LES CASTELS
Hôtellerie de Plein Air

41 4
ca

C000221537

LES CASTELS
DEPUIS - SINCE 1959

Les Castels chain has been working with The Caravan Club since 1981

Camping
Caravaning
Chalets
Mobile home
Gîtes
Glamping
Unusual

Are you dreaming of a camping holiday in a natural and authentic setting?

Come camp at Les Castels! Located near castles, lakes, rivers, in the mountains, or by the sea, our campsites are set apart by their exceptional surroundings.

Spacious camping pitches, exceptionally comfortable top-of-the-range accommodations, high-quality facilities and flawless service await you.

To benefit from the very best Les Castels has to offer, discover the VIP services in our Premium offer, on our properties' finest camping pitches.

Discover a Castel site that matches your idea of a perfect holiday destination!

Win a week holiday in a Castel camping!

When ordering a brochure or booking on line or by phone, please indicate this special code CARAVANCLUB15 on your form and you will enter our lucky draw. Free game with no obligation to purchase anything, available until 30/08/15. Only one participation per household is admitted.

Booking : + 33 (0)2 23 16 45 02

contact@les-castels.com

www.camping-castels.co.uk

Explanation of a Campsite Entry
Touring France 2015

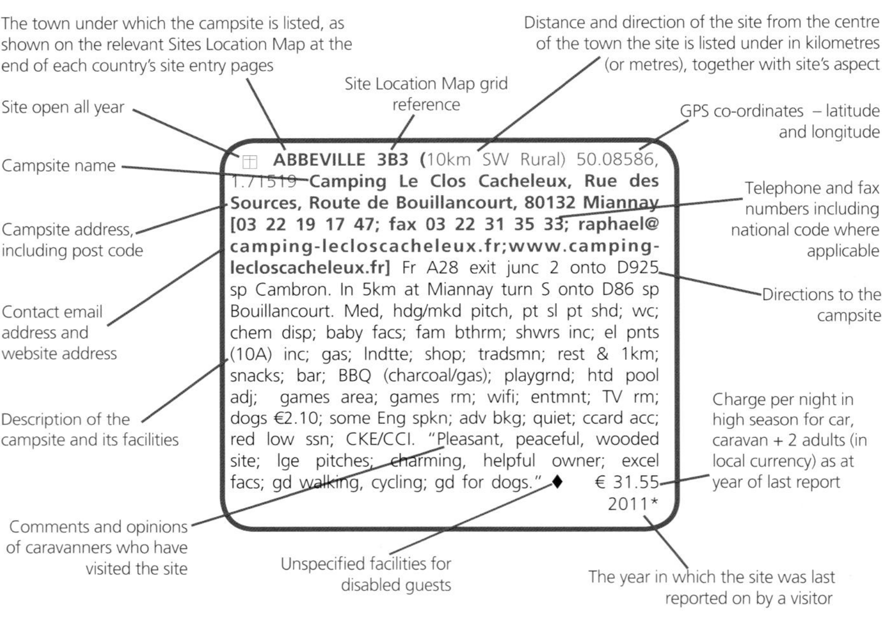

Popular Abbreviations

(for a full list of abbreviations please see page 10).

Site Description

hdg: hedged
mkd: marked
sm: max 50 pitches
hdstg: some hard standing or gravel pitches
pt shd: part shaded
terr: terraced site
sl: sloping site
unshd: no shade
lge: 151-500 pitches
pt sl: sloping in parts
v lge: 501+ pitches
med: 51–150 pitches
shd: plenty of shade

Popular Abbreviations for Site Facilities

Adv bkg: advanced booking accepted
CCI or CCS: Camping Card International or Camping Card Scandinavia accepted
chem disp: dedicated chemical toilet disposal facilities
chem disp (wc): no dedicated point; disposal via wc only
CL-type: very small, privately-owned, informal and usually basic, farm or country site
El pnts: mains electric hook-ups
Eng spkn: English spoken
entmnt: entertainment (facilities or organised)
lndtte: washing machine(s) with or without tumble dryers
NH: suitable as a night halt;
quiet: peaceful, tranquil site
rest: restaurant
shwrs: hot showers available at a fee
shwrs inc: cost included in site fee quoted
tradsmn: tradesman call at the site, e.g. baker
sbs: Site Booking Service – Ref No. for a site included in the Caravan Club's network i.e. bookable through the Club
ssn: season
⊞ open all year

Popular Generic Abbreviations

Adj: adjacent, nearby; **app**: approach, on approaching; **arr**: arrival, arriving **bef**: before **bet**: between **c'van**: caravan; **ccard acc**: Credit and/or debit cards accepted; **CChq acc:** Camping Cheques accepted **clsd**: closed **E**: East; **ent**: entrance/entry to **excel**: excellent; **facs**: facilities; **foll**: follow; **fr**: from; **gd**: good; **inc**: included/inclusive; **L**: left; **m'van**: motorhome/motor caravan; **narr**: narrow **N**: North; **o'fits**: outfits; **R**: right; **rec**: recommend/ed ; **red**: reduced/reduction; **rte**: route **S**: South; **sh**: short; **sp**: sign post/signposted; **strt**: straight, straight ahead **sw**: swimming **vg**: very good; **W**: West

Touring France
and Andorra

Also available:

Published by The Caravan Club Limited
East Grinstead House, East Grinstead
West Sussex RH19 1UA

General Enquiries: 01342 326944
Travel Service Reservations: 01342 316101
Red Pennant Overseas Holiday Insurance: 01342 336633
Website: www.caravanclub.co.uk
Email: enquiries@caravanclub.co.uk

Editor: Kate Walters
Email: kate.walters@caravanclub.co.uk

Printed by Stephens & George Ltd
Merthyr Tydfil

ISBN 978-0-9569510-6-9

Maps and distance charts generated from Collins Bartholomew Digital Database
Maps © Collins Bartholomew Ltd 2014, reproduced by permission of HarperCollins Publishers.

Cover: Mont St Michel ©Shutterstock/Max Topchii

Welcome
to Touring France 2015

The Caravan Club has been producing the ***Caravan Europe*** guides for over 50 years, and in that time there have been a lot of changes in the way people tour on the continent. We know that those who use this guide travel in a wide range of outfits – not just caravans, but motorhomes, trailer tents and tents as well. This, above all else, is the reason for the change in the name of this publication to ***Touring France***.

The way that people research their trip has also changed considerably. The availability of information, especially online, means that there is far more content accessible than we are able to provide within these books. With this in mind, you will see a change to the introductory chapters - giving you the essential information you need when touring, while directing you to further good sources if you need to delve deeper.

One thing that hasn't changed over the years is our reliance on you, the users of the sites and these guides, to collate the information. We very much appreciate the time and effort you continue to give in contributing to the guides. You can find site report forms at the back of the guide, or visit www.caravanclub.co.uk/europereport to fill in reports online.

This edition has one other major change; the site entries are now listed by region. Within each region you will still find the sites listed alphabetically by town name, but the alteration has been made to help those looking for sites in a specific region or along a route. If you're struggling to find a site by it's town name within the new regions, there is an index of towns at the back of the book.

I hope the changes will make the guides much easier to use, but we always welcome feedback on the changes or what you would like to see in future editions. Happy touring!

Kate Walters

Kate Walters, Editor

Contents

How To Use This Guide

Planning your trip

Motoring advice

During your stay

Continental Campsites

Site Listings

See also alphabetical index at the back of the guide

How to use this guide

The information contained within *Touring France* is presented in the following categories:

The Handbook

This includes general information about touring in France and Andorra, such as legal requirements, advice and regulations. The Handbook chapters are at the front of the guide and are separated as follows:

Purple section	Planning your trip - information you'll need before you travel including information on the documents and insurance you'll need, advice on money, customs regulations and planning your channel crossings.
Green section	Motoring advice - advice on motoring overseas, essential equipment and roads in Europe including mountain passes and tunnels.
Turquoise section	During your stay - information for while you're away including telephone, internet and TV advice, medical information and advice on staying safe.
Blue section	Continental Campsites - advice on choosing your site and the differences you might find overseas.

Regional Introduction

Following on from the Handbook chapters you will find the Regional Introductions which contain a brief introduction to the region, list the major towns and cities and some attractions you might like to visit. There are also contact details to find out more local information.

Campsite Entries

After the Regional Introduction you will find the campsite entries - for the first time the site entries in this edition of the book has been separated by regions. You can find details of these regions on page 91, and a full index of town names at the back of the book.

Within each region sites are listed alphabetically under their nearest town or village. Where several campsites are shown in and around the same town they will be listed in clockwise order from the north.

Regionalisation is based on the site postcode rather than the location of the listing towns, so you may find towns listed under more than one region. For example the town of Aire-Sur-l'Ardour is situated in Aquitaine, but right on the border with Midi-Pyrenees; sites listed under the town are located in both regions.

To find a campsite all you need to do is look for the town or village of where you would like to stay, or use the maps at the back of the book to find a town where sites are listed. Where there are no sites listed in a relatively large or popular town you may find a cross reference, directing you to closest town which does have sites.

In order to provide you with the details of as many site as possible in *Touring France* we use abbreviations in the site entries.

For a full and detailed list of these abbreviations please see the following pages of this section.

We have also included some of the most regularly used abbreviations, as well as an explanation of a campsite entry, on the tear-out bookmark page.

Campsite Fees

Campsite entries show high season fees per night for an outfit plus two adults, as at the year of the last report. Prices given may not include electricity or showers, unless indicated. Outside of the main holiday season many sites offer discounts on the prices shown and some sites may also offer a reduction for longer stays.

Campsite fees may vary to the prices stated in the site entries, especially if the site has not been reported on for a few years. You are advised to always check fees when booking, or at least before pitching, as those shown in site entries should be used as a guide only.

Site Maps

Each town and village listed alphabetically in the site entry pages has a map grid reference number, e.g. 3B4. The map grid reference number is shown on each site entry. The maps can be found at the end of the book. The reference number will show you where each town or village is located, and the site entry will tell you how far the site is from that town. Place names are shown on the maps in two colours:

Red where we list a site which is open all year (or for at least eleven months of the year)

Black where we only list seasonal sites which close in winter.

These maps are intended for general campsite location purposes only; a detailed road map or atlas is essential for route planning and touring.

Town names in capital letters (**RED**, **BLACK** or in *ITALICS*) correspond with towns listed on the Distance Chart.

The scale used for the map means that it is not possible to pinpoint every town or village where a campsite exists, so some sites in small villages may be listed under a nearby larger town instead.

Satellite Navigation
Most campsite entries now show a GPS (sat nav) reference. There are several different formats of writing co-ordinates, and in this guide we use decimal degrees, for example 48.85661 (latitude north) and 2.35222 (longitude east).

Minus readings, shown as -1.23456, indicate that the longitude is west of the Greenwich meridian. This will only apply to sites in the west of France, most of Spain and all of Portugal as the majority of Europe (including all countries covered in this edition of the guide) are east of the Greenwich meridian.

Manufacturers of sat navs all use different formats of co-ordinates so you may need to convert the co-ordinates before using them with your device. There are plenty of online conversion tools which enable you to do this quickly and easily - just type 'co-ordinate converter' into your search engine.

Please be aware if you are using a sat nav device some routes may take you on roads that are narrow and/or are not suitable for caravans or large outfits.

The GPS co-ordinates given in this guide are provided by members and checked wherever possible, however we cannot guarantee their accuracy due to the rural nature of most of the sites. The Caravan Club cannot accept responsibility for any inaccuracies, errors or omissions or for their effects.

Site Report Forms

With the exception of campsites in The Club's Overseas Site Booking Service (SBS) network, The Caravan Club does not inspect sites listed in this guide. Virtually all of the sites listed in *Touring France* are from site reports submitted by users of these guides. You can tell us about great sites you have found or update the details of sites already within the books.

Sites which are not reported on for five years are deleted from the guide, so even if you visit a site and find nothing different from the site listing we'd appreciate a update to tell us as much.

You will find site report forms towards the back of this guide which we hope you will complete and return to us by freepost (please post when you are back in the UK). Use the abbreviated site report form if you are reporting no changes, or only minor changes, to a site entry. The full report form should be used for new sites or sites which have changed a lot since the last report.

You can complete both the full and abbreviated versions of the site report forms by visiting www.caravanclub.co.uk/europereport.

Please submit reports as soon as possible. Information received by **mid August 2015** will be used wherever possible in the next edition of *Touring France*. Reports received after that date are still very welcome and will appear in the following edition. The editor is unable to respond individually to site reports submitted due to the large quantity that we receive.

Tips for Completing Site Reports

- If possible fill in a site report form while at the campsite. Once back at home it can be difficult to remember details of individual sites, especially if you visited several during your trip.
- When giving directions to a site, remember to include the direction of travel, e.g. 'from north on D137, turn left onto D794 signposted Combourg' or 'on N83 from Poligny turn right at petrol station in village'. Wherever possible give road numbers, junction numbers and/or kilometre post numbers, where you exit from motorways or main roads. It is also helpful to mention useful landmarks such as bridges, roundabouts, traffic lights or prominent buildings.

We very much appreciates the time and trouble you take submitting reports on campsites that you have visited; without your valuable contributions it would be impossible to update this guide.

Acknowledgements

The Caravan Club's thanks go to the AIT/FIA Information Centre (OTA), the Alliance Internationale de Tourisme (AIT), the Fédération International de Camping et de Caravaning (FICC) and to the national clubs and tourist offices of those countries who have assisted with this publication.

Every effort is made to ensure that information contained in this publication is accurate and that the details given in good faith in the site report forms are accurately reproduced or summarised. The Caravan Club Ltd has not checked these details by inspection or other investigation and cannot accept responsibility for the accuracy of these reports as provided by members and non-members, or for errors, omissions or their effects. In addition The Caravan Club Ltd cannot be held accountable for the quality, safety or operation of the sites concerned, or for the fact that conditions, facilities, management or prices may have changed since the last recorded visit. Any recommendations, additional comments or opinions have been contributed by caravanners and people staying on the site and are not generally those of The Caravan Club.

The inclusion of advertisements or other inserted material does not imply any form of approval or recognition, nor can The Caravan Club Ltd undertake any responsibility for checking the accuracy of advertising material.

Explanation of a Campsite Entry

The town under which the campsite is listed, as shown on the relevant Sites Location Map at the end of each country's site entry pages

Distance and direction of the site from the centre of the town the site is listed under in kilometres (or metres), together with site's aspect

Site Location Map grid reference

Indicates that the site is open all year

Campsite name

Telephone and fax numbers including national code where applicable

Description of the campsite and its facilities

Contact email and website address

Directions to the campsite

Charge per night in high season for car, caravan + 2 adults as at year of last report

Unspecified facilities for disabled guests. If followed by 'ltd' this indicates that the facilities are limited.

The year in which the site was last reported on by a visitor

⊞ **ABBEVILLE** *3B3* (10km SW Rural) *50.08586, 1.71519* **Camping Le Clos Cacheleux, Rue des Sources, Route de Bouillancourt, 80132 Miannay [03 22 19 17 47; fax 03 22 31 35 33; raphael@camping-lecloscacheleux.fr; www.camping-lecloscacheleux.fr]** Fr A28 exit junc 2 onto D925 sp Cambron. In 5km at Miannay turn S onto D86 sp Bouillancourt. Site thro vill of R opp sister site Camping Le Val de Trie which is sp fr A28. Med, hdg/mkd pitch, pt sl pt shd; wc; chem disp; baby facs; fam bthrm; shwrs inc; el pnts (10A) inc (poss long lead req); gas; lndtte (inc dryer); shop; tradsmn; rest & 1km; snacks; bar; BBQ (charcoal/gas); playgrnd; htd, covrd pool adj; paddling pool adj; jacuzzi; sand beach 20km; fishing pond; tennis 3km; games area; games rm; farm animals; wifi; entmnt; TV rm; dogs €2.10; no c'vans/m'vans over 18m; some Eng spkn; adv bkg; quiet; ccard acc; red low ssn; CKE/CCI. "Pleasant, peaceful, wooded site; lge pitches; charming, helpful owner; excel facs; all services (inc shop, rest & pool) are on sister site 'Le Val de Trie' on opp side of rd, accessed via steep track 50m fr site ent; gd walking, cycling; gd for dogs." ♦ € 31.55

2011*

Campsite address

GPS co-ordinates – latitude and longitude in decimal degrees. Minus figures indicate that the site is west of the Greenwich meridian

Comments and opinions of caravanners who have visited the site (within inverted commas)

Opening dates

The site accepts Camping Cheques, see the ***Continental Campsites*** chapter for details

Booking reference for a site the Club's Overseas Travel Service work with, i.e. bookable via The Club.

ST PALAIS SUR MER 7B1 (2km E Coastal) 45.64396,-1.06325 **Camping Le Val Vert, 108 Ave Frédéric Garnier,17640 Vaux-sur-Mer [05 46 38 25 51; fax 05 46 38 06 15;camping-val-vert@wanadoo.fr; www.val-vert.com]** Fr Saintes on N150 dir Royan; join D25 dir St Palais-sur-Mer; turn L at rndabt sp Vaux-sur-Mer & Centre Hospitaliers; at traff lts ahead; at 2nd rndabt take 3rd exit & then turn immed R. Site on R in 500m. Med, hdg pitch; wc; chem disp; mv service pnt; baby facs; shwrs inc; el pnts (6A) €5.50 or (10A) €6.00; gas; lndtte; shop; rest, snacks; gas/elec BBQ; playgrnd; htd pool; paddling pool; sand beach 900m; watersports; fishing; cycle hire; tennis 400m; horseriding & golf 5km; games area; games rm; some wifi; entmnt; dogs €3.40; no c'vans/m'vans over 6.50m high ssn; adv bkg; ccard acc; red low ssn; "Well kept, family-run site; gd sized pitches; unisex san facs; no twinaxles; a stream runs alongside site; sh walk to pleasant vill; daily mkt in Royan; excel" ♦ ltd
6 Apr-30 Sep. € 31.30 (CChq acc)

SBS - A25 2013*

Site Description Abbreviations

Each site entry assumes the following unless stated otherwise:

Level ground, open grass pitches, drinking water on site, clean wc unless otherwise stated (own sanitation required if wc not listed), site is suitable for any length of stay within the dates shown.

aspect

urban – within a city or town, or on its outskirts
rural – within or on edge of a village or in open countryside
coastal – within one kilometre of the coast

size of site

sm – max 50 pitches
med – 51 to 150 pitches
lge – 151 to 500 pitches
v lge – 501+ pitches

pitches

hdg pitch – hedged pitches
mkd pitch – marked or numbered pitches
hdstg – some hard standing or gravel

levels

sl – sloping site
pt sl – sloping in parts
terr – terraced site

shade

shd – plenty of shade
pt shd – part shaded
unshd – no shade

Site Facilities

adv bkg

Advance booking accepted;
adv bkg rec – advance booking recommended

baby facs

Nursing room/bathroom for babies/children

beach

Beach for swimming nearby;
1km – distance to beach
sand beach – sandy beach
shgl beach – shingle beach

bus/metro/tram

Public transport within an easy walk of the site

chem disp

Dedicated chemical toilet disposal facilities;
chem disp (wc) – no dedicated point; disposal via wc only

CKE/CCI

Camping Key Europe and/or Camping Card International accepted

CL-type

Very small, privately-owned, informal and usually basic, farm or country site similar to those in the Caravan Club's network of Certificated Locations

dogs

Dogs allowed on site with appropriate certification (a daily fee may be quoted and conditions may apply)

el pnts

Mains electric hook-ups available for a fee;
inc – cost included in site fee quoted
10A – amperage provided
conn fee – one-off charge for connection to metered electricity supply
rev pol – reversed polarity may be present

(see ***Electricity and Gas*** in the section ***DURING YOUR STAY***)

Eng spkn

English spoken by campsite reception staff

entmnt

Entertainment facilities or organised entertainment for adults and/or children

fam bthrm

Bathroom for use by families with small children

gas

Supplies of bottled gas available on site or nearby

internet

Internet point for use by visitors to site;
wifi – wireless local area network available

lndtte

Washing machine(s) with or without tumble dryers, sometimes other equipment available, eg ironing boards;
lndtte (inc dryer) – washing machine(s) and tumble dryer(s)
lndry rm – laundry room with only basic clothes-washing facilities

Mairie

Town hall (France); will usually make municipal campsite reservations

mv service pnt

Special low level waste discharge point for motor caravans; fresh water tap and rinse facilities should also be available

NH
Suitable as a night halt

noisy
Noisy site with reasons given;
quiet – peaceful, tranquil site

open 1 Apr-15 Oct
Where no specific dates are given, opening dates are assumed to be inclusive, ie Apr-Oct – beginning April to end October
(NB: opening dates may vary from those shown; check before travelling, particularly when travelling out of the main holiday season)

phone
Public payphone on or adjacent to site

playgrnd
Children's playground

pool
Swimming pool (may be open high season only);
htd – heated pool
covrd – indoor pool or one with retractable cover

poss cr
During high season site may be crowded or overcrowded and pitches cramped

red CCI/CCS
Reduction in fees on production of a Camping Card International or Camping Card Scandinavia

rest
Restaurant;
bar – bar
BBQ – barbecues allowed (may be restricted to a separate, designated area)
cooking facs – communal kitchen area
snacks – snack bar, cafeteria or takeaway

SBS
Site Booking Service (pitch reservation can be made through the Caravan Club's Travel Service)

serviced pitch
Electric hook-ups and mains water inlet and grey water waste outlet to pitch;
all – to all pitches
50% – percentage of pitches

shop(s)
Shop on site;
adj – shops next to site
500m – nearest shops
supmkt – supermarket
hypmkt – hypermarket
tradsmn – tradesmen call at the site, eg baker

shwrs
Hot showers available for a fee;
inc – cost included in site fee quoted

ssn
Season;
high ssn – peak holiday season
low ssn – out of peak season

50% statics
Percentage of static caravans/mobile homes/ chalets/fixed tents/cabins or long term seasonal pitches on site, including those run by tour operators

sw
Swimming nearby;
1km – nearest swimming
lake – in lake
rv – in river

TV
TV available for viewing by visitors (often in the bar);
TV rm – separate TV room (often also a games room)
cab/sat – cable or satellite connections to pitches

wc
Clean flushing toilets on site;
(cont) – continental type with floor-level hole
htd – sanitary block centrally heated in winter
own san – use of own sanitation facilities recommended

Other Abbreviations

AIT	Alliance Internationale de Tourisme
a'bahn	Autobahn
a'pista	Autopista
a'route	Autoroute
a'strada	Autostrada
adj	Adjacent, nearby
alt	Alternative
app	Approach, on approaching
arr	Arrival, arriving
avail	Available
Ave	Avenue
bdge	Bridge
bef	Before
bet	Between
Blvd	Boulevard
C	Century, eg 16thC
c'van	Caravan
CC	Caravan Club
ccard acc	Credit and/or debit cards accepted (check with site for specific details)
CChq acc	Camping Cheques accepted

cent	Centre or central
clsd	Closed
conn	Connection
cont	Continue or continental (wc)
conv	Convenient
covrd	Covered
dep	Departure
diff	Difficult, with difficulty
dir	Direction
dist	Distance
dual c'way	Dual carriageway
E	East
ent	Entrance/entry to
espec	Especially
ess	Essential
excel	Excellent
facs	Facilities
FIA	Fédération Internationale de l'Automobile
FICC	Fédération Internationale de Camping & de Caravaning
FFCC	Fédération Française de Camping et de Caravaning
FKK/FNF	Naturist federation, ie naturist site
foll	Follow
fr	From
g'ge	Garage
gd	Good
grnd(s)	Ground(s)
hr(s)	Hour(s)
immac	Immaculate
immed	Immediate(ly)
inc	Included/inclusive
indus est	Industrial estate
INF	Naturist federation, ie naturist site
int'l	International
irreg	Irregular
junc	Junction
km	Kilometre
L	Left
LH	Left-hand
LS	Low season
ltd	Limited
mkd	Marked
mkt	Market
mob	Mobile (phone)
m'van	Motor caravan
m'way	Motorway
N	North
narr	Narrow
nr, nrby	Near, nearby
opp	Opposite
o'fits	Outfits
o'look(ing)	Overlook(ing)
o'night	Overnight
o'skts	Outskirts
PO	Post office
poss	Possible, possibly
pt	Part
R	Right
rd	Road or street
rec	Recommend/ed
recep	Reception
red	Reduced, reduction (for)
reg	Regular
req	Required
RH	Right-hand
rlwy	Railway line
rm	Room
rndabt	Roundabout
rte	Route
RV	Recreational vehicle, ie large motor caravan
rv/rvside	River/riverside
S	South
san facs	Sanitary facilities ie wc, showers, etc
snr citizens	Senior citizens
sep	Separate
sh	Short
sp	Sign post, signposted
sq	Square
ssn	Season
stn	Station
strt	Straight, straight ahead
sw	Swimming
thro	Through
TO	Tourist Office
tour ops	Tour operators
traff lts	Traffic lights
twd	Toward(s)
unrel	Unreliable
vg	Very good
vill	Village
W	West
w/end	Weekend
x-ing	Crossing
x-rds	Cross roads

Symbols Used

◆	Unspecified facilities for disabled guests check before arrival
⊞	Open all year
*	Last year site report received (see Campsite Entries in Introduction)

Documents

Camping Card Schemes

Camping Key Europe (CKE) is a useful companion for touring in France. Not only does it serve as a valid ID at campsites, meaning that you don't have to leave you passport with the site reception, it also entitles you to discounts at over 2200 sites.

CKE also offers Third Party Liability Insurance for up to 6 people travelling in one party, and Personal Accident Cover while on site. Full Terms and Conditions and details of the levels of cover of this insurance are provided with the card.

CKE is available to purchase from The Caravan Club by calling 01342 336633, or is provided free for all members taking out the 'Motoring' level of cover of The Club's Red Pennant Overseas Holiday Insurance.

An alternative scheme is Camping Card International (CCI) which offers similar benefits as CKE.

If you are using a CKE or CCI card as a method of ID at a site, make sure that you retrieve your card on leaving the site. Also check that you have been given your own card instead of someone else's.

See www.campingkey.com or www.campingcardinternational.com for full details of the schemes.

Driving Licence

A full, valid driving licence should be carried at all times when driving abroad as you must produce it when asked to do so by the police and other authorities. Failure to do so may result in an immediate fine and confiscation of your vehicle(s). If your driving licence is due to expire while you are away it can normally be renewed up to three months before the expiry date - contact the DVLA if you need to renew more than three months ahead.

All European Union countries recognise the pink EU-format driving licence introduced in the UK in 1990, subject to the minimum age requirements (normally 18 years for a vehicle with a maximum weight of 3,500 kg carrying no more than 8 people). However, there are exceptions in some European Countries and the Country Introductions contain specific details. Holders of an old-style green UK paper licence or a licence issued in Northern Ireland prior to 1991, which are not to EU format, should update it to a photocard licence before

travelling in order to avoid any difficulties with local authorities. A photocard driving licence is also useful as a means of identification in other situations, e.g. when using a credit card. Remember to carry both the plastic card and its paper counterpart.

Allow enough time for your application to be processed and do not apply if you will need to use your licence in the near future, e.g. to hire a car. Selected post offices and DVLA local offices offer a premium checking service for photocard applications but the service is not available for online applications.

MOT Certificate

You are advised to carry your vehicle's MOT certificate (if applicable) when driving on the Continent as you may need to show it to the authorities if your vehicle is involved in an accident, or in the event of random vehicle checks. If your MOT certificate is due to expire while you are away you should have the vehicle tested before you leave home.

Passport

In France everyone is required you to carry photographic ID (e.g. your passport or photocard driving licence) at all times. Enter next-of-kin details in the back of your passport and keep a separate photocopy or record of your passport details. It's also a good idea to leave a photocopy of it with a relative or friend at home.

The following information applies to British passport holders only. For people who's passports are issued by other countries you should contact the local embassy for more information.

Applying for a Passport

Each person travelling out of the UK (including babies) must hold a valid passport. It is no longer possible to add or include children on a parent's British passport. A standard British passport is valid for ten years, or 5 years for children under 16.

All new UK passports are now biometric passports, also known as e-passports, which contain a microchip with information which can be used to authenticate the holder's identity. When your passport expires and you apply for a new one it will be replaced with a biometric passport.

Full information and application forms are available from main post offices or from the

Identity & Passport Service's website, www.gov.uk where you can complete an online application. Allow at least six weeks for first-time passport applications, for which you may need to attend an interview at your nearest Identity and Passport Service (IPS) regional office. Allow three weeks for a renewal application and the replacement of a lost, stolen or damaged passport.

Main post offices offer a 'Check & Send' service for passport applications. To find your nearest 'Check & Send' post office call 0845 611 2970 or see www.postoffice.co.uk

Passport Validity
Most countries in the EU only require your passport to be valid for the duration of your stay. However, in case your return home is delayed for any reason it is a good idea to renew your passport before you travel if there is less than 6 month's validity remaining. Any time left on a passport (up to a maximum of 9 months) will be added to the validity of your new passport.

Schengen Agreement
The Schengen Agreement allows people and vehicles to pass freely without border checks from country to country within the Schengen area (a total of 26 countries) . Where there are no longer any border checks you should still not attempt to cross land borders without a full, valid passport. It is likely that random identity checks will continue to be made for the foreseeable future in areas surrounding land borders.

The United Kingdom and Republic of Ireland do not fully participate in the Schengen Agreement.

Regulations for Pets

Some campsites in France do not accept dogs at all and some have restrictions on the number and breed of dogs allowed. Further information can be found at www.caravanclub.co.uk/overseasadvice.

In popular tourist areas local regulations may ban dogs from beaches during the summer months.

In preparation for your return home with your dog you can find the names and addresses of vets in France in 'Pages Jaunes' (the equivalent of the Yellow Pages) on www.pagesjaunes.fr. Alternatively you can ask the campsite staff to recommend a local vet.

Pet Travel Scheme (PETS)
The Pet Travel Scheme (PETS) allows owners of dogs, cats and ferrets from qualifying European countries, to bring their pets into the UK (up to a limit of five per person) without quarantine. The animal must have an EU pet passport, be microchipped and be vaccinated against rabies. Dogs must also have been treated for tapeworm. It also allows pets to travel from the UK to other EU qualifying countries. Some countries may not allow entry to certain types or breeds of dogs and may have rules relating to matters such as muzzling and transporting dogs in cars – check the Country Introductions for any specific details or see www.caravanclub.co.uk/pets for more details. Pets normally resident in the Channel Islands, Isle of Man and the Republic of Ireland can also enter the UK under the PETS scheme if they comply with the rules. Pets resident anywhere in the British Isles (including the Republic of Ireland) are able to travel freely within the British Isles and are not subject to PETS rules.

Travelling with Children

Some countries require evidence of parental responsibility from single parents travelling alone with children before allowing them to enter the country or, in some cases, before permitting children to leave the country. The authorities may want to see a birth certificate, a letter of consent from the other parent and evidence of your responsibility for the child.

If you are travelling with a minor under the age of 18 who is not your own, you must carry a letter of authorisation, naming the adult in charge of the child, from the child's parent or legal guardian.

For further information on exactly what will be required at immigration contact the Embassy or Consulate of the countries you intend to visit before your visit.

Vehicle Excise Licence

While driving abroad you still need to have current UK vehicle excise licence. If your vehicle's tax is due to expire while you are abroad you may apply to re-license the vehicle at a post office, by post, or in person at a DVLA local office, up to two months in advance.

Vehicle Registration Certificate (V5C)

You must always carry your Vehicle Registration Certificate (V5C) and MOT Certificate (if applicable) when taking your vehicle abroad. If yours has been lost, stolen or destroyed you should apply to a DVLA local office on form V62. Call DVLA Customer Enquiries on 0300 790 6802 for more information.

Caravan – Proof of Ownership (CRIS)

In Britain and Ireland, unlike most other European countries, caravans are not formally registered in the same way as cars. This may not be fully understood by police and other authorities on the Continent. You are strongly advised, therefore, to carry a copy of your Caravan Registration Identification Scheme (CRIS) document.

Hired or Borrowed Vehicles

If using a borrowed vehicle you must obtain a letter of authority to use the vehicle from the registered owner. You should also carry the Vehicle Registration Certificate (V5C).

In the case of hired or leased vehicles, including company cars, when the user does not normally possess the V5C, ask the company which owns the vehicle to supply a Vehicle On Hire Certificate, form VE103, which is the only legal substitute for a V5C. The BVRLA, the trade body for the vehicle rental and leasing sector, provide advice on hired or leased vehicles - see www.bvrla.co.uk or call them on 01494 434747 for more information.

If you are caught driving a hired vehicle abroad without this certificate you may be fined and/or the vehicle impounded.

Visas

British citizens holding a full UK passport do not require a visa for entry into any countries covered by this guide. EU countries may require a permit for stays of more than three months and you should contact the relevant country's UK embassy before you travel for information.

British subjects, British overseas citizens, British dependent territories citizens and citizens of other countries may need visas that are not required by British citizens. Again check with the authorities of the country you are due to visit at their UK embassy or consulate. Citizens of other countries should apply to their own embassy, consulate or High Commission for information.

Insurance

Car, Motorhome and Caravan Insurance

Insurance cover for your outfit whilst travelling abroad is an absolute essential. Your car or motorhome insurance should cover you for driving in the EU or associated countries, but you should check what you are covered for before you travel. If you are travelling outside the EU or associated countries you'll need to inform your insurer and may have to pay an additional premium.

Make sure your Caravan insurance covers travel outside of the UK, speak to your insurer – most will require the dates of your holiday and it is possible there will be an extra premium to pay.

The Caravan Club's Car, Caravan and Motorhome Insurance schemes extend to provide policy cover for travel within the EU free of charge, provided the total period of foreign travel in any one year does not exceed 270 days for Car Insurance, 182 for Caravan Insurance and 270 days for Motorhome Insurance. It may be possible to extend this period, although a charge may apply.

Should you be delayed beyond these limits speak to your broker or insurer immediately in order to maintain your cover until you can return to the UK.

If your outfit is damaged during loading, unloading or travel on a ferry it must be reported to the carrier at the time the damage occurred. Most insurance policies will cover short sea crossings (up to 65 hours) but check with your insurer before travelling.

For full details of The Caravan Club's Caravan Insurance telephone 01342 336610 or for Car Insurance and Motorhome insurance, telephone 0800 0284809 or visit our website, www.caravanclub.co.uk/insurance.

European Accident Statement

Your car or motorhome insurer may provide you with a European Accident Statement form (EAS), or you may be given one if you are involved in an accident abroad. The EAS is a standard form, available in different languages, which gives all parties involved in an accident the opportunity to agree on the facts. Signing the form doesn't mean that you are accepting liability, just that you agree with what has been stated on the form. Only sign an EAS if you are completely sure that you understand what has been written and always make sure that you take a copy of the completed EAS.

Legal Costs Abroad

If an accident abroad leads to you being taken to court you may find yourself liable for legal costs – even if you are not found to be at fault. Most UK vehicle insurance policies include cover for legal costs or have the option to add cover for a small additional cost – check if you are covered before you travel.

Holiday Travel Insurance

Having insured your vehicles, there are other risks to consider and it is essential to take out adequate travel insurance. Your vehicle insurance policy won't cover you for all eventualities, such as vehicle breakdown, medical expenses or accommodation. Make sure that the holiday insurance you take out is suitable for a caravan or motorhome holiday.

The Caravan Club's Red Pennant Overseas Holiday Insurance is designed specifically for touring holidays and can cover both motoring and personal use. Depending on the level of cover chosen the policy will cover you for vehicle recovery and repair, holiday continuation, medical expenses and accommodation.

For full details visit www.caravanclub.co.uk/redpennant or call 01342 336633.

Look carefully at the exemptions to your insurance policy, including those relating to preexisting medical conditions or the use of alcohol. Be sure to declare any preexisting medical conditions to your insurer.

Holiday Insurance for Pets

Make sure that your pet is also covered if you take them on holiday with you. Some holiday insurance policies, including The Club's Red Pennant, can be extended to cover pet expenses relating to an incident normally covered under the policy – such as pet repatriation in the event that your vehicle is written off.

However in order to provide cover for pet injury or illness you will need a separate pet insurance policy which covers your pet while out of the UK. For details of The Club's Pet Insurance scheme visit www.caravanclub.co.uk/petins or call 0800 015 1396.

Home Insurance

Your home insurer may require advance notification if you are leaving your home unoccupied for 30 days or more. You may be required to turn off mains services (except electricity), drain water down and have somebody visit the home once a week. Check your policy documents or speak to your insurer or broker.

The Caravan Club's Home Insurance policy provides full cover for up to 90 days when you are away from home (for instance when touring) and requires only common sense precautions for longer periods of unoccupancy. See www.caravanclub.co.uk/homeins or call 0800 028 4815 for details.

Personal Belongings

The majority of travellers are able to cover their valuables such as jewellery, watches, cameras, laptops, and bikes under a Home insurance Policy. This includes The Caravan Club's Home Insurance scheme.

Vehicles Left Behind Abroad

If you are involved in an accident or breakdown abroad which prevents you taking your vehicle home, you must ensure that your normal insurance will cover your vehicle if left overseas while you return home. Also check if you are covered for the cost of recovering it to your home address.

You should remove all items of baggage and personal belongings from your vehicles before leaving them unattended. If this is not possible you should check with your insurer/broker to establish whether extended cover can be provided. In all circumstances, you must remove any valuables and items liable for customs duty, including wine, beer, spirits and cigarettes.

Customs Regulations

Caravans and Vehicles

A caravan, motorhome or trailer tent imported into France from an EU country may remain indefinitely. The importer must be in possession of the purchase invoice showing that tax (VAT) has been paid in the country of purchase. The temporary importation of a caravan by persons other than the owner requires written authorisation from the owner.

Although a permit is not required for vehicles being imported on a permenant basis, they must be covered by a certificate of conformity to EU standards issued by the manufacturer or his representative in France or by the "Direction Régionale de l'Environnement, de l'Aménagement et du Logement" (DREAL). Any vehicles that do not conform to these standards, and vehicles over 4 years old, must be presented to the DREAL for an inspection.

Borrowed vehicles
If you are borrowing a vehicle from a friend or relative, or loaning yours to someone, you should be aware of the following:

- The total time the vehicle spends abroad must not exceed the limit for temporary importation (generally six months).
- The owner of the caravan must provide the other person with a letter of authority.
- The owner cannot accept a hire fee or reward.
- The number plate on the caravan must match the number plate on the tow car.
- Both drivers' insurers must be informed if a caravan is being towed and any additional premium must be paid.

Currency

Any person entering or leaving the EU will have to declare the money that they are carrying if this amounts to €10,000 (or equivalent in other currencies) or more. This includes cheques, travellers' cheques, bankers' drafts and any cash - notes and coins. This ruling does not apply to anyone travelling within the EU.

For further information contact HMRC Excise & Customs Helpline on 0845 010 9000.

Customs Allowances

Travelling within the European Union
If you are travelling to the UK from within the

EU you can bring an unlimited amount of most goods without being liable for any duty or tax, but certain rules apply. The goods must be for your own personal use, which can include use as a gift (if the person you are gifting the goods to reimburses you in any way this is not classed as a gift), and you must have paid duty and tax in the country where you purchased the goods.If a customs official suspects that any goods are not for your own personal use they can question you, make further checks and ultimately sieze both the goods and the vehicle used to transport them. Although no limits are in place, customs officials are less likely to question you regarding your goods if they are under the following limits:

- 800 cigarettes
- 400 cigarillos
- 200 cigars
- 1kg tobacco
- 10 litres of spirits
- 20 litres of fortified wine (e.g. port or sherry)
- 90 litres of wine
- 110 litres of beer

The same rules and guidance limits apply for travel between other EU countries.

Travelling outside the EU
There are set limits to the amount of goods you can buy in countries outside of the EU to bring back into the UK. Even within these limits goods must still be for your own personal use. Each person aged 17 and over is entitled to the following allowance:

- 200 cigarettes, or 100 cigarillos, or 50 cigars, or 250gms tobacco
- 1 litre of spirits or strong liqueurs over 22 per cent volume, or 2 litres of fortified wine, sparkling wine or any other alcoholic drink that's less than 22 per cent volume
- 4 litres of still wine
- 16 litres of beer
- £390 worth of all other goods including perfume, gifts and souvenirs without having to pay tax and/or duty
- For further information contact HM Revenue & Customs National Advice Service on 0845 010 9000 (+44 2920 501 261 from outside the UK).

Duty-Free Imports from Andorra
Duty-free shopping is permitted in Andorra, which is not a member of the EU, but there are strict limits on the amount of goods which can be exported from there into France and Spain, and Customs checks are frequently made. Each person aged 17 years or over is permitted to export the following items from Andorra free of duty or tax:

1.5 litre of spirits over 22 % vol or 3 litres spirits or apertifs under 22 % vol or sparkling wine

5 litres of table wine

300 cigarettes or 150 cigarillos or 75 cigars or 400 gm of tobacco

75g of perfumes + 375 ml of eau de cologne

Other items (industrial products) up to the value of €900

There are no Customs formalities when entering Andorra from France or Spain.

Medicines

There is no limit to the amount of medicines you can take abroad if they are obtained without prescription (i.e. over the counter medicines), but medicines prescribed by your doctor may contain controlled drugs (e.g. those containing morphine). You must obtain a licence if you are leaving the UK for 3 months or more with medication containing a controlled drug. Visit www.gov.uk/travelling-controlled-drugs or tel. 020 7035 0771 for a list of controlled drugs and to apply for a licence.

You don't need a licence if you carry supplies for less than 3 months or if your medication doesn't contain controlled drugs, but you should carry a letter from your doctor stating your name, a list of your prescribed drugs and dosages for each drug. You may have to show this letter when going through customs.

Personal Possessions

Visitors to countries within the EU are free to carry reasonable quantities of any personal possessions such as jewellery, cameras, and electrical equipment required for the duration of their stay. It is sensible to carry sales receipts for new items in case you need to prove that tax has already been paid.

Prohibited and Restricted Goods

Regardless of where you are travelling from the importation of some goods into the UK is restricted or banned, mainly to protect health and the environment. These include:

- Endangered animals or plants including live animals, birds and plants, ivory, skins, coral, hides, shells and goods made from them such as jewellery, shoes, bags and belts.
- Controlled, unlicensed or dangerous drugs.
- Counterfeit or pirated goods such as watches, CDs and clothes; goods bearing a false indication of their place of manufacture or in breach of UK copyright.
- Offensive weapons such as firearms, flick knives, knuckledusters, push daggers or knives disguised as everyday objects.
- Pornographic material depicting extreme violence or featuring children such as DVDs, magazines, videos, books and software.

This list is not exhaustive; if in doubt contact HM Revenue & Customs National Advice Service on 0845 010 9000 or +44 2920 501 261 from outside the UK for more information or, when returning to the UK, go through the red Customs channel or use the telephone at the Red Point and ask a Customs officer. It is your responsibility to make sure that you are not breaking the law. Never attempt to mislead or hide anything from Customs officers; penalties are severe.

Plants and food

Travellers from within the EU may bring into the UK any fruit, vegetable or plant products without restriction as long as they are grown in the EU, are free from pests or disease and are for your own consumption. For food products Andorra, the Channel Islands, the Isle of Man, San Marino and Switzerland are treated as part of the EU.

From most countries outside the EU you are not allowed to bring into the UK any meat or dairy products. Other animal products may be severely restricted or banned and it is important that you declare any such products on entering the UK.

For up to date information please contact the Food and Environment Research Agency (Fera) on 0844 248 0071. If you are unsure about any item you are bringing in, or are simply unsure of the rules, you must go to the red Customs channel or use the phone provided at the Red Point to speak to a Customs officer.

Money

Being able to safely access your money while you're away is a necessity for you to enjoy your break. It isn't a good idea to rely on one method of payment, so always have a backup plan. A mixture of a small amount of cash plus one or two electronic means of payment are a good idea.

Travellers' cheques have become less popular in recent years as fewer banks and hotels are willing or able to cash them. There are alternative options which offer the same level of security but are easier to use, such as pre-paid credit cards.

Local Currency

It is a good idea to take enough foreign currency for your journey and immediate needs on arrival, don't forget you may need change for tolls or parking on your journey. Currency exchange facilities will be available at ports & on ferries but rates offered may not be as good as you would find elsewhere. The Post Office, many high -street banks, exchange offices and travel agents offer commission free foreign exchange, some will charge a flat fee and some offer a 'buy back' service. All should stock Euros but during peak holiday times they may be running low so it can be a good idea to pre-order your currency. You should also pre-order any less common currencies. Shop around and compare commission and exchange rates, together with minimum charges.

Banks and money exchanges in central and eastern Europe won't usually accept Scottish and Northern Irish bank notes and may be reluctant to change any sterling which has been written on or is creased or worn

Foreign Currency Bank Accounts

Frequent travellers or those who spend long periods abroad may find a Euro bank account useful. Most such accounts impose no currency conversion charges for debit or credit card use and allow fee-free cash withdrawals at ATMs. Some banks may also allow you to spread your account across different currencies, depending on your circumstances. Speak to your bank about the services they offer.

This will also overcome a potential issue where automated payment machines, such as those found at petrol stations and toll booths, rejecting cards issued by foreign banks.

Travel Money Cards

Travel money cards are issued by various providers including the Post Office, Travelex, Lloyds Bank and American Express. For a comparison table see www.which-prepaid-card.co.uk.

They are increasingly popular as the PIN protected travel money card offers the security of Travellers Cheques, with the convenience of paying by card. You load the card with the amount you need before leaving home, and then use cash machines to make withdrawals or use the card to pay for goods and services as you would a credit or debit card. You can top the card up over the telephone or online while you are abroad. Please note that pre-paid cards cannot be used when you are not required to enter a PIN, so cannot be used on the French toll system.

These cards can be cheaper to use than credit or debit cards for both cash withdrawals and purchases as there are usually no loading or transaction fees to pay. In addition, because they are separate from your bank account, if the card is lost or stolen there is less risk of identity theft. However they are not accepted by automated payment machines where you don't have to enter a PIN such as those found at toll booths.

The Caravan Club have partnered with Moneycorp to offer the Explorer prepaid card to members. For more information visit www.caravanclub.co.uk/travelmoney.

Credit and Debit Cards

Credit and debit cards offer a convenient way of spending abroad. For the use of cards abroad most banks impose a foreign currency conversion charge (typically 2.75% per transaction) which is usually the same for both credit and debit cards. If you use your card card to withdraw cash there will be a further commission charge of up to 3% and you will be charged interest (possibly at a higher rate than normal) as soon as you withdraw the money.

If you have several cards, take at least two in case you encounter problems. Credit and debit 'chip and PIN' cards issued by UK banks may not be universally accepted abroad so check before incurring expenditure.

Contact your credit or debit card issuer before you leave home to let them know that you will be travelling abroad. In the battle against card fraud, card issuers are frequently likely to query transactions which they regard as unusual or suspicious, causing your card to be declined or temporarily stopped. You should always carry your card issuer's helpline number with you so that you can contact them if this happens. You will also need this number should you need to report the loss or theft of your card.

Dynamic Currency Conversion

When you pay with a credit or debit card, retailers may offer you the choice of currency for payment, e.g. a euro amount will be converted into sterling and then charged to your card account. You may be asked to sign an agreement to accept the conversion rate used and final amount charged and, having done so, there is no opportunity to change your mind or obtain a refund. This is known as a 'dynamic currency conversion' but the exchange rate used is likely to be worse than the rate offered by your card issuer.

Emergency Cash

If an emergency or theft means that you need cash in a hurry, then friends or relatives at home can send you emergency cash via money transfer services.

The Post Office, MoneyGram and Western Union all offer services which, allows the transfer of money to over 233,000 money transfer agents around the world. Transfers take approximately ten minutes and charges are levied on a sliding scale.

Ferries & the Channel Tunnel

Booking Your Ferry

If travelling in July or August, or peak weekends, such as Easter and half-term, make your reservation as early as possible. Space for caravans and large vehicles is usually limited and cheaper off-peak crossings can fill up quickly. If you need any special assistance or arrangements make sure you request this at the time of booking.

When booking any ferry crossing, make sure you give the correct measurements for your outfit including bikes, roof boxes or anything else which may add to the length or height of your vehicle. If your vehicle is larger than your booking states you may be turned away at boarding.

The Caravan Club is an agent for most major ferry companies operating services. Call The Club's Travel Service on 01342 316 101 or see www.caravanclub.co.uk/ferries to book and for details of special offers, some of which are exclusive to Caravan Club members.

The tables on the following page show current ferry routes from the UK to the Continent and Ireland. Some ferry routes may not be operational all year, and during peak holiday periods the transportation of caravans or motorhomes may be restricted. For the most up-to-date information on ferry routes and prices visit www.caravanclub.co.uk/ferries or speak to The Club's Travel Services team.

Channel Tunnel

The Channel Tunnel operator, Eurotunnel, accepts cars, caravans and motorhomes (except those running on LPG) on their service between Folkestone and Calais. You can just turn up and see if there is availability on the day, however prices increase as the crossing gets fuller so if you know your plans in advance it is best to book as early as possible.

You will be asked to open your roof vents prior to travel and you will also need to apply the caravan brake once you have parked your vehicle on the train. You will not be able to use your caravan until arrival.

On the Journey

Arrive at the port with plenty of time before your boarding time. Motorhomes and car/caravan outfits will usually either be the first or last vehicles boarded onto the ferry. Almost all ferries are now 'drive on – drive off' so

you won't be required to do any complicated manoeuvres. You may be required to show ferry staff that your gas is switched off before boarding the ferry.

Be careful using the ferry access ramps, as they are often very steep which mean there is a risk of grounding the tow bar or caravan hitch. Drive slowly and, if your ground clearance is low, consider whether removing your stabiliser and/or jockey wheel would help.

Vehicles are often parked close together on ferries, meaning that if you have towing extension mirrors they could get knocked or damaged by people trying to get past your vehicle. If you leave them attached during the ferry crossing then make sure you check their position on returning to your vehicle.

Pets on Ferries and Eurotunnel

It is possible to transport your pet on a number of ferry routes to the Continent and Ireland, as well as on Eurotunnel services from Folkestone to Calais. Advance booking is essential as restrictions apply to the number of animals allowed on any one crossing. Make sure you understand the carrier's terms and conditions for transporting pets.

Once on board pets are normally required to remain in their owner's vehicle or in kennels on the car deck and you won't be able to access your vehicle to check on your pet while the ferry is at sea. On longer crossings you should make arrangements at the on-board information desk for permission to visit your pet in order to check its well-being. You should always make sure that ferry staff know your vehicle has a pet on board.

Information and advice on the welfare of animals before and during a journey is available on the website of the Department for Environment, Food and Rural Affairs (Defra), www.gov.uk/defra.

Gas on Ferries and in the Channel Tunnel

UK based ferry companies usually allow up to three gas cylinders per caravan, including the cylinder currently in use, however some may restrict this to a maximum of two cylinders. Some operators may ask you to hand over your gas cylinders to a member of the crew so that they can be safely stored during the crossing. Check that you know the rules of your ferry operator before you travel.

Cylinder valves should be fully closed and covered with a cap, if provided, and should remain closed during the crossing. Cylinders should be fixed securely in or on the caravan in the position specified by the manufacturer.

Gas cylinders must be declared at check-in and the crew may ask to inspect each cylinder for leakage before travel.

Eurotunnel will allow vehicles fitted with LPG tanks for the purposes of heating, lighting, cooking or refrigeration to use their service, but regulations stipulate that a total of no more than 47 kg of gas can be carried through the Channel Tunnel. Tanks must be switched off before boarding and must be less than 80% full; you will be asked to demonstrate this before you travel. Vehicles powered by LPG cannot be carried through the Channel Tunnel.

Most ferry companies will accept LPG-powered vehicles but you must let them know at the time of booking. During the crossing the tank must be no more than 75% full and it must be turned off. In the case of vehicles converted to use LPG, some ferry companies also require a certificate showing that the conversion has been carried out to the manufacturer's specification.

The carriage of spare petrol cans, whether full or empty, is not permitted on ferries or through the Channel Tunnel. Caravan Club Sites Near Ports

Caravan Club Sites Near Ports

If you've got a long drive to the ferry port, or want to catch an early ferry then an overnight stop near to the port gives you a relaxing start to your holiday. The following table lists Caravan Club sites which are close to ports.

Members can book online at www.caravanclub.co.uk or call 01342 327490. If you aren't a Club member you will need to contact the sites directly when they are open.

Please note that Commons Wood, Daleacres, Fairlight Wood, Hunter's Moon, Mildenhall, Old Hartley and Rookesbury Park are open to Caravan Club members only. Non-members are welcome at all the other Caravan Club sites listed below.

Port	Nearest Club Site and Town	Tel No.
Cairnryan, Stranraer	New England Bay (Drummore)	01776 860275
Dover, Folkestone, Channel Tunnel	Bearsted (Maidstone)	01622 730018
	Black Horse Farm* (Folkestone)	01303 892665
	Daleacres (Hythe)	01303 267679
	Fairlight Wood (Hastings)	01424 812333
Fishguard, Pembroke	Freshwater East (Pembroke)	01646 672341
Harwich	Cambridge Cherry Hinton*	01223 244088
	Commons Wood* (Welwyn Garden City)	01707 260786
	Mildenhall	01638 713089
Holyhead	Penrhos (Benllech)	01248 852617
Hull	York Beechwood Grange	01904 424637
	York Rowntree Park	01904 658997
Newcastle upon Tyne	Old Hartley (Whitley Bay)	0191 237 0256
Newhaven	Brighton*	01273 626546
Plymouth	Plymouth Sound	01752 862325
Poole	Hunter's Moon*, Wareham	01929 556605
Portsmouth	Rookesbury Park, Fareham	01329 834085
Rosslare	River Valley, Wicklow	00353 (0)404 41647
Weymouth	Crossways, Dorchester	01305 852032

** Site open all year*

Ferry routes and Operators

Route	Operator	Approximate Crossing Time	Maximum Frequency
Belgium			
Hull – Zeebrugge	P & O Ferries	12½ hrs	1 daily
Denmark			
Harwich – Esbjerg	DFDS Seaways	18¼ hrs	3 per week
France			
Dover – Calais	P & O Ferries	1½ hrs	22 daily
Dover – Dunkerque	DFDS Seaways	2 hrs	12 daily
Folkestone – Calais	Eurotunnel	35 mins	3 per hour
Newhaven – Dieppe	Transmanche Ferries	4 hrs	2 daily
Plymouth – Roscoff	Brittany Ferries	6 hrs	2 daily
Poole – Cherbourg	Brittany Ferries	4½ hrs	1 daily
Poole – St Malo (via Channel Islands)	Condor Ferries	5 hrs	1 daily (May to Sep)
Portsmouth – Caen	Brittany Ferries	3¾ / 7½ hrs	4 daily
Portsmouth – Cherbourg	Brittany Ferries	3 / 4½ hrs	3 daily
Portsmouth – Cherbourg	Condor Ferries	5½ hrs	1 weekly (May to Sep)
Portsmouth – Le Havre	LD Lines	3¼ / 8 hrs	2 daily
Portsmouth – St Malo	Brittany Ferries	9 hrs	1 daily
Weymouth – St Malo (via Channel Islands)	Condor Ferries	9½ hrs	1 daily
Ireland – Northern			
Cairnryan/Troon – Larne	P & O Irish Sea	1 / 2 hrs	11 daily
Liverpool (Birkenhead) – Belfast	Stena Line	8 hrs	2 daily
Cairnryan – Belfast	Stena Line	2 / 3 hrs	7 daily
Ireland – Republic			
Cork – Roscoff†	Brittany Ferries	14 hrs	1 per week
Fishguard – Rosslare	Stena Line	2 / 3½ hrs	3 daily
Holyhead – Dublin	Irish Ferries	1¾ / 3¼ hrs	4 daily
Holyhead – Dublin	Stena Line	3¼ hrs	4 daily
Holyhead – Dun Loaghaire	Stena Line	2 hrs	2 daily
Liverpool – Dublin	P & O Irish Sea	8 hrs	2 daily
Liverpool (Birkenhead) – Dublin	Stena Line	7 hrs	2 daily
Pembroke – Rosslare	Irish Ferries	4 hrs	2 daily
Rosslare – Cherbourg†	Irish Ferries	19½ hrs	3 per week
Rosslare – Cherbourg†	Celtic Link Ferries	17 hrs	3 per week
Rosslare – Roscoff†	Irish Ferries	19½ hrs	4 per week
Netherlands			
Harwich – Hook of Holland	Stena Line	6½ hrs	2 daily
Hull – Rotterdam	P & O Ferries	10¼ hrs	1 daily
Newcastle – Ijmuiden (Amsterdam)	DFDS Seaways	15½ hrs	1 daily
Spain			
Portsmouth – Bilbao	Brittany Ferries	24 hrs	2 per week
Portsmouth or Plymouth – Santander	Brittany Ferries	24 / 20 hrs	4 per week

† *Not bookable through the Club's Travel Service.*

Note: Services and routes correct at time of publication but subject to change.

Motoring Advice

Preparing for Your Journey

The first priority in preparing for your outfit for your journey should be to make sure it has a full service. Make sure that you have a fully equipped spares kit, and a spare wheel and tyre for your caravan – it is easier to get hold of them from your local dealer than to have to spend time searching for spares where you don't know the local area.

If you're a member of The Caravan Club then carry your UK Sites Directory & Handbook with you, as it contains a section of technical advice which may be useful when travelling. If you have any queries you can also contact The Club's free advice service who have information on all things caravanning – you can download free information leaflets at www.caravanclub.co.uk/advice or contact the team by calling 01342 336611 or emailing technical@caravanclub.co.uk.

For advice on issues specific to countries other than the UK, Club members should contact the Travel Service Information Officer, email: travelserviceinfo@caravanclub.co.uk or call 01342 336766.

Weight Limits

From both a legal and a safety point of view, it is essential not to exceed vehicle weight limits. It is advisable to carry documentation confirming your vehicle's maximum permitted laden weight - if your Vehicle Registration Certificate (V5C) does not clearly state this, you will need to produce alternative certification, e.g. from a weighbridge.

If you are pulled over by the police and don't have certification you will be taken to a weighbridge. If your vehicle(s) are then found to be overweight you will be liable to a fine and may have to discard items to lower the weight before you can continue on your journey.

Some Final Checks

Before you start any journey make sure you complete the following checks:

- All car and caravan or motorhome lights are working and sets of spare bulbs are packed.
- The coupling is correctly seated on the towball and the breakaway cable is attached.
- Windows, vents and hatches are shut.

- All on-board water systems are drained.
- Mirrors are adjusted for maximum visibility.
- Corner steadies are fully wound up and the brace is handy for your arrival on site.
- Any fires or flames are extinguished and the gas cylinder tap is turned off. Fire extinguishers are fully charged and close at hand.
- The over-run brake is working correctly.
- The jockey wheel is raised and secured, the handbrake is released.

Driving in France

Driving abroad for the first time can be a daunting prospect, especially when towing a caravan. Here are a few tips to make the transition easier:

- Remember that sat navs may take you on unsuitable roads, so have a map or atlas to hand to help you find an alternative route.
- It can be tempting to try and get to your destination as quickly as possible but we recommend travelling a maximum of 250 miles a day when towing. Share the driving if possible, and if you're going a long way then plan in an overnight stop.
- Remember that if you need to overtake a slow moving vehicle or pull out around an obstruction you will not be able to see clearly from the driver's seat. If possible, always have a responsible adult in the passenger seat who can advise you when it is clear to pull out. If that is not possible then stay well back to get a better view and pull out slowly.
- If traffic builds up behind you, pull over safely and let it pass.
- Driving on the right should become second nature after a while, but pay particular attention when turning left, leaving a rest area, petrol station or site, or after a one-way system.
- Stop at least every two hours to stretch your legs and take a break.

Accidents

A driver involved in an accident or one who has committed a traffic offence may be required to take a saliva or urine drugs test as well as a breathalyser test. In the event of an accident where people are injured or if emergency assistance is required, dial 17 (police) or 112 from any phone.

Alcohol

In both France and Andorra the maximum legal level of alcohol is 50 milligrams in 100 millilitres of blood, i.e. less than permitted in the UK (80 milligrams). It is advisable to adopt the 'no drink and drive' rule at all times. The police carry out random breath tests and penalties are severe.

There is a legal requirement to carry a breathalyser, however there is currently no punishment for non-compliance. Check www.caravanclub.co.uk/overseasadvice for the most up-to-date advice before you travel.

Breakdown Service

Breakdown and accident assistance on motorways and on motorway service and rest areas can only be obtained by contacting the police direct. They can be called from one of the orange emergency telephones placed every 2km along motorways. If you are in a service area, ask service station staff to contact the police for you, or dial 17 or 112 from a public phone and the police will be able to pinpoint your exact whereabouts. The police will arrange breakdown and towing assistance. No breakdown vehicle will enter a motorway without police authority.

Charges for motorway assistance are fixed by the government and vary according to category/weight of vehicle, time of day and whether the breakdown occurred over a weekend or public holiday. The basic cost (2013) of repairing a vehicle up to 1,800 kg in weight, on the spot, between Monday and Friday, from 0800 to 1800, is €119.75 or €148.00 for vehicles over 1800kg. Higher charges apply at night and over weekends and public holidays.

If you have taken out breakdown insurance you should contact your insurance provider once the breakdown service has arrived in order to establish a means of payment. Your insurance provider cannot summon the police on your behalf if you breakdown on a motorway.

Fuel

Unleaded petrol pumps are marked 'Essence Sans Plomb'. Diesel pumps are marked Gas Oil or Gazole.

Petrol stations may close on Sundays and those at supermarkets, where petrol is generally cheaper, may close for lunch. At supermarkets it is advisable to check the height and width clearance before towing past the pumps. Credit cards are generally accepted. Some automatic pumps at unmanned petrol stations are operated by credit cards and increasingly these accept cards issued outside France and have instructions in English, but you should not rely on this being the case. Away from major roads and towns it is a good idea not to let your fuel tank run too low as you may have difficulty finding a petrol station, especially at night or on Sundays.

Fuel containing 10% bioethanol is on sale at many petrol stations in France alongside the regular Euro 95 unleaded fuel, which it will eventually replace. Pumps are labelled SP95-E10. This fuel can be used in most modern vehicles manufactured since 2000 but if you are in any doubt about using it then regular Euro 95 or 98 Super Plus unleaded fuel is still available at most petrol stations. For a list of vehicles which can safely use SP95-E10 see the French website www.carburante10.fr or check with your vehicle manufacturer.

To find the cheapest fuel in any area log on to www.zagaz.com and simply click on the map of France to find the locations of petrol stations, together with prices charged. Alternatively view the French government website,
www.prix-carburants.gouv.fr which gives fuel prices all over the country.

Members of The Caravan Club can check current average fuel prices by country at www.caravanclub.co.uk/overseasadvice.

Automotive Liquified Petroleum Gas (LPG)
The increasing popularity of dual-fuelled vehicles means that the availability of LPG – also known as 'autogas' or GPL – has become an important issue for more drivers. LPG (also called Gepel or GPL) is available in petrol stations across France, especially on motorways. However LPG may not be available in more rural areas so you are advised to fill up at the first opportunity. Maps showing their company's outlets are issued free by most LPG suppliers, e.g. Shell, Elf, etc. A list of locations is available online on http://stations.gpl.online.fr. LPG is not available in Andorra.

Low Emission Zones

There are currently no Low Emission Zones in force in French cities. For up-to-date information visit www.lowemissionzones.eu.

Motorhomes Towing Cars

It is illegal to tow a vehicle with another motor vehicle in France. While this law was introduced to prevent the use of tow ropes, the French authorities have never specified whether A-frames are excluded from this law and therefore it is possible that you may be stopped and fined for towing with an A-frame. To ensure that you stay within the law motorhome users towing a small car should transport it on a braked trailer so that all four of the car's wheels are off the road.

Motorways

France has over 11,400 kilometres of excellent motorways and more are under construction or planned. Tolls are payable on most routes according to distance travelled and category of vehicle(s) and, because motorways are privately financed, prices per kilometre vary in different parts of the country. Emergency telephones connected to the police are located every 2km.

Motorway Service Areas
Stopping is allowed for a few hours at the service areas of motorways, called 'aires', and some have sections specially laid out for caravans. Most have toilet facilities and a water supply but at 'aires' with only basic facilities, water may not be suitable for

drinking, indicated by a sign 'eau non potable'. In addition there are 'aires de repos' which have picnic and play areas, whereas 'aires de services' resemble UK motorway service areas with fuel, shop, restaurant and parking facilities for all types of vehicle.

Motorway Tolls

Motorways tolls are charged extensively throughout France by a number of different operating companies, although there are numerous stretches, particularly around large cities, where no tolls are levied. Vehicles are classified as follows:

Category 1: (Light Vehicles) Vehicle with overall height under 2m and gross vehicle weight not exceeding 3,500kg. Train with overall height under 2m and gross vehicle weight of towing vehicle not exceeding 3,500kg.

Category 2: (Intermediate Vehicles) Vehicle with overall height from 2m to 3m and gross vehicle weight up to 3,500kg. Train with overall height from 2m to 3m and gross vehicle weight up to 3,500kg.

Category 3: (HGV or bus with two axles) Vehicle with overall height of 3m or more. Vehicle with gross vehicle weight of more than 3,500kg. On the A14 all twin-axle buses are in category 4.

Category 4: (HGV or bus with three or more axles) Vehicle with more than two axles and height of 3m or more, or gross vehicle weight of more than 3,500kg. Train with overall height of 3m or more. Train with towing vehicle having gross vehicle weight of more than 3,500kg.

Motorists driving Category 2 vehicles adapted for the transport of disabled persons pay the toll specified for Category 1 vehicles. Holding a disabled person's Blue Badge does not automatically entitle foreign motorists to pay Category 1 charges, and the decision whether to downgrade from Category 2 to 1 will be made by the person at the toll booth, based on experience of similar vehicles registered in France.

To calculate the tolls payable on your planned route see www.viamichelin.com and tick the box marked 'Caravan' (ticking this box will also give the toll for a motorhome) and select the 'Michelin recommended' route. For more detailed information, consult the websites of the individual motorway operating companies, a list of which can be found on www.autoroutes.fr/en/asfa/french-motorway-companies (English option). Alternatively calculate tolls payable on your chosen route on www.autoroutes.fr.

Payment

Payments may be made in cash or by credit card, but be aware that when paying with a credit card you may not be asked for a signature or required to key in a PIN. Pre-paid credit cards, Maestro and Electron are not accepted.

On less frequently-used motorways, toll collection is increasingly by automatic machines equipped with height detectors. It is simplest to pay with a credit card but there should be a cash/change machine adjacent. There are lanes at nearly all toll plazas specifically for drivers who have a Liber-t toll tag which allows them to pay for tolls directly from their bank account. Caravan Club members can benefit from a free Liber-t tag application (normally €10) - visit www.caravanclub.co.uk/sanef for details.

Overtaking and Passing

Crossing a solid single or double centre line is heavily penalised.

Outside built-up areas, outfits weighing more than 3,500 kg, or more than 7m in length, are required by law to leave at least 50m between themselves and the vehicle in front. They are only permitted to use the two right-hand lanes on roads with three or more lanes and, where overtaking is difficult, should slow down or stop to allow other smaller vehicles to pass.

Parking

As a general rule, all prohibitions are indicated by road signs or by yellow road markings. Stopping or parking on the left-hand side of the road is prohibited except in one-way streets.

In most French cities parking meters have largely been replaced by 'pay and display' machines which take coins and credit or debit cards. Where parking signs show 'Horodateur' or 'Stationnement Payant' you must obtain a ticket from a nearby machine.

In Paris two red routes ('axe rouge') have been created on which stopping and parking are absolutely prohibited. Elsewhere, drivers must observe parking restrictions indicated by signs. Car parks are expensive and the best advice is to use public transport which is cheap and efficient.

In many cities and towns there are blue zones (indicated by blue street markings) where you can sometimes park for free, usually for one hour between 9am and 12pm, and between 2pm and 7pm, from Monday to Saturday. You must display a parking disc ('disque de contrôle/stationnement') in your windscreen; these are available free, or for a small fee, from garages, travel agencies, motoring organisations, tourist offices, police stations, tobacconists and some shops.

Priority

In built up areas, give way to traffic coming from the right, unless otherwise indicated. Outside built-up areas traffic on all main roads of any importance has right of way, indicated by the following signs:

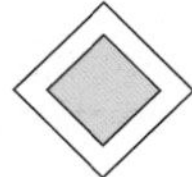

Priority road   Priority road

On entering towns, the same sign will often have a line through it, warning that vehicles may pull out from a side road on the right and will have priority.

End of priority road

On steep gradients, vehicles travelling downhill must give way to vehicles travelling uphill.

Public Transport

In general in built-up areas be prepared to stop to allow a bus to pull out from a bus stop when the driver is signalling his intention to do so. Take particular care when school buses have stopped and passengers are getting on and off.

Overtaking trams in motion is normally only allowed on the right, unless on a one way street where you can overtake on the left if there is not enough space on the right. Do not overtake a tram near a tram stop. These may be in the centre of the road. When a tram or bus stops to allow passengers on and off, you should stop to allow them to cross to the pavement. Give way to trams which are turning across your carriageway. Don't park or stop across tram lines; trams cannot steer round obstructions!

Pedestrian Crossings

Stopping to allow pedestrians to cross at zebra crossings is not always common practice on the Continent as it is in the UK. Pedestrians expect to wait until the road is clear before crossing, while motorists behind may be taken by surprise by your stopping. The result may be a rear-end shunt or vehicles overtaking you at the crossing and putting pedestrians at risk.

Roads

French roads fall into three categories: autoroutes (A) i.e. motorways; national (N) roads; and departmental (D) roads. There are over 10,500 kilometres of motorways, on most of which tolls are levied. British motorists will find French roads relatively uncongested.

Re-Numbering of French Roads

The French government has transferred the administration of approximately 18,000 kilometres of national N roads to local authorities, resulting in the significant re-classification and re-numbering of roads. For example, the N21 has become the D821 and a part of the N20 is now the D820.

Andorra

Travellers to Andorra from France should be aware that conditions on the road from Toulouse to Andorra, the N20/E9, can quickly become difficult in severe winter weather and you should be prepared for delays.

It is advisable to stick to main roads in Andorra when towing and not to attempt the many unsurfaced roads.

Road Signs and Markings

Directional signposting on major roads is generally good. Signs may be placed on walls pointing across the road they indicate and this may be confusing at first until you get the feel for them. Generally a sign on the right pointing left means that you go straight ahead. The same sign on the right pointing right means 'turn right' at the first opportunity. The words 'tout droit' mean 'go straight ahead' or 'straight on'.

Road signs on approach to roundabouts and at junctions usually do not show road numbers, just the destination, with numbers being displayed once you are on the road itself. Make sure you know the names of places along your proposed route, and not just the road numbers. Once you have seen your destination town signposted continue along the road until directed otherwise. Intermediate junctions or roundabouts where you do not have to turn usually omit the destination name if the route to it is straight on.

Lines on the carriageway are generally white. A yellow zigzag line indicates a bus stop, blue markings indicate that parking is restricted and yellow lines on the edge of the roadway also indicate that stopping and/or parking is prohibited. A solid single or double white line in the centre of the road indicates that overtaking is not permitted.

STOP signs mean stop - you must come to a complete halt otherwise you may be liable to a fine if caught.

Whilst road signs conform to international standards, some other commonly used signs you may see include:

French	English translation
Allumez vos feux	Switch on lights
Attention	Caution
Bouchon	Traffic jam
Chausée deformée	Uneven road
Chemin sans issue	No through road
Col	Mountain pass
Créneau de dépassement	2-lane passing zone, dual carriageway
Déviation	Diversion
Fin d'interdiction de stationner	End of parking restrictions
Gravillons	Loose chippings
Interdit aux piétons	No pedestrians
Itineraire bis	Alternative route
Péage	Toll
Ralentissez	Slow down
Rappel	Continued restriction
Rétrécissement	Narrow lane
Route barrée	Road closed
Sens interdit	No entry
Sens unique	One-way street
Serrez à gauche/ droite	Keep left/right
Stationnement interdit	No parking
Tout droit	Straight on
Toutes directions	All directions
Travaux	Road works
Virages	Bends

Andorra

Main roads are prefixed 'CG' (Carretera General) and side roads are prefixed 'CS' (Carretera Secundaria). CG road signs are white on red and CS signs are white on green.

Recently-Qualified Drivers

The minimum age to drive in France is 18 years and this also applies to foreign drivers. Driving without professionally qualified supervision/ instruction on a provisional licence is not allowed.

Roundabouts

At roundabouts drivers must give way to traffic already on the roundabout, i.e. on the left, if indicated by a red-bordered triangular sign showing a roundabout symbol with the words 'Vous n'avez pas la priorité' or 'Cédez le passage' underneath.

Traffic on the roundabout has priority

In the absence of these signs traffic entering the roundabout has priority, however it is always very important to be watchful and to take extra care at roundabouts and junctions to avoid accidents.

Speed Limits

Police are strict about speeding - motorists caught driving more than 40 km/h (25mph) over the speed limit face immediate confiscation of their driving licence. Motorway toll booths will also calculate your speed from the distance you have travelled and the time it has taken, and the police will be alerted if you have driven over the speed limit.

Speed limits on motorways (in dry weather) are higher than in the UK – although they are lower on ordinary roads.

Fixed speed cameras are common on both motorways and major roads. The use of mobile speed cameras and radar traps is frequent, even on remote country roads, and may be operated from parked vans or motor bikes, or they may be hand-held. They may also be in use on exit slip roads from motorways or major roads where there is a posted speed limit.

Radar Detectors

Radar detectors, laser detectors or speed camera jammers are illegal in France. If caught carrying one – even if it is not in use – you are liable to both a fine of up to €1,500 and confiscation of the device, and possibly confiscation of your vehicle if unable to pay the fine. GPS or sat nav devices which pinpoint the position of fixed speed cameras are illegal in France, Germany and Switzerland. You can still use the device, but you must disable the function which pinpoints speed cameras.

Inside Built-up Areas

The general speed limit is 50 km/h (31 mph) which may be raised to 70 km/h (44 mph) on important through roads, indicated by signs. The beginning of a built-up area is marked by a road sign giving the name of the town or village in blue or black letters on a light background with a red border. The end of the built-up area is indicated by the same sign with a red diagonal line through it. See examples below:

Therefore, when you enter a town or village, even if there is no actual speed limit warning sign, the place name sign itself indicates that you are entering a 50 km/h zone. The end of the 50 km/h zone is indicated by the place name sign crossed out. The word 'rappel' on a speed limit sign is a reminder of that limit.

The speed limit on stretches of motorway in built-up areas is 110 km/h (68 mph), except on the Paris ring road where the limit is 80 km/h (50 mph).

Outside Built-up Areas

General speed limits are as follows:

- On single carriageway roads 90 km/h (56 mph)
- On dual-carriageways separated by a central reservation 110 km/h (68 mph)
- On motorways 130 km/h (81 mph)

These general speed limits also apply to private cars towing a trailer tent or caravan, provided the gross train mass (fully laden weight of the car, plus the cars towing limit) of the vehicle does not exceed 3,500 kg. If the gross train mass of the towing vehicle is over 3,500 kg the speed limits are 90 km/h (56 mph) on motorways, 80-90 km/h (50 mph) on dual carriageways and 80 km/h (50 mph) on single carriageways.

Large motorhomes over 3,500 kg have a speed limit of 110 km/h (68 mph) on motorways, 100 km/h (62 mph) on dual carriageways and 80 km/h (50 mph) on single carriageway roads.

For full details of speed regulations see www.caravanclub.co.uk/overseasadvice.

Adverse Weather Conditions

In case of rain or adverse weather conditions, general speed limits are lowered as follows:

- On motorways 110 km/h (68 mph)
- On urban motorways and dual carriageways 100 km/h (62 mph)
- Outside built-up areas 80 km/h (50 mph)

A speed limit of 50 km/h (31 mph) applies on all roads (including motorways) in foggy conditions when visibility is less than 50 metres.

Traffic Jams

The A6/A7 (the Autoroute du Soleil) from Paris via Lyon to the south are busy motorways prone to traffic jams. Travelling from the north, bottlenecks are often encountered at Auxerre, Chalon-sur-Saône, Lyon, Valence and Orange. An alternative route to the south is the A20, which is largely toll-free, or the toll-free A75 via Clermont-Ferrand.

During periods of severe congestion on the A6, A7 and A10 Paris-Bordeaux motorways, traffic police close off junctions and divert holiday traffic onto alternative routes or 'Itinéraires Bis' which run parallel to main roads. Yellow and black signs indicate these routes. For a summer traffic calendar, indicating when certain areas are most prone to traffic jams, together with a real-time congestion map and regional phone numbers to call for traffic/travel information, see www.bison-fute.equipement.gouv.fr.

Alternative holiday routes

Information centre for holiday route

Realtime traffic information on traffic conditions on motorways can be found on www.autoroutes.fr.

In general, Friday afternoons and Saturday mornings are busiest on roads leading south, and on Saturday and Sunday afternoons roads leading north may well be congested. Many French people drop everything for lunch and, therefore, between noon and 2pm roads are quieter.

At the start of the school holidays in early July, at the end of July and during the first and last few days of August, roads are particularly busy. Avoid the changover weekend at the end of July/beginning of August when traffic both north and south bound can be virtually at a standstill. Traffic can also be very heavy around the Christmas/New Year period and on the weekend of any public holiday.

Andorra

There is heavy traffic in Andorra-la-Vella town centre on most days of the year. During the peak summer holiday period you are likely to encounter queues of traffic on the Envalira pass from France on the N22. Traffic is at its worst in the morning from France and in the afternoon and evening from Andorra and you are recommended to use the Envalira Tunnel to avoid some of the congestion and reduce travel time.

Traffic Lights

There is no amber light after the red light in the traffic light sequence.

A flashing amber light indicates caution, slow down, proceed but give way to vehicles coming from the right. A flashing red light indicates no entry; it may also be used to mark level crossings, obstacles, etc.

A yellow arrow at the same time as a red light indicates that drivers may turn in the direction of the arrow, traffic permitting, and providing they give way to pedestrians.

Watch out for traffic lights which may be mounted high above the road and hard to spot.

Violation of Traffic Regulations

Severe fines and penalties are in force for motoring offences and the police are authorised to impose and collect fines on the spot. Violations include minor infringements such as not wearing a seat belt, not carrying a set of spare bulbs or not respecting a STOP sign. More serious infringements such as dangerous overtaking, crossing a continuous central white line and driving at very high speeds, can result in confiscation of your driving licence.

If the offence committed is serious and likely to entail a heavy fine and the suspension of your driving licence or a prison sentence, a motorist who is not resident in France and has no employment there must deposit a guarantee. The police may hold a vehicle until payment is made.

Drivers who are deemed to have deliberately put the lives of others in danger face a maximum fine of €15,000 and a jail sentence. Failure to pay may result in your car being impounded. Your driving licence may also be suspended for up to five years.

By paying fines on the spot (request a receipt) or within three days, motorists can avoid court action and even reduce the fine. Standard fines can now be paid electronically in post offices and newsagents equipped with a dedicated terminal or by visiting www.amendes.gouv.fr.

Motoring Equipment

Essential Equipment

The equipment that you legally have to carry differs by country. For a full list see the Essential Equipment table at the end of this chapter, or see the Country Introductions of this book for country specific information. Please note equipment requirements and regulations can change frequently. To keep up to date with the latest equipment information please visit www.caravanclub.co.uk/overseasadvice.

Child Restraint Systems

Children under 10 years of age are not permitted to travel in front seats of vehicles, unless there are no rear seats in the vehicle, or the rear seats are already occupied with other children, or there are no seat belts in the rear. In these situations a child must not be placed in the front seats in a rear-facing child seat, unless any airbag is deactivated. Children up to 10 must travel in an approved child seat or restariant system, adapted to their size. A baby up to 13kg in weight must be carried in a rear facing baby seat. A child between 9kg and 18kg in weight must be seated in a child seat. A child from 15kg in weight up to the age of 10 can use a booster seat with a seat belt.

In Andorra children under 10 years of age and under 1.5m in height must always use a restaraint system that has been approved by the EU and has been adapted to their size. Children must not travel in the front of a vehicle if there are rear seats available. If they travel in the front the airbag must be deactivated and again they must use an EU approved restaraint system adapted to their size.

Fire Extinguisher

As a safety precaution, an approved fire extinguisher should be carried in all vehicles. This is a legal requirement in several countries in Europe.

Glasses

In some countries it is a legal requirement for residents to carry a spare pair of glasses if they are needed for driving, and it is recommended that visitors also comply. Elsewhere, if you do not have a spare pair, you may find it helpful to carry a copy of your prescription.

Lights

When driving on the Continent headlights need to be adjusted to deflect to the right if

they are likely to dazzle other road users. You can do this by applying beam deflectors, or some newer vehicles have a built-in adjustment system. Some modern high-density discharge (HID), xenon or halogen-type lights, may need to be taken to a dealer to make the necessary adjustment. Remember also to adjust headlights according to the load being carried and to compensate for the weight of the caravan on the back of your car. Even if you do not intend to drive at night, it is important to ensure that your headlights are correctly adjusted as you may need to use them in heavy rain, fog or in tunnels. If using tape or a pre-cut adhesive mask remember to remove it on your return home.

The use of dipped headlights is recommended at all times, day and night. Headlights must be adjusted for driving on the right if they are likely to dazzle other road users.

Headlight-Flashing
On the Continent headlight-flashing is used as a warning of approach or as an overtaking signal at night, and not, as is commonly the case in the UK, an indication that you are giving way. Be more cautious with both flashing your headlights and when another driver flashes you. If a driver flashes his headlights in France he is generally indicating that he has priority and you should give way, contrary to standard practice in the UK.

Hazard Warning Lights
Hazard warning lights should not be used in place of a warning triangle, but they may be used in addition to it.

Nationality Plate (GB/IRL)

A nationality plate must be fixed to the rear of both your car or motorhome and caravan. Checks are made and a fine may be imposed for failure to display a nationality plate correctly. If your number plates have the Euro-Symbol on them there is no requirement to display an additional GB sticker within the EU and Switzerland. If your number plate doesn't have the EU symbol or you are planning to travel outside of the EU you will need a GB sticker.

GB is the only national identification code allowed for cars registered in the UK.

Reflective Jackets/Waistcoats

It is a legal requirement for all vehicle occupants (driver and passengers) to wear a reflective jacket when getting out of a vehicle which is stationary on the carriageway or on the side of the road at any time of the day or night, regardless of visibility. Keep the jacket(s) to hand in your vehicle, not in the boot.

Route Planning

It is always a good idea to carry a road atlas or map of the countries you plan to visit, even if you have Satellite Navigation. You can find information on UK roads from Keep Moving – www.keepmoving.co.uk or call 09003 401100. Websites offering a European route mapping service include www.google.co.uk/maps, www.mappy.com or www.viamichelin.com.

Satellite Navigation/GPS

Continental postcodes don't cover just one street or part of a street in the same way as UK postcodes. A French five-digit postcode, for example, can cover a very large area.

GPS co-ordinates and full addresses are given for most site entries in this guide wherever possible, so that you can programme your sat nav as accurately as possible.

It is important to remember that sat nav devices don't usually allow for towing or driving a large motorhome and may try to send you down unsuitable roads. Always use your common sense, and if a road looks unsuitable find an alternative route.

Use your sat nav in conjunction with the directions given in the site entries, which have been provided by members who have actually visited. Please note that the directions given in site entries have not been checked by The Caravan Club.

In nearly all European countries it is illegal to use car navigation systems which actively search for mobile speed cameras or interfere with police equipment (laser or radar detection). Car navigation systems which give a warning of fixed speed camera locations are legal in most countries with the exception of France, Germany, and Switzerland where this function must be de-activated.

Seat Belts

The wearing of seat belts is compulsory throughout Europe and beyond. On-the-spot fines will be incurred for failure to wear them and, in the event of an accident failure to wear a seat belt may reduce any claim for injury. See the country introductions for specific regulations on both seat belts and car seats.

Spares

Caravan Spares

It will generally be much harder to get hold of spare parts for caravans on the continent, especially for UK manufactured caravans. It is therefore advisable to carry any commonly required spares (such as light bulbs) with you.

Take contact details of your UK dealer or manufacturer with you, as they may be able to assist in getting spares delivered to you in an emergency.

Car Spares Kits

Some car manufacturers produce spares kits; contact your dealer for details. The choice of spares will depend on the vehicle and how long you are away, but the following is a list of basic items which should cover the most common causes of breakdown:

- Radiator top hose
- Fan belt
- Fuses and bulbs
- Windscreen wiper blade
- Length of 12V electrical cable
- Tools, torch and WD40 or equivalent water repellent/ dispersant spray

Spare Wheel

Your local caravan dealer should be able to supply an appropriate spare wheel. If you have any difficulty in obtaining one, The Caravan Club's Technical Department can provide Club members with a list of suppliers on request.

Tyre legislation across Europe is more or less consistent and, while the Club has no specific knowledge of laws on the Continent regarding the use of space-saver spare wheels, there should be no problems in using such a wheel provided its use is in accordance with the manufacturer's instructions. Space-saver spare wheels are designed for short journeys to get to a place where it can be repaired and there will usually be restrictions on the distance and speed at which the vehicle should be driven.

Towbar

The vast majority of cars registered after 1 August 1998 are legally required to have a European Type approved towbar (complying with European Directive 94/20) carrying a plate giving its approval number and various technical details, including the maximum noseweight. Your car dealer or specialist towbar fitter will be able to give further advice.

From 2011 for brand new motorhome designs (launched on or after that date) and 2012 for existing designs (those already being built before 29 April 2011), all new motorhomes will need some form of type approval before they can be registered in the UK and as such can only be fitted with a type approved towbar. Older vehicles can continue to be fitted with non-approved towing brackets.

Tyres

Tyre condition has a major effect on the safe handling of your outfit. Caravan tyres must be suitable for the highest speed at which you can legally tow, even if you choose to drive slower.

Most countries require a minimum tread depth of 1.6mm but motoring organisations recommend at least 3mm. If you are planning a long journey, consider if they will still be above the legal minimum by the end of your journey.

Tyre Pressure

Tyre pressure should be checked and adjusted when the tyres are cold; checking warm tyres will result in a higher pressure reading. The correct pressures will be found in your car handbook, but unless it states otherwise to add an extra 4 - 6 pounds per square inch to the rear tyres of a car when towing to improve handling. Make sure you know what pressure your caravan tyres should be. Some require a pressure much higher than that normally used for cars. Check your caravan handbook for details.

Tyre Sizes

It is worth noting that some sizes of radial tyre to fit the 13" wheels commonly used on older UK caravans are virtually impossible to find in stock at retailers abroad, e.g. 175R13C.

After a Puncture

A lot of new cars now have a liquid sealant puncture repair kit instead of a spare wheel. These sealants should not be used to achieve a permanent repair and in some cases have been known to make repair of the tyre impossible. If you need to use a liquid sealant you should get the tyre repaired or replaced as soon as possible.

Following a caravan tyre puncture, especially on a single-axle caravan, it is advisable to have the opposite side (non-punctured) tyre removed from its wheel and checked inside and out for signs of damage resulting from overloading during the deflation of the punctured tyre.

Winter driving

Snow chains must be fitted to vehicles using snow-covered roads in compliance with the relevant road signs. Fines may be imposed for non-compliance. Vehicles fitted with chains must not exceed 50 km/h (31mph).

They are not difficult to fit but it's a good idea to carry sturdy gloves to protect your hands when handling the chains in freezing conditions. Polar Automotive Ltd sells and hires out snow chains (10% discount for Caravan Club members), tel 01892 519933 www.snowchains.com, email: polar@snowchains.com.

In Andorra winter tyres are recommended. Snow chains must be used when road conditions necessitate their use and/or when road signs indicate.

Warning Triangles

It is compulsory to carry a warning triangle which, in the event of vehicle breakdown or accident, must be placed (providing it is safe to do so) on the carriageway at least 30 metres from the vehicle. In some instances it is not compulsory to use the triangle but only when this action would endanger the driver. The French Tourist Board recommends carrying two triangles, as do the authorities in Andorra.

A warning triangle should be placed on the road approximately 30 metres (100 metres on motorways) behind the broken down vehicle on the same side of the road. Always assemble the triangle before leaving your vehicle and walk with it so that the red, reflective surface is facing oncoming traffic. If a breakdown occurs round a blind corner, place the triangle in advance of the corner. Hazard warning lights may be used in conjunction with the triangle but they do not replace it.

Essential Equipment Table

The table on the following page shows the essential equipment required for each country. The Country Introduction chapters also include details of specific rules for each country. Please note that this information was correct at the time of going to print but is subject to change. For up to date information on equipment requirements for countries in Europe visit www.caravanclub.co.uk/overseasadvice.

Country	Warning Triangle	Spare Bulbs	First Aid Kit	Reflective Jacket	Additional Equipment to be Carried/Used
Andorra	Yes (2)	Yes	Rec	Yes	Dipped headlights in poor daytime visibility. Winter tyres recommended; snow chains when road conditions or signs dictate.
Austria	Yes	Rec	Yes	Yes	Winter tyres from 1 Nov to 15 April.*
Belgium	Yes	Rec	Rec	Yes	Dipped headlights in poor daytime visibility.
Croatia	Yes (2 for vehicle with trailer)	Yes	Yes	Yes	Dipped headlights at all times from last Sunday in Oct - last Sunday in Mar. Spare bulbs compulsory if lights are xenon, neon or LED. Snow chains compulsory in winter in certain regions.*
Czech Rep	Yes	Yes	Yes	Yes	Dipped headlights at all times. Replacement fuses. Winter tyres or snow chains from 1 Nov - 31st March.*
Denmark	Yes	Rec	Rec	Rec	Dipped headlights at all times. On motorways use hazard warning lights when queues or danger ahead.
Finland	Yes	Rec	Rec	Yes	Dipped headlights at all times. Winter tyres Dec - Feb.*
France	Yes	Rec	Rec	Yes	Dipped headlights recommended at all times. Legal requirement to carry a breathalyser, but no penalty for non-compliance.
Germany	Rec	Rec	Rec	Rec	Dipped headlights recommended at all times. Winter tyres to be used in winter weather conditions.*
Greece	Yes	Rec	Yes	Rec	Fire extinguisher compulsory. Dipped headlights in towns at night and in poor daytime visibility.
Hungary	Yes	Rec	Yes	Yes	Dipped headlights at all times outside built-up areas and in built-up areas at night. Snow chains compulsory on some roads in winter conditions.*
Italy	Yes	Rec	Rec	Yes	Dipped headlights at all times outside built-up areas and in poor visibility. Snow chains from15 Oct - 15 April.*
Luxembourg	Yes	Rec	Rec	Yes	Dipped headlights at night and daytime in bad weather.
Netherlands	Yes	Rec	Rec	Rec	Dipped headlights at night and in bad weather and recommended during the day.
Norway	Yes	Rec	Rec	Rec	Dipped headlights at all times. Winter tyres compulsory when snow or ice on the roads.*
Poland	Yes	Rec	Rec	Rec	Dipped headlights at all times. Fire extinguisher compulsory.
Portugal	Yes	Rec	Rec	Rec	Dipped headlights in poor daytime visibility, in tunnels and in lanes where traffic flow is reversible.
Slovakia	Yes	Rec	Yes	Yes	Dipped headlights at all times. Winter tyres compulsory when compact snow or ice on the road.*
Slovenia	Yes (2 for vehicle with trailer)	Yes	Rec	Yes	Dipped headlights at all times. Hazard warning lights when reversing. Use winter tyres or carry snow chains 15 Nov - 15 Mar.
Spain	Yes (2 Rec)	Rec	Rec	Yes	Dipped headlights at night, in tunnels and on 'special' roads (roadworks).
Sweden	Yes	Rec	Rec	Rec	Dipped headlights at all times. Winter tyres 1 Dec to 31 March.
Switzerland (inc Liechtenstein)	Yes	Rec	Rec	Rec	Dipped headlights recommended at all times, compulsory in tunnels. Snow chains where indicated by signs.

NOTES:

1) *All countries: seat belts (if fitted) must be worn by all passengers.*
2) *Rec: not compulsory for foreign-registered vehicles, but strongly recommended*
3) *Headlamp converters, spare bulbs, fire extinguisher, first aid kit and reflective waistcoat are strongly recommended for all countries.*
4) *In some countries drivers who wear prescription glasses must carry a spare pair.*
5) *Please check information for any country before you travel. This information is to be used as a guide only and it is your responsibility to make sure you have the correct equipment.*

* *For more information and regulations on winter driving please see the Country Introduction.*

Route planning

Motorways
Major roads
Main roads
Ferry routes
Major airports

Gedser
Sassnitz
Gdańsk
Kiel
Rostock
Olsztyn
Bremerhaven
Hamburg
Schwerin
Szczecin
Groningen
Bremen
Assen
Bydgoszcz
Gorzów Wielkopolski
AMSTERDAM
Berlin
Hannover
Potsdam
Poznań
Osnabrück
Apeldoorn
Arnhem
Magdeburg
POLAND
Łódź
Bocholt
Essen
Dortmund
Düsseldorf
Leipzig
Wrocław
Erfurt
Dresden
Opole
Troisdorf
Liège
GERMANY
Liberec
Katowice
Karlovy Vary
Hradec Králové
Wiesbaden
Mainz
Frankfurt am Main
PRAHA
Ostrava
LUXEMBOURG
Plzeň
CZECH REPUBLIC
Olomouc
Zlín
Zilina
Saarbrücken
Nürnberg
Brno
Metz
České Budějovice
Trenčín
Karlsruhe
SLOVAKIA
Stuttgart
Sindelfingen
Trnava
Nitra
Strasbourg
Linz
WIEN
BRATISLAVA
München
BUDAPEST
Salzburg
Sopron
Győr
Basel
Zürich
Szombathely
Innsbruck
AUSTRIA
Veszprém
BERN
LIECHTENSTEIN
Graz
Luzern
HUNGARY
SWITZERLAND
Klagenfurt
Nagykanizsa
Lausanne
Maribor
Bolzano
Pécs
Genève
SLOVENIA
Trento
LJUBLJANA
ZAGREB
Osijek
Trieste
Slavonski Brod
Milano
Verona
Venezia
Karlovac
Grenoble
Rijeka
Torino
CROATIA
Banja Luka
Pula
Tuzla
BOSNIA AND HERZEGOVINA
Bologna
Genova
Zenica
SARAJEVO
Zadar
SAN MARINO
Nice
MONACO
Firenze
Ancona
Split
Mostar
Livorno
Adriatic Sea
Perugia
Dubrovnik
Bastia
ITALY
Pescara
L'Aquila
Corse (Corsica) (France)
Ajaccio
ROMA
Campobasso
Bari
Sardegne (Sardinia)
Olbia
Napoli
Potenza
Tyrrhenian

Mountain Passes & Tunnels

Advice for Drivers

Mountain Passes

Mountain passes can create difficult driving conditions, especially when towing or driving a large vehicle. You should only use them if you have a good power to weight ratio and in good driving conditions. If in any doubt as to your outfit's suitability or the weather then stick to motorway routes across maintain ranges if possible.

The tables on the following pages show which passes are not suitable for caravans, and those where caravans are not permitted. Motorhomes aren't usually included in these restrictions, but relatively low powered or very large vehicles should find an alternative route. Road signs at the foot of a pass may restrict access or offer advice, especially for heavy vehicles. Warning notices are usually posted at the foot of a pass if it is closed, or if chains or winter tyres must be used.

Caravanners are particularly sensitive to gradients and traffic/road conditions on passes. The maximum gradient is usually on the inside of bends but exercise caution if it is necessary to pull out. Always engage a lower gear before taking a hairpin bend and give priority to vehicles ascending. On mountain roads it is not the gradient which puts strain on your car but the duration of the climb and the loss of power at high altitudes: approximately 10% at 915 metres (3,000 feet) and even more as you get higher. To minimise the risk of the engine overheating, take high passes in the cool part of the day, don't climb any faster than necessary and keep the engine pulling steadily. To prevent a radiator boiling, pull off the road safely, turn the heater and blower full on and switch off air conditioning. Keep an eye on water and oil levels. Never put cold water into a boiling radiator or it may crack. Check that the radiator is not obstructed by debris sucked up during the journey.

A long descent may result in overheating brakes; select the correct gear for the gradient and avoid excessive use of brakes. Even if you are using engine braking to control speed, caravan brakes may activate due to the overrun mechanism, which may cause them to overheat.

Travelling at altitude can cause a pressure build up in tanks and water pipes. You can prevent this by slightly opening the blade valve of your portable toilet and opening a tap a fraction.

Tunnels

Long tunnels are a much more commonly seen feature in Europe than in the UK, especially in mountainous regions. Tolls are usually charged for the use of major tunnels.

Dipped headlights are usually required by law even in well-lit tunnels, so switch them on before you enter. Snow chains, if used, must be removed before entering a tunnel in lay-bys provided for this purpose.

'No overtaking' signs must be strictly observed. Never cross central single or double lines. If overtaking is permitted in twin-tube tunnels, bear in mind that it is very easy to underestimate distances and speed once inside. In order to minimise the effects of exhaust fumes close all car windows and set the ventilator to circulate air, or operate the air conditioning system coupled with the recycled air option.

If you break down, try to reach the next lay-by and call for help from an emergency phone. If you cannot reach a lay-by, place your warning triangle at least 100 metres behind your vehicle. Modern tunnels have video surveillance systems to ensure prompt assistance in an emergency. Some tunnels can extend for miles and a high number of breakdowns are due to running out of fuel so make sure you have enough before entering the tunnel.

In recent years safety features in both the Mont Blanc and Fréjus tunnels have been significantly overhauled and improved. Both tunnels are heavily used by freight vehicles and traffic is subject to a number of restrictions including minimum and maximum speed limits. All drivers should listen to the tunnels' radio stations and if your vehicle runs on LPG you should tell the toll operator before entering the tunnel. See www.tunnelmb.net and www.sftrf.fr.

Mountain Pass Information

The dates of opening and closing given in the following tables are approximate. Before attempting late afternoon or early morning journeys across borders, check their opening times as some borders close at night.

Gradients listed are the maximum which may be encountered on the pass and may be steeper at the inside of curves, particularly on older roads.

Gravel surfaces (such as dirt and stone chips) vary considerably; they can be dusty when dry and slippery when wet. Where known to exist, this type of surface has been noted.

In fine weather winter tyres or snow chains will only be required on very high passes, or for short periods in early or late summer. In winter conditions you will probably need to use them at altitudes exceeding 600 metres (approximately 2,000 feet).

Converting Gradients

20% = 1 in 5	11% = 1 in 9
16% = 1 in 6	10% = 1 in 8
14% = 1 in 7	8% = 1 in 12
12% = 1 in 8	6% = 1 in 16

Tables and maps

Much of the information contained in the following tables was originally supplied by The Automobile Association and other motoring and tourist organisations. The Caravan Club haven't checked this information and cannot accept responsibility for the accuracy or for errors or omissions to these tables.

The mountain passes, rail and road tunnels listed in the tables are shown on the following maps. Numbers and letters against each pass or tunnel in the tables, correspond with the numbers and letters on the maps.

Abbreviations

MHV	Maximum height of vehicle
MLV	Maximum length of vehicle
MWV	Maximum width of vehicle
MWR	Minimum width of road
OC	Occasionally closed between dates
UC	Usually closed between dates
UO	Usually open between dates, although a fall of snow may obstruct the road for 24-48 hours.

Major Alpine Mountain Passes

Before using any of these passes, PLEASE READ CAREFULLY THE ADVICE AT THE BEGINNING OF THIS CHAPTER

	Pass Height In Metres (Feet)	From To	Max Gradient	Conditions and Comments
1	**Allos** (France) 2250 (7382)	Colmars *Barcelonette*	10%	UC early Nov-early Jun. MWR 4m (13'1") Very winding, narrow, mostly unguarded pass on D908 but not difficult otherwise; passing bays on southern slope; poor surface, MWV 1.8m (5'11"). **Not recommended for caravans.**
2	**Aravis** (France) 1498 (4915)	La Clusaz *Flumet*	9%	OC Dec-Mar. MWR 4m (13'1"). Fine scenery; D909, fairly easy road. Poor surface in parts on Chamonix side. Some single-line traffic.
3	**Ballon d'Alsace** (France) 1178 (3865)	Giromagny *St Maurice-sur-Moselle*	11%	OC Dec-Mar. MWR 4m (13'1") Fairly straightforward ascent/descent; narrow in places; numerous bends. On road D465.
4	**Bayard** (France) 1248 (4094)	Chauffayer *Gap*	14%	UO. MWR 6m (19'8") Part of the Route Napoléon N85. Fairly easy, steepest on the S side with several hairpin bends. Negotiable by caravans from N-to-S via D1075 (N75) and Col-de-la-Croix Haute, avoiding Gap.
5	**Brouis** (France) 1279 (4196)	Nice *Col-de-Tende*	12.50%	UO. MWR 6m (19'8") Good surface but many hairpins on D6204 (N204)/S20. Steep gradients on approaches. Height of tunnel at Col-de-Tende at the Italian border is 3.8m (12'4) **Not recommended for caravans.**
6	**Bussang** (France) 721 (2365)	Thann *St Maurice-sur-Moselle*	7%	UO. MWR 4m (13'1") A very easy road (N66) over the Vosges; beautiful scenery.
7	**Cabre** (France) 1180 (3871)	Luc-en-Diois *Aspres-sur-Buëch*	9%	UO. MWR 5.5m (18') An easy pleasant road (D93/D993), winding at Col-de-Cabre.
8	**Cayolle** (France) 2326 (7631)	Barcelonnette *Guillaumes*	10%	UC early Nov-early Jun. MWR 4m (13'1") Narrow, winding road (D902) with hairpin bends; poor surface, broken edges with steep drops. Long stretches of single-track road with passing places. **Caravans prohibited.**
9	**Croix Haute** (France) 1179 (3868)	Monestier-de-Clermont *Aspres-sur-Buëch*	7%	UO on N75. MWR 5.5m (18') Well-engineered road (D1075/N75); several hairpin bends on N side.
10	**Faucille** (France) 1323 (4341)	Gex *Morez*	10%	UO. MWR 5m (16'5") Fairly wide, winding road (N5) across the Jura mountains; negotiable by caravans but probably better to follow route via La Cure-St Cergue-Nyon.

Before using any of these passes, PLEASE READ CAREFULLY THE ADVICE AT THE BEGINNING OF THIS CHAPTER

	Pass Height In Metres (Feet)	From To	Max Gradient	Conditions and Comments
11	**Forclaz** (Switzerland – France) 1527 (5010)	Martigny *Argentière*	8.50%	UO Forclaz; OC Montets Dec-early Apr. MWR 5m (16'5") MWV 2.5m (8'2") Good road over the pass and to the French border; long, hard climb out of Martigny; narrow and rough over Col-des-Montets on D1506 (N506).
12	**Galibier** (France) 2645 (8678)	La Grave *St Michel-de-Maurienne*	12.50%	UC Oct-Jun. MWR 3m (9'10") Mainly wide, well-surfaced road (D902) but unprotected and narrow over summit. From Col-du-Lautaret it rises over the Col-du-Telegraphe then 11 more hairpin bends. Ten hairpin bends on descent then 5km (3.1 miles) narrow and rough; easier in N to S direction. Limited parking at summit. **Not recommended for caravans.** (There is a single-track tunnel under the Galibier summit, controlled by traffic lights; caravans are not permitted).
13	**Gorges-du-Verdon** (France) 1032 (3386)	Castellane *Moustiers-Ste Marie*	9%	UO. MWR probably 5m (16'5") On road D952 over Col-d'Ayen and Col-d'Olivier. Moderate gradients but slow, narrow and winding. Poss heavy traffic.
14	**Iseran** (France) 2770 (9088)	Bourg-St Maurice *Lanslebourg*	11%	UC mid Oct-late Jun. MWR 4m (13'1") Second highest pass in the Alps on road D902. Well-graded with reasonable bends, average surface. Several unlit tunnels on N approach. **Not recommended for caravans.**
15	**Izoard** (France) 2360 (7743)	Guillestre *Briançon*	12.50%	UC late Oct-mid Jun. MWR 5m (16'5") Fine scenery. Winding, sometimes narrow road (D902) with many hairpin bends; care required at several unlit tunnels near Guillestre. **Not recommended for caravans.**
16	**Larche (della Maddalena)** (France – Italy) 1994 (6542)	La Condamine-Châtelard *Vinadio*	8.50%	OC Dec-Mar. MWR 3.5m (11'6") An easy, well-graded road (D900); long, steady ascent on French side, many hairpins on Italian side (S21). Fine scenery; ample parking at summit.
17	**Lautaret** (France) 2058 (6752)	Le Bourg-d'Oisans *Briançon*	12.50%	OC Dec-Mar. MWR 4m (13'1") Modern, evenly graded but winding road (D1091), and unguarded in places; very fine scenery; suitable for caravans but with care through narrow tunnels.
18	**Leques** (France) 1146 (3760)	Barrême *Castellane*	8%	UO. MWR 4m (13'1") On Route Napoléon (D4085). Light traffic; excellent surface; narrow in places on N ascent. S ascent has many hairpins.
19	**Mont Cenis** (France – Italy) 2083 (6834)	Lanslebourg *Susa*	12.50%	UC Nov-May. MWR 5m (16'5") Approach by industrial valley. An easy highway (D1006/S25) with mostly good surface; spectacular scenery; long descent into Italy with few stopping places. Alternative Fréjus road tunnel available. See ***Road Tunnels*** in this section.
20	**Montgenèvre** (France – Italy) 1850 (6070)	Briançon *Cesana-Torinese*	9%	UO. MWR 5m (16'5") An easy, modern road (N94/S24) with some tight hairpin bends on French side; road widened & tunnels improved on Italian side. Much used by lorries; may be necessary to travel at their speed and give way to oncoming large vehicles on hairpins.
	Montets (See **Forclaz**)			

Before using any of these passes, PLEASE READ CAREFULLY THE ADVICE AT THE BEGINNING OF THIS CHAPTER

	Pass Height In Metres (Feet)	From To	Max Gradient	Conditions and Comments
21	**Morgins** (France – Switzerland) 1369 (4491)	Abondance *Monthey*	14%	UO. MWR 4m (13'1") A lesser used route (D22) through pleasant, forested countryside crossing French/Swiss border. **Not recommended for caravans.**
22	**Petit St Bernard** (France – Italy) 2188 (7178)	Bourg-St Maurice *Pré-St Didier*	8.50%	UC mid Oct-Jun. MWR 5m (16'5") Outstanding scenery, but poor surface and unguarded broken edges near summit. Easiest from France (D1090); sharp hairpins on climb from Italy (S26). **Closed to vehicles towing another vehicle.**
23	**Restefond (La Bonette)** (France) 2802 (9193)	Barcelonnette *St Etienne-de-Tinée*	16%	UC Oct-Jun. MWR 3m (9'10") The highest pass in the Alps. Rebuilt, resurfaced road (D64) with rest area at summit – top loop narrow and unguarded. Winding with hairpin bends. **Not recommended for caravans.**
24	**Schlucht** (France) 1139 (3737)	Gérardmer *Munster*	7%	UO. MWR 5m (16'5") An extremely picturesque route (D417) crossing the Vosges mountains, with easy, wide bends on the descent. Good surface.
25	**Tenda (Tende)** Italy – France 1321 (4334)	Borgo-San Dalmazzo *Tende*	9%	UO. MWR 6m (19'8") Well-guarded, modern road (S20/ND6204) with several hairpin bends; road tunnel (height 3.8m) at summit narrow with poor road surface. Less steep on Italian side. **Caravans prohibited during winter.**
26	**Vars** (France) 2109 (6919)	St Paul-sur-Ubaye *Guillestre*	9%	OC Dec-Mar. MWR 5m (16'5") Easy winding ascent and descent on D902 with 14 hairpin bends; good surface.

Technical information by courtesy of the Automobile Association. Additional update and amendments supplied by caravnners and tourers who have themselves used the passes and tunnels. The Caravan Club has not checked the information contained in these tables and cannot accept responsibility for their accuracy, or for any errors, omissions, or their effects.

The Alpine maps only show the major Alpine mountain passes for France. For other countries please refer to Caravan Europe Guide to Sites and Touring in Austria, Benelux, Central Europe, Germany, Greece, Italy, Scandinavia and Switzerland.

Major Alpine Road Tunnels - France

Before using any of these tunnels, PLEASE READ CAREFULLY THE ADVICE AT THE BEGINNING OF THIS CHAPTER

	Tunnel	Route and Height above Sea Level	General Information and Comments
(A)	**Frejus** (France – Italy) 12.8 km (8 miles)	**Modane to Bardonecchia** 1220m (4000')	MWR 9m (29'6"), tunnel height 4.3m (14'). Min/max speed 60/70 km/h (37/44 mph). Return tickets valid until midnight on 7th day after day of issue. Season tickets are available. Approach via A43 and D1006; heavy use by freight vehicles. Good surface on approach roads. **Tolls charged.** www.sftrf.fr
(B)	**Mont Blanc** (France – Italy) 11.6 km (7.2 miles)	**Chamonix to Courmayeur** 1381m (4530')	MHV 4.7m (15'5"), MWV 6m (19'6") On N205 France, S26 (Italy). Max speed in tunnel 70 km/h (44 mph) – lower limits when exiting; min speed 50 km/h. Leave 150m between vehicles; ensure enough fuel for 30km. Return tickets valid until midnight on 7th day after issue. Season tickets are available. **Tolls charged.** www.tunnelmb.net
-	**Ste Marie-aux-Mines (France)** 6.8 km (4.25 miles)	**St Dié to Ste-Marie-aux Mines** 772m (2533')	At 7km, this is the longest road tunnel situated entirely in France. Also known as Maurice Lemaire Tunnel, through the Vosges in north-east France from Lusse on N159 to N59. **Tolls charged.** Alternate route via Col-de-Ste Marie on D459.

NOTES: *Dipped headlights should be used (unless stated otherwise) when travelling through road tunnels, even when the road appears to be well lit. In some countries police make spot checks and impose on-the-spot fines.*

During the winter wheel chains may be required on the approaches to some tunnels. These must not be used in tunnels and lay-bys are available for the removal and refitting of wheel chains.

For information on motorway vignettes, see the relevant Country Introductions.

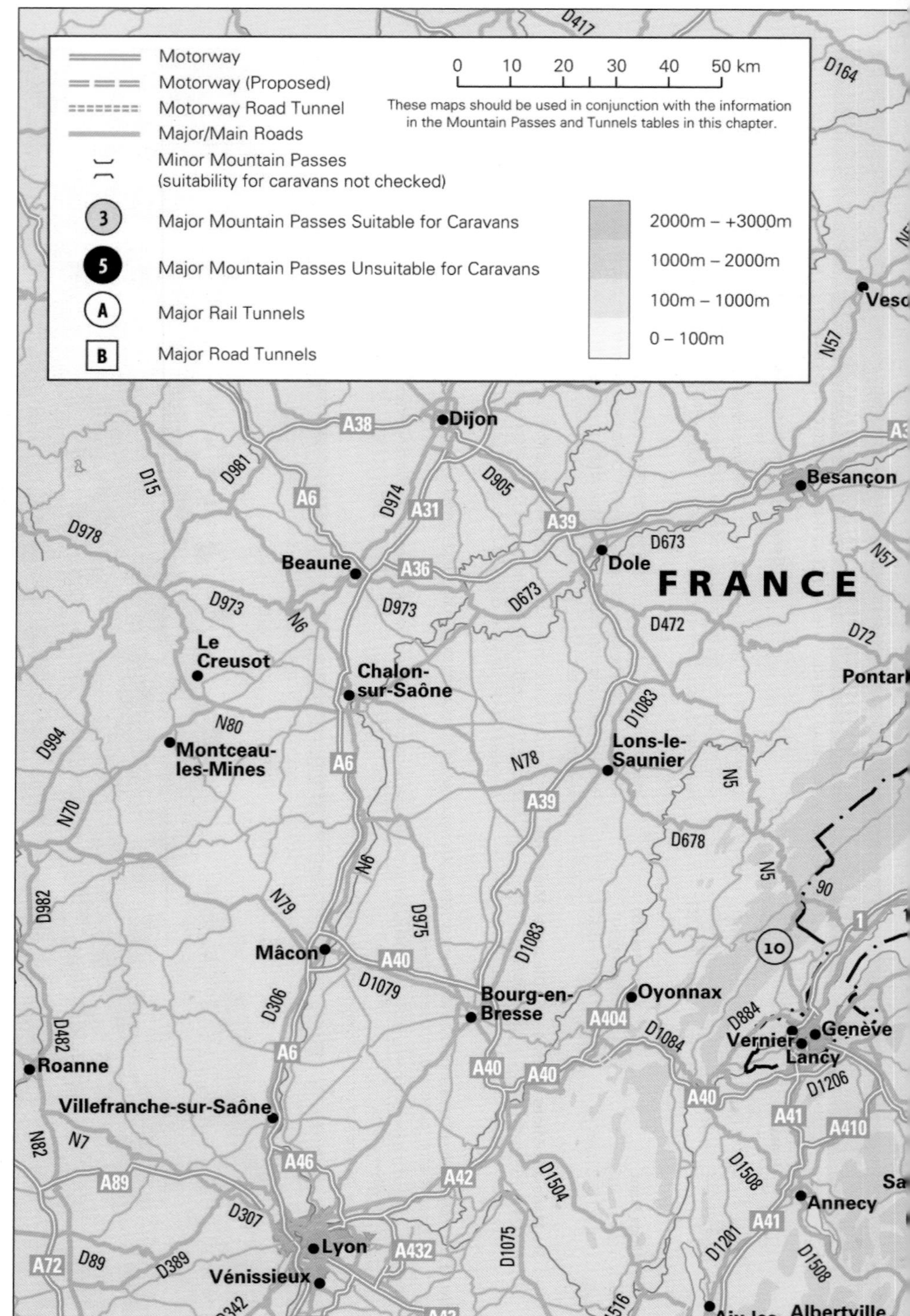

Motorway
Motorway (Proposed)
Motorway Road Tunnel
Major/Main Roads
Minor Mountain Passes
(suitability for caravans not checked)
Major Mountain Passes Suitable for Caravans
Major Mountain Passes Unsuitable for Caravans
Major Rail Tunnels
Major Road Tunnels
0 10 20 30 40 50 km
These maps should be used in conjunction with the information in the Mountain Passes and Tunnels tables in this chapter.
2000m – +3000m
1000m – 2000m
100m – 1000m
0 – 100m
FRANCE
Dijon
Besançon
Dole
Beaune
Le Creusot
Chalon-sur-Saône
Montceau-les-Mines
Lons-le-Saunier
Mâcon
Bourg-en-Bresse
Oyonnax
Vernier
Genève
Lancy
Roanne
Villefranche-sur-Saône
Annecy
Lyon
Vénissieux
Albertville

GERMANY
SWITZERLAND
Rottweil
Emmendingen
Freiburg im Breisgau
Schwenningen
Tuttlingen
Colmar
Remiremont
Guebwiller
Mulhouse
Belfort
Singen
(Hohentwiel)
Schaffhausen
Weil am
Rhein
Basel
Rheinfelden
(Baden)
Liestal
Delémont
Aarau
Dietikon
Winterthur
Dübendorf
Zürich
Uster
Solothurn
Biel
Zug
Emmen
Luzern
Kriens
Schwyz
Neuchâtel
BERN
Köniz
Stans
Altdorf
Sarnen
Yverdon
Fribourg
Thun
Lausanne
Montreux
Sion
Bellinzona
Lugano
Verbania
Varese
Aosta
B

Chamond
Roussillon
Col de la République 1161
Annonay
Voiron
Col du Granier
Col de la Croix de Fer
Fontaine
Grenoble
Échirolles
Romans-sur-Isère
Valence
Col de la Bataille
Col de Rousset
Col de l'Escrinet
Aubenas
Montélimar
Col du Festre
Gap
Col de Maure
Bagnols-sur-Cèze
Orange
FRANCE
Carpentras
Col
L'Isle-sur-la-Sorgue
Avignon
Nîmes
Beaucaire
Cavaillon
Manosque
Arles
Salon-de-Provence
Miramas
Istres
Aix-en-Provence
Draguignan
Martigues
Marseille
Aubagne
Col de la Bigue
La Ciotat
Toulon
La Valette-du-Var
Six-Fours-les-Plages
Hyères
A48
A43
A41
A7
A49
A51
A9
A54
A55
A52
A8
A57
A50
A570
D1082
N88
D82
D1085
D520
D1090
D1006
D1092
D1532
D1075
D532
N532
D86
D1091
N7
N85
D111
D164
N102
D104
D93
D107
D993
D994
D94
D900B
N85
D981
D6086
N100
D12
D4
N202
D900
N113
D7N
D570N
D4096
N568
D113
D560
D1
DN7
D97
DN8
D98
12
17
9
7
4
18
13

Ivrea
Novara
Magenta
Vercelli
Vigevano
Venaria
Chivasso
Torino
Rivoli
Orbassano
Moncalieri
Casale Monferrato
ITALY
Valenza
Pinerolo
Carmagnola
Asti
Alessandria
Tortona
Col de la Croix
Col Agnel
Col de la Traversette
Bra
Alba
Novi Ligure
Acqui Terme
Fossano
Cuneo
Mondovì
Genova
Savona
Albenga
Imperia
San Remo
Menton
Ventimiglia
Monte-Carlo
MONACO
Nice
Antibes
Cannes
© Collins Bartholomew Ltd 2014

Major Pyrenees Mountain Passes

Before using any of these passes, PLEASE READ CAREFULLY THE ADVICE AT THE BEGINNING OF THIS CHAPTER

	Pass Height In Metres (Feet)	From To	Max Gradient	Conditions and Comments
27	**Aubisque** (France) 1710 (5610)	Eaux Bonnes *Argelés-Gazost*	10%	UC mid Oct-Jun. MWR 3.5m (11'6") Very winding; continuous on D918 but easy ascent; descent including Col-d'Aubisque 1709m (5607 feet) and Col-du-Soulor 1450m (4757 feet); 8km (5 miles) of very narrow, rough, unguarded road with steep drop. **Not recommended for caravans** .
28	**Col-d'Haltza and Col-de-Burdincurutcheta** (France) 782 (2565) and 1135 (3724)	St Jean-Pied-de-Port *Larrau*	11%	UO. A narrow road (D18/D19) leading to Iraty skiing area. Narrow with some tight hairpin bends; rarely has central white line and stretches are unguarded. Not for the faint-hearted. **Not recommended for caravans.**
29	**Envalira** (France – Andorra) 2407 (7897)	Pas-de-la-Casa *Andorra*	12.5%	OC Nov-Apr. MWR 6m (19'8") Good road (N22/CG2) with wide bends on ascent and descent; fine views. MHV 3.5m (11'6") on N approach near l'Hospitalet. Early start rec in summer to avoid border delays. Envalira Tunnel (toll) reduces congestion and avoids highest part of pass. See ***Pyrenean Road Tunnels*** in this section.
30	**Ibañeta (Roncevalles)** (France – Spain) 1057 (3468)	St Jean-Pied-de-Port *Pamplona*	10%	UO. MWR 4m (13'1") Slow and winding, scenic route on N135.
31	**Peyresourde** (France) 1563 (5128)	Arreau *Bagnères-de-Luchon*	10%	UO. MWR 4m (13'1") D618 somewhat narrow with several hairpin bends, though not difficult. **Not recommended for caravans.**
32	**Port** (France) 1249 (4098)	Tarascon-sur-Ariège *Massat*	10%	OC Nov-Mar. MWR 4m (13'1") A fairly easy, scenic road (D618), but narrow on some bends.
33	**Portet-d'Aspet** (France) 1069 (3507)	Audressein *Fronsac*	14%	UO. MWR 3.5m (11'6") Approached from W by the easy Col-des-Ares and Col-de-Buret; well-engineered but narrow road (D618); care needed on hairpin bends. **Not recommended for caravans.**
34	**Pourtalet** (France – Spain) 1792 (5879)	Laruns *Biescas*	10%	UC late Oct-early Jun. MWR 3.5m (11'6") A fairly easy, unguarded road, but narrow in places. Easier from Spain (A136), steeper in France (D934). **Not recommended for caravans.**
35	**Puymorens** (France) 1915 (6283)	Ax-les-Thermes *Bourg-Madame*	10%	OC Nov-Apr. MWR 5.5m (18') MHV 3.5m (11'6") A generally easy, modern tarmac road (N20). Parallel toll road tunnel available. See ***Pyrenean Road Tunnels*** in this section.

Before using any of these passes, PLEASE READ CAREFULLY THE ADVICE AT THE BEGINNING OF THIS CHAPTER

	Pass Height In Metres (Feet)	From To	Max Gradient	Conditions and Comments
36	**Quillane** (France) 1714 (5623)	Axat *Mont-Louis*	8.5%	OC Nov-Mar. MWR 5m (16'5") An easy, straightforward ascent and descent on D118.
37	**Somport** (France – Spain) 1632 (5354)	Accous *Jaca*	10%	UO. MWR 3.5m (11'6") A favoured, old-established route; not particularly easy and narrow in places with many unguarded bends on French side (N134); excellent road on Spanish side (N330). Use of road tunnel advised – see ***Pyrenean Road Tunnels*** in this section. NB Visitors advise re-fuelling no later than Sabiñánigo when travelling south to north.
38	**Tourmalet** (France) 2114 (6936)	Ste Marie-de-Campan *Luz-St Sauveur*	12.5%	UC Oct-mid Jun. MWR 4m (13'1") The highest French Pyrenean route (D918); approaches good, though winding, narrow in places and exacting over summit; sufficiently guarded. Rough surface & uneven edges on west side. **Not recommended for caravans.**

Major Pyrenean Road Tunnels

Before using any of these tunnels, PLEASE READ CAREFULLY THE ADVICE AT THE BEGINNING OF THIS CHAPTER

	Tunnel	Route and Height Above Sea Level	General Information and Comments
AA	**Bielsa** (France – Spain) 3.2 km (2 miles)	**Aragnouet to Bielsa** 1830m (6000')	Open 24 hours but possibly closed October-Easter. On French side (D173) generally good road surface but narrow with steep hairpin bends and steep gradients near summit. Often no middle white line. Spanish side (A138) has good width and is less steep and winding. Used by heavy vehicles. No tolls. Please note the tunnel may be undergoing repair works and as a result may be closed at certain times and on certain days.
BB	**Envalira** (France – Spain via Andorra) 2.8 km (1.75 miles)	**Pas de la Casa to El Grau Roig** 2000m (6562')	Tunnel width 8.25m. On N22/CG2 France to Andorra. **Tolls charged.**
CC	**Puymorens** (France –Spain) 4.8 km (2.9 miles)	**Ax-les-Thermes to Puigcerda** 1515m (4970')	MHV 3.5m (11'6"). Part of Puymorens pass on N20/E9. **Tolls charged.**
DD	**Somport** (France – Spain) 8.6 km (5.3 miles)	**Urdos to Canfranc** 1116m (3661')	Tunnel height 4.55m (14'9"), width 10.5m (34'). Max speed 90 km/h (56 mph); leave 100m between vehicles. On N134 (France), N330 (Spain). No tolls.

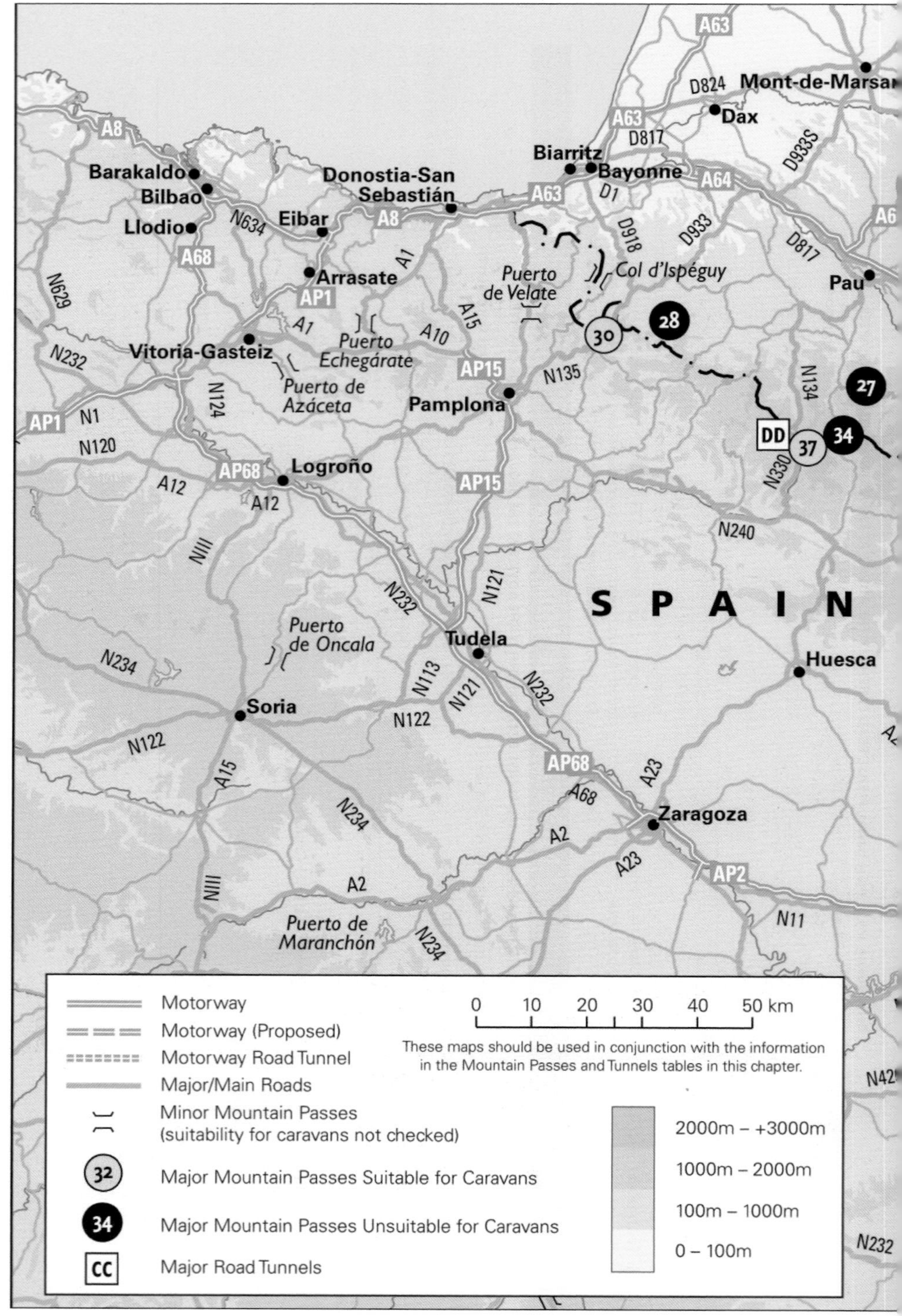

Barakaldo
Bilbao
Llodio
Donostia-San Sebastián
Eibar
Arrasate
Vitoria-Gasteiz
Puerto Echegárate
Puerto de Azáceta
Puerto de Velate
Col d'Ispéguy
Biarritz
Bayonne
Dax
Mont-de-Marsan
Pau
Pamplona
Logroño
Tudela
Puerto de Oncala
Soria
Huesca
Zaragoza
Puerto de Maranchón
SPAIN
Motorway
Motorway (Proposed)
Motorway Road Tunnel
Major/Main Roads
Minor Mountain Passes
(suitability for caravans not checked)
Major Mountain Passes Suitable for Caravans
Major Mountain Passes Unsuitable for Caravans
Major Road Tunnels
0 10 20 30 40 50 km
These maps should be used in conjunction with the information in the Mountain Passes and Tunnels tables in this chapter.
2000m – +3000m
1000m – 2000m
100m – 1000m
0 – 100m

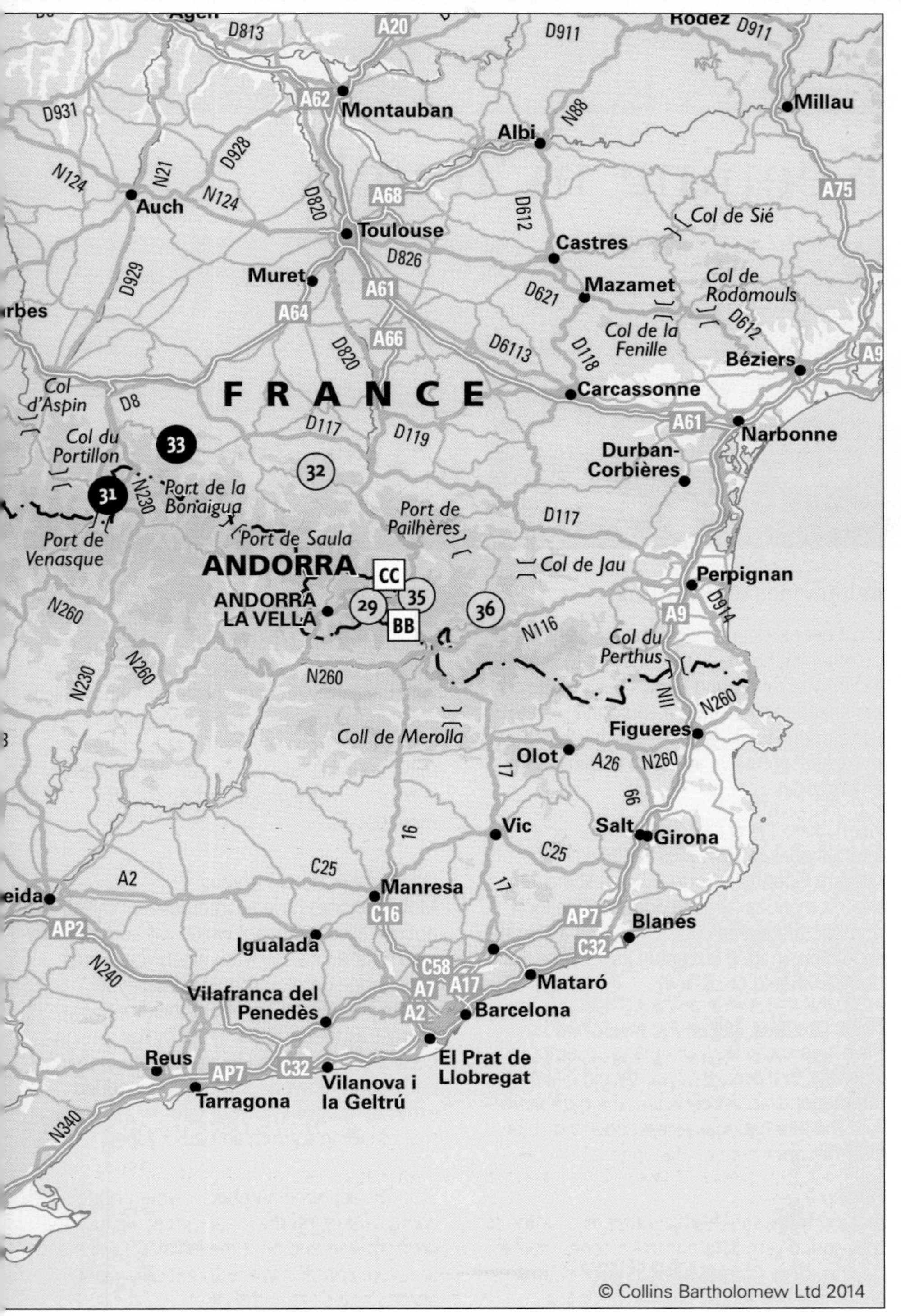
FRANCE
ANDORRA
ANDORRA LA VELLA
Montauban
Albi
Millau
Auch
Toulouse
Castres
Muret
Mazamet
Béziers
Carcassonne
Narbonne
Durban-Corbières
Perpignan
Col de Sié
Col de Rodomouls
Col de la Fenille
Col d'Aspin
Col du Portillon
Port de la Bonaigua
Port de Venasque
Port de Saula
Port de Pailhères
Col de Jau
Col du Perthus
Coll de Merolla
Figueres
Olot
Vic
Salt
Girona
Manresa
Igualada
Blanes
Mataró
Vilafranca del Penedès
Barcelona
El Prat de Llobregat
Reus
Tarragona
Vilanova i la Geltrú
33
31
32
29
35
36
CC
BB
© Collins Bartholomew Ltd 2014

Keeping in Touch

Telephones and Calling

Most people need to use a telephone at some point while they're away, whether to keep in touch with family and friends back home or call ahead to sites. Even if you don't plan to use a phone while you're away, it is best to make sure you have access to one in case of emergencies.

International Direct Dial Calls
International access codes are given in the relevant Country Introduction - first dial the international access code then the local number. If the area code starts with a zero this should be omitted (except in Italy where the full number should be dialled).

Some countries' telephone numbers do not have area codes (e.g. Denmark, Luxembourg, Norway). In these cases you should dial the international access code and the number in full. The international access code to dial the UK from anywhere in the world is 0044.

Ringing Tones
Ringing tones vary from country to country, so may sound very different to UK tones. Some ringing tones sound similar to error or engaged tones that you would hear on a UK line.

Phone cards
You can buy pre-paid international phone cards which offer much lower rates for international calls than most mobile phone providers. You load the card with your chosen amount (which you can top up at any time) and then dial an access code from any mobile or landline to make your call. See www.planetphonecards.com or www.thephonecardsite.com for more details.

Using Mobile Phones Abroad
Mobile phones have an international calling option called 'roaming' which will automatically search for a local network when you switch your phone on. You should contact your service provider to ask about their roaming charges as these are partly set by the foreign networks you use and fluctuate with exchange rates. Most network providers offer added extras or 'bolt-ons' to your tariff to make the cost of calling to/from abroad cheaper.

Storing telephone numbers in your phone's contact list in international format (i.e. use the prefix of +44 and omit the initial '0') will mean that your contacts will automatically work abroad as well as in the UK.

Global SIM Cards
If you're planning on spending a while in one country consider buying a global SIM card. This will enable your mobile phone to operate on a foreign mobile network, which will be more cost effective than your service provider's roaming charges.

When you go abroad you simply replace the SIM card in your phone with the new card. For details of SIM cards available, speak to your service provider or see www.0044.co.uk.

You may, however, find it simpler to buy a SIM card abroad but before doing this, check with your UK service provider to find out whether it has locked your phone against the use of a different SIM card and what, if anything, it will charge to unlock it. If you plan to use a mobile phone a lot while abroad, e.g. to book campsites, restaurants, etc, then give some thought to buying a cheap 'pay-as-you-go' phone in the country you are visiting.

Hands-Free
Legislation in Europe forbids the use of mobile or car phones while driving except when using hands-free equipment. If you are involved in an accident whilst driving and, at the same time, you were using a hand-held mobile phone, your insurance company may refuse to honour the claim.

Accessing the internet

Mobile Internet Costs - Data Roaming
Please be aware that accessing the internet overseas via your mobile can be very expensive. It is recommended that you disable your internet access by switching 'data roaming' to off, in order to avoid a large mobile phone bill on your return.

Internet Access
Wi-Fi is available on lots of campsites in Europe, sometimes the cost in included in your pitch fee and other sites charge extra for access. Most larger towns may have internet cafés or libraries where you can access the internet, however lots of fast food restaurants and coffee chains now offer free Wi-Fi for customers and visiting them for a cup of coffee or bite to eat is often the most economical way if you only need access for a short time.

Many people now use their smartphones for internet access or have a dongle – a device which, when connected to your laptop or tablet, allows you to access the internet using a mobile phone network. While these methods are economical in the UK, if you do the same abroad you will be charged data roaming charges which can run into hundreds or thousands of pounds depending on how much data you use. If you plan on using your smartphone or a dongle abroad speak to your service provider before you leave the UK to make sure you understand the costs. There may even be an overseas package that you can add to your plan to make data roaming cheaper.

Making Calls from your Laptop

If you download Skype to your laptop you can make free calls to other Skype users anywhere in the world using a Wi-Fi connection. Rates for calls to non-Skype users (landline or mobile phone) are also very competitively-priced. You will need a computer with a microphone and speakers, and a webcam is handy too. It is also possible to download Skype to an internet-enabled mobile phone to take advantage of the same low-cost calls – see www.skype.com.

Club Together

If you want to chat to other members either at home or while you're away, you can do so on The Club's online community Club Together. You can ask questions and gather opinions on the forums, as well as asking for expert advice on a number of caravanning topics. Just visit www.caravanclub.co.uk/together.

Radio and Television

Radio

The BBC World Service broadcasts radio programmes 24 hours a day worldwide and you can listen on a number of platforms: online, via satellite or cable, DRM digital radio, internet radio or mobile phone. You can find detailed information and programme schedules at www.bbc.co.uk/worldservice.

Listeners in northern France can currently listen to BBC Radio 5 Live on either 693 or 909 kHz

medium wave or BBC Radio 4 on 198 kHz long wave. Whereas analogue television signals were switched off in the UK during 2012, no date has yet been fixed for the switch off of analogue radio signals.

Digital Terrestrial Television

As in the UK, television transmissions in most of Europe have been converted to digital. The UK's high definition transmission technology may be more advanced than any currently implemented or planned in Europe. This means that digital televisions intended for use in the UK might not be able to receive HD terrestrial signals in some countries.

Satellite Television

For English-language TV programmes the only realistic option is satellite, and satellite dishes are a common sight on campsites all over Europe. A satellite dish mounted on the caravan roof or clamped to a pole fixed to the drawbar, or one mounted on a foldable free-standing tripod, will provide good reception and minimal interference. Remember however that obstructions to the south east (such as tall trees or even mountains) or heavy rain, can interrupt the signals. A specialist dealer will be able to advise you on the best way of mounting your dish. You will also need a satellite receiver and ideally a satellite-finding meter.

The main entertainment channels such as BBC1, ITV1 and Channel 4 can be difficult to pick up in mainland Europe as they are now being transmitted by new narrow-beam satellites. A 60cm dish should pick up these channels in most of France, Belgium and the Netherlands but as you travel further afield, you'll need a progressively larger dish. See the website www.satelliteforcaravans.co.uk (created and operated by a Caravan Club member) for the latest changes and developments, and for information on how to set up your equipment.

Medical Matters

Before You Travel

You can find country specific medical advice, including details of any vaccinations you may need, from the NHS choices website www.nhs.uk/healthcareabroad. Your GP surgery should also be able to give you advice on vaccinations and precautions. For general enquiries about medical care abroad you can contact NHS England on 0300 311 22 33 or email england.contactus@nhs.uk.

If you have any pre-existing medical conditions you should check with your GP that you are fit to travel. Ask your doctor for a written summary of any medical problems and a list of medications currently used. This is particularly important for travellers whose medical conditions require them to use controlled drugs or hypodermic syringes, in case customs officers question why you are carrying them.

Always make sure that you have enough of your medication to last the duration of your holiday and some extra in case you are delayed in returning to the UK. Ask your doctor for the generic name of any drugs you use, as brand names may be different abroad. If possible carry a card giving your blood group and details of any allergies or dietary restrictions (a translation of these may be useful when visiting restaurants).

If you have any doubts about your teeth or plan to be away a long time, have a dental check-up before departure. An emergency dental kit is available from High Street chemists which will allow you temporarily to restore a crown, bridge or filling or to dress a broken tooth until you can get to a dentist.

A good website to check before you travel is www.nathnac.org/travel. This website gives general health and safety advice and reports of disease outbreaks, as well as highlighting potential health risks by country.

European Heath Insurance Card (EHIC)
Before leaving home apply for a European Health Insurance Card (EHIC). British residents temporarily visiting another EU country are entitled to receive state-provided emergency treatment during their stay on the same terms as residents of those countries, but you must have a valid EHIC to claim these services.

Apply online for your EHIC on www.ehic.org.uk, call 0845 6062030 or pick up an application form from a post office. An EHIC is required by each individual family member -

children under 16 must be included in a parent or guardian's application.

The EHIC is free of charge, is valid for up to five years and can be renewed up to six months before its expiry date. Before you travel remember to check that your EHIC is still valid.

British nationals requiring emergency treatment can take advantage of the French health service on production of a European Health Insurance Card (EHIC). This will allow you to claim reimbursement of around 70% of standard doctors' and dentists' fees, and between 35% and 65% of the cost of most prescribed medicines.

For the address of a doctor 'conventionné', i.e. working within the French state healthcare system, ask at a pharmacy. After treatment make sure you are given a signed statement of treatment ('feuille de soins') showing the amount paid as you will need this for a refund.

Pharmacies dispense prescriptions and first aid. Your prescription will be returned to you and you should attach this, together with the stickers (vignettes) attached to the packaging of any medication or drugs, to the 'feuille de soins' in order to obtain a refund.

If you are admitted to hospital make sure you present your EHIC on admission. This will save you from paying any refundable costs up front and ensure that you only pay the patient contribution. You may have to pay a co-payment towards your treatment and if you are an inpatient you will have to pay a daily hospital charge. These charges are not refundable in France but you may be able to seek reimbursement when you are back in the UK.

Applications for refunds should be sent to a local sickness insurance office (Caisse Primaire d'Assurance-Maladie) and you should receive payment at your home address within about two months.

Andorra is not a member of the EU and, therefore, the EHIC is not accepted and there are no reciprocal emergency health care arrangements with Britain. You will be required to pay the full cost of medical treatment so make sure that you have comprehensive travel and medical insurance which includes cover for travel to non-EU countries.

An EHIC is not a substitute for travel insurance and it is strongly recommended that you arrange full travel insurance before leaving home regardless of the cover provided by your

EHIC. Some insurance companies require you to have an EHIC and some will waive the policy excess if an EHIC has been used.

If your EHIC is stolen or lost while you are abroad contact 0044 191 2127500 for help. If you experience difficulties in getting your EHIC accepted, telephone the Department for Work & Pensions for assistance on the overseas healthcare team line 0044 (0)191 218 1999 between 8am to 5pm Monday to Friday. Residents of the Republic of Ireland, the Isle of Man and Channel Islands, should check with their own health authorities about reciprocal arrangements with other countries.

Holiday Travel Insurance

Despite the fact that you have an EHIC you may incur thousands of pounds of medical costs if you fall ill or have an accident. The cost of bringing a person back to the UK, in the event of illness or death, is never covered by the EHIC. You may also find that you end up with a bill for treatment as not all countries offer free healthcare.

Separate additional travel insurance adequate for your destination is essential, such as The Caravan Club's Red Pennant Overseas Holiday Insurance, available to Club members – see www.caravanclub.co.uk/redpennant.

First Aid

A first aid kit containing at least the basic requirements is an essential item, and in some countries it is compulsory to carry one in your vehicle (see the Essential Equipment Table in the chapter Motoring – Equipment). Kits should contain items such as sterile pads, assorted dressings, bandages and plasters, antiseptic wipes or cream, cotton wool, scissors, eye bath and tweezers. Also make sure you carry something for upset stomachs, painkillers and an antihistamine in case of hay fever or mild allergic reactions.

If you're travelling to remote areas then you may find it useful to carry a good first aid manual. The British Red Cross publishes a comprehensive First Aid Manual in conjunction with St John Ambulance and St Andrew's Ambulance Association.

During Your Stay

Accidents and Emergencies

If you are involved in or witness a road accident the police may want to question you about it. If possible take photographs or make sketches of the scene, and write a few notes about what happened as it may be more difficult to remember the details at a later date.

For sports activities such as skiing and mountaineering, travel insurance must include provision for covering the cost of mountain and helicoptor rescue. Visitors to the Savoie and Haute-Savoie areas should be aware that an accident or illness may result in a transfer to Switzerland for hospital treatment. There is a reciprocal healthcare agreement for British citizens visiting Switzerland but you will be required to pay the full costs of treatment and afterwards apply for a refund.

The telephone numbers for police, fire brigade and ambulance services are given in each Country Introduction, however all EU member states the number 112 can be used from landlines or mobile phones to call any of the emergency services.

Sun Protection

Never under-estimate how ill exposure to the sun can make you. If you are not used to the heat it is very easy to fall victim to heat exhaustion or heat stroke. Avoid sitting in the sun between 11am and 3pm and cover your head if sitting or walking in the sun. Use a good quality sun-cream with high sun protection factor (SPF) and re-apply frequently. Make sure you drink plenty of fluids.

Tick-Borne Encephalitis (TBE) and Lyme Disease

Hikers and outdoor sports enthusiasts planning trips to forested, rural areas should be aware of tick-borne encephalitis, which is transmitted by the bite of an infected tick. If you think you may be at risk, seek medical advice on prevention and immunisation before you leave the UK.

There is no vaccine against Lyme disease, an equally serious tick-borne infection, which, if left untreated, can attack the nervous system and joints.

You can minimise the risk by using an insect repellent containing DEET, wearing long sleeves and long trousers, and checking for ticks after outdoor activity. Avoid unpasteurised dairy products in risk areas. See www.tickalert.org or telephone 01943 468010 for more information.

Water and food

Water from mains supplies throughout France is safe to drink, but may be treated with chemicals which make it taste different to tap water in the UK. If in any doubt, always drink bottled water or boil it before drinking. Food poisoning is potential anywhere, and a complete change of diet may upset your stomach as well. In hot conditions avoid any food that hasn't been refrigerated or hot food that has been left to cool. Be sensible about the food that you eat – don't eat unpasteurised or undercooked food and if you aren't sure about the freshness of meat or seafood then it is best avoided.

Returning Home

If you become ill on your return home tell your doctor that you have been abroad and which countries you have visited. Even if you have received medical treatment in another country, always consult your doctor if you have been bitten or scratched by an animal while on holiday.

If you were given any medicines in another country, it may be illegal to bring them back into the UK. If in doubt, declare them at Customs when you return.

Electricity and Gas

Electricity – General Advice

The voltage for mains electricity is 230V across the EU, but varying degrees of 'acceptable tolerance' mean you may find variations in the actual voltage. Most appliances sold in the UK are 220-240V so should work correctly. However, some high-powered equipment, such as microwave ovens, may not function well – check your instruction manual for any specific instructions. Appliances marked with 'CE' have been designed to meet the requirements of relevant European directives.

The table below gives an approximate idea of which appliances can be used based on the amperage which is being supplied (although not all appliances should be used at the same time). You can work it out more accurately by making a note of the wattage of each appliance in your caravan. The wattages given are based on appliances designed for use in caravans and motorhomes. Household kettles, for example, have at least a 2000W element. Each caravan circuit will also have a maximum amp rating which should not be exceeded.

Electrical Connections – EN60309-2 (CEE17)

EN60309-2 (formerly known as CEE17) is the European Standard for all newly fitted connectors. Most sites in France should now have these connectors, however there is no

Amps	Wattage (Approx)	Fridge	Battery Charger	Air Conditioning	LCD TV	Water Heater	Kettle (750W)	Heater (1kW)
2	400	✓	✓					
4	900	✓	✓		✓	✓		
6	1300	✓	✓	*	✓	✓	✓	
8	1800	✓	✓	✓**	✓	✓	✓	✓**
10	2300	✓	✓	✓**	✓	✓	✓	✓**
16	3600	✓	✓	✓	✓	✓	✓	✓**

* *Usage possible, depending on wattage of appliance in question*
** *Not to be used at the same time as other high-wattage equipment*

requirement to replace connectors which were installed before this was standardised so you may still find some sites where your UK 3 pin connector doesn't fit. For this reason it is a good idea to carry a 2-pin adapter. If you are already on site and find your connector doesn't fit, ask campsite staff to borrow or hire an adaptor. You may still encounter a poor electrical supply on site even with an EN60309-2 connection.

If the campsite does not have a modern EN60309-2 (CEE17) supply, ask to see the electrical protection for the socket outlet. If there is a device marked with IDn = 30mA, then the risk is minimised.

Hooking Up to the Mains

Connection
Connection should always be made in the following order:

- Check your outfit isolating switch is at 'off'.
- Uncoil the connecting cable from the drum. A coiled cable with current flowing through it may overheat. Take your cable and insert the connector (female end) into your outfit inlet.
- Insert the plug (male end) into the site outlet socket.
- Switch outfit isolating switch to 'on'.
- Use a polarity tester in one of the 13A sockets in the outfit to check all connections are correctly wired. Never leave it in the socket. Some caravans have these devices built in as standard.

It is recommended that the supply is not used if the polarity is incorrect (see Reversed Polarity overleaf).

Warnings:
If you are in any doubt of the safety of the system, if you don't receive electricity once connected or if the supply stops then contact the site staff.

If the fault is found to be with your outfit then call a qualified electrician rather than trying to fix the problem yourself.

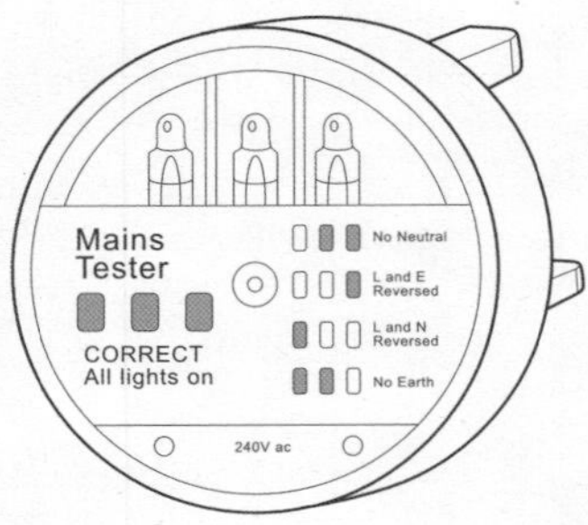

To ensure your safety you should never use an electrical system which you can't confirm to be safe. Use a mains tester such as the one shown above to test the electrical supply. Always check that a proper earth connection exists before using the electrics. Please note that these testers may not pick up all earth faults so if there is any doubt as to the integrity of the earth system do not use the electrical supply.

Disconnection

- Switch your outfit isolating switch to 'off'.
- At the site supply socket withdraw the plug.
- Disconnect the cable from your outfit.

Motorhomes – if leaving your pitch during the day, don't leave your mains cable plugged into the site supply, as this creates a hazard if the exposed live connections in the plug are touched or if the cable is not seen during grass-cutting.

Reversed Polarity

Even if the site connector meets European Standard EN60309-2 (CEE17), British caravanners are still likely to encounter the problem known as reversed polarity. This is where the site supply 'live' line connects to the outfit's 'neutral' and vice versa. You should always check the polarity immediately on connection, using a polarity tester available from caravan accessory shops. If polarity is reversed the caravan mains electricity should not be used. Try using another nearby socket instead. Frequent travellers to the Continent can make up an adaptor themselves, or ask an electrician to make one for you, with the live and neutral wires reversed. Using a reversed polarity socket will probably not affect how an electrical appliance works, however your protection is greatly reduced. For example, a lamp socket may still be live as you touch it while replacing a blown bulb, even if the light switch is turned off.

Shaver Sockets

Most campsites provide shaver sockets with a voltage of 220V or 110V. Using an incorrect voltage may cause the shaver to become hot or break. The 2-pin adaptor available in the UK may not fit Continental sockets so it is advisable to buy 2-pin adaptors on the Continent. Many modern shavers will work on a range of voltages which make them suitable for travelling abroad. Check you instruction manual to see if this is the case.

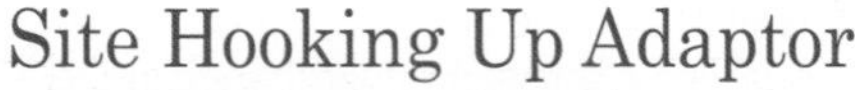

Site Hooking Up Adaptor

ADAPTATEUR DE PRISE AU SITE (SECTEUR)
CAMPINGPLATZ-ANSCHLUSS (NETZ)

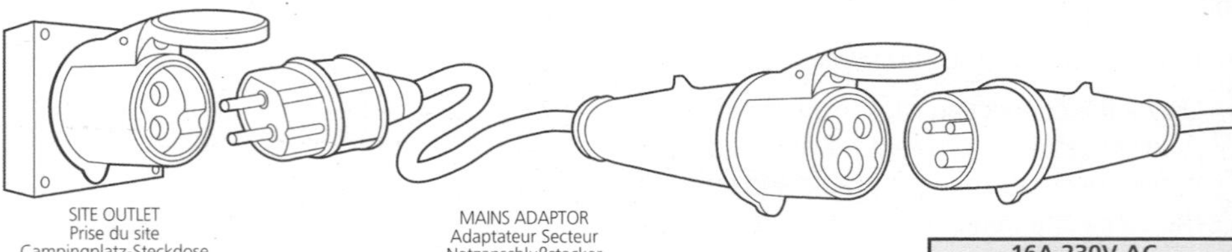

Gas – General Advice

Gas usage can be difficult to predict as so many factors, such as temperature and how often you eat out, can affect the amount you need. As a rough guide allow 0.45kg of gas a day for normal summer usage.

With the exception of Campingaz, LPG cylinders normally available in the UK cannot be exchanged abroad. If possible, take enough gas with you and bring back the empty cylinders. Always check how many you can take with you as ferry and tunnel operators may restrict the number of cylinders you are permitted to carry for safety reasons.

The full range of Campingaz cylinders is widely available from large supermarkets and hypermarkets, although at the end of the holiday season stocks may be low. Other popular brands of gas are Primagaz, Butagaz, Totalgaz and Le Cube. A loan deposit is required and if you are buying a cylinder for the first time you may also need to buy the appropriate regulator or adaptor hose.

If you are touring in cold weather conditions use propane gas instead of butane. Many other brands of gas are available in different countries and, as long as you have the correct regulator, adaptor and hose and the cylinders fit in your gas locker these local brands can also be used.

Gas cylinders are now standardised with a pressure of 30mbar for both butane and propane within the EU. On UK-specification caravans and motorhomes (2004 models and later) a 30mbar regulator suited to both propane and butane use is fitted to the bulkhead of the gas locker. This is connected to the cylinder with a connecting hose (and sometimes an adaptor) to suit different brands or types of gas. Older outfits and some foreign-built ones may use a cylinder-mounted regulator, which may need to be changed to suit different brands or types of gas.

Warnings:

- Refilling gas cylinders intended to be exchanged is against the law in most countries, however you may still find that some sites and dealers will offer to refill cylinders for you. Never take them up on this service as it can be dangerous; the cylinders haven't been designed for user-refilling and it is possible to overfill them with catastrophic consequences.
- Regular servicing of gas appliances is important as a faulty appliance can emit carbon monoxide, which could prove fatal. Check your vehicle or appliance handbook for service recommendations.
- Never use a hob or oven as a space heater.

The Caravan Club publishes a range of technical leaflets for its members including detailed advice on the use of electricity and gas – you can request copies or see www.caravanclub.co.uk/advice-and-training.

Safety and Security

France has good legislation in place to protect your safety wherever possible. However accidents and crime will still occur and taking sensible precautions can help to minimise your risk of being involved.

Beaches, Lakes and Rivers

Check for any warning signs or flags before you swim and ensure that you know what they mean. Check the depth of water before diving and avoid diving or jumping into murky water as submerged objects may not be visible. Familiarise yourself with the location of safety apparatus and/or lifeguards.

Use only the designated areas for swimming, watersports and boating and always use life jackets where appropriate. Watch out for tides, undertows, currents and wind strength and direction before you or your children swim in the sea. This applies in particular when using inflatables, windsurfing equipment, body boards, kayaks or sailing boats. Sudden changes of wave and weather conditions combined with fast tides and currents are particularly dangerous.

Campsite safety

Once you've settled in, take a walk around the site to familiarise yourself with its layout and locate the nearest safety equipment. Ensure that children know their way around and where your pitch is.

Natural disasters are rare, but always think about what could happen. A combination of heavy rain and a riverside pitch could lead to flash flooding, for example, so make yourself aware of site evacuation procedures.

Be aware of sources of electricity and cabling on and around your pitch – electrical safety might not be up to the same standards as in the UK.

Poison for rodent control is sometimes used on sites or surrounding farmland. Warning notices are not always posted and you are strongly advised to check when staying on a rural site with dogs or children.

Incidents of theft on campsites are rare but when leaving your caravan unattended make sure you lock all doors and shut windows. Conceal valuables from sight and lock bicycles to a tree or to your caravan.

Lake Annecy, French Alps

Children

Watch out for children as you drive around the site and don't exceed walking pace.

Children's play areas are generally unsupervised. Check which are suitable for your children's ages and abilities and agree with them which ones they may use. Read and respect the displayed rules. Remember it is your responsibility to know where your children are at all times.

Be aware of any campsite rules concerning ball games or use of play equipment, such as roller blades and skateboards. When your children attend organised activities, arrange when and where to meet afterwards.

Make sure that children are aware of any places where they should not go and never leave children alone inside a caravan.

Fire

Fire prevention is important on sites, as fire can spread quickly between outfits. Certain areas of southern France experience severe water shortages in summer months with a consequent increased fire risk. This may result in some local authorities imposing restrictions at short notice on the use of barbecues.

Fires can be a regular occurrence in forested areas, especially along the Mediterranean coast and in Corsica during summer months. They are generally extinguished quickly and efficiently but short term evacuations are sometimes necessary. If visiting forested areas familiarise yourself with local emergency procedures in the event of fire.

The following fire safety measures should be followed:

- Don't use portable paraffin or gas heaters inside your caravan. Gas heaters should only be fitted when air is taken from outside the caravan.
- Don't change your gas cylinder inside the caravan. If you smell gas (or in the event of a fire starting), turn off the cylinder immediately, extinguish all naked flames and seek professional help.
- Know where the fire points and telephones are on site and know the site fire drill. Establish a family fire drill. Make sure everyone knows how to call the emergency services.
- Where site rules permit the use of barbecues, take the following precautions to prevent fire:

- Never locate a barbecue near trees or hedges. Have a bucket of water to hand in case of sparks.
- Only use recommended fire-lighting materials.
- Do not leave a barbecue unattended when lit and dispose of hot ash safely.
- Never take a barbeque into an enclosed area or awning – even when cooling they continue to release carbon monoxide which can lead to fatal poisoning.

Swimming Pools
Familiarize yourself with the pool area before you venture in for a swim, especially if you're travelling with children. Check the pool layout – identify shallow and deep ends and the location of safety equipment. Check the gradient of the pool bottom as pools which shelve off sharply can catch weak or non-swimmers unawares.

Never dive or jump into a pool without knowing the depth – if there is a no diving rule it usually means the pool isn't deep enough for safe diving.

For pools with a supervisor or lifeguard, note any times or dates when the pool is not supervised. Read safety notices and rules posted around the pool.

On the Road

Don't leave valuables on on view in cars or caravans, even if they are locked. Make sure items on roof racks or cycle carriers are locked securely.

In and around Calais and Dunkerque, British owned cars have been targetted by thieves, both while parked and on the move, e.g. by flagging drivers down or indicating that a vehicle has a flat tyre. If you stop in such circumstances be wary of anyone offering help, ensure that car keys are not left in the ignition and that vehicle doors are locked while you investigate.

Always keep car doors locked and windows closed when driving in populated areas of the south of France, especially in the Marseille to Menton area.

Beware of a 'snatch' through open car windows at traffic lights, filling stations or in traffic jams. When driving through towns and cities keep your doors locked. Keep handbags, valuables and documents out of sight at all times.

Stowaways in vehicles can be a problem on ferries and Eurotunnel, so check that your outfit is free from unexpected guests at the last practical opportunity before boarding.

If flagged down by another motorist for whatever reason, take care that your own car is locked and windows closed while you check outside, even if someone is left inside. Be particularly careful on long, empty stretches of motorway and when you stop for fuel. Even if the people flagging you down appear to be officials (e.g. wearing yellow reflective jackets or dark, 'uniform-type' clothing) show presence of mind and lock yourselves in immediately. They may appear to be friendly and helpful, but could be opportunistic thieves. Have a mobile phone to hand and, if necessary, be seen to use it.

Road accidents are a significant risk in some countries where traffic laws may be inadequately enforced, roads may be poorly maintained, road signs and lighting inadequate, and driving standards poor. It's a good idea to keep a fully-charged mobile phone with you in your car with the number of your breakdown organisation saved into it.

Overnight Stops

Overnight stops should always be at campsites and not at motorway service areas, ferry terminal car parks, petrol station forecourts or isolated 'aires de services' on motorways where robberies and muggings. If you decide to use these areas for a rest then take appropriate precautions, for example, shutting all windows, securing locks and making a thorough external check of your vehicle(s) before departing. Safeguard your property, e.g. handbags, while out of the caravan and beware of approaches by strangers.

For a safer place to take a break, there is a wide network of 'Aires de Services' in cities, towns and villages across Europe, many specifically for motorhomes with good security and overnight facilities. It is rare that you will be the only vehicle staying on such areas, but avoid any that are isolated, take sensible precautions and trust your instincts. For example, if the area appears run down and there are groups of people hanging around who seem intimidating, then you are probably wise to move on.

Personal Security

Petty crime happens all over the world; however as a tourist you are more vulnerable to it. This shouldn't stop you from exploring new horizons, but there are a few sensible precautions you can take to minimise the risk.

- Leave valuables and jewellery at home. If you do take them, fit a small safe in your caravan or lock them in the boot of your car. Don't leave money or valuables in a car glovebox or on view. Don't leave bags in full view when sitting outside at cafés or restaurants, or leave valuables unattended on the beach.
- When walking be security-conscious. Avoid unlit streets at night, walk away from the kerb edge and carry handbags or shoulder bags on the side away from the kerb. The less of a tourist you appear, the less of a target you are.
- Keep a separate note of your holiday insurance details and emergency telephone numbers.
- Beware of pickpockets in crowded areas, at tourist attractions and in cities. Pickpockets operate on the Paris metro and RER (regional suburban rail network) and you should be extra vigilant.

- Be cautious of bogus plain-clothes policemen who may ask to see your foreign currency or credit cards and passport. If approached, decline to show your money or to hand over your passport but ask for credentials and offer instead to go to the nearest police station.
- Laws and punishment vary from country to country so make yourself aware of anything which may affect you before you travel. Be especially careful on laws involving alcohol consumption (such as drinking in public areas), and never buy or use illegal drugs abroad.
- Respect Customs regulations - smuggling is a serious offence and can carry heavy penalties. Do not carry parcels or luggage through Customs for other people and do not cross borders with people you do not know in your vehicle, such as hitchhikers.

The Foreign & Commonwealth Office produces a range of material to advise and inform British citizens travelling abroad about issues affecting their safety - www.gov.uk/foreign-travel-advice has country specific guides.

Money security

We would rarely walk around at home carrying large amounts of cash, but as you may not have the usual access to bank accounts and credit cards you are more likely to do so on holiday. You are also less likely to have the same degree of security when online banking as you would in your own home. Take the following precautions to keep your money safe:

- Carry only the minimum amount of cash and don't rely on one person to carry everything. Never carry a wallet in your back pocket. Moneybelts are the most secure way to carry cash and passports.
- Keep a separate note of bank account and credit/debit card numbers. Carry your credit card issuer/bank's 24-hour UK contact number with you.
- Be careful when using cash machines (ATMs) – try to use a machine in an area with high footfall and don't allow yourself to be distracted. Put your cash away before moving away from the cash machine.
- Always guard your PIN number, both at cash machines and when using your card to pay in shops and restaurants. Never let your card out of your sight while paying.
- If using internet banking do not leave the PC or mobile device unattended and make sure you log out fully at the end of the session.

Winter Sports

If you are planning a skiing holiday in Andorra you should contact the Andorran Embassy in London (tel 020 8874 4806) for advice on safety and weather conditions before travelling. All safety instructions should be followed meticulously given the dangers of avalanches in some areas. See www.ski.andorra.com or www.avalanches.org for more information.

British Consular Services Abroad

British Embassy and Consular staff offer practical advice, assistance and support to British travellers abroad. They can, for example, issue replacement passports, help Britons who have been the victims of crime, contact relatives and friends in the event of an accident, illness or death, provide information about transferring funds and provide details of local lawyers, doctors and interpreters. But there are limits to their powers and a British Consul cannot, for example, give legal advice, intervene in court proceedings, put up bail, pay for legal or medical bills, or for funerals or the repatriation of bodies, or undertake work more properly done by banks, motoring organisations and travel insurers.

If you are charged with a serious offence, insist on the British Consul being informed. You will be contacted as soon as possible by a Consular Officer who can advise on local procedures, provide access to lawyers and insist that you are treated as well as nationals of the country which is holding you. However, they cannot get you released as a matter of course.

British Embassy in France
35 RUE DU FAUBOURG ST HONORE
75363 PARIS CEDEX 08 PARIS
Tel: 01 44 51 31 00
www.ukinfrance.fco.gov.uk/en/

There are also Consulates in Bordeaux, Lille, Lyon and Marseilles.

Irish Embassy in France
12 AVENUE FOCH, 75116 PARIS
Tel: 01 44 17 67 00
www.embassyofireland.fr

There are also Irish Consulates-General/ Consulates in Cannes, Cherbourg, Lyon and Monaco.

For Consular help while in Andorra contact the British Consulate-General in Barcelona:

AVDA DIAGNOL 477-13, 08036 BARCELONA
Tel: 00 34 902 109 356
www.ukinspain.fco.gov.uk/en/

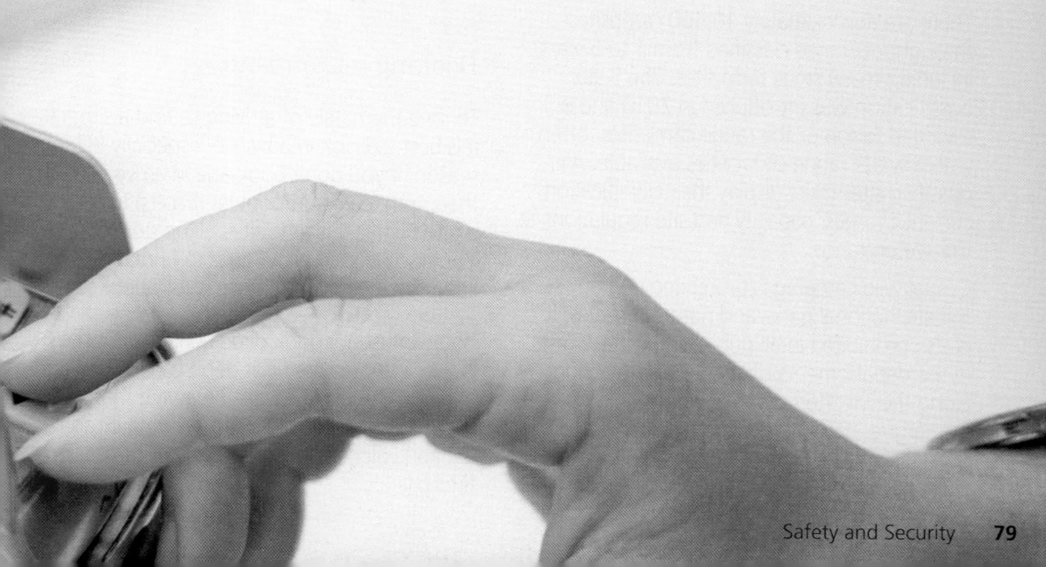

Continental Campsites

The quantity and variety of sites across France means you're sure to find one that suits your needs – from full facilities and entertainment to quiet rural retreats. If you haven't previously toured outside of the UK you may notice some differences, such as pitches being smaller or closer together. In hot climates hard ground may make putting up awnings difficult.

Camping in France

There are approximately 10,400 campsites throughout France classified from 1 to 5 stars, including many small farm sites. The 5 star classification was introduced in 2010 and is awarded to top of the range campsites, often with a wider range of facilities available. All classified sites must display their classification, current charges, capacity and site regulations at the site entrance.

Casual/wild camping is prohibited in many state forests, national parks and nature reserves. It is also prohibited in all public or private forests in the départements of Landes and Gironde, along the Mediterranean coast including the Camargue, parts of the Atlantic and Brittany coasts, Versailles and Paris, and along areas of coast that are covered by spring tides.

The Camping Club de France owns a number of sites in France (some of which are listed in this guide and marked CC de F in their site entries) and has partnership agreements with others including the Campéole, Camping du Midi and Huttopia chains. Caravanners wishing to join the CC de F pay an annual fee of €50 per family (2013). Email the CC de F secretariat@campingclub.asso.fr or visit their website www.campingclub.asso.fr.

Booking a Campsite

To save the hassle of arriving to find a site full it is best to book in advance, especially in high season. If you don't book ahead arrive no later than 4pm (earlier at popular resorts) to secure a pitch, after this time sites fill up quickly. You also need to allow time to find another campsite if your first choice is fully booked.

You can usually book directly via a campsite's website using a credit or debit card to pay a deposit if required. Please be aware that some sites regard the deposit as a booking or admin fee and will not deduct the amount from your final bill.

Overseas Travel Service

The Caravan Club's Travel Service offers Club members an overseas site booking service to over 200 campsites in Europe. Full details of these sites plus information on Ferry special offers and Red Pennant Overseas Holiday Insurance can be found in the Club's Continental Caravanning brochure – call 01342 327410 to request a copy or visit www.caravanclub.co.uk/overseas.

Overseas Site Booking Service sites are marked 'SBS' in the site listings. Many of them can be booked at www.caravanclub.co.uk. The Caravan Club cannot make advance reservations for any other campsites listed in this guide. Only those sites marked SBS have been inspected by Caravan Club staff.

Camping Cheques

The Caravan Club operates a low season scheme in association with Camping Cheques, offering flexible holidays. The scheme covers approximately 635 sites in 29 countries.

Camping Cheques are supplied as part of a package which includes return ferry fare and a minimum of seven Camping Cheques. Those sites which feature in the Camping Cheques scheme and which are listed in this guide are marked 'CChq' in their site entries. For full details of the Camping Cheque scheme visit www.caravanclub.co.uk/campingcheques.

Caravan Storage Abroad

Storing your caravan on a site in France can be a great way to avoid a long tow and to save on ferry and fuel costs. Even sites which don't offer a specific long-term storage facility may be willing to negotiate a price to store your caravan for you. You can download a list of sites which offer storage facilities in France from www.caravanclub.co.uk.

Before you leave your caravan in storage abroad always check whether your insurance covers this, as many policies don't. If you aren't covered then look for a specialist policy - Towergate Bakers (tel: 0800 4961516 or www.towergatebakers.co.uk) or K Drewe Insurance (tel: 0845 408 5929 or www.lookinsuranceservices.co.uk) both offer policies.

Facilities and Site Description

All of the site facilities shown in the site listings of this guide have been taken from member reports, as have the comments at the end of each site entry. Please remember that opinions and expectations can differ significantly from one person to the next.

The year of report is indicated at the end of each site listing – sites which haven't been reported on for a few years may have had changes to their prices, facilities, opening dates and standards. It is always best to check any specific details before travelling by contacting the site or looking at their website.

Many French campsites ban the wearing of loose or boxer-style shorts in swimming pools on grounds of hygiene. Sites may also require swimmers to wear swimming caps.

Sanitary Facilities

Facilities normally include toilet and shower blocks with shower cubicles, wash basins and razor sockets. In site listings the abbreviation 'wc' indicates that the site has the kind of toilets we are used to in the UK (pedestal style). Some sites have footplate 'squat' toilets and, where this is known, you will see the abbreviation 'cont', i.e. continental. French sites do not always provide sink plugs, toilet paper or soap so it is best to take them with you. During low season it is not uncommon for only a few toilet and shower cubicles to be in use on a 'unisex' basis.

Waste Disposal

Site entries show (when known) where a campsite has a chemical disposal and/or a motorhome service point, which is assumed to include a waste (grey) water dump station and toilet cassette-emptying point. Use of the site facilities is very common on continental sites, meaning you may find fewer waste water disposal facilities.

Chemical disposal points may be fixed at a high level requiring lifting of cassettes in order to empty them. Disposal may simply be down a toilet – continental or otherwise. Wastemaster-style emptying points are not very common in Europe.

Finding a Campsite

Directions are given for all campsites listed in this guide and most listings also include GPS co-ordinates. Where known full street addresses are also given. The directions have been supplied by member reports and haven't been checked in detail by The Club.

For information about using satellite navigation to find a site see the Motoring Equipment section.

Overnight Stops

Many towns and villages in France provide dedicated overnight or short stay areas specifically for motorhomes, usually with security, electricity, water and waste facilities. These are known as 'Aires de Services' and are usually well signposted with a motorhome icon. Aires vary from region to region. Some are free of charge while others charge a small fee. Facilities also vary - some will have electrics available as well as other facilities, whilst others will just provide a basic parking area.

Many campsites in popular tourist resorts have separate overnight areas of hardstanding with appropriate facilities, often adjacent to, or just outside, the main campsite area. Look for the 'Stop Accueil Camping-Car' sign.

Motorhomes are also welcome to park overnight free of charge at approximately 1,500 vineyards and farms throughout France through an organisation called France Passion. Membership is open to motorhomes only - write to France Passion, BP 57, 84202 Carpentras. Alternatively join online at www.france-passion.com. It is illegal to spend the night at the roadside.

The Fédération Française de Camping et de Caravaning (FFCC) publishes a 'Guide Officiel Aires de Services Camping-Car', listing 'aires' and stopping places specifically set aside for motorhomes in France and in a number of other countries. Vicarious books publish an English guide to Aires including directions, GPS co-ordinates and photographs. Contact 0131 208 333 or visit their website www.vicariousbooks.co.uk.

For security reasons you shouldn't spend the night on petrol station service areas, ferry terminal car parks or isolated 'aires de repos' or 'aires de services' along motorways.

Municipal Campsites

Municipal sites are found in towns and villages all over France. Once very basic, many have improved in standard in recent years – although you may still find some which are outdated. They can usually be booked in advance through the local town hall ('Mairie') or tourist office during office hours. Most municipal sites are clean, well-run and very reasonably priced but security may be rudimentary – at best there may be a barrier at the main entrance which is lowered at night.

You may sometimes find that these sites are used by seasonal workers, market traders and travellers in low season – where sites try to discourage these visitors you may find that twin-axle or very large caravans aren't accepted or are charged at a much higher rate. If you may be affected check for any restrictions when you book.

Naturist Campsites

Some naturist sites are included in this guide and are shown with the word 'naturist' after their site name. Those marked 'part naturist' have separate areas for naturists. The French Government Tourist Board has links to naturist centres approved by the French Federation of Naturism, or visit www.naturisme.fr and www.france4naturisme.com for details of naturist centres throughout the country.

Visitors aged 15 and over are recommended to have a Naturist Licence, although this is no longer compulsory at many naturist centres. A licence can be obtained in advance from British Naturism (tel 01604 620361, www.british-naturism.org.uk, email headoffice@british-naturism.org.uk) or on arrival at any recognised naturist campsite (passport-size photo required).

For further details contact the French Federation of Naturism, email contact@ffn-naturisme.com, or visit www.ffn-naturisme.com.

Opening Dates and times

Opening dates (where known) are given for campsites in this guide. However sites may close without notice due to refurbishment work, a lack of visitors or bad weather. Outside the high season it is always best to contact campsites in advance, even if the site advertises itself as open all year.

Following incidents in recent years some authorities in southern France have introduced tighter regulations concerning sites liable to flooding, including limiting opening dates from April/May until August/September in some areas.

Most sites will close their gates or barriers overnight – if you are planning to arrive late or are delayed on your journey you should call ahead to make sure you will be able to gain access to the site. There may be a late arrivals area outside of the barriers where you can pitch overnight. Motorhomers should also consider barrier closing times if leaving site in your vehicle for the evening.

Check out time is usually between 10am and 12 noon – advise staff if you will have to leave the site very early for any reason to make sure you can check out before you leave. Sites may also close for an extended lunch break, so if you're planning to arrive or check out around lunchtime check that the office will be open.

Pets on Campsites

Well behaved dogs are welcome on many sites, although you may have to prove that all of their vaccinations are up to date before they are allowed onto the site. Certain breeds of dogs are banned in France and other breeds will need to be muzzled and kept on a lead at all times. A list of breeds with restrictions can be found at www.caravanclub.co.uk/pets.

Sites usually charge for dogs and may limit the number allowed per pitch. On arrival make yourself aware of site rules regarding dogs, such as keeping them on a lead, muzzling them or not leaving them unattended in your outfit.

In popular tourist areas local regulations may ban dogs from beaches during the summer. Some dogs may find it difficult to cope with prolonged periods of hot weather if they are used to UK weather. Also watch out for diseases transmitted by ticks, caterpillars, mosquitoes or sandflies to which dogs from the UK have no natural resistance. Consult your vet about preventative treatment before you travel.

Visitors to parts of central France should be aware of the danger of Pine Processionary Caterpillars from mid-winter to late spring. Dogs should be kept away from pine trees if possible or fitted with a muzzle that prevents the nose and mouth from touching the ground. This will also protect against poisoned bait sometimes used by farmers and hunters.

In the event that your pet is taken ill abroad a campsite should have information about local vets.

Dogs are required to wear a collar identifying their owners at all times. If your dog goes missing, report the matter to the local police and the local animal welfare organisation.

See the Documents section of this book for more information about the Pet Travel Scheme.

Prices

Campsite prices per night (for an outfit and two adults) are shown in the site entries. If you stay on site after midday you may be charged for an extra day. Many campsites have a minimum amount for credit card transactions, meaning they can't be used to pay for overnight or short stays. Check which methods of payment are accepted when you check in.

Sites with automatic barriers may ask for a deposit for a swipe card to operate it.

Sites may impose extra charges for the use of facilities such as swimming pools, showers or laundry facilities. You may also be charged extra for dogs, Wi-Fi, tents and extra cars. Often campsites have a daily discounted charge for children, other sites will charge a fixed rate per person, regardless of age.

Visitors are usually required to pay a tourism tax (taxe de séjour) that is imposed by local authorities. This tax is collected by campsite owners and will be included in your bill.

Registering on Arrival

Local authority requirements mean you will usually have to produce an identity document on arrival, which will be retained by the site until you check out. If you don't want to leave your passport with reception then most sites will accept a camping document such as the Camping Key Europe (CKE) or Camping Card International (CCI) - if this is known site entries are marked CKE/CCI.

CKE are available for Caravan Club members to purchase by calling 01342 336633 or are free to members if you take out the 'motoring' level of cover from the Club's Red Pennant Overseas Holiday Insurance.

General Advice

If you've visiting a new site see if it is possible to take a look round the site and facilities before booking in. If your pitch is allocated at check in ask to see it first to check the condition and access, as marked or hedged pitches can sometimes be difficult for large outfits. Riverside pitches can be very scenic but keep an eye on the water level; in periods of heavy rain this may rise rapidly.

A tourist tax, eco tax and/or rubbish tax may be imposed by local authorities. VAT may also be payable on top of your campsite fees.

Speed limits on campsites are usually restricted to 10 km/h (6 mph). You may be asked to park your car in a separate area away from your caravan, particularly in the high season.

The use of the term 'statics' in the campsite reports in this guide may refer to long-term seasonal pitches, chalets, cottages, tour operators' fixed tents and cabins, as well as mobile homes.

Complaints

If a situation arises where you want to make a complaint, take it up with site staff or owners at the time. It is much better to make staff aware of a problem while something could be done to rectify the situation for the rest of your stay than to complain once you are home.

The Caravan Club has no control or influence over day to day campsite operations or administration of the sites listed in this guide. Therefore we aren't able to intervene in any dispute you should have with a campsite, unless the booking has been made through our Site Booking Service - see listings marked 'SBS' for sites we are able to book for you.

Campsite groups

Across Europe there are many 'groups' of campsites with sites in various locations. While you may find that sites within a group can be slightly more expensive than independent sites, there are also many benefits to choosing a group campsite.

You will generally find that group sites will be consistent in their format and the quality and variety of facilities they offer. If you liked one site you can be fairly confident that you will like other sites within the same group.

If you're looking for a full facility site, with swimming pools, play areas, bars and restaurants on site you're likely to find these on sites which are part of a group. You might even find organised excursions and activities such as archery on site.

Introduction to France

Banon, Provence

Population France (approx): 63 million

Capital: Paris (population approx 12 million)

Area: 543,965 sq km

Bordered by: Andorra, Belgium, Germany, Italy, Luxembourg, Monaco, Spain, Switzerland

Terrain: Mostly flat plains or gently rolling hills in north and west; mountain ranges in south and east

Climate: Temperate climate with regional variations; generally warm summers and cool winters; harsh winters in mountainous areas; hot summers in central and Mediterranean areas

Coastline: 3,427km

Highest Point: Mont Blanc 4,807m

Language: French

Local Time: GMT or BST + 1, i.e. 1 hour ahead of the UK all year

Currency: Euros divided into 100 cents; £1 = €1.26, €1 = £0.79 (September 2014)

Telephoning: From the UK dial 0033 for France and omit the initial 0 of the 10-digit number you are calling. Mobile phone numbers start 06. For Monaco the code is 00377. To call the UK from France dial 0044 omitting the initial zero of the area code

Emergency Numbers: Police 112; Fire brigade 112; Ambulance 112.

Public Holidays 2015

France: Jan 1; Apr 6; May 1, 8 (VE Day), 14, 25; Jul 14 (Bastille Day); Aug 15; Nov 1, 11 (Armistice Day); Dec 25.

Find out more

French Government Tourist Board
Maison de la France
Lincoln House
300 High Holborn
London
WC1V 7JH
Tel: 09068 244123
Website: www.franceguide.com
Email: info.uk@atout-france.fr

Opening Hours

Banks – Mon-Fri 9am-noon & 2pm-4pm/5pm/6pm; in Paris Mon-Fri 10am-5pm; some open Sat & close on Mon. Early closing the day before a public holiday.

Museums – Daily 10am-5pm; closed Mon or Tues, check locally. In Paris many are open late once a week.

Post Offices – Mon-Fri 8am/9am-6pm/7pm; Sat 8am/9am-noon.

Shops: Food shops - Tues-Sat 7am/9am-6.30pm/7.30pm; some food shops i.e. bakers, grocers, etc, are open sun morning. Other shops - Tues-Sat 9am/10am-7.30pm. Shops generally close all or half day on Mon; in small towns shops close for lunch from noon to 2pm. Major Shops - Mon-Sat 9am/10am-7pm. Supermarkets may stay open until 9pm/10pm. Shops in tourist areas may open on Sunday.

Touring in France

France is divided administratively into 'régions', each of which consists of several 'départements'. There are 96 départements in total including Corsica, and these are approximately equivalent to our counties.

Paris, the capital and hub of the region known as the Ile-de-France, remains the political, economic, artistic, cultural and tourist centre of France. Visit www.parisinfo.com for a wealth of information on what to see and do in the city. A Paris Pass, valid for 2 to 6 days, entitles you to free entrance (ahead of the queues) to over 60 Paris attractions and free unlimited public transport plus discounts and free offers – see www.parispass.com.

Visitors under the age of 26 are admitted free to permanent collections in national museums; show your passport as proof of age. National museums, including the Louvre, are closed on Tuesday, with the exception of Versailles and the Musée d'Orsay which are closed on Monday. Entrance to national museums is free on the first Sunday of every month. Municipal museums are usually closed on Monday and public holidays.

Restaurants must display priced menus outside and most offer a set menu 'plat du jour' or 'table d'hôte' which usually represents good value. A service charge of 15% is included in restaurant bills but it is also expected to leave a small tip if you have received good service. Smoking is not allowed in bars and restaurants.

France has a large network of well-marked, long-distance footpaths and hiking trails – Les Sentiers de Grande Randonnée – which generally follow ancient tracks formerly used by pilgrims, merchants and soldiers. In addition to these 'GR' paths there are also 'PR' paths (Chemins de Petite Randonnée) which are most suited for local hiking. For a list of GR routes see www.gr-infos.com or contact the French Tourist Board or local tourist offices in France for more information.

For personalised itineraries based on your interests and recommended places to visit during your break visit www.france-voyage.com.

Channel Islands

Ferry services operate for cars and passengers between Poole and Portsmouth and St Malo via Jersey and Guernsey. Caravans and motorhomes are permitted to enter Jersey, subject to certain conditions, including pre-booking direct with a registered campsite and the acquisition of a permit. For further information and details of the campsites on Jersey where caravans are permitted, see www.jersey.com or contact The Club's Travel Service Information Officer, email: travelserviceinfo@caravanclub.co.uk.

There are three campsites on Guernsey but, for the moment, the authorities in Guernsey do not permit entry to trailer caravans. Motorhomes can only be taken onto the island if they are stored under cover and not used for human habitation. Trailer tents can be taken onto the island without restrictions.

Local Travel

Several large cities have metro or tram systems and all have a comprehensive bus network.

The Paris metro network comprises 16 lines and around 300 stations, and has many connections to the RER (regional suburban rail network) and the SNCF national railway system. Tickets for the metro, also valid on RATP buses, can be bought singly from vending machines at the turnstiles or from ticket offices, but a 'carnet' of 10 tickets is a more economical option. Your ticket is valid for an hour and a half from the time it is validated at the machines, on buses or at metro stations.

For tourists Paris Visite travel passes are available allowing unlimited travel for one to five days across some or all of the travel zones and a range of discounts at attractions. For further information see www.ratp.fr.

Senior citizens aged 60 and over are entitled to a discount of up to 25% when using French railways. Show your passport as proof of age.

Ferries

Car ferry services operate all year across the Gironde estuary between Royan and Le Verdon eliminating a 155km detour. Approximate 2013 prices are €40.60 single journey for car, caravan under 3m and 2 adults or €53.20 for car, caravan over 3m and 2 adults or €47 for motorhome and 2 adults. Between Blaye and Lamarque north of Bordeaux approximate 2013 prices are €28.80 single journey for car, caravan under 3m and 2 adults or for a motorhome and 2 adults, or €34.20 for car, caravan over 3m – see www.bernezac.com for more details.

Ferry services operate from Marseille, Nice and Toulon to Corsica. For information contact:

Southern Ferries
30 Churton Street
London
SW1V 2LP
Tel: 0844 8157785
www.southernferries.co.uk
mail@southernferries.com

Cycling

A number of French towns are actively promoting the use of bicycles. Initiatives i nclude increasing the number of cycle paths, providing parking space for bicycles and constructing shelters and cycle hire points in car parks. You may hire bicycles at many local tourist offices and from some railway stations.

Recent initiatives have included the improvement of cycle tracks along rivers and canals and many former gravel tracks have been replaced with tarmac along the Rivers Rhône, Loire and Yonne/Canal de Nivernais. It is understood that similar improvements will take place along the Canal de Bourgogne.

In and around Paris there are 370 kilometres of cycle lanes, and bicycles, known as 'Les Vélibs', are available for hire at very reasonable rates at more than 1,600 self-service stations – roughly one every 300 metres.

The French Tourist Board has information on cycle routes and tours throughout France.

Place names used in the Site Entry listings which follow can be found in Michelin's France Atlas, scale 1:200,000 (1 cm = 2 km).

Site listings

In a change to previous editions of this guide, the site listings have now been separated into regional sections. If you know the site you are looking for, you can find an index of town names at the rear of this book to help you find which section the site is now listed under.

On the following page you will find a map showing the regions of France, and listing the departments which fall within each region. Each region is a separate section of the listings starting with a regional introduction, with sites within that region listed alphabetically by town name.

Regionalisation is based on the site postcode rather than the location of the listing town, so you may find towns listed under more than one region. For example the town of Aire-Sur-l'Ardour is situated in Aquitaine, but right on the border with Midi-Pyrenees; sites listed under the town are located in both regions.

France

Regions and Departments

Please note the first two digits of a French postal code refer to the department in which it is located.

Departmental numbers are listed below.

Alsace
67 Bas-Rhin
68 Haut-Rhin

Aquitaine
24 Dordogne
33 Gironde
40 Landes
47 Lot-et-Garonne
64 Pyrénées-Atlantiques

Auvergne
03 Allier
15 Cantal
43 Haute-Loire
63 Puy-de-Dôme

Burgundy
21 Côte-d'Or
58 Nièvre
71 Saône-et-Loire
89 Yonne

Brittany
22 Côtes-d'Armor
29 Finistère
35 Ille-et-Vilaine
56 Morbihan

Centre
18 Cher
28 Eure-et-Loir
36 Indre
37 Indre-et-Loire
41 Loir-et-Cher
45 Loiret

Champagne-Ardenne
08 Ardennes
10 Aube
51 Marne
52 Haute-Marne

Corsica
02A Corse-du-Sud
02B Haute-Corse

Cote d'Azur
06 Alpes-Maritimes

Franche-Comté
25 Doubs
39 Jura
70 Haute-Saône
90 Territoire-de-Belfort

Languedoc-Roussillon
11 Aude
30 Gard
34 Hérault
48 Lozère
66 Pyrénées-Orientales

Limousin
19 Corréze
23 Creuse
87 Haute-Vienne

Lorraine
54 Meurthe-et-Moselle
55 Meuse
57 Moselle
88 Vosges

Midi-Pyrénées
09 Ariège
12 Aveyron
31 Haute-Garonne
32 Gers
46 Lot
65 Hautes-Pyrénées
81 Tarn
82 Tarn-et-Garonne

Nord Pas-De-Calais
59 Nord
62 Pas-de-Calais

Normandy
14 Calvados
27 Eure
50 Manche
61 Orne
76 Seine-Maritime

Paris-Île-de-France
75 Paris
77 Seine-et-Marne
78 Yvelines
91 Essonne
92 Haut-de-Seine
93 Seine-St-Denis
94 Val-de-Marne
95 Val-d'Oise

Pays de la Loire
44 Loire-Atlantique
49 Maine-et-Loire
53 Mayenne
72 Sarthe
85 Vendée

Picardy
02 Aisne
60 Oise
80 Somme

Poitou-Charentes
16 Charente
17 Charente-Maritime
79 Deux-Sèvres
86 Vienne

Provence
04 Alpes-de-Haute-Provence
05 Hautes-Alpes
13 Bouches-du-Rhône
83 Var
84 Vaucluse

Rhône-Alps
01 Ain
07 Ardèche
26 Drôme
38 Isère
42 Loire
69 Rhône
73 Savoie
74 Haute-Savoie

Alsace

Regional Introduction

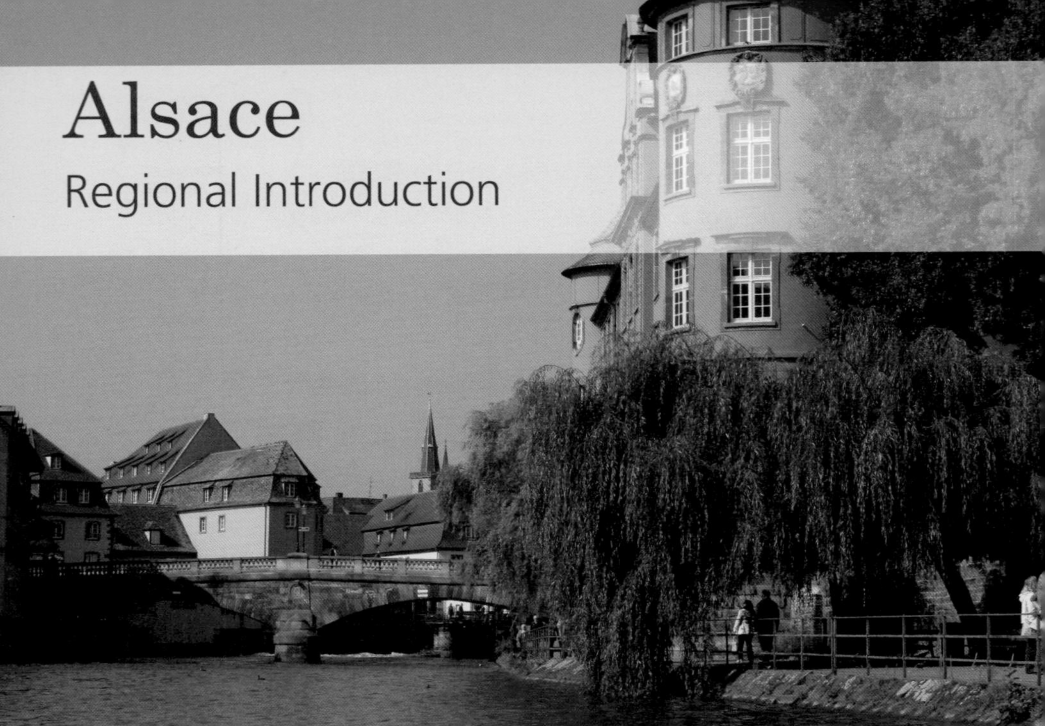

Strasbourg

Welcome to Alsace

Located in north-east France, and neighbouring Switzerland and Germany, Alsace is in the heart of Europe. The region you is home to many villages of quaint, brightly-painted houses, with an eclectic mix of German and French cultures.

Alsace is also renowned for its wine production and there are many vineyards to visit during your stay, especially along the 105 miles of the Route des Vins d'Alsace from Marlenheim to Thann.

Strasbourg is one of the major cities in this region and has a rich history to discover as well as many popular tourist spots, including the magnificent gothic cathedral.

Local highlights

A local variety of sauerkraut, choucroute garnie is the gastronomic highlight of the region. Used in many dishes, it is traditionally served with different types of German sausage.

During winter festivities, over a hundred Christmas markets can be found throughout Alsace and the Christmas tree of Strasbourg has the title of being the tallest in Europe.

Major towns and cities

- Strasbourg – the capital city of Alsace.
- Mulhouse – an industrial town famous for its historical museums.
- Colmar – renowned for its well-preserved old town.
- Guebwiller – a city with a rich history and three stunning churches to visit.
- Obernai – a popular city full of old charm and cobbled lanes.

Regional attractions

- Bibliothèque Humaniste, Sélestat – one of the oldest public libraries in the world.
- Cathédrale Notre Dame de Strasbourg – a fine example of Gothic architecture.
- Northern Vosges Nature Park – a UNESCO listed World Biosphere Reserve, ideal for exploration on foot or bike.

Find out more

www.tourisme-alsace.com

Tel: (0)3 89 20 68 92 Colmar Tourist Office

Tel: (0)3 88 52 28 28 Strasbourg Tourist Office

⊞ **ALTKIRCH** *6F3* (1km SE Rural) *47.61275, 7.23336* **Camp Municipal Les Acacias, Route de Hirtzbach, 68130 Altkirch [03 89 40 69 40 or 03 89 40 00 04 (Mairie); camping.les.acacias@gmail.com; www.sundgau-sudalsace.com]** Sp on D419 on app to town fr W. Sp in town. Sm, mkd pitch, shd; htd wc (some cont); chem disp; baby facs; shwrs inc; el pnts (10A) €3; shop in ssn & 1km; rest, snacks; bar; playgrnd; pool 1km; 20% statics; dogs; Eng spkn; adv bkg rec high ssn; CKE/CCI. "Lovely quiet site; gd, clean facs; office clsd until 1700 - site yourself & pay later; gd NH." € 13.50 2013*

BIESHEIM see Neuf Brisach *6F3*

BURNHAUPT LE HAUT see Cernay *6F3*

CERNAY *6F3* (500m S Urban) *47.80448, 7.16999* **Camping Les Acacias, 16 Rue René Guibert, 68700 Cernay [03 89 75 56 97; fax 03 89 39 72 29; www.camping-les-acacias.com]** Fr N on D83 by-pass, exit Cernay Est. Turn R into town at traff lts, immed L bef rv bdge, site sp on L; well sp. Lge, mkd pitch, pt shd; wc; chem disp; mv service pnt; shwrs inc; el pnts (5A) €3.50 (poss rev pol); Indtte; shop, rest, bar & pool (high ssn); entmnt; 25% statics; dogs €1.20; poss cr; quiet; red long stay; 10% red CKE/CCI (pitch only). "Friendly staff; clean, tidy site; storks nesting over some pitches; sh walk to town." ♦ 1 Apr-1 Oct. € 12.00 2010*

CERNAY *6F3* (6km S Rural) *47.74684, 7.12423* **Camping Les Castors, 4 Route de Guewenheim, 68520 Burnhaupt-le-Haut [03 89 48 78 58; fax 03 89 62 74 66; camping.les.castors@wanadoo.fr; www.camping-les-castors.fr]** Exit A36 junc 15 sp Burnhaupt-le-Haut onto D83, then D466 sp Masevaux. Site on R. Med, mkd pitch, pt shd; htd wc; chem disp; baby facs; shwrs inc; el pnts (5-10A) €4-5; gas; Indtte; shop 2km; tradsmn; rest, snacks; bar; BBQ; playgrnd; games rm; wifi; 40% statics; dogs €15; phone; poss cr; Eng spkn; adv bkg; quiet; CKE/CCI. "Conv German & Swiss borders, Black Forest; wine rte; Mulhouse motor museum; gd san facs; vg; excel site, nice area. Friendly owner. Gd cycle path." ♦ 1 Apr-31 Oct. € 12.80 (CChq acc) 2013*

COLMAR *6F3* (2km E Urban) *48.07942, 7.38665* **Camping de l'Ill, 1 Allée du Camping, 68180 Horbourg-Wihr [tel/fax 03 89 41 15 94; camping@agglo-colmar.fr; www.campingdelill.com]** Exit A35 junc 25 onto D415, foll Freibourg sp. At 2nd rndabt turn L to Colmar cent, site on rvside on L bef bdge. Lge, hdg/mkd pitch, hdstg, pt sl, terr, shd; htd wc; chem disp; mv service pnt; shwrs; el pnts (10A) €4.80 (poss rev pol); Indtte (inc dryer); shop & tradsmn (high ssn); supmkt nr; rest, snacks; bar; playgrnd; cycle hire; wifi; entmnt; TV; 10% statics; dogs €4.; bus/train to city cent; poss cr; some Eng spkn; adv bkg; much noise fr a'route; ccard acc (over €20); CKE/CCI. "Lovely, clean, rvside site; excel san facs; gd rest; some pitches req steel pegs; gd for town; sep area for NH." ♦ ltd 21 Mar-31 Dec. € 22.50 2013*

COLMAR *6F3* (7km S Rural) *48.01613, 7.34983* **Camping Clair Vacances, Route de Herrlisheim, 68127 Ste Croix-en-Plaine [03 89 49 27 28; fax 03 89 49 31 37; clairvacances@orange.fr; www.clairvacances.com]** Exit D83 at sp Herrlisheim onto D1 bis. Take 2nd rd to vill sp camping, foll site sp thro vill. NB Rd thru vill narr with traff calming bollards. Fr A35 turn off at junc 27 sp Herrlisheim/Ste Croix-en-Plaine onto D1 dir Herrlisheim to site in 1km. Med, hdg/mkd pitch, some hdstg, pt shd; htd wc; chem disp; baby facs; shwrs inc; el pnts (16A) €4 (long lead poss req); Indry rm; gas; service wash; shop 2km; tradsmn; snacks high ssn; BBQ (gas); playgrnd; htd pool; paddling pool; tennis 3km; cycle hire; child entmnt; no dogs; phone; wifi; poss cr; Eng spkn; adv bkg; quiet; ccard acc; red low ssn; CKE/CCI. "Beautiful site; well-kept & supervised; can be busy, adv bkg rec; helpful, friendly owners; gd size pitches; excel, clean san facs; gd touring base Alsace wine rte; excel." ♦ 10 Apr-19 Oct. € 37.50 2014*

See advertisement

COLMAR *6F3* (7km SW Rural) *48.04238, 7.29935* **Camping des Trois Châteaux, 10 Rue du Bassin, 68420 Eguisheim [03 89 23 19 39; fax 03 89 24 10 19; camping.eguisheim@orange.fr; www.camping-eguisheim.fr]** Foll D83 S (Colmar by-pass) R at sp Eguisheim. R into vill to site at top of vill, foll camp sp. Med, mkd pitch, pt sl, terr, pt shd; wc; chem disp; mv service pnt; shwrs inc; el pnts (8-10A) €3-5 (poss rev pol); gas; lndtte; shops, rest & bars in vill 300m; hypmkt 5km; playgrnd; dogs €3; phone adj; poss cr; adv bkg (tel 2 days bef arr); poss noisy; ccard acc; red low ssn; CKE/CCI. "Popular, well-run, busy site; no c'vans over 7m (inc draw bar); mv pitches flat but some c'van pitches sl & poss diff; gd touring base; weekly wine-tasting events; stork park adj; rec arr early; excel; cycle rte to cent of Colmar." ♦ ltd 23 Mar-27 Oct, 29Nov-22 Dec. € 21.00 2014*

See advertisement

COLMAR *6F3* (7km W Urban) *48.08517, 7.27253* **Camping Le Médiéval (formerly Municipal Les Cigognes), Quai de la Gare, 68230 Turckheim [03 89 27 02 00; fax 03 89 80 86 93; reception@camping-turckheim.fr; www.camping.turckheim.fr]** Fr D83 twd Turchkeim turn W onto D11 to Turckheim. On ent vill, turn immed L down 1-way rd after x-ing rlwy lines. Do not cross rv bdge. Site on L bef bdge, adj stadium. Med, hdg pitch, pt shd; htd wc; chem disp; mv service pnt; baby facs; shwrs inc; el pnts (16A) €4; lndtte (inc dryer); shop 500m; hypmkt nrby; BBQ; playgrnd; pool; games rm; wifi; entmnt; TV rm; 5% statics; dogs €2.50; bus adj; train 250m; twin axles; Eng spkn; poss cr; quiet; ccard acc; red low ssn; CKE/CCI. "Lovely site with spacious pitches; ltd low ssn; cycle rtes nr; resident storks; sh walk to interesting, beautiful old vill with rests; gd touring base; gd, new san facs block (2014); poss cr in June & high ssn; under new management; deposit for barrier key; friendly helpful staff; open 28 Dec-26 Dec for Christmas mkt; vg; close to historic sites and medieval castles." ♦ 4 Apr-26 Oct. € 21.00 2014*

DAMBACH LA VILLE see Sélestat *6E3*

EGUISHEIM see Colmar *6F3*

FRELAND see Kaysersberg *6F3*

HAGUENAU *5D3* (2km S Urban) *48.80289, 7.76911* **Camp Municipal Les Pins, Route de Strasbourg, 67500 Haguenau [03 88 73 91 43 or 03 88 93 70 00; fax 03 88 93 69 89; tourisme@ville-haguenau.fr; www.ville-haguenau.fr]** Fr S on D263, after passing Haguenau town sp turn L at 2nd set of traff lts (opp Peugeot g'ge). Site sp fr D263. Med, mkd pitch, terr, pt shd; htd wc; chem disp; shwrs inc; el pnts (6A) inc; gas; lndtte; shop, rest, snack & bar 2km; BBQ; playgrnd; pool 1km inc; dogs €0.90; phone; bus 500m; Eng spkn; adv bkg; quiet; CKE/CCI. "Lge pitches; helpful staff; clean, modern san facs; meals avail fr warden; grnd firm even after heavy rain; excel." ♦ 1 May-30 Sep. € 13.00 2010*

HEIMSBRUNN see Mulhouse *6F3*

"There aren't many sites open at this time of year"

If you're travelling outside peak season remember to call ahead to check site opening dates – even if the entry says 'open all year'.

KAYSERSBERG *6F3* (1km NW Rural) *48.14899, 7.25405* **Camping Municipal de Kayserberg, Rue des Acacias, 68240 Kaysersberg [tel/fax 03 89 47 14 47 or 03 89 78 11 11 (Mairie); camping@ville-kaysersberg.fr; www.camping-kaysersberg.com]** Fr A35/N83 exit junc 23 onto D4 sp Sigolsheim & Kaysersberg; bear L onto N415 bypass dir St Dié; site sp 100m past junc with D28. Or SE fr St Dié on N415 over Col du Bonhomme; turn L into Rue des Acacias just bef junc with D28. Med, hdg/mkd pitch, pt shd; wc; chem disp; shwrs inc; baby facs; el pnts (8-13A) inc (may need cable); gas; lndtte; shops 150m; supmkt 700m; bread delivery; pool 1km; playgrnd; fishing & tennis adj; wifi; TV; dogs €2 (no dogs Jul/Aug); quiet. "Excel, well-kept, busy site; rec arr early high ssn; many gd sized pitches; friendly staff; clean san facs; rv walk to lovely town, birth place Albert Schweitzer; many mkd walks/cycle rts; Le Linge WWI battle grnd nr Orbey; Excel site; if arr when clsd, choose pitch nbr bef registering." ♦ 1 Apr-30 Sep. € 18.60 2014*

KAYSERSBERG *6F3* (7km NW Rural) *48.18148, 7.18449* **Camping Les Verts Bois, 3 Rue de la Fonderie, 68240 Fréland [tel/fax 03 89 47 57 25 or 06 81 71 89 38 (mob); gildas.douault@sfr.fr; www.camping-lesvertsbois.com]** Sp off N415 Colmar/St Dié rd bet Lapoutroie & Kaysersberg. Site approx 5km after turn fr main rd on D11 at far end of vill. Turn L into rd to site when D11 doubles back on itself. Sm, pt sl, terr, pt shd; htd wc; chem disp; shwrs inc; el pnts (6-10A) €2.70-3.20; gas; Indtte (inc dryer); shop & bank in vill; tradsmn; rest (open to non-campers); snacks, bar; BBQ; dogs €0.70; poss cr; Eng spkn; poss cr; adv bkg; quiet; ccard acc; red low ssn; CKE/CCI. "Lovely site in beautiful, peaceful setting adj rv; friendly welcome; excel; fishing & bird watching; cheese farms 2 miles away; a must for cheese lovers; v helpful owners; excel rest." 1 Apr-31 Oct. € 19.00 2014*

KESKASTEL *5D3* (700m NE Rural) *48.97684, 7.05354* **Camp Municipal Les Sapins, Centre des Loisirs, 67260 Keskastel [03 88 00 19 25 (Mairie); fax 03 88 00 34 66; camping.keskastel@orange.fr; www.keskastel.fr/camping-municpal-les-sapins]** Exit A4 junc 42 fr N or junc 43 fr S dir Sarralbe/Keskastel. In Keskastel cent turn onto D338 twds Herbitzheim. Cont for approx 1km; turn R for approx 400m; site on L, well sp on lakeside. Med, hdg/mkd pitch, pt shd; htd wc (some cont); chem disp; shwrs inc; el pnts (10A) €4.30 (poss rev pol); Indtte; shop 1km; tradsmn; rest, snacks; bar; BBQ; playgrnd; sand beach adj; lake sw & fishing; tennis nr; 60% statics; dogs; phone; poss cr; some Eng spkn; quiet; adv bkg; ccard acc; CKE/CCI. "Relaxing location; conv m'way; spacious pitches; helpful warden lives above recep, ring bell if office clsd; basic san facs, ltd low ssn; office poss clsd Sun morn; barrier clsed 2300; vg." ♦ 1 Jan-21 Feb, 8 Mar-23 Oct, 8 Nov-18 Dec. € 15.45 2013*

LIEPVRE see Seléstat *6E3*

MASEVAUX *6F3* (950m N Urban) *47.77820, 6.99090* **Camping de Masevaux, 3 Rue du Stade, 68290 Masevaux [tel/fax 03 89 82 42 29; contact-masevaux@tv-com.net; www.camping-masevaux.com]** Fr N83 Colmar-Belfort rd take N466 W to Masevaux; site sp. NB D14 fr Thann to Masevaux narr & steep - not suitable c'vans. Med, mkd pitch, pt shd; htd wc; chem disp; mv service pnt; baby facs; shwrs inc; el pnts (3-6A) €3.20-3.80; Indtte; shop 1km; tradsmn; snacks; bar; playgrnd; htd pool & sports complex adj; entmnt; internet; TV rm; 40% statics; dogs €0.50; no twin-axles; poss cr; Eng spkn; adv bkg; quiet; some rd noise; ccard acc; red long stay; CKE/CCI. "Pleasant walks; interesting town - annual staging of Passion Play; helpful, friendly owners; excel facs; gd cycle rtes; excel; gd site in nice little town; supmkt nrby; close to Ballon d'Alsace." ♦ 15 Mar-31 Oct. € 19.00 2014*

MITTLACH see Munster *6F3*

MOLSHEIM *6E3* (900m SE Urban) *48.54124, 7.50003* **Camp Municipal de Molsheim, 6 Rue des Sports, 67120 Molsheim [03 88 49 82 45 or 03 88 49 58 58 (LS); fax 03 88 49 58 59; camping-molsheim@orange.fr; www.mairie-molsheim.fr]** On ent town fr Obernai on D1422 site sp on R immed after x-ing sm rv bdge. Med, mkd pitch, pt shd; wc; chem disp; mv service pnt; shwrs inc; el pnts (10A) €3; Indtte; tradsmn; BBQ; pool adj; cycle hire; dogs €1.30; train to Strasbourg 700m; poss cr; Eng spkn; adv bkg; quiet, but poss rock concerts nrby Sat in summer; red low ssn; CKE/CCI. "Pleasant site; san facs unisex low ssn. easy walk to town cent & shops; Bugatti museum in town." ♦ 8 Apr-16 Oct & 1 - 25 Dec. € 12.80 2011*

MOOSCH see Thann *6F3*

⊞ **MULHOUSE** *6F3* (4km NE Urban) *47.78267, 7.39453* **Camping Le Safary, 35 Rue de la Forêt-Noire, 68390 Sausheim [tel/fax 03 89 61 99 29 or 06 85 44 16 64 (mob); camping.safary@wanadoo.fr; www.campinglesafary.fr]** Exit A36/E54 junc 20 onto D201 N dir Battenheim & Baldersheim, site on E of D201, sp. Med, hdg/mkd pitch, pt shd; wc; chem disp; shwrs inc; el pnts (6-10A) €3-4; Indtte; shops 2km; snacks; bar; 60% statics; dogs €1; quiet; CKE/CCI. "Barrier clsd 2200-0800; few facs for size of site, poss inadequate if site full; poss travellers." € 13.00 2009*

MULHOUSE *6F3* (2km SW Rural) *47.73405, 7.3235* **Camping de l'Ill, 1 Rue de Pierre Coubertin, 68100 Mulhouse [03 89 06 20 66; fax 03 89 61 18 34; campingdelill@wanadoo.fr; www.camping-de-lill.com]** Fr A36 take Mulhouse/Dornach exit & foll sp Brunstatt at 1st traff lts. At 2nd traff lts turn R, foll University/Brunstatt/Camping sps, site approx 2.5km on rvside. Lge, some mkd pitch, pt sl, pt shd; wc; chem disp; mv service pnt; baby facs; shwrs inc; el pnts (5A) €3.70; gas; supmkt & rest 1km; tradsmn; snacks; pool; internet; dogs €1.50; tram 500m; quiet but some rlwy noise; red low ssn/CKE/CCI. "Welcoming recep; cycle along rv to town cent; OK NH." 1 Apr-17 Oct. € 14.70 2009*

⊞ **MULHOUSE** *6F3* (10km SW Rural) *47.72225, 7.22590* **FFCC Camping Parc La Chaumière, 62 Rue de Galfingue, 68990 Heimsbrunn [tel/fax 03 89 81 93 43 or 03 89 81 93 21; accueil@camping-lachaumiere.com; www.camping-lachaumiere.com]** Exit A36 junc 15; turn L over m'way; at rndabt exit on D166 sp Heimsbrunn; in vill turn R at rndabt; site end of houses on R. Med, hdg pitch, hdstg, pt sl, shd; htd wc; chem disp; mv service pnt; shwrs inc; el pnts (10A) €3 (poss rev pol); Indry rm; shop 1km; tradsmn; snacks; playgrnd; pool; 50% statics; dogs €1; quiet; ccard acc; CKE/CCI. "Sm pitches not suitable long o'fits; beautiful wine vills on La Route des Vins; museum of trains & cars in Mulhouse." € 10.50 2010*

ALSACE

MUNSTER *6F3* (800m E Rural) *48.03944, 7.14250* **Camping Le Parc de la Fecht, Route de Gunsbach, 68140 Munster [03 89 77 31 08 or 04 99 57 21 21; dirparcdelafecht@village-center.com; www.village-center.com]** Clear site sp on all app to Munster & in town. Site on D10. Lge, hdg/mkd pitch, pt shd; wc; chem disp; mv service pnt; sauna; shwrs inc; el pnts (6A) inc; Indtte (inc dryer); shops adj; rest, snacks; bar; BBQ; playgrnd; htd pool complex, paddling pool, waterslide adj; fishing; games rm; wifi; entmnt; TV; some statics; dogs €3; phone; Eng spkn; quiet; ccard acc; CKE/CCI. "Pleasant, wooded site; friendly & helpful staff; gd walking & cycling; o'night waiting area." ♦ 1 May-12 Sep. € 16.80 (CChq acc) 2010*

MUNSTER *6F3* (4km E Rural) *48.05160, 7.20527* **Camping La Route Verte, 13 Rue de la Gare, 68230 Wihr-au-Val [03 89 71 10 10; info@camping-routeverte.com; www.camping-routeverte.com]** Take D417 out of Colmar twd Munster & turn R int Wihr-au-Val. Site on L 800m. Well sp. Med, mkd pitch, pt sl, shd; wc; chem disp; mv service pnt; shwrs inc; el pnts (4-6A) €2.80-3.95; Indtte; shops, rest, bar 50m; pool 4km; games rm; dogs €1.50; phone; poss cr; adv bkg; quiet; red long stay; CKE/CCI. "Delightful, popular, clean site amid vineyards; owner helpful & friendly; not suitable lge c'vans (6m max); excel san facs; highly rec; excel." ♦ 26 Apr-30 Sep. € 17.50 2014*

MUNSTER *6F3* (2km SW Rural) *48.03105, 7.11350* **FFCC Camping Les Amis de la Nature, 4 Rue du Château, 68140 Luttenbach-près-Munster [03 89 77 38 60; fax 03 89 77 25 72; an-munster@wanadoo.fr; www.camping-an.fr]** Fr Munster take D10 sp Luttenbach; site sp. Lge, mkd pitch, pt shd; htd wc; chem disp; mv service pnt; baby facs; sauna; shwrs inc; el pnts (4-6A) €3.25-4.40/6.20; Indtte (inc dryer); shop; rest, snacks; bar; BBQ; playgrnd; htd pool; dir access to rv; tennis 1km; fishing; games area; games rm; wifi; entmnt; TV; 50% statics; dogs €1.50; poss cr; Eng spkn; quiet; ccard acc; quiet. "Lovely setting by stream; basic san facs, some grubby (2010); gd value." ♦ 6 Feb-30 Nov & 18 Dec-7 Jan. € 10.50 2010*

MUNSTER *6F3* (9km SW Rural) *47.98250, 7.01865* **Camp Municipal de Mittlach Langenwasen, 68380 Mittlach [03 89 77 63 77; fax 03 89 77 74 36; mairiemittlach@wanadoo.fr; www.mittlach.fr]** Fr Munster on D10 to Metzeral then R onto D10. Site at end rd in 6km. Med, hdg/mkd pitch, pt sl, pt shd; wc; chem disp; shwrs inc; el pnts (6-10A) €2.45-6: gas; Indtte (inc dryer); sm shop & 6km; tradsmn; playgrnd; 10% statics; dogs €0.80; Eng spkn; adv bkg; quiet; red low ssn; CKE/CCI. "Peaceful, wooded site at bottom of valley; helpful staff; san facs gd & clean; gd walking base; plenty of interest locally; excel." ♦ ltd 15 Apr-30 Sep. € 10.25 2010*

NEUF BRISACH *6F3* (6km NE Rural) *48.02724, 7.57230* **Camping de L'Ile du Rhin, 68600 Biesheim [03 89 72 57 95; fax 03 89 72 14 21; info@campingiledurhin.com; www.campingiledurhin.com]** On D415 Colmar to Freiburg (Germany). Site on island in Rv Rhine, on R after French Customs point off D415. Lge, hdstg, pt shd; wc; shwrs inc; el pnts (4-10A) inc; Indtte; shop; snacks; htd, covrd pool adj; rv fishing 100m; tennis; 50% statics; poss cr; Eng spkn; ccard acc. "Excel facs; gates clsd 2000-0700; poss flooding some pitches; gd touring base; vg." ♦ 6 Apr-4 Oct. € 19.00 (CChq acc) 2009*

NEUF BRISACH *6F3* (1.2km E Urban) *48.01638, 7.53565* **Camp Municipal Vauban, Entrée Porte de Bâle, 68600 Neuf-Brisach [tel/fax 03 89 72 54 25 or 03 89 72 51 68 (Mairie); contact@camping-vauban.fr; www.camping-vauban.fr]** Fr D415 (Colmar-Freiburg) at E of Neuf-Brisach turn NE on D1 bis (sp Neuf-Brisach & Camping Vauban). At next junc turn L & immed R into site rd. Med, pt shd; wc; mv service pnt; shwrs €1; el pnts (10A) €4; shops in town; playgrnd; pool 3km; 40% statics; dogs €1; adv bkg; quiet; red low ssn; CKE/CCI. "Gd, well-run site; fascinating ramparts around town; excel NH; lge pitches; friendly, helpful staff; most statics being removed." 1 Jan-2 Jan, 20 Mar-31 Dec. € 20.40 2013*

NEUF BRISACH *6F3* (6km SE Rural) *47.97988, 7.59639* **FFCC Camping L'Orée du Bois, 5 Rue du Bouleau, 68600 Geiswasser [tel/fax 03 89 72 80 13; valerie.schappler@wanadoo.fr; http://camping-oree-du-bois.pagesperso-orange.fr/]** Site in vill cent; rd name on bungalow; ent bet bungalow & vegetable garden - tight turn, watch out bungalow gutters. Sm, hdg pitch, pt shd; htd wc; chem disp; shwrs inc; el pnts (10A) €2.50; Indtte; BBQ; playgrnd; dogs free; Eng spkn; adv bkg; quiet; CKE/CCI. "Gd touring base; friendly owner; vg." ♦ ltd 1 Apr-30 Sep. € 6.60 2009*

NIEDERBRONN LES BAINS *5D3* (1.5km N Rural) *48.96221, 7.64522* **Camp Municipal du Heidenkopf, Route de la Lisière, 67110 Niederbronn-les-Bains [03 88 09 08 46; camping-niederbronn@laregie.fr; www.niederbronn-les-bains.fr]** Fr Niederbronn NW on D1062/D662 & foll sp rd R into forest fr mineral spring. NB Last 500m single track - poss diff lge o'fits. Med, pt sl, terr, pt shd; htd wc (some cont); chem disp; mv service pnt; baby facs; shwrs inc; el pnts (6A) €3.30; gas; Indtte; shops 3km; tradsmn; BBQ; playgrnd; pool, tennis 600m; dogs €1.40; adv bkg; quiet; red long stay/low ssn. "V peaceful site; warm welcome; forest walks; rec pay day bef dep." ♦ 1 Apr-31 Oct. € 14.00 2010*

NIEDERBRONN LES BAINS *5D3* (1.5km SW Rural) *48.92958, 7.60428* **Camping Oasis Oberbronn, 3 Rue de Frohret, 67110 Oberbronn [03 88 09 71 96; fax 03 88 09 97 87; oasis.oberbronn@laregie.fr; http://campingalsaceoberbronn.jimdo.com]** Fr D1062 turn S on D28 away fr Niederbronn; thro Oberbronn, site sp. Lge, mkd pitch, pt sl, pt shd; wc; chem disp; mv service pnt; sauna; shwrs inc; el pnts (6A) €4.30; Indtte; shop & 1.5km; tradsmn; rest, snacks; bar; BBQ; playgrnd; htd, covrd pool high ssn; paddling pool; tennis; wellness centre; fitness rm; walking, cycling, horseriding rtes; golf, games rm; fishing 2km; 20% statics; dogs €2.65; clsd 1200-1300; poss cr; adv bkg rec high ssn; quiet; red long stay/low ssn; ccard acc; CKE/CCI. "Vg site with views; pt of leisure complex; sl area for tourers; some san facs tired; site gravel paths not suitable wheelchair users." ♦ ltd 1 Apr-30 Sep. € 15.00 2011*

OBERNAI *6E3* (1km W Urban) *48.46460, 7.46750* **Camp Municipal Le Vallon de l'Ehn, 1 Rue de Berlin, 67210 Obernai [03 88 95 38 48; fax 03 88 48 31 47; camping@obernai.fr; www.obernai.fr]** Fr N exit A35 junc 11 onto D426 sp Obernai. Foll D426 W around Obernai & foll sp Mont St Odile & Camping VVF; at final rndabt turn R & immed L to site. Fr S on A35 exit junc 12 sp Obernai. At 3rd rndabt turn L onto D426 Ottrott-Mont Ste Odile (look for sp Camping VVF). Do not tow into Obernai. Lge, mkd pitch, hdstg, pt sl, pt shd; htd wc; chem disp; mv service pnt; 75% serviced pitches; baby facs; shwrs inc; el pnts (16A) €4; gas 1km; Indtte (inc dryer); sm shop & 1km; tradsmn; BBQ; playgrnd; lge pool 200m; tennis, horseriding adj; wifi; dogs €1.10; phone; bus to Strasbourg & Obernai adj; train; poss cr; Eng spkn; adv bkg; quiet; ccard acc; 10% red CC members low ssn; red long stay/low ssn/CKE/CCI. "Attractive, well-kept, busy site on edge of picturesque town; sm pitches; welcoming, helpful staff; superb, clean san facs but stretched in high ssn; no entry after 19.30; rec arr early high ssn; c'vans, m'vans & tents all sep areas; excel bus/train links; ideal NH; highly rec; v well run site; lots of refurb 2013; gd site; office cls 1230-1400." ♦ 1 Jan-11 Jan, 14 Mar-31 Dec. € 23.50 2014*

ORBEY see Munster *6F3*

RIBEAUVILLE *6E3* (2km E Urban) *48.19490, 7.33648* **Camp Municipal Pierre-de-Coubertin, Rue de Landau, 68150 Ribeauville [tel/fax 03 89 73 66 71; camping.ribeauville@wanadoo.fr; www.camping-alsace.com]** Exit N83 junc 20 at Ribeauville onto D106 & foll rd to o'skts; at traff lts turn R & then immed R again. Site on R in 500m. Camp at sports grnd nr Lycée. Lge, mkd pitch, pt sl, pt shd; htd wc; chem disp; baby facs; shwrs inc; el pnts (16A) €3.50; gas; Indtte; sm shop; pool adj; wifi; dogs €1; poss cr; quiet; red low ssn;CKE/CCI. "Well-run site; friendly, helpful staff; park outside site bef checking in; clean san facs; resident storks; gd size pitches; gd touring base; mkt Sat; highly rec; excel." ♦ 15 Mar-15 Nov. € 22.60 2014*

RIBEAUVILLE *6E3* (4.5km S Rural) *48.16200, 7.31691* **Camp Intercommunal, 1 Route du Vin, 68340 Riquewihr [03 89 47 90 08; fax 03 89 49 05 63; camping.riquewihr@wanadoo.fr; www.ribeauville-riquewihr.com]** Fr Strasbourg on N83/E25, take junc 21 (fr opp dir take junc 22) to Blebenheim/Riquewihr. D416 & D3 thro Blebenheim. At T-junc turn R onto D1B, site on R at rndabt. Lge, hdg/mkd pitch, some hdstg, pt sl, pt shd; htd wc; chem disp; mv service pnt; baby facs; shwrs inc; el pnts (6A) €3.50 (poss rev pol); gas; Indtte (inc dryer); shops 5km; tradsmn in ssn; snacks; playgrnd; tennis; games area adj; dogs €1.20; poss cr; adv bkg; noise fr main rd;wifi; ccard acc;CKE/CCI ess. "Rec arr early; friendly staff; san facs clean; gd for sm children; lovely town; m'van o'night area; office clsd 12.00-14.00." 28 Mar-31 Dec. € 21.00 2013*

RIQUEWIHR see Ribeauville *6E3*

ROMANSWILLER see Wasselonne *6E3*

ROUFFACH *6F3* (400m SW Urban) *47.9557, 7.2964* **Camp Municipal, 4 Rue de la Piscine, 68250 Rouffach [03 89 49 78 13; fax 03 89 78 03 09; campingmunicipal.rouffach@orange.fr]** On D83 S fr Colmar bet Colmar & Cernay. Foll sp 'Sport, Loisirs, Piscine'. Sm, pt shd; htd wc; chem disp; mv service pnt; shwrs €1.50; el pnts (6A) €2.50; Indry rm; shop 500m; pool nr; quiet; CKE/CCI. "Clean site; pitch self, contact office when open; vg NH." 1 May-30 Sep. € 6.40 2009*

STE CROIX EN PLAINE see Colmar *6F3*

ST LOUIS *6G3* (2km N Rural) *47.59428, 7.58930* **Camping au Petit Port, 10 Allée des Marronniers, 68330 Huningue [tel/fax 03 89 69 05 25 03 89 70 01 71; contact@campinghuningue.fr; www.campinghuningue.fr]** S fr Mulhouse on A35, exit onto D105 & foll sps to Huningue; after level x-ing site sp on rvside. Sm, shd; wc; mv service pnt; shwrs inc; el pnts (6A) €2; shop 1km; rest, bar 500m; htd pool 2km; 50% statics; dogs; bus to Basle; poss cr; quiet. "Excel NH on banks of Rv Rhine; helpful staff; clean facs; poss diff access lge o'fits." ♦ 15 Apr-15 Oct. € 10.40 2010*

SAUSHEIM see Mulhouse *6F3*

SAVERNE *6E3* (1.3km SW Urban) *48.73148, 7.35561* **FFCC Camping de Saverne, Rue du Père Libermann, 67700 Saverne [tel/fax 03 88 91 35 65; info@campingsaverne.com; www.campingsaverne.com]** Take Saverne exit fr A4, junc 45. Site well sp nr town cent. Med, hdg/mkd pitch, hdstg, pt sl, terr, pt shd; htd wc; chem disp; mv service pnt; shwrs inc; el pnts (6-10A) €3.10-5.70 (poss rev pol); Indry rm; supmkt 1.5km; playgrnd; pool 1km; 20% statics; dogs €1.60; poss cr; adv bkg; quiet; ccard acc; red low ssn/CKE/CCI. "Pleasant, busy, well-run site; pitches mostly terr; warm welcome, friendly staff; excel san facs; long steep walk back fr town; m'van aire de service nr ent; trains to Strasbourg fr town; poss travellers; gd." ♦ 1 Apr-30 Sep. € 12.40 2011*

SAVERNE *6E3* (5km SW Rural) *48.69172, 7.32958* **Camping au Paradis Perdu, 31 Rue de Hirschberg, St Gall, 67440 Thal-Marmoutier [03 88 70 60 59]** Fr Saverne, use minor rds rather than by-pass; foll sp Thal-Marmoutier then foll camp sps to St Gall & site; access thro archway - poss tight for lge vans. Sm, pt sl, pt shd; wc; chem disp; shwrs; el pnts (3-6A); shops 3km; rest, snacks; bar; playgrnd; dogs €1.20; adv bkg; quiet. "Pleasant setting in orchard; facs basic but gd." 1 Apr-15 Oct. 2009*

SELESTAT *6E3* (4km N Rural) *48.29144, 7.48236* **Camping à la Ferme St Paul (Loos), 67600 Ebersheim [03 88 85 71 80; fax 03 88 85 71 05; fermest.paul@orange.fr]** Exit Sélestat on N83 to N & site on R in approx 4km, sp. Sm, pt shd; wc; chem disp; mv service pnt; shwrs €1; el pnts €2; gas 1km; Indtte; shops 1km; snacks; rest & bar Sat eve; playgrnd; horseriding, tennis 1km; dogs €1; adv bkg; quiet; CKE/CCI. "CL-type site; friendly owner." 1 Apr-30 Oct. € 7.00 2009*

SELESTAT *6E3* (5km N Rural) **Camping Rural (Weiss), 17 Rue du Buhl, 67600 Ebersheim [03 88 85 72 97; elizabeth.trau@wanadoo.fr]** Fr S or N on N83 in vill of Ebersheim foll green Camping Rural sps. Sm, pt shd; wc; shwrs inc; el pnts inc; shop 500m; cooking facs; quiet; adv bkg; ccard not acc; CKE/CCI. "Gd touring base; friendly, helpful warden." ♦ 15 Jun-15 Sep. € 10.00 2010*

SELESTAT *6E3* (6km N Rural) *48.32600, 7.42510* **Camping de l'Ours, Route d'Ebersheim, 67650 Dambach-la-Ville [06 50 92 00 26; camping-de-l-ours@orange.fr; www.pays-de-barr.com]** Exit A35 at junc 16 for D1422 dir Obernai. After approx 2km take D210 for Dambach-la-Ville & foll sp. Med, mkd pitch, pt shd; wc; chem disp; shwrs inc; el pnts (5A) €2.50; Indtte; shop, rest, snacks, bar 1km; BBQ; playgrnd; sports area; tennis adj; dogs €1.90; quiet; lake 15km; pool 7km; library 1km; cinema 7km; . "Attractive medieval town; spacious site, lge pitches." ♦ Easter-1 Nov. € 11.70 2013*

SELESTAT *6E3* (1.3km SW Urban) *48.25470, 7.44781* **Camp Municipal Les Cigognes, Rue de la 1ère D.F.L, 67600 Sélestat [03 88 92 03 98 or 03 88 58 87 20; fax 03 88 92 88 63; camping-selestat@orange.fr; www.selestat-tourisme.com]** Site sp D1083 & D424. Fr S town cent turn E off D1083 & foll sps to site adj schools & playing fields. Med, mkd pitch, pt shd; wc; mv service pnt; chem disp; shwrs inc; el pnts (5-16A) inc; gas; Indtte; shops; rest, snacks, bar 500m; playgrnd; pool 300m; rv & lake nrby; entmnt; dogs €1; train to Strasbourg nrby; poss cr; Eng spkn; adv bkg rec high ssn; quiet but some noise fr local football area; CKE/CCI. "Well-run site; helpful staff; clean san facs; easy walk to old town; mkt Sat; rec." ♦ 15 Apr-30 Sep. € 17.30 (3 persons) 2013*

SELESTAT *6E3* (12km W Rural) *48.27287, 7.29052* **Camping du Haut-Koenigsbourg, Rue de la Vancelle, 68660 Lièpvre [03 89 58 43 20; fax 03 89 58 98 29; camping.haut-koenigsbourg@wanadoo.fr; www.liepvre.fr/camping]** Fr Sélestat W on N59 twd Lièpvre vill then R at factory car park & foll site sps. Fr Ste Marie-aux-Mines on N59 turn L at rndabt after tunnel. Med, mkd pitch, pt sl, pt shd; htd wc; mv service pnt; shwrs inc; el pnts (4-8A) €3-4.20; Indtte; shop 1km; tradsmn; bar; BBQ; playgrnd; TV rm; 10% statics; dogs €2; poss cr; quiet; CKE/CCI. "V well maintained site; gd location; would rec. gd walks and cycling lovely site." ♦ 15 Mar-15 Oct. € 12.40 2012*

SELESTAT *6E3* (5km NW Rural) *48.28915, 7.41787* **Aire Naturelle (Palmer), 11 Rue Faviers, 67759 Scherwiller [03 88 92 94 57; fax 03 88 82 05 39; campingpalmer@yahoo.fr; www.campingpalmer.fr]** Fr N foll N83 to Ebersheim then D81 to Scherwiller. Site sp off D35 at N end vill. Sm, pt shd; wc; chem disp; shwrs €2.40; el pnts (6A) €2.80; gas 1km; tradsmn; shop, rest, snacks & bar 1km; BBQ; playgrnd; pool 5km; dogs €1; Eng spkn; quiet; ccard acc; CKE/CCI. "Friendly site on wine rte; facs basic; easy walk to vill; easy access to Rhine/Germany; vg." 15 May-15 Sep. € 9.80 2011*

SEPPOIS LE BAS see Altkirch *6F3*

THANN *6F3* (7km NW Rural) *47.85071, 7.03058* **FFCC Camping La Mine d'Argent, Rue des Mines, 68690 Moosch [03 89 82 30 66 or 03 89 60 34 74; fax 03 89 42 15 12; moosch@camping-la-mine-argent.com; www.camping-la-mine-argent.com]** Turn L off N66 Thann-Thillot rd in cent of Moosch opp church; foll sps for 1.5km, ent on R, narr app. Med, mkd pitch, pt sl, pt terr, pt shd; wc; chem disp; mv service pnt; shwrs inc; el pnts (6-10A) €3.00-5.60; gas; Indtte; tradsmn; shops 1.5km; playgrnd; 10% statics; dogs €0.60; phone; adv bkg; quiet; ccard acc; red low ssn/CKE/CCI. "Well-kept site in wooded valley; busy w/end; helpful staff; excel walking; highly rec." 5 Apr-15 Oct. € 19.00 2013*

TURCKHEIM see Colmar *6F3*

WASSELONNE *6E3* (1km W Urban) *48.63739, 7.43209* **FFCC Camp Municipal, Rue des Sapins, 67310 Wasselonne [tel/fax 03 88 87 00 08; camping-wasselonne@wanadoo.fr; www.suisse-alsace.com]** Fr D1004 take D244 to site. Med, mkd pitch, terr, pt shd; wc; mv service pnt; shwrs inc; el pnts (5-10A) €2.30-3.70; gas; Indtte; shop; rest, snacks; bar; playgrnd; htd, covrd pool high ssn; 30% statics; dogs €0.60; quiet; CKE/CCI. "Pleasant town; facs OK; cycle rte to Strasbourg; gd NH." 15 Apr-15 Oct. € 11.70 2010*

WASSELONNE *6E3* (5km NW Urban) *48.64487, 7.39953* **Camp Municipal, La Vosgesia, 67310 Romanswiller [tel/fax 03 88 87 45 54]** Fr Saverne take D1004 twd Strasbourg. 1km N of Wasselonne turn R onto D260 & cont twd town cent, turn R onto D224 sp Romanswiller & 'Camping Piscine'. Turn L into 'Centre des Loisirs'. Sm, hdg pitch, pt shd; wc; chem disp; all serviced pitches; shwrs inc; el pnts (10A) inc; Indry rm; shops 2km; rest, snacks; BBQ; playgrnd; htd pool 5km; games area; cycle hire; 90% statics; dogs; poss cr; some Eng spkn; poss noisy; CKE/CCI. "Well-kept, scenic site; pleasant town." 1 May-30 Sep. € 12.00 2010*

WATTWILLER see Cernay *6F3*

WINGEN SUR MODER *5D3* (1.3km W Rural) *48.91565, 7.36934* **Camp Municipal/Aire Naturelle, Rue de Zittersheim, 67290 Wingen-sur-Moder [03 88 89 71 27 (Mairie); fax 03 88 89 86 99; mairie@wingen-moder.com; www.wingen-moder.com]** W fr Haguenau on D919 to W end Wingen-sur-Moder. Site sp by rlwy arch. Sm, mkd pitch, terr, pt shd; wc; chem disp; shwrs inc; el pnts (13A) inc; shop 500m; rest nr; Eng spkn; adv bkg; quiet; CKE/CCI. "Excel, peaceful site but adj sports field poss used by youth groups/motorbikers high ssn; clean facs; warden calls am & pm; gd walking/cycling." 1 May-30 Sep. € 11.40 2009*

Aquitaine

Regional Introduction

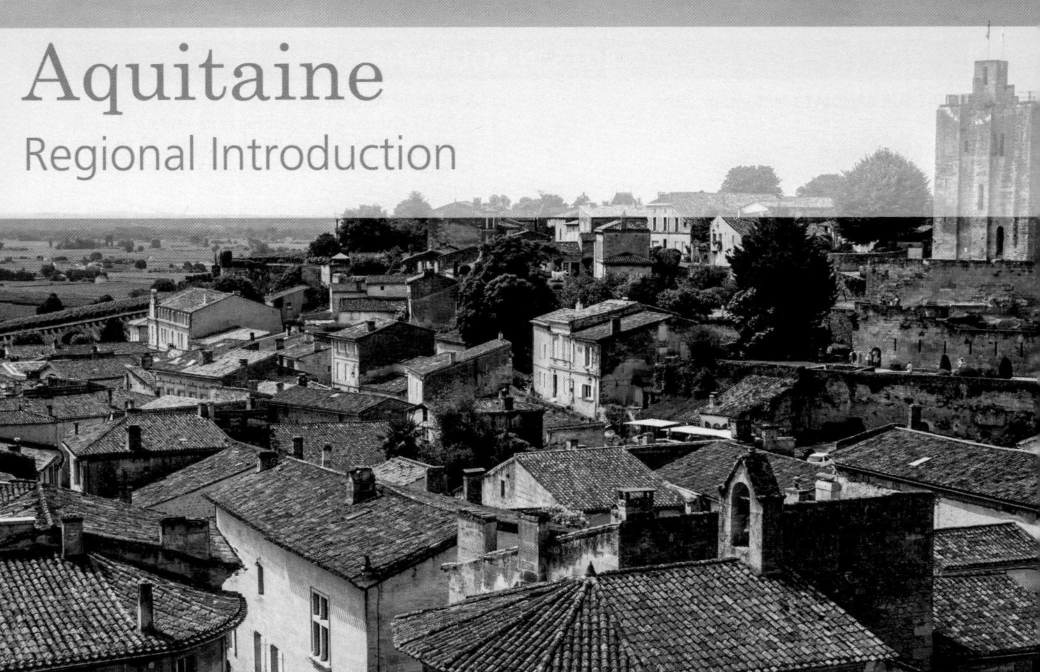

St Emilion

Welcome to Aquitaine

With an outstanding heritage, a beautiful coastline and mountains for all seasons, Aquitaine is one of the largest and most varied regions of France.

The Dordogne department is famous worldwide for its beautiful countryside and has many prehistoric sites to visit.

The region benefits from mild temperatures all year round, making it a wonderful place to stay during any season, whether relaxing on the beach or exploring the mountains and wooded valleys to find hidden traditional villages.

Local highlights

Bordeaux wine events take place throughout the year, with the most notable festivals in the summer when you can visit one of the many vineyards and sample the produce direct from the source.

Specialities can be found in the many renowned food festivals and markets, so make sure you sample the local culinary delights along the way. Try poule au pot (chicken stew) or the famous Bayonne ham.

Major towns and cities

- Bordeaux – the capital city of Aquitaine.
- Bayonne – giving ideal access to the Pyrénées Mountains and the Atlantic coast.
- Mont de Marsan – located in the centre of the largest forest in Europe.
- Biarritz – the beaches have made this town a prime destination for surfers.
- St Emilion – fascinating churches and ruins stretch along the steep and narrow streets.

Regional attractions

- Dune du Pilat, La Teste-de-Buch – the highest dune in Europe, offering panoramic views.
- Château de Commarque, near Sarlat-la-Canéda – a medieval fortified encampment.
- Lascaux, Montignac – a UNESCO site of prehistoric caves.
- St Emilion Monolithic Church – walk through centuries of history.

Find out more

www.tourisme-aquitaine.com
Tel: (0)5 56 01 70 00 Aquitaine Tourist Office

ABJAT SUR BANDIAT see Nontron *7B3*

ABZAC see Coutras *7C2*

ACCOUS *8G2* (500m NW Rural) *42.97717, -0.60592* **Camping Despourrins, Route du Somport, D'Arrechau, 64490 Accous [05 59 34 71 16]** On N134 rte to & fr Spain via Somport Pass. Site sp on main rd. Sm, pt shd; wc (some cont); chem dis (wc); shwrs inc; el pnts (6A) €2.70; Indtte; shop, rest, snacks, bar nrby; BBQ; fishing; 10% statics; dogs free; quiet but some rd noise. "Clean, tidy NH; conv Col de Somport." 1 Mar-31 Oct. € 10.50 2014*

AGEN *8E3* (8km NW Rural) *44.24368, 0.54290* **Camping Le Moulin de Mellet, Route de Prayssas, 47450 St Hilaire-de-Lusignan [05 53 87 50 89; fax 05 53 47 13 41; moulin.mellet@wanadoo.fr; www.camping-moulin-mellet.com]** NW fr Agen on N113 twd Bordeaux for 5km. At traff lts just bef Colayrac-St Cirq take D107 N twd Prayssas for 3km. Site on R. Sm, mkd pitch, shd; wc; chem disp; baby facs; shwrs inc; el pnts (10A) €3.80 (poss rev pol); gas; Indtte (inc dryer); shop 3km; tradsmn high ssn; rest, snacks; BBQ; playgrnd; 2 pools; games rm; dogs €2.85; phone; adv bkg; quiet; Eng spkn; adv bkg; quiet, but some rd noise & poss croaking fr frogs at night; red low ssn; CKE/CCI. "Delightful, well-run site; helpful, friendly new owners, who are working hard to improve site further; sm children's farm; RVs & twin-axles phone ahead; excel; spotless facs; rest & bar open in ls; pretty location; quiet at night; gd for long stay." ♦ 1 Apr-15 Oct. € 40.20 2014*

AGNAC see Eymet *7D2*

AIGUILLON *7D2* (900m NE Rural) *44.30467, 0.34491* **Camp Municipal du Vieux Moulin, Route de Villeneuve, 47190 Aiguillon [05 53 79 61 43; fax 05 53 79 82 01; mairie@ville-aiguillon.fr; www.ville-aiguillon.eu]** On ent town on D813, turn E onto D666 to site on bank of Rv Lot. Clearly sp. Or exit A62 junc 6 at Damazan onto D8 to Aiguillon. Med, mkd pitch, shd; wc; chem disp (wc); shwrs; el pnts (10A) inc; tradsmn; supmkt, rest & bar 1km; playgrnd; rd noise. "Gd site adj old mill house by rv; gd san facs; conv A62; NH only." 1 Jul-31 Aug. € 10.00 2014*

AINHOA *8F1* (400m NW Urban) *43.30913, -1.50178* **Aire Naturelle Harazpy (Zaldua), 64250 Ainhoa [tel/fax 05 59 29 89 38 or 05 59 29 90 26 (LS)]** Take D918 E fr St Jean-de-Luz sp Espelette: in approx 20km turn R on D20 sp Ainhoa. App church in Ainhoa turn R thro open car park to rd at rear; site on R in 250m. Site sp. Sm, mkd pitch, terr, pt sl, pt shd; wc; chem disp; mv service pnt; shwrs; el pnts (10A) inc; Indtte; sm shop; tradsmn; lake sw 10km; dogs; phone; adv bkg; quiet; ccard not acc; CKE/CCI. "Beautiful location; conv Spanish border; helpful staff; excel walking area." ♦ 1 Apr-30 Sep. € 13.50 2009*

AIRE SUR L'ADOUR *8E2* (700m NE Urban) *43.70259, -0.25792* **Camping Les Ombrages de l'Adour, Rue des Graviers, 40800 Aire-sur-l'Adour [tel/fax 05 58 71 75 10; hetapsarl@yahoo.fr; www.camping-adour-landes.com]** Turn E on S side of bdge over Rv Adour in town. Site close to bdge & sp, past La Arena off rd to Bourdeaux. Med, pt shd; wc; chem disp; mv service pnt; shwrs inc; el pnts (10A) €3; Indtte; sm shop; snacks; BBQ; playgrnd; pool 500m; sports area; canoeing, fishing, tennis 500m; wifi; dogs €1.80; poss cr; red low ssn. "Vg." 6 Apr-24 Oct. € 13.50 2009*

ALLAS LES MINES see Sarlat la Canéda *7C3*

ALLEMANS DU DROPT see Miramont de Guyenne *7D2*

ALLES SUR DORDOGNE see Bugue, Le *7C3*

ANDERNOS LES BAINS *7D1* (3km NE Rural) *44.75777, -1.07194* **Camping Les Arbousiers, 134 Ave de Bordeaux, 33510 Andernos-les-Bains [05 56 82 12 46; fax 05 56 26 15 21; lesarbousiers@yahoo.fr; www.camping-les-arbousiers.fr]** E of Arès fr Bordeaux on D106 for approx 7km, take D215 sp Andernos. Site on L in 2km, ent rd to airport. Lge, hdg/mkd pitch, pt shd; htd wc; chem disp; baby facs; shwrs inc; el pnts (6A) inc (poss rev pol); Indtte (inc dryer); shop 2km; snacks; bar; BBQ; pool; sand beach 3km; wifi; 50% statics; dogs €1; Eng spkn; quiet; ccard acc. "Friendly staff; pleasantly situated site." 1 Apr-30 Sep. € 21.00 2009*

ANDERNOS LES BAINS *7D1* (2.5km SE Coastal) *44.72568, -1.08083* **Camping Fontaine Vieille, 4 Blvd du Colonel Wurtz, 33510 Andernos-les-Bains [05 56 82 01 67; fax 05 56 82 09 81; contact@fontaine-vieille.com; www.fontaine-vieille.com]** Take D106 fr Bordeaux then D215 on L after 40km sp Andernos. Well sp. Site situated 600m off D3. V lge, hdg/mkd pitch, pt shd; wc (some cont); chem disp; mv service pnt; baby facs; shwrs inc; el pnts (5A) inc; gas; Indtte; shop & 3km; tradsmn; rest, snacks; bar; BBQ; pool/waterpark; sand beach adj; watersports; windsurfing; tennis; games area; wifi; entmnt; TV; dogs €3; adv bkg rec high ssn; quiet; ccard acc; red long stay/low ssn. "Nice site; some pitches sea view (extra charge); excel for families & beach holiday; organised bus trips & sports." ♦ 1 Apr-30 Sep. € 29.00 2011*

⊞ **ANDERNOS LES BAINS** *7D1* (5km SE Coastal) *44.70435, -1.04856* **Camping Domaine du Roumingue, 60 Ave de la Libération, 33138 Lanton [05 56 82 97 48; fax 05 56 82 96 09; info@roumingue.fr; www.roumingue.fr]** Approx 7km SE of Andernos-les-Bains on D3 bet Cassy & Lanton. Lge, hdg/mkd pitch, pt shd; htd wc (some cont); mv service pnt; chem disp; serviced pitches; shwrs inc; el pnts (6A) €3.50; gas; Indtte; shop; tradsmn; rest, snacks; bar; playgrnd; pool; guarded private sand beach adj; lake sw; fishing; windsurfing; tennis; archery; games/sports area; cycle hire; entmnt; sat TV; 30% statics; dogs €2; phone; site clsd Jan; Eng spkn; adv bkg; ccard acc; red low ssn/long stay; CKE/CCI. "Excel family site; many facs/activities; lge pitches avail; helpful, friendly staff; vg." ♦ € 22.00 2009*

ANDERNOS LES BAINS *7D1* (6km W Coastal) *44.73443, -1.1960* **Airotel Camping Les Viviers, Ave Léon Lesca, Claouey, 33950 Lège-Cap-Ferret [05 56 60 70 04 or 01 76 76 70 10; fax 05 57 70 37 77; reception@lesviviers.com; www.airotel-les-viviers.com]** Fr N exit A10/A630 W of Bordeaux onto D106 sp Cap-Ferret. Foll D106 thro Arès & vill of Claouey on W side of Bassin d'Arcachon, site on L after LH bend (approx 1.5km after Claouey). V lge, hdg/mkd pitch, pt shd; htd wc; mv service pnt; chem disp; baby facs; sauna; shwrs inc; el pnts (10A) €9; gas; Indtte (inc dryer); supmkt; rest, snacks; bar; BBQ (gas/elec); playgrnd; htd, covrd pool; paddling pool; waterslide; sea water lagoon with private sand beach adj; fishing; sailing; windsurfing; tennis; cycle hire; games area; games rm; cinema; wifi; entmnt; TV rm; 27% statics; dogs €5; bus; Eng spkn; adv bkg ess; quiet; ccard acc; red long stay/low ssn/CKE/CCI. "Sand pitches, various positions & prices; clean san facs; vg leisure facs; free night bus along peninsular; vg site." ♦ 27 Mar-30 Sep. € 50.00 2010*

ANDERNOS LES BAINS *7D1* (5km NW Coastal) *44.77108, -1.14306* **Camping Domaine des Abberts, 17 Rue des Abberts, 33740 Arès [tel/fax 05 56 60 26 80; campinglesabberts@wanadoo.fr; www.lesabberts.com]** Fr town sq in Arès, take D106 twd Cap Ferrat, turn 1st L to site in 100m. Med, hdg/mkd pitch, pt shd; wc; chem disp; shwrs inc; el pnts (6A) €5; gas; Indtte; snacks; shops 400m; tradsmn; snacks; bar; BBQ; playgrnd; pool; sand beach 600m; cycle hire; 25% statics; dogs €2; poss cr; adv bkg; quiet; CKE/CCI. "Nr cycle paths to Arès; mkt Tues; gd." ♦ 1 Jun-15 Sep. € 24.00 2010*

ANDERNOS LES BAINS *7D1* (5km NW Coastal) *44.75799, -1.11931* **Camping Les Goëlands, Ave de la Libération, 33740 Arès [05 56 82 55 64; fax 05 56 82 07 51; camping-les.goelands@wanadoo.fr; www.goelands.com]** Fr Bordeaux m'way by-pass take D106 for Cap-Ferret. At Arès take D3 SE twd Andernos. Site on R 200m after end of Arès town sp. Site sp. Lge, mkd pitch, shd; wc; chem disp; shwrs inc; el pnts (10A) inc; gas; Indtte (inc dryer); shop; tradsmn; snacks; bar; playgrnd; htd pool; sand beach 200m; seawater lake 200m; games rm; wifi; TV; 90% statics; dogs; phone; poss cr; adv bkg; poss noisy; ccard acc; red low ssn; CKE/CCI. "Many gd beaches." ♦ 1 Mar-31 Oct. € 27.45 2010*

ANDERNOS LES BAINS *7D1* (5km NW Coastal) *44.77792, -1.14280* **FLOWER Camping La Canadienne, 82 Rue du Général de Gaulle, 33740 Arès [05 56 60 24 91; fax 05 57 70 40 85; info@lacanadienne.com; www.lacanadienne.com / www.flowercampings.com]** N fr town sq at Arès on D3 (Rue du Général de Gaulle) dir Cap Ferret. Site on R after 1km. Med, shd; wc; baby facs; shwrs inc; el pnts (15A) inc; gas; Indtte; shop; rest, snacks; bar; sand beach 2km; playgrnd; pool; paddling pool; cycle & canoe hire; fishing, sailing & windsurfing 1km; tennis; archery; entmnt; games/TV rm; dogs €2.50; adv bkg rec high ssn; quiet, but some rd noise; red low ssn. ♦ 1 Feb-30 Nov. € 31.00 2012*

ANDERNOS LES BAINS *7D1* (7.5km NW Rural) *44.80288, -1.13362* **Camping La Prairie, 93 Ave du Médoc, 33950 Lège-Cap-Ferret [tel/fax 05 56 60 09 75; camping-la-prairie@wanadoo.fr; www.campinglaprairie.com]** Site 1km N of Lège-Cap-Ferret on D3 dir Porge. Med, pt shd; htd wc; chem disp; shwrs inc; el pnts (10A) €3.10; Indtte; shop; snacks; BBQ; playgrnd; pool; sand beach 5km; games area; games rm; entmnt; some statics; dogs €1.50; Eng spkn; adv bkg; quiet; CKE/CCI. "Poss run down & unclean low ssn; friendly owner; long dist cycle paths; gd baker nrby." 1 Mar-1 Nov. € 14.70 2009*

ANDERNOS LES BAINS *7D1* (8km NW Rural) *44.80330, -1.13264* **FFCC Camping Mer et Forêt, 101 Ave du Médoc, 33950 Lège-Cap-Ferret [05 56 60 18 36 or 05 56 60 16 99; fax 05 56 60 39 47]** Fr Bordeaux take D106 W dir Arès. Fr cent Arès take D3 N sp Lège-Cap-Ferret. Site on L in 5km adj 'Camping Prairie'. Med, mkd pitch, pt shd; wc; chem disp; mv service pnt; shwrs €1; el pnts (3-6A) €1.25-2.50; shop 2km; tradsmn; sand beach 6km; dogs; phone; quiet; CKE/CCI. "Lovely site; generous pitches; warm welcome, friendly owner; excel, clean san facs; vg." ♦ ltd 1 Jun-30 Sep. € 9.50 2009*

ANTONNE ET TRIGONANT see Périgueux *7C3*

ARAMITS *8F1* (1km SW Rural) *43.12135, -0.73215* **Camping Barétous-Pyrénées, Quartier Ripaude, 64570 Aramits [05 59 34 12 21; atso64@hotmail.com; www.camping-pyrenees.com]** SW fr Oloron-Ste Marie take D919 sp Aramits, Arette. Fr Aramits cont on D919 sp Lanne; site on R; well sp. Sm, mkd pitch, pt shd; wc; chem disp; mv service pnt; serviced pitches; shwrs inc; el pnts (10A) €4.90; Indtte (inc dryer); supmkt 500m; tradsmn; rest 3km; snacks, bar high ssn; playgrnd; htd pool; paddling pool; cycle hire; games rm; TV; 50% statics; dogs €2.80; poss cr; Eng spkn; adv bkg; CKE/CCI. "Friendly, helpful owner; well-kept, clean site but muddy when wet; ltd facs low ssn; twin-axles extra; gd base for Pyrenees; poss unrel opening dates - phone ahead low ssn." ♦ ltd 12 Feb-29 Oct. € 21.30 (CChq acc) 2011*

ARCACHON *7D1* (10km E Coastal) *44.64400, -1.11167* **Camping de Verdalle, 2 Allée de l'Infante, La Hume, 33470 Gujan-Mestras [tel/fax 05 56 66 12 62; camping.verdalle@wanadoo.fr; www.camping-bassin-arcachon.fr]** Fr A63 take A660 twd Arcachon. Turn R at rndabt junc with D652 sp La Hume. In vill at junc with D650 turn L, then R at rndabt; then 3rd turning on R after rlwy line. Med, hdg pitch, pt shd; wc; chem disp; mv service pnt; shwrs inc; el pnts (10A) inc; Indtte; shops nrby; snacks; BBQ (sep area); playgrnd nrby; sand beach adj; wifi; dogs €1.50; bus adj; phone; poss cr; Eng spkn; adv bkg; ccard acc; red low ssn; CKE/CCI. "Lovely, well-kept site in excel position; friendly, helpful owner; pitches uncomfortable in wet - dirty sand (2011); cycling/walking; conv local attractions; vg." ♦ 1 Apr-3 Oct. € 26.00 2013*

AQUITAINE

⊞ **ARCACHON** *7D1* (2km S Coastal) *44.65089, -1.17381* **Camping Club d'Arcachon, 5 Allée de la Galaxie, 33312 Arcachon [05 56 83 24 15; fax 05 57 52 28 51; info@camping-arcachon.com; www.camping-arcachon.com]** Exit A63 ont A660 dir Arcachon. Foll sp 'Hôpital Jean Hameau' & site sp. Lge, hdg/mkd pitch, some hdstg, terr, pt shd; htd wc; chem disp; mv service pnt; baby facs; private san facs avail; shwrs inc; el pnts (10A) €4; gas; Indtte (inc dryer); shop; tradsmn; rest, snacks; bar; BBQ; playgrnd; pool; sand beach 1.5km; lake sw 10km; cycle hire; wifi; entmnt; TV rm; 40% statics; dogs €4; site clsd mid-Nov to mid-Dec; adv bkg; Eng spkn; quiet; ccard acc; red low ssn; CKE/CCI. "Vg site in pine trees; excel touring base; gd facs; access rds narr - poss diff manoeuvring into pitches; gd network cycle tracks." ♦ € 32.00 (CChq acc) 2010*

ARES see Andernos les Bains *7D1*

ASCAIN see St Jean de Luz *8F1*

ATUR see Périgueux *7C3*

AUBAS see Montignac *7C3*

AUDENGE *7D1* (1km E Rural) *44.68410, -1.00433* **Camping Le Braou, Route de Bordeaux, 33980 Audenge [tel/fax 05 56 26 90 03; info@camping-audenge.com; www.camping-audenge.com]** SW fr Bordeaux turn R off D1250 twd Andernos onto D3; at traff lts in Audenge turn R; site 750m on R. Lge, mkd pitch, pt shd; wc; mv service pnt; shwrs inc; el pnts (3A) €3.50; Indtte (inc dryer); shops 1km; tradsmn; snacks; BBQ; pool; beach 1.5km; cycle hire; games area; internet; entmnt; some statics; dogs €3.50; bus 1km; quiet; CKE/CCI. ♦ ltd 27 Mar-2 Oct. € 19.50 2010*

AUDENGE *7D1* (10km SE Urban) *44.60486, -0.94225* **Camp Municipal de l'Eyre, Allée de la Plage, 33380 Mios [05 56 26 42 04; fax 05 56 26 41 69]** Fr N or S on A63, join A660 sp Arcachon; leave at junc 1 to Mios. After vill turn L after traff lts (sm sp) bet tourist & PO. Site adj Rv Eyre. Med, mkd pitch, pt shd; htd wc; shwrs inc; el pnts (10A) inc; Indtte; shop 500m; sports hall adj; canoe hire; cycle hire for adj rte; many statics; dogs €1.50; CKE/CCI. "Excel touring base; helpful warden; ltd facs low ssn; park outside site to book in; san facs poss stretched if site full; poss noisy at night." ♦ 15 Jun-15 Sep. € 18.50 2010*

AUDENGE *7D1* (5km S Urban) *44.65076, -0.97914* **Camping Le Marache Vacances, 25 Rue Gambetta, 33380 Biganos [05 57 70 61 19; fax 05 56 82 62 60; contact@marachevacances.com; www.marachevacances.com]** Exit A660 junc 2 sp Facture; take D3 dir Audenge, site clearly sp. NB Height restriction 2.6m in Facture, use ring rd. Med, mkd pitch, pt shd; wc; mv service pnt; baby facs; shwrs inc; el pnts (6A) €4.50; Indtte (inc dryer); shops 1km; tradsmn; rest, snacks; bar; BBQ; playgrnd; htd pool; rv & fishing 1km; tennis 1km; games rm; wifi; entmnt; TV; dogs €3.80; adv bkg; quiet; ccard acc. "Pleasant staff; basic facs, ltd low ssn; NH only." ♦ 1 Mar-31 Oct. € 24.50 2010*

AUGIGNAC see Nontron *7B3*

AUREILHAN see Mimizan *7D1*

AZUR see Soustons *8E1*

BAUDREIX see Nay *8F2*

BAYAS see Coutras *7C2*

⊞ **BAYAS** *7C2* (3.2km N Rural) *45.07947, -0.20719* **Camping Le Chene du Lac, 3 lieu-dit "Chateauneuf" 33230, Bayas (Gironde) [05 57 69 13 78 06 10 64 94 98 (mob); lechenedulac@orange.fr; www.camping-lechenedulac.com]** Fr N10 Bordeaux - Angouleme exit Laruscade/Guitres. Site sp fr D247 N of Guitres. Sm, shd; wc; shwrs; el pnts €4.30; Indtte; shop; tradsmn; snacks; dog €2. "Excel site." € 12.00 2013*

BAYONNE *8F1* (8km NE Rural) *43.54858, -1.40381* **Aire Naturelle L'Arrayade (Barret), 280 Chemin Pradillan, 40390 St Martin-de-Seignanx [05 59 56 10 60; www.seignanx-tourisme.com]** On D26 midway bet D810 & D817, 3km W of St Martin. (Opp tall crenellated building). Sm, pt sl, pt shd; wc (some cont); shwrs; el pnts €2.50 (long lead rec); Indry rm; BBQ; playgrnd; dogs; quiet. "Delightful little site; warm welcome; helpful owner; simple facs poss stretched high ssn; gd base for exploring Basque country." 1 Jun-30 Sep. € 12.00 2013*

⊞ **BAYONNE** *8F1* (10km NE Rural) *43.55588, -1.36115* **FFCC Camping Le Ruisseau, 40390 St André-de-Seignanx [05 59 56 71 92; campingle@aol.com; www.campingleruisseau.fr]** Fr Bayonne, take D817 dir Orthez. Turn L after 10km at traff lts in St Martin & foll sp for 5km to site. Sp fr all dir. Take care on ent - by rd junc. Med, hdg/mkd pitch, terr, pt shd; wc; chem disp; 15% serviced pitches; shwrs inc; el pnts (6A) €4; Indtte; shop; tradsmn; rest, snacks & bar 1km; playgrnd; pool; sand beach 10km; TV; 20% statics; dogs €2.50; adv bkg; quiet; red long stay/low ssn; CKE/CCI ess. "Away fr busy coastal area; helpful owner; not suitable lge o'fits." € 24.50 (3 persons) 2009*

BAYONNE *8F1* (11km NE Rural) *43.52820, -1.39157* **Camping Lou P'tit Poun, 110 Ave du Quartier Neuf, 40390 St Martin-de-Seignanx [05 59 56 55 79; fax 05 59 56 53 71; contact@louptitpoun.com; www.louptitpoun.com]** Fr Bordeaux exit A63 junc 6 dir Bayonne Nord; then take D817 dir Pau & St Martin-de-Seignanx; site sp on R in 7km. Lge, hdg/mkd pitch, terr, pt shd; wc; chem disp; mv service pnt; serviced pitch; baby facs; shwrs inc; el pnts (10A) inc; gas; Indtte (inc dryer); shop 4km; tradsmn; rest (high ssn); snacks; bar; BBQ (el/gas); playgrnd; pool; paddling pool; sand beach 10km; tennis; games area; entmnt; games/TV rm; 17% statics; dogs €5; phone; Eng spkn; adv bkg; quiet, rd noise some pitches; ccard acc; red low ssn/long stay; CKE/CCI. "Charming, spacious, family-run site; gd sized pitches; friendly staff; gd clean san facs; ltd facs low ssn; conv Biarritz, St Jean-de-Luz & a'route; excel." ♦ ltd 15 Jun-12 Sep. € 34.30 SBS - A39 2011*

See advert on previous page

BEAUMONT DU PERIGORD *7D3* (6km W Rural) *44.75603, 0.70216* **Centre Naturiste de Vacances Le Couderc (Naturist), 24440 Naussannes [05 53 22 40 40; fax 05 53 23 90 98; info@lecouderc.com; www.lecouderc.com]** Fr D660 at D25 W thro Naussannes & hamlet of Leydou. Just beyond Leydou turn R into site, well sp. Lge, mkd pitch, pt sl, pt shd; wc; chem disp; sauna; shwrs inc; el pnts (5A) €4.50; shop; rest, snacks; bar; playgrnd; htd pool; paddling pool; jacuzzi; sm lake; cycle hire; wifi; entmnt; some statics; dogs €4.65; adv bkg, ess high ssn; quiet; ccard acc; red long stay/low ssn. "Beautiful site with relaxed atmosphere; friendly, helpful Dutch owners; gd san facs; superb pool; naturist walks on site; gd walking/cycling area; Bastide towns nrby." ♦ 1 Apr-1 Oct. € 37.00 2014*

BEAUVILLE *7D3* (500m SE Rural) *44.27210, 0.88850* **Camping Les Deux Lacs, 47470 Beauville [tel/fax 05 53 95 45 41; camping-les-2-lacs@wanadoo.fr; www.les2lacs.info]** Fr D656 S to Beauville, site sp on D122. NB Steep descent to site - owners help when leaving if necessary. Med, hdg/mkd pitch, terr, shd; wc; chem disp; mv service pnt; shwrs inc; el pnts (6A) €2.45; Indtte; rest, snacks; bar; shop 600m; playgrnd; lake sw adj; games area; fishing; watersports; wifi; 10% statics; dogs €2.15; Eng spkn; adv bkg; quiet; ccard acc; red long stay/low ssn; CKE/CCI. "Peaceful; gd fishing; pleasant walk to vill; vg." ♦ 1 Apr-31 Oct. € 15.00 2012*

BELUS see Peyrehorade *8F1*

BELVES *7D3* (4km N Rural) *44.82560, 0.98902* **Camping du Port, 24170 Siorac-en-Périgord [05 53 28 63 81 or 06 18 12 64 75 (mob); contact@campingduport.net; www.campingduport.net]** On D25 in vill turn down beside Carrefour supmkt. Site ent strt ahead. Med, hdg/mkd pitch, shd; wc; shwrs; el pnts (10A) €3; Indtte; shops 1km; snacks; bar; playgrnd; rv beach, sw & fishing; Eng spkn; adv bkg rec; quiet; red low ssn. "Friendly owners; pleasant site; low trees - poss fruit drop onto vehicles." ♦ 15 May-30 Sep. € 12.00 2010*

BELVES *7D3* (2km S Rural) *44.76192, 1.01457* **RCN Le Moulin de la Pique, 24170 Belvès [05 53 29 01 15; fax 05 53 28 29 09; info@rcn-lemoulindelapique.fr; www.rcn-campings.fr]** Site sp S of Belvès on L. Med, shd; htd wc; chem disp; baby facs; shwrs inc; el pnts (6A) inc; Indtte (inc dryer); shop; rest, snacks; bar; BBQ; playgrnd; 3 pools (1 htd); paddling pool; waterslides; boating; fishing; tennis; games area; wifi; entmnt; TV; some statics; dogs €6; Eng spkn; adv bkg; red low ssn. "Well-kept, well-run site in great location; friendly, helpful Dutch owners; vg for children; poss soft in wet weather; rd to to town 2.5km uphill; gd Sat mkt." ♦ 9 Apr-1 Oct. € 44.00 (CChq acc) 2011*

See advertisement

BELVES *7D3* (4km SW Rural) *44.75258, 0.98330* **FLOWER Caming Les Nauves, Le Bos-Rouge, 24170 Belvès [05 53 29 12 64; campinglesnauves@hotmail.com; www.lesnauves.com / www.flowercampings.com]** On D53 fr Belvès. Site on L just after junc to Larzac. Avoid Belves cent - use lorry rte dir Monpazier. Med, hdg pitch, pt sl, pt shd; wc; chem disp; mv service pnt; baby facs; shwrs inc; el pnts (6A) inc; Indtte; shop adj; rest, snacks; bar; BBQ; playgrnd; pool; paddling pool; games rm; horseriding; cycle hire; games rm; internet; entmnt; TV; some statics; dogs €2.30; adv bkg; quiet. "Excel site; gd views fr some pitches." ♦ 23 Apr-25 Sep. € 19.50 2012*

BELVES *7D3* (8km SW Rural) *44.75813, 0.90222* **Camping Terme d'Astor (Naturist), St Avit-Rivière, 24480 Bouillac [05 53 63 24 52; fax 05 53 63 25 43; termdastor@wanadoo.fr; www.termedastor.com]** Leave D710 at Belvès onto D53; in 4km turn R onto D26 to Bouillac; pass thro vill; then turn 2nd L. Well sp. Med, mkd pitch, pt sl, shd; wc (some cont); chem disp; shwrs inc; el pnts (6A) €5.20; gas; Indtte; shop; tradsmn; rest, snacks; bar; BBQ; playgrnd; pool; paddling pool; jacuzzi; excursions; rafting; archery; tennis, horserding & canoeing nrby; games rm; internet; entmnt; TV; 10% statics; dogs free; phone; Eng spkn; adv bkg; quiet; ccard acc; red low ssn; INF. "Gd cent for Dordogne rv & chateaux; vg." ♦ ltd 23 Apr-25 Sep. € 28.00 2012*

BERGERAC *7C3* (500m S Urban) *44.84902, 0.47635* **Camp Municipal La Pelouse, 8 bis Rue Jean-Jacques Rousseau, 24100 Bergerac [tel/fax 05 53 57 06 67; population@mairie-bergerac.fr; www.ville-bergerac.com]** On S bank of Rv Dordogne 300m W of old bdge opp town cent. Do not ent town, foll camping sp fr bdge, ent on R after L turn opp block of flats. Well sp, on Rv Dordogne. Med, mkd pitch, pt sl, pt shd; htd wc; chem disp; mv service pnt; shwrs inc; el pnts (6A) €3.20-4.50; gas; Indtte; shop in town; playgrnd; rv fishing adj; dogs €1.25; poss cr; adv bkg; Eng spkn; quiet; CKE/CCI. "Peaceful, spacious site on rv bank; friendly warden; san facs need update & ltd low ssn; easy walk by rv into attractive old town; no twin-axles & c'vans over 6m; site poss clsd earlier if weather bad; pitches poss muddy when wet; rec arr bef 1400 high ssn site has lots of trees so not all pitches in sun; Facs updated 2012." ♦ 1 Apr-31 Oct. € 17.20 2014*

BERGERAC *7C3* (8km W Rural) *44.83849, 0.33052* **FFCC Camping Parc Servois, 11 Rue du Bac, 24680 Gardonne [06 84 38 24 33; mfounaud24@orange.fr; www.bergerac-tourisme.com]** Fr D936 Bergerac to Bordeaux, in vill of Gardonne turn R into sm rd 100m after traff lts; site at end of rd by rv. Well sp in vill. Sm, pt shd; wc; chem disp; mv service pnt; shwrs inc; el pnts (10A) €2.60 (poss rev pol); shops 200m; rest 300m; dogs €0.70; phone 200m; Eng spkn; quiet; CKE/CCI. "Pretty, CL-type site on bank of Rv Dordogne; lge pitches; helpful warden; facs immac but dated & poss stretched when site full; gates clsd 2200-0800 with pedestrian access; sm mkt Wed & Sun; excel, well run site." 1 Jun-30 Sep. € 9.20 2013*

BEYNAC ET CAZENAC see Sarlat la Canéda *7C3*

BIARRITZ *8F1* (3.5km E Rural) *43.46416, -1.53222* **Camping de Parme, 2 Allée Etchécopar, 64600 Anglet [05 59 23 03 00; fax 05 59 41 29 55; campingdeparme@wanadoo.fr; www.campingdeparme.com]** On D810 fr St Jean-de-Luz to Bayonne. Site sp on R bef Biarritz aerodrome, 500m down tarmac app rd. Lge, pt sl, terr, shd; htd wc (some cont); shwrs inc; el pnts (6-10A) €4-4.50; gas; Indtte; shops 3km; rest, snacks; bar; playgrnd; pool; paddling pool; sand beach 3km; tennis; golf 2km; wifi; entmnt; TV; dogs €3; ccard acc. "Diff exit up steep slope & by blind corner - owner will advise alt R-turn rte; pleasant site." ♦ 4 Apr-7 Nov. € 28.00 2009*

See advertisement

BIARRITZ *8F1* (3km S Coastal) *43.43838, -1.58184* **Village Camping Sunêlia Berrua, Rue Berrua, 64210 Bidart [05 59 54 96 66; fax 05 59 54 78 30; contact@berrua.com; www.berrua.com]** Exit A63 junc 4 dir Bidart, fr Bidart on D810 sp St Jean de Luz, L at 1st traff lts, site sp. Lge, pt sl, pt shd; wc; chem disp; mv service pnt; steam rm; shwrs inc; baby facs; el pnts (6A) €6.20; (poss long lead req); gas; Indtte (inc dryer); shop; tradsmn; rest, snacks; bar; BBQ; playgrnd; htd pool & paddling pool; waterslides; beach 1km; tennis; cycle hire; archery; golf 2km; wifi; TV; 50% statics; dogs €4.20; phone; bus 1km; poss cr; Eng spkn; adv bkg; some rd & rlwy noise; ccard acc; red low ssn; CKE/CCI. "Busy, well-kept site in attractive location; excel, clean facs; pitches tight lge o'fits; site rds narr, low trees, some high kerbs; muddy after rain; gd rest; sh walk to vill; gd; pleasant staff." ♦ 5 Apr-28 Sep. € 39.00 (CChq acc) 2014*

BIARRITZ *8F1* (3km S Coastal) *43.45305, -1.57277* **Yelloh! Village Ilbarritz, Ave de Biarritz, 64210 Bidart [05 59 23 00 29; fax 05 59 41 24 59; contact@camping-ilbarritz.com; www.yellohvillage.co.uk]** S fr Bayonne on D810, by-pass Biarritz. 1km after A63 junc turn R at rndabt immed after Intermarché on R; sp to Pavillon Royal. Site 1km on R sp. Lge, mkd pitch, pt sl, terr, shd; wc; chem disp; shwrs inc; baby facs; el pnts (10A) inc; gas; lndtte; shop; tradsmn; rest & snacks high ssn; bar; playgrnd; htd pool; sand beach 600m; tennis; games area; cycle hire; golf nr; horseriding; internet; TV; many statics & tour ops; dogs €4; phone; poss cr; Eng spkn; adv bkg over 15 days & high ssn; ccard acc; red low ssn; CKE/CCI. "Attractive, mature site; lge pitches; narr access rds poss diff long o'fits; excel pool; gd beaches nrby; gd." ♦ 8 Apr-25 Sep. € 39.00 2009*

BIARRITZ *8F1* (5km S Coastal) *43.43371, -1.59040* **Camping Ur-Onéa, Rue de la Chapelle, 64210 Bidart [05 59 26 53 61; fax 05 59 26 53 94; contact@uronea.com; www.uronea.com]** Exit A63 junc 4 dir Bidart, fr Bidart on D810 sp St Jean de Luz, L at traff lts in town where site sp, then 2nd R, L at motel, site is 300m on L. Access fr main rd a bit tricky, 2nd access further S is easier for lge o'fits. Lge, mkd pitch, hdstg, pt terr, pt shd; wc (some cont); chem disp; some serviced pitches; baby facs; fam bthrm; shwrs inc; el pnts (10A) inc; gas; lndtte (inc dryer); shop high ssn; tradsmn; rest, snacks; bar, BBQ; playgrnd; htd pool; paddling pool; sand beach 600m; lake sw 12km; wifi; entmnt; TV; 20% statics; dogs €2.50; phone; Eng spkn; adv bkg; quiet; ccard acc; red low ssn; CKE/CCI. "Well-kept site 600m fr Bidart; various pitch sizes, most not terr; suitable for o'fits up to 8m; staff friendly & helpful; excel, clean san facs; conv Pays Basque vills; new covered/open pool (2014)." ♦ 12 Apr-19 Sep. € 45.60 2014*

See advertisement

BIARRITZ *8F1* (2km SW Coastal) *43.4625, -1.5672* **Camping Biarritz, 28 Rue Harcet, 64200 Biarritz [05 59 23 00 12; fax 05 59 43 74 67; info@biarritz-camping.fr; www.biarritz-camping.fr]** S fr Bayonne on D810, by-pass Biarritz & cont to junc of D810 coast rd sp Bidart & Biarritz; double back on this rd, take 1st exit at next rndabt, 1st L dir Biarritz Cent, foll sp to site in 2km. Lge, mkd pitch, pt sl, terr, pt shd; wc; chem disp; shwrs inc; el pnts (10A) €4; gas; lndtte; shop; tradsmn; rest, snacks; bar; playgrnd; htd pool; padddling pool; sand beach 1km; tennis 4km; entmnt; 10% statics; no dogs; bus at gate; poss cr; adv bkg; ccard acc; noisy in high ssn; red low ssn/CKE/CCI. "One of better sites in area, espec low ssn." ♦ ltd 12 May-14 Sep. € 24.00 2010*

BIARRITZ *8F1* (3.5km SW Coastal) *43.45525, -1.58119* **Camping Pavillon Royal, Ave du Prince de Galles, 64210 Bidart [05 59 23 00 54; fax 05 59 23 44 47; info@pavillon-royal.com; www.pavillon-royal.com]** Exit A63/E4 junc 4; then take D810 S dir Bidart. At rndabt after Intermarché supmkt turn R (sp Biarritz). After 600m turn L at site sp. Lge, hdg/mkd pitch, pt sl, pt shd, wc (some cont); chem disp; mv service pnt; serviced pitch; baby facs; shwrs inc; el pnts (10A) inc (long lead poss req); gas; lndtte (inc dryer); shop; tradsmn; rest, snacks; bar; BBQ; playgrnd; htd pool; paddling pool; sand beach adj; tennis nr; fitness rm; games rm; golf 500m; horseriding 2km; wifi; entmnt; games rm/TV; no statics; no dogs; no c'vans/m'vans over 8m; poss cr; Eng spkn; adv bkg (ess Jul/Aug); ccard acc; red low ssn. "Lovely, well-kept, busy site in beautiful location beside beach; various pitch sizes, some with sea views, some sm & diff lge o'fits; direct access via steps to excel beach; san facs poss irreg cleaning low ssn; mkt Sat; excel; adv bkg rec as ess; avoid pitches on perimeter fence as damage to vehicles fr stray golf balls; vg, helpful, friendly staff; excel shwrs, wc, shop, bar & rest." ♦ 15 May-29 Sep. € 83.00 SBS - A06 2014*

BIDART see Biarritz *8F1*

BIGANOS see Audenge *7D1*

"Satellite navigation makes touring much easier"

Remember most sat navs don't know if you're towing or in a larger vehicle – always use yours alongside maps and site directions.

BIRON *7D3* (220m W Rural) *44.6305, 0.8733* **Aire Communale, Route de Vergt de Biron, 24540 Biron [05 53 63 15 23; fax 05 53 24 28 12]** Fr Villeréal or Monpazier on D104/D2 turn onto D53 to Biron, foll sp for Information. M'vans only. Sm, unshd; own san; chem disp; mv service pnt; water €2; el pnts €2; shop 8km; rest, snacks & bar 100m; dogs; poss cr; quiet. "Extensive views fr site; gd NH." 1 Apr-31 Oct. € 2.00 2009*

BISCARROSSE *7D1* **See also sites listed under Gastes, Sanguinet and Parentis-en-Born.**

AQUITAINE

BISCARROSSE *7D1* (3km N Coastal) *44.42955, -1.16792* **Campéole Camping Navarrosse, 712 Chemin de Navarrosse, 40600 Biscarrosse [05 58 09 84 32; fax 05 58 09 86 22; navarrosse@campeole.com; www.camping-navarrosse.com / www.campeole.com]** Fr Biscarrosse N on D652 dir Sanguinet; 1km beyond turning to L to Biscarrosse-Plage, turn L onto D305 & foll sp to Navarrosse. V lge, mkd pitch, pt shd; htd wc; baby facs; mv service pnt; baby facs; shwrs inc; el pnts (10A) inc (poss rev pol); Indtte (inc dryer); tradsmn; supmkt adj; rest 200m; snacks; bar; BBQ: playgrnd; sand beach & lake sw adj; fishing; sailing; tennis; cycle hire; games area; games rm; wifi; entmnt; TV; 40% statics; dogs; late arr area; Eng spkn; quiet; ccard acc; red low ssn/CKE/CCI. "Pleasant site; vg for children; helpful staff; gd walking; sailing lessons; cycle rtes; gd value." ♦ 30 Apr-12 Sep. € 32.80 2012*

BISCARROSSE *7D1* (4.5km N Rural) *44.42715, -1.16078* **Camping Bimbo, 176 Chemin de Bimbo, 40600 Biscarrosse [05 58 09 85 33; info@campingbimbo.fr; www.campingbimbo.fr]** Fr Biscarrosse take D652 N. At rndabt take 2nd exit (D305) sp Biscarrosse Lac. After 1.5km turn R twds Chemin de Bimbo, site on R in 500m. Med, shd; wc; chem disp (wc); shwrs €1.10; baby facs; el pnts (3-10A) inc (poss rev pol); shop; rest; bar; play area; sandy beach 10km; Lake beach & watersports 1km; htd pool, paddling pool; adv bkg; 80% statics; Wifi. "Excel full facs site; beach 10km excel for surfing; bakery, pizzeria & creperie on site." 1 Apr-30 Sep. € 50.00 2014*

See advertisement

BISCARROSSE *7D1* (5km N Rural) *44.43996, -1.14068* **Aire Naturelle Le Frézat (Dubourg), 2583 Chemin de Mayotte, 40600 Biscarrosse [06 22 65 57 37; www.biscarrosse.com]** Fr Biscarrosse on D652 dir Sanguinet; after 5km turn L at water tower onto D333; site 2nd on R in 1km. Med, shd; wc (some cont); chem disp (wc); shwrs €1.20; el pnts (6A) inc; shops 4km; tradsmn; BBQ; playgrnd; lake & sand beach 3km; dogs; Eng spkn; adv bkg; quiet; CKE/CCI. "Lovely site; friendly owners; clean facs; cycle paths." 15 Apr-15 Oct. € 15.00 2014*

BISCARROSSE *7D1* (5km N Rural) *44.43535, -1.15496* **Camping Village Mayotte Vacances, 368 Chemin des Roseaux, 40600 Biscarrosse [05 58 78 00 00; fax 05 58 78 83 91; camping@mayottevacances.com; www.mayottevacances.com]** Twd NE fr Biscarrosse on D652 L sp Navarrosse & at 1st fork R to Mayotte, foll camping sp. V lge, mkd pitch, pt shd; wc; chem disp; mv service pnt; shwrs inc; el pnts (10A) inc (poss rev pol); snacks; gas; Indtte; shop; rest, snacks; bar; BBQ; playgrnd; pool complex; waterslide; jacuzzi; lake sw adj; sailing school; sand beach 9km; tennis; cycle hire; games rm; entmnt; TV; 95% statics; dogs €5; Eng spkn; adv bkg (ess Jul/Aug); quiet; ccard acc; red low ssn/CKE/CCI. "Excel leisure facs; vg for families; suitable o'fits up to 8m; rec." ♦ 3 Apr-3 Oct. € 43.00 2010*

See advertisement

BISCARROSSE *7D1* (8km NE Rural) *44.46230, -1.12900* **Camping de la Rive, Route de Bordeaux, 40600 Biscarrosse [05 58 78 12 33; fax 05 58 78 12 92; info@larive.fr; www.larive.fr]** Fr Bordeaux on A63 dir Bayonne/San Sebastian; at junc 22 turn off onto A660; cont until 1st junc where turn L onto D216; cont for 17km to Sanguinet; cont on A652 for 3km; site sp on R nr Lake Cazaux. V lge, hdg/mkd pitch, pt shd; htd wc; chem disp; mv service pnt; baby facs; shwrs inc; el pnts (6A) inc; gas; lndtte (inc dryer); shop; rest, snacks; bar; BBQ zone (gas); playgrnd; 7 pools (1 htd covrd) inc paddling pool; waterslide; jacuzzi; lake sw & private, sand beach adj; watersports; tennis; cycle hire; games area; games rm; wifi; entmnt; games/TV rm; 30% statics; dogs €8.20; no c'van/m'van over 9m; poss cr; phone; Eng spkn; adv bkg; some noise fr entmnt high ssn; ccard acc; red low ssn; CKE/CCI. "On banks of Lake Cazaux-Sanguinet in delightful area; bustling, noisy site high ssn; many acitivies for all ages; some pitches diff lge o'fits due trees; gd beaches; gd cycling; lovely rest, pleasant staff." ♦ 12 Apr-30 Aug. € 68.20 (CChq acc) SBS - A38 2013*

See advert on next page

BISCARROSSE *7D1* (1.5km S Rural) *44.38869, -1.18170* **Camping Latécoère, 265 Rue Louis Bréguet, 40600 Biscarrosse [05 58 78 13 01; fax 05 58 78 16 26; latecoere.biscarrosse@wanadoo.fr]** S on D652 Sanguinet-Biscarrosse rd to cent of town. Strt in front of church by mkt sq; site in 1.5km adj lake. Lge, mkd pitch, pt shd; wc; shwrs inc; el pnts (10A) inc; lndtte; shop; snacks; bar; BBQ; playgrnd adj; pool; lake sw & sand beach adj; watersports; 40% statics; dogs €2; quiet. "Yacht club adj; museums opp; seaplanes." 1 May-30 Sep. € 25.00 2009*

BISCARROSSE *7D1* (8km NW Coastal) *44.45804, -1.23968* **Campéole Camping Le Vivier, 681 Rue du Tit, 40600 Biscarrosse-Plage [05 58 78 25 76; fax 05 58 78 35 23; vivier@campeole.com; www.camping-biscarrosse.info / www.campeole.com]** Fr Arcachon & Pyla-sur-Mer, take D218, D83 to Biscarrosse Plage. Town o'skts site sp to R. Foll sps. Lge, pt shd; wc; chem disp; baby facs; shwrs; el pnts (10A) inc (poss rev pol); lndtte (inc dryer); shop; rest, snacks; bar; playgrnd; htd pool; paddling pool; sand beach 800m; boating; fishing; tennis; games rm; horseriding nr; cycle hire; wifi; entmnt; some statics; dogs €3.50; quiet; ccard acc; red low ssn. "Sandy site in pine forest; access to beach via path thro dunes." 1 May-19 Sep. € 31.70 2010*

BISCARROSSE *7D1* (9km NW Coastal) *44.44133, -1.24558* **Campéole Camping Plage Sud, 230 Rue des Bécasses, 40600 Biscarrosse-Plage [05 58 78 21 24; fax 05 58 78 34 23; plage-sud@campeole.com; www.landes-camping.net / www.campeole.com]** Clearly sp on D146 on ent to Biscarrosse-Plage in pine forest. V lge, mkd pitch, pt sl, pt shd; wc; chem disp; baby facs; shwrs inc; el pnts (6A) inc; lndtte (inc dryer); shop adj; tradsmn; snacks; bar; BBQ; playgrnd; htd pool; paddling pool; sand beach 800m; cycle hire; wifi; entmnt; 50% statics; dogs €3.50; Eng spkn; adv bkg (rec high ssn); ccard acc; red low ssn; CKE/CCI. "Gd site, lively high ssn; helpful staff; facs stretched high ssn; gd beach, inc surfing; some pitches on soft sand; sm, modern town, lots of rests; New entmnt, pool and san facs (2013); excel for sh or long stay." 27 Apr-15 Sep. € 54.45 2013*

BLAYE *7C2* (5km NE Rural) *45.16708, -0.61666* **Aire Naturelle Les Tilleuls (Paille), Domaine Les Alberts, 33390 Mazion [05 57 42 18 13; fax 05 57 42 13 01; chateau-alberts@hotmail.com]** Fr Blaye on D937 N, sp to site on L. Sm, pt sl, pt shd; own san; el pnts (3-10A) €2.50; BBQ; dogs; some Eng spkn; rd noise; CKE/CCI. "Lovely, family-run site in vineyards; charming owners; clean basic san facs; wine-tasting; easy cycling nrby, cycle track to Blaye." 1 May-15 Oct. € 12.50 2013*

BLAYE *7C2* (1km W Urban) *45.12936, -0.66621* **Camp Municipal La Citadelle, 33390 Blaye [05 57 42 00 20 or 05 57 42 16 79 (LS); info@tourisme-blaye.com; www.tourisme-blaye.com]** Fr N ent town, over x-rds, sp in town; ent thro narr gateways in fortifications; access by narr track, single in places. Fr S on D669 cont thro town passing citadel on L; turn L at mini rndabt, go over bdge & take 1st L; sp strt on thro arches - recep to R of barrier. NB Site access unsuitable m'vans higher than 2.7m due to narr, curved arches. Sm, terr, pt shd; wc (mostly cont); serviced pitches; shwrs inc; el pnts (10-15A) €2.60; shops 500m; tradsmn high ssn; no BBQ; pool 250m; tennis; phone adj; poss cr; quiet; no ccard acc. "Lovely site within ancient monument, partly o'lookng rv; spacious pitches; clean but basic san facs; vineyards nr." 1 May-30 Sep. € 10.00 2011*

⊞ **BORDEAUX** *7C2* (7km N Rural) *44.89701, -0.58317* **Camping Le Village du Lac Bordeaux, Blvd Jacques Chaban Delmas, 33520 Bordeaux-Bruges [05 57 87 70 60; fax 05 57 87 70 61; contact@village-du-lac.com; www.camping-bordeaux.com]** On ring rd A630 take exit 5 twd lake; site sp on N side of lake, 500m N of Parc des Expositions. Lge, mkd pitch, some hdstg, pt shd; htd wc; chem disp; mv service pnt; baby facs; shwrs inc; elec pnts (10A) inc; lndtte (inc dryer); shop; tradsmn; rest, snacks; bar; BBQ; playgrnd; pool; paddling pool; lake sw & fishing adj; cycle hire; games rm; wifi; TV; 50% statics; dogs €5; bus/tram to city; Eng spkn; adv bkg; quiet; ccard acc; red low ssn; CKE/CCI. "Busy, poorly laid out, modern site; friendly staff; san facs poss streched high ssn; plenty elec & water pnts; excel rest; conv Bordeaux; easy access fr ring rd; pitches poss soft and muddy after rain; bus/tram conn to city; vg rest; gd unisex facs." ♦ € 45.80 2014*

⊞ **BORDEAUX** *7C2* (4km S Urban) *44.75529, -0.62772* **Camping Beausoleil, 371 Cours du Général de Gaulle, 33170 Gradignan [tel/fax 05 56 89 17 66; campingbeausoleil@wanadoo.fr; www.camping-gradignan.com]** Fr N take exit 16 fr Bordeaux ring rd onto D1010 sp Gradignan. Fr S exit A63 junc 24 onto D211 to Jauge then D1010 to Gradignan. Site S of Gradignan on R after Beau Soleil complex, sp. Sm, hdg/mkd pitch, hdstg, pt sl, pt shd; htd wc; chem disp; shwrs inc; el pnts (6-10A) €1.50 -3. (poss rev pol); lndtte (inc dryer); shop 3km; rest, snacks, bar 1km; gas/elec BBQ; htd pool & waterslides 5km; rv/lake sw 2km; wifi; 70% statics; dogs €1; bus/tram 250m; poss cr; Eng spkn; adv bkg rec; quiet; red low ssn; CKE/CCI. "Pleasant, family-run site; helpful owners; vg, modern, clean san facs; ltd touring pitches; sm pitches not suitable lge o'fits; adv bkg rec; excel; gd sm site; booking necessary; highly rec; excel & cheap park & ride tram sys 6km away." ♦ € 23.00 2014*

A 5000 m² aquatic complex with slides and jacuzzis, covered and heated swimming pool !

Campsite La Cote d'Argent is a very attractive 20 acre park, situated in the heart of the pine forest and on only 300m distance from the Atlantic Ocean Beach. This characteristic park is protected for the ocean wind by the dunes and the forest. The Village Club Cote d'Argent is the perfect destination for your calm holiday in nature.

33990 Hourtin Plage
Tél : +33 (0)5.56.09.10.25 Fax : +33 (0)5.56.09.24.96

www.cca33.com

CAMPING RESORT & SPA
★★★★★

La Rive

Alongside the lake in the heart of the Landes forest. Aquatic area of more than 5500 m², of which 1300m² covered and heated. Wave pool - Water slides - Jacuzzi - Spa - whirlpool - Massage-lane. Bar - Restaurant - Theater - Kids club - Animation. Chalet and mobile home rental.

Route de Bordeaux 40600 Biscarrosse
Tél : + 33 5 58 78 12 33 Fax : + 33 5 58 78 12 92

www.larive.fr

BOURG SUR GIRONDE *7C2* (500m S Urban) *45.03880, -0.56065* **Camp Municipal La Citadelle, 33710 Bourg-sur-Gironde [05 56 68 40 04; fax 05 57 68 39 84; commune-de-bourg@wanadoo.fr]** Take D669 fr St André-de-Cubzac (off A10) to Bourg. Foll sp Halte Nautique & Le Port into Rue Franklin on L twd town cent & foll sp to site. Or fr Blaye, foll Camping sp on app Bourg, cont round by-pass to other end of town to Rue Franklin. NB Do not attempt to take c'van thro town. Sm, mkd pitch, pt shd; wc; chem disp; mv service pnt; shwrs inc; el pnts (3-10A) €3-6 (poss long lead req); shops in town; BBQ; pool, playgrnd adj; dogs; no statics; adv bkg; quiet; CKE/CCI. "Scenic, CL-type rvside site; well-maintained but basic facs; poss variable opening dates; excel." ♦ ltd 15 May-30 Sep. € 13.00 2013*

BOURNEL see Villereal *7D3*

"There aren't many sites open at this time of year"

If you're travelling outside peak season remember to call ahead to check site opening dates – even if the entry says 'open all year'.

BRANTOME *7C3* (1km E Rural) *45.36074, 0.66035* **Camping Brantôme Peyrelevade, Ave André Maurois, 24310 Brantôme [05 53 05 75 24; fax 05 53 05 87 30; info@camping-dordogne.net; www.camping-dordogne.net]** Fr N on D675 foll sp Centre Ville; ent vill & turn L onto D78 Thiviers rd, site sp at turn; in 1km on R past stadium opp g'ge. Fr S D939 foll sp 'Centre Ville' fr rndabt N of town. Then L onto D78 Thiviers rd & foll sp. Do not foll 'Centre Ville' sp fr rndabt S of town, use by-pass. Football stadium best ref point for ent. Lge, hdg/mkd pitch, pt shd; htd wc; chem disp; mv service pnt; baby facs; shwrs inc; el pnts (10A) €4; Indtte (inc dryer); shop 1km; supmkt 2km; tradsmn (bread baked on site); snacks, bar high ssn; BBQ; playgrnd; pool; paddling pool; rv sw & sand beach adj; tennis nr; games area adj; wifi; entmnt; 7% statics; dogs €2; Eng spkn; adv bkg; quiet; ccard acc; red low ssn/CKE/CCI. "Spacious, well-kept rvside site; attractive courtyard layout; friendly, helpful owners; excel modern san facs; gd facs; grnd poss soft after heavy rain; 10 min walk to lovely town (the Venice of Périgord); mkt day in town on wednesdays; beautiful countryside; gd walking & cycling; excel." ♦ ltd 1 May-30 Sep. € 36.00 2014*

BRANTOME *7C3* (4km SW Rural) *45.32931, 0.63690* **Camping du Bas Meygnaud, 24310 Valeuil [05 53 05 58 44; camping-du-bas-meygnaud@wanadoo.fr; www.basmeygnaud.fr]** Fr Brantôme, take D939 S twd Périgueux; in 4.5km turn R at sp La Serre. In 1km turn L to in 500m, well sp. Winding, narr app thro lanes; poss diff lge o'fits. Sm, pt sl, pt shd; wc; chem disp; shwrs inc; el pnts (6A) €3.50; gas 4km; Indtte; shop; tradsmn; rest 4km; snacks; bar; BBQ; playgrnd; pool; entmnt; wifi; dogs €2.50; phone; Eng spkn; quiet; CKE/CCI. "Most pitches shd by pine trees; helpful & friendly owner; dated san facs; unspoilt countryside." 1 Apr-30 Sep. € 15.50 2013*

BUGUE, LE *7C3* (1km SE Urban) *44.90980, 0.93160* **FFCC Camping Les Trois Caupain, Le Port, 24260 Le Bugue Dordogne [05 53 07 24 60 or 06 85 48 44 25 (mob); fax 05 53 08 72 66; info@camping-bugue.com; www.camping-des-trois-caupain.com]** Exit Le Bugue town cent on D703 twd Campagne. Turn R at sp after 400m to site in 600m on rvside. Med, mkd pitch, pt shd; wc; chem disp; mv service pnt; baby facs; shwrs inc; el pnts (6-16A) €3.60-4 (rev pol); gas; shops 1km; rest & snacks (high & low ssn); bar; playgrnd; htd covrd pool; rv & games area adj; wifi; 25% statics, sep area; dogs €2; adv bkg; quiet; red low ssn. "Beautiful site; pleasant, helpful owners; cycle along rv to pretty town; excel; lovely site; new pool; mkt in Le Bugue well worth a visit; Ideal cent for touring the Dordogne region; lots of attractions." 1 Apr-30 Oct. € 30.40 2014*

BUGUE, LE *7C3* (7km SE Rural) *44.86199, 0.98150* **Camping Le Clou, Meynard, 24220 Coux-et-Bigaroque [05 53 31 63 32; fax 05 53 31 69 33; info@camping-le-clou.com; www.camping-le-clou.com]** S fr Le Bugue on D703 twd Belvès; site 8km on R. Med, mkd pitch, pt sl, pt shd; htd wc; chem disp; mv service pnt; serviced pitches; baby facs; fam bthrm; shwrs inc; el pnts (4-6A) €3.80; gas; Indtte; tradsmn; rest, snacks; bar; BBQ; playgrnd; 2 pools & paddling pool; waterslide; fishing; canoeing; horseriding; entmnt; games rm; TV; phone; 10% statics; dogs €2.50; Eng spkn; adv bkg; quiet; ccard acc; red long stay/low ssn/CKE/CCI. "Pleasant owners; ideal base for Dordogne; lovely wooded site with much wildlife." ♦ 17 Apr-3 Apr. € 23.70 2009*

BUGUE, LE *7C3* (8km S Rural) *44.85416, 0.91208* **Camping Le Pont de Vicq, 24480 Le Buisson-de-Cadouin [05 53 22 01 73; fax 05 53 22 06 70; le.pont.de.vicq@wanadoo.fr; www.campinglepontdevicq.com]** Fr Le Bugue foll sp to Le Buisson. Site immed S of bdge over Rv Dordogne on rd D51E. Sp fr all dir in Le Buisson. Med, hdg/mkd pitch, pt shd; wc; baby facs; shwrs inc; el pnts (6A) €3.50 (poss rev pol); Indtte; shops 1.5km; rest adj; snacks in ssn; playgrnd; shgl beach & rv; games area; games rm; entmnt; TV; 60% statics; dogs €1.10; phone adj; poss cr; adv bkg; quiet; CKE/CCI. "Pleasant site on rv; poss mosquitoes." 27 Mar-30 Oct. € 20.40 2009*

BUGUE, LE *7C3* (5km SW Rural) *44.89323, 0.87955* **Camping La Ferme des Poutiroux, 24510 Limeuil [05 53 63 31 62; fax 05 53 58 30 84; infos@poutiroux.com; www.poutiroux.com]** W fr Le Bugue on D703 twd Bergerac; in 2km take D31 S for 4km; bef bdge take R fork twd Trémolat/Lalinde; in 300m fork R (sp), site well sp. Sm, mkd pitch, pt sl, terr, pt shd; wc; chem disp; mv service pnt; baby facs; shwrs; el pnts (6A) €4; Indtte; shop; tradsmn; snacks; playgrnd; htd pool; paddling pool; canoes & rv sw nrby; wifi; 50% statics; dogs €1; phone; Eng spkn; adv bkg; quiet; ccard not acc; red low ssn; CKE/CCI. "Peaceful, well-kept, well-positioned, family-run site; friendly, helpful farmer; facs clean; vg value low ssn; highly rec." ♦ 1 Apr-2 Oct. € 17.40 2013*

AQUITAINE

BUGUE, LE *7C3 (6km SW Rural) 44.87990, 0.88576* **Camping du Port de Limeuil, 24480 Alles-sur-Dordogne [05 53 63 29 76; fax 05 53 63 04 19; didierbonvallet@aol.com; www.leportdelimeuil.com]** Exit Le Bugue on D31 sp Le Buisson; in 4km turn R on D51 sp Limeuil; at 2km turn L over rv bdge; site on R after bdge. Med, hdg/mkd pitch, pt sl, pt shd; wc; chem disp; 50% serviced pitches; shwrs inc; el pnts (5A) €3.50; gas; Indtte; shop & 1km; bar; snacks; BBQ; playgrnd; htd pool; shgl beach & rv adj; games rm; canoe & cycle hire; 40% statics (tour ops); dogs €2; poss cr; Eng spkn; adv bkg; quiet; red low ssn; CKE/CCI. "Superb location & site for all ages; lge pitches; clean san facs, ltd low ssn; tour ops." ♦ ltd 1 May-30 Sep. € 25.00 2012*

BUGUE, LE *7C3 (7km SW Rural) 44.87390, 0.85840* **Camping La Pénétie, Route de Trémolat, 24510 Paunat [05 53 22 80 53; fax 05 53 74 17 88; ferme-la-penetie@orange.fr; www.penetie.fr]** Fr Le Bugue take D31 S dir Le Buisson. After 5km turn R to Limeuil then D31 sp Trémolat. Site on L 5km out of Limeuil. Sm, hdg pitch, terr, pt shd; wc; chem disp (wc); baby facs; shwrs inc; el pnts €3; Indtte; shop, rest 2km; bar; playgrnd; games area; wifi; dogs €0.80; adv bkg; red low ssn; CKE/CCI. "Gd views fr pitches on S side of site; friendly, helpful staff; gd touring base Dordogne; excel." 1 Apr-30 Sep. € 13.00 2010*

BUGUE, LE *7C3 (9km SW Rural) 44.87909, 0.82751* **Camping de Trémolat, Centre Nautique, Route de Mauzac, 24510 Trémolat [05 53 22 81 18 or 05 53 05 65 65 (res); fax 05 53 06 30 94; semitour@perigord.tm.fr]** Fr Le Bugue, take D703 W twd Pezuls. In vill, turn L onto D30 twd Trémolat. Site 700m N of Trémolat, well sp fr all dir. Med, hdg pitch, pt shd; wc; chem disp; shwrs inc; el pnts (10A) inc; Indtte; shops 700m; rest, snacks; BBQ; pool; rv adj; fishing; canoeing; 20% statics; dogs; phone; poss cr; Eng spkn; adv bkg; quiet; CKE/CCI. "Peaceful site; most touring pitches have rv frontage, excel for fishing & canoeing; facs poss stretched high ssn." ♦ ltd 1 May-30 Sep. € 21.40 2009*

BUGUE, LE *7C3 (10km W Rural) 44.91527, 0.82083* **Camping La Forêt, Ste Alvère, 24510 Pezuls [05 53 22 71 69; camping.laforet@wanadoo.fr; www.camping-la-foret.com]** Off D703 fr Le Bugue to Lalinde rd, sp on L 1.5km bef Pezuls. In Le Bugue do not foll sp to Lalinde but cont thro town on D703, turn R, L & R, passing fire stn. Med, pt sl, pt shd; wc; chem disp; baby facs; shwrs inc; el pnts (10A) inc; gas; Indtte; sm shop; bar; BBQ (gas/charcoal only); playgrnd; pool; tennis; games area; games/TV rm; entmnt; dogs free; no c'vans/m'vans over 5.50m high ssn; poss cr; adv bkg; quiet; ccard not acc; red low ssn; CKE/CCI. "Simple, peaceful site set amongst sm oak trees; nature lovers' paradise; friendly, helpful Dutch owner; gd san facs, ltd low ssn; manoeuvring poss diff lge o'fits due trees; under-used low ssn; gd touring base; excel." ♦ 1 Apr-1 Oct. € 21.50 2010*

BUGUE, LE *7C3 (5km NW Rural) 44.95130, 0.85070* **Camping St Avit Loisirs, 24260 St Avit-de-Vialard [05 53 02 64 00; fax 05 53 02 64 39; contact@saint-avit-loisirs.com; www.saint-avit-loisirs.com / www.les-castels.com]** Leave N89/E70 SE of Périgueux & turn S onto D710 for approx 32km; about 3km N of Le Bugue turn R sp St Avit-de-Vialard. Turn R in vill & conf for approx 1.5km, site on R. NB Narr, twisting app rd. Lge, hdg pitch, pt sl, pt shd; wc; chem disp; mv service pnt; baby facs; shwrs inc; el pnts (6A) inc; gas; Indtte (inc dryer); shop; rest, snacks; bar; BBQ; playgrnd; 2 pools (1 htd, covrd); waterslide; paddling pool; tennis; golf, watersports, archery & horseriding nr; cycle hire; games area; wifi; entmnt; games/TV rm; many static tents/vans; dogs €2-5.10; no c'vans/m'vans over 7m; poss cr; adv bkg; quiet; ccard acc; red low ssn; CKE/CCI. "Excel, well-kept, well-run, busy site; gd sized pitches; friendly welcome; gd, clean san facs; gd touring base; conv for Lascaux." ♦ 5 Apr-14 Sep. € 42.70 SBS - D10 2011*

See advertisement

BUISSON DE CADOUIN, LE see Bugue, Le *7C3*

BUZY see Louvie Juzon *8F2*

CALVIAC EN PERIGORD see Sarlat la Canéda *7C3*

CAMBO LES BAINS *8F1* (1.3km SW Rural) *43.35526, -1.41484* **Camping Bixta-Eder, Route de St Jean-de-Luz, 64250 Cambo-les-Bains [05 59 29 94 23; fax 05 59 29 23 70; contact@camping-bixtaeder.com; www.camping-bixtaeder.com]** Fr Bayonne on D932 (ignore 1st sp Cambo-les-Bains) exit at junc with D918 L twd Cambo. Site on L nr top of hill (Intermarché supmkt at by-pass junc). Med, mkd pitch, pt sl, pt shd; wc; baby facs; shwrs inc; el pnts (6-10A) €3.55-4; Indtte; shops 500m; rest, bar 100m; sand beach 20km; playgrnd; pool, tennis 400m; wifi; TV; dogs €1.50; poss cr; adv bkg; ccard acc; red low ssn/long stay. "Gd, well-run site; clean san facs; muddy when wet." ♦ 4 Apr-25 Oct. € 23.00 2011*

⊞ **CAMBO LES BAINS** *8F1* (3km SW Rural) *43.33863, -1.40129* **Camping L'Hiriberria, 64250 Itxassou [05 59 29 98 09; fax 05 59 29 20 88; hiriberria@wanadoo.fr; www.hiriberria.com]** Fr Cambo-les-Bains on D932 to Itxassou. Site on L 200m fr D918. Lge, hdg/mkd pitch, hdstg, pt sl, pt shd; htd wc (some cont); chem disp; mv service pnt; shwrs inc; baby facs; el pnts (5A) €3.25; gas; Indtte; shops 2km; tradsmn; rest, bar 1km; snacks 3km; BBQ; playgrnd; htd, covrd pool; rv 2km; games area; wifi; TV rm; 20% statics; dogs €1; Eng spkn; phone; quiet; 10% red 21+ days; CKE/CCI. "Popular site, phone ahead rec; gd views Pyrenees; pretty vill in 1km; some rd noise; vg walks; friendly owners." ♦ € 35.00 2013*

"That's changed – Should I let The Club know?"

If you find something on site that's different from the site entry, fill in a report and let us know. See www.caravanclub.co.uk/europereport.

CAMBO LES BAINS *8F1* (5km W Rural) *43.33969, -1.47000* **Camping Alegera, 64250 Souraïde [05 59 93 91 80 / 06 13 76 66 87 (mob); www.camping-alegera.com]** Fr St Jean-de-Luz take D918 to Souraïde, site sp on L on rvside. Lge, hdg/mkd pitch, pt shd; wc (cont); chem disp; mv service pnt; baby facs; shwrs inc; el pnts (4-10A) €3.40-4 (poss rev pol); gas; Indtte; ice, shop (high ssn) & 150m; snacks; BBQ (gas/elec); playgrnd; pool; fishing 4km; games rm; tennis; golf; 10% statics; dogs €1.30; poss cr; adv bkg; quiet. "Excel for coast & Pyrenees; spacious pitches; red facs low ssn; pretty vill; v quiet, clean, lovely site." ♦ 1 Apr-31 Oct. € 17.80 2013*

CANCON *7D3* (5km N Rural) *44.57728, 0.62128* **Camp Municipal de St Chavit, 47290 Lougratte [05 53 01 68 25; fax 05 53 41 18 04; mairie.lougratte@wanadoo.fr; www.lougratte.com]** N on N21 fr Cancon, site at lake, L turn 50m bef church, site seen fr rd 500m fr turn. Med, pt hdg pitch, pt shd; wc; chem disp (wc); shwrs; el pnts (10A) €2.70; Indtte; shop 500m; bar; BBQ; playgrnd; games rm; sand beach; boating; fishing; tennis nr; phone; v quiet. "Nice position; spacious; clean san facs high ssn; warden calls eves; gd touring base; highly rec." ♦ 15 Jun-15 Sep. € 8.60 2010*

⊞ **CANCON** *7D3* (8km W Rural) *44.53461, 0.50555* **Camping Le Moulin, Lassalle, 47290 Monbahus [05 53 01 68 87; info@lemoulin-monbahus.com; www.lemoulin-monbahus.com]** Fr N21 turn W at Cancon on D124 sp Miramont. In 7.5km at Monbahus pass thro vill cent take L turn, still on D124 sp Tombeboeuf. In 3km lge grain silos on L, site next on R. Sm, mkd pitch, hdstg, pt shd; wc; chem disp; shwrs inc; fam bthrm; el pnts (5-10A) €3 (most pitches 5A only avail); Indtte; tradsmn; shop 3km; bistro; snacks; BBQ; playgrnd; htd pool; lake 5km; cycle hire; wifi; entmnt; dogs; poss cr; Eng spkn; adv bkg; some rd noise; ccard not acc; CKE/CCI. "CL-type site in garden; friendly British owners; clean, basic san facs; vg pool; B & B avail; extra for twin-axles over 5m; excel." € 13.00 2010*

CARCANS *7C1* (8km W Rural) *45.06657, -1.13903* **Camping Le Maubuisson, 81 Ave de Maubuisson, 33121 Carcans [05 56 03 30 12; fax 05 56 03 47 93; camping.maubuisson@orange.fr; www.camping-maubuisson.com]** Fr D1215 at Castelnau-de-Médoc turn W onto D207 to Carcans & onto Maubuisson, in vill camp ent on L, sp. V lge, mkd pitch, pt sl, shd; wc; baby facs; shwrs inc; el pnts (5A) €3.50; gas; Indtte; shop; rest, snacks; bar; playgrnd; sand beach 3km; lake sw 100m; fishing; watersports; windsurfing; tennis; some statics; dogs €1.60; poss cr; adv bkg; quiet. "Site in wooded park; conv Médoc wine region & many sandy beaches." ♦ 1 Mar-30 Nov. € 19.60 2009*

CARLUX see Sarlat la Canéda *7C3*

CARSAC AILLAC see Sarlat la Canéda *7C3*

CASTELJALOUX *7D2* (500m N Urban) *44.31472, 0.09153* **Camp Municipal de la Piscine, Rue du Souvenir Français, Route de Marmande, 47700 Casteljaloux [05 53 93 54 68; fax 05 53 89 48 07; www.casteljaloux.com]** On N side of town on D933 visible fr rd. Sm, pt shd; wc; shwrs inc; el pnts (10A) €2.15; shops 750m; rest; bar; pool adj inc; rv & lake sw; fishing; rd noise. "Gd, old-fashioned site; sm park nr; helpful warden; gd san facs; conv for town; useful NH; extra charge c'vans over 4m." ♦ 1 Apr-15 Nov. € 7.35 2009*

CASTELJALOUX *7D2* (8km SE Rural) *44.27262, 0.18969* **Camping Moulin de Campech, 47160 Villefranche-du-Queyran [05 53 88 72 43; fax 05 53 88 06 52; camping@moulindecampech.co.uk; www.moulindecampech.co.uk]** Fr A62 exit junc 6 (sp Damazan & Aiguillon). Fr toll booth take D8 SW sp Mont-de-Marsan. In 3km turn R in Cap-du-Bosc onto D11 twd Casteljaloux. Site on R in 4km. Or fr Casteljaloux S on D655 then SW on D11 after 1.5km. Site on L after 9.5km. Sm, hdg/mkd pitch, pt shd; wc (some cont); chem disp; shwrs inc; el pnts (6A) €4; Indtte (inc dryer); sm shop; tradsmn; rest, snacks; bar; BBQ; htd pool; lake fishing; golf nr; games rm; entmnt; wifi; dogs €2.40; no c'vans/m'vans over 8.20m; phone; poss cr; adv bkg; quiet ; ccard acc; red low ssn; CKE/CCI. "Superb, peaceful rvside site in wooded valley; well-run; lge pitches; friendly, helpful & welcoming British owners; clean, dated san facs, poss tired early ssn (2011); gd pool; excel, gd value rest; BBQ suppers; gd cycling; interesting area ideal for nature lovers; excel site; many social events." ♦ 1 Apr-6 Oct. € 39.80 SBS - D16 2014*

CASTELNAUD LA CHAPELLE see Sarlat la Canéda *7C3*

CASTETS *8E1* (800m E Urban) *43.88069, -1.13768* **Camp Municipal Le Galan, 73 Rue du Stade, 40260 Castets [05 58 89 43 52 or 05 58 89 40 09; fax 05 58 55 00 07; contact@camping-legalan.com; www.camping-legalan.com]** Exit N10 junc 12 onto D947; foll sp Castets centre; turn R onto D42; in 500m (after passing over rndabt) turn R onto Rue de Galan; in 200m turn R into Rue du State. Site on L at end of wide cul-de-sac. Site sp in Castets. Lge, pt sl, shd; wc; hot water & shwrs inc; el pnts (10A) inc; gas; Indtte; shop high ssn & 1km; tradsmn; rest 100m; playgrnd; paddling pool; tennis; few statics; dogs €1.70; bus to Dax; adv bkg; quiet but some rd noise; twin-axles extra; red low ssn; CKE/CCI. "Peaceful, clean site in pleasant vill; NH area poss cr; rv walks; excel." ♦ 1 Feb-30 Nov. € 14.45 2011*

CASTILLON LA BATAILLE *7C2* (600m E Urban) *44.85350, -0.03550* **Camp Municipal La Pelouse, Chemin de Halage, 33350 Castillon-la-Bataille [05 57 40 04 22 or 05 56 40 00 06 (Mairie)]** Site in town on N bank of Rv Dordogne. After x-ing rv on D17 fr S to N, take 1st avail rd on R to rv. Sm, shd; wc; shwrs inc; el pnts (15A) inc; shop; poss cr; adv bkg; quiet; CKE/CCI. "Peaceful site by rv; busy high ssn; pitches poss rough & muddy when wet; helpful warden; facs dated but clean; conv St Emillion & wine area; gd NH." 1 May-15 Oct. € 15.50 2011*

CASTILLONNES *7D3* (300m N Urban) *44.65566, 0.59111* **Camp Municipal La Ferrette, Route de Bergerac, 47330 Castillonnès [05 53 36 94 68 or 05 58 36 80 49 (Mairie); fax 05 53 36 88 77; mairie.castillonnes@wanadoo.fr]** On N21, 27km S of Bergerac, on N side of Castillonnès. Easily seen fr main rd. Med, mkd pitch, pt sl, pt shd; wc (cont); mv service pnt; shwrs inc; el pnts (6A) €2; Indtte; shops 300m; pool 100m; playgrnd; tennis adj; some statics; quiet. "Beautiful situation; interesting town; gd san facs." ♦ 15 Jun-15 Sep. € 9.50 2010*

CAUDECOSTE see Agen *8E3*

CAZOULES see Souillac *7C3*

CENAC ET ST JULIEN see Sarlat la Canéda *7C3*

CHALUS *7B3* (12km S Rural) *45.54711, 0.95487* **FFCC Camping Le Périgord Vert, Fardoux, 24450 La Coquille [05 53 52 85 77; fax 05 53 55 14 25; leperigordvert@aol.com]** On N21 Périgueux/Châlus rd bet Thiviers & Châlus, turn L in vill of La Coquille at traff lts foll sps for Mialet. In 1.5km turn R, site 500m on L; sp. Sm, pt shd, pt sl; wc; chem disp; mv service pnt; shwrs inc; el pnts (6A) inc; gas; Indtte; shops 2km; tradsmn; rest, snacks, bar high ssn; playgrnd; pool high ssn; free fishing; tennis; 5% statics; dogs; phone; poss cr; Eng spkn; adv bkg; quiet; red low ssn; CKE/CCI. "Pleasant site; helpful staff; choice of meadow or woodland pitch; poor facs, ltd low ssn." ♦ 15 Apr-30 Oct. € 13.30 2010*

CHAMPAGNAC LA RIVIERE see Chalus *7B3*

CHAMPS ROMAIN see Nontron *7B3*

CONTIS PLAGE *8E1* (500m E Coastal) *44.08895, -1.31678* **Yelloh! Village Lous Seurrots, 40170 Contis-Plage [05 58 42 85 82; fax 05 58 42 49 11; info@lous-seurrots.com; www.lous-seurrots.com / www.yellohvillage.co.uk]** S fr Mimizan take D652; 14km turn R onto D41 sp Contis-Plage; site on L. Or fr N10/E5/E70 exit junc 14 onto D38/D41 to Contis. V lge, hdg pitch, shd; htd wc; chem disp; baby facs; fam bthrm; shwrs inc; el pnts (6A) €4; gas; Indtte (inc dryer); shop; tradsmn; rest, snacks; bar; BBQ; playgrnd; pool; paddling pool; sand beach 400m; tennis; cycle hire; games area; wifi; entmnt; TV; 30% statics; dogs €4; adv bkg; quiet; Eng spkn; ccard acc; red low ssn. "Pitches vary in size, some req levelling blocks; excel." ♦ 9 Apr-27 Sep. € 36.00 2010*

COQUILLE, LA see Chalus *7B3*

COURBIAC *7D3* (1.7km W Rural) *44.37818, 1.01807* **FFCC Le Pouchou, 47370 Courbiac [tel/fax 05 53 40 72 68 or 06 80 25 15 13 (mob); le.pouchou@wanadoo.fr; www.camping-le-pouchou.com]** S fr Fumel on D102 thro Tournon-d'Agenais; Courbiac sp to L on S side of town; site on R in 2.5km (1.5km bef Courbiac). Sm, pt sl, pt shd; wc; chem disp; mv service pnt; baby facs; shwrs inc; el pnts (10A) €4 (poss rev pol); Indry rm; shop; snacks; bar; playgrnd; pool & paddling pool; cycle hire; fishing; horseriding; archery; wifi; sat TV; some statics; dogs €1.80; site clsd 21 Dec-9 Jan; Eng spkn; adv bkg ess high ssn; quiet; red low ssn; CKE/CCI. "Vg site in lovely setting; lge pitches each with picnic table; many sl pitches poss diff; gd, clean facs; gd views; friendly, hospitable owners; gd cycling; peaceful location." ♦ 1 Mar-30 Jun, 1 Jul-31 Aug, 1 Sep-30 Nov. € 16.00 2014*

COUTRAS *7C2* (3km SW Rural) *45.01335, -0.10856* **Camping Résidential de Loisir Le Paradis, 8 Champ des Ardouins, Port-du-Mas, 33230 Abzac [05 57 49 05 10; fax 05 57 49 18 88; campingleparadis@free.fr; http://campingleparadis.free.fr/]** Fr Coutras on S on D17 to Abzac, site well sp. Sm, pt shd; htd wc; mv service pnt; baby facs; shwrs inc; el pnts (6A) €3; gas; Indtte; shop; tradsmn; rest, snacks; BBQ; playgrnd; pool; lake sw, sand beach; fishing; games rm; entmnt;TV rm; 90% statics; dogs €1.50; ccard acc; m'vans only; CKE/CCI. "Excel site; san facs need refurb; gd for vineyards." 1 May-15 Sep. € 15.20 2009*

⊞ **COUTRAS** *7C2* (7.5km NW Rural) *45.07944, -0.20622* **Camping Le Chêne du Lac, 3 Lieu-dit Chateauneuf, 33230 Bayas [05 57 69 13 78 or 06 07 98 92 65 (mob); lechenedulac@orange.fr; www.camping-lechenedulac.com]** Fr Coutras W on D10 to Guitres; N fr Guitres on D247 to Bayas; site 2km N of Bayas, sp. Sm, mkd ptch, pt shd; wc (some cont); chem disp; shwrs inc; el pnts (10A) €4.30-5; gas; Indry rm; shop; tradsmn; snacks; bar; BBQ sep area; playgrnd; internet; 25% statics; no twin-axles; dogs €2; adv bkg; Eng spkn; quiet; CKE/CCI. "Helpful owner; pedalos & canoes adj; vg; red facs in winter; great site; friendly, helpful new owners; v relaxed atmosphere." ♦ ltd € 24.00 2013*

COUX ET BIGAROQUE see Bugue, Le *7C3*

CREON *7D2* (3km NW Rural) *44.78372, -0.37108* **FFCC Camping Caravaning Bel Air, 33670 Créon [05 56 23 01 90; fax 05 56 23 08 38; info@camping-bel-air.com; www.camping-bel-air.com]** Fr A10/E70 at junc 24 take D936 E fr Bordeaux sp Bergerac. Approx 15km E turn SE onto D671 sp Créon & cont for 5km. Site on L, 1.5km after Lorient. Med, hdg/mkd pitch, hdstg, pt shd; htd wc (some cont); chem disp; mv service pnt; shwrs inc; el (10A) €3.60 ; gas; Indtte (inc dryer); shop high ssn; tradsmn; rest, snacks; bar; playgrnd; pool; wifi; 50% statics; dogs €2.50; clsd to vehicles 2200-0800; Eng spkn; adv bkg; quiet; ccard acc; red long stay; CKE/CCI. "Helpful owners; immac, modern san facs; rest sm & ltd; facs v ltd low ssn; no twin-axles; some pitches v restricted and tight; phone ahead to check open low ssn; gd NH; poss music festival in next field; poss rd noise." ♦ ltd 16 Jan-15 Dec. € 26.00 2014*

DAGLAN *7D3* (4km N Rural) *44.76762, 1.17590* **Camping Le Moulin de Paulhiac, 24250 Daglan [05 53 28 20 88; fax 05 53 29 33 45; info@moulin-de-paulhiac.com; www.moulin-de-paulhiac.com]** D57 SW fr Sarlat, across rv into St Cybranet & site in 2km. Fr Souillac W on D703 alongside Rv Dordogne; x-ing rv onto D46 (nr Domme) & D50, to site. Med, hdg/mkd pitch, shd; wc (some cont); chem disp; mv service pnt; shwrs; el pnts (6-10A) €3.70-4.40; gas; Indtte; shop; rest, snacks; bar; playgrnd; 4 htd pools; waterslide; TV rm; entmnt; shgl beach/rv adj with canoeing/fishing; 20% statics; dogs €1.90; poss cr; Eng spkn; adv bkg; quiet with some rd noise; red low ssn; ccard acc; CKE/CCI. "Pretty site; friendly, helpful staff; vg fruit/veg mkt Sun in vill; highly rec." ♦ ltd 15 May-16 Sep. € 25.00 2011*

DAMAZAN *7D2* (2km S Rural) **Camp Municipal du Lac, Route de Buzet-sur-Baïse, 47160 Damazan [05 53 79 40 15; fax 05 53 79 26 92; mairie.damazan@wanadoo.fr]** Fr A62 take junc 6, turn R at rndabt onto D8; almost immed take slip rd sp Damazan/Buzet-dur-Baïse; at top take 2nd R sp Buzet (1st turning goes to lake only). Site 1km on R, sp fr rd. Med, some hdg/mkd pitch, pt sl, pt shd; wc (some cont); chem disp (wc); shwrs inc; el pnts (10A) €3; gas 2km; Indtte; shops, rest, snacks, bar 2km; BBQ; playgrnd adj; lake sw adj; 2% statics; dogs; phone adj; poss cr; adv bkg; quiet but nr a'route; CKE/CCI. "Pretty site by lake; helpful staff; warden calls am & pm; if office clsd, pitch self; next to cricket club; clean basic san facs; attractive Bastide town; conv NH; excel." ♦ ltd 1 Jul-31 Aug. € 11.40 2014*

DAX *8E1* (1.5km W Rural) *43.71189, -1.07304* **Camping Les Chênes, Allée du Bois de Boulogne, 40100 Dax [05 58 90 05 53; fax 05 58 90 42 43; camping-chenes@orange.fr; www.camping-les-chenes.fr]** Fr D824 to Dax, foll sp Bois de Boulogne, cross rlwy bdge & rv bdge & foll camp sp on rv bank. Well sp. Lge, mkd pitch, shd; htd wc (cont); chem disp; mv service pnt; some serviced pitches; shwrs inc; el pnts (5A) inc; gas; Indtte (inc dryer); shop; tradsmn; rest adj; snacks; bar; playgrnd; pool; beach 20km; wifi; TV rm; cycle hire; many statics; dogs €1.50; poss cr; Eng spkn; adv bkg; ccard acc; red low ssn; CKE/CCI. "Excel position; easy walk along rv into town; poss noise fr school adj; conv thermal baths at Dax; modernised site with uptodate htd, clean san facs; lovely pool and child area." ♦ 15 Mar-8 Nov. € 27.70 2014*

DAX *8E1* (6km W Rural) *43.72680, -1.12302* **Camping L'Etang d'Ardy, Route de Bayonne, 40990 St Paul-lès-Dax [05 58 97 57 74; info@etangardy.com; www.etangardy.com]** Fr E on D824 dir Dax; turn R onto D16 dir Magescq; then L sp Ardy; foll camping sp. Fr W leave D824 sp La Pince/Dax/Magescq; at rndabt U-turn onto D824 going E; take 1st exit & foll site sp. Med, hdg pitch, shd; wc; chem disp; serviced pitches; shwrs inc; el pnts (5A) inc; Indtte (inc dryer); shops; tradsmn; BBQ; playgrnd; pool; paddling pool; lake fishing; wifi; 30% statics; dogs €1.60; adv bkg; quiet; red long stay. "Friendly site." ♦ 3 Apr-22 Oct. € 20.50 2010*

DAX *8E1* (9km W Rural) *43.68206, -1.14974* **Camping Lou Bascou, 40180 Rivière-Saas-et-Gourby [05 58 97 57 29; fax 05 58 97 59 52; loubascou@orange.fr; www.campingloubascou.fr]** Leave N10 at junc 9 for D824 twd Dax. In 3.5km turn R onto D13 sp Rivière-Saas-et-Gourby. Well sp fr D824. Beware speed humps in Rivière vill. Med, hdg/mkd pitch, pt shd; htd wc; chem disp; mv service pnt; shwrs inc; el pnts (6-10A) €3-5; Indtte; shop 300m; tradsmn; snacks; bar; BBQ; playgrnd; pool 9km; sand beach 25km; tennis; entmnt; 50% statics in sep area; dogs €1.50; Eng spkn; adv bkg; red long stay/low ssn. "Quiet, friendly site; excel, clean facs; thermal facs in Dax; nrby wetlands wildlife inc storks worth seeing; vg NH." ♦ 1 Apr-31 Oct. € 16.00 2009*

⊞ **DAX** *8E1* (11km W Rural) *43.68706, -1.14687* **FFCC Camping à la Ferme Bertranborde (Lafitte), 975 Route des Clarions, 40180 Rivière-Saas-et-Gourby [05 58 97 58 39; bertranborde@orange.fr]** Turn S off D824 5km W of Dax onto D113, sp Angoumé; at x-rd in 2km turn R (by water tower); then immed L; site on R in 100m, well sp. Or fr N10/A63, exit junc 9 onto D824 dir Dax; in 5km turn R onto D113, then as bef. Sm, pt shd, pt sl; wc (own san); chem disp; mv service pnt; shwrs inc; el pnts (4-10A) €2.50-4; Indtte; ice; shops 3km; BBQ; playgrnd; rv sw 7km; dogs €0.50; poss cr; Eng spkn; quiet; adv bkg; CKE/CCI. "Peaceful CL-type site; beautiful garden; friendly, helpful owners; meals on request; min 2 nights high ssn; poss travellers festival time; excel." € 9.50 2009*

DAX *8E1* (3km NW Rural) *43.72020, -1.09365* **FFCC Camping Les Pins du Soleil, Route des Minières, La Pince, 40990 St Paul-les-Dax [05 58 91 37 91; fax 05 58 91 00 24; info@pinsoleil.com; www.pinsoleil.com]** Exit N10 junc 11 sp Dax onto D16. Cross D824 & turn R onto D459 S. Cross rndabt & cont on D459, Route des Minières. Site sp in pine forest. Med, hdg/mkd pitch, pt sl, pt shd; htd wc, chem disp; mv service pnt; serviced pitches; baby facs; shwrs inc; el pnts (5A) €2; gas; Indtte (inc dryer); shop; tradsmn; rest 1km; snacks; bar; BBQ; playgrnd; pool; paddling pool; tennis 2km; cycle hire; games area; wifi; entmnt; TV rm; 25% statics; dogs €2; phone; Eng spkn; some rd noise; red long stay/low ssn; ccard acc. "Nice, quiet site (low ssn); various pitch sizes, some spacious; soft, sandy soil poss problem when wet; helpful, friendly staff; excel pool; spa 2km; conv Pyrenees & Biarritz; vg." ♦ 1 Apr-6 Nov. € 24.00 (CChq acc) 2010*

AQUITAINE

DAX *8E1* (12km NW Rural) *43.82364, -1.15103* **FFCC Camping Aire Naturelle Le Toy (Fabas), 1284 Chemin de Carroués, 40990 Herm [05 58 91 55 16; www.camping-du-toy.com]** Exit N10 junc 11 at Magescq; foll sps for cent vill & then Herm on D150; at Herm x-rds by church turn L onto rd to Castets. Site 1km on R. Sm, hdg/mkd pitch, shd; wc; shwrs inc; el pnts (4-10A) €3-5; shops 1km; lndtte; playgrnd; sand beach 20 mins; games area; trampolines; dogs €1.50; Eng spkn; quiet. "Pleasant woodland site." Easter-31 Oct. € 12.00 2011*

DEVILLAC see Villéreal *7D3*

DOMME see Sarlat la Canéda *7C3*

DOUVILLE *7C3* (2km S Rural) *44.99271, 0.59853* **Camping Lestaubière, Pont-St Mamet, 24140 Douville [05 53 82 98 15; fax 05 53 82 90 17; lestaubiere@cs.com; www.lestaubiere.com]** Foll sp for 'Pont St Mamet' fr N21; then watch for camping sp. Med, pt sl, pt shd; wc; chem disp; baby facs; fam bthrm; shwrs inc; el pnts (6-10A) €4-5; gas; lndtte; shop in ssn; tradsmn; rest & snacks (high ssn); bar; BBQ; playgrnd; pool; paddling pool; lake sw, sm sand beach; fishing lake; tennis 5km; games area; games rm; child entmnt (high ssn); wifi; TV; dogs €3.50; phone; twin-axles (high ssn only); Eng spkn; adv bkg; quiet but some rd noise; ccard acc; red low ssn; CKE/CCI. "Spacious, park-like site with beautiful views; v lge pitches; owned by friendly, helpful Dutch couple; vg modern san facs; superb out of ssn; excel." ♦ 29 Apr-15 Sep. € 26.50 2011*

DOUZE, LA *7C3* (3km E Rural) *45.06493, 0.88817* **Camping Laulurie en Périgord (Naturist), 24330 La Douze [05 53 06 74 00; fax 05 53 06 77 55; toutain@laulurie.com; www.laulurie.com]** Fr Périgueux S on N221; in 8km turn S on D710 twd Le Bugue. Or exit A89 onto D710 S. On ent La Douze turn L & foll arrow signs. Sm, hdg/mkd pitch, pt sl, pt shd; wc (some cont); chem disp; shwrs inc; el pnts (3-10A); gas; shop; rest, snacks; bar; playgrnd; pool; dogs €3.00; sep car park; adv bkg; quiet; red low ssn; ccard acc. "Excel site; friendly owners; gd touring base for Dordogne & Périgueux; INF card req." ♦ ltd 15 May-15 Sep. € 34.50 2013*

⊞ **DURAS** *7D2* (500m N Rural) *44.68293, 0.18602* **Camping Le Cabri, Malherbe, Route de Savignac, 47120 Duras [05 53 83 81 03; fax 05 53 83 08 91; holidays@lecabri.eu.com; www.lecabri.eu.com]** Fr N on D708, turn R on ent Duras onto D203 at mini-rndabt by tourist info shop; site in 800m. Sm, hdg pitch, hdstg, terr, unshd; htd wc; chem disp; baby facs; shwrs inc; el pnts (4-10A) €3-5; gas 500m; lndtte (inc dryer); shop 500m; rest, snacks; bar; BBQ; playgrnd; sm pool; tennis 1km; games area; games rm; entmnt; wifi; 30% statics; dogs €2; bus 500m; Eng spkn; adv bkg; quiet; ccard acc; red low ssn; CKE/CCI. "Spacious site with wide views; lge pitches; British owners (CC members); san facs poss tired high ssn (2011); vg rest; Duras an attractive town; excel." ♦ € 17.00 2012*

EAUX BONNES see Laruns *8G2*

EYMET *7D2* (5km SW Rural) *44.63211, 0.39977* **Camping Le Moulin Brûlé, 47800 Agnac [tel/fax 05 53 83 07 56; thebeales@wanadoo.fr; www.campingswfrance.co.uk]** Fr S on D933 at Miramont-de-Guyenne (6km S of Eymet) turn E onto D1; in 4km turn L onto C501 dir Eymet; site on L in 2km. Or fr N approx 1km after Eymet turn L onto C1 sp Chateau Pèchalbet. In 1.5km at x-rds turn L sp Bourgougnague, site on R in 2km. NB Narr lanes & bends on app. Sm, mkd pitch, hdstg, sl, unshd; wc; shwrs; chem disp (wc); shwrs inc; el pnts (10-16A) €3; lndtte; shops, rest, snacks & bar 6km; BBQ (charcoal); playgrnd; pool; games area; 1% statics; no twin axles; adv bkg. "Lovely, peaceful, well-kept site in pleasant surroundings; friendly British owners; excel san facs; gd cycling & walking; excel." Apr-Oct. € 12.00 2011*

EYMET *7D2* (500m W Urban) *44.66923, 0.39615* **Camping du Château (formerly Municipal), Rue de la Sole, 24500 Eymet [05 53 23 80 28 / 06 98 16 97 93 (mob); fax 05 53 22 22 19; eymetcamping@aol.com; www.eymetcamping.fr]** Thro Miramont onto D933 to Eymet. Turn opp Casino supmkt & foll sp to site. Sp on ent to Eymet fr all dirs. Sm, hdg/mkd pitch, pt shd, wc; chem disp; mv service pnt; shwrs inc; el pnts (10A) €3 (poss rev pol); gas 300m; lndtte; shops, rest, snacks & bar 300m; playgrnd; pool 1.5km; lake & rv sw nrby; boat & cycle hire; wifi; dogs; poss cr; Eng spkn; adv bkg; no twin-axles; quiet; red long stay; CKE/CCI. "Lovely, well-kept site by rv behind medieval chateau; friendly, helpful owner; immac san facs; wine tasting on site; Thur mkt; excel; Peaceful site nr lovely Bastide town." ♦ 1 Apr-30 Sep. € 10.50 2013*

EYZIES DE TAYAC, LES *7C3* (4km N Rural) *44.98070, 1.04457* **Camping Bouyssou, Lespinasse, 24620 Tursac [05 53 06 98 08; campingbouyssou@wanadoo.fr; http://campingbouyssou24.pagesperso-orange.fr]** N fr Les Eyzies on D707, turn L across rv bdge sp La Madelaine. Take R fork, site sp on L. Sm, hdg pitch, pt shd; wc; chem disp; shwrs inc; el pts (10A) €2; shop, rest 1km; playgrnd; pool; paddling pool; rv fishing 200m; some statics; poss cr; adv bkg; quiet. "Pleasant site with views; friendly, helpful owner; vg modern, unisex san facs; excel touring base." 2 Jun-29 Sep. € 10.00 2010*

EYZIES DE TAYAC, LES *7C3* (4km NE Rural) *44.95633, 1.04410* **Camping La Ferme du Pelou, 24620 Tursac [05 53 06 98 17; www.lafermedupelou.com]** Fr Les Eyzies-de-Tayac take D706 dir Tursac. In 3km turn R, site sp. 1km up hill on L. Ent poss diff for lge o'fits. Med, hdg pitch, pt shd; wc; chem disp; mv service pnt; shwrs inc; el pnts (6A) €2.80 (long lead poss req); lndtte; shop, rest & bar 4km; BBQ; playgrnd; htd pool; mainly statics; dogs free; phone; adv bkg; quiet low ssn; CKE/CCI. "Well-kept, clean site; views fr pt of site without el pnts; friendly, helpful owners; gd san facs, poss too few high ssn; vg pool; gd walking; many dogs, inc owner's; site too sm for v lge o'fits; highly rec." ♦ 15 Mar-15 Nov. € 10.50 2009*

EYZIES DE TAYAC, LES *7C3* (5km NE Rural) *44.96935, 1.04623* **Camping Le Pigeonnier, Le Bourg, 24620 Tursac [tel/fax 05 53 06 96 90; campinglepigeonnier@orange.fr; www.campinglepigeonnier.fr]** NE fr Les Eyzies for 5km on D706 to Tursac; site is 200m fr Mairie in vill cent; ent tight. Sm, hdg/mkd pitch, pt sl, terr, shd; wc; chem disp in vill; shwrs inc; el pnts (10A) €3; gas; Indtte; tradsmn; shop 5km; snacks; bar; playgrnd; sm pool; shgl beach, rv sw, fishing & canoeing 1km; horseriding; cycle hire; dogs €1; adv bkg; quiet; no ccard acc; CKE/CCI. "Freshwater pool (v cold); spacious, grass pitches; facs poss stretched high ssn; v quiet hideaway site in busy area; close to prehistoric sites; friendly Brit owners." 1 Jun-30 Sep. € 20.50 2012*

"I like to fill in the reports as I travel from site to site"

You'll find report forms at the back of this guide, or you can fill them in online at www.caravaclub.co.uk/europereport.

⊞ **EYZIES DE TAYAC, LES** *7C3* (6km NE Rural) *44.95277, 1.08820* **FFCC Camping Auberge (Veyret), Bardenat, 24620 Marquay [05 53 29 68 44 / 05 53 31 58 00 ls; fax 05 53 31 58 28; contact@auberge-veyret.com; www.auberge-veyret.com]** Leave Les Eyzies dir Sarlat on D47; in 4km go L onto D48 (dir Tamniès); in 3.5km turn L & foll sp for Auberge Veyret. Sm, sl, pt shd; wc; chem disp (wc); shwrs inc; el pnts (16A) €3; tradsmn; rest, snacks; playgrnd; pool; adv bkg low ssn ess; quiet; CKE/CCI. "Excel rest; simple CL-type site with sl grass pitches & views; v quiet and lovely site, lovely views; helpful owner." € 12.00 2013*

EYZIES DE TAYAC, LES *7C3* (2km S Rural) *44.92370, 1.02910* **Camping Le Pech Charmant, 24620 Les Eyzies-de-Tayac [05 53 35 97 08; fax 05 53 35 97 09; info@lepech.com; www.lepech.com]** Fr Sarlat take D47 to Les Eyzies then take D706 dir Le Bugue. Turn L immed after g'ge & foll sm site sps round 1-way system. Med, mkd pitch, terr, pt shd; wc; chem disp; mv service pnt; shwrs; el pnts (10A) €3; gas; Indtte (inc dryer); shop; tradsmn; snacks; bar; BBQ (gas); playgrnd; pool; paddling pool; rv sw 2km; horseriding; children's farm; games area; games rm; wifi; entmnt; 10% statics; dogs €1.80; phone; Eng spkn; adv bkg; quiet; ccard acc; CKE/CCI. ♦ 1 Apr-1 Oct. € 21.00 2009*

EYZIES DE TAYAC, LES *7C3* (1km NW Rural) *44.93695, 1.00563* **Camping La Rivière, 3 Route du Sorcier, 24620 Les Eyzies-de-Tayac [05 53 06 97 14; fax 05 53 35 20 85; la-riviere@wanadoo.fr; www.lariviereleseyzies.com]** Site off D47 Rte de Périgueux. Lge o'fits use 2nd ent by sw pool & walk to recep. Med, hdg/mkd pitch, pt shd; wc; chem disp; mv service pnt; shwrs; el pnts (6-10A) €3.60-4; Indtte; shop; rest, snacks; bar; playgrnd; pool; paddling pool; canoe hire 500m; tennis; internet; TV rm; 5% statics; dogs €1; phone; Eng spkn; adv bkg; quiet; ccard acc; red low ssn; CKE/CCI. "Pleasant site; sm pitches; gd clean facs; walking dist many prehistoric caves." ♦ 4 Apr-1 Nov. € 19.00 2009*

FUMEL *7D3* (2km E Rural) *44.48929, 0.99704* **Camping de Condat/Les Catalpas, Route de Cahors, 47500 Fumel [05 53 71 11 99 or 06 30 24 20 04; fax 05 53 71 36 69; les-catalpas@wanadoo.fr; www.les-catalpas.com]** Take D811 fr Fumel E twd Cahors. Clearly sp after Condat. Med, mkd pitch, hdstg, pt sl, pt shd; htd wc; chem disp (wc); mv service pnt; shwrs inc; el pnts (10A) €3; Indtte; shops 1km; rest in vill; snacks; BBQ; playgrnd; pool; fishing adj; wifi; entmnt; 15% statics; dogs; Eng spkn; adv bkg; red low ssn; CKE/CCI. "New owners, friendly helpful, improvements to site, sec barrier, by rv." ♦ ltd 1 Apr-31 Oct. € 21.00 2012*

GABARRET *8E2* (700m SE Rural) *43.98250, 0.01562* **Camp Municipal La Chêneraie, 454 Ave de la Chêneraie, 40310 Gabarret [05 58 44 92 62; fax 05 58 44 35 38; la-cheneraie@orange.fr]** Fr cent of vill take D656 dir Mézin & Nérac. After 300m turn R onto D35, site in 300m on R. Sm, hdg pitch, pt sl, pt shd; htd wc; chem disp; shwrs inc; el pnts (10A) inc; Indtte; shops, rest, bar 500m; playgrnd; htd pool; adv bkg ess Jul/Aug; quiet; CKE/CCI. ♦ 1 Mar-31 Oct. € 9.00 2010*

GARDONNE see Bergerac *7C3*

GASTES *7D1* (3km SW Rural) *44.31331, -1.16856* **Camping La Réserve, 1229 Ave Félix Ducourneau, 40160 Gastes [05 58 09 74 79 or 05 58 09 79 23; fax 05 58 09 78 71; lareserve@siblu.fr; www.siblu.com/lareserve]** At traff lts in cent Parentis-en-Born, turn L sp Pontenx & Gastes on D652. After 3km turn R dir Gastes, Ste Eulalie & Mimizan-Plage. Cont onto rndabt & take 2nd exit D652, then turn immed R sp La Réserve. Site sp. V lge, pt shd; wc; chem disp; shwrs inc; el pnts (6A) inc; gas; Indtte; rest, snacks; bar; shop; BBQ (gas only); playgrnd; pools (1 htd, covrd); waterslide; lake sw & private sandy beach adj; watersports high ssn; sailing school; windsurfing; cycle hire; tennis; games area; archery; wifi; entmnt; mostly statics; no dogs; Eng spkn; adv bkg ess high ssn; ccard acc; red low ssn; CKE/CCI. "Lakeside site by pine forest; lge pitches; mostly statics, but gd facs for tourers; children's club inc in site fee; highly rec." ♦ 9 Apr-16 Sep. € 67.00 2011*

GAUGEAC see Monpazier *7D3*

GOURDON *7D3* (10km W Rural) *44.75491, 1.23999* **Camping Le Convivial, La Gréze, 24250 St Martial de Nabirat [05 53 28 43 15; contact@campingleconvivial.com; www.campingleconvivial.com]** SW fr Gourdon, take D673 twd Salviac. Bef Pont Carral turn R onto D6 which becomes D46. Site 1.5km N St Martial on L. Sm, hdg pitch, pt sl, pt shd; htd wc; chem disp; baby facs; shwrs; el pnts (8A); Indtte (inc dryer); shops 6km; rest; snacks; bar; BBQ; fishing 1km; playgrnd; pool; games area; wifi; 25% statics; dogs €1.60; twin axles; Eng spkn; quiet; ccard acc; CCI. "Beautiful, spacious site off tourist track; friendly & welcoming owners; cycle trail in pretty valley of Céon nrby; vg." ♦ 1 Apr-31 Oct. € 19.70 2014*

GRAYAN ET L'HOPITAL see Soulac sur Mer *7B1*

GROLEJAC see Sarlat la Canéda *7C3*

GUJAN MESTRAS see Arcachon *7D1*

HAGETMAU *8E2* (200m S Urban) *43.65020, -0.59190* **Camp Muncipal de la Cité Verte, Chemin des Loussets, 40700 Hagetmau [tel/fax 05 58 79 79 79]** On D933 S fr Mont-de-Marsan, go thro St Sever & cont on D933 to Hagetmau. Take ring rd & ent town fr S, sp 'Cité Verte'. Heading N fr Orthez on D933, also foll sp 'Cité Verte'. Sm, hdg pitch, pt shd; wc; chem disp (wc); mv service pnt; serviced pitch; fam bthrm; sauna; shwrs inc; el pnts (16A) inc; shops 500m; rest, snacks, bar 1km; BBQ; playgrnd; htd, covrd pool; jacuzzi; gym; dogs; phone; adv bkg ess; quiet. "Unique site with sports cent inc Olympic-sized pool; 24 pitches with personal facs; gd base for touring area; attractive town; excel." 1 Jun-30 Sep. € 22.00 2009*

HAUTEFORT *7C3* (3km NE Rural) *45.28081, 1.15917* **Camping La Grenouille, Brégérac, 24390 Hautefort [tel/fax 05 53 50 11 71; info@lagrenouillevacances.com; www.lagrenouillevacances.com]** Fr N on D704 at Cherveil-Cubas take D77 dir Boisseuilh/Teillots. In 4km turn R & in 800m turn L to site. Fr S on D704 at St Agnan take D62 sp Hautefort/Badefols d'Ans. Pass 'Vival' (sm shop on L) in Hautefort & turn L dir Boisseuilh. After 1st bdge turn L to La Besse & site in 2km. Sm, pt sl, pt shd; wc; chem disp; shwrs inc; el pnts (8A) €3.50; Indtte (inc dryer); ice; shop & 3km; tradsmn; rest; bar 3km; BBQ; playgrnd; pool; wifi; dogs free; Eng spkn; adv bkg; v quiet; ccard not acc; red low ssn; CKE/CCI. "Tranquil, scenic, well-kept site; friendly, helpful, Dutch owners; vg san facs; meals avail; goats, guinea pigs, chickens in pens on site; gd walking; highly rec." 22 Apr-15 Oct. € 17.00 2010*

HAUTEFORT *7C3* (8km W Rural) *45.28032, 1.04845* **Camping Les Tourterelles, 24390 Tourtoirac [05 53 51 11 17; les-tourterelles@orange.fr; www.les-tourterelles.com]** Fr N or S on D704 turn W at Hautefort on D62/D5 to Tourtoirac. In Tourtoirac turn R over rv then L. Site in 1km. Med, hdg/mkd pitch, terr, pt shd; wc; chem disp; mv service pnt; baby facs; shwrs; el pnts (6A) €4.50; gas; Indtte; shop 2km; rest, snacks; bar; playgrnd; pool; tennis; horseriding; TV rm; 20% statics; dogs €5; bus 1km; phone; poss cr; Eng spkn; adv bkg; quiet; low ssn/snr citizens red; ccard acc; CKE/CCI. "Beautiful Auvézère valley; rallies welcome; owners helpful; equestrian cent; gd walks." ♦ 25 Apr-27 Sep. € 29.00 2014*

> ## "We must tell The Club about that great site we found"
> Get your site reports in by mid-August and we'll do our best to get your updates into the next edition.

HENDAYE *8F1* (2km W Urban/Coastal) *43.37335, -1.75608* **Camping Ametza, Blvd de l'Empereur, 64700 Hendaye-Plage [05 59 20 07 05; fax 05 59 20 32 16; contact@camping-ametza.com; www.camping-ametza.com]** Exit A63 junc 2 St Jean-de-Luz S onto D192. Foll sp to site. Turn L on hill down to seafront, cross rlwy, site immed on L. Lge, sl, shd; wc; chem disp; baby facs; shwrs inc; el pnts (6A) €5 (poss rev pol); Indry rm; shop; snacks; bar; playgrnd; pool; sand beach 900m; games area; wifi; entmnt; 30% statics; dogs €2; poss cr; Eng spkn; quiet but rd & rlwy noise; red low ssn; CKE/CCI. "Lovely relaxed site; some gd sized pitches, some sm; excel facs; Hendaye pleasant resort; excel beach in walking dist; excel." 1 May-30 Sep. € 24.50 2009*

HOSSEGOR *8E1* (6km N Coastal) *43.69490, -1.42953* **Village Camping Océliances, Ave des Tucs, 40510 Seignosse [05 58 43 30 30; fax 05 58 41 64 21; oceliances@wanadoo.fr; www.oceliances.com]** Take D79 N fr Hossegor. After 6km turn L at rndabt. Site sp. Lge, mkd pitch, pt sl, pt shd; htd wc; chem disp; baby facs; shwrs inc; el pnts (6A) inc; gas; Indtte (inc dryer); shop; rest, snacks; bar; BBQ; playgrnd; pool; paddling pool; sand beach 600m; windsurfing; lake 2km; games area; games rm; cycle hire; wifi; entmnt; 65% statics; dogs €3.40; Eng spkn; adv bkg; quiet; ccard acc; red long stay/low ssn. "Pleasant site in pine forest." ♦ Easter-30 Sep. € 30.50 2010*

> ## "I need an on-site restaurant"
> We do our best to make sure site information is correct, but it is always best to check any must-have facilities are still available or will be open during your visit.

HOSSEGOR *8E1* (1.5km NE Urban) *43.67212, -1.42035* **Camping Le Lac, 580 Routes des Lacs, 40150 Hossegor [05 58 43 53 14; fax 05 58 43 55 83; info@camping-du-lac.com; www.camping-du-lac.com]** Exit A63 junc 8 or N10 onto D28 sp Hossegor/Capbreton & foll sp for town cent. Site well sp at Soorts-Hossegor. Lge, hdg/mkd pitch, pt shd; wc (some cont); chem disp (wc); mv service pnt; shwrs inc; el pnts (6A) inc; gas; Indtte (inc dryer); shop; tradsmn; rest, snacks; bar; playgrnd; pool; paddling pool; sand beach 2km; lake 300m; games area; cycle hire; wifi; 80% statics; dogs €4; poss cr; Eng spkn; adv bkg; some rd noise; ccard acc; CKE/CCI. "Ltd space for tourers." ♦ ltd 1 Apr-30 Sep. € 34.00 2009*

HOSSEGOR *8E1* (2km S Coastal) *43.62947, -1.43270* **Camping La Civelle, Rue des Biches, 40130 Capbreton [05 58 72 15 11; campinglacivelle@orange.fr; www.campinglacivelle.fr]** Fr N on A63, take exit 8 & foll sps to Capbreton; cont twds cent. At 1st rndabt, turn L past Intermarché. Strt on at 2nd rndabtat. At 3rd rndabt take 3rd exit & foll sp for site. Lge, mkd pitch, shd; wc (some cont); chem disp; 10% serviced pitches; el pnts €3.80; gas; Indtte; shop 1.5km; rest, snacks; BBQ; pool; sand beach 1km; games area; games rm; 40% statics; dogs €2.20; phone; ccard acc; CKE/CCI. "Busy site; no arr bef 1500; some sandy pitches; conv for area; cycle rte dir to beach." 22 Mar-5 Oct. € 21.50 2010*

⊞ **HOSSEGOR** *8E1* (3km S Coastal) *43.65168, -1.42998* **Camp Municipal Bel Air, Ave de Bourret, 40130 Capbreton [05 58 72 12 04; www.capbreton-tourisme.com]** Fr N10 or A63, take D28 to Capbreton; turn R onto D152; turn L at 4th rndabt, site on L in 200m. Diff access long o'fits. Med, hdg pitch, pt sl, pt shd; wc; chem disp; shwrs; el pnts (10A) inc; gas; Indtte; shops 500m; tradsmn; playgrnd; sand beach 1km; cycle hire adj; dogs €2.05; site clsd New Year; quiet; 10% red low ssn; CKE/CCI. "No arr bef 1500; card-op barrier, rec phone ahead to arrange access; arr bef 2000 unless late arr agreed in adv; vg winter NH/sh stay but phone ahead to check open; marina nrby, gd fishing; network of cycle paths; excel surfing; walking dist to Cap Breton & Hossegor; conv Biarritz." ♦ € 24.40 2011*

HOURTIN *7C1* (7.5km SSW Rural) *45.13915, -1.07096* **Aire Naturelle de Camping l'Acacia, Route de Carcans, 33990 (Gironde) [05 56 73 80 80 06 72 94 12 67 (mob); camping.lacacia@orange.fr; www.campinglacacia.com]** Fr Carcans on main rd to Hourtin, sp for site about 5km. Turn off rd on L and travel for 1.5km. Sm, v lge pitches, pt shd; wc; shwrs; el pnts inc; tradsmn; snacks; bar; cooking facs; playgrnd; lakes with beaches 5km; beach 16km; games area; games rm; bicycles; twin axles acc; adv bkg; red low ssn; "Site well maintained; immac san facs; owner v helpful, ltd Eng; volleyball; table tennis; v lge field; quiet peaceful site; great for families and couples; excel." Apr-Sep. € 20.20 2013*

HOURTIN *7C1* (1.5km W Rural) *45.17919, -1.07502* **Camping Les Ourmes, 90 Ave du Lac, 33990 Hourtin Port [05 56 09 12 76; fax 05 56 09 23 90; info@lesourmes.com; www.lesourmes.com]** Fr vill of Hourtin (35km NW Bordeaux), foll sp Houtin Port. In 1.5km, L at sp to site. Lge, mkd pitch, pt shd; wc; chem disp; mv service pnt; baby facs; shwrs inc; el pnts (6A) inc; gas; Indtte; shops 1.5km; tradsmn; rest, snacks, bar 1.5km; BBQ; playgrnd; pool; lake sw 1km; sand beach (sea) 10km; watersports; fishing; horseriding; games rm; entmnt; TV; 50% statics; dogs €2; phone; bus; poss cr in ssn; Eng spkn; adv bkg; quiet; CKE/CCI. "Excel for family holiday; Lake Hourtin shallow & vg for bathing, sailing etc; vg beaches nrby; nr Les Landes & Médoc vineyards." 27 Apr-22 Sep. € 41.00 2013*

"Satellite navigation makes touring much easier"

Remember most sat navs don't know if you're towing or in a larger vehicle – always use yours alongside maps and site directions.

HOURTIN *7C1* (10km W Coastal) *45.22296, -1.16472* **Camping La Côte d'Argent, Rue de la Côte d'Argent, 33990 Hourtin-Plage [05 56 09 10 25; fax 05 56 09 24 96; info@camping-cote-dargent.com; www.camping-cote-dargent.com]** On D1215 at Lesparre-Médoc take D3 Hourtin, D101 to Hourtin-Plage, site sp. V lge, mkd pitch, pt sl, some terr, shd; wc; chem disp; mv service pnt; baby facs; fam bthrm; shwrs inc; el pnts (10A) inc; Indtte (inc dryer); ice; shop; rest, snacks; bar; BBQ; playgrnd; 3 htd, pools (1 covrd); waterslide; jacuzzi; huge sand beach 300m; watersports; lake sw & fishing 4km; horseriding; cycle hire; games area; games rm; wifi; entmnt; 30% statics; dogs €5.50; phone; Eng spkn; adv bkg; quiet; ccard acc; red low ssn/long stay; CKE/CCI. "Pleasant, peaceful site in pine trees & dunes; poss steel pegs req; conv Médoc region chateaux & vineyards; ideal for surfers & beach lovers." ♦ 14 May-18 Sep. € 53.00 (CChq acc) 2011*

See advert on page 106

HOURTIN PLAGE see Hourtin *7C1*

⊞ **LABENNE** *8E1* (4km S Rural) *43.56470, -1.45240* **Camping du Lac, 518 Rue de Janin, 40440 Ondres [05 59 45 28 45 or 06 80 26 91 51 (mob); fax 05 59 45 29 45; contact@camping-du-lac.fr; www.camping-du-lac.fr]** Fr N exit A63 junc 8 onto N10 S. Turn R just N of Ondres sp Ondres-Plage, at rndabt turn L & foll site sp. Fr S exit A63 junc 7 onto N10 to Ondres. Cont thro town cent & turn L at town boundary, then as above; tight turns thro housing est. Med, hdg/mkd pitch, terr, pt shd; htd wc; chem disp; baby facs; shwrs inc; el pnts (10A) €4; gas; Indtte; shop 500m; rest in ssn; snacks; bar; playgrnd; pool in ssn; sand beach 4km; fishing; boating; games area; entmnt; cycle hire; 60% statics; dogs €5; phone; twin-axles acc low ssn only; Eng spkn; adv bkg (dep); quiet; red long stay/low ssn; CKE/CCI. "Peaceful, charming lakeside site by lake; gd welcome; helpful staff; ltd facs low ssn; vg pool; excel." ♦ € 30.00 2011*

"There aren't many sites open at this time of year"

If you're travelling outside peak season remember to call ahead to check site opening dates – even if the entry says 'open all year'.

LABENNE *8E1* (3km SW Coastal) *43.59533, -1.45651* **Camping Le Sylvamar, Ave de l'Océan, 40530 Labenne [05 59 45 75 16; fax 05 59 45 46 39; camping@sylvamar.fr; www.sylvamar.fr / www.yellohvillage.co.uk]** Exit A63 junc 7 onto D85; then take N10 N to Labenne; turn L onto D126; site sp. Lge, hdg/mkd pitch, pt shd; wc; chem disp; serviced pitches; sauna; spa; baby facs; shwrs inc; el pnts (10A) inc; Indtte (inc dryer); shop adj; tradsmn; rest, snacks; bar; BBQ; pool complex; paddling pool; waterslide; playgrnd; creche; sand beach 800m; fitness rm; beauty cent; wifi; entmnt; 50% statics; adv bkg; quiet; Eng spkn; red low ssn; ccard acc; CKE/CCI. "Site amongst pine trees; sandy pitches; gd location; v gd facs." ♦ 9 Apr-25 Sep. € 43.00 2011*

LABENNE *8E1* (2km W Coastal) *43.59547, -1.45695* **Camping La Côte d'Argent, 60 Ave de l'Océan, 40530 Labenne-Océan [05 59 45 42 02; fax 05 59 45 73 31; info@camping-cotedargent.com; www.camping-cotedargent.com]** Fr N10 take D126 W fr Labenne to Labenne-Plage & site. Lge, hdg/mkd pitch, shd; htd wc; 10% serviced pitches; mv service pnt; chem disp; baby facs; shwrs inc; el pnts (6A) €3.95; gas 300m; Indtte (inc dryer); shop 200m; tradsmn, rest, snacks, bar high ssn; BBQ; playgrnd; 2 pools (1 htd, covrd); paddling pool; sand beach 900m; fishing 300m; cycle hire; games area; games rm; archery; tennis 500m; wifi; entmnt; TV rm; 50% statics; dogs €2.50; poss cr; Eng spkn; adv bkg rec; quiet; ccard acc; CKE/CCI. "Nice pool area; children's park; gd cycle tracks; ltd facs low ssn; conv Biarritz; excel for family hols." ♦ ltd 1 Apr-31 Oct. € 25.75 (CChq acc) 2010*

*Last year of report

LABENNE *8E1* (3km W Coastal) *43.59628, -1.46104* **Camp Atlantique Le Boudigau, 45 Avenue de la Plage, 40530 Labenne-Océan [02 51 20 41 94; fax 05 59 45 43 0; http://boudigau.camp-atlantique.co.uk/]** Turn W off N10 in Labenne at traff lts in town cent onto D126 to Labenne-Plage. Site 2km on R. Lge, shd; wc; baby facs; shwrs inc; el pnts (6A) inc; gas; lndtte; shop; rest, snacks; bar; BBQ; playgrnd; htd, covrd pool; sandy beach 500m; games area; 90% statics; 1 dog per pitch; adv bkg;. "Sm touring area - only 25 pitches; excel san facs;gd site; lively high ssn - gd kids activities." 1 Apr-30 Sep. € 28.00 2014*

See advertisement

LACANAU *7C1* (3.3km NNW Rural) *45.00178, -1.09241* **Camping Les Fougères, Ave de l'Océan, 33680 Talaris [05 56 03 56 76; contact@campinglesfougereslacanau.com; www.campinglesfougereslacanau.com]** A630 bypass exit at junc 8 sp Lacanau - Le Verdon. Med, pt shd; wc; chem disp; mv service pnt; shwrs; el (4A) inc; tradsmn; BBQ; playgrnd; sw 2km; games area; wifi; 10% statics; dogs €2.10; twin axles; Eng spkn; adv bkg acc; CKE/CCI; "Excel site; watersports 1.5km; tennis 9km." ♦ 1 Jun-30 Sep. € 32.85 2013*

LACANAU OCEAN *7C1* (1km N Coastal) *45.01166, -1.19305* **Yelloh! Village Les Grands Pins, Plage Nord, Ave des Grands Pins, 33680 Lacanau-Océan [05 56 03 20 77; fax 05 57 70 03 89; reception@lesgrandspins.com; www.lesgrandspins.com / www.yellohvillage.co.uk]** Fr E on D6, on ent Lacanau-Océan, at 2nd rndabt fork R (2nd exit) onto Voie Pénétrante Nord; foll sp 'Plage Nord' & 'Les Grands Pins'. Site a turning to R in 1km. V lge, hdg/mkd pitch, terr, pt shd; htd wc; serviced pitches; chem disp; mv service pnt; baby facs; shwrs inc; el pnts (10A) inc; gas; lndtte; shop; rest, snacks; bar; playgrnd; htd pool; sand beach 500m; cycle hire; internet; entmnt; TV; 20% statics; dogs €4; poss cr; adv bkg red high ssn; quiet; red low ssn; 7 nights min 13 Jul-25 Aug. "Excel, well organised site; lge pitches; doesn't feel overcr - even when full." 14 Apr-22 Sep. € 49.00 2011*

LACANAU OCEAN *7C1* (7km E Rural) *45.00808, -1.11230* **Camping Talaris Vacances, Route de L'Océan, 33680 Lacanau [05 56 03 04 15; fax 05 56 26 21 56; www.talaris-vacances.fr]** Fr Lacanau-Océan twds Lake Lacanau, site on R. Lge, mkd pitch, hdstg, shd; wc (some cont); chem disp; mv service pnt; baby facs; shwrs inc; el pnts (6A) €3.90; gas; lndtte; shop; rest, snacks; bar; BBQ area; playgrnd; pool; waterslide; lake sw 2km; tennis; 50% statics; dogs €4; bus adj; Eng spkn; adv bkg; some rd noise; red low ssn; CKE/CCI. "Nr Lake Lacanau, sw & watersports; excel network cycle tracks." ♦ 4 Apr-26 Sep. € 32.00 2009*

LACANAU OCEAN *7C1* (5km SE Rural) *44.98620, -1.13410* **Camping Le Tedey, Par Le Moutchic, Route de Longarisse, 33680 Lacanau-Océan [05 56 03 00 15; fax 05 56 03 01 90; camping@le-tedey.com; www.le-tedey.com]** Fr Bordeaux take D6 to Lacanau & on twd Lacanau-Océan. On exit Moutchic take L fork twd Longarisse. Ent in 2km well sp on L. V lge, mkd pitch, shd; wc (some cont); chem disp; mv service pnt; baby facs; shwrs inc; el pnts (10A) €4.30; gas; lndtte; shop; snacks; bar; playgrnd; lake sw & sand beach adj; boating; cycle hire; golf 5km; entmnt; internet; TV rm; some statics; no dogs; poss cr; Eng spkn; adv bkg (ess Jul/Aug); quiet, but poss live music Sat night high ssn; red low ssn; ccard acc; CKE/CCI. "Peaceful, friendly, family-run site in pine woods - avoid tree sap; golf nr; gd cycle tracks; no el pnts for pitches adj beach; access diff some pitches; excel site." ♦ 25 Apr-19 Sep. € 29.40 2013*

See advert on next page

LALINDE *7C3* (2.2km E Urban) *44.83956, 0.76298* **Camping Moulin de la Guillou, Route de Sauveboeuf, 24150 Lalinde [09 61 46 06 96 or 05 53 73 44 60 (Mairie); fax 05 53 57 81 60; la-guillou@wanadoo.fr; www.pays-de-bergerac.com]** Take D703 E fr Lalinde (Rv Dordogne on R) & keep strt where rd turns L over canal bdge. Site in 300m; sp. Med, shd; wc; shwrs inc; el pnts (5A) €2.60; shops 1km; tradsmn; pool; playgrnd; rv sw & fishing adj; entmnt; tennis adj; dogs €2; adv bkg. "Charming, peaceful site on bank of Rv Dordogne; lovely views; clean san facs, in need of upgrade; poss travellers; vg." 1 May-30 Sep. € 15.00 2012*

LALINDE *7C3* (8.5km SE Rural) *44.7944, 0.8336* **Camping La Grande Veyière, Route de Cadouin, 24480 Molières [05 53 63 25 84; la-grande-veyiere@wanadoo.fr; www.lagrandeveyiere.com]** Fr Bergerac take D660 E for 19km to Port-de-Couze. Turn SW still on D660 sp Beaumont. In 6km turn L on D27. Site sp fr here. In approx 6km, ent on R. Med, hdg/mkd pitch, pt sl, terr, pt shd; wc; chem disp; baby facs; shwrs inc; el pnts (6A) €3; gas; Indtte; shop; rest, snacks; bar; BBQ (charcoal); playgrnd; pool; games area; games/TV rm; some statics; dogs €1; Eng spkn; adv bkg (rec Jul/Aug); phone; red low ssn; ccard acc; CKE/CCI. "Wooded site off beaten track, worth finding; warm welcome, owners friendly & helpful; excel facs; tractor tow avail in wet weather; excel; rec." ♦ 15 Jun-15 Sep. € 16.00 2011*

LALINDE *7C3* (4km W Urban) *44.82639, 0.70468* **Camping des Moulins, Route de Cahors, 24150 Couze-St Front [05 53 61 18 36; fax 05 53 24 99 72; camping-des-moulins@wanadoo.fr; www.campingdesmoulins.com]** Fr Lalinde take D703 dir Bergerac. In 2km turn L on D660 sp Port-de-Couze; over bdge (Dordogne Rv) into Couze. Turn R on D37 sp Lanquais, turn immed L, site sp. (NB Do not take D37E.) Sm, hdg pitch, pt sl, pt shd; wc; chem disp; mv service pnt; shwrs inc; el pnts (10A) €4.50; gas; Indtte; snacks; bar; BBQ; playgrnd; 3 pools; lake sw 3km; games area; games rm; 40% statics; dogs €2; phone adj; poss cr; Eng spkn; adv bkg; quiet; ccard acc; CKE/CCI. "Generous pitches; friendly, helpful owner; ltd facs low ssn & poss unclean; gd pools; conv Bergerac; excel." 18 Mar-5 Nov. € 29.00 (4 persons) 2011*

LANTON see Andernos les Bains *7D1*

⊞ **LARUNS** *8G2* (6km N Rural) *43.02085, -0.42043* **FFCC Camp Municipal de Monplaisir, Quartier Monplaisir, 64260 Gère-Bélesten [05 59 82 61 18]** Site sp on E side of D934 S of Gère-Bélesten. Med, mkd pitch, pt shd, htd wc; shwrs inc; el pnts (6A) €3.90; tradsmn; shops 4km; bar 100m; htd pool 4km; fishing; TV; 75% statics; Eng spkn; adv bkg; quiet; red low ssn. "Helpful warden calls am & pm." € 10.30 2014*

LARUNS *8G2* (6km SE Rural) *42.96972, -0.38220* **Camping d'Iscoo, 64440 Eaux-Bonnes [05 59 05 36 81 or 06 98 23 54 93 (mob); camping.iscoo@live.fr; http://iscoo.free.fr]** Site is on R 1.4km fr Eaux-Bonnes on climb to Col d'Aubisque. Site ent in middle of S-bend so advise cont 500m & turn on open grnd on L. Sm, mkd pitch, pt sl, pt shd; wc (some cont); shwrs; el pnts (2-5A) €2.50; shops 1.5km; playgrnd; pool 3km; dogs; quiet; ccard not acc; CKE/CCI. "V pleasant location; friendly owner; beautiful sunny site in hills; excel shwrs." 1 Jun-30 Sep. € 12.00 2014*

"That's changed – Should I let The Club know?"

If you find something on site that's different from the site entry, fill in a report and let us know. See www.caravanclub.co.uk/europereport.

⊞ **LARUNS** *8G2* (800m S Rural) *42.98241, -0.41591* **Camping Les Gaves, Quartier Pon, 64440 Laruns [05 59 05 32 37; fax 05 59 05 47 14; campingdesgaves@wanadoo.fr; www.campingdesgaves.com]** Site on S edge of town, N of Hôtel Le Lorry & bdge. Fr town sq cont on Rte d'Espagne (narr exit fr sq) to end of 1-way system. After Elf & Total stns turn L at site sp immed bef bdge (high fir tree each side of bdge ent). Ignore 1st site on L. At v constricted T-junc at ent to quartier 'Pon', turn R & foll rd into site. App no suitable lge o'fits. Med, mkd pitch, pt shd; htd wc; chem disp; serviced pitch; shwrs inc; el pnts (3-10A) €2.60-4.50; Indtte; shops 800km; tradsmn; bar; playgrnd; htd, covrd pool 800m; fishing; rv fishing adj; games area; games rm; TV; 75% statics; dogs €3; quiet; CKE/CCI. "Beautiful site; excel facs; level walk to vill." € 18.80 2009*

LARUSCADE *7C2* (4km SW Rural) *45.09274, -0.36742* **Aire Naturelle Le Lac Vert (Saumon), 33620 Laruscade [tel/fax 05 57 68 64 43]** N on N10 fr Bordeaux for 28km, about 1km S of Cavignac, sp off to R. Access over narr bdge. Sm, pt shd; wc; chem disp; shwrs inc; ltd el pnts €2.70 (long cable req); shops 1km; rest, snacks; bar; lake sw; playgrnd; dogs; Eng spkn; quiet but some rlwy noise; CKE/CCI. "Pretty site nr lake; Auberge rest on site; fair NH." 1 May-30 Sep. € 8.00 2009*

LEGE CAP FERRET see Andernos les Bains *7D1*

LELIN LAPUJOLLE see Aire sur l'Adour *8E2*

LEON *8E1* (4km N Rural) *43.90260, -1.31030* **Camping Sunêlia Le Col Vert, Lac de Léon, 40560 Vielle-St Girons [08 90 71 00 01; fax 05 58 42 91 88; contact@colvert.com; www.colvert.com]** Exit N10 junc 12; at Castets-des-Landes turn R onto D42 to Vielle-St Girons. In vill turn L onto D652 twd Léon sp Soustons. In 4km, bef Vielle, take 2nd of 2 RH turns twd Lac de Léon. Site on R at end of rd in 1.5km. V lge, shd; wc; chem disp; mv service pnt; baby facs; serviced pitches; shwrs inc; el pnts (3A) inc; gas; Indtte (inc dryer); shop; tradsmn; rest, snacks; bar; BBQ (gas/elec); playgrnd; 2 pools (1 htd, covrd); wellness centre; paddling pool; sand beach 6km; lake sw, fishing, sailing, canoeing, windsurfing nrby; tennis; fitness rm; wellness cent; archery; horseriding; cycle hire; wifi; entmnt; games/TV rm; 60% statics; dogs €4.70; no c'van/m'van over 6.50m; poss cr; adv bkg; poss noisy (nightclub); ccard acc; red low ssn/long stay; CKE/CCI. "Lakeside site in pine forest; some pitches 800m fr facs; ideal for children & teenagers; daily mkt in Léon in ssn; excel location." ♦ 12 Apr-20 Sep. € 57.40 (CChq acc) SBS - A08 2013*

See advertisement

LEON *8E1* (1.5km NW Rural) *43.88528, -1.31510* **Camping Lou Puntaou, 1315 Route du Lac, 40550 Léon [05 58 48 74 30; fax 05 58 48 70 42; reception@loupuntaou.com; www.louputaou.com]** Site sp fr D142 on Etang de Léon. V lge, mkd pitch, pt shd; wc; chem disp; mv service pnt; shwrs inc; el pnts (15A) inc; Indtte; supmkt; rest 100m; snacks; bar; playgrnd; 2 pools (1 htd, covrd); paddling pool; waterslide; jacuzzi; lake sw 100m; sand beach 5km; tennis; watersports; games area; cycle hire; fitness rm; cash machine; entmnt; 20% statics; dogs €4; adv bkg; quiet. "Excel sports facs; lovely location." ♦ 3 Apr-4 Oct. € 35.00 2009*

LEON *8E1* (9km NW Coastal) *43.90830, -1.36380* **Domaine Naturiste Arna (Naturist), Arnaoutchot, 5006 Route de Pichelèbe, 40560 Vielle-St Girons [05 58 49 11 11; fax 05 58 48 57 12; contact@arna.com; www.arna.com]** Fr St Girons turn R onto D328 at Vielle sp Pichelèbe. Site in 5km on R. Lge, pt sl, shd; wc (some cont); chem disp; mv service pnt; baby facs; shwrs inc; Arna Forme Spa; el pnts (3-6A) €4.50-6.10 inc; gas; Indtte (inc dryer); shop; rest, snacks; bar; BBQ (gas/elec); playgrnd; 2 pools (1 htd covrd); spa centre; paddling pool; waterslide; sand beach adj; lake adj; watersports 5km; tennis; cycle hire; golf nr; archery; games area; wifi; entmnt; games/TV rm; many statics (sep area); dogs €3.50; no c'vans/m'vans over 6.50m; Eng spkn; adv bkg; quiet; ccard acc; red long stay/low ssn. "Excel site in pine forest; some pitches soft sand; clean san facs, ltd low ssn; excel long stay site; access lge o'fits poss diff due trees; vg beach; daily mkt in Léon in ssn." ♦ 9 Apr-25 Sep. € 40.00 (CChq acc) 2011*

LESCAR see Pau *8F2*

LESCUN *8G2* (1.5km SW Rural) *42.92805, -0.64147* **Camp Municipal Le Lauzart, 64490 Lescun [tel/fax 05 59 34 51 77; campinglauzart@wanadoo.fr; www.tourisme-aquitaine.fr]** Turn L (W) off N134 8km N of Urdos on D339 sp Lescun & foll camping sp for 5km - rd gd but steep with hairpins; foll Camping sp to fork L - do not ent Lescun vill, v narr & steep, unsuitable for c'vans. Sm, mkd pitch, terr, pt shd; htd wc; chem disp; mv service pnt; shwrs inc; el pnts (10A) €2.80; gas; Indtte; shop; rest & bar nr; dogs €0.80; adv bkg; quiet. "Mountain views; basic san facs, poss stretched high ssn; gd walks; vg." ♦ 1 May-30 Sep. € 12.30 2010*

LESPERON *8E1* (4km SW Rural) *43.96657, -1.12940* **FFCC Parc de Couchoy, Route de Linxe, 40260 Lesperon [tel/fax 05 58 89 60 15; info@parcdecouchoy.com; www.parcdecouchoy.com]** Exit N10 junc 13 to D41 sp Lesperon; in 1km turn L, thro vill of Lesperon; L at junc onto D331; bottom of hill turn R & immed L; site on R in 3km dir Linxe. Med, mkd pitch, pt shd; wc; chem disp; child/baby facs; shwrs inc; el pnts (6A) €3; gas; Indtte; shops 3km; tradsmn; snacks; bar; playgrnd; pool; sand beach 8km; lake sw 5km; 10% statics; dogs €1; phone; poss cr; adv bkg; quiet; ccard acc high ssn; 10% red long stay; CKE/CCI. "Lovely but isolated site on edge of wine country; gd facs on lakes for sailing, windsurfing; British owners; clean san facs; vg." 1 Jun-15 Sep. € 22.00 2009*

LEVIGNAC DE GUYENNE see Miramont de Guyenne *7D2*

LIMEUIL see Bugue, Le *7C3*

LINXE *8E1* (1km N Rural) *43.93203, -1.25770* **Camp Municipal Le Grandjean, 190 Route de Mixe, 40260 Linxe [05 58 42 90 00; fax 05 58 42 94 67; camping.grandjean@wanadoo.fr]** Exit N10 junc 12 dir Castets; take D42 to Linxe; turn R & R into site. Site well sp at N of Linxe cent. Med, mkd pitch, pt shd; wc, chem disp; baby facs; shwrs inc; el pnts (10A) inc; Indtte; supmkt 5km; rest, snacks, bar 1km; playgrnd; cycle hire, tennis 1km; dogs; Eng spkn; adv bkg; quiet. "Gd, quiet site; friendly warden; immac facs." End Jun-mid Sep. € 18.45 2010*

LISLE *7C3* (6km SW Rural) *45.25731, 0.49573* **Camp Municipal Le Pré Sec, 24350 Tocane-St Apre [05 53 90 40 60 or 05 53 90 70 29; fax 05 53 90 25 03; commune-de-tocane-st-apre@orange.fr; www.campingdupresec.com]** Fr Ribérac E on D710 sp Brantôme. Fr E or W at Tocane St Apre, take bypass rd at rndabt. Site sp at both rndabts - distance 500m. Site is on N side of D710 (fr Riberac dir, there is a gab bet cent reservation to turn L.) Ent thro lge car park for Tocan Sports, barrier to site 100m back. Med, hdg pitch, shd; wc; chem disp; mv service pnt; baby facs; shwrs; el pnts (6-10A) €1.80; mv service pnt; shops in vill; BBQ; playgrnd; wifi; 10% statics; dogs; phone; bus 200m; twin axles; poss cr; Eng spkn; adv bkg; quiet; CKE/CCI. "Gd; canoeing nrby on Rv Dronne." ♦ ltd 2 May-30 Sep. € 9.00 2014*

LIT ET MIXE *8E1* (8km W Coastal) *44.03861, -1.33477* **Camp Municipal de la Plage du Cap de l'Homy, Ave de l'Océan, 40170 Lit-et-Mixe [05 58 42 83 47; fax 05 58 42 49 79; contact@camping-cap.com; www.camping-cap.com]** S fr Mimizan on D652. In Lit-et-Mixe R on D88 to Cap de l'Homy Plage. Site on R when rd becomes 1-way. Lge, hdg/mkd pitch, pt sl, shd; wc (some cont); chem disp; mv service pnt; shwrs inc; el pnts (10A) €6.90 (poss rev pol); Indtte; shop, rest high ssn; playgrnd; beach 300m; surfing; wifi; dogs €2.80; poss cr; quiet. "Popular site, adv bkg rec high ssn; site in pine woods on sandy soil; gd for beach holiday; gd walks; interesting flora & fauna; Aire de Service for m'vans at ent; vg." 1 May-30 Sep. € 18.70 2011*

⊞ **LOUVIE JUZON** *8F2* (1km E Rural) *43.08940, -0.41019* **FFCC Camping Le Rey, Quartier Listo, Route de Lourdes, 64260 Louvie-Juzon [05 59 05 78 52; fax 05 59 05 78 97; nadia@camping-pyrenees-ossau.com; www.camping-pyrenees-ossau.com]** Site on L at top of hill E fr Louvie; v steep app. Sm, mkd pitch, pt sl, pt shd; htd wc; chem disp; shwrs inc; el pnts (6A) €3.30; Indtte; shops 1km; tradsmn; rest 1km; snacks; bar; playgrnd; sm pool; watersports, fishing nr; games area; entmnt; 50% statics; dogs €2; phone; site clsd last 2 weeks Nov & last 2 weeks Jan; adv bkg; quiet; CKE/CCI. "Fascinating area; chateau nr." ♦ € 13.25 2009*

LOUVIE JUZON *8F2* (500m S Rural) *43.08277, -0.42050* **Camp Municipal de la Vallée d'Ossau, Route d'Ossau, 64260 Izeste [05 59 05 68 67; fax 05 59 05 73 82; mairie.izeste@9business.fr]** Site 300m fr rv bdge in Louvie-Juzon, on L heading S on D934. Sm, mkd pitch, shd; wc; shwrs inc; el pnts (6A) inc; shops, rest 300m; no statics; quiet; adv bkg; CKE/CCI. "Vg, attractive site adj fast-flowing rv & weir; ideal for access to Vallée d'Ossau; some rd & water noise." 1 Jun-15 Sep. € 14.60 2014*

⊞ **LOUVIE JUZON** *8F2* (6km NW Rural) *43.15180, -0.44499* **FFCC Aire Naturelle Les Jardins d'Ossau (Dunan), 2 Chemin de Départ, 64250 Buzy [05 59 21 05 71; dunan.pascal@wanadoo.fr]** S fr Pau on N134; approx 12 km past Gan sp Camping; after rest at Belair turn L onto D34 sp Buzy; in 2km turn L after going under 1st rlwy bdge. Site on R, sp. Sm, pt shd; wc; chem disp (wc); shwrs inc; el pnts (6A) €2.10 (long lead poss req); Indtte; games area; games rm; dogs €0.50; Eng spkn; adv bkg; quiet; no ccard acc; CKE/CCI. "Peaceful site on fruit farm with views; san facs basic but clean; easy access; helpful owners; NH only to/fr Spain." ♦ ltd € 11.40 2009*

MARCILLAC ST QUENTIN see Sarlat la Canéda *7C3*

MAREUIL *7B2* (5km N Rural) *45.49504, 0.44860* **FFCC Camping Les Graulges, Le Bourg, 24340 Les Graulges [tel/fax 05 53 60 74 73; info@lesgraulges.com; www.lesgraulges.com]** Fr D939 at Mareuil turn L onto D708 & foll sp to Les Graulges in 5km. Sm, mkd pitch, pt sl, terr, pt shd; wc; chem disp (wc); baby facs; shwrs inc; el pnts (6A) €3.50; Indtte; tradsmn; rest, snacks; bar; BBQ; playgrnd; pool; lake fishing; some statics; dogs €2; phone 300m; poss cr; Eng spkn; adv bkg; quiet; red 7+ days. "Tranquil site in forested area; ideal touring base; friendly Dutch owners; excel rest; Not suitable for elderly; pool dirty; lge dog lives on site (2012)." ♦ 1 Apr-15 Sep. € 20.50 2012*

MAREUIL *7B2* (4km SE Rural) *45.44481, 0.50474* **Camping L'Etang Bleu, 24340 Vieux-Mareuil [05 53 60 92 70; fax 05 53 56 66 66; marc@letangbleu.com; www.letangbleu.com]** On D939 Angoulême-Périgueux rd, after 5km turn L cent of Vieux-Mareuil onto D93, foll camping sp to site in 2km. Narr app thro vill. Lge, hdg/mkd pitch, pt shd; wc; chem disp; mv service pnt; baby facs; fam bthrm; shwrs inc; el pnts (10A) €4.75 (poss rev pol); gas; Indtte; shop; tradsmn; rest, snacks; bar; BBQ; playgrnd; pool; paddling pool; lake fishing 500m; TV; entmnt; 10% statics; dogs €3; adv bkg; ccard acc; red low ssn; CKE/CCI. "Pleasant site in unspoilt countryside; lge pitches, but narr site rds; access diff lge o'fits without mover; friendly British owners; gd san facs, ltd low ssn; gd walking/cycling area; excel." ♦ 01 Apr-20 Oct. € 30.50 2013*

MAREUIL *7B2* (6km SE Rural) *45.42465, 0.53012* **Camping La Charrue, Les Chambarrières, 24340 Vieux-Mareuil [tel/fax 05 53 56 65 59; info@la-charruefrance.com; www.la-charruefrance.com]** SE fr Angoulême on D939 sp Périgueux to Mareuil. Fr Mareuil stay on D939 twds Brantôme, thro Vieux-Mareuil then in 2km site immed on L after passing a lge lay-by on R with white stone chippings. Awkward turn. Sm, mkd pitch, pt shd; wc; chem disp; shwrs inc; el pnts (4A) €3; gas 3km; Indtte; shop 2km; tradsmn; rest & bar 500m; snacks; BBQ; playgrnd; pool; sand beach, lakes & watersports nr; fishing 3km; cycle hire; golf nr; dogs (low ssn only); adv bkg (full payment req); some rd noise; red long stay/low ssn; CKE/CCI. "CL-type site in Regional Park; friendly, helpful British owners; immac facs; gd touring base for beautiful area; B&B & gites avail; excel." 1 May-31 Oct. € 13.00 2009*

MAREUIL *7B2* (500m SW Rural) *45.44680, 0.45153* **Camp Municipal Vieux Moulin, Rue des Martyrs/Rue Arnaud de Mareuil; 24340 Mareuil [05 53 60 91 20 (Mairie) or 05 53 60 99 80; fax 05 53 60 51 72; mariemareuil@wanadoo.fr]** Fr town cent take D708 (sp Ribérac); after 300m turn L on D99 (sp 'La Tour Blanche'); after 100m turn L opp lge school, site 100m ahead. Well sp all dirs. Sm, mkd pitch, shd; wc; shwrs; el pnts (6A) €1.70; shop 500m; rest, snacks, bar 400m; playgrnd; rv 1km; dogs €0.50; adv bkg; quiet. "Clean, tidy site; friendly warden; ltd, well-kept facs; lovely walk by stream to vill; interesting chateau; vg, immac site." ♦ 1 Jun-30 Sep. € 8.00 2012*

MARQUAY see Eyzies de Tayac, Les *7C3*

MAULEON LICHARRE *8F1* (2km S Rural) *43.20795, -0.89695* **Camping Uhaitza Le Saison, Route de Libarrenx, 64130 Mauléon-Licharre [05 59 28 18 79; fax 05 59 28 06 23; camping.uhaitza@wanadoo.fr; www.camping-uhaitza.com]** Fr Sauveterre take D936 twd Oloron. In 500m turn R onto D23 to Mauléon, then take D918 dir Tardets, site on R. Sm, hdg/mkd pitch, pt sl, pt shd; wc; chem disp; mv service pnt; baby facs; shwrs inc; el pnts (4-10A) €2.65-4.90; Indtte (inc dryer); shops 1.5km; tradsmn; snacks; bar high ssn; BBQ; playgrnd; pool 2km; rv fishing adj; tennis 2km; games rm; some statics; dogs €2; adv bkg; quiet; CKE/CCI. "Lovely, quiet site beside rv - steep access; friendly owners." ♦ 1 Mar-15 Nov. € 13.50 2010*

MENESPLET see Montpon Ménestérol *7C2*

MESSANGES *8E1* (2km S Coastal) *43.80070, -1.39220* **Camping La Côte, Route de Vieux-Boucau, 40660 Messanges [05 58 48 94 94; fax 05 58 48 94 44; info@campinglacote.com; www.campinglacote.com]** On D652 2km S of Messanges. Med, pt shd; wc; chem disp; mv service pnt; serviced pitches; shwrs inc; el pnts (6-10A) €3.90-4.90; Indtte; sm shop; supmkt 1km; tradsmn; snacks; playgrnd; pool complex; paddling pool; sand beach 1km; horseriding 300m; golf 2km; cycle hire; wifi; 5% statics; dogs €2.20; phone; adv bkg; Eng spkn; quiet but poss early noise fr builders yard adj; red low ssn; CKE/CCI. "Peaceful, well-kept site adj pine woods; spacious pitches; easy access; helpful staff; clean san facs; vg pool; gd access to beaches; gd cycle tracks; excel." ♦ 1 Apr-30 Sep. € 20.50 2011*

MESSANGES *8E1* (2km SW Coastal) *43.79790, -1.40135* **Airotel Camping Le Vieux Port, Plage Sud, 40660 Messanges [01 76 76 70 00; fax 05 58 48 01 69; contact@levieuxport.com; www.levieuxport.com]** Fr S take D652 past Vieux-Boucau; site sp. Turn W at Super U rndabt. V lge, mkd pitch, hdstg, shd; wc; chem disp; mv service pnt; baby facs; fam bthrm; shwrs inc; el pnts (6-8A) €8.50; gas; Indtte (inc dryer); shop; supmkt 500m; tradsmn; rest, snacks; bar; BBQ; playgrnd; htd, pt cvrd pool + pool complex; paddling pool; waterslides; dir access to sand beach 400m; tennis; games area; cycle hire; horseriding; quadbikes; wifi; entmnt; TV; 10% statics; dogs €5.50; Eng spkn; adv bkg; poss cr; quiet; ccard acc; red low ssn/long stay; CKE/CCI. "V pleasant, clean site; superb, v lge pool complex; excel touring base." ♦ 2 Apr-25 Sep. € 48.50 (CChq acc) 2010*

MEZOS *8E1* (1km SE Rural) *44.07980, -1.16090* **Le Village Tropical Sen Yan, 40170 Mézos [05 58 42 60 05; fax 05 58 42 64 56; reception@sen-yan.com; www.sen-yan.com]** Fr Bordeaux on N10 in 100km at Laharie turn W onto D38 dir Mimizan; in 12km turn L onto D63 to Mézos; turn L at mini-rndabt; site on L in approx 2km. Site 1.5km fr D63/D38 junc NE of Mézos. Lge, hdg/mkd pitch, shd; wc (some cont); chem disp; baby facs; sauna; shwrs inc; el pnts (6A) inc; gas; Indtte (inc dryer); shop; rest, snacks; bar; BBQ (gas only); playgrnd; 2 pools (1 htd & covrd); paddling pool; waterslides; jacuzzi; sand beach 12km; rv adj; fishing; canoe hire 1km; watersports 15km; tennis; cycle hire; many sports & games; fitness cent; wifi; entmnt; games/TV (cab/sat) rm; 80% statics; dogs €5; no c'vans/m'vans over 8m; phone; Eng spkn; adv bkg; quiet; ccard acc; red low ssn;CKE/CCI. "Attractive, restful site; many plants, inc banana trees; modern, clean san facs; excel facs for families; mkt Mimizan Fri & Morcenx Wed." ♦ 1 Jun-9 Sep. € 47.00 2012*

MIMIZAN *7D1* (2km N Rural) *44.21997, -1.22968* **Camping du Lac, Ave de Woolsack, 40200 Mimizan [05 58 09 01 21; fax 05 58 09 43 06; lac@mimizan-camping.com; www.mimizan-camping.com]** Fr Mimizan N on D87, site on R. Lge, mkd pitch; pt shd; sandy; wc; chem disp; mv service pnt; baby facs; shwrs inc; el pnts (3A) inc; gas; Indtte; shop; (rest, snacks; bar; high ssn only); BBQ; playgrnd; sand beach 6km; lake adj - no sw; boating; fishing; entmnt; some statics; dogs €1.70; poss cr; adv bkg; quiet; red low ssn. "Nice site in lovely location; o'night area for m'vans; rec." ♦ ltd 27 Apr-20 Sep. € 20.00 2012*

MIMIZAN *7D1* (3km E Rural) *44.22296, -1.19445* **Camping Aurilandes, 1001 Promenade de l'Etang, 40200 Aureilhan [05 58 09 10 88 or 05 46 55 10 01; fax 05 46 55 10 00; www.village-center.com]** Fr N10 S of Bordeaux take D626 W fr Labouheyre twds Mimizan. Site 1km fr D626 by Lake Aureilhan. V lge, mkd pitch, pt shd; wc; mv service pnt; sauna; shwrs inc; el pnts (6-10A) inc; Indtte; shop; tradsmn; rest; playgrnd; htd pool complex; paddling pool; spa; sand beach 10km; dir access to lake; watersports; tennis; games rm; entmnt; statics; dogs €3; Eng spkn; adv bkg; ccard acc; quiet; ccard acc. ♦ 27 Apr - 09 Sep. € 44.00 (CChq acc) 2013*

MIMIZAN PLAGE *7D1* (700m E Coastal) *44.21629, -1.28584* **Camping de la Plage, Blvd d'Atlantique, 40200 Mimizan-Plage [05 58 09 00 32; fax 05 58 09 44 94; contact@mimizan-camping.com; www.mimizan-camping.com]** Turn off N10 at Labouheyre on D626 to Mimizan (28km). Approx 5km after Mimizan turn R. Site in approx 500m. V lge, pt sl, shd; wc; mv service pnt; baby facs; shwrs; el pnts (10A) inc; lndtte (inc dryer); shop; BBQ; playgrnd; sand beach 850m; games area; wifi; entmnt; 20% statics; dogs €1.80; poss cr; no adv bkg; noisy. "Gd facs; town nrby." ♦ 2 Apr-26 Sep. € 20.50 2010*

MIMIZAN PLAGE *7D1* (3km E Coastal) *44.20420, -1.2908* **Club Marina-Landes, Rue Marina, 40202 Mimizan-Plage-Sud [05 58 09 12 66; fax 05 58 09 16 40; contact@clubmarina.com; www.marinalandes.com]** Turn R off N10 at Labouheyre onto D626 to Mimizan (28km). Approx 5km fr Mimizan-Plage turn L at Camping Marina sp on dual c'way. Site sp on S bank of rv. V lge, hdg pitch, hdstg, pt shd; wc; chem disp; mv service pnt; baby facs; shwrs inc; el pnts (10A) €7; gas; lndtte; ice; shop; rest, snacks; bar; BBQ; playgrnd; 2 pools (1 htd, covrd); paddling pool; waterslide; sand beach 500m; tennis; horseriding; games area; cycle hire; games rm; fitness rm; golf 7km; wifi; entmnt; TV rm; some statics; dogs €5; poss cr; Eng spkn; adv bkg; ccard acc; quiet; red CKE/CCI. "Excursions to Dax, Biarritz & Bordeaux areas; excel leisure facs; vg." ♦ 1 May-12 Sep. € 42.00 (3 persons) 2010*

MIOS see Audenge *7D1*

MIRAMBEAU *7C2* (8km S Rural) *45.31430, -0.60290* **Camping Chez Gendron, 33820 St Palais [tel/fax 05 57 32 96 47; info@chezgendron.com; www.chezgendron.com]** N fr Blaye on N137; turn to St Palais, past church 1km; turn L twd St Ciers. Site sp R down narr lane. Or N fr Bordeaux on A10 exit juncs 37 or 38 onto N137 to St Palais & as above. Sm, mkd pitch, terr, pt sl, pt shd; htd wc; chem disp; shwrs; fam bthrm; el pnts (6A) inc; lndtte; shops 3km; tradsmn; rest, snacks; bar; BBQ; playgrnd; pool; paddling pool; games area; tennis 3km; games rm; wifi; TV; dogs free; phone; Eng spkn; adv bkg rec; quiet; red low ssn; CKE/CCI. "Peaceful & relaxed site in vineyards; lovely ambience; friendly, helpful Dutch owners; sep car park high ssn; superb san facs; ltd facs low ssn; pitches nr bar/recep poss noisy till late peak ssn; poss waterlogged after heavy rain; chem disp poor; excel Sun mkt." ♦ 1 Mar-31 Oct. € 25.50 2014*

⊞ **MIRAMONT DE GUYENNE** *7D2* (13km W Rural) *44.62918, 0.22126* **Camping Parc St Vincent, 47120 Lévignac-de-Guyenne [05 53 83 75 17 or 01425 275080 (UK); sara.batchelor777@orange.fr; www.psv47.com]** Fr Miramont take D668 to Allemans-du-Dropt, then D211. At junc D708 turn S to Lévignac, site sp. Fr Marmande N on D708 sp St Foy & Duras. Turn E at Lévignac church to further green site sp on D228. Sm, hdstg, pt shd; wc; chem disp; mv service pnt; shwrs inc; el pnts (5A) €2; gas; lndtte; shops 2.5km; tradsmn; rest, snacks; BBQ; playgrnd; pool; lake sw 6km; entmnt; TV rm; 90% statics; no dogs; phone; adv bkg; quiet; red low ssn; CKE/CCI. "Peaceful site; British owners make visitors welcome; gd NH or longer to/fr Spain." ♦ € 13.00 2010*

MIRAMONT DE GUYENNE *7D2* (7km NW Rural) *44.62877, 0.29135* **Camp Municipal Le Dropt, Rue du Pont, 47800 Allemans-du-Dropt [05 53 20 25 59 or 05 53 20 23 37 (Mairie); fax 05 53 20 68 91]** Fr D668 site well sp in vill. Sm, shd; wc (some cont); chem disp (wc); shwrs inc; el pnts (20A) €2; shop 400m; rest, snacks & bar 400m; playgrnd; canoeing, kayaking; quiet, but poss noise fr canoe/kayak pnt on site; CKE/CCI. "Attractive site on opp side of Rv Dropt to vill; friendly warden; ltd pitches for c'vans & lge o'fits due trees & o'hanging branches; basic but clean facs; excel." 1 Apr-15 Oct. € 7.00 2014*

MOLIERES (DORDOGNE) see Lalinde *7C3*

MOLIETS ET MAA *8E1* (2km W Coastal) *43.85166, -1.38375* **Camping Les Cigales, Ave de l'Océan, 40660 Moliets-Plage [05 58 48 51 18; fax 05 58 48 53 27; reception@camping-les-cigales.fr; www.camping-les-cigales.fr]** In Moliets-et-Maa, turn W for Moliets-Plage, site on R in vill. Lge, pt sl, shd; wc; chem disp; mv service pnt; shwrs inc; el pnts (5A) €3.50; lndtte; shop; tradsmn; rest, snacks; bar; BBQ; playgrnd; sand beach 300m; games area; TV; many statics; dogs €2; adv bkg; quiet; ccard acc; CKE/CCI. "Site in pine wood - sandy soil; narr access tracks; excel beach & surfing; many shops, rests 100m; gd forest walk to N." 1 Apr-30 Sep. € 36.00 2014*

MOLIETS ET MAA *8E1* (2km W Coastal) *43.85210, -1.38730* **Camping St Martin, Ave de l'Océan 40660 Moliets-Plage [05 58 48 52 30; fax 05 58 48 50 73; contact@camping-saint-martin.fr; www.camping-saint-martin.fr]** On N10 exit for Léon, Moliets-et-Maa. At Moliets foll sp to Moliets-Plage. Camp site after Les Cigales, by beach. V lge, hdg/mkd pitch, pt sl, terr, pt shd; htd wc (some cont); chem disp; some serviced pitches; baby facs; sauna; shwrs inc; el pnts (10A) €5.30; gas; Indtte; shops; supmkt; rests; snacks; bar; playgrnd; 3 pools (1 htd, covrd); paddling pool; jacuzzi; dir access to sand beach 300m; rv 250m; watersports; tennis, golf nr; games area; cycle paths; entmnt; TV rm; dogs €5 (free low ssn); Eng spkn; adv bkg rec high ssn (fee); quiet; ccard acc; red low ssn; CKE/CCI. "Excel family site; vg san facs; gd for teenagers; gd cycling, walking." 8 Apr-1 Nov. € 43.30 2011*

See advert on previous page

MONBALEN *7D3* (2.2km NE Rural) *44.32142, 0.74084* **Ferme Equestre Crinière au Vent, Bouillon, 47340 Monbalen [05 53 95 18 61 or 06 70 68 79 92 (mob); www.criniereauvent.com]** Site 15km N Agen & 13km S Villeneuve-sur-Lot. Fr Agen, take N21 N dir Villeneuve-sur-Lot. In approx 15km turn R onto D110 sp Laroque-Timbaut & foll 'Camping' sp. Fr Villeneuve-sur-Lot, take N21 S dir Agen. In approx 10km turn L onto D110 sp Laroque-Timbaut & foll 'Camping' sp. Sm, pt sl, shd; wc (some cont); chem disp; shwrs inc; el pnts (10A) €2.20; Indry rm; tradsmn; bar (soft drinks only); horseriding; no statics; dogs €1; little Eng spkn; no ccard acc; CKE/CCI. "Owner v pleasant; horseriding for all ages on site; vg." ♦ 15 Apr-30 Sep. € 8.20 2009*

"I need an on-site restaurant"

We do our best to make sure site information is correct, but it is always best to check any must-have facilities are still available or will be open during your visit.

MONPAZIER *7D3* (3km SW Rural) *44.65875, 0.87925* **Camping Moulin de David, Route de Villeréal, 24540 Gaugeac-Monpazier [05 53 22 65 25 or 04 99 57 20 25; fax 05 53 23 99 76; contact@moulindedavid.com; www.moulindedavid.com]** Fr Monpazier, take D2 SW twd Villeréal, site sp on L after 3km. Narr app rds. Lge, hdg/mkd pitch, pt shd; htd wc; chem disp; mv service pnt; serviced pitches; baby facs; shwrs inc; el pnts (10A) inc gas; Indtte; shop; tradsmn; rest, snacks; bar; BBQ €8.; playgrnd; pool; paddling pool; lake sw & waterslide high ssn; fishing adj; tennis; games area; wifi; games/TV rm; cycle hire; archery; internet; entmnt; many statics; dogs €3; poss cr; Eng spkn; adv bkg; quiet; ccard acc; red low ssn; CKE/CCI. "Charming site nr lovely town; welcoming, helpful owners; excel facs, ltd low ssn; poss mosquitoes nr rv thro site; mkt Thu Monpazier; highly rec; v rural; superb rest." ♦ 30 Mar-30 Sep. € 34.80 2014*

MONTIGNAC *7C3* (7km E Rural) *45.05375, 1.23980* **Yelloh! Village Lascaux Vacances, Route des Malénies, 24290 St Amand-de-Coly [05 53 50 81 57; fax 05 53 50 76 26; mail@campinglascauxvacances.com; www.campinglascauxvacances.com / www.yellohvillage.co.uk]** Exit A89 junc 17 (Peyrignac) SE onto D6089 to Le Lardin-St Lazare. Join D62 S to Coly & then foll sp to Saint Amand-de-Coly. Site well sp. Med, hdg/mkd pitch, pt shd; wc; chem disp; mv service pnt; sauna; baby facs; shwrs; el pnts (10A) inc; Indtte; supmkt; rest, snacks; bar; BBQ; playgrnd; pool complex; paddling pool; waterslides; fishing nr; cycle hire nr; games area; games rm; wifi; entmnt; TV; 60% statics; dogs €4; phone; adv bkg; quiet; ccard acc; red long stay/low ssn. "Excel, peaceful, renovated site in superb location; warm welcome; lge pitches; excel touring base." ♦ 15 Apr-11 Sep. € 33.00 2011*

MONTIGNAC *7C3* (6.5km SE Rural) *45.07211, 1.23431* **Camping La Tournerie Ferme, La Tournerie, 24290 Aubas [05 53 51 04 16; la-tournerie@orange.fr; www.la-tournerie.com]** Fr Montignac on D704 dir Sarlat-la-Canéda; in 5.5km turn L onto C1 sp St Amand-de-Coly; in 1.6km at x-rds turn L sp Malardel & Drouille; in 400m at Y-junc foll rd to R sp Manardel & La Genèbre; cont on this rd ignoring minor rds; in 1.6km at elongated junc take rd to R of post box; immed after passing Le Treuil farm on R turn R at x-rds La Tournerie. Site opp farm. Sm, terr, hdstg, terr, sl, unshd; htd wc; chem disp; shwrs inc; el pnts (6A) inc; Indtte; shop 6.5km; rest, bar 2.5km; BBQ; dogs; adv bkg ess. "Lovely, tranquil site; adults only; lge pitches with beautiful views; dogs; friendly, helpful British owners (CC members); excel san facs; twin-axles OK; request detailed dirs or see website - Sat Nav not rec; excel touring base; excel site." ♦ ltd 1 Mar-30 Nov. € 23.00 2013*

MONTIGNAC *7C3* (500m S Urban) *45.05980, 1.15860* **Camping Le Moulin du Bleufond, Ave Aristide Briand, 24290 Montignac [05 53 51 83 95; fax 05 53 51 19 92; info@bleufond.com; www.bleufond.com]** S on D704, cross bdge in town & turn R immed of rv on D65; site sp in 500m nr stadium, adj Rv Vezere. Med, hdg pitch, pt shd; wc (some cont); shwrs inc; el pnts (10A) €3.50; shops 500m; rest, snacks; bar; BBQ; htd pool high ssn; paddling pool; tennis adj; fishing; wifi; entmnt; dogs €2; poss cr; quiet; ccard acc; red low ssn. "Pleasant site; pleasant, helpful owners; facs excel; poss diff lge o'fits due trees; conv Lascaux caves & town; gd walking area; lovely site." 1 Apr-15 Oct. € 31.40 2012*

MONTIGNAC *7C3* (7km S Rural) *45.01765, 1.18811* **FFCC Camping La Fage, 24290 La Chapelle-Aubareil [tel/fax 05 53 50 76 50 / 06 87 37 5 891 (Mob); contact@camping-lafage.com; www.camping-lafage.com]** Fr Montignac take D704 twd Sarlat. In approx 7km take 2nd rd L & foll camp sp to site ent thro woods, 1km bef La Chapelle. Med, some hdstg, pt sl, pt shd; wc; mv service pnt; baby facs; shwrs inc; el pnts (10A); Indtte (inc dryer); shop; tradsmn; rest, snacks; bar; BBQ; playgrnd; htd pool; paddling pool; games area; wifi; entmnt; TV; 30% statics; dogs €1.80; adv bkg; red low ssn/CKE/CCI. "Excel site; helpful owners; vg, clean san facs; red facs low ssn; gd rest at auberge in vill; conv Lascaux 2 & other pre-historic sites; gd walking." ♦ 1 May-30 Sep. € 23.60 (CChq acc) 2013*

"Satellite navigation makes touring much easier"

Remember most sat navs don't know if you're towing or in a larger vehicle – always use yours alongside maps and site directions.

MONTIGNAC *7C3* (8km SW Rural) *45.04107, 1.11915* **Camping La Castillonderie, 24290 Thonac [05 53 50 76 79; fax 05 53 51 59 13; castillonderie@wanadoo.fr; www.castillonderie.nl]** Take D706 dir Les Eyzies. At rndabt in Thonac turn R onto D65 sp Fanlac in 1km after x-rd take R, site is sp 1.5km. Narr app rd. Med, hdg/mkd pitch, hdstg, pt sl, pt shd; htd wc; chem disp; mv service pnt; baby facs; fam bthrm; shwrs inc; el pnts (10A) €4; gas 5km; Indtte (inc dryer); sm shop & 2km; tradsmn; rest, snacks; bar; BBQ; playgrnd; pool; paddling pool; canoeing 3km; wifi; entmnt; TV rm; 10% statics; dogs €0.50; phone; Eng spkn; adv bkg; quiet; ccard acc; red low ssn; CKE/CCI. "Peaceful, well-kept site; friendly, helpful Dutch owners;on site lake fishing; canoeing 3km; gd cent for historic visits & walks." ♦ 15 May-15 Sep. € 23.00 2013*

See advertisement

MONTIGNAC *7C3* (9km SW Rural) *45.00178, 1.07155* **Camping Le Paradis, La Reybeyrolle, 24290 St Léon-sur-Vézère [05 53 50 72 64; fax 05 53 50 75 90; le-paradis@perigord.com; www.le-paradis.com]** On W bank of Rv Vézère on D706 Montignac-Les Eyzies rd, 1km fr Le Moustier. D706 poss rough rd. Med, hdg pitch, pt shd; htd wc; chem disp; mv service pnt; baby facs; shwrs inc; el pnts (10A) €3.50; Indtte (inc dryer); shop; tradsmn; rest, snacks; bar; BBQ; playgrnd; 2 htd pools; paddling pool; beach adj; boat hire; rv sw & fishing; tennis; cycle hire; games area; wifi; entmnt; TV rm; 25% statics; dogs €2.50; phone; poss cr; Eng spkn; adv bkg; poss rd noise; ccard acc; red low ssn/long stay; CKE/CCI. "Excel, high standard site in gd location; friendly, conscientious Dutch owners; immac san facs; gd pool, rest & takeaway; vg for families; tropical vegetation around pitches - grnds like a garden; excel, espec low ssn." ♦ 26 Mar-20 Oct. € 28.00 2012*

See advertisement

"There aren't many sites open at this time of year"

If you're travelling outside peak season remember to call ahead to check site opening dates – even if the entry says 'open all year'.

MONTPON MENESTEROL *7C2* (1km N Rural) *45.01280, 0.15828* **Camping La Cigaline, 1 Rue de la Paix, Route de Ribérac, 24700 Montpon-Ménestérol [05 53 80 22 16; contact@lacigaline.fr; www.lacigaline.fr]** Fr Montpon town cent traff lts take D730 N to Ménestérol. Site on L bef bdge beside Rv Isle. Med, hdg/mkd pitch, shd; wc; chem disp; shwrs inc; el pnts (10A) inc; gas 500m; lndtte (inc dryer); shop 800m; rest, snacks; bar; BBQ; playgrnd; lake sw 500m; boat hire; fishing; tennis 200m; cycle hire 500m; leisure park nrby; internet; wifi; 1% statics; dogs €1.50; train 1km; Eng spkn; adv bkg; quiet; ccard acc; red low ssn; CKE/CCI. "Gd touring base for St Emilion region; gd walking, cycling; vg; new young owners (2014); gd food in bar/rest; terrace overlooks rv; site improving." ♦ ltd 12 Apr-30 Sep. € 16.00 2014*

MONTPON MENESTEROL *7C2* (10km SE Rural) *44.94153, 0.21260* **Camping Domaine de Chaudeau (Naturist), 24700 St Géraud-de-Corps [05 53 82 49 64; fax 05 53 81 18 94; chaudeau.naturiste@wanadoo.fr; www.domainedechaudeau.com]** Fr Montpon take D708 S; after 8km turn E on D33 for St Géraud-de-Corps; foll black & white sp Chaudeau. Fr St Foy-la-Grande take D708 N; after 11km on exit St Méard-de-Gurçon turn E & foll sp as above. Med, hdg/mkd pitch, shd; wc; chem disp; shwrs inc; el pnts (5A) €3.90; lndtte; shop; snacks; bar; pool; lake sw; fishing; games area; entmnt; some statics; dogs €2.40; phone; quiet; ccard not acc; red low ssn. "Excel site; INF card req but holiday membership avail; v lge pitches." 1 Apr-30 Sep. € 19.00 2009*

⊞ **MONTPON MENESTEROL** *7C2* (9km W Rural) *44.99857, 0.07228* **Camp'Gite Les Loges, 24700 Ménesplet [05 53 81 84 39; fax 05 53 81 62 74; aquabrite@hotmail.com; www.camp-gite.com]** Fr Montpon-Ménestérol W on D6089. After Ménesplet turn S onto D10 sp Minzac. Turn L after level x-ing, foll sp. Sm, pt hdg pitch, hdstg, pt shd; wc; chem disp; shwrs inc; el pnts (16A) €4; lndtte (inc dryer); shops 2.5km; rest; BBQ; playgrnd; games area; no statics; dogs €2; Eng spkn; adv bkg; quiet; CKE/CCI. "Excel, peaceful site in pleasant countryside; friendly, attentive staff." ♦ € 15.00 2009*

MORCENX *8E1* (7km W Rural) *44.03529, -0.94612* **Aire Naturelle La Réserve (Lemercier), 1870 Ave de l'Océan, 40110 Garrosse [05 58 04 38 12; dlemercier@club-internet.fr; www.camping-lareserve.com]** Exit N10 junc 14 onto D38 dir Morcenx; foll camping sps for 5km; site on L. Sm, pt sl, shd; wc; chem disp (wc); shwrs inc; el pnts (6-10A) €4.50; playgrnd; sm pool; snacks; games area; 25% statics; dogs €1; some Eng spkn; quiet. "Site in pine trees; conv N10; friendly, helpful owners." ♦ 1 Apr-30 Sep. € 9.00 2010*

NAUSSANNES see Beaumont du Périgord *7D3*

NAVARRENX *8F1* (200m S Urban) *43.31988, -0.76143* **Camping Beau Rivage, Allée des Marronniers, 64190 Navarrenx [05 59 66 10 00; beaucamping@free.fr; www.beaucamping.com]** Fr E exit A64 junc 9 at Artix onto D281 dir Mourenx, then Navarrenx. Fr N on D947 thro Orthez to Navarrenx (D947 fr Orthez much improved). Site well sp bet walled (Bastide) town & rv. Med, hdg/mkd pitch, some hdstg, pt sl, terr, pt shd; htd wc; chem disp; mv service pnt; some serviced pitches; baby facs; fam bthrm; shwrs inc; el pnts (8-10A) inc; lndtte (inc dryer); shop, rest & bar 300m; snacks; BBQ; playgrnd; pool; rv fishing; rafting; tennis; cycle hire in town; games rm; wifi; 15% statics; dogs €1.50; no c'vans/m'vans over 9m high ssn; phone; Eng spkn; adv bkg; quiet; ccard acc; red low ssn; CKE/CCI. "Lovely, peaceful, well-run site; nr interesting walled town; helpful, friendly, British owners; clean san facs; gd pool; gd area for walking, cycling; conv local shops & rests; mkt Wed; rec; outstanding." ♦ 29 Mar-11 Oct. € 35.00 SBS - D26 2014*

NAY *8F2* (2km N Rural) *43.20027, -0.25722* **Camping Les Ô Kiri, Ave du Lac, 64800 Baudreix [05 59 92 97 73; fax 05 59 13 93 77; les-okiri@wanadoo.fr; www.lesokiri.net]** Exit A64 junc 10 onto Pau ring rd D317 S, then D938 dir Nay & Lourdes. Exit sp Baudreix & in 2km turn R at rndabt & foll sp to lake & site. Med, hdg/mkd pitch, pt shd; htd wc; chem disp; mv service pnt; shwrs inc; el pnts (6-10A) €4-5.50; lndtte (inc dryer); shop; tradsmn; supmkt 4km; rest, snacks; bar; BBQ; playgrnd; lake sw complex; waterslides; tennis; cycle hire; wifi; 50% statics; dogs €2; adv bkg; quiet; ccard acc. "Conv Biarritz, N Spain & Pyrennees; booking ess; on arr use carpark for recep; excel rest; superb lake facs; picturesque; basic but ok san facs, poss stretched if site full." ♦ 1 Apr-30 Sep. € 19.50 (CChq acc) 2014*

NERAC *8E2* (5.7 km SW Rural) *44.09948, 0.31028* **Aire Naturelle Les Contes d'Albret, 47600 Nérac [05 53 65 18 73; fax 05 53 97 18 62; lescontesdalbret@orange.fr; www.albret.com]** Exit A62 junc 7 onto D931 to Laplume. Then turn W onto D15 & D656 to Nérac. Cont on D656 dir Mézin & foll site sp to end of rd in 3km. Sm, pt sl, pt shd; htd wc; baby facs; shwrs inc; el pnts (6A) €2; farm shop, other shops in vill; rest; playgrnd; pool; kayaking; Eng spkn; adv bkg; quiet. "Vg, peaceful, CL-type site; excel views; glorious garden." 1 May-30 Sep. € 13.00 2014*

NEUVIC (DORDOGNE) *7C3* (800m N Rural) *45.10571, 0.46930* **Camping Le Plein Air Neuvicois, Ave de Planèze, 24190 Neuvic [05 53 81 50 77; fax 05 53 80 46 50; camping.le.plein.air.neuvicois@cegetel.net; www.campingneuvicdordogne.com]** On D6089, 26km SW fr Périgueux. After 24km, turn R sp Neuvic. Site clearly sp thro vill, by rv after bdge. Med, pt shd; htf wc; baby facs; shwrs inc; el pnts (6-10A) €3-4; lndtte; shop; tradsmn; rests 800m; snacks; bar; pool; fishing; tennis; games rm; some statics; dogs €0.50; phone; adv bkg; quiet; red low ssn/long stay. "Beautiful location; lge pitches; charming owners; clean modern san facs; vg." 1 Jun-15 Sep. € 12.00 2010*

NONTRON *7B3* (7km NE Rural) *45.56185, 0.71979* **Camping Manzac Ferme, Manzac, 24300 Augignac [05 53 56 31 34; info@manzac-ferme.com; www.manzac-ferme.com]** Fr Nontron take D675 N dir Rochechouart & after 7km on ent Augignac turn R sp Abjat-sur-Bandiat then immed R sp Manzac. Site on R 3.5km. Sm, mkd pitch, pt hdstg, sl, pt shd; htd wc; chem disp; shwrs inc; el pnts (6A) inc; gas 6km; shops, rest, bar 5km; BBQ; rv fishing; dogs by arrangement; adv bkg; quiet. "Superb, peaceful, well-kept CL-type site; adults only; helpful British owners; excel san facs; phone ahead in winter; ideal for birdwatching & wildlife; highly rec." ♦ ltd Mar-Oct. € 24.00 2012*

NONTRON *7B3* (11km NE Rural) *45.55138, 0.79472* **Kawan Village Le Château Le Verdoyer, 24470 Champs-Romain [05 53 56 94 64; fax 05 53 56 38 70; chateau@verdoyer.fr; www.verdoyer.fr]** Fr Limoges on N21 twd Périgueux. At Châlus turn R sp Nontron (D6 bis-D85). After approx 18km turn L twd Champs Romain on D96 to site on L in 2km. Lge, terr, pt shd; wc; chem disp; mv service pnt; baby facs; shwrs inc; el pnts (5-10A) inc (poss rev pol); gas; lndtte (inc dryer); shop; rest, snacks; bar; B&B in chateau; BBQ (charcoal/gas); playgrnd; htd pool; paddling pool; waterslide; lake fishing & boating (sm boats); tennis; cycle hire; golf 25km; wifi; entmnt; games/TV rm; 20% statics; dogs €3; no c'vans/m'vans over 10m; phone; poss cr; Eng spkn; adv bkg; quiet; ccard acc; red low ssn; CKE/CCI. "Peaceful, Dutch-run site in grnds of chateau; lovely location; gd sized pitches, but terr; friendly staff; superb facs; poss steep access some pitches; grnd hard, but awnings poss; excel; highly rec." ♦ 19 Apr-29 Sep. € 42.00 (CChq acc) SBS - D21 2013*

See advertisement

⊞ **NONTRON** *7B3* (1km S Urban) *45.51992, 0.65876* **Camping de Nontron, St Martiel-de-Valette, 24300 Nontron [05 53 56 02 04 or 06 30 66 25 74 (mob); camping-de-nontron@orange.fr; www.campingdenontron.com]** Thro Nontron S twd Brantôme on D675. Site on o'skts of town on L nr stadium. Sp. Med, hdg/mkd pitch, pt shd; htd wc; mv service pnt; shwrs; el pnts (10A) €3.50; gas; lndtte; shops adj; tradsmn; rest, snacks, bar 600m; playgrnd; pool adj; paddling pool; games area; games rm; entmnt; TV rm; statics; dogs €1; site clsd mid-Dec to early Jan; poss cr; Eng spkn; quiet; CKE/CCI. "Pleasant owners; excel, modern san facs; gd touring base." € 18.50 2012*

OLORON STE MARIE *8F2* (2km W Urban) *43.17886, -0.62328* **Camping-Gîtes du Stade, Chemin de Lagravette, 64400 Oloron-Ste Marie [05 59 39 11 26 or 06 08 35 09 06 (mob); fax 05 59 36 12 01; camping-du-stade@wanadoo.fr; www.camping-du-stade.com]** Fr N on ring rd foll sp to Saragosse (Spain); at rndabt take 2nd exit onto D6 still sp Saragosse, site sp on R just after sports field. Fr S on D55 join ring rd & turn W at rndabt by McDonalds; sp. Med, hdg/mkd pitch, pt shd; wc; chem disp; shwrs inc; el pnts (6-10A) €4-6 (some rev pol); lndry rm; tradsmn; supmkt 1km; rest, snacks; BBQ; playgrnd; pool adj; rv fishing & sw 1km; tennis; cycle hire; wifi; entmnt; TV; dogs €1.20; adv bkg; quiet; twin-axles extra; red low ssn; CKE/CCI. "Well-kept site; lge pitches; helpful staff; clean facs but ltd low ssn & stretched high ssn; take care low tree; grnd poss soft & damp after rain; barrier clsd 1200-1500; excel base for Pyrenees; gd walking." ♦ 1 May-30 Sep. € 26.00 2014*

ONESSE ET LAHARIE *8E1* (500m N Rural) *44.06344, -1.07257* **FFCC Camping Le Bienvenu, 259 Route de Mimizan, 40110 Onesse-et-Laharie [05 58 07 30 49 or 06 81 32 12 56 (mob); www.camping-onesse.fr]** On N10 Bordeaux-Bayonne rd, turn W onto D38 at Laharie. Site in 5km. Med, mkd pitch, pt shd; wc (some cont); chem disp; mv service pnt; shwrs inc; el pnts (10A) €4; lndtte; shop 100m; rest, bar adj; playgrnd; beach 20km; TV rm; some statics; dogs €1; adv bkg; quiet; red long stay; CKE/CCI. "Well-run, nice, family site; gd facs; v helpful staff." 1 Mar-30 Sep. € 18.00 2014*

ORTHEZ *8F1* (1.5km SE Rural) *43.48793, -0.75882* **Camping La Source, Blvd Charles de Gaulle, 64300 Orthez [05 59 67 04 81; fax 05 59 67 02 38; campingdelasource@orange.fr; www.camping-orthez.com]** Leave Orthez on D817 twd Pau, turn L at sp Mont-de-Marsan & site on R in 300m at crossrds between pedestrian x-ings. Sm, pt sl, some hdstg, ltd shd; wc; mv service pnt; shwrs inc; chem disp; el pnts (10A) €3.50; tradsmn; snacks; playgrnd; pool 2km; fishing; some statics; dogs €1.80; phone; wifi; v quiet; red low ssn; CKE/CCI. "Peaceful, basic but well-maintained site; friendly & helpful staff; gd, clean facs but need updating; some pitches soft in wet weather; interesting historical town; gd security; rec; gd NH." 1 Apr-31 Oct. € 18.40 2014*

OUSSE see Pau *8F2*

PARENTIS EN BORN *7D1* (6km SW Rural) *44.34562, -1.09241* **Camping L'Arbre d'Or, 75 Route du Lac, 40160 Landes [05 58 78 41 56; fax 05 58 78 49 62; contact@arbre-dor.com; www.arbre-dor.com]** Leave the Bordeaux m'way A63/ N10 in Liposthey and drive twds Parentis (D43). The campsite is sp in Parentis. Med, mkd pitch shd or pt shd; wc, chem disp, child/baby facs, shwrs, el inc; Indtte inc dryer; rest, snacks, bar; BBQ; playgrnd; pool; sw 400m; games area; entmnt; wifi; dogs free; poss cr; Eng spkn; adv bkg acc; ccard acc; CKE/CCI; red low ssn. "Vg; lake 500m fr site." ♦ € 37.30 1 Apr-31 Oct (CChq acc) 2014*

PARENTIS EN BORN *7D1* (2km W Rural) *44.34593, -1.10106* **FFCC Camp Municipal Pipiou, Route du Lac, 40160 Parentis-en-Born [05 58 78 57 25; fax 05 58 78 93 17; pipiou@parentis.com; www.parentis.com]** Site on D43 rd twds lake beach. In vill foll sp 'Lac'. After 2km where rest on R, turn R. Site is 150m on R. Lge, hdg/mkd pitch, pt shd; wc; chem disp; mv service pnt; 100% serviced pitches; baby facs; shwrs inc; el pnts (10A) €3.50 (poss rev pol); gas high ssn; Indtte; shop; rest, snacks; bar; playgrnd; lake sw & sand beach adj, fishing & watersports adj; entmnt; TV; 25% statics; dogs €1.30; phone; poss cr; adv bkg; quiet but pitches adj rd noisy; ccard acc; red low ssn/long stay/CKE/CCI. "Lovely lakeside location; phone to check open low ssn; some pitches tight; facs stretched high ssn; cycle tracks thro vill & woods; office not open w/ends low ssn or public hols when access/leaving site not poss; excel." 15 Feb-15 Nov. € 19.00 2009*

PARENTIS EN BORN *7D1* (3km NW Rural) *44.35153, -1.10959* **Camping Calède, Quartier Lahitte, 40160 Parentis-en-Born [05 58 78 44 63; fax 05 58 78 40 13; contact@camping-calede.com; www.camping-calede.com]** Exit N10 junc 17 onto D43 to Parentis-en-Born; then take D652 dir Biscarrosse; site in 3km on L. Sp adj lake. Med, hdg pitch, pt shd; wc; chem disp; baby facs; shwrs inc; el pnts (5A) €3.25; gas; Indtte; shop 3km; tradsmn; snacks; bar; BBQ; playgrnd; lake sw & sand beach adj; sailing; fishing; dogs €0.50; phone; poss cr; Eng spkn; quiet; adv bkg; red low ss; CKE/CCI. "Peaceful site in remote location; well-kept pitches & san facs; friendly, helpful staff; site yourself if office clsd; rec." ♦ 1 May-30 Sep. € 17.00 2009*

PARRANQUET see Villeréal *7D3*

⊞ **PAU** *8F2* (5km E Rural) *43.28909, -0.26985* **FFCC Camping Les Sapins, Route de Tarbes, 64320 Ousse [05 59 81 79 03 or 05 59 81 74 21 (LS); lessapins64@orange.fr]** Site adj Hôtel des Sapins on S side of D817 (Pau-Tarbes rd). Sm, pt shd; wc; mv service pnt; shwrs inc; el pnts (4-6A) €2-3; shop adj; rest in hotel adj; fishing; poss cr; noisy; some rd noise. "Popular, pleasant NH; red facs low ssn; helpful owners; NH only." € 10.00 2014*

⊞ **PAU** *8F2* (6km W Rural) *43.32081, -0.45096* **Camping Le Terrier, Ave du Vert-Galant, 64230 Lescar [05 59 81 01 82; fax 05 59 81 26 83; contact@camping-terrier.com; www.camping-terrier.com]** Exit A64 junc 9.1 onto D817; in 3km, at rndabt junc with D509, turn L onto Blvd de L'Europe; in 1.5km at rndabt turn R onto Av du Vert Galant; site on R in 1km, 200m bef rv bdge. NB. If app on Av du Galant fr S, rec cont to next rndabt & app fr opp dir due tight, concealed ent. Med, hdg/mkd pitch, pt shd; htd wc; chem disp; mv service pnt; baby facs; shwrs inc; el pnts (3-10A) €2.80-6.10; gas; Indtte (inc dryer); shop 500m; tradsmn; hypmkt 2km; snacks & bar high ssn; playgrnd; htd pool high ssn; rv fishing adj; tennis; car wash; entmnt; wifi; 10% statics; dogs €1.60; bus 500m; poss cr; Eng spkn; adv bkg; quiet; ccard acc; red long stay; CKE/CCI. "Gd base for Pau & district; helpful new owners (2010); improved access (2011); vg clean san facs; excel food; no twin-axles; 2 golf courses nr; vg." ♦ ltd € 13.00 2011*

PAUILLAC *7C2* (1km S Rural) *45.18515, -0.74218* **FFCC Camp Municipal Les Gabarreys, Route de la Rivière, 33250 Pauillac [05 56 59 10 03 or 05 56 73 30 50; fax 05 56 73 30 68; camping.les.gabarreys@wanadoo.fr; www.pauillac-medoc.com]** On ent Pauillac on D206, turn R at rndabt, sp site. On app Quays, turn R bef 'Maison du Vin'. Site on L in 1km. Med, hdg/mkd pitch, hdstg, pt shd; wc; chem disp; mv service pnt; shwrs inc; el pnts (5-10A) €4-5.20; Indtte; shop 1km; tradsmn; BBQ; playgrnd; htd, covrd pool 1km; games rm; TV; 6% statics; dogs €2; Eng spkn; adv bkg; quiet; red low ssn; ccard acc; CKE/CCI. "Peaceful, well-kept, well-equipped site on estuary; nice clean san facs; conv wine chateaux; cycle rtes; mkt Sat; excel." ♦ 2 Apr-10 Oct. € 15.00 2011*

PAULHIAC see Biron *7D3*

PAUNAT see Bugue, Le *7C3*

⊞ **PERIGUEUX** *7C3* (12km NE Rural) *45.21975, 0.86383* **Camping Le Bois du Coderc, Route des Gaunies, 24420 Antonne-et-Trigonant [05 53 05 99 83; fax 05 53 05 15 93; coderc-camping@wanadoo.fr; www.campinglecoderc.com]** NE fr Périgueux on N21 twd Limoges, thro Antonne approx 1km turn R at x-rds bet car park & Routiers café. Site in 500m. Sm, pt shd; wc; chem disp; baby facs; shwrs inc; el pnts (6-10A) €3-4; gas 5km; Indtte (inc dryer); ice; shop 4km; tradsmn; rest 1km; snacks; bar; BBQ; playgrnd; htd pool; rv sw & shgl beach adj; games area; games rm; wifi; TV; some statics; dogs €1; phone; Eng spkn; adv bkg; quiet; ccard acc; red low ssn/CKE/CCI. "Secluded site; most pitches spacious; friendly, helpful owners; vg, clean san facs; rallies welcome; gd value, inc rest; highly rec; quiet; well maintained; excel site; view of website a must." ♦ € 26.80 2014*

PERIGUEUX *7C3* (1.5km E Urban) *45.18693, 0.74132* **Camping de Barnabé, 80 Rue des Bains, 24750 Boulazac [05 53 53 41 45; fax 05 53 54 16 62; contact@barnabe-perigord.com; www.barnabe-perigord.com]** Exit A89 junc 15 onto D6021 to Périgueux; at rndabt by rv, cont strt on; at mini rndabt in 200m cont strt on; in 500m at T-junc turn R into Blvd du Petit Changé; in 500m turn L into Rue des Bains & site. Site will sp. Med, hdg/mkd pitch, pt shd; htd wc; chem disp; shwrs inc; el pnts (5-10A) €3.40-3.90; shops 500m; supmkt 1km; rest, snacks; bar; rv fishing; no statics; dogs €1.20; poss v cr; Eng spkn; adv bkg; quiet; red long stay/low ssn; ccard acc. "Pleasant rvside site in nice spot; sm pitches & cramped for lge o'fits; many pitches dark & v shady; san facs dated & poss unclean (2010); poss clsd low ssn - phone ahead; access to public using adj café; 15 min rvside walk to Périgueux delightful; sm site with narr app; helpful friendly owners; excel Sat mkt." 1 Apr-31 Oct. € 19.50 2014*

"I need an on-site restaurant"

We do our best to make sure site information is correct, but it is always best to check any must-have facilities are still available or will be open during your visit.

PERIGUEUX *7C3* (20km SE Rural) *45.13165, 0.92867* **Camping de la Pélonie, La Bourgie, 24330 St Antoine-d'Auberoche [05 53 07 55 78; fax 05 53 03 74 27; www.lapelonie.com]** Fr Périgueux on A89 twd Brive; 5km past St Pierre-de-Chignac, site sp on L; turn L at picnic area - go under rlwy bdge; site ent on L. Med, mkd pitch, pt shd; wc; chem disp; shwrs inc; el pnts (10A) €3.80 (poss req long cable); Indtte; gas; shop; tradsmn; rest, snacks; bar; playgrnd; htd pool; paddling pool; wifi; TV; 20% statics; dogs €2; phone; poss cr; Eng spkn; adv bkg; quiet; ccard acc; red low ssn; CKE/CCI. "Delightful site; pleasant, welcoming owners; gd, clean facs; excel facs for children; some pitches diff lge o'fits; gd touring base." ♦ 11 Apr-17 Oct. € 17.50 2013*

See advertisement

PERIGUEUX *7C3* (7km S Rural) *45.14900, 0.77880* **Camping Le Grand Dague, Route du Grand Dague, 24750 Atur [05 53 04 21 01; fax 05 53 04 22 01; info@legranddague.fr; www.legranddague.fr]** Fr cent Périgueux, take N21 & A89 twd Brive. Fork L onto D2 to Atur (main rd bears R). In Atur turn L after bar/tabac; foll site sp for 2.5km. Lge, pt sl, shd; htd wc; chem disp; baby facs; shwrs inc; el pnts (6A) inc; Indtte (inc dryer); ltd shop; tradsmn; rest, snacks; bar; BBQ; playgrnd; htd pool; paddling pool; cycle hire; games area; games rm; wifi; entmnt; TV rm; 70% statics; dogs €2; phone; Eng spkn; adv bkg; quiet; red low ssn; ccard acc; red low ssn; CKE/CCI. "Gd family site; friendly owners; site immac, even end of ssn; poss unkempt early ssn; lots to do; ltd touring pitches; excel." ♦ 20 Apr-26 Sep. € 29.00 2010*

PETIT PALAIS ET CORNEMPS see St Médard de Guizières *7C2*

PEYREHORADE *8F1* (7km N Rural) *43.60318, -1.12970* **Camping La Comtesse, Lieu-dit Claquin, 40300 Bélus [05 58 57 69 07; fax 05 58 57 62 50; campinglacomtesse@wanadoo.fr; www.campinglacomtesse.com]** N fr Peyrehorade on D33; in 4km turn R sp Bélus; in 1.5km turn L; site on R in 1.5km, sp. Med, hdg/mkd pitch, pt shd; wc; chem disp; shwrs incl; el pnts (10A) €3.10; Indtte (inc dryer); shops, rests nrby; bar; BBQ; playgrnd; htd pool; games rm; entmnt; 50% statics; dogs €1.70; phone; adv bkg; red low ssn. "By pretty lake; friendly staff; ltd facs low ssn; vg." ♦ ltd 1 Apr-30 Sep. € 13.00 2009*

⊞ **PEYRIGNAC** *7C3* (1km W Rural) *45.16048, 1.18594* **Camping La Garenne, La Brousse, 24210 Peyrignac [tel/fax 05 53 50 57 73; s.lagarenne@wanadoo.com; www.lagarennedordogne.com]** E fr Périgueux on A89. At Peyrignac foll site sp. Narr, steep rd poss diff lge o'fits. Med, mkd pitch, pt sl, shd; htd wc; chem disp; mv service pnt; baby facs; shwrs inc; el pnts (6-10A) €4 (poss rev pol); gas; Indtte; shop; tradsmn; snacks; bar; playgrnd; sm pool; games area; 50% statics; dogs €1.50; poss cr; adv bkg; quiet; red low ssn; CKE/CCI. "Gd touring base; gd size pitches; clean san facs; v kind owners; vg site would rec." ♦ € 15.00 2011*

PEYRILLAC ET MILLAC see Souillac *7C3*

PEZULS see Bugue, Le *7C3*

PINSAC see Souillac *7C3*

PISSOS *7D1* (500m E Rural) *44.30831, -0.76987* **Camp Municipal l'Arriu, 40410 Pissos [05 58 08 90 38 or 05 58 04 41 40 (LS); fax 05 58 08 92 93; mairie.pissos@wanadoo.fr; www.pissos.fr]** Fr N exit N10 junc 18 onto D834 to Pissos; at x-rds turn L onto D43 sp Sore; site on R in 500m, sp. Med, shd; wc; chem disp; shwrs inc; el pnts €2.10; ice; playgrnd; pool 500m; rv fishing 300m; quiet; red long stay. "Lge pitches; excel." 1 Jul-15 -Sep. € 11.50 2012*

PORGE, LE *7C1* (9km W Coastal) *44.89430, -1.20181* **Camping La Grigne, Ave de l'Océan, 33680 Le Porge [05 56 26 54 88; fax 05 56 26 52 07; campingduporge2@wanadoo.fr; www.leporge.fr]** Fr Bordeaux ring rd take N215 twd Lacaneau. In 22km at Ste Hélène D5 to Saumos & onto Le Porge. Site on L of rd to Porge-Océan in approx 9km. V lge, mkd pitch, terr, pt sl, shd; wc; chem disp; shwrs inc; el pnts (10A) €5; gas; shop; lndtte; bar; snacks; playgrnd; beach 600m; tennis; games area; TV; dogs €1.90; poss cr; adv bkg; quiet. "Vg facs; great beach; excel cycle path network; red long stay/low ssn." ♦ 1 Apr-30 Sep. € 22.00 2011*

PRATS DE CARLUX see Sarlat la Canéda *7C3*

PROISSANS see Sarlat la Canéda *7C3*

PYLA SUR MER *7D1* (7km S Coastal) *44.58517, -1.20868* **Camping Village Centre La Forêt, Route de Biscarosse, 33115 Pyla-sur-Mer [05 56 22 73 28; fax 05 56 22 70 50; contact@village-center.com; www.village-center.com]** Fr Bordeaux app Arcachon on A660 by-pass rd; at La Teste-de-Buch at rndabt foll sp for Dune du Pilat & 'campings'. At T-junc in 4km turn L; foll 'plage' & camping sp on D218. Site on R. Lge, hdg/mkd pitch, sl, shd; wc; chem disp; mv service pnt; shwrs inc; el pnts (6A) inc; lndtte; shop; rest, snacks; bar; BBQ; playgrnd; pool; sand beach 600m; solarium; tennis; cycle hire; many statics (sep area); dogs €2; adv bkg; red low ssn; ccard acc; CKE/CCI. "Forest setting at foot of sand dune; well-organised; new san facs 2010; many facs; hang-gliding, surfing, sailing, cycle rtes nrby." ♦ 4 Apr-20 Sep. € 34.80 (CChq acc) 2010*

PYLA SUR MER *7D1* (7km S Coastal/Rural) *44.57474, -1.22217* **Yelloh! Village Panorama du Pyla, Route de Biscarosse, 33115 Pyla-sur-Mer [05 56 22 10 44; fax 05 56 22 10 12; mail@camping-panorama.com; www.camping-panorama.com / www.yellohvillage.co.uk]** App Arcachon fr Bordeaux on A63/A660, at rndabt foll sp for Dune-du-Pilat & 'campings'. Foll sp for 'plage' & 'campings' on D218. Site on R next to Camping Le Petit Nice. Lge, mkd pitch, pt sl, terr, pt shd; wc (some cont); chem disp; mv service pnt; sauna; shwrs inc; el pnts (3-10A) inc; gas; rest, snacks; bar; shop; playgrnd; htd pool; sand beach adj; tennis; TV; entmnt; dogs €5; Eng spkn; adv bkg; quiet; red low ssn; CKE/CCI. "Pleasant site on wooded dune; direct steep access to excel beach; site rds v narr; ltd pitches for v lge o'fits; some pitches sandy; gd facs; paragliding adj." ♦ 13 Apr-2 Oct. € 52.80 2013*

RAUZAN *7D2* (200m N Rural) *44.78237, -0.12712* **Camping du Vieux Château, 33420 Rauzan [05 57 84 15 38; fax 05 57 84 18 34; contact@camping-levieuxchateau.com; www.camping-levieuxchateau.com]** Fr Libourne S on D670, site is on D123 about 1.5km fr D670, sp. Sm, mkd pitch, shd; wc; chem disp; baby facs; shwrs inc; el pnts (6A) €3.30 (poss rev pol); gas; lndtte; shop, tradsmn; rest 200m; snacks; sm bar & in 200m; playgrnd; pool; tennis; rv/lake 5km; cycle hire; horseriding; wine-tasting; entmnt; TV; 10% statics; dogs €2; poss cr; Eng spkn; adv bkg; quiet; red low ssn; ccard acc; CKE/CCI. "Lovely site but take care tree roots on pitches; helpful owners; basic san facs - ltd low ssn & poss not well-maintained, & poss stretched high ssn; access to some pitches diff when wet; conv vineyards." ♦ 29 Mar-11 Oct. € 24.50 2012*

REOLE, LA *7D2* (1.6km SE Urban) *44.57778, -0.03360* **Camp Municipal La Rouergue, Bords de Garonne, 33190 La Réole [05 56 61 13 55; fax 05 56 61 89 13; lareole@entredeuxmers.com; www.entredeuxmers.com]** On N113 bet Bordeaux & Agen or exit A62 at junc 4. In La Réole foll sps S on D9 to site on L immed after x-ing suspension bdge. Med, pt shd; wc; shwrs inc; el pnts (3A) inc; gas; shop; tradsmn; snacks; pool 500m; fishing, boating; dogs €2; some rd noise. "Resident warden; 2m barrier clsd 1200-1500; Sat mkt on rv bank." 15 May-15 Oct. € 14.00 2009*

RIBERAC *7C2* (500m N Rural) *45.25668, 0.34280* **Camp Municipal La Dronne, Route d'Angoulême, 24600 Ribérac [05 53 90 50 08 or 05 53 90 03 10; fax 05 53 91 35 13; ot.riberac@perigord.tm.fr]** Site on L of main rd D709 immed N of bdge over Rv Dronne on o'skts of Ribérac. Med, some hdg pitches, pt shd; wc (some cont); shwrs inc; el pnts (10A) €2.50; lndtte; supmkt 500m; tradsmn; snacks; playgrnd; pool 1km; dogs €0.50; no twin-axles; quiet. "Vg, well-run site; pitches in cent hdgd & shady; facs gd & clean but inadequate high ssn; Fri mkt." ♦ 1 Jun-15 Sep. € 8.55 2010*

RIVIERE SAAS ET GOURBY see Dax *8E1*

ROCHE CHALAIS, LA *7C2* (500m S Rural) *45.14892, -0.00245* **Camp Municipal Les Gerbes, Rue de la Dronne, 24490 La Roche-Chalais [05 53 91 40 65 or 06 38 82 40 08 (mob); fax 05 53 90 32 01; campinggerbes@orange.fr; www.larochechalais.com]** Fr S on D674 turn sharp L in vill at site sp. Site on R in 500m. Fr N take Coutras-Libourne rd thro vill; site sp on L beyond sm indus est. Med, mkd pitch, terr, pt shd; wc; shwrs inc; el pnts (5-10A) €2.60-3.60 (poss rev pol); lndtte; tradsmn; shops 500m; playgrnd; municipal pool inc; rv sw, fishing, boating & canoeing adj; leisure pk 5km; wifi; adv bkg; rlwy & factory noise; red long stay;CKE/CCI. "Pleasant, well-kept, well-run site nr rv; gd sized pitches, some rvside; gd clean san facs; rec pitch N side of site to avoid factory noise; mkt Sat am; rec." ♦ 15 Apr-30 Sep. € 14.00 2014*

ROQUE GAGEAC, LA see Sarlat la Canéda *7C3*

ROQUEFORT *8E2* (2.5km S Rural) *44.02093, -0.31032* **Camp Municipal, Route de Pau, 40120 Sarbazan [05 58 45 64 93 (Mairie); fax 05 58 45 69 91]** Fr Roquefort take D934 S twd Villeneuve-de-Marsan & Pau. In 2km camp sp on L in Sarbazan. Sm, mkd pitch, pt sl, shd; wc (some cont); shwrs inc; el pnts (5A) €1.60-2.40 (poss rev pol); Indtte; shops 2.5km; tradsmn; BBQ; playgrnd; tennis; dogs; quiet; red low ssn; CKE/CCI. "Peaceful, friendly; site yourself, warden calls am & pm; dated, clean san facs; some pitches soft after heavy rain; nr arena; highly rec." ♦ ltd 1 Apr-30 Oct. € 9.00 2009*

ROUFFIGNAC *7C3* (300m N Rural) *45.05473, 0.98708* **Camping Bleu Soleil, Domaine Touvent, 24580 Rouffignac-St-Cernin-de-Reilhac [05 53 05 48 30; infos@camping-bleusoleil.com; www.camping-bleusoleil.com]** On D6 in Rouffignac, take D31 NE twd Thenon. Site clearly sp on R after 300m. Med, hdg/mkd pitch, pt sl, terr, pt shd; wc; chem disp; 75% serviced pitches; shwrs inc; el pnts (10A) €3.70; Indtte; shop; tradsmn; rest, snacks & bar high ssn; BBQ; playgrnd; htd pool; tennis; games rm; wifi; TV rm; 10% statics; dogs €2; phone; Eng spkn; adv bkg; quiet; red low ssn; ccard acc; CKE/CCI. "Relaxing site with views nr pretty vill; v friendly, helpful owners; ltd facs low ssn; poss diff for lge o'fits; excel." ♦ ltd 15 Apr-23 Sep. € 22.00 2011*

ST AMAND DE COLY see Montignac *7C3*

ST ANDRE DE CUBZAC *7C2* (4km NW Rural) *45.00703, -0.47724* **FFCC Camping Le Port Neuf, 1125 Route du Port Neuf, 33240 St André-de-Cubzac [tel/fax 05 57 43 16 44; camping.port.neuf@wanadoo.fr; www.camping-port-neuf.com/]** Fr A10 or N10 take exit sp St André. Well sp fr St André (narr rds) on D669. Sm, mkd/hdg pitch, hdstg, pt shd; htd wc; chem disp; mv service pnt; shwrs inc; el pnts (6A) €3.50 (poss long lead req); Indry rm; tradsmn; rest, snacks; bar; cycle hire; trout-fishing & boating in sm lake + rv 100m; horseriding nrby; pedalo hire; wifi; dogs €1; rlwy stn in vill to Bordeaux; quiet; Eng spkn; adv bkg; quiet; red/ CKE/CCI. "Lovely spot; friendly, helpful staff; san facs clean; terraine rather scruffy (2011); vg." ♦ ltd 1 May-30 Sep. € 12.00 2014*

ST ANDRE DE SEIGNANX see Bayonne *8F1*

ST ANTOINE D'AUBEROCHE see Thenon *7C3*

ST ANTOINE DE BREUILH see Ste Foy la Grande *7C2*

ST ASTIER *7C3* (600m E Rural) *45.14735, 0.53308* **Flower Camping Le Pontet, Route de Montanceix, 24110 St Astier [05 53 54 14 22; fax 05 53 04 39 36; camping.lepontet@flowercampings.com; www.camping-dordogne-lepontet.com]** Take D6089 SW fr Périgueux; in 14km turn R sp St Astier; site on R on D41 on banks of Rv Isle. Med, mkd pitch, shd; wc; chem disp; shwrs inc; el pnts (6A) €2.55; gas; Indtte; shops 400m; snacks; BBQ; playgrnd; pool; paddling pool; sand beach adj; fishing; canoing; entmnt; statics; dogs; poss cr; adv bkg; v quiet; CKE/CCI. "Some areas soft in wet weather." 1 Apr-30 Sep. € 25.00 2012*

ST AVIT DE VIALARD see Bugue, Le *7C3*

ST CREPIN ET CARLUCET see Sarlat la Canéda *7C3*

ST CYBRANET see Sarlat la Canéda *7C3*

"Satellite navigation makes touring much easier"

Remember most sat navs don't know if you're towing or in a larger vehicle – always use yours alongside maps and site directions.

ST CYPRIEN (DORDOGNE) *7C3* (1km S Rural) *44.85547, 1.03788* **Camping du Garrit, Le Garrit, 24220 St Cyprien [05 53 29 20 56; pbecheau@aol.com; www.campingdugarritendordogneperigord.com]** Fr W on D703 turn R bef town sp; cross rlwy & bear R; then sharp R at rv. Sp on D703 fr St Cyprien as 'Le Garrit'. Med, hdg/mkd pitch, pt shd; wc; chem disp; baby facs; shwrs inc; el pnts (6A) €3; Indtte; shop; BBQ; playgrnd; pool; canoeing; sailing; boat hire; fishing; dogs €1; phone; Eng spkn; adv bkg; rd & rlwy noise some pitches; CKE/CCI. "Lovely, rvside site; lge pitches; excel san facs; gd touring base for prehistoric caves; NH or sh stay." 1 May-15 Sep. € 15.00 2009*

ST EMILION *7C2* (3km N Rural) *44.91695, -0.14160* **Camping Yelloh Saint Emilion, 2 lieu dit Les Combes, 33330 St Emilion [05 57 24 75 80; fax 05 57 24 69 68; info@camping-saint-emilion.com; www.camping-saint-emilion.com]** NB Trailer c'vans not permitted in cent of St Emilion. Fr A10 exit junc 39a sp Libourne onto D670. In Libourne turn E on D243 twd St Emilion. On o'skts of St Emilion turn L onto D122 dir Lussac & Montagne; site on R by lake in 3km. Or fr S, foll site sp off D670 to Libourne, nr Les Bigaroux. NB D122 S of St Emilion unsuitable for c'vans. Lge, hdg/mkd pitch, hdstg, shd; wc (some cont); chem disp; mv service pnt; baby facs; shwrs inc; el pnts (10A) inc; gas; Indtte (inc dryer); sm shop; tradsmn; rest, snacks;bar; BBQ (gas); playgrnd; htd pool; paddling pool; waterslide; fishing; canoes & pedalos avail; watersports nr; horseriding 8km; tennis; mountain bike circuit; cycle hire; wifi; entmnt; games/ TV rm; 40% statics; dogs €4; no c'vans/m'vans over 10m; phone; poss cr; Eng spkn; adv bkg; quiet; ccard acc; red low ssn; CKE/CCI. "Lovely, peaceful, well-run lakeside site; owners friendly & helpful; gd sized & shd pitches; suitable lge o'fits; clean, modern san facs but inadequate; free shuttle bus service to St Emilion; gd cycle rtes; poss boggy when wet; excel." ♦ 25 Apr-12 Oct. € 52.00 SBS - D08 2014*

See advert on previous page

⊞ **ST EMILION** *7C2* (4km SE Rural) *44.85138, -0.10683* **Aire St Emilion Domaine du Château Gerbaud, 33000 St Pey-d'Armens [06 03 27 00 32 (mob); fax 05 57 47 10 53; contact@chateau-gerbaud.com; www.chateau-gerbaud.com]** Fr Libourne SE on D670/D936 dir Castillon-la-Bataille. In St Pey-d'Armens at bar/tabac foll sp Château Gerbaud vineyard. Parking & service pnt for m'vans for max 48 hours. "Friendly, Eng-speaking owners." 2010*

STE ENGRACE *8F1* (5km NW Rural) *43.01600, -0.85786* **FFCC Camping Ibarra, Quartier Les Casernes, 64560 Ste Engrâce [05 59 28 73 59; maryse@ibarra-chantina.com; www.ibarra-chantina.com]** D918 S fr Tardets-Sorholus; in 2km turn R onto D26; in 6km to L onto D113 sp Ste Engrâce; site on R in 5km. Site clearly sp just bef La Caserne. NB not suitable car+c'van. Sm, mkd pitch, pt shd; wc (some cont); chem disp; shwrs inc; el pnts (5A) €1.80; Indry rm; tradsmn; snacks 500m; bar; BBQ (sep area); playgrnd; 8% statics; dogs; quiet; CKE/CCI. "Pleasant site on rv bank; scenic views; spectacular Kakuetta gorges nrby; vg; narr rd thro gorge for several Kms bef site." ♦ ltd 1 Apr-30 Sep. € 11.50 2013*

ST ETIENNE DE BAIGORRY *8F1* (500m N Rural) *43.18370, -1.33569* **Camp Municipal L'Irouleguy, Borciriette, 64430 St Etienne-de-Baïgorry [05 59 37 43 96 or 05 59 37 40 80 (Mairie); fax 05 59 37 48 20; comstetiennebaigorry@wanadoo.fr]** W on D15 fr St Jean-Pied-de-Port to St Etienne-de-Baigorry; site on R 300m bef junc with D948; ent next to wine co-operative. Fr N on D948, on ent St Etienne-de-Baïgorry turn L onto D15; site in 300m on L. NB Don't be put off by entry down track L of winery - can't see site fr rd. Med, shd; wc; chem disp; shwrs inc; el pnts (6A) €2.70; Indtte; gas, shop 100m; htd pool adj; tennis adj; troutfishing; birdwatching; poss cr; adv bkg; quiet. "Scenic site by rv; lge pitches; plenty hot water; gd hill walking cent; out of ssn call at Mairie to open site for NH; Gd modern san facs." ♦ 1 May-30 Nov. € 9.23 2013*

ST ETIENNE DE VILLEREAL see Villeréal *7D3*

STE EULALIE EN BORN *7D1* (4.7km N Rural) *44.30808, -1.18103* **Camp Municipal du Lac, 1590 Route du Lac, 40200 Ste Eulalie-en-Born [05 58 09 70 10 or 05 58 09 73 48 (Mairie); fax 05 58 09 76 89; contact@lecampingdulac.com; www.lecampingdulac.com]** N fr Mimizan on D87/D652. Pass Ste Eulalie & turn W at water tower, site sp. Med, mkd pitch, pt shd; wc; chem disp; mv service pnt; baby facs; shwrs inc; el pnts (10A) €3.90; gas; Indtte; snacks; bar; pool; lake sw & beach adj; boat hire; games area; some statics; dogs €2.10; phone; poss cr; Eng spkn; adv bkg; quiet; ccard acc; CKE/CCI. "On Lake Biscarrosse; vg for familes; do not confuse with site of similar name on Lac Aureilhan, 2km N of Mimizan." 1 Apr-30 Oct. € 17.50 2009*

ST FELIX DE REILLAC see Douze, La *7C3*

STE FOY LA GRANDE *7C2* (1.5km NE Rural) *44.84426, 0.22468* **Camping de la Bastide, Allée du Camping, 2 Les Tuileries, Pineuilh, 33220 Ste Foy-la-Grande [tel/fax 05 57 46 13 84; contact@camping-bastide.com; www.camping-bastide.com]** Fr W go thro town & turn off at D130 to site, well sp on Rv Dordogne. Med, mkd pitch, pt shd; wc; chem disp; mv service pnt; baby facs; shwrs inc; el pnts (10A) €3 (poss rev pol); Indtte; shops, snacks & bar 500m, playgrnd; pool; jacuzzi; fishing, canoeing; games rm; wifi; 10% statics; dogs €2; phone; poss cr; Eng spkn; adv bkg; v quiet; ccard acc; red low ssn; CKE/CCI. "Pretty, well-cared for site; sm pitches; helpful British owners; immac, modern san facs; high kerb stones onto pitches - poss diff lge o'fits; no twin-axles; mkt Sat; excel." ♦ 1 Apr-30 Oct. € 23.00 2013*

STE FOY LA GRANDE *7C2* (6km W Rural) *44.82954, 0.12290* **FLOWER Camping La Rivière Fleurie, 180 Rue Théophile, 24230 St Antoine-de-Breuilh [tel/fax 05 53 24 82 80; info@la-riviere-fleurie.com; www.la-riviere-fleurie.com / www.flowercampings.com]** Turn S off D936 at W end of St Antoine-de-Breuilh; site 2.7km fr main rd in vill of St Aulaye adj Rv Dordogne. Well sp. Med, mkd pitch, pt shd; wc; chem disp; baby facs; shwrs inc; el pnts (10A) inc; gas; Indtte (inc dryer); shops 4km; hypmkt 5km; tradsmn; rest; bar; BBQ; playgrnd; htd pool; paddling pool; games rm; rv sw adj; tennis, horseriding; golf; canoeing & fishing nrby; wifi; entmnt; TV rm; 10% statics; dogs €2; phone; Eng spkn; adv bkg; quiet; red low ssn/long stay; CKE/CCI. "Peaceful, well-maintained site; some spacious pitches; welcoming, helpful owners; excel san facs; church bells during day; vg cycling; mkt Sat in Ste Foy; highly rec." ♦ 10 Apr-20 Sep. € 27.00 (CChq acc) 2014*

ST GEOURS DE MAREMNE *8E1* (500m W Rural) *43.68981, -1.23376* **Camping Les Platanes, 3 Route de Lecoume, 40230 St Geours-de-Maremne [05 58 57 45 35; fax 05 58 57 37 85; info@platanes.com; www.platanes.com]** Fr N10 take junc sp St Geours-de-Maremne. Site sp fr town cent. Med, pt sl, pt shd; htd wc; chem disp; shwrs inc; el pnts (6A) €4.70; gas; Indtte; shop nr; tradsmn; rest, snacks; bar; BBQ; playgrnd; pool (high ssn); sand beach 8km; tennis; games area; games rm; wifi; TV; 50% statics; dogs €1.50; phone; poss cr; adv bkg; quiet; ccard acc; red low ssn/long stay; CKE/CCI. "Friendly British owners; useful NH on N10." 1 Mar-15 Nov. € 27.50 2012*

ST GERAUD DE CORPS see Montpon Ménestérol *7C2*

ST GERMAIN DU BEL AIR see Gourdon *7D3*

ST GIRONS PLAGE *8E1* (Coastal) *43.95105, -1.35276* **Camping Eurosol, Route de la Plage, 40560 St Girons-Plage [05 58 47 90 14 or 05 58 56 54 90; fax 05 58 47 76 74; contact@camping-eurosol.com; www.camping-eurosol.com]** Turn W off D652 at St Girons on D42. Site on L in 4km. Lge, pt sl, pt shd; wc; chem disp; baby facs; serviced pitches; shwrs inc; el pnts (6-10A) inc; gas; Indtte; shop; rest, snacks; playgrnd; 2 pools; paddling pool; sand beach 700m; tennis; games area; games rm; horseriding adj; cycle hire; entmnt; TV rm; some statics; dogs €2.50; poss cr; red low ssn; quiet. "Pitches poss tight for long vans." ♦ 10 May-13 Sep. € 39.00 (4 persons) 2014*

See advertisement

ST GIRONS PLAGE *8E1* (800m NE Coastal) *43.95436, -1.35689* **Campéole Camping Les Tourterelles, 40560 St Girons-Plage [05 58 47 93 12; tourterelles@campeole.com; www.camping-tourterelles.com / www.campeole.com]** Exit N10 at Castets & take D42 W to St Girons, then to St Girons-Plage. Lge, pt sl, shd; wc; shwrs inc; el pnts (6A) €3.90; Indtte; shops 1km; BBQ; playgrnd; sand beach 200m; games area; games rm; entmnt; dogs €1; poss cr; quiet; red low ssn. "Site in pine trees; footpath to dunes & beach." 15 Mar-15 Oct. € 20.20 (CChq acc) 2012*

ST HILAIRE DE LUSIGNAN see Agen *8E3*

ST JEAN DE LUZ *8F1* (3km N Coastal) *43.40549, -1.64222* **Camping Bord de Mer, 71 chemin d'Erromardie, 64500 St Jean-de-Luz [tel/fax 05 59 26 24 61; bord-de-mer64@orange.fr; www.camping-le-bord-de-mer.fr]** Exit A63 junc 3 onto D810 dir St Jean-de-Luz. In 1km cross rlwy & immed turn sharp R sp Erromardie. Site on sharp turn L bef beach. Ent by plastic chain fence bef ent to prom, but easy to miss. App poss diff lge o'fits due hairpin turn - drive on to car park where may be poss to turn. Med, hdg pitch, pt sl; terr; wc (mainly cont); chem disp; mv service pnt; shwrs inc; el pnts (10A) €3,50; Indy rm; tradsmn; snacks; bar; BBQ; sand beach adj; dogs; quiet; red low ssn. "Nice site in excel position; owner connects el pnts; cliff walk to town; NH en rte Spain; San facs refurbished; wonderful location." ♦ ltd 11 Apr-2 Nov. € 43.00 2014*

ST JEAN DE LUZ *8F1* (3km N Urban/Coastal) *43.40777, -1.63777* **Chadotel Camping International Erromardie, Ave de la Source, 64500 St Jean-de-Luz [05 59 26 07 74 or 02 51 33 05 05 (LS); fax 05 59 51 12 11; camping-international@wanadoo.fr or info@chadotel.com; www.chadotel.com]** Fr A63 exit junc 3 sp St Jean-de-Luz. At traff lts at end of slip rd turn L onto D810 sp St Jean; in 1km cross rlwy & immed turn sharp R sp Erromardie, site on R in 1km opp beach. Lge, hdg/mkd pitch, pt sl, shd; wc; chem disp (wc); shwrs inc; el pnts (5A) inc; Indtte; shop; rest, snacks; bar; BBQ (charcoal); playgrnd; pool; sand/shgl beach adj; fishing 2km; watersports 3km; golf, entmnt; wifi; TV rm; many statics; dogs €3.20; c'vans over 7m not acc high ssn; adv bkg; quiet; ccard acc; red long stay. "Facs & office poss clsd after 1800 low ssn; poss poor security; twin-axle c'vans acc;mkd Tue & Fri." 7 Apr-11 Nov. € 32.50 2011*

ST JEAN DE LUZ *8F1* (2km NE Coastal) *43.40563, -1.64216* **Camping de la Ferme Erromardie, 40 Chemin d'Erromardie, 64500 St Jean-de-Luz [05 59 26 34 26; fax 05 59 51 26 02; contact@camping-erromardie.com; www.camping-erromardie.com]** Exit A63 junc 3 onto D810 sp St Jean-de-Luz. After 1km x rlwy and turn immed sharp R sp Erromardie. Site ent on R in 3km just bef rest/bar. Lge, hdg/mkd pitch, shd; wc; chem disp; mv service pnt; baby facs; shwrs inc; el pnts (6-16A) €3.80-4.30; gas; Indtte; tradsmn; rest, snacks; bar; playgrnd; sand beach adj; many statics; dogs €1.50; poss cr; Eng spkn; adv bkg; red low ssn; CKE/CCI. "Well-run, popular site; cheerful, helpful staff; ltd water pnts in 2nd field; lovely, sandy beaches; coastal walk into St Jean-de-Luz; Basque museum nrby; site in 3 sections, lge o'fits should ask for pitch on touring field; excel modern san facs." ♦ 15 Mar-30 Sep. € 36.30 2014*

ST JEAN DE LUZ *8F1* (3km NE Coastal) *43.41339, -1.61710* **Camping Itsas-Mendi, Acotz, 64500 St Jean-de-Luz [05 59 26 56 50; fax 05 59 26 54 44; itsas@wanadoo.fr; www.itsas-mendi.com]** Exit A63 junc 3 sp St Jean-de-Luz; take D810 dir Biarritz; in 3km turn L sp Acotz Plage & Camping; site well sp. Lge, hdg pitch, pt sl, terr, shd; htd wc; chem disp; mv service pnt; sauna; shwrs inc; fam bthrm; el pnts (10A) inc; Indtte (inc dryer); shop; rest, snacks; bar; BBQ; playgrnd; htd pools; paddling pool; waterslides & aquatic area; tennis; games area; beach 500m; wifi; TV rm; dogs €2.20; phone; poss cr; Eng spkn; quiet but rlwy adj; red low ssn; CKE/CCI. "Friendly staff; excel." ♦ 3 Apr-13 Oct. € 40.00 (CChq acc) 2012*

ST JEAN DE LUZ *8F1 (4km NE Rural) 43.41527, -1.61666* **Camping Atlantica, Quartier Acotz, 64500 St Jean-de-Luz [05 59 47 72 44; fax 05 59 54 72 27; info@campingatlantica.com; www.campingatlantica.com]** Exit A63 at junc 3 sp St Jean-de-Luz-Nord. Take D810 twd Biarritz & at top of hill foll sp Acotz Plage; site well sp. Lge, mkd pitch, pt sl, pt shd; wc; mv service pnt; shwrs inc; baby facs; el pnts (6A) €4.70; Indtte; shop; rest, snacks; bar; playgrnd; pool; paddling pool; beach 500m; entmnt; games/TV rm; 35% statics; dogs €2.50; bus; poss cr; Eng spkn; adv bkg; some rd & rlwy noise; ccard acc; red low ssn; CKE/CCI. "Vg pool; gd san facs; various pitch sizes; not suitable v lge o'fits due narr site rds; excel." ♦ 1 Apr-30 Sep. € 29.50 2010*

ST JEAN DE LUZ *8F1 (4km NE Coastal) 43.41674, -1.62274* **Camping Duna-Munguy, 881 Chemin Duhartia, Quartier Acotz, 64500 St Jean-de-Luz [05 59 47 70 70; fax 05 59 47 78 82; camping-duna-munguy@wanadoo.fr; www.camping-dunamunguy.com]** Exit A63 at junc 3 St Jean-de-Luz Nord. Take D810 twd Biarritz, turn L at 2nd rise then R at T-junc & down hill under rlwy bdge sp Acotz Plages. Site well sp. NB Steep downhill app. Sm, mkd pitch, hdstg, pt shd; htd wc; chem disp; shwrs inc; jacuzzi; el pnts (10A) €4 (poss rev pol); Indtte; playgrnd; sm pool; sandy beach 300m; golf 5km; wifi; TV; 80% statics; dogs €4; phone; bus 1km (at top of hill); poss cr; Eng spkn; adv bkg; quiet but rlwy noise; ccard not acc; CKE/CCI. "Steep app poss diff long o'fits; sm pitches - poss liable to flood; gd san facs with smart shwrs; helpful owner; no sea views but sheltered in storms; gd coastal walks; rec." ♦ ltd 15 Feb-15 Nov. € 26.00 2009*

ST JEAN DE LUZ *8F1 (4km NE Coastal) 43.41861, -1.62320* **Camping Merko Lacarra, 820 Route des Plages, Plage d'Acotz, 64500 St Jean-de-Luz [05 59 26 56 76; fax 05 59 54 73 81; contact@merkolacarra.com; www.merkolacarra.com]** Exit A63 at junc 3 St Jean-de-Luz Nord. Take D810 twd Biarritz, turn L at 2nd rise then R at T-junc & down hill under rlwy bdge sp Acotz Plages, site on L. NB steep downhill app. Med, pt sl, pt shd; wc; chem disp; shwrs; el pnts (16A) £4; Indtte; shop; café/bar; sand beach over rd; wifi; 15% statics; dogs €1.50; m'van o'night sep area; Eng spkn; quiet; ccard acc; red low ssn; CKE/CCI. "Well-kept, busy site; some pitches awkward due trees/bushes; poss cr high ssn; lovely walking/cycling; gd." ♦ 27 Mar-16 Oct. € 27.00 2010*

⊞ **ST JEAN DE LUZ** *8F1 (6km SE Rural) 43.34591, -1.61724* **Camping Chourio, Luberriaga, 64310 Ascain [05 59 54 06 31 or 05 59 54 04 32; www.tourisme-aquitaine.fr]** Fr St Jean-de-Luz take D918 sp Ascain. In 6km turn R at traff lts, in 250m over rv bdge & turn L at mini-rndabt. Site sp in town. Med, pt shd; wc; chem disp; mv service pnt; shwrs inc; el pnts (6A) €2.80; tradsmn; rest, snacks, bar 1km; phone; poss cr; quiet; CKE/CCI; "Friendly, family-owned, relaxed site in lovely countryside; conv Spanish border; Tues & Sat mkt St Jean-de-Luz; vg; v helpful owners." 20 Mar-15 Nov. € 14.00 2013*

ST JEAN DE LUZ *8F1 (10km SE Rural) 43.35748, -1.57465* **Camping d'Ibarron, 64310 St Pée-sur-Nivelle [05 59 54 10 43; fax 05 59 54 51 95; camping.dibarron@wanadoo.fr; www.camping-ibarron.com]** Fr St Jean take D918 twd St Pée, site 2km bef St Pée on R of rd. Lge, shd; wc (mainly cont); chem disp; mv service pnt; shwrs inc; el pnts (6A) €3.95; gas 3km; Indtte; shop, tradsmn, snacks high ssn; supmkt adj; playgrnd; pool; sand beach 10km; wifi; TV/games rm; 5% statics; dogs €1.60; phone; Eng spkn; adv bkg; quiet, a little traff noise; red low ssn; CKE/CCI. "Well-kept site in scenic location; spacious pitches; welcoming, helpful owner; gd san facs; on main rd & no footpath to vill; walk along rv into vill; mkt Sat; excel." ♦ 1 May-30 Sep. € 19.80 2011*

ST JEAN DE LUZ *8F1 (10km SE Rural) 43.36288, -1.56638* **Camping Goyetchea, Route d'Ahetze, 64310 St Pée-sur-Nivelle [05 59 54 19 59; info@camping-goyetchea.com; www.camping-goyetchea.com]** Fr St Jean-de-Luz take D918 twd St Pée-sur-Nivelle. Turn L at Hotel Bonnet at Ibarron D855. Site on R in 800m. Med, pt shd; wc (some cont); chem disp; baby facs; shwrs inc; el pnts (6A) €3.80; gas; Indtte; shop; supmkt 800m; tradsmn; rest, snacks; bar; BBQ; playgrnd; pool; paddling pool; sand beach 10km; lake sw 4km; games area; wifi; entmnt; TV rm; 10% statics; dogs €1.50; adv bkg; quiet; ccard acc; red low ssn; CKE/CCI. "Excel site in lovely area; friendly, helpful owners; vg." ♦ 5 Jun-18 Sep. € 20.60 2010*

⊞ **ST JEAN DE LUZ** *8F1* (3km SW Rural) *43.37064, -1.68629* **Camping Larrouleta, 210 Route de Socoa, 64122 Urrugne [05 59 47 37 84; fax 05 59 47 42 54; info@larrouleta.com; www.larrouleta.com]** Exit A63 junc 2 St Jean-de-Luz Sud. Pass under D810 & take 1st L sp Urrugne. Loop back up to N10 & turn R, site sp in 500m. Or fr S on D810, 2km beyond Urrugne vill (by-pass vill), turn L into minor rd, site 50m on R. Lge, hdg/mkd pitch, hdstg, pt shd; htd wc; chem disp; baby facs; shwrs inc; el pnts (10A) inc (poss rev pol); gas; lndtte; shop; hypmkt 1.5km; tradsmn; rest (Jul/Aug); snacks; bar; playgrnd; htd, covrd pool; lake sw, fishing & boating; sand beach 3km; tennis; games; wifi; entmnt; no statics (2010); dogs €2; phone; bus 200m; poss cr; some Eng spkn; adv bkg ess high ssn; ccard acc; red low ssn; CKE/CCI; "Pleasant, well-run family site nr lake; satisfactory san facs (unisex low ssn) & pool; friendly & helpful (ask for dir on dep to avoid dangerous bend); some pitches unrel in wet but can park on site rds/ hdstg; poss ltd facs low ssn; conv A63, Biarritz & en rte Spain; gd; Conv m'way & hypermkt/fuel." ♦ ltd € 36.00 2014*

See advert on previous page

"There aren't many sites open at this time of year"

If you're travelling outside peak season remember to call ahead to check site opening dates – even if the entry says 'open all year'.

ST JEAN DE LUZ *8F1* (4km SW Coastal) *43.39320, -1.69310* **Camping Juantcho, Route de la Corniche, Socoa, 64122 Urrugne [tel/fax 05 59 47 11 97; camping.juantcho@orange.fr; www.camping-juantcho.com]** Leave A63 at junc 2. Keep to L lane & immed after passing toll booth take exit to Socoa, site on R on cliff top rd - busy & steep. Lge, hdg/mkd pitch, terr, pt shd; wc; chem disp; shwrs inc; el pnts (5A) €4.20; lndtte; shop & snacks in ssn; playgrnd; beach 500m; fishing, watersports; entmnt 500m; some statics; dogs €2.50; poss cr; quiet; red low ssn/long stay; CKE/CCI. "Pleasant site; beautiful beach; helpful, friendly staff; ltd facs low ssn; can get v windy at top of site; ferry fr Socoa to St Jean high ssn." 1 May-30 Sep. € 18.30 2010*

"That's changed – Should I let The Club know?"

If you find something on site that's different from the site entry, fill in a report and let us know. See www.caravanclub.co.uk/europereport.

ST JEAN DE LUZ *8F1* (7km SW Rural) *43.33277, -1.68527* **Camping Sunêlia du Col d'Ibardin, Route d'Ascain, 64122 Urrugne [05 59 54 31 21; fax 05 59 54 62 28; info@col-ibardin.com; www.col-ibardin.com]** Exit A63 junc 2, ignore slip rd to R 50m, turn L & in 100m turn R onto D810 S. In 2km at rndabt foll sp Col d'Ibardin, Ascain; after 4km site on R immed past minor rd to Col d'Ibardin. Med, hdg/mkd pitch, some hdstg, pt sl, pt terr, pt shd; 5% serviced pitch; wc; chem disp; baby facs; shwrs inc; el pnts (5-10A) €5.50-6.50 (poss rev pol); gas; lndtte (inc dryer); shop; tradsmn; supmkt 5km; rest, snacks & bar in ssn; BBQ; playgrnd; htd pool; paddling pool; sand beach 6km; tennis; games area; games rm; wifi; entmnt; TV; 5% statics; dogs €2.80; phone; Eng spkn; adv bkg; quiet; ccard acc; red low ssn/long stay; CKE/CCI. "Lovely, well-run site in woodland; fair sized pitches; helpful, friendly owner; gd san facs; pleasant bar/rest; mountain rlwy nr; gd touring base for Pyrenees & N Spain; excel." ♦ 1 Apr-30 Sep. € 32.00 2011*

See advertisement

ST JEAN PIED DE PORT *8F1* (3km E Rural) *43.17763, -1.21317* **Aire Naturelle La Paix des Champs (Jasses), Ferme Asoritzia, Route de Jaxu, 64220 St Jean-le-Vieux [05 59 37 02 63]** E fr St Jean-Pied-de-Port on D933. In 2km turn L onto D22 sp Jaxu, site on R in 1km. Sm, pt shd, wc; chem disp (wc); shwrs inc; el pnts (10A) inc; lndry facs; supmkt 1km; playgrnd; pool 2km; trout-fishing; dogs €0.50; quiet; CKE/CCI. "Lovely, peaceful site with mountain views; san facs OK but basic, stretched high ssn; poss run down low ssn; interesting town on pilgrim rte to Spain." ♦ ltd 15 Apr-30 Sep. € 12.50 2010*

ST JEAN PIED DE PORT *8F1* (200m S Urban) *43.16126, -1.23662* **Camp Municipal de Plaza Berri, Ave de Fronton, 64220 St Jean-Pied-de-Port [05 59 37 11 19 or 05 59 37 00 92; fax 05 59 37 99 78; mairie.stjeanpieddeport@wanadoo.fr; www.saintjeanpieddeport-paysbasque-tourisme.com]** Fr N on D933 thro town & cross rv. In 50m bear L at sm rndabt, site in 200m, sp. Enquire at Hôtel de Ville (Town Hall) off ssn. Narr app rds. Med, some mkd pitch; pt sl, pt shd; wc; chem disp; mv service pnt; shwrs inc; el pnts (5A) €2.50 (poss rev pol); shops 400m; pool 500m; quiet; CKE/CCI. "Nice site; busy, rec arr early high ssn; dogs; friendly warden; if recep unmanned, site yourself & report later; san facs need refurb (2011); gd walks & scenery; used by walkers on pilgrim rte; pelota court adj; mkt Mon; gd NH; lovely site." ♦ 23 Apr-1 Nov. € 13.00 2012*

ST JEAN PIED DE PORT *8F1* (1.5km W Rural) *43.17304, -1.25416* **Europ Camping, 64220 Ascarat [05 59 37 12 78; fax 05 59 37 29 82; europcamping64@orange.fr; www.europ-camping.com]** Site on D918 bet Uhart-Cize & Ascarat. Well sp. Med, hdg/mkd pitch, pt shd; wc; chem disp; mv service pnt; sauna; shwrs inc; el pnts (6A) €4 (poss rev pol); lndtte; shop 2km; tradsmn; rest, snacks; bar; playgrnd; pool; paddling pool; games area; games rm; 30% statics; dogs €2.50; adv bkg; quiet; ccard acc; red low ssn; CKE/CCI. "Beautiful location; helpful staff; ltd facs low ssn; only basic food in bar/rest; grnd v soft when wet; vg." ♦ 1 Apr-30 Sep. € 23.50 2011*

ST JEAN PIED DE PORT *8F1* (3km W Rural) *43.17745, -1.25970* **Camping Narbaïtz Vacances Pyrénées Basques, Route de Bayonne, 64220 Ascarat [05 59 37 10 13 or 05 59 37 09 22 (LS); fax 05 59 37 21 42; camping-narbaitz@wanadoo.fr; www.camping-narbaitz.com]** Site on L of D918 St Jean to Bayonne 3km fr St Jean, sp. Med, hdg/mkd pitch, pt sl, pt shd; htd wc (some cont); chem disp; mv service pnt; baby facs; shwrs inc; el pnts (6-10A) €4.50-5.50 (poss rev pol); lndtte (inc dryer); shop, snacks & bar in ssn; tradsmn; playgrnd; htd pool; trout-fishing; canoeing; kayaking; cycling; internet; entmnt; 5% statics; dogs free; phone; poss cr; Eng spkn; adv bkg; quiet; ccard acc high ssn; red low ssn; CKE/CCI. "Attractive, clean, family-run site; lovely views; helpful owners; vg facs; rec m'vans use top of site when wet; nr Spanish border (cheaper petrol); excel ." ♦ 26 Apr-12 Sep. € 45.80 2014*

ST JORY DE CHALAIS see Thiviers *7C3*

ST JULIEN DE LAMPON see Sarlat la Canéda *7C3*

ST JULIEN EN BORN *8E1* (2km W Rural) *44.07107, -1.24557* **Aire Naturelle Piou de Pelle, 1312 Route du Sable-Blanc, 40170 St Julien-en-Born [05 58 42 88 87; jacques.vigneres@orange.fr; http://vigneres.monsite-orange.fr]** Fr St Julien-en-Born cent take D652 N dir Bias; in 900m take 2nd turning to L after bdge over rv into Route du Stade; site on R in 1.5km. Sm, pt shd; wc; chem disp; shwrs inc; el pnts €3; shops 2km; BBQ; playgrnd; sand beach 5km; dogs; phone; adv bkg. "Quiet site; beautiful beaches nrby; friendly owners; vg." 1 May-30 Sep. € 10.50 2010*

ST JUSTIN *8E2* (2km NW Rural) *44.00166, -0.23502* **Camping Le Pin, Route de Roquefort, 40240 St Justin [tel/fax 05 58 44 88 91; campinglepin@wanadoo.fr; www.campinglepin.com]** Fr St Justin on D933, take D626 twd Roquefort. Site on L in 2km, well sp fr town. Sm, shd; wc; shwrs inc; el pnts (6A) €3; lndtte; shop & 2km; rest, snacks; bar; playgrnd; pool; rv fishing 2km; cycle hire; horseriding; games area; entmnt; TV; some statics; dogs €1.50; poss cr; adv bkg; quiet; red low ssn/snr citizens; CKE/CCI. "Pleasant, spacious site; facs old but clean & poss stretched when site full; beautiful vill." ♦ 1 Apr-30 Sep. € 18.00 2009*

ST LAURENT MEDOC *7C1* (2km N Rural) *45.17479, -0.83994* **Camping Le Paradis, 8 Rue Fournon, 33112 St Laurent-Médoc [tel/fax 05 56 59 42 15 or 06 27 73 50 00 (mob); leparadismedoc@orange.fr; www.leparadismedoc.com]** On W side of D1215 at Ballac. Med, hdg/mkd pitch, pt shd; wc; chem disp; mv service pnt; baby facs; shwrs inc; el pnts (10A) €4; lndtte; tradsmn; snacks; bar; playgrnd; pool; paddling pool; games area; wifi; entmnt; TV; some statics; dogs €1.60; adv bkg; quiet. "Excel site; helpful staff." 3 Apr-24 Oct. € 14.30 2010*

ST LEON SUR VEZERE see Montignac *7C3*

ST MARTIAL DE NABIRAT see Gourdon *7D3*

ST MARTIN DE SEIGNANX see Bayonne *8F1*

ST MEDARD DE GUIZIERES *7C2* (500m N Rural) *45.01989, -0.05876* **Camp Municipal Le Gua, Terrain du Guâ, 33230 St Médard-de-Guizières [tel/fax 05 57 69 82 37]** On N89 bet Libourne & Montpon-Ménestérol; in St Médard foll sp 'Base de Loisirs'; site adj sw pool. Med, mkd pitch, shd; wc (some cont); chem disp (wc); shwrs inc; el pnts €2.60; shop, rest, snacks, bar 500m; playgrnd; pool adj; rv fishing adj; dogs; quiet. "Conv Bordeaux, St Emillion & vineyards; vg." ♦ ltd 15 Jun-15 Sep. € 7.00 2009*

⊞ **ST MEDARD DE GUIZIERES** *7C2* (4km S Rural) *44.99694, -0.06330* **FLOWER Camping Le Pressoir, Queyrai, 33570 Petit-Palais-et-Cornemps [05 57 69 73 25; fax 05 57 69 77 36; contact@campinglepressoir.com; www.campinglepressoir.com / www.flowercampings.com]** Leave A89/E70 junc 11 onto D1089 E to St Médard-de-Guizières; then take D21 S & foll site sp 'Le Pressoir' (site bef Petit-Palais). Fr Castillon-la-Bataille on D936 Bergerac-Bordeaux rd take D17/D21 sp St Médard & foll site sp. Take care on access & exit. Med, hdg/mkd pitch, pt sl, pt shd; htd wc; chem disp; shwrs inc; el pnts (10A) inc; gas; lndtte; shop; tradsmn; rest, snacks; bar; BBQ; playgrnd; htd pool; cycle hire; games area; wifi; entmnt; TV rm; 30% statics; dogs €1.90; Eng spkn; adv bkg; quiet; ccard acc; red low ssn; CKE/CCI. "Close to vineyards; basic san facs; gd rest; 90% static tents and chalets not much space for tourers; facs excel but busy; lovely area for cycling." ♦ € 26.50 2012*

ST MICHEL ESCALUS see Léon *8E1*

STE NATHALENE see Sarlat la Canéda *7C3*

ST PALAIS (GIRONDE) see Mirambeau *7C2*

ST PEE SUR NIVELLE see St Jean de Luz *8F1*

ST SEURIN DE PRATS see Ste Foy la Grande *7C2*

ST SEVER *8E2* (1km N Urban) *43.76570, -0.56312* **FFCC Camping Les Rives de l'Adour, Ave René Crabos, 40500 St Sever [05 58 76 04 60; camping.deladour@orange.fr; www.camping-lesrivesdeladour.com]** S on D933 fr Mont-de-Marsan, cross D924 then bdge over Rv Adour. Look immed for access rd on L bef rlwy x-ing & steep climb up to St Sever. Site sp adj Parc des Sports. Med, hdg/mkd pitch, shd; htd wc; mv service pnt; shwrs inc; el pnts (13A) €2.50; sm shop & 1km; Indtte (inc dryer); playgrnd; pool nrby inc; tennis; sailing; fishing; cycle hire; games rm; wifi; TV; dogs €1.50; quiet; red low ssn/long stay. "Gd san facs; gd." 1 Apr-31 Oct. € 12.50 2009*

ST SOZY see Souillac *7C3*

ST SYLVESTRE SUR LOT see Villeneuve sur Lot *7D3*

"I like to fill in the reports as I travel from site to site"

You'll find report forms at the back of this guide, or you can fill them in online at www.caravaclub.co.uk/europereport.

⊞ **ST SYMPHORIEN** *7D2* (1km S Rural) *44.41831, -0.49232* **FFCC Camping La Hure, Route de Sore, 33113 St Symphorien [tel/fax 05 56 25 79 54 or 06 86 77 09 27 (mob); campingdelahure@wanadoo.fr]** S thro Langon on app to . Foll sp Villandraut, St Symphorien. Sp fr vill 1km S on D220, opp Intermarché. Med, shd; htd wc; chem disp; mv service pnt; shwrs inc; el pnts (5A) €2.50; Indtte; shops; rest, snacks; playgrnd; pool adj; tennis; rv fishing; many statics; dogs €1.30; adv bkg; red low ssn. "Helpful staff; basic facs; site in pinewoods; gd cycling, walks, beaches." € 9.00 2009*

ST VINCENT DE COSSE see Sarlat la Canéda *7C3*

ST VINCENT DE PAUL see Dax *8E1*

SALIES DE BEARN *8F1* (2km NW Urban) *43.47639, -0.9382* **Camp Municipal de Mosquéros, Ave Al Cartéro, 64270 Salies-de-Béarn [05 59 38 12 94; mairie-salies@wanadoo.fr]** Leave A64 at exit 7 onto D430 S sp Salies de Béarn. After 500m take D330 on R sp 'Casino' & turn R onto D17 at rndabt. Site sp in town, on D17 Bayonne rd NW of town. Site next to 'Base Plein Aire des Mosquéros'. NB Avoid town - narr streets & diff when busy. Med, hdg/mkd pitch, pt sl, terr, pt shd; wc; chem disp; shwrs inc; el pnts inc (10A) inc; Indtte; shops 2km; rest, snacks, bar 1km; pool, sports facs adj; fishing 1km; golf 2km; horseriding 3km; TV; quiet; "Excel site; excel serviced pitches; helpful warden; old but clean san facs; levelling blocks req some pitches; poss diff lge o'fits; barrier clsd 2200-0700; mkt Thu." ♦ 15 Mar-15 Oct. € 14.30 2009*

SALIGNAC EYVIGNES see Sarlat la Canéda *7C3*

SALLES (GIRONDE) *7D1* (500m SW Rural) *44.54475, -0.87506* **FFCC Camping Parc du Val de l'Eyre, 8 Route du Minoy, 33770 Salles [05 56 88 47 03; fax 05 56 88 47 27; levaldeleyre2@wanadoo.fr; www.camping-parcduvaldeleyre.com]** Exit junc 21 fr A63, foll dir to Salles on D3. On edge of Salles turn L on D108 at x-rds. Ent to site on L after rv opp Super U supmkt building. Lge, pt shd; wc; chem disp; mv service pnt; baby facs; shwrs inc; el pnts (6A) €4 (poss rev pol); gas; Indtte; shops adj; supmkt nr; rest, snacks; bar; BBQ; playgrnd; htd pool; lake & rv sw; fishing; canoeing; tennis 500km; games area; horseriding 8km; entmnt; 80% statics; dogs €4; quiet but entmnt poss noisy; ccard acc; red low ssn. "Attractive site; gd san facs but poss stretched when site busy; ltd facs low ssn; gd NH only; peaceful site by rv; gd size mkd pitches with access to water & drainage; refurbished unizex san facs (2013) v clean; conv for m'way; Carrefour opp; gd for long/sh stay." ♦ 01 Apr-15 Oct. € 49.80 2014*

⊞ **SALLES (GIRONDE)** *7D1* (4km SW Rural) *44.52039, -0.89631* **Camping Le Bilos, 37 Route de Bilos, 33770 Salles [05 56 88 36 53; fax 05 56 88 45 14; lebilos@aol.com; www.lebilos.com]** Exit A63 junc 21; foll sp Salles on D3; turn L onto D108/D108E3 sp Lugos; pass Carrefour supmkt on R; in 2km bear R & site on R in 2km. Med, pt shd; htd wc; chem disp; shwrs inc; el pnts (3-6A) €2.20-3.50; gas; Indtte; shop; supmkt 2.5km; BBQ sep area; playgrnd; 80% statics; dogs; adv bkg; quiet; "Pleasant, peaceful site in pine forest; sm, well-drained pitches, ltd space for tourers, friendly owners, old but clean san facs, ltd low ssn, cycle lane thro forest, vg NH en rte Spain; friendly welcome." € 16.00 2013*

SANGUINET *7D1* (3km N Rural) *44.49915, -1.07911* **Camping Lou Broustaricq, 2315 Route de Langeot, 40460 Sanguinet [05 58 82 74 82; fax 05 58 82 10 74; loubrousta@wanadoo.fr; www.lou-broustaricq.com]** Take Arcachon exit off Bordeax-Bayonne m'way. After 5km twd S on D3 & D216 to Sanguinet. Site sp in town off Bordeaux rd. V lge, mkd pitch, pt shd; htd wc (some cont); chem disp; shwrs inc; el pnts (10A) inc; Indtte (inc dryer); shop; rest, snacks, bar high ssn; BBQ; playgrnd; pool; waterslide; lake sw & sand beach 500m; watersports; sailing school; tennis; games area; cycle hire; entmnt; golf nr; wifi; TV rm; 60% statics; no dogs; Eng spkn; adv bkg; quiet; red low ssn; ccard acc; CKE/CCI. "In lovely wooded area; gd cycle tracks; gd for children; vg; touring pitches sep fr statics; nice pool; nr army base, some aircraft noise." ♦ 1 Apr-30 Sep. € 51.00 2013*

SANGUINET *7D1* (1.5km S Rural) *44.48372, -1.09449* **Campéole Camping Le Lac Sanguinet, 526 Rue de Pinton, 40460 Sanguinet [05 58 82 70 80; fax 05 58 82 14 24; lac-sanguinet@campeole.com; www.campeole.com]** Foll Le Lac sp at rndabt in Sanguinet, turn L on lakeside, site on L in 600m. Lge, mkd pitch, pt shd; wc; mv service pnt; shwrs inc; el pnts (6-10A) €4.10; Indtte; shops 500m; tradsmn; snacks; bar; BBQ (not charcoal); playgrnd; htd pool; paddling pool; sand beach, lake sw & sailing nrby; watersports; games area; games rm; cycle hire; wifi; entmnt; some statics; dogs €3.10; extra €26 for twin-axles; poss cr; quiet; red low ssn; CKE/CCI. "Spacious site in pine woods; cycle path around lake; san facs poss run down low ssn; friendly, helpful staff." 30 Apr-19 Sep. € 26.50 (CChq acc) 2009*

AQUITAINE

SARLAT LA CANEDA *7C3* (12km N Rural) *44.97450, 1.18832* **Camping Les Tailladis, 24200 Marcillac-St Quentin [05 53 59 10 95; fax 05 53 29 47 56; info@tailladis.com; www.tailladis.com]** N fr Sarlat on D704 dir Montignac. After 7km turn L & foll sp to site. NB Access along fairly narr lane. Med, hdg pitch, pt sl, terr, pt shd; wc; chem disp; mv service pnt; shwrs inc; el pnts (10A) €4.20; gas; lndtte; shop; rest, snacks & bar (Apr-Oct); pool; lake sw; fishing; canoeing; 6% statics; dogs €2.20; phone; poss cr; Eng spkn; adv bkg; ccard acc; red low ssn. "Excel site; friendly & helpful Dutch owners; immac san facs, ltd early ssn; vg food in rest; c'van storage." ♦ 1 Mar-30 Nov. € 22.00 2014*

SARLAT LA CANEDA *7C3* (6km NE Rural) *44.90404, 1.28210* **Camping Les Grottes de Roffy, 24200 Ste Nathalène [05 53 59 15 61; fax 05 53 31 09 11; contact@roffy.fr; www.roffy.fr]** Fr N end of Sarlat take D47 NE for Ste Nathalène. Site on R 1km bef vill. Or fr A20 exit junc 55 onto ND804/D703 dir Carlux. Turn R onto D61B then D47 to Ste Nathalène, site thro vill on L. Lge, hdg/mkd pitch, terr, pt shd; htd wc; chem disp; baby facs; shwrs inc; el pnts (6A) €3; gas; lndtte; shop; tradsmn; rest, snacks; bar; BBQ; playgrnd; 4 pools inc paddling pool; canoeing; tennis; games area; games rm; cycle hire; entmnt; 40% statics (inc tour ops); dogs €2.10; extra for 'comfort' pitches; Eng spkn; adv bkg (ess Jul/Aug); CKE/CCI. "Excel rest & shop; helpful staff; lovely site." ♦ 17 Apr-19 Sep. € 25.30 2009*

SARLAT LA CANEDA *7C3* (7km NE Rural) *44.91825, 1.27870* **Camping Domaine des Mathévies, Les Mathévies, 24200 Ste Nathalène [05 53 59 20 86 or 06 14 10 95 86 (mob); mathevies@mac.com; www.mathevies.com]** Exit A20 junc 55 Souillac & foll sp Roufillac. At Roufillac, foll sp to Carlux & cont to Ste Nathalène, site sp N of Ste Nathèlene. Sm, hdg/mkd pitch, pt shd; wc; chem disp; mv service pnt; shwrs; el pnts (10A) €4; snacks; bar; playgrnd; pool; paddling pool; tennis; games area; wifi; sat TV; some statics; dogs €1.50; adv bkg; quiet. "Gd, British-owned site; lge pitches, most with views." ♦ 19 Apr-20 Sep. € 21.50 SBS - D04 2010*

SARLAT LA CANEDA *7C3* (8km NE Rural) *44.90030, 1.29700* **Camping La Châtaigneraie, 24370 Prats-de-Carlux [05 53 59 03 61 or 05 53 30 29 03 (LS); fax 05 53 29 86 16; lachataigneraie@orange.fr; www.lachataigneraie24.com]** Fr Sarlat take D704 E twd Souillac, after 3km turn L onto D704A/D703. At Rouffillac turn L opp rv bdge onto D61 sp Carlux. In Carlux fork L onto D47B & in 4km turn L at site sp, site on R in 500m. Med, hdg/mkd pitch, terr, pt shd; wc; chem disp; baby facs; shwrs inc; jaccuzi; el pnts (10A) inc (poss rev pol); gas; lndtte; shop; rest, snacks; sm bar; BBQ (elec/charcoal); playgrnd; htd pool; paddling pool; waterslide; fishing; tennis; games area; cycle circuit; wifi; entmnt; games/TV rm; dogs €2.30; no c'vans/m'vans over 7m (inc towbar) high ssn; poss cr; quiet; ccard acc; red low ssn. "Excel site; friendly, helpful owners; vg clean san facs; vg pool area; some pitches diff due position of trees; mkt Sarlat Wed & Sat am." ♦ 21 Apr-16 Sep. € 32.50 2011*

SARLAT LA CANEDA *7C3* (9km NE Rural) *44.90803, 1.29212* **Camping La Palombière, 24200 Ste Nathalène [05 53 59 42 34; fax 05 53 28 45 40; la.palombiere@wanadoo.fr; www.lapalombiere.fr]** Take D47 fr Sarlat to Ste Nathalène, thro vill, past Mill Rest, fork L on o'skts by cemetary. Site sp on R in 300m - sharp R turn & access poss diff. Med, terr, shd; wc; chem disp; baby facs; shwrs inc; el pnts (10A) €3; lndtte; shop; rest, snacks; bar; BBQ; htd pools; waterslide; tennis; gym; games rm; games area; entmnt; TV; 70% statics (tour ops); dogs €2; Eng spkn; adv bkg; quiet; 10% red low ssn. "Lovely, well-run site; friendly owners; immac san facs; vg rest with views; poss diff for lge o'fits due trees, narr site rds & pitch sizes; highly rec." ♦ 30 Apr-13 Sep. € 25.70 2009*

SARLAT LA CANEDA *7C3* (10km NE Rural) *44.95778, 1.27280* **Camping Les Péneyrals, Le Poujol, 24590 St Crépin-et-Carlucet [05 53 28 85 71; fax 05 53 28 80 99; camping.peneyrals@wanadoo.fr; www.peneyrals.com]** Fr Sarlat N on D704; D60 E dir Salignac-Eyvignes to Le Poujol; S to St Crépin. Site sp. Lge, hdg pitch, pt sl, terr, pt shd; htd wc; chem disp; mv service pnt; all serviced pitch; baby facs; shwrs inc; el pnts (5-10A) €3.40-3.90; lndtte; shop; rest, snacks; bar; playgrnd; 4 pools (1 htd, covrd); paddling pool; waterslide; fishing; tennis; games area; entmnt; 50% statics; dogs €2.40; phone adj; Eng spkn; adv bkg; quiet; red low ssn; ccard acc; red low ssn. "Friendly owners; superb family & touring site." ♦ 11 May-12 Sep. € 29.20 2010*

SARLAT LA CANEDA *7C3* (12km NE Rural) *44.96347, 1.32817* **FLOWER Camping Le Temps de Vivre, Route de Carlux, 24590 Salignac-Eyvignes [tel/fax 05 53 28 93 21; contact@temps-de-vivre.com; www.temps-de-vivre.com / www.flowercampings.com]** Fr Sarlat N on D704, bear R onto D60 to Salignac-Eyvigues. Fr Salignac take D61 S dir Carlux, site sp in 1.5km on R. Sm, hdg/mkd pitch, terr, pt shd; wc; chem disp; mv service pnt; baby facs; fam bthrm; shwrs inc; el pnts (10A) €4; gas; lndtte; shop; tradsmn; BBQ; supmkt 2km; rest & bar (high ssn); snacks; pool; playgrnd; games area; golf; tennis; fishing; dogs €2; 40% statics; poss cr; quiet; phone; adv bkg (fee); Eng spkn; ccard acc; CKE/CCI. "Lovely, well-kept site; gd sized pitches; friendly, helpful owners; lge o'fits poss diff access some pitches; rec." ♦ 23 Apr-24 Sep. € 21.50 2011*

SARLAT LA CANEDA *7C3* (1km E Rural) *44.89328, 1.22756* **Camping Indigo Sarlat Les Périères, Rue Jean Gabin, 24200 Sarlat-la-Canéda [05 53 59 05 84; fax 05 53 28 57 51; sarlat@camping-indigo.com; www.camping-indigo.com]** Site on R of D47 to Proissans & Ste Nathalène. NB steep access rds. Med, mkd pitch, terr, shd; wc; mv service pnt; sauna; baby facs; shwrs inc; el pnts (6A) €3.90; gas; lndry rm; shop; tradsmn; bar; BBQ (gas/charcoal); playgrnd; 2 pools (1 htd covrd); games rm; tennis; some statics; dogs; poss cr; Eng spkn; adv bkg; quiet; ccard acc; red low ssn. "Lovely site; friendly, helpful staff; san facs clean too few; excel pool complex; steep site rds; access poss diff med & lge o'fits; excel." ♦ ltd Easter-30 Sep. € 27.50 2010*

See advert on next page

SARLAT LA CANEDA *7C3* (10km E Rural) *44.8674, 1.3578* **Camping Les Ombrages, Rouffillac, 24370 Carlux [09 53 53 25 55; fax 05 53 28 62 18; ombragesperigord@free.fr; www.ombrages.fr]** 12km W thro Souillac on D703. Turn L at x-rds in Rouffillac & immed turn L bef rv bdge into site. Med, some mkd pitch, pt shd; wc; chem disp; shwrs inc; el pnts (6A) €2.70; gas 1km; Indtte; shop 1km; tradsmn (high ssn); rest 500m; snacks; bar; BBQ; playgrnd; pool adj; rv sw adj; fishing; tennis; games area; cycle & canoe hire; internet; TV rm; 2% statics; dogs €2; phone; poss cr; Eng spkn; adv bkg; quiet but some rd noise; ccard acc; red low ssn; CKE/CCI. "Pleasant, well-kept, rvside site; enthusiastic new owners live on site; pitching poss diff due trees; san facs (open air) poss stretched high ssn; cycle track; vg; lovely peaceful site; lots of entmnt." 15 Apr-15 Oct. € 13.00 2012*

SARLAT LA CANEDA *7C3* (12km E Rural) *44.86345, 1.37350* **Camping Le Mondou, Le Colombier, 24370 St Julien-de-Lampon [tel/fax 05 53 29 70 37; lemondou@camping-dordogne.info; www.camping-dordogne.info]** Fr Sarlat-la-Canéda take D704/D703 E; cross rv at Rouffillac, ent St Julien-de-Lampon & turn L at x-rds; site sp on R in 2km. Med, hdg/mkd pitch, pl, pt shd; wc; chem disp; mv service pnt; baby facs; shwrs inc; el pnts (6A) €3.50; gas 700m; Indtte; shop 2km; tradsmn; rest, snacks; bar; BBQ; playgrnd; pool & paddling pool; rv sw, fishing & waterports 300m; games rm; games area; cycle hire; wifi; 10% statics; dogs €1; phone; poss cr; Eng spkn; adv bkg; quiet; red low ssn. "Beautiful views; friendly, helpful owners; sm, uneven pitches; gd cycle paths." ♦ 1 May-15 Oct. € 21.00 2012*

SARLAT LA CANEDA *7C3* (5km SE Rural) *44.85480, 1.23760* **Camping Les Acacias, Route de Cahors, 24200 Sarlat-la-Canéda [05 53 31 08 50; fax 05 53 59 29 30; camping-acacias@wanadoo.fr; www.acacias.fr]** Foll sp La Canéda vill & site fr D704 S fr Sarlat. NB Last few metres of app v narr rd. Med, hdg/mkd pitch, pt sl, shd; wc; chem disp; mv service pnt; baby facs; shwrs inc; el pnts (6-10A) €3.50-4.50; gas; Indtte; supmkt 3km; tradsmn; rest, snacks; bar; playgrnd; 2 pools; games area; wifi; entmnt; some statics; dogs €1.50; phone; bus; adv bkg; quiet; ccard acc; red low ssn/CKE/CCI. "Clean, modern san facs; helpful, enthusiastic owners; ideal touring base; mkt Wed & Sat." 1 Apr-30 Sep. € 16.50 2010*

SARLAT LA CANEDA *7C3* (10km SE Rural) *44.81536, 1.29245* **Camping Les Granges, 24250 Groléjac [05 53 28 11 15; fax 05 53 28 57 13; contact@lesgranges-fr.com; www.lesgranges-fr.com]** Fr Sarlat take D704 SE, sp Gourdon. Site sp nr cent of Groléjac on R. Care on acute corner after rlwy bdge. Med, hdg, terr, pt shd; wc; chem disp; baby facs; serviced pitches; shwrs inc; el pnts (6A) €3.80; gas; Indtte (inc dryer); shop; rest, snacks; bar; playgrnd; htd pool; paddling pool; waterslide; rv & lake fishing 1km; cycle hire; games rm; wifi; entmnt; TV; 40% statics; dogs €3; poss cr; Eng spkn; adv bkg; ccard acc; red low ssn; CKE/CCI. "Historical & beautiful area; vg site & facs." ♦ 23 Apr-11 Sep. € 26.50 2014*

SARLAT LA CANEDA *7C3* (11km SE Rural) *44.83274, 1.26626* **Camping Le Plein Air des Bories, 24200 Carsac-Aillac [tel/fax 05 53 28 15 67; camping.lesbories@wanadoo.fr]** Take D704 SE fr Sarlat sp Gourdon; diff RH turn to site after Carsac vill. Easier access on D703 fr Vitrac. Med, pt sl, shd; wc (male cont); baby facs; shwrs; el pnts (3-6A) inc; gas; Indtte; sm shop & 1.5km; tradsmn; snacks; bar; htd pool; rv sw, canoe hire, boating & fishing; tennis 700m; dogs €1.30; poss cr; Eng spkn; quiet; CKE/CCI. "Clean, shady rvside site; friendly owners." ♦ 1 Jun-15 Sep. € 18.00 2012*

SARLAT LA CANEDA *7C3* (13km SE Rural) *44.80227, 1.29448* **Camping du Lac de Groléjac, Plan d'Eau, 24250 Groléjac [05 53 59 48 70; fax 05 53 29 39 74; contact@camping-dulac-dordogne.com; www.camping-dulac-dordogne.com]** On D704 SE fr Sarlat twd Goudon, Groléjac in 11km. In vill cent, foll sp 'Plan d'Eau'; pass thro vill & turn R in front of Le Marais Rest, in 100m turn L dir Nabirat. Site on L in 500m. Med, hdg pitch, pt shd; wc; chem disp; baby facs; shwrs; el pnts (10A) €3; gas; Indtte; sm shop; sm rest, snacks; bar; playgrnd; sand beach & lake sw; fishing; watersports; cycle hire; wifi; dogs €1.50; Eng spkn; adv bkg; quiet; ccard acc; CKE/CCI. "Popular site on man-made lake with artificial sand beach; excel." ♦ 15 Apr-15 Oct. € 11.50 2009*

AQUITAINE

SARLAT LA CANEDA *7C3* (6km S Rural) *44.82375, 1.25080* **Camping La Bouysse de Caudon, 24200 Vitrac [05 53 28 33 05; fax 05 53 30 38 52; info@labouysse.com; www.labouysse.com]** S fr Sarlat on D46 dir Vitrac. At Vitrac 'port' bef bdge turn L onto D703 sp Carsac. In 2km turn R & foll site sp, site on L. Well sp. Med, hdg/mkd pitch, pt shd; wc; chem disp; baby facs; shwrs inc; el pnts (10A) €4.80; gas; lndtte; shop; tradsmn; rest, snacks; bar; BBQ; playgrnd; pool; rv sw & shgl beach; fishing; canoe hire; tennis; games area; wifi; entmnt; 8% statics; dogs €2; phone; poss cr; Eng spkn; adv bkg (dep); quiet; ccard acc; red low ssn; CKE/CCI. "Beautiful family-run site on Rv Dordogne; helpful owner; plenty gd clean san facs; gd access rv beach; muddy when wet; many Bastides in area; excel." ♦ 2 Apr-25 Sep. € 21.70 2014*

See advertisement

“We must tell The Club about that great site we found”

Get your site reports in by mid-August and we'll do our best to get your updates into the next edition.

SARLAT LA CANEDA *7C3* (8km S Rural) *44.82525, 1.25360* **Domaine de Soleil-Plage, Caudon-par-Montfort, 24200 Vitrac [05 53 28 33 33; fax 05 53 28 30 24; info@soleilplage.fr; www.soleilplage.fr]** On D46, 6km S of Sarlat twd Vitrac, turn L onto D703 to Château Montfort, R to site dir Caudon, sp. Site beyond Camping La Bouysse on rvside, 2km E of Vitrac. If coming fr Souillac on D703, when app Montfort rd v narr with overhanging rock faces. Narr access rds on site. Lge, hdg pitch, pt shd; htd wc; chem disp; mv service pnt; baby facs; serviced pitches; shwrs inc; el pnts (16A) inc (poss rev pol); gas; lndtte (inc dryer); shop; rest, snacks; bar; BBQ; playgrnd; htd pool; paddling pool; waterslide; rv sand beach adj; fishing; canoeing; tennis; cycle hire; golf 1km; horseriding 5km; games rm; wifi; entmnt; TV; 45% statics; dogs €3.50; no c'vans/m'vans over 7m Jun-Aug; phone; Eng spkn; adv bkg ess Jul/Aug; quiet; ccard acc; red low ssn/groups; CKE/CCI. "Lovely site in beautiful location; friendly, welcoming owner; variety of pitches - extra for serviced/rvside (shady); san facs clean; superb aquatic complex; poss muddy when wet; highly rec; first class comprehensive site." ♦ 11 Apr-29 Sep. € 51.20 (CChq acc) SBS - D15 2014*

See advertisement

SARLAT LA CANEDA *7C3* (9km S Rural) *44.81628, 1.21508* **Camping Beau Rivage, Gaillardou, 24250 La Roque-Gageac [05 53 28 32 05; fax 05 53 29 63 56; camping.beau.rivage@wanadoo.fr; www.beaurivagedordogne.com]** On S side of D703, 1km W of Vitrac adj Rv Dordogne. Lge, mkd pitch, pt shd; htd wc (some cont); chem disp; baby facs; shwrs inc; el pnts (6A) €3.50; gas; lndtte; shop; rest 200m; snacks; bar; playgrnd; htd pool; rv beach; canoeing; tennis; games area; cycle hire; horseriding; archery; golf 2km; wifi; entmnt; TV; some statics; dogs €3; phone; poss cr; Eng spkn; adv bkg rec high ssn; quiet; red low ssn. "Gd touring base." ♦ 4 Apr-20 Sep. € 23.65 2013*

"I need an on-site restaurant"

We do our best to make sure site information is correct, but it is always best to check any must-have facilities are still available or will be open during your visit.

SARLAT LA CANEDA *7C3* (9km S Rural) *44.82442, 1.16939* **Camping La Plage, 83 Près La Roque-Gageac, 24220 Vézac [06 85 23 22 16; campinglaplage24@orange.fr; www.camping-laplage.fr]** On banks of Rv Dordogne, 500m W of La Roque-Gageac on D703. Med, mkd pitch, shd; wc; chem disp (wc); shwrs inc; el pnts (3A) €2.40; gas; sm shop 1km; BBQ; playgrnd; pool; shgl beach & rv sw; fishing; canoeing; some statics; poss cr; adv bkg; quiet; red CKE/CCI. "Attractive site; excel pitches; kind, helpful owers; ltd facs low ssn; highly rec; ccard not acc; new (2012) immac san facs." 1 Apr-30 Sep. € 20.00 2012*

SARLAT LA CANEDA *7C3* (9km S Rural) *44.78648, 1.20930* **Camping Le Pech de Caumont, 24250 Cénac-et-St-Julien [05 53 28 21 63 or 05 53 28 30 67; fax 05 53 29 99 73; jmilhac@pech-de-caumont.com; www.pech-de-caumont.com]** D46 fr Sarlat to Cénac, cross rv & cont on D46 thro Cénac; site ent on L 500m past End of Vill sp. Do not go thro Domme. Med, hdg/mkd pitch, pt sl, terr, pt shd; wc; chem disp; shwrs inc; el pnts (6A) €3.10; lndtte; shops 1km; snacks & sm bar (400 high ssn); BBQ; playgrnd; pool; rv sw 2km; TV rm; 20% statics; dogs; phone; poss cr; Eng spkn; adv bkg; quiet; ccard acc; red low ssn; CKE/CCI. "Views fr most pitches; modern, clean san facs; helpful owners; popular, tidy, family-run site; excel." 15 Jun-15 Sept. € 15.45 2012*

SARLAT LA CANEDA *7C3* (10km S Rural) *44.80436, 1.20589* **Camp Municipal, Le Port de Domme, 24250 Cénac-et-St Julien [05 53 28 31 91 or 05 53 31 41 31 (Mairie)]** D46 fr Sarlat to Vitrac then Cénac; cross rv & site on L on ent Cénac. Med, mkd pitch, pt shd; wc; chem disp; shwrs inc; el pnts (6A) inc (poss long lead req); lndtte; shop, rest, snacks, bar 200m; playgrnd; rv sw, boating & fishing adj; games area; dogs; phone; adv bkg; quiet; no ccard acc. "Pleasant site in excel rvside location; clean facs but dated & ltd low ssn; grnd rather rough & poss flooded after rain; site opens earlier if demand; vg NH." 1 Jun-15 Sep. € 13.60 2009*

SARLAT LA CANEDA *7C3* (10km S Rural) *44.81521, 1.22362* **Camping La Rivière de Domme, 24250 Domme [05 53 28 33 46; fax 05 53 29 56 04; contact@camping-riviere-domme.com; www.camping-riviere-domme.com]** Fr Sarlat take D46 to Vitrac. Cross rv bdge on D46E. In 1km at T-junc turn R on D50 & in 1km turn R at sp into site. Sm, pt shd; wc; chem disp; shwrs inc; el pnts (10A) €2.50 (poss rev pol); lndtte; shops 4km; playgrnd; pool; games area; few statics; Eng spkn; adv bkg; quiet; red low ssn. "Generous pitches; pleasant owner; modern san facs; many walks fr site." ♦ 4 Apr-3 Oct. € 32.00 2014*

"Satellite navigation makes touring much easier"

Remember most sat navs don't know if you're towing or in a larger vehicle – always use yours alongside maps and site directions.

SARLAT LA CANEDA *7C3* (11km S Rural) *44.82527, 1.24222* **Camping La Sagne, Lieu dit Lassagne, 24200 Vitrac [05 53 28 18 36; info@camping-la-sagne.com; www.camping-la-sagne.com]** On A20 exit 55 (Souillac) & head twds Sarlat; take D703 in dir Montfort; turn L & foll sp to site. Med, mkd pitch; wc; chem disp; el pnts (16A) inc; shop; bar; playgrnd; pool; paddling pool; jacuzzi; rv fishing; wifi; dogs €3; Eng spkn; quiet; ccard acc. "Superb location in the Dordogne; undergoing major refurb for the 2012 ssn." 6 Apr-30 Sep. € 30.00 2011*

See advertisement

SARLAT LA CANEDA *7C3* (10km S Rural) *44.82181, 1.22587* **Camping Le Bosquet, La Rivière, 24250 Domme [05 53 28 37 39; fax 05 53 29 41 95; info@lebousquet.com; www.lebosquet.com]** Fr Sarlat take D46 S to Vitrac cross rv on D46E. Sp at junc, site 500m on R. Sm, hdg/mkd pitch, pt shd, wc; chem disp; shwrs inc; el pnts (6A) €2.50 (long lead poss req); gas; lndtte; sm shop; tradsmn; snacks; pool; rv sw & fishing 500m; wifi; 50% statics; dogs €2; Eng spkn; adv bkg; quiet; CKE/CCI. "Lovely peaceful site with friendly, helpful owners; excel updated san facs but poss stretched high ssn; gd shd but sm pitches; gd views of Domme." ♦ 11 Apr-27 Sep. € 27.70 2014*

SARLAT LA CANEDA *7C3* (10km S Rural) *44.81725, 1.21944* **Camping Le Perpetuum, 24250 Domme [05 53 28 35 18; fax 05 53 29 63 64; luc.parsy@wanadoo.fr; www.campingleperpetuum.com]** Fr Sarlat take D46 to Vitrac; cross rv bdge to D46E; in 1km turn R onto D50, R again in 1km at site sp. Med, hdg/mkd pitch, hdstg, pt shd; wc; chem disp; mv service pnt; baby facs; shwrs inc; el pnts (10A) €3.50; lndtte; sm shop (farm produce); supmkt 3km; tradsmn; snacks; bar; BBQ; playgrnd; pool; rv sw & beach adj (Rv Dordogne); canoeing; games area; entmnt; TV rm statics; dogs €2; poss cr; some Eng spkn; adv bkg; quiet; ccard acc; red low ssn/CKE/CCI; wifi. "Site fronts rv; busy high ssn; relaxed, friendly atmosphere; gd sized pitches; cheerful, helpful owners; gd san facs; gd pool; gd local dog walks; late arr area at ent." ♦ 1 May-10 Oct. € 36.40 2014*

See advertisement

"There aren't many sites open at this time of year"

If you're travelling outside peak season remember to call ahead to check site opening dates – even if the entry says 'open all year'.

SARLAT LA CANEDA *7C3* (12km S Rural) *44.79175, 1.16266* **Camping Bel Ombrage, 24250 St Cybranet [05 53 28 34 14; fax 05 53 59 64 64; belombrage@wanadoo.fr; www.belombrage.com]** Fr Sarlat take D46 sp Bergerac, rd then conts as D57; after 8km turn L at Vézac sp Castelnaund. After 1.6km at T-junc turn L onto D703 & in 180m turn R onto D57. Cont thro Castelnaund on D57; site on L in 3km. Lge, hdg pitch, shd; wc; chem disp; baby facs; shwrs inc; el pnts (10A) inc; gas 800m; lndtte (inc dryer); tradsmn; shop 800m; rest, snacks & bar 100m; BBQ; playgrnd; pool; paddling pool; rv sw & beach; fishing; tennis 800m; cycle hire; horseriding 2km; games area; wifi; games/TV rm; library; dogs free; no c'vans/m'vans over 8m high ssn; adv bkg; quiet; ccard acc; red long stay; CKE/CCI. "Attractive, well-run site by rv; popular with British; lge pitches; modern san facs; peaceful early ssn; ideal base for Dordogne; mkt Thur; excel." ♦ 1 Jun-4 Sep. € 22.70 SBS - D01 2012*

SARLAT LA CANEDA *7C3* (8km SW Rural) *44.83560, 1.15873* **Camping Les Deux Vallées, La Gare, 24220 Vézac [05 53 29 53 55; fax 05 53 31 09 81; contact@campingles2vallees.com; www.campingles2vallees.com]** Exit A20 junc 55 onto D804 dir Sarlat-la-Caneda; cont onto D703/D704A/D704 to Sarlat; then take D57 SW to Vézac; immed after sp for vill take 1st R to site. Or fr E leave D703 onto D57; 250m after junc with D49 turn L & foll sp to site. Med, hdg/mkd pitch, hdstg, pt shd; htd wc; chem disp; baby facs; shwrs inc; el pnts (6-10A) €4.10; gas; Indtte (inc dryer); ice; shop; tradsmn; rest, snacks; bar; BBQ; 2 playgrnds; 3 pools; rv 500m, shgl beach; cycle hire; games area; games rm; entmnt July/Aug (in Dutch); TV; 6% statics; dogs €2; poss cr; Eng spkn; adv bkg ess Jul/Aug; quiet but rlwy adj; ccard acc; red low ssn/long stay; CKE/CCI; "Excel site; helpful, friendly Dutch owners; ltd san facs low ssn; poss muddy when wet; gd local walks; poss long leads req; some reverse polarity; ltd water points; pitch 71,72 &73 too restricted for caravan access." ♦ 17 Feb-12 Nov. € 41.00 2013*

See advert on previous page

"That's changed – Should I let The Club know?"

If you find something on site that's different from the site entry, fill in a report and let us know. See www.caravanclub.co.uk/europereport.

SARLAT LA CANEDA *7C3* (9km SW Rural) *44.82585, 1.15322* **Camping La Cabane, 24220 Vézac [05 53 29 52 28; fax 05 53 59 09 15; contact@lacabanedordogne.com; www.lacabanedordogne.com]** Fr Sarlat-La-Canéda take D57 thro Vézac. On leaving Vézac turn L immed bef rlwy bdge, site sp on R on bank of Rv Dordogne. Lge, hdg/mkd pitch, pt shd; wc; shwrs inc; el pnts (6-10A) €2;60-3.20; gas; Indtte; shop high ssn; rest & snacks 3km; BBQ; playgrnd; htd covrd pool; rv sw & shgl beach adj; TV rm; internet; some statics; dogs €1; phone; poss cr; Eng spkn; adv bkg; quiet; ccard acc; red low ssn; CKE/CCI. "Well-shd, rvside site; lge pitches; clean facs; friendly, helpful family owners; rvside walk to Beynac Château; gd." ♦ ltd 1 Apr-30 Sep. € 12.20 2010*

SARLAT LA CANEDA *7C3* (10km SW Rural) *44.83819, 1.14846* **Camping Le Capeyrou, 24220 Beynac-et-Cazenac [05 53 29 54 95; fax 05 53 28 36 27; lecapeyrou@wanadoo.fr; www.campinglecapeyrou.com]** Fr W on D703 on R (opp sm supmkt & baker) immed past vill of Beynac. Or fr N on D57 fr Sarlat; in vill immed on L on rv. Med, hdg pitch, some hdstg, pt shd; wc; chem disp; mv service pnt; baby facs; shwrs inc; el pnts (6-10A) €3.50-4.20; Indtte; shop & rest adj; snacks; bar; playgrnd; pool; wifi; dogs €2: poss cr; Eng spkn; adv bkg; some rd & rlwy noise; ccard acc; red low ssn. "View of chateau most pitches; helpful, friendly owners; clean san facs; excel lge pool; rvside walk to attractive vill; excel NH." ♦ Apr-30 Sep. € 27.80 2012*

"I like to fill in the reports as I travel from site to site"

You'll find report forms at the back of this guide, or you can fill them in online at www.caravaclub.co.uk/europereport.

SARLAT LA CANEDA *7C3* (10km SW Rural) *44.80519, 1.15852* **Camping Maisonneuve, Vallée de Céou, 24250 Castelnaud-la-Chapelle [05 53 29 51 29; fax 05 53 30 27 06; contact@campingmaisonneuve.com; www.campingmaisonneuve.com]** Take D57 SW fr Sarlat sp Beynac. Cross Rv Dordogne at Castelnaud; site sp 500m on L out of Castelnaud on D57 twd Daglan. Foll narr rd across bdge (or alt ent - cont on D57 for 2km, sp on L for c'vans). Med, hdg/mkd pitch, some hdstg, pt shd; htd wc (some cont); chem disp; mv service pnt; child/baby facs; fam bthrm; shwrs inc; el pnts (6-10A) €4-4.90; gas; Indtte; shop, rest, snacks & bar high ssn; BBQ; playgrnd; pool; paddling pool; rv & shgl beach; fishing; tennis 2km; cycle hire; games rm; wifi; entmnt; TV rm; 10% statics; dogs €2; Eng spkn; adv bkg ess high ssn; quiet; ccard acc; red low ssn/CKE/CCI. "Vg, spacious site; helpful owners; modern, clean facs; gd walking, cycling." ♦ 27 Mar- 2 Nov. € 20.40 2011*

See advertisement

SARLAT LA CANEDA *7C3* (18km SW Rural) *44.83610, 1.06230* **Domaine Le Cro Magnon, La Raisse, 24220 Allas-les-Mines [05 53 29 13 70; fax 05 53 29 15 79; contact@domaine-cro-magnon.com; www.domaine-cro-magnon.com]** Fr Sarlat two Bergerac/Le Buisson on D57/D703 turn L after St Cyprien & rv x-ing onto D48 sp site & Berbiguières. Approx 1.5km after Berbiguières turn L at site sp. Do not foll any earlier sp to site as rds impassable to c'vans & m'vans. App steep, narr & twisting but gd surface. NB App via Berbiguières only. Med, pt shd; wc; chem disp; mv service pnt; baby facs; sauna; jaccuzi; shwrs inc; el pnts (6A) inc; gas; lndtte (inc dryer); shop; rest, snacks; bar; BBQ (gas/elec); playgrnd; 2 pools (1 htd covrd); waterslides; paddling pool; rv fishing 800m; horseriding nrby; tennis; cycle hire; games area; sm gym; wifi; entmnt; games/TV rm; dogs €3.60; no c'vans/m'vans over 10m; adv bkg; quiet; ccard acc; red low ssn. "Lge pitches, many in shady, woodland setting; gd, clean san facs." ♦ 16 Jun-15 Sep. € 30.40 2011*

SARLAT LA CANEDA *7C3* (9km W Rural) *44.90805, 1.11527* **Camping Le Moulin du Roch, Le Roch, Route des Eyzies, 24200 Sarlat-la-Canéda [05 53 59 20 27; fax 05 53 59 20 95; moulin.du.roch@wanadoo.fr; www.moulin-du-roch.com / www.les-castels.com]** Fr A20 take exit 55 at Souillac dir Sarlat. Head for D704 twds Sarlat La Caneda. At rndabt in Sarlat (just under rlwy viaduct) take 2nd exit onto bypass. Take 2nd exit at next rndabt staying on D704. At next rndabt take 2nd exit onto D6 dir Les Eyzies (becomes D47). Site on L in approx 9 km on D47. Fr N on D704 to Sarlat, turn R at hypmkt, then as above. Lge, hdg/mkd pitch, terr, pt shd; htd wc; chem disp; mv service pnt; baby facs; some serviced pitches; shwrs inc; el pnts (6A) inc; gas; lndtte (inc dryer); shop; rest, snacks; bar; BBQ (gas/charcoal only); playgrnd; htd pool; paddling pool with mini waterslide; fishing lake; tennis; canoeing & horseriding nrby; wifi; entmnt; games/TV rm; 45% statics; no dogs; twin-axles; Eng spkn; adv bkg rec Jun-Aug; quiet; ccard acc; red low ssn/long stay; CKE/CCI. "Well-run, family owned site; lge pitches; clean facs but poss long, steep walk;some noise fr adj rd; gd rest & pool; m'vans poss not acc after prolonged heavy rain due soft grnd; mkt Sat." ♦ 17 May-20 Sep. € 52.00 (CChq acc) SBS - D02 2014*

SARLAT LA CANEDA *7C3* (9km W Rural) *44.89382, 1.11322* **Camping Les Charmes, Malartigue-Haut, 24200 St André-d'Allas [05 53 31 02 89 or 06 74 22 45 70 (mob); fax 05 53 31 06 32; les.charmes@wanadoo.fr; www.campinglescharmesdordogne.com]** Fr Sarlat dir St Cyprien on D25; site on R 200m bef rd forks with D35 to Le Bugue; 8km along narr rd; poss hard to find. Med, hdg/mkd pitch, pt sl, pt shd; wc; chem disp; baby facs; shwrs inc; el pnts (6A) €3.40; lndtte (inc dryer); shop; tradsmn; rest, snacks; bar; BBQ; playgrnd; 2 pools (1 htd, covrd); paddling pool; waterslide; bicycle & canoe hire; tennis; games area; games rm; wifi; entmnt; TV; 10% statics; dogs €1.50; phone; Eng spkn; adv bkg; quiet; ccard acc; red low ssn; CKE/CCI. "Friendly & helpful; sep car park; excel." ♦ ltd 1 Apr-30 Sep. € 17.80 2010*

SARLAT LA CANEDA *7C3* (4km NW Rural) *44.90929, 1.18738* **FFCC Camping Le Rivaux, Route de Périgueux, 24200 Sarlat-la-Canéda [05 53 59 04 41]** Fr Sarlat take D47 sp Les Eyzies & Périgueux; after approx 2km, take D6. Site on R after approx 300m. Med, hdg/mkd pitch, pt sl, pt shd; wc; chem disp; shwrs inc; el pnts (2-6A) €1.50-2.80; gas; lndry rm; shops 3km; tradsmn high ssn; BBQ; playgrnd; pool 4km; games rm; dogs; phone; quiet; adv bkg rec high ssn; CKE/CCI. "Spacious pitches; gd touring base; vg." ♦ ltd 1 Apr-30 Sep. € 11.00 2009*

SAUVETERRE DE GUYENNE *7D2* (8km NW Rural) *44.72564, -0.15066* **Camping Château Guiton (Naturist), 33760 Frontenac [05 56 23 52 79; fax 05 56 23 99 40; accueil@chateau-guiton.com; www.chateau-guiton.com]** N of Sauveterre-de-Guyenne turn W onto D123 sp Frontenac. Turn L just bef vill sp Château Guiton. Sm, mkd pitch, pt sl, pt shd; wc; chem disp; sauna; shwrs; el pnts (6-10A) €3.50; lndtte; shop; tradsmn; rest & bar 4km; playgrnd; pool; gym; TV rm; dogs €2; phone; Eng spkn; adv bkg; quiet; ccard acc; red low ssn; INF card req. "Pt-wooded site in cent wine region; friendly owner; gd cycling; conv Bordeaux; gd." 15 May-30 Sep. € 23.50 2009*

SAUVETERRE LA LEMANCE see Villefranche du Périgord *7D3*

SEIGNOSSE see Hossegor *8E1*

SERIGNAC PEBOUDOU see Cancon *7D3*

SIGOULES *7D2* (1.5km N Rural) *44.77135, 0.41076* **Camp Municipal La Gardonnette, Les Coteaux de Sigoulès, 24240 Pomport-Sigoulès [tel/fax 05 53 58 81 94; campingdelagardonnette@wanadoo.fr]** S fr Bergerac take D933 S. After 6km at top of hill turn R by La Grappe d'Or Rest onto D17 sp Pomport/Sigoulès. Thro Pomport, site at bottom of hill on R by lake. Med, mkd pitch, pt sl, shd; wc; chem disp; shwrs inc; el pnts (6A); lndtte; shop, snacks, bar 1km; playgrnd; lake sw adj; fishing; canoeing; tennis; games area; entmnt; TV; 25% statics; dogs; phone; Eng spkn; adv bkg; ccard acc; CKE/CCI. "Barrier ent; facs clean but well worn & in need of refurb; gd security." 1 Apr-30 Sep. 2009*

SOUILLAC *7C3* (5km SW Rural) *44.87340, 1.43389* **Camp Municipal La Borgne, 24370 Cazoulès [05 53 29 81 64 or 05 53 31 45 25 (Mairie); fax 05 53 31 45 26; campingcazoules@orange.fr; http://cazoules.pagesperso-orange.fr]** Fr Souillac, take D804/D703 twd Sarlat. In 4km in vill of Cazoulès turn L & foll site sps. Site on R just bef rv bdge & adj Rv Dordogne. Lge, pt shd; wc; baby facs; shwrs inc; el pnts (10A) €3; lndtte; sm shop; supmkt 4km; BBQ; playgrnd; pool; paddling pool; canoe trips; boat hire; fishing; tennis adj; 15% statics; dogs €1; quiet; "Poss mosquito problem; helpful staff." ♦ 15 Jun-15 Sep. € 15.00 2013*

SOUILLAC *7C3* (6km W Rural) *44.88577, 1.40678* **Camping La Périgourdine (Levet), Le Bourg, 24370 Peyrillac-et-Millac [05 53 29 72 12 or 06 07 22 15 07 (mob); francoislevet@aol.com; www.campinglaperigourdine.fr]** Fr cent of Souillac, W on D804 then D703 to Peyrillac-et-Millac; in vill turn L at sp to site. Drive past farmhouse, ent 75m on R, narr app rd. Sm, pt shd; htd wc; shwrs inc; el pnts (16A) €3; Indtte; tradsmn; shop, rest, bar etc 5km; BBQ; playgrnd; pool; games area; rv 2km; dogs €2; adv bkg; quiet; no ccard acc; CKE/CCI. "CL-type site; friendly, helpful owners; ltd facs low ssn; not suitable lge o'fits as access narr, sloping & sharp bend; gd cycle rtes." € 13.50 2010*

SOULAC SUR MER *7B1* (1km S Coastal) *45.50136, -1.13185* **Camping Le Palace, 65 Blvd Marsan-de-Montbrun, Forêt Sud, 33780 Soulac-sur-Mer [05 56 09 80 22; fax 05 56 09 84 23; info@camping-palace.com; www.camping-palace.com]** Fr ferry at Le Verdon-sur-Mer S on D1215, site sp. Or fr S on D101. V lge, hdg/mkd pitch, shd; wc; mv service pnt; baby facs; shwrs inc; el pnts; Indtte; shop; rest, snacks; bar; BBQ; playgrnd; htd, covrd pool; paddling pool; waterslide; sand beach 400m; cycle hire; internet; entmnt; 65% statics; dogs €3-6; adv bkg; quiet. "Ideal for family beach holiday." 1 May-27 Sep. € 36.00 2014*

See advertisement

SOULAC SUR MER *7B1* (2km S Rural) *45.48568, -1.11909* **Camping Club de Soulac Le Lilhan, 8 Allée Michel Montaigne, 33780 Soulac-sur-Mer [tel/fax 05 56 09 78 78; contact@lelilhan.com; www.camping-club-soulac.com]** Fr S on D1215 dir Le Verdon, turn W dir Lilhan & L'Amélie-sur-Mer, site sp. Lge, hdg/mkd pitch, pt shd; htd wc; chem disp; mv service pnt; sauna; shwrs; el pnts (10A) inc; Indtte (inc dryer); shop; supmkt 3m; rest, snacks; bar; playgrnd; pool; sand beach 2km; tennis; wifi; entmnt; some statics; dogs €2.95; adv bkg; quiet. ♦ 1 Apr-30 Sep. € 25.00 2009*

SOULAC SUR MER *7B1* (3km SW Coastal) *45.48068, -1.14538* **Camping L'Océan, 62 Allée de la Négade, L'Amélie, 33780 Soulac-sur-Mer [05 56 09 76 10; fax 05 56 09 74 75; camping.ocean@wanadoo.fr; http://camping.ocean.pagesperso-orange.fr/]** Fr S on D1215 dir Soulac-sur-Mer; turn L onto D102 to Vendays-Montalivet; then turn N onto D101 Soulac-sur-Mer; in 14km turn L onto D101E2 sp L'Amélie-sur-Mer; in 2km at sp Camping L'Océan turn L into Allée de la Négade. Site on R. Lge, mkd pitch, pt shd; wc; chem disp; shwrs inc; el pnts (10A) €4; Indtte; shop; rest 500m; snacks; bar; BBQ (charcoal, sep area); playgrnd; sand beach 600m; cycle hire; tennis; games area; games rm; initernet; TV; dogs €2.50; adv bkg; ccard not acc; red low ssn; CKE/CCI. "Sandy pitches; several cycle tracks; vg." ♦ ltd 1 Jun-15 Sep. € 22.40 2010*

SOULAC SUR MER *7B1* (13km S Coastal) *45.43357, -1.14519* **Camp Municipal du Gurp, 51 Route de l'Océan, 33590 Grayan-et-L'Hôpital [05 56 09 44 53 or 05 56 09 43 01 (Mairie); fax 05 56 09 54 73; mairie.grayan@orange.fr; www.grayan.fr]** Take D101 fr Soulac. Turn R after 5km sp Grayan & R at x-rds. Site clearly sp. V lge, mkd pitch, hdstg, shd; wc; chem disp; baby facs; shwrs inc; el pnts (4-10A) €2.88; Indtte; shop; rest, snacks; bar; playgrnd; sand beach adj; tennis; games area; games rm; entmnt; wifi; TV; dogs €1.50; poss cr; quiet. "In pine forest; gd, vast beaches; mv service pnt outsite site (fee payable)." 1 Jun-15 Sep. € 17.40 2011*

SOULAC SUR MER *7B1* (13km S Coastal) *45.41600, -0.12930* **Centre Naturiste Euronat (Naturist), 33590 Grayan-l'Hôpital [05 56 09 33 33; fax 05 56 09 30 27; info@euronat.fr; www.euronat.fr]** Fr Soulac, take D101 twd Montalivet, turn W at camp sp onto rd leading direct to site. Fr Bordeaux, take D1215 sp Le Verdon-sur-Mer. Approx 8km after Lesparre-Médoc turn L onto D102. In Venday-Montalivet bear R onto D101. In 7.5km turn L sp Euronat. V lge, mkd pitch, hdstg, shd; htd wc (some htd); chem disp; mv service pnt; all serviced pitches; baby facs; shwrs inc; el pnts (10A) inc; gas; Indtte (inc dryer); shop; rest, snacks; bar; BBQ; playgrnd; 3 htd pools (1 covrd); paddling pool; thalassotherapy & beauty treatment cent; sand beach adj; tennis; horseriding; cinema; archery; cycle hire; golf driving range; wifi; entmnt; TV; 30% statics; dogs €3; phone; Eng spkn; adv bkg; quiet; red low ssn; INF card req. "Expensive, but well worth it; lge pitches; excel." ♦ 1 Apr-1 Nov. € 50.40 (CChq acc) 2013*

SOULAC SUR MER *7B1* (1.5km SW Coastal) *45.49958, -1.13899* **Camping Les Sables d'Argent, Blvd de l'Amélie, 33780 Soulac-sur-Mer [05 56 09 82 87; fax 05 56 09 94 82; sables@lelilhan.com; www.sables-d-argent.com]** Drive S fr Soulac twd L'Amélie-sur-Mer. Clearly sp on R. Med, mkd pitch, pt sl, pt shd; wc; shwrs inc; el pnts (10A) inc (poss long lead req); Indtte; shop; rest, snacks; bar; private sand beach adj; fishing; tennis; internet; entmnt; TV; 60% statics; dogs €2.95; poss cr; red low ssn. "Nice area, but major erosion of coast so no access to beach (2009); poss diff lge o'fits; old san facs (2009); Soulac sm, lively mkt town." 1 Apr-30 Sep. € 25.00 2009*

SOURAIDE see Cambo les Bains *8F1*

SOUSTONS *8E1* (6km NE Rural) *43.79193, -1.29455* **Camping Le Tuc, 155 Rue Henri Goalard, 40140 Azur [05 58 48 22 52 or 06 77 60 22 75 (mob); fax 05 58 48 33 53; campingletuc@wanadoo.fr; www.campingletuc.com]** Exit N10 junc 11 at Magescq onto D150 dir Azur; site on R 1km SE fr Azur. Site sp fr Azur. Med, hdg pitch, pt shd; wc; chem disp; shwrs inc; el pnts (6-10A) €3.20; gas; Indtte; shop, tradsmn (high ssn); BBQ; playgrnd; pool; paddling pool; lake watersports & fishing 2km; tennis; games area; games rm; wifi; TV rm; 50% statics; dogs €2; phone; poss cr; adv bkg; quiet; red low ssn; CKE/CCI. "Woodland walks; excel." ♦ 1 Apr-15 Sep. € 15.40 2010*

SOUSTONS *8E1* (6km NE Rural) *43.78694, -1.30861* **Camping Village La Paillotte, 40140 Azur [05 58 48 12 12; fax 05 58 48 10 73; paillotte@franceloc.fr; www.paillotte.com / www.campings-franceloc.fr]** Exit N10 junc 11; cont thro Magescq & after a sh dist, turn L onto D150 to Azur. Turn L by church, after 1.5km site sp on L. Lge, mkd pitch, pt shd; wc (some cont); chem disp; mv service pnt; baby facs; shwrs inc; el pnts (10A) inc; Indtte (inc dryer); shop; rest, snacks; bar; BBQ (gas/elec); playgrnd; htd, covrd pool; paddling pool; waterslide; lake sw & sand beach adj; dinghy sailing; windsurfing; fishing; cycle hire; tennis; horseriding 7km; wifi; entmnt; games/TV rm; statics (tour ops); no dogs; no c'vans/m'vans over 7m high ssn; bus; adv bkg; ccard acc; red low ssn; CKE/CCI. "Lakeside site with stream thro; facs ltd low ssn; mkt Soustons Mon." ♦ ltd 28 May-25 Sep. € 39.00 2010*

SOUSTONS *8E1* (6.5km NE Rural) *43.78430, -1.30473* **Camping Azu'Rivage, 720 Route des Campings, 40140 Azur [tel/fax 05 58 48 30 72; info@campingazurivage.com; www.campingazurivage.com]** Exit m'way A10 at exit Magescq & take D150 W for 8km to Azur, site sp fr church adj La Paillotte. Med, pt shd; wc; baby facs; shwrs inc; el pnts (10A) €7.40; Indtte; sm shop & 6km; rest, snacks; playgrnd; pool; paddling pool; sand beach & lake sw; tennis; boating; watersports; entmnt; TV rm; dogs €2; poss cr; adv bkg; ccard acc; red long stay; red low ssn. "Delightful forest setting adj lake; v busy high ssn; san facs poss stretched high ssn; rec." ♦ 15 May-30 Sep. € 15.00 2010*

TARDETS SORHOLUS *8F1* (1km S Rural) *43.11143, -0.86362* **Camping du Pont d'Abense, 64470 Tardets-Sorholus [tel/fax 05 59 28 58 76 or 06 78 73 53 59 (mob); camping.abense@wanadoo.fr; www.camping-pontabense.com]** Take D918 S to Tardets, turn R to cross bdge onto D57. Site sp on R. Tardets cent narr. Med, shd; wc; chem disp; shwrs inc; el pnts (3A) €3.20; Indry rm; shop, rest, snacks & bar 500m; tradsmn; rv & beach nrby; fishing; some statics; dogs €2; quiet; adv bkg; red low ssn; CKE/CCI. "Informal pitching; facs old; gd birdwatching; lovely, quaint site; nr gorges." Easter-Mid Nov. € 14.70 2012*

TEICH, LE *7D1* (1.5km W Rural) *44.63980, -1.04272* **Camping Ker Helen, Ave de la Côte d'Argent, 33470 Le Teich [05 56 66 03 79; fax 05 56 66 51 59; camping.kerhelen@wanadoo.fr; www.kerhelen.com]** Fr A63 take A660 dir Arcachon & exit junc 2 onto D3 then D650 thru Le Teich. Site sp on L. Med, hdg pitch, pt shd; htd wc; chem disp; mv service pnt; baby facs; shwrs inc; el pnts (10A) €3.70; Indtte (inc dryer); rest, snacks; bar; no BBQ; playgrnd; pool; canoeing; horseriding; wifi; entmnt; TV; 75% statics; adv bkg; some rd noise; CKE/CCI. "Less cr than coastal sites in Arcachon region; bird reserve nrby; vg." ♦ 16 Apr-16 Oct. € 23.00 2011*

TERRASSON LAVILLEDIEU *7C3* (4km W Rural) *45.12041, 1.26199* **Camping La Salvinie, Bouillac-Sud, 24120 Terrasson-Lavilledieu [05 53 50 06 11 or 06 03 61 55 72; camping.lasalvinie@orange.fr; www.camping-salvinie.com]** Exit A89 junc 18 onto D6089 dir Terrasson-Lavilledieu. Cross Rv Vézère & turn immed L, site in 4km sp. Med, hdg/mkd pitch, shd; wc; chem disp; mv service pnt; shwrs; el pnts (6A) €2.60; gas; Indtte; shop & 4km; tradsmn; ice; supmkt 3km; rest, snacks; bar; BBQ; playgrnd; pool; games area; games rm; wifi; 10% statics; dogs €1; no twin-axles; poss cr; Eng spkn; adv bkg; quiet; ccard acc. "Excel, scenic site; friendly owners; Terrasson interesting town; mkt Thurs." ♦ 1 Apr-31 Oct. € 11.00 2009*

TEUILLAC *7C2* (Rural) *45.09163, -0.54808* **Camp Municipal, Le Bourg, 33710 Teuillac [05 57 64 34 55; accueil@mairie-teuillac.com; www.teuillac.a3w.fr]** Fr D137 turn onto D134 at Le Poteau twd Teuillac, site in 2km adj Mairie. Sm, pt shd; wc; baby facs; shwrs; el pnts €3; snacks; pool; fishing nr; quiet. "Pleasant, peaceful site surrounded by grape vines; conv Bordeaux; vg, useful NH." May- Sep. € 7.00 2011*

THENON *7C3* (3km SE Rural) *45.11883, 1.09119* **Camping Le Verdoyant, Route de Montignac, 24210 Thenon [05 53 05 20 78; fax 05 67 34 05 00; contact@campingleverdoyant.fr; www.campingleverdoyant.fr]** Sp fr A89, take D67 fr Thenon to Montignac. Site on R in 4km. Med, mkd pitch, pt sl, terr, pt shd; wc; chem disp (wc); shwrs inc; el pnts (10A) €3.15; shops 2km; tradsmn; snacks; bar; gas; Indtte; playgrnd; pool; lake fishing; wifi; dogs €1.60; adv bkg; quiet; 20% statics; dogs €1.75; Eng spkn; quiet; red low ssn; CKE/CCI. "Beautiful setting away fr tourist bustle; friendly owners; excel base for area." ♦ 1 Apr-30 Sep. € 14.00 2011*

THIVIERS *7C3* (10km N Rural) *45.49950, 0.90690* **Camping Maisonneuve, 1 Chemin de Maisonneuve, 24800 St Jory-de-Chalais [tel/fax 05 53 55 10 63; camping.maisonneuve@wanadoo.fr; www.camping-maisonneuve.com]** N fr Thiviers on N21 for 6km; turn L on D98 thro Chaleix; site on L bef ent St Jory. Other rtes v narr. Sm, hdg/mkd pitch, hdstg, pt sl, pt shd; wc (some cont); chem disp; mv service pnt; sauna; shwrs inc; el pnts (10A) €3.50; Indtte (inc dryer); shop 500m; rest, snacks; bar; playgrnd; pool; fishing lake; games rm; internet; TV; 10% statics; dogs €1; Eng spkn; adv bkg; quiet; red low ssn/long stay/CKE/CCI. "Pretty site in attractive countryside; lge pitches, some v shd; helpful, welcoming owners; excel." ♦ 1 Apr-31 Oct. € 20.50 2010*

THIVIERS *7C3* (10km N Rural) *45.50255, 0.91447* **Camping Moulin du Touroulet, Moulin du Tourelet, 24800 Chaleix [tel/fax 05 53 55 23 59; touroulet@hotmail.com; www.camping-touroulet.com]** Fr Limoges on N21 S twd Périgueux, thro vill of La Coquille, in about 4.5km turn R onto D98 twd St Jory-de-Chalais & Chaleix. In 4km turn L to vill & site 1km further on. Take care narr bdge & site ent. Sm, pt sl, some hdstg, pt shd; pt htd wc; chem disp; shwrs inc; el pnts (8A) €3; Indry rm; shop 1.5km; tradsmn; rest; bar; BBQ; pool; fishing; games rm; entmnt; internet; dogs €0.50; adv bkg; quiet; CKE/CCI. "Beautiful site in tranquil rvside setting; spacious & well-kept; welcoming, helpful British owners; fishing avail on site; basic, ltd san facs, stretched high ssn; excel bar/rest; hdstg pitches sl & uneven; Xmas package; excel." 1 Mar-31 Dec. € 18.00 2012*

⊞ **THIVIERS** *7C3* (7km NE Rural) *45.47390, 0.93808* **Camping La Petite Lande, Lieu-dite La Petitie Lande, 24800 St Jory-de-Chalais [09 64 44 82 79; fax 05 53 62 42 89; info@la-petite-lande.com; www.la-petite-lande.com]** N fr Thiviers on D21; in 6km turn L onto unclassified rd sp 'La Petite Lande' campsite; foll sps to site in 500m. Sm, unshd; htd wc; chem disp; mv service pnt; shwrs inc; el pnts (10A) €3.50; Indtte; shops 6km; rest & bar 3km; BBQ; sm playgrnd; pool (above grnd); dogs €1; Eng spkn; quiet; ccard acc; red low ssn. "Relaxing, CL-type site; new site (2011); helpful Dutch owners; v gd, clean facs plans to expand." ♦ ltd € 13.75 2014*

⊞ **THIVIERS** *7C3* (2km E Rural) *45.41299, 0.93209* **Camping Le Repaire, Ave de Verdun, 24800 Thiviers [tel/fax 05 53 52 69 75; contact@camping-le-repaire.fr; www.camping-le-repaire.fr]** N21 to Thiviers; at rndabt take D707 E dir Lanouaille; site in 1.5km on R. Med, hdg/mkd pitch, pt sl, terr, pt shd; htd wc; chem disp; mv service pnt; shwrs inc; el pnts (12A) €3; Indtte; shop 2km; snacks; BBQ; playgrnd; covrd pool; lake fishing; entmnt; games rm; TV rm; 5% statics; dogs €1.60; phone; no twin-axles; poss cr; Eng spkn; adv bkg; quiet; red low ssn; CKE/CCI. "Lovely site - one of best in area; friendly owners; clean san facs; some pitches unrel in wet weather; excel." ♦ ltd € 14.00 2009*

THONAC see Montignac *7C3*

TOUZAC see Fumel *7D3*

TREMOLAT see Bugue, Le *7C3*

TURSAC see Eyzies de Tayac, Les *7C3*

URRUGNE see St Jean de Luz *8F1*

⊞ **URT** *8F1* (900m E Rural) *43.49353, -1.27960* **Camping Ferme Mimizan, 64240 Urt [tel/fax 05 59 56 21 51; contact@lafermedemimizan.fr; www.lafermedemimizan.fr]** E fr Bayonne on A64/E80, exit junc 4 sp Urt; in vill turn sharp R at PO & foll sps; site on R in 1km. Fr N on D12 cross Rv Adour by metal bdge & turn L immed past church, site on R in 1.5km. Med, pt shd; wc; shwrs inc; el pnts (10A) €3.50; playgrnd; pool; paddling pool; wifi; some statics; adv bkg; poss noise fr static residents; red low ssn; CKE/CCI. "V peaceful out of ssn; friendly owners; gd walking & cycling; conv coast & Pyrenees; gd NH." € 19.50 2009*

URT *8F1* (500m S Rural) *43.49165, -1.29677* **Camping Etche Zahar, Allée des Mesplès, 64240 Urt [05 59 56 27 36; fax 05 59 56 29 62; info@etche-zahar.fr; www.etche-zahar.fr]** Exit A64 at junc 4 dir Urt. Fr N on N10 exit junc 9 at St Geours-de-Maremne onto D12 S to Urt, site sp. Fr town cent head W, L at rndabt, L again to site. Sm, hdg pitch, pt sl, pt shd; wc; chem disp; baby facs; shwrs inc; el pnts (10A) €3.50; Indtte (inc dryer); shop 500m; tradsmn; snacks; bar; BBQ; rest 500m; playgrnd; pool; paddling pool; fishing; games area; cycle hire; wifi; entmnt; 25% statics; dogs €2.20 (not acc Aug); phone; Eng spkn; adv bkg; quiet; CKE/CCI. "Peaceful site; welcoming, pleasant owners; gd walking & cycling." ♦ 1 Mar-15 Nov. € 21.30 2010*

"I need an on-site restaurant"

We do our best to make sure site information is correct, but it is always best to check any must-have facilities are still available or will be open during your visit.

VENDAYS MONTALIVET *7C1* (6km NE Rural) *45.39875, -1.04828* **Camp Municipal du Vieux Moulin, 15 Route du Moulin, 33590 Vensac [tel/fax 05 56 09 45 98 or 06 64 64 13 12 (mob); campingduevieuxmoulin@vensac-medoc.com; www.campingduvieuxmoulin.fr]** Turn off D1215 to Vensac. Foll sp to windmill (moulin à vent), which is adj site. Site is 500m to W of Vensac. Med, pt shd, mkd pitch; wc; chem disp; shwrs inc; el pnts (3A) €3; Indtte (inc dryer); shop; rest, snacks; bar; BBQ (charcoal, sep area); playgrnd; pool; sand beach 8km; surfing, sand yachting & horseriding 8km; games area; games rm; wifi; entmnt; TV; 65% statics; dogs €1.50; adv bkg; quiet; ccard acc; CKE/CCI. "Excel ambiance; ltd facs low ssn; tourers in sep field; now municipal site - many changes planned (2010)." ♦ ltd 17 Mar-31 Oct. € 14.60 2010*

VENDAYS MONTALIVET *7C1* (3km W Rural) *45.36698, -1.09885* **Camping Le Mérin, 7 Route de Mérin, 33930 Vendays-Montalivet [tel/fax 05 56 41 78 64; www.campinglemerin.com]** NW fr Lesparre-Médoc on D1215 for 9km; then W on D102 to Vendays-Montalivet. Cont on D102 twds Montalivet-les-Bains. Site on L in 3km. Lge, hdg pitch, pt shd; wc; shwrs; el pnts (6-10A) €2.80-3.30; Indtte; shop 3km; tradsmn in ssn; BBQ; playgrnd; sand beach 4km; fishing; cycle hire; games area; entmnt; 5% statics; dogs €1; adv bkg; CKE/CCI. "Working farm; basic facs; gd." 1 Apr-31 Oct. € 11.50 2010*

VENDAYS MONTALIVET *7C1* (6km W Coastal) *45.37040, -1.14442* **Camp Municipal de Montalivet, Ave de l'Europe, 33930 Vendays-Montalivet [05 56 09 33 45; fax 05 56 09 33 12; campingmunicipal-vendays@wanadoo.fr]** Take D101 fr Soulac to Vendays, D102 to Montalivet-les-Bains. Site sp bef ent to Montalivet. Turn L at petrol stn, site 500m on L. V lge, mkd pitch, shd; wc; chem disp; mv service pnt; shwrs inc; el pnts inc; lndtte; shop; rest, snacks; bar; playgrnd; paddling pool; beach 700m; dogs €1.87; quiet; adv bkg. "Site in pine forest; gd mkt 1km; naturist beaches N & S of Montalivet." ♦ 1 May-30 Sep. € 14.70 (CChq acc) 2010*

⊞ **VENDAYS MONTALIVET** *7C1* (6km W Coastal) *45.36325, -1.14496* **Camping CHM Montalivet (Naturist), 46 Ave de l'Europe, 33340 Vendays-Montalivet [05 56 73 26 81 or 05 56 73 73 73; fax 05 56 09 32 15; infos@chm-montalivet.com; www.chm-montalivet.com]** D101 fr Soulac to Vendays-Montalivet; D102 to Montalivet-les-Bains; site bef ent to vill; turn L at petrol stn; site 1km on R. V lge, mkd pitch, pt sl, pt shd; wc; chem disp; mv service pnt; shwrs inc; el pnts (6A) inc; gas; lndtte (inc dryer); 2 supmkts; rests; snacks; bar; playgrnd; htd pool; sand beach adj; games area; games rm; cycle hire; wifi; entmnt; wifi; TV rm; 50% statics; dogs €6.90; phone; poss cr; Eng spkn; adv bkg; quiet; red long stay/low ssn; ccard acc; INF card. "Vast, peaceful site in pine forest; superb lge naturist beach adj; excel facs for children of all ages; vg." ♦ ltd € 40.00 2011*

VENDAYS MONTALIVET *7C1* (9.5km NE Rural) *45.41032, -1.03531* **Camping Village Vacances Les Acacias, Route de St-Vivien, 33590 Vensac [05 56 09 58 81; fax 05 56 09 50 67; contact@les-acacias-du-medoc.fr; www.les-acacias-du-medoc.fr]** Via Bordeaux exit 8 on the A10 dir Le Verdon/Pointe de Grave. Lge, mkd pitch, pt shd; wc; chem disp; baby facs; shwrs inc; el pnts (6A) inc; gas; lndtte; shop; mkt (once a wk); rest; bar; BBQ; playgrnd; pool (solar htd); paddling pool; cycle hire; wifi; dogs €3.50; adv bkg. "Set in woodlands; friendly staff - welcome drink on Sun; v gd site." ♦ 01 Apr-30 Sep. € 24.50 2011*

> "Satellite navigation makes touring much easier"
>
> Remember most sat navs don't know if you're towing or in a larger vehicle – always use yours alongside maps and site directions.

⊞ **VENDOIRE** *7B2* (3km W Rural) *45.40860, 0.28079* **Camping du Petit Lion, 24320 Vendoire [05 53 91 00 74; info@lepetitlion.co.uk; www.lepetitlion.co.uk]** S fr Angoulême on D939 or D674, take D5 to Villebois-Lavalette, then D17 to Gurat. Then take D102 to Vendoire, site sp. Sm, hdg pitch, some hdstg, pt shd; htd wc; shwrs inc; el pnts (10A) €3; lndtte; sm shop on site & 7km; rest, snacks; bar; playgrnd; pool; paddling pool; lake fishing; tennis; internet; 10% statics; dogs €2; rally fields; British owners; adv bkg; quiet; CKE/CCI. ♦ ltd € 11.00 2010*

VENSAC see Vendays Montalivet *7C1*

VERTEILLAC *7C2* (600m NE Urban) *45.35064, 0.37010* **Camp Municipal Le Pontis Sud-Est, 24320 Verteillac [05 53 90 37 74; fax 05 53 90 77 13; j-c.rouvel@wanadoo.fr; www.camping-le-pontis.com]** N fr Ribérac on D708 dir Angoulême; leaving Verteillac turn R at 'Camping' sp, then L at gendarmerie, then 1st R. Site adj stadiium. Sm, hdg pitch, sl, unshd; wc, chem disp (wc); mv service pnt; shwrs inc; el pnts (6A) €1.90; lndry rm; shop, rest, snacks, bar nrby; BBQ; pool 500m; wifi; 70% statics; dogs €0.50; quiet; CKE/CCI. "Easy access to pitches; m'van pitches sm; facs modern but ltd & in need of maintenance (2009); ltd el pnts; attractive vill; Ribérac mkt Fri." ♦ 4 Apr-15 Nov. € 8.00 2009*

VEZAC see Sarlat la Canéda *7C3*

VIELLE ST GIRONS see Léon *8E1*

> "There aren't many sites open at this time of year"
>
> If you're travelling outside peak season remember to call ahead to check site opening dates – even if the entry says 'open all year'.

VIEUX BOUCAU LES BAINS *8E1* (800m N Coastal) *43.79309, -1.40607* **Camp Municipal Les Sablères, Bldv du Marensin, 40480 Vieux-Boucau-les-Bains [05 58 48 12 29 or 05 58 48 13 22; fax 05 58 48 20 70; camping-lessableres@wanadoo.fr; www.les-sableres.com]** Foll sps fr cent of vill twd beach, site sp fr D652. V lge, mkd pitch, pt sl, shd; wc (some cont); chem disp; mv service pnt; baby facs; shwrs inc; el pnts (8A) €3.90; lndtte; shops, rest & snack 1km; BBQ; playgrnd; sand/surf beach 300m; lake sw nrby; games area; 20% statics; dogs €1.80; phone; poss cr; Eng spkn; adv bkg; quiet; red low ssn; CKE/CCI. "Site by lge sand dune; vg." ♦ ltd 1 Apr-15 Oct. € 18.30 2010*

VIGAN, LE (LOT) see Gourdon *7D3*

VILLEFRANCHE DU PERIGORD *7D3* (1km E Urban) *44.62757, 1.08159* **FFCC Camping La Bastide, Route de Cahors, 24550 Villefranche-du-Périgord [05 53 28 94 57; fax 05 53 29 47 95; campinglabastide@wanadoo.fr; www.camping-la-bastide.com]** On N660 fr Villefranche-du-Périgord dir Cahors; site past PO on R nr top of hill on town o'skts. Med, hdg/mkd pitch, terr, pt shd; wc; chem disp; mv service pnt; baby facs; shwrs inc; el pnts (6-10A) €3-4; lndtte; shops 300m; rest, snacks; bar; playgrnd; pool; tennis 300m; fishing; entmnt; 25% statics; dogs €1; poss cr; adv bkg; quiet; red low ssn; CKE/CCI. ACSI; wifi; "Steep, terr site but easy access, can be soft in wet weather; charming owners; excel touring base; vg; V nice town within walking dist." ♦ ltd 3 Apr-16 Oct. € 22.00 2012*

VILLEFRANCHE DU PERIGORD *7D3* (6km SW Rural) *44.59025, 1.04799* **Moulin du Périé Camping - Caravaning, 47500 Sauveterre-la-Lémance [05 53 40 67 26; fax 05 53 40 62 46; moulinduperie@wanadoo.fr; www.camping-moulin-perie.com / www.flowercampings.com]** FrN fr Villefranche-du-Périgord take D710 S dir Fumel. At Sauveterre-la-Lémance turn L at traff lts, cross level x-ing & in 400m turn L sp Loubejac & site; site on R in 4km. Tight ent bet tall hedges 2.6m apart for 30m. Fr E fr Cahors on D660 & turn L onto D46 sp Loubejac. Cont thro Loubejac & turn L at T-junc, foll sp Sauveterre. Site on R in 4km. Med, pt sl, pt shd; wc; chem disp; mv service pnt; baby facs; shwrs inc; el pnts (10A) inc (poss rev pol); gas; Indtte (inc dryer); shop; rest, snacks; bar; BBQ; playgrnd; pool; paddling pool; sm lake & beach; trout fishing; tennis 3km; cycle hire; archery; entmnt; games/TV rm; 25% statics; dogs €4.60; poss cr; Eng spkn; adv bkg rec; quiet; ccard acc; red low ssn; CKE/CCI. "Beautiful, well-run site in grnds of old mill; welcoming, friendly family owners; clean, dated san facs; vg rest; site rds narr, not suitable v lge o'fits; gd touring base; excel." ♦ 14 May-17 Sep. € 32.00 (CChq acc) 2011*

VILLEFRANCHE DU QUEYRAN see Casteljaloux *7D2*

"That's changed – Should I let The Club know?"

If you find something on site that's different from the site entry, fill in a report and let us know. See www.caravanclub.co.uk/europereport.

⊞ **VILLENEUVE SUR LOT** *7D3* (7km E Rural) *44.39590, 0.78664* **Camping Le Sablon, 47140 St Sylvestre-sur-Lot [05 53 41 37 74; campinglesablon@wanadoo.fr]** Fr Villeneuve E on D911 sp Cahors; in 5km, site on R immed on ent St Sylvestre. Sm, hdg/mkd pitch, shd; htd wc; mv service pnt; shwrs; el pnts (6-10A) €2.50-3.50; Indtte; snacks; playgrnd; pools & paddling pool; waterslide; fishing adj; 25% statics; dogs €1.50; quiet. "Pleasant, family-owned site; gd facs but run down low ssn; muddy when wet - no hdstg; poss travellers." € 10.00 2009*

VILLENEUVE SUR LOT *7D3* (8km E Urban) *44.39576, 0.80491* **Camping Les Berges du Lot, Place de la Mairie, 47140 St Sylvestre-sur-Lot [05 53 41 22 23 or 05 53 41 24 58 (Mairie)]** Exit Villeneuve-sur-Lot on D911 sp Cahors. Site in cent of St Sylvestre-sur-Lot. Foll Camping sp to rear of La Mairie (Town Hall) & supmkt; site accessed via car park to R of main rd. Sm, mkd pitch, pt shd; wc; chem disp; shwrs inc; el pnts (16A) €3.30 (poss long lead req); shops & supmkt adj; rest, bar 1km; sm pool; boating; fishing; birdwatching; Eng spkn; quiet. "Popular, comfortable, scenic site; clean facs; helpful staff; adv bkg rec high ssn; 2 pin cont el conn; many long term residents, inc British; mkt Wed & Sun am, when access diff; rec." ♦ 15 May-30 Sep. € 11.50 2014*

VILLENEUVE SUR LOT *7D3* (3km S Urban) *44.39483, 0.68680* **Camping Lot et Bastides, Allée de Malbentre, 47300 Pujols [05 53 36 86 79 or 06 14 13 78 93 (mob); fax 09 70 63 28 07; contact@camping-lot-et-bastides.fr; www.camping-lot-et-bastides.fr]** Fr Villeneuve Sur Lot on D911 take L onto D118. At rndabt take 1st exit onto D911. Turn L onto Rue du General. Site on the R. Med, hdg pitch, pt shd; wc; chem disp; mv service pnt; shwr inc; el pnts (16A); Indtte (inc dryer); shops; tradsmn; snacks; bar; BBQ; playgrnd; pool; games area; entmnt; wifi; 25% statics; dogs €2; bus adj; twin axles; adv bkg; quiet; ccard acc; red low ssn; CCI. "New site 2012; neat and clean; views of Pujols, most beautiful vill in France; lots to see & do in area; v scenic; friendly staff; bike hire." ♦ 1 Apr-30 Sep. € 31.00 2014*

See advertisement

VILLEREAL *7D3* (2km N Rural) *44.65723, 0.72820* **Camping Château de Fonrives, 47210 Rives, Villeréal [05 53 36 63 38; fax 05 53 36 09 98; contact@campingchateaufonrives.com; www.campingchateaufonrives.com]** Fr Bergerac take N21 S for 8km, turn L onto D14 thro Issigeac; site is just outside vill of Rives in grnds of chateau. Med, pt sl, pt shd; wc; baby facs; shwrs inc; el pnts (6A) inc; gas; Indtte; shop; rest; bar; BBQ; playgrnd; 2 pool (1 htd, covrd); waterslide; lake sw; fishing; golf; cycle hire; games rm; entmnt; some statics; dogs €5; Eng spkn; adv bkg; quiet but some noise fr weekly disco; ccard acc; CKE/CCI. "Spacious site; gd, lge pool; van poss manhandled on some shady pitches; easier access pitches without shd; friendly owners; B&B avail; interesting town; mkt Sat; huge pitches nr pool/bar; poss noisy." ♦ 13 Apr-28 Sep. € 47.00 2013*

VILLEREAL *7D3* (7km NE Rural) *44.65331, 0.80953* **Camping Le Moulin de Mandassagne, 47210 Parranquet [tel/fax 05 53 36 04 02; isabelle.pimouguet@orange.fr; www.haut-agenais-perigord.com]** Fr D104/D2 bet Villeréal & Monpazier turn N sp Parranquet, site sp. Sm, mkd pitch, pt shd; wc; chem disp; shwrs inc; el pnts (6A) inc; gas; lndry rm; snacks; playgrnd; pool; fishing; tennis; entmnt; TV; poss cr; Eng spkn; adv bkg; v quiet. "Lovely countryside; v relaxing; slightly bohemian site; friendly owners." ♦ 1 Apr-1 Oct. € 15.00 2014*

VILLEREAL *7D3* (10km SE Rural) *44.61426, 0.81889* **Camping Fontaine du Roc, Les Moulaties, 47210 Dévillac [05 53 36 08 16; fax 05 53 61 60 23; fontaine.du.roc@wanadoo.fr; www.fontaineduroc.com]** Fr Villeréal take D255 sp Dévillac, just beyond Dévillac at x-rds turn L & L again sp Estrade; site on L in 500m. Med, hdg/mkd pitch, hdstg, pt shd; wc; chem disp; shwrs inc; el pnts (5-10A) €3.50-4.50 gas; lndtte; shop 7km; tradsmn; rest, snacks; bar; BBQ; playgrnd; pool; paddling pool; fishing 500m; cycle hire; games rm; wifi; TV; 2% statics; dogs €3.50; phone; Eng spkn; adv bkg; quiet; red low ssn/long stay; no ccard acc; CKE/CCI. "Peaceful, well-cared for site; helpful owner; lge pitches." 1 Apr-30 Sep. € 19.00 2010*

VITRAC see Sarlat la Canéda *7C3*

YCHOUX *7D1* (10km E Rural) *44.33060, -0.97975* **Camp Municipal du Lac des Forges, 40160 Ychoux [05 58 82 35 57 or 05 58 82 36 01 (Mairie); fax 05 58 82 35 46]** Fr Bordeaux take N10 S & turn onto D43 at Liposthey W twd Parentis-en-Born. Site in 8km on R, past vill of Ychoux. Sm, pt sl, pt shd; wc; chem disp; mv service pnt; shwrs; el pnts (5-10A) €3.50 (rev pol); lndtte; shops 1km; rest; bar; playgrnd; TV rm; lake adj; fishing; sailing; dogs €1.50; quiet. "Levelling blocks poss req; pitches nr rd poss noisy." 15 Jun-10 Sep. € 14.00 2013*

Auvergne

Regional Introduction

Clermont Ferrand

Welcome to Auvergne

Time seems to move at a slower pace in this region of hills, mountains and valleys. Auvergne is home to the largest volcanic area in Europe, which provides hot springs for the region's many spas.

Natural lakes have formed in volcanic craters and the small villages and winter ski resorts on the slopes of the volcanoes make a visit to this incredible part of France an unforgettable experience.

An area much appreciated by ramblers and nature lovers, Auvergne is an ideal place to get away from the crowds and see the great outdoors.

Local highlights

With 10 traditional spa towns and 109 hot springs, the region has a unique sense of relaxation, well-being and hospitality. The quality of the water means that it is bottled and sold internationally by renowned brands.

Auvergne is also a paradise for cheese lovers, accounting for the production of over a quarter of France's quality-labelled cheeses.

Major towns and cities

- Clermont Ferrand – famous for the chain of extinct volcanoes that ring the city.
- Vichy – a renowned spa and resort town.
- Moulins – a town of art and history.
- Le Puy-en-Velay – a small city that is famous for its lace-making.

Regional attractions

- Church of Saint-Austremoine, Issoire – a 12th-century church with Moorish influence.
- Château de Chavaniac, Chavaniac-Lafayette – a fortified manor house furnished in the Louis XIII style.
- Auvergne Volcanoes Nature Park – Europe's largest regional park famous for its volcanos and natural beauty.
- Fortress of Polignac, Le Puy-en-Velay - a medieval Ducal fortress built on a platform formed by volcanic rock.

Find out more

www.auvergne-tourism.com

Tel: (0)4 70 98 71 94 Vichy Tourist Office
Tel: (0)4 70 44 14 14 Moulins Tourist Office

ABREST see Vichy *9A1*

ALBEPIERRE BREDONS see Murat *7C4*

ALLEGRE *9C1* (300m NE Rural) *45.20834, 3.71873* **Camp Municipal La Pinède, Le Chier, 43270 Allègre [04 71 00 76 79 or 04 71 00 71 21 (Mairie); mairie.allegre@wanadoo.fr; www.mairie-allegre.com]** N on D13 fr Allègre, then take D21; site visible on N edge of Allègre adj football pitch, sp. Sm, pt shd; wc (some cont); chem disp (wc); shwrs inc; el pnts (3-6A) €1.90-2.70; gas; lndtte; shop, rest, bar in vill; playgrnd; no statics; dogs €0.95; bus 300m; quiet; red long stay. "Attractive pine-shd site; gd cent for S Auvergne & Le Puy; gd NH & longer." ♦ ltd 15 Jun-15 Sep. € 10.00 2010*

AMBERT *9B1* (1km S Urban) *45.53951, 3.72867* **Camping Les Trois Chênes, Rue de la Chaise-Dieu, 63600 Ambert [04 73 82 34 68 or 04 73 82 23 95 (LS); fax 04 73 82 44 00; tourisme@ville-ambert.fr; www.camping-ambert.com]** On main rd D906 S twd Le Puy on L bet Leisure Park & Aquacentre. Med, hdg/mkd pitch, pt shd, serviced pitch; wc (some cont); chem disp; shwrs inc; el pnts (10A) €3.25; gas 400m; lndtte; supermkt adj; tradsmn; snacks; rest nrby; playgrnd; htd pool adj; waterslide; many statics; dogs €1; poss cr; adv bkg; quiet but some traff noise; ccard not acc; CKE/CCI. "Excel, well-kept site; gd, clean san facs; rvside walk to town; rec arrive bef noon peak ssn; recep & barrier clsd 1900 low ssn; steam museum & working paper mill nr; steam train 1.5km; vg." ♦ 8 May-30 Sep. € 27.00 2014*

AMBERT *9B1* (10km W Rural) *45.57449, 3.63393* **Camp Municipal Saviloisirs, 63890 St Amant-Roche-Savine [tel/fax 04 73 95 73 60 or 04 73 95 70 22 (Mairie); saviloisirs@wanadoo.fr; www.saviloisirs.com]** W fr Ambert on D996 to St Amant, turn R onto D37 into vill. In vill cent turn R & foll site sp. Bear L at lge building facing site on L. Sm, hdg/mkd pitch, pt shd; wc; shwrs inc; el pnts (16A) inc (rev pol); lndtte; shops adj; playgrnd; TV; dogs €0.30; quiet; CKE/CCI. "Tranquil vill site in wooded area; clean, modern facs; pleasant staff; easy walk to vill." 1 May-30 Oct. € 11.00 2009*

ARFEUILLES see Châtel Montagne *9A1*

ARLANC *9C1* (1km W Rural) *45.41344, 3.71866* **Camp Municipal Le Metz, Loumas, 63220 Arlanc [04 73 95 15 62; fax 04 73 95 78 31; jardin-terre.arlanc@wanadoo.fr; www.arlanc.fr]** Fr Ambert on D906 to Arlanc, turn R (W) onto D300 dir St Germain-l'Herm. Site on R in 800m, sp. Med, some hdg pitch, pt shd; wc (some cont); chem disp (wc); shwrs inc; el pnts (6A) inc (long lead poss req); lndtte (inc dryer); shop 800m; rest, snacks & bar 150m; playgrnd; pool 100m; games area; 10% statics; dogs; phone; adv bkg; quiet. "Lace-making museum in Arlanc." ♦ 15 Jun-30 Sep. € 11.40 2009*

AURILLAC *7C4* (2km NE Urban) *44.93551, 2.45596* **Camp Municipal de l'Ombrade, Chemin du Gué Bouliaga, 15000 Aurillac [tel/fax 04 71 48 28 87]** Take D17 N fr Aurillac twd Puy-Mary; site on banks of Rv Jordanne. Well sp fr town. Lge, mkd pitch, pt sl, shd; wc; shwrs inc; el pnts (10A) €2.10; lndtte; shops adj; BBQ; entmnt; TV & games rm; dogs; quiet. "Well-managed, spacious site; lge pitches; old san facs, but clean; poss not well-kept low ssn; interesting, lge mkt town; vg." ♦ ltd 15 Jun-15 Sep. € 10.50 2010*

AURILLAC *7C4* (2km S Urban) *44.89858, 2.46265* **Camp Municipal de la Cère, Rue Félix Ramond, 15130 Arpajon-sur-Cère [tel/fax 04 71 64 55 07; sebastienpradel@yahoo.fr]** Fr Rodez take D920 twd Aurillac. Site sp 2km bef Aurillac on S side of Arpajon. Med, hdg pitch, pt shd; wc; shwrs inc; el pnts (10A) inc; gas; lndtte; shops adj; pool; rv fishing adj; beach 20km; sports facs adj; golf 5km; some statics; dogs; adv bkg; some rd noise; ccard acc; CKE/CCI. "Pleasant site in pretty area; public access to site - not secure; generous pitches." ♦ ltd 1 Jun-30 Sep. € 14.00 2010*

AYDAT *9B1* (2km NE Rural) *45.66777, 2.98943* **Camping du Lac d'Aydat, Forêt du Lot, 63970 Aydat [04 73 79 38 09; fax 04 73 79 34 12; info@camping-lac-aydat.com; www.camping-lac-aydat.com]** Exit A75 S fr Clermont-Ferrand at junc 5 onto D13 W. Foll sp Lake Aydat. At x-rds at end of Rouillas-Bas, turn L at rndabt & foll site sp. Med, mkd pitch, some hdstg, terr, shd; wc (some cont); chem disp; mv service pnt; serviced pitches; shwrs inc; el pnts (10A) €4; lndtte; shop 1km; tradsmn high ssn; rest 500m; snacks; bar 500m; playgrnd; lake sw 500m; fishing; entmnt; 30% statics; dogs €1.50; phone; poss cr; adv bkg; quiet; red low ssn; CKE/CCI. "On shore of Lake Aydat; gd for m'vans; Charming woodland pitches, facs tired." ♦ 1 Apr-30 Sep. € 24.00 2012*

AYDAT *9B1* (3km W Rural) *45.66195, 2.94857* **Camping Les Volcans, La Garandie, 63970 Aydat [tel/fax 04 73 79 33 90; campinglesvolcans@akeonet.com; www.campinglesvolcans.com]** Fr N exit A75 junc 2 onto D2089 dir Bourboule; in 18km turn S onto D213 to Verneuge; in 1km fork R onto D5 dir Murol; in 1.5km turn R onto D788 sp La Grandie; turn R into vill; turn R again & site on L in 100m. Fr S exit A73 junc 5 onto D213 W; in 16km turn S in Verneuge onto D5; after 1.5km turn W onto D788 sp La Garandie; in vill turn R just after phone box, site on L in 100m. Sm, mkd pitch, pt sl, pt shd; wc; chem disp; mv service pnt; shwrs inc; el pnts (6A) €5; lndtte; sm shop; tradsmn; rest 4km; snacks; bar; playgrnd; htd pool; lake sw, sand beach & water sports 3km; horseriding 3km; games area; wifi; 2% statics; dogs €2; phone adj; Eng spkn; adv bkg; quiet; red low ssn. "Relaxing site; friendly, helpful new owners improving (2011); lge pitches; no twin-axles; excel walking & cycle rtes nr; beautiful area; gd touring base; excel clean & well stocked facs; loads of hot water always on supply." 1 May-30 Sep. € 18.00 2014*

BERT see Donjon, Le *9A1*

BLAVOZY see Puy en Velay, Le *9C1*

BLESLE see Massiac *9C1*

BORT LES ORGUES *7C4* (4km N Rural) *45.43213, 2.50461* **Camping Les Ch'tis de la Siauve, Rue du Camping, 15270 Lanobre [04 71 40 31 85; canoubgdeschtisdelasiauve@orange.fr; www.camping-chtis-15.com]** On D992 Clermont-Ferrand to Bort-les-Orgues, site on R 3km S of Lanobre. Site sp. Lge, hdg/mkd pitch, terr, pt shd; wc; chem disp; mv service pnt; baby facs; shwrs inc; el pnts (6A) €3; Indtte (inc dryer); shop & 3km; tradsmn; rest, snacks; bar; BBQ; playgrnd; htd pool; paddling pool; lake sw adj; fishing; tennis nr; games area; cycle hire; wifi; entmnt; TV rm; dogs €2; phone; Eng spkn; adv bkg; noisy high ssn; ccard acc; red low ssn; CKE/CCI. "Scenic, family-run site; friendly & helpful; gd clean san facs; high hedges make some pitches dark; footpaths (steep) to lake; gd sw, boating etc; excel touring base; interesting area." ♦ 1 Apr-15 Oct. € 16.00 2011*

BORT LES ORGUES *7C4* (6km S Rural) *45.33671, 2.47379* **Camp Municipal de Bellevue, 15240 Saignes [04 71 40 68 40 or 04 71 40 62 80 (Mairie); saignes-mairie@wanadoo.fr; www.saignes-mairie.fr]** Fr Bort-les-Orgues take D922 S twd Mauriac. In 5km, turn L onto D22. Site sp on R after ent vill. Foll sp 'Piscine/Stade'. Sm, hdg/mkd pitch, pt shd; wc (some cont); chem disp; shwrs inc; el pnts (6-10A) €2.25; Indtte; shops, rest 500m; snacks; bar; BBQ; playgrnd; 3 pools adj; 2 tennis courts adj; dogs; Eng spkn; adv bkg; quiet; no ccard acc; CKE/CCI. "Pleasant situation with views; roomy pitches; vill in walking dist; gd touring base." 1 Jul-31 Aug. € 6.50 2010*

BORT LES ORGUES *7C4* (7km SW Rural) *45.33249, 2.48713* **Camping à la Ferme (Chanet), Domaine de la Vigne, 15240 Saignes [tel/fax 04 71 40 61 02 or 06 83 12 39 32 (mob); chanetcollete@wanadoo.fr]** Take D922 S fr Bort-les-Orgues sp Mauriac. After 5.5km at junc with D15 take sharp L sp Saignes; then turn R onto D22. In cent of Saignes turn L at T-junc onto D30. After 200m turn L onto C14 sp La Vigne & Camping. Farmhouse on L after 400m, site on R. Sm, pt sl, pt shd; wc; cold shwrs inc; el pnts (6A) €2.30 (rev pol); shops 800m; sm pool; poss cr; adv bkg; quiet. "Beautiful, peaceful setting; CL-type site; friendly owners; ltd facs; san facs poss neglected low ssn." Mar-Nov. € 10.50 2009*

BOURBON L'ARCHAMBAULT *9A1* (10km NE Rural) *46.66050, 3.09490* **Camping Domaine Naturiste Les Fourneaux (Naturist), Route Limoise, 03160 Couzon [tel/fax 04 70 66 23 18; lesfourneaux@wanadoo.fr; www.lesfourneaux.org]** Fr Bourbon NE on D139 to Couzon, then L onto D13, site in 2.5km on L. Med, pt sl, pt shd; wc; chem disp; shwrs el pnts (4-6A) €4; tradsmn; bar; playgrnd; pool; cycle hire; no dogs; phone; Eng spkn; quiet; red long stay; INF card req. "V lge pitches; helpful Dutch owners; site not suitable children; conv touring base; many pitches o'grown/unkempt (2009)." ♦ ltd 1 Jun-30 Aug. € 22.00 2009*

BOURBON L'ARCHAMBAULT *9A1* (1km W Rural) *46.58058, 3.04804* **Camp Municipal de Bignon, 03160 Bourbon-l'Archambault [04 70 67 08 83; fax 04 70 67 35 35; mairie-bourbon-archambault@wanadoo.fr]** Exit D953 at Bourbon-l'Archambault onto D1 northwards; in 400m turn L into Boulevard Jean Bignon. Site sp. Lge, sl, pt shd; wc (some cont); shwrs inc; el pnts (6-10A) €2-2.20; Indtte; shops 1km; htd pool & waterslide 300m; tennis nr; wifi; 75% statics (sep area); poss cr; quiet. "Beautifully laid-out in park surroundings; gd pitches; excel updated san facs (2013); charming town; excel." 1 Mar-12 Nov. € 6.40 2014*

BOURBOULE, LA *7B4* (1km N Rural) *45.59680, 2.75130* **FFCC Camping Le Panoramique, Le Pessy, 63150 Murat-le-Quaire [04 73 81 18 79; fax 04 73 65 57 34; info@campingpanoramique.fr; www.campingpanoramique.fr]** Exit A89 junc 25; cont strt until junc with D922; turn R; in 3km turn R onto D219 dir Mont-Dore; in 5km pass thro Murat-le-Quaire; in 1km turn L in Le Pessy; site on L in 300m. Site well sp fr D922. Med, mkd pitch, terr, pt shd; htd wc; chem disp; mv service pnt; baby facs; shwrs inc; el pnts (6-10A) €4.30-5.60; gas; Indtte; shop & snacks 2km; tradsmn; rest 1km; bar; playgrnd; pool; games rm; 30% statics; dogs €1.70; phone; adv bkg; quiet; CKE/CCI. "Site well set-out; mountain views; friendly, helpful recep; clean facs; vg." 15 May-30 Sep. € 24.00 2012*

BOURBOULE, LA *7B4* (1km E Rural) *45.58980, 2.75257* **Camp Municipal des Vernières, Ave de Lattre de Tassigny, 63150 La Bourboule [04 73 81 10 20 or 04 73 81 31 00 (Mairie); fax 04 73 65 54 98]** Fr N on N89 or S on D922 turn E onto D130 dir Le Mont-Dore, site sp. Lge, some hdg pitch; pt terr, pt shd; htd wc (some cont); chem disp; shwrs inc; el pnts (10A) €3.50; Indtte; supmkt nr; playgrnd; pool nr; fishing nr; dogs €1; poss cr; no adv bkg; some rd noise daytime. "Lovely setting in mountains; gd clean facs; sh walk to fine spa town; gd family site; rec." ♦ Easter-30 Sep. € 10.00 2012*

BOURBOULE, LA *7B4* (4km E Rural) *45.59456, 2.76347* **Camping Les Clarines, 1424 Ave Maréchal Leclerc, 63150 La Bourboule [04 73 81 02 30; fax 04 73 81 09 34; clarines.les@wanadoo.fr; www.camping-les-clarines.com]** Fr La Bourboule take D996/D88 on N bank of rv (old rd sp Piscine & Gare); fork L at exit fr town. Site sp on R, nr junc with D219. Lge, terr, pt shd; htd wc (some cont); baby facs; shwrs inc; el pnts (6-10A) €3.50-€5.80; gas; Indtte (inc dryer); shop & adj; bar; BBQ; htd pool; paddling pool; playgrnd; games area; wifi; entmnt; TV rm; dogs €2; poss cr; adv bkg rec; quiet; 15% red low ssn. "Gd winter sports cent; excel htd facs." ♦ 19 Dec-17 Oct. € 16.00 2012*

BRAIZE see Urcay *4H3*

BRIOUDE *9C1* (2km S Rural) *45.2813, 3.4045* **Camping La Bageasse, Ave de la Bageasse, 43100 Brioude [04 71 50 07 70; fax 04 73 34 70 94; labageasse@orange.fr; www.aquadis-loisirs.com]** Turn off N102 & foll sp for Brioude town centre; then foll site sp. Narr app rd. Site on Rv Allier. Med, mkd pitch, terr, pt shd; wc (some cont); chem disp; baby facs; shwrs inc; el pnts (6A) €2 (some rev pol); lndtte (inc dryer); sm shop; tradsmn; snacks; bar; BBQ; playgrnd; pool 2km; fishing & boating adj; canoe hire; 8% statics; dogs €1.50; phone; Eng spkn; adv bkg; quiet; ccard acc; red long stay; htd pool; CKE/CCI. "Well-kept site; lge pitches; helpful warden; gd, clean san facs; phone ahead to check open low ssn; interesting basilica; easy cycle to Brioude." ♦ Easter-15 Oct. € 14.50 (CChq acc) 2014*

BRUGHEAS see Vichy *9A1*

BUXIÈRES-SOUS-MONTAIGUT *9A1* (3.8km SW Rural) *46.19271, 2.81994* **Camping Les Suchères, Les Sucheres, 63700 Buxierères-sous-Montaigut [33 04 73 85 92 66; sucheres@gmail.com; www.campinglessucheres.com]** Head SE on D92, cont on Buxières. Take Les Gouttes to Les Sucheres, Take the 1st R onto Buxières, cont onto Les Gouttes after 700 mtrs turn R twrd Les Sucheres, turn L twrd Les Sucheres, take 1st R onto Les Sucheres, turnn L to stay on Les Sucheres, take the 1st L to stay on Les Sucheres your dest will be on your R. Sm, pt sl; wc; shwrs; chem disp; el pnts (6A) €3; lndry; rest; bar; BBQ; playgrnd; pool; wifi; TV in bar; dogs €1.50; Eng spkn; CCI. "Helpful Dutch owners; lovely peaceful site; good walking area; Montaigut within walking distance; sm supmkt; access to the site could be difficult for lge o'fits as rd narrow for last km; very quiet." € 20.40 2014*

CERILLY *4H3* (8km N Rural) *46.68210, 2.78630* **Camping des Ecossais, La Salle, 03360 Isle-et-Bardais [04 70 66 62 57 or 04 70 67 55 89 (LS); fax 04 70 66 63 99; ecossais@campingstroncais.com; www.campingstroncais.com]** Fr Lurcy-Lévis take D978A SW, turn R onto D111 N twd Isle-et-Bardais & foll camp sp. Ent tight. Med, hdg, pt sl, pt shd; wc; Chem disp; mv service pnt; child/baby facs; shwrs inc; el pnts (10A) inc; lndtte; shop, tradsmn, snack, bar, BBQ, playgrnd; rest nr; lake sw; fishing; dogs €1.50; games area/rm, wifi, 10% statics, twin axle acc, adv bkg; quiet; red low ssn; CKE/CCI. "Excel; v busy high ssn; ltd facs low ssn; gd cycling; site in oak forest; rec." 1 Apr-30 Sep. € 11.55 2013*

CEYRAT see Clermont Ferrand *9B1*

CHAISE DIEU, LA *9C1* (2km NE Rural) *45.33526, 3.70388* **Camp Municipal Les Prades, 43160 La Chaise-Dieu [04 71 00 07 88; fax 04 71 00 03 43; andre.brivadis@orange.fr]** Site well sp fr D906. Med, pt sl, shd; wc (some cont); chem disp; baby facs; shwrs inc; el pnts (10A) inc (long lead poss req); lndtte; shops 2km; tradsmn; BBQ; playgrnd; lake sw 300m; 10% statics; quiet. "Fair sh stay/NH; tourist info office in vill; 14thC church; vg for mushrooms in ssn." 1 Jun-30 Sep. € 12.20 2010*

CHATEAUNEUF LES BAINS see St Gervais d'Auvergne *7A4*

CHATEL DE NEUVRE *9A1* (1.3km NE Rural) *46.4131, 3.31884* **Camping Deneuvre, Route De Moulins, 03500 Châtel-de-Neuvre [04 70 42 04 51; fax 09 72 25 62 63; campingdeneuvre@wanadoo.fr; www.deneuvre.com]** S fr Moulins on D2009; sp N of vill on E side of D2009. Med, mkd pitch, hdstg, pt shd; wc; chem disp; mv service pnt; baby facs; shwrs inc; el pnts (4A) inc; gas; lndtte; tradsmn; rest, snacks; bar; playgrnd; canoe hire; wifi; dogs €1; adv bkg; Eng spkn; quiet; ccard not acc; CKE/CCI. "Site by Rv Allier in nature reserve; clean but not smart; useful NH without unhitching; Dutch management; friendly welcome; excel clean san facs; ltd facs low ssn; meals avail; splendid place for walking, fishing, cycling & birdwatching; diff ent/exit for lge o'fits; no twin-axles." ♦ 1 Apr-30 Sep. € 28.00 2013*

⊞ **CHATEL DE NEUVRE** *9A1* (400m W Rural) *46.40320, 3.31350* **FFCC Canoë Camping de la Courtine, 7 Rue de St Laurant, 03500 Châtel-de-Neuvre [04 70 42 06 21; fax 04 70 42 82 89; campinglacourtine@gmail.com; www.camping-lacourtine.com]** Fr N on D2009 to cent of vill, turn L at x-rds onto D32; site in 500m. Sm, mkd pitch, hdstg, pt shd; htd wc; chem disp; mv service pnt; baby facs; shwrs inc; el pnts (6-10A) €3-5 (poss rev pol); lndtte (inc dryer); shop 400m; tradsmn; rest 400m; snacks; bar; playgrnd; wifi; TV; dogs €1; poss cr; Eng spkn; adv bkg; quiet; red low ssn; CKE/CCI. "Friendly welcome; untidy ent masks v nice site; German family-owned site; access to Rv Allier for canoeing, fishing; walking in nature reserve; liable to flood & poss clsd low ssn, phone ahead to check; conv low ssn NH." ♦ € 12.50 2012*

CHATEL GUYON see Riom *9B1*

CHATEL MONTAGNE *9A1* (10km NE Rural) *46.15938, 3.73506* **Camp Municipal La Boulère, 03120 Arfeuilles [04 70 55 50 11 (Mairie); fax 04 70 55 53 28]** Site off D207 at NE exit to Arfeuilles 50m fr town name sp. 8km fr N7. Sm, pt sl, pt shd; wc (some cont); chem disp; shwrs inc; el pnts (6A) inc; lndry rm; shops, rest, snacks, bar 500m; sm playgrnd; tennis; dogs; quiet; CKE/CCI. "Lovely, peaceful, under-used site set in beautiful countryside; local fishing; gd walking; excel." ♦ 1 May-1 Oct. € 11.50 2010*

CHATEL MONTAGNE *9A1* (1km NW Rural) *46.11526, 3.67700* **FFCC Camping La Croix Cognat, 03250 Châtel-Montagne [tel/fax 04 70 59 31 38 or 06 65 53 91 93 (mob); campinglacroixcognat@wanadoo.fr; http://campinglacroixcognat.monsite-orange.fr/]** SW fr Lapalisse on D7; in 15km L on D25 to Châtel-Montagne in 5km & foll sp; site on L bef vill. 'Sleeping policemen' at ent. Sm, mkd pitch, terr, sl, pt shd; wc (some cont); chem disp; mv service pnt; baby facs; shwrs inc; el pnts (6A) €3; gas; lndtte; supmkt 6km; rest, snacks; playgrnd; pool (high ssn); paddling pool; fishing; tennis 100m; mountain bike hire; horseriding & windsurfing adj; entmnt; 5% statics; dogs €0.50; adv bkg; quiet; CKE/CCI. "Sm pitches poss diff o'fits over 6m." 1 May-30 Sep. € 11.00 2010*

CHAUDES AIGUES *9C1* (3km SW Rural) *44.84583, 3.00039* **Camp Municipal Le Château du Couffour, 15110 Chaudes-Aigues [tel/fax 04 71 23 57 08 or 04 71 23 52 47 (Mairie); www.chaudesaigues.com]** Sp on L of D921 N dir Laguiole. Lge, pt shd; wc; shwrs inc; el pnts (6A) €2.50; Indtte; shops, rest, snacks, bar 2.5km; BBQ; playgrnd; pool 3km; sports area; tennis; fishing 1km; golf 2km; TV; quiet. "Scenic area; attractive, family-run site with fine views; gd walking; 1000m altitude; thermal spa in town; excel." ♦ 1 May-20 Oct. € 8.00 2009*

⊞ **CLERMONT FERRAND** *9B1* (7km SE Rural) *45.70018, 3.16902* **Camping Le Clos Auroy, Rue de la Narse, 63670 Orcet [tel/fax 04 73 84 26 97; aanvraag@camping-le-clos-auroy.com; www.camping-le-clos-auroy.com]** S on A75 take exit 5 sp Orcet; foll D213 to Orcet for 2km, at rndabt onto D52, take 1st L, site on R, sp. Med, hdg/mkd pitch, hdstg, terr, pt shd; htd wc; chem disp; mv service pnt; shwrs inc; el pnts (10A) €5 (poss rev pol); gas; Indtte; sm shop 500m; supmkt 4km; tradsmn; snacks; bar; playgrnd; htd pool; paddling pool; rv fishing 500m; tennis; wifi; entmnt; 5-10% statics; dogs €2.25; site poss open all year; phone; Eng spkn; adv bkg; quiet; ccard acc; red low ssn/long stay/snr citizens; CKE/CCI. "Excel, well-kept; easy access; lge pitches, poss v high hedges; superb htd san facs; pitches by rv poss liable to flood; extra charge for sh stay m'vans; ltd fresh water points & diff to use for refill; vg winter site; interesting town; gd dog walks adj; snack & bar only open high ssn; vg value; helpful staff; gd site." ♦ € 40.00 2014*

CLERMONT FERRAND *9B1* (9km SE Urban) *45.74015, 3.22247* **Camp Municipal Le Pré des Laveuses, Rue des Laveuses, 63800 Cournon-d'Auvergne [04 73 84 81 30; fax 04 73 84 65 90; camping@cournon-auvergne.fr; www.cournon-auvergne.fr/camping]** Fr S o'skts Clermont-Ferrand take D212 E to Cournon & foll sp in town; by Rv Allier, 1km E of Cournon. Lge, mkd pitch, pt shd; wc (some cont); chem disp; baby facs; shwrs inc; el pnts (5-10A) €3.30; Indtte; shop; supmkt nrby; snacks; bar; playgrnd; htd pool; slide paddling pool; rv sw/lake adj; fishing & boating; 40% statics; dogs €2.70; poss cr; Eng spkn; quiet low ssn; red low ssn; ccard acc; CKE/CCI. "Well-kept site - even low ssn; lge pitches; helpful manager; sports grnd adj; excel; clean new facs." ♦ 1 Apr-25 Oct. € 33.00 2014*

⊞ **CLERMONT FERRAND** *9B1* (6km SW Urban) *45.73866, 3.06168* **Camp Municipal Le Chanset, Ave Jean-Baptiste Marrou, 63122 Ceyrat [tel/fax 04 73 61 30 73; camping.lechanset@wanadoo.fr; www.campingdeceyrat63.com]** Exit A75 junc 2 onto D2089 dir Aubière/Beaumont. Foll sp Beaumont then in approx 7km at rndabt junc foll sp Ceyrat. Uphill into Ceyrat; curve R to traff lts; cross main rd & take L fork up hill. Site at top on R - turn poss diff so cont 50m for U-turn back to site. Lge, hdg/mkd pitch, terr, pt sl, pt shd; htd wc (some cont); chem disp; mv service pnt; baby facs; shwrs inc; Indry rm; el pnts (10A) €4.50 (poss rev pol); gas; Indtte; shop; rest, snacks; bar; BBQ; playgrnd; htd pool high ssn; games & TV rm; 25% statics; dogs €1.80; bus; phone; security barrier; poss cr; some Eng spkn; adv bkg; poss noisy when cr; ccard acc; red low ssn/long stay; CKE/CCI. "Gd base for Clermont Ferrand - gd bus service; friendly, helpful staff; shops & supmkt in Vill; late arr can park nr recep." ♦ € 16.70 2013*

CLERMONT FERRAND *9B1* (5km W Rural) *45.75845, 3.05453* **Camping Indigo Royat, Route de Gravenoire, Quartier de l'Oclède, 63130 Royat [04 73 35 97 05; fax 04 73 35 67 69; royat@camping-indigo.com; www.camping-indigo.com]** Site diff to find fr Clermont-Ferrand cent. Fr N, leave A71 at Clermont-Ferrand. Foll sp Chamalières/Royat, then sp Royat. Go under rlwy bdge & pass thermal park on L. At mini-rndabt go L & up hill. At statue, turn L & go up long hill. Look for site sp & turn R. Site on R. NB Do not go down steep rd with traff calming. NB Sat Nav directs up v narr rds & steep hills. Lge, mkd/hdstg pitch, terr, pt shd; htd wc; chem disp; mv service pnt; some serviced pitches; baby facs; shwrs inc; el pnts (10A) €5.20; gas; Indtte (inc dryer); sm shop; tradsmn; rest, snacks high ssn; bar; BBQ; playgrnd; htd pool; paddling pool; tennis; cycle hire; internet; entmnt; TV rm; some statics; dogs €4; phone; Eng spkn; adv bkg; quiet; ccard acc; red low ssn; CKE/CCI. "Excel, clean, spacious, lovely site; set on hillside in trees; gd size earth pitches; views at top levels over Clermont; clean san facs; facs ltd in low ssn; conv touring base." ♦ 29 Apr-3 Nov. € 41.00 (CChq acc) SBS - L18 2014*

COUBON see Puy en Velay, Le *9C1*

COURNON D'AVERGNE see Clermont Ferrand *9B1*

COURPIERE *9B1* (5km NE Rural) *45.79199, 3.60583* **Camping Le Grün du Chignore, Les Plaines, 63120 Vollore-Ville [tel/fax 04 73 53 73 37; camping-du-chignore@hotmail.fr; www.campingauvergne.fr]** D906 S fr Thiers; at Courpière turn L onto D7 to Vollore-Ville; cont on D7 past vill; site on R in 500m. Sm, hdg/mkd pitch, pt shd; wc (some cont); chem disp (wc); mv service pnt; shwrs inc; el pnts (10A) €4.: Indtte; shop 500m; tradsmn; rest, snacks; bar; BBQ (sep area); playgrnd; pool; games area; some statics; wifi; dogs €1.50; some Eng spkn; adv bkg; quiet; ccard acc. "Situated above fishing lake; rolling hills; helpful & welcoming owners; facs poss stretched high ssn; poss clsd on Weds in April; gd walks; chateau in Vollore-Ville; bar pt of vill life; highly rec; excel; vg, new deep pool." ♦ 1 Apr-31 Oct. € 11.00 2013*

⊞ **COURPIERE** *9B1* (10km E Rural) *45.79966, 3.61633* **Campsite Le Montbartoux, Montbartoux, 63120 Vollore-Ville, Auvergne [04 73 53 7005; contact@camping-montbartoux.com; www.camping-montbartoux.com]** D906 S fr Thiers to Courpiere. Then E on D7 to Vollore-Ville. Cont twd Vollore-Montagne. Sp to camp. Sm, mkd pitch, sl, terr, pt shd; wc; chem disp; fam bthrm; shwr; el pnts(10A); Indtte; rest; snacks; bar; BBQ; playgrnd; pool; games area; games rm; entmnt; wifi; tv; dogs €1; twin axles; Eng spkn; adv bkg; quiet; CCI. "Attractive site, beautiful views of Auvergne Valley and Vocanoes of Puy-de-Dome; helpful owner; gd; lge o'fits should phone for dir to avoid hairpin on app rd; new san fac's being built(2013)." ♦ ltd € 23.00 2014*

COUZON see Bourbon L'Archambault *9A1*

DALLET see Pont du château

DEUX CHAISES see Montmarault *9A1*

DIOU see Dompierre sur Besbre *9A1*

AUVERGNE

DOMPIERRE SUR BESBRE *9A1* (5km E Rural) *46.53546, 3.74388* **Camping du Gué de Loire, 03290 Diou [03 85 53 97 79; (Mairie); info@campingguedeloire.com; www.campingguedeloire.com]** Sp in cent of vill in both dirs on rvside, off N79. Sm, hdg/mkd pitch, pt sl, shd; wc; chem disp; mv service pnt; shwrs inc; el pnts €2.50; Indry rm; shop 800m; rest, bar 500m; cycle hire; dogs €1; rd noise; no ccard acc; CKE/CCI. "Simple site; vg, modern san facs; gd touring base." ♦ 15 Jun-31 Aug. € 9.50 2010*

DOMPIERRE SUR BESBRE *9A1* (1.5km S Urban) *46.51378, 3.68276* **Camp Municipal, La Madeleine, Parc des Sports, 03290 Dompierre-sur-Besbre [04 70 34 55 57 or 04 70 48 11 39 (Mairie); camping@mairie-dsb.fr; www.dompierre-sur-besbre.fr]** At E end of town nr rv behind stadium; sp. Med, hdg pitch, shd, pt sl; htd wc; chem disp; mv service pnt; baby facs; shwrs inc; el pnts (10A) €2.20; Indtte; shop 500m; BBQ; full sports facs adj; dogs; phone; poss cr; Eng spkn; adv bkg; quiet; CKE/CCI. "Smart, well-run, busy site; clean san facs, but poss stretched high ssn; excel sports complex; gd for Loire Valley, vineyards & chateaux; highly rec low ssn; excel." ♦ 15 May-15 Sep. € 7.00 2011*

DONJON, LE *9A1* (500m N Urban) *46.35317, 3.79188* **Camp Municipal, 4 Chemin Denys Bournatot, 03130 Le Donjon [04 70 99 56 35 or 04 70 99 50 25 (Mairie); fax 04 74 99 58 02; mairie-le-donjon@wanadoo.fr; www.allier-tourisme.com]** Fr Lapalisse N on D994. Site sp fr town cent on D166 dir Monétay-sur-Loire. Sm, pt sl, pt shd; wc (some cont); mv service pnt; shwrs inc; el pnts (10A) €2.50; shop 500m; rest & bar 400m; playgrnd; fishing, sailing & windsurfing 900m; dogs; quiet; CKE/CCI. ♦ 1 May-31 Oct. € 7.00 2009*

EBREUIL see Gannat *9A1*

FAVEROLLES *9C1* (200m S Rural) *44.93932, 3.14759* **Camp Municipal, 15320 Faverolles [04 71 23 49 91 or 04 71 23 40 48 (Mairie); fax 04 71 23 49 65; faverolles.mairie@wanadoo.fr]** Fr A75 exit junc 30 & take D909 S, turn L onto D13 at Viaduct de Garabit & foll sp for Faverolles for 5km, then sp to site dir St Chély-d'Apcher. Sm, mkd pitch, pt sl, pt shd; htd wc (some); chem disp; shwrs inc; el pnts (6A) inc (rev pol); shops 500m; Indtte; playgrnd; some statics; phone; ccard not acc; quiet. "Nr pretty lake; excel, clean san facs; vg rest in vill." ♦ 1 Jun-15 Oct. € 11.40 2009*

FERRIERES SUR SICHON *9B1* (300m SE Rural) *46.02246, 3.65326* **Camp Municipal, 03250 Ferrières-sur-Sichon [04 70 41 10 10; fax 04 70 41 15 22]** Well sp in Ferrières-sur-Sichon. At x-rds of D995 & D122. Sm, pt sl, pt shd; htd wc; shwrs inc; el pnts €2.20; shop 500m; playgrnd; dogs; quiet. "CL-type site; friendly warden visits 1930; gd san facs; excel NH; lake adj; pleasant vill." 1 Jun-30 Sep. € 7.00 2014*

GANNAT *9A1* (7km N Rural) *46.16588, 3.18975* **Camp Municipal Champ de la Sioule, Route de Chantelle, 03800 Jenzat [04 70 56 86 35 or 04 70 56 81 77 (Mairie); fax 04 70 56 85 38; mairie-jenzat@pays-allier.com; www.bassin-gannat.com]** D2009 N fr Gannat for 4.5km, turn L onto D42, site in 3km in Jenzat on R, just after rv bdge. Med, pt shd; wc; shwrs inc; el pnts (6-10) €1.90-2.95; Indtte; shops 250m; playgrnd; rv sw adj; Eng spkn; clean facs; quiet; CKE/CCI. "Pleasant site on rv bank; helpful warden; clean facs, poss stretched high ssn; muddy after heavy rain; pitches nr rv, some mosquitos." ♦ ltd 19 Apr-21 Sep. € 16.00 2014*

GANNAT *9A1* (1km SW Rural) *46.09106, 3.19385* **Camp Municipal Le Mont Libre, 10 Route de la Bâtisse, 03800 Gannat [tel/fax 04 70 90 12 16 or 06 73 86 04 95 (mob); camping.gannat@wanadoo.fr; www.camping-gannat.fr]** App Gannat fr S on D2009; at rndabt just after town name sp, turn L for 150m; turn R (stadium on R) for 700m; turn L uphill for 200m, turn R to site. Site sp. Or S fr Gannat on D2009; in 600m to R into Route de la Bâtisse; then R, sp site. Med, hdstg, pt sl, terr, pt shd; wc; chem disp; mv service pnt; el pnts (10A) €2.60 (poss rev pol); Indtte; shop & 500m, supmkt 1km; tradsmn; playgrnd; sm pool; rv 5km; games area; games/TV rm; some statics; dogs free; poss cr; adv bkg; quiet; ccard acc. "Pretty, well-kept site; gd sized pitches; helpful warden; clean facs, but poss tired end of ssn; grnd soft after heavy rain; no twin-axles; pleasant town; popular, busy NH." ♦ 1 Apr-31 Oct. € 10.40 2011*

GANNAT *9A1* (10km W Rural) *46.11077, 3.08082* **Camp Municipal Les Nières, Rue des Nières, 03450 Ebreuil [04 70 90 70 60 or 04 70 90 71 33 (Mairie); fax 04 70 90 74 90; mairie-ebreuil@wanadoo.fr; www.valdesioule.com]** Site 1km SW of Ebreuil, sp fr D915. Sm, shd; wc (cont); chem disp; shwrs; el pnts (4-8A) €1.95-2.80; Indtte; shops 1km; snacks; playgrnd; fishing; access to rv; quiet. "Nice setting on Rv Sioule; san facs dated but clean, poss stretched high ssn; warden present 1700-2000 only low ssn; sh walk into vill." ♦ 1 Jun-30 Sep. € 8.00 2012*

GANNAT *9A1* (10km W Rural) *46.10838, 3.07347* **Camping La Filature de la Sioule, Route de Chouvigny, 03450 Ebreuil [04 70 90 72 01; camping.filature@gmail.com; www.campingfilature.com]** Fr A71 exit 12 (avoid 12.1); foll sp to Ebreuil N 500m, then W for 5km thro vill. Turn W onto D915 dir Chouvigny, site in 1km. Med, hdg/mkd pitch, pt shd; wc (some cont); chem disp; mv service pnt 800m; baby facs; shwrs inc; el pnts (6A) €3.50; gas; Indtte; shop; tradsmn; snacks; bar; BBQ; playgrnd; canoeing; trout-fishing; tennis 800m; cycle hire; horseriding; TV rm; wifi; some statics; dogs free; Eng spkn; adv bkg; v quiet; ccard acc; red long stay/low ssn; CKE/CCI. "Peaceful, pleasant site in orchard; lge pitches; helpful British owners; clean facs, ltd low ssn; vg value food high ssn (gd home cooking); vg walking area; conv A71; No hdstg, v soft grnd." ♦ 31 Mar-1 Oct. € 20.00 2013*

HERISSON *7A4* (500m NW Rural) *46.51055, 2.70576* **Camp Municipal de l'Aumance, Rue de Crochepot, 03190 Hérisson [04 70 06 88 22 , 04 70 06 80 45 or 06 63 46 21 49 (mob); www.allier-tourisme.com]** Exit A71 junc 9 onto D2144 N; turn R onto D11 dir Hérisson; immed bef T-junc with D3 turn L at blue sp (high on L) into Rue de Crochepot; site on R down hill. Med, mkd pitch, pt shd; wc; shwrs inc; el pnts (5A) €2.60; playgrnd; games area; rv adj; phone. "Delightful rvside site; idyllic setting; gd clean san facs; warden calls eves; rec; peaceful and picturesque; easy walk to vil; lovely site." 1 Apr-31 Oct. € 8.00 2014*

HERMENT *7B4* (450m N Rural) *45.75481, 2.56683* **Camp Municipal de Herment, Rue de la Chapelle, 63470 Herment [04 73 22 11 98]** Fr main rd thro vill, foll sp upwards thro older pt of town. No name on rd to site. Sm, hdg/mkd pitch, pt shd; wc; el pnts (6A) €0.76; shops 500m; quiet. "Pitches poss diff access lge o'fits; el pnts hidden behind bushes on pitch." ♦ ltd € 5.50 2009*

ISLE ET BARDAIS see Cérilly *4H3*

ISSOIRE *9B1* (2.5km E Rural) *45.55113, 3.27423* **FFCC Camp Municipal du Mas, Ave du Dr Bienfait, 63500 Issoire [04 73 89 03 59 or 04 73 89 03 54 (LS); fax 04 73 89 41 05; camping-mas@wanadoo.fr; www.camping-issoire.com]** Fr Clermont-Ferrand S on A75/E11 take exit 12 sp Issoire; turn L over a'route sp Orbeil; at rndabt, take 1st exit & foll site sp. Med, unshd; htd wc (mostly cont); chem disp; mv service pnt; baby facs; shwrs inc; el pnts (10-13A) €3.35 (long lead poss req); gas; lndtte; supmkt 500m; shops 2km; tradsmn; snacks; playgrnd; fishing in adj lake; tennis 500m; wifi; TV rm; 5% statics; dogs €0.50; phone; poss cr; some Eng spkn; adv bkg (rec high ssn); quiet but some rd noise; ccard acc; red long stay/low ssn; CKE/CCI. "Lovely, well-kept, basic site in park-like location; lge pitches; helpful warden; new, modern san facs; site poss boggy after rain; conv A75; excel touring base or NH; easy cycle rte to Issoire." ♦ 1 Apr-5 Nov. € 25.00 2014*

ISSOIRE *9B1* (6km SE Rural) *45.50908, 3.2848* **FFCC Camping Château La Grange Fort, 63500 Les Pradeaux [04 73 71 05 93 or 04 73 71 02 43; fax 04 73 71 07 69; chateau@lagrangefort.com; www.lagrangefort.com]** S fr Clermont Ferrand on A75, exit junc 13 onto D996 sp Parentignat. At 1st rndabt take D999 sp St Rémy-Chargnat (new rd); at next rndabt take 1st exit onto D34 & foll sp to site on hill-top. Narr app rd & narr uphill ent. Med, hdg/mkd pitch, shd; htd wc; chem disp; mv service pnt; baby facs; sauna; shwrs inc; el pnts (6A) €3.50; lndtte; gas; shop in vill; tradsmn; rest in chateau; snacks; bar; playgrnd; 2 pools (1 htd, covrd); paddling pool; rv fishing; tennis; canoe & mountain bike facs; internet; TV rm; some statics; dogs €3; phone; Eng spkn; adv bkg (fee); quiet; ccard acc; red low ssn; CKE/CCI. "Pleasant, peaceful Dutch-run site in chateau grnds with views; excel san facs but long walk fr some pitches & ltd low ssn; some sm pitches; most pitches damp & gloomy under lge trees & muddy after rain; mosquito problem on shadiest pitches; ltd parking at recep; conv A75; gd." 1 Apr-31 Oct. € 27.00 2014*

ISSOIRE *9B1* (11km S Rural) *45.47373, 3.27161* **Camping Les Loges, 63340 Nonette [04 73 71 65 82; fax 04 73 71 67 23; les.loges.nonette@wanadoo.fr; www.lesloges.com]** Exit 17 fr A75 onto D214 sp Le Breuil, dir Nonette. Turn L in 2km, cross rv & turn L to site. Site perched on conical hill. Steep app. Med, hdg/mkd pitch, pt shd; wc; chem disp; child/baby facs; shwrs inc; el pnts (10A) €3.50; gas; lndtte; shop; tradsmn; rest, snacks; bar; playgrnd; htd pool; rv sw & fishing adj; entmnt; TV; 30% statics; dogs €1.80; quiet; red low ssn; CKE/CCI. "Friendly site; conv Massif Cent & A75; gd NH." Easter-10 Sep. € 21.00 2012*

LACAPELLE VIESCAMP *7C4* (1.6km SW Rural) *44.91272, 2.24853* **Camping La Presqu'île du Puech des Ouilhes, 15150 Lacapelle-Viescamp [04 71 46 42 38 or 06 80 37 15 61 (mob); contact@cantal-camping.fr; www.camping-lac-auvergne.com]** W fr Aurillac on D120; at St Paul-des-Landes turn S onto D53 then D18 to Lacapelle-Viescamp. Foll sp Base de Loisirs, Plage-du-Puech des Ouilhes & Camping. Site beside Lake St Etienne-Cantalès. Med, hdg/mkd pitch, hdstg, pt shd; wc; chem disp; baby facs; shwrs inc; el pnts (16A) €3; lndtte; shop 200m; rest, snacks; bar; playgrnd; pool; sand beach adj; lake sw adj; watersports; canoeing; fishing; tennis; games rm; some statics; dogs €2; Eng spkn; quiet; red low ssn/long stay. "Friendly, helpful young owners; excel." ♦ 15 Jun-15 Sep. € 19.00 2014*

LANGEAC *9C1* (1km N Rural) *45.10251, 3.49980* **Camp Municipal du Pradeau/Des Gorges de l'Allier, 43300 Langeac [04 71 77 05 01; fax 04 71 77 27 34; infos@campinglangeac.com; www.campinglangeac.com]** Exit N102 onto D56 sp Langeac; in 7km join D585 into Langeac; pass under rlwy; at 2nd rndabt in 1km turn L to site, just bef junc with D590. Fr S on D950 to Langeac, take 1st R after rv bdge; then 1st exit at rndabt in 100m. Lge, pt shd; wc (some cont); chem disp; mv service pnt; shwrs inc; el pnts (10A) €2.60 (poss long lead req); gas 500m; lndtte; shop 1km; tradsmn; rest 500m; snacks; playgrnd; pool (high ssn); rv sw, fishing, canoeing & walking rtes adj; cycle hire; entmnt; TV rm; some statics; dogs €1.05; phone; bus 1km; poss cr; Eng spkn; quiet; red low ssn; CKE/CCI. "Beautiful location on Rv Allier; tourist train thro Gorges d'Allier fr Langeac; barrier to site poss clsd after sept 11am-5pm; gd san facs; gd local mkt; excel NH." ♦ 1 Apr-31 Oct. € 13.00 2014*

LANOBRE see Bort les Orgues *7C4*

LAPALISSE *9A1* (250m S Urban) *46.24322, 3.63950* **Camping de la Route Bleue, Rue des Vignes, 03120 Lapalisse [04 70 99 26 31, 04 70 99 76 29 or 04 70 99 08 39 (LS); office.tourisme@cc-paysdelapalisse.fr; www.cc-paysdelapalisse.fr]** S fr Moulins on N7; at rndabt junc with D907 just bef Lapalisse, take 3rd exit onto Ave due Huit Mai 1945 (to town cent), foll rd for 1.5km, over rv bdg, round RH bend onto Rue des Vignes, site on R in 500m. Med, mkd pitch, pt shd; htd wc (some cont); mv service pnt; shwrs inc; el pnts (6-9A) €2.40; lndtte; shops 300m; tradsman; playgrnd; dogs €1; quiet; Eng spkn; CKE/CCI. "Popular, excel NH off N7 in pleasant parkland setting; gd clean san facs; pleasant 10 min walk thro adj park to town; no twin-axles; poss flooding after heavy rain; adequate sans but need upgrade." ♦ 1 Apr-30 Sep. € 14.80 2014*

LAPEYROUSE *7A4* (2km SE Rural) *46.22159, 2.88339* **Camp Municipal Les Marins, La Loge, 63700 Lapeyrouse [04 73 52 02 73 or 04 73 52 00 79 (Mairie); fax 04 73 52 03 89; mairie-lapeyrouse63@wanadoo.fr; http://63lapeyrouse.free.fr]** Fr Montluçon S on D2144 sp Montaigut. In 24km turn L on D13 sp Lapeyrouse. In 7km turn R onto D998, site on R at end of vill, well sp. Med, hdg/mkd pitch, pt shd; wc; chem disp; baby facs; shwrs inc; el pnts (10-16A) inc; Indtte; bar nr; playgrnd; lake sw adj; windsurfing; fishing; tennis; games area; cycle hire; TV; adv bkg; quiet; CKE/CCI. "Delightful countryside; gd." 15 Jun-1 Sep. € 15.00 (3 persons) (CChq acc) 2010*

LAVOUTE SUR LOIRE see Puy en Velay, Le *9C1*

LEMPDES SUR ALLAGNON *9C1* (1.2km N Rural) *45.38699, 3.26598* **Camping Le Pont d'Allagnon (formerly CM au Delà de l'Eau), Rue René Filiol, off Route de Chambezon, 43410 Lempdes-sur-Allagnon [04 71 76 53 69; centre.auvergne.camping@orange.fr; www.campingenauvergne.com]** Going S on A75 exit junc 19 (ltd access) onto D909; turn R on D654 bef vill, site sp at junc. Or fr junc 20 going N; foll sp. Site just outside vill. Med, hdg pitch, pt shd; wc (some cont); chem disp; mv service pnt; shwrs inc; baby facs; el pnts (16A) €3.40; Indtte; shops 500m; bar; playgrnd; pool 100m; rv fishing; tennis; games area; games rm; phone; adv bkg; quiet; ccard acc; red low ssn. "Pleasant site in beautiful area; conv NH A75; gd." ♦ 28 Mar-19 Oct. € 25.00 2014*

MARSAC EN LIVRADOIS see Ambert *9B1*

MARTRES DE VEYRE, LES see Clermont Ferrand *9B1*

MASSIAC *9C1* (7km N Rural) *45.31217, 3.17278* **Camp Municipal La Bessière, 43450 Blesle [04 71 76 25 82; mairie.de.blesle@wanadoo.fr; www.blesle.fr]** Fr Massiac take D909 N. In 5km at Babory turn L onto D8. In 1km turn L immed after x-ing rv bdge. Site sp. Sm, some hdg/mkd pitch, terr, pt shd; wc (some cont); chem disp (wc); mv service pnt; shwrs inc; el pnts (10A) €2.50; Indtte; BBQ; playgrnd; tennis; wifi; 30% statics; dogs €1; phone 200m; poss cr; quiet; red long stay; CKE/CCI. "Pleasant, clean site nr pretty vill; warm welcome, helpful warden; gd touring base; vg." ♦ ltd 1 Apr-2 Oct. € 8.30 2011*

MASSIAC *9C1* (800m SW Rural) *45.24703, 3.18765* **FFCC Camp Municipal de l'Allagnon, 17 Ave de Courcelles, 15500 Massiac [04 71 23 03 93 or 04 71 23 02 61; camping.allagnon15@orange.fr; www.paysdemassiac.com]** Exit A75 at Massiac onto N122 or N122e; cont on N122 dir Murat; site sp on L on rvside 800m along Ave de Courcelles (pt of N122). Med, mkd pitch, shd; wc; mv service pnt; shwrs; el pnts (6A) €3; gas; Indtte; shops adj; playgrnd; pool adj; fishing; tennis; wifi; dogs €0.60; poss cr; Eng spkn; ccard acc; CKE/CCI. "Simple, popular site; helpful staff; conv A75; vg." ♦ 1 May-31 Oct. € 10.00 2011*

MASSIAC *9C1* (6km SW Rural) *45.23353, 3.13432* **Camp Municipal, Pré Mongeal, 15500 Molompize [04 71 73 62 90 or 04 71 73 60 06; fax 04 71 73 60 24; mairie.molompize@wanadoo.fr]** Fr N exit A75 junc 23 onto N122 dir Aurillac; site on L just bef Molompize. Or fr S exit A75 junc 24 onto N122e to Massiac; then join N122 dir Aurillac; then as bef. Med, pt shd; wc; chem disp (wc); shwrs inc; el pnts (10A); Indry rm; shops 500m; playgrnd; 6% statics; quiet; CKE/CCI. "Rvside site behind stadium; tennis courts; friendly warden; gd." ♦ ltd 15 Jun-15 Sep. € 7.00 2010*

MAURIAC *7C4* (1km SW Rural) *45.21865, 2.31639* **Camping Le Val St Jean, Lac du Barrage d'Enchanet, 15200 Mauriac [04 71 67 31 13 or 06 80 14 59 45 (mob); fax 04 71 68 17 34; valsaintejean@mauriac.fr; www.tourismevalsaintjean.fr]** Site adj lake; well sp. Med, hdg/mkd pitch, terr, unshd; htd wc; chem disp; mv service pnt; shwrs inc; el pnts (10A) €3.60; Indtte (inc dryer); shop; tradsmn; rest 1km; snacks; playgrnd; htd pool; paddling pool; waterslide; sand beach & lake sw adj; fishing; golf adj; wifi; TV rm; some statics; dogs €1.50; adv bkg; quiet; red low ssn; CKE/CCI. "Excel, clean, tidy site; ltd facs low ssn; gd touring base." ♦ 1 May-25 Sep. € 19.50 (CChq acc) 2010*

MAURS *7D4* (6km SE Rural) *44.68140, 2.26050* **FFCC Camping Le Moulin de Chaules, Route de Calvinet, 15600 St Constant [04 71 49 11 02; fax 04 71 49 13 63; camping@moulin-de-chaules.com; www.moulin-de-chaules.com]** Fr N122 in Maurs, foll sp to St Constant on D663. Take by-pass round St Constant & turn L to Calvinet, well sp fr Maurs. Med, mkd pitch, terr, shd; wc; chem disp; baby facs; shwrs inc; el pnts (4A) €3; Indtte (inc dryer); sm shop; tradsmn; rest, snacks; bar; BBQ (gas); playgrnd; pool; games area; games rm; wifi; some statics; no twin-axles; dogs €1.50; Eng spkn; adv bkg; quiet; red low ssn/long stay; CKE/CCI. "Friendly Dutch owner; excel facs; excel for young children; terr access steep - care needed (tractor tow avail); gd." ♦ ltd 11 Apr-11 Oct. € 21.50 2009*

MAURS *7D4* (800m S Rural) *44.70522, 2.20586* **Camp Municipal Le Vert, Route de Decazeville, 15600 Maurs [04 71 49 04 15; fax 04 71 49 00 81; camping@ville-maurs.fr; www.ville-maurs.fr/tourisme/camping]** Fr Maurs take D663 dir Decazeville. Site on L 400m after level x-ing thro sports complex. Narr ent. Med, mkd pitch, shd; wc; chem disp; baby facs; shwrs inc; el pnts (15A) inc; Indtte; shops 1km; playgrnd; pool; tennis; rv fishing; poss cr; adv bkg; quiet. "V pleasant on side of rv; sports complex adj; friendly helpful warden." ♦ 1 May-30 Sep. € 11.00 2014*

MEAULNE *7A4* (800m S Urban) *46.59667, 2.61352* **Camp Municipal Le Cheval Blanc, Route de Montluçon, 03360 Meaulne [04 70 06 91 13 or 04 70 06 95 34; fax 04 70 06 91 29; mairie.meaulne@wanadoo.fr; www.meaulne-ami.com]** Site off D2144 on bank Rv Aumance. Sm, pt shd; wc; chem disp (wc); shwrs inc; el pnts (12A) €2; Indtte; shop, rest, bar 300m; BBQ; playgrnd; rv fishing; canoeing; dogs; phone; quiet, some rd noise; CKE/CCI. "Pleasant, well-kept, basic site in beautiful rvside position; clean san facs; site yourself, warden calls 1300 & 1900 or put money in letterbox; poss flooding in high rainfall; excel NH." ♦ ltd 1 May-30 Sep. € 10.00 2009*

MENAT *7A4* (2km E Rural) *46.09579, 2.92899* **Camp Municipal des Tarteaux, 63560 Menat [04 73 85 52 47 or 04 73 85 50 29 (Mairie); fax 04 73 85 50 22; mairiemenat@wanadoo.fr; www.ville-menat.com]** Heading SE fr St Eloy-les-Mines on D2144 foll sp Camping Pont de Menat. Exit D2144 at Menat opp Hôtel Pinal. Site alongside Rv Sioule. Med, terr, pt sl, shd; wc (cont); mv service pnt; shwrs inc; el pnts (16A) €2.70; Indtte; shop 2km; playgrnd; rv adj; fishing & boating 2km; wifi; adv bkg; quiet; CKE/CCI. "Beautiful site beside rv; basic san facs clean but in need of update (2011) - own san facs rec; Chateau Rocher ruins nrby; ok NH." 1 Apr-30 Sep. € 8.00 2013*

MOLOMPIZE see Massiac *9C1*

MONASTIER SUR GAZEILLE, LE *9C1* (1km SW Rural) *44.93662, 3.98453* **Camping Estela, Route du Moulin de Savin, 43150 Le Monastier-sur-Gazeille [06 87 48 60 28 04 71 03 82 24 (mob); contact@campingestela.com]** Fr Le Puy-en-Velay E on D535; in 4km fork R continuing on D535 to Le Monastier-sur-Gazeille; site sp fr ent to vill. App only fr N end of vill. Site in bottom of valley; gd power-weight ratio needed on dep. Sm, pt shd; wc; shwrs; el pnts (3-10A) €3.20; Indtte; tradsmn; snack bar; BBQ; playgrnd; rv sw; dog €2.50; wifi; quiet. "Lovely rvside site in beautiful area; friendly staff; Le Monastier was start of R. L. Stevenson's 'Travels with a Donkey'." 1 Jun-30 Sep. € 18.00 2013*

"I need an on-site restaurant"

We do our best to make sure site information is correct, but it is always best to check any must-have facilities are still available or will be open during your visit.

MONISTROL D'ALLIER *9C1* (4km N Rural) *44.99148, 3.67781* **Camp Municipal Le Marchat, 43580 St Privat-d'Allier [04 71 57 22 13; fax 04 71 57 25 50; info@mairie-saintprivatdallier.fr; www.mairie-saintprivatdallier.fr]** Fr Le Puy-en-Velay W on D589. Turn R in cent of vill at petrol stn, site on R in 200m. Sm, hdg pitch, terr, shd; wc; chem disp; shwrs inc; el pnts (10A) €1.10; shops, bar in vill; playgrnd; quiet. "Beautifully-kept site; poss unkempt low ssn; friendly warden; not suitable lge o'fits." ♦ ltd 1 May-1 Nov. € 6.00 2014*

MONISTROL D'ALLIER *9C1* (350m E Rural) *44.96912, 3.64793* **Camp Municipal Le Vivier, 43580 Monistrol-d'Allier [04 71 57 24 14 or 04 71 57 21 21 (Mairie); fax 04 71 57 25 03; mairie-monistroldallier@wanadoo.fr; www.monistroldallier.fr/camping.php]** Fr Le Puy-en-Velay W on D589 to Monistrol-d'Allier. Turn L in vill immed after rlwy stn & cont down steep entry rd bef x-ing bdge. Site sp in town cent. Sm, mkd pitch, pt shd; wc; chem disp; shwrs inc; el pnts (5-10A) €2.60; shops, rest, snacks; bar 200m; BBQ; dogs; phone; train 500m; quiet; CKE/CCI. "Vg site steep valley." ♦ ltd 15 Apr-15 Sep. € 12.00 2014*

MONISTROL SUR LOIRE *9C1* (7km SE Rural) *45.21630, 4.21240* **Kawan Village Camping de Vaubarlet, 43600 Ste Sigolène [04 71 66 64 95; fax 04 71 66 11 98; camping@vaubarlet.com; www.vaubarlet.com]** Fr Monistrol take D44 SE twd Ste Sigolène & turn R into vill. In vill take D43 dir Grazac for 6km. Site by Rv Dunière, ent L bef bdge. Site well sp fr vill. Med, mkd pitch, pt shd; wc; chem disp; mv service pnt; shwrs inc; el pnts (6A) €3 (poss rev pol); Indtte (inc dryer); shop & 6km; tradsmn; rest, snacks; bar; BBQ; playgrnd; htd pool; paddling pool; rv sw adj; trout fishing; cycle hire; games area; wifi; entmnt; TV rm; 15% statics; phone; dogs €1; Eng spkn; adv bkg; quiet; red low ssn; ccard acc; CKE/CCI. "Friendly, helpful staff; well-run site; excel san facs; interesting museums nrby." ♦ 1 May-30 Sep. € 25.00 (CChq acc) 2014*

MONT DORE, LE *7B4* (500m NW Urban) *45.57711, 2.80387* **Camp Municipal des Crouzets, 4 Ave des Crouzets, 63240 Le Mont-Dore [tel/fax 04 73 65 21 60 or 04 73 65 22 00 (Mairie); camping.crouzets@orange.fr; www.mairie-mont-dore.fr]** Take D130 fr Bourboule to Le Mont-Dore; site ent just on L after entering town. Poor sps. Lge, mkd pitch, hdstg, pt sl, unshd; htd wc; chem disp; mv service pnt adj; shwrs inc; el pnts (10A) €4.10 (poss rev pol); Indtte; tradsmn; shops & rests adj; BBQ; playgrnd; pool 4km; sports area; dogs €1.60; poss cr; Eng spkn; ccard acc; red low ssn. "Well-run site in town cent, but quiet; gd sized pitches; excel san facs; helpful warden; gd touring base; cable car to Puy de Sancy." ♦ 19 Dec-30 Sep. € 10.00 2010*

MONTLUCON *7A4* (12km NW Rural) *46.37795, 2.46695* **Camp Municipal Le Moulin de Lyon, 03380 Huriel [06 11 75 05 63 or 04 70 28 60 08 (Mairie); fax 04 70 28 94 90; mairie.huriel@wanadoo.fr; www.huriel.planet-allier.com]** Exit A71 junc 10 & foll sp Domérat, then D916 to Huriel. Site well sp. Or fr N D943 turn SW at La Chapelaude to Huriel on D40, foll sp to site. Last km single track (but can pass on level grass) with steep incline to site ent. Site adj Rv Magieure. Med, hdg pitch, pt sl, pt shd; wc (some cont); chem disp; shwrs; el pnts (10A) €2.40 (poss rev pol); gas; Indry rm; shops, tradsmn; snacks, bar 1km; BBQ; playgrnd (on other side of rv); lake/rv fishing; tennis; TV; few statics; Eng spkn; quiet. "Peaceful, wooded site in lovely setting by lake; well-kept; friendly; site yourself, warden calls am & pm; no apparent security; uphill walk to vill (1km); lovely quiet site, clean facs." 15 Apr-15 Oct. € 9.00 2014*

MONTMARAULT *9A1* (4.5km NE Rural) *46.35995, 2.99213* **Camping La Petite Valette, La Vallette, 03390 Sazeret [04 70 07 64 57 or 06 80 23 15 54 (mob); la.petite.valette@wanadoo.fr; www.valette.nl]** Leave A71 at junc 11 & take 3rd exit at 1st rndabt onto D46; after 400m turn L at next rndabt, site sp on L in 3km. Or N of Montmarault in vill of Sazeret site well sp. Narr rd fr vill to site poss diff lge o'fits. Easy to find. Med, hdg/mkd pitch, pt shd; htd wc; chem disp; baby facs; fam bthrm; shwrs inc; el pnts (6A) €2.95; gas; Indtte (inc dryer); tradsmn; rest (high ssn); snacks; bar; BBQ; playgrnd; htd pool; paddling pool; cycle hire; fishing; games area; dogs €2; Eng spkn; adv bkg; quiet; red low ssn. "Attractive, popular, well-run site; a bit isolated; Dutch family owners; spacious, clean san facs; gd rest; grassy pitches muddy when wet; pleasant walks; vg." ♦ 1 Apr-3 Oct. € 18.00 2011*

MONTMARAULT *9A1* (10.8km NE Rural) *46.38107, 3.03926* **Camp Municipal, 03240 Deux-Chaises [04 70 47 12 33 or 04 70 47 12 74 (Mairie); fax 04 70 47 31 33; mairie-deux-chaises@pays-allier.com; www.auvergne-tourisme.info]** Exit A71 junc 11 onto N79 dir Moulins; in 8km turn off N79 to Deux-Chaises. Site in vill, well sp. Sm, hdg pitch, terr, pt sl, unshd; wc; shwrs; el pnts (16A) €2; shop; rest & bar 200m; playgrnd; tennis; lake fishing adj. "Well-kept site in beautiful setting; gd, basic facs; warden calls for fees pm; phone to check open bef arr, esp low ssn; vg rest nrby; gd NH." 1 Apr-30 Sep. € 10.50 2013*

MURAT *7C4* (1km SW Urban) *45.10303, 2.86599* **Camp Municipal de Stalapos, 8 Rue de Stade, 15300 Murat [04 71 20 01 83 or 04 71 20 03 80; fax 04 71 20 20 63; agyl@camping-murat.com; www.murat.fr]** Fr N122 site sp fr cent of Murat dir Aurillac (thro indus est), adj Rv Alagnon. Lge, some hdstg, pt sl, pt shd; wc (cont); chem disp; shwrs inc; el pnts (6-16A) €2.50-6.30; Indtte; shops 1km; playgrnd; rv fishing adj; dogs free; poss cr; no adv bkg; also winter ssn, phone ahead; quiet; red CKE/CCI. "Peaceful location; basic but clean san facs; warden lives on site; excel touring base; gd views medieval town." ♦ 1 May-30 Sep. € 13.00 2014*

MURAT *7C4* (5km SW Rural) *45.07781, 2.83047* **Aire Naturelle Municipal, 15300 Albepierre-Bredons [04 71 20 20 49]** SW fr Murat on D39 dir Prat-de-Bouc; site sp fr cent of Albepierre. Sm, pt shd; wc (some cont); chem disp (wc); shwrs inc; el pnts (10A) €2; shops, rest & bar 300m; dogs free; quiet; ccard not acc; CKE/CCI. "Excel, peaceful location; basic, clean facs; warden visits am & pm; vg walking amidst extinct volcanoes; gd." 15 Jun-15 Sep. € 6.80 2014*

MURAT *7C4* (6km W Rural) **Camp Municipal Le Vallognon, 15300 Laveissière [04 71 20 11 34; fax 04 71 20 20 48; campinglaveissiere@orange.fr]** Site sp fr N122 W fr Murat Sp Aurilla, after 4km turn R onto D439 site on L after 300m. Med, pt shd; wc; shwrs inc; el pnts inc; Indtte; shops 300m; playgrnd; htd pool adj; quiet, some rd noise; CKE/CCI. "Conv for Cantal Mountains; gd hill walking; gd site." ♦ 1 Jan-3 Apr, 1Jun-4 Sep, 20 Dec-31 Dec. € 14.60 2013*

MUROL *7B4* (1km S Rural) *45.56275, 2.93825* **Camping Sunêlia La Ribeyre, Route de Jassat, St Victor-la-Rivière, 63790 Murol [04 73 88 64 29; fax 04 73 88 68 41; info@laribeyre.com; www.laribeyre.com]** Exit 6 fr A75 onto D978 S sp Champeix/St Nectaire, then D996 to Murol. In Murol take D5 S sp Besse-et-St Anastaise. In approx 500m take D618 twd Jassat & site in 500m on rvside. Sp fr Murol. Lge, mkd pitch, pt shd; wc (some cont); chem disp; serviced pitches; baby facs; shwrs inc; el pnts (6-10A) €6.45-11.40 (poss rev pol); Indtte (inc dryer); shop 1km; tradsmn; rest; bar; BBQ; playgrnd; pools (1 htd, covrd) & aqua park; paddling pool; waterslides; lake sw & sand beach adj; fishing; boat hire; tennis; horseriding; hiking; games area; games rm; wifi; entmnt; TV rm; 30% statics; dogs €2.80; Eng spkn; adv bkg; quiet; ccard acc; red low ssn; CKE/CCI. "Beautiful setting by lake; spacious pitches, some by lake; gd san facs; excel sw complex; ideal touring base & family site; great walks fr site; activities for all ages; barrier operated 2300-0700; quiet low ssn; groups welcome low ssn; vg." ♦ 1 May-15 Sep. € 27.00 2011*

MUROL *7B4* (1km S Rural) *45.57400, 2.95735* **FFCC Camp Le Repos du Baladin, Groire, 63790 Murol [04 73 88 61 93; fax 04 73 88 66 41; reposbaladin@free.fr; www.camping-auvergne-france.com]** Fr D996 at Murol foll sp 'Groire' to E, site on R in 1.5km just after vill. Med, hdg/mkd pitch, pt sl, terr, shd; htd wc (some cont); chem disp; sauna; baby facs; shwrs inc; el pnts (5A) €4; Indtte (inc dryer); shop 1.5km; tradsmn; snacks; bar; playgrnd; htd pool; lake sw 5km; wifi; dogs €3; poss cr; poss noise high ssn; Eng spkn; CKE/CCI. "Lovely site with immac san facs; friendly, helpful owners; easy walk into town thro fields." 27 Apr-7 Sep. € 34.00 2013*

MUROL *7B4* (2km W Rural) *45.56902, 2.93005* **Camping de la Plage, Lac Chambon, 63790 Murol [04 73 88 60 04; fax 04 73 88 80 08; lac.chambon@wanadoo.fr; http://lac-chambon-plage.fr]** Exit A75 junc 6 sp Champeix/St Nectaire; cont for 34km thro St Nectaire to Murol on D996; 1km past Murol turn L sp Lac Chambon/Centre Touristique; bear L past lge car park to site ent. Lge, hdg/mkd pitch, terr, pt shd; htd wc; chem disp; mv service pnt; shwrs inc; baby facs; el pnts (6A) €3.70; gas & 2km; Indtte; shop; rest, snacks & bar in hotel; playgrnd; lake sw & fishing adj; tennis; cycle hire; entmnt; TV; statics; dogs €1; phone; Eng spkn; adv bkg; quiet; ccard acc; CKE/CCI. "Vg site; facs stretched high ssn; gd birdwatching & walking." ♦ ltd 1 May-15 Sep. € 16.50 2010*

"Satellite navigation makes touring much easier"

Remember most sat navs don't know if you're towing or in a larger vehicle – always use yours alongside maps and site directions.

MUROL *7B4* (2km W Rural) *45.57516, 2.91428* **Camping Le Pré Bas, 63790 Chambon-sur-Lac [04 73 88 63 04; fax 04 73 88 65 93; prebas@campingauvergne.com; www.campingauvergne.com]** Take D996 W fr Murol twd Mont-Dore. Site 1.5km on L, twd lake. Lge, hdg/mkd pitch, pt sl, pt shd; wc; chem disp; mv service pnt; serviced pitches; baby facs; shwrs inc; el pnts (6A) €4.70; gas 1km; Indtte; ice/freezer; shop & 1km; tradsmn; snacks; bar (high ssn); BBQ; playgrnds; 2 pools (1 htd, covrd); waterslides; lake sw; games area; library; entmnt; TV rm; 40% statics; dogs €2.10; phone; poss cr; Eng spkn; adv bkg; quiet; red low ssn; CKE/CCI. "Excel family-run site by Lac Chambon; superb views; friendly, helpful staff; immac san facs; excel pool complex; rock pegs ess; access to sm pitches poss diff lge o'fits; excel walking area." ♦ 24 Apr-30 Sep. € 24.00 2012*

MUROL *7B4* (5km W Rural) *45.56979, 2.90185* **Camping Les Bombes (formerly Municipal), Chemin de Pétary, 63790 Chambon-sur-Lac [04 73 88 64 03 or 06 88 33 25 94 (mob); les-bombes-camping@orange.fr; www.camping-les-bombes.com]** Site is on D996. Nr exit fr vill Chambon. Well sp. Med, mkd pitch, pt shd; wc (some cont); chem disp; mv service pnt; shwrs; el pnts (6A) €4.50; Indtte; shops; tradsmn; rest 500m; snacks; bar; BBQ; playgrnd; pool; lake sw 1km; TV rm; 5% statics; dogs €2.20; phone; quiet; Eng spkn; adv bkg; red low ssn; CKE/CCI. "Beautiful area; gd, clean, well-maintained facs stretched in high ssn; lge pitches; friendly, helpful owners; excel." ♦ 15 May-30 Sep. € 24.00 2012*

NERIS LES BAINS *7A4* (1km NW Urban) *46.28695, 2.65215* **Le Camping du Lac (Formerly Municipal), Ave Marx Dormoy, 03310 Néris-les-Bains [04 70 03 17 59 or 04 70 03 24 70 (recep); fax 04 70 03 79 99; campingdulac-neris@orange.fr; www.ville-neris-les-bains.fr]** Site on N side of Néris off D2144. Turn W at rndabt by blue TO, opp park, & foll sp round 1 way system to site in 500m. Med, hdg/mkd pitch, hdstg, pt sl, terr, pt shd; wc (some cont); chem disp; shwrs inc; el pnts (10A); gas; shops 1km; tradsmn; snacks; bar; playgrnd; covrd pool 500m; some statics; dogs €1; quiet; red long stay. "6 pitches for m'vans at ent to site; space to wait on car park if barrier clsd; pleasant town; vg; gd facs, quiet lower pitches, gd NH." 1 Apr-22 Oct. € 15.00 2013*

NEUSSARGUES MOISSAC see Murat *7C4*

NEUVEGLISE *9C1* (5km S Rural) *44.89500, 3.00157* **Flower Camping Le Belvédère, Le Pont-de-Lanau, 15260 Neuvéglise [04 71 23 50 50; fax 04 71 23 58 93; contact@campinglebelvedere.com; www.campinglebelvedere.com]** S on A75/E11 exit junc 28 at St Flour; take D921 S twd Chaudes-Aigues. Turn R sp 'Villages de Vacances de Lanau' & site - do not app site thro Neuvéglise. Steep access poss diff lge o'fits. Med, terr, pt shd; wc; chem disp; mv service pnt; baby facs; sauna; shwrs inc; el pnts (6A) inc; gas; Indtte (inc dryer); shop; rest, snacks; bar; BBQ (gas/charcoal); playgrnd; htd pool; paddling pool; fishing; canoeing, windsurfing & tennis nrby; sailing 15km; fitness rm; horseriding 20km; fitness rm; wifi; entmnt; games/TV rm; 25% statics; dogs free; twin-axles acc (rec check in adv); adv bkg; quiet; ccard acc; red low ssn/long stay; CKE/CCI. "Views over Rv Truyère; friendly, peaceful, family-run site; steep terrs & tight pitches poss diff; gd, clean san facs; mkt Neuvéglise Fri; excel site, beautiful views." ♦ 30 Mar-29 Sep. € 39.00 2013*

NEUVEGLISE *9C1* (300m SW Rural) *44.92406, 2.97936* **Camp Municipal Fontbielle, 15260 Neuvéglise [04 71 23 50 50]** S fr St Flour on D921 for approx 20km. Turn R to Neuvéglise & foll sp thro town. Sm, terr, pt shd; wc (some cont); chem disp (wc); mv service pnt in town; shwrs inc; el pnts (6A) €2; Indtte (inc dryer); shop, rest, snacks, bar 300m; BBQ; playgrnd; htd pool 5km; tennis 150m; some statics; dogs €1; bus 300m; adv bkg; quiet; CKE/CCI. "Well-maintained & well-run site; clean san facs; gd touring base." ♦ ltd 1 Jun-30 Sep. € 5.50 2010*

NONETTE see Issoire *9B1*

OLLIERGUES *9B1* (1.75km E Rural) *45.69008, 3.63289* **Camping Les Chelles, 63880 Olliergues [tel/fax 04 73 95 54 34; info@camping-les-chelles.com; www.camping-les-chelles.com]** Fr Olliergues take D37 N up hill dir Le Brugeron; then sharp L onto D87 dir La Chabasse; site sp. Med, hdg/mkd pitch, terr, shd; wc; chem disp; shwrs inc; el pnts (15A) €2.80; Indtte (inc dryer); shop 5km; rest, snacks; bar; playgrnd; pool; games area; games rm; wifi; TV; dogs €1; phone; Eng spkn; adv bkg; ccard acc. "Facs excel for families with young children; enthusiastic, helpful & kind Dutch owners; gd walking; gd touring base; vg." ♦ ltd 1 Apr-31 Oct. € 21.00 2014*

ORCET see Clermont Ferrand *9B1*

⊞ **ORCIVAL** *7B4* (6km NE Rural) *45.7067, 2.8593* **FFCC Camping La Haute Sioule, Route du Camping, 63210 St Bonnet-près-Orcival [04 73 65 83 32; fax 04 73 65 85 19; info@camping-auvergne.info; www.camping-auvergne.info]** Fr Clermont-Ferrand take N89 S then W twds La Bourboule for approx 20km. At junc with D216 turn L twds Orcival. Site in 4km. Foll site sp. Med, sl, pt shd; wc; mv service pnt; shwrs inc; el pnts (4-13A) €3-6.10; gas; Indtte; shops 250m; snacks; playgrnd; rv sw adj; golf; fishing adj; games rm; entmnt; 50% statics; dogs free; poss cr; Eng spkn; CKE/CCI. "Pleasant site; gd views; friendly owners; poss diff lge o'fits; many sheep & chickens on site (Jun 2011)." € 15.00 2010*

ORLEAT see Thiers *9B1*

PAULHAGUET *9C1* (500m SE Rural) *45.19900, 3.52000* **Camping La Fridière, 6 Route d'Esfacy, 43230 Paulhaguet [04 71 76 65 54; campingpaulhaguet@wanadoo.fr; www.campingfr.nl]** On SE side of town on D4. Sm, hdg/mkd pitch, pt shd; htd wc; chem disp; mv service pnt; shwrs inc; el pnts (10-16A) €3.50; gas 500m; Indtte; shop, snacks 500m; tradsmn; bar; playgrnd; rv fishing; wifi; dogs €1; Eng spkn; quiet; CKE/CCI. "Useful NH; lge pitches; friendly Dutch owners; vg, clean san facs; vg facs for children; popular with young Dutch families; site unkempt end ssn (2010); mkt Mon; excel." ♦ 1 Apr-1 Oct. € 13.00 2010*

"There aren't many sites open at this time of year"

If you're travelling outside peak season remember to call ahead to check site opening dates – even if the entry says 'open all year'.

PERS *7C4* (4.8km NE Rural) *44.90619, 2.25568* **Camping Du Viaduc, Le Ribeyres Village, 15290 Pers [04 71 64 70 08; infos@camping-cantal.com; www.camping-cantal.com]** Fr Aurillac take N122 S twrds Figeac. After Sansac turn R onto D61 sp Pers. Site well sp fr here. Final 2km narr rd with passing places. Med, hdg/mkd pitch, terr, pt shd; wc; chem disp; mv service pnt; shwrs inc; el pnts (10A) €3.60; Indtte (inc dryer); shop; tradsmn (Jul-Aug); snack; takeaway; bar; BBQ; playgrnd; pool; lake 0.5km; wifi; 20% statics; dogs €2-3.10; twin axles; adv bkg; red in low ssn; CKE/CCI. "Adj to lge lake with watersports avail; nearest town for shops is Aurillac 25km; local shops in Le Rouget 7km; beautiful location; many pitches with lake view; excel." ♦ ltd 26 Apr-11 Nov. € 26.50 2014*

PONT DU CHATEAU *9B1* (4.5km SSW Urban) *45.77546, 3.24197* **Camping Les Ombrages, Rue Pont du Château, 63111 Dallet [tel/fax 04 73 83 10 97; lesombrages@hotmail.com; www.lesombrages.com]** E fr Clermont Ferrand on D769; 200m bef x-ing Rv Allier turn R onto D783/D769A; 50m after x-ring rv turn L into Rue Pont du Château; site on L in 400m. Sm, shd; wc; shwrs inc; el pnts (6A) €3.50; Indtte; shop; rest, snacks; bar; playgrnd; 2 pools; paddling pool; rv sw adj; fishing; canoeing; games rm; wifi; entmnt; TV; no dogs; quiet; red low ssn. "Peaceful site; excel pitches by rv; gd for fishing & canoeing." 12 May-15 Sep. € 17.50 2011*

PONTGIBAUD *7B4* (3km NE Rural) *45.84436, 2.87672* **Camping Bel-Air, 63230 St Ours [04 73 88 72 14; contact@campingbelair.fr; www.campingbelair.fr]** Exit A89 junc 26 onto D941 dir Pontgibaud; cont past Pontigibaud; in 1.5km turn L onto D943; site in 1.3km on L. Site sp. Med, mkd pitch, pt sl, shd; wc; chem disp; mv service pnt; baby facs; shwrs inc; el pnts (6A) €3.30; gas; lndry rm; shop 1.5km; tradsmn; rest, snacks; bar; BBQ; playgrnd; golf; games area; 5% statics; dogs €1; Eng spkn; adv bkg; quiet, but some rd noise; CKE/CCI. "Peaceful, basic site in beautiful area; helpful owner; clean facs, ltd low ssn; conv Vulcania; excel." ♦ 1 May-27 Sep. € 18.00 2013*

PONTGIBAUD *7B4* (200m S Rural) *45.82978, 2.84517* **FFCC Camp Municipal La Palle, Route de la Miouze, 63230 Pontgibaud [04 73 88 96 99 or 04 73 88 70 42 (LS); fax 04 73 88 77 77; mairie.pontgibaud@wanadoo.fr; www.campongibaud.free.fr]** At W end of Pontgibaud turn S over bdge on D986 & site in 500m on L, past site for La Palle Chalets. Med, hdg/mkd pitch, hdstg, pt shd; htd wc (some cont); chem disp; mv service pnt; shwrs inc; el pnts (10-16A) inc; gas 400m; lndtte; shops 400m; tradsmn; rest; BBQ; playgrnd; lake sw & beach 1km; games area; tennis, cycle hire 400m; entmnt; 5% statics; dogs; Eng spkn; adv bkg; wifi; rd & rlwy noise; red long stay/low ssn; CKE/CCI. "Pleasant site nr sm rv; helpful staff; gd touring base; pop concerts once a week high ssn; conv Vulcania exhibition cent." ♦ 15 Apr-30 Sep. € 19.00 2014*

PRADEAUX, LES see Issoire *9B1*

PUY EN VELAY, LE *9C1* (500m N Urban) *45.05014, 3.88044* **Camping Bouthezard, Chemin de Bouthezard, Ave d'Aiguilhe, 43000 Le Puy-en-Velay [04 71 09 55 09 or 06 15 08 23 59 (mob); romain.margerit@hotmail.fr; www.ot-lepuyenvelay.fr]** Fr Le Puy heading NW on N102 to city cent; look for sp Clermont & Vichy; turn R at traff lts in Place Carnot at sp for Valence; site on L on bank of rv. Site ent immed opp Chapel St Michel & 200m fr volcanic core. Med, some hdg pitches, pt shd; wc; chem disp; mv service pnt; shwrs inc; el pnts (6A) inc (rev pol); lndtte; sm shop; shop 200m & supmkt 500m; snacks; playgrnd adj; pool & tennis adj; games rm; dogs €0.85; poss cr; Eng spkn; adv bkg; noise of church bells (not night-time); ccard not acc; red low ssn; CKE/CCI. "Popular, well-kept site in gd location; busy - rec arr early; efficient staff;gates clsd 2100-0700 low ssn; no twin-axles; may flood in v heavy rain; unrel opening dates - phone ahead low ssn; vg touring base on pilgrim rte to Spain." ♦ ltd 15 Mar-31 Oct. € 19.00 2014*

PUY EN VELAY, LE *9C1* (9km N Rural) *45.12473, 3.92177* **Camp Municipal Les Longes, Route des Rosières, 43800 Lavoûte-sur-Loire [04 71 08 18 79 or 04 71 08 50 13; mairie.lavoutesurloire@wanadoo.fr; www.lavoutesurloire.fr]** Fr Le Puy take N on D103 sp Lavoûte & Retournac. In Lavoûte turn R onto D7 bef rv bdge, site on L in 1km on rvside. Med, mkd pitch, pt shd; wc; mv service pnt; shwrs €1; el pnts (6A) €2.50; lndtte; shops 9km; bread 1km; tradsmn (high ssn); playgrnd; pool 1km; rv sw, fishing 50m; tennis; dogs €1.50; quiet. "Gd, friendly, scenic site; gd walking." ♦ 30 Apr-2 Oct. € 13.00 2011*

PUY EN VELAY, LE *9C1* (3km E Urban) *45.04431, 3.93030* **Camp Municipal d'Audinet, Ave des Sports, 43700 Brives-Charensac [tel/fax 04 71 09 10 18; camping.audinet@wanadoo.fr; www.camping-audinet.fr]** Fr Le Puy foll green sp E twd Valence. Fr S on N88 foll sp twd Valence & on E side of town foll white sp. Lge, pt shd; wc (mostly cont); chem disp; mv service pnt; baby facs; shwrs inc; el pnts (6A) €3.30; lndtte; sm shop & shops 500m; supmkt 1.5km; rest, snacks; bar; BBQ; playgrnd; pool; rv & lake sw/fishing; internet; bus to town; quiet; red low ssn/long stay. "Spacious site on rvside; friendly, helpful staff; gd san facs, poss stretched high ssn; poss travellers - but not a prob; no twin-axles; vg; 12 min bus to town every 1/2 hour." ♦ 30 Apr-17 Sep. € 22.70 2014*

PUY EN VELAY, LE *9C1* (9km E Rural) *45.06020, 3.95660* **Camping Le Moulin de Barette, Le Pont de Sumène, 43540 Blavozy [04 71 03 00 88; fax 04 71 03 00 51; hotel@lemoulindebarette.com; www.lemoulindebarette.com]** Take N88 dir St Etienne. Exit after 7km at D156 Blavozy. At rndabt foll sp for Rosières & 1st L to Moulin-de-Barette. Med, mkd pitch, pt sl, pt shd; wc; chem disp; mv service pnt; shwrs inc; el pnts €4; rest; bar; playgrnd; TV rm; few statics; dogs €1; quiet; red long stay; ccard acc; CKE/CCI. "Pt of hotel complex; dated san facs in need of refurb; gd rest; ltd el pnts; v quiet low ssn; site run down (2011); NH only." ♦ 20 Mar-30 Oct. € 14.70 2011*

PUY EN VELAY, LE *9C1* (7km S Rural) *44.99369, 3.90345* **Camping Comme au Soleil, Route du Plan d'Eau, 43700 Coubon [tel/fax 04 71 08 32 55; dumoulin-patrick@club-internet.fr; www.camping-le-puy.fr]** S fr Puy-en-Velay on N88, turn E onto D38 to Coubon, site sp. Please do not use SatNav for final appr, cross bdge then foll sp to site. Sm, terr, pt shd; htd wc; chem disp; baby facs; shwrs inc; el pnts (10A) €3.50 (poss long lead req, poss rev pol); lndtte (inc dryer); ice; tradsmn; rest, snacks; bar; BBQ; playgrnd; pool; games area; cycle hire; 5% statics; dogs €1; bus1m; some Eng spkn; adv bkg; quiet; red low ssn; CKE/CCI; "Well-kept site; helpful owners; clean facs; vg rest; excel." ♦ 01 Feb - 31 Dec. € 11.80 2013*

PUY GUILLAUME *9B1* (1km W Rural) *45.96231, 3.46632* **Camping de la Dore, 86 Rue Joseph Claussat, 63290 Puy-Guillaume [04 73 94 78 51 or 06 70 14 56 10 (mob); contact@camping-auvergne-63.com; www.camping-auvergne-63.com]** N fr Thiers on D906 as far as Puy-Guillaume; at ent to town (lge sculpture on rndabt), turn L at rndabt onto D343 (which joins D63); then L again at next rndabt onto D63. Site on R by rv. Med, pt shd; wc (some cont); chem disp; some serviced pitches; shwrs inc; el pnts (6A) €3.65; lndtte; shops 1km; rest, snacks; bar; playgrnd; 3 pools; jacuzzi; rv fishing adj; dogs; phone adj; bus 1km; adv bkg (rec high ssn); ccard acc; CKE/CCI. "Neat & tidy site in pleasant location; friendly staff; clean san facs; excel pool with bar; unrel opening/closing dates, rec phone ahead low ssn; excel." ♦ ltd 1 May-3 Sep. € 12.00 2011*

RIOM *9B1* (5km NW Rural) *45.90614, 3.06041* **Camping de la Croze, St Hippolyte, 63140 Châtel-Guyon [04 73 86 08 27 or 06 87 14 43 62 (mob); fax 04 73 86 08 51; info@campingcroze.com; www.campingcroze.com]** Fr A71 exit junc 13; ring rd around Riom sp Châtel-Guyon to Mozac, then D227. Site L bef ent St Hippolyte. Fr Volvic on D986 turn L at rndabt after Leclerc supmkt & L again to D227. NB Not rec to tow thro Riom. Lge, mkd pitch, pt sl, pt shd; htd wc; chem disp; shwrs inc; el pnts (6-10A) €2.50; Indtte (inc dryer); shops 2km; tradsmn; playgrnd; htd pool; wifi; 10% statics; dogs €1.30; quiet; CKE/CCI. "Gd sightseeing area; mini-bus to Châtel-Guyon (2km) high ssn; vg." 1 May-20 Oct. € 10.00 2010*

RIOM *9B1* (6km NW Rural) *45.91597, 3.07682* **Camping Clos de Balanède, Route de la Piscine, 63140 Châtel-Guyon [04 73 86 02 47; fax 04 73 86 05 64; clos-balanede.sarl-camping@wanadoo.fr; www.balanede.com]** Fr Riom take D227 to Châtelguyon, site on R on o'skts of town. Tight turn into ent. Lge, pt sl, pt shd; wc; shwrs inc; el pnts (6-10A) €3-3.50.; gas; Indtte; shop; rest, snacks; bar; playgrnd; 3 pools; tennis; dogs €1.50; poss cr; Eng spkn; adv bkg; quiet; poss open until 31 Dec; red low ssn/long stay. "Pleasant, well-run site; san facs dated; some pitches steep & poss uneven; sh walk to town; m'vans/campers not allowed up to Puy-de-Dôme - must use bus provided; Conv for A71, gd NH; Gd quiet site; conv for Clermont-Ferrand and Puy de Dôme." ♦ 12 Apr-30 Sep. € 24.00 2013*

RIOM ES MONTAGNES *7C4* (10km SW Rural) *45.24821, 2.53650* **Camp Municipal Le Pioulat, 15400 Trizac [04 71 78 64 20 or 04 71 78 60 37 (Mairie); fax 04 71 78 65 40; mairie.trizac@wanadoo.fr; www.chalets-decouverte.com]** D678 W fr Riom-ès-Montagnes to Trizac. Site on R after leaving vill S twd Mauriac. Sm, hdg pitch, pt sl, pt shd; htd wc; chem disp; el pnts (5A) inc; gas, tradsmn, rest, bar, shops 1km; BBQ; Indtte; playgrnd; tennis nr; sand beach; lake sw; quiet; Eng spkn; adv bkg; phone; CKE/CCI. "Beautiful site, lovely scenery; friendly staff; clean facs; vg walking area; highly rec." ♦ 16 Jun-16 Sep. € 11.00 2010*

RUYNES EN MARGERIDE *9C1* (4km E Rural) **Camping à la Ferme (Rolland), 15320 Clavières [04 71 23 45 50]** Fr St Flour, S on N9. After 7km turn L onto D4 thro Clavières & foll sps. Site in Chirol, foll Chirol sp. Sm, wc; shwrs inc; el pnts (long lead req); farm food avail; shops 2.5km; playgrnd; rv 2.5km; pool, tennis, golf, horseriding 10km; sailing, fishing 15km; quiet. "Isolated, with beautiful views, gd facs for a basic site; pay at old white house in Chirol." 1 Jun-30 Sep. 2009*

RUYNES EN MARGERIDE *9C1* (300m SW Rural) *44.99910, 3.21893* **Camp Municipal du Petit Bois, 15320 Ruynes-en-Margeride [tel/fax 04 71 23 42 26; contact@revea-vacances.com; www.revea-vacances.fr/campings]** Fr St Flour SE on D909. After 7km turn L onto D4. Site in 7km, sp. Or exit junc 30 fr A75, turn R into vill & foll sp. Lge, pt sl, pt shd; htd wc (some cont); chem disp; mv service pnt; baby facs; shwrs inc; el pnts (6-10A) €3.50; gas; Indtte; shops, rest, bar 600m; BBQ; playgrnd; htd pool adj; TV rm; some log statics; dogs €1.50; phone; Eng spkn; adv bkg; quiet; ccard acc; CKE/CCI. "Attractive site with pine trees; gd views; few flat pitches; excel san facs; barrier clsd 1200-1500; gd cent for walking, horseriding & fishing; used as field work cent in term time; gd." ♦ 30 Apr-17 Sep. € 16.00 (CChq acc) 2011*

ST AMANT ROCHE SAVINE see Ambert *9B1*

ST BONNET PRES ORCIVAL see Orcival *7B4*

ST BONNET TRONCAIS see Cérilly *4H3*

ST FLOUR *9C1* (2km N Rural) *45.05120, 3.10778* **Camping International La Roche Murat, N9 15100 St Flour [04 71 60 43 63; fax 04 71 60 02 10; courrier@camping-saint-flour.com; www.camping-saint-flour.com]** Fr N or S on A75 exit junc 28; sp off rndabt on St Flour side of m'way. Site ent visible 150m fr rndabt. Med, hdg/mkd pitch, terr, pt shd; htd wc; chem disp; mv service pnt; shwrs inc; el pnts (10A) inc; gas; Indry rm; shops 4km; tradsmn; playgrnd; pool 2km; dogs; Eng spkn; adv bkg; quiet, v little rd noise; ccard not acc; CKE/CCI. "Busy site with gd views; sunny & secluded pitches; helpful warden; gd, clean facs; some pitches sm; when pitches waterlogged use site rds; old town high on hill worth visit; excel touring cent & conv NH fr A75; vg; v clean facs." ♦ 1 Apr-1 Nov. € 19.80 2014*

ST GERVAIS D'AUVERGNE *7A4* (500m N Rural) *46.03706, 2.81733* **Camp Municipal L'Etang Philippe, 63390 St Gervais-d'Auvergne [tel/fax 04 73 85 74 84; campingstgervais@wanadoo.fr; www.camping-loisir.com]** Fr N144 3km S of St Eloy-les-Mines, take D987 S to St Gervais. Site on R just bef town. Lge, hdg pitch, pt shd; wc; chem disp; mv service pnt; shwrs inc; el pnts (10A) inc; Indtte; shop 500m; tradsmn (Jul/Aug); playgrnd; lake sw & beach adj; cycle hire; tennis; archery; entmnt; some statics; dogs €0.50; Eng spkn; adv bkg; quiet; CKE/CCI. "Popular, well-maintained site; clean facs; poss untidy low ssn & ltd facs; vg." ♦ Easter-30 Sep. € 10.00 2010*

ST GERVAIS D'AUVERGNE *7A4* (8km E Rural) *46.02741, 2.89894* **Camp Municipal Les Prés Dimanches, 63390 Châteauneuf-les-Bains [04 73 86 41 50 or 04 73 86 67 65 (LS); fax 04 73 86 41 71; mairie-chat-les-bains@wanadoo.fr]** Fr Montaigut take N144 S twd Riom & Clermont-Ferrand. In 9km at La Boule S onto D987 to St Gervais. Take D227 E to Chateuneuf-les-Bains. In 7km L onto D109. Site thro vill on R. Sm, pt shd, hdg/mkd pitch; htd wc; shwrs inc; el pnts (6A) inc; Indtte; shop 250m; rest adj; playgrnd; fishing, tennis, canoeing nrby; spa baths 500m; quiet; adv bkg; excel; CKE/CCI. "Lovely, well-kept site; helpful warden. gd walks." ♦ ltd 30 Apr-15 Oct. € 13.00 2012*

ST JACQUES DES BLATS *7C4* (600m SE Rural) *45.05181, 2.71377* **Camp Municipal Les Blats, Route de la Gare, 15800 St Jacques-des-Blats [04 71 47 06 00 or 04 71 47 05 90 (Mairie); fax 04 71 47 07 09; i-tourisme-st-jacques@wanadoo.fr]** Sp fr N122, 3km SW of Lioran Tunnel in vill of St Jacques-des-Blats; 300m fr N122 down steep app rd; sp in vill adj rv. Sm, hdg pitch, pt shd; htd wc; chem disp; shwrs; el pnts (10A); Indtte; shops 200m; rest 200m; bar; BBQ; playgrnd; TV; 30% statics; quiet; CKE/CCI. "Gd walking trails fr site; lift to summit Plomb du Cantal." 1 May-30 Sep. € 9.00 2009*

AUVERGNE

AUVERGNE

ST JUST (CANTAL) *9C1* (450m W Urban) *44.89035, 3.21079* **FFCC Camp Municipal, 15320 St Just [04 71 73 72 57, 04 71 73 70 48 or 06 31 47 05 15 (mob); fax 04 71 73 71 44; info@saintjust.com; www.saintjust.com]** Exit junc 31 fr A75, foll sp St Chély-d'Apcher D909; turn W onto D448 twds St Just (approx 6km); sp with gd access. Med, mkd pitch, pt sl, terr, pt shd; htd wc; chem disp; mv service pnt; shwrs inc; el pnts (10A) €2.20; Indtte; shop; snacks; bar; pool high ssn; fishing; tennis; cycle hire; dogs; phone; some Eng spkn; v quiet; ccard acc; red low ssn/long stay. "Vg site; friendly, helpful warden; ltd facs low ssn; excel tennis & pool; gd touring base; area for m'vans." Easter-30 Sep. € 9.80 2011*

ST MAURICE DE LIGNON *9C1* (1km E Rural) *45.22299, 4.15156* **FFCC Camping du Sabot, 813 Route du Stade, 43200 St Maurice-de-Lignon [04 71 65 32 68; campingdusabot@aol.com; www.campingdusabot.fr]** Take N88 N fr Yssingeaux or S fr St Etienne. Site well sp in St Maurice. Med, mkd pitch, pt terr, pt shd; htd wc (some cont); chem disp; mv service pnt; shwrs; el pnts (6A) €3.60; Indtte; shops; rest, snacks 250m: BBQ; playgrnd; games area; wifi; 70% statics; dogs €1; phone 500m; poss cr; Eng spkn; adv bkg; quiet. "Warm welcome; helpful owner; blocks poss req; v busy w/ends; ltd touring pitches; conv touring base; mkd walks fr site." 15 Apr-15 Oct. € 11.00 2010*

ST NECTAIRE *9B1* (1km SE Rural) *45.57971, 3.00173* **Camping Le Viginet, chemin du Manoir, 63710 St Nectaire [04 73 88 53 80 or 08 25 80 14 40; fax 04 73 88 41 93; info@camping-viginet.com; www.camping-viginet.com]** Exit A75/E11 junc 14 onto D996 dir Mont-Doré. In E side of St Nectaire (opp Ford g'ge) turn sharp L up v steep hill; rd widens after 100m; site on R after bends. Car park at site ent. Med, hdg/mkd pitch, pt sl, pt shd; wc; chem disp; mv service pnt; baby facs; shwrs inc; el pnts (10A) €4; gas; Indry rm; shops, rest & bar 1.5km; snacks; playgrnd; pool; dogs €2;Eng spkn; poss cr; adv bkg; quiet; ccard not acc; CKE/CCI. "Nice pitches; gd views; gd sm pool; gd walking in hills around site." ♦ ltd 1 Apr-30 Sep. € 30.00 2013*

ST NECTAIRE *9B1* (500m S Rural) *45.57556, 3.00169* **Camping La Clé des Champs, Les Sauces, Route des Granges, 63710 St Nectaire [04 73 88 52 33; campingcledechamps@free.fr; www.campingcledeschamps.com]** S bound exit A75 at junc 6 to join D978 sp Champeix; N bound exit junc 14 to join D996 sp Champeix/St Nectaire. In St Nectaire turn L at g'ge on L (site sp); site 300m on L. Med, hdg/mkd pitch, pt sl, pt shd; wc (some cont); chem disp; mv service pnt; shwrs inc; el pnts (2-6A) €2.10-3.50 (poss rev pol); gas; Indtte; shops 1km; playgrnd; pool; wifi; some statics; dogs €2; poss cr; adv bkg; poss noisy high ssn; red low ssn; CKE/CCI. "Well-kept, clean site; spectacular scenery; helpful owner; vg san facs." ♦ 1 Apr-30 Sep. € 37.00 2014*

ST NECTAIRE *9B1* (1km S Rural) *45.57541, 2.99942* **Camping La Vallée Verte, Route des Granges, 63710 St Nectaire [04 73 88 52 68; lavalleeverte@neuf.fr; www.valleeverte.com]** Fr A75 exit junc 6 onto D978 & D996 to St Nectaire. On ent o'skts St Nectaire turn L immed at site sp, site in 300m. Med, pt shd; htd wc; chem disp; mv service pnt; fam bthrm; shwrs inc; el pnts (5-8A) €3-3.50; Indtte (inc dryer); shop; tradsmn; snacks; bar; playgrnd; lake sw 5km; 20% statics; dogs €1.50; phone; Eng spkn; adv bkg; quiet; red low ssn; CKE/CCI. "Vg, friendly, well-maintained, family-run site." ♦ 15 Apr-18 Sep. € 15.00 2011*

ST PARDOUX *9A1* (4km SW Rural) *46.03752, 2.95436* **Camping Elan, Route de Villemorie, 63440 Blot-l'Eglise [04 73 97 51 70 or 06 10 21 40 58 (mob); info@camping-elan.com; www.camping-elan.com]** Fr N on N144 take D16 to Blot, fr S take D50, foll site sp. Sm, hdg/mkd pitch, pt shd; wc; chem disp (wc); shwrs inc; el pnts (5-10A) €2.50-4.50; gas 200m; Indry rm; shop 200m; rest, snacks; bar; playgrnd; tennis; games area; TV; dogs €1; no twin-axles; Eng spkn; adv bkg; quiet; red low ssn/long stay/CKE/CCI. "In beautiful area; lge pitches; friendly Dutch owners; clean but basic san facs; site open low ssn by arrangement; gd touring base; conv Vulcania; gd." 1 Apr-30 Sep. € 12.50 2009*

ST PAULIEN *9C1* (2.5km SW Rural) *45.12041, 3.79357* **Camping de la Rochelambert, 43350 St Paulien [tel/fax 04 71 00 54 02; infos@camping-rochelambert.com; www.camping-rochelambert.com]** Fr St Paulien take D13; turn L onto D25 sp La Rochelambert; site on L in 1.5km. Med, mkd pitch, terr, pt shd; wc (some cont); chem disp; mv service pnt; shwrs inc; el pnts (10A) €3.10; Indtte; shop 3km; tradsmn; snacks; bar; BBQ; playgrnd; pools; paddling pool; tennis; wifi; 15% statics; dogs €1.50; phone; poss cr; Eng spkn; adv bkg; quiet; red low ssn; CKE/CCI. "Gd touring base; gd walking & fishing; app poss diff lge/long o'fits; gd." ♦ ltd 1 Apr-30 Sep. € 30.00 2014*

ST POURCAIN SUR SIOULE *9A1* (650m SE Urban) *46.30643, 3.29207* **Camp Municipal de l'île de la Ronde, Quai de la Ronde, 03500 St Pourçain-sur-Sioule [04 70 45 45 43 or 06 60 94 75 20 (mob); camping.iledelaronde@live.fr/contact@campingiledelaronde.fr; www.ville-saint-pourcain-sur-sioule.com]** On D2009, 31km S of Moulins; in St Pourçain-sur-Sioule town cent turn R immed bef rv bdge; site ent on L in 100m. NB Sp in town easily missed. Med, hdg pitch, pt shd; wc; chem disp; mv service pnt; shwrs; el pnts (6A) inc; Indtte; shops adj; playgrnd; pool 1km; dogs; adv bkg; quiet; CKE/CCI. "Well-run, magnificent, busy site in pretty town; extra charge for lger pitches; barrier clsd 2000-0800; gd rest nr; mkt Sat; great value; excel; recep and barrier clsd 1200-1400." ♦ 1 Apr-1 Oct. € 15.50 2014*

ST PRIVAT D'ALLIER see Monistrol d'Allier *9C1*

ST SATURNIN (PUY DE DOME) *9B1* (9km W Rural) *45.66977, 3.00054* **Camping La Clairière, Rouillas-Bas, 63970 Aydat [tel/fax 04 73 79 31 15; info@campinglaclairiere.com; www.campinglaclairiere.com]** S fr Clermont-Ferrand exit A75 junc 5 onto D213 W & foll sp Lac d'Aydat. At x-rds at end Rouillas-Bas turn L, site 100m on L. Sm, hdg pitch, terr, pt shd; htd wc; chem disp; shwrs inc; el pnts (10A) €3.50 (poss rev pol); Indtte; shop 600m; rest 250m; snacks high ssn; playgrnd; wifi; 10% statics; dogs €1; Eng spkn; adv bkg rec high ssn; quiet; red low ssn. "V pleasant site; friendly, helpful owner; clean facs poss stretched when site full; excel walking." 15 Apr-30 Sep. € 13.00 2009*

STE SIGOLENE see Monistrol sur Loire *9C1*

SALERS *7C4* (800m NE Rural) *45.14756, 2.49857* **Camp Municipal Le Mouriol, Route de Puy-Mary, 15410 Salers [04 71 40 73 09 or 04 71 40 72 33 (Mairie); fax 04 71 40 76 28; www.salers.fr]** Take D922 SE fr Mauriac dir Aurillac; turn onto D680 E dir Salers; site 1km NE of Salers on D680 dir Puy Mary, opp Hôtel Le Gerfaut; sp fr all dir. Med, hdg/mkd pitch, sl, pt shd, wc (some cont); chem disp; shwrs inc; el pnts (16A) €4.60 (long lead poss req); Indtte; shops, rest, snacks & bar 1km; BBQ; playgrnd; tennis; hill-walking; WIFI; dogs; bus 1km; phone; poss cr; no adv bkg; quiet; 10% red 10 days; CKE/CCI. "Generous pitches; san facs gd but stretched if site full; peaceful low ssn; excel cycling & walking; beautiful medieval vill; vg; well kept." ♦ 1 Apr-30 Oct. € 12.00 2012*

SALERS *7C4* (800m W Rural) *45.13304, 2.48762* **Camping à la Ferme (Fruquière), Apcher, 15140 Salers [04 71 40 72 26]** D922 S fr Mauriac for 17km; L on D680 sp Salers; in lane on R sp Apcher - immed after passing Salers town sp. Sm, pt shd; wc (some cont), chem disp (wc); shwrs inc; el pnts (10A) €2.30; shop 300m; dogs; poss cr; quiet; CKE/CCI. "Sm farm site; welcoming, friendly owner; excel clean san facs, plenty hot water; beautiful countryside; gd." 1 May-30 Sep. € 8.20 2011*

SAUXILLANGES *9B1* (500m SW Rural) *45.54578, 3.36451* **FFCC Camping Les Prairies, Chemin des Prairies, 63490 Sauxillanges [04 73 96 80 22 or 06 50 51 95 75; contact@camping-lesprairies.fr; www.camping-lesprairies.fr]** Exit A75/E11 junc 13 to D996, E twd Sauxillanges. Turn R 100m after Gendarmerie in vill. Sp. Med, mkd pitch, shd; wc (some cont); chem disp; some serviced pitches; shwrs inc; el pnts (6A) inc (poss rev pol); Indtte; shop; BBQ; playgrnd; pool adj (Jul/Aug); paddling pool; fishing adj; tennis; 5% statics; dogs €2; Eng spkn; adv bkg ess high ssn; quiet; ccard acc. "Charming, interesting town; excel." ♦ 15 Jun-15 Sep. € 16.50 2010*

THIERS *9B1* (7km NE Rural) *45.89874, 3.59888* **Camping Les Chanterelles, Chapon 63550 St Rémy-sur-Durolle [04 73 93 60 00; fax 04 73 94 31 71; contact@revea-vacances.com; www.revea-vacances.fr]** On A72/E70 W dir Clermont-Ferrand, exit at junc 3 sp Thiers. Foll sp twd Thiers on N89 into L Monnerie. Fr vill, take D20 & foll sp St Rémy. In St Rémy, foll 'Camping' sp. Do not app thro Thiers as narr rds v diff for lge o'fits. Med, terr, pt shd; htd wc; chem disp; mv service pnt; shwrs inc; el pnts (10A) €3.50; gas; Indtte (inc dryer); shop; tradsmn; BBQ; playgrnd; htd pool; paddling pool; waterslide; lake sw 600m; windsurfing; tennis 600m; TV rm; some statics; dogs €1.50; adv bkg; quiet; ccard acc; CKE/CCI. "Vg site in beautiful situation with views; modern, clean facs; some noise at w/end fr statics; excel." ♦ 30 Apr-15 Sep. € 26.00 (CChq acc) 2013*

THIERS *9B1* (8km W Rural) *45.86845, 3.47616* **Camp Municipal Pont Astier, 63190 Orléat [tel/fax 04 73 53 64 40; mairie.orleat@orleat.com]** On A72 take exit 2 onto D906 S for 2.5km. Turn R on N89 for Clermont-Ferrand. Turn R at Pont-de-Dore onto D224. Site 3km on R. Med, hdg pitch, pt sl, pt shd; wc (some cont); chem disp; shwrs inc; el pnts (10A) €4; Indtte; shop 3km; tradsmn; snacks; bar; BBQ; playgrnd; pool; fishing; tennis; dogs €0.90; Eng spkn; adv bkg; red low ssn; CKE/CCI. "By Rv Dore; lge pitches, but some damp; poss mosquito prob; site ent poss diff; unrel opening dates." ♦ 1 May-30 Sep. € 12.00 2009*

THIERS *9B1* (4km NW Rural) *45.87168, 3.48538* **Camping Base de Loisirs Iloa, Courty, 63300 Thiers [04 73 80 92 35 or 04 73 80 88 80 (LS); fax 04 73 80 88 81; http://ville-thiers.fr]** Exit A72 junc 2 for Thiers; at rndabt turn L sp Vichy but take D44 sp Dorat; pass under m'way, site beyond Courty on L sp Les Rives-de-Thiers. Sm, mkd pitch, pt shd; wc (some cont); chem disp; mv service pnt; some serviced pitches; shwrs inc; el pnts (6A) €2.20; gas 5km; Indtte; supmkt 5km; tradsmn; playgrnd; pool & sports adj; lake fishing; tennis; entmnt; TV rm; dogs; CKE/CCI. "Well-maintained; vg, clean san facs; friendly warden; quiet low ssn; vg NH." ♦ ltd 9 May-7 Sep. € 12.00 (3 persons) 2011*

THIEZAC see Vic sur Cère *7C4*

TRIZAC see Riom ès Montagnes *7C4*

URCAY *4H3* (6km NE Rural) *46.6430, 2.6620* **Camping Champ de la Chapelle, St Bonnet-Tronçais, 03360 Braize [04 70 06 15 45; info@champdelachapelle.com; www.champdelachapelle.com]** Fr D2144 take D978A for Tronçais. 1.5km on L fr rndabt(Montaloyer) x-ing D28. Site sp. Med, mkd pitch, pt sl, pt shd; wc; chem disp; shwrs; el pnts (10A) €3.50; Indtte; shop; tradsmn; rest 5km; snacks; bar; playgrnd; pool; lake & rv sw 5km; games area; some statics; dogs €1; Eng spkn; adv bkg; ccard acc; red low ssn/CKE/CCI. "Excel walking & flora/fauna in ancient oak forest; some lge pitches; peaceful site." 10 Apr-30 Oct. € 24.50 2014*

VALLON EN SULLY *7A4* (500m S Rural) *46.53019, 2.61447* **Camp Municipal Les Soupirs, Allée des Soupirs, 03190 Vallon-en-Sully [04 70 06 50 96 or 04 70 06 50 10 (LS); fax 04 70 06 51 18; mairie.vallonensully@wanadoo.fr; www.vallonensully.com]** N fr Montluçon on N144; in 23km at traff lts where D11 crosses N144 turn L & foll camping sp for Vallon-en-Sully. After bdge over Rv Cher turn L in 50m. Site in 100m. If N or S on A71 exit at junc 9 Vallon-en-Sully; turn N on N144; in 3km at traff lts turn L. Med, pt shd; wc (cont); chem disp (wc); shwrs; el pnts (6-20A) €2-4; shops 500m; rest, snacks, bar adj; TV rm; dogs; bus 500m; adv bkg; quiet. "Peaceful, spacious site on banks of rv & canal; immac san facs; lge pitches; risk of flooding in wet; gd cycling along canal; gd NH; vg." 13 Jun-12 Sep. € 6.00 2009*

VIC SUR CERE *7C4* (500m E Rural) *44.98136, 2.62930* **Camp Municipal du Carladez, Ave des Tilleuls, 15800 Vic-sur-Cère [04 71 47 51 04 or 04 71 47 51 75 (Mairie); fax 04 71 47 50 59; vic-sur-cere@wanadoo.fr; www.vicsurcere.com]** Fr Aurillac on N122 site sp on ent Vic-sur-Cère on R. Lge, pt shd; wc (some cont); shwrs inc; el pnts (6A) €2.50; supmkt 100m; pool 500m; playgrnd, tennis & mini-golf nrby; rv fishing; poss cr; adv bkg; quiet. "Gate clsd 2000; office clsd Sun; no pitching without booking in; plenty of rm high ssn; helpful warden; clean facs." ♦ 1 Apr-30 Sep. € 7.00 2011*

VIC SUR CERE *7C4* (1.5km SE Rural) *44.97142, 2.63319* **Camping La Pommeraie, 15800 Vic-sur-Cère [04 71 47 54 18; fax 04 71 49 63 30; pommeraie@wanadoo.fr; www.camping-la-pommeraie.com]** Fr Vic-sur-Cère take D54 twd Pierrefort & Chaudes-Aigues, initially sp Salvanhac. Foll yellow site sp over rv, under rlwy bdge. Foll D154 up steep, narr, winding hill for 1.5km. Foll camp sp R into narr lane. Med, terr, pt shd; wc (some cont); baby facs; serviced pitches; shwrs inc; el pnts (6A) €4.20; Indtte; shop high ssn; rest, snacks; bar; no BBQ; playgrnd; pool; paddling pool; fishing; tennis; wifi; entmnt; TV rm; many statics; dogs €2.50; poss cr; adv bkg rec; red low ssn; ccard acc. "Peaceful, scenic site; best pitches at top but steep access; not suitable elderly or infirm; gd san facs; mkt Tue, Fri." ♦ 1 Jun-10 Sep. € 26.00 2011*

VICHY *9A1* (2km SE Urban) *46.10756, 3.43670* **FFCC Camping La Croix St Martin, Allée du Camping, 99 Ave des Graviers, 03200 Abrest [tel/fax 04 70 32 67 74 or 06 10 94 70 90 (mob); camping-vichy@orange.fr; www.camping-vichy.com]** Exit D906 at Abrest onto D426 N (Ave des Graviers); in 900m turn L into Allée du Camping. Site sp fr D906, both N & S of Abrest. Med, hdg/mkd pitch, shd; wc; chem disp; baby facs; mv service pnt; shwrs inc; el pnts (10A) €3.60; dogs €1; Indtte (inc dryer); tradsmn; snacks; bar; BBQ hire; conv store; playgrnd; htd pool; games area; entmnt; wifi; phone; 15% statics; phone; Eng spkn; adv bkg; quiet; ccard acc; red low ssn; CKE/CCI. "Gd cycling along rv allier thro Vichy; san facs in need of updating but clean; well maintain attractive site." ♦ 10 Apr-10 Oct. € 28.60 2014*

VICHY *9A1* (1.5km S Rural) *46.11555, 3.43006* **Camping Beau Rivage, Rue Claude Decloître, 03700 Bellerive-sur-Allier [04 70 32 26 85; fax 04 70 32 03 94; camping-beaurivage@wanadoo.fr; www.camping-beaurivage.com]** Fr Vichy cross rv bdge over Rv Allier onto D1093, turn L at rndabt foll sp Campings, sp to Beau Rivage. Site on L on rv bank, past Cmp Les Acacias. Med, shd; wc; chem disp; mv service pnt; baby facs; shwrs inc; el pnts (10A) €3.10; gas; Indtte (inc dryer); shop; supmkt 1km; tradsmn; snacks; BBQ; playgrnd; 2 htd, covrd pools; waterslide; fishing; canoeing; cycle hire; games area; tennis 2km; archery; wifi; entmnt; TV rm; 50% statics; dogs €1; poss cr; quiet; red low ssn. "Lovely rvside site, but no rv sw allowed; Lge o'fits have diff pitching; easy cycle ride to lovely city." ♦ 1 Apr-15 Oct. € 31.05 (CChq acc) 2013*

VICHY *9A1* (1km SW Rural) *46.11648, 3.42560* **Camping Les Acacias, Rue Claude Decloître, 03700 Bellerive-sur-Allier [04 70 32 36 22; fax 04 70 32 88 52; camping-acacias03@orange.fr; www.camping-acacias.com]** Cross bdge to Bellerive fr Vichy & foll Hauterive sp onto D1093. Strt over at 1st rndabt & turn L at 2nd rndabt onto D131 dir Hauterive. At 3rd rndabt turn L sp 'piscine'. Foll sm camping sps along rv side. Or fr S leave D906 at St Yorre & cross Rv Allier, then foll sp to Bellerive. Site sp at rndabt on app to Bellerive adj Rv Allier. On final app, at sp showing site in either dir, keep L & foll site sp along rv bank to recep. NB Many other sites in area, foll sp carefully. Med, hdg/mkd pitch, shd; wc; chem disp; baby facs; shwrs inc; el pnts (10A) €3.40; gas; shops 1km; snacks; BBQ; playgrnd; pool; wifi; fishing; boating; TV; 20% statics; dogs €1; adv bkg; ccard acc; red low ssn; CKE/CCI. "Well-run site; helpful owner; gd san facs; free Vichy Célestins water at spring in lovely town." 7 Apr-7 Oct. € 19.00 2014*

VICHY *9A1* (5km SW Rural) *46.07961, 3.38213* **FLOWER Camping La Roseraie, 1093 Route de Randan, 03700 Brugheas [04 70 32 43 33; fax 04 70 32 26 23; camping.laroseraie@wanadoo.fr; www.flowercampings.com]** Fr Vichy on D1093, foll sp to Brugheas. Site well sp. Med, hdg/mkd pitch, some hdstg, pt shd; wc; chem disp; baby facs; shwrs inc; el pnts (6A) inc; gas; Indtte; shop on site & 3km; tradsmn; rest; snacks, bar high ssn; BBQ; playgrnd; htd pool; paddling pool; waterslide; mini-farm; games area; games rm; wifi; entmnt; TV rm; 10% statics; dogs free; adv bkg; quiet; ccard acc; red long stay; CKE/CCI. "Lovely pool." ♦ 15 Mar-15 Nov. € 19.50 2010*

VIEURE *7A4* (2km NE Rural) *46.50305, 2.90754* **Plan d'eau de Vieure, La Borde, 03430 Vieure [tel/fax 04 70 02 04 46; plandeau03@orange.fr; www.loctionschaletscampingdelaborde.fr]** Exit A71-E11 at junc 10. Take D94 NE to Cosne d'Allier, then R onto D11. L onto D459, 1st R onto La Bordé. Foll sp to campsite. Med, hdg pitch, pt sl, pt shd; wc; twin axles; baby facs; shwrs inc; el pnts (10A) €3.10; Indtte (inc dryer); rest; snacks; bar; playgrnd; sw lake; dogs; 35% statics; phone; poss cr; quiet; ccard acc; CCI. "Large, open & shd pitches; dated san facs; v pleasant remote site by lake; fishing & canoeing; family friendly; gd." ♦ ltd 11 Apr-30 Sep. € 11.50 2014*

⊞ **VOLLORE-VILLE** *9B1* (1km NE Rural) *45.79199, 3.60583* **Camping Des Plaines, Le Grun de Chignore, Les Plaines, 63120 Vollore-Ville [04 73 53 73 37; jenny-loisel@orange.fr; www.campingauvergne.fr]** Leave A89/E70 at junc 29 onto D906 S to Courpiere. Fr Courpiere take D7 to Vollore-Ville. Site on the R at turning to Chabrier. Sm, hdg/mkd pitch, pt shd; wc; mv service pnt; baby facs; shwr inc; gas; lndtte; shops 800m; rest; snacks; bar; BBQ; playgrnd; pool; internet; wifi; 20% statics; Y €1.50; twin axles; adv bkg; quiet; ccard acc; red low ssn; CKE/CCI. "Excel, well-kept little site; friendly owners; pleasant vill; conv for A89/E70." ♦ ltd € 15.00 2014*

VOLVIC *9B1* (600m E Urban) *45.87208, 3.04591* **Camp Municipal Pierre et Sources, Rue de Chancelas, 63530 Volvic [04 73 33 50 16; fax 04 73 33 54 98; camping@ville-volvic.fr; www.ville-volvic.fr]** Exit Riom on D986: foll sp for Pontgibaud & Volvic. Site sp to R on app to town. Sm, shd; htd wc; chem disp; mv service pnt (open all year); shwrs inc; el pnts (12A) €3.50; lndtte; sm shop; tradsmn; some statics; dogs €1.50; Eng spkn; adv bkg; quiet; red low ssn. "Pleasant site with lovely views; welcoming & helpful; excel, cleans san facs; access some pitches poss diff, particularly for lge o'fits; conv Volvic factory tour." 1 May-30 Sep. € 15.00 2011*

VOREY *9C1* (4km NE Rural) *45.20305, 3.94464* **Camping Domaine du Pra de Mars, Le Chambon de Vorey, 43800 Vorey-sur-Arzon [tel/fax 04 71 03 40 86; leprademars@wanadoo.fr; www.leprademars.com]** On D103 dir Retournac. Med, hdg/mkd pitch, pt sl, pt shd; htd wc (some cont); chem disp; some serviced pitches; mv service pnt; baby facs; fam bthrm; shwrs inc; el pnts (5A) €3; lndtte; rest, snacks; bar; BBQ; htd pool; dogs €1.50; bus; phone; Eng spkn; adv bkg; quiet; ccard acc; CKE/CCI. "Beautiful rvside setting; welcoming owners; facs clean but need update (2009); vg." 3 Apr-27 Sep. € 13.50 2009*

VOREY *9C1* (300m SW Rural) *45.18576, 3.90679* **Camping Les Moulettes, Chemin de Félines, 43800 Vorey-sur-Arzon [04 71 03 70 48 or 04 71 03 79 49; fax 04 71 03 72 06; contact@camping-les-moulettes.fr; www.camping-les-moulettes.fr]** Fr Le Puy take D103 sp Vorey. Site sp in vill; L in main sq. Sm, hdg pitch, pt shd; wc; shwrs inc; el pnts (10A) €3.50; lndtte; shops in vill; rest, snacks; bar; playgrnd; pool; paddling pool; waterslide; fishing adj; games area; some statics; dogs €1.50; Eng spkn; adv bkg; quiet; red low ssn. "Peaceful site by rv; gd sized pitched, many on rv bank; friendly owners." ♦ May-Sep. € 20.00 2014*

Brittany

Regional Introduction

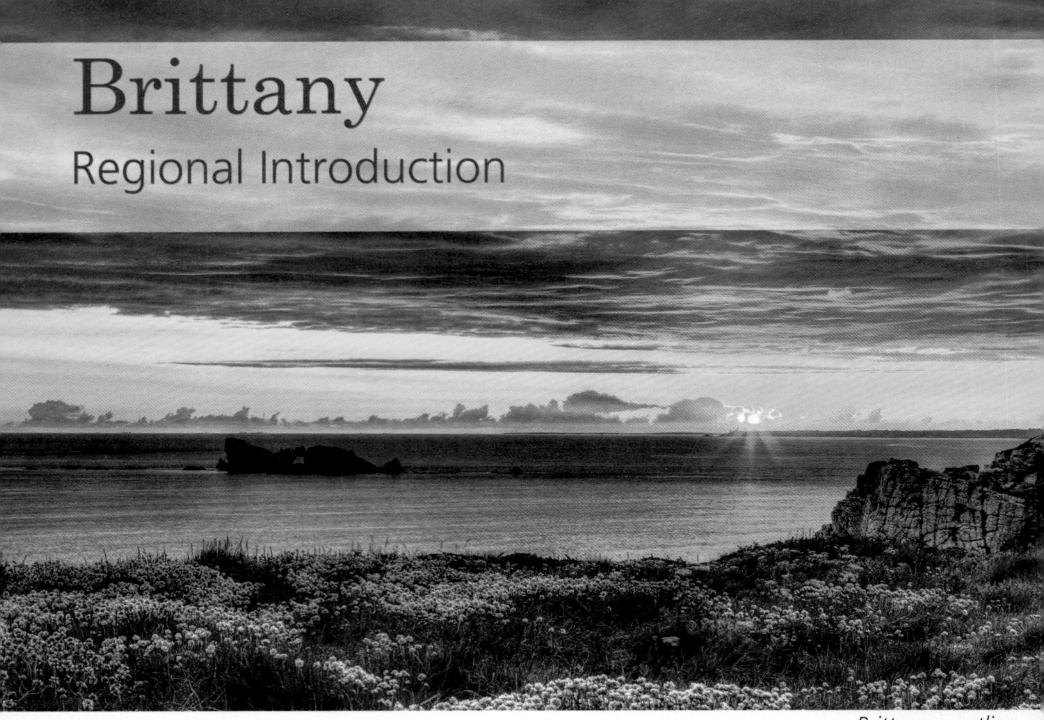

Brittany coastline

Welcome to Brittany

Boasting a stunning 1700 miles of coastline, Brittany is a top destination for a seaside break. Towering cliffs, rugged rock formations and sandy shores make for some of the most spectacular coastal scenery in France.

An independent duchy until the 16th-century, Brittany has retained its own unique personality. The Breton language is still widely spoken and you will find that the Breton culture is strongest in the west of the region.

Brittany's climate can be compared to that of south-west England, although you can expect temperatures to be a couple of degrees warmer most of the time.

Local highlights

Crepes with a variety of savoury fillings are a regional speciality, and Brittany is renowned for its superb seafood. Roscoff is particularly noted for its delicious shellfish, while Cancale oysters are world famous. Locally-brewed sweet cider is the traditional tipple.

The world's largest Celtic event, the Inter-Celtic Festival, takes place over 10 days in August in the city of Lorient.

Major towns and cities

- Rennes – the regional capital and a centre for art and history.
- Vannes – a walled town in southern Brittany.
- St. Malo – built as a fortified island in the Middle Ages.
- Quimper – the oldest Breton city.
- Dinan – an attractive walled town.

Regional attractions

- Huelgoat Forest, Finistère – features include amazing rock formations and caves.
- Fougères, Ille-et-Vilaine – a medieval fortress city with an impressive château.
- Carnac stones – the most famous megalith site in France, predating the pyramids in Egypt.
- Belle-Ile – the largest of Brittany's islands, ideal for walking and relaxing on beaches.

Find out more

www.brittanytourism.com

Tel: (0)2 99 28 44 30 Brittany Tourism
Tel: (0)2 99 67 11 11 Rennes Tourist Office
Tel: (0)8 25 13 52 00 St Malo Tourist Office

AMBON PLAGES see Muzillac *2G3*

ARRADON see Vannes *2F3*

ARZAL *2G3* (4.5km W Rural) *47.5143, -2.4343* **Camping de Kernéjeune, 56190 Arzal [02 97 45 01 60 or 06 18 79 65 10 (mob); fax 02 97 45 05 42; contact@camping-de-kernejeune.com; www.camping-de-kernejeune.com]** Fr E on N165 exit onto D139 sp Arzal. Opp town hall turn L sp Billiers & foll sp to site. Site on rd on R after vill of Bourgerelle. Med, mkd pitch, pt shd; htd wc; shwrs; el pnts (6-10A) €3.05; Indtte; shop; tradsmn; BBQ; playgrnd; htd pool high ssn; fishing; games area; entmnt; TV; 30% statics; dogs €1.50; phone; red low ssn; quiet. "Gd base for interesting area; helpful, friendly owners; rec." ♦ 1 Apr-1 Nov. € 13.80 2009*

ARZON *2G3* (800m NE Coastal) *47.55303, -28.8294* **Camp Municipal Le Tindio, Kerners, 56640 Arzon [02 97 41 25 59; fax 02 97 53 91 23; letindio@arzon.fr; www.arzon.eu]** Fr Vannes or Muzillac on D780 turn R at rndabt on o'skts of Arzon. Site clearly sp. Lge, pt sl, pt shd; wc; chem disp; mv service pnt; shwrs; el pnts (6A) €2.50; Indtte; playgrnd; sand beach 1km; golf nr; dogs €1.20; poss cr; adv bkg; red low ssn. "Site o'looks Gulf of Morbihan; direct access to sea; excel san facs." ♦ 1 Apr-3 Nov. € 14.20 2010*

AUDIERNE *2F1* (700m SE Coastal/Rural) *48.02458, -4.52863* **Camping Le Loquéran, Bois de Loquéran, 29770 Audierne [02 98 74 95 06; fax 02 98 74 91 14; pointe.raz@free.fr; http://pointe.raz.free.fr]** Fr Quimper on D784 thro Plozévet & Plouhinec dir Audierne. Look out for sm, yellow/purple camping sp on R, site 500m on L. Sm, mkd pitch, terr, pt shd; wc; chem disp; shwrs inc; el pnts (6A) €2; Indtte; shop & 600m; playgrnd; beach 1km; dogs €1; ccard acc; quiet; CKE/CCI. "Gd san facs; peaceful site." 15 May-30 Sep. € 9.00 2010*

AUDIERNE *2F1* (3km SE Coastal) *48.00723, -4.50799* **Camping de Kersiny-Plage, 1 Rue Nominoé, 29780 Plouhinec [02 98 70 82 44; info@kersinyplage.com; www.kersinyplage.com]** Fr Audierne on D784 turn R at 2nd traff lts in Plouhinec, cont for 1km; turn L into Rue Nominoé (sp diff to see) for 100m. Or fr Quimper on D784 to Plouhinec, turn L at 1st traff lts & as bef. Med, hdg pitch, terr, pt shd; wc; chem disp; baby facs; shwrs inc; el pnts (8A) €3; Indry rm; tradsmn high ssn; BBQ (gas); playgrnd; direct access to sand beach; wifi; dogs €2; Eng spkn; quiet; barrier clsd 2300-0730; red low ssn; CKE/CCI. "Quiet, peaceful site; beautiful location & beach; most pitches superb sea views; welcoming, friendly owner; clean san facs; not much in area for children except beach; gd coastal walks; vg, rec." 14 May-17 Sep. € 14.80 2011*

AUDIERNE *2F1* (8km W Coastal) *48.02527, -4.61830* **Camp Municipal de Kermalero, 29770 Primelin [tel/fax 02 98 74 84 75 or 02 98 74 81 19 (LS); campingkermalero@wanadoo.fr]** Exit D784 Audierne-Pointe-du-Raz for Primelin; in Primelin turn R dir Ecomarché supmkt; site on L in 500m; site sp. Med, hdg pitch, terr, pt shd; wc; chem disp; mv service pnt; shwrs inc; el pnts (6A) €2.50; Indtte; supmkt 1km; tradsmn; playgrnd; games area; sand beach 1km; tennis; TV; 5% statics; quiet. "Pleasant site; gd outlook/views; helpful warden; clean facs; gd." ♦ 1 Mar-22 Oct. € 12.00 2010*

AUDIERNE *2F1* (1.5km NW Urban) *48.02859, -4.55675* **FFCC Camping de Kerivoas, Route de la Pointe du Raz, 29770 Audierne [02 98 70 26 86 or 02 98 70 27 75 (LS); camping.kerivoas@wanadoo.fr]** W fr Audierne on D784 sp Pointe du Raz; site on L at top of hill opp Leclerc supmkt. Sm, pt sl, pt shd; wc; chem disp (wc); shwrs inc; Indry rm; el pnts (6-10A) €2.60- 3.20 (poss long lead req); Indry rm; shops & rests nrby; beach 1.5km; dogs €1.20; bus; no twin-axles; adv bkg; some rd noise; red long stay; CKE/CCI. "Sm pitches poss diff long o'fits." 1 Apr-31 Oct. € 11.00 2009*

AURAY *2F3* (5km SE Coastal) *47.64909, -2.92540* **Camp Municipal Kergouguec, Route de Bequerel, 56400 Plougoumelen [02 97 57 88 74; marie.plougoumelen@wanadoo.fr; www.plougoumelen.fr]** Site is S of N165, 13km W of Vannes; sp fr vill sq 500m S on R, nr stadium. Med, pt sl, pt shd; wc (some cont); chem disp; shwrs; el pnts (6A) €3.16; playgrnd; beach & windsurfing 300m; tennis; dogs €1.58; adv bkg; quiet; CKE/CCI. "Well-run, under-used site; report (2011) site may close due to lack of visitors, phone ahead; gd touring base." ♦ 1 Jul-28 Aug. € 9.52 2011*

AURAY *2F3* (7km SE Rural) *47.64320, -2.89890* **Aire Naturelle La Fontaine du Hallate (Le Gloanic), 8 Chemin du Poul Fétan, La Hallate, 56400 Plougoumelen [09 64 04 90 16 or 06 16 30 08 33 (mob); clegloanic@orange.fr; www.camping-hallate.fr]** Fr N165 Vannes-Lorient, turn S onto D101E to Plougoumelen; watch for sp after Plougoumelen, site in La Hallate. Narr, bumpy app rd. Sm, hdg/mkd pitch, pt sl, pt shd; shwrs inc; el pnts (6A) €3.40 (poss rev pol); Indtte; shops 2km; playgrnd; golf/tennis adj; 2% statics; dogs €2.88; phone; adv bkg ess Jul/Aug; CKE/CCI. "Gd alt to lge/noisier sites; gd coast paths; conv local boat trips & Ste Anne-d'Auray; vg." 29 Mar-24 Oct. € 16.00 2013*

AURAY *2F3* (5km S Rural) *47.64402, -2.93774* **FFCC Camping du Parc-Lann, 52 Rue Thiers, Le Varquez, 56400 Le Bono [02 97 57 93 93; campingduparclann@wanadoo.fr; www.campingduparclann.fr]** S fr Auray on D101 sp Le Bono. Site well sp in Le Bono. Med, hdg/mkd pitch, pt shd; wc; chem disp; mv service pnt; baby facs; shwrs inc; el pnts (6A) €2.30; Indtte; ice; shop 2km; tradsm; rest, snacks; bar; BBQ; playgrnd; pool 5km; sand beach 9km; games area; dogs €0.70; bus; phone; red low ssn; CKE/CCI. "Lovely quiet site in pretty area; gd, clean san facs poss stretched high ssn & ltd low ssn; warden on site 1800-1900 only low ssn; gd walking." ♦ ltd 1 May-30 Sep. € 13.20 2014*

⊞ **AURAY** *2F3* (8km W Rural) *47.66406, -3.09985* **FFCC Camp Municipal Le St Laurent, Kergonvo, 56400 Ploemel [tel/fax 02 97 56 85 90; info@campingdesaintlaurent.com; www.campingdesaintlaurent.com]** Fr Auray on D22 twd Belz/Etel; after 8km turn L on D186 to Ploemel & site on L in 200m. Med, some hdstg, shd; htd wc; chem disp; mv service pnt; baby facs; shwrs inc; el pnts (10A) €4; Indtte; shop & 3km; rest; bar; BBQ; playgrnd; htd pool; paddling pool; sand beach 6km; games area; some statics; dogs €1.40; adv bkg; quiet. "Peaceful site; friendly staff; red facs low ssn." ♦ € 26.80 2014*

BADEN *2F3* (500m SW Rural) *47.61410, -2.92540* **Camping Mané Guernehué, 52 Rue Mané er Groëz, 56870 Baden [02 97 57 02 06; fax 02 97 57 15 43; info@camping-baden.com; www.camping-baden.com]** Exit N165 sp Arradon/L'Ile aux Moines onto D101 to Baden (10km); in Baden vill turn R at camp sp immed after sharp L-hand bend; in 200m bear R at junc; site on R. Sp at both ends of vill. Lge, hdg/mkd pitch, terr, pt shd; htd wc; chem disp; mv service pnt; sauna; baby facs; some serviced pitches; shwrs inc; el pnts (10A) €4.70; gas 1km; Indtte (inc dryer); sm shop; rest/snacks; bar; BBQ; playgrnd; lge htd pool complex (covrd & outdoor); paddling pool; waterslide; jacuzzi; sand beach 3km; fishing; tennis 600m; fitness rm; games area; games rm; cycle hire; golf 1.5km; wifi; entmnt; TV rm; 35% statics; dogs €3.90; phone; Eng spkn; quiet; ccard acc; red low ssn/long stay. "Mature, pleasant site; gd views; excel san facs; some narr site rds; excel." ♦ 12 Apr-2 Nov. € 58.40 (CChq acc) 2014*

BAGUER PICAN see Dol de Bretagne *2E4*

BAIN DE BRETAGNE *2F4* (500m SE Rural) *47.83000, -1.67083* **Camping du Lac, Route de Launay, 35470 Bain-de-Bretagne [02 99 43 85 67; info@campinglac.fr; www.campinglac.fr]** Fr Bain-de-Bretagne take N772 SE dir Châteaubriant, foll sp. Up hill & turn R into narr lane & foll site sp; narr ent. Not rec to tow thro Bain-de-Bretagne. Med, hdg/mkd pitch, pt shd; wc; chem disp; mv service pnt; sauna; shwrs inc; el pnts (10A) €2.50; shop 1km; tradsmn; rest, snacks; bar; playgrnd; htd, covrd pool 500m; lake sw, sailing school nr; some statics; dogs €2; no twin-axles; phone; poss cr; Eng spkn; quiet; red low ssn; CKE/CCI. "Pretty site with lake views; friendly, helpful new owners (2010) - much improved site; attractive sm town; many leisure facs in walking dist; conv NH; lovely location, conv for a'route, Vitre & Fougeres." ♦ 15 Mar-15 Oct. € 24.00 2014*

BAIN DE BRETAGNE *2F4* (11km W Rural) *47.8200, -1.8299* **Camp Municipal Le Port, Rue de Camping, 35480 Guipry [02 99 34 72 90 (Mairie) or 02 99 34 28 26; fax 02 99 34 28 06]** W fr Bain-de-Bretagne on D772, cross rv at Messac; cont on D772 sharp L at Leader supmkt into Ave du Port; site sp bef ent Guipry. NB Do not app after dark as rv is at end of app rd. Med, hdg/mkd pitch, pt shd; wc; mv service pnt; shwrs; el pnts (6A) €2.65 (poss long lead req); shop & rest nrby; playgrnd; pool nrby; rv fishing; train noise; CKE/CCI. "Excel site; friendly; warden on duty am & late pm; barrier 1.90m locked at times but phone for help or go to pitch 30; delightful rv walks & cycle paths; cruising & hire boats avail; nr classic cars museum." ♦ ltd Easter-15 Oct. € 9.80 2013*

BANNALEC see Pont Aven *2F2*

BAUD *2F3* (3.5km S Rural) *47.84613, -3.01354* **Camp Municipal du Petit Bois, Route de Lambel-Camors, 56330 Camors [02 97 39 18 36 or 02 97 39 22 06; fax 02 97 39 28 99; commune.de.camors@wanadoo.fr]** S fr Baud on D768 to Camors. Sp in vill on D189. Sm, mkd pitch, pt sl, terr, unshd; wc; chem disp; mv service pnt; shwrs inc; el pnts (10A) €2.50; Indtte; playgrnd; horseriding adj; dogs; adv bkg; quiet; CKE/CCI. "Pleasant surroundings; vg facs; well-managed site." ♦ 1 Jul-31 Aug. € 9.60 2010*

BELZ *2F3* (2.6km NW Coastal) *47.68268, -3.18796* **Camping St Cado, Port de St Cado, 56550 Belz [02 97 55 31 98; fax 02 97 55 27 52; info@camping-saintcado.com; www.camping-saintcado.com]** W fr Auray on D22 then D16. Well sp fr Belz. Med, hdg pitch, pt shd; wc; el pnts (3-6A) €2.60-3.60; Indtte; tradsmn; shop, rest 300m; playgrnd; fishing, boat hire 300m; tennis; volleyball; boules; games area; games rm; some statics; dogs €1.60; Eng spkn; adv bkg; quiet. "Popular site in beautiful location; seas views fr some pitches; helpful owner; rec phone ahead high ssn; vg; rec." 1 Apr-30 Sep. € 15.00 2013*

BENODET *2F2* (1.5km E Coastal) *47.86670, -4.09080* **Camping Du Letty, Rue du Canvez, 29950 Bénodet [02 98 57 04 69; fax 02 98 66 22 56; reception@campingduletty.com; www.campingduletty.com]** Fr N ent town on D34, foll sp Fouesnant D44. Le Letty sp R at rndabt. Fr E on N165 take D44 sp Fouesnant & foll rd to o'skirts Bénodet. After town sp, site is sp. Lge, hdg/mkd pitch, hdstg, pt sl, pt shd; wc (some cont); chem disp; mv service pnt; baby facs; sauna; shwrs €0.60; el pnts (10A) €4; gas; lndtte; shop; snacks; bar; BBQ (gas); playgrnd; htd, covrd pool; paddling pool; waterslides & aquapark (new in 2011); sand beach adj; kayak hire; tennis; squash; games area; games rm; gym; golf & horseriding nr; library; wifi; entmnt; TV rm; dogs €2.30; phone; poss cr; Eng spkn; adv bkg; quiet; ccard acc; red low ssn; CKE/CCI. "Excel, well-run, beautifully laid-out site; clean & well-equipped; lovely beach adj; excel playgrnd; many activities; friendly, helpful staff; highly rec." ♦ 11 Jun-5 Sep. € 33.20 2011*

See advert on previous page

BENODET *2F2* (500m SE Coastal) *47.86780, -4.09750* **Camping du Poulquer, 23 rue du Poulquer, 29950 Bénodet [02 98 57 04 19; fax 02 98 66 20 30; contact@campingdupoulquer.com; www.campingdupoulquer.com]** Fr N ent town on D34. At rndabt after junc with D44 strt onto Rue Penfoul. At next rndabt (tourist info office on R after rndabt) go strt dir La Plage until reach seafront; turn L at seafront then L at end of prom at camping sp; site in 100m on R. Fr E on N165 take D44 sp Fouesnant & foll rd to o'skirts Bénodet. After town sp, site is sp. Lge, hdg/mkd pitch, pt sl, pt shd; wc; chem disp; baby facs; shwrs inc; jaccuzi; el pnts (6-10A) inc (long lead poss req, poss rev pol); lndtte (inc dryer); shop; rest 600m; snacks; bar; BBQ; playgrnd; htd pool; covrd pool planned (2011); paddling pool; waterslide; aqua park; sand beach adj; tennis; golf & boat trips nr; cycle hire 1km; entmnt; wifi; games/TV rm; dogs €2; no c'vans/m'vans over 7.50m high ssn; Eng spkn; adv bkg; quiet; ccard not acc; red low ssn; CKE/CCI. "Lovely, well-kept, family-run site; friendly, helpful owner; gd, clean san facs, poss tired end of ssn; quiet site low ssn; mkt Mon; rec." ♦ 1 May-29 Sep. € 35.05 SBS - B16 2013*

BENODET *2F2* (7km W Coastal) *47.86903, -4.12848* **Camping Le Helles, 55 Rue du Petit-Bourg, 29120 Combrit-Ste Marine [tel/fax 02 98 56 31 46; contact@le-helles.com; www.le-helles.com]** Exit D44 S dir Ste Marine, site sp. Med, mkd pitch, pt sl, pt shd; htd wc; chem disp; baby facs; fam bthrm; shwrs inc; el pnts (6-10A) €3.50-4.40; lndtte; shop; tradsmn; snacks; BBQ; playgrnd; htd pool; paddling pool; sand beach 300m; some statics; dogs €2.60; Eng spkn; adv bkg; quiet; ccard acc; red low ssn; CKE/CCI. "Vg site with lge pitches, some shd; gd, clean modern san facs; friendly, helpful owners; excel beach within 5 min walk; vg long stay." ♦ 1 Apr-30 Sep. € 32.25 2014*

BENODET *2F2* (1km NW Rural) *47.88237, -4.10334* **Yelloh! Village Port de Plaisance, Route de Quimper, Clohars-Fouesnant, 29950 Bénodet [tel/fax 02 98 57 02 38; info@campingbenodet.fr; www.campingbenodet.fr / www.yellohvillage.co.uk]** Fr Bénodet take D34 twd Quimper, site on R 200m bef rndabt at ent to town. Lge, hdg pitch, pt sl, pt shd; wc; chem disp; mv service pnt; shwrs inc; baby facs; el pnts (6A) inc; lndtte; shop; tradsmn; rest, snacks; bar; playgrnd; htd pool; sand/shgl beach 1.5km; tennis; games area; cycle hire; internet; entmnt; 80% statics; dogs €4; phone; poss cr; Eng spkn; poss noisy (disco); adv bkg; ccard acc; red low ssn; CKE/CCI. "Many tour ops on site; some pitches poss diff lge o'fits; excel." ♦ ltd 8 Apr-18 Sep. € 39.00 2009*

BEUZEC CAP SIZUN see Douarnenez *2E2*

BINIC *2E3* (1km S Coastal) *48.59216, -2.8238* **Camping Le Panoramic, Rue Gasselin, 22520 Binic [02 96 73 60 43; fax 02 96 69 27 66; camping.le.panoramic@wanadoo.fr; www.lepanoramic.net]** D786 St Brieuc-Paimpol. 1st slip rd for Binic & 1st R up hill 100m, site sp. Med, mkd pitch, pt sl, terr, pt shd; htd wc; chem disp; shwrs; el pnts (10A) €5 (poss rev pol); gas; lndtte; shop; snacks; bar; BBQ; htd pool; paddling pool; sand beach 500m; golf adj; wifi; entmnt; 75% statics; dogs €2.50; quiet; red low ssn. "Pleasant site; clean facs; coastal path nr; excel facs, easy walk to beach." 1 Apr-30 Sep. € 18.70 2012*

BINIC *2E3* (2.5km S Coastal) *48.58269, -2.80477* **Camping Les Madières, Rue du Vau Madec, 22590 Pordic [02 96 79 02 48; fax 02 96 79 46 67; campinglesmadieres@wanadoo.fr; www.campinglesmadieres.com]** Site at E end of Pordic vill, sp. Med, pt sl,pt shd; htd wc (mainly cont); shwrs inc; el pnts (10A) €4; gas; lndtte; sm shop; rest, snacks; bar; htd pool; shgl beach 800m; sand beach & watersports 3km; entmnt; 10% statics; dogs €2.50; adv bkg; quiet; red low ssn/CKE/CCI. "Pleasant, clean, child-friendly site; helpful, friendly owners; immac facs; poss diff access to shgl beach, Binic beach OK; highly rec; quiet site." ♦ 30 Mar-2 Nov. € 32.00 2013*

BINIC *2E3* (4km S Coastal) *48.57875, -2.78498* **Camping Le Roc de l'Hervieu, 19 Rue d'Estienne d'Orves, 22590 Pordic [tel/fax 02 96 79 30 12; le.roc.de.lhervieu@wanadoo.fr; www.campinglerocdelhervieu.fr]** Site on E side of vill off N786, Binic-St Brieuc rd. Turn E in cent of vill, sp to Les Madières then sp Le Roc de l'Hervieu. Med, hdg pitch, pt shd; wc (some cont); chem disp; mv service pnt; shwrs inc; el pnts (10A) €3.60; lndtte; shop; bar; BBQ; playgrnd; sand beach 600m; fishing; some statics; quiet. "Gd walking; pleasant site." ♦ 1 May-30 Sep. € 16.20 2009*

BINIC *2E3* (8km SW Rural) *48.55622, -2.94635* **Camping à la Ferme La Corderie (Hello), Le Courtil Rault, 22170 Plélo [02 96 74 21 21 or 06 71 05 12 49 (mob); hello.odile@22.wanadoo.fr]** Fr Binic take D4 dir Châtelaudren, site on R at La Corderie. Sm, pt shd; wc; chem disp; shwrs inc; el pnts (10A); lndtte; playgrnd; sand beach 8km; TV; 20% statics; no dogs; quiet. "CL-type site." May-Sep. 2010*

BRITTANY

BINIC *2E3* (1.2km W Rural) *48.60539, -2.84124* **Camping des Palmiers, Ker Viarc'h, 22520 Binic [tel/fax 02 96 73 72 59 or 06 67 32 78 66 (mob); campingpalmiers.chantal@laposte.net; www.campingpalmiers.com]** N fr St Brieuc on D786 dir Pordic/Paimpol on coast rd. Foll sp to site on o'skts on Binic. Sm, mkd pitch, hdstg, terr, pt shd; htd wc; chem disp; mv service pnt; baby facs; shwrs inc; el pnts (10A) €6; Indtte; gas; shop; supmkt 1km; tradsmn; rest 1.5km; snacks; bar; BBQ; playgrnd; htd, covrd pool; paddling pool; sand beach 1.5km; tennis 1km; games rm; wifi; entmnt; TV; 6% statics; dogs €2; Eng spkn; adv bkg; quiet; red low ssn/CKE/CCI. "Warm welcome; excel site in gd situation." ♦ 1 Jun-30 Sep. € 21.00 2009*

BINIC *2E3* (6km W Rural) *48.60640, -2.86160* **FFCC Camping Les Etangs, Pont de la Motte, Route de Châtelaudren, 22410 Lantic [02 96 71 95 47; contact@campinglesetangs.com; www.campinglesetangs.com]** D786 fr Binic twd Paimpol; turn L approx 1km on D4 sp Châtelaudren & Lantic; in 3km at x-rds turn L foll camping sp; site in 50m on R. Fr N12 Guingamp-St Brieuc take D4 at Châtelaudren. Med, hdg/mkd pitch, pt sl, terr, pt shd; wc (cont); chem disp; mv service pnt; shwrs inc; el pnts (6A) €3.40; gas; Indtte (inc dryer); sm shop; tradsmn; snacks; BBQ; playgrnd; htd pool; paddling pool; beach 3km; wifi; TV; 2% statics; dogs €1.30; phone; poss v cr; Eng spkn; adv bkg; quiet; ccard acc; CKE/CCI. "Gd base slightly away fr cr coast sites; helpful, friendly owners; gd pool; excel." ♦ 1 Apr-30 Sep. € 13.80 2010*

BONO, LE see Auray *2F3*

⊞ **BREST** *2E2* (6km W Coastal) *48.36544, -4.54163* **Camping du Goulet, Ste Anne-du-Porzic, 29200 Brest [tel/fax 02 98 45 86 84; campingdugoulet@wanadoo.fr; www.campingdugoulet.com]** On D789 turn L at site sp. Approx 4km fr Brest after R bend at T junc, turn L & L again at site sp; down hill to site. Med, pt sl, terr, unshd; htd wc; chem disp; baby facs; shwrs inc; el pnts (6-10A) €3-3.50; Indtte; shop high ssn; snacks; playgrnd; pool complex; waterslides; sand beach 1km; games area; games rm; 15% statics; dogs €1.50; adv bkg; quiet; CKE/CCI. ♦ € 23.00 2010*

BRIGNOGAN PLAGES *1D2* (1km NW Coastal) *48.67278, -4.32916* **Camping de la Côte des Légendes, Keravezan, 29890 Brignogan-Plages [02 98 83 41 65; fax 02 98 83 59 94; contact@campingcotedeslegendes.com; www.campingcotedeslegendes.com]** Fr Roscoff on D10, fr Brest on D788/770 or fr N12 exit dir Lesneven. In Brignogan foll sp Brignogan-Plages & 'Centre Nautique'. Lge, hdg/mkd pitch, some hdstg, pt shd; wc; chem disp; mv service pnt; baby facs; shwrs inc; el pnts (5-10A) €3.15-4.05 (poss rev pol); Indtte; shop; tradsmn; snacks; bar; BBQ; playgrnd; dir access to sand beach adj; sailing & watersports; entmnt; TV rm; site guarded 24 hrs; 30% statics; dogs €1.40; phone; Eng spkn; adv bkg; quiet; ccard acc; red long stay/low ssn/CKE/CCI. "On beautiful sandy cove; friendly, helpful staff; ltd facs low ssn; vg touring base in interesting area; vg." ♦ 29 Mar-12 Nov. € 24.00 2014*

BRIGNOGAN PLAGES *1D2* (2km NW Coastal) *48.67535, -4.34534* **Camping du Phare, Plage du Phare, 29890 Brignogan-Plages [02 98 83 45 06; fax 02 98 83 52 19; camping.du.phare@orange.fr; www.camping-du-phare.com]** Take D770 N fr Lesneven to Brignogan-Plages; take L fork in town cent & foll site sp dir Kerverven. Med, some hdg pitch, some hdstg, pt shd; wc; chem disp; mv service pnt; shwrs €1; el pnts (6A) €3; gas; Indtte; shop 1km; tradsmn; snacks; playgrnd; sand beach adj; wifi; 10% statics; dogs €2; poss cr; Eng spkn; adv bkg; quiet; CKE/CCI. "Next to pretty bay & gd beach; helpful owner; vg site nr walking rte GR34." 1 Apr-30 Sep. € 22.30 2014*

CAMARET SUR MER *2E1* (2km NE Coastal) *48.28070, -4.56490* **Camping Le Grand Large, Lambézen, 29570 Camaret-sur-Mer [02 98 27 91 41; fax 02 98 27 93 72; contact@campinglegrandlarge.com; www.campinglegrandlarge.com]** On D8 bet Crozen & Camaret, turn R at ent to Camaret onto D355, sp Roscanvel. Foll sps to site in 3km. Med, hdg/mkd pitch, pt sl, pt shd; wc; chem disp; mv service pnt; baby facs; shwrs inc; el pnts (10A) inc; gas; Indtte (inc dryer); shop; tradsmn; snacks; bar; BBQ; playgrnd; htd pool; paddling pool; sandy & shgl beach 500m; boating; tennis; wifi; TV; dogs €2; adv bkg; quiet; ccard acc; red low ssn. "Coastal views fr some pitches, lovely beach; pleasant, helpful owners; cliff top walk to town; excel." ♦ 1 Apr-30 Sep. € 26.50 (CChq acc) 2014*

"We must tell The Club about that great site we found"

Get your site reports in by mid-August and we'll do our best to get your updates into the next edition.

CAMARET SUR MER *2E1* (3.5km NE Coastal) *48.28788, -4.56540* **Camping Plage de Trez-Rouz, Route de Camaret à Roscanvel, 29160 Crozon [02 98 27 93 96; fax 02 98 27 84 54; contact@trezrouz.com; www.trezrouz.com]** Foll D8 to Camaret-sur-Mer & at rndabt turn N sp Roscanvel/D355. Site on R in 3km. Med, hdg/mkd pitch, pt sl, pt shd; wc; chem disp; mv service pnt; baby facs; shwrs inc; el pnts (16A) €3.50; Indtte (inc dryer); shop; tradsmn; rest, snacks; playgrnd; sand beach; tennis 500m; horseriding 2km; wifi; 10% statics; dogs €1.50; poss cr; adv bkg; poss cr; quiet; CKE/CCI. "Great position opp beach; conv for Presqu'île de Crozon; gd facs but stretched high ssn; site scruffy low ssn; friendly owner." ♦ 15 Mar-15 Oct. € 16.50 2010*

⊞ **CAMARET SUR MER** *2E1* (500m W Urban) *48.27698, -4.60430* **Camp Municipal du Lannic, Rue du Grouanoc'h, 29570 Camaret-sur-Mer [02 98 27 91 31 or 02 98 27 94 22; camaret@wanadoo.fr; www.camaret-sur-mer.com]** On ent town foll sp to Port, on quayside to L turn sp Camping-Golf Miniature/m'van parking. Foll sp to site in 500m behind sports cent. Lge, pt sl, pt shd; wc; chem disp; mv service pnt; baby facs; shwrs inc; el pnts €3; Indtte (inc dryer); shops 500m; playgrnd; sand beach 500m; some statics; dogs €1.10; poss cr; quiet. "Gd site bet town & beach; sections for vans & tents." € 12.00 2010*

CANCALE *2E4* (3km N Coastal) *48.70369, -1.84829* **Camp Municipal La Pointe du Grouin, 35260 Cancale [02 99 89 63 79 or 02 99 89 60 15; fax 02 99 89 54 25; campingcancale@orange.fr; www.ville-cancale.fr]** Take D76 twd Cancale & cont on D201 sp Pointe de Grouin; site on R in 3km on cliffs above sea, on N side of Cancale (diff to see, on RH bend mkd with chevrons); sp 'Camp Municipal'. Care req at ent. Med, pt sl, terr; wc (mainly cont); mv service pnt; shwrs inc; el pnts (8-13A) €3.40-445 (poss long lead req); Indtte; shop; rest in town; BBQ; playgrnd; rocky beach adj; watersports; fishing; dogs €1.75, Eng spkn; poss cr; quiet; ccard acc; red low ssn. "Lovely, well-kept site in gd location; sea views; some pitches uneven; excel san facs; gates clsd 2300-0700; conv Dinan, Mont-St Michel, St Malo; gd walking." 9 Mar-25 Oct. € 16.80 2014*

CANCALE *2E4* (6km S Coastal) *48.61893, -1.84946* **Camp Municipal des Ondes, Rue Bord de la Mer, 35114 St Benoît-des-Ondes [02 99 58 65 21]** In vill cent on D155. Med, unshd; wc; chem disp (wc); mv service pnt; shwrs inc; el pnts (6A) €2.55; Indtte; shop, rest, snacks adj; playgrnd; sand/shgl beach adj; dogs; phone; rd noise; CKE/CCI. "Site adj main rd; gd san facs; gd walking & cycling." 1 Jun-30 Sep. € 12.75 2009*

CANCALE *2E4* (6km S Coastal) *48.61592, -1.85151* **Camping de l'Ile Verte, 42 Rue de l'Ile Verte, 35114 St Benoît-des-Ondes [02 99 58 62 55; camping-ile-verte@sfr.fr; www.campingdelileverte.com]** Site on S side of vill. Fr Cancale, take D76 SW for approx 4km, then turn L onto D155 into St Benoît. Foll site sp. Sm, hdg pitch, pt shd; htd wc (cont); chem disp; mv service pnt; shwrs inc; el pnts (6A) €4 (poss rev pol); gas; Indtte; shop; rest, bar adj; playgrnd; sand beach adj; dog €2.50; 3% statics; phone; adv bkg; quiet; red low ssn; CKE/CCI; "Well-kept site on edge of vill; facs poss stretched high ssn." 30 Mar-2 Nov. € 30.00 2013*

CANCALE *2E4* (2km W Rural) *48.68823, -1.86061* **Camping La Ville ès Poulain, 35260 Cancale [02 99 89 87 47; www.ville-cancale.fr]** Turn of D201 coast rd on o'skts of town onto D355 at traff lts. Turn R at rndabt by bar & foll sp; site in 1km. Sm, hdg pitch, pt shd; wc; chem disp; shwrs; el pnts (10A) €2.60; Indry rm; supmkt 1.5km; sand beach 2km; dog €1; quiet; no ccard acc; CKE/CCI. "CL-type site; lge pitches; gd base but no views - entire site surrounded by high hdg; conv St-Malo ferry & Mont St Michel." 15 Apr-30 Sep. € 13.50 2010*

CANCALE *2E4* (2.3km NW Coastal) *48.68995, -1.86130* **Camping Les Close Fleuris, La Ville es Poulains et Les, Clos Fleuris, La Ville es Polains, 35260 Cancale [02 99 89 97 68; fax 09 58 18 10 82; campingdosfleuris@free.fr; www.canale-camping.fr]** Foll D76 to D355, foll D355 to Boulevard d'Armor, cont on Boulrvard D'Armor. Drive on to La Ville Es Poulains, exit the rndbt onto Boulevard d'Armor, go over rdbt, bear L twrds Rue du Saussaye, cont onto Rue du Saussaye, turn L onto La Ville Es Poulains, take 1st R to stay on La Ville Es Poulains and the site will be on your L. Med, mkd, pt shd; wc; shwrs; chem disp; el pnts (16A) €4.40; Indtte; playgrnd; pool; games rm; wifi; dogs (€2); Eng spkn. "Lots of walking trails and coastal walks." 15 Mar-15 Nov. € 19.90 2014*

CANCALE *2E4* (7km NW Coastal) *48.68861, -1.86833* **Camping Le Bois Pastel, 13 Rue de la Corgnais, 35260 Cancale [02 99 89 66 10; fax 02 99 89 60 11; camping.bois-pastel@wanadoo.fr; www.campingboispastel.fr]** Fr Cancale take D201 dir Pointe du Grouin & St Malo by Rte Touristique. Site sp on L 2.5km after Pointe du Grouin. Med, mkd pitch, pt shd; wc; shwrs inc; chem disp; mv service pnt; shwrs inc; el pnts (6A) €4; Indtte (inc dryer); shop; tradsmn; snacks; bar; BBQ; playgrnd; htd, covrd pool; paddling pool; sand beach 800m; fishing; games area; games rm; 25% statics; dogs €2.50; adv bkg; quiet; red long stay/low ssn. "Conv Mont-St Michel, St Malo; gd touring base." 1 Apr-30 Sep. € 22.00 2012*

CARANTEC see St Pol de Léon *1D2*

CARHAIX PLOUGUER *2E2* (1.5km W Rural) *48.27763, -3.60183* **Camp Municipal La Vallée de l'Hyères, Rue de Kerniguez, 29270 Carhaix-Plouguer [02 98 99 10 58; fax 02 98 99 15 92; tourismecarhaux@wanadoo.fr; www.ville-carhaix.com]** SE fr Huelgoat on D794 for 17km; sm site sps on all apps to Carhaix. Med, pt shd; wc (some cont); chem disp (wc); shwrs inc; el pnts (6A) €2.20; Indtte; shop 1.5km; tradsmn, snacks; bar; playrnd nr; pool 1.5km; canoe/kayak hire; 5% statics; adv bkg; quiet; CKE/CCI. "Pleasantly situated in parkland; resident warden; muddy after rain; poss waterlogged due adj rv; forest trail nrby." ♦ ltd 1 May-15 Sep. € 7.45 2010*

CARNAC *2G3 (1km N Rural) 47.59683, -3.06035* **Camping La Grande Métairie, Route des Alignements de Kermario, 56342 Carnac [02 97 52 24 01; fax 02 97 52 83 58; info@lagrandemetairie.com; www.lagrandemetairie.com / www.les-castels.com]** Fr Auray take N768 twd Quiberon. In 8km turn L onto D119 twd Carnac. La Métairie site sp 1km bef Carnac (at traff lts) turn L onto D196 to site on R in 1km. V lge, hdg/mkd pitch, pt shd; htd wc; chem disp; mv service pnt; baby facs; shwrs inc; el pnts (6A) €3; gas; Indtte (inc dryer); shop; tradsmn; rest, snacks; bar; BBQ; playgrnd; 2 pools (1 htd, covrd); paddling pool; waterslide; sand beach 2.5km; watersports, sailing 2.5km; tennis; games rm; wifi; entmnt; TV; 80% statics; dogs €4; Eng spkn; adv bkg; quiet; ccard acc; red low ssn. "Excel facs; vg pool complex; friendly, helpful staff; rec." ♦ 2 Apr-10 Sep. € 42.00 2011*

See advert on previous page

CARNAC *2G3 (1km N Rural) 47.5964, -3.0617* **Camping Le Moulin de Kermaux, Route de Kerlescan, 56340 Carnac [02 97 52 15 90; fax 02 97 52 83 85; moulin-de-kermaux@wanadoo.fr; www.camping-moulinkermaux.com]** Fr Auray take D768 S sp Carnac, Quiberon. In 8km turn L onto D119 twds Carnac. 1km bef Carnac take D196 (Rte de Kerlescan) L to site in approx 500m opp round, stone observation tower for alignments. Med, hdg/mkd pitch, pt shd; htd wc; chem disp; mv service pnt; baby facs; sauna; shwrs inc; el pnts (6A) €4 (poss rev pol); gas; Indtte (inc dryer); shop; tradsmn; snacks; bar; BBQ; playgrnd; htd, covrd pool; paddling pool; waterslide; jacuzzi; sand beach 3km; games area; wifi; entmnt; TV; 50% statics; dogs €2.50; phone; bus adj; Eng spkn; adv bkg; quiet; ccard acc; red low ssn; CKE/CCI. "Well-kept, friendly, attractive site nr standing stones; peaceful & comfortable low ssn; many repeat visitors; excel." ♦ 1 May-10 Sep. € 27.00 2011*

CARNAC *2G3 (1km N Rural) 47.60225, -3.07869* **Camping Les Ombrages, Kerlann, 56340 Carnac [02 97 52 16 52 (Jul & Aug) or 02 97 52 14 06]** Exit Auray SW on D768; in 9.5km turn L onto D119; in 3km turn R at carwash, sp Kerlann; site 600m on R. Sp fr D119. Med, hdg/mkd pitch, shd; wc; shwrs; el pnts (6A) €2.70; Indtte; shops 1km; playgrnd; sand beach 3km; tennis; dogs €1; some statics; poss cr; quiet. "Well-kept site in wooded area; san facs old but clean." 15 Jun-15 Sep. € 15.20 2010*

CARNAC *2G3 (3km N Rural) 47.60801, -3.09049* **Camping Les Bruyères, Kerogile, 56340 Plouharnel [02 97 52 30 57; fax 09 71 70 46 47; contact@camping-lesbruyeres.com; www.camping-lesbruyeres.com]** Fr Vannes W on E60/N165, at Auray take D768 dir Quiberon. At rndabt approx 2km fr Plouharnel turn L into Rte du Hahon, site in 500m, sp. Med, hdg/mkd pitch, hdstg, pt shd; htd wc; chem disp; mv service pnt; baby facs; shwrs inc; el pnts (6A) €3.70; Indtte (inc dryer); shop; rest, snacks; bar; BBQ; playgrnd; sand beach 3km; tennis; bicycles; games area; wifi; child entmnt; TV rm; library; pony rides; 30% statics; dogs €2; Eng spkn; adv bkg; quiet; ccard acc; red low ssn; CKE/CCI. "V pleasant, well-run, peaceful site; vg." ♦ 5 Apr- 30 Sep. € 33.50 2014*

CARNAC *2G3 (2km NE Rural) 47.60820, -3.06605* **Kawan Village Le Moustoir, 71 Route du Moustoir, 56340 Carnac [02 97 52 16 18; fax 02 97 52 88 37; info@lemoustoir.com; www.lemoustoir.com]** Fr N165 take D768 at Auray dir Carnac & Quiberon. In 5km take D119 dir Carnac, site on L at ent to Carnac. Lge, hdg/mkd pitch, pt sl, pt shd; wc; chem disp; mv service pnt; baby facs; shwrs inc; el pnts (6A) €4.80; Indtte (inc dryer); shop; tradsmn; rest, snacks; bar; BBQ; playgrnd; 2 htd pools (1 covrd); paddling pool; waterslide; sand beach 4km; tennis; games area; cycle hire; wifi; TV rm; 30% statics; dogs free; phone; poss cr & noisy; Eng spkn; adv bkg; red low ssn; ccard acc; CKE/CCI. "Attractive, friendly, well-run site; facs clean but stretched; megaliths nrby; Sun mkt." ♦ 13 Apr-22 Sep. € 46.00 (4 persons) (CChq acc) 2012*

CARNAC *2G3 (3.5km NE Rural) 47.60198, -3.03672* **Camping de Kervilor, Route du Latz, 56470 La Trinité-sur-Mer [02 97 55 76 75; fax 02 97 55 87 26; camping.kervilor@wanadoo.fr; www.camping-kervilor.com]** Sp fr island in cent of Trinité-sur-Mer. Lge, hdg/mkd pitch, hdstg, pt shd; wc; chem disp; mv service pnt; baby facs; shwrs inc; el pnts (6-10A) €3.85-4.35; gas; Indtte; shop; snacks; bar; BBQ; playgrnd; htd, covrd pool; paddling pool; waterslides; solarium; sand beach 4km; tennis; games area; cycle hire; internet; entmnt; 5% statics; dogs €2.90; poss cr; Eng spkn; adv bkg; ccard acc; red low ssn; CKE/CCI. "Busy, well-kept family site; lge pitches; clean dated unisex san facs; 20 min walk into La Trinité-sur-Mer (1.5km); gd cycling to Carnac & megaliths; gd." ♦ 1 Apr-18 Sep. € 29.25 2010*

BRITTANY

CARNAC *2G3* (8km NE Rural) *47.61538, -2.98965* **Camping Le Fort Espagnol, Route de Fort Espagnol, 56950 Crac'h [02 97 55 14 88; fax 02 97 30 01 04; fort-espagnol@wanadoo.fr; www.fort-espagnol.com]** Fr Auray take D28 S; in Crac'h turn L at rndabt; site sp in 1km on R. Lge, pt shd; htd wc (some cont); chem disp; baby facs; shwrs inc; el pnts (10A) €4; gas; lndtte; shops 1km; tradsmn; snacks; bar; playgrnd; pool; waterslide; sand beach 5km; tennis; sports facs; entmnt; 30% statics; dogs €3.50; poss cr; adv bkg rec high ssn; quiet; ccard acc; CKE/CCI. "Helpful, pleasant management; popular with British; some lge pitches." 1 May12 Sep. € 28.00 2009*

CARNAC *2G3* (2km E Rural/Coastal) *47.5810, -3.0576* **Camping Les Druides, 55 Chemin de Beaumer, 56340 Carnac [02 97 52 08 18; fax 02 97 52 96 13; contact@camping-les-druides.com; www.camping-les-druides.com]** Go E on seafront Carnac Plage to end; turn N onto Ave d'Orient; at junc with Rte de la Trinité-sur-Mer, turn L, then 1st R; site 1st on L in 300m. Med, hdg pitch, pt sl, pt shd; wc; chem disp; mv service pnt; baby facs; shwrs inc; el pnts (6A) €3.70; lndtte; shop 1km; rest adj; playgrnd; htd pool; sand beach 500m; entmnt; games/TV rm; 5% statics; dogs €2.50; phone adj; Eng spkn; adv bkg; quiet; ccard acc; CKE/CCI. "Friendly welcome." ♦ ltd 12 Apr-6 Sep. € 49.30 2014*

CARNAC *2G3* (1.5km SE Coastal) *47.58116, -3.05804* **Camping Le Dolmen, Chemin de Beaumer, 56340 Carnac [02 97 52 12 35; fax 02 97 52 63 91; contact@campingledolmen.com; www.campingledolmen.com]** Fr N on D768 twd Quiberon; turn L onto D781 twd La Trinité-sur-Mer. At Montauban turn R at rndabt dir Kerfraval & Beaumer, site in 700m, sp. Med, hdg/mkd pitch, hdstg, pt sl, pt shd; htd wc (some cont); chem disp; mv service pnt; baby facs; shwrs €2; el pnts (10A) €4.70; lndtte; shop 800m; tradsmn; rest, snacks; BBQ; playgrnd; htd pool; paddling pool; sand beach 500m; games area; games rm; wifi; entmnt; 2% statics; dogs €3; Eng spkn; adv bkg; quiet; ccard acc; red low ssn/CKE/CCI. "Excel, pleasant site." ♦ 1 Apr-20 Sep. € 28.00 2011*

CARNAC *2G3* (3km SE Coastal) *47.57566, -3.02900* **Camping de la Plage, Plage de Kervilen, 56470 La Trinité-sur-Mer [02 97 55 73 28; fax 02 76 01 33 05; info@camping-plage.com; www.camping-plage.com]** Fr Auray on D28 & D781 dir La Trinite. Foll sp Kervilen-Plage to S. Lge, hdg pitch, pt shd; wc; chem disp; mv service pnt; chem disp; serviced pitches; baby facs; shwrs inc; el pnts (6-10A) €3.50-4.30; gas; lndtte (inc dryer); shop 200m; rest, snacks; bar; BBQ; playgrnd; htd pool; paddling pool; waterslide; jacuzzi; sand beach adj; fishing; tennis adj; cycle hire; wifi; 80% statics; dogs €1.30; poss cr; Eng spkn; adv bkg; quiet; red long stay/low ssn; ccard acc; CKE/CCI. "Pleasant site; friendly staff; tight ent; variable pitch sizes." ♦ 7 May-19 Sep. € 36.50 2010*

CARNAC *2G3* (4km SE Coastal) *47.57396, -3.02653* **Camping La Baie, Plage de Kervillen, 56470 La Trinité-sur-Mer [02 97 55 73 42; fax 02 97 55 88 81; contact@campingdelabaie.fr; www.campingdelabaie.fr]** Fr Carnac take D186. Turn R after causeway, keep R, past Camping de la Plage site, & site on L. Fr E app vill along seafront sp Carnac, cont strt thro traff lts, after 2nd traff lts take 1st L & foll rd for 1km. Site ent on L. Lge, hdg/mkd pitch, hdstg, pt shd; wc; chem disp; mv service pnt; baby facs; serviced pitches; shwrs inc; el pnts (6-10A) €3.50-5; lndtte; shops, snacks, rest, bar 500m; playgrnd; entmnt; htd pool; sand beach 50m; fishing; boat hire, mini-golf & tennis 250m; TV rm; 30% statics; dogs €1.30; phone; poss cr; Eng spkn; adv bkg; quiet; red low ssn; ccard acc. "Excel, well-kept site in superb location; vg recep; excel san facs; sm pitches; some narr site rds - pitching poss diff lge o'fits inc lge m'vans; vg family beach across rd; v sm pool; highly rec." ♦ 8 May-12 Sep. € 42.20 2010*

See advert on previous page

CARNAC *2G3* (1km S) *47.57667, -3.06817* **Camping Les Menhirs, Allé saint michel, 56343 Carnac [02 97 52 94 67; fax 02 97 52 25 38; contact@lesmenhirs.com; www.lesmenhirs.com]** Fr Auray foll sps to Carnac, Carnac Plage. Site past shopping cent rd on L, sp by camping sps. Lge, pt sl, pt shd; wc (some cont); chem disp; shwrs inc; el pnts (6A) €4.80; gas; shop & 500m; lndtte; htd pool; jacuzzi; sauna; games rm; sandy beach 350m; 50% statics; adv bkg; quiet; 20-50% red low ssn. "Extra charge for larger pitches; excel san facs; ♦ May-Sep. € 49.00 2014*

See advert above

BRITTANY

CARNAC *2G3* (1.5km NW Rural) *47.59468, -3.09659* **Camping Les Goélands, Kerbachic, 56340 Plouharnel [02 97 52 31 92; angelina.oliviero@wanadoo.fr]** Take D768 fr Auray twd Quiberon. In Plouharnel turn L at rndabt by supmkt onto D781 to Carnac. Site sp to L in 500m. Med, pt shd; wc (some cont); chem disp; shwrs inc; el pnts (3-5A) €2-3; gas; lndtte; shops 1km; playgrnd; sand beach 3km; dogs €1; poss cr; adv bkg. "Friendly owners; excel facs; gd-sized pitches; gate clsd at 2200; nr beaches with bathing & gd yachting; bells fr adj abbey not too intrusive; conv for megalithic sites; high standard site; Pleasant quiet site; facs basic; clean and tidy." 1 Jun-15 Sep. € 15.00 2012*

"I need an on-site restaurant"

We do our best to make sure site information is correct, but it is always best to check any must-have facilities are still available or will be open during your visit.

CARNAC *2G3* (7.5km NW Rural) *47.62882, -3.14511* **Camping Les Mégalithes, Kerfélicité, 56410 Erdeven [tel/fax 02 97 55 68 76 or 02 97 55 68 09; campingdesmegalithes@orange.fr; www.campingdesmegalithes.fr]** Fr Carnac take D781 thro Plouharnel after further 4km; site on L in 500m. Med, hdg/mkd pitch, pt sl, pt shd; mv service pnt; wc; shwrs inc; el pnts (10A) inc; lndtte; shop high ssn; rest, bar 1km; playgrnd; pool; sand/shgl beach 2km; some statics; dogs €1; quiet. "Excel, well maintained site with lge pitches but poorly lit; poss diff to manoeuvre lge c'vans; conv for megalithic alignments; v clean facs; helpful staff; family run site; pool area beautiful but busy." 1 May-21 Sep. € 33.00 2014*

CARNAC *2G3* (8km NW Rural) *47.63282, -3.14743* **Camping Kerzerho, Route de Plouharnel, 56410 Erdeven [tel/fax 02 97 55 63 17; info@camping-kerzerho.com; www.camping-kerzerho.com]** N fr Carnac on D781, site sp 400m S of Erdeven. Med, hdg/mkd pitch, pt shd; wc; baby facs; sauna; baby facs; shwrs; el pnts (10A) €5.30; lndtte (inc dryer); shop; tradsmn; rest, snacks; bar; playgrnd; htd, covrd pool; paddling pool; waterslide; beach 2km; cycle hire; excursions; entmnt; some statics; dogs €3.20; adv bkg; quiet; red low ssn. "Busy site; some sm pitches diff lge o'fits." 1 Jun-3 Sep. € 24.00 2010*

CARNAC *2G3* (8km NW Coastal) *47.62165, -3.16462* **Idéal Camping, Route de la Plage de Kerhilio, Lisveur, 56410 Erdeven [02 97 55 67 66; contact@camping-l-ideal.com; www.camping-l-ideal.com]** Fr Carnac take D781 to Erdeven, turn L at rndabt. Site 2km on R at hotel/cafe. Sm, hdg pitch, pt shd; wc; chem disp (wc); baby facs; shwrs inc; el pnts (6A) €5; gas; lndtte; rest; shops 500m; tradsmn; rest, snacks; bar; BBQ; playgrnd; htd, covrd pool; paddling pool; sand beach 800m; sailing; fishing; tennis nr; games rm; TV; 90% statics; dogs €4; sep parking area for cars; Eng spkn; no adv bkg; quiet; ccard acc; red low ssn; CKE/CCI. "Peaceful site nr excel beach & cent of mkt town; not rec twin-axles or lge o'fits due narr site rds." ♦ 1 Apr-30 Oct. € 23.00 (3 persons) 2009*

CARNAC *2G3* (12.5km NW Rural) *47.65500, -3.17194* **Camping Les Sept Saints, 56410 Erdeven [02 97 55 52 65; fax 02 97 55 22 67; info@septsaints.com; www.septsaints.com]** Fr Erdeven on D781 going NW dir Lorient; site on L in 2km. Lge, hdg/mkd pitch, pt sl, pt shd; wc; chem disp; baby facs; shwrs inc; el pnts (10A) inc; gas; lndtte; shop; snacks; bar; BBQ (charcoal/gas); playgrnd; htd pool; paddling pool; waterslide; sand beach 4km; watersports 1.5km; cycle hire; internet; entmnt; games/TV rm; many statics; dogs €5; c'vans over 8m not acc high ssn; adv bkg; quiet; ccard acc; red low ssn; CKE/CCI. "V pleasant site; gd lge pitches; superb unspoilt beaches nrby; excel cycling rtes; Etel 3km worth visit; vg." ♦ 1 May-15 Sep. € 37.50 2009*

CAUREL see Mûr de Bretagne *2E3*

CHAPELLE AUX FILTZMEENS, LA see Combourg *2E4*

CHATEAULIN *2E2* (1.5km S Rural) *48.18754, -4.08515* **Camping La Pointe, Route de St Coulitz, 29150 Châteaulin [tel/fax 02 98 86 51 53; lapointecamping@aol.com; www.lapointesuperbecamping.com]** Exit N165 onto D887 to Châteaulin; in town cent, cross bdge & turn L along rv on D770; after approx 750m, turn L at sp for St Coulitz; in 100m turn R into site. NB if app fr S to Châteaulin on D770, do not attempt to turn R at sp for St Coulitz (tight turn); go into town & turn round. Med, hdg/mkd pitch, some hdstg, pt sl, pt shd; wc; chem disp; mv service pnt; baby facs; shwrs inc; el pnts (10A) €3 (poss rev pol); lndtte (inc dryer); shop; supmkt 1.5km; tradsmn; rest, snacks & bar 1km; BBQ; playgrnd; covrd pool 1km; sand beach 15km; rv fishing nr; cycle hire; games rm; wifi; dogs €1; phone; bus 1.5km; Eng spkn; adv bkg; quiet but some rd noise; no ccard acc; red low ssn; CKE/CCI. "Charming, peaceful, spacious site in wooded setting; well-run; helpful & friendly British owners; immac san facs; rvside path to town; gd cycling, walking & fishing; gd touring base; gd." ♦ 12 Mar-15 Oct. € 17.00 (CChq acc) 2013*

"Satellite navigation makes touring much easier"

Remember most sat navs don't know if you're towing or in a larger vehicle – always use yours alongside maps and site directions.

CHATEAULIN *2E2* (500m SW Urban) *48.19099, -4.08597* **Camping de Rodaven (formerly Municipal), Rocade de Prat Bihan 29150 Châteaulin [02 98 86 32 93; fax 02 98 86 31 03; contact@campingderodaven.fr; www.campingderodaven.fr]** Fr canal/rv bdge in town cent take Quai Moulin (SE side of rv) for about 350m; site down track on R opp sw pool. Med, pt shd; wc; chem disp; mv service pnt; shwrs inc; el pnts (10A) €2.90; shops 200m; snacks; playgrnd; htd, covrd pool 300m; direct rv access, fishing; sand beach 5km; wifi; entmnt; dogs free, 2nd dog €1.00; phone; poss cr; Eng spkn; adv bkg; quiet; CKE/CCI. "Well-kept site; pleasant, helpful owner; vg clean facs; walk along rv bank to town; gd touring base; Locronan vill well worth the visit." ♦ ltd 7 Apr-30 Sep. € 18.60 (CChq acc) 2013*

CHATEAUNEUF D'ILLE ET VILAINE *2E4* (1.5km NE Rural) *48.57589, -1.91941* **Camping Le Bel Event, 35430 St Père [02 99 58 83 79; fax 02 99 58 82 24; contact@camping-bel-event.com; www.camping-bel-event.com]** Fr terminal at St Malo, at 1st rndabt foll sp Toutes Directions; at 2nd traff lts turn R & cont foll dir Toutes Directions, then sp Rennes; cont twd Rennes on D137 for approx 10km & take exit for Dinan/ Châteauneuf; take immed L twds Cancale; past an old rlwy stn on R & take 1st little rd on L (500m fr stn) opp rest; site 100m further on L. Fr S on D137 at Châteauneuf junc turn R onto D74 sp Cancale, then as above. Med, mkd pitch, pt sl, pt shd; wc; chem disp; shwrs inc; el pnts (10A) €4.20 (rev pol poss); Indtte; tradsmn; sm shop; snacks; bar; htd pool (high ssn); playgrnd; lake sw, fishing & watersports adj; sand beach 5km; cycle hire; tennis; TV; 75% statics (sep area); dogs €2.10; quiet, some rd noise; adv bkg; red low ssn . "Excel NH for St Malo & ferry; clean & tidy site; immac san facs, ltd low ssn; some sm pitches - 4 per enclave; gd touring base." 9 Apr-25 Sep. € 18.60 2011*

CHATILLON EN VENDELAIS see Vitre *2F4*

CHERRUEIX see Dol de Bretagne *2E4*

CLOHARS CARNOËT see Pouldu, Le *2F2*

COMBOURG *2E4* (8km NE Rural) *48.45304, -1.65031* **Camping Le Bois Coudrais (Ybert), 35270 Cuguen [02 99 73 27 45; fax 02 99 73 13 08; info@vacancebretagne.com; www.vacancebretagne.com]** Fr Combourg take D796 twd Pleine-Fougères, 5km out of Combourg turn L on D83 to Cuguen; 500m past Cuguen, turn L, site sp. Or fr Dol-de-Bretagne, take D795 then turn L onto D9 to Cuguen. Sm, hdg/mkd pitch, pt shd; wc; chem disp; shwrs inc; el pnts (10A) €3; shop 500m; snacks; bar; BBQ; playgrnd; pool; fishing, watersports, golf, zoo, adventure park nr; cycle hire; wifi; dogs €1; Eng spkn; adv bkg; v quiet; red long stay; no ccard acc; red CKE/CCI. "CL-type site, friendly British owners, gd clean facs, great for young children, sm animal-petting area, gd touring base." ♦ 27 Apr-30 Sep. € 18.50 2013*

COMBOURG *2E4* (1.5km SE Rural) *48.40449, -1.74271* **Camp Municipal Le Vieux Châtel, Route de Lanrigan, Ave de Waldmünchen, 35270 Combourg [02 99 73 13 93; campingcombourg@gmail.com; www.camping-combourg.com]** Fr W, N & E foll sp for D795 dir Rennes, Hede. Take 1st L after lake twd Lanrigan. Fr S on D795, turn R at lake. Site on L in approx 500m. Med, hdg/mkd pitch, pt shd; wc; chem disp; shwrs inc; el pnts (5A) €2.35; Indtte; shop, rest, snacks, bar 500m; BBQ; playgrnd; htd, covrd pool 1km; lake fishing nrby; tennis; games area; games rm; entmnt; dogs €1.50; phone; Eng spkn; adv bkg; quiet; ccard acc; CKE/CCI. "Forests, chateaux & churches nrby; 20 mins to Emerald Coast; castle in Combourg." ♦ 28 May-18 Sep. € 10.87 2010*

"There aren't many sites open at this time of year"

If you're travelling outside peak season remember to call ahead to check site opening dates – even if the entry says 'open all year'.

COMBOURG *2E4* (6km SW Rural) *48.38090, -1.83290* **FFCC Camping Domaine du Logis, 35190 La Chapelle-aux-Filtzméens,Ille-et-Vilaine [02 99 45 25 45 or 06 85 78 69 71 (mob); fax 02 99 45 30 40; domainedulogis@wanadoo.fr; www.domainedulogis.com]** Fr N176 at junc for Dol-de-Bretagne branch R onto D155 sp Dol & take D795 S to Combourg. Then take D13 twd St Domineuc, go thro La Chapelle-aux-Filtzméens & site on R in 1km. Lge, hdg/mkd pitch, pt shd; wc; chem disp; mv service pnt; shwrs inc; el pnts (10A) inc; gas; Indtte (inc dryer); shop 5km; tradsmn; rest, snacks; bar; BBQ; playgrnd; htd pool; paddling pool; sand beach 20km; fitness rm; canoes 800m; fishing nr; cycle hire; gym; games area; games rm; wifi; entmnt; TV rm; 10% statics; dogs €2; no c'vans/m'vans over 12m; phone; Eng spkn; adv bkg; quiet; ccard acc; red low ssn/ long stay/CKE/CCI. "Set in chateau grnds; lge grassy pitches; helpful staff; gd san facs; gd touring base, conv St Malo, Mont St Michel, Dinan & Channel Islands; mkt Mon; excel." ♦ 1 Apr-1 Nov. € 15.00 (CChq acc) SBS - B02 2013*

See advertisement

COMBRIT STE MARINE see Bénodet *2F2*

CONCARNEAU *2F2* (2km S Coastal) *47.85628, -3.89999* **Camping Le Cabellou Plage, Ave de Cabellou, Kersaux, 29185 Concarneau [02 98 97 37 41; fax 02 98 60 78 57; info@le-cabellou-plage.com; www.le-cabellou-plage.com]** Fr N165 turn onto D70 dir Concarneau. At 5th rndabt (Leclerc supmkt) foll dir Tregunc. After Moros bdge take 2nd exit at next rndabt dir Le Cabellou-Plage. Site sp on L. Lge, mkd/hdg pitch, hdstg, pt shd; wc (cont); chem disp; baby facs; shwrs; el pnts (10A) inc; Indtte; tradsmn; snacks; bar; playgrnd; htd pool; paddling pool; sand beach adj; watersports; cycle hire; games area; games rm; wifi; TV; 16% statics; dogs €2; bus at site ent; Eng spkn; adv bkg; quiet; ccard acc; red low ssn. "Pleasant seaside site; vg san facs; gd walking fr site." ♦ 25 May-18 Sep. € 27.00 2009*

CONCARNEAU *2F2* (3km W Coastal) *47.88910, -3.94070* **Camping Les Prés Verts, Kernous-Plage, 29186 Concarneau [02 98 97 09 74; info@presverts.com; www.presverts.com]** Exit N165 onto D70 dir Concarneau. At rndabt by Leclerc supmkt foll sp 'Centre Ville' (Town Centre) with Leclerc on L. At x-rds with traff lts go strt over, then fork R into Rue de Kerneach & down slope. Bear L at 1st rndabt & R at next. Keep R to join coast rd & foll sp La Forêt-Fouesnant; pass Hôtel Océans; site 3rd rd on L in 1.5km. Med, hdg/mkd pitch, pt sl, pt shd; wc; chem disp; mv service pnt; serviced pitch; shwrs inc; el pnts (6A-10A) inc (poss rev pol & long lead req); gas 2km; Indtte; rest 3km; BBQ (charcoal/gas); playgrnd; htd pool; paddling pool; dir access to sand beach 300m; sailing 1km; horseriding 1km; games rm; wifi; TV; 10% statics; dogs €2; no c'vans/m'vans over 8m; poss cr; adv bkg; quiet; ccard acc; red low ssn. "Peaceful, scenic, busy site; path to sandy cove below; gd sized pitches, lge pitches extra; family-run, friendly staff; basic san facs, ltd low ssn; poss unkempt low ssn; gd touring base; walk along coastal path to Concarneau; mkt Mon & Fri." 1 May-29 Sep. € 19.50 SBS - B24 2011*

CONCARNEAU *2F2* (1.5km NW Urban/Coastal) *47.8807, -3.9311* **Camping Les Sables Blancs, Ave du Dorlett, 29900 Concarneau [tel/fax 02 98 97 16 44; contact@camping-lessablesblancs.com; www.camping-lessablesblancs.com]** Exit N165 to Concarneau dir 'Centre Ville'. Then foll sp 'La Côte' 300m after traff lts. Site on R, sp. Med, hdg/mkd pitch, hdstg, pt sl, terr, pt shd; htd wc; chem disp; mv service pnt; baby facs; fam bthrm; shwrs inc; el pnts (10A) €4; Indtte; shop 1.5km; tradsmn; rest, snacks; bar; BBQ; playgrnd; htd pool; paddling pool; sand beach 300m; games area; games rm; wifi; entmnt; TV rm; 3% statics; dogs €2; phone; bus 300m; poss cr; Eng spkn; adv bkg; quiet; ccard acc; red low ssn/long stay; CKE/CCI. "Nice, clean, family site in woodland; many sm pitches; friendly staff; excel san facs; superb pool; gd rest; pleasant walk to town; mkt Fri; vg." ♦ 3 Apr-31 Oct. € 23.00 2011*

CONQUET, LE *2E1* (2km N Coastal) *48.36748, -4.75990* **Camping Les Blancs Sablons, 29217 Le Conquet [tel/fax 02 98 89 06 90]** Exit Brest on D789 to Le Conquet. Turn R after 22km (1.8km bef Le Conquet) on D67 twd St Renan, turn L after 700m on D28 twd Ploumoguer. After 2km, turn L at x-rds twd Plage des Blancs Sablons, site on L in 1km. Lge, mkd pitch, pt sl, unshd; wc; chem disp (wc); shwrs inc; el pnts (16A) €3 (long lead poss req); Indtte; shop in ssn & 1km; rest, snacks 1km; bar 500m; playgrnd; htd pool; sand beach 100m; adv bkg; ccard acc; CKE/CCI. "Gd views fr some pitches; some soft pitches; ltd facs low ssn; site badly run down & office hardly ever open (2010); lovely old fishing town." ♦ 1 Apr-31 Oct. € 16.40 2010*

⊞ **CONQUET, LE** *2E1* (7km SE Coastal) *48.34154, -4.70749* **Camping Les Terrasses de Bertheaume, Rue de Perzel, 29217 Plougonvelin [tel/fax 02 98 48 32 37; camping-lesterrassesdebertheaume@wanadoo.fr; www.camping-brest.com]** Sp nr town. Sm, mkd pitch, pt sl, terr, unshd; wc (some cont); chem disp (wc); shwrs €1; el pnts €2.50; Indtte; shop 1km; snacks; bar; BBQ; playgrnd; htd pool; sand beach adj (steps); TV rm; 80% statics; dogs €1; poss cr; CKE/CCI. "Some sea views; Le Fort de Bertheaume 500m interesting; cliff walk; steep access poss diff lge o'fits." ♦ ltd € 17.00 2010*

CRAC'H see Carnac *2G3*

CROZON *2E2* (5km E Coastal) *48.24204, -4.42932* **Camping L'Aber, Tal-ar-Groas,50 Route de la Plage de l'Aber, 29160 Crozon [02 98 27 02 96 or 06 75 62 39 07 (mob); contact@camping-aber.com; www.camping-aber.com]** On D887 turn S in Tal-ar-Groas foll camp sp to site in 1km on R. Med, mkd pitch, pt sl, terr, pt shd; wc; shwrs inc; el pnts (5A) €3.40; gas; Indtte; snacks; bar; htd pool; sand beach 1km; sailing; fishing; windsurfing; dogs €1.50; 50% statics; adv bkg; quiet. ♦ 1 Apr-1 Oct. € 24.00 2013*

CROZON *2E2* (3km SW Rural) *48.22138, -4.52285* **Camping Les Bruyères, Le Bouis, 29160 Crozon-Morgat [tel/fax 02 98 26 14 87; info@camping-bruyeres-crozon.com; www.camping-bruyeres-crozon.com]** Take D887 then D255 SW fr Crozon (sp Cap de la Chèvre). In 1.5km turn R & site on R in 700m. Lge, mkd pitch, pt shd; wc (mainly cont); baby facs; shwrs inc; el pnts (5A) €3; gas; Indtte; shop in ssn; playgrnd; sand beach 1.8km; dogs €1.50; Eng spkn; adv bkg; quiet. "Conv beaches & mkt town." 1 Jun-15 Sep. € 16.80 2010*

DAMGAN see Muzillac *2G3*

DINAN *2E3* (3km N Rural) *48.48903, -2.00855* **Camping Beauséjour (formaly municipal), La Hisse, 22100 St Samson-sur-Rance [02 96 39 53 27 or 02 96 39 16 05 (Mairie); fax 02 96 87 94 12; beausejour-stsamson@orange.fr; www.beausejour-camping.com]** Fr Dinan take N176/D766 N twd Dinard. In 3km turn R onto D12 dir Taden then foll sp thro Plouer-sur-Rance to La Hisse; site sp. Fr N exit N176/E401 dir Plouer-sur-Rance, then foll sp La Hisse. Med, hdg/mkd pitch, pt sl, pt shd; wc; chem disp; mv service pnt; baby facs; shwrs inc; el pnts (10A) €3.45 (poss rev pol); Indtte; sm shop; supmkt 5km; tradsmn; rest, snacks; bar; playgrnd; htd pool; tennis; games area; sailing; wifi; 40% statics; dogs €2.05; phone; poss cr; Eng spkn; adv bkg; quiet; red low ssn/long stay; CC acc; CKE/CCI. "Pleasant, well-kept site; helpful, friendly staff; gd pool; quiet & spacious Jun & Sep; no twin-axles; excel rv walks; excel well maintained site; footpath down to Rance and rvside walks." ♦ ltd 1 Jun-30 Sep. € 14.50 2013*

DINAN *2E3* (3km NE Rural) *48.47138, -2.02277* **Camp International de la Hallerais, 4 rue de la Robardais, 22100 Taden [02 96 39 15 93 or 02 96 87 63 50 (Mairie); fax 02 96 39 94 64; contact@camping-lahallerais.com; www.camping-lahallerais.com]** Fr Dinan take N176/D766 N twd Dinard. In 3km turn R onto D12 to Taden. Foll La Hallerais & Taden sp to site. Fr N176 take exit onto D166 dir Taden; turn onto D766 dir Taden, then L onto D12A sp Taden & Camping. At rndabt on ent Taden take 1st exit onto D12 sp Dinan; site rd is 500m on L. Do not ent Dinan. Site adj Rv Rance. Lge, mkd pitch, terr, pt shd; wc; chem disp; mv service pnt; serviced pitches; shwrs inc; el pnts (6A) inc (rev pol); gas; Indtte; shop adj; tradsmn; snacks (high ssn); rest & bar adj; BBQ; playgrnd; htd pool; paddling pool; shgl beach 10km; tennis; fishing; horseriding 500m; wifi; games/TV rm; many statics (sep area); dogs free; no c'vans/m'vans over 9m (check in adv rec); storage facs; Eng spkn; adv bkg; quiet; ccard acc; red low ssn. "Lovely site; excel, clean san facs; vg pool; phone ahead if arr late at night low ssn; ltd office hours low ssn - report to bar; sh walk to Taden; rvside walk to Dinan medieval town; rv trips; gd walking, cycling; mkt Thur am & Fri eve; rec; excel." ♦ 15 Mar-11 Nov. € 27.00 SBS - B01 2014*

DINAN *2E3* (10km NE Coastal) *48.52466, -1.96617* **Camping Ville Ger, 22690 Pleudihen-sur-Rance [02 96 83 33 88; reservation@campingdelavilleger.fr; www.campingdelavilleger.fr]** Fr Dinan take D675/D676 in dir Dol de Bretagne; turn L on D29 after 6km; site sp after 4km on L. Sm, mkd pitch; pt shd; wc (cont); rec own san high ssn; shwrs €1; el pnts (3-10A) €2.30-4.80; Indtte; shops 1.5km; rest; bar; playgrnd; dogs €1; poss cr; adv bkg ess high ssn; quiet; CKE/CCI. "Lovely area; close to rv; gd for dog-walking." 1 Apr-15 Oct. € 9.30 2011*

DINAN *2E3* (200m S Urban) *48.44743, -2.04631* **Camp Municipal Châteaubriand, 103 Rue Châteaubriand, 22100 Dinan [02 96 39 11 96 or 02 96 39 22 43 (LS); fax 02 96 87 08 40; campingmunicipaldinan@wanadoo.fr; www.brittanytourism.com/accommodation/campsites/camping-municipal-chateaubriand]** Fr N176 (E or W) take slip rd for Dinan cent; at lge rndbt in cent take 2nd R; down hill to site on L (500m). Sm, mkd pitch, pt sl, pt shd; wc; chem disp; mv service pnt; shwrs inc; el pnts (6A) €2.70; gas 500m; Indry rm; shop, rest, snacks 500m; bar adj; BBQ; sand beach 18km; games area; dogs €1.50; phone; poss cr; Eng spkn; adv bkg; daytime rd noise; ccard not acc; CKE/CCI. "Pleasant, helpful staff; high kerb onto pitches; poss mkt traders; opening dates vary each year; check time when barrier locked, espec low ssn; gd cent for Rance valley, St Malo & coast; gd location." 01 Jun- 30 Sep. € 11.35 2014*

DINARD *2E3* (1.5m W Coastal) *48.6309, -2.08413* **Camping La Touesse, 171 Rue de la Ville Gehan, La Fourberie, 35800 St Lunaire [02 99 46 61 13; fax 02 99 16 02 58; camping.la.touesse@wanadoo.fr; www.campinglatouesse.com]** Exit Dinard on St Lunaire coast rd D786, site sp. Med, mkd pitch, pt shd; wc; mv service pnt; baby facs; shwrs inc; el pnts (5-10A) €3.30-3.70; Indtte; shop; snacks; bar; playgrnd; sand beach 300m; tennis 1.5km; golf 2km; entmnt; TV rm; dog €1.50; adv bkg (dep); quiet, some late night noise; red low ssn; CKE/CCI. "Vg well-kept site; gd beach & rocks nr; friendly recep." ♦ 1 Apr-30 Sep. € 21.80 2011*

See advertisement

BRITTANY

DINARD *2E3* (1km W Coastal) *48.63486, -2.07928* **Camping Le Port Blanc, Rue de Sergent Boulanger, 35800 Dinard [02 99 46 10 74; fax 02 99 16 90 91; info@camping-port-blanc.com; www.camping-port-blanc.com]** Fr Dinard foll sp to St Lunaire on D786 for 1.5km. Turn R at traff lts by football grnd to site. Lge, mkd pitch, pt sl, terr, pt shd; wc (some cont); chem disp; child/baby facs; shwrs inc; el pnts (10A) €3.95; Indtte; sm shop; supmkt 800m; rest 500m; snacks; bar; playgrnd; sand beach adj; 40% statics; dogs €1.90; phone; bus; poss cr; adv bkg; quiet at night; ccard acc; CKE/CCI. "O'looks sand beach; gd san facs; excel site; walk along coast to town; well run site; gd pitches; gd acces to beach." ♦
1 Apr-30 Sep. € 33.00 2014*

DINARD *2E3* (4km W Coastal) *48.63406, -2.12039* **Camping Longchamp, Blvd de St Cast, 35800 St Lunaire [02 99 46 33 98; fax 02 99 46 02 71; contact@camping-longchamp.com; www.camping-longchamp.com]** Fr St Malo on D168 turn R sp St Lunaire, In 1km turn R at g'ge into St Lunaire, site sp to W of vill on D786 dir St Briac. Lge, hdg/mkd pitch, pt shd; wc; chem disp; mv service pnt; baby facs; shwrs inc; el pnts (4-10A) €3.40-4.20; gas; Indtte; shop; tradsmn; rest, snacks; bar; BBQ; playgrnd; sand beach 300m; 30% statics; dogs €2; phone adj; bus 500m; Eng spkn; adv bkg rec; quiet; red low ssn. "Excel, well-run site; clean facs; friendly, helpful staff; clean beach 300m; conv Brittany Ferries at St Malo; Site under new ownership, much improved (2013); heated pool; friendly quiet site nr beautiful seaside town."
♦ ltd 1Apr-30 Sep. € 34.70 2013*

See advert above

DOL DE BRETAGNE *2E4* (6km N Coastal) *48.60290, -1.77241* **Camp Municipal L'Abri des Flots, 35960 Le Vivier-sur-Mer [02 99 48 91 57; fax 02 99 48 98 43; campinglabridesflots@orange.fr; www.pays-de-dol.com]** Site ent off D155/D797 (coast rd) in Le Vivier-sur-Mer. On sea front at E end of town, ent almost opp Mairie, sp. Med, mkd pitch, pt shd; wc; mv service pnt; shwrs; el pnts (6A) inc (long lead poss req); Indtte; sm shop & in vill; tradsmn; dogs €1; poss cr; no adv bkg; noise fr adj port; Eng spkn; CKE/CCI. "Clean site in vill cent & on sea front; resident warden; friendly; muddy beach not suitable for sw; gd NH to see mussel/oyster beds; tours fr museum nrby."
1 Apr-15 Oct. € 15.60 2010*

DOL DE BRETAGNE *2E4* (7km NE Coastal) *48.60052, -1.71182* **Camping de l'Aumône, 35120 Cherrueix [02 99 48 84 82 or 06 48 64 60 16 (mob); laumone@orange.fr; www.camping-de-laumone.fr]** Exit D797 Pontorson-Cancale rd S onto D82, opp rd leading into vill of Cherrueix. Site in 100m. Med, unshd; wc; chem disp; mv service pnt; baby facs; shwrs inc; el pnts (10A) €3.50; gas; Indtte (inc dryer); shops 300m; snacks; bar; BBQ; playgrnd; muddy beach 1km (not suitable for sw); sand yachting nrby; cycle hire; internet; 5% statics; dogs free; Eng spkn; adv bkg rec high ssn; noise fr adj rd daytime; red low ssn/CKE/CCI. "Friendly; sm chateau; gd sized pitches; modern san facs; vg; pleasant friendly owners." 22 Apr-14 Nov. € 13.00 2013*

DOL DE BRETAGNE *2E4* (4km E Rural) *48.54941, -1.68386* **FFCC Camping du Vieux Chêne, Le Motais, 35120 Baguer-Pican [02 99 48 09 55; vieux.chene@wanadoo.fr; www.camping-vieuxchene.fr]** Leave N176 E of Dol on slip rd sp Baguer-Pican. At traff lts turn L thro vill, site on R of D576 at far end vill adj lake. Lge, hdg/mkd pitch, pt sl, pt shd; wc; chem disp; mv service pnt; baby facs; shwrs inc; el pnts (10A) inc (poss rev pol & poss long cable req); gas; lndtte (inc dryer); shop; supmkt nr; rest, snacks; bar; BBQ (charcoal & gas); playgrnd; 2 htd pools; paddling pool; lake fishing; horseriding; tennis; games area; games rm; wifi; entmnt; TV rm; dogs €3; no c'vans/m'vans over 7.50m high ssn; phone; Eng spkn; adv bkg; quiet; ccard acc; red low ssn/long stay; CKE/CCI. "Well-kept site in grnds of former farm; 3 sm unfenced lakes; plenty rm for pitch access; various pitch sizes, some sm & some with fruit trees; friendly & helpful; gd san facs; shop & rest ltd low ssn; mkt in Dol Sat; gd." ♦ 12 May-23 Sep. € 29.00 2011*

DOL DE BRETAGNE *2E4* (7km SE Rural) *48.49150, -1.72990* **Camping Le Domaine des Ormes, 35120 Epiniac [02 99 73 53 60 or 02 99 73 53 01; fax 02 99 73 53 55; info@lesormes.com; www.lesormes.com / www.les-castels.com]** Exit N176/E401 at W end of Dol-de-Bretagne; then S fr Dol on D795 twd Combourg & Rennes, in 7km site on L of rd, clearly sp. V lge, hdg/mkd pitch, pt sl, pt shd; wc; chem disp; baby facs; shwrs inc; el pnts (6A) inc (poss long lead req); gas; lndtte (inc dryer); shop; tradsmn; rest, snacks; bar; BBQ (charcoal/gas); playgrnd; htd pool complex; waterslide; covrd aquacentre; paddling pool; lake fishing, canoeing; pedalos; sand beach 25km; tennis; cycle hire; horseriding; archery; golf course adj (discount to campers); cricket; cycle hire; wifi; entmnt; games/TV rm; 80% statics; dogs €2; c'vans/m'vans 8m & over by request only; poss cr; adv bkg; Eng spkn; poss noisy (disco); ccard acc; red low ssn; CKE/CCI. "Busy site set in well-kept chateau grnds; helpful staff; clean san facs; suitable RVs; conv Mont St Michel, St Malo & Dinan; disco at night; mkt Sat; excel all round." ♦ 12 Apr-21 Sep. € 44.60 SBS - B08 2011*

See advert on previous page

DOUARNENEZ *2E2* (2km W Rural) *48.09270, -4.35220* **Camping de Trézulien, Route de Trézulien, 29100 Douarnenez [02 98 74 12 30 or 06 80 01 17 98 (mob); fax 09 70 06 31 74; contact@camping-trezulien.com; www.camping-trezulien.com]** Ent Douarnenez fr E on D7; foll sp 'Centre Ville'; turn L at traff lts sp to Tréboul. Cross rv bdge into Ave de la Gare, at PO turn L, then 1st L. Turn R at island, foll site sp. Lge, pt terr, pt shd; wc; baby facs; shwrs inc; el pnts (10A) €3.50; gas; lndtte; shops 1km; playgrnd; sand beach 1.5km; dogs €2; quiet. "Pleasant site; steep hill fr ent to recep; 1km by foot to Les Sables Blancs; conv Pointe du Raz." 1 Apr-30 Sep. € 14.00 2013*

“We must tell The Club about that great site we found”

Get your site reports in by mid-August and we'll do our best to get your updates into the next edition.

DOUARNENEZ *2E2* (6km W Rural) *48.08166, -4.40722* **Camping de la Baie de Douarnenez, Route de Douarnenez, 29100 Poullan-sur-Mer [02 98 74 26 39; fax 02 98 74 55 97; info@pil-koad.com; www.camping-douarnenez.com / www.flowercampings.com]** Fr E take circular rd around Douarnenez on D7/D765 dir Audierne & Poullan-sur-Mer, Tréboul & Pointe-du-Van. Site on L off D7 1km fr Poullan-sur-Mer vill, shortly after church spire becomes visible. Med, hdg/mkd pitch, pt shd; htd wc; chem disp; mv service pnt; baby facs; shwrs inc; el pnts (10A) inc; gas; lndtte; shop; rest, snacks; bar; BBQ (charcoal/gas); playgrnd; htd, covrd; paddling pool; sand beach 5km; watersports 4km; lake fishing; tennis; cycle hire; games area; wifi; entmnt; games/TV rm; statics (tour ops); dogs €4; no c'vans/m'vans over 10m high ssn; Eng spkn; adv bkg; quiet; ccard acc; red low ssn; CKE/CCI. "Tranquil site in woodland; gd sized pitches; staff friendly; ltd facs low ssn; entmnt well away fr most pitches; gd for families; mkd walks, guided high ssn; mkt Mon & Fri; pools & water slides great fun." ♦ 26 Apr-13 Sep. € 35.85 SBS - B04 2013*

See advertisement

DOUARNENEZ *2E2* (11km W Coastal) *48.08416, -4.48194* **Camping Pors Péron, 29790 Beuzec-Cap-Sizun [02 98 70 40 24; fax 02 98 70 54 46; info@campingporsperon.com; www.campingporsperon.com]** W fr Douarnenez take D7 sp Poullan-sur-Mer. Thro Poullan & in approx 4km turn R sp Pors-Piron, foll site & beach sp. Site bef Beuzec-Cap-Sizun vill. Med, hdg/mkd pitch, pt sl, pt shd; wc (some cont); chem disp; mv service pnt; baby facs; shwrs inc; el pnts (10A) inc (long lead req); gas; Indtte (inc dryer); shop & 3km; snacks; BBQ; playgrnd; sand beach 200m; games area; cycle hire; wifi; 5% statics; dogs €1.60; phone 200m; poss cr; adv bkg; quiet; red low ssn; CKE/CCI. "Pleasant site nr beautiful sandy cove; friendly, helpful British owners; gd san facs, poss insufficient high ssn & long way fr some pitches; poss ltd privacy in ladies' facs; site rds poss diff lge o'fit; gd." ♦ ltd 1 Apr-30 Sep. € 24.65 2013*

EPINIAC see Dol de Bretagne *2E4*

ERDEVEN see Carnac *2G3*

"I need an on-site restaurant"

We do our best to make sure site information is correct, but it is always best to check any must-have facilities are still available or will be open during your visit.

ERQUY *2E3* (1km N Coastal) *48.63838, -2.45561* **Yelloh! Village Les Pins, Le Guen, Route des Hôpitaux, 22430 Erquy [02 96 72 31 12; fax 02 96 63 67 94; camping.des.pins@wanadoo.fr; www.yellohvillage.co.uk/camping/les_pins]** Site sp on all app rds to Erquy. Lge, hdg/mkd pitch, pt sl, pt shd; wc (some cont); chem disp; sauna; baby facs; shwrs inc; el pnts (6A) inc; Indtte (inc dryer); shop; tradsmn; rest, snacks; bar; BBQ; playgrnd; htd, covrd pool; paddling pool; waterslide; sand beach 600m; tennis; fitness rm; jacuzzi; games area; games rm; internet; entmnt & TV rm; 40% statics; dogs €4; Eng spkn; adv bkg; quiet; ccard acc; red low ssn; CKE/CCI. "Gd family holiday site; excel facs." ♦ 29 Apr-17 Sep. € 36.00 2011*

ERQUY *2E3* (3km NE Coastal) *48.64201, -2.42456* **Camping Les Hautes Grées, Rue St Michel, Les Hôpitaux, 22430 Erquy [02 96 72 34 78; fax 02 96 72 30 15; hautesgrees@wanadoo.fr; www.camping-hautes-grees.com]** Fr Erquy NE D786 dir Cap Fréhel & Les Hôpitaux sp to site. Med, hdg/mkd pitch, hdstg, pt shd; htd wc (some cont); chem disp; mv service pnt; sauna; shwrs inc; el pnts (10A) €4.70 (rec long lead); gas; Indtte; shop; tradsmn; rest & snacks or 2km; bar; BBQ; playgrnd; htd pool; sand beach 400m; fishing; tennis; horseriding; gym; child entmnt; TV rm; some statics; dogs €1.70; adv bkg; ccard acc; red low ssn; CKE/CCI. "Lovely, well-run site; well-kept pitches, extra charge lge ones; helpful staff; clean, modern facs." ♦ 10 Apr-2 Oct. € 21.00 2010*

ERQUY *2E3* (1km E Coastal) *48.63828, -2.44233* **Camping Le Vieux Moulin, 14 Rue des Moulins, 22430 Erquy [02 96 72 34 23 or 06 42 22 20 36 (mob); fax 02 96 72 36 63; www.camping-vieux-moulin.com]** Sp fr all dirs on D786. Lge, mkd pitch, sl, pt shd; wc; mv service pnt; shwrs inc; el pnts (6-10A) €5-5.50; gas; Indtte (inc dryer); shop; tradsmn; rest, snacks; bar; 2 htd pools (1 covrd); paddling pool; waterslide; sand beach 900m; games rm; wifi; entmnt; TV; statics; dogs €4; poss cr; quiet; red low ssn. "Site set in pine woods; plenty of beaches in 20 mins drive; ideal for family holiday; poss diff access lge o'fits; lower pitches subject to flooding." ♦ 25 Apr-5 Sep. € 41.00 2010*

ERQUY *2E3* (5km S Rural) *48.59410, -2.48530* **Camping Bellevue, Route de Pléneuf-Val-André, La Couture, 22430 Erquy [02 96 72 33 04; fax 02 96 72 48 03; campingbellevue@yahoo.fr; www.campingbellevue.fr]** Fr Erquy, take D786 twd Le Val-André, site sp. Med, hdg/mkd pitch, hdstg, pt shd; wc; chem disp; mv service pnt; baby facs; shwrs inc; el pnts (6-10A) €3.30-4.80; gas; Indtte; shop; tradsmn; snacks; bar; BBQ; 3 playgrnds; htd, covrd pool; paddling pool; sand beach 2km; watersports; tennis 2km; games area; games rm; entmnt; child entmnt high ssn; TV rm; 40% statics; dogs €1.70; phone; Eng spkn; adv bkg; quiet; red low ssn/long stay; ccard acc; CKE/CCI. "Excel for families; rec." ♦ 12 Apr-15 Sep. € 19.50 2009*

See advertisement

ERQUY *2E3* (4km SW Rural/Coastal) *48.60695, -2.49723* **Camping de la Plage de St Pabu, 22430 Erquy [02 96 72 24 65; fax 02 96 72 87 17; camping@saintpabu.com; www.saintpabu.com]** Sp on D786 bet Erquy & Le Val-André at St Pabu. Narr rd, restricted passing places. Lge, hdg/mkd pitch, hdstg, terr, pt shd; wc; chem disp; mv service pnt; baby facs; shwrs inc; el pnts (10A) €4.80; gas; Indtte (inc dryer); shop; tradsmn; snacks; bar; BBQ; playgrnd; sand beach adj; wind surfing; cycle hire; games/TV rm; wifi; entmnt; some statics; dogs €1.60; Eng spkn; adv bkg; quiet; ccard acc; red long stay/low ssn; CKE/CCI. "In beautiful location; vg beach adj; lge pitches; upper terrs poss diff lge o'fits; friendly; san facs gd; vg touring base; conv St Malo, Dinan, Granit Rose coast; excel." ♦ 1 Apr-10 Oct. € 20.00 2010*

ETABLES SUR MER *2E3* (1km S Coastal) *48.63555, -2.83526* **Camping L'Abri Côtier, Rue de la Ville-ès-Rouxel, 22680 Etables-sur-Mer [02 96 70 61 57 or 06 07 36 01 91 (mob LS); fax 02 96 70 65 23; camping.abricotier@wanadoo.fr; www.camping-abricotier.fr]** Fr N12 round St Brieuc take D786 N thro Binic & 500m after Super U supmkt turn L to Etables. Go thro vill for approx 3 km & turn L into Rue de la Ville-es-Rouxel just after R turn for Plage-du-Moulin. Site ent just after sm x-rds. NB Long c'vans & big m'vans (to avoid going thro vill): cont on D786, past Chapel, down hill & turn L at boatyard dir Etables; take 2nd turn on R. To avoid manoeuvring, park on rd & go to recep on foot. Med, mkd pitch, pt sl, pt shd; htd wc; chem disp; mv service pnt; 15% serviced pitch; baby facs; shwrs inc; el pnts (10A) inc; gas; Indtte (inc dryer); shop; tradsmn; snacks; bar; BBQ; playgrnd; htd pool; paddling pool; jacuzzi; sand beach 500m; watersports 2km; tennis in vill; golf 4km; games rm; wifi; entmnt; TV; 10% statics; dogs €2; adv bkg; quiet; ccard acc; red low ssn; CKE/CCI. "Popular, immac site; excel beach (poss strong currents); entry narr & steep, narr corners on site rds poss diff lge o'fits; mkt Tues & Sun; vg." ♦ 1 May-14 Sep. € 31.00 SBS - B09 2013*

FAOUET, LE *2F2* (2km SE Rural) *48.01826, -3.47142* **Camp Municipal Beg er Roch, Route de Lorient, 56320 Le Faouët [02 97 23 15 11 or 06 89 33 75 70 (mob); fax 02 97 23 11 66; camping.lefaouet@wanadoo.fr]** SE fr Le Faouët on D769 site sp on L. Med, hdg/mkd pitch, pt shd; wc; mv service pnt; chem disp; shwrs inc; el pnts (10A) €3; gas 2km; Indtte; shops, tradsmn; rest, bar 2km; playgrnd; htd pool; lake sw 2km; fishing; tennis; games area; golf; games/TV rm; 25% statics; dogs €1.05; Eng spkn; adv bkg; ccard acc; red long stay/CKE/CCI. "Pleasant, well-kept, quiet rvside site; helpful warden; kingfishers on rv; many mkd walks; lovely, historic area." ♦ 10 Mar-30 Sep. € 16.50 2010*

FEINS *2E4* (2km N Rural) *48.33923, -1.63816* **Camp Municipal L'Etang de Boulet/La Bijouterie, La Bijouterie, 35440 Feins [02 99 69 63 23 or 02 99 69 70 52 (Mairie); fax 02 99 69 70 52; feins@wanadoo.fr; www.feins.fr]** N fr Feins on D91; site on L in 1.5km. Sp fr Feins & fr Marcillé-Raoul. Sm, hdg/mkd pitch, pt shd; wc; chem disp (wc); shwrs inc; el pnts €3; Indtte; shops, rest & snacks nrby; playgrnd; lake & beach adj; sailing & canoe hire; 40% statics; dogs; quiet; CKE/CCI. "Vg site; cycle track." ♦ ltd May-30 Sep. € 11.00 2009*

FOUESNANT *2F2* (5km SE Coastal) *47.85938, -3.98650* **Camping Kerolland, Chemin de Kerolland, Route des Dunes, Beg Meil, 29170 Fouesnant [02 98 94 91 00; camping.kerolland@orange.fr; www.camping-kerolland.com]** S fr Quimper on D34/D45; 400m bef Beg Meil, turn R after church into Chemin de Kerolland. Site sp. Route des Dunes is pt of D45. Lge, mkd pitch, pt shd; wc (cont); mv service pnt; shwrs inc; el pnts €2.50; Indtte (inc dryer); shops 200m; playgrnd; sand beach 500m; wifi; 60% statics; dogs €1.10; bus 1km; Eng spkn; adv bkg; quiet; red low ssn. "Nr lovely beaches & coastal walks; helpful staff; san facs clean but tired; in walking dist of beaches or vill; gd touring base. 1 May-30 Sep. € 14.80 2011*

FOUESNANT *2F2* (3km S Rural) *47.88202, -4.01863* **Camping Les Hortensias, La Grande Allée, 29170 Fouesnant [02 98 56 52 95 or 06 20 45 73 74 (mob); information@campingleshortensias.com; www.campingleshortensias.com]** Fr Quimper on D34 dir Fouesnant, then S twds Mousterlin, site sp. Med, hdg pitch, pt shd; htd wc; chem disp; mv service pnt; baby facs; shwrs; el pnts (6A) €3; gas; Indtte (inc dryer); tradsmn; snacks; BBQ; playgrnd; beach 3km; games area; games rm; wifi; entmnt; TV; dogs €2; phone; adv bkg; quiet. "Guided walks & cycle rides." Easter-30 Sep. € 15.00 2010*

FOUESNANT *2F2* (3.5km SW Rural) *47.86667, -4.01556* **Camping La Piscine, 51 Hent Kerleya, 29170 Fouesnant [02 98 56 56 06; fax 02 98 56 57 64; contact@campingdelapiscine.com; www.campingdelapiscine.com]** Turn R off D45 on exit Fouesnant onto D145 sp Mousterlin; in 1km L at site sp. Lge, hdg/mkd pitch, some hdstg, pt shd; wc; chem disp; mv service pnt; baby facs; sauna; shwrs inc; el pnts (6-10A) €4-4.60; gas; Indtte; shop; tradsmn; rest 2km; snacks; BBQ; playgrnd; htd pool; paddling pool; waterslide; sand beach 1.5km; lake adj; golf, tennis nr; golf 7km; games rm; wifi; entmnt; 30% statics; dogs €2.20; Eng spkn; adv bkg; quiet; ccard acc; red low ssn; CKE/CCI. "Highly rec, family-run site; gd walking, cycling." ♦ 13 May-12 Sep. € 26.00 2009*

FOUESNANT *2F2* (4.5km SW Coastal) *47.85851, -4.02009* **Camping Sunêlia L'Atlantique, Hent Poul an Corre, 29170 Fouesnant [02 98 56 14 44; fax 02 98 56 18 67; sunelia@latlantique.fr; www.camping-bretagne-atlantique.com]** Exit Quimper on D34 sp Fouesnant, take D45 L to Fouesnant & after lge intersection with D44 look for next R to Mousterlin, site sp. Lge, hdg/mkd pitch, pt shd; htd wc; chem disp; mv service pnt; baby facs; sauna; shwrs inc; el pnts (6-10A) inc; gas; Indtte (inc dryer); shop; rest, snacks; bar; BBQ; playgrnd; htd pools (1 covrd); paddling pool; waterslide; sand beach 400m; watersports; spa, fitness rm & beauty treatments; lake fishing 200m; tennis; cycle hire; games rm; games area; golf 12km; wifi; entmnt; TV rm; 70% statics; no dogs; phone; poss cr; adv bkg rec; ccard acc; red long stay/low ssn; CKE/CCI. "Excel leisure facs; helpful, friendly staff; ideal for families." ♦ 23 Apr-10 Sep. € 41.00 (CChq acc) 2011*

BRITTANY

FOUESNANT *2F2* (5km SW Coastal) *47.85055, -4.03444* **Camping Kost-Ar-Moor, Route du Grande Large, 29170 Mousterlin [02 98 56 04 16; fax 02 98 56 65 02; contact@camping-fouesnant.com; www.camping-fouesnant.com]** S fr Fouesnant on D145, site sp. Lge, hdg/mkd pitch, pt shd; htd wc; chem disp; baby facs; fam bthrm; shwrs inc; el pnts (10A) €3.50; gas; Indtte; shop; tradsmn; snacks; bar; playgrnd; pools; waterpark; sand beach 400m; lake adj; cycle hire; games area; golf, horseriding nr; wifi; entmnt; TV rm; 10% statics; dog €2.50; phone; Eng spkn; adv bkg; quiet; ccard acc; CKE/CCI. "Vg clean site; helpful owner; gd for beach holiday & walking, cycling." ♦ 24 Apr-11 Sep. € 21.00 2009*

FOUGERES *2E4* (1.5km E Urban) *48.3544, -1.1795* **Camp Municipal de Paron, Route de la Chapelle-Janson, 35300 Fougères [02 99 99 40 81; fax 02 99 99 70 83; campingmunicipal35@orange.fr; www.ot-fougeres.fr]** Fr A84/E3 take junc 30 then ring rd E twd N12. Turn L at N12 & foll sp. Site on D17 sp R after Carrefour. Well sp on ring rd. Med, hdg pitch, hdstg, pt sl, pt shd; wc; serviced pitches; chem disp; shwrs inc; el pnts (5-10A) €3.60-4.10 (poss rev pol); Indtte; shops 1.5km; hypmkt 800m; tradsmn high ssn; rest 600m; playgrnd; pool 1km; tennis; horseriding adj; internet; dogs; adv bkg; quiet; ccard acc; red low ssn; CKE/CCI. "Well-kept site in pleasant parkland setting; lge pitches, poss soggy when wet; popular NH; helpful warden; gd clean facs; gates clsd 2200-0900 card pass avail; tours of 12thC castle; old town worth visit; Sat mkt; excel; excel new (2013) san facs." Apr 25- 30 Sep. € 14.85 2013*

GACILLY, LA *2F3* (200m E Rural) *47.76325, -2.12544* **Camping de l'Aff, Le Bout du Pont, 35550 Sixt-sur-Aff [02 99 08 10 59, 06 58 04 16 62 (mob); fax 02 99 08 25 38; lepage.roselyne@orange.fr; www.paysdelagacilly.com]** On ent La Gacilly exit rv bdge onto D777 dir Sixt-sur-Aff. Site on L outside town sp. Well sp fr town cent. Sm, mkd pitch, pt shd; wc; mv service pnt; shwrs inc; el pnts (6A) €2.50; shops 500m; tradsmn; rests 200m; playgrnd; rv adj; boat hire; cycle hire; dogs €0.50; Eng spkn; quiet; CKE/CCI. "Rvside site; new owners (2011); gd san facs; easy walk to pretty vill; vg." ♦ ltd 20 Jun-19 Sep. € 13.00 2011*

GOUAREC *2E3* (600m SW Rural) *48.22555, -3.18307* **Camping Tost Aven, Au Bout du Pont, 22570 Gouarec [tel/fax 02 96 24 87 86; bertrand.cocherel@orange.fr; www.brittanycamping.com]** Sp fr town cent bet rv & canal. Med, mkd pitch, pt shd; wc (some cont); chem disp; shwrs inc; el pnts (10A) €2.40; gas adj; Indry rm; shops adj; supmkt nr; rest, snacks, bar 500m; BBQ; sm playgrnd; sw adj (rv & canal); cycle, canoe hire; entmnt; dogs; bus 200m; Eng spkn; adv bkg; quiet. "Clean, tidy site bet Nantes-Brest canal & rv on edge of vill; towpath for cycling; great!" ♦ ltd 1 May-15 Sep. € 10.00 2013*

GOUDELIN *2E3* (3km NE Rural) *48.61433, -2.99288* **Camping à la Ferme Kérogel (Le Faucheur), 22290 Goudelin [tel/fax 02 96 70 03 15; kerogel@wanadoo.fr; www.kerogel.com]** NE fr Guingamp on D9 to Goudelin. Fr cent of vill take rd dir Lanvollon, site sp on R. Sm, pt sl, pt shd; wc; chem disp (wc); shwrs inc; el pnts (6A) inc; Indry rm; tradsmn; rest, snacks, bar 3km; BBQ; playgrnd; games rm; dogs €0.50; Eng spkn; adv bkg; quiet; CKE/CCI. "Well-kept farm site; lge pitches; clean facs; helpful owner; gd touring base away fr cr coastal sites." ♦ 1 Apr-30 Sep. € 13.85 2011*

GUEGON see Josselin *2F3*

⊞ **GUERCHE DE BRETAGNE, LA** *2F4* (6km E Rural) *47.94383, -1.17233* **Camp Municipal, 35130 La Selle-Guerchaise [02 99 96 46 72]** Fr N on D178 Vitré to Châteaubriant rd 3km N of of La Guerche-de-Bretagne; turn L onto D106 to Availles-sur-Seiche, then foll sp La Selle-Guerchaise; site behind Mairie in vill. Sm, hdg/mkd pitch, pt sl, pt shd; htd wc; chem disp (wc); shwrs inc; el pnts (4A); (rev pol, poss long cable req); Indtte; playgrnd, multisports area; fishing adj; 50% statics; dogs; adv bkg; poss noisy; CKE/CCI. "Welcoming; gd san facs; fair NH." ♦ 2009*

GUERNO, LE see Muzillac *2G3*

GUIDEL see Pouldu, Le *2F2*

GUILVINEC *2F2* (2.5km W Coastal) *47.80388, -4.31222* **Yelloh! Village la Plage, Chemin des Allemands, Penmarc'h, 29760 Guilvinec [02 98 58 61 90; fax 02 98 58 89 06; info@yellohvillage-la-plage.com; www.villagelaplage.com / www.yellohvillage.co.uk]** Fr Quimper, Pont l'Abbé on D785 SW to Plomeur; turn S onto D57 sp Guilvinec. Bear R on app to town & v soon after turn R sp Chapelle de Tremor. Foll site to site in 1.5km. Lge, pt shd; wc; chem disp; mv service pnt; baby facs; sauna; shwrs inc; el pnts (5A) inc; gas; Indtte (inc dryer); shop; rest, snacks; bar; BBQ; playgrnd; 2 htd pools (1 covrd); paddling pool; waterslide; direct accesss sand beach adj; tennis; archery; games rm; fitness rm; cycle hire; wifi; entmnt; 70% statics; dogs €4; no c'vans/m'vans over 8m high ssn; poss cr; adv bkg; quiet; ccard acc; red low ssn. "Ideal for families; spacious pitches; site rds poss diff lge o'fits; excel touring base; mkt Tue & Sun." ♦ 12 Apr-14 Sep. € 43.00 SBS - B15 2011*

GUILVINEC *2F2* (3.5km NW Coastal) *47.81819, -4.30942* **Camping Les Genêts, Rue Gouesnac'h Nevez, 29760 Penmarc'h [02 98 58 66 93 or 06 83 15 85 92 (mob); campinglesgenets29@orange.fr; www.camping-lesgenets.com]** S fr Pont-l'Abbé on D785 to Plomeur; cont on D785 for another 4km, then turn L onto D53 sp Guilvinec; in 300m turn L into Rue Gouesnac'h Nevez to site. Med, hdg/mkd pitch, pt shd; htd wc; chem disp; baby facs; shwrs inc; el pnts (10A) €3.40; gas; Indtte; ice; tradsmn; rest, snacks; bar; BBQ; playgrnd, htd pool; covrd pool & waterslide planned (2010); sand beach 1.5km; cycle hire nrby; horseriding 800m; games area; games rm; wifi; entmnt; TV rm; 25% statics; dogs €2; bus; phone; poss cr; Eng spkn; adv bkg; red low ssn/long stay; CKE/CCI. "Peaceful, well-kept site in beautiful, unspoilt area; family-run; friendly atmosphere; welcoming, helpful owners; easy access to spacious pitches; excel, clean, modern san facs; gd value; excel." ♦ 1 Apr-30 Sep. € 22.00 (CChq acc) 2013*

GUIPRY see Bain de Bretagne *2F4*

GUISSENY see Plouguerneau *2E2*

HENNEBONT see Lorient *2F2*

HENVIC see St Pol de Léon *1D2*

HILLION see St Brieuc *2E3*

HUELGOAT *2E2* (3km E Rural) *48.36275, -3.71532* **FFCC Camping La Rivière d'Argent, La Coudraie, 29690 Huelgoat [02 98 99 72 50; fax 02 98 99 90 61; campriviere@orange.fr; www.larivieredargent.com]** Sp fr town cent on D769A sp Poullaouen & Carhaix. Med, some hdg/mkd pitch, shd; wc; chem disp; mv service pnt; shwrs inc; el pnts (6-10A) €3.60-4.30; Indtte; shops 3km; rest, snacks, playgrnd; pool, tennis & entmnt high ssn; dogs €1.60; adv bkg; quiet; red long stay/low ssn. "Lovely wooded site on rv bank; some rvside pitches; helpful owner; ltd facs low ssn; gd walks with maps provided; Shwrs and cabinas locked o'night; water not V hot, san facs well maintained." 10 Apr-12 Oct. € 15.50 2012*

HUELGOAT *2E2* (800m W Rural) *48.36388, -3.76361* **Camp Municipal du Lac, Le Faô, 29690 Huelgoat [02 98 99 78 80; fax 02 98 99 75 72; mairie.huelgoat@wanadoo.fr]** Fr cent of Huelgoat foll unnumbered rd W sp La Feuillée/Brest; foll site sp. Med, pt hdstg pitch, pt shd; wc; chem disp; shwrs inc; el pnts (3-10A) €2.10; Indry rm; shops 600m; rest, bar 500m; playgrnd; htd pool adj; dogs €1.20; no adv bkg; quiet; no ccard acc; CKE/CCI. "Peaceful site at end of lake (no sw); gd size pitches; gd san facs; gd walking." Jul-Aug. € 11.40 2009*

JOSSELIN *2F3* (1.5km W Rural) *47.95230, -2.57338* **Domaine de Kerelly, Le bas de la lande; 56120 Guégon [02 97 22 22 20 or 06 27 57 22 79 (mob); domainedekerelly@orange.fr; www.camping-josselin.com]** Exit N24 by-pass W of town sp Guégon; foll sp 1km; do not attempt to cross Josselin cent fr E to W. Site on D724 just S of Rv Oust (canal). Med, hdg pitch, terr, pt shd; wc; chem disp; mv service pnt; baby facs; shwrs inc; el pnts (6-10A) €3.80-4.50; Indtte; shops 2km; tradsmn; rest; snacks; bar high ssn; BBQ; playgrnd; pool; wifie; tv rm; cycle hire; dogs; phone; Eng spkn; adv bkg; quiet but rd noise; ccard acc; red low ssn/CKE/CCI. "Vg, clean san facs; site rds steep; pleasant walks; poss diff if wet; walk to Josselin, chateau & old houses; gd cycling; family run; gd food; mini golf." ♦ 1 Apr-31 Oct. € 19.80 2014*

JUGON LES LACS *2E3* (S Rural) *48.40166, -2.31678* **Camping au Bocage du Lac, Rue Du Bocage, 22270 Jugon-les-Lacs [02 96 31 60 16; fax 02 96 31 75 04; contact@campinglacbretagne.com; www.camping-location-bretagne.com]** Bet Dinan & Lamballe by N176. Foll 'Camping Jeux' sp on D52 fr Jugon-les-Lacs. Situated by lakes, sp fr cent of Jugon. Lge, pt sl, pt shd; wc; mv service pnt; baby facs; shwrs inc; el pnts (10A) €3-4.60; Indtte; shops adj; tradsmn; bar; playgrnd; htd pool; paddling pool; waterslide; fishing & watersports in lake/rv adj; games area; games rm; entmnt; TV; some statics; dogs €3.20; adv bkg; red low ssn. "Well-situated nr pretty vill; many sports & activities; vg, modern san facs; vg, attractive site." 5 Apr-27 Sep. € 24.90 (CChq acc) 2013*

See advertisement

LAMBALLE *2E3* (700m NE Urban) *48.47576, -2.50472* **Camp Municipal, Rue St Sauveur, 22400 Lamballe [02 96 34 74 33 or 02 96 50 13 50 (LS)]** NE side of town beyond church; nr water tower. Clearly sp. Sm, mkd pitch, terr, pt shd; wc; shwrs inc; el pnts (5A) €3.20; shops 700m; htd pool 700m; dogs free; quiet. "Interesting town, historic 17thC church." 1 Jul-2 Sep. € 9.00 2009*

LAMPAUL PLOUDALMESEAU *2E1* (500m NW Coastal) *48.56780, -4.65674* **Camp Municipal Les Dunes, Le Vourc'h, 29830 Lampaul-Ploudalmézon [02 98 48 14 29 or 02 98 48 11 28; fax 02 98 48 19 32; lampaul-ploudalmezeau.mairie@wanadoo.fr; www.vacanceseniroise.com]** Exit Ploudalmézeau E on D28 dir St Pabu & Lannilis; in 500m turn L at campsite sp onto C1 Route du Bourg (opp picnic site on R); foll rd & sp to site on beach. Med, pt sl, pt shd; wc; mv service pnt; shwrs inc; el pnts €2.40; Indry rm; shops 5km; tradsmn; snacks & bar 1km; playgrnd; sand beach adj; games area; dogs; phone; bus adj; quiet. "Spacious site nr amazing sandy beach used for many non-motorised water sports; san facs dated but clean; vg." ♦ ltd 15 Jun-15 Sep. € 10.20 2011*

LANDEBIA see Plancoët *2E3*

BRITTANY

LANDEDA *2E1* (2km NW Coastal) *48.59333, -4.60333* **Camping des Abers, 51 Toull Tréaz, Plage de Ste Marguerite, 29870 Landéda [02 98 04 93 35; fax 02 98 04 84 35; info@camping-des-abers.com; www.camping-des-abers.com]** Exit N12/E50 at junc with D788 & take D13 to Lannilis. Then take D128A to Landéda & foll green site sp. Lge, some hdg/mkd pitch, terr, pt shd; wc; chem disp; mv service pnt; baby facs; fam bthrm; shwrs €0.80; el pnts (10A) €3 (long lead poss req); gas; lndtte (inc dryer); shop & snacks in ssn; rest & bar 200m; BBQ; playgrnd; sand beach adj; fishing; cycle hire; wifi; entmnt; games/TV rm; 10% statics; dogs €2.20; Eng spkn; no c'vans/m'vans over 8m high ssn; adv bkg (rec high ssn); quiet; ccard acc; red low ssn/long stay; CKE/CCI. "Attractive, landscaped site on wild coast; views fr high pitches; friendly, helpful manager; san facs clean, some new, others old; some pitches muddy when wet; access to many pitches by grass tracks, some sloping; gd walks, cycling; excel." ♦ 1 May-29 Sep. € 24.00 SBS - B30 2013*

LANDEDA *2E1* (3km NW Coastal) *48.60310, -4.59882* **Camp Municipal de Penn-Enez, 29870 Landéda [02 98 04 99 82; info@camping-penn-enez.com; www.camping-penn-enez.com]** Proceed NW thro Landéda, turn R in 1km sp Penn-Enez then L in 600m. Site sp. Med, pt hdg pitch, pt sl, unshd; wc; chem disp (wc); shwrs €1; el pnts (16A) €2.80; playgrnd; sand beach 500m; 2% statics; dogs €1.65; Eng spkn; quiet. "Site on grassy headland; beach views fr some pitches; site self if warden absent; friendly, helpful staff; vg clean san facs; gd walks; excel." ♦ ltd 25 Apr-30 Sep. € 16.20 2014*

LANDERNEAU *2E2* (1.6km SW Urban) *48.44575, -4.25854* **Camp Municipal Les Berges de l'Elorn, Route de Calvaire, 29800 Landerneau [02 98 85 44 94 or 02 98 85 00 66 (Mairie); fax 02 98 85 43 35; ti-ker-landerne@mairie-landerneau.fr; www.ville-landerneau.fr]** Site S of rv. Foll sps to pool, sports stadium & site. Sm, hdg pitch, hdstg, pt shd; wc; chem disp; mv service pnt; shwrs €0.50; el pnts (7A) €3.35; shops; rest; snacks bar 250m; BBQ; playgrnd adj; pool 500m; tennis; dogs €1.15; phone adj; Eng spkn; adv bkg; quiet, some rd noise; CKE/CCI. "Historic, pretty town on tidal rv; conv touring base. Note: An Aire de Service for m'vans 100m E of site on same rd." ♦ Apr-Oct. € 9.60 2014*

LANDIVISIAU *2E2* (9.3km NE Urban) *48.57724, -4.03006* **Camp Municipal Lanorgant, 29420 Plouvorn [02 98 61 32 40 (Mairie); fax 02 98 61 38 87; commune-de-plouvorn@wanadoo.fr; www.plouvorn.com]** Fr Landivisiau, take D69 N twd Roscoff. In 8km turn R onto D19 twd Morlaix. Site sp, in 700m turn R. NB Care req entry/exit, poss diff lge o'fits. Sm, hdg/mkd pitch, terr, pt shd; wc (cont for men); mv service pnt; shwrs; el pnts (10A) €2; lndtte; shops, snacks, bar 500m; rest 1km; BBQ; playgrnd; sand beach; lake sw; sailboards & canoes for hire; fishing; tennis; adv bkg; quiet. "Ideal NH for ferries; lge pitches; nr lake." 26 Jun-15 Sep. € 10.00 2009*

LANDRELLEC see Trégastel *1D2*

LANDUDEC *2F2* (2km SW Rural) *47.99190, -4.35353* **Camping Domaine de Bel-Air, Keridreuff, 29710 Landudec [02 98 91 50 27; fax 02 98 91 55 82; camping-dubelair@wanadoo.fr; www.belaircamping.com]** Fr N165 exit dir Quimper Cent. On ring rd foll sp Douarnenez & Audierne & exit ring rd onto D765 immed after Carrefour supmkt sp Douarnenez. Turn L at rndabt onto D784 dir Audierne/Landudec. Strt on at traff lts in Landudec, site on L in 750m. Lge, hdg/mkd pitch, terr, pt shd; wc; chem disp; shwrs inc; el pnts (10A) inc; gas; lndtte; shop; tradsmn; rest, snacks; playgrnd; htd pool; paddling pool; beach 10km; lake adj; waterslide; watersports; tennis; games rm; entmnt; TV; dogs €2; poss cr; Eng spkn; adv bkg; quiet; ccard acc; red low ssn; CKE/CCI. "Well-situated, family site; excel." ♦ 1 May-30 Sep. € 24.00 2009*

LANILDUT *2E1* (1km N Coastal) *48.48012, -4.75184* **Camping du Tromeur, 11 Route du Camping, 29840 Lanildut [02 98 04 31 13; tromeur@vive-les-vacances.com; www.vive-les-vacances.com/tromeur]** Site well sp on app rds to vill. Med; wc; chem disp (wc); shwrs inc; el pnts €3 (poss long lead req & poss rev pol); lndry rm; tradsmn; shop, bar, crêperie & gd rest in vill; BBQ; dogs €1; phone; quiet. "Clean, sheltered site; san facs gd; harbour & sm beach; low ssn warden am & pm only - site yourself." 1 May-30 Sep. € 9.00 2014*

LANLOUP *2E3* (350m W Rural) *48.71369, -2.96711* **FFCC Camping Le Neptune, 22580 Lanloup [02 96 22 33 35; fax 02 96 22 68 45; contact@leneptune.com; www.leneptune.com]** Take D786 fr St Brieuc or Paimpol to Lanloup, site sp. NB Take care Sat Nav dirs (2011). Med, hdg/mkd pitch, pt shd; wc (some cont); chem disp; mv service pnt; baby facs; shwrs inc; el pnts (10A) €4 (long lead poss req); gas; lndtte (inc dryer); shop (high ssn) or 500m; tradsmn; rest 2km; snacks, bar (high ssn) or 500m; BBQ; playgrnd; htd, covrd pool; sand beach 2km; tennis 300m; horseriding 4km; cycle hire; wifi; TV rm; 15% statics; dogs €3; phone; poss cr; Eng spkn; adv bkg; quiet, rd noise some pitches; red low ssn; CKE/CCI. "Excel, well-maintained site nr beautiful coast; various pitch sizes; clean san facs; friendly, helpful owner; highly rec." ♦ 3 Apr-17 Oct. € 21.00 (CChq acc) 2011*

⊞ **LANNION** *1D2* (2.6km SE Urban) *48.72300, -3.44600* **Camp Municipal Les Deux Rives, Rue du Moulin du Duc, 22300 Lannion [02 96 46 31 40 or 02 96 46 64 22; fax 02 96 46 53 35; infos@ville.lannion.fr; www.ville-lannion.fr]** SW fr Perros-Guirec on D788 to Lannion; fr Lannion town cent foll dir Guincamp on D767; site well sp, approx 1.5km, turn R at Leclerc supmkt (do not confuse with hypmkt). Fr S on D767 sp at rndabts; turn L at Leclerc supmkt. Med, mkd pitch, unshd; wc; chem disp; shwrs inc; el pnts (6A) €2.50; lndtte; shop high ssn & 1km; bar high ssn; playgrnd; security barrier; dogs €1.10; adv bkg; red low ssn; CKE/CCI. "Rvside walk to old town; vg, clean san facs; phone ahead low ssn to check open; warden lives on site but poss no arr acc Sun." ♦ € 19.85 2014*

LANNION *1D2* (4km NW Rural) *48.75143, -3.50693* **Kawan Village Les Alizés, Route de Trébeurden, 22300 Lannion [tel/fax 02 96 47 28 58; info@camping-lesalizes.fr; www.camping-lesalizes.fr]** D65 fr Lannion twd Trébeurden, site sp on L. Med, pt shd; wc; baby facs; shwrs; el pnts (10A) inc; Indtte (inc dryer); shop 2km; tradsmn; rest 3km; snacks; bar; BBQ; playgrnd; 2 pools (1 htd, covrd); paddling pool; waterslide; sand beach 3.5km; games area; games rm; wifi; entmnt; 60% statics; dogs €2; adv bkg; quiet; red low ssn. "Vg touring base." ♦ 1 Apr-1 Oct. € 24.00 (CChq acc) 2010*

LANNION *1D2* (8km NW Coastal) *48.73833, 3.54500* **FFCC Camping Les Plages de Beg-Léguer, Route de la Côte, 22300 Lannion [02 96 47 25 00; fax 02 96 47 27 77; info@campingdesplages.com; www.campingdesplages.com]** Fr Lannion take rd out of town twd Trébeurden then twd Servel on D65, then head SW off that rd twd Beg Léguer (sp). Lge, hdg/mkd pitch, pt shd; wc (some cont); chem disp; mv service pnt; baby facs; shwrs inc; el pnts (6A) €3.50 (poss long lead req); gas; Indtte; sm shop & 5km; tradsmn; rest, snacks; bar; playgrnd; htd, covrd pool; paddling pool; sand beach 500m; fishing; sailing; windsurfing; tennis; wifi; TV; 20% statics; dogs €1; phone; bus 400m; Eng spkn; adv bkg; quiet; red long stay/low ssn; ccard acc; red CKE/CCI. "Pleasant, peaceful, wel-run family site; charming French owner who speaks excel Eng; superb pool complex & vg children's play area; lge grass pitches; immac, modern san facs; one of the best sites in France; many superb rest in nrby seaside resorts; stunning beaches." ♦ 12 Apr-2 Nov. € 39.00 2014*

"Satellite navigation makes touring much easier"

Remember most sat navs don't know if you're towing or in a larger vehicle – always use yours alongside maps and site directions.

LANVEOC *2E2* (1km N Coastal) *48.29176, -4.46072* **Camp Municipal La Cale, Route de la Grève, 29160 Lanvéoc [02 98 27 58 91]** N fr Crozon dir Roscanvel. After approx 5.5km turn R onto D55 for Lanvéoc. Site sp. Med, mkd pitch, terr, unshd; shwrs inc; el pnts (10A) €2.90; Indtte; rest, snacks; bar; dir access to coast; fishing; no statics; dogs €1; quiet; CKE/CCI. "Sea views; low ssn unisex san facs; site rd steep with sharp bends to upper levels." 1 Jun-15 Sep. € 8.00 2009*

LESCONIL see Pont l'Abbé *2F2*

LOCMARIAQUER *2G3* (800m N Rural) *47.57339, -2.95774* **Camping La Ferme Fleurie, Kerlogonan, 56740 Locmariaquer [tel/fax 02 97 57 34 06; www.campinglafermefleurie.com]** Sp off D781. Sm, mkd pitch, pt shd; wc; shwrs inc; el pnts (10A) €2.50; shop; Indtte; playgrnd; beach 1km; fishing; sailing; entmnt; some statics; dogs €1; adv bkg ess high ssn; quiet. "Lovely, well-kept CL-type site in great position; coastal path nr; attractive area; friendly; excel, clean facs but poss stretched when site full; midge repellent rec; unrel opening dates - phone ahead low ssn; conv megalith sites." 15 Mar-20 Oct. € 13.80 2010*

LOCMARIAQUER *2G3* (2km S Coastal) *47.55598, -2.93939* **Camp Municipal de la Falaise, Route de Kerpenhir, 56740 Locmariaquer [tel/fax 02 97 57 31 59 or 02 97 57 32 32 (LS); campinglafalaise@wanadoo.fr; www.campingmunicipallafalaise.com]** Site sp fr Locmariaquer. On ent vill, site sp R avoiding narr cent (also sp fr vill cent). Lge, mkd pitch, pt sl; wc (some cont); shwrs; chem disp; mv service pnt; el pnts (6A) inc; gas; Indtte; shop 1km tradsmn; rest & 500m; playgrnd; sand beach adj; entmnt (high ssn); dogs €2.10; poss cr; ccard acc. "Gd, quiet site in pleasant countryside; clean san facs, some modern & some dated; archaeological remains; gd fishing, boating, cycling & coastal walking; rest simple but superb food." ♦ 15 Mar-15 Oct. € 16.60 2013*

LOCMARIAQUER *2G3* (2km NW Coastal) *47.57982, -2.97394* **Camping Lann Brick, Lieu Dit Lann-Brick, 56740 Locmariaquer [02 97 57 32 79 or 06 42 22 29 69 (mob); camping.lanbrick@wanadoo.fr; www.camping-lannbrick.com]** N165/E60, exit Crach via D28 dir Locmariaquer. L Onto D781. Sp on R 2km bef Locmariaquer. Med, hdg/ mkd pitch, shd; wc (cont); chem disp; mv service pnt; baby facs; shwr inc; el pnts (6/10A); Indtte (inc dryer); shop 2.5km; tradsmn; snack; bar; BBQ; playgrnd; htd pool; paddling pool; beach 0.5km; bike hire; entmnt; wifi; tv rm; 40% statics; dogs €2.60; phone; bus adj; twin axles; Eng spkn; adv bkg; quiet; ccard acc; red low ssn; CKE/CCI. "Excel; quiet well managed site; helpful & friendly owners; facs well maintained & spotless; easy walk to beach; delightful site; gd location for Gulf of Morbihan; easy cycle rte." ♦ ltd 15 Apr-15 Oct. € 28.00 2014*

⊞ **LOCQUIREC** *2E2* (1.5km SW Coastal) *48.67940, -3.65320* **Camping Municipal Du fond de la Baie, Route de Plestin, 29241 Locquirec [02 98 67 40 85; campingdufonddelabaie@gmail.com; www.campinglocquirec.com]** Fr D786 Morlaix-Lannion, turn L (traff lts) at Plestin-Les-Graves onto D42. At T junc on reaching Bay turn L onto D64. Site on R on app Locquirec. Lge, mkd pitch, pt shd; wc; chem disp; mv service pnt; shwrs; gas; Indtte; shop; rest; snacks; bar; BBQ; sand beach adj; entmnt; wifi; 6% statics; dogs €1; phone; bus adj; twin axles; Eng spkn; adv bkg; quiet; Ccard acc; red low ssn. "Beautifully situated beachside site; vill 1.5km; flat site; fishing, boating & shellfishing." ♦ € 24.00 2014*

LOCRONAN *2E2* (1km ESE Urban) *48.09657, -4.19774* **Camping de Locronan, Rue de la Troménie, 29180 Locronan [02 98 91 87 76 / 06 28 80 44 74; contact@camping-locronan.fr; www.camping-locronan.fr]** Fr Quimper/Douarnenez foll sp D7 Châteaulin; ignore town sp, take 1st R after 3rd rndabt. Fr Châteaulin, turn L at 1st town sp & foll site sp at sharp L turn. NB Foll sp around town, do not ent Locronan. Med, hdg pitch, steeply terr, pt shd; wc; chem disp; baby facs; fam bathrm; shwrs; el pnts (10A) €4.30; Indtte (inc dryer); shops 1.5km; tradsmn; rest & bar 400m; playgrnd; htd covrd pool; paddling pool; games area; wifi; dogs €2.20; phone; Eng spkn; adv bkg (rec indicate o'fit size when bkg); quiet; ccard acc; CKE/CCI. "Gd touring cent with gd views; gd walks; historic town; excel; ltd san facs low ssn." ♦ 13 Apr-10 Nov. € 32.30 (CChq acc) 2013*

LOCUNOLE see Quimperle *2F2*

⊞ **LORIENT** *2F2* (6km N Rural) *47.82041, -3.40689* **Camping Ty Nénez, Route de Lorient, 56620 Pont-Scorff [02 97 32 51 16; fax 02 97 32 43 77; contact@camping-tynenez.com; www.lorient-camping.com]** N fr N165 on D6, look for sp Quéven in approx 5km on R. If missed, cont for 1km & turn around at rndabt. Site sp fr Pont-Scorff. Med, hdg pitch, pt shd; htd wc; chem disp; mv service pnt; baby facs; shwrs inc; el pnts (16A) €3; Indtte; supmkt 1km; bar; games area; some statics; dogs €1; adv bkg; quiet; red low ssn. "Site barrier locked 2200-0800; excel low ssn; peaceful NH." ♦ € 10.00 2010*

LORIENT *2F2* (10km NE Rural) *47.80582, -3.28347* **Camp Municipal St Caradec, Quai St Caradec, 56700 Hennebont [02 97 36 21 73; camping.municipal.stcaradec@wanadoo.fr]** Fr S on D781 to Hennebont. In town cent turn L & cross bdge, then sharp R along Rv Blavet for 1km. On R on rv bank. Med, mkd pitch, pt shd; wc; chem disp; shwrs inc; el pnts inc; Indtte; shop 2km; playgrnd; sand beach 12km; some statics; adv bkg; quiet; CKE/CCI. "Pretty site." 15 Jun-15 Sep. 2009*

⊞ **LORIENT** *2F2* (4km SW Coastal) *47.70955, -3.39228* **Camping La Fontaine, Rue de Québello, Kerderff, 56260 Larmor-Plage [02 97 33 71 28 or 02 97 65 11 11; fax 02 97 33 70 32; contact@campingdelafontaine.com; www.camping-la-fontaine.com]** At Larmor-Plage 300m fr D152. Well sp. Med, hdg pitch, pt sl, pt shd; htd wc; mv service pnt; chem disp; baby facs; shwrs inc; el pnts (10A) €2.45 (rev pol); Indtte; shop adj; snacks; bar; playgrnd; beach 800m; tennis adj; horseriding; sailing; sports; dogs €1.55; Eng spkn. "Excel site; gd facs." ♦ € 15.00 2009*

LOUDEAC *2E3* (2km E Rural) *48.17827, -2.73010* **Camp Municipal Pont es Bigots, 22600 Loudéac [02 96 28 14 92 or 02 96 66 85 00 (Mairie); fax 02 96 66 08 93; mairie.loudeac@wanadoo.fr; www.ville-loudeac.fr]** Fr Loudéac, take N164 twd Rennes, site on L by lake in 1km, sp. Height barrier into site 1.8m. Med, hdg pitch, pt shd; wc; shwrs; el pnts €2; shops 1km; playgrnd; entmnt; lake sw; fishing; horseriding; quiet. "V pleasant; site clsd 1100-1700." 15 Jun-15 Sep. € 6.35 2009*

LOYAT see Ploërmel *2F3*

MALESTROIT *2F3* (500m E Urban) *47.80865, -2.37922* **Camp Municipal de la Daufresne, Chemin des Tanneurs, 56140 Malestroit [02 97 75 13 33 or 02 97 75 11 75 (Mairie); fax 02 97 73 71 13; tourisme@malestroit.com; www.malestroit.com]** S fr Ploërmel on N166 dir Vannes for 9km. Turn L onto D764 to Malestroit; site sp just off Blvd du Pont Neuf on E bank of Rv Oust, not well sp. Sm, some hdg pitch, pt shd; wc; chem disp; mv service pnt; shwrs inc; el pnts (10A) €2.70 (poss long lead req); Indtte; shop, rest, snacks, bar 300m; playgrnd; tennis; adv bkg; rv & fishing adj; canoeing nr; dogs free; poss cr; ccard not acc; CKE/CCI. "Pleasant site in excel location; narr site rds, some pitches poss diff to manoeuvre; no twin-axles; clean san facs poss stretched high ssn; canal towpath adj; gd cycle rtes; Museum of Breton Resistance in St Marcel; v nice site, highly rec." ♦ ltd 1 May-15 Sep. € 10.35 2012*

MATIGNON see St Cast le Guildo *2E3*

MERDRIGNAC *2E3* (1.9km N Rural) *48.19786, -2.41622* **Camping Le Val de Landrouët, 14 rue du Gouède, 22230 Merdrignac [02 96 28 47 98; fax 02 96 26 55 44; contact@valdelandrouet.com; www.valdelandrouet.com]** Sp fr town cent, 500m fr town on D793 twd Broons, site on L. Med, hdg/mkd pitch, pt sl, pt shd; wc; chem disp; mv service point (emptying only); baby facs; shwrs inc; el pnts (4A) €3; Indtte; shops adj; bar; BBQ; playgrnd; htd pool; entmnt; tennis; lake sw 3km; fishing; 5% statics; dogs; phone adj; bus adj; twin axles; adv bkg; quiet; ccard acc; CKE/CCI. "Superb, spacious site; gd touring ctr; activities adj; excel." 1 May-30 Sep. € 15.00 2014*

MOELAN SUR MER see Pont Aven *2F2*

MONTERBLANC see Vannes *2F3*

MORLAIX *2E2* (13km N Coastal) *48.65950, -3.84847* **Camping De La Baie de Terenez, 29252 Plouezoch [02 98 67 26 80; campingbaiedeterenez@wanadoo.fr; www.campingbaiedeterenez.com]** Take D46 on exit Morlaix, turn L on D76 to site. Lge, pt sl, pt shd; wc; shwrs inc; el pnts (6A) €3.20; gas; Indtte; baby facs; bar; snacks; shop & 3km; sand beach 2km; playgrnd adj; games rm; tv rm; mv service pnt; htd pool; fishing; windsurfing; dogs; wifi; adv bkg; quiet. ♦ 5 Apr-28 Sep. € 26.45 2014*

"There aren't many sites open at this time of year"

If you're travelling outside peak season remember to call ahead to check site opening dates – even if the entry says 'open all year'.

MORLAIX *2E2* (6km NE Rural) *48.61583, -3.76822* **Camping Vert de Morlaix (Berric), Ferme de Kerroyal, Bois de La Roche, 29610 Garlan [02 98 79 12 54 or 06 14 39 21 61 (mob); fax 02 98 63 24 47; nills.bretagne@wanadoo.fr]** Fr Morlaix take D786 dir Lannion; in 6km turn R; farm on L in 1km. Foll blue & white camping sps. Clearly sp fr D786. Sm, hdg pitch, pt shd; wc; chem disp forbidden (2009); shwrs inc; el pnts €2; bar (in ssn); Indtte; playgrnd; htd pool 5km; TV; dogs; quiet; ccard not acc. "Pleasant CL-type site; goats, pony & duckpond; conv Roscoff & Marlaix; gd." ♦ Easter-31 Oct. € 10.00 2009*

MORLAIX *2E2* (11km E Rural) *48.60283, -3.73833* **Camping Aire Naturelle la Ferme de Croas Men (Cotty), Garlan, 29610 Plouigneau [tel/fax 02 98 79 11 50; fermecroasmen@free.fr; http://camping.croamen.pagesperso-orange.fr]** Fr D712 rndabt W of Plouigneau twd Morlaix (exit fr N12) 2km R sp Garlan; thro Garlan site 1km on L, well sp. Sm, hdg pitch, pt shd; wc; 50% serviced pitches; chem disp; baby facs; shwrs; el pnts (6A) €3.20; playgrnd; horseriding 200m; farm museum; donkey/tractor rides; some statics; dogs €1; Eng spkn (daughter); quiet; CKE/CCI. "Lovely, well-kept CL-type farm site; excel facs; ideal for children; produce avail inc cider & crêpes." ♦ 1 Apr-31 Oct. € 11.40 2010*

MOUSTERLIN see Fouesnant *2F2*

MUR DE BRETAGNE *2E3* (6km N Rural) *48.25568, -2.98801* **Camping Le Boterff d'en Haut, 22320 St Mayeux [02 96 24 00 65; info@leboterff.com; www.brittanyforholidays.com]** N fr Mur-de-Bretagne on D767 to St Mayeux. Turn R into vill & R after vill hall (Salle Municipal); to T-junc, turn R & site on L. App via 750m single-track lane. Car parking in rd outside. Sm, unshd; wc; chem disp; shwrs inc; el pnts (6A) inc; gas 8km; shops, snacks & bar 2km; rest 5km; BBQ; lake sw & watersports 8km; adv bkg; dogs €1 (2 max); quiet; ccard not acc; red low ssn/long stay. "Peaceful, remote CL-type site; gd san facs; gd touring cent; gd walks & cycling; when wet, cars parked off site; excel; (2013) Chgd owner, still British, v welcoming; superb CL type site; beautiful area." € 20.00 2013*

MUR DE BRETAGNE *2E3* (2km SW Rural) *48.19872, -3.01282* **Camping Le Point de Vue, 104 Rue du Lac, 22530 Mur-de-Bretagne [02 96 26 01 90; fax 02 96 28 59 44; camping-lepointdevue@orange.fr; www.camping-lepointdevue.fr]** Fr Mur-de-Bretagne take D18 & foll site sp; ent opp view point of Lake Guerlédan. Med, terr, pt sl, pt shd; wc (mainly cont); chem disp; shwrs inc; el pnts (10A) inc; lndry rm; shops, rest 1.5km; bar 50m; playgrnd; sand beach/lake 500m; dogs €1; poss cr; wifi; quiet; CKE/CCI. "Gd watersports; hot water may be ltd to a few hrs a day in low ssn; gd walking & cycling around lake." ♦ 15 Feb-15 Nov. € 15.00 2013*

MUR DE BRETAGNE *2E3* (4km NW Rural) *48.20950, -3.05150* **Camping Nautic International, Route de Beau Rivage, 22530 Caurel [02 96 28 57 94; fax 02 96 26 02 00; contact@campingnautic.fr; www.campingnautic.fr]** Fr Loudéac on N164 into Caurel. Fork L 100m past church, site is 1st on L, beside Lac de Guerlédan. NB App fr Pontivy on D767 via Mur-de-Bretagne v steep in places & not rec when towing. Med, mkd pitch, terr, pt shd; wc (some cont); chem disp; mv service pnt; baby facs; sauna; shwrs inc; el pnts (10A)€4.90; Indtte (inc dryer); shop (high ssn); BBQ; playgrnd; htd pool; paddling pool; jacuzzi; lake fishing; watersports & horseriding nr; cycle hire; tennis; fitness rm; games/TV rm; sauna; dogs €2.50; adv bkg; no c'vans/m'vans over 8m; quiet; ccard acc; red low ssn; CKE/CCI. "Peaceful site in attractive countryside by lake; gd pitches, some poss diff lge o'fits; dated facs, poss stretched when site full; wonderful pool & lake." ♦ 15 May-25 Sep. € 24.00 2013*

MUZILLAC *2G3* (12km N Rural) *47.66220, -2.46837* **Camp Municipal de l'Etang de Célac, Route de Damgan, 56230 Questembert [02 97 26 11 24 or 02 97 26 11 38 (LS); fax 02 97 26 54 15; accueil@mairie-questembert.fr; www.questembert.com]** Fr N on N166, at Bohal exit onto D5 to Questembert; in town turn R dir La Vraie-Croix; site in 1km on D1C, by lake. Camping sp in town. Med, mkd pitch, pt sl, pt shd; htd wc (some cont); chem disp; mv service pnt; shwrs inc; el pnts (12A) €2.90; lndry rm; supmkt 500m; rest nrby; playgrnd; fishing; games rm; TV rm; dogs €1.50; quiet; CKE/CCI. "Site in attractive location by lake; nice pitches; clean san facs; diff access lge o'fits as ent zig-zags around concrete flower tubs; no twin-axles; m'van aire de service at ent; mkt Mon sp fr vill; vg." ♦ 15 Jun-15 Sep. € 11.35 2011*

MUZILLAC *2F3* (2.5km NE Rural) *47.56236, -2.44719* **Camping de la Blanche Hermine, Le Petit Boissignan, 56190 Muzillac [02 97 45 67 03 or 06 76 81 95 79 (mob); fax 02 97 45 67 06; info@lablanchehermine.fr; www.lablanchehermine.fr]** Exit Muzillac on D20 E dir Redon; site on R in 2.5km. Clearly sp. Med, hdg/mkd pitch, pt sl, shd; wc; chem disp; shwrs inc; el pnts (10A) €3.40; Indtte; snacks; bar; playgrnd; htd pool; paddling pool; games area; entmnt; wifi; 70% statics; dogs €2.10; red low ssn; CKE/CCI. "Gd site." 1 Apr-15 Oct. € 15.00 2011*

MUZILLAC *2G3* (7km NE Rural) *47.58261, -2.41582* **Camp Municipal Borgnehue, Le Borg-Nehué, 56190 Le Guerno [02 97 42 99 38 or 02 97 42 94 76 (Mairie); fax 02 97 42 84 36; mairie-leguerno@wanadoo.fr; www.camping-leguerno.com]** Exit N165 onto D139 dir Questembert. In 5km turn L onto D20 dir Muzillac then in 2km R onto D139A to Le Guerno. Just pass vill sp do not foll rd round to R into vill but take C104 strt for 100m, then foll camping sp. Site on R just after leaving Le Guerno. When turning R into site, keep to L. Sm, hdg pitch, pt shd; wc; chem disp (wc); mv service pnt; baby facs; shwrs inc; el pnts (6-10A) €2.14-3.25; Indtte; playgrnd; some statics; phone; adv bkg; quiet. "Warden high ssn only; book in at vill shop or Mairie (site clsd 1300-1600); pitches lge but poss diff lge o'fits - need to unhitch; gd site." 1 Apr-31 Oct. € 8.00 2010*

MUZILLAC *2G3* (8km SW Coastal) *47.51780, -2.55539* **Camping Ty Breiz, 15 Grande Rue, Kervoyal, 56750 Damgan [tel/fax 02 97 41 13 47; info@campingtybreiz.com; www.campingtybreiz.com]** Fr Muzillac on D153 dir Damgan, turn S for Kervoyal; site on L opp sm church. Med, hdg/mkd pitch, pt shd; wc; shwrs inc; el pnts (6-10A) €3-3.50; Indtte; wifi; playgrnd; sand beach 300m; dogs €1.50; Eng spkn; adv bkg rec high ssn; quiet; ccard acc; red low ssn; CKE/CCI. "Pleasant, welcoming, family-run site; excel san facs; quiet low ssn; cycle path to Damgan; mkt Wed; vg." ♦ 26 Apr-15 Oct. € 21.40 2012*

MUZILLAC *2G3* (4km W Coastal) *47.52552, -2.51231* **Camping Le Bédume, Bétahon-Plage, 56190 Ambon-Plages [02 97 41 68 13; fax 02 97 41 56 79; cledelles.ambon@free.fr; www.bedume.com]** Fr N165 take D20 W dir Ambon, foll to Bétahon, site sp. Lge, hdg pitch, pt shd; wc; chem disp; baby facs; shwrs inc; el pnts (5A) €4; Indtte; shop; tradsmn; snacks; bar; BBQ; playgrnd; htd pool; paddling pool; waterslide; sand beach adj; games area; games rm; entmnt; TV rm; 75% statics; dogs €2; Eng spkn; adv bkg req; quiet; ccard acc; red low ssn. ♦ 1 Apr-30 Sep. € 35.00 2009*

NEANT SUR YVEL *2F3* (3.5km N Rural) *48.04382, -2.33063* **Camping Koad-Ar-Roc'h (Naturist), Le Bois de la Roche, 56430 Néant-sur-Yvel [02 97 74 42 11; koad-ar-roc-h@wanadoo.fr; www.koad-ar-roch.com]** NE fr Ploërmel on D766 for 12km; D134 W for 3km to vill of Le Bois-de-la Roche & site ent in vill on L. Med, pt sl, pt shd; wc; chem disp (wc); mv service pnt in Mauron; shwrs inc; el pnts (6A) €3.50; shop; tradsmn; rest, snacks; bar; BBQ; playgrnd; pool; lake sw & fishing; games rm; TV; 10% statics; dogs €4; no twin axles; Eng spkn; adv bkg; quiet; ccard acc; INF card. "Unsophisticated, tranquil site in extensive grnds; friendly owners; lge pitches; gd walking & cycling." ♦ ltd 15 May-15 Sep. € 23.00 2010*

NEVEZ see Pont Aven *2F2*

PAIMPOL *1D3* (2.5km SE Coastal) *48.76966, -3.02209* **Camp Municipal Crukin, Rue de Crukin, Kérity, 22500 Paimpol [02 96 20 78 47 or 02 96 55 31 70 (Mairie); fax 02 96 20 75 00; contact@camping-paimpol.com; www.camping-paimpol.com]** On D786 fr St Brieuc/Paimpol, site sp in vill of Kérity 80m off main rd shortly bef abbey. Med, hdg pitch, pt shd; htd wc; chem disp; mv service pnt; baby facs; shwrs inc; el pnts (6A) €3.90 (poss rev pol); lndtte (inc dryer); shops 1km; tradsmn; playgrnd; shgl beach 250m; fishing; watersports; wifi; TV rm; 10% statics; dogs €2.10; bus 100m; poss cr; quiet; CKE/CCI. "Clean & tidy; sep m'van area; Beaufort Abbey nrby; excel sh stay/NH; plenty of space; facs ltd low ssn; walk to town along coast rd gd views." ♦ 1 Apr-4 Oct. € 16.55 2013*

PAIMPOL *1D3* (5km SE Coastal) *48.75993, -2.96233* **Camping Cap de Bréhat, Route de Port-Lazo, 22470 Plouézec [02 96 20 64 28; fax 02 96 20 63 88; info@cap-de-brehat.com; www.cap-de-brehat.com]** Site sp fr D786 at Plouézec dir Port-Lazo. Site 3km NE of Plouézec. Med, hdg/mkd pitch, pt sl, terr, pt shd; wc; chem disp; baby facs; shwrs inc; el pnts (6A) inc (poss rev pol); gas; lndtte; shop; rest 1km; snacks; bar; playgrnd; htd pool; paddling pool; direct access to shgl beach 500m; boating; games rm; entmnt; 30% statics; dogs €4.50; adv bkg; quiet; ccard acc; red C'Club members; red low ssn/long stay/CKE/CCI. "On 2 levels in valley & hillside; sea views; steep path to beach; gd facs; gd." ♦ 1 Apr-25 Sep. € 26.50 2011*

See advertisement

PAIMPONT see Plélan le Grand *2F3*

PEILLAC *2F3* (1km N Rural) *47.72635, -2.21430* **Camp Municipal du Pont d'Oust, 56220 Peillac [02 99 91 39 33 or 02 99 91 26 76 (Mairie); fax 02 99 91 31 83; www.peillac.fr]** SW fr La Gacilly on D777; in 6km turn L onto D14 sp Les Fougerêts; cont thro Les Fougerêts, site on R in 1km opp canal. Or N fr Peillac on D14, folls sp Pont d'Oust; site on L. Med, pt shd; htd wc; shwrs inc; el pnts (10A) €2.75 (poss rev pol); lndtte; shops 1km; rest, bar 300m; BBQ; pool adj; quiet. "Nice, peaceful site by Rv Oust & canal; spacious pitches; helpful warden calls, site yourself; v flat, ideal for cycling; pretty vill; vg." 1 Jun-30 Sep. € 9.40 2011*

PENESTIN *2G3* (1.5km N Coastal) *47.47687, -2.45204* **Camping Les Pins, Chemin du Val au Bois de la Lande, 56760 Pénestin [tel/fax 02 99 90 33 13; camping.lespins@wanadoo.fr; www.camping-despins.com]** Fr Roche-Bernard take D34 dir Pénestin, 2km bef town turn L sp Camping Les Pins. Site on R in 250m. Med, hdg/mkd pitch, pt sl, pt shd; htd wc; chem disp; mv service pnt; baby facs; shwrs inc; el pnts (10A) €3; gas; lndtte (inc dryer); shop & 2km; tradsmn; snacks; bar; BBQ; playgrnd; htd, covrd pool; outdoor pool with waterslides; paddling pool; waterslide; playgrnd; sand beach 3km; cycle hire; games area; games rm; wifi; entmnt; TV; 33% statics; dogs €1.20; phone; bus; poss cr; Eng spkn; adv bkg; quiet; red low ssn/long stay/CKE/CCI. "Sun mkt; excel." ♦ ltd 1 Apr-16 Oct. € 19.00 2011*

PENESTIN *2G3* (1.5km E Rural) *47.47890, -2.45390* **Camping Le Cénic, Route de la Roche-Bernard, 56760 Pénestin-sur-Mer [02 99 90 45 65; fax 02 99 90 45 05; info@lecenic.com; www.lecenic.com]** Fr La Roche-Bernard take N774 sp La Baule. In 1.5km turn R onto D34. At Pénestin turn L opp Intermarché & foll sp to site in 800m. Lge, mkd pitch, pt sl, pt shd; wc; chem disp; mv service pnt; shwrs inc; el pnts (4-6A) €4; lndtte; shop adj; snacks; bar; playgrnd; htd, covrd pool/aquatic park; paddling pool; waterslides; jacuzzi; beach 3km; lake fishing; tennis; games area; games rm; few statics; dogs €2.50; Eng spkn; adv bkg rec high ssn; poss noisy high ssn; red low ssn; CKE/CCI. "Vg site nr unspoilt coastline; lge pitches; pleasant staff; clean san facs, ltd number; take care when pitching due trees; vg Sun mkt." ♦ 3 Apr-16 Sep. € 27.00 2010*

PENESTIN *2G3* (2km S Rural) *47.47150, -2.46695* **Yelloh! Village Le Domaine d'Inly, Route de Couarne, 56760 Pénestin [02 99 90 35 09; fax 02 99 90 40 93; inly-info@wanadoo.fr; www.camping-inly.com / www.yellohvillage.co.uk]** Fr Vannes or Nantes on N165, exit junc 15 W onto D34 fr La Roche-Bernard to Pénestin, then onto D201, site sp on L. Lge, hdg/mkd pitch, hdstg, pt shd; wc; chem disp; shwrs inc; el pnts (10A) inc; lndtte; shop; rest, snacks; bar; BBQ (charcoal); playgrnd; 2 pools (1 htd, covrd); paddling pool; waterslide; sand beach 1.8km; lake fishing; canoe hire; pony hire; cycle hire; tennis; games area; games rm; wifi; entmnt; TV rm; 75% statics; dogs €4; Eng spkn; adv bkg; ccard acc; red long stay/low ssn; CKE/CCI. "V pleasant, family site; excel." ♦ 6 Apr-22 Sep. € 40.00 2011*

PENESTIN *2G3* (3km S Coastal) *47.44527, -2.48416* **Camping Les Iles, La Pointe du Bile, 56760 Pénestin [02 99 90 30 24; fax 02 99 90 44 55; contact@camping-des-iles.fr; www.camping-des-iles.fr]** Fr La Roche Bernard take D34 to Pénestin; cont on D201 for 2.5km & foll site sp. Lge, hdg/mkd pitch, pt shd; wc; chem disp; mv service pnt; some serviced pitches; baby facs; shwrs inc; el pnts (10A) inc (poss rev pol); gas; Indtte (inc dryer); shop; tradsmn; rest, snacks; bar; BBQ (elec/charcoal); playgrnd; htd pool complex; paddling pool; waterslide; sand beach nrby; fishing adj; tennis; cycle hire; horseriding; wifi; entmnt; games/TV rm; some statics; dogs €4; no c'vans/m'vans over 7m high ssn; poss cr; Eng spkn; adv bkg; quiet but noisy nr rd; ccard acc; red low ssn; CKE/CCI. "Lovely site o'looking sea; direct access to shoreline; some pitches sm; helpful staff; clean modern unisex san facs; mkt Sun (also Wed in Jul/Aug); gd cycling, walking; vg." ♦ 12 Apr-30 Sep. € 41.00 (CChq acc) SBS - B06 2012*

PENVINS see Sarzeau *2G3*

PERROS GUIREC *1D2* (5km E Coastal) *48.81439, -3.38372* **Camp Municipal Le Palud, Port L'Epine, 22660 Trélévern [02 96 91 73 11 or 02 96 23 71 91 (LS); fax 02 96 91 76 30; campinglepalud.trelevern@orange.fr; www.trelevern.fr]** Fr Lannion on D788 to Perros-Guirec; at rndabt on sea front turn R onto D6 dir Louannec & Trélévern; in 3km turn L to Trélévern. Foll sps Port L'Epine & Camping Municipal. Med, mkd pitch, unshd; wc; chem disp; baby facs; shwrs inc; el pnts (10A) inc; gas 1km; Indtte; sm shop & 1km; tradsmn; rest, snacks; bar; BBQ; playgrnd; beach adj; entmnt; internet; dogs €1.10; phone adj; Eng spkn; adv bkg; quiet; ccard acc; red low ssn; CKE/CCI. "Peaceful site with views; many pitches beside sea; rocks & sand adj; excel." ♦ 4 Jun-12 Sep. € 20.55 2010*

PERROS GUIREC *1D2* (10km E Coastal/Rural) *48.81310, -3.38590* **RCN Port l'Epine, 10 Venelle de Pors-Garo, 22660 Trélévern [02 96 23 71 94; fax 02 96 23 77 83; portlepine@rcn.fr; www.rcn-campings.fr]** N fr Guingamp on D767 dir Lannion for approx 30km, then D788 dir Perros-Guirec; at rndabt just outside Perros-Guirec turn R onto D38 dir Trélévern. In Trélévern turn L at petrol stn & cont twd beach, sp Port L'Epine & Cmp Municipal; site on L opp Municipal site. NB Park on R at bottom of hill & walk to site to collect check-in information. Med, hdg/mkd pitch, pt sl, pt shd; wc; chem disp; serviced piches; shwrs inc; el pnts (16A) inc (poss rev pol); gas; Indtte; shop; tradsmn; rest, snacks; bar; BBQ; playgrnd; htd pool; paddling pool; dir access shgl beach; cycle hire; games rm; wifi; entmnt; 30% statics; dogs €7; no c'vans/m'vans over 6m high ssn; poss cr; Eng spkn; adv bkg; quiet; ccard acc; red long stay/low ssn; CKE/CCI. "Pleasant, family-run, friendly site; sea view & v lge pitches extra; narr site rds; clean san facs, poss stretched high ssn; barrier clsd 2300-0700; vg for families with young children but not rec for teenagers; mkt Perros-Guirec Fri." ♦ 6 Apr-29 Sep. € 45.65 2011*

See advertisement

PERROS GUIREC *1D2* (1km SE Coastal) *48.79657, -3.42689* **Camp Municipal Ernest Renan, 22700 Louannec [02 96 23 11 78; fax 02 96 23 35 42; mairie-louannec@wanadoo.fr; www.camping-louannec.fr]** 1km W of Louannec on D6. Lge, unshd; wc (some cont); chem disp; mv service pnt; shwrs inc; el pnts (6A) inc; gas; shop high ssn; rest; bar; playgrnd; htd pool; sand beach adj; fishing & watersports adj; games rm; TV; dogs €1.35; poss cr; adv bkg; Eng spkn; traff noise early am (minimal away fr rd). "Well-kept site; pitches on seashore; clean san facs; clsd 1200-1530, little parking space outside; highly rec." ♦ 1 Jun-30 Sep. € 16.55 2014*

BRITTANY

PERROS GUIREC *1D2* (3km NW Coastal) *48.82798, -3.47623* **Yelloh! Village Le Ranolien, Ploumanac'h, 22700 Perros-Guirec [02 96 91 65 65; fax 02 96 91 41 90; info@yellohvillage-ranolien.com; www.leranolien.fr / www.yellohvillage.co.uk]** At Perros-Guirec harbour turn R at Marina foll sp Trégastel. Up hill above coast into Perros Guirec town. Cont strt thro traff lts & into La Clarté vill; strt at traff lts & sharp R at Camping & Le Ranolien sp. Ent shortly on L. Foll Trégastel sp all way. Lge, mkd pitch, pt sl, pt shd; htd wc; mv service pnt; baby facs; shwrs inc; el pnts (16A) inc; lndtte; shop; rest, snacks; bar; 2 pools (1 htd,covrd); waterslide; spa; sand & rock beach; fishing; tennis; golf; horseriding; entmnt; many tour op statics; dogs €4; poss cr; Eng spkn; adv bkg; ccard acc. "Excel beaches; vg coastal walks nrby." ♦ 9 Apr-18 Sep. € 40.00 2010*

PERTRE, LE *2F4* (1km W Rural) *48.03287, -1.03965* **Camp Municipal Le Chardonneret, Rue de Chardonneret, 35370 Le Pertre [02 99 96 99 27 or 06 79 50 41 77; marielepertre@wanadoo.fr; www.lepertre.fr]** W fr Laval on D57 turn S at La Gravelle onto D43 to Le Pertre. Or exit A81 junc 5 S. Sm, hdg pitch, pt sl, pt shd; htd wc; shwrs; el pt (16A) €1.80; lndry rm; BBQ; 20% statics; dogs; phone; quiet but factory adj & church bells at night. "Warden calls am/pm; o'night area for m'vans; basic shops in town; some run down statics; gd NH." ♦ ltd 1 Jan-30 Sep. € 7.00 2009*

PLANCOET *2E3* (650m SE Urban) *48.52035, -2.23213* **Camp Municipal Les Vergers, Rue du Verger, 22130 Plancoët [02 96 84 03 42 or 02 96 84 39 70 (Mairie); fax 02 96 84 19 49; mairie.plancoet@wanadoo.fr; www.mairie-plancoet.fr]** On D974 fr Dinan descend to bdge over rlwy lines & site well sp on L. Med, mkd pitch, pt shd; wc; chem disp; shwrs inc; el pnts (5A) inc; lndtte; shops 50m; sand beach 13km; rv fishing; cycle hire; TV; some statics; adv bkg rec high ssn; quiet; CKE/CCI. "Excel sand beach at Pen Guen; adj park & rv with canoeing; poss travellers/mkt traders." 1 Jun-15 Sep. € 9.00 2010*

⊞ **PLELAN LE GRAND** *2F3* (7km SW Rural) *47.95950, -2.15260* **Camping du Château d'Aleth, Rue de l'Ecole, 56380 St Malo-de-Beignon [06 78 96 10 62 (mob); contact@camping-aleth.com; www.camping-aleth.com]** Fr N24 twds Rennes exit N onto D773 to St Malo-de-Beignon in 5km, site L by church. Sm, pt sl, pt shd; wc; chem disp; mv service pnt; shwrs inc; el pnts (10A) inc; lndtte; shop; snacks; BBQ; playgrnd; wifi; dogs free; quiet. "Pleasant, tranquil, well-kept site by lake; clean san facs; themed cowboy & indian site." ♦ € 19.50 2013*

PLELAN LE GRAND *2F3* (8km NW Rural) *48.02403, -2.17282* **Camp Municipal Brocéliande, Rue du Chevalier Lancelot du Lac, 35380 Paimpont [02 99 07 89 16 or 02 99 07 81 18 (Mairie); fax 02 99 07 88 18; mairie.paimport@wanadoo.fr; www.camping-paimpont-broceliande.com]** Sp on N edge of Paimpont vill. On D773 dir St Méen-le-Grand/Concoret, 500m fr Paimpont. Med, hdg/mkd pitch, pt shd; wc (some cont); chem disp; shwrs inc; el pnts (5A) €3; gas 500m; lndtte; playgrnd; rv & lake sw & fishing adj; cycle hire; tennis; entmnt; internet; phone; bus in vill; quiet; red low ssn; CKE/CCI. "Pleasant, spacious, clean site; friendly; conv NH; no barrier; gd facs for children; sh walk to attractive vill; excel." ♦ 1 Apr-30 Sep. € 10.00 2009*

PLELO see Binic *2E3*

PLESTIN LES GREVES *2E2* (2km NE Coastal) *48.66805, -3.60060* **Camp Municipal St Efflam, Rue Lan-Carré, 22310 Plestin-les-Grèves [02 96 35 62 15; fax 02 96 35 09 75; campingmunicipalplestin@wanadoo.fr; www.camping-municipal-bretagne.com]** Fr Morlaix on D786 thro Plestin-les-Grèves; foll D786 sp St Efflam down hill to bay; site on R 850m along bay; sp. Lge, mkd pitch, pt sl, terr, pt shd; wc; chem disp; mv service pnt; shwrs inc; el pnts (7A) €2.50; gas; lndtte; tradsmn; rest; bar; BBQ; playgrnd; sand beach 150m; sw, fishing, boating adj; dogs €1.30; Eng spkn; adv bkg ess high ssn; ccard acc; red low ssn; CKE/CCI. "Excel; helpful recep." ♦ ltd 1 Apr-30 Sep. € 11.00 2009*

PLEUBIAN see Tréguier *1D3*

PLEUMEUR BODOU see Trébeurden *1D2*

PLOBANNALEC LESCONIL see Pont l'Abbé *2F2*

PLOEMEUR see Lorient *2F2*

PLOERMEL *2F3* (2km N Rural) *47.94866, -2.42077* **Camping du Lac, Les Belles Rives, 56800 Taupont [tel/fax 02 97 74 01 22; contact@camping-du-lac-ploermel.com; www.camping-du-lac-ploermel.com]** Fr N24 foll D766e around Ploërmel or foll sp for Taupont (D8). Cent, take D8 twds Taupont & Lac-au-Duc 3km. Site clearly sp on R on edge of lake. Med, hdg/mkd pitch, pt shd; htd wc; mv service pnt; chem disp; shwrs inc; el pnts (5A) €3.50; gas; lndtte; shop; tradsmn; snacks; bar; BBQ; playgrnd; pool & waterslide nrby; sand beach & lake sw adj; watersports adj; cycle hire nrby; tennis; 10% statics; dogs €2.40; Eng spkn; adv bkg; quiet; ccard acc high ssn; red low ssn; CKE/CCI. "Pleasant site in lovely location; golf & horse riding 1km; friendly staff; vg; excel shopping in Ploermel; excel cent to explore Brittany." ♦ 1 Apr-30 Sep. € 14.80 2014*

⊞ **PLOERMEL** *2F3* (6km N Rural) *47.98425, -2.38191* **FFCC Camping Parc Merlin l'Enchanteur, 8 Rue du Pont, Vallée de l'Yvel, 56800 Loyat [02 97 93 05 52 or 02 97 73 89 45; fax 02 97 73 89 37; camelotpark@wanadoo.fr; www.campingmerlin.com]** Fr Ploërmel take D766 N sp St Malo. In 5km turn L to Loyat. Site on L on ent vill opp g'ge, adj sm lake. Med, hdg/mkd pitch, pt shd; htd wc; chem disp; mv service pnt; shwrs inc; el pnts (10-16A) €3.50-6 (poss rev pol); gas; lndtte; sm shop & other shops 600m; tradsmn high ssn; rest, bar 200m; BBQ; htd covrd pool; sand beach/lake sw with watersports 4km; fishing; tennis; games area; cycle hire; wifi €3; 10% statics; dogs €2; phone 1km; adv bkg; quiet, but some rd noise; red long stay; ccard acc; red CKE/CCI. "Lovely, peaceful site; spacious pitches; welcoming British owners; vg clean facs; gd indoor pool; poss soggy in winter; new 60km tarmac cycle trail adj; conv Château Josselin, Lizio & Brocéliande forest with legend of King Arthur; pleasant site; excel walking and cycling." ♦ € 21.00 (CChq acc) 2013*

PLOERMEL *2F3* (8km S Rural) *47.86354, -2.44612* **Camping Domaine du Roc, Rue Beaurivage, 56460 Le Roc-St André [02 97 74 91 07 or 06 48 07 68 05 (mob); contact@domaine-du-roc.com; www.domaine-du-roc.com]** Fr N on N166 turn R onto D764/D4 to Le Roc-St André. Site in approx 3km at end of bdge over Nantes & Brest Canal. Med, hdg/mkd pitch, pt shd; wc; baby facs; shwrs inc; el pnts (6A) €3.50; Indtte; shop adj; rest, snacks, bar in town; BBQ; playgrnd; htd, covrd pool; 50% statics; dogs €3; phone adj; poss cr; adv bkg; quiet; ccard acc; CKE/CCI. "Peaceful, well-situated site; gd touring base; excel cycle rtes adj canal." 1 Apr-31 Oct. € 15.00 2009*

PLOERMEL *2F3* (7km NW Rural) *47.96932, -2.47010* **Camping La Vallée du Ninian, Route du Lac, Le Rocher, 56800 Taupont [02 97 93 53 01; fax 02 97 93 57 27; infos@camping-ninian.com; www.camping-ninian.com]** Fr Ploërmel cent foll sp to Taupont or Lac au Duc; N on D8. Thro vill Taupont take L hand turn sp La Vallée du Ninian; site on L 1km fr Helléan. Sm, hdg pitch (lge), pt shd; wc; chem disp; shwrs inc; baby facs; el pnts (3-6A) €2-3.50; Indtte; shop; bar; playgrnd; htd pool; paddling pool; lake sw & watersports 4km; sand beach 4km; entmnt; dogs €1; quiet; adv bkg. "Farm produce; helpful owners; peaceful; gd facs for children; vg." ♦ 1 Apr-30 Sep. € 16.00 2009*

PLOMEUR see Pont l'Abbe *2F2*

PLONEOUR LANVERN see Pont l'Abbé *2F2*

PLONEVEZ PORZAY *2E2* (4km W Coastal) *48.14458, -4.26915* **Camping La Plage de Tréguer, Plage de Ste Anne-la-Palud, 29550 Plonévez-Porzay [02 98 92 53 52; fax 02 98 92 54 89; camping-treguer-plage@wanadoo.fr; www.camping-treguer-plage.com]** On D107 S fr Châteaulin. After 8km turn R to Ste Anne-la-Palud & foll sp. Lge, hdg/mkd pitch, hdstg, pt shd; wc (some cont); chem disp; mv service pnt; shwrs inc; el pnts (6A) €3.90; gas; Indtte; shop; tradsmn; snacks; bar; BBQ; playgrnd; sand beach adj; games area; games rm; entmnt; TV rm; some statics; dogs €2.20; Eng spkn; adv bkg; ccard acc; red low ssn; CKE/CCI. "Well-situated touring base; vg, friendly site; excel beach." ♦ 4 Apr-24 Sep. € 34.65 (CChq acc) 2013*

PLONEVEZ PORZAY *2E2* (4km W Coastal) *48.11042, -4.27983* **Camping Trezmalaouen, 20 Route de la Baie, 29550 Plonévez-Porzay [tel/fax 02 98 92 54 24; camping.trezmalaouen@wanadoo.fr; www.camping-trezmalaouen.com]** Fr Douarnenez take D107 N dir Plonévez-Porzay, site sp to L. Med, hdg/mkd pitch, some hdstg, pt shd; wc; chem disp; mv service pnt; baby facs; shwrs inc; el pnts; Indtte; BBQ; playgrnd; sand beach adj; tennis; games area; 75% statics; dogs €1.70; 2 accesible mobile homes; dogs €3; adv bkg; ccard acc; red long stay/low ssn/CKE/CCI. "Sea views; vg touring base." 1 Apr-15 Nov. € 18.00 (CChq acc) 2010*

PLOUGASNOU *1D2* (1.5km SE Rural) *48.68548, -3.78530* **Camping Le Trégor, 130 route du Cosquerou, 29630 Plougasnou [tel/fax 02 98 67 37 64; bookings@campingdutregor.com; www.campingdutregor.com]** At junc of D46 to Plougasnou. Site is on L just bef town sp. Sm, hdg/mkd pitch, pt shd; wc; chem disp (wc); shwrs inc; el pnts (6-10A) inc; gas; Indtte; shop 1km; BBQ; playgrnd; sand beach 1.2km; lake sw & watersports 3km; 40% statics; dogs €1; poss cr; adv bkg; quiet; no ccard acc; CKE/CCI. "Well-run site in beautiful area; dated but clean facs; ideal for walking, cycling & fishing; conv Roscoff ferries & Morlaix; phone if req NH after end Oct." Easter-11 Nov. € 15.00 2014*

PLOUGASNOU *1D2* (2km S Rural) *48.66472, -3.78062* **Camping Domaine de Mesqueau, 870 Route de Mesqueau, 29630 Plougasnou [02 98 67 37 45; fax 02 96 47 28 58; domaine-de-mesqueau@orange.fr; www.camping-bretagne-mer.com]** N fr Morlaix on D46 dir Primel-Trégastel, site sp 2km S of Plougasnou. Med, mkd pitch, pt shd; wc; chem disp; mv service pnt; baby facs; shwrs; el pnts (6A) inc; Indtte; shop 4km; tradsmn; rest, snacks; bar; BBQ; playgrnd; htd pool complex; sand beach 4km; lake fishing; tennis; games area; wifi; 30% statics; dogs €2; adv bkg; quiet. 1 May-25 Sep. € 20.00 2010*

PLOUGASNOU *1D2* (3km NW Coastal/Urban) *48.71421, -3.81563* **Camp Municipal de la Mer, 29630 Primel-Trégastel [02 98 72 37 06 or 02 98 67 30 06; fax 02 98 67 82 79; primel-tregastel.camping-de-la-mer@wanadoo.fr]** Fr Morlaix take D46 to Plougastel on to Primel-Trégastel. Bear R in vill & 1st L opp cafe to site on R in 100 m. Med, unshd, wc; chem disp; mv service pnt; shwrs €1.80; el pnts (10A) inc; gas 1.5km; Indtte; shop, rest, bar 500m; tradsmn high ssn; playgrnd; sand beach 500m; dogs €1; phone; poss cr; no adv bkg; quiet; no ccard acc; CKE/CCI. "Fine coastal views; gd walking & cycling; ltd facs low ssn." ♦ ltd 1 Jun-30 Sep. € 17.00 2014*

PLOUGASTEL DAOULAS *2E2* (4.5km NE Coastal) *48.40134, -4.35419* **Camping Saint Jean, 29470 Plougastel-Daoulas [02 98 40 32 90; fax 02 98 04 23 11; info@campingsaintjean.com; www.campingsaintjean.com]** Fr Brest, take N165 E for approx 12km then leave m'way after Plougastel exit & foll sp. Site in 2km at end of rd by rv. Med, hdg pitch, some hdstg, pt sl, terr, pt shd; htd wc; chem disp; mv service pnt; baby facs; shwrs; el pnts (6A) €3 (poss rev pol); Indtte (inc dryer); shop; supmkt 2km; snacks; bar; BBQ; playgrnd; htd, covrd pool; paddling pool; waterslide; games area; wifi; entmnt; TV rm; some statics; dogs €2; poss cr; quiet; red low ssn. "Nice site by rv; steep in places; gd facs." ♦ 9 Apr-30 Sep. € 22.00 (CChq acc) 2011*

PLOUGONVELIN see Conquet, Le *2E1*

PLOUGOULM see Roscoff *1D2*

PLOUGRESCANT see Tréguier *1D3*

PLOUGUENAST *2E3* (2km NW Rural) *48.28653, -2.72145* **Pinábre Camping & Caravaning, Lingouet 22150 [02 96 26 80 04; www.campgite-brittany.com]** Site is 50 miles fr St. Malo ferry port, bet Loudeac and Moncontour off the D768. Sm, pt sl, pt shd; wc; chem dis; fam bthrm; shwrs; el (16A) €3; Eng spkn; adv bkg; CKE/CCI; "Gd for walks & cycling; sm friendly site; excel facs; close to N & S coast; open plan, grassy site." Apr-Sep. € 12.00 2013*

PLOUGUERNEAU *2E2* (3km N Coastal) *48.63048, -4.52402* **Camping La Grève Blanche, St Michel, 29880 Plouguerneau [02 98 04 70 35 or 02 98 04 63 97 (LS); fax 02 98 04 63 97; lroudaut@free.fr; www.campinggreveblanche.com]** Fr Lannilis D13 to Plouguerneau, D32 sp La Grève, St Michel (look out for lorry rte sp). Avoid Plouguerneau vill when towing - tight RH bend. Med, pt sl, terr, unshd; wc; chem disp; mv service pnt; shwrs €1; el pnts (9A) €2.80; bar; shops 3km; playgrnd; sand beach; dogs €1.90; Eng spkn; adv bkg; red low ssn; CKE/CCI. "Excel location; sea views; helpful staff; facs clean & well-kept; low ssn recep open eves only; in fog lighthouse sounds all night otherwise quiet." ♦ ltd 16 Apr-10 Oct. € 11.60 2010*

PLOUGUERNEAU *2E2* (6km N Coastal) *48.63112, -4.44972* **Camping du Vougot, Route de Prat-Leden, 29880 Plouguerneau [02 98 25 61 51; campingduvougot@hotmail.fr; www.campingplageduvougot.com]** Fr N12 at Landerneau exit N onto D770 to Lesneven, then D28/D32 to Plouguerneau. Fr Plouguerneau take D10 dir Guissény then turn W onto D52 dir Grève-du-Vougot, site sp. Med, hdg/mkd pitch, pt shd; wc; chem disp; mv service pnt; shwrs €0.50; el pnts (10A) €3.30; Indtte; shop 6km; tradsmn; snacks; playgrnd; sand beach 250m; watersports nr; wifi; entmnt; 30% statics; dogs €2.60; adv bkg; quiet; ccard acc; red long stay/low ssn; CKE/CCI. "Gd walking (GR34); interesting area; excel touring base." ♦ 1 Apr-31 Oct. € 16.40 (CChq acc) 2011*

PLOUHARNEL see Carnac *2G3*

PLOUHINEC *2F2* (1km SE Coastal) *47.66489, -3.22105* **Camping Le Moténo, Rue du Passage d'Etel, 56680 Plouhinec [02 97 36 76 63; fax 02 97 85 81 84; info@camping-moteno.com; www.camping-le-moteno.com]** App Auray on D22, take 2nd turn L after Pont Lerois & foll sps. Lge, hdg/mkd pitch, pt shd; wc; chem disp; shwrs inc; el pnts (10A) inc; gas; Indtte; shop; rest, snacks; bar; playgrnd; htd, covrd pool; waterslide; jacuzzi; sand beach 800m; fishing & watersports 100m; cycle hire; games area; games rm; entmnt; TV; some statics; dogs €5; Eng spkn; adv bkg; quiet; red low ssn. "Pleasant site; gd base Carnac & Quiberon Peninsula." ♦ 3 Apr-11 Sep. € 32.00 2009*

PLOUHINEC *2F2* (9.4km SE Coastal) *47.65269, -3.20174* **Camp Municipal de la Falaise, Rue de la Barre, 56410 Etel [02 97 55 33 79; fax 02 97 55 33 79; www.morbihan.com]** S fr L'Orient on D194/D9/D781 dir Carnac; in 1.5km after x-ing rv brdge turn R onto D16 to Etel; foll sps for La Plage or Camping. Or N fr Carnac on D781; at Erdeven turn L onto D105 to Etel & then as bef. Med, mkd pitch, pt sl, pt shd; wc; mv service pnt; shwrs inc; el pnts inc; Indtte; shop 500m; tradsmn; playgrnd; sand beach; lake sw; boat trips; windsurfing; canoeing; phone; quiet; CKE/CCI. 1 Apr-18 Sep. € 16.50 2011*

PLOUVORN see Landivisiau *2E2*

PLOZEVET *2F2* (500m SW Rural) *47.98006, -4.43071* **Camping La Corniche, Route de la Corniche, 29710 Plozévet [02 98 91 33 94 or 02 98 91 32 93; fax 02 98 91 41 53; infos@campinglacorniche.com; www.campinglacorniche.com]** Fr N165 foll sp Audierne onto D784 to Plozévet & foll sps to site. Med, hdg pitch, pt shd; wc; chem disp; mv service pnt; baby facs; shwrs inc; el pnts (10A) €3.20 (poss rev pol); Indtte; shop; tradsmn; playgrnd; pool; beach 2km; wifi; 10% statics; dogs €2.20; red low ssn; CKE/CCI. "Clean site; lge pitches; vg pool; helpful owner; excel facs; gd cycling." ♦ 1 Apr-1 Oct. € 15.00 (CChq acc) 2010*

PLUMERGAT see Ste Anne d'Auray *2F3*

PONT AVEN *2F2* (10km N Rural) *47.92512, -3.68888* **Camping Les Genêts d'Or, KermerourPont Kereon 29380 Bannalec [tel/fax 02 98 39 54 35; info@holidaybrittany.com; www.holidaybrittany.com]** Fr Pont Aven/Bannalec exit on N165 N to Bannalec on D4; after rlwy x-ing turn R sp Quimperlé. In 1km turn R, sp Le Trévoux; site on L 500m. Sm, hdg/mkd pitch, pt sl, pt shd; wc; chem disp; shwrs inc; el pnts (6A) €3.50; Indtte (inc dryer); shop 500m; supmkt 1km; rest, snacks; bar; BBQ (gas); playgrnd; pool 10km; sand beach 15km; games rm; cycle hire; some statics; dogs €1.50; Eng spkn; adv bkg; quiet, some non-intrusive rd/rlwy noise; ccard not acc; red long stay; CKE/CCI; ACSI acc. "Lovely, peaceful, well-kept site in orchard; lge pitches; welcoming, helpful British owners; immac san facs; Bannalec in walking dist; lovely area - excel touring base; highly rec; lovely hosts; easy walk into Bannalac." 1 Apr-30 Sep. € 24.00 2013*

PONT AVEN *2F2* (8km SE Coastal) *47.78799, -3.70064* **Camping de l'Ile Percée, Plage de Trénez, 29350 Moëlan-sur-Mer [02 98 71 16 25; camping-ilepercee-am@orange.fr; www.camping-ile-percee.fr]** App thro Moëlan-sur-Mer, 6km SE of Pont-Aven or 6km SW of Quimperlé - watch for R turn after Moëlan. Take D116 sp to Kerfany. Keep strt at Kergroës, turn L after 500m sp L'Ile Percée. Med, pt sl, unshd; wc (some cont); baby facs; shwrs; el pnts (4-6A) €2.60-3.70; Indtte; snacks; bar; BBQ; playgrnd; sandy/rocky beach adj; sw, fishing & watersports adj; games area; entmnt; TV; some statics; dogs €1; phone; poss cr; adv bkg; v quiet. "Well-run site; sea views; ent narr & winding; sm pitches; manhandling ess; not suitable lge o'fits; san facs poss stretched high ssn." 1 Apr-19 Sep. € 17.50 2013*

PONT AVEN *2F2* (8km S Coastal) *47.79640, -3.77489* **Camping Les Chaumières, 24 Hameau de Kerascoët, 29920 Névez [02 98 06 73 06; info@camping-des-chaumieres.com; www.camping-des-chaumieres.com]** S fr Pont-Aven thro Névez to Kerascoët. Med, hdg/mkd pitch, pt shd; wc; chem disp; mv service pnt; serviced pitches; shwrs inc; el pnts (4-10A) €3.40-4.30; gas 3km; Indtte (inc dryer); shop 3km; tradsmn high ssn; rest, snacks, bar adj; BBQ; playgrnd; sand beach 800m; dogs €1.50; Eng spkn; adv bkg ess; quiet; red low ssn; CKE/CCI. "Excel, well-organised site; facs poss stretched high ssn; gd play & games areas; sandy bay/beaches, cliff walks; san facs refurbished and upgraded; excel site; highly rec." ♦ 15 May-15 Sep. € 17.40 2013*

PONT AVEN *2F2* (10km S Coastal) *47.80492, -3.74510* **Camping Le St Nicolas, Port Manec'h, 29920 Névez [02 98 06 89 75; fax 02 98 06 74 61; info@campinglesaintnicolas.com; www.campinglesaintnicolas.com]** Take D783 W fr Pont-Aven for 2km, turn L onto D77 S thro Névez to Port Manech. Site well sp. Narr app to site. Lge, hdg/mkd pitch, pt sl, pt shd; wc (some cont); chem disp; shwrs inc; el pnts (6-10A) €3.70-4.70; gas; Indtte; tradsmn high ssn; rest, snacks, bar in vill; playgrnd; htd pool; paddling pool; sand beach 200m; watersports; games area; games rm; tennis, horseriding nrby; entmnt; TV rm; dogs €1.70; Eng spkn; adv bkg; quiet; ccard acc; red low ssn; CKE/CCI. "Pleasant, wooded site; friendly owners; sh walk to beach & cliff walks; gd touring base." ♦ 1 May-19 Sep. € 28.80 2014*

PONT AVEN *2F2* (3km SW Rural) *47.84500, -3.79000* **Domaine de Kerlann, Land Rosted, 29930 Pont Aven [02 98 06 01 77; fax 02 98 06 18 50; reservations@ledomainedekerlann.fr; www.siblu.fr/domainedekerlann]** Fr Pont Aven foll sp twd Concarneau. After 1.5km, turn L onto D77 twd Névez. Site approx 1.5km on R. V lge, hdg/mkd pitch, hdstg, pt sl, pt shd; htd wc; chem disp; baby facs; shwrs inc; el pnts (8A) inc; gas; Indtte; shop; rest, snacks; bar; playgrnd; htd pools (1 covrd); waterslide; sand beach 3km; tennis; cycle hire; entmnt; child entmtn; TV rm; 85% statics; Eng spkn; adv bkg ess high ssn; ccard acc; red low ssn/low ssn; CKE/CCI. "Wooded site & areas poss muddy after rain; children's club all ssn; teenagers' club Jul/Aug; sports pitch; all facs open all ssn." ♦ ltd 4 Apr-21 Sep. 2009*

PONT AVEN *2F2* (5km SW Rural) *47.81749, -3.79959* **Camping Les Genêts, Route St Philibert, 29920 Névez [02 98 06 86 13 or 02 98 06 72 31; campinglesgenets@aol.com; www.campinglesgenets-nevez.com]** Turn S off D783 onto D77 to Névez. At church in town, bear R & turn immed R to exit Névez with PO on R. Site on L, clearly sp. Med, hdg/mkd pitch, pt shd; wc (some cont); baby facs; shwrs inc; el pnts (3-6A) €2.40-5; gas 500m; Indtte; shops 500m; playgrnd; sand beach; 10% statics; dogs €1; some Eng spkn; adv bkg; quiet; CKE/CCI. "Excel beaches adj; vg." 15 Jun-15 Sep. € 15.00 2012*

PONT AVEN *2F2* (6km SW Coastal) *47.79906, -3.79033* **Camping Les Deux Fontaines, Raguenès, 29920 Névez [02 98 06 81 91; fax 02 98 06 71 80; info@les2fontaines.fr; www.les2fontaines.fr]** Leave N165/E60 at Kérampaou foll sp D24 twds Pont Aven. In approx 4.5km turn R (S) foll sp Névez then Raguenès. Site 3km fr Névez. Lge, mkd pitch, pt shd; wc (some cont); shwrs inc; baby facs; el pnts (10A) €4.90; Indtte; shop; rest; bar; sand beach 800m; htd pool; tennis; 80% statics (tour ops); dogs €3.40; o'night facs for m'vans; adv bkg; red low ssn; 25 meter conn lead req'd; price inc waterpark acc & kids club "Busy high ssn; popular with British families." ♦ ltd 27 Apr-7 Sep. € 33.00 (CChq acc) 2013*

PONT AVEN *2F2* (8km SW Coastal) *47.7946, -3.79816* **Camping de l'Océan, Impasse des Mouettes, Keroren, Raguenès, 29920 Névez [02 98 06 87 13; fax 02 98 06 78 26; campingocean@orange.fr; www.camping-ocean.fr]** Leave N165 at Kérampaou; foll sp D24 dir Pont Aven; in 4.5km turn R onto D77; foll sp Névez then Raguenès; site 3km fr Névez. Med, hdg/mkd pitch, pt sl, pt shd; wc (some cont); serviced pitches; chem disp; baby facs; shwrs inc; el pnts (4-10A) €3.50-4.70; Indtte; shops 3km; tradsmn; rest, snacks & bar 2km; BBQ; sm playgrnd; htd covrd pool; sand beach 300m; sailing; fishing; games area; games rm; TV; 4% statics; dogs €1.50; phone; bus; poss cr; some Eng spkn; adv bkg rec high ssn; quiet; ccard acc; red low ssn; CKE/CCI. "Peaceful, well-run, family-owned site; dir access to beach; excel." ♦ ltd 15 May-15 Sep. € 20.60 2009*

PONT AVEN *2F2* (8km SW Coastal) *47.79597, -3.79877* **Camping du Vieux Verger - Ty Noul, Raguenès-Plage, 29920 Névez [02 98 06 86 08 or 02 98 06 83 17 (LS); fax 02 98 06 76 74; contact@campingduvieuxverger.com; www.campingduvieuxverger.com]** Fr Pont-Aven take D783 dir Concarneau; in 2.5km L onto D77 to Névez; foll sp Raguenès-Plage; 1st site on R. Foll 'Vieux Verger' sps. Med, hdg/mkd pitch, pt shd; wc; chem disp (wc); shwrs inc; el pnts (4-10A) €3.20-4.20 (poss rev pol); shop (high ssn); rest 500m; playgrnd; sand beach 500m; statics in sep area; dogs free; phone; poss cr; quiet; red low ssn; CKE/CCI. "Well-run, well-kept site with pool & waterslides; highly rec low ssn." 16 Apr-25 Sep. € 15.50 2011*

BRITTANY

PONT AVEN *2F2* (8km SW Coastal) *47.79330, -3.80110* **Camping Raguénès-Plage, 19 Rue des Îles à Raguénès, 29920 Névez [02 98 06 80 69; fax 02 98 06 89 05; info@camping-le-raguenes-plage.com; www.camping-le-raguenes-plage.com]** Fr Pont-Aven take D783 dir Trégunc; in 2.5km turn L for Névez, foll sps to Raguénès fr Névez. Or fr N165 take D24 at Kérampaou exit; in 3km turn R to Nizon; at church in vill turn R onto D77 to Névez; site on L 3km after Névez. Lge, mkd pitch, hdstg, pt shd; htd wc (some cont); chem disp; mv service pnt; baby facs; sauna; shwrs inc; el pnts (6-15A) €4-6.90; gas; Indtte; shop; rest; snacks adj; bar; BBQ; playgrnd; htd, covrd pool; paddling pool; waterslide; direct access to sand beach adj; watersports school adj; tennis nr; games area; games rm; cycle hire; trampoline; games area; horseriding; wifi; entmnt; 20% statics (sep area); dogs €3.20; Eng spkn; adv bkg rec; quiet; red low ssn; ccard acc; CKE/CCI. "Pretty, wooded, family-run site; private path to beach; clean facs; 1st class site." ♦ 1 Apr-30 Sep. € 32.80 2011*

See advert on previous page

PONT CROIX see Audierne *2F1*

PONT L'ABBE *2F2* (6km S Rural/Coastal) *47.79715, -4.22868* **Camping des Dunes, 67 Rue Paul Langevin, 29740 Plobannalec-Lesconil [02 98 87 81 78; fax 02 98 82 27 05; contact@camping-lesdunes.com; www.camping-lesdunes-29.com]** Fr Pont l'Abbé, S on D102 for 5km to Plobannelec; over x-rds; in 1km turn R, 100m after sports field; green sp to site in 1km. Med, hdg/mkd pitch, pt shd; wc (few cont); chem disp; mv service pnt; baby facs; shwrs inc; el pnts (8A) €3.70; Indtte (inc dryer); shop & rests 1km; tradsmn; snacks; bar; BBQ; playgrnd; sand beach 100m; games rm; games area; dogs €2.10; poss cr high ssn; adv bkg; ccard acc; red early ssn; CKE/CCI. "Helpful owner; nr fishing port; gd walking, cycling & birdwatching; site gd for children." ♦ 5 Apr-30 Sep. € 33.05 2014*

PONT L'ABBE *2F2* (7km S Rural) *47.81241, -4.22147* **Camping L'Océan Breton, Route Kerlut, 29740 Lesconil [02 98 82 23 89; fax 02 98 82 26 49; info@yellohvillage-loceanbreton.com; www.camping-bretagne-oceanbreton.fr / www.yellohvillage.co.uk]** Fr Pont l'Abbé S on D102 to Plobannalec & head for Lesconil; site on L after supmkt. Lge, hdg/mkd pitch, hdstg, pt shd; htd wc; serviced pitches; mv service pnt; chem disp; sauna; shwrs inc; el pnts (5A) inc; gas; Indtte; shop; tradsmn; rest, snacks; bar; playgrnd; htd, covrd pool; waterslide; sand beach 2km; cycle hire; fitness rm; tennis; games area; 80% statics; dogs €4; phone; Eng spkn; adv bkg; quiet; ccard acc; red long stay/low ssn; CKE/CCI. "Excel site for families; spacious pitches." ♦ 28 May-18 Sep. € 39.00 2014*

PONT L'ABBE *2F2* (3km W Rural) *47.86113, -4.26766* **Aire Naturelle Keraluic, 29120 Plomeur [tel/fax 02 98 82 10 22; camping@keraluic.fr; www.keraluic.fr]** Leave Quimper S on D785 to o'skts Pont L'Abbe; turn R at 1st rndabt (junc with D44); strt on at 2nd rndabt (junc with D2); in 1km turn R at 3rd rndabt up narr rd sp St Jean-Trolimon; site on R in 1.5km. Site 2km NE of Plomeur & well sp. Sm, pt shd; wc; chem disp; baby facs; shwrs inc; el pnts (6A) €2.90; gas; Indtte; sm shop or 3km; tradsmn; BBQ; playgrnd; surfing 5km; games area; games rm; internet; no dogs high ssn, £1.50 low ssn; no twin-axles; Eng spkn; adv bkg (rec high ssn); quiet; ccard acc; red low ssn; CKE/CCI. "Excel, well-kept, family-run site; friendly, helpful Dutch owners; spacious pitches; gd leisure facs; ideal for children; gd walking; gd surfing nrby; facs poss stretched high ssn, highly rec low ssn; no motorhomes." ♦ ltd 1 May-31 Oct. € 19.00 2014*

PONT L'ABBE *2F2* (5km NW Urban) *47.90602, -4.28339* **Camp Municipal de Mariano, 29720 Plonéour-Lanvern [02 98 87 74 80; fax 02 98 82 66 09; mairie@ploneour-lanvern.fr; www.ploneour-lanvern.fr]** Fr Pont l'Abbé, take D2 to Plonéour-Lanvern, site sp fr cent town; fr cent L of church & strt to T-junc, turn R 2nd on L. Med, hdg pitch, pt shd; wc; shwrs inc; el pnts (5A) €3; Indtte; shops 400m; pool 6km; playgrnd; sand beach 13km; tennis adj; dogs €1; adv bkg; quiet. "Pleasant site; warden visits am & pm; gd touring base." ♦ 15 Jun-15 Sep. € 9.50 2009*

PONT L'ABBE *2F2* (10km NW Rural) *47.89462, -4.32863* **Camping Kerlaz, Route de la Mer, 29670 Tréguennec [tel/fax 02 98 87 76 79; contact@kerlaz.com; www.kerlaz.com]** Fr Plonéour-Lanvern take D156 SW to Tréguennec. Med, hdg pitch, pt shd; wc; chem disp; mv service pnt; shwrs inc; el pnts (3-6A) €2.40-3.50; Indtte (inc dryer); shops 4km; snacks; BBQ; playgrnd; htd, covrd pool; sand beach 2km; cycle hire; 30% statics; dogs €1.30; Eng spkn; adv bkg; quiet; ccard acc; red low ssn. "Nice, friendly site." 1 Apr-30 Sep. € 15.30 2011*

PONTORSON *2E4* (7.5km NW Rural) *48.59415, -1.59855* **Camping Les Couesnons, Route de St Malo, 35610 Roz-sur-Couesnon [02 99 80 26 86; fax 02 99 80 31 04; contact@les-couesnons.com; www.lescouesnons.com]** Exit N175/N176 NW onto D797 dir St Malo on coastal rd; site sp 700m past Roz-sur-Couesnon on R. Med, hdg/mkd pitch, pt shd; htd wc; chem disp; baby facs; fam bthrm; shwrs inc; el pnts (6A) €3; Indtte; tradsmn; rest, snacks; bar; BBQ (charcoal & gas); playgrnd; games area; games rm; wifi; TV; 10% statics; dogs €2; Eng spkn; adv bkg; quiet; ccard acc; red low ssn/long stay; CKE/CCI. "Excel site; Mont St Michel 8km." ♦ 31 Mar-3 Nov. € 17.00 2010*

PONTRIEUX *2E3* (4km E Rural) **Camp Municipal du Bois d'Amour, 22260 Quemper-Guézennec [02 96 95 13 40 or 02 96 95 62 62; fax 02 96 95 36 07]** Exit N12 at Guincamp Est; D787 twds Pontrieux. At rndabt ent to Pontrieux, turn R & foll rd to indus est over level x-ing. Turn R along rv front, site in approx 200 yrds. Sm, hdg/mkd pitch, pt shd, mkd pitch; wc; shwrs; el pnts (16A) inc; Indtte; sm shop high ssn & 4km; tradsmn; playgrnd; fishing; 10% statics; ccard not acc; quiet; CKE/CCI. "Attractive site; some rvside pitches; clean, spacious san facs; pay at Marie in town low ssn; rv walks nrby; gd touring base." ♦ 15 Jun-15 Sep. € 13.00 2010*

BRITTANY

⊞ **PONTRIEUX** *2E3* (500m W Rural) *48.69493, -3.16365* **Camping de Traou Mélédern (Moisan), Traou Mélédern, 22260 Pontrieux [02 96 95 69 27; campingpontrieux@free.fr; http://campingpontrieux.free.fr]** N on D787 fr Guingamp; on ent town sq turn sharp L sp Traou Mélédern, cross rv bdge & turn R alongside church. Site in 400m. Access poss diff for lge o'fits; steep exit on 1-way system. Med, hdg/mkd pitch, pt sl, pt shd; wc; chem disp; shwrs inc; el pnts (8A) €3; Indtte; shops, supmkt 1km; tradsmn; playgrnd; BBQ; dogs €1; phone; poss cr; Eng spkn; adv bkg; quiet but some daytime factory noise; CKE/CCI. "In orchard; excel touring base; friendly owner; steep junc nr site poss problem for lge o'fits; gd." ♦ € 11.00 2010*

PORDIC see Binic *2E3*

"I need an on-site restaurant"

We do our best to make sure site information is correct, but it is always best to check any must-have facilities are still available or will be open during your visit.

POULDU, LE *2F2* (4.8km ESE Coastal) *47.78401, -3.54463* **FFCC Camping de Croas An Ter, Quelvez, Le Pouldu, 29360 Clohars-Carnoët [02 98 39 94 19 or 06 24 88 68 20 (mob); campingcroasanter@orange.fr; www.campingcroasanter.com]** On D49 fr Quimperlé to Le Pouldu. Site on L 3km after junc with D224. Med, pt sl, pt shd; wc; chem disp; mv service pnt; shwrs inc; el pnts (6A) €3.20; Indtte; shop & rest 1.5km; snacks & bar 200m; playgrnd; beach 1.5km; internet; dogs; bus 1.5km; Eng spkn; quiet; ccard acc; CKE/CCI. "Lge pitches; friendly owners; gd bathing & sailing; walks in wood & rv fr site; Tues mkt; vg." ♦ ltd 1 Jun-15 Sep. € 11.80 2011*

POULDU, LE *2F2* (300m N Urban/Coastal) *47.76850, -3.54540* **Camping Les Embruns, 2 Rue du Philosophe Alain, Clohars-Carnoët, 29360 Le Pouldu [02 98 39 91 07; fax 02 98 39 97 87; camping-les-embruns@wanadoo.fr; www.camping-les-embruns.com]** Exit N165 dir Quimperlé Cent, onto D16 to Clohars-Carnoët. Cont on D16/D24/D1214 to Le Pouldu. Site on R on ent 1-way traff system. Site sp. Lge, hdg/mkd pitch, hdstg, terr, pt shd; htd wc; chem disp; mv service pnt; all serviced pitches; baby facs; fam bthrm; shwrs inc; el pnts (10A) inc; gas; Indtte (inc dryer); shop; tradsmn; rest, snacks; bar; BBQ; playgrnd; htd, covrd pool; paddling pool; sand beach 250m; watersports; tennis 200m; fishing; cycle hire; horseriding nr; children's farm; tennis; games area; games rm; wifi; TV rm; 40% statics; dogs €2.70; bus nrby; Eng spkn; adv bkg; quiet; ccard acc; red low ssn; CKE/CCI. "Excel family-run site in great location; luxury pitches extra charge; friendly, helpful owners; vg clean san facs; superb facs; gd walking along coastal paths; cycle rtes; great for dogs; town was home of Paul Gauguin; highly rec." ♦ 6 Apr-22 Sep. € 31.50 2011*

See advertisement

"Satellite navigation makes touring much easier"

Remember most sat navs don't know if you're towing or in a larger vehicle – always use yours alongside maps and site directions.

POULDU, LE *2F2* (2km N Rural) *47.78669, -3.55110* **Camping du Quinquis, 29360 Le Pouldu [02 98 39 92 40; fax 02 98 39 96 56; andrew.munro@clara.co.uk; www.campingquinquis.com]** On D16 fr Quimperlé, 2km S of x-rds with D224. Or fr N165 exit Guidel junc 45; foll sps to Le Pouldu & zoo adj to site. Med, hdg pitch, pt sl, pt shd; wc; shwrs; el pnts (10A) inc; gas; Indtte; sm shop; snacks; bar; playgrnd; pool & paddling pool; sand beach 2km; tennis; cycle hire; games rm; entmnt; TV; 80% statics; dogs; phone; poss cr; quiet; red low ssn. "Vg, peaceful, British-owned site." ♦ 23 May-5 Sep. € 21.00 2009*

BRITTANY

POULDU, LE *2F2* (500m NE Rural) *47.77274, -3.54433* **Camping Keranquernat, 29360 Keranquernat [02 98 39 92 32; fax 02 98 39 99 84; camping.keranquernat@wanadoo.fr; www.camping-keranquernat.com]** Fr Quimperlé D16 to Clohars-Carnoët, then D24 to Le Pouldu - twd port; turn R at x-rds nr Ar Men Résidence; site ent immed on R. Fr S on N165 exit junc 45 sp Guidel; in 1km turn W onto D162/D224, then foll sp Le Pouldu; site sp at town ent. Med, hdg/mkd pitch, pt shd; wc (some cont); chem disp; baby facs; shwrs; el pnts (3-5A) €3-4; Indtte; shops 300m; tradsmn; rest & bar nrby; BBQ; playgrnd; htd pool; paddling pool; sand beach 700m; fishing; sailing; tennis; cycle hire; games rm; TV; dogs €0.50; adv bkg; quiet; red low ssn; CKE/CCI. "Beautifully-kept, pretty site; welcoming owners; highly rec." 1 May-6 Sep. € 27.40 2014*

POULDU, LE *2F2* (2km E Rural/Coastal) *47.77466, -3.50616* **Camping Les Jardins de Kergal, Route des Plages, 56520 Guidel [02 97 05 98 18; fax 02 97 32 88 27; jardins.kergal@wanadoo.fr; www.camping-lorient.com]** Fr N165 Brest-Nantes take Guidel exit; thro Guidel & onto Guidel-Plages; camp sp in 1km. Lge, hdg/mkd pitch, hdstg, pt sl, pt shd; wc; chem disp; baby facs; shwrs inc; el pnts (10A) inc; Indtte; gas; shops 2km; tradsmn high ssn; rest, snacks, bar high ssn; BBQ; playgrnd; 2 pools (1 covrd); waterslide; sand beach 1.5km; tennis; entmnt; cycle hire; games area; games rm; wifi; TV; 75% statics; dogs €3; adv bkg; quiet but poss noisy youth groups high ssn; red low ssn; CKE/CCI. "Friendly, helpful, welcoming staff; well-run, peaceful site; conv beaches & touring." ♦ 29 Mar-30 Sep. € 41.00 2013*

POULLAN SUR MER see Douarnenez *2E2*

QUESTEMBERT see Muzillac *2G3*

QUIBERON *2G3* (1.5km N Coastal) *47.49978, -3.12021* **Camping Do Mi Si La Mi, 31 Rue de la Vierge, St Julien-Plage, 56170 Quiberon [02 97 50 22 52; fax 02 97 50 26 69; camping@domisilami.com; www.domisilami.com]** Take D768 down Quiberon Peninsular, 3km after St Pierre-Quiberon & shortly after sp for rlwy level x-ing turn L into Rue de la Vierge, site on R in 400m. Lge, hdg/mkd pitch, pt sl, pt shd; wc (some cont); chem disp; mv service pnt; baby facs; serviced pitches; shwrs inc; el pnts (3-10A) €2.80-4.30; gas; Indtte (inc dryer); shop, snacks, bar adj; BBQ; playgrnd; sand/shgl beach 100m; games area; cycle hire; sailing, horseriding, tennis nr; wifi; 40% statics; dogs €2.40; poss cr; Eng spkn; quiet; red low ssn; ccard acc; CKE/CCI. "Gd touring base; vg." ♦ 1 Apr-2 Nov. € 21.60 2011*

QUIBERON *2G3* (800m SE Urban) *47.47919, -3.10090* **Camping Les Joncs du Roch, Rue de l'Aérodrome, 56170 Quiberon [tel/fax 02 97 50 24 37; www.campingquiberon.com]** Foll sp to aerodrome. Site ent opp. Lge, pt shd; wc (some cont); chem disp; shwrs inc; el pnts (10A) €4.20 (poss rev pol); gas; shops 1km; sand beach 500m; some statics; dogs €2; poss cr; quiet, but minimal aircraft noise. "Well-maintained, clean, friendly, sheltered site; facs old but clean; easy access town/beach; vg cycling." Easter-30 Sep. € 22.00 2010*

QUIBERON *2G3* (1.5km SE Coastal/Rural) *47.47641, -3.10441* **Camping Le Bois d'Amour, Rue St Clément, 56170 Quiberon [02 97 50 13 52 or 04 42 20 47 25 (LS); fax 02 97 50 42 67; info@homair.com; www.homair.com]** Exit N165 at Auray onto D768. In Quiberon foll sp 'Thalassothérapie', site sp. Lge, hdg/mkd pitch, pt shd; wc; mv service pnt; chem disp; baby facs; shwrs inc; el pnts (10A) €5; gas; Indtte; shop; rest, snacks; bar; BBQ; playgrnd; htd pool; beach 200m; games area; tennis; horseriding; cycle hire; entmnt; dogs €5; adv bkg; quiet; Eng spkn; red low ssn; ccard acc; CKE/CCI. ♦ 3 Apr-2 Oct. € 36.00 2012*

QUIBERON *2G3* (1.5km SE Coastal) *47.47690, -3.09246* **Camping Le Conguel, Blvd de la Teignouse, 56175 Quiberon [02 97 50 19 11; fax 02 97 30 46 66; info@campingduconguel.com; www.campingduconguel.com]** On D768 fr N, turn E at rlwy stn on ent Quiberon, foll sps for Pointe du Conguel, site sp. Lge, mkd pitch, pt sl, unshd; wc; baby facs; sauna; shwrs; el pnts €3.65; gas; Indtte; shop; rest, snacks; bar; playgrnd; htd pool; paddling pool; waterslide; sand beach adj; watersports; tennis; games area; games rm; fitness rm; cycle hire; entmnt; internet; TV rm; adv bkg; quiet; red low ssn. "Beautiful, varied coastline; excel family site." ♦ 4 Apr-31 Oct. € 43.30 2009*

"There aren't many sites open at this time of year"

If you're travelling outside peak season remember to call ahead to check site opening dates – even if the entry says 'open all year'.

QUIBERON *2G3* (1km S Coastal) *47.47424, -3.10563* **Camp Municipal Le Goviro, Blvd du Goviro, 56170 Quiberon [02 97 50 13 54]** Fr D768 at Quiberon foll sp Port Maria & 'Centre Thalassothérapie'. Site 1km on L nr Sofitel hotel. Lge, hdg/mkd pitch, terr, pt shd; wc (some cont); chem disp; mv service pnt; shwrs; el pnts (13A) €3; gas; Indtte; rest adj; playgrnd; sand beach, fishing & watersports adj; dogs €1.65; poss cr; quiet. "Popular, well-run site in excel location; lovely bay, gd sea views & coastal path; smallish pitches; clean, adequate san facs, ltd low ssn." ♦ ltd 1 Apr-8 Oct. € 12.45 2010*

QUIMPER *2F2* (9km SE Rural) *47.93811, -3.99959* **Camping Vert de Creac'h-Lann (Hemidy), 202 Route de Concarneau, 29170 St Evarzec [02 98 56 29 88 or 06 68 46 97 25 (mob); contact@campingvertcreachlann.com; www.campingvertcreachlann.com]** S fr Quimper on D783, 1.5km fr St Evarzec rndabt at brow of hill (easily missed). Sm, hdg pitch, pt sl, pt shd; wc; chem disp; shwrs; el pnts (4-13A) €3-3.50; Indtte; shop, rest, snacks & bar 3km; playgrnd; sand beach 5km; 50% statics; dogs; poss cr; Eng spkn; adv bkg; quiet; ccard not acc. "Lovely spacious site; lge pitches; friendly, helpful owner; gd playgrnd; poss to stay after end Sep by arrangement; lovely old town; gd touring base; daily mkt; excel." 1 Jun-30 Sep. € 10.00 2011*

QUIMPER *2F2* (2km S Rural) *47.97685, -4.11060* **Camping L'Orangerie de Lanniron, Château de Lanniron, 29000 Quimper [02 98 90 62 02; fax 02 98 52 15 56; camping@lanniron.com; www.lanniron.com]** Fr Rennes/Lorient: on N165 Rennes-Quimper, Quimper-Centre, Quimper-Sud exit, foll dir Pont l'Abbé on S bypass until exit sp Camping de Lanninon on R. At top of slip rd turn L & foll site sp, under bypass then 2nd R to site. Recep at Old Farm 500m bef site. Lge, mkd pitch, pt shd; wc; chem disp; mv service pnt; some serviced pitches; baby facs; shwrs inc; el pnts (10A) inc; gas; Indtte (inc dryer); shop; tradsmn; supmkt adj; rest, snacks; bar; BBQ; playgrnd; htd pool; paddling pool; aquapark; rv fishing & beach; canoeing; 9-hole golf course on site; tennis; cycle hire; wifi; entmnt; games/TV rm; 40% statics; dogs €4.70; bus; phone; poss cr; Eng spkn; adv bkg; ccard acc; red low ssn; CKE/CCI. "Excel, busy, family-run site in grnds of chateau by Rv Odet; well-spaced pitches; vg san facs; vg leisure facs." ♦ 29 Mar-15 Nov. € 54.20 SBS - B21 2014*

⊞ **QUIMPER** *2F2* (1km W Urban) *47.99198, -4.12536* **Camp Municipal Bois du Séminaire, Ave des Oiseaux, 29000 Quimper [tel/fax 02 98 55 61 09; camping-municipal@quimper.fr; www.mairie-quimper.fr]** Fr E on D765 to Quimper, bear L on 1-way system along rv. In 1km bear R over rv into Blvd de Boulguinan - D785. In 500m turn R onto Blvd de France (lge junc). In 1km bear R into Ave des Oiseaux, site on R in front of Auberge de Jeunesse. Med, hdg pitch, terr, pt shd; wc; chem disp (wc); shwrs inc; el pnts (5A) €3.30; Indry facs; shops, rest, snacks, bar 500m; BBQ; pool nr; sand beach 15km; 10% statics; phone; bus adj; poss cr; quiet; ccard acc; CKE/CCI. "Conv NH/sh stay." ♦ ltd 01 Jun-30 Sep. € 10.85 2013*

QUIMPER *2F2* (12km W Rural) *48.00126, -4.26925* **Camping La Rocaille, Kérandoaré, 29710 Plogastel-St Germain [02 98 54 58 13 or 06 72 34 73 13 (mob)]** Fr N165 exit Quimper Sud & foll sp dir Audierne onto D784; in 9km turn R at Kérandoaré; site sp in 200m. NB Avoid Quimper town cent. Sm, hdg/mkd pitch, terr, pt shd; wc (some cont); shwrs inc; el pnts (6A) inc; Indtte; shop 500m; tradsmn; beach 10km; Eng spkn; quiet. "Lovely touring area; friendly, helpful owner; vg san facs; poss diff m'vans if wet." 1 Jun-15 Sep. € 13.00 2009*

QUIMPERLE *2F2* (7km NE Rural) *47.90468, -3.47477* **Camping Le Ty-Nadan, Route d'Arzano, 29310 Locunolé [02 98 71 75 47; fax 02 98 71 77 31; info@tynadan-vacances.fr; www.tynadan-vacances.fr / www.les-castels.com]** To avoid Quimperlé cent exit N165 dir Quimperlé. As ent town turn R onto D22 dir Arzano. In 9km turn L at W end of Arzano (un-numbered rd) sp Locunolé & Camping Ty Nadan; site on L just after x-ing Rv Elle. Or fr Roscoff on D69 S join N165/E60 but take care at uneven level x-ing at Pen-ar-Hoat 11km after Sizun. Lge, hdg/mkd pitch, pt shd; htd wc; chem disp; mv service pnt; sauna; serviced pitches; baby facs; shwrs inc; el pnts (10A) inc (long lead poss req); gas; Indtte (inc dryer); shop; rest, snacks; bar; BBQ (gas/charcoal); playgrnd; htd pools (1 covrd); paddling pool; waterslides; spa; sand beach 18km; rv fishing, canoeing adj; tennis; cycle hire; horseriding; archery; games area; wifi; entmnt; sat TV/games rm; 40% statics; dogs €5.50; no c'vans/m'vans over 8.50m high ssn; Eng spkn; adv bkg; ccard acc; red low ssn/CKE/CCI. "Excel, peaceful site by rv; pitches poss narr for lge o'fits; friendly staff; barrier clsd 2300-0800; many activities; gd touring base." ♦ 18 Apr-31 Aug. € 46.00 (CChq acc) SBS - B20 2011*

QUIMPERLE *2F2* (1.5km SW Urban) *47.87250, -3.56952* **Camp Municipal de Kerbertrand, Rue du Camping, 29300 Quimperlé [02 98 39 31 30 or 02 98 96 04 32 (TO); fax 02 98 96 16 12; contact@quimperletourisme.com; www.quimperletourisme.com]** Exit N165 at Kervidanou junc SW of town. Foll sp 'Centre Ville' along Rue de Pont-Aven. In 1km turn L bef supmkt, sp v sm. Sm, hdg pitch, pt shd; wc; shwrs; el pnts €1.80; playgrnd; TV; dogs. "Delightful site; helpful warden." 1 Jun-15 Sep. € 10.29 2011*

"That's changed – Should I let The Club know?"

If you find something on site that's different from the site entry, fill in a report and let us know. See www.caravanclub.co.uk/europereport.

QUINTIN *2E3* (550m SE Urban) *48.40128, -2.90672* **Camp Municipal du Lac, Chemin des Côtes, 22800 Quintin [02 96 74 92 54 or 02 96 74 84 01 (Mairie); fax 02 96 74 06 53; mairie@quintin.fr]** Fr N exit D790 at rndabt & foll sp 'Centre Ville'; at 2nd rndabt site sp; site on L 200m after 5th ped x-ing (narr rd, easy to miss). Fr S on D790 do not take slip rd (D7) but cont to rndabt - narr rds in town; then as above. Site N (100m) of town gardens & boating lake. Sm, pt sl, pt shd; wc (some cont); mv service pnt; shwrs; el pnts (6A) €2.80; BBQ; shops, rest, snacks, bar 500m; playgrnd; fishing; quiet, but poss noise fr sports complex adj. "Fair site; helpful warden; poss insufficient of security (2011); interesting town." ♦ 15 Apr-30 Sep. € 8.52 2011*

RAGUENES see Pont Aven *2F2*

REGUINY *2F3* (1km S Urban) *47.96928, -2.74083* **Camp Municipal de l'Etang, Rue de la Piscine, 56500 Réguiny [02 97 38 66 11; fax 02 97 38 63 44; mairie.requiny@wanadoo.fr; www.reguiny.com]** On D764 fr Pontivy to Ploërmel, turn R into D11 to Réguiny then foll sp. Med, pt shd; wc; chem disp; mv service pnt; baby facs; shwrs inc; el pnts (10A) €2.50; Indtte; shop 2km; rest, bar 1km; playgrnd; htd pool 500m; dogs €2; phone; Eng spkn; quiet; ccard acc; "Gd facs; gd touring base." 15 Jun-15 Sep. € 9.80 2013*

⊞ **RENNES** *2F4* (2km NE Urban) *48.13529, -1.64597* **Camp Municipal des Gayeulles, Rue du Maurice Audin, 35700 Rennes [02 99 36 91 22; fax 02 23 20 06 34; info@camping-rennes.com; www.camping-rennes.com]** Exit Rennes ring rd N136 junc 14 dir Maurepas & Maison Blanche, foll sp 'Les Gayeules' & site. Narr app to site. Med, mkd pitch, hdstg, pt sl, pt shd; wc; chem disp; mv service pnt; baby facs; some serviced pitches; shwrs; el pnts (10A) €3.50-4; Indtte (inc dryer); shops 500m; tradsmn; snacks; office clsd 12.30-16.00; BBQ; playgrnd; pool adj; tennis, archery & mini-golf nrby; internet; dogs €1; phone; bus; m'van o'night area; Eng spkn; adv bkg; quiet; red low ssn/long stay; ccard acc; CKE/CCI. "Lovely, well-kept, well-run site adj park; friendly, helpful staff; lge pitches; slight sl for m'vans; 1st class facs; park adj; reg bus to Rennes, a lovely city; sm m'van Aire de Service adj; excel." ♦ € 17.00 (CChq acc) 2014*

ROC ST ANDRE, LE see Ploërmel *2F3*

BRITTANY

ROCHE BERNARD, LA *2G3* (500m S Urban) *47.51946, -2.30517* **Camp Municipal Le Patis, Chemin du Patis, 56130 La Roche-Bernard [02 99 90 60 13 or 02 99 90 60 51 (Mairie); fax 02 99 90 88 28; camping.lrb56@gmail.com; www.camping-larochebernard.com]** Leave N165 junc 17 (fr N) junc 15 (fr S) & foll marina sp. NB Arr/exit OK on mkt day (Thurs) if avoid town cent. Med, mkd pitch, hdstg, pt shd; wc; chem disp; mv service pnt; shwrs inc; el pnts (6A) €4; Indtte; shops & snacks 500m; playgrnd; pool 1km; sand beach 18km; rv adj; sailing, boating at marina adj; dogs €2.30; m'van o'night area; poss cr; Eng spkn; adv bkg; quiet; ccard acc; red low ssn/long stay. "Excel clean site in lovely spot on rv bank; helpful staff; facs poss stretched high ssn; grass pitches poss soft - heavy o'fits phone ahead in wet weather; Thurs mkt; organic mkt Sat; ancient, pretty town up steep hill; gd walks; highly rec." ♦ 1 Apr-30 Sep. € 17.00 2014*

ROCHEFORT EN TERRE *2F3* (9.8km NE Urban) *47.74455, -2.25997* **Camp Municipal de La Digue, Route 77 Le Guélin, 56200 St Martin sur Oust [02 99 91 55 76 or 02 99 91 49 45; fax 02 99 91 42 94; st-martin-oust@wanadoo.fr; www.tourismebretagne.com]** On D873 14km N of Redon at Gacilly, turn W onto D777 twd Rochefort-en-Terre; site sp in 10km in St Martin. Med, pt shd; wc; shwrs; el pnts (3-5A) €2.40; Indtte; shops adj; BBQ; playgrnd; rv fishing 50m; dogs €0.30; adv bkg; quiet; "Towpath walks to vill & shops; clean facs but ltd low ssn; well-maintained site; site yourself, warden calls am & eve; excel, refurbished facs (2013)." 1 May-30 Sep. € 8.00 2013*

ROCHEFORT EN TERRE *2F3* (600m S Rural) *47.69217, -2.34794* **Camping Au Gré des Vents (formerly du Moulin Neuf), Chemin de Bogeais, Route de Limerzel, 56220 Rochefort-en-Terre [02 97 43 37 52; fax 02 97 43 35 45; gredesvents@orange.fr; www.campingaugredesvents.com]** Fr Redon W on D775 twd Vannes, approx 23km turn R onto D774 sp Rochefort-en-Terre; immed after vill limit sp, turn sharp L up slope to ent. NB Do not drive thro vill. Med, hdg/mkd pitch, terr, pt sl, pt shd; mv service pnt; wc; chem disp; shwrs inc; el pnts ltd (10A) €4.50; Indtte; shops in vill; tradsmn; rest nr; BBQ; play area; htd pool high ssn; lake beach & sw 500m; some statics; dogs €3; poss cr; adv bkg; quiet; ccard acc;CKE/CCI. "Peaceful base for touring area; helpful owners; no vehicle movement or shwrs 2200-0700 (0800 low ssn), but wcs open; no twin-axles; excel." ♦ ltd 1 Apr-28 Sep. € 34.60 2014*

ROHAN *2F3* (200m NW Rural) *48.07078, -2.75525* **Camp Municipal du Val d'Oust, Rue de St Gouvry, 56580 Rohan [02 97 51 57 58 or 02 97 51 50 33 (Mairie); fax 02 97 51 52 11; mairie.rohan@wanadoo.fr; www.morbihan.com]** Rue de St Gouvry runs NW fr Rohan parallel to D11, but other side of canal. Sm, mkd pitch, pt shd; wc; chem disp (wc); shwrs inc; el pnts €3.10; Indtte; shop, rest, snacks & bar 200m; BBQ; playgrnd; dogs €0.90; phone; adv bkg; CKE/CCI. "Pleasant site beside Nantes/Brest canal; gd cycling." ♦ 1 Jun-15 Sep. € 10.20 2014*

ROSCANVEL *2E1* (500m S Coastal) *48.30893, -4.55851* **Camp Municipal Le Kervian, Route du Camping, 29570 Roscanvel [02 98 27 43 23 or 02 98 27 48 51 (Mairie); fax 02 98 27 41 10; mairie@roscanvel.com]** Fr Crozon foll D355 dir Le Fret/Roscanvel. After Le Fret x-rds foll Municipal sp. Turn L just bef Roscanvel. Sm, mkd pitch, terr, unshd; wc (some cont); chem disp (wc); shwrs inc; el pnts (10A) €3.50; Indry rm; shop & bar 1km; tradsmn; playgrnd; sand beach 800m; horseriding nrby; some statics; dogs; phone adj; quiet; ccard not acc; CKE/CCI. "Vg site; gd views; if office clsd go to Mairie to check in." 15 Jun-15 Sep. € 7.50 2010*

ROSCOFF *1D2* (7km SW Coastal/Rural) *48.67142, -4.05088* **Camp Municipal du Bois de la Palud, 29250 Plougoulm [02 98 29 81 82 or 02 98 29 90 76 (Mairie); fax 02 98 29 90 76; mairie-de-plougoulm@wanadoo.fr]** Fr D58 turn W on D10 sp Cléder/Plouescat; after 3km on ent Plougoulm foll sp to site. Sm, hdg/mkd pitch, terr, pt shd; wc; chem disp; shwrs inc; el pnts (8A) €3.50; Indry rm; shop 800m; sand beach 500m; playgrnd; phone; some Eng spkn; adv bkg; quiet; ccard acc; CKE/CCI. "Clean, tidy site in delightful area; lovely views to sandy inlet; conv ferry; if arr late, site yourself; warden calls am & pm; access all hrs with c'van; walk in first, turning diff inside; also lower field with el pnts; sh walk to vill; excel." ♦ ltd 15 Jun-5 Sep. € 13.50 2014*

"I like to fill in the reports as I travel from site to site"

You'll find report forms at the back of this guide, or you can fill them in online at www.caravaclub.co.uk/europereport.

ROSCOFF *1D2* (10km SW Coastal) *48.69033, -4.13879* **Camping Village de Roguennic, 29233 Cléder [02 98 69 63 88; fax 02 98 61 95 45; semcleder@wanadoo.fr; www.campingvillageroguennic.com]** Fr D10 bet St Pol-de-Léon & Lesneven, take coast rd at either Plouescat or Cléder, foll Camping sp twd sea. Site sp. Lge, mkd pitch, pt sl, pt shd; wc; mv service pnt; shwrs inc; el pnts (6A) €2.50; gas; Indtte; shop, rest, snacks, bar (high ssn); playgrnd; htd pool (high ssn); sand beach adj; tennis; games area; sailing school nr; entmnt; statics sep area; dogs €1.10; phone; bus; adv bkg; quiet; ccard acc; CKE/CCI. "Holiday vill, lovely early ssn; direct access to beach." ♦ 1 May-15 Sep. € 15.40 2010*

ROSCOFF *1D2* (3.5km W Coastal) *48.71411, -4.00866* **Camping aux Quatre Saisons, Perharidy, Le Ruguel, 29680 Roscoff [02 98 69 70 86; fax 02 98 61 15 74; camping.roscoff@wanadoo.fr; www.camping-aux4saisons.com]** Fr dock foll exit & camping sps; at rndbt exit N on D169 twd cent ville; in 800m turn W dir Santec, foll camping sps, pass travellers' site. Lge, hdg pitch, unshd; wc; chem disp; shwrs inc; baby facs; el pnts (4-8A) €2.80-4.40; Indtte; shops 2km; BBQ; playgrnd; sand beach; windsurfing; fishing; sailing; wifi; entmnt; dogs €1; poss cr; adv bkg rec high ssn; quiet; red low ssn. "Conv ferry; will open low ssn if bkd in adv; cheap & cheerful." ♦ 1 Apr-9 Oct. € 11.80 2010*

⊞ **ROSTRENEN** *2E2* (2km S Rural) *48.23063, -3.29881* **Camping Fleur de Bretagne, Kerandouaron, 22110 Rostrenen [02 96 29 16 45 or 02 96 29 15 45; fax 02 96 29 16 45; info@fleurdebretagne.com; www.fleurdebretagne.com]** Fr Rostrenen town cent foll dir Champion supmkt & take next R turn sp D31 Silfiac. In approx 1km turn L, site sp. NB Rough, steep ent/exit. Med, mkd pitch, pt sl, terr, pt shd; wc; chem disp; mv service pnt; shwrs inc; el pnts (6A) €3 (poss rev pol); lndry rm; shop 2km; snacks; bar; BBQ; playgrnd; pool; fishing lake; watersports, horseriding nr; dogs €2; phone; Eng spkn; adv bkg; quiet; red low ssn; CKE/CCI. "Helpful British owners; san facs clean but need refurb (2010), ltd low ssn; wooded walks; poss muddy when wet; ltd opening Nov-Mar - phone ahead." ♦ € 16.00 2011*

ROZ SUR COUESNON see Pontorson *2E4*

"We must tell The Club about that great site we found"

Get your site reports in by mid-August and we'll do our best to get your updates into the next edition.

SABLES D'OR LES PINS *3E2* (5.5km NE Coastal) *48.66418, -2.34260* **Camp Municipal Cap Fréhel/Les Grèves d'en Bas, 22240 Plévenon [02 96 41 43 34 or 02 96 29 60 51 (Mairie); mairie.plevenon.capfrehel@wanadoo.fr]** W fr St Malo on D168/D786; in 30km turn R onto D34 or D341 dir Cap Fréhel; site on R 2.5km bef Cap Fréhel. Med, pt hdg/mkd pitch, pt sl, pt shd; wc; chem disp; shwrs inc; el pnts (5A) €2.05; tradsmn; rest 2km; sand beach adj; 10% statics; dogs €0.75; quiet. "Access to coast path fr site; gd." Apr-Nov. € 9.75 2009*

SABLES D'OR LES PINS *2E3* (1.2km NW Coastal/Rural) *48.63230, -2.41229* **Camp Municipal Sables d'Or Les Pins (formerly La Saline), Rue du Lac, 22240 Plurien [02 96 72 17 40 or 02 96 72 17 23 (Mairie)]** Fr D786 turn N at Plurien onto D34 to Sables-d'Or. In 1km turn L & site on L after 200m. Med, pt sl, terr, pt shd; wc (some cont); chem disp; shwrs inc; el pnts (6A) €2.35; lndtte; shops 500m; playgrnd; sand beach 400m; dogs €0.50; phone; poss cr; Eng spkn; adv bkg; quiet; CKE/CCI. "Lovely, tranquile hillside site; some sea views; friendly, helpful warden; vg san facs; gates clsd 2200-0700; no pitching when office clsd, but lge car park opp; excel access to nature reserve & beautiful beaches." ♦ 1 Jun-15 Sep. € 10.00 2014*

STE ANNE D'AURAY *2F3* (6km N Rural) *47.72889, -2.95349* **FFCC Aire Naturelle Nerhouit, 56400 Plumergat [02 97 57 70 62; nerhouit@tromp.net]** Fr N165 turn N on D17 to Plumergat; site 3km W of Plumergat, sp. Sm, pt shd; wc; chem disp (wc); shwrs €0.50; el pnts (6A) inc (poss long lead req); lndtte; shop, rest, bar 3km; playgrnd; dogs; Eng spkn; adv bkg; quiet; CKE/CCI. "Pitches on lge grassy area; friendly Dutch owner; own cider avail; gd touring base." ♦ ltd 1 Jun-15 Sep. € 12.50 2009*

STE ANNE D'AURAY *2F3* (500m SW Rural) *47.69842, -2.96226* **Camp Municipal du Motten, Allée des Pins, 56400 Ste Anne-d'Auray [02 97 57 60 27 or 02 97 57 63 91; fax 02 97 57 72 33; secretariat.general@sainte-anne-auray.com; www.sainte-anne-auray.com]** Fr W on N165 take D17bis N to St Anne-d'Auray; then L onto D19 to town. This rte avoids Pluneret. Foll site sp. Med, mkd pitch, pt shd; wc; chem disp; shwrs inc; el pnts (10A) €3.20; lndtte; shops 1km; tradsmn; snacks; playgrnd; sand beach 20km; tennis; games area; TV; dogs; Eng spkn; adv bkg; poss cr; quiet; "Peaceful, well-kept site; best pitches immed R after ent; welcoming, helpful warden; gd clean san facs; excel touring base; conv Basilica Ste Anne d'Auray; excel." ♦ 15 Jun-15 Sep. € 16.40 2014*

ST AUBIN DU CORMIER *2E4* (300m E Urban) *48.25990, -1.39609* **Camp Municipal, Rue de l'Etang, 35140 St Aubin-du-Cormier [06 83 38 93 63 (mob) or 02 99 39 10 42 (Mairie); fax 02 99 39 23 25; mairie@ville-staubinducormier.fr]** NE fr Rennes on A84; in 20km exit junc 28 dir St Aubin-du-Cormier. Foll sp 'Centre Ville' then site sp. Poss diff for lge o'fits - narr app. Sm, pt sl, pt shd; wc; shwrs inc; el pnts (6-10A) inc; shops adj; supmkt 1km; lake fishing; 10% statics; dogs €0.65; poss cr; adv bkg; quiet; CKE/CCI. "Pleasant site adj lake; friendly; gd san facs; forest walks & around lake; pretty vill; vet 1km; excel; lovely site." 1 Apr-30 Sep. € 14.34 2013*

ST BENOIT DES ONDES see Cancale *2E4*

ST BRIAC SUR MER *2E3* (1km N Urban) *48.62765, -2.13056* **FFCC Camping Emeraude, 7 Chemin de la Souris, 35800 St Briac-sur-Mer [tel/fax 02 99 88 34 55; campingemeraude@wanadoo.fr; www.camping-emeraude.com]** SW fr Dinard to St Lunaire on N786, after passing Dinard golf course, site is sp to L. Lge, hdg/ pitch, pt shd; wc; chem disp; mv service pnt; baby facs; shwrs inc; el pnts (6A) €3.80; gas; lndtte (inc dryer); sm shop & 200m; tradsmn; snacks; bar; playgrnd; htd pool; paddling pool; water park; beach 700m & sand beach 1.5km; cycle hire; games area; games rm; wifi; entmnt; 40% statics; dogs €2.50; poss cr; adv bkg; red low ssn. "Excel, well-run site, quiet low ssn." ♦ 3 Apr-19 Sep. € 25.80 2010*

ST BRIAC SUR MER *2E3* (500m S Coastal) *48.61493, -2.12779* **Camping Le Pont Laurin, Route de la Vallée Gatorge, 35800 St Briac-sur-Mer [02 99 88 34 64; fax 02 99 16 38 19; lepontlaurin@ouest-camping.com; www.ouest-camping.com]** Fr St Briac, 500m S on D3. Lge, hdg/mkd pitch, some hdstg, pt shd; wc; chem disp; mv service pnt; baby facs; shwrs inc; el pnts (10A) €3 (poss rev pol); lndtte (inc dryer); shop & 500m; tradsmn; snacks; playgrnd; sand beach 1km; sailing; canoe hire nr; tennis nr; games area; sports cent adj; wifi; 4% statics; dogs €1.50; twin-axles not acc; Eng spkn; adv bkg; quiet; ccard acc; CKE/CCI. "Peaceful site; welcoming, helpful staff; clean, modern san facs; excel beaches; gd walking; interesting town; highly rec." ♦ 1 Apr-30 Sep. € 26.30 2013*

BRITTANY

ST BRIAC SUR MER *2E3* (500m SW Coastal) *48.60422, -2.15616* **Camp Municipal des Mielles, Rue Jules Jeunet, 22770 Lancieux [02 96 86 22 98 or 02 96 86 22 19; fax 02 96 86 28 20; campinglesmielles@orange.fr; www.mairie-lancieux.fr]** Fr S on D786 at 500m past windmill turn L into Rue du Fredy. Site on R in 300m, sp. Lge, mkd pitch, unshd; wc (some cont); chem disp; shwrs inc; el pnts (6A) €3.20; Indtte; shop 500m; playgrnd; sand beach 400m; watersports 150m; tennis; wifi; entmnt; 2% statics; dogs €1.70; poss cr; CKE/CCI. "Well-managed, popular site; gd security in ssn; excel facs; hot water ltd low ssn." ♦ 1 Apr-30 Sep. € 10.50 2009*

ST BRIEUC *2E3* (5km E Coastal) *48.53311, -2.67193* **FFCC Camping Bellevue Mer, Pointe de Guettes, 22120 Hillion [02 96 32 20 39 or 02 96 31 25 05 (HS); fax 02 96 32 20 39; contact@bellevuemer.com; www.bellevuemer.com]** Fr St Brieuc twds Dinan on N12 turn N at exit St René onto D712 to Hillion, then rd to Lermot. Site well sp. Narr, winding app rd. Med, unshd; wc; chem disp; mv service pnt; shwrs €0.15; el pnts (6A) 3 (poss rev pol); Indtte; shops 1.5km; tradsmn; bar; playgrnd; wifi; dogs €0.50; quiet; red low ssn. "Sea views fr most pitches; well-maintained site; welcoming, friendly owners; facs basic; narr site rds poss diff lge o'fits; vg." 28 Apr-16 Sep. € 19.20 2011*

ST CAST LE GUILDO *2E3* (500m N Coastal) *48.64198, -2.25601* **Camping La Crique, Plage de la Mare, 22380 St Cast-Le-Guildo [02 96 41 89 19; fax 02 96 81 04 77; info@campings-vert-bleu.com; www.campings-vert-bleu.com]** On ent town foll site sp. Med, mkd pitch, unshd; wc; chem disp; shwrs inc; el pnts (6A) €4.60; Indtte; snacks; bar; playgrnd; beach 200m; some statics (sep area); dogs €2.50; poss cr; adv bkg; quiet; CKE/CCI. "Site on top of low cliff with path to beach; vg." 15 Mar-15 Sep. € 16.00 2010*

ST CAST LE GUILDO *2E3* (500m N Coastal) *48.63690, -2.26900* **Camping Le Châtelet, Rue des Nouettes, 22380 St Cast-le-Guildo [02 96 41 96 33; fax 02 96 41 97 99; info@lechatelet.com; www.lechatelet.com]** Site sp fr all dir & in St Cast-le-Guildo but best rte: fr D786 at Matignon take D13 into St Cast-le-Guildo, turn L after Intermarché supmkt on R; foll sm site sp. Or app on D19 fr St Jaguel. Care needed down ramp to main site. (NB Avoid Matignon cent Wed due to mkt). Lge, hdg/mkd pitch, pt sl, terr, pt shd; wc; chem disp; mv service pnt; baby facs; shwrs inc; el pnts (8A) inc (50m cable req); gas; Indtte (inc dryer); shop; snacks; bar; BBQ (charcoal/elec); playgrnd; htd covrd pool; paddling pool; dir access sand beach 300m (via steep steps); fishing; cycle hire 500m; games rm; golf 2km; wifi; entmnt; TV; 10% statics (tour ops); dogs €4; no c'vans/m'vans over 7m high ssn, otherwise by req; adv bkg; ccard acc; red low ssn. "Site o'looks coast; extra for sea view pitches; some pitches round fishing pond; gd for families with young children; helpful staff; modern unisex san facs; gates clsd 2230-0700; access to some pitches diff lge o'fits; steep climb to beaches; mkt Mon." ♦ 14 Apr-11 Sep. € 40.82 SBS - B11 2011*

ST CAST LE GUILDO *2E3* (1.2km S Coastal) *48.62666, -2.25552* **Camping Les Mielles, Blvd de la Vieux Ville, 22380 St Cast-le-Guildo [02 96 41 87 60; info@campings-vert-bleu.com; www.campings-vert-bleu.com]** Fr D786 at Matignon turn onto D13 into St Cast. Cross over staggered x-rds foll site sp down long gentle hill. R at next x-rds & site on R in 200m. Lge, unshd; wc (mainly cont); chem disp; baby facs; shwrs inc; el pnts (3-10A) €4.45-6.20; Indtte; shop; snacks; bar; playgrnd; htd pool; sand beach 350m; entmnt; 95% statics; dogs €2.40; poss cr; poss noisy; red low ssn. "Plenty of facs for teenagers; gd san facs; ltd space for tourers." 15 Mar-2 Jan. € 20.00 2009*

ST CAST LE GUILDO *2E3* (3.5km S Rural) *48.58441, -2.25691* **Camping Le Château de Galinée, Rue de Galinée, 22380 St Cast-le-Guildo [02 96 41 10 56; fax 02 96 41 03 72; contact@chateaudegalinee.com; www.chateaudegalinee.com]** W fr St Malo on D168 thro Ploubalay. At La Ville-es-Comte branch onto D786 & go thro Notre Dame-du-Guildo. Approx 2km after Notre Dame-du-Guildo turn 3rd L into Rue de Galinée & foll sp to site. Do not go into St Cast. Lge, hdg/mkd pitch, pt shd; htd wc; chem disp; mv service pnt; baby facs; fam bthrm; sauna; shwrs inc; el pnts (10A) inc; Indtte (inc dryer); shop; rest, snacks; bar; BBQ; playgrnd; htd pool complex inc covrd pool; waterslide; paddling pool; sand beach 4km; fishing pond; tennis; games area; horseriding 6km; golf 3km; wifi; entmnt; games/TV rm; 30% statics; dogs €4; Eng spkn; adv bkg; quiet; ccard acc; red low ssn/long stay/CKE/CCI. "Peaceful, family site in lovely area; spacious, well laid-out pitches; helpful staff; modern, clean, excel san facs; pitches poss muddy after rain; excel rest; mkt Fri & Mon; identity bracelet to be worn at all times." ♦ 10 May-5 Sep. € 54.55 (CChq acc) SBS - B27 2014*

ST CAST LE GUILDO *2E3* (6km SW Rural) *48.59111, -2.29578* **Camping Le Vallon aux Merlettes, Route de Lamballe, 22550 Matignon [02 96 41 11 61 or 06 70 31 03 22 (mob); giblanchet@orange.fr; www.camping-matignon.com]** Fr E & W take D786 to Matignon; 500m fr town cent turn SW on D13 twds Lamballe. Med, pt sl, pt shd; wc (cont); chem disp; mv service pnt; shwrs inc; el pnts (8A) €3.10; gas; Indtte; shop; snacks; playgrnd; pool 4km; tennis; sand beach 6km; some statics; dogs €0.75; adv bkg rec; quiet; ccard not acc; CKE/CCI. "Lovely site on playing fields outside attractive town; vg clean facs." ♦ Easter-30 Oct. € 12.70 2009*

ST COULOMB see St Malo *2E4*

ST EVARZEC see Quimper *2F2*

ST GILDAS DE RHUYS see Sarzeau *2G3*

ST JOUAN DES GUERETS see St Malo *2E4*

ST LUNAIRE see Dinard *2E3*

ST MALO *2E4* (2km NE Coastal) *48.68173, -1.97748* **Camp Municipal Le Nicet, Ave de la Varde, Rothéneuf, 35400 St Malo [02 99 40 26 32; fax 02 99 21 92 62; camping@ville-saint-malo.fr; www.ville-saint-malo.fr/campings]** Fr St Malo take coast (busy & narr) rd Ave JF Kennedy twd Cancale; pass Camping Nielles on L bef district of Rotheneuf; turn L at camping sp just after sm g'ge on L; turn L at T-junc; site in view. Lge, mkd pitch, pt sl, pt terr, unshd; wc; chem disp, shwrs inc; el pnts (5-10A) inc (rev pol); Indtte; shops 800m; tradsmn; playgrnd; sand beach adj; dogs €2.30; poss cr & noisy high ssn; Eng spkn; adv bkg; ccard acc; CKE/CCI. "Clean, well-run site on cliff top; can be exposed if pitched nr edge with sea view; secluded beach via steep steps; some pitches sm." ♦ 1 Jul-1 Sep. € 17.50 2009*

ST MALO *2E4* (8km NE Coastal) *48.69000, -1.94200* **Camping des Chevrets, La Guimorais, 35350 St Coulomb [02 99 89 01 90; fax 02 99 89 01 16; campingdeschevrets@wanadoo.fr; www.campingdeschevrets.fr]** St Malo to Cancale coast rd D201; La Guimorais on L 3km E of Rothéneuf, strt thro vill; fairly narr app. V lge, hdg/mkd pitch, pt sl, pt shd; wc; chem disp; mv service pnt; baby facs; shwrs inc; el pnts (6A) €3.35 (poss rev pol); gas; Indtte; shop; rest, snacks; bar; BBQ; playgrnd; sand beach adj; games area; cycle hire; internet; entmnt; 50% statics; dogs; poss cr; Eng spkn; adv bkg; quiet; ccard acc; red low ssn/long stay; CKE/CCI. "Vg location with 2 bays; vg site." ♦ 6 Apr-1 Nov. € 22.00 2009*

ST MALO *2E4* (1km E Coastal) *48.66737, -1.98486* **Camp Municipal Les Nielles, 47 Ave du Président Kennedy, Paramé, 35400 St Malo [02 99 40 26 35; fax 02 99 21 92 62; camping@ville-saint-malo.fr; www.ville-saint-malo.fr/campings]** Fr cent of St Malo (avoiding old walled town) E on D201 parallel & adj to coast; few site sp & poss not easy to find. Med, mkd pitch, unshd; wc (some cont); shwrs inc; el pnts (10A) inc; shop 900m; rest, bar 500m; playgrnd; sand beach adj; fishing; dogs €2.40; poss cr; some rd noise. "Excel for beach & ferry; pitches nr beach v exposed if weather bad." ♦ 1 Jul-31 Aug. € 17.25 2009*

ST MALO *2E4* (3km S Rural) *48.61469, -1.98663* **Camping Domaine de la Ville Huchet, Rue de la Passagère, Quelmer, 34500 St Malo [02 99 81 11 83; fax 02 99 81 51 89; info@lavillehuchet.com; www.lavillehuchet.com]** Fr ferry port, foll sps for D137 dir Rennes; site sp fr 'Madeleine' rndabt on leaving St Malo. Or fr S on D137 take D301 sp St Malo centre. Take 1st exit at next 2 rndabts (thro indus est) & cont on this rd (sharp R-hand bend), then under bdge, site on R. Fr S head N on D137, merge onto D301, at rndabt take 1st exit onto Rue de la Grassinais, thro next rndabt. At next rndabt take 1st exit. Site on the L. Lge, hdg/mkd pitch, pt sl, pt shd; wc; chem disp; mv service pnt; baby facs; shwrs inc; el pnts (6A) inc; Indtte (inc dryer); shop; rest, snacks; bar; BBQ (charcoal/gas, sep area); playgrnd; 2 htd pools (1 covrd pool planned for 2011); paddling pool; water park; sand beach 4km; cycle hire; games area; games rm; wifi; entmnt; TV; 40% statics; dogs €3.50; no c'vans/m'vans over 7.50m except by request; poss cr; Eng spkn; adv bkg; quiet, but some rd noise; red low ssn. "Spacious site in grnds of sm chateau; helpful owner; modern san facs; lge pitches avail; some pitches v shady; conv ferries & Mont St Michel." ♦ 11 Apr-21 Sep. € 45.00 SBS - B32 2014*

See advertisement

⊞ **ST MALO** *2E4* (5km E Urban) *48.65762, -1.95932* **Camping De La Fontaine, 40 Rue de la Fontaine aux Pèlerins, 35400 St Malo [02 99 81 62 62; fax 02 99 81 68 95; contact@campinglafontaine.com; www.campinglafontaine.com]** N fr Rennes on D137 turn R onto D301 sp Cancale. Turn R onto D155 sp Mont-St Michel, site in L in 100m. Med, hdg/mkd pitch, pt shd; htd wc; chem disp; mv service pnt; baby facs; fam bthrm; shwrs; el pnts (10A) €3.80 (poss rev pol); gas; Indtte; shop & 250m; tradsmn; rest, snacks; bar; BBQ; htd pool; sand beach 5km; cycle hire; games area; bouncy castle; table tennis; wifi; entmnt; 80% statics; dogs €3; phone; Eng spkn; poss cr; quiet; ccard acc; red low ssn; CKE/CCI. "Gd touring base; conv ferry; excel site; looks like garden cent fr rd; v clean & tidy site; gd covrd pool; clean san facs; supermkts nrby; san facs poss stretched in high ssn; pleasant site very friendly; gd wifii coverage." € 27.90 2014*

ST MALO *2E4* (5km SE Rural) *48.60916, -1.98663* **Camping Le P'tit Bois, La Chalandouze, 35430 St Jouan-des-Guérets [02 99 21 14 30; fax 02 99 81 74 14; camping.ptitbois@wanadoo.fr; www.ptitbois.com]** Fr St Malo take D137 dir Rennes; after o'skts of St Malo turn R twd St Jouan-des-Guérets, site sp. Lge, hdg/mkd pitch, pt shd; wc; chem disp; mv service pnt; baby facs; shwrs inc; el pnts (10A) inc; gas; Indtte (inc dryer); shop; rest, snacks; bar; BBQ (gas/elec); playgrnd; 2 htd pools; (1 covrd); waterslides; paddling pool; jacuzzi; turkish bath; sand beach 2km; tidal rv fishing, watersports 2km; tennis; cycle hire; wifi; entmnt; games/TV rm; 50% tour ops/statics; dogs €4-6; lge c'vans/m'vans by request; adv bkg; ccard acc; min 3 persons high ssn; red low ssn/CKE/CCI. "Well-kept, well-run site; busy even low ssn; friendly, helpful staff; gd clean san facs, one block unisex; some narr site rds poss diff lge o'fits; conv Le Mont-St Michel & ferries; excel." ♦ 11 Apr-20 Sep. € 58.60 (3 persons) SBS - B03 2013*

ST MARTIN SUR OUST see Rochefort en Terre *2F3*

ST MAYEUX see Mur de Bretagne *2E3*

ST MICHEL EN GREVE *2E2* (1km NE Coastal) *48.69277, -3.55694* **Camping Les Capucines, Voie Romaine, Kervourdon, 22300 Trédez-Locquémeau [02 96 35 72 28; fax 02 96 35 78 98; les.capucines@wanadoo.fr; www.lescapucines.fr]** Fr Lannion on D786 SW twd St Michel-en-Grève, sp Morlaix; in approx 700m, after steep descent & 'Landebouch' sp, turn R & R again in 100m at x-rds. Fr Roscoff take D58 to join N12 at junc 17; NE of Morlaix at next junc turn onto D786 twd Lannion; site down narr app rd on L on leaving St Michel-en-Grève (slow down at town exit sp), then R at x-rds. Med, hdg/mkd pitch, pt sl, pt shd; wc; chem disp; mv service pnt; all serviced pitches; baby facs; shwrs inc; el pnts (10A) inc; gas; Indtte (inc dryer); shop & 1km; tradsmn; snacks; bar; BBQ (charcoal/gas); playgrnd; htd, covrd pool; paddling pool; sand beach 1km; watersports 1km; cycle hire; games rm; games area; wifi; games/TV rm; 15% statics; dogs €2.10; phone; no c'vans/m'vans over 9.50m high ssn; Eng spkn; adv bkg; quiet; ccard acc; red low ssn/long stay; CKE/CCI. "Excel, peaceful, well-kept site; gd sized pitches; helpful owners; clean san facs; gd pool; gd touring base; mkt Lannion Thu." ♦ 1 Apr-20 Sep. € 28.20 SBS - B13 2011*

See advertisement

ST NIC *2E2* (1.5km SW Coastal) *48.19373, 4.30157* **Camping Domaine de Ker-Ys, Pentrez-Plage, 29550 St Nic [02 98 26 53 95; fax 02 98 26 52 48; info@homair.com; www.ker-ys.com]** Turn W off D887 onto D108 & into St Nic, & foll sp Pentrez-Plage & site. Lge, pt shd; wc; chem disp; baby facs; shwrs inc; el pnts (10A) inc; gas; Indtte (inc dryer); shop; snacks; BBQ; bar; htd pool complex; paddling pool; waterslide; sand beach adj; watersports; tennis; games area; wifi; entmnt; TV rm; some statics; dogs €2.50; adv bkg; ccard acc; red low ssn. "Gd family site in lovely location; vg beach; friendly, helpful staff." ♦ 1 Apr-15 Sep. € 28.00 2010*

ST NICOLAS DU PELEM *2E3* (1.5km SW Rural) *48.30983, -3.17923* **Camp Municipal de la Piscine, Croas-Cussuliou, Rue de Rostrenen, 22480 St Nicolas-du-Pélem [02 96 29 51 27; fax 02 96 29 59 73]** Fr Rostrenen, take D790 NE twd Corlay. In 11km, turn L sp St Nicolas-du-Pélem. Site in 500m on R, opp pool. Med, pt shd; wc (some cont); chem disp (wc); shwrs inc; el pnts (10A) inc; gas, shops 1.5km; htd pool opp; dogs; quiet; CKE/CCI. "Clean, well-kept site; choose own pitch, warden will call; excel touring base." ♦ ltd 15 Jun-15 Sep. € 10.00 2012*

ST PABU *2E1* (2km NW Coastal) *48.57643, -4.62854* **Camping FFCC de L'Aber Benoît, 89 Rue de Corn ar Gazel, 29830 St Pabu [02 98 89 76 25; info@camping-aber-benoit.com; www.camping-aber-benoit.com]** E fr Ploudalmézeau on D28; in 5km L to St Pabu. Site sp in vill. Med, hdg pitch, pt shd; wc; chem disp; mv service pnt; baby facs; shwrs inc; el pnts (6A) €3; Indtte; shop, rest (high ssn); snacks; BBQ; playgrnd; beach 100m; wifi; entmnt; TV rm; 10% statics; dogs €1; poss cr; CKE/CCI. "Facs stretched high ssn; vg." ♦ Easter-30 Sep. € 12.00 2013*

ST PIERRE QUIBERON *2G3* (1.5km SE Coastal) *47.50400, -3.12028* **Camp Municipal du Petit Rohu, Rue des Men-Du, 56510 St Pierre-Quiberon [02 97 50 27 85 or 02 97 30 92 00 (Mairie)]** On D768 dir Quiberon, 1km past exit for St Pierre-Quiberon turn L at camp sp. Turn R in 200m & L after 250m at T-junc sp Le Petit Rohu. Site on R in 50m on beach. Well sp. Med, mkd pitch, pt sl, unshd; wc; shwrs; mv service pnt; el pnts (10A) inc; gas; Indtte; sm shop & bar nrby; snacks adj; playgrnd; sand beach adj; boating; fishing; sports area; some statics; dogs; poss cr; quiet. "Well-kept site in excel location on beach front; excel facs; gd cycling; gd footpath to Quiberon & Port-Haliguen." ♦ 3 Apr-3 Oct. € 14.00 2009*

ST PIERRE QUIBERON *2G3* (3km SE Coastal) *47.53981, -3.13417* **Camp Municipal de Kerhostin, Allée du Camping, 56510 St Pierre-Quiberon [02 97 30 95 25 or 02 97 30 92 00 (Mairie); fax 02 97 30 87 20; mairie.saintpierrequiberon@wanadoo.fr; www.saintpierrequiberon.fr]** Off D768 turn SE onto Rue des Goélettes by rlwy x-ing (no thro rd sp), turn L at 1st sm island, turn L at end, site 300m on R. Med, mkd pitch, pt shd; wc; shwrs inc; el pnts (6A) inc; Indtte; shops adj; rest, snacks, bar 500m; playgrnd; pool 2km; sand beach 200m; dogs; poss cr; no adv bkg; red low ssn. 28 Apr-11 Sep. € 15.50 2010*

ST PIERRE QUIBERON *2G3* (1.5km NW Coastal) *47.53400, -3.14000* **FLOWER Camping Relais de l'Océan, 16 Ave de Groix, Kerhostin, 56510 St Pierre-Quiberon [02 97 30 91 29; fax 02 97 30 80 18; info@relaisdelocean.com; www.relaisdelocean.com / www.flowercampings.com]** S on D768 fr Carnac at traff lts in Kerhostin turn R into Rue de Sombreuil then Ave de Groix, site sp. Lge, hdg/mkd pitch, pt shd; wc; chem disp; baby facs; shwrs inc; el pnts (12A) inc; gas; Indtte; shop 1km; tradsmn; rest, snacks; bar; BBQ; playgrnd; sand beach adj; games area; games rm; cycle hire; golf 15km; entmnt; TV; 20% statics; dogs €3; Eng spkn; adv bkg; quiet; ccard acc; red low ssn/CKE/CCI. "Pleasant site; gd sized pitches; gd amenities; gd for families; popular with surfers; vg." ♦ 1 Apr-30 Sep. € 23.00 2010*

ST POL DE LEON *1D2* (2km E Coastal) *48.69103, -3.9673* **Camping Ar Kleguer, Plage de Ste Anne, 29250 St Pol-de-Léon [02 98 69 18 81; fax 02 98 29 12 84; info@camping-ar-kleguer.com; www.camping-ar-kleguer.com]** In St Pol-de-Léon foll Centre Ville sp. At cathedral sq (2 towers) with cathedral on L descend hill & in 150m, bef church with tall belfry, turn L foll Plage & camping sp. On reaching sea turn L (N); site at end, well sp. NB Narr, busy rds in town. Med, mkd pitch, terr, pt sl, pt shd; wc (some cont); chem disp; mv service pnt; baby facs; shwrs inc; el pnts (10A) €4.20 (long lead poss req); Indtte; shops 500m; tradsmn; snacks; bar; htd pool; paddling pool; waterslide; beach adj; tennis; games rm; 40% statics; dogs €2.80; poss cr; adv bkg; poss noisy; CKE/CCI. "Well-kept, attractive site; modern facs; gd views; conv Roscoff ferry." 1 Apr-30 Sep. € 18.70 2009*

ST POL DE LEON *1D2* (2km E Coastal) *48.69355, -3.96930* **Camping de Trologot, Grève du Man, 29250 St Pol-de-Léon [02 98 69 06 26 or 06 62 16 39 30 (mob); fax 02 98 29 18 30; camping-trologot@wanadoo.fr; www.camping-trologot.com]** Fr the port of Roscoff take D58 go briefly on the D769 then back on to the D58 foll the sp to Morlaix over six rndabts (approx 4miles/6.5km). Just after passing under a rlwy bdge, take the exit for the D769 (sp St Pol de Léon, Kerlaudy, Penzé) then turn L. Stay on the D769 for 1.8 km, just past the graveyard turn R at the rndabt and go strt over the next rndabt (sp Campings/Plage) at the end of the rd turn L and the turning for the site will be on L after 1km and is sp. Do not use SatNav. Fr the E on the N12 take the exit for the D19 (sp Morlaix St pol de Leon) at the rndabt take the 2nd exit cont twds St-Pol-de Leon on the D58. Take the exit to the D769 (SP St-Pol-de Leon) then foll above dirs fr the graveyard. Med, hdg/mkd pitch, unshd; wc (some cont); chem disp; mv service pnt; baby facs; shwrs inc; el pnts (10A) €3.65; Indtte (inc dryer); sm shop & 600m; tradsmn; snacks; bar; BBQ (gas/charcoal only); playgrnd; htd pool; paddling pool; sm sand beach adj; wifi; entmnt; games/TV rm; 20% statics; dogs €2.05; no c'vans/m'vans over 7m high ssn; poss cr; adv bkg; quiet; ccard acc; red long stay/low ssn/CKE/CCI. "Lovely, well-kept site; ideal NH for Roscoff ferry; gd sized pitches; helpful owners; clean, modern san facs; gd for family beach holiday; peaceful area, many walks nrby; beautiful town; highly rec." ♦ 1 May-29 Sep. € 18.50 (CChq acc) SBS - B29 2013*

ST POL DE LEON *1D2* (5km SE Coastal) *48.65805, -3.92805* **Yelloh! Village Les Mouettes, La Grande Grève, 29660 Carantec [02 98 67 02 46; fax 02 98 78 31 46; camping@les-mouettes.com; www.les-mouettes.com / www.yellohvillage.co.uk]** Fr Morlaix take D58 N sp Roscoff; at lge rndabt turn R sp Carantec on D173; turn L at 1st rndabt; strt on at 2nd & 3rd rndabt past Casino supmkt; turn L next rndabt; site on L. Or fr Roscoff take D58 sp Mortaix, then D173 to Carantec; foll sp town cent, then site. Lge, mkd pitch, pt shd; wc; chem disp; mv service pnt; baby facs; shwrs inc; sauna/jaccuzi; el pnts (10A) inc (poss rev pol); gas; Indtte (inc dryer); shop; snacks; 2 bars; BBQ (charcoal only); playgrnd; htd pool complex (1 covrd); waterslide; paddling pool; sand/shgl beach 1km; fishing; golf 1.5km; tennis; cycle hire; games area; wifi; entmnt; games/TV rm; 50% statics; dogs €5; no c'vans/m'vans over 8m; poss cr; Eng spkn; adv bkg; noise fr boatyard; ccard acc; red low ssn; CKE/CCI. "Attractive site with sea views; clean, modern san facs; impressive pool complex; plenty to do on site; mkt Thu." ♦ 11 Apr-6 Sep. € 46.00 SBS - B14 2011*

ST POL DE LEON *1D2* (7km SE Rural) *48.64912, -3.92126* **Camping Les Hortensias (Jacq), Kermen, 29660 Carantec [02 98 67 08 63; contact@leshortensias.fr; www.leshortensias.fr]** Fr Roscoff on D58 dir Morlaix. Turn L after approx 10km onto D173, then turn R at 1st rndabt, site in 200m, site sp. Sm, mkd pitch, unshd; wc; chem disp; mv service pnt; shwrs inc; el pnts (6A) €3; gas 3km; Indtte (inc dryer); shop 3km; playgrnd; htd, covrd pool 6km; beach 2.5km; dogs €0.80; adv bkg; quiet; CKE/CCI. "Conv Roscoff ferry; views of bay; friendly staff; poss unkempt low ssn; organic produce in shop; gd touring base; no gates allows early deparature; excel NH." ♦ 1 May-30 Sep. € 12.56 2013*

ST POL DE LEON *1D2* (6km S Urban) *48.63476, -3.92962* **Camp Municipal de Kerilis, Menez Izella, 29670 Henvic [02 98 62 82 10 or 02 98 62 81 11 (Mairie); fax 02 98 62 81 56; commune-henvic@wanadoo.fr]** Exit D58 (St Pol-de-Léon to Morlaix rd) at Henvic; foll sp. Site 800m after exit main rd, behind football stadium. NB 2m height barrier open 0830-1230 & 1300-2000, so unsuitable late arr/early deps. Med, pt shd; wc; shwrs inc; el pnts €2.10 (poss long lead req); Indry rm; supmkt nr; playgrnd; sand beach 8km; quiet; CKE/CCI. "Pleasant, simple, well-run site; helpful warden; access only poss bef 1230 or bet 1630 & 1900 (2011), or phone Mairie in office hours." 1 Jul-31 Aug. € 9.45 2009*

ST POL DE LEON *1D2* (6km W Coastal) *48.68622, -4.07682* **Camping Ar Roc'h, Moguériec, 29250 Sibiril [02 98 29 97 14]** S fr Roscoff on D58 for approx 6km, then take D10 W & in 4km turn N to Moguériec. Site sp just bef ent Moguériec. Sm, hdg/mkd pitch, unshd; wc; chem disp; shwrs €1; el pnts (2-4A) €2.80; Indry rm; BBQ; sand beach 500m; no statics; dogs €1; quiet; CKE/CCI. "Well-kept, pretty site; old facs but well-maintained; gd views across estuary fr some pitches; vg." 15 Jun-15 Sep. € 14.00 2010*

⊞ **ST POL DE LEON** *1D2* (7km W Coastal) *48.68972, -4.08396* **Camp du Theven, Moguériec, 29250 Sibiril [02 98 29 96 86; fax 02 98 61 23 30; roudaut.theven.29@wanadoo.fr; http://camping.theven.29.pagesperso-orange.fr]** Fr Roscoff ferry on D58, at junc with D10 take Sibiril/Cléder turn. In Sibiril pass church & turn R past water tower, foll sp Port de Moguériec, site sp. Sm, hdg/mkd pitch, terr, pt shd; wc; shwrs €1; el pnts (4-6A) €3.80; Indtte; shop; supmkt 5km; snacks; bar; BBQ; playgrnd; sand/rocky beach adj; fishing; boat hire; entmnt; 90% statics; dogs €1; Eng spkn; adv bkg; quiet; CKE/CCI. "Friendly, helpful owner; liable to close for 10 day periods low ssn - phone ahead to check open; san facs ltd & need refurb (2010)." € 11.40 2010*

"I need an on-site restaurant"

We do our best to make sure site information is correct, but it is always best to check any must-have facilities are still available or will be open during your visit.

ST QUAY PORTRIEUX *2E3* (600m NW Coastal) *48.66269, -2.84550* **Camping Bellevue, 68 Blvd du Littoral, 22410 St Quay-Portrieux [02 96 70 41 84; fax 02 96 70 55 46; campingbellevue22@orange.fr; www.campingbellevue.net]** Foll D786 thro St Quay-Portrieux twd Paimpol; turn R at traff lts sp St Quay-Portrieux; foll site sp; site in 2.5km. Lge, hdg/mkd pitch, hdstg, pt sl, terr, pt shd; wc (some cont); chem disp; mv service pnt; baby facs; shwrs inc; el pnts (6A) €3; gas; Indtte (inc dryer); shop; tradsmn; snacks; BBQ; playgrnd; htd pool; paddling pool; sand beach adj & 600m; games area; golf 3km; wifi; TV rm; 8% statics; dogs free; Eng spkn; adv bkg; quiet; ccard acc; red low ssn; CKE/CCI. "Beautiful position with sea views; direct access to sm cove; friendly staff; gd, clean facs; vg." ♦ 28 Apr-16 Sep. € 19.20 2011*

ST RENAN *2E1* (2km NW Urban) *48.43899, -4.62959* **Camp Municipal Lokournan, Route de Brêles, 29290 St Renan [02 98 84 37 67 or 02 98 84 20 08 (Mairie); fax 02 98 32 43 20]** On D27 fr St Renan dir Lanildut, site sp in 2km. Sm, hdg pitch, pt sl, pt shd; wc; chem disp; shwrs inc; el pnts €3.10; shop 1km; no statics; dogs; adv bkg; CKE/CCI. "Vg." ♦ ltd 1 Jun-15 Sep. € 9.00 2010*

SARZEAU *2G3* (7km SE Coastal) *47.50551, -2.68308* **Camping Manoir de Ker An Poul, 1 Route de la Grée, Penvins, 56370 Sarzeau [02 97 67 33 30; fax 02 97 67 44 83; manoirdekeranpoul@wanadoo.fr; www.manoirdekeranpoul.com]** Fr E exit N165 1km E of Muzillac, sp Sarzeau D20 & cont approx 20km to junc of D20 & D199, S on D199 sp Penvins. Fr W, 6km E of Vannes, exit N165 onto N780 sp Sarzeau, in 9.5km S onto D199 sp Penvins. Lge, hdg pitch, pt sl, pt shd; wc (some cont); chem disp; baby facs; shwrs inc; el pnts (6-10A) €4; Indtte (inc dryer); shop; rest adj; snacks; bar; BBQ; playgrnd; htd pool; sand beach 700m; tennis; games area; cycle hire; wifi; entmnt; TV rm; 30% statics; dogs €4; poss cr; Eng spkn; adv bkg; quiet; red low ssn; CKE/CCI. "Spacious pitches; warm welcome; lovely situation in grnds of chateau." ♦ 3 Apr-25 Sep. € 25.00 2010*

See advertisement

"Satellite navigation makes touring much easier"

Remember most sat navs don't know if you're towing or in a larger vehicle – always use yours alongside maps and site directions.

SARZEAU *2G3* (2.5km S Coastal) *47.50720, -2.76083* **Camping La Ferme de Lann Hoëdic, Rue Jean de la Fontaine, Route de Roaliguen, 56370 Sarzeau [02 97 48 01 73; contact@camping-lannhoedic.fr; www.camping-lannhoedic.fr]** Fr Vannes on N165 turn onto D780 dir Sarzeau. Do not ent Sarzeau, but at Super U rndabt foll sp Le Roaliguen. After 1.5km turn L to Lann Hoëdic. Med, mkd pitch, pt shd; htd wc; chem disp; mv service pnt; baby facs; fam bthrm; shwrs inc; el pnts (10A) €3.20; gas; Indtte (inc dryer); shop 800m; tradsmn; rest 2km; snacks; bar 1km; playgrnd; sand beach 800m; cycle hire; wifi; 10% statics; dogs €2; phone; Eng spkn; adv bkg; quiet; red low ssn; CKE/CCI. "Peaceful, well-managed, family-run site; warm welcome; excel, clean facs; beautiful coastline - beaches & dunes; highly rec." ♦ 1 Apr-31 Oct. € 17.80 (CChq acc) 2011*

SARZEAU *2G3* (4km S Coastal/Rural) *47.50589, -2.77139* **Camping An Trest, Route de la Plage de Roaliguen, 56370 Sarzeau [02 97 41 79 60; fax 02 97 41 36 21; letreste@campingletreste.com; www.an-trest.com]** Fr E on D780 turn L at 1st rndabt nr Super U supmkt sp Le Roaliguen, site sp on L. NB ignore R turn to Sarzeau after sp Port Navalo. Lge, hdg/mkd pitch, pt sl, pt shd; wc (some cont); chem disp; baby facs; shwrs inc; el pnts (10A) €4.20; gas; Indtte (inc dryer); supmkt 2km; tradsmn; snacks; bar in ssn; BBQ; playgrnd; htd pool & paddling pool; waterslide; sand beach 800m; tennis, horseriding, golf 3km; wifi; TV rm; 5% statics; dogs €2.50; phone; Eng spkn; adv bkg; quiet; 20% red low ssn; ccard acc; CKE/CCI. "Pleasant, well-run site; gd touring base; helpful owners." ♦ Easter-26 Sep. € 23.50 2010*

SARZEAU *2G3* (2km SW Rural) *47.52255, -2.79713* **Lodge Club Presqu'île de Rhuys (formerly Le Bohat), Route d'Arzon Lower Bohat, 56370 Sarzeau [02 97 41 78 68; fax 02 97 41 71 97; info@lodgeclub.fr; www.lodgeclub.fr]** Fr Vannes on N165, exit onto D780 to Sarzeau. Do not turn off this main rd to Sarzeau (town not suitable for m'vans or c'vans) but cont twd Arzon; 1km after 2nd rndabt turn L for Le Bohat & Spernec, then take 1st R. Fr S on N165 take D20 at Muzillac, thro Surzur & cont to join D780 to Sarzeau. Then as above. Lge, hdg/mkd pitch, pt shd; wc; chem disp; mv service pnt; baby facs; shwrs inc; el pnts (10A) inc; gas; Indtte; shop; tradsmn; rest, snacks; bar; BBQ (gas/charcoal); playgrnd; 2 htd pools (1 covrd); paddling pool; waterslide; sand beach, watersports 4km; fishing; cycle hire; golf 6km; pony rides; horseriding 2km; wifi; entmnt; games/TV rm; 4% statics; dogs €3.70; phone; poss cr; Eng spkn; adv bkg; quiet; ccard acc; red low ssn; CKE/CCI. "Busy, well-kept, Dutch-owned site; lge pitches; excel, helpful staff; clean san facs; excel pools; gd for families; cycle tracks; gd touring base; mkt Thu; vg." ♦ 5 Apr-29 Sep. € 34.30 SBS - B07 2012*

SARZEAU *2G3* (3km SW Rural) *47.50941, -2.80747* **Camping à la Ferme L'Abri-Côtier (Rio), 90 Route de Sarzeau, 56730 St Gildas-de-Rhuys [02 97 45 27 42 or 06 11 97 31 76 (mob); contact@abri-cotier.com; www.abri-cotier.com]** Fr Sarzeau take D198 sp St Gildas-de-Rhuys. Site in 3km. Med, hdg/mkd pitch, pt shd; wc; chem disp; mv service pnt; baby facs; fam bthrm; shwrs inc; el pnts (10A) €3 (poss long lead req); gas; Indtte; shop, rest & bar 2km; tradsmn; snacks; BBQ (charcoal/gas); beach 2.5km; games area; wifi; TV; dogs €1; bus 100m; Eng pkn; adv bkg; v quiet; ccard acc. "Well-run, clean, reliable site; lge pitches; friendly staff; cannot fault!" ♦ 1 Apr-30 Sep. € 15.00 2011*

SARZEAU *2G3* (5km SW Coastal) *47.48976, -2.80075* **Camping Saint Jacques, 1 Rue Pratel Vihan, 56370 Sarzeau [02 97 41 79 29; fax 02 97 48 04 45; info@camping-stjacques.com; www.camping-stjacques.com]** Fr Sarzeau on D780, at 2nd rndabt foll dir St Jacques, site sp. Lge, mkd pitch, pt shd; wc (come cont); chem disp; baby facs; shwrs inc; el pnts (4-6A) €2.55; gas; Indtte; shop; snacks; bar; BBQ; playgrnd; sand beach adj; tennis; fishing; sailing school; cycle hire; entmnt; 10% statics; dogs €1; Eng spkn; adv bkg; quiet; red low ssn; ccard acc; CKE/CCI. "Poss untidy site; many long-stay c'vans; excel beach & dunes; gd sea sw; NH only." ♦ 1 Apr-30 Sep. € 13.55 2009*

SARZEAU *2G3* (6km W Coastal) *47.52865, -2.84772* **Camping du Menhir, La Saline, 56730 St Gildas-de-Rhuys [02 97 45 22 88; contact@camping-bretagnesud.com; www.camping-bretagnesud.com]** Take D780 Vannes-Port Navalo rd; 6km after Sarzeau turn L sp La Saline & Camping Menhir. Lge, mkd pitch, pt shd; wc; baby facs; shwrs inc; el pnts (6-10A) €4-5; gas; Indtte (inc dryer); sm shop high ssn or 3km; tradsmn; rest, snacks; bar; playgrnd; htd pool; waterslides; paddling pool; sand beach 1km; tennis; games area; games rm; dogs €3; adv bkg; quiet; red low ssn. "Lge pitches; gd san facs; excel." ♦ 26 May-6 Sep. € 29.50 2009*

SCAER *2F2* (200m E Rural) *48.02765, -3.69628* **Camp Municipal de Kérisole, Rue Pasteur, 29390 Scaër [02 98 57 60 91 or 02 98 59 42 10 (LS); fax 02 98 57 66 89; mairie.scaer@altica.com; www.ville-scaer.fr]** Fr N165 take D70 to Rosporden, then N on D782, site well sp in Scaër. Thro town foll sp to site. Med, pt sl, pt shd; wc; chem disp; mv service pnt; baby facs; shwrs; el pnts (10A) €2.65; Indtte (inc dryer); shop, rest, snacks & bar 300m; playgrnd; pool 700m; fishing; 5% statics; dogs; Eng spkn; adv bkg; quiet; CKE/CCI. "Site at ent to forest, forest walk adj; excel san facs; isolated at night, gate locked 2200; warden visits 2hrs am, 2hrs pm; vill poorly served with rests/bars; fair." ♦ 15 Jun-31 Aug. € 10.00 2011*

"There aren't many sites open at this time of year"

If you're travelling outside peak season remember to call ahead to check site opening dates – even if the entry says 'open all year'.

SERENT *2F3* (500m NE Rural) *47.82479, -2.50182* **Camp Municipal du Pont Salmon, Rue Général de Gaulle, 56460 Sérent [02 97 75 91 98 or 06 61 09 49 56; mairie.serent@fr.oleane.com; www.serent.fr]** S fr Ploërmel on N166 take D10 W 5km to Sérent. At E end of vill turn R twd Le Pont Salmon, site on R. Med, hdg pitch, pt sl, pt shd; htd wc (male all cont); chem disp; mv service pnt; shwrs inc; el pnts (10A) €2.35 (poss rev pol); Indtte (inc dryer); shops 300m; BBQ; playgrnd; htd pool; 5% statics; adv bkg; quiet. "Excel, well-kept site; gd san facs; Resistance Museum at St Marcel-Malestroit." ♦ ltd 1 Jun-31 Aug. € 8.00 2009*

SIBIRIL see St Pol de Léon *1D2*

SIXT SUR AFF see Gacilly, La *2F3*

SIZUN *2E2* (1km S Rural) *48.40038, -4.07635* **Camp Municipal du Gollen, 29450 Sizun [02 98 24 11 43 or 02 98 68 80 13 (Mairie); fax 02 98 68 86 56; mairie.sizun@wanadoo.fr; www.mairie-sizun.fr]** Fr Roscoff take D788 SW onto D69 to Landivisiau, D30 & D764 to Sizun. In Sizun take D18 at rndabt. At end of by-pass, at next rndabt, take 3rd exit. Site adj pool. Sm, pt shd; wc (some cont); shwrs inc; el pnts (10A) 2.50 (poss rev pol); Indry rm; shops 500m; playgrnd; htd pool adj high ssn; phone; no twin-axles; poss cr; no adv bkg; quiet; ccard not acc; CKE/CCI. "Lovely little site; simple & restful by rv in nature park; friendly recep; site yourself if warden not avail; vg." 16 Apr-30 Sep. € 10.50 2011*

SURZUR *2G3* (1.5km NE Urban) *47.58775, -2.61913* **Camping Ty-Coët, 38 rue du Bois, 56450 Surzur [02 97 42 09 05; contact@camping-tycoet.com; www.camping-tycoet.com]** N165/E60 Vannes-Nantes. Take Exit 22. D183 twd Surzur. At rndabt bef Surzur cont onto D183, then 1st L onto Rue des Lutins. Foll sp to site. Med, hdg pitch, mkd pitch, unshd; wc; chem disp; baby facs, fam bthrm; shwr; el pnts(16A); lndtte (inc dryer); tradsmn; snacks; bar; BBQ; playgrnd; sw 0.5km; games area; games rm; wifi; 50% statics; dogs €1; bus 0.5km; twin axles; Eng spkn; adv bkg; quiet; CCI. "BBQ except Jul & Aug; conv for Golfe de Morbihan; gd mkt in Vannes (Sat & Tue); lovely, quiet, well-kept site with super clean san facs; excel." ♦ ltd 1 Jan-15 Nov. € 23.00 2014*

TADEN see Dinan *2E3*

TAUPONT see Ploërmel *2F3*

TELGRUC SUR MER *2E2* (1km S Coastal) *48.22386, -4.37223* **Camping Le Panoramic, 130 Route de la Plage, 29560 Telgruc-sur-Mer [02 98 27 78 41; fax 02 98 27 36 10; info@camping-panoramic.com; www.camping-panoramic.com]** Fr D887 Crozon-Châteaulin rd, turn W on D208 twd Trez-Bellec Plage, site sp on R in approx 1.5km. Med, hdg/mkd pitch, terr, pt shd, wc (some cont); chem disp; mv service pnt; baby facs; shwrs inc, el pnts (6-10A) €3.50-4.50; lndtte (inc dryer); shop & rest ltd opening time; snacks; bar; BBQ; playgrnd; htd, covrd pool; paddling pool; jacuzzi; sand beach 700m; tennis; cycle hire; games rm; wifi; TV rm; some statics; dogs €2; adv bkg; quiet; ccard acc; red low ssn; CKE/CCI. "Vg, well-run, welcoming site; access to pitches poss diff due trees & narr site rds; rec; some facs tired need updating; sea views; excel rest, pool & all facs; helpful owner." ♦ 1 May-15 Sep. € 34.40 2014*

See advertisement

TELGRUC SUR MER *2E2* (2.5km S Coastal) *48.21003, -4.36881* **Camping Pen-Bellec, Trez Bellec, 29560 Telgruc-sur-Mer [02 98 27 31 87 or 02 98 27 76 55; camping.penbellec@orange.fr; www.camping-telgruc.fr]** Fr D887 turn S onto D208 for Telgruc-sur-Mer. In Telgruc take rd mkd 'Plage Trez Bellec' & cont to far end where rd rises & turns inland. Sm, mkd pitch, unshd; wc; mv service pnt; shwrs €1.50; el pnts (3A) €3; shop 3km; tradsmn; rest 3km; playgrnd; sand beach adj; watersports adj; cycle hire; games area; dogs €1.50; poss cr; Eng spkn; adv bkg; poss noisy. "Excel location by beach with views; well-kept; friendly, helpful owners; san facs adequate; exposed in bad weather; gd cliff walking; gd touring base; highly rec." Jun-Sep. € 11.50 2011*

TELGRUC SUR MER *2E2* (1.5km SW Coastal) *48.22553, -4.37103* **Camping L'Armorique, 112 Rue de la Plage, 29560 Telgruc-sur-Mer [02 98 27 77 33; fax 02 98 27 38 38; contact@campingarmorique.com; www.campingarmorique.com]** Fr D887 Châteaulin to Crozon; turn S on D208 at sea end of Telgruc-sur-Mer. NB Steep hairpins on site access rds poss diff long/low powered o'fits. Med, hdg/mkd pitch, terr, pt shd; wc; chem disp; mv service pnt; baby facs; shwrs inc; el pnts (10A) €3.50; shop; lndtte (inc dryer); tradsmn; snacks; takeaway; bar; playgrnd; htd pool; waterslide pool; paddling pool; sand beach 700m; deep-sea diving, climbing & horseriding nrby; games area; games rm; entmnt; wifi; TV; 20% statics; dogs €2.50; adv bkg; quiet; ccard acc; red low ssn; CKE/CCI. "Pleasant, peaceful, well-wooded site; run by enthusiastic couple; clean san facs; lge playgrnd; walking & cycling rtes nrby; vg." ♦ ltd 2 Apr-30 Sep. € 19.00 (CChq acc) 2011*

TELGRUC SUR MER *2E2* (1km W Coastal) *48.22696, -4.36844* **Camping Les Mimosas, Kergreis, 106 Rue de la Plage, 29560 Telgruc-sur-Mer [tel/fax 02 98 27 76 06; campingmimosa@wanadoo.fr; www.campingmimosa.com]** Fr D887 Crozon-Châteaulin rd turn SW onto D208 into Telgruc. Fr town sq foll sp Trez-Bellec-Plage. In 900m, after exiting town, turn L & L, site clearly sp. Med, hdg/mkd pitch, terr, pt shd; wc; chem disp; shwrs inc; el pnts (10A) €1.80; lndtte; shop 600m; sand beach 1km; playgrnd; tennis; dogs €0.80; poss cr; adv bkg rec high ssn; quiet; CKE/CCI. "Gd." 1 Apr-30 Sep. € 10.20 2009*

TINTENIAC *2E4* (500m N Rural) *48.33111, -1.83315* **Camp Municipal du Pont L'Abbesse, Rue du 8 Mai 1945, 35190 Tinténiac [02 99 68 09 91 or 02 99 68 02 15 (Mairie); fax 02 99 68 05 44]** Fr D137 turn E onto D20 to Tinténiac; go strt thro vill to canal; sp just bef canal bdge; turn L. Site behind Brit Hôtel La Guinguette, on Canal d'Ille et Rance. Sm, hdg/mkd pitch, pt sl, pt shd; htd wc; shwrs; el pnts inc; shops, rest, snacks & bar adj; playgrnd; fishing; few statics; quiet; CKE/CCI. "Delightful, busy site; gd san facs; lovely walks/cycling along canal." ♦ 1 Mar-31 Oct. € 10.00 2013*

TINTENIAC *2E4* (2km S Rural) *48.31058, -1.82027* **Camping Les Peupliers, Manoir de la Besnelais, 35190 Tinténiac [02 99 45 49 75; fax 02 99 45 52 98; camping.les.peupliers@wanadoo.fr; www.les-peupliers-camping.fr]** On D137 Rennes to St Malo rd; after Hédé foll rd to Tinténiac about 2km; site on main rd on R, sp. Med, hdg/mkd pitch, pt sl, pt shd; wc (some cont); chem disp; mv service pnt; shwrs inc; el pnts (6A) €2.90 (poss rev pol); Indtte; shops 2km; tradsmn high ssn; rest, snacks; bar; playgrnd; htd pool; lake fishing; tennis; games area; internet; TV rm; 30% statics; dogs €1.60; phone; adv bkg; red low ssn; CKE/CCI. "Pleasant, quiet, well-kept site; gd pool & park; on pilgrim rte to Spain." ♦ ltd 1 Apr-30 Sep. € 18.20 2010*

TOUR DU PARC, LE see Sarzeau *2G3*

TREBEURDEN *1D2* (4km N Coastal) *48.79078, -3.55787* **Camping L'Espérance, Penvern, 22560 Trébeurden [02 96 91 95 05; fax 02 96 91 98 12; accueil@camping-esperance.com; www.camping-esperance.com]** Fr Lannion on D65 to Trébeurden, then D788 sp Trégastel, site in 5km. Med, hdg/mkd pitch, pt shd; wc (some cont); chem disp; mv service pnt; baby facs; shwrs inc; el pnts (5-10A) €2.80-3.50; gas; Indtte; shop 2km; playgrnd; sand beach adj; golf adj; TV; 10% statics; dogs €1.50; bus; Eng spkn; adv bkg; quiet; ccard not acc; CKE/CCI. "Pleasant site; some pitches sm; nr GR34 long dist walking rte." ♦ 1 Apr-30 Sep. € 16.80 2010*

TREBEURDEN *1D2* (3.5km NW Coastal) *48.79905, -3.58386* **Camp Municipal Le Dourlin, L'Île Grande, 22560 Pleumeur-Bodou [02 96 91 92 41 or 02 96 23 91 17 (Mairie); infos.tourisme@pleumeur-bodou.com; www.pleumeur-bodou.com]** Off D788 N fr Trébeurden. Foll minor rd thro vill to site on coast. Well sp. Med, mkd pitch, unshd; wc; chem disp; mv service pnt; shwrs inc; el pnts (6A) €2.35; Indtte; shops 500m; supmkt nrby; rest, snacks; bar; BBQ; playgrnd; sand/shgl beach adj; sailing; fishing; games area; wifi; dogs €0.60; phone; bus; poss cr; Eng spkn; quiet; CKE/CCI. "Popular site in excel location - fine sea views; excel facs; gd walking, cycling; ornithological cent nr; 8km circular coast rd round peninsula; gd." ♦ 30 Apr-27 Sep. € 8.75 2010*

TREDION *2F3* (1.3km S Rural) *47.78295, -2.59060* **Camp Municipal l'Etang aux Biches, Route d'Elven, 56350 Trédion [02 97 67 14 06; fax 02 97 67 13 41]** E fr Vannes on N166 for 15km to Elven; in town foll sps N on D1 for Trédion. Site on L in 5km. Sm, hdg/mkd pitch, pt sl, pt shd; wc; shwrs €1.10; el pnts (3A) €1.90; shop 1.5km; tradsmn; playgrnd; quiet. "Peaceful; inland fr v busy coast." ♦ 1 Jul-31 Aug. € 5.40 2010*

TREGASTEL *1D2* (1.5km N Coastal) *48.82549, -3.49135* **Tourony Camping, 105 Rue de Poul-Palud, 22730 Trégastel [02 96 23 86 61; fax 02 96 15 97 84; contact@camping-tourony.com; www.camping-tourony.com]** On D788 fr Trébeurden dir Perros Guirec, site on R immed after exit Trégastel town sp & immed bef bdge over Traouieros inlet, opp Port de Ploumanac'h. Med, hdg/mkd pitch, pt shd; wc (some cont); chem disp; mv service pnt; baby facs; shwrs inc; el pnts (6A) €3; gas; Indtte; shop 400m; tradsmn; snacks; bar; BBQ; playgrnd; sand beach adj; lake fishing; tennis; cycle hire; games area; golf, horseriding nrby; entmnt; TV; 15% statics; dogs €1.50; Eng spkn; adv bkg; quiet; ccard acc; red long stay/low ssn; CKE/CCI. "Pleasant site in gd location; friendly, helpful staff; gd touring base Granit Rose coast." ♦ 4 Apr-25 Sep. € 17.40 2009*

TREGASTEL *1D2* (3km W Coastal/Rural) *48.80995, -3.54140* **Camping du Port, 3 Chemin des Douaniers, 22560 Landrellec [02 96 23 87 79 or 06 73 78 32 64 (mob); renseignements@camping-du-port-22.com; www.camping-du-port-22.com]** Turn off D788 to Landrellec & foll rd thro vill past shop for 100m, take care tight turn L. Site in 500m. Med, hdg/mkd pitch, pt sl, pt shd; htd wc; chem disp; mv service pnt; serviced pitches; baby facs; shwrs inc; el pnts (10-15A) €3.20-3.50; gas; Indtte (inc dryer); shop; tradsmn; rest, snacks; bar; BBQ; playgrnd; pool 2km; direct access to sandy/rocky beach; fishing, boating, waterskiing; cycle hire; games rm; wifi; entmnt; TV rm; 25% statics; dogs €2.50; Eng spkn; adv bkg; quiet; ccard acc; red low ssn; CKE/CCI. "Immac, family-owned site; beautiful location; direct access beach; beach front pitches extra charge but narr; coastal path runs thro site; lots of lovely beaches nrby; telecoms museum worth visit; excel." ♦ 3 Apr-3 Oct. € 17.00 2011*

See advertisement

TREGUENNEC see Pont l'Abbé *2F2*

TREGUIER *1D3* (8km N Coastal) *48.84877, -3.21065* **Camp Municipal de Beg Vilin, 22820 Plougrescant [02 96 92 56 15 or 02 96 92 51 18 (Mairie); fax 02 96 92 59 26; mairie.plougrescant@wanadoo.fr; www.plougrescant.fr]** Take D8 N out of Tréguier to Plougrescant. At St Gonéry/Plougrescant turn R foll sp. Site 1.5km NE of Plougrescant. Med, pt shd; wc; shwrs inc; el pnts €3.60; Indtte (inc dryer); shops 2km; tradsmn; sand/rock beach adj; some statics; dogs free; phone; quiet. "Quiet, peaceful site low ssn; busy, cr site high ssn; rocky beach, some sand; gd." ♦ 12 Jun-12 Sep. € 10.35 2010*

TREGUIER *1D3* (10km N Coastal) *48.85810, -3.22013* **FFCC Camping Le Varlen, 4 Pors-Hir, 22820 Plougrescant [02 96 92 52 15; fax 02 96 92 50 34; info@levarlen.com; www.levarlen.com]** Take D8 N out of Tréguier to Plougrescant. Go past old chapel then immed bef church turn R sp Pors-Hir to site in 1km on R. Sm, mkd pitch, pt sl, pt shd; wc; mv service pnt; baby facs; shwrs inc; el pnts (6-10A) €3.50-3.90 (poss rev pol); Indtte; shop; tradsmn; bar; playgrnd; sports area; shgl beach 300m; 90% statics; dogs €1.50; adv bkg; quiet; ccard acc; red low ssn. "Friendly, helpful owners; some pitches sm & poss diff lge o'fits/m'vans; coastal walks." 1 Mar-15 Nov. € 14.70 2013*

TREGUIER *1D3* (9km NE Coastal) *48.85537, -3.13231* **Camping Port La Chaîne, 22610 Pleubian [02 96 22 92 38; fax 02 96 22 87 92; info@portlachaine.com; www.portlachaine.com]** Fr Paimpol take old D786 W & pick up new D786 over estuary & thro Lézardrieux. After 3km at rndabt turn R (N) onto D33 thro Pleumeur-Gautier to Pleubian; then D20 twds Larmor-Pleubian; turn L after 2km twd coast & foll site sp. Lge, mkd pitch, pt sl, pt shd; wc (some cont); chem disp; serviced pitch; baby facs; shwrs inc; el pnts (16A) inc; gas; Indtte (inc dryer); tradsmn; rest, snacks; bar; BBQ (charcoal/gas); playgrnd; htd pool; paddling pool; shgl beach adj; watersports nr; sea-fishing; open air gym; cycle hire in vill; wifi; entmnt; games/TV rm; 30% statics; dogs €2.90; no c'vans/m'vans over 7m high ssn; poss cr; Eng spkn; adv bkg ess; quiet; ccard acc; red low ssn. "Lovely, peaceful site; excel views fr some pitches; helpful owners; gd clean san facs." ♦ 9 Apr-22 Sep. € 26.60 2011*

TREGUNC *2F2* (3km S Coastal) *47.81065, -3.85091* **Camping des Etangs de Trévignon, Kerlin, 29910 Trégunc [tel/fax 02 98 50 00 41; camp.etangdetrevignon@wanadoo.fr; www.camping-etangs.com]** Exit N165/E60 at Kérampaou. S on D122 to Trégunc, then cont S on D1 to Trévignon. Site in 3km. Foll sp. Lge, hdg/mkd pitch, pt shd; wc (some cont); chem disp; baby facs; shwrs inc; el pnts (5A) €3.20; gas; Indtte; shop 2km; tradsmn; rest 3km; snacks; bar; BBQ; playgrnd; htd, covrd pool high ssn; waterslide; sand beach 800m; cycle hire; TV rm; 5% statics; dogs €1.80; phone; Eng spkn; adv bkg; quiet; red low ssn/long stay; ccard acc; red CKE/CCI. "In nature reserve with bird sanctuary nr; excel." ♦ 1 Jun-15 Sep. € 20.50 2009*

TREGUNC *2F2* (5.5km S Coastal) *47.80705, -3.83863* **Camping La Pommeraie, St Philibert, 29910 Trégunc [02 98 50 02 73; fax 02 98 50 07 91; info@campingdelapommeraie.com; www.campingdelapommeraie.com]** Fr D783 bet Concarneau & Pont-Aven, turn S in Trégunc onto D1 twd Pointe de Trévignon. In 5.5km look for site sp. Turn L to St Philibert & Névez. Ent immed on L. Lge, hdg/mkd pitch, pt shd; wc (some cont); chem disp; shwrs inc; mv service pnt; some serviced pitches; el pnts (10A) €2; gas; Indtte; shop on site & 250m; rest, snacks; bar; playgrnd; htd pool; paddling pool; sand beach 1km; boating; fishing; games rm; cycle hire; entmnt; TV; 60% statics; dogs €3.50; Eng spkn; adv bkg; quiet; ccard acc; red low ssn; CKE/CCI. "Pleasant site in apple orchard; warm welcome." ♦ 1 May-26 Sep. € 29.00 2009*

TREGUNC *2F2* (3.5km SW Coastal) *47.83384, -3.89173* **Camping La Plage Loc'h Ven, Plage de Pendruc, 29910 Trégunc [02 98 50 26 20; fax 02 98 50 27 63; contact@lochven.com; www.lochven.com]** Fr N165 exit at Kérampaou sp Trégunc. At rndbt W of Trégunc foll Loc'h Ven sp thro Lambell, site on coast. Med, hdg/mkd pitch, pt sl, pt shd; htd wc; chem disp; baby facs; shwrs inc; el pnts (4-10A) €3.50-4.70; gas; Indtte; shop 4km; tradsmn; rest, snacks, bar 4km; playgrnd; sand/shgl beach adj; games area; TV; 40% statics; dogs free (€1.60 high ssn); poss cr; Eng spkn; adv bkg; quiet. "Easy walk to beach, rock pools & coastal footpath; helpful owners." 28 Apr-20 Sep. € 18.50 2014*

TRELEVERN see Perros Guirec *1D2*

TRINITE SUR MER, LA see Carnac *2G3*

VAL ANDRE, LE *2E3* (3km S Coastal) *48.58944, -2.55083* **Campéole Camping Les Monts Colleux, 26 Rue Jean Le Brun, 22370 Pléneuf-Val-André [02 96 72 95 10; fax 02 96 63 10 49; monts-colleux@campeole.com; www.camping-montscolleux.com / www.campeole.com]** Site 800m off D786 & off D78, sp fr Pléneuf town cent. Rec app only fr Pléneuf centre; at traff lts turn twds Les Plages, then site sp - adj municipal pool. Med, hdg/mkd pitch, hdstg, pt sl, pt shd; htd wc; chem disp; mv service pnt; shwrs inc; el pnts (6-10A) €4.10 (poss rev pol); Indtte (inc dryer); shops, rest nr; tradsmn; bar; BBQ; playgrnd; covrd pool adj; sand/shgl beach 300m; tennis; games area; golf 1km; wifi; entmnt; TV rm; 40% statics; dogs €2.60; phone; Eng spkn; adv bkg; quiet; ccard ac; red low ssn/CKE/CCI. "Pleasant combination of gd beach, port & vill with mkt; san facs basic but clean." ♦ 1 Apr-30 Sep. € 18.00 (CChq acc) 2009*

⊞ **VANNES** *2F3* (5km N Rural) *47.73035, -2.72795* **Camping du Haras, 5 Kersimon-Vannes/Meucon, 56250 Monterblanc [02 97 44 66 06 or 06 71 00 05 59 (mob); fax 02 97 44 49 41; contact@campingvannes.com; www.campingvannes.com]** App fr N165 turn L onto D767 sp Airport. Go N for 7km & turn R onto D778 for 1km & turn R again. After 1km approx, turn L onto Airport Perimeter Rd, site sp on W side. App fr N on D767, join D778 & as above. Med, hdg/mkd pitch, hdstg, pt shd; htd wc; chem disp; mv service pnt; fam bthrm; shwrs inc; el pnts (4-16A) €3-8; gas; Indtte (inc dryer); sm shop; tradsmn; snacks; bar; BBQ; playgrnd (covrd); htd pools (covrd); paddling pool; waterslides; sauna; wellness cent; sand beach 12km; lake sw 3km; fishing; tennis; horseriding 300m; trampoline; cycle hire; outdoor fitness; games rm; wifi €2; 30% statics; dogs €4; ltd facs low ssn; NH; Eng spkn; adv bkg; quiet with minimal airplane noise in the day; ccard acc; red long stay/long ssn/CKE/CCI. "Lovely site; ltd space for tourers; rec." ♦ € 36.00 2013*

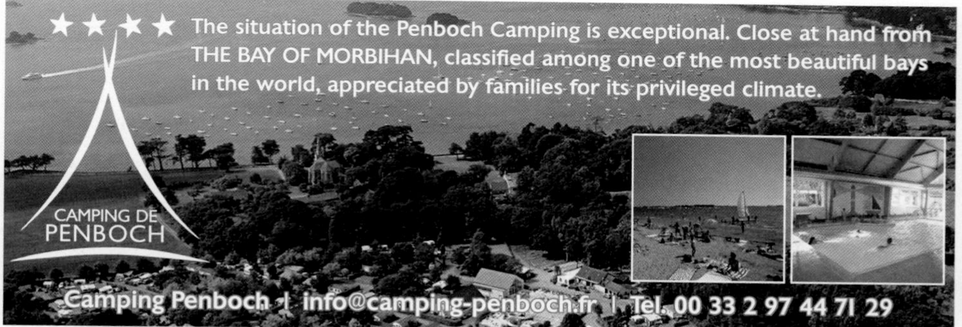

VANNES *2F3* (3km S Rural) *47.62754, -2.74117* **FFCC Camping Moulin de Cantizac, 2 Rue des Orchidées, 56860 Séné [tel/fax 02 97 66 90 26; info@camping-vannes.com; www.camping-vannes.com]** S fr Vannes on D199 twds Séné. Site on L at rndabt beside rv. Med, hdg pitch, pt sl, pt shd; wc (some cont); chem disp; baby facs; shwrs inc; el pnts (10A) €3.90; gas; Indtte (inc dryer); tradsmn; sm shop; snacks; playgrnd; htd pool; sand beach 4km; boating; games area; games rm; wifi; 10% statics; dogs €2.30; quiet; red low ssn. "Superb cent for birdwatching." 1 May-15 Oct. € 22.00 2010*

VANNES *2F3* (4km SW Coastal) *47.63365, -2.78008* **FFCC Camp Municipal de Conleau, 188 Ave Maréchal Juin, 56000 Vannes [02 97 63 13 88; fax 02 97 40 38 82; camping.conleau@flowercampings.com; www.vannes-camping.com]** Exit N165 at Vannes Ouest junc; Conleau sp on R. Site twd end of rd on R. If on N165 fr Auray take 1st exit sp Vannes & at 2nd rndabt R (sp) to avoid town cent. C'vans not allowed thro town cent. Lge, mkd pitch, pt sl, pt shd; wc; chem disp; mv service pnt; shwrs; el pnts (6A) €3.50 (some rev pol); Indtte; tradsmn; rest; bar; BBQ; playgrnd; htd pool; paddling pool; sea water pool nr; sand beach 300m; entmnt; wifi; TV; 10% statics; dogs €3; bus adj; twin axles; End spkn; adv bkg; quiet; ccard acc; red in low ssn; CKE/CCI. "Most pitches sl; sep area for m'vans by rd - little shd & poss long walk to san facs; v busy/noisy in high ssn; lovely easy walk to Port Conleau; site full of atmosphere - rec; vg." ♦ 5 Apr-28 Sep. € 33.00 2014*

VANNES *2F3* (5km SW Coastal) *47.62190, -2.80056* **Camping de Penboch, 9 Chemin de Penboch, 56610 Arradon [02 97 44 71 29; fax 02 97 44 79 10; camping.penboch@wanadoo.fr; www.camping-penboch.fr]** Exit Brest-Nantes N165 Vannes by-pass at junc with D127 sp Ploeren & Arradon. Foll sp Arradon. Site well sp. Lge, hdg/mkd pitch, pt shd; wc (some cont); chem disp; mv service pnt; baby facs; shwrs inc; el pnts (10A) inc (poss rev pol); gas; Indtte (inc dryer); sm shop on site & 2km; tradsmn; sm shop; snacks; bar; BBQ; playgrnd; 2 htd pools (1 covrd); paddling pools; waterslide; sand beach 200m; cycle hire 2km; games area; games rm; wifi; TV rm; some statics; dogs €3.50; no c'vans/m'vans over 7m high ssn; Eng spkn; adv bkg rec high ssn; quiet; ccard acc; red low ssn; CKE/CCI. "Excel site; gd clean san facs; some pitches sm; steel pegs req; o'flow area with facs; plenty for youngsters; 20 mins walk to Arradon; gd coast walks." ♦ 12 Apr-26 Sept. € 58.50 SBS - B33 2012*

See advertisement

VANNES *2F3* (6km SW Coastal) *47.62108, -2.84025* **Camping de l'Allée, 56610 Arradon [02 97 44 01 98; fax 02 97 44 73 74; contact@camping-allee.com; www.camping-allee.com]** Fr Vannes take D101 & D101A to Arradon. Take by-pass & take 1st exit at rndabt & foll sp. Site to SW of Arradon. Fr Auray on D101 turn R on C203 immed after Moustoir. App rd to site is narr. Med, some hdg/mkd pitch, pt sl, pt shd; wc; chem disp; baby facs; shwrs inc; el pnts (10A) €4.60 (poss long leads req); gas; Indtte; sm shop on site & 2km; tradsmn; snacks; playgrnd; htd pool; shgl beach 600m; games/TV rm; 5% statics; dogs €2; poss cr; Eng spkn; adv bkg; quiet; red low ssn; CKE/CCI. "Delightful, helpful, family-run site partly in orchard; site yourself if office clsd; immac modern san facs; gd walks; gd touring base; highly rec; roomy site with gd atmosphere; rec." ♦ 1 Apr-30 Sep. € 34.45 2014*

VITRE *2F4* (14km N Rural) *48.23090, -1.18087* **Camp Municipal du Lac, 35210 Châtillon-en-Vendelais [02 99 76 06 32 or 02 99 76 06 22 (Mairie); fax 02 99 76 12 39]** Take D178 fr Vitré to Fougères. In 11km branch L onto D108, sp Châtillon-en-Vendelais. Foll sp thro vill & turn R immed after level x-ing & bef bdge; site in 1km. Med, pt sl, pt shd; wc; shwrs inc; el pnts (6A) €3.10 (poss rev pol); Indtte; shop & 1km; playgrnd; tennis; lake adj; fishing; 10% statics; quiet; CKE/CCI. "Pleasant site; clean san facs; warden on site 0900-1000 only; levelling blocks req most pitches; quiet low ssn; gd walks; nature reserve (birds) nr." 15 May-30 Sep. € 11.50 2012*

VIVIER SUR MER, LE see Dol de Bretagne *2E4*

Burgundy
Regional Introduction

Chalon-sur-Saône

Welcome to Burgundy

A great historical region of France popular with tourists, Burgundy is famous for its fine and expensive wines.

The area's colourful history has produced a rich heritage of Romanesque architecture, still standing as testaments to the skilled labourers of the time.

After a long day of sightseeing and exploring all that the region has to offer, round the evening off by trying one of the many local liqueurs. Marcs liqueur is very popular in Burgundy but also well known outside of France and achieves its rich flavour by maturing for years in oak casks.

Local highlights

Numerous celebrations, fairs, fetes and carnivals are held throughout the year but the high point is the 'vendange', or harvest, which concludes with three days of feasting, tasting and auctions.

Similar to other regions of France, Burgundy has been producing famous cheeses and wines since Roman times. Bresse chicken, Charolles beef and Dijon mustard are a few of the well-known dishes from the area.

Major towns and cities

- Auxerre – the River Yonne is the main focal point of this historical port town.
- Beaune – this walled city is known as the centre for Burgundy wines.
- Dijon – capital city of Burgundy, filled with medieval and Renaissance buildings.
- Chalon-sur-Saône – an old town with a picturesque centre and ancient narrow streets.

Regional attractions

- Musée de l'Hotel-Dieu – a historical hospital dating back to the 15th century.
- St Madeleine – a huge medieval cathedral dominating the village of Vezelay.
- L'Abbaye de Fontenay – one of the oldest Cistercian abbeys in Europe.
- Cathédrale St-Etienne – the oldest of the Gothic cathedrals in France.

Find out more

www.burgundy-tourism.com

Tel: (0)3 80 26 21 30 Beaune Tourist Office
Tel: (0)8 92 70 05 58 Dijon Tourist Office

AMPILLY LE SEC see Châtillon sur Seine *6F1*

ANDRYES see Clamecy *4G4*

ARNAY LE DUC *6H1* (1km E Rural) *47.13388, 4.49835* **Camping L'Etang de Fouché, Rue du 8 Mai 1945, 21230 Arnay-le-Duc [03 80 90 02 23; fax 03 80 90 11 91; info@campingfouche.com; www.campingfouche.com]** App by D906 to Arnay (site sp); turn E onto D17, site on R in 2km. Lge, hdg/mkd pitch, hdstg, pt shd; htd wc; chem disp; baby facs; shwrs inc; el pnts (6A) €4; Indtte; shop; tradsmn; rest, snacks; bar; BBQ; playgrnd; htd pool; paddling pool; waterslide; lake sw & beach adj; fishing; tennis; cycle hire; games rm; wifi; entmnt; sat TV/TV rm; dogs €2; Eng spkn; adv bkg; quiet; ccard acc; red low ssn; CKE/CCI. "Excel lakeside site with pleasant views; lge pitches; friendly staff; gd san facs; attractive sm town; gd touring base S Burgundy; gd for young families." ♦ 15 Apr-15 Oct. € 39.60 2014*

ARTAIX see Marcigny *9A1*

AUTUN *6H1* (1km N Rural) *46.96478, 4.29381* **Camp Municipal de la Porte d'Arroux, Les Chaumottes, 71400 Autun [03 85 52 10 82; fax 03 86 37 79 20; camping.autun@orange.fr; www.camping-autun.com]** Foll sp fr town on D980 dir Saulieu & site on L; only site in Autun. Med, some hdg pitch, some hdstg, pt shd; wc (some cont); mv service pnt; baby facs; shwrs inc; el pnts (10A) €3.30; (poss rev pol); gas high ssn; Indry rm; shop; rest high ssn; snacks; playgrnd; rv sw & fishing; canoe & cycle hire; wifi; dogs €1.35; phone; Eng spkn; adv bkg; rd noise some pitches; ccard acc; red low ssn; CKE/CCI. "Lovely, quiet, clean site; busy NH high ssn; sm pitches, views fr some; friendly, helpful staff; gd san facs, poss stretched high ssn; no twin-axles; v muddy when wet (tow avail); vg, lively rest; medieval architecture & Roman walls around town; m'van Aire de Service nr lake in town; mkt Wed/Fri." ♦ 1 Apr-31 Oct. € 16.50 (CChq acc) 2014*

AUXERRE *4F4* (3km SE Urban) *47.78678, 3.58721* **Camp Municipal, 8 Rue de Vaux, 89000 Auxerre [03 86 52 11 15 or 03 86 72 43 00 (Mairie); fax 03 86 51 17 54; camping.mairie@auxerre.com; www.auxerre.com]** Exit A6 at Auxerre; at junc N6 ring rd foll sp Vaux & 'Stade'; site sp by Rv Yonne. Or fr N6 (N) take ring rd, site/stadium sp. Site also well sp fr town cent as 'L'Arbre Sec'. Lge, mkd pitch, pt shd; wc; chem disp; mv service pnt; shwrs inc; el pnts (6A) inc (long lead poss req); Indtte; shop; supmkt 400m; bar/café; playgrnd; pool 250m; fishing 300m; TV; 10% statics; dogs; adv bkg; quiet; ccard acc; CKE/CCI. "Lovely, peaceful, well-kept site; lge pitches; friendly staff; gd clean san facs; poss cr & noisy during football ssn; site poss flooded stormy weather; no c'vans/m'vans over 5m; ltd el pnts for site size; no vehicles 2200-0700; pretty town; popular NH." 15 Apr-30 Sep. € 12.80 2011*

AUXERRE *4F4* (10km S Rural) *47.70704, 3.63563* **FFCC Camping Les Cerisellles, Route de Vincelottes, 89290 Vincelles [03 86 42 50 47; fax 03 86 42 39 39; camping@cc-payscoulangeois.fr; www.campingceriselles.com]** Leave A6 at Auxerre Sud. Fr Auxerre, take D606 S twd Avallon. 10km fr Auxerre turn L into Vincelles. In 400m immed after 'Atac Marche', turn L into site access rd, sp as Camping Les Ceriselles. Site is approx 16km fr a'route exit. Med, mkd pitch, some hdstg, pt shd; htd wc; chem disp; mv service pnt; baby facs; shwrs inc; el pnts (10A) inc (poss rev pol); gas adj; Indtte (inc dryer); sm supmkt adj; tradsmn; rests 500m; snacks; bar; BBQ; playgrnd; sm pool; rv adj; cycle hire; wifi; TV rm; 10% statics; dogs free (2nd €1.50); phone; no twin-axles; poss v cr; some Eng spkn; adv bkg; quiet but rd noise; ccard acc; high ssn overflow area; red long stay/low ssn; CKE/CCI. "Excel, busy site by canal, poss full late Jun; friendly, helpful owner; gd san facs, poss insufficient high ssn & ltd low ssn; lovely walks to vill & along canal; cycle track to Auxerre & Clamecy; highly rec; secure o'night area; v popular." ♦ 1 Apr-30 Sep. € 22.00 (CChq acc) 2014*

"We must tell The Club about that great site we found"

Get your site reports in by mid-August and we'll do our best to get your updates into the next edition.

AUXONNE *6G1* (500m NW Rural) *47.19838, 5.38120* **Camping L'Arquebuse, Route d'Athée, 21130 Auxonne [03 80 31 06 89; fax 03 80 31 13 62; camping.arquebuse@wanadoo.fr; www.campingarquebuse.com]** On D905 Dijon-Geneva, site sp on L bef bdge at ent to Auxonne. Med, pt shd; htd wc (some cont); chem disp; mv service pnt; shwrs inc; el pnts (10A) €3.70 (poss rev pol); gas; Indry rm; shop 500m; rest, snacks; bar; BBQ; playgrnd; htd pool adj; fishing; sailing; windsurfing; waterskiing; wifi; entmnt; TV rm; 20% statics; dogs €1.80; adv bkg; quiet; clsd 2200-0700; CKE/CCI. "Pleasant rvside site; friendly staff; san facs poss tatty; poss busy w/ends as NH; interesting town; Child friendly site." 20 Jan-19 Dec. € 27.00 2014*

AVALLON *4G4* (2km SE Rural) *47.48030, 3.91246* **Camp Municipal Sous Roches, Rue Sous Roche; 89200 Avallon [tel/fax 03 86 34 10 39; campingsousroche@ville-avallon.fr; www.campingsousroche.com]** App town fr a'route or fr SE on N6. Turn sharp L at 2nd traff lts in town cent, L in 2km at sp Vallée du Cousin (bef bdge), site 250m on L. If app fr S care needed when turning R after bdge. Med, some hdstg pitches, terr, pt shd; wc; mv service pnt; shwrs inc; el pnts (6A) €3.50; Indtte; shop; tradsmn; snacks 1km; rest 2km; BBQ; playgrnd; pool 1km; rv & fishing adj; wifi; dogs free; phone adj; CKE/CCI. "Popular, well-kept site in lovely location nr rv; friendly, helpful staff; excel immac san facs; conv Morvan National Park; poss flood warning after heavy rain; no twin-axles or o'fits over 2,500kg; attractive town; excel." ♦ 1 Apr-15 Oct. € 19.50 2013*

BEAUNE *6H1* (800m NE Urban) *47.03304, 4.83911* **Camp Municipal Les Cent Vignes, 10 Rue Auguste Dubois, 21200 Beaune [03 80 22 03 91; fax 03 80 20 15 51; campinglescentvignes@mairie-beaune.fr; www.beaune.fr]** Fr N on A31 & fr S on A6 at junc with m'ways A6/A31 take A6 sp Auxerre-Paris; after 1km leave at junc 24 to join D974 twd Beaune; after approx 1.5km, turn R at 2nd traff lts fr a'route to site (sp) in 200m. If app fr S on D974 site well sp fr inner ring rd & foll sp to Dijon (not a'route sps). Also sp fr Mersault/L'Hôpital x-rds. Med, hdg/mkd pitch, some hdstg, pt shd; htd wc; chem disp; mv service pnt; shwrs inc; el pnts (6A) €3.80 (some rev pol); gas; Indtte (inc dryer); shop; hypmkt 2km; rest, snacks; bar; BBQ; playgrnd; pool 800m; tennis; cycle hire; games area; wifi; TV rm; dogs; phone; some Eng spkn; adv bkg in writing only bef 30 May; red low ssn; ccard acc; CKE/CCI. "Popular, well-run site; rec arr early even low ssn; gd modern san facs; vg rest; most pitches gd size but narr site rds makes access some pitches diff, a mover useful; tight turns & low trees poss diff lge o'fits; twin-axles; in walking dist of Beaune; v conv site; superb new san facs 2013; excel site." ♦ 15 Mar-31 Oct. € 26.30 2014*

⊞ **BEAUNE** *6H1* (3.5km NE Rural) *47.02458, 4.88711* **Camping Les Bouleaux, 11 Rue Jaune, 21200 Vignoles [tel/fax 03 80 22 26 88]** Exit A6 at junc 24.1; 500m after toll turn R at rndabt, in 1.5km turn R sp Dole rndabt. Immed after x-ing m'way turn L sp Vignoles. L again at next junc then R & foll camping sp. Site in approx 1.5km in cent Chevignerot; fr town cent take D973 (E) sp Dole. In 2km cross a'route & 1st L (N) sp Vignoles. Well sp. Sm, hdg/mkd pitch, pt shd; htd wc; chem disp; shwrs inc; el pnts (6A) inc (rev pol altered on request); shop; tradsmn; supmkt 2km; dogs; adv bkg rec; quiet but some rd noise; CKE/CCI. "Attractive, well-kept, busy site; rec arr early high ssn; some gd sized pitches, most sm; superb clean new san facs, poss stretched high ssn & ltd low ssn; poss muddy after rain - park on rdways; conv NH fr a'route; basic site; long lead may be req'd; excel site; excel walking in area." ♦ € 20.00 2014*

BEAUNE *6H1* (8km SW Rural) *46.98573, 4.76855* **La Grappe d'Or (formally Kawan Village), 2 Route de Volnay, 21190 Meursault [03 80 21 22 48; fax 03 80 21 65 74; info@camping-meursault.com; www.camping-meursault.com]** Fr N-S, Exit A6 Junc 24.1 SP Beaune Centre Hospices, at rndabt foll sp to Chalon sur Saône RN 74, after 7km foll sp to Meursault, turn r, foll sp for site. Med, mkd pitch, terr, pt shd; htd wc; chem disp; mv service pnt; baby facs; shwrs inc; el pnts (10A) inc; gas; Indtte (inc dryer); shop; rest, snacks; bar; playgrnd;sw; paddling pool; waterslide; tennis; rambling;games court; cycle hire; wifi; phone; dogs €1.40; poss cr; Eng spkn; adv bkg ess in ssn; some rd noise; red low ssn; CKE/CCI. "Lovely family site; busy high ssn - arr early; all pitches views over vineyards; friendly, helpful owners; basic facs stretched; ltd water pnts & poss steep climb fr lower pitches; some pitches uneven, sm or obstructed by trees - poss diff access lge o'fits; poss muddy when wet; barrier clsd 2200-0730; sh walk to lovely vill; gd cycle paths; vg; popular site; well run; if full use site at Santenay." ♦ 1 Apr-15 Oct. € 28.50 2014*

BEAUNE *6H1* (5km NW Rural) *47.06861, 4.80292* **FFCC Camping Les Premiers Prés, Route de Bouilland, 21420 Savigny-lès-Beaune [tel/fax 03 80 26 15 06 or 06 83 23 93 37 (mob); contact.camping@x-treme-bar.fr; www.camping-savigny-les-beaune.fr]** Fr Beaune ring rd turn N on D974 sp Dijon; in 200m turn L sp Savigny; in 100m ignore camping sp & bear R to Savigny (3km); site 1km thro vill on L. Med, mkd pitch, pt sl, pt shd; wc; chem disp; mv service pnt; shwrs inc; el pnts (6A) €3.50 (some rev pol); shops 1km; supmkt 3km; tradsmn; snacks; BBQ; playgrnd; cycle hire; internet; dogs €1.20; adv bkg; quiet; CKE/CCI. "Pleasant, busy NH in beautiful area; pleasant staff; modern basic san facs; no twin-axles; gd touring base; conv A6, A31, A36 & Beaune; easy walk to vill; excel quiet site." ♦ ltd 15 Mar-15 Oct. € 15.00 2013*

BLENEAU *4G3* (600m N Rural) *47.70473, 2.94891* **Camp Municipal La Pépinière, Rue du Lieutenant Travers, 89220 Bléneau [03 86 74 93 73 or 03 86 74 91 61 (Mairie); fax 03 86 74 86 74; mairiedebleneau@wanadoo.fr; www.bleneau.fr]** At junc of D47/D22 & D90 in Bléneau take D64 twd Champcevrais & site. Sp in Bléneau. Sm, hdg pitch, shd; wc (cont); chem disp; shwrs inc; el pnts (10A); shops, rest, snacks, bar 600m; pool adj; paddling pool; tennis; games rm; fishing adj; poss cr; adv bkg; quiet; CKE/CCI. "Set in orchard; gd." 1 Apr-30 Sep. 2009*

⊞ **BLENEAU** *4G3* (12km NE Rural) *47.75833, 3.09960* **Camping Le Bois Guillaume, 89350 Villeneuve-les-Genêts [03 86 45 45 41; fax 03 86 45 49 20; camping@bois-guillaume.com; www.bois-guillaume.com]** Fr W on D965 dir St Fargeau. At Mézilles take D7 thro Tannerre-en-Puisaye; stay on D7 & after 3.5km foll sp for site. Or fr A6 exit junc 18 onto D16 thro Charny, then turn L onto D119 to Champignelles; take D7 dir Tannere for approx 2km; turn R & foll sp to site. Med, hdg/mkd pitch, some hdstg, shd; htd wc; chem disp; mv service pnt; shwrs inc; el pnts (5-10A) €3.10-4.60; gas; rest; bar; playgrnd; htd pools; games area; cycle hire; tennis; wifi; dogs €1.40; poss cr; Eng spkn; CKE/CCI. "Friendly staff; clean, tidy site; facs ltd low ssn; vg rest." € 14.30 2011*

BLENEAU *4G3* (7km NW Urban) *47.74321, 2.88508* **Camp Municipal Les Lancières, Rue André Henriat, 89220 Rogny-Les-Sept-Ecluses [03 86 74 57 50 or 06 74 43 43 04 (mob); fax 03 86 74 56 91; campingleslancieres@orange.fr; www.campingdeslancieres.fr]** Site sp fr D90 on S edge of vill on rvside. Sm, pt shd; wc; mv service pnt; shwrs inc; el pnts €2.10; Indtte; shop, rest, snacks, bar in vill; playgrnd; games area; fishing; tennis nr; some statics; quiet. "Pretty site." 1 May-30 Sep. € 5.50 2010*

BLIGNY SUR OUCHE *6H1* (500m NW Rural) *47.10858, 4.66000* **Camping des Isles, 2 Allée de la Gare, 21360 Bligny-sur-Ouche [03 80 20 00 64 or 06 62 97 19 28 (mob)]** On D17/D970 fr Arnay-le-Duc, site on L on ent vill. Med, pt shd; wc (mainly cont); shwrs inc; el pnts (15A) €2.35; shop 500m; café/rest 300m; playgrnd; quiet; red long stay. "Peaceful, clean & tidy; helpful owner; in reach of Côte d'Or wine areas; steam rlwy 100m; noise fr cornmill at harvest time; poss flooding in adverse weather; gd." 1 May-30 Sep. € 11.75 2009*

BONNARD see Joigny *4F4*

BOURBON LANCY *4H4* (300m Urban) *46.62098, 3.76557* **Camping St Prix, Rue de St Prix, 71140 Bourbon-Lancy [tel/fax 03 85 89 20 98 or 03 86 37 95 83; aquadis1@wanadoo.fr; www.aquadis-loisirs.com]** Fr N turn L fr D979 on D973 & foll into Bourbon-Lancy. Turn R at traff lts after Attac Sup'mkt, keep L, site on R after mini-rndabt. Med, hdg pitch, hdstg, terr, pt sl, shd; htd wc (some cont); chem disp; shwrs inc; el pnts (10A) €2; lndry rm; shop; snacks; playgrnd; htd pool; lake sw/fishing; 25% statics; dogs €3.10; Eng spkn; quiet; CKE/CCI. "Tidy, well-run site; helpful staff; new san facs; lovely old town 10 min uphill walk; rec." ♦ Easter-1 Nov. € 14.50 2012*

BOURBON LANCY *9A1* (1km S Rural) **Camping Le Plan d'Eau du Breuil, 71140 Bourbon Lancy [03 86 37 95 83; fax 03 86 37 79 20; aquadis1@orange.fr; www.aquadis-loisirs.com]** Site sp fr town, on lakeside. Sm, pt sl, pt shd; wc; chem disp; shwrs inc; el pnts (6A); snacks; tradsmn; lake adj; poss cr; quiet; adv bkg; excel; CKE/CCI; WiFi; Tv rm; lndtte (inc dryer); BBQ; dogs; pool; paddling pool. 1 Jun-15 Sep. € 16.00 (CChq acc) 2013*

CERCY LA TOUR *4H4* (900m S Urban) *46.86680, 3.64328* **Camp Municipal Le Port, 58360 Cercy-la-Tour [03 86 50 55 27 or 03 86 50 07 11 (Mairie)]** At Decize take D981 E; in 12 km L onto D37, then L onto D10 to Cercy-la-Tour; site sp in vill. Adj municipal pool, Rv Aron & canal. Med, hdstg, pt shd; wc; chem disp; shwrs inc; el pnts inc; pool nrby; dogs; phone; quiet; CKE/CCI. "Clean & tidy site; immac san facs; gd cycling/walking along canal; great value; excel." 15 May-15 Sep. € 9.00 2014*

CHABLIS *4F4* (600m W Rural) *47.81376, 3.80563* **Camp Municipal Le Serein, Quai Paul Louis Courier, 89800 Chablis [03 86 42 44 39 or 03 86 42 80 80 (Mairie); fax 03 86 42 49 71; mairie-chablis@chablis.net; www.chablis.net]** W fr Tonnere on D965; in approx 16km exit D965 for Chabilis; in 300m, just bef x-ing Rv Serein, turn L at camping sp onto Quai Paul Louis Courier; site in 300m on R. Med, hdg/mkd pitch, shd; wc (some cont); shwrs inc; el pnts (5A) €2; gas 1km; lndtte; shops, rest & snacks 1km; tradsmn; playgrnd; rv adj; dogs €1.50; poss cr; Eng spkn; adv bkg; quiet; CKE/CCI. "Attractive, tidy site; facs poss stretched high ssn; friendly & helpful warden,calls 0800-1200 & 1600-2000; easy walk to attractive town; vineyards & wine cellars nrby; excel Sun mkt; warden attaches elec supply to locked post." ♦ ltd 2 Jun-15 Sep. € 12.40 2014*

CHAGNY *6H1* (650m W Urban) *46.91187, 4.74567* **FFCC Camp Municipal du Pâquier Fané, 20 Rue du Pâquier Fané, 71150 Chagny [03 85 87 21 42 or 06 18 27 21 99 (mob); camping-chagny@orange.fr; www.chagny-bourgogne-tourisme.com]** Clearly sp in town. Med, hdg/mkd pitch, pt shd; wc; chem disp; mv service pnt; shwrs inc; el pnts (6A) €3.50 (rev pol); gas; lndtte; shop, rest, snacks & bar 500m; playgrnd; htd pool adj; fishing; tennis adj; dogs €1; Eng spkn; adv bkg (ess Jul/Aug); quiet except rlwy noise adj; red low ssn; CKE/CCI. "Well laid-out, well-lit site; friendly, helpful resident wardens; clean san facs; many pitches sm & diff med/lge o'fits; on wine rte; gd cycling nrby (voie verte)." ♦ 1 Apr-31 Oct. € 18.00 2011*

CHALON SUR SAONE *6H1* (1km E Rural) *46.78411, 4.87136* **Camping du Pont de Bourgogne, Rue Julien Leneveu, 71380 St Marcel [03 85 48 26 86 or 03 85 94 16 90 (LS); fax 03 85 48 50 63 or 03 85 94 16 97 (LS); campingchalon71@wanadoo.fr; www.camping-chalon.com]** Fr A6 exit junc 26 (sp Chalon Sud) onto N80 E; foll sp Chalon-sur-Saône; at 1st rndabt go strt over (sp Louhans & St Marcel) & over flyover; take 4th exit on 2nd rndbt; immed after this rndabt fork R thro Les Chavannes (still on N80). Turn R at traff lts bef bdge. (DO NOT CROSS BDGE). Site in 500m. Med, hdg/mkd pitch, hdstg, terr, pt shd; htd wc; chem disp; mv service pnt; shwrs inc; el pnts (6A) inc; gas; lndtte (inc dryer); sm shop; hypmkt nr; tradsmn; rest, snacks; bar; BBQ; playgrnd; pool 500m; rv fishing; canoeing nrby; cycle hire; wifi; games/TV rm; dogs €2.60; no c'vans/m'vans over 12m; Eng spkn; some noise fr rd & rv pathway; ccard acc; red low ssn; CKE/CCI. "Peaceful, well-run rvside site; lge pitches, some by rv; helpful, friendly staff; excel clean san facs, poss stretched high ssn; vg rest/bar; rvside walks; lovely town; conv NH fr A6; vg; gd cycling." ♦ 1 Apr-30 Sep. € 39.70 (CChq acc) SBS - L17 2014*

CHALON SUR SAONE *6H1* (12km SE Rural) *46.69813, 4.92751* **Mini-Camping Les Tantes, 29 Route de Grigny, 71240 Marnay [03 85 44 23 88 or 06 19 22 09 73 (mob)]** On D978 SE fr Chalon-sur-Saône, turn R in vill of Ouroux-sur-Saône onto D6 twd Marnay. Over bdge, foll site sp. Sm, hdg pitch, pt shd; wc; chem disp; shwrs inc; el pnts (5-10A) €2.90-4.20; lndry rm; tradsmn; snacks; BBQ; sm playgrnd; pool; games area; 30% statics; dogs; phone; no twin-axles; o'night area; quiet. "Gd." ♦ 1 Apr-30 Sept. € 9.00 2012*

CHAMPAGNAT (SAONE ET LOIRE) see Cuiseaux *9A2*

CHARNY *4F3* (500m N Rural) *47.89078, 3.09419* **FFCC Camping des Platanes, 41 Route de la Mothe, 89120 Charny [tel/fax 03 86 91 83 60; campingdesplatanes@wanadoo.fr; www.campingdesplatanes.com]** Exit A6 junc 18 onto D943 to Montargis. Turn S onto D950 to Charny, site on R as ent vill; sp. Med, hdg/mkd pitch, pt shd; htd wc; chem disp; mv service pnt; serviced pitch; shwrs inc; el pnts (10A) inc; gas; lndtte (inc dryer); shop 500m; tradsmn; snacks; BBQ; playgrnd; pool; rv fishing 150m; tennis 500m; cycle hire; wifi; TV rm; 60% statics; dogs €3; Eng spkn; adv bkg; quiet; red low ssn/long stay; CKE/CCI. "Pleasant, peaceful site; gd sized pitches; friendly, helpful owners; excel, clean san facs; sh walk to vill; gd walking; gd touring base." ♦ 1 Apr-30 Oct. € 20.50 2013*

CHAROLLES *9A2* (500m E Rural) *46.43972, 4.28208* **FFCC Camp Municipal, Route de Viry, 71120 Charolles [03 85 24 04 90; fax 03 85 24 08 20; camping.charolles@orange.fr]** Exit N79 at E end of by-pass sp Vendenesse-lès-Charolles; at rndabt foll camping sp; then sharp R bottom hill bef town; site on L, next to Municipal pool. Med, hdg/mkd pitch, hdstg, pt sl, pt shd; htd wc; chem disp; mv service pnt (outside ent); shwrs inc; el pnts (6A) €2; lndtte; shops 300m; rest, snacks; bar; playgrnd; pool adj high ssn (proper sw trunks req); wifi; TV; dogs €1; adv bkg rec; quiet, but faint rd noise; ccard acc; CKE/CCI. "Well-kept site; sm pitches; friendly, helpful warden; gd, modern san facs; m'van area outside site; negligible security." ♦ 1 Apr-5 Oct. € 9.00 2010*

CHARRIN see Decize *4H4*

BURGUNDY

CHATEAU CHINON *4H4* (6km S Rural) *47.00587, 3.90548* **FFCC Camping L'Etang de la Fougeraie, Hameau de Champs, 58120 St Léger-de-Fougeret [03 86 85 11 85; fax 03 86 79 45 72; campingfougeraie@orange.fr; www.campingfougeraie.com]** Fr Château-Chinon S on D27; in approx 3km turn R onto D157 to St Léger-de-Fougeret; in vill foll sps S dir Onlay to site in 2.5km. Med, hdg/mkd pitch, terr, pt shd; wc; chem disp; baby facs; shwrs inc; el pnts (6A) €3.20; Indtte; shop; tradsmn; rest, snacks; bar; BBQ; playgrnd; cycle hire; lake sw & fishing; donkey rides; games area; games rm; TV; dogs €1.70; Eng spkn; quiet; red low ssn; CKE/CCI. "Beautiful, tranquil situation; most pitches lge & face lake; welcoming, efficient owners; facs at top of terr - poss stretched high ssn & ltd low ssn; gd rest; poss diff lge o'fits; pitches muddy when wet; excel." 3 Apr-2 Oct. € 13.50 2010*

CHATEL CENSOIR see Coulanges sur Yonne *4G4*

CHATILLON SUR SEINE *6F1* (500m E Urban) *47.85955, 4.57975* **Camp Municipal Louis Rigoly, Esplanade Saint Vorles, 21400 Châtillon-sur-Seine [03 80 91 03 05 or 03 80 91 13 19 (LS); fax 03 80 91 21 46; camping-chatillon-sur-seine@orange.fr; www.mairie-chatillon-sur-seine.fr]** Fr N, cross rv bdge (Seine); cont approx 400m twd town cent; at lge fountain forming rndabt turn L into rd with Bureau de Tourisme on corner; foll sp to site. Fr S ignore all camping sp & cont into town cent to fountain, turn R & cont as above. Med, hdg/mkd pitch, pt sl, pt shd; wc; chem disp; mv service pnt; shwrs inc; el pnts (4-6A) €2.30-4.65; gas; Indtte; shops 500m; snacks adj municipal pool; playgrnd; htd pool adj; jacuzzi; wifi; fishing; tennis; riding; dogs; Eng spkn; adv bkg; quiet; CKE/CCI. "Pretty site adj park; clean, tidy, well-spaced pitches; helpful, welcoming warden; excel, clean new san facs; easy walk to old town; no twin-axles; vg." ♦ ltd 1 Apr-30 Sep. € 18.20 2014*

CHATILLON SUR SEINE *6F1* (6km S Rural) *47.81390, 4.53896* **Camping de la Forge, La Forge, 21400 Ampilly-le-Sec [tel/fax 03 80 91 46 53; campingdelaforge@gmail.com; www.campinglaforge.com]** S fr Châtillon-sur-Seine on D971, on leaving Buncey take 1st turn R immed after layby (narr rd); site on R in 1km, on bend immed bef rv bdge, sp. Or app fr S on D971, after passing Chamesson, Ampilly-le-Sec & site sp - note sharp R turn in Ampilly. Sm, pt shd; wc; chem disp; shwrs inc; el pnts (6-16A) €3 (poss long lead req); Indtte; shop 2km; tradsmn; rest 2.5km; BBQ; rv sw adj; fishing; dogs; phone; Eng spkn; adv bkg rec high ssn; ltd facs winter - phone ahead Dec to Feb to check open; quiet; red long stay; CKE/CCI. "Beautiful, secluded, CL-type site in woodland by rv; helpful, friendly British owners; clean, basic san facs; area for lge m'vans across rd; access diff lge o'fits; levelling blocks poss req; phone ahead rec; NH only; facs V basic." ♦ ltd 1 May-30 Sep. € 19.00 2014*

CHAUFFAILLES see Clayette, La *9A2*

CHEVENON see Nevers *4H4*

CLAMECY *4G4* (5km NE Rural) *47.51665, 3.48001* **Camping Le Bois Joli, 2 Route de Villeprenoy, 89480 Andryes [tel/fax 03 86 81 70 48; info@campingauboisjoli.com; www.campingauboisjoli.com]** S on N151 fr Auxerre to Coulanges-sur-Yonne; W on D39 to Andryes. Foll sps `Camping Andryes'; site in 500m after vill. Med, mkd pitch, terr, shd; htd wc; chem disp; baby facs; baby facs; fam bthrm; shwrs inc; el pnts (10A) €4.80 (poss rev pol); gas; Indry rm; shop; tradsmn; BBQ; playgrnd; pool inc; rv sw, fishing & boat hire 2km; tennis; cycle hire; wifi; TV; 10% statics; dogs €3.50; phone; Eng spkn; quiet; ccard acc; red low ssn; CKE/CCI; "Dutch owners; beautiful countryside; gd pitches; muddy in rain; excel facs & site; v quiet; nice site in wooded area." ♦ 1 Apr-31Oct. € 25.00 2014*

CLAMECY *4G4* (1.3km SE Urban) *47.45133, 3.52770* **Camp Municipal du Pont-Picot, Rue de Chevroche, 58500 Clamecy [03 86 27 05 97; clamecycamping@orange.fr; www.clamecy.fr]** On N151 fr S, exit N151 at rndabt 3km SW of town cent, cross level x-ing then R at rndabt on D23, take 1st L, site sp in 2.4km. Narr app rd. App fr N or E thro town not rec. Med, pt sl, pt shd; wc; chem disp; shwrs inc; el pnts (6A) inc; Indry rm; shops 1km; tradsmn; playgrnd; sw; no twin-axles; poss cr; Eng spkn; quiet: red low ssn; CKE/CCI. "Pleasant, peaceful site bet rv & canal in beautiful location; friendly, helpful staff; facs poss inadequate when busy; town 10 min walk on towpath; gd cycling; gd NH; narr bdge just bef ent." ♦ 25 Mar-30 Sep. € 14.50 2013*

"I need an on-site restaurant"

We do our best to make sure site information is correct, but it is always best to check any must-have facilities are still available or will be open during your visit.

CLAMECY *4G4* (8km SE Rural) *47.41390, 3.60828* **Camp Municipal Les Fontaines, 58530 Brèves [tel/fax 03 86 24 25 26; mairie-breves@wanadoo.fr; www.vaux-yonne.com]** On D985 (Clamecy-Corbigny) at Brèves. Both app clearly sp. Med, pt sl, unshd; wc; chem disp (wc); shwrs inc; el pnts (6A) €2; Indtte; tradsmn; shop; BBQ; playgrnd; 4% statics; dogs; phone; adv bkg rec; CKE/CCI. "Quiet site in pretty area nr Rv Yonne & canal; friendly staff; grnd soft after heavy rain; ltd level sites for m'van vg." ♦ 1 Jun-30 Sep. € 8.60 2014*

CLAYETTE, LA *9A2* (500m E Urban) *46.29159, 4.32020* **Camping des Bruyères, 9 Route de Gibles, 71800 La Clayette [03 85 28 09 15 or 03 86 37 95 83 (LS); contact@campingbruyeres.com; http://campingbruyeres.com/]** Site on D79, 100m fr D987 & lake. Med, hdg/mkd pitch, hdstg, pt sl, shd; htd wc; chem disp; mv service pnt; shwrs inc; el pnts (6A) inc; gas; Indtte; shops adj; tradsmn; snacks, bar 500m; BBQ; playgrnd; htd pool adj Jun-Aug inc; boating; tennis; games area; entmnt; 10% statics; dogs €1.60; phone; poss cr; adv bkg; quiet; CKE/CCI; free wifi. "Pleasant, well-kept site o'looking lake & chateau; friendly, helpful staff; gd-sized pitches, mostly sloping; excel; 20 min walk to town; supmkt 10 min walk." ♦ 18 Apr-30 Sep. € 25.30 2014*

CLAYETTE, LA *9A2* (13km S Rural) *46.2011, 4.3391* **FFCC Camping Les Feuilles, 18 Rue de Châtillon, 71170 Chauffailles [03 85 26 48 12; fax 03 85 26 55 02; campingchauffailles@gmail.com / chalets@chalets-decouverte.com; www.chauffailles.fr / www.chalets-decouverte.com]** S fr La Clayette on D985 (dir Les Echarmeaux), turn R at camp sp down hill & cross Rv Botoret to site. Med, mkd pitch, hdstg, pt shd; htd wc; chem disp; mv service pnt; shwrs; el pnts (5A) inc; Indtte; supmkt 500m; playgrnd; pool adj; fishing; tennis; games rm; wifi; TV; Eng spkn; adv bkg ess; quiet; red CKE/CCI. "Attractive site; poss rallies May/June & Sep (poss noisy); gd san facs but hot water to shwrs & dishwashing only; easy walk to interesting town; sep m'van Aire de Service adj rear ent." 1 May-30 Sep. € 18.80 2013*

CLUNY *9A2* (500m E Urban) *46.43086, 4.66756* **Camp Municipal St Vital, 30 Rue de Griottons, 71250 Cluny [tel/fax 03 85 59 08 34; camping.st.vital@orange.fr; www.camping-cluny.blogspot.com]** E fr Cluny on D15 (sp Azé & Camping) across narr rv bdge; in 200m turn R into Rue de Griottonste; site on L in 100m. Site adj sw pool. Lge, mkd pitch, some hdstg, sl, pt shd; htd wc (some cont); chem disp; shwrs inc; el pnts (6A) €4.50 (poss rev pol); gas; Indtte (inc dryer); sm shop open w/ends & 500m; tradsmn; BBQ; playgrnd; htd pool adj inc; tennis; fishing; horseriding nrby; cycle hire; games rm; wifi; dogs; poss cr; adv bkg rec high ssn; frequent rlwy noise daytime; ccard acc; twin-axles extra. "Well-run, tidy site; helpful staff; gd clean san facs; cycle & walking rte adj (Voie Verte); interesting town; excel, reliable site; well organised and pleasant; busy site." ♦ 1 May-10 Oct. € 24.60 2014*

CLUNY *9A2* (10km S Rural) *46.81195, 6.30285* **Camping du Lac de St Point-Lamartine, 8 Rue du Port, 71520 St Point [03 85 50 52 31; reservation@campingsaintpoint.com; www.campingsaintpoint.com]** Turn S off N79, Mâcon/Paray-le-Monial rd, turn L bef Ste Cécile on D22; site sp at junc; site 100m on R after St Point vill. Med, hdg/mkd pitch, pt terr, pt sl, pt shd; htd wc; chem disp; mv service pnt; shwrs inc; el pnts (16A) inc; gas 800m; Indtte (inc dryer); shop 800m; rest, snacks; bar; BBQ; playgrnd; TV; lake sw adj; fishing; boat hire; tennis 4km; wifi; 30% statics; dogs €1; phone; adv bkg; quiet; CKE/CCI. "Cluny attractive town & abbey; lge pitches; clean & basic san facs & ltd LS; lovely scenery & pleasant lake; on edge of Beaujolais; sp walks fr site; peaceful area with wooded hills & valleys." 1 Apr-31 Oct. € 19.00 (4 persons) 2014*

CLUNY *9A2* (11km NW Rural) *46.51775, 4.59865* **FFCC Camp Municipal de la Clochette, Place de la Clochette, 71250 Salornay-sur-Guye [03 85 59 90 11; fax 03 85 59 47 52; mairie.salornay@wanadoo.fr; www.cluny-tourisme.com]** Sp fr N or S on D980; turn E on D14 sp Cormatin & Taizé. Ent in 300m. Well sp in vill & fr D980. Med, mkd pitch, pt shd; wc; shwrs €1; chem disp; mv service pnt; el pnts (8-10A) €2-3; Indry rm; shop & bar 200m; BBQ; playgrnd; rv adj; fishing; adv bkg; quiet; CKE/CCI. "Pleasant, tidy site on sm rv & mill pond; site yourself, warden comes 0930-1030 & 1900-2000; clean, dated san facs; poss long walk to chem disp & rubbish disposal (2011); rvside pitches poss subject to flooding; well sp walks around vill; vill shops poss clsd Mon." 21 May-4 Sep. € 8.00 2011*

CORBIGNY *4G4* (3.5km W Rural) *47.25858, 3.64131* **Camp Intercommunal L'Ardan, Route de Germeney, 58800 Chaumot [03 86 20 07 70; campingdelardan@wanadoo.fr; www.camping-bourgogne.com]** D977 fr Corbigny to Chaumot. Turn on D130 sp Germenay. Site on R after 50m. Med, shd; wc (some cont); chem disp; shwrs inc; el pnts €3; shop 3.5km; rest; bar; playgrnd; lake adj; fishing; boat hire; some statics; dogs €1; Eng spkn; adv bkg; quiet. 1 Apr-1 Oct. € 12.00 2009*

CORMATIN *9A2* (500m N Rural) *46.54841, 4.68351* **Camping Le Hameau des Champs, Route de Chalon, 71460 Cormatin [03 85 50 76 71; fax 03 85 50 76 98; camping.cormatin@wanadoo.fr; www.le-hameau-des-champs.com]** Fr Cluny N on D981 dir Cormatin for approx 14km, site N of town sp on L, 300m after chateau. Look for line of European flags. Sm, hdg/mkd pitch, pt sl, unshd; htd wc; chem disp; mv service pnt; shwrs inc; el pnts (13A) €3.25 (long lead poss req); gas 500m; Indtte; shop 500m; tradsmn; rest, snacks; bar; BBQ (gas/elec); cooking facs; playgrnd; rv sw 1km; shgle beach 7km; cycle hire; TV rm; 10% statics; dogs €1; phone; wifi; Eng spkn; adv bkg; quiet; ccard acc; red low ssn; CKE/CCI. "Well-kept, secure site in lovely countryside; welcoming, friendly owner; lge pitches; ltd el pnts, adv bkg rec; gd facs, poss stretched high ssn; rest open low ssn; Voie Verte cycling rte adj; excel municipal site. Small town but gd local store; Chateau closeby." ♦ 1 Apr-30 Sep. € 21.55 2014*

CORMATIN *9A2* (6km NW Rural) *46.57139, 4.66245* **Camping du Gué, Messeugne, 71460 Savigny-sur-Grosne [03 85 92 56 86; camping.messeugne@orange.fr; www.camping-messeugne.monsite-orange.fr]** Fr Cluny N on D981, 2km N of Cormatin fork L sp Malay. Site 3km on R bef rv bdge. Med, mkd pitch, shd; htd; chem disp; shwrs €1.20; el pnts €3; tradsmn; snacks; bar; BBQ; playgrnd; games area; dir access to rv; fishing; 80 - 90% statics; dogs €1.20; CKE/CCI. "Pleasant, friendly site; nr St Genoux-le-National (national monument), Cluny & Taizé; on Burgundy wine rte; fairly boggy when wet; caravans parked on concrete bases." ♦ 29 Mar-27 Oct. € 10.70 2013*

CORMORANCHE SUR SAONE see Macon *9A2*

COUCHES see Nolay *6H1*

COULANGES SUR YONNE *4G4* (9km E Rural) *47.53610, 3.63326* **Camp Municipal Le Petit Port, 89660 Châtel-Censoir [03 86 81 01 98 (Mairie) or 06 80 32 59 50 (mob); campinglepetitport@orange.fr / mairie-de-chatel-censoir@wanadoo.fr; www.chatel-censoir.com]** Fr Auxerre or Clamecy on N151 at Coulanges turn E onto D21, S side of rv & canal to Châtel-Censoir; site sp. Med, pt shd; wc (some cont); chem disp; shwrs inc; el pnts (6A) €2 (poss rev pol); Indry rm; basic shop 400m; snacks; bar; BBQ; playgrnd; rv sw & fishing adj; wifi; some statics; dogs €0.50; twin-axles extra; phone; Eng spkn; some rlwy noise; CKE/CCI. "Attractive, peaceful site bet rv & canal; friendly, busy resident warden; ok san facs; some pitches muddy when wet; beautiful area with gd cycling; concerts at w/ends." 27 Apr-30 Sep. € 8.50 2013*

COULANGES SUR YONNE *4G4* (600m S Rural) *47.52269, 3.53817* **Camping des Berges de l'Yonne, 89480 Coulanges-sur-Yonne [03 86 81 76 87]** On N151 dir Nevers. Med, pt shd; wc; chem disp; shwrs; el pnts (10A) €2.80; shop; snacks; playgrnd; pool; fishing; tennis. "V pleasant site in beautiful area; dated facs but adequate & clean; superb pool." 1 May-30 Sep. € 14.40 2012*

"Satellite navigation makes touring much easier"

Remember most sat navs don't know if you're towing or in a larger vehicle – always use yours alongside maps and site directions.

CUISEAUX *9A2* (5km W Rural) *46.49570, 5.32662* **Camping Le Domaine de Louvarel, 71480 Champagnat [03 85 76 62 71; info@louvarel.com; www.louvarel.com]** Exit A39 junc 9 dir Cuiseaux; foll sp 'Base de Loisirs de Louvarel'. Or fr D1083 exit Champagnat & foll sp to site on lakeside. Med, hdg/mkd, terr, pt shd; htd wc; chem disp; mv service pnt; baby facs; fam bthrm; shwrs inc; el pnts (10A) incl; Indtte (inc dryer); tradsmn; rest, snacks; bar; BBQ; playgrnd; htd pool; paddling pool; lake sw adj, sand beach; fishing; boating; games area; cycle hire; wifi; 7% statics; dogs €2; phone; o'night area for m'vans; Eng spkn; adv bkg; quiet; red low ssn; CKE/CCI. "Excel, clean site; helpful manager; excel, immac san facs; nice rest & bar; gd walking; free use of canoes; busy." ♦ 12 Apr-27 Sep. € 38.20 2014*

DECIZE *4H4* (500m NE Urban) *46.83487, 3.45552* **Camping des Halles, Allée Marcel Merle, 58300 Decize [03 86 25 14 05 or 03 86 25 03 23 (Mairie); fax 03 86 77 11 48; aquadis1@wanadoo.fr; www.des-vacances-vertes.com / www.aquadis-loisirs.com]** Fr Nevers take D981 to Decize, look for sp for 'Stade Nautique Camping'. Lge, mkd pitch, pt shd; wc (some cont); snacks; shwrs inc; el pnts (6A) €2.30 (poss rev pol); gas; shop; rv & sand beach adj; sat TV; dogs €1.60; poss cr; some Eng spkn; quiet; ccard acc; CKE/CCI. "Site on banks of Rv Loire; lge pitches, some by rv; helpful staff; san facs clean but need update; no twin-axles; poss diff access pitches due trees; shady, flat walk into town; mkt Fri; town v interesting,15 min walk." ♦ 1 May-15 Oct. € 17.70 2013*

DIGOIN *9A1* (500m W Urban) *46.47985, 3.96780* **Camping de la Chevrette, 41 Rue de la Chevrette, 71160 Digoin [03 85 53 11 49; fax 03 85 88 59 70; info@lachevrette.com; www.lachevrette.com]** Fr S exit N79/E62 at junc 24 sp Digoin-la-Grève D994, then on D979 cross bdge over Rv Loire. Take 1st L, sp campng/piscine. Sm, some hdg pitch, hdstg, pt sl, terr for tents, pt shd; htd wc (some cont); chem disp; mv service pnt; shwrs inc; el pnts (10A) inc; tradsmn; Indtte (inc dryer); shops 500m; sm rest & 500m; snacks high ssn; playgrnd; htd pool adj; fishing; wifi; dogs €1; poss cr w/ends; Eng spkn; adv bkg; red low ssn; CKE/CCI. "Pleasant, well-run site by rv; diff sized pitches, some lge; friendly, helpful owner; ltd facs low ssn; barrier clsd 2200-0700; pleasant walk by rv to town; lovely cycle rides along canals; gd dog walking along the rv." ♦ 1 Apr-10 Oct. € 26.70 2014*

DIJON *6G1* (2km W Urban) *47.32127, 5.01108* **Camping du Lac Kir, 3 Blvd du Chanoine Kir, 21000 Dijon [tel/fax 03 80 30 54 01; campingdijon@wanadoo.fr / reservation@camping-du-lac-dijon.com; www.camping-du-lac-dijon.com]** Site situated nr N5, Lac Kir. Fr Dijon ring rd take N5 exit (W) sp A38 twd Paris. At traff lts L sp A31, site immed on R under 3m high bdge. Do not tow thro town cent. Med, mkd pitch, pt hdstg, pt shd; wc; chem disp; shwrs inc; el pnts (10A & 16A) inc; (poss rev pol, poss long lead req); gas; supmkt nr; tradsmn; sw lake 1km; fishing, sw & boating; dogs €2.vaccinated on lead; bus adj; poss cr; Eng spkn; quiet but some rd noise; ccard acc; red low ssn; CKE/CCI. "Site a bit unkempt (2012/13); rvside path to town; wonderful surrounding area; easy bus to town; gd security; poss flooding; new ownership 2013." 30 Mar-13 Oct. € 22.30 2014*

DOMPIERRE LES ORMES *9A2* (500m NW Rural) *46.36369, 4.47460* **Camp Municipal Le Village des Meuniers, 71520 Dompierre-les-Ormes [03 85 50 36 60; fax 03 85 50 36 61; contact@villagedesmeuniers.com; www.villagedesmeuniers.com]** Fr A6 exit Mâcon Sud onto N79 dir Charolles. After approx 35km take slip rd onto D41 for Dompierre-les-Ormes. Well sp nr stadium. Med, hdg/mkd pitch, terr, pt shd; wc; chem disp; mv service pnt; 50% serviced pitch; shwrs inc; el pnts (16A) €4.50; gas; Indtte; shops 2km; tradsmn; rest, snacks; bar; playgrnd; htd pools; waterslide; cycle hire; tennis; wifi; entmnt; dogs €2; adv bkg (ess high ssn); quiet; ccard acc; red low ssn; CKE/CCI. "Excel, clean site with views; v lge pitches; o'flow field with full facs high ssn; facs stretched high ssn; excel for children; gd sp walks in area; pools, rest, bar etc used by public; free m'van hdstg outside site ent." ♦ 15 Mar-1 Nov. € 23.00 2010*

ENTRAINS SUR NOHAIN *4G4* (200m N Rural) *47.46574, 3.25870* **Camping Salixcamp, 12 Route d'Etais, 58410 Entrains-sur-Nohain [tel/fax 03 45 50 20 45 or 06 34 44 71 46 (mob); salixcamp@camping58.com; www.camping58.com]** On D1 fr Entrains-sur-Nohain, sp on R. Sm, hdg pitch, pt shd; wc (some cont); chem disp; mv service pnt; shwrs inc; el pnts (10A) inc (poss rev pol); Indry rm; shop, rest, bar 300m; BBQ; htd pool 500m; entmnt; 1% statics; dogs €1.50; phone 300m; quiet, but church bells & cockerel (2011); CKE/CCI. "Basic site; friendly warden; san facs clean but v ltd; poss unkempt early ssn; NH only." ♦ ltd 1 Jun-30 Sep. € 13.20 2011*

EPINAC *6H1* (500m SW Rural) *46.98577, 4.50617* **Camp Municipal du Pont Vert, Rue de la Piscine, 71360 Epinac [03 85 82 00 26; fax 03 85 82 13 67; info@campingdupontvert.com; www.campingdupontvert.com]** On D973 Autun dir Beaune for 16km. Turn L on D43 to Epinac, site nr public sports facs, sp in town. Med, pt shd; wc; chem disp; shwrs inc; el pnts (10A) €3.70; Indtte; shops in vill; snacks; cycle hire; wifi; some statics; dogs €1.05; extra charge for twin axles (€44 in 2009); quiet. 1 Apr-1 Nov. € 11.65 2009*

⊞ **ETANG SUR ARROUX** *4H4* (900m SE Rural) *46.86190, 4.19177* **FFCC Camping des 2 Rives, 26-28 Route de Toulon, 71190 Etang-sur-Arroux [03 85 82 39 73; fax 03 85 82 32 97; camping@des2rives.com; www.des2rives.com]** Fr Autun on N81 SW for 11km; turn L onto D994 to Etang-sur-Arroux; site on R after passing thro main pt of town. Med, shd; wc; chem disp; mv service pnt; shwrs inc; el pnts (6-10A) €3.60; Indtte; shop 1km; rest, snacks & bar high ssn or 1km; playgrnd; pool 500m; rv sw adj; canoeing; kayaking; 20% statics; dogs €2.40; phone; Eng spkn; adv bkg; wifi; CKE/CCI. "Well-kept site bet two rvs; Dutch owners; dated but adequate san facs; gd rv sports; ltd opening Jan & Feb; nice site; helpful owners." ♦ € 27.30 2013*

ETRIGNY see Tournus *9A2*

FOURCHAMBAULT see Nevers *4H4*

GIBLES see Clayette, La *9A2*

GIGNY SUR SAONE see Sennecey le Grand *6H1*

ISLE SUR SEREIN, L' *4G4* (850m S Rural) *47.58011, 4.00561* **Camp Municipal Le Parc de Château, 89440 L'Isle-sur-Serein [03 86 33 93 50 or 03 86 33 80 74 (Mairie); fax 03 86 33 91 81; mairie-isle-sur-serein@wanadoo.fr; www.isle-sur-serein.com]** Exit A6 junc 21 or 22 & foll sp Noyers or Montréal & L'Isle-sur-Serein on D117. Or fr Avallon, take D957 twd Sauvigny-le-Bois; then D86 to L'Isle-sur-Serein; site on L on ent to vill. Sm, hdg/mkd pitch, some hdstg, shd; wc; chem disp; shwrs inc; el pnts (6A) 2.60; Indtte; shop 1km; rest; bar; BBQ; playgrnd; tennis & boating adj; games area; some statics; dogs; adv bkg; quiet, some rd noise; CKE/CCI. "Basic, well-kept site in attractive area; helpful warden; dated facs; site poss poorly maintained end of ssn (2010); vg." 15 Apr-30 Sep. € 8.20 2010*

"There aren't many sites open at this time of year"

If you're travelling outside peak season remember to call ahead to check site opening dates – even if the entry says 'open all year'.

JOIGNY *4F4* (8km E Urban) *47.95646, 3.50657* **Camping Les Confluents, Allée Léo Lagrange, 89400 Migennes [tel/fax 03 86 80 94 55; planethome2003@yahoo.fr; www.les-confluents.com]** A6 exit at junc 19 Auxerre Nord onto N6 & foll sp to Migennes & site, well sp. Med, hdg/mkd pitch, hdstg, pt shd; htd wc (some cont); chem disp; mv service pnt; baby facs; fam bthrm; shwrs inc; el pnts (6-10A) €3.50-4.90; gas; Indtte; shop; rest, snacks; bar; BBQ; playgrnd; pool; watersports 300m; lake sand beach; canoe, cycle hire; games area; entmnt; TV rm; 8% statics; dogs €0.90; phone; bus 10 mins; quiet; red long stay; ccard acc; CKE/CCI. "Friendly, family-run, clean site nr canal & indust area; no twin-axles; medieval castle, wine cellars, potteries nrby; walking dist to Migennes; mkt Thurs; excel." ♦ ltd 1 Apr-1 Nov. € 24.00 2012*

JOIGNY *4F4* (12km SE Rural) *47.92802, 3.51932* **Camp Municipal Le Patis, 28 Rue du Porte des Fontaines, 89400 Bonnard [03 86 73 26 25 or 03 86 73 26 91 (Mairie); mairie.bonnard@wanadoo.fr; www.tourisme-yonne.com]** Exit A6 junc 19; N on N6 dir Joigny; in 8.5km at Bassou turn R & foll sp Bonnard. Site on L immed after rv bdge. Sm, mkd pitch, shd; wc; chem disp; shwrs inc; el pnts (10A) €2.20; Indtte; shop 1km; rest 500m; playgrnd; rv sw, fishing, boating, tennis adj; dogs; phone; poss cr; adv bkg; quiet. "Super little site on banks of Rv Yonne; well-kept; friendly, helpful warden; immac san facs; gd security; vg fishing." ♦ ltd 15 May-30 Sep. € 7.80 2013*

JOIGNY *4F4* (3.5km NW Rural) *47.99550, 3.34468* **Camp Municipal L'Ile de L'Entonnoir, Route de St Aubin-sur-Yonne, 89410 Cézy [03 86 63 17 87 or 03 86 63 12 58 (LS); fax 03 86 63 02 84; info@camping-cezy.com]** Site sp off N6 N & S-bound (Joigny by-pass). Thro St Aubin vill, cross bdge over Rv Yonne. Site on L bank of rv. Or exit N6 Joigny by-pass at N of rndabt onto N2006 twd St Aubin. After St Aubin turn R to Cézy & site in 1km. Rec app via St Aubin - narr bdge 3.5t weight restriction. Alt route for lge o'fits, N6 onto N2006 to St Aubin, sp in vill. Sm, mkd pitch, pt shd; wc; shwrs inc; chem disp; mv service pnt; el pnts (6-10A) inc; Indtte; shop 1km; rest, snacks, bar, BBQ; playgrnd; rv sw & beach 100m; dogs €1; Eng spkn; adv bkg; quiet; CKE/CCI. "V pleasant, quiet site; helpful staff; conv Chablis area; barrier clsd 2200." 1 May-31 Oct. € 15.40 2012*

⊞ **LAIGNES** *6F1* (500m N Rural) **Aire Communale, Le Moulin Neuf, 21300 Laignes [03 80 81 43 03; mairie@laignes.fr]** Fr E or W to Laignes on D965; in town foll sp 'Camping pour Camping Cars', N on D953. Sm (10 m'vans), pt shd; own san; chem disp; mv service pnt; water points; el pnts; picnic tables; shops & rest 15 min walk; m'vans only. "Free of charge; delightful site by mill-pond." 2009*

LAIVES see Sennecey le Grand *6H1*

LEZINNES *4F4* (400m S Urban) *47.79955, 4.08957* **La Graviere du Moulin, 7 route de Frangey, 89160 Lezinnes [tel/fax 03 86 75 68 67 / 02 29 59 27 (mob); lagraviereduмoulin@lezinnes.fr; www.gravieredumoulin.lezinnes.fr]** Fr N on Route Nationale D905 turn L onto D200, foll rd round to the R onto Route de Frangey to site. Sm, wc; shwrs inc; el pnts €2.70; Indtte; playgrnd; canoeing; football; basketball; handball; tennis. "Gated strictly run, great café in vill." 29 Mar-7Oct. € 7.20 2013*

LIGNY LE CHATEL *4F4* (500m SW Rural) *47.89542, 3.75288* **Camp Municipal La Noue Marrou, 89144 Ligny-le-Châtel [03 86 47 56 99 or 03 86 47 41 20 (Mairie); fax 03 86 47 44 02; camping.lignylechatel@orange.fr; www.mairie-ligny-le-chatel-89.fr]** Exit A6 at junc 20 Auxerre S onto D965 to Chablis. In Chablis cross rv & turn L onto D91 dir Ligny. On ent Ligny turn L onto D8 at junc after Maximart. Cross sm rv, foll sp to site on L in 200m. Sm, mkd pitch, pt shd; wc; chem disp (wc); mv service pnt; shwrs inc; el pnts (10A) inc (poss rev pol, poss long lead req); Indtte; shop; rest, snacks; bar; wifi; playgrnd; rv sw adj; tennis; dogs; phone; bus 200m; quiet; red low ssn; CKE/CCI. "Well-run site; lge pitches; no twin-axles; friendly warden lives on site; san facs dated but clean; pleasant vill with gd rests; popular NH; excel." ♦ 1 May-30 Sep. € 12.00 2014*

LOUHANS *6H1* (2km W Urban) *46.62286, 5.21733* **Camp Municipal de Louhans, 10, Chemin de la Chapellerie, 71500 Louhans [03 85 75 19 02 or 03 85 76 75 10 (Mairie); fax 03 85 76 75 11; mairiedelouhanschateaurenaud@ yahoo.fr]** In Louhans foll sp for Romenay on D971. Go under rlwy & over rv. Site on L just after stadium. Med, hdg/mkd pitch, hdstg, shd; wc (some cont); chem disp; mv service pnt 700m; shwrs inc; el pnts €3.60; Indtte; snacks; playgrnd; pool & tennis courts adj; sw rv adj; poss cr; adv bkg; some rlwy noise; CKE/CCI. "Rv location; clean & well-appointed; sports complex adj; lovely cycling area; lge town mkt Mon am; poss travellers; vg." ♦ ltd 1 Apr-30 Sep. € 7.40 2012*

LUCENAY L'EVEQUE *6H1* (550m S Rural) *47.07668, 4.24675* **Camp Municipal du Ternin, 71540 Lucenay-l'Evêque [03 85 82 61 86; mairie.lucenay.l.eveque@wanadoo.fr; www.lucenay71.fr]** On D980 Autun to Saulieu rd, 300m S of Lucenay site ent immed bef vill sp. Ent narr; easier when warden opens 2nd gate. Sm, hdg/mkd pitch, pt shd; wc (some cont); shwrs inc; el pnts €3; playgrnd; shops 300m; dogs €1.50; tennis; quiet; ccard acc; CKE/CCI. "Neat site with brook running thro; gd walking country; quiet low ssn; warden visits am & pm - site yourself; narr ent to pitches with el pnts." 1 May-1 Sep. € 10.00 2010*

LUGNY see Pont de Vaux *9A2*

LUZY *4H4* (1km NE Rural) *46.79622, 3.97685* **Camping La Bédure, Route d'Autun, 58170 Luzy [03 86 30 68 27; info@campinglabedure.com; www.campinglabedure.com]** Foll sps on D981 to site. Med, mkd pitch, pt sl, pt shd; wc (some cont); baby facs; shwrs inc; shops 1km; el pnts (6A) €3 (poss rev pol); tradsmn; playgrnd; pool adj; dogs 1.50; quiet. "Pleasant site; gd walking & touring base." May-Sep. € 10.00 2010*

LUZY *4H4* (7km NE Rural) *46.81680, 4.05650* **Camping Domaine de la Gagère (Naturist), 58170 Luzy [03 86 30 48 11; fax 03 86 30 45 57; info@la-gagere.com; www.la-gagere.com]** Fr Luzy take D981 dir Autun; in 6.5km over rlwy, turn R onto unclassified rd sp 'La Gagère'. Site at end of rd in 3.5km on L; this rd narr in places. Med, mkd pitch, hdstg, pt sl, terr, pt shd; wc; chem disp; mv service pnt; child/ baby facs; fam bthrm; sauna; shwrs inc; el pnts (6A) €4.50; gas 10km; Indtte; sm shop & shops 10km; tradsmn; rest, snacks; bar; BBQ; playgrnd; 2 htd pools; lake, shgle beach 12km; wifi; entmnt; TV rm; 20% statics; dogs €4; bus 10km; phone; poss cr; Eng spkn; adv bkg; quiet; ccard acc; red low ssn; INF card req. ACSI acc; "Excel, wooded, scenic site in beautiful area; gd views; friendly, helpful owners; superb san facs; gd touring base." ♦ 1 Apr-30 Sep. € 42.65 2014*

LUZY *4H4* (2km SW Rural) *46.75790, 3.94472* **Camping Château de Chigy, 58170 Tazilly [03 86 30 10 80; fax 03 86 30 09 22; reception@chateaudechigy.com.fr; www.chateaudechigy.com.fr]** Fr Luzy take D973 S twd Bourbon-Lancy, in 4km turn L on minor rd sp Chigy, site sp. Fr S turn R onto rd to Chigy. Site is E of D973 - do not take sp rd to Tazilly vill. V lge, pt sl, pt terr, pt shd; wc; chem disp; baby facs; shwrs inc; private san facs some pitches; el pnts (6A) €4; gas; Indtte; rest, snacks (high ssn); bar; playgrnd; htd covrd pool; paddling pool; fishing; games area; entmnt; TV; some statics; dogs €2; adv bkg; quiet; red low ssn/long stay/snr citizens; CKE/CCI. "Lovely site in grnds of château; lge pitches; gd." ♦ 26 Apr-30 Sep. € 22.00 2009*

MACON *9A2* (3km N Urban) *46.33023, 4.84491* **Camp Municipal Les Varennes, 1 Route des Grandes Varennes, Sancé, 71000 Mâcon [03 85 38 16 22 or 03 85 38 54 08; fax 03 85 39 39 18; camping@ville-macon.fr; www.macon.fr]** Fr both N & S exit A6 junc 28 & cont S on N6 twd Mâcon; site on L in approx 3km, sp. (Fr S, leaving A6 at junc 28 avoids long trip thro town). Lge, mkd pitch, pt sl, pt shd; htd wc (some cont); chem disp; mv service pnt; baby facs; shwrs inc; el pnts (5-10A) inc (poss rev pol); gas; Indtte; shop; supmkt nr; hypmkt 1km; rest, snacks; bar; playgrnd; 2 pools; tennis 1km; golf 6km; wifi; TV; dogs €1.40; phone; bus; poss cr; Eng spkn; adv bkg; quiet but some rd & rlwy noise; ccard acc; red low ssn/long stay; CKE/CCI. "Well-kept, busy NH nr A6; rec arr early as poss full after 1800; friendly staff; vg, immac san facs; excel rest; gates clsd 2200-0630; poss flooding bottom end of site; twin-axles extra; long level walk to town; excel." ♦ 15 Mar-31 Oct. € 32.80 2014*

MACON *9A2* (8km S Rural) *46.24106, 4.80643* **Camp Municipal du Port d'Arciat, Route du Port d'Arciat, 71680 Crêches-sur-Saône [03 85 37 11 83 or 03 85 37 48 32 (LS); fax 03 85 36 51 57; campingduportdarciat@wanadoo.fr; http://campingduportdarciat.pagesperso-orange.fr]** S fr Mâcon on N6 to Crêches-sur-Saône. Site sp (1 sm sp) at 3rd set of traff lts in cent vill on N6, turn E, cross m'way bdge; site on R by rv, sp on rndabt. Lge, mkd pitch, pt sl, pt shd; wc (some cont); chem disp; mv service pnt; shwrs inc; el pnts (6A) €4; gas; Indtte; shop; supmkt 1km; rest, snacks; bar; playgrnd; pool 1km; fishing & boating; entmnt; dogs €1.40; gates clsd 2200-0700; some Eng spkn; adv bkg; ccard acc; red low ssn; CKE/CCI. "Gd touring base; gd facs; gate to lake/beach clsd bef 1900; twin-axles extra; poss flooding in heavy rain; conv a'route; ideal NH, espec low ssn; vg." ♦ 15 May-15 Sep. € 22.65 2014*

MAILLY LE CHATEAU *4G4* (2.5km SE Rural) *47.58906, 3.65332* **Camp Municipal Le Pré du Roi, Pertuis des Bouchets, 89660 Mailly-le-Château [03 86 81 44 85 or 03 86 81 40 37 (Mairie); fax 03 86 81 40 37; mairie-maillylechateau@wanadoo.fr]** NW on N6 fr Avallon twd Auxerre, turn W in Voutenay-sur-Cure on D950 to Mailly-la-Ville. Cross bdge twd Mailly-le-Château, site sp. Heading S fr Auxerre, turn R off N6 SE of Vincelles on D100 to Bazarnes & Mailly-le-Château. Med, mkd pitch, pt shd; wc; shwrs; el pnts (20A) €3; shops 2km; fishing; dogs; quiet. "Pleasant, peaceful situation by Rv Yonne; helpful warden; gd san facs; some pitches uneven & soft when wet." 1 Jun-3 Sep. € 11.00 2010*

MARCENAY *6F1* (1km N Rural) *47.87070, 4.40560* **Camping Les Grèbes du Lac de Marcenay, 5 Route du Lac, 21330 Marcenay [03 80 81 61 72; fax 03 25 81 02 64; info@campingmarcenaylac.com; www.campingmarcenaylac.com]** On D965 bet Laignes & Châtillon-sur-Seine. Fr Châtillon sp on R 8km after vill of Cérilly. Foll sp to lake & camp. Med, hdg/mkd pitch, hdstg, shd; htd wc; chem disp; mv service pnt; baby facs; shwrs inc; el pnts (10A) €3; gas; Indtte (inc dryer); shop; tradsmn; rest adj; snacks; bar adj; BBQ; playgrnd; pool; lake sw adj; fishing; watersports; boat, canoe & cycle hire; golf; horseriding; games rm; games area; wifi; TV rm; 5% statics; dogs €1; phone; Eng spkn; adv bkg rec; quiet; ccard acc; red low ssn; CKE/CCI. "Lovely, peaceful, well-run site by lake; beautiful area; friendly, helpful Dutch owners; excel san facs; pitches poss soft after rain; gd touring base; gd walking & cycling; Châtillon museum & Abbey de Fontenay worth visit." ♦ 1 May-30 Sep. € 29.70 2013*

MARCIGNY *9A1* (7km W Rural) *46.26489, 3.95756* **Camping La Motte aux Merles, 71110 Artaix [03 85 25 37 67]** Leave D982 (Digoin-Roanne) at Marcigny by-pass. Take D989 twd Lapalisse. In 2km at Chambilly cont on D990, site sp in 5km on L, 200m down side rd. Sm, pt sl, pt shd; wc; shwrs inc; el pnts (8A) €2.40; Indry rm; snacks; playgrnd; pool (high ssn); fishing, tennis; golf nrby; dogs €1; quiet. "Friendly owners; gd sightseeing in peaceful area; site diff in wet; excel." ♦ 1 Apr-15 Oct. € 10.00 2012*

MARNAY (SAONE ET LOIRE) see Chalon sur Saône *6H1*

MATOUR *9A2* (1km W Rural) *46.30475, 4.47858* **Camp Municipal Le Paluet, Rue de la Piscine, 71520 Matour [03 85 59 70 92; lepaluet@matour.fr; www.matour.com]** On W o'skts of Matour off Rte de la Clayette D987. Med, hdg/mkd pitch, pt shd; wc; chem disp; shwrs inc; el pnts (10A) inc; Indtte (inc dryer); shop 500m; bar; snacks; BBQ; playgrnd; pool high ssn; waterslide; lake fishing adj; tennis; games area; wifi; entmnt; TV; adv bkg; quiet; ccard acc; CKE/CCI. "Conv touring vineyards; highly rec; facs poss inadequate high ssn." ♦ 1 May-30 Sep. € 18.50 2012*

MEURSAULT see Beaune *6H1*

MIGENNES see Joigny *4F4*

MONTBARD *6G1* (1km W Urban) *47.6314, 4.33303* **Camp Municipal Les Treilles, Rue Michel Servet, 21500 Montbard [03 80 92 69 50; fax 03 80 92 21 60; camping.montbard@wanadoo.fr; www.montbard.com]** Lies off N side D980. Camping sp clearly indicated on all app including by-pass. Turn onto by-pass at traff lts at rndabt at junc of D905 & D980. Site nr pool. Med, hdg pitch, pt shd, wc; chem disp; shwrs inc; el pnts (16A) €4; Indry rm; shop 1km; supmkt 300m; tradsmn; BBQ; snacks; playgrnd; pool complex adj inc; cycle hire; rv sw 100m; dogs €2; phone; poss cr; quiet but rd/rlwy noise at far end; CKE/CCI. "Pleasant & well-kept site; gd pitches; lge, smart san facs; poss contract worker campers; quiet low ssn; interesting area; excel NH." ♦ 1 Mar-23 Oct. € 27.00 2014*

MONTIGNY EN MORVAN *4H4* (2km E Rural) *47.15627, 3.87476* **Camp Municipal Plat du Lac, Bonin, 58120 Montigny-en-Morvan [03 86 84 75 76; fax 03 86 84 73 05; montignyenmorvan@free]** N fr Château-Chinon on D944. At Montigny take D303 on R sp Barrage de Pannecière. Foll sp Bonin & site. Access fr D303 narr & not rec lge o'fits. Med, pt sl, shd; wc; chem disp; shwrs; el pnts (10A) inc (poss rev pol); tradsmn; lake sw; fishing; CKE/CCI. "Pitches poss soft after rain." 1 May-30 Sep. € 12.00 2009*

MONTSAUCHE LES SETTONS *4G4* (5km SE Rural) *47.17114, 4.06037* **Camping L'Hermitage de Chevigny, 58230 Moux-en-Morvan [03 86 84 50 97; www.mouxenmorvan.fr]** Fr Montsauche take D520 S & after approx 5km turn L on D290; at T-junc in 3km turn L & in further 800m turn L into Chevigny & foll sp to L'Hermitage. App rds narr & twisting. Med, hdg/mkd pitch, pt shd; htd wc (mainly cont); chem disp; shwrs inc; el pnts (6A) €4.70; gas; Indtte (inc dryer); sm shop; tradsmn; snacks, bar; playgrnd; lake sw; watersports; fishing; games area; dogs €1.80; adv bkg; Eng spkn; quiet; ccard not acc; CKE/CCI. "Peaceful, secluded woodland site; clean facs; friendly, helpful owner; gd cycling & walking; less well-known pt of France; excel." 15 Apr-30 Sep. € 15.60 2010*

"I like to fill in the reports as I travel from site to site"

You'll find report forms at the back of this guide, or you can fill them in online at www.caravaclub.co.uk/europereport.

MONTSAUCHE LES SETTONS *4G4* (5.4km SE Rural) *47.19276, 4.06047* **FFCC Camping de la Plage des Settons, Rive Gauche, Lac des Settons, 58230 Montsauche-les-Settons [03 86 84 51 99; fax 03 86 84 54 81; camping@settons-tourisme.com; www.settons-tourisme.com]** Fr Montsauche foll sp Château-Chinon. In 500m fork L to Les Settons. After 2km foll sp for Rive Gauche, after 1km L at bend for site. Med, hdg/mkd pitch, terr, pt shd; wc; chem disp; mv service pnt; shwrs inc; el pnts (4A) inc (long lead req); Indtte; shops 500m; tradsmn; BBQ; playgrnd; pool nrby; sand/shgl lake beach adj; fishing; pedalos; lake sw; cycle hire; dogs free; Eng spkn; poss noisy; ccard acc; CKE/CCI. "In cent of Parc du Morvan; direct access to Lac des Settons; access rd busy pm." ♦ ltd 15 Apr-15 Oct. € 20.00 2011*

MONTSAUCHE LES SETTONS *4G4* (6km SE Rural) *47.18175, 4.05293* **FFCC Camping Les Mésanges, Rive Gauche, 58230 Montsauche-les-Settons [tel/fax 03 86 84 55 77; campinglesmesanges@orange.fr]** Fr Montsauche take D193 to Les Settons, then D520 dir Chevigny. Foll sp to site on W side of lake. Med, mkd pitch, terr, pt sl, pt shd; wc (some cont); chem disp; mv service pnt; baby facs; shwrs inc; el pnts (16A) inc; gas; Indtte (inc dryer); shop; rest 1km; snacks; playgrnd; lake sw; fishing; games area; games rm; dogs €0.80; poss cr; Eng spkn; quiet; adv bkg; CKE/CCI. "Beautiful, lakeside site; well-maintained; gd for families - lge play areas; excel." ♦ 15 May-15 Sep. € 19.00 2010*

BURGUNDY

MONTSAUCHE LES SETTONS *4G4* (7km SE Rural) *47.18578, 4.07056* **Camping Plage du Midi, Lac des Settons Les Branlasses, 58230 Montsauche-les-Settons [03 86 84 51 97; fax 03 86 84 57 31; campplagedumidi@aol.com; www.settons-camping.com]** Fr Salieu take D977 bis to Montsauche, then D193 'Rive Droite' to Les Settons for 5km. Cont a further 3km & take R fork sp 'Les Branlasses' Centre du Sport. Site on L after 500m at lakeside. Med, mkd pitch, terr, pt shd; htd wc; chem disp; mv service pnt; baby facs; shwrs inc; el pnts (10A) €3.60; gas; Indtte (inc dryer); shop; tradsmn; rest 3km; snacks; bar; BBQ; playgrnd; htd, covrd pool; lake sw; sand beach adj; watersports; cycle hire; horseriding 2km; wifi; entmnt; dogs €1; phone; poss cr; Eng spkn; adv bkg; poss noisy; red low ssn; ccard acc; CKE/CCI. "Site in gd situation; muddy when wet." ♦ Easter-15 Oct. € 14.00 2010*

MOTTE TERNANT, LA *6G1* (75m W Rural) *47.32309, 4.33086* **Camping Le Village, 21210 La Motte-Ternant [tel/fax 03 80 84 30 11; campinglevillagelamotte-t@orange.fr; www.campinglamotteternant.eu]** Exit A6 junc 23 onto D980 to Précy-sous-Thil; then take D36 to Fontangy; turn R onto D26 to La Motte-Ternant. Fr Saulieu take D26 to La Motte-Ternant. Site in 10km. Site sp, but diff to see fr S (obscured by building). Sm, pt sl, shd; wc; chem disp (wc); shwrs inc; el pnts (16A) €3.50; tradsmn; shop & bar 800m; tradsmn; BBQ; dogs free; Eng spkn; adv bkg; quiet; ccard acc. "Delightful, friendly site with views; helpful Dutch owners; hot water poss extremely hot - children take care; gd." 1 Apr-15 Oct. € 12.00 2010*

NEVERS *4H4* (500m S Rural) *46.98210, 3.16110* **FFCC Camping de Nevers, Rue de la Jonction, 58000 Nevers [06 84 98 69 79; info@campingnevers.com; www.campingnevers.com]** Fr E exit A77 junc 37 & foll dir 'Centre Ville'. Site on R immed bef bdge over Rv Loire. Fr W (Bourges) on D976 foll sp 'Nevers Centre' onto D907. In approx 3km bef bdge turn R, site on L. Med, mkd pitch, hdstg, terr, pt shd; htd wc; chem disp; mv service pnt; baby facs; shwrs inc; el pnts (6-10A) €3-4.75; Indtte (inc dryer); supmkt 2km; tradsmn; rest 500m; snacks; bar; BBQ; playgrnd; sand beach 200m; rv fishing; cycle hire; internet; TV; 3% statics; dogs €0.50; phone; bus 20m; poss cr; Eng spkn; adv bkg; rd noise; ccard not acc; red low ssn; CKE/CCI. "Pleasant, scenic site on bank of Rv Loire; on 3 levels - ltd el pnts on lower; gd clean san facs, poss stretched high ssn; cycle paths along Loire; no twin-axles; poss noisy when events at Nevers Magny-Cours racing circuit; gd site; easy walk over bdge to interesting town; nr town." ♦ 11 Apr-12 Oct. € 27.00 2014*

NEVERS *4H4* (7km NW Urban) *47.01222, 3.07822* **FFCC Camping La Loire, 2 Rue de la Folie, 58600 Fourchambault [03 86 60 81 59 or 06 11 05 18 69 (mob); fax 03 86 60 96 24; campingdelaloire@dbmail.com; www.camping-de-loire.fr.st]** Fr Nevers on D40 thro town, site on L bef rv bdge. Med, pt shd; wc; chem disp; mv service pnt; shwrs inc; el pnts (6-10A) €3-4.50; Indtte; shop 500m; rest 100m; snacks; bar; BBQ; rv adj; dogs €0.50; bus; red long stay/ CKE/CCI. "Friendly, helpful staff; san facs need update & poss unclean." ♦ ltd 9 Apr-31 Oct. € 10.50 2010*

NOLAY *6H1* (9km SW Rural) *46.87604, 4.55877* **Camp Municipal La Gabrelle, 39 La Varenne, 71490 Couches [03 85 45 59 49 or 03 85 98 19 20 (Mairie); fax 03 85 98 19 29; camping-la-gabrelle@orange.fr]** Exit A6 at junc 25 Chalon-sur-Saône Nord onto D978 sp Autun. In 26km at Couches, site NW of vill. Sm, hdg pitch, terr, pt shd; wc; shwrs inc; el pnts (6A) €2.80; Indtte; supmkt 5km; snacks; bar; playgrnd; lake adj; some daytime rd noise. "Attractive countryside nr wine area; gd facs; excel." ♦ 1 May-30 Sep. € 11.00 2010*

⊞ **NOLAY** *6H1* (1km NW Rural) *46.95084, 4.62266* **Camping La Bruyère, Rue du Moulin Larché, 21340 Nolay [tel/fax 03 80 21 87 59 or 06 88 16 06 18 (mob); www.nolay.com/fr/?/Logement/Les-campings]** Fr Beaune take D973 W dir Autun. In approx 20km, arr in vill of Nolay & cont on D973 thro vill. Site on L in 1km after vill, opp supmkt. Sm, hdg/mkd pitch, terr, pt shd; htd wc; chem disp; mv service pnt; shwrs inc; el pnts (10-12A) €3.60-4; Indtte; shop adj; supmkt, rest & bar 1km; BBQ; a few statics; phone adj; bus adj; Eng spkn; quiet; ccard acc; red low ssn; CKE/CCI. "Lovely, peaceful, well-kept site; friendly staff; gd, clean san facs, poss stretched if site busy; poss grape pickers in Sep; poss school & youth groups; attractive walk to bustling old town; gd touring base in wine area or NH." ♦ € 14.65 2014*

NOYERS *4G4* (200m S Rural) *47.69423, 3.99421* **Camp Municipal, Promenade du Pré de l'Echelle, 89310 Noyers-sur-Surein [03 86 82 83 72 (Mairie); fax 03 86 82 63 41; mairie-de-noyers@wanadoo.fr]** Exit A6 at Nitry & turn R onto D944. In 2km at N edge of Nitry, turn R onto D49 sp Noyers. In 10km in Noyers, turn L onto D86 sp Centre Ville/ Camping. Immed after x-ing rv & bef gate, turn L bet 2 obelisks. Site at end of track. Sm, mkd pitch, terr, shd; wc; own san; chem disp; shwrs inc; el pnts €1.05; shop, rest, snacks & bar 200m; BBQ; playgrnd; dogs; quiet, except church bells. "Attractive, secluded site nr Rv Serein (6 pitches); ent key fr Mairie on R after going thro town gate; pretty old vill; ltd san facs." € 4.30 2014*

NUITS ST GEORGES *6G1* (3km SW Urban) *47.10323, 4.94148* **Camping Le Moulin de Prissey, 21700 Premeaux-Prissey [03 80 62 31 15; fax 03 80 61 37 29; www.cpg-moulin-prissey.fr]** Exit Beaune on D974 twd Nuits-St Georges & Dijon; app Premeaux-Prissey turn R soon after vill sp, under rlwy bdge & foll site sp. Fr A31 exit at Nuits-St Georges & foll camp sp for Saule-Guillaume, thro Premeaux-Prissey & foll site sp. Sm, mkd pitch, pt sl, pt shd; wc (some cont); chem disp (wc); mv service pnt; shwrs inc; el pnts (6A) inc; gas; Indtte; shops 3km; tradsmn; snacks; rest, bar 4km; BBQ; playgrnd; dogs €0.90; poss cr; adv bkg; noisy rlwy adj; ccard not acc; CKE/CCI. "Popular NH - arr early; sm pitches; access poss diff lge o'fits; untidy & run down early ssn (2011); basic facs; gd cycling." ♦ ltd 1 Apr-15 Oct. € 18.20 2012*

PALINGES *9A2* (1km N Rural) *46.56118, 4.22516* **Camp Municipal du Lac, Le Fourneau, 71430 Palinges [03 85 88 14 49 or 06 06 88 14 49 (mob); camping.palinges@hotmail.fr]** N70 Montceau-les-Mines dir Paray, turn L onto D92 into Palinges cent (4km). By church turn L church onto D128. Site in 1km. Sm, hdg/mkd pitch, pt sl, pt shd; htd wc; chem disp; baby facs; shwrs inc; el pnts (10A) inc; Indtte; shop, rest 1km; snacks; bar; playgrnd; lake sw & fishing adj with beach; cycle hire; tennis; dogs €1.60; adv bkg; Eng spkn; quiet; no ccard acc; CKE/CCI. "Lge pitches; friendly & helpful owners; gd clean facs; poss a little unkempt; gd walking, cycling & lake sw; conv canal; highly rec." ♦ 1 Apr-30 Oct. € 18.50 2010*

PARAY LE MONIAL *9A1* (1km NW Urban) *46.45750, 4.10472* **Camping de Mambré, Route du Gué-Léger, 71600 Paray-le-Monial [03 85 88 89 20; fax 03 85 88 87 81; camping.plm@gmail.com; www.campingdemambre.com]** Fr N79 Moulin to Mâcon; site at W end of town; just after level x-ing turn NE into Rte du Gué-Léger. Turn R into site after x-ing rv; well sp. Lge, hgd/mkd pitch, pt shd; wc; chem disp; shwrs inc; el pnts (10A) €3.40; Indtte; sm shop & 500m; snacks high ssn; bar; playgrnd; pool high ssn; dogs €2; quiet, but some rd noise; red low ssn; CKE/CCI. "Paray-le-Monial is pilgrimage cent; ltd facs & poorly maintained low ssn (2011); no designated fresh water pnts (2011); 15min walk to town along rv; excel cycling cent." 3 May-4 Oct. € 25.60 (CChq acc) 2014*

PONT DE VAUX *9A2* (15km W Rural) *46.47686, 4.80908* **Camp Municipal St Pierre, 71260 Lugny [03 85 33 20 25 or 03 85 33 21 96 (Mairie); fax 03 85 33 00 58]** W of A6/N6; take C7 off D56 N out of Lugny; foll sp for Rest St Pierre; site adj & sp fr town. Diff app for lge o'fits. Sm, mkd pitch, pt shd; wc; shwrs inc; el pnts inc; Indry rm; shop 1.5km in Lugny; rest adj; v quiet; ccard not acc. "Simple site; lovely views of vineyards; warden calls am & pm; facs clean; gd local walks - steep fr town to site; gd rest adj." 1 May-30 Sep. 2010*

PONTAILLER SUR SAONE *6G1* (750m E Rural) *47.30817, 5.42518* **Camping La Chanoie, 46 Rue de la Chanoie, 21270 Pontailler-sur-Saône [03 80 36 10 58; fax 03 80 47 84 42; otpontailler@wanadoo.fr; www.pontailler-tourisme.fr]** E fr Pontailler-sur-Saône on D959; pass town hall & TO on R; after bdg take 1st L sp Camping; site in 500m. Fr W on D959 turn R bef bdg & bef ent town. Med, hdg/mkd pitch, pt shd; htd wc (some cont); chem disp (wc); mv service pnt; baby facs; shwrs inc; el pnts (6-10A) €2.85-4.10; gas 1km; Indtte; shops 750m; rest, snacks; bar; BBQ; playgrnd; rv sw, water sports & fishing adj; tennis; games area; games rm; 80% statics; dogs €1.55; bus; poss cr; adv bkg; quiet, poss noisy if busy; red long stay; CKE/CCI. "Attractive sm town; polite & helpful owner; clean san facs, poss stretched high ssn; vg; ok NH." ♦ ltd 15 Apr-15 Oct. € 21.20 2014*

POUGUES LES EAUX *4H4* (1km N Urban) *47.08430, 3.09349* **Camp Municipal Les Chanternes, Ave du Paris, 58320 Pougues-les-Eaux [03 86 68 86 18 or 03 86 37 32 91; accueil@ot-pouguesleseaux.fr; www.ot-pouguesleseaux.fr]** On E side of D907 in Pougues-les-Eaux at rear of open-air pool & thro same ent. Med, mkd pitch, pt shd; htd wc (some cont); mv service pnt; shwrs inc; el pnts; shops, rest & snacks in vill; pool adj; adv bkg; rd & rlwy noise; CKE/CCI. 1 Jun-30 Sep. 2009*

POUILLY SUR LOIRE *4G3* (1km N Rural) *47.28742, 2.94427* **Camp Municipal Le Malaga, Rue des Champs-sur-Loire, Les Loges, 58150 Pouilly-sur-Loire [tel/fax 03 86 39 14 54 or 03 86 58 74 38 (LS); www.ot-pouillysurloire.fr]** Fr S exit A77 junc 26 onto D28a, turn L onto D59/D4289 W, bef rv bdge turn R, site in 1km on rv. Fr N on ent vill turn R at site sp into narr rd. Turn R along rv as above. Med, pt shd; wc; chem disp; shwrs inc; el pnts (10A) inc (poss long lead req & poss rev pol); Indry rm; shop & 1km; tradsmn; snacks; bar; BBQ; playgrnd; dogs €1; phone; no twin-axles or o'fits over 5m; poss cr; Eng spkn; quiet, but some rlwy noise & poss noisy w/end. "Beautifully kept site on banks of Loire; busy NH; spacious but uneven pitches; mixed reports san facs; poss youth groups; beautiful area; wine tasting nrby; poss mosquitoes; excel; delightful site adjacent to the Loire, spacious and leafy areas, wonderful wines in Pouilly and Sancerre, excellent museum closeby." ♦ 1 Jun-10 Sep. € 14.20 2014*

PRECY SOUS THIL *6G1* (350m NW Rural) *47.38721, 4.30645* **Camp Municipal du Parc de l'Hôtel de Ville, 17 Rue de l'Hôtel de Ville, 21390 Précy-sous-Thil [03 80 64 57 18 (Mairie); fax 03 80 64 43 37; precysousthil@orange.fr; www.cotedor-tourisme.com]** Exit A6 at junc 23 Bierre-lès-Semur exit onto D980 to Précy. Site sp in vill. Sm, pt sl, pt shd; wc; shwrs inc; el pnts (6A) inc; Indtte; shops 150m; rest & bar 300m; playgrnd; rv adj; tennis nr; horseriding; entmnt; TV; some statics; dogs €1.30; quiet. "In grnds of Town Hall; warden calls 1900-2100; mostly sl pitches; conv NH on way S." Easter-1 Nov. € 12.00 2013*

PREMEAUX PRISSEY see Nuits St Georges *6G1*

PREMERY *4G4* (500m NW Urban) *47.17804, 3.33692* **Camp Municipal Le Plan D'eau (Les Prés de la Ville), 58700 Prémery [03 86 37 99 42 or 03 86 68 12 40 (Mairie); fax 03 86 37 98 72; mairie-premery@wanadoo.fr; www.mairie-premery.fr]** N fr Nevers on D977 to Prémery; turn R after 2nd rndabt. Site sp on D977. Med, pt shd; wc (some cont); chem disp (wc); shwrs inc; el pnts (8-10A) €1-1.80; shops 500m; lake & rv adj with sand beach, sw, fishing & boating; tennis adj; adv bkg; quiet; 10% red 10+ days. "Lovely, well-run lakeside site in town park; excel facs; popular NH; nice walk to interesting town; poss mkt traders; excel value." ♦ 1 May-30 Sep. € 14.50 2013*

RIEL LES EAUX *6F1* (1.8km W Rural) *47.97050, 4.64990* **Camp Municipal du Plan d'Eau, 21570 Riel-les-Eaux [tel/fax 03 80 93 72 76; bar-camping-du-marais@wanadoo.fr]** NE fr Châtillon-sur-Seine on D965 twd Chaumont: after 6km turn N onto D13 at Brion-sur-Ource; cont thro Belan-sur-Ource. Site almost opp junc with D22 turning to Riel-les-Eaux; site well sp. Sm, hdg pitch, pt shd; wc; chem disp; shwrs inc; el pnts (6A) €3; tradsmn; snacks; bar; playgrnd; lake adj; fishing; Eng spkn; quiet; CKE/CCI. "Conv Champagne area; excel." ♦ 1 Apr-31 Oct. € 8.60 2009*

ROGNY LES SEPT ECLUSES see Bleneau *4G3*

SACQUENAY *6G1* (500m S Rural) *47.58924, 5.32178* **Aire Naturelle La Chênaie (Méot), 16 Rue du 19 Mars, 21260 Sacquenay [03 80 75 89 43 or 03 80 75 97 07; fax 03 80 75 89 43; eric.meot@wanadoo.fr; www.cotedor-tourisme.com/bourgogne/camping/aire-naturelle-de-camping-de-la-chenaie]** S on D974 turn L onto D171A sp Occey & Sacquenay, site sp. Sm, pt sl, pt shd; wc; shwrs inc; el pnts (6A); shop 400m; lndtte; playgrnd; poss cr; Eng spkn; adv bkg; quiet; red 10+ days; CKE/CCI; "Peaceful site in orchard." 1 Apr-1 Oct. € 12.00 2013*

ST AGNAN *4G4* (50m N Rural) *47.31812, 4.09520* **Camping du Lac, Le Château, 58230 St Agnan [03 86 78 73 70 or 01772 700531 (UK tel LS); fax 03 86 78 74 94; info@campingburgundy.co.uk; www.campingburgundy.co.uk]** Exit A6 junc 22 onto D646 then D906 dir Saulieu; at La Roche-en-Brenil turn R onto D226 to St Agnan. Site ent on R opp junc. Fr Saulieu leave town S on D980 sp Autun; on o'skts turn W onto D26B to Eschamps then D106 to St Agnan. Med, pt sl, pt shd; wc (some cont); chem disp; shws inc; el pnts (6A) €3; lndtte; shop; tradsmn; rest, snacks; bar; BBQ; playgrnd; lake sw adj; kayak & pedalo hire nr; games rm; dogs €1.50; Eng spkn; adv bkg; quiet; ccard acc; CKE/CCI. "Pretty, British-owned site in grnds of chateau; v ltd facs low ssn." 15 Apr-15 Oct. € 13.00 2010*

ST BOIL *6H1* (1.5km S Rural) *46.64621, 4.69480* **Camping Moulin de Collonge, Route des Vins, 71940 St Boil [03 85 44 00 40 or 03 85 44 00 32; fax 03 85 44 00 40; millofcollonge@wanadoo.fr; www.moulindecollonge.com]** S on A6 take N80 at Chalon-Sud; W dir Le Creusot; 9km turn S on D981 thro Buxy to St Boil; sp on L thro vill. Sm, hdg/mkd pitch, pt shd; wc (few cont); baby facs; shwrs inc; el pnts (6A) €3.50 (poss no earth or rev pol); gas; lndtte; sm shop & 2km; tradsmn; rest, snacks; bar; BBQ; playgrnd; htd, covrd pool; lake fishing; cycle hire; wifi; entmnt; some statics; dogs; v cr high ssn; some Eng spkn; adv bkg; quiet; ccard acc; red low ssn; CKE/CCI. "Busy but quiet site; clean, dated san facs; uneven pitches & some sm - poss muddy when wet; gd cycling." ♦ 1 Apr-29 Sep. € 19.00 2009*

ST BONNET DE JOUX *9A2* (400m E Urban) *46.48388, 4.44276* **Camp Municipal, Route de Cluny, 71220 St Bonnet-de-Joux [03 85 24 73 87 (Mairie); st.bonnet.de.joux.mairie@wanadoo.fr]** Site sp fr vill cent - also sp for tennis. Sm, hdg pitch, pt shd; wc (some cont); chem disp (wc); shwrs inc; shop, rest, bar in vill; BBQ; playgrnd; tennis adj; quiet. "Simple, ungated site in sm vill, beside sm lake; facs clean but ltd." 1 Jun-. € 9.00 2010*

ST FLORENTIN *4F4* (1km S Rural) *47.99252, 3.73450* **Camping L'Armançon, 89600 St Florentin [tel/fax 03 86 35 08 03 13 or 03 86 35 11 86 (mob); ot.saint-florentin@wanadoo.fr]** N fr Auxerre on N77 site on R app rv bdge S of town. Fr N pass traff islands, exit town up slope, x-ing canal & rv. Site immed on S side of rv bdge - turn R immed at end of bdg then under bdg to site. Site well sp fr all dirs. Med, hdg pitch, pt sl, pt shd; wc (cont); chem disp; shwrs inc; el pnts (10A) inc (poss long lead req); gas; lndtte; shop; café/bar; snacks; playgrnd; fishing; dogs €0.20; poss cr; some rd noise at night. "Well-kept site; excel, lge pitches; friendly manager; dated but clean san facs; diff, steep exit to main rd; gd nh." ♦ ltd 2 Apr-11 Oct. € 12.60 2013*

ST GERMAIN DU BOIS *6H1* (500m S Rural) *46.74661, 5.24613* **Camp Municipal de l'Etang Titard, Route de Louhans, 71330 St Germain-du-Bois [03 85 72 06 15 or 03 85 72 01 47; fax 03 85 72 03 38; mairie-71330-saint-germain-du-bois@wanadoo.fr]** Fr Chalon-sur Saône E on N78, exit at Thurey onto D24 to St Germain. Site sp on D13 adj lake. Sm, mkd pitch, terr, pt shd; wc; chem disp; mv service pnt; shwrs inc; el pnts (6A); lndtte; shop, rest, bar 300m; BBQ; playgrnd, htd, covrd pool in sports grnd adj; fishing; dogs; adv bkg; quiet; CKE/CCI. "Lge pitches; friendly warden; no sw in lake; pleasant town; gd cycling area." ♦ 1 May-15 Sep. € 7.60 2009*

ST HONORE LES BAINS *4H4* (450m W Urban) *46.90413, 3.83919* **Camp Municipal Plateau du Guet, 13 Rue Eugène Collin, 58360 St Honoré-les-Bains [03 86 30 76 00 or 03 86 30 74 87 (Mairie); fax 03 86 30 73 33; mairie-de-st-honore-les-bains@wanadoo.fr; www.st-honore-les-bains.com]** On D985 fr Luzy to St Honoré-les-Bains. In cent vill turn L on D106 twd Vandenesse. Site on L in 150m. Or N fr Château-Chinon 27km. Then D985 to St Honoré. Med, mkd pitch, pt hdstg, pt terr, pt shd; htd wc; mv service pnt; shwrs inc; el pnts (10A) €2.90; lndtte; shop, rest, snacks, bar 300m; playgrnd; htd pool 300m; adv bkg; quiet; CKE/CCI. "Gd, modern san facs; pleasant, conv site town, gd walking ." ♦ 1 Apr-26 Oct. € 8.60 2012*

ST HONORE LES BAINS *4H4* (1km W Rural) *46.90680, 3.82843* **Camping & Gîtes Les Bains, 15 Ave Jean Mermoz, 58360 St Honoré-les-Bains [03 86 30 73 44; fax 03 86 30 61 88; camping-les-bains@wanadoo.fr; www.campinglesbains.com]** Fr St Honoré-les-Bains foll site sp as 'Village des Bains' fr town cent on D106 twd Vandenesse. Med, hdg/mkd pitch, some hdstg, pt sl, shd; wc (some cont); chem disp; mv service pnt; baby facs; shwrs inc; el pnts (6A) €3.50; gas; lndtte (inc dryer); shop 1km; rest, snacks; bar; BBQ; playgrnd; pool; paddling pool; waterslide; fishing; tennis; horseriding 300m; cycle hire; wifi; entmnt; games/TV rm; dogs €1.50; Eng spkn; adv bkg; quiet low ssn; ccard acc; CKE/CCI. "Helpful staff; poor maintenance & san facs need refurb; gd walking; sm pitches & poss waterlogged after rain; mkt Thu." ♦ 1 Apr-31 Oct. € 16.00 2011*

ST LEGER DE FOUGERET see Château-Chinon *4H4*

ST LEGER SOUS BEUVRAY *4H4* (1km N Rural) *46.93157, 4.10088* **Camping De La Boutière, 71990 St Léger-sous-Beuvray [06 80 40 81 28 / 03 85 82 48 86 (ls); camping@la-boutiere.com; www.la-boutiere.com]** Take N81 SW fr Autun dir Bourbon-Lancy & in approx 10km, turn R onto D61 to St Léger. Site sp in vill. Sm, mkd pitch, pt sl, pt shd; wc; chem disp; shwrs inc; el pnts (6-10A) €3.70; shops 1km; 5% statics; dogs €2.70; phone; wifi; twin-axle c'vans €80; poss cr; quiet; red low ssn; CKE/CCI; "Pleasant, well-kept, Dutch-owned site; gd, modern san facs; vg." 1 Apr-31 Aug. € 16.00 2013*

ST PEREUSE *4H4* (1km SE Rural) *47.05720, 3.81580* **Camping Le Manoir de Bezolle, 58110 St Péreuse-en-Morvan [03 86 84 42 55; fax 03 86 84 43 77; info@camping-bezolle.com; www.camping-bezolle.com]** 9km W of Château-Chinon on D978 Autun-Nevers. Site sp at junc with D11 to St Péreuse on N side of D978. Med, pt sl, pt terr, pt shd; wc htd; chem disp; mv service pnt; baby facs; shwrs inc; el pnts (10A) inc (long lead poss req & avail on loan); Indtte; vg shop; rest, snacks; bar; BBQ (charcoal/gas/elec); playgrnd; 2 pools; paddling pool; lakeside walks; fishing; wifi; entmnt; dogs €2; no c'vans/m'vans over 8m; quiet; ccard acc; red low ssn; CKE/CCI. "Peaceful, well-kept site; most pitches shd; gd views fr upper pitches; some steep site rds; friendly, helpful Eng owners; modern, well-kept san facs; gd pool; gd food in rest; rest, shop, bar & pools clsd low ssn; gd touring base Morvan National Park & Burgundy; excel walks adj to site; excel." ♦ € 32.00 (CChq acc) SBS - L19 2011*

ST POINT see Cluny *9A2*

"I need an on-site restaurant"

We do our best to make sure site information is correct, but it is always best to check any must-have facilities are still available or will be open during your visit.

ST SAUVEUR EN PUISAYE *4G4* (2km N Rural) *47.63076, 3.19231* **FFCC Camping Parc des Joumiers, Route de Mézilles, 89520 St Sauveur-en-Puisaye [03 86 45 66 28; fax 03 86 45 60 27; campingmoteljoumiers@wanadoo.fr; www.camping-motel-joumiers.com]** Fr A6 S, exit at sp Joigny-Toucy onto D955 thro Aillant-sur-Tholon to Toucy, then cont to St Sauveur. Or N fr St Sauveur on D7 sp Mézilles, site on R in 1.5km. Site well sp at main x-rds in town. Med, hdg/mkd pitch, pt shd; htd wc; chem disp; shwrs inc; el pnts (5-10A) €2.80-3.80; gas; Indtte; tradsmn; rest, snacks; bar; BBQ; playgrnd; htd pool; lake sw & beach adj; fishing; games area; cycle hire; wifi; some statics; dogs €1.80; phone; poss cr; no adv bkg; quiet; ccard acc; 5% red long stay/CKE/CCI. "Helpful staff; lge pitches with lake views." ♦ ltd 16 Mar-16 Oct. € 16.30 2010*

ST SEINE L'ABBAYE *6G1* (1.8km N Rural) *47.44073, 4.79236* **Camp Municipal, Rue de la Foire aux Vaches, 21440 St Seine-l'Abbaye [03 80 35 00 09 or 03 80 35 01 64 (Mairie)]** On D971 in vill of St Seine-l'Abbaye, turn N onto D16. Turn R uphill, sp camping & turn R thro gateway in stone wall. Narr rds in vill. Or fr N on D974, avoiding Dijon, turn R onto D959 at Til-Châtel, then D901 Moloy/Lamargelle. Turn L in Lamargelle onto D16 St Seine-l'Abbaye. Turn L uphill at edge of vill & as above (avoids narr rds). Sm, pt sl, hdstg, pt unshd; wc (cont); chem disp; shwrs inc; el pnts (10A) €2.50 (rev pol); shops 500m; pool 4km; rv 500m; dogs; v quiet; CKE/CCI. "Pleasantly situated & peaceful site; basic but immac san facs; fees collected fr 1900 hrs; lovely vill; conv Dijon or as NH; excel; gd." 1 May-30 Sep. € 11.00 2014*

SALORNAY SUR GUYE see Cluny *9A2*

SAULIEU *6G1* (1km N Rural) *47.28936, 4.22401* **Camping Le Perron/Camping de Saulieu, Route de Paris, 21210 Saulieu [03 80 64 16 19; camping.salieu@wanadoo.fr; www.aquadis-loisirs.com]** On D906 on L of rd on ent fr N. Sp. Lge, hdg/mkd pitch, pt sl, pt shd; htd wc; chem disp; mv service pnt; shwrs inc; el pnts (10A) €3.90; gas; Indtte; sm shop; tradsmn; rest in ssn; bar; playgrnd; pool; paddling pool; lake fishing; tennis; wifi; dogs €1.50; adv bkg; quiet, but poss rd noise some pitches; red low ssn; CKE/CCI. "Nr town but rural feel; quiet at far end of site, away fr pool & playgrnd; no twin-axles; many rests in town; gd walking area; gd." ♦ ltd 15 Mar-30 Oct. € 25.30 (CChq acc) 2014*

"Satellite navigation makes touring much easier"

Remember most sat navs don't know if you're towing or in a larger vehicle – always use yours alongside maps and site directions.

SELONGEY *6G1* (500m SW Rural) *47.58248, 5.18408* **Camp Municipal Les Courvelles, Rue Henri Jevain, 21260 Selongey [03 80 75 52 38 or 03 80 75 70 74 (Mairie); fax 03 80 75 56 65; info@solongey.com; www.selongey.com]** Exit A31 junc 5 N of Dijon onto D974 N for 3km to Orville: turn W in Orville sp Selongey & site; site in approx 2km. Sm, some hdstg, unshd; wc; chem disp; shwrs inc; el pnts (6A) €2; shop 1km; tennis; quiet; CKE/CCI. "Well-kept, friendly site; warden calls am & eve; rec arr bef 1600 & site yourself if req hdstg; no twin-axles; poss travellers; conv m'way/NH; excel." ♦ 1 May-30 Sep. € 10.00 2011*

"There aren't many sites open at this time of year"

If you're travelling outside peak season remember to call ahead to check site opening dates – even if the entry says 'open all year'.

SEMUR EN AUXOIS *6G1* (3.5km S Rural) *47.46812, 4.35589* **FFCC Camping Lac de Pont, 16 Rue du Lac, 21140 Pont-et-Massène [03 80 97 01 26 or 03 80 97 01 26 (Low Ssn); contact@camping-lacdepont.fr/camping-lacdepont@orange.fr; www.campinglacdepont.fr]** Exit A6 junc 23 twd Semur-en-Auxois on D980; after sh dist turn R sp 'Lac de Pont' D103. Med, some hdg pitch, pt sl, pt shd; wc; chem disp; mv service pnt; baby facs; shwrs inc; el pnts (6A) €3.50; gas; Indtte; shop; tradsmn; rest 500m; snacks; bar; BBQ; playgrnd; lake sw, sand beach adj; diving platform; watersports on lake; tennis; games rm; cycle hire; 30% statics; dogs €2; phone; poss cr; Eng spkn; quiet; ccard acc; CKE/CCI. "Warm welcome, helpful owners; generous pitches, some shady; san facs dated; vg for teenagers - games/meeting rm; 'Petit Train' goes round site & into Semur; cycle rte/walks adj; gd touring base; nr A6 m'way; walled, medieval town; muddy pitches." 1 May-30 Sep. € 25.30 2014*

SENNECEY LE GRAND *6H1* (6km E Rural) *46.65480, 4.94461* **Château de L'Epervière, Rue du Château, 71240 Gigny-sur-Saône [03 85 94 16 90; fax 03 85 94 16 97; info@domaine-eperviere.com; www.domaine-eperviere.com]** Fr N exit A6 junc 26 (Chalon Sud) onto N6 dir Mâcon & Tournus; at Sennecey-le-Grand turn E onto D18 sp Gigny-sur-Saône; site sp 1km S of Gigny-sur-Saône. Or fr S exit A6 junc 27 (Tournus) onto N6 N to Sennecey-le-Grand, then as above. NB Diff to find signs fr main rd. Lge, hdg/mkd pitch, hdstg, pt shd; htd wc; chem disp; mv service pnt; baby facs; jacuzzi/sauna; shwrs inc; el pnts (6A) inc; gas; Indtte (inc dryer); sm shop; tradsmn; rest, snacks; pizzeria; bar high ssn; BBQ; playgrnd; 2 pools (1 htd, covrd); paddling pool; lake & rv nr; fishing; tennis 400m; cycle hire; wifi; entmnt; games/TV rm; tour op statics; dogs €3; no c'vans/m'vans over 18m high ssn; poss v cr; Eng spkn; adv bkg; quiet; ccard acc; red low ssn; CKE/CCI. "Superb, spacious, well-run site in grnds of chateau nr sm lake; lovely, lge pitches; warm welcome, pleasant staff; excel san facs; gd pools & rest; vg for families; wine tasting; interesting wild life; boggy when wet; conv NH fr a'route; fantastic site; level pitches; great facs." ♦ 1 Apr-1 Oct. € 49.40 SBS - L12 2013*

SENNECEY LE GRAND *6H1* (5km NW Rural) *46.67160, 4.83301* **Camping La Héronnière, Les Lacs de Laives, 71240 Laives [tel/fax 03 85 44 98 85; camping.laives@wanadoo.fr; www.camping-laheronniere.com]** Exit A6 junc 26 (fr N) or junc 27 (fr S) onto N6. Turn W at Sennecey-le-Grand to Laives. Foll sp 'Lacs de Laives'. Sp on D18. Med, hdg/mkd pitch, some hdstg, pt shd; wc; chem disp; shwrs inc; el pnts (6A) €4.80; Indtte; shop; rest 300m; snacks; playgrnd; sm htd pool; lake sw & beach nrby; fishing; windsurfing; watersports; cycle hire; dogs €1.60; Eng spkn; adv bkg; quiet, but some rd noise fr A6; CKE/CCI. "Lovely, level, lakeside site; excel, busy NH; may fill up after 1500; gd shwrs; rest at lakeside (high ssn); popular with bikers; vg; Pretty site, laid back helpful staff, gd nh, romantic rest by lakeside 3 mins walk; excel facs; clean modern san facs." ♦ 29 Mar-13 Oct. € 36.00 2013*

SENS *4F4* (1km S Urban) *48.18312, 3.28803* **Camp Municipal Entre Deux Vannes, Ave de Senigallia, 89100 Sens [03 86 65 64 71 or 03 86 65 37 42 (LS); fax 03 86 95 39 41; http://ville-sens.fr]** D606/D1060 S of town. Take D606a sp sens. Site on R in 600m. Med, mkd pitch, pt shd; wc (some cont); chem disp (wc); mv service pnt; baby facs; shwrs inc; el pnts (16A) inc; Indtte; shops 1km; tradsmn high ssn; rest nrby; playgrnd; adv bkg rec; some noise fr rd & commercial premises nrby during day; ccard acc; CKE/CCI. "Excel site; opp rv & superb park area; friendly, helpful warden; san facs old but clean; gate locked 2200; easy walk to town; ensure height barrier moved bef ent." 15 May-15 Sep. € 13.50 2014*

TIL CHATEL *6G1* (2km E Rural) *47.53042, 5.18700* **Camping Les Sapins, 21120 Til-Châtel [03 80 95 16 68; www.restaurantlessapins.eresto.net]** Leave A31 junc 5 onto D974 dir Til-Châtel. Site on R in 500m adj Rest Les Sapins. Sm, pt sl, pt shd, serviced pitch; wc (some cont); shwrs inc; el pnts (10A) inc; shops 2km; rest, snacks; bar; poss v cr; Eng spkn; adv bkg; minimal rd noise; CKE/CCI. "Clean site; basic san facs; no twin-axles; conv NH fr a'route." 1 Apr-30 Sep. € 17.00 2014*

TIL CHATEL *6G1* (5km W Urban) *47.52204, 5.10918* **Camp Municipal des Capucins, Rue des Capucins, 21120 Is-sur-Tille [03 80 95 02 08; fax 03 80 95 08 33; www.is-sur-tille.com]** Leave A31 at junc 5 S onto D974 dir Til-Châtel; turn R onto D959 to Is-sur-Tille. Site on L at sports grnd, well sp. Sm, shd; wc (cont); chem disp; shwrs inc; el pnts (3A) inc; Indry rm; shops, rest, bar 1km; tradsmn; pool adj; poss cr; quiet. "Delightful, floral vill; site yourself; warden calls am & pm; facs old but clean; poss travellers; poss security probs - NH only." 1 Jun-30 Sep. € 10.05 2010*

TONNERRE *4F4* (1.5km NE Urban) *47.86003, 3.98429* **Camp Municipal de la Cascade, Ave Aristide Briand, 89700 Tonnerre [03 86 55 15 44 or 03 86 55 22 55 (Mairie); fax 03 86 55 30 64; ot.tonnerre@wanadoo.fr; www.tonnerre.fr]** Best app via D905 (E by-pass); turn at rndabt twd town cent L after x-ing 1st rv bdge. Foll site sp to avoid low bdge (height 2.9m, width 2.4m). Or fr D444 strt over rndabt in town cent, over canal bdge & site on L. On banks of Rv Armançon & nr Canal de l'Yonne, 100m fr junc D905 & D944. Med, pt shd; htd wc; chem disp; mv service pnt; baby facs; shwrs inc; el pnts (6A) inc; Indtte (inc dryer); shop; tradsmn; bar; playgrnd; htd pool 1km; rv sw adj; fishing; entmnt; TV rm; 10% statics; Eng spkn; adv bkg; noise fr nrby rlwy; ccard acc; CKE/CCI. "Pleasant, spacious, shady site in arboretum; friendly warden; lge pitches; excel clean san facs; often damp underfoot; no twin-axles; interesting town; gd cycling/walking along canal; conv site; excel." ♦ 1 Apr-15 Oct. € 15.00 (CChq acc) 2014*

TOUCY *4F4* (300m S Urban) *47.73159, 3.29677* **Camping des Quatre Merlettes, Rue du Pâtis, 89130 Toucy [03 86 44 13 84; fax 03 86 44 28 42; campingdetoucy@wanadoo.fr]** On D3, 25km SW of Auxerre to Toucy. After rv x-ing take 1st L sp 'Base de Loisirs'. Site on S bank of Rv Quanne. Med, pt shd; wc; mv service pnt; shwrs inc; el pnts (3A) €3.10; shops 500m; htd pool; fishing; some statics; dogs; poss cr; adv bkg; quiet. "Pleasant vill; pleasant, helpful warden; no twin-axles; mkt Sat." 1 Apr-15 Oct. € 7.50 2010*

TOULON SUR ARROUX *4H4* (500m W Urban) *46.69419, 4.13233* **Camp Municipal Le Val d'Arroux, Route d'Uxeau, 71320 Toulon-sur-Arroux [03 85 79 51 22 or 03 85 79 42 55 (Mairie); fax 03 85 79 62 17]** Fr Toulon-sur-Arroux NW on D985 over rv bdge; rturn L in 100m, site sp. Med, pt shd; wc; chem disp; mv service pnt; shwrs inc; el pnts (6A) €3.25; Indtte; shops 500m; playgrnd; rv sw adj; 30% statics; dogs; quiet but some rd noise. "Rvside site; boules park adj; beautiful Buddhist temple 6km; gd." ♦ 16 Apr-15 Oct. € 9.55 2013*

TOURNUS *9A2* (1km N Urban) *46.57244, 4.90854* **Camping de Tournus, 14 Rue des Canes, 71700 Tournus [tel/fax 03 85 51 16 58; reception@camping-tournus.com; www.camping-tournus.com]** Fr N6 at N of town turn E opp rlwy stn & rest 'Le Terminus;' foll site sp. Med, some mkd pitch, hdstg, pt sl, pt shd; wc (some cont); chem disp; mv service pnt; shwrs inc; el pnts (10A) €4.70 (long lead poss req)(poss rev pol); gas; Indtte (inc dryer); tradsmn; snacks; bar; BBQ; playgrnd; htd pools adj; rv fishing 100m; wifi; TV; dogs €2.60; Eng spkn; quiet but rd & rlwy noise some pitches; red low ssn; CKE/CCI. "Peaceful, rvside site in nice position; popular NH, conv A6 - rec arr early; helpful staff; clean facs poss stretched high ssn & ltd low ssn; poss extra charge twin-axles; rv walk into town; gd cycling nrby; abbey worth visit; vg; well kept site; helpful staff." ♦ 1 Apr-30 Sep. € 34.40 (CChq acc) 2013*

TOURNUS *9A2* (9km S Rural) *46.48768, 4.91286* **FFCC Camping International d'Uchizy - Le National 6, 71700 Uchizy [tel/fax 03 85 40 53 90; camping.uchizylen6@wanadoo.fr; www.camping-lenational6.com]** Exit A6 junc 27 & foll N6 S; sp on L, turn L over rwly bdge on lane to site on L. Adj Rv Saône. Med, shd; wc; shwrs inc; el pnts (6A) €3.90; gas; shop; snacks; playgrnd; pool; fishing; boat hire; dogs €1; poss cr; adv bkg; m'way & train noise; red low ssn. "Attractive, well-maintained site; gd, modern san facs; pitches soft & muddy in rain; arr early for rvside pitch." 1 Apr-30 Sep. € 30.40 2014*

TOURNUS *9A2* (10km W Rural) *46.59182, 4.77746* **Aire Naturelle de Camping à la Ferme de Malo (Goujon), Champlieu, 71240 Etrigny [03 85 92 21 47 or 03 85 92 23 40; fax 03 85 92 22 13; fam@aubergemalo.com; www.aubergemalo.com]** S on N6 to Tournus; after rwly stn turn R onto D14; after passing under rlwy DO NOT fork L to foll D14 - cont strt onto D215 dir St Gengoux-le-National. In 8km, in Nogent, turn R at lge stone drinking trough onto D159; at 2nd x-rds turn L onto D459 (sp Champlieu); at 1st x-rds turn L into Champlieu; site on L 500m after vill, bef rv. Sm, pt shd; wc (cont); chem disp (wc); shwrs inc; el pnts (6-10A) €3 (long lead poss req); Indtte; tradsmn; rest 1km; playgrnd; tennis 3km; horseriding; dogs; adv bkg ess high ssn; quiet; no ccard acc; CKE/CCI. "Pitch yourself, owner calls 1800; san facs poss stretched high ssn; additional pitches & pool opp main site; adj to Rv Grison." 1 May-1 Nov. € 9.80 2010*

UCHIZY see Tournus *9A2*

VANDENESSE EN AUXOIS *6G1* (3km NE Rural) *47.23661, 4.62880* **Camping Le Lac de Panthier, 21320 Vandenesse-en-Auxois [03 80 49 21 94; fax 03 80 49 25 80; info@lac-de-panthier.com; www.lac-de-panthier.com]** Exit A6 junc 24 (A38) at Pouilly-en-Auxois; foll D16/D18 to Vandenesse; turn L on D977bis, cross canal bdge & cont strt for 3km to site on L. Fr SW (Autun) on D981 approx 12km after Arnay-le-Duc turn R onto D994 sp Châteauneuf. At x-rds cont onto D977bis then as above. Lge, hdg/mkd pitch, pt sl, terr, pt shd; wc; chem disp (wc); sauna; baby facs; shwrs inc; el pnts (6A) inc (some rev pol); Indtte (inc dryer); shop on site & 6km; rest, snacks; bar; BBQ; playgrnd; 2 pools (1 htd, covrd); paddling pool; waterslide; lake beach 50m; fishing; cycle hire; wifi; entmnt; sat TV; dogs €3; adv bkg ess; Oct open Fri, Sat & Sun; CKE/CCI. "Lovely area; views fr higher pitches; well-run site operating with Les Voiliers adj; lge pitches, most sl & blocks req; facs poss stretched high ssn; gd cycling & walks round lake; popular NH; vg." ♦ 9 Apr-8 Oct. € 28.00 2011*

VARZY *4G4* (1km N Rural) *47.37242, 3.38311* **Camp Municipal du Moulin Naudin, 58210 Varzy [03 86 29 43 12; fax 03 86 29 72 73]** Fr N151 in Varzy, turn N onto D5, site sp. Sm, pt shd; some hdg pitch; wc; shwrs inc; el pnts (6A) inc; tradsmn; shops 1.5km; fishing; tennis nrby; quiet. "Quiet site on edge of town; gd NH." 30 Apr-1 Oct. € 12.00 2011*

VENAREY LES LAUMES *6G1* (600m W Urban) *47.54448, 4.45043* **Camp Municipal Alésia, Rue du Docteur Roux, 21150 Venarey-les-Laumes [tel/fax 03 80 96 07 76 or 03 80 96 01 59 (Mairie); camping@ville-venareyleslaumes.fr; www.venareyleslaumes.fr]** SE fr Montbard on D905, site well sp fr Venarey on D954. Med, hdg/mkd pitch, hdstg, pt shd, some hdstg; htd wc; shwrs inc; el pnts (16A) €3; Indtte (inc dryer); shops 1km; tradsmn; BBQ; playgrnd; sand beach & lake sw; cycle hire; TV rm; some statics; dogs €1; phone; poss cr; Eng spkn; adv bkg; red low stay; ccard acc; CKE/CCI. "Well-kept site in scenic area; lge pitches; pleasant wardens; gd, clean san facs; barrier clsd 2200-0700; cycle tracks to Canal de Bourgogne." ♦ 1 Apr-15 Oct. € 12.00 2013*

"I like to fill in the reports as I travel from site to site"

You'll find report forms at the back of this guide, or you can fill them in online at www.caravaclub.co.uk/europereport.

VERDUN SUR LE DOUBS *6H1* (500m W Rural) *46.90259, 5.01777* **Camp Municipal La Plage, Quai du Doubs Prolongé, 71350 Verdun-sur-le-Doubs [03 85 91 55 50 or 03 85 91 52 52; fax 03 85 91 90 91; mairie.verdunsurledoubs@wanadoo.fr; www.tourisme-verdun-en-bourgogne.com]** SE on D970 fr Beaune to Verdun-sur-le-Doubs & foll sp in town. Or on D973 or N73 twd Chalon fr Seurre, turn R onto D115 to Verdun; site on bank of Rv Saône. Lge, mkd pitch, pt sl, shd; wc (some cont); chem disp; shwrs inc; el pnts (10A) €2.10; shops 500m; rest, snacks & bar 500m; BBQ; playgrnd; htd pool adj; waterslide; fishing; tennis; wifi €3; dog €1; phone; quiet. "Lovely rvside location; lge pitches; helpful warden; interesting sm town; confluence of 3 rvs: La Saône, Le Doubs & La Dheune; fishermen's paradise; excel." May-Sep. € 13.50 2014*

VERMENTON *4G4* (500m W Rural) *47.65897, 3.73087* **Camp Municipal Les Coullemières, route de Coullemières, 89270 Vermenton [03 86 81 53 02; fax 03 86 81 63 95; contact@camping-vermenton.com; www.camping-vermenton.com]** Lies W of D606 - turn off D606 into Rue Pasteur (tight turn & narr rd), strt on at x-rds into Ave de la Gare. Turn R at stn, L over level x-ing. Well sp in vill adj to rv but sps low down & easy to miss. Med, hdg/mkd pitch, pt shd; htd wc (some cont); chem disp; shwrs inc; el pnts (6A) €3; Indtte; shop 500m; rest 200m; playgrnd; tennis; fishing, boating; cycle hire; TV rm; 5% statics; dogs €1; bus; adv bkg rec high ssn; quiet; ccard acc. "Peaceful, well-run rvside site; gd facs; absolutely immac; weight limit on access rds & pitches; no twin-axles; gd walks & cycling; conv Chablis vineyards; beautiful town with 12thC church; excel site; staff helpful." ♦ 1 Apr-30 Sep. € 18.00 2013*

VERMENTON *4G4* (2km W Rural) *47.66199, 3.70493* **Camp Municipal Le Moulin Jacquot, Route de Bazarnes, 89460 Accolay [tel/fax 03 86 81 56 48 or 03 86 81 56 87 (Mairie); mairie.accolay@wanadoo.fr]** N fr Vermenton on N6 dir Auxerre; in 2km turn L onto D39 sp Accolay. Cross bdge, turn R thro vill; site on R at 200m adj Canal du Nivernais. Sm, mkd pitch, shd; wc; chem disp; mv service pnt; shwrs inc; el pnts (6A) €2.20; Indtte; shops, rest 300m; bar 200m; playgrnd; adv bkg; quiet; ccard not acc; red long stay; CKE/CCI. "Site yourself; grassy pitches poss boggy; pleasant sm vill; caves 11km; gd, flat cyling along canal." ♦ ltd 1 Apr-1 Oct. € 8.20 2009*

VEZELAY *4G4* (2km SE Rural) *47.45879, 3.77150* **Camp Municipal, 89450 St Père [03 86 33 36 58 or 03 86 33 26 62 (Mairie); fax 03 86 33 34 56; mairie-saint-pere@wanadoo.fr; www.saint-pere.fr]** Fr Vézelay take D957, turn onto D36 to St Père. Site sp. Med, pt shd; wc (cont); shwrs inc; el pnts (10A) €2.20 (poss rev pol); shops 500m; playgrnd; rv adj; fishing; canoeing; tennis; some statics; poss cr; quiet. "Pleasant site; conv Morvan National Park; warden comes am & pm; basic san facs need update; gd walking area." 1 Apr-30 Sep. € 11.00 2014*

VEZELAY *4G4* (600m S Rural) *47.45675, 3.78768* **FFCC Camping de Vézelay L'Ermitage, 1 Route de l'Étang, 89450 Vézelay [tel/fax 03 86 33 24 18; auberge.jeunesse.vezelay@orange.fr; www.vezelaytourisme.com]** Foll sp fr cent of Vézelay to 'Camping Vézelay' & Youth Hostel. Sm, pt sl, pt shd; wc; chem disp; mv service pnt; some serviced pitches; shwrs inc; el pnts (4-6A) €2.50 (rev pol); shops 500m; tradsmn (high ssn); poss cr; Eng spkn; quiet; no ccard acc; CKE/CCI. "Pleasant, peaceful, scenic site; welcoming; gd, clean facs; some pitches diff lge o'fits & blocks req; recep eve only - site self & sign in when open; some pitches muddy after heavy rain; Vézelay the starting point of one of the pilgrim rtes - superb abbey; excel." 1 Apr-31 Oct. € 8.50 2014*

VILLENEUVE LES GENETS see Bléneau *4G3*

VINCELLES see Auxerre *4F4*

Centre

Regional Introduction

Chateau de Villandry

Welcome to Centre

'Le Centre' is not the middle of France; it could more aptly be described as being the centre section of the northern part of the country.

The northern part of the region benefits from its proximity and good transport links to Paris, allowing for day trips to the capital.

The Loire Valley is the highlight of the region and has many sights and activities for you to enjoy, including a wealth of impressive chateaux and historic towns.

Local highlights

Centre offers rich products and delicious traditional dishes. Examples of this are the andouillettes, a traditional French sausage that is cooked in Vouvray wine and the well-known Rillettes de Tours, a pork product similar to pâté.

The International Garden Festival in Chaumont-sur-Loire sees around 30 artists from around the world create landscaped gardens, which remain on display for six months of the year.

Major towns and cities

- Tours – site of the Paris-Tours road bicycle race and largest city in the region.
- Orléans – the town boasts many historical sites and pretty streets.
- Chateauroux – enjoys a tranquil, laid-back atmosphere for holidaymakers.
- Olivet – castles and water mills can be found in this old commune.

Regional attractions

- Château de Chenonceau, near Tours – Country villa inspired by the Italian Renaissance.
- Loire Valley – France's biggest UNESCO-listed site, known as the Garden of France.
- Cathédrale de Chartres – the magnificent stained-glass windows and fine sculptures make this well-preserved cathedral a must-see.
- Château de Villandry – famous gardens encompass this classical countryside villa.

Find out more

www.about-france.com

Tel: (0)2 47 70 37 37 Tours Tourist Office
Tel: (0)2 38 63 49 68 Olivet Tourist Office

AMBOISE *4G2* (4km N Rural) *47.43113, 0.95430* **Camp Municipal des Patis, 37530 Nazelles-Négron [02 47 57 71 07 or 02 47 23 71 71; mairie.nazelles-negron@wanadoo.fr; www.ville-amboise.fr]** Fr Amboise, take D952 on N bank of rv twd Tours & turn R (N) onto D5 to Nazelles-Négron. Foll sp to vill. Site N of bdge over Rv Cisse, on R immed after x-ing bdge. Sm, mkd pitch, pt shd; wc (some cont); chem disp; shwrs inc; el pnts (3-5A) inc (long lead poss req); shops 100m; playgrnd; dogs €0.90; poss cr; quiet; CKE/CCI. "Peaceful, clean, well-kept site; some lge pitches; no lge c'vans or twin-axles; boggy in wet weather; excel." 12 Apr-15 Sep. € 11.00 2014*

AMBOISE *4G2* (1km NE Rural) *47.41763, 0.98717* **Camp Municipal L'Ile d'Or, 37400 Amboise [02 47 57 23 37 or 02 47 23 47 38 (Mairie); fax 02 47 23 19 80; camping@ville-amboise.fr; www.camping-amboise.com]** Fr N exit A10 exit junc 18 onto D31/D431 to Amboise; at rndabt by rv turn R onto D751 dir Blois & get in L lane to cross bdge on D431; site a turning L off bdge, on lge wooded island in Rv Loire. Fr S exit A85 junc 11 onto D31 dir Amboise; at lge rndabt (where main rd swings R) foll Centre Ville sp to rv on D431; get in L/H lane to cross bdge (dir Nazelles); turn R off bdge to site on island. Lge, mkd pitch, pt shd; wc; chem disp; mv service pnt; baby facs; shwrs inc; el pnts (6A) €2.35 (poss rev pol); Indtte (inc dryer); shop 1km; rest, snacks; bar; playgrnd nrby; htd pool & waterslide 500m (high ssn); fishing; tennis; games area; entmnt; wifi; TV; no statics; dogs €1.15; phone; poss cr; Eng spkn; adv bkg; quiet, but rd noise if pitched nr rd; ccard acc; red low ssn/long stay; CKE/CCI. "Lovely, spacious, secure site in gd location adj Rv Loire & park; well-kept; lge pitches; gd clean san facs; nice rest & bar; easy walk to interesting old town; vg dog walking; conv Parc Léonardo Da Vinci (last place he lived) & Château d'Amboise; midsummer week music festival in adj park - check date; no twin-axles; m'van o'night area open all year, excel stop out of ssn; gd value; vg." ♦ 30 Mar-30 Sep. € 19.00 2014*

⊞ **AMBOISE** *4G2* (6km NE Rural) *47.44580, 1.04669* **Camping Le Jardin Botanique, 9 bis, Rue de la Rivière, 37530 Limeray [02 47 30 13 50; fax 02 47 30 17 32; info@camping-jardinbotanique.com; www.camping-jardinbotanique.com]** NE fr Amboise on D952 on N side of Rv Loire dir Blois; in approx 6km turn L for Limeray & then immed turn L onto Rue de la Rivière; site on L in 500m. NB Rec not to app fr Limeray, narr rds & diff for lge o'fits. Med, hdg/mkd pitch, hdstg, pt shd; htd wc; chem disp; mv service pnt; baby facs; fam bthrm; shwrs inc; el pnts (10A) €5 (poss rev pol); gas; Indtte; shop 2km; tradsmn; rest, snacks; bar; BBQ; playgrnd; pool; sand beach 15km; tennis; games area; cycle hire; TV; 20% statics; dogs €1.50; Eng spkn; adv bkg; rd & rlwy noise; red long stay/CKE/CCI. "Gd for Loire chateaux; 500m fr rv; friendly & helpful owner; gd for children; gd gourmet rest adj; poss muddy when wet; gd cycle rtes." ♦ € 17.00 2011*

ANET *3D2* (500m N Urban) *48.86183, 1.44166* **Camp Municipal Les Eaux Vives, 1 Route des Cordeliers, 28260 Anet [02 37 41 42 67 or 06 09 74 16 90 (mob); fax 02 37 62 20 99; martine.desrues@cegetel.net; www.camping-anet.fr]** Take D928 NE fr Dreux; in Anet thro town & take 1st L after chateau; turn L on rd to Ezy & Ivry (camp sp on corner), site in 150m N of rv. Lge, pt shd; htd wc; chem disp (wc); mv service pnt; 75% serviced pitches; shwrs €1.10; el pnts (10A) €3; Indry rm; supmkt 1km; playgrnd; rv adj; lake sw & fishing 2km; tennis; 95% statics; dogs €1.10; poss cr; Eng spkn; ccard not acc; red low ssn; CKE/CCI. "Rvside pitches; helpful warden; clean, v basic san facs, poss stretched high ssn; grnd soft in wet - site poss clsd early; gd walks in forest; chateau in vill; easy drive to Paris; untidy statics (2010); conv NH." 1 Mar-31 Oct. € 14.20 2013*

ARGENTON SUR CREUSE *7A3* (12km SE Rural) *46.50709, 1.58355* **La Chaumerette Camping Club à Tou Vert, 36190 Gargilesse-Dampierre [02 54 47 73 44; campinglachaumerette@wanadoo.fr]** Fr A20 take exit 17 for D48 to Badecon-le-Pin then R onto D40. Turn R sp Barsize then foll sp to site. Sm, shd; wc; chem disp; baby facs; shwrs inc; el pnts (6A) inc; tradsmn; snacks; bar; playgrnd; fishing; adv bkg; quiet; CKE/CCI. "Superb location in wooded valley adj rv; v isolated & poor security; gd san facs; additional o'flow area when site full." 1 May-31 Oct. € 12.00 2011*

ARGENTON SUR CREUSE *7A3* (12km SW Rural) *46.54192, 1.40328* **Camping La Petite Brenne (Naturist), La Grande Metairie, 36800 Luzeret [02 54 25 05 78; fax 02 54 25 05 97; la.petite.brenne@wanadoo.fr; www.lapetitebrenne.com]** Fr A20 exit junc 18 sp Luzeret/Prissac; foll D55 to Luzeret vill. After bdge in vill turn L, then next L to site. Lge, pt sl, unshd; wc; chem disp; sauna; shwrs inc; el pnts (10A) €5 (long leads poss req); Indtte; shop 12km; tradsmn; rest; bar; playgrnd; 2 pools (1 htd); horseriding; wifi; no dogs; Eng spkn; adv bkg rec high ssn; quiet; ccard acc; red long stay/low ssn. "Excel family site; friendly Dutch owners; lge pitches; excel san facs; ideal for children; pools excel; gd rest; gd walking in National Park." 26 Apr-30 Sep. € 24.00 2013*

ARGENTON SUR CREUSE *7A3* (2km NW Rural) *46.59636, 1.50619* **Camp Municipal Les Chambons, 37 Rue des Chambons, 36200 Argenton-sur-Creuse [02 54 24 15 26; camping-les-chambons@orange.fr; www.entreprisefrery.com]** Fr A20 exit junc 17 onto D937 dir Argenton; turn R at rndabt, then L at mini rndabt nr supmkt sp St Marcel; foll rd downhill over rlwy bdge; then 1st R in 100m. But best app fr N on D927 to avoid traff calming rd humps; at town sp cross rlwy bdge & turn R immed past LH turn for Roman archaeological museum; foll camping sp on narr, busy app rd. Med, mkd pitch, some hdstg, pt sl, shd; wc; chem disp; shwrs inc; el pnts (5A) €3.60 (poss long lead req); gas; shop 1.5km; tradsmn; bar; rest 1km; playgrnd; wifi; quiet but some rd noise. "Beautiful, peaceful, well-kept site by rv; helpful warden; v muddy after heavy rain & poss uneven pitches by rv; rvside walk into interesting old town; no need to unhitch so useful for early start; quiet in day, busy in evening as popular NH high ssn; excel." 1 May-30 Sep. € 23.50 2014*

ARGENTON SUR CREUSE *7A3* (6km NW Rural) *46.62965, 1.47882* **Camp Municipal Les Rives de la Bouzanne, 36800 Le Pont Chrétien-Chabenet [02 54 25 80 53 or 02 54 25 81 40 (Mairie); fax 02 54 25 87 50; commune. pontchretien@wanadoo.fr]** Exit A20 junc 17 onto D927; site well sp over rv bdge. Or fr St Gaultier on D927 dir Argenton-sur-Creuse; turn R in Le Pont Chrétien-Chabenet, bef rv bdge, site 50m on L. Med, pt shd; wc (some cont); chem disp (wc); shwrs inc; el pnts inc; Indtte; shop & bar adj; supmkt 3km; BBQ; playgrnd; rv adj; dogs €0.50; phone; Eng spkn; adv bkg rec; quiet; CKE/CCI. "Picturesque, quiet, rvside site; site yourself, warden calls; gd, drained pitches; immac san facs; conv A20; excel NH." 15 Jun-10 Sep. € 11.50 2014*

ARROU *4F2* (850m NW Rural) *48.10189, 1.11556* **Camp Municipal du Pont de Pierre, 28290 Arrou [02 37 97 02 13 (Mairie); fax 02 37 97 10 28; mairie. arrou@wanadoo.fr; www.loirevalleytourism.com]** Take D15 fr Cloyes. Site sp in vill of Arrou. Med, hdg/mkd pitch, pt sl, unshd; wc; chem disp; mv service pnt; shwrs inc; el pnts (6-10A) €2-3; Indry rm; supmkt nr; rest, bar, snacks in vill; BBQ; playgrnd; htd pool & paddling pool adj; lake fishing & sand beach adj; tennis; horseriding; cycle hire; 10% statics; phone; adv bkg; quiet; CKE/CCI. "Lovely, peaceful, well-kept site in park-like setting; lge pitches; excel san facs; gd security; phone warden (or call at house) if office & barrier clsd; gd rvside walks/cycle rides; excel value." ♦ 1 May-30 Sep. € 4.60 2013*

AUBIGNY SUR NERE *4G3* (1.5km E Rural) *47.48435, 2.45703* **FLOWER Camping des Etangs, Route de Sancerre, 18700 Aubigny-sur-Nère [02 48 58 02 37; camping. aubigny@orange.fr; www.camping-aubigny.com / www. flowercampings.com]** D940 fr Gien, turn E in vill of Aubigny onto D923, foll sp fr vill; site 1km on R by lake, after Camp des Sports & just bef end of vill sp. Avoid town cent due congestion. Med, mkd pitch, some hdstg, pt shd; htd wc; chem disp; shwrs inc; el pnts (6-10A) inc; Indtte; shop, rest & bar nr; tradsmn; snacks; BBQ; playgrnd; htd, covrd pool; paddling pool; fishing; cycle hire; games rm; wifi; TV; 10% statics; dogs €2; phone; poss cr; Eng spkn, adv bkg; quiet; red low ssn/CKE/CCI. "Vg site with lake views; pretty medieval vill with historical links to Scotland; mkt Sat; 2nd w/e July Scottish Son & Lumière event adj site!" ♦ 1 Apr-30 Sep. € 30.00 2014*

⊞ **AZAY LE FERRON** *4H2* (8km N Rural) *46.91949, 1.03679* **Camping Le Cormier, Route de St Flovier, 36290 Obterre [02 54 39 27 95 or 0844 232 7271 (UK); mike@ loireholidays.biz; www.loireholidays.biz]** Fr Azay-le-Ferron N on D14, site on R just N of Obterre. Or fr Loches S on D943 for 3.5km, turn onto D41 to St Flovier then turn L onto D21 sp Obterre. In 1km turn R onto D14, site on L in 4km. Sm, hdg/ mkd pitch, hdstg, pt shd; htd wc; chem disp; shwrs inc; el pnts (10A) €4; Indry rm; ice; tradsmn; rest, snacks & bar 5km; BBQ; pool; games area; games rm; wifi; TV; dogs free; Eng spkn; adv bkg; twin axle acc; quiet; red low ssn. "Friendly, helpful British owners (CC members); spacious pitches; gd san facs; excel touring/walking base; nr Brenne National Park; excel birdwatching; vg." € 19.00 2014*

AZAY LE RIDEAU *4G1* (300m E Urban) *47.25919, 0.46992* **FFCC Camp Municipal Le Sabot, Rue du Stade, 37190 Azay-le-Rideau [02 47 45 42 72 or 02 47 45 42 11 (Mairie); fax 02 47 45 49 11; camping.lesabot@wanadoo.fr; www. azaylerideau.fr]** Best app is fr D751 by-pass to avoid narr town - ignore Azay-le-Rideau sps until Carrefour rndabt. Strt ahead for 1km, site visible at 2nd rndabt. Lge, mkd pitch, pt shd; wc (some cont); chem disp; mv service pnt; shwrs inc; el pnts (10A) €4.50 (poss rev pol); gas 1km; shop, snacks, rest in town; BBQ; htd pool adj; playgrnd; fishing; wifi; TV; phone; dogs; poss cr fr Son et Lumière in high ssn; Eng spkn; adv bkg rec; quiet; ccard acc; red low ssn/long stay; CKE/CCI. "Pleasant, spacious, scenic site by rv & chateau; friendly, helpful recep; poss long dist to san facs fr some pitches - cent facs have steps; san facs stretched high ssn, ltd low ssn; site prone to flooding; recep open 0800-1200 & 1400-1700; when site clsd m'vans can stay on car park by rv o'night - no facs but well lit (enq at TO); gd loc nr to town and rests." ♦ 1 Apr-31 Oct. € 24.00 2014*

BARROU *4H2* (Rural) *46.86500, 0.77100* **FFCC Camping Les Rioms, Les Rioms, 37350 Barrou [02 47 94 53 07; campinglesrioms@orange.fr; www.lesrioms.com]** Fr D750 Descartes to La Roche-Posay rd turn R at sp Camping at ent to Barrou vill. Site sp. NB Site has barriers, phone if clsd. Sm, hdg/ mkd pitch, pt shd; wc; chem disp (wc); shwrs inc; el pnts (16A) €4; Indry rm; tradsmn; shop, rest & snacks nr; BBQ; playgrnd; htd pool; sand rv beach 2km; 35% statics; dogs free; Eng spkn; adv bkg; quiet; red low ssn; CKE/CCI. "Pleasant, peaceful site on bank of Rv Creuse; clean san facs; friendly owners; gd pool; excel." ♦ 30 Mar- 26 Oct. € 10.50 2013*

BEAUGENCY *4F2* (500m E Rural) *47.77628, 1.64294* **Camp Municipal du Val de Flux, Route de Lailly-en-Val, 45190 Beaugency [02 38 44 50 39 or 02 38 44 83 12; fax 02 38 46 49 10; camping@ville-beaugency.fr; www. beaugency.fr]** Exit A10 junc 15 onto N152. In Beaugency turn L at traff lts nr water tower onto D925 & again over rd bdge. Site sp on S bank of Rv Loire. Med, mkd pitch, pt shd; htd wc; chem disp; mv service pnt; shwrs inc; el pnts (10A)€3.60 incl; Indry rm; sm shop & 500m; rest 1km; snacks; bar; playgrnd; sand beach; fishing; watersports; entmnt; 10% statics; dogs €1.10; poss cr w/end in ssn; quiet; Eng spkn; ccard acc; red long stay; CKE/CCI. "Beautiful, well-kept site; views over Loire; helpful staff; free 1 night site for m'vans over rv on other side of town; poss unrel opening dates low ssn, rec phone ahead; vg location close to town." ♦ 12 Apr-1 Sep. € 18.00 2013*

⊞ **BEAUGENCY** *4F2* (8km S Rural) *47.68679, 1.55802* **Camp Municipal L'Amitié, 17 Rue du Camping, Nouan-sur-Loire, 41220 St Laurent-Nouan [02 54 87 01 52; fax 02 54 87 09 93; campingdelamitie@stlaurentnouan.fr; www.campingdelamitie.fr]** On D951 SW fr Orléans cont past power stn into Nouan-sur-Loire. Site on R sp. Med, hdg/ mkd pitch, pt shd; htd wc; mv service pnt; shwrs; el pnts (6A) €4.60; Indtte (inc dryer); shop, rest 500m; pools & sports activities nr; direct access to rv; 50% statics; dogs €1; site clsd Xmas & New Year; adv bkg; quiet; 10% red CKE/CCI. "Interesting area; view of Rv Loire; workers poss resident on site; friendly, helpful staff; well-maintained site; clean san facs in Portacabins; phone ahead low ssn to check open; being redeveloped; excel facs; conv for Chateau Chambord; supmkt 100mts fr ent." € 8.20 2014*

CENTRE

BEAULIEU SUR LOIRE *4G3* (300m E Rural) *47.54407, 2.82167* **FFCC Camp Municipal du Canal, Route de Bonny, 45630 Beaulieu-sur-Loire [02 38 35 89 56 or 02 38 35 32 16 (LS); fax 02 38 35 86 57; renault.campingbeaulieu@orange.fr; www.beaulieu-sur-loire.fr]** Exit A77 junc 21 Bonny-sur-Loire, cross rv to Beaulieu-sur-Loire on D296. On E o'skirts of vill on D926, nr canal. Sm, hdg/mkd pitch, hdstg, pt shd; wc; chem disp; mv service pnt; shwrs inc; el pnts (10A) €3.10; shop 2km; rest/takeaway & bar 500m; poss cr; Eng spkn; adv bkg; some rd noise; CKE/CCI. "Well-kept site in pleasant area; direct access to canal; some sm pitches diff lge o'fits; site yourself, warden calls 0800-0900 & 1830-1930; no security; clean modern san facs; gd walking along canal & Rv Loire; boat trips; poss workers' statics low ssn; mkt Wed." ♦ Easter-1 Nov. € 6.60 2011*

BLANC, LE *4H2* (2km E Rural) *46.63202, 1.09389* **Camping L'Ile d'Avant, Route de Châteauroux, 36300 Le Blanc [02 54 37 88 22; fax 02 54 36 35 42; info@tourisme-leblanc.fr; www.tourisme-leblanc.fr]** Fr town cent take D951 twd St Gaultier/Argenton; site on R 1km after supmkt. Med, hdg/mkd pitch, pt shd; wc; mv service pnt; shwrs inc; el pnts (6A) inc; lndtte; shops 1km; rest, snacks, bar 2km; BBQ; playgrnd; htd pool adj inc; fishing; tennis adj; adv bkg; quiet but some rd noise. "Gd pitches; adj sports field & club house; open Apr with adv bkg only, otherwise May." 1 Apr-30 Sep. € 14.00 2012*

BLERE *4G2* (500m NE Urban) *47.32791, 0.99685* **Camping Bléré Plage (Formaly Municipal La Gâtine), Rue de Cdt Le Maître, 37150 Bléré [tel/fax 02 47 57 92 60; info@campingblereplage.com; www.campingblereplage.com]** Exit A10 S of Tours onto A85 E. Exit A85 junc 11 dir Bléré. Site in 5km adj sports cent on S side of Rv Cher. Lge, mkd pitch, pt shd; wc; chem disp; mv service pnt; shwrs inc; el pnts (10A) €4 (poss rev pol & long lead poss req); lndtte (inc dryer); shops 300m; supmkt 400m; htd pool adj high ssn; rv fishing adj; wifi; dogs €1.20; no adv bkg; quiet; ccard acc; CKE/CCI. "Excel, well-kept, peaceful, pleasant site; wardens are enthusiastic & helpful; clean san facs, some dated & stretched when site full; some dated el pnts poss unrel in wet; gd security; gd cent for wine rtes & chateaux; unrel opening dates low ssn; rec." ♦ 1 Apr-15 Oct. € 14.30 2014*

BLOIS *4G2* (12km NE Rural) *47.68666, 1.48583* **Camping Le Château de la Grenouillère, 41500 Suèvres [02 54 87 80 37; fax 02 54 87 84 21; la.grenouillere@wanadoo.fr; www.camping-loire.com / www.les-castels.com]** Exit A10 junc 16 sp Chambord, Mer; take rd to Mer; go thro Mer on D2152 dir Blois; site in 5km, 2km NE of Suèvres. Lge, mkd pitch, pt shd; wc; chem disp; mv service pnt; sauna; baby facs; shwrs inc; el pnts (10A) inc; gas; lndtte (inc dryer); shop; rest; pizzeria; snacks; bar; BBQ (gas/charcoal); playgrnd; 2 pools (1 covrd); paddling pool; waterslide; boating; fishing; tennis; cycle hire; gym; wifi; entmnt; games/TV; statics (tour ops); no c'vans/m'vans over 15m; Eng spkn; adv bkg (min 3 nts); some pitches some rd & rlwy noise; ccard acc; red low ssn; CKE/CCI. "Ideal for Loire area; clean modern san facs, poss ltd low ssn; some superb leisure facs; mkt Wed & Sat Blois." ♦ 19 Apr-12 Sep. € 46.00 SBS - L04 2014*

BLOIS *4G2* (10km E Rural) *47.59149, 1.45894* **Camping de Chatillon (Formerly Aire Naturelle), 6 Rue de Châtillon, 41350 Huisseau-sur-Cosson [02 54 20 35 26]** Fr Blois cross Rv Loire on D765 dir Vineuil. 1km S turn L onto D33. Site at E end of vill of Huisseau on R. Sm, hdg/mkd pitch, pt sl, pt shd; wc; chem disp; mv service pnt; shwrs inc; el pnts (10A) €4.20 (poss rev pol); gas; shops 400m, supmkt 4km; dogs €1.50; poss cr; adv bkg; quiet; ccard not acc; red low ssn; CKE/CCI. "Pretty, peaceful, garden site; lovely, even low ssn; beautiful area; friendly owner; gd clean san facs, but ltd; conv Loire Valley chateaux; cycle rte thro Chambord forest; Son et Lumière show in town; rec; delightful, spacious and spotless site, recommended " ♦ ltd 1 May-20 Sep. € 18.00 2014*

BLOIS *4G2* (8km S Rural) *47.52539, 1.38675* **Camp Municipal, Rue du Conon, 41120 Cellettes [02 54 70 48 41 or 02 54 70 47 54 (Mairie)]** On D956, Blois to Châteauroux rd, pass almost thro Cellettes, site 120m fr D956 down 1st L after rv bdge, site on L in 100m, well sp. NB Turn-in narr fr v busy main rd. Med, pt shd; wc; chem disp; shwrs inc; el pnts (5A)€2.80; snacks; shops, pool, playgrnd & tennis adj; fishing; games area; poss cr; phone; quiet, some daytime rd noise; ccard acc; CKE/CCI. "Lovely, peaceful site in pleasant rvside location; lge pitches; friendly, helpful warden; gd san facs; don't checkout late without telling warden - she locks el pnts boxes; poss boggy after rain; excel for Loire châteaux; rec." ♦ ltd 1 Jun-30 Sep. € 9.45 2013*

"We must tell The Club about that great site we found"

Get your site reports in by mid-August and we'll do our best to get your updates into the next edition.

BLOIS *4G2* (6km SW Rural) *47.54379, 1.31114* **FFCC Camping Le Cosson, 1 Rue de la Forêt, 41120 Chailles [02 54 79 46 49]** Fr Blois foll sp dir Montrichard (D751); after x-ing rv bdge at rndabt take 1st exit sp Montrichard/Chailles (D751); after x-ing sm rv bdge in Chailles take 1st L onto Rue de la Forêt; site in 50m; sm sp easily missed. Sm, hdg pitch, pt shd; wc (cont); chem disp (wc); shwrs inc; baby facs; el pnts (6A) €3.50; shops 1km; baker 500m; games area; playgrnd; dogs; phone; poss cr; adv bkg; rd noise; CKE/CCI. "Well-maintained, quiet site nr chateaux; pleasant, helpful owners; walks & cycle paths in local forest; poss tired pitches & facs end of ssn; tel no at gate for warden to come and unlock toilet block if site is empty." 15 Jun-10 Sep. € 15.00 2014*

BLOIS *4G2* (18km W Rural) *47.54427, 1.15712* **Ferme de Prunay, 41150 SEILLAC [2 54 70 02 01; fax 2 08 42 17 56; contact@prunay.com; www.prunay.fr]** Take exit Blois on the A10; foll dir for Angers Chateau Renault until Molineuf, then Chambon sur Cisse and Seillac, rd D131. Med, mkd pitch, pt shd; wc; chem disp; baby facs; shwrs inc; el pnts €3.70; lndtte (inc dryer); shop; rest, snacks; bar; BBQ; playgrnd; pool; paddling pool; lake; fishing; cycle hire; games area; entmnt; internet; TV; statics; dogs; Eng spkn; ccard acc. "In the heart of the Loire Valley; spacious pitches; v nice site." 31 Mar-7 Oct. € 23.00 2011*

BONNEVAL *4F2* (1km SE Rural) *48.17080, 1.38640* **Camping Le Bois Chièvre, Route de Vouvray, St Maurice, 28800 Bonneval [02 37 47 54 01; fax 02 37 96 26 79; camping-bonneval-28@orange.fr]** Rec app fr N (Chartres), or SE (D27 fr Patay/Orléans) as app fr S thro town is narr & diff. Fr Chartres take N10 into Bonneval & foll camp sp (mainly to L). Med, hdg/mkd pitch, hdstg, pt sl, shd; htd wc; chem disp; mv service pnt; shwrs inc; el pnts (6A) inc (rev pol); Indtte; shop 1km; tradsmn; rest, snacks; bar; BBQ; playgrnd; htd pool adj inc; some statics; dogs €1.20; Eng spkn; adv bkg; quiet; CKE/CCI. "Well-run, well-kept site in woodland; gd, lge pitches; friendly, helpful staff; vg facs but poss stretched in ssn; vg NH for Le Havre or Dieppe." ♦ 1 April-20 Oct. € 21.00 2014*

BOURGES *4H3* (1km S Urban) *47.07228, 2.39497* **Camp Municipal Robinson, 26 Blvd de l'Industrie, 18000 Bourges [02 48 20 16 85; fax 02 48 50 32 39; camping@ville-bourges.fr; www.ville-bourges.fr]** Exit A71/E11 at junc 7, foll sp Bourges Centre & bear R at 'Autres Directions' sp; foll site sp; site at traff lts on N side of S section of inner ring rd half-way bet junc with D2144 & D2076. NB: site access is via a loop - no L turn at traff lts, but rndabt just past site if turning missed. If on outer ring rd D400, app city on D2144 & then as above. Sp on app rds to site gd. Med, hdg/mkd pitch, hdstg, pt shd; htd wc; chem disp; some serviced pitches; shwrs inc; el pnts (6-16A) €3.40-8.00 (poss rev pol); gas 3km; Indtte; rest, snacks & bar 1km; BBQ (gas/elec); playgrnd; pool 300m inc; dogs €2.15; bus adj; poss cr; Eng spkn; quiet; extra for twin-axles; ccard acc; red long stay; CKE/CCI. "Attractive, well-kept, busy, rvside site in gd location; friendly staff; excel, immac san facs; some v lge pitches, some sm & poss diff entry; most pitches hdstg; excel NH or longer." ♦ 15 Mar-15 Nov. € 24.00 2013*

BOURGUEIL *4G1* (750m S Rural) *47.26991, 0.16873* **Camp Municipal Parc Capitaine, 37140 Bourgueil [02 47 97 85 62 or 02 47 97 25 00 LS; www.bourgueil.fr]** N on D749 fr junc 5 of A85, site 1km on R. Fr W (Longue) via D10 & by-pass, S at rndabt on D749 to site on L in 200m. Do not app fr N via D749 thro town cent. Med, hdg/mkd pitch, pt shd; wc; chem disp; mv service pnt; shwrs inc; el pnts (10A) €2.15 (poss long lead req); gas; Indtte; shops 1km; supmkt 400m; playgrnd; sw lake; dogs €1.25; quiet; ccard acc; CKE/CCI. "Gd san facs; ideal cent Loire châteaux; 2 sites - one on R for tourers; excel; barrier ent & exit by code; office clsd 1230-1500 but warden lives upstairs; conv fr A85 & Loire valley; vg." ♦ ltd 15 May-15 Sep. € 14.00 2014*

BOUZONVILLE AUX BOIS see Pithiviers *4F3*

BRACIEUX *4G2* (500m N Urban) *47.55060, 1.53743* **Camping Indigo les Châteaux, 11 Rue Roger Brun, 41250 Bracieux [02 54 46 41 84; fax 02 54 46 41 21; chateaux@camping-indigo.com; www.camping-indigo.com]** Fr S take D102 to Bracieux fr Cour-Cheverny. Fr N exit Blois on D765 dir Romorantin; after 5km take D923 to Bracieux & site on R on N o'skts of town opp church, sp. Lge, pt hdg/mkd pitch, hdstg, pt shd; wc (some cont); chem disp; shwrs inc; el pnts (10A) €2.75 (poss long lead req); gas 300m; Indtte; shop 300m; supmkt 1km; tradsmn high ssn; rest, snacks 300m; playgrnd; htd pool high ssn adj; tennis; cycle hire & tracks; games rm; TV; 10% statics; dogs €2.80; Eng spkn; adv bkg; quiet; ccard acc; red long stay/low ssn; CKE/CCI. "Peaceful spot; attractive forest area; busy high ssn; gd security; gd touring base; excel; well run site; all san blocks replaced (2013); superb." ♦ 10 Apr-3 Nov. € 38.50 2014*

See advertisement

BRIARE *4G3* (7km S Rural) *47.59713, 2.76617* **Camping L'ecluse des Combles, Chemin de Loire, 45360 Châtillon-sur-Loire [tel/fax 02 38 36 25 32; campingchatillonsurloire@recrea.fr; www.campingdescombles.fr]** SE fr Briare on N7, in 4km turn SW onto D50. Site immed bef rv bdge on R. Care needed over bdge after ent. Med, terr, pt shd; htd wc; chem disp; mv service pnt; shwrs inc; el pnts (6A) inc ; gas; Indtte; shops 1km & 4km; tradsmn; rest, snacks & bar adj; BBQ; playgrnd; fishing; games rm; dogs €1.20; no twin-axles; Eng spkn; quiet; red low ssn; CKE/CCI. "Lovely, peaceful site by Rv Loire & historic canal; pleasant staff; right of way along rv bank passes thro site; mkt 2nd Thurs of month; vg." ♦ 1 Apr-31 Oct. € 17.00 2013*

BRIARE *4G3* (500m W Rural) *47.64137, 2.72560* **Camping Le Martinet, Quai Tchékof, 45250 Briare [02 38 31 24 50 or 02 38 31 24 51; fax 02 38 31 39 10; campingbriare@recrea.fr; www.campinglemartinet.fr]** Exit N7 into Briare. Fr N immed R after canal bdge; fr S L bef 2nd canal bdge; sp. Lge, mkd pitch, unshd; wc (some cont); shwrs inc; el pnts (10A) €3.60; Indry rm; shops 500m; rest, snacks, bar 500m; fishing adj; dogs €1; poss cr; adv bkg; quiet; red low ssn. "Gd views some pitches; pretty bars & rests along canal; gd walking & cycling; interesting town; gates close 2200; slightly neglected (2009); ok sh stay." ♦ 1 Apr-30 Sep. € 16.70 2012*

BRUERE ALLICHAMPS see St Amand Montrond *4H3*

CENTRE

BUZANCAIS *4H2* (500m N Urban) *46.89309, 1.41801* **Camp Municipal La Tête Noire, Allée des Sports, 36500 Buzançais [02 54 84 17 27 or 06 15 85 53 04 (mob); fax 02 54 02 13 45; buzancais@wanadoo.fr]** D943 fr Châteauroux thro town cent, cross rv, immed turn R into sports complex. Lge, some hdstg, pt shd; wc (some cont); mv service pnt; shwrs inc; el pnts (16A) inc; lndtte; shop, rest, snacks, bar 500m; playgrnd; pool 500m; entmnt; some statics; dog €1.50; adv bkg; quiet; red low ssn/long stay; CKE/CCI. "Pleasant, peaceful, well-kept site on rv; clean facs; no access when office clsd but ample parking; no twin-axles; gd fishing." ♦ 1 May-30 Sep. € 15.00 (CChq acc) 2014*

"I need an on-site restaurant"

We do our best to make sure site information is correct, but it is always best to check any must-have facilities are still available or will be open during your visit.

CANDE SUR BEUVRON *4G2* (500m S Rural) *47.48952, 1.25834* **La Grande Tortue, 3 Route de Pontlevoy, 41120 Candé-sur-Beuvron [02 54 44 15 20; fax 02 54 44 19 45; grandetortue@wanadoo.fr; www.la-grande-tortue.com]** Exit A10 junc 17 (Blois) & foll 'Autres/Toutes Directions' or 'Vierzon' to cross Rv Loire; immed after bdge R onto D951/ D971 dir Chaumont; ignore D173 R fork & foll D751 thro Chailles & Villelouet; R at rndabt to go thro Cande; fork L after Cande; site on L in abt 100m. Lge, hdg/mkd pitch, some hdstg, pt sl, pt shd; htd wc (some cont); chem disp; mv service pnt; baby facs; shwrs inc; el pnts (10A) €3.50; gas; lndtte (inc dryer); shop; tradsmn; rest, snacks; bar; BBQ; playgrnd; htd, covrd pool; paddling pool; cycle hire; horseriding; games area; wifi; entmnt; TV rm; 50% statics; dogs €3.70; Eng spkn; adv bkg; quiet; ccard acc; red low ssn; CKE/CCI. "Excel, rustic site amongst trees; poss diff access due trees; helpful staff; vg, clean san facs; gd pool; gd for children; gd cycling; gourmet rest by rv bdge in vill; conv Loire chateaux." ♦ 12 Apr-21 Sep. € 55.50 (CChq acc) 2014*

See advertisement

CELLETTES see Blois *4G2*

⊞ **CHAILLAC** *7A3* (550m SW Rural) *46.43260, 1.29602* **Camp Municipal Les Vieux Chênes, 36310 Chaillac [02 54 25 61 39 or 02 54 25 74 26 (Mairie); fax 02 54 25 65 41; chaillac-mairie@wanadoo.fr]** Exit N20 S of Argenton-sur-Creuse at junc 20 onto D36 to Chaillac. Thro vill, site 1st L after sq by 'Mairie', adj Lac du Rochegaudon. Sm, hdg/mkd pitch, pt sl, pt shd; htd wc (some cont); chem disp; shwrs inc; el pnts (16A) inc (poss rev pol); lndry rm; shop, rest, bar 200m; BBQ; playgrnd; lake sw & fishing adj; waterslide; tennis adj; 35% statics; dogs; phone adj; poss cr; adv bkg; quiet; CKE/CCI. "Excel site, beautiful location, friendly wardens, well kept san facs, gd local supmkt 2 mins walk." ♦ € 9.60 2013*

CHAILLES see Blois *4G2*

⊞ **CHAMBON LA FORET** *4F3* (800m N Rural) *48.06381, 2.28192* **Camping Domaine La Rive du Bois, Route de la Forêt, 45340 Chambon-la-Forêt [02 38 32 29 73/ 06 79 95 26 53 (mob); rive.bois@ wanadoo.fr; www.larivedubois.com]** Fr Pithiviers take D921 S. Immed after x-ing over A19 turn L onto D30 sp Chambon-la-Forêt, Sully-sur-Loire. At La Rive-du-Bois traff lts foll sp to site on R. Sm, pt shd; htd wc; chem disp; shwrs inc; el pnts (10A) inc; lndtte; BBQ; playgrnd; pool; fishing; tennis; games area; cycle hire; 70% statics; dogs free; Eng spkn; adv bkg; quiet; CKE/CCI. "Helpful, friendly manager; gd walking & cycling fr site; deer & red squirrels in woods around; gd; lovely woodland setting." ♦ € 15.00 2013*

CHAPELLE D'ANGILLON, LA *4G3* (1km SE Rural) *47.36044, 2.44261* **Camp Municipal Les Murailles, Route d'Henrichemont, 18380 La Chapelle-d'Angillon [02 48 73 40 12 (Mairie); fax 02 48 73 48 67]** Fr Bourges or Aubigny-sur-Nère on D940, turn E onto D926; turn onto D12 in vill, site on R, sp. Sm, pt sl, pt shd; wc (some cont); chem disp (wc); shwrs inc; el pnts (6A) €3.20; gas, shop, rest, & bar 1km; BBQ; playgrnd; lake fishing adj; some statics; dogs; ccard acc; CKE/CCI. "Lake adj with castle o'looking; v quiet; facs dated but adequate; site yourself, warden calls; vg." ♦ ltd 1 Jun-15 Sep. € 7.00 2009*

CHARITE SUR LOIRE, LA *4G4* (500m W Urban) *47.17683, 3.01058* **FFCC Camp Municipal La Saulaie, Quai de la Saulaie, 58400 La Charité-sur-Loire [tel/fax 03 86 70 00 83 / 03 86 70 15 06 (ls); contact@lacharitesurloire-tourisme.com; www.lacharitesurloire-tourisme.com / www.nievre-tourisme.com]** Exit A77 junc 30 & foll sp 'Centre Ville'. Turn L over Rv Loire sp Bourges; take 2nd R bef next bdge. Fr Bourges on N151, turn L immed after x-ing 1st bdge over Rv Loire. Foll sp. NB Take care when turn R over narr rv bdge when leaving site - v high kerb. Med, mkd pitch, pt shd; wc; chem disp; shwrs inc; el pnts (10A) €3.10; Indtte; shop 500m; tradsmn; snacks; playgrnd & htd pool, paddling pool adj inc (pool opens 1 Jul); rv beach & sw adj; dogs €2; no twin-axles; quiet; ccard not acc; red long stay; CKE/CCI. "Lovely, well-kept site on rv island; warm welcome, helpful staff; san facs in need of refurb (2013) & ltd low ssn; gd security; poss school groups high ssn; low ssn phone to check open; beautiful town; welcoming staff, site scruffy and in need of maintenance." ♦ 28 Apr-23 Sep. € 19.20 2014*

CHARTRES *4E2* (1.5km SE Urban) *48.43433, 1.49914* **Camping Les Bords de l'Eure, 9 Rue de Launay, 28000 Chartres [tel/fax 02 37 28 79 43; camping-roussel-chartres@wanadoo.fr; www.camping-de-chartres.com]** Exit N123 ring rd at D935, R at T-junc dir Chartres; then R at 2nd traff lts dir Chartres immed after rlwy bdge; site on L in 400m; inside of ring rd. Also sp fr town cent on N154 fr N, foll sp town cent under 2 rlwy bdges, L at traff lts sp Orléans, after 1km site sp. Fr SE on N154 cross ring rd, foll site sp & turn L at 2nd traff lts; site on R. Med,some hdg/mkd pitch, pt shd; htd wc (mostly cont); chem disp; mv service pnt; baby facs; shwrs inc; el pnts (6A) €3.40 (poss rev pol); Indry rm; shop; tradsmn; BBQ; shop in ssn; supmkt 1km; playgrnd; fishing; wifi; some statics; dogs €1.08; poss cr; Eng spkn; adv bkg; quiet, some rlwy noise; ccard acc; red low ssn; CKE/CCI; Wifi. "Popular, spacious, well laid-out, direct access to rv; friendly, helpful staff; unisex san facs clean but need update (2010) & insufficient when site busy; some pitches diff lge o'fits; gates clsd 2200-0700; poor security (2011); poss travellers & long-stay workers; poss unkempt early ssn; when wet grnd soft & muddy in places; walk along rv to Chartres; rec Son et Lumière; ideal NH & longer; vg; attractive site, bottom of hill, next rv; some awkward pitches; needs barrier, pass to ent during day, friendly helpful staff excellent situation, easy walk to Chartres, well lit at night." ♦ 1 Mar-15 Nov. € 21.00 2014*

CHARTRES *4E2* (9km S Rural) *48.40100, 1.48918* **Camp Municipal de Morancez, Rue de Chartres, 28630 Morancez [02 37 30 02 80, 07 86 40 65 49 (mob) or 02 37 28 49 71 (Mairie); fax 02 37 33 05 25; mairie.morancez@wanadoo.fr; www.morancez.fr]** S on Chartres by-pass (N123) take exit D935; L at T-junc twd Morancez; R on D114/Base de Loisirs at S end of vill (abrupt turn); cross bdge; after 200m turn R onto track, site at end of lake 300m. Travelling N on N10/D910 turn R onto D114 sp Morancez; strt over at x-rds at La Varenne; cont on narr rd for 1.5km; cross rv bdge, site on L. Sm, hdg/mkd pitch, shd; wc (some cont); chem disp (wc); shwrs inc; el pnts (6A) €2.90 (poss rev pol); shops & supmkt 2km; playgrnd adj; fishing adj; 20% statics; adv bkg; quiet but some rd noise; CKE/CCI. "Pleasant, peaceful site; surrounded by woods, lakes & rvs; friendly, helpful warden; san facs could be improved (2009); site locked 2200-0700; unrel opening dates; bus fr vill to Chartres every hr (high ssn); excel NH." 17 May-31 Aug. € 14.50 (3 persons) 2013*

CHATEAU LA VALLIERE *4G1* (500m W Rural) *47.54565, 0.31354* **FFCC Camp Municipal du Val Joyeux, 37330 Château-la-Vallière [02 47 24 00 21 or 02 47 24 04 93; fax 02 47 24 06 13; info@chateaulavalliere.com; www.chateaulavalliere.com]** Turn L off D959, in vill 1km S on D749. Site on R after x-ing bdge with lake on L. Med, hdg/mkd pitch, pt shd; wc; chem disp; mv service pnt; serviced pitch; shwrs inc; el pnts (5A) €2.50; shops 1km; tradsmn; playgrnd; lake beach & fishing adj; dogs €0.80; Eng spkn; adv bkg rec high ssn; quiet; CKE/CCI. "Friendly welcome; modern san facs; mkd walks; conv Loire chateaux; v soft grnd after heavy rain; site untidy & irreg cleaning of facs (2010) due being run by students; unrel opening dates." ♦ 27 Apr-17 Sep. € 10.50 2010*

CHATEAU RENAULT *4G2* (6km S Urban) *47.54471, 0.88786* **Camp Municipal du Moulin, Rue du Lavoir, 37110 Villedômer [02 47 55 05 50 or 02 47 55 00 04 (Mairie); fax 02 47 55 06 27; mairie.villedomer@wanadoo.fr]** Fr A10 exit junc 18 onto D31 dir Château-Renault. Turn W onto D73 sp to Auzouer & Villedômer. Fr Château-Renault S on D910, site sp dir Villedômer. Sm, hdg pitch, shd; wc (male cont); chem disp; shwrs inc; el pnts (10A) €3; shops, rest, bar adj; rv fishing; lake & fishing 2km; dogs €1; adv bkg. "Gd, clean facs but old-fashioned; pitch yourself if warden not present; does not accept twin axles." 15 Jun-15 Sep. € 7.00 2014*

CHATEAU RENAULT *4G2* (500m W Urban) *47.59283, 0.90687* **Camp Municipal du Parc de Vauchevrier, Rue Paul-Louis-Courier, 37110 Château-Renault [02 47 29 54 43 or 02 47 29 85 50 (LS); fax 02 47 56 87 50]** At Château-Renault foll sp to site 800m fr D910. If app fr a'route turn L on ent town & site on R of main rd adj Rv Brenne. Med, mkd pitch, pt shd; wc; chem disp; mv service pnt; shwrs inc; el pnts (6A) €2.20 (long lead poss req); shops 800m; rest 600m; bar 300m; playgrnd; htd pool; fishing; tennis; some rd noise; ccard not acc; CKE/CCI. "Pleasant site by rv in park; lge pitches; friendly, helpful warden; clean san facs, ltd low ssn; gd NH nr D910; no twin axles." ♦ 1 May-15 Sep. € 9.00 2014*

CHATEAUDUN *4F2* (1km N Urban) *48.08008, 1.33141* **Camp Municipal Le Moulin à Tan, Rue de Chollet, 28200 Châteaudun [02 37 45 05 34 or 02 37 45 22 46 (LS); fax 02 37 45 54 46; tourisme-chateaudun@wanadoo.fr]** App Châteaudun fr N on N10; turn R onto D3955 at 2nd rndabt (supmkt & Buffalo Grill on L); L at next rndabt onto D955; in 800m turn L into Rue de Chollet. App Chââteaudun fr S on N10, turn L onto D3955 & then as bef. Site adj Rv Loir & well sp fr D955. Med, mkd pitch, pt shd; wc (some cont); chem disp; mv service pnt; shwrs inc; el pnts (5A) inc; Indtte; tradsmn; shops, rest & snacks 2km; playgrnd; htd, covrd pool 2km; fishing; canoeing; games area; TV; 5% statics; CKE/CCI. "Gd touring base; quiet/under-used low ssn; helpful warden; some night flying fr nrby military airfield; security gate 2.10m height; no twin-axles; gd; reception open from 0700 - 2200; walks from site." 1 Apr-30 Sep. € 9.00 2014*

CENTRE

CHATEAUMEILLANT *7A4* (500m NW Rural) *46.56807, 2.18823* **Camp Municipal L'Etang Merlin, 18370 Châteaumeillant [02 48 61 31 38; fax 02 48 61 39 89; www.camping-etangmerlin.e-monsite.com]** Rec app fr W to avoid narr town rds. Site sp fr rndabt at W end of town on D80 N of Châteaumeillant on lakeside. Fr Culan by pass town on D943, then as above. Sm, hdg/mkd pitch, pt shd; wc; serviced pitches; chem disp; shwrs inc ; el pnts (5A) inc; lndry rm; shop 3km; playgrnd; pool; lake adj (no sw); fishing; tennis & basketball at sports complex adj; dogs €1; Eng spkn; adv bkg; quiet; no ccard acc; CKE/CCI. "Superb, well-kept site; lge pitches; friendly & helpful staff; rec arr early high ssn to secure pitch; easy walk to town." ♦ 1 May-30 Sep. € 11.45 2012*

"Satellite navigation makes touring much easier"

Remember most sat navs don't know if you're towing or in a larger vehicle – always use yours alongside maps and site directions.

CHATEAUNEUF SUR LOIRE *4F3* (500m S Rural) *47.85643, 2.22426* **FFCC Camping de la Maltournée, Sigloy, 45110 Châteauneuf-sur-Loire [02 38 58 42 46 or 06 32 11 41 13 (mob); contact@camping-chateauneufsurloire.fr; www.camping-chateauneufsurloire.fr]** S fr Chateauneuf cent, cross rv on D11; take 1st L, site in 300m on S bank of Rv Loire. Lge, pt shd; htd wc; chem disp; mv service pnt; shwrs inc; el pnts (10A) €3.90; lndtte; shops 1.5km; tradsmn; snacks; playgrnd; pool 2km; canoeing; wifi; 75% statics in sep area; dogs free; security barrier; poss cr; adv bkg; quiet; CKE/CCI. "Well-kept, busy site; helpful, pleasant staff; clean, modern san facs; chem disp v basic; m'van pitches beside rv; conv Orléans." ♦ 1 Apr-31 Oct. € 12.80 2013*

CHATEAUNEUF SUR LOIRE *4F3* (7km W Urban) *47.86884, 2.11597* **Camping de l'Isle aux Moulins, Rue du 44ème Régiment d'Infanterie, 45150 Jargeau [tel/fax 02 38 59 70 04 or 02 54 22 26 61 (LS); camping.jargeau@orange.fr; www.jargeau.fr]** Exit Châteauneuf W on D960 dir Orléans; at St Denis-de l'Hôtel turn sharp L onto D921 to Jargeau over Loire bdge; immed after x-ing bdge turn R into Blvd Jeanne d'Arc sp Camping; in 200m cont strt on into Rue du 44ème Régiment d'Infanterie; site on R in 300m. Site clearly visible on R of bdge on W bank of rv. NB App rd & turning to site is v narr; do not arr 1200-1330 (lunch time) as parking diff. Lge, mkd pitch, pt sl, pt shd; htd wc (mainly cont); chem disp; mv service pnt; baby facs; shwrs inc; el pnts (5A) €3.50; lndtte; tradsmn; shop, rest, bar 500m; BBQ; playgrnd; pool adj; rv fishing adj; cycle hire; games area; entmnt; wifi; twin axle; 2% statics; dogs €1.20; bus 500m; poss cr; Eng spkn; adv bkg; quiet; ccard acc; red long stay/low ssn/CKE/CCI. "Pleasant rvside site; lge pitches amongst trees; friendly farming family; modern san facs; poss muddy when wet; sh walk to sm town." ♦ 1 Apr-31 Oct. € 22.40 2014*

CHATEAUROUX *4H2* (1km N Rural) *46.82368, 1.69496* **Camp Municipal Le Rochat-Belle Isle, Rue du Rochat, 36000 Châteauroux [02 54 34 26 56 or 02 54 22 26 61; camping-le-rochat@orange.fr; www.aquadis-loisirs.com]** Exit A20 junc 13 onto D943/N143 S; foll sp Châteauroux; site sp bef town. Site on banks of Rv Indre, just S of Lac de Belle-Isle. Sp in town. Med, pt shd; wc (some cont); chem disp; mv service pnt; baby facs; shwrs inc; el pnts (5-10A) inc; gas; lndtte; shops 300m; rest, snacks, bar 100m; playgrnd; wifi; dogs €1.50; Eng spkn; poss noise fr low-flying aircraft. "Leisure park adj with pool & windsurfing on lake; friendly welcome & helpful; modern, clean san facs; poss music till late w/end high ssn; poss travellers; pleasant walk into town along rv; lge brocante mkt 1st Sun of month; vg." ♦ 2 Apr-16 Oct. € 19.00 (CChq acc) 2014*

CHATEAUROUX *4H2* (9km SW Rural) *46.74214, 1.61983* **Camping Les Grands Pins, Les Maisons-Neuves, 36330 Velles [02 54 36 61 93; contact@les-grands-pins.fr; www.les-grands-pins.fr]** Fr N exit A20 junc 14 dir Châteauroux; in 500m turn R onto D920 parallel with m'way. Foll sp Maisons-Neuves & site. Fr S exit A20 junc 15, turn R then L onto D920, site on R. Med, pt sl, pt shd; wc; chem disp; some serviced pitches; shwrs inc; el pnts (10A) €4.50 (poss rev pol; long lead req if in open field); shop 8km; tradsmn; rest high ssn; bar; playgrnd; pool; tennis; wifi; entmnt; dogs €1.50; site clsd w/end 1 Nov-14 Dec; Eng spkn; adv bkg; quiet; ccard acc; CKE/CCI. "Gd, tidy site in pine forest; clean facs; gd rest; low ssn recep in rest; max weight m'van 3,500kg Oct-Apr - heavier acc in summer; vet in Châteauroux; excel NH nr m'way, some noise; nice site, pitches in the woods; san facs need attention; pleasant helpful staff; popular NH." ♦ 22 Mar-23 Oct. € 28.00 2014*

See advert on next page

"There aren't many sites open at this time of year"

If you're travelling outside peak season remember to call ahead to check site opening dates – even if the entry says 'open all year'.

CHATILLON COLIGNY *4F3* (500m S Rural) *47.81717, 2.84447* **Camp Municipal La Lancière, Rue de la Lancière, 45230 Châtillon-Coligny [02 38 92 54 73 or 06 16 09 30 26 (mob); lalanciere@wanadoo.fr]** N fr Briare twd Montargis on N7; E fr Les Bézards on D56 twd Châtillon-Coligny; site sp on ent town on R immed bef canal bdge. Fr town cross Canal de Briare on D93 twd Bléneau; immed turn S along canal rd sp Camping & Marina. Med, mkd pitch, pt shd; wc (some cont); chem disp (wc); shwrs inc; el pnts (3-6A) €2.-3.10 (poss long lead req & rev pol); lndtte; shops, rest, bar in town; playgrnd; pool high ssn; rv fishing; games area; quiet;dogs; 25% statics; no ccard acc; CKE/CCI. "Attractive, peaceful, tidy site; many lge pitches; clean, dated facs; site yourself, warden calls; gd walking/cycling along canal & historic vill; superb site for simple caravaning, excel value." 1 Apr-30 Sep. € 10.00 2013*

CHATILLON SUR INDRE *4H2* (500m N Rural) *46.99116, 1.17382* **Camp Municipal Les Rives de L'Indre (formerly Camp Municipal de la Ménétrie), Rue de Moulin de la Grange, 36700 Châtillon-sur-Indre [06 78 27 16 39 or 02 54 38 75 44 (Mairie); fmadjointdgs@orange.fr; www.chatillon-sur-indre.fr]** Site well sp in vill. N twd Loches then foll sp. Med, some hdg/mkd pitch, pt shd; wc; shwrs inc; el pnts (6A) €3; gas, shop & rest 400m; BBQ; playgrnd adj; htd pool 400m (proper sw trunks only); dogs; no twin-axles; no adv bkg; quiet; CKE/CCI. "Lovely, relaxed, well-kept site; friendly, helpful warden; gd, clean san facs; conv Loire chateaux; gd birdwatching area; interesting old town; lge mkt Fri; excel value; barrier open & warden present 0800-1100 / 1630-2000." ♦ 15 May-15 Sep. € 11.00 2014*

CHATILLON SUR LOIRE see Briare *4G3*

CHATRE, LA *7A4* (3km N Rural) *46.60131, 1.97808* **Camp Municipal Solange-Sand, Rue du Pont, 36400 Montgivray [02 54 06 10 34 or 02 54 06 10 36; fax 02 54 06 10 39; mairie.montgivray@wanadoo.fr]** Fr La Châtre take rd to Montgivray, foll camping sp. Fr Châteauroux on D943 SE twd La Châtre turn R 2km S of Nohant on D72. Site behind church. Med, mkd pitch, pt shd; wc; chem disp; shwrs inc; el pnts (6A) inc (poss rev pol); Indry rm; BBQ; dogs; quiet; CKE/CCI. "Pleasant site in chateau grnds; new san facs planned (2010); gd access; warden calls am & pm; gd rest adj; gd walks." ♦ 15 Mar-15 Oct. € 10.80 2010*

CHATRE, LA *7A4* (2km SE Rural) *46.56862, 1.99921* **Camping Intercommunal Le Val Vert, Route de Briantes, 36400 La Châtre [02 54 48 32 42; fax 02 54 48 32 87]** Fr La Châtre take D943 dir Montluçon. On o'skts La Châtre turn R to Briantes, site sp at this junc. Or fr Montluçon on D943, turn L just bef La Châtre; site sp. Sm, hdg pitch, terr, pt shd; wc; chem disp; mv service pnt; shwrs inc; el pnts (10A) €2.50; Indry rm; shop 1km; tradsmn; BBQ; playgrnd; htd pool 5km; some statics; adv bkg; quiet; ccard not acc; CKE/CCI. "Spacious, pleasant site; excel grnds; dated san facs; walk/cycle to shops; poss travellers." ♦ 1 Jun-12 Sep. € 8.50 2009*

CHATRES SUR CHER see Villefranche sur Cher *4G3*

CHAUMONT SUR LOIRE *4G2* (500m NE Rural) *47.48444, 1.19417* **Camp Municipal Grosse Grève, Ave des Trouillas, 41150 Chaumont-sur-Loire [02 54 20 95 22 or 02 54 20 98 41 (Mairie); fax 02 54 20 99 61; mairie.chaumontsloire @ wanadoo.fr; www.camping-chaumont-sur-loire.com]** Fr N side of rv on D952 cross bdge to Chaumont on D1, turn R immed & R under bdge. Site sp in vill on D751. Med, pt shd; htd wc; chem disp; shwrs inc; el pnts (6-16A) €2-3.50 (poss long lead req); Indry rm; rest & bar 1km; BBQ; playgrnd; fishing; horseriding; canoeing; tennis; cycle hire; quiet, but some rd/rlwy noise; no ccard acc; CKE/CCI. "Pleasant site by rv; gd, clean san facs; no twin-axles; interesting chateau; cycle track along Loire; gd value; excel." ♦ 1 May-30 Sep. € 11.40 2014*

CHEMERY see Contres *4G2*

CHENONCEAUX *4G2* (1.5km E Rural) *47.32905, 1.08816* **Camping de l'Ecluse, Route de la Plage, 37150 Chisseaux [02 47 23 87 10 or 06 15 83 21 20 (mob); sandrine@campingdelecluse-37.fr; www.campingdelecluse-37.fr]** E fr Chenonceaux on D176; cross bdge; immed hard R & foll rv bank; site in 300m. Med, mkd pitch, pt shd; wc; chem disp; mv waste; shwrs inc; el pnts (16A) €3.90 (rev pol); Indtte; shop 1km; supmkt 6km; tradsmn; snacks; bar; playgrnd; fishing; canoeing; watersports; dogs €1.50; phone; poss cr; Eng spkn; adv bkg; quiet tho some rd/rlwy noise; ccard acc; CKE/CCI. "Rv trips; fishing; gd walking; gd." ♦ 1 Mar-31 Oct. € 12.50 2014*

CHENONCEAUX *4G2* (280m S Rural) *47.33033, 1.06947* **Camp Municipal, Fontaine des Prés, 37150 Chenonceaux [02 47 23 90 13 (Mairie); fax 02 47 23 94 46; www.chenonceaux-blere-tourisme.com]** In town cent foll sp Château de Chenonceaux & site. Ent as if visiting chateau & attendants will direct you. Site ent narr & twisting, poss not suitable long o'fits. Sm, pt sl, pt shd; wc (some cont); chem disp; mv service pnt; shwrs inc; el pnts (6A) €2.65; shop, rest, bar 500m; BBQ; sm playgrnd; dogs €1; phone; bus adj; poss cr; no adv bkg; some rlwy noise; CKE/CCI. "Simple site conv for chateau; v nr rlwy." ♦ 1 Jun-15 Sep. € 8.55 2011*

CHENONCEAUX *4G2* (1.5km S Rural) *47.32765, 1.08936* **Camping Le Moulin Fort, Pont de Chisseaux, 37150 Francueil [02 47 23 86 22; fax 02 47 23 90 83; lemoulinfort@wanadoo.fr; www.lemoulinfort.com]** Exit A85 junc 11 N, then take D976 E dir Montrichard; site on S bank of Rv Cher just off D976. Fr Tours take D976 sp Vierzon; keep on D976 by-passing Bléré until sm rndabt (5km) where site sp to L twd rv. Take sm rd on R to site, bef actually x-ing bdge. Site well sp. Med, hdg/mkd pitch, pt shd; wc; chem disp; baby facs; shwrs inc; el pnts (6A) €4. (long lead poss req); gas; lndtte (inc dryer); shop; tradsmn; rest, snacks; bar; BBQ (gas/ charcoal); playgrnd; pool; paddling pool; fishing; cycle hire; wifi; entmnt; games/TV rm; dogs €3; no c'vans/m'vans over 8m high ssn; lge o'fits check in adv; Eng spkn; adv bkg rec for Jul & Aug; min 3 nights preferred; rd noise & a little rlwy noise; ccard acc; red low ssn; CKE/CCI. "Lovely, well-kept site on rv bank; beautiful area; friendly, helpful British owners; gd san facs; easy access most pitches; many sm & v shady pitches; some pitches suitable for lge o'fits; footpath by rv with view of chateau; gd cycle rtes; poss security probs due access to site fr rv bank; Fri mkt Montrichard & Sun mkt Amboise; excel; well laid site to rv view for many pitches." ♦ 12 Apr -25 Sep. € 36.00 SBS - L08 2014*

CHEVERNY *4G2* (2km S Rural) *47.47798, 1.45070* **Camping Les Saules, 102 Route de Contres, 41700 Cheverny [02 54 79 90 01; fax 02 54 79 28 34; contact@camping-cheverny.com; www.camping-cheverny.com]** Exit A10 junc 17 dir Blois Sud onto D765 to Romorantin. At Cour-Cheverny foll sp Cheverny & chateau. Fr S on D956 turn R onto D102 just N of Contres, site on L just bef Cheverny. Well sp fr all dirs. Lge, mkd pitch, shd; htd wc; chem disp; mv service pnt; baby facs; shwrs inc; el pnts (10A) €3.50 (poss long lead req); gas; lndtte (inc dryer); shop; tradsmn; rest, snacks; bar; BBQ; playgrnd; htd pool; paddling pool; fishing; tennis, golf nr; excursions; games rm; cycle hire; wifi; 2% statics; TV; dogs €2; phone; Eng spkn; adv bkg rec high ssn; quiet but some rd noise; ccard acc; red long stay/low ssn; CKE/CCI. "Beautiful, well-run site; friendly, welcoming, helpful owners; excel san facs; castle adj; excel pool; all pitches under trees; muddy after heavy rain; many excel cycle & walking rtes nr; Cheverny chateau worth visit; little train & boat rides." ♦ 1 Apr-19 Sep. € 37.50 SBS - L01 2014*

CHINON *4G1* (500m SW Rural) *47.16397, 0.23377* **FFCC Camping de L'Ile Auger, Quai Danton, 37500 Chinon [02 47 93 08 35; fax 02 47 93 91 15; camping-ile-auger@hotmail.fr; www.camping-chinon.com]** On S side of rv at bdge. Fr S foll sp Chinon St Jacques; when app 2nd bdge on 1-way 'loop', avoid R lane indicated for x-ing bdge & cont strt past S end of main bdge to site on R. Fr N foll sp 'Centre Ville' round castle, cross bdge, site on R. Well sp in town & opp castle. Lge, hdg/mkd pitch, pt shd; wc (some cont); chem disp (wc); mv service pnt; baby facs; shwrs inc; el pnts (8-12A) €3.10 (poss rev pol); lndtte; shop 200m; snacks adj; playgrnd; canoe hire; htd pool 300m; wifi sat TV; dogs €1.20; phone; quiet; ccard acc; red long stay/CKE/CCI. "Excel, well-kept site in gd location; clean, dated san facs, poss stretched if site busy; twin-axles discretionary; poss midge prob; poss travellers; gd cycle rtes; gd views of chateau; rec; automatic ent barrier." ♦ 1 Apr-31 Oct. € 19.00 2014*

See advertisement

CHINON *4G1* (14km NW Rural) *47.20693, 0.08127* **Camping Belle Rive, 2 Route de Chinon, 37500 Candes-St Martin [02 47 95 98 11; fax 02 47 95 80 95; contact@campingcandes37.com; www.cdc-rivegauchevienne.com]** Fr Chinon take D751. Site on R bef junc with D7, on S bank of Rv Vienne. Med, mkd pitch, pt shd; wc; shwrs; el pnts (16A) €3.10; lndtte (inc dryer); shops 1km; tradsmn; rvside café; bar; rv sw 1km; playgrnd; fishing adj; dogs €1.30; adv bkg; quiet; CKE/CCI. "Pleasant rvside site; san facs, on 2 floors, need update & poss stretched if site busy; conv Saumur & chateaux." ♦ 15 Apr-30 Sep. € 13.40 2012*

CLOYES SUR LE LOIR *4F2* (1km N Rural) *48.00240, 1.23304* **Parc de Loisirs Le Val Fleuri, Route de Montigny, 28220 Cloyes-sur-le-Loir [02 37 98 50 53; fax 02 37 98 33 84; info@parc-de-loisirs.com; www.val-fleuri.fr]** Located on L bank of Rv Loir off N10; site sp. Med, hdg pitch, pt shd; wc; chem disp; shwrs inc; lndry rm (inc dryer); el pnts (5A) inc; shop; rest, snacks; bar; playgrnd; pool; wifi €3; waterslide; cycle hire; 50% statics; dogs €2; adv bkg; quiet. "Facs gd for children but ltd low ssn; well-run, pleasant site in wooded valley; site fees inc use of sm leisure park, pedalos & rowing boats on Rv Loir." 15 Mar-15 Nov. € 24.60 2014*

CLOYES SUR LE LOIR *4F2* (2km S Rural) *47.97326, 1.23292* **FFCC Aire Naturelle Camping Les Fouquets (Fetter), 41160 St Jean-Froidmentel [02 54 82 66 97; lesfouquets@aol.com]** Off N10 twd Vendôme. Sp Les Fouquets 200m SE of N10. Sm, shd; wc; shwrs inc; el pnts (15A) €3; lndry rm; shop, rest 2km; pool; fishing, tennis & sailing 2km; dogs €1; quiet; CKE/CCI. "Lovely, family-run site in woodland; friendly, welcoming owner; gd pool." ♦ 1 Apr-30 Sep. € 9.00 2011*

CONTRES *4G2* (6km SW Rural) *47.38261, 1.36251* **Camping à la Ferme La Presle (Boucher), 41700 Oisly [02 54 79 52 69 or 06 15 70 74 02; fax 02 54 79 80 44; lapresle@lapost.net; www.gites-centre-loire.com]** Fr Contres take D675 SW for 3km D21 to just past Oisly. Well sp. Sm, pt sl, pt shd; wc; el pnts (4A) €2.20 (poss no earth); shops 1.5km; lake fishing; v quiet. "Excel CL-type site; owner helpful." Easter-1 Nov. € 12.00 2011*

COSNE COURS SUR LOIRE *4G3* (1km SW Rural) *47.40923, 2.91792* **Camping de l'Ile, Ile de Cosne, 18300 Bannay [03 86 28 27 92; fax 03 86 28 18 10; contact@restaurantcamping.com; www.restaurantcamping.com]** Fr Cosne take Bourges rd, D955, over 1st half of bdge, ent immed on L, 500m strt. On rv island. Lge, shd; htd wc; chem disp; shwrs inc; el pnts (10A) €4; Indtte; ltd shop; rest, snacks; bar; BBQ; playgrnd; paddling pool; entmnt; cycle hire; TV; some statics; dogs €0.90; quiet; ccard acc; CKE/CCI. "Helpful staff; views of Rv Loire; gd san facs; gd NH; supmkt Carrefour closeby; gd rest opp; town within walking distance." ♦ 1 Apr-30 Oct. € 23.70 2014*

COULLONS *4G3* (1km W Rural) *47.62319, 2.48444* **Camp Municipal Plancherotte, Route de la Brosse, 45720 Coullons [02 38 29 20 42 or 06 86 73 94 94 (mob); coullons.mairie@wanadoo.fr; www.coullons.fr]** Fr cent of Coullons foll sp twd Cerdon (D51). Bef leaving vill & after passing lake, take 1st rd on L. Site in 500m on L side of lake. Med, pt shd, hdg/mkd pitch; wc (cont); chem disp; some serviced pitches; shwrs; el pnts (15A) inc; gas 1km; shop 1km; playgrnd; tennis; 30% statics; phone; adv bkg; CKE/CCI. "Excel, well-kept site; pleasant mkd walks nrby." ♦ 1 May-31 Oct. € 9.85 2010*

COURVILLE SUR EURE *4E2* (500m S Urban) *48.44629, 1.24157* **Camp Municipal Les Bords de l'Eure, Ave Thiers, 28190 Courville-sur-Eure [02 37 23 76 38 or 02 37 18 07 90 (Mairie); fax 02 37 18 07 99; secretaria-mairie@courville-sur-eure.fr; www.courville-sur-eure.fr]** Turn N off D923 19km W of Chartres. Site on bank of rv. Foll sp. Med, hdg pitch, pt shd; htd wc (some cont); chem disp; mv service pnt (outside ent); shwrs; el pnts (6A) €3.30; Indtte; supmkt 1km; rest in town; pool 200m; dogs; poss cr; quiet. "Lovely, peaceful rvside site; spacious pitches; friendly warden; san facs clean but need update & poss stetched high ssn; poss no twin-axles; conv Chartres; mkt Thurs; easy walk into town." 1 May - 22 Sep. € 12.00 2013*

CROUY SUR COSSON see Muides sur Loire *4G2*

DESCARTES *4H2* (700m SW Urban) *46.97152, 0.69586* **Camp Municipal La Grosse Motte, Allée Léo Lagrange, 37160 Descartes [02 47 59 85 90 or 02 47 92 42 20; fax 02 47 59 72 20; www.ville-descartes.fr]** Fr S on D750 turn L just bef Descartes sp, cross rlwy line & in 500m turn L into site. Fr N turn R after Descartes sp. V narr turn into site due stone house walls. Sm, hdg pitch, pt sl, shd; wc (some cont); baby facs; shwrs inc; shops in town; el pnts (10A) €2.10 (poss rev pol); pool adj; playgrnd, tennis, mini-golf nr; boating on rv; dogs €1; adv bkg; quiet; ccard not acc; CKE/CCI. "Beautiful site; public gardens adj; spacious pitches; friendly staff; clean facs; popular with school parties; gd NH." 1 Jun-30 Sep. € 6.80 2009*

⊞ **DREUX** *4E2* (6km NW Rural) *48.76149, 1.29041* **Camping Etangs de Marsalin, 3 Place du Général de Gaulle, 28500 Vert-en-Drouais [02 37 82 92 23; fax 02 37 82 85 47; contact@campingdemarsalin.fr; www.campingdemarsalin.fr]** Fr W on N12 dir Dreux, cross dual c'way bef petrol stn onto D152 to Vert-en-Drouais; on ent turn R to church, site on L. Well sp. Med, hdg/mkd pitch, some hdstg, pt sl, pt shd; htd wc (some cont); chem disp; shwrs inc; el pnts (6-10A), €4.60 (poss rev pol, long leads poss req, avail at recep); Indtte (inc dryer); shop; tradsmn; rest 4km; snacks; bar 100m; lake fishing 2km; wifi; 80% statics; dogs; phone adj; poss cr; Eng spkn; quiet; CKE/CCI. "Peaceful location; working families on site; friendly, helpful staff; basic, clean san facs; touring pitches at far end far fr facs; muddy when wet; lovely vill; conv Versailles; NH only; new owners (2014); site tidy and clean." ♦ ltd € 18.44 2014*

EGUZON CHANTOME *7A3* (300m N Urban) *46.44562, 1.58331* **Camping La Garenne, 1 Rue Yves Choplin, 36270 Éguzon-Chantôme [02 54 47 44 85; info@campinglagarenne.eu; www.campinglagarenne.eu]** Exit A20 junc 20 onto D36 to Eguzon; on ent vill sq cont strt on, foll sp; site on L in 300m. Med, hdg pitch, pt sl, pt shd; wc; chem disp; mv service pnt; baby facs; shwrs inc; el pnts (6A) €3.20; gas 300m; Indtte (inc dryer); shop 300m; rest, snacks; bar; BBQ; playgrnd; htd pool; cycling; lake sw & water sports 4km; entmtn; wifi; TV rm; 20% statics; dogs €1.50; phone; site clsd 16 Dec-14 Jan; poss cr; Eng spkn; adv bkg; poss open all year, phone ahead; quiet; red low ssn; CKE/CCI. "All you need on site or in vill; excel." ♦ ltd 11 Mar-18 Oct. € 31.60 2013*

⊞ **EGUZON CHANTOME** *7A3* (3km SE Rural) *46.43372, 1.60399* **Camp Municipal du Lac Les Nugiras, Route de Messant, 36270 Eguzon-Chantôme [02 54 47 45 22; fax 02 54 47 47 22; nugiras@orange.fr; www.eguzonlaccreuse.com]** Fr A20 exit junc 20, E on D36 to Eguzon; in vill turn R & foll site sp. Lge, hdg/mkd pitch, pt sl, terr, pt shd; htd wc; shwrs inc; el pnts (10A) €3 (rev pol); Indtte; shop; tradsmn; rest, snacks; bar; playgrnd; sand beach 300m; watersports; waterski school; entmnt; games rm; some statics; security barrier; quiet but poss noise fr statics or entmnt; red low ssn; CKE/CCI. "Scenic site & region; ample, clean facs but v ltd low ssn; site yourself on arr; warden avail early eves; gd winter site; muddy after heavy rain." ♦ € 9.40 2014*

FAVEROLLES SUR CHER see Montrichard *4G2*

FERRIERES EN GATINAIS *4F3* (300m N Rural) *48.09198, 2.78482* **Camp Municipal Le Perray/Les Ferrières, Rue du Perray, 45210 Ferrières-en-Gâtinais [06 71 43 25 95 (mob) or 02 38 87 15 44 (Mairie); fax 02 38 96 62 76; ferrieres.mairie@wanadoo.fr or cyril.martin@ferrieresengatinais.fr; www.metiers-art-gatinais.com]** N fr Mantargis on N7; R onto D96/D32 sp Ferrières & foll camp sp. Med, mkd pitch, pt shd; wc; chem disp; mv service pnt; shwrs inc; el pnts (10A) €4.10; Indtte; shops, supmkt & rests 300m; playgrnd; pool & sports facs adj; tennis; rv fishing adj; entmnt; 5% statics; quiet. "Vg site; direct access to sm rv; gd facs & security; 2 gd rests nrby; old pretty town with lovely church; supmkt." 1 Apr-30 Oct. € 10.80 2014*

FERTE ST AUBIN, LA *4F3* (1km N Urban) *47.72553, 1.93565* **Camp Municipal Le Cosson, Ave Löwendal, 45240 La Ferté-St Aubin [02 38 76 55 90; campingducosson@recrea.fr; www.campingducosson.fr]** S fr Orléans on D2020; ent on R on N o'skts twd Municipal pool. Turning onto Rue Lowendal. Sm, pt shd; wc; chem disp (wc); shwrs inc; el pnts (6A) inc (poss rev pol); shops 1km; tradsmn; rest 100m; htd pool; fishing adj; wifi; dogs €2; phone; Eng spkn; train noise; ccard not acc; red low ssn; CKE/CCI. "Agreeable, spacious site; friendly, helpful recep; clean, ltd facs; easy walk to delightful town & gd rests; nr park & chateau; poss travellers low ssn; conv A71; gd NH." 26 Apr-29 Sep. € 16.00 2014*

⊞ **FONTAINE SIMON** *4E2* (800m N Rural) *48.51314, 1.01941* **Camping du Perche, 3 Rue de la Ferrière, 28240 Fontaine-Simon [02 37 81 88 11 or 06 23 82 90 28 (mob); info@campingduperche.com; www.campingduperche.com]** Fr La Loupe on D929 take D25 N to Fontaine-Simon, site sp. Med, hdg pitch, pt sl, pt shd; htd wc (some cont); chem disp; shwrs inc; el pnts €3.60; Indtte (inc dryer); shop; tradsmn; BBQ; playgrnd; htd, covrd pool adj; lake sw adj; fishing; wifi; few statics; dogs €3; adv bkg; quiet; CKE/CCI. "Undulating, lakeside site; gd." ♦ € 15.00 2012*

FRETEVAL see Morée *4F2*

GIEN *4G3* (1km SW Rural) *47.68233, 2.62289* **Camping Touristique de Gien, Rue des Iris, 45500 Poilly-lez-Gien [02 38 67 12 50; fax 02 38 67 12 18; camping-gien@wanadoo.fr; www.camping-gien.com]** Off D952 Orléans-Nevers rd; turn R over old rv bdge in Gien & then R again onto D951; site on R on Rv Loire. Alt dir fr D940 (Argent-sur-Sauldre - Gien) at rndbt take rd sp Gien. Take L at traff lts bef old bdge; site on R, 1km S of rv. Lge, hdg/mkd pitch, hdstg, pt sl, pt shd; htd wc; chem disp; mv service pnt; baby facs; shwrs inc; el pnts (10A) €3.50-5; gas adj; Indtte (inc dryer); shop; rest, snacks; bar adj; BBQ; playgrnd; covrd pool; paddling pool; lake sw 3km; canoeing; tennis; cycle hire; games rm; wifi; entmnt; TV rm; 20% statics; dogs €2; phone; adv bkg; Eng spkn; quiet; ccard acc; red long stay/CKE/CCI. "Lovely rvside site; views of old bdge & town some pitches; excel staff; gd san facs; vg facs; no sw allowed in rv; easy walk to town across bdge; porcelain factory 'seconds'; vg value; gd rest; san facs unisex; excel site, highly rec; nice situation; flock of sheep/goats traverse the site daily." ♦ 2 Mar-10 Nov. € 32.00 2014*

GIEN *4G3* (5km SW Rural) *47.64152, 2.61528* **Kawan Village Les Bois du Bardelet, Route de Bourges, Poilly 45500 Gien [02 38 67 47 39; fax 02 38 38 27 16; contact@bardelet.com; www.bardelet.com]** Fr Gien take D940 dir Bourges; turn R onto D53, then R again onto unclassified rd to go back across D940; foll sp to site on L side of this rd. Site well sp fr D940. Lge, hdg/mkd pitch, some hdstg, pt shd; htd wc; chem disp; mv service pnt; baby facs; shwrs inc; el pnts (10-16A) inc (some rev pol); gas; Indtte (inc dryer); shop; rest, snacks; bar; BBQ; playgrnd; 2 htd pools (1 covrd); paddling pool; jacuzzi; lake fishing & canoeing; horseriding 5km; tennis; games area; games rm; fitness rm; cycle hire; archery; wifi; entmnt; TV; 17% statics; dogs €4; twin-axles acc (rec check in adv); phone; adv bkg; quiet; ccard acc; red couples/low ssn/long stay; CKE/CCI. "Pleasant, well-kept, well-run site; friendly welcome; modern, immac san facs, poss stretched high ssn; some pitches poss diff access; beautiful o'door pool; gd for young children; guided walks; remote site in countryside." ♦ 19 Apr-30 Sep. € 48.20 (CChq acc) SBS - L05 2014*

See advertisement

GRACAY see Vatan *4H3*

GRAND PRESSIGNY, LE *4H2* (300m S Rural) *46.91723, 0.80600* **Camp Municipal Croix Marron, Rue St Martin, 37350 Le Grand-Pressigny [02 47 94 90 37 (Mairie); fax 02 47 91 04 77]** Fr Descartes take D750 S for 3km, L onto D42 to Le Grand-Plessigny. Site at SE end of vill by rv. Sm, mkd pitch, pt shd; wc; chem disp; mv service pnt; shwrs €0.50; el pnts €2.35; shop, rest, bar in vill; playgrnd; pool adj; quiet. "Pleasant location; prehistoric sites nr." 9 Apr-30 Sep. € 6.55 2010*

GUERCHE SUR L'AUBOIS, LA *4H3* (2km SE Rural) *46.94029, 2.95852* **Camp Municipal Robinson, 2 Rue de Couvache, 18150 La Guerche-sur-l'Aubois [02 48 74 18 86 or 02 48 77 53 53; fax 02 48 77 53 59; camping-laguerche@orange.fr; www.mairie-la-guerche-sur-laubois.com]** Site sp fr D976 opp church in vill cent. Sm, hdg/mkd pitch, pt shd; wc; shwrs inc; el pnts (10A) €3; Indry rm; shop; tradsmn; rest, bar 300m; playgrnd; lake sw adj; fishing; boating; entmnt; dogs; phone; poss cr; quiet, some rlwy noise; CKE/CCI. "Pleasantly situated; v welcoming; clean san facs; gd cycling area; excel; ideal for visits to Parc Floral gardens at Apremont." ♦ ltd 1 May-30 Sep. € 8.50 2013*

HUISSEAU SUR COSSON see Blois *4G2*

ILE BOUCHARD, L' *4H1* (500m N Urban) *47.12166, 0.42857* **Camping Les Bords de Vienne, 4 Allée du Camping, 37220 L'Ile-Bouchard [02 47 95 23 59; fax 02 47 98 45 29; info@campingbordsdevienne.com; www.campingbordsdevienne.com]** On N bank of Rv Vienne 100m E of rd bdge nr junc of D757 & D760. Fr E, turn L bet supmkt & pharmacy. Med, mkd pitch, pt sl, pt shd; wc; chem disp; shwrs inc; el pnts (6-16A) €3.50; gas; Indtte; supmkt adj; snacks; playgrnd; pool & tennis 500m; rv sw adj; wifi; some statics; dogs €1.50; phone adj; Eng spkn; adv bkg; quiet; ccard acc; red low ssn/long stay; CKE/CCI. "Lovely, clean rvside site; attractive location; poss travellers; conv Loire chateaux." 15 Mar-25 Oct. € 28.00 2014*

ILLIERS COMBRAY *4E2* (2km SW Rural) *48.28667, 1.22697* **FLOWER Camping Le Bois Fleuri, Route de Brou, 28120 Illiers-Combray [02 37 24 03 04; infos@camping-chartres.com; www.camping-chartres.com / www.flowercampings.com]** S on D921 fr Illiers for 2km twd Brou. Site on L. Med, hdg pitch, some hdstg, pt shd; htd wc; chem disp; some serviced pitches; shwrs inc; el pnts (6A) €3.50; gas; Indtte; shop 2km; rest 2km; snacks; bar; htd pool 200m; paddling pool; playgrnd; fishing adj; games area; entmnt; 30% statics; dogs €4; poss cr; adv bkg; quiet, some rd noise; red low ssn; CKE/CCI. "Many pitches wooded & with flowers; popular NH; excel san facs, poss insufficient cleaning (2010); ltd water/el pnts; uneven grnd makes access diff; gd security; excel cycle path to vill." ♦ 2 Apr-29 Oct. € 20.00 (CChq acc) 2014*

JARGEAU see Châteauneuf sur Loire *4F3*

LANGEAIS *4G1* (1km E Urban) *47.32968, 0.41848* **Camp Municipal du Lac, rue Carnot, 37130 Langeais [02 47 96 85 80; fax 02 47 96 69 23; patrimoine@langeais.fr; www.langeais.fr]** Exit A85 junc 7 onto D952 dir Langeais & foll 'Camping Municipal' sp. Med, mkd pitch, pt shd; wc; chem disp; shwrs inc; el pnts (6A) €3.50; shop 1km; rest 1km; snacks; bar1km; playgrnd; htd pool; fishing nr; 5% statics; dogs; rlwy noise; ccard acc; CKE/CCI. "Busy site high ssn; easy walk to town; dated san facs, inadequate when busy; nr Rv Loire cycle path; lovely chateau; gd; poss rd/rlwy noise." 1 Jun-15 Sep. € 19.00 2013*

⊞ **LIGUEIL** *4H2* (2km N Rural) *47.05469, 0.84615* **Camping de la Touche, Ferme de la Touche, 37240 Ligueil [02 47 59 54 94; booklatouche@hotmail.co.uk; www.theloirevalley.com]** Fr Loches SW on D31; turn L at x-rds with white cross on R 2km after Ciran; in 500m turn R, site on R bef hotel. Fr A10 exit junc 25 Ste Maure-de-Touraine & foll sp to Ligueil; then take D31 dir Loches; turn L at white cross. Sm, mkd ptch, hdstg, pt shd; wc; chem disp (wc); shwrs inc; el pnts (10A) €5; Indtte (inc dryer); sm shop; snacks; playgrnd; pool; cycle hire; fishing; wifi; dogs free; adv bkg; ccard acc; quiet; CKE/CCI. "Well-maintained, relaxed CL-type site; lge pitches; welcoming, helpful British owners; c'van storage; excel san facs; gd walking & touring base; much wild life; conv m'way; gd." € 14.00 2011*

LIMERAY see Amboise *4G2*

LOCHES *4H2* (500m S Urban) *47.12255, 1.00175* **Kawan Village La Citadelle, Ave Aristide Briand, 37600 Loches [02 47 59 05 91 or 06 21 37 93 06 (mob); fax 02 47 59 00 35; camping@lacitadelle.com; www.lacitadelle.com]** Fr any dir take by-pass to S end of town & leave at Leclerc rndabt for city cent; site well sp on R in 800m. Lge, hdg/mkd pitch, pt shd; htd wc (some cont); chem disp; mv service pnt; shwrs inc; el pnts (10A) €4.30 (poss rev pol) (poss long lead req); gas; Indtte (inc dryer); shop & 2km; tradsmn; rests, snacks; bar; BBQ; playgrnd; htd pool on site & 2 htd pools adj; fishing; boating; tennis nr; games area; cycle hire; golf 9km; wifi; entmnt; sat TV rm; 30% statics; dogs €3; poss cr; Eng spkn; adv bkg rec; poss night noise fr entmnt; ccard acc; red long stay/low ssn; CKE/CCI. "Attractive, well-kept, busy site nr beautiful old town; views of citadel; gd sized pitches, poss uneven; helpful staff; facs poss stretched; barrier clsd 2200-0800; poss no night security (2010); rvside walk into town; poss mosquitoes; site muddy after heavy rain; mkt Wed & Sat am; excel site; lge serviced pitches; sh walk to a beautiful mediaeval town." ♦ 18 Mar - 29 Sep. € 39.00 2013*

LOUROUX, LE *4G2* (350m N Rural) *47.16270, 0.78697* **Camping à la Ferme La Chaumine (Baudoin), 37240 Le Louroux [tel/fax 02 47 92 82 09 or 06 85 45 68 10 (mob); bruno.baudoin@free.fr]** Fr Tours, take D50 S for 30km. Site immed on R bef Le Louroux. Sm, hdg pitch, shd; wc; chem disp; shwrs inc; el pnts (10A) inc; BBQ; playgrnd; dogs; bus 200m; Eng spkn; adv bkg; quiet. "Superb CL-type site nr quaint vill; helpful owners; gd, clean san facs; gd walks fr site." 1 May-15 Oct. € 11.50 2013*

LUYNES see Tours *4G2*

LUZERET see Argenton sur Creuse *7A3*

CENTRE

⊞ **MAINTENON** *4E2* (4km NW Rural) *48.60890, 1.54760* **Camping Les Ilots de St Val, Le Haut Bourray, 28130 Villiers-le-Morhier [02 37 82 71 30; fax 02 37 82 77 67; lesilots@campinglesilotsdestval.com; www.campinglesilotsdestval.com]** Take D983 N fr Maintenon twd Nogent-le-Roi, in 5km 2nd L onto D101 sp Néron/Vacheresses-les-Basses/Camping to site in 1km on L at top of hill. NB App fr N on D929 not rec as rds in Nogent-le-Roi narr. Lge, some hdg/mkd pitch, hdstg, pt shd; htd wc; chem disp; mv service pnt; shwrs inc; el pnts (6-10A) €4-7; gas; lndtte; shops 4km; tradsmn; BBQ; playgrnd; pool 4km; rv fishing 1km; tennis; games rm; wifi; 50% statics; dogs €2; train 4km; little Eng spkn; adv bkg; quiet but some aircraft noise; red long stay/ CKE/CCI. "Pleasant, peaceful site in open countryside; lge private pitches; some vg, modern san facs; helpful staff; gd value site; conv Chartres, Versailles, Maintenon Château, train to Paris; dog walking fr the site is gd; improved access for lge o'fits; phone ahead late Dec to mid Feb as site may be clsd to tourers." HCAP] 01 Mar-31 Dec. € 33.00 2014*

MEHUN SUR YEVRE *4H3* (500m N Urban) *47.14797, 2.21725* **Camp Municipal, Ave Jean Châtelet, 18500 Mehun-sur-Yèvre [02 48 57 44 51 or 02 48 57 30 25 (Mairie); fax 02 48 57 34 16; www.ville-mehun-sur-yevre.fr/Le-camping]** Leave A71 junc 6 onto D2076 (N76) dir Bourges. App Mehun & turn L into site at 2nd traff lts. Ave Jean Châtelet is pt of D2076. Sm, mkd pitch, pt shd; wc; chem disp; mv service pnt; shwrs inc; el pnts (6A) €2.80 (poss rev pol & long lead req some pitches); lndtte; shop, rest & bar 600m; supmkts 1km; playgrnd; pool & tennis adj; quiet with some rd noise; twin-axles extra; ccard not acc. "Excel NH conv for m'way; clean, modern san facs; water pnts poss long walk; gates locked 2200-0700 (high ssn); facs open to elements; town rather run down, nice park." ♦ 8 May-30 Sep. € 16.65 2013*

MEHUN SUR YEVRE *4H3* (6km NE Rural) *47.09648, 2.18165* **Camp Municipal Pierre Sicard, 18120 Preuilly [02 48 57 12 04 or 02 48 51 30 08 (Mairie); fax 02 48 51 06 28; mairie.preuilly@wanadoo.fr]** S fr Vierzon on D27 sp Brinay & Quincy to Preuilly; take 2nd L to site in 500m; on R just past rv bdge. Med, hdg/mkd pitch, pt shd; wc; chem disp; shwrs inc; el pnts (5A) inc; lndtte; shop; snacks; bar; playgrnd; games area; tennis opp; a few statics; dogs €0.80; phone adj; adv bkg; quiet, but poss noise fr rest adj; CKE/CCI. "Gd touring base for wine rte; san facs old but clean; direct access to rv fishing & boating; fair." ♦ 1 May-30 Sep. € 9.80 2009*

MENNETOU SUR CHER see Villefranche sur Cher *4G3*

MESLAND see Onzain *4G2*

MEZIERES EN BRENNE *4H2* (6km E Rural) *46.79817, 1.30595* **Camping Bellebouche, 36290 Mézières-en-Brenne [02 54 38 32 36; fax 02 54 38 32 96; v.v.n@orange.fr; www.village-vacances-bellebouche.com]** Sp on D925. Med, mkd pitch, pt sl, pt shd; wc (cont); chem disp (wc); baby facs; shwrs inc; el pnts €3.50; lndtte; shop 6km; rest high ssn; bar; BBQ (elec); playgrnd; lake sw adj; watersports; fishing; some statics; no dogs; phone; quiet; ccard acc;CKE/CCI. "In country park; gd walking, cycling, birdwatching; vg; san facs dated." 30 Apr-30 Sep. € 11.00 2013*

MONTBAZON *4G2* (300m N Rural) *47.29044, 0.71595* **Camping de la Grange Rouge, 37250 Montbazon [02 47 26 06 43; fax 02 47 26 03 13; infos@camping-montbazon.com; www.camping-montbazon.com]** On D910 thro Montbazon fr S to N, after x-ing bdge (pt of D910) immed turn L to site. Clearly visible & clearly sp on W side of rd at N end of town. Med, mkd pitch, pt shd; wc (male cont); chem disp; shwrs inc; el pnts (10A) €4; lndtte; shops 300m; rest & bar adj; playgrnd; sm htd pool; fishing; tennis; TV rm; some statics; dogs €2; Eng spkn; adv bkg; quiet; ccard acc; red low ssn; CKE/CCI. "Lovely, rvside site in pretty town; helpful, friendly owner; basic facs dated but clean; conv Tours & a'routes." ♦ 1 Apr-15 Oct. € 26.00 2014*

MONTBAZON *4G2* (2km E Rural) *47.28924, 0.73436* **Camping de la Plage, 37250 Veigné [02 47 26 23 00; fax 02 47 73 11 47; campingveigne@aol.com; www.touraine-vacance.com]** Exit A10 junc 23 dir Montbazon onto D910. N of Montbazon after 'Les Gues' turn SE onto D50 to Veigné & site. Site in 2km on R at rvside. Med, mkd pitch, pt shd; htd wc; chem disp; mv service pnt; baby facs; shwrs, el pnts (10A) €4.50; gas 200m; lndtte; shop 200m; rest, snacks; BBQ; playgrnd; htd pool high ssn; canoeing; fishing; games area; entmnt; 13% statics; dogs €1.20; phone; Eng spkn; adv bkg; quiet, some rd/rwly noise; ccard acc; red low ssn/long stay; CKE/CCI. "Rvside site nr vill; gd san facs; gd for Loire chateaux & Tours; gd walking & cycling; site used as sh cut by locals; poss clsd Oct, phone ahead." ♦ 1 Apr-31 Oct. € 13.00 2009*

MONTOIRE SUR LE LOIR *4F2* (500m S Rural) *47.74750, 0.86351* **Camp Municipal Les Reclusages, Ave des Reclusages, 41800 Montoire-sur-le Loir [tel/fax 02 54 85 02 53; camping.reclusages@orange.fr; www.mairie-montoire.fr]** Foll site sp, out of town sq, over rv bdge & 1st L on blind corner at foot of old castle. Med, some mkd pitch, pt shd; wc (some cont); chem disp; mv service pnt; shwrs inc; el pnts (6-10A) €3.10-3.93; lndtte; shops 500m; bar; snacks; playgrnd; htd pool adj; playgrnd; canoeing; fishing; wifi; dogs €0.97; 5% statics; Eng spkn; adv bkg; quiet; ccard acc; CKE/CCI. "Lovely location nr Rv Loir; peaceful, well-kept, secure site; some rvside pitches; friendly, helpful warden; excel clean san facs, ltd low ssn; gd cycling; conv troglodyte vills; excel; pleasant sh walk into town across rv; attractive town; International Folk Festival mid Aug." ♦ 28 Apr-22 Sep. € 20.00 2014*

MONTRESOR *4H2* (3km W Rural) *47.15782, 1.16026* **Camping Les Coteaux du Lac, 37460 Chemillé-sur-Indrois [02 47 92 77 83; fax 02 47 92 72 95; lescoteauxdulac@wanadoo.fr; www.lescoteauxdulac.com]** Fr Loches on D764; then D10 dir Montrésor; cont to Chemillé-sur-Indrois. Med, pt sl; wc; chem disp; mv service pnt; baby facs; shwrs inc; el pnts (6A) €3.90; lndtte (inc dryer); sm shop; rest, snacks; bar; BBQ: playgrnd; htd pool; paddling pool; lake fishing & boating; trekking in Val d'Indrois; games rm; wifi; entmnt; TV rm; dogs €1.70; phone; Eng spkn; quiet. "Excel setting by lake; immac, modern san facs; beautiful vill 600m; 3km along cycle track (old rlwy)." ♦ 3 Mar-15 Oct. € 34.00 2013*

MONTRICHARD *4G2* (1km S Rural) *47.33384, 1.18766* **Camping Couleurs du Monde, 1 Rond Point de Montparnasse, 41400 Faverolles-sur-Cher [02 54 32 06 08 or 06 74 79 56 29 (mob); fax 02 54 32 61 35; touraine-vacances@wanadoo.fr; www.camping-couleurs-du-monde.com]** E fr Tours on D796 thro Bléré; at Montrichard turn S on D764 twd Faverolles-sur-Cher, site 200m fr junc, adj to Carrefour supmkt - on L by 2nd rndabt. Med, mkd pitch, hdstg, pt shd; wc; chem disp; mv service pnt; baby facs; sauna; shwrs inc; el pnts (10A) €4 (rev pol); Indtte (inc dryer); supmkt adj; rest, snacks; bar; BBQ; playgrnd; htd pool; paddling pool; waterslide 500m; beach & sw 600m; tennis 500m; cycle hire; games area; games rm; beauty cent; wifi; entmnt; TV rm; dogs €2; Eng spkn; adv bkg; quiet, but some rd noise; ccard acc; red low ssn/CKE/CCI. "Site in gd location nr vineyards; gd sports activities; vg; excel facs; gd sw pool with canopy; ideal for exploring Cher & Loire Valley." ♦ ltd 29 Mar-27 Sep. € 38.50 2014*

MOREE *4F2* (2.5km SW Urban) *47.88932, 1.20109* **Camping La Maladrerie, Rue du Plessis, 41160 Fréteval [02 54 82 62 75 or 06 88 69 21 92 (mob); fax 02 54 82 62 75; campingdelamaladrerie@orange.fr; www.camping-de-la-maladrerie.fr]** E fr Le Mans on D357 to Fréteval; turn L in vill. Sp. Med, mkd pitch, pt shd; wc; chem disp; mv service pnt; shwrs inc; el pnts (4-6A) €1.55-2.30; gas; Indtte; shops 800m; bar; BBQ; playgrnd; pool; rv sw 200m; lake fishing on site; 5% statics; Eng spkn; ccard acc; CKE/CCI. "Delightful, well-kept, quiet site; friendly owner; some facs in need of update (2011); poss ltd facs low ssn; site was a medieval leper colony; highly rec." ♦ ltd 1 Apr-30 Oct. € 10.45 2013*

MOREE *4F2* (2km W Rural) *47.88885, 1.21101* **Camp Municipal, Route de l'Etang, 41160 Fréteval [02 54 82 63 52 (Mairie); fax 02 54 82 07 15; freteval.mairie@wanadoo.fr]** Site 100m fr D357 by Rv Loir in vill cent, 500m fr lake. NB Chicane ent/exit thro concrete posts & fencing - not for lge o'fits. Med, mkd pitch, pt shd; wc (some cont); shwrs inc; el pnts inc; shops 500m; playgrnd; fishing; quiet, some rd noise. "Lovely, location on Rv Loir; diff ent/exit, esp med/lge o'fits; facs need update; conv beautiful town of Vendôme; site run down (2009)." 1 Jun-31 Aug. € 7.50 2009*

MOREE *4F2* (500m NW Rural) *47.90643, 1.22755* **Camp Municipal La Varenne, Plan d'Eau de la Varenne, 41160 Morée [02 54 82 06 16 or 02 54 89 15 15; fax 02 54 89 15 10; mairie-de-moree@wanadoo.fr]** W fr Orléans on N157/D357 or N fr Vendôme on D910 & foll sp in vill onto D19 to site. Sm, pt shd; htd wc; chem disp; mv service pnt; shwrs inc; el pnts (8A) €3; gas, shops 400m; snacks; bar; playgrnd; lake sw & beach adj; fishing; canoeing; tennis 500m; golf 5km; wifi; adv bkg; red long stay; CKE/CCI. "Lovely, lakeside site; ltd san facs stretched if site full; popular with school parties high ssn; poss unrel opening dates." 1 May-30 Sep. € 11.50 2010*

MORNAY SUR ALLIER see St Pierre le Moûtier *4H4*

MUIDES SUR LOIRE *4G2* (1km N Rural) *47.67191, 1.52596* **Camp Municipal Belle Vue, Ave de la Loire, 41500 Muides-sur-Loire [02 54 87 01 56 or 02 54 87 50 08 (Mairie); fax 02 54 87 01 25; mairie.muides@wanadoo.fr; www.muides.fr]** Fr A10/E5/E60 exit junc 16 S onto D205. Turn R onto D2152 then D112 over rv. Site on S bank of rv on D112 W of bdge. Tight U-turn into site fr N. Med, mkd pitch, pt shd; wc; chem disp/mv service pnt; shwrs inc; el pnts (6A) €3.90 (poss long lead req),(poss rev pol); gas in vill; Indtte; shops 200m; rest, snacks adj; playgrnd; rv fishing adj; sw 4km; cycling; dogs €2; vehicle barrier; quiet; no ccard acc; CKE/CCI. "Neat, clean, basic, spacious site; ladies shwrs need upgade (2011); gd views over rv; some pitches by fast-flowing (unfenced) rv; little shd; excel cycling." ♦ 1 May-15 Sep. € 15.47 2014*

MUIDES SUR LOIRE *4G2* (6km E Rural) *47.64803, 1.61165* **Camp Municipal du Cosson, Route de la Cordellerie, 41220 Crouy-sur-Cosson [02 54 87 08 81; fax 02 54 87 59 44; mairie-de-crouy-sur-cosson@wanadoo.fr]** Fr Muides-sur-Loire, take D103 E dir Crouy-sur-Cosson. In vill, turn R onto D33 dir Chambord. Site 200m fr village, well sp. Med, mkd pitch, pt shd; wc; shwrs inc; el pnts (6A) inc (poss rev pol); Indry rm; shops 500m; tradsmn; rest 300m; snacks; bar 300m; BBQ; playgrnd; rv fishing nr; few statics; dogs; phone; adv bkg; quiet; CKE/CCI. "V pleasant site; woodland setting; nr Rv Loire; poss long-stay workers." 1 Apr-15 Oct. € 15.55 2014*

MUIDES SUR LOIRE *4G2* (500m S Rural) *47.66611, 1.52916* **Camping Le Château des Marais, 27 Rue de Chambord, 41500 Muides-sur-Loire [02 54 87 05 42; fax 02 54 87 05 43; chateau.des.marais@wanadoo.fr; www.chateau-des-marais.com]** Exit A10 at junc 16 sp Chambord & take D2152 sp Mer, Chambord, Blois. At Mer take D112 & cross Rv Loire; at Muides-sur-Loire x-rds cont strt on for 800m; then turn R at Camping sp; site on R in 800m. Lge, mkd pitch, pt sl, shd; htd wc; chem disp; mv service pnt; all serviced pitches; baby facs; sauna; shwrs inc; el pnts (6A) inc (poss rev pol); gas; Indtte (inc dryer); shop; rest, snacks; bar; BBQ; playgrnd; htd covrd pool complex; waterslides; paddling pool; jaccuzi; lake fishing; watersports nrby; cycle hire; tennis; games area; games rm; wifi (€3 per day); TV; 50% statics (tour ops); dogs €6; twin-axles acc (rec check in adv); Eng spkn; adv bkg; ccard acc; red low ssn; CKE/CCI. "Busy lively site in wooded area in chateau grnds; gd sized pitches; excel, clean san facs; friendly staff; plenty of gd quality children's play equipment; sh walk to rv; conv Loire chateaux; plenty to do in area; mkt Sat Blois; pitches grass, can be a problem when wet." ♦ 8 May-13 Sep. € 60.00 SBS - L10 2014*

NANCAY *4G3* (500m NW Rural) *47.35215, 2.18522* **Camp Municipal des Pins, Route de Salbris, La Chaux, 18330 Nançay [02 48 51 81 80 or 02 48 51 81 35 (Mairie); fax 02 48 51 80 60; info@les-pins-camping.com; www.les-pins-camping.com]** Site on D944 fr Salbris twd Bourges clearly sp on L immed bef ent Nançay. Med, mkd pitch, hdstg, shd; htd wc; chem disp; shwrs inc; el pnts (6A) inc; gas; Indtte; shops 1km; playgrnd; tennis; golf 2km; fishing; 50% statics; no twin-axles; adv bkg; quiet; CKE/CCI. "Lovely spot in pine woods; friendly recep; clean san facs; poor site lighting; beautiful vill; gd walking; reception open am and pm." 20 Apr- 08 Sep. € 9.40 2014*

NERET *4H3* (3km N Rural) *46.58885, 2.13425* **Campsite Le Bonhomme, Mulles 36400 Neret [02 54 31 46 11; info@camping-lebonhomme.com; www.camping-lebonhomme.com]** Fr Vierzon on the A20 take exit 12 to Chateauroux, then the D943 twds Montlucon.Turn L at Neret exit and foll Aire Naturelle signs. Site is 2km beyond Neret on L. Sm, mkd pitch; hdstg; sl, pt shd; wc; chem disp; mv service pnt; shwr; el pnts(6A); Indtte; tradsmn; rest; games area; BBQ; wifi; Eng spkn; adv bkg; quiet. "Excel." 1 Apr-1 Oct. € 23.40 2014*

NEUNG SUR BEUVRON *4G3* (500m NE Rural) *47.53893, 1.81488* **FFCC Camp Municipal de la Varenne, 34 Rue de Veilleas, 41210 Neung-sur-Beuvron [tel/fax 02 54 83 68 52 or 06 27 92 39 14 (mob); camping.lavarenne@wanadoo.fr; www.neung-sur-beuvron.fr/camping]** On A10 heading S take Orléans Sud exit & join N20 S. At end of La Ferté-St Aubin take D922 SW twd Romorantin-Lanthenay. In 20km R onto D925 to Neung. Turn R at church pedestrian x-ing in cent of vill ('stade' sp), R at fork (white, iron cross) & site on R in 1km. Site by rvside. Fr A71 exit junc 3 onto D923; turn R onto D925 & as above. Sm, hdg/mkd pitch, pt sl, pt shd; wc; chem disp; mv service pnt; shwrs inc; el pnts (6A) €3.10; gas; Indtte; shops 1km; tradsmn; rest, bar 500m; playgrnd; tennis; few statics; dogs; poss cr (Aug); Eng spkn; adv bkg; v quiet; ccard acc. "Friendly, helpful warden; gd, immac facs; lge pitches; barrier clsd 2200-0800; vg cent for hiking, cycling, birdwatching; mkt Sat; excel well maintained site." Easter-20 Oct. € 12.20 2014*

"That's changed – Should I let The Club know?"

If you find something on site that's different from the site entry, fill in a report and let us know. See www.caravanclub.co.uk/europereport.

NONANCOURT *4E2* (4km E Urban) *48.76410, 1.23686* **Camp Municipal du Pré de l'Eglise, Rue Pré de l'Eglise, 28380 St Rémy-sur-Avre [02 37 48 93 87 or 02 37 62 52 00 (LS); fax 02 37 48 80 15; mairiesaintremy2@wanadoo.fr; www.ville-st-remy-sur-avre.fr]** Fr Dreux take N12 W to St Rémy; strt over 1st rndabt & at traff lts complex in 500m turn R & then immed R & foll site sp. Fr Evreux (W) on N12 to St Rémy; after x-ing rv bdge at traff lts complex strt ahead to rndabt (no L turn at traff lts), then immed R at end rv bdge as above. Site clearly sp in vill cent, sp 'Oscar' is for sports cent adj. NB Speed ramps on site app rd. Sm, hdg/mkd pitch (some grouped x 4), pt shd; wc; chem disp; fam bthrm; shwrs inc; el pnts (6A) €2.83 (poss rev pol); Indtte (inc dryer); tradsmn; rest 500m; playgrnd; tennis & trout fishing adj; TV; dogs; phone; poss cr; Eng spkn; adv bkg rec high ssn; factory adj poss noisy; ccard not acc; CKE/CCI. "Pleasant, popular, well-kept NH nr rv; welcoming warden; clean facs, some modern, ltd low ssn; no twin-axles (but negotiable); some pitches poss diff access; vill in walking dist; a gd find; Carrefour with fuel 1km; excel site in middle of vill; warm welcome. ♦ 1 Apr-30 Sep. € 15.65 2014*

NOUAN LE FUZELIER *4G3* (700m S Urban) *47.53328, 2.03508* **Camping La Grande Sologne, Rue des Peupliers, 41600 Nouan-le-Fuzelier [02 54 88 70 22; fax 02 54 88 41 74; info@campingrandesologne.com; www.campingrandesologne.com]** On E side of D2020, at S end of Nouan opp rlwy stn. Sp fr town cent & opp rlwy stn. NB Sat Nav not rec. Med, mkd pitch, pt shd; wc (some cont); chem disp; mv service pnt; baby facs; shwrs inc; el pnts (10A) €3 ; Indtte; shops 800m; tradsmn; playgrnd; htd pool adj; tennis; games area; fishing; golf 15km; 2% statics; wifi; dogs €1; poss cr; Eng spkn; adv bkg; quiet; red long stay/low ssn; CKE/CCI. "Pretty site adj lake (no sw); some pitches boggy when wet; facs poss stretched high ssn; ltd facs end of ssn & poss unclean; public park at ent to site, but quiet; rec arr early; excel NH; phone for entry low ssn; excel site; office open 0700-1500; voucher for nrby sw pool; san facs dated; friendly owners." 1 Apr-15 Oct. € 32.00 (CChq acc) 2014*

"I like to fill in the reports as I travel from site to site"

You'll find report forms at the back of this guide, or you can fill them in online at www.caravaclub.co.uk/europereport.

ONZAIN *4G2* (4km N Rural) *47.52620, 1.18718* **Camping Domaine de Dugny, 45 Route de Chambon-sur-Cisse, 41150 Onzain [02 54 20 70 66; fax 02 54 33 71 69; info@dugny.fr; www.siblu.com/domainededugny]** Exit A10 junc 17 Blois onto D952 dir Tours. After 16km at rndabt at bdge to Chaumont, turn N dir Onzain. Take D45 N dir Chambon-sur-Cisse to Cabinette. Site sp on a minor rd to L, beside sm lake. Site well sp fr Onzain cent. Lge, hdg/mkd pitch, hdstg, pt sl, pt shd; htd wc; chem disp; mv service pnt; serviced pitches; baby facs; fam bthrm; shwrs inc; el pnts (6-10A) inc; gas; Indtte; shop; tradsmn; rest, snacks; bar; BBQ; playgrnd; htd pool & paddling pool; waterslide; lake sw & 10km; fishing; cycle hire; games rm; games area; golf 8km; boat hire; entmnt; ultra-light flights; internet; TV rm; 90% statics; dogs €4.50; train 4km; Eng spkn; adv bkg; quiet; ccard acc; red low ssn; CKE/CCI. "Peaceful site; welcoming; clean san facs, but ltd low ssn; gd facs for children; poss diff in wet weather; chateaux close by - World Heritage site; gd NH." ♦ 9 Apr-1 Oct. € 45.00 2010*

ONZAIN *4G2* (1.5km SE Urban) *47.49081, 1.18847* **Camp Municipal, Rue de la Liberté, 41150 Onzain [02 54 20 85 15 or 02 54 51 20 40 (Mairie); fax 02 54 20 74 34; marie@ville-onzain.fr; www.ville-onzain.fr]** Fr N of Chaumont-sur-Loire, at rndabt at junc D952 & D1 take D1 N twds Onzain then take 1st turn on R. Foll sp. Sm, hdg pitch, pt sl, pt shd; wc (some cont); chem disp; mv service pnt; shwrs inc; el pnts (10A) €2 (poss rev pol); gas; Indtte; shops, rest 500m; playgrnd; dogs €1.53; no twin-axle vans; gates locked 2000-0800; poss cr; rd & rlwy noise; ccard not acc; CKE/CCI. "Cent for Loire chateaux; clsd 2200-0800." ♦ 1 May-15 Sep. € 7.80 2010*

www.lesalicourts.com
My Holiday ?
My little prince discovered the baby pool and swims like Nemo. My eldest has made good friends with the ponies. Their dad has been improving his handicap on the 9 hole golf course!!! And me? I have learnt the meaning of total relaxation. You see when my family is happy I am too, so for once I can think about only me.
ovely campsite located
he heart of Loire Valley
the whole family
ly perfect world
nty of activities to share with your family :
lness centre, spa, gym, heated pools,
e pool, slides and water park,
ole golf, tennis court, football,
eyball, basketball, kayaking,
nery, bike rental, fishing,
club.
Alicourts
300 Pierrefitte-sur-Sauldre
+33 (0) 2 54 88 63 34
+33 (0) 2 54 88 58 40
@lesalicourts.com
alan rogers
LeadingCampings
les alicourts
resort by nature

ONZAIN *4G2* (6km W Rural) *47.51030, 1.10400* **Yelloh! Village Le Parc du Val de Loire, 155 Route de Fleuray, 41150 Mesland [02 54 70 27 18; fax 02 54 70 21 71; parcduvaldeloire@orange.fr; www.parcduvaldeloire.com / www.yellohvillage.co.uk]** Fr Blois take D952 SW twd Amboise. Approx 16km outside Blois turn R to Onzain & foll sp to Mesland; go thro Mesland vill & turn L dir Fleuray; site on R after 1.5km. Lge, hdg/mkd pitch, pt sl, pt shd; wc; chem disp; mv service pnt; some serviced pitches; baby facs; shwrs inc; fam bthrm; el pnts (10A) inc; gas; lndtte (inc dryer); shop; tradsmn; rest, snacks; bar; BBQ (charcoal/gas); playgrnd; 2 htd pools (1 covrd); paddling pool; waterslide; tennis; games area; cycle hire; wine-tasting; wifi; entmnt; games/TV rm; 30% statics; dogs €4; no twin-axles; Eng spkn; adv bkg; ccard acc; red low ssn/CKE/CCI. "Secluded site; excursions to vineyards; mkt Thu Onzain; excel." ♦ 11 Apr-20 Sep. € 35.00 SBS - L02 2011*

ORLEANS *4F3* (10km E Rural) *47.88830, 2.02744* **Camp Municipal Les Pâtures, 55 Chemin du Port, 45430 Chécy [02 38 91 13 27; camping@checy.fr; www.checy.fr]** Take D960 E twd Châteauneuf. In Chécy, foll site sp. Access thro town via narr rds. Sm, hdg pitch, pt shd; wc; chem disp; mv service pnt; shwrs €0.30/3 mins; el pnts (16A) €3.80; lndtte; shop 1km; BBQ; tennis; fishing; golf 5km; no statics; dogs €1; twin-axles extra; Eng spkn; adv bkg; some noise fr adj site; CKE/CCI. "Vg, well-run site on Rv Loire; vg location; friendly, helpful warden; gd san facs; conv Orléans; poss open bef & after dates given; popular NH." ♦ 30 May-2 Oct. € 12.00 2011*

"We must tell The Club about that great site we found"

Get your site reports in by mid-August and we'll do our best to get your updates into the next edition.

ORLEANS *4F3* (5km S Rural) *47.85603, 1.92555* **Camp Municipal d'Olivet, Rue du Pont-Bouchet, 45160 Olivet [02 38 63 53 94; fax 02 38 63 58 96; infos@camping-olivet.org; www.camping-olivet.org]** To avoid height restriction, best app fr A71 exit junc 2 onto N271 dir Orléans-La Source. Cont on N271 until rd crosses N20 into Rue de Bourges. Pass commercial estate & hotel on L & turn L at traff lts into Rue de Châteauroux. Pass university (Parc Technologique), cross tramway & turn L at traff lts onto D14, Rue de la Source, then in 500m turn R (watch for pharmacy on L & green site sp) into Rue du Pont-Bouchet (narr rd). Site well sp on D14. NB Beware height restrictions on junc underpasses in Orléans cent. Sm, hdg pitch, pt sl, pt shd; htd wc); baby facs; chem disp; mv service pnt; shwrs inc; el pnts (16A) €3.10; lndtte; shop on site; tradsmn; snacks; playgrnd; wifi; dogs €2.05; bus 400m; tram 2km (secure car park); poss cr; Eng spkn; adv bkg rec, confirm by tel bef 1800 (booking fee & dep); quiet - poss noisy at w/end; ccard not acc; red low ssn; CKE/CCI. "Well-run, busy site by Rv Loiret; friendly; excel clean san facs; guided tours of Orléans by site staff; gd walking; vineyards nr; vg." ♦ 5 Apr-11 Oct. € 19.50 2014*

ORLEANS *4F3* (10km SW Urban) *47.85539, 1.75352* **Camp Municipal Fontaine de Rabelais, Chemin de la Plage, 45130 St Ay [02 38 88 44 44 (Mairie); fax 02 38 88 82 14; maire@ville-saint-ay.fr; www.ville-saint-ay.fr]** Exit A10/E60 at junc 15 Meung-sur-Loire onto N152 dir Orléans, sp La Chapelle-St Mesmin; site sp on app to St Ay on N bank Rv Loire. Fr A71 exit junc 1 dir Blois & Beaugency onto N152. Lge, pt sl, pt shd; wc; chem disp; mv service pnt; shwrs inc; el pnts (6A) inc (poss rev pol); gas; shops 500m; tradsmn; rest 500m; BBQ; playgrnd; rv fishing & boating adj; dogs; phone; bus 500m; no twin-axles; Eng spkn; adv bkg; quiet but some rlwy noise; ccard not acc; red long stay; CKE/CCI. "Pleasant, clean, tidy site on Rv Loire; excel modern facs for sm site but poss stretched high ssn; rvside cycling/walking; conv Orléans & chateaux; poss early closure or late opening - rec call in adv to check; perfect NH." ♦ 15 Apr-31 Oct. € 14.20 2014*

ORLEANS *4F3* (3km W Urban) *47.89492, 1.86196* **Camp Municipal Gaston Marchand, Rue de la Roche, 45140 St Jean-de-la-Ruelle [02 38 88 39 39 or 02 38 79 33 00 (Mairie); fax 02 38 79 33 62; sports@ville-saintjeandelaruelle.fr; www.ville-saintjeandelaruelle.fr]** App Orléans fr Blois on D2152/D152; 500m after passing under A71, turn R into Rue de la Roche. Or app Orléans fr E on D2151/D215; 1km after passing Pont de l'Europe (still on D2151/D215) turn L into Rue de la Roche. Site sp. Med, mkd pitch, pt sl, pt shd; wc (some cont); chem disp; shwrs inc; el pnts (6A) €2.60; gas; shops 2km; pool 1.5km; dogs €1.10; bus; poss cr; adv bkg; some rd noise. "Well-kept site on bank of Rv Loire; ltd san facs; gd value; conv Orléans; NH only." 1 Jul-31 Aug. € 9.80 2011*

PIERREFITTE SUR SAULDRE *4G3* (6km NE Rural) *47.54444, 2.19138* **Les Alicourts Resort, Domaine des Alicourts, 41300 Pierrefitte-sur-Sauldre [02 54 88 63 34; fax 02 54 88 58 40; info@lesalicourts.com; www.lesalicourts.com]** Fr S of Lamotte-Beuvron, turn L on D923. After 14km turn R on D24E sp Pierrefitte. After 750m turn L, foll sp to site approx 750m on R. Med, pt shd; wc; mv service pnt; chem disp; baby facs; shwrs inc; el pnts (6A) inc; lndtte; shop; rest, snacks; bar; BBQ; playgrnd; 3 pools; waterslide; tennis; lake sw; kayak/pedalo hire; skating rink; cycle hire; fitness cent; games rm; entmnt; some statics; dogs €7; extra for lakeside pitches; poss cr (but roomy); Eng spkn; adv bkg; quiet; ccard acc; red low ssn; CKE/CCI. "Excel, peaceful site; gd, clean facs; v lge pitches." ♦ 29 Apr-6 Sep. € 52.00 2011*

See advert on previous page

⊞ **PITHIVIERS** *4F3* (8km S Rural) *48.10365, 2.24142* **Camping Le Clos des Tourterelles, Rue des Rendillons, 45300 Bouzonville-aux-Bois [02 38 33 01 00]** S fr Pithiviers on D921 twds Jargeau; enter Bouzonville; turn R immed bef cafe; site 500m on R; sp in vill. Med, pt shd; htd wc; chem disp; shwrs inc; el pnts (16A) inc; lndtte; shop 8km; playgrnd; 90% statics; adv bkg; quiet; CKE/CCI. "Ltd space for tourers - phone ahead rec; friendly, helpful owners; gd NH; cash only." ♦ € 15.00 2014*

POILLY LEZ GIEN see Gien *4G3*

PREUILLY see Mehun sur Yevre *4H3*

RICHELIEU *4H1* (500m S Rural) *47.00774, 0.32078* **Camp Municipal, 6 Ave de Schaafheim, 37120 Richelieu [02 47 58 15 02 / 02 47 58 10 13 (mob); commune-de-richelieu@wanadoo.fr; www.tourisme-richelieu.fr]** Fr Loudun, take D61 to Richelieu, D749 twd Châtellerault; site sp. Sm, hdg/mkd pitch, pt shd; wc; chem disp; shwrs inc; el pnts (5-15A); Indtte; shop nr; playgrnd; pool 500m; fishing; tennis; quiet; CKE/CCI. "Phone ahead to check site open low ssn; clean site and facs; gd value." ♦ 15 May-15 Sep. € 10.00 2014*

RILLE *4G1* (4km W Rural) *47.45750, 0.21840* **Camping Huttopia Rillé, Base de Loisirs de Pincemaille, Lac de Rillé, 37340 Rillé [02 47 24 62 97; fax 02 47 24 63 61; rille@huttopia.com; www.huttopia.com]** Fr N or S D749 to Rillé, foll sp to Lac de Pincemaille, site sp on S side of lake. Med, shd; htd wc; chem disp; mv service pnt; baby facs; fam bthrm; shwrs inc; el pnts (6-10A) €4.20-6.20; shop; rest, snacks; bar; playgrnd; htd pool; lake sw & beach adj; fishing; watersports; tennis; games rm; some statics; dogs €3.50; sep car park; adv bkg. "Peaceful site; vg walking; excel." 24 Apr-5 Nov. € 24.00 2014*

ROCHE POSAY, LA *4H2* (3km E Rural) *46.78274, 0.86942* **Camp Municipal Les Bords de Creuse, Rue de Pont, 37290 Yzeures-sur-Creuse [tel/fax 02 47 94 48 32 or 02 47 94 55 01 (Mairie); www.yzeuressurcreuse.com]** Fr Châtellerault take D725 E twds La Roche-Posay; after x-ing Rv Creuse, turn L onto D750 twds Yzeures-sur-Creuse; at traff lts in vill turn S onto D104; site on R in 200m at T-junc. Med, mkd pitch, pt sl, pt shd; wc; chem disp; shwrs inc; el pnts (6A) inc; Indtte; shop 500m BBQ; pool, rv sw, tennis adj; games rm; dogs; quiet. ♦ 15 Jun-31 Aug. € 15.40 2013*

ROMORANTIN LANTHENAY *4G2* (500m E Urban) *47.35486, 1.75568* **Camping de Tournefeuille, Rue de Long Eaton, 41200 Romorantin-Lanthenay [02 54 76 16 60; fax 02 54 76 00 34; camping.romo@wanadoo.fr; www.ethicetapes-sologne.com]** Fr town cent on D724 to Salbis, foll sp thro several traff lts over bdge turn R into Rue de Long-Eaton, site sp. Med, pt shd; htd wc; shwrs inc; el pnts (10A) €3; gas; shop 500m; snacks; pool adj; playgrnd; fishing; cycle hire; wifi; dogs free; quiet; red low ssn. "Rv walk to town rec." 1 Apr-30 Sep. € 15.00 (3 persons) 2010*

ROSNAY *4H2* (500m N Rural) *46.70647, 1.21161* **Camp Municipal Les Millots, Route de St Michel-en-Brenne, 36300 Rosnay [02 54 37 80 17 (Mairie); fax 02 54 37 02 86; rosnay-mairie@wanadoo.fr]** NE on D27 fr Le Blanc to Rosnay; site sp 500m N of Rosnay on D44. Sm, some mkd pitch, pt shd; htd wc; chem disp; baby facs; shwrs inc; el pnts (6-10A) €2-3.50 (poss rev pol); Indtte; rest & shop 500m; BBQ; playgrnd; lake fishing; cycling; tennis; dogs; phone; poss cr; adv bkg; quiet; CKE/CCI. "Lovely, tranquil, popular site; well-kept; excel modern san facs; warden collects fees twice daily; lakeside walks; excel walking, cycling, birdwatching & fishing; gd base for exploring Brenne National Park; vg value; excel." ♦ 16 Feb-15 Nov. € 8.50 2014*

⊞ **ST AIGNAN SUR CHER** *4G2* (7km N Rural) *47.32361, 1.36983* **FFCC Camping Domaine du Bien Vivre, 13-15 Route du Petit Village, 41140 St Romain-sur-Cher [02 54 71 73 74; fax 02 54 71 72 81; domainedubienvivire@orange.fr; http://domainedubienvivre.pagespro-orange.fr]** Fr St Aignan-sur-Cher N on D675; in 6km in St Romain-sur-Cher site sp to L; foll sps for 3km. Sm, mkd pitch, pt sl, pt shd; wc; chem disp (wc); shwrs inc; el pnts (6A) inc; shops & bar 3km; shops, rest & snacks 6km; BBQ; playgrnd; dogs; Eng spkn; quiet; ccard acc; CKE/CCI. "A vineyard site; helpful owner; ltd facs in winter; sale of wines; conv Blois; gd." € 13.50 2010*

ST AIGNAN SUR CHER *4G2* (2km SE Rural) *47.26530, 1.38875* **Camping Les Cochards, 1 Rue du Camping, Seigy, 41110 St Aignan-sur-Cher [02 54 75 15 59 or 06 72 09 45 24 (mob); fax 02 54 75 44 72; camping@lesclochards.com; www.lescochards.com]** On D17 heading SE fr St Aignan twd Seigy on S bank of Rv Cher. Lge, mkd pitch, pt shd; htd wc; chem disp; mv service pnt; baby facs; shwrs inc; el pnts (5-10A) €3.80; Indtte (inc dryer); sm shop; snacks; bar; BBQ; playgrnd; pool; rv sw adj; rv fishing; canoeing; games area; horseriding 3km; wifi; entmnt; TV rm; 20% statics; dogs €1.60; phone; Eng spkn; quiet; ccard acc; red low ssn; CKE/CCI. "Attractive, open site; helpful owners; gd san facs; recep clsd 20.00; some pitches waterlogged after rain; easy walk to attractive town; excel; discount vouchers avail for local attractions." ♦ 1 Apr-15 Oct. € 32.00 (CChq acc) 2014*

ST AIGNAN SUR CHER *4G2* (4km NW Rural) *47.29411, 1.33041* **Camp Municipal Le Port, 3 rue du Passeur, 41110 Mareuil-sur-Cher [tel/fax 02 54 75 10 01; camping-leport@orange.fr; www.camping-leport.fr]** Fr St Aignan take D17 twd Tours (on S bank of Cher); site in 4km in vill of Mareuil-sur-Cher behind church, thro new archway, on Rv Cher. By Mareuil chateau. Or fr A85 sp. Sm, mkd pitch, pt shd; htd wc; chem disp; shwrs inc; el pnts (16A) €5.50; ice/gas 50m; shop & baker 100m; supmkt adj; rest 4km; playgrnd; rv sw (shgl beach); fishing; canoe hire; internet at supmkt; dogs €2; Eng spkn; quiet, but some rd noise & poss events in chateau; no ccard acc; CKE/CCI. "Beautiful, simple, rvside site; friendly staff; clean san facs but ltd; opening/closing dates variable, phone ahead to check; if office clsd enquire at supmkt adj (same owners); no access 1300-1500; diff lge o'fits; no twin-axles; m'vans extra; gd touring area." ♦ 15 Apr-30 Sep. € 28.60 2013*

ST AMAND MONTROND *4H3* (3km SW Rural) *46.71258, 2.49000* **Camp Municipal La Roche, Rue de la Roche, 18200 St Amand-Montrond [tel/fax 02 48 96 09 36; camping-la-roche@wanadoo.fr; www.st-amand-tourisme.com]** Exit A71/E11 junc 8 dir St Amand-Montrond on D300. Then foll sp to Montluçon on D2144 until rndabt on canal, turn R onto Quai Pluviôse/Rue de la Roche, site on R. Site sp on far side of town. Med, shd, pt sl; htd wc (some cont); shwrs inc; chem disp (wc); el pnts (5A) €2.90 (poss rev pol); Indtte (inc dryer); shops 900m; playgrnd; pool nr; rv fishing; tennis; wifi; entmnt; dogs; phone; quiet; CKE/CCI. "Popular NH, rec arr by 1700 high ssn; helpful warden; clean facs; tight for lge o'fits; rvside walk to pleasant town; gd." ♦ 1 Apr-30 Sep. € 17.60 2014*

ST AMAND MONTROND *4H3* (8km NW Rural) *46.77033, 2.42907* **FFCC Camping Les Platanes, 18200 Bruère-Allichamps [02 48 61 06 69 or 02 48 61 02 68 (Mairie); www.bruere-allichamps.fr]** Site on N edge of town on rvside. Sm, pt shd; wc; chem disp; shwrs €1; el pnts (10A) inc; shops 10 min walk; tradsmn; snacks; playgrnd; rv fishing; quiet. "Lovely surroundings; san facs dated but clean; friendly staff; level walk to interesting vill; excel; vill is cent of France; site is like lge CL." 1 May-30 Sep. € 9.00 2014*

ST AVERTIN see Tours *4G2*

STE CATHERINE DE FIERBOIS see Ste Maure de Touraine *4H2*

ST FLORENT SUR CHER *4H3* (7km SE Rural) *46.93663, 2.27071* **Camp Intercommunal, 6 Rue de l'Abreuvoir, 18400 Lunery [02 48 68 07 38 or 02 48 23 22 08; fax 02 48 55 26 78; fercher@fr-oleane.com]** Fr N151 turn S onto D27 at St Florent-sur-Cher, cont for 7km, site in vill cent of Lunery. Sm, hdg/mkd pitch, pt shd; wc; chem disp; mv service pnt; shwrs inc; el pnts (6A) €3.50 (poss rev pol); shop, rest in vill; playgrnd; fishing; tennis nr; no statics; bus 200m, train in vill; phone 100m; Eng spkn; red long stay; CKE/CCI. "Charming, peaceful, rvside site; quiet even high ssn; gd clean san facs; liable to flood low ssn - phone ahead to check open; gd." ♦ 15 Apr-15 Sep. € 15.00 2009*

ST GAULTIER *4H2* (300m W Rural) *46.63470, 1.42172* **Camp Municipal L'Illon, Rue de Limage, 36800 St Gaultier [02 54 47 11 22 or 02 54 01 66 00 (Mairie); fax 02 54 01 66 09; st-gaultier.mairie@wanadoo.fr; www.mairie-saintgaultier.fr]** Site well sp in town. V narr thro town - best app fr W. NB App down short, steep hill with sharp R turn into site ent. Med, mkd pitch, pt sl, pt shd; wc (some cont); shwrs inc; el pnts inc; gas; shops 500m; playgrnd; rv & fishing 50m; quiet. "Lovely, peaceful setting nr rv; pitch yourself, warden calls; site ent poss too narr for twin-axles/ lge o'fits; gd cycle path on old rlwy track nrby." Easter-30 Sep. € 8.50 2010*

ST GAULTIER *4H2* (1km W Rural) *46.63406, 1.40863* **Camping L'Oasis du Berry, Rue de la Pierre Plate, 36800 St Gaultier [02 54 47 17 04; www.campoasisduberry.com]** Appr fr W (fr Le Blanc) on D951; turn R at sp St Gaultier, then foll sp L'Oasis du Berry. Look out for sp in vill. Med, hdg/mkd pitch, terr, pt shd; wc; chem disp; shwrs inc; el pnts (4-10A) €2.50-3.50; lndtte (inc dryer); shop; tradsmn; rest, snacks; takeaway; bar; BBQ; playgrnd; htd pool; games area; wifi; 60% statics; dogs €1.40; Eng spkn; adv bkg; quiet; CKE/CCI. "Pleasant site in wooded surroundings; nice clean san facs; gd pool; gd walks nrby; nr Voie Verte track; nr Brenne Regional Park; most pitches sl; gd." 1 Apr-6 Nov. € 19.00 2014*

ST JEAN FROIDMENTEL see Cloyes sur le Loir *4F2*

ST LAURENT NOUAN see Beaugency *4F2*

STE MAURE DE TOURAINE *4H2* (6km NE Rural) *47.14831, 0.65453* **Camping Le Parc de Fierbois, 37800 Ste Catherine-de-Fierbois [02 47 65 43 35; fax 02 47 65 53 75; contact@fierbois.com; www.fierbois.com / www.les-castels.com]** S on D910 fr Tours, thro Montbazon & cont twd Ste Maure & Châtellerault. About 16km outside Montbazon nr vill of Ste Catherine look for site sp. Turn L off main rd & foll sp to site. Or exit A10 junc 25 onto D760E, then D910 N sp Tours; in 6.5 km turn R to Ste Catherine-de-Fierbois; site on L 1.5km past vill. Lge, hdg/mkd pitch, pt shd; wc; chem disp; mv service pnt; baby facs; shwrs inc; el pnts (10A) €5; lndtte (inc dryer); shop; rest, snacks; bar; BBQ; playgrnd; 2 htd pools (1 covrd); waterslide; paddling pool; sand/shgl beach at lake; boating; fishing; tennis; cycle hire; games area; games rm; wifi; entmnt; TV; statics; dogs free; twin-axles acc (rec check in adv); poss cr; Eng spkn; adv bkg; ccard acc; red low ssn; CKE/CCI. "Excel, well-kept family site; helpful staff; gd touring base; peaceful low ssn; rec." ♦ 19 May-6 Sep. € 44.00 SBS - L20 2011*

See advertisement

STE MAURE DE TOURAINE *4H2* (1.5km SE Rural) *47.10483, 0.62574* **Camp Municipal Marans, Rue de Toizelet, 37800 Ste Maure-de-Touraine [02 47 65 44 93 / 06 72 18 05 41; fax 02 47 65 65 76; www.tourisme-saintemauredetouraine.fr]** Fr A10 take Ste Maure exit junc 25 & foll D760 twd Loches. At 4th rndabt turn L & then immed R. Site on R in 500m. Site sp fr m'way. Med, mkd pitch, pt shd; wc; chem disp; mv service pnt; shwrs inc; el pnts (10A) €3.20 (poss long cables req); supmkt 500m; shops, rest, bar 1km; BBQ; playgrnd; pool 1.5km; fishing; tennis; roller blade court; wifi; dogs €1.42; phone; Eng spkn; adv bkg; quiet. "Well-kept, basic site; cheerful staff; gd, clean facs - poss stretched when busy; if office clsd site yourself; barrier down 2200-0700; late arr area outside barrier; no twin-axles; poss travellers in sep area; vg; wifi around office area." ♦ 10 Apr-30 Sep. € 7.80 2014*

⊞ **STE MAURE DE TOURAINE** *4H2* (1.5km S Rural) *47.10861, 0.61440* **Aire de Service Camping-Cars Bois de Chaudron, 37800 Ste Maure-de-Touraine [02 47 34 06 04]** Fr S on D910 dir Tours, as ent town, site on R adj junc at traff lts; sm sp on dual-c'way. Sm; wc; mv service pnt; shwrs; el pnts €2 (on only some pitches); Indtte; wifi; m'vans only. "New Aire de Service (2009); warden calls; conv N/S journeys." € 5.00 2009*

STE MAURE DE TOURAINE *4H2* (6km W Rural) *47.10705, 0.51016* **Camping du Château de la Rolandière, 37220 Trogues [tel/fax 02 47 58 53 71; contact@larolandiere.com; www.larolandiere.com]** Exit A10 junc 25 onto D760 dir Chinon & L'Ile-Bouchard. Site sp on S side of rd in 5.5km. Sm, hdg/mkd pitch, pt sl, pt shd; wc; chem disp; baby facs; shwrs inc; el pnts (10A) €4.40 (poss long lead req); gas 6km; Indtte (inc dryer); shop 4km; supmkt 9km; tradsmn; snacks; bar; BBQ; playgrnd; htd pool; paddling pool; rv & sand beach 4km; games area; games rm; wifi; TV rm; dogs €3; Eng spkn; adv bkg; quiet; red low ssn; CKE/CCI. "Beautiful, well-maintained, family-run site in chateau grnds; friendly, helpful owners; gd clean san facs; excel for young families; gd dog walking; conv Loire chateaux." ♦ Apr-30 Sep. € 24.50 2011*

ST PIERRE LE MOUTIER *4H4* (8km NW Rural) *46.81730, 3.02746* **Camp Municipal La Bruyère, 18600 Mornay-sur-Allier [02 48 74 57 01 or 02 48 74 56 07 (Mairie); www.mornaysurallier.fr]** Fr W on D2076 turn R onto D45 & foll sp. Site just bef x-ing Rv Allier. Sm, pt shd; wc; shwrs inc; el pnts (12A); shop 500m; bar 200m; quiet. "Tidy site with clean facs, run by volunteers; pitch self & warden collects fees; excel NH." 15 May-15 Sep. 2009*

ST ROMAIN SUR CHER see St Aignan sur Cher *4G2*

STE SEVERE SUR INDRE *7A4* (6km SE Rural) *46.47194, 2.14660* **Camping Pérassay, Le Bourg, 36160 Pérassay [02 54 30 63 25; camping@the-french-connection.net; www.the-french-connection.net]** Fr Ste Sévère take D917 S & after approx 6km turn L onto D71 sp Pérassay. Site on L in cent of vill opp tabac. Sm, pt sl, pt shd; wc; chem disp (wc); shwrs inc; el pnts (16A) €2.50; Indtte; BBQ; lake sw 10km; 1 static; dogs €2.50; adv bkg; quiet; red low ssn. "Lovely CL-type site in quiet location; friendly British owner; vg san facs; vg." ♦ 1 Apr-31 Oct. € 15.00 2009*

SALBRIS *4G3* (500m NE Urban) *47.43006, 2.05427* **Camping de Sologne, 8 Allée de la Sauldre, Route de Pierrefitte, 41300 Salbris [02 54 97 06 38; fax 02 54 97 33 13; campingdesologne@wanadoo.fr; www.campingdesologne.fr]** Exit A71 junc 4; take D724 bypass, then take D2020 N (do not take D724 into town); turn E onto D55 (Route de Pierrefitte); Impasse de la Sauldre leading to Allée de la Sauldre is 2nd turning on R in 200m (narr & easy to miss). Med, hdg/mkd pitch, pt shd; wc; chem disp; baby facs; shwrs inc; el pnts (10A) inc (some rev pol); gas; Indtte; shop 200m; hypmkt 1km; rest, snacks; bar high ssn; playgrnd; lake adj; fishing; boat hire; karting 6km; wifi; TV rm; 25% statics; dogs €1; phone; poss cr; Eng spkn; adv bkg; some noise fr rlwy, rd & motor circuit; ccard acc; red low ssn; CKE/CCI. "Excel, well-kept site in pleasant lakeside location; friendly, helpful owners; gd san facs poss stretched if site busy & ltd low ssn; poss scruffy early ssn (2009); gd rest; gd dog walks adj; conv NH for m'way; beautiful site by lake, easy access to town." ♦ 1 Apr-30 Sep. € 26.50 2013*

SANCERRE *4G3* (4km N Rural) *47.34215, 2.86571* **Flower Camping Les Portes de Sancerre, Quai de Loire, 18300 St Satur [02 48 72 10 88; camping.sancerre@flowercampings.com; www.camping-cher-sancerre.com]** Fr Sancerre on D955 thro cent St Satur & St Thibault. Turn L immed bef Loire bdge. Site on R in 100m. Med, hdg pitch, shd; wc; chem disp; mv service pnt; shwrs inc; el pnts (10A) inc (long lead poss req); Indtte (inc dryer); shop 500m; tradsmn; rest 500m; playgrnd; pool adj; rv sw via slipway; canoe hire adj; tennis; cycle hire; games area; entmnt; TV rm; 50% statics; dogs €2; poss cr; some Eng spkn; adv bkg; quiet, but poss noise fr public rv slipway & watersports; CKE/CCI. "Nice site; some pitches sm, some with rv view; friendly & helpful staff; gd clean san facs, rec own in peak ssn; rvside walks; gd touring cent; vg." ♦ 5 Apr-19 Oct. € 30.00 2014*

SANCERRE *4G3* (9.4km SW Rural) *47.30353, 2.74555* **Camping Crezancy en Sancerre, 9 Route de Veagues, 18300 Crezancy en Sancerre [06 12 55 69 98; campingcrezancy@orange.fr]** Fr Sancerre take D955 dir Bourges. In 5km turn R onto D22 sp Crezancy, Henrichement. After 5km at vill turn L onto D86 sp Veagues. Site 100m on L. Sm, hdg/mkd pitch, shd; wc; chem disp; fam bthrm; shwrs; el pnts (6A); Indtte (inc dryer); BBQ; cooking facs; playgrnd; dogs; phone; public transport 100m; twin axles; Eng spkn; adv bkg; quiet; CKE/CCI. "Site in Sancerre vineyards with wine tasting and purchase opportunities; gd walking & cycling, but a bit hilly; easy acc to Sancerre and The Loire; hospitable site manager; excel. ♦ 1 Apr-31 Oct. € 10.00 2014*

SAVIGNY EN VERON *4G1* (500m W Rural) *47.20059, 0.13932* **FFCC Camping La Fritillaire, Rue Basse, 37420 Savigny-en-Véron [02 47 58 03 79; fax 02 47 58 03 81; www.aquadis-loisirs.com]** Fr Montsoreau on D751 or D7 on S bank of Rv Loire, foll sp to Savigny-en-Véron & site. Med, mkd pitch, pt shd; htd wc; chem disp; mv service pnt; baby facs; shwrs inc; el pnts (10A) inc (poss rev pol); Indtte; rest, snacks & bar 500m; BBQ; playgrnd; htd, covrd pool 4km; games area (under-7s); tennis; cycle hire; horseriding; some statics; dogs €1; adv bkg; quiet; red low ssn; CKE/CCI. "Excel, peaceful site; friendly owners; gd clean facs, ltd low ssn; gd touring base Loire chateaux; vg cycle rtes; poss workers staying on site (2009)." ♦ 29 Mar - 20 Oct. € 13.00 2013*

CENTRE

SELLES SUR CHER *4G2* (300m E Rural) *47.27666, 1.55935* **Camp Municipal Les Châtaigniers, Blvd Kléber Lousteau, 41130 Selles-sur-Cher [02 54 97 67 26; camping.les.chataigniers@orange.fr; http://campingleschataigniers.e-monsite.com]** N fr Valençay on D965 dir Blois to Selles-sur-Cher; site on R, 250m after rndabt junc with D51. Med, mkd pitch, pt shd; wc; chem disp; mv service pnt (outside gate); shwrs inc; el pnts €3.50; tradsmn; shop, rest & bar 500m; BBQ; playgrnd; pool 1km; canoeing; no rv sw; 4% statics; dogs free; no twin-axles; adv bkg; quiet; CKE/CCI. "Well-kept, spacious site by Rv Cher; lge pitches; walks by rv; attractive sm town; gd." ♦ 15 Apr-24 Sep. € 7.00 2011*

SENONCHES *4E2* (500m S Rural) *48.55569, 1.03851* **Huttopia Senonches, Ave de Badouleaux, 28250 Senonches [04 37 64 22 35 or 02 37 37 81 40 (reservations); fax 04 72 85 08 02; senonches@huttopia.com; www.huttopia.com]** Fr Senonches cent take D155 dir Etang de Badouleaux, site sp. Med, pt shd; htd wc; baby facs; shwrs; el pnts (6-10A) €4.60-6.80; rest, snacks; bar; playgrnd; pool; tennis adj; cycle hire; games area; entmnt; internet; TV rm; some statics; dogs €4; adv bkg; quiet. ♦ 3 Jul-5 Nov. € 18.00 2009*

"I need an on-site restaurant"

We do our best to make sure site information is correct, but it is always best to check any must-have facilities are still available or will be open during your visit.

SERGE SUR BRAY *4F2* (500m SW Rural) *47.92268, 0.84921* **Camp Municipal, Ave de la Gare, 41170 Sargé-sur-Bray [02 54 72 73 17 (Mairie)]** E fr Le Mans on D357, turn L onto D921 to Sargé-sur-Bray, site sp. Sm, shd; wc; chem disp (wc); shwrs inc; el pnts (10A) €1; Indtte; shop, rest, snacks, bar 1km; BBQ; rv sw 100m; some statics; dogs; quiet; ccard acc; CKE/CCI. "Helpful warden; gd local shops; gd birdwatching; vg." ♦ 1 Apr-30 Sep. € 10.00 2010*

SONZAY *4G1* (500m W Rural) *47.52620, 0.45070* **Kawan Village L'Arada Parc, 88 Rue de la Baratière, 37360 Sonzay [02 47 24 72 69; fax 02 47 24 72 70; info@laradaparc.com; www.laradaparc.com]** Exit A28 junc 27 to Neuillé-Pont-Pierre; then D766 & D6 to Sonzay; turn R in town cent. Site on R on o'skirts immed past new houses; sp. Med, hdg/mkd pitch, pt sl, pt shd; wc; chem disp; mv service pnt; 20% serviced pitches; baby facs; shwrs inc; el pnts (10A) €4.10 (poss rev pol); gas; Indtte (inc dryer); shop; tradsmn; rest, snacks; bar; BBQ; playgrnd; 2 pools (1 htd, covrd); paddling pool; spa; lake sw 9km; rv fishing 500m; gym; cycle hire; games area; wifi; entmnt; TV rm; 15% statics; dogs €2; phone; bus to Tours; Eng spkn; adv bkg; quiet; ccard acc; red long stay/low ssn; CKE/CCI. "Peaceful, well-kept site; friendly, helpful owners & staff; clean, modern facs; gd views; vg rest; poss diff for lge o'fits when site full/cr; barrier clsd 2300-0800; many walks, inc in attractive orchards; 60km fr Le Mans circuit; rec." ♦ 26 Mar-1 Nov. € 30.80 2012*

SUEVRES see Blois *4G2*

SULLY SUR LOIRE *4F3* (500m NW Rural) *47.77180, 2.36200* **Camping Le Jardin de Sully, 1Route Orleans, 45600 Pope-sur-Loire [02 38 67 10 84 or 07 81 11 47 65 (mob); info-camping-lejardindesully@orange.fr; www.camping-lejardindesully.fr]** Fr N on D948 to Sully then turn R at rndabt immed bef x-ing bdge over Rv Loire onto D60 in St Père-sur-Loire, dir Châteauneuf-sur-Loire. Sp to site in 200m. Fr S thro Sully on D948, cross Rv Loire & turn L at rndabt onto D60. Well sp fr town. Med, hdg/mkd pitch, hdstg, pt shd; htd wc (some cont); chem disp; mv service pnt; baby facs; serviced pitches; shwrs inc; el pnts (10A) inc (poss rev pol); gas; Indtte; shop; tradsmn; snacks; pizzeria; bar; BBQ; playgrnd; htd, covrd pool 500m; sand beach adj; tennis; cycle hire; games rm; cycle hire; wifi; entmnt; sat TV; 18% statics; dogs €2; phone; bus; some Eng spkn; adv bkg rec; quiet; ccard acc; red low ssn/CKE/CCI. "Pleasant, well-kept, well laid-out site on rvside adj nature reserve; gd, well-kept san facs; pleasant walk along rv to town; long dist footpath (grande randonnée) along Loire passes site; gd dog walks; gd cycling; gd winter site & NH en rte S; recep might be clsd low ssn, need to phone for barrier code ent; fairy-tale chateau in Sully; gd loc; san facs inadequate; new owner keen to bring the standards up." ♦ 1 Jan-31 Dec. € 29.00 2014*

THORE LA ROCHETTE see Vendôme *4F2*

⊞ **TOURS** *4G2* (6km E Rural) *47.40226, 0.77845* **Camping Les Acacias, Rue Berthe Morisot, 37700 La Ville-aux-Dames [02 47 44 08 16 or 02 62 19 18 08 (LS); fax 02 47 46 26 65; contact@camplvad.com; www.camplvad.com]** Fr Tours take D751 E sp Amboise; after 6km at rndabt where La Ville-aux-Dames sp to R, go strt on for 200m, then turn R, site sp. Med, shd; htd wc; chem disp; mv service pnt; serviced pitch; shwrs; el pnts (10A) €4.50; gas; Indtte; sm shop; supmkt 1km; rest nrby; playgrnd; pool 500m; tennis 600m; fitness trail, mountain bike circuit, fishing 100m; wifi; 30% statics; dogs €2; bus nr; Eng spkn; adv bkg; rd & rlwy noise; CKE/CCI. "Well-kept, well-run site; excel san facs, ltd low ssn; conv town cent; many long-term residents; gd site; conv NH; lovely friendly helpful English speaking owners; lge supmkt nr; bus to city nr; childrens playgrnd; gd for long or sh stays." ♦ € 24.00 2014*

TOURS *4G2* (8km E Rural) *47.39273, 0.81085* **Camping Les Peupliers, 37270 Montlouis-sur-Loire [02 47 50 81 90 or 03 86 37 95 83; aquadis1@wanadoo.fr; www.aquadis-loisirs.com]** On D751, 2km W of vill of Montlouis. Fr N foll sp to Vouvray (keep on N side of Rv Loire to avoid Tours) & cross rv by bdge to Montlouis. Sp at last min. NB App fr E a 'Q-turn' to get into site. Lge, hdg pitch, pt shd; htd wc; chem disp; mv service pnt; baby facs; shwrs inc; el pnts (6A) €2; Indtte; shop 2km; tradsmn; playgrnd; tennis; 12% statics; dogs €1.90; Eng spkn; adv bkg; some rd & rlwy noise; ccard acc; CKE/CCI. "Clean, tidy site; poss clsd mid-Oct; lge pitches; mkt Sun in Amboise; vg." ♦ 1 Apr-31 Oct. € 15.50 (CChq acc) 2012*

TOURS *4G2 (5km SE Urban) 47.37070, 0.72305* **Camping Les Rives du Cher, 61 Rue de Rochepinard, 37550 St Avertin [02 47 27 87 47; fax 02 47 25 82 89; contact@camping-lesrivesducher.com; www.camping-lesrivesducher.com]** Fr Tours, take D976 S of rv sp Bléré/Vierzon into St Avertin vill. Take next L at traff lts over 1st of 2 bdges. Site on R in 450m, not well sp. Med, hdg/mkd pitch, some hdstg, pt shd; wc (some cont); chem disp; mv service pnt; shwrs inc; el pnts (10A) €4.20 (poss rev pol); lndtte; shops 400m; rest, snacks & bar adj; playgrnd; htd pool adj; tennis; fishing; wifi; dogs €1.20; bus nr by; phone; Eng spkn; adv bkg; quiet; ccard acc; red long stay; CKE/CCI. "Clean & tidy site but needs updating; some lge pitches; friendly owner; some resident workers; frequent bus to Tours." ♦ 1 Apr-15 Oct. € 19.00 2013*

TOURS *4G2 (8km SW Urban) 47.35530, 0.63401* **Camping La Mignardière, 22 Ave des Aubépines, 37510 Ballan-Miré [02 47 73 31 00; fax 02 47 73 31 01; info@mignardiere.com; www.mignardiere.com]** Fr A10 exit junc 24 onto N585 & D37 by-pass. At exit for Joué-lès-Tours foll sp Ballan-Miré onto D751. Turn R at 1st set traff lts & foll site sp to W of lake. Lge, hdg/mkd pitch, hdstg, pt shd; htd wc; chem disp; mv service pnt; 10% serviced pitch; baby facs; shwrs inc; el pnts (6-10A) €3.50; lndtte (inc dryer); sm shop; tradsmn; snacks; bar 200m; BBQ; playgrnd; htd, covrd pool; windsurfing & fishing 1km; tennis; cycle hire; squash; wifi; entmnt; TV rm; dogs; phone; Eng spkn; adv bkg; quiet, but some rd/rlwy noise; red low ssn; CKE/CCI. "Conv Loire valley & chateaux; friendly, helpful staff; unisex facs low ssn; gd cycle paths; vg site; rec." ♦ 1 Apr-23 Sep. € 22.00 2009*

> **"Satellite navigation makes touring much easier"**
>
> Remember most sat navs don't know if you're towing or in a larger vehicle – always use yours alongside maps and site directions.

TOURS *4G2 (8km W Rural) 47.38950, 0.59616* **Camping L'Islette, 23 Rue de Vallières, 37230 Fondettes [02 47 42 26 42; www.camping-de-lislette.ruedesloisirs.com]** Foll D952 W fr Tours twd Saumur. In approx 6km turn R at traff lts onto D276 at Port-de-Vallières. Site on L in approx 2km. Sm, hdg pitch, pt shd; wc (some cont); mv service pnt; shwrs inc; el pnts (10A) €2.50; shop 2km; playgrnd; pool 4km; dogs; bus; poss cr; adv bkg; quiet; CKE/CCI. "Pleasant site; helpful owners; facs poss stretched if site full; poss boggy when wet; conv for Langeais & Luynes chateaux." ♦ ltd 1 Apr-31 Oct. € 9.40 2013*

TOURS *4G2 (10km W Rural) 47.38110, 0.55830* **Camping Club Les Granges, Le Bourg, 37230 Luynes [02 47 55 79 05 or 01 76 61 65 94; fax 02 47 40 92 43; reception@campinglesgranges.fr; www.campinglesgranges.fr]** W fr Tours on D952 dir Saumur; in 9km turn R at Le Port-de-Luynes dir Luynes, site on R in 500m. Med, hdg/mkd pitch, pt shd; htd wc; mv service pnt; baby facs; shwrs inc; el pnts (10A) €3.70; lndtte; shops; tradsmn; snacks; bar; BBQ; playgrnd; pool; fishing 500m; tennis 700m; games area; games rm; wifi; TV; some statics; dogs €2.50; adv bkg; quiet; ccard acc. "Pleasant site; gd touring base Loire valley." ♦ 2 May-27 Sep. € 20.00 2009*

TOURS *4G2 (10km W Rural) 47.35054, 0.54964* **Camping de la Confluence, Route de Bray, 37510 Savonnières [02 47 50 00 25; fax 02 47 50 15 71; camping.confluence37@orange.fr; www.campinglaconfluence.fr/]** Fr Tours take D7 on S of Rv Cher. Site on R on ent Savonnières on rvside. Med, hdg/mkd pitch, hdstg, pt shd; wc (some cont); chem disp; mv service pnt; baby facs; shwrs; el pnts (10A) €4.20; lndtte; shops 500m; tradsmn; rest 100m; bar adj; BBQ; playgrnd; canoe hire; tennis adj; dogs €1.20; phone; bus 200m; Eng spkn; adv bkg; quiet; red low ssn; CKE/CCI. "Well-kept site with rv views; friendly, efficient staff; modern unisex san facs; some pitches narr & awnings diff; lovely vill with basic facs; gd touring base; gd birdwatching, cycling; highly rec." ♦ 25 Apr-28 Sep. € 23.00 2014*

TOURY *4F3 (1.4km S Urban) 48.19361, 1.93260* **Camp Municipal, Rue de Boissay, 28310 Toury [02 37 90 50 60 (Mairie); fax 02 37 90 58 61; mairie-toury@wanadoo.fr; www.ville-toury.fr]** Fr Orléans take N20 N. Site well sp. Sm, pt shd; wc; chem disp (wc); shwrs inc; el pnts (6A) €3; gas 1km; shop 800m; rest 200m; bar 100m; BBQ; playgrnd; no statics; dogs; poss cr' rd & rlwy noise. "NH only; warden calls; poss travellers low ssn & unclean san facs; high ssn rec arrive bef 1600 to ensure pitch." 15 Apr-15 Oct. € 10.00 2014*

TROGUES see Ste Maure de Touraine *4H2*

VALENCAY *4H2 (1km W Urban) 47.15656, 1.55202* **Camp Municipal Les Chênes, Route de Loches, 36600 Valençay [tel/fax 02 54 00 03 92 or 02 54 00 32 32]** App town fr E on D960 or N/S on D956, foll sp for D960 Luçay-le-Mâle. Ignore 1st sp for camping (Veuil); D960 is next L in town. Foll sp for pool & camping. Site adj pool mkd by flags. Sm, hdg/mkd pitch, pt shd; wc; chem disp; shwrs inc; el pnts (6A) €3.20 (poss rev pol); lndtte; shop; tradsmn; BBQ; playgrnd; htd pool adj (high ssn); tennis adj; fishing; TV rm; dogs; adv bkg; quiet; red long stay; CKE/CCI. "Excel, well-kept site in parkland with lake; lge pitches; gd, clean facs; poss muddy after heavy rain; gate clsd 2200-0700; sh walk to impressive chateau; day's drive to Calais or Le Havre ferries." ♦ ltd 1 May-30 Sep. € 12.00 2010*

VATAN *4H3 (8km N Rural) 47.13479, 1.85121* **Camp Municipal St Phalier, 2 Chemin Trompe-Souris, 18310 Graçay [02 48 51 24 14 or 02 48 51 42 07 (Mairie); fax 02 48 51 25 92; camping-gracay@wanadoo.fr; www.camping.gracay.info]** Leave A20 at junc 9 & take D83 to Graçay. On o'skts of vill turn L & immed turn L foll sp to Cent Omnisport & site. Sm, pt shd; wc (some cont); chem disp; shwrs €1.02; el pnts (10A) €2.69; rest, bar & shop 1km; tradsmn; playgrnd & pool adj; fishing; dogs €1.02; phone; Eng spkn; quiet; CKE/CCI. "Lovely, peaceful, well-kept site by sm unfenced lake & park; plenty of space lge o'fits - site yourself; excel clean san facs; poss travellers, but no problem; vill in walking dist; gd NH fr A20." 1 Apr-15 Sep. € 10.40 2014*

VATAN *4H3* (1km S Rural) *47.06540, 1.80043* **Camping Le Moulin de la Ronde (Naturist), Route de la Ronde, 36150 Vatan [02 54 49 83 28; www.moulindelaronde.com]** Fr town cent take D136 S twds A20; at supmkt turn R; site on L 500m; sp. Sm, hdg/mkt pitch, pt shd; htd wc; chem disp; shwrs inc; el pnts (10A) €2.50 (long lead poss req); gas 1km; supmkt 400m; tradsmn; snacks; bar; BBQ; playgrnd; pool; games area; games rm; dogs €1.60; adv bkg; quiet; red low ssn/ long stay; INF card req. "Pleasant, simple site; helpful owners; dated & modern san facs; mkt Wed; gd NH." 1 Apr-30 Sep. € 16.50 2011*

VATAN *4H3* (500m W Urban) *47.07131, 1.80573* **Camp Municipal de la Ruelle au Loup, Rue du Collège, 36150 Vatan [02 54 49 91 37 or 02 54 49 76 31 (Mairie); fax 02 54 49 93 72; vatan-mairie1@wanadoo.fr; www.vatan-en-berry.com]** Exit A20 junc 10 onto D922 to town cent. Take D2 dir Guilly & foll site sp - 2nd on L (easily missed). Med, hdg/ mkd pitch, pt shd; wc; mv service pnt; shwrs inc; el pnts (10A) €3 (rev pol); Indtte; shops, rests 200m; playgrnd; pool adj; adv bkg; quiet; ccard not acc; CKE/CCI. "Pleasant, well-kept site in park; spacious pitches; basic but clean san facs; twin-axles extra; site yourself, warden calls pm; easy access fr a'route; conv Loire chateaux." ♦ 15 Apr-15 Sep. € 15.00 2014*

VEIGNE see Montbazon *4G2*

VELLES see Châteauroux *4H2*

VENDOME *4F2* (500m E Urban) *47.79122, 1.07586* **Camping au Coeur de Vendôme, Rue Geoffroy-Martel, 41100 Vendôme [02 54 77 00 27; fax 02 54 89 41 01; aucoeurdevendome@camp-in-ouest.com; www.aucoeurdevendome.com]** Fr N10 by-pass foll sp for town cent; in town foll sp Camping; site adj to pool 500m. Lge, mkd pitch, pt shd; wc; chem disp; baby facs; shwrs inc; el pnts (6A) €3.40; Indry rm; shops, rest & bar 500m; BBQ; wifi; playgrnd adj; htd pool adj; rv fishing adj; games area adj; 5% statics in sep area; dogs €2.50; phone; some Eng spkn; quiet but some rd noise; ccard not acc; red long stay; CKE/CCI. "Pleasant rvside setting; new ownership (2011) & improvements in hand; clean san facs - a trek fr outer pitches; sports cent, pool & theatre adj; recep 0900-2100; barrier clsd 2200-0630; vg." ♦ 18 Apr-1 Nov. € 23.60 (CChq acc) 2014*

VENDOME *4F2* (8km W Rural) *47.80206, 0.95835* **Camp Municipal de la Bonne Aventure, Route de Cunaille, 41100 Thoré-la-Rochette [02 54 72 00 59; fax 02 54 89 41 01; camping@cpvendome.com]** Fr Vendôme take D917 twd Montoire. After 6km turn R onto D82 for Thoré; thro vill & cont to vill exit sign, foll site sp. NB: there are 2 rds to Montoire - foll sp to vill. Med, pt shd; wc; chem disp; shwrs; el pnts (5A) €2.70 (long lead poss req); Indtte; shop 2km; tradsmn; snacks; fishing & watersports adj; playgrnd; tennis; entmnt; games area; dogs €1; Eng spkn; adv bkg; CKE/ CCI. "Peaceful, pretty site by Rv Loir; well-kept facs; helpful warden; gd." 6 Jun-1 Sep. € 10.00 2010*

VERT EN DROUAIS see Dreux *4E2*

VEURDRE, LE see St Pierre le Moûtier *4H4*

VIERZON *4G3* (2.5km SW Urban) *47.20937, 2.08079* **Camp Municipal de Bellon, Route de Bellon, 18100 Vierzon [02 48 75 49 10 / 02 48 53 06 14 (ls); fax 02 48 71 40 94; campingmunicipal-vierzon@wanadoo.fr / ot-vierzon@wanadoo.fr; www.officedetourismedevierzon.com]** Fr N on A71 take A20 dir Châteauroux, leave at junc 7 onto D2020 & then D27 dir Bourges; pass Intermarché supmkt on L, after next traff lts turn L into Route de Bellon; site in 1km on R, sp. NB Do not go into town cent. Med, hdg/mkd pitch, pt sl, pt shd; wc; chem disp; mv service pnt; shwrs inc; el pnts (6A) €3 (some rev pol); gas; Indry rm; shops 1km; rest, snacks; bar; BBQ (gas/elec); playgrnd; fishing; boat hire; internet; no statics; dogs; phone; poss cr; Eng spkn; adv bkg; quiet but some rlwy noise; no ccard acc; CKE/CCI. "Attractive, well-kept site by rv; gd sized pitches but some poss diff to negotiate; gd san facs, poss tired high ssn; nice little rest o'looking rv; gates clsd 2300-0700; warden on site 1700-2200; poss travellers; ideal NH; gd site; friendly recep." ♦ 1 May-30 Sep. € 13.00 2013*

"There aren't many sites open at this time of year"

If you're travelling outside peak season remember to call ahead to check site opening dates – even if the entry says 'open all year'.

⊞ **VIERZON** *4G3* (5km NW Rural) *47.24590, 1.99000* **Aire Communale, Place de la Mairie, 18100 Méry-sur-Cher [02 48 75 38 18]** Fr Vierzon on D2076 dir Tours. Site clearly sp on L on ent Méry-sur-Cher. Sm, mkd pitch, hdstg, ltd shd; wc; chem disp; mv service pnt; el pnts inc; shop 100m; dogs; phone; bus; rd noise; m'vans only - max 48 hrs. "Well-maintained site; pay at machine on ent (ccards only); excel NH." € 5.00 2011*

VILLEFRANCHE SUR CHER *4G3* (9km SE Rural) *47.26917, 1.86265* **FFCC Camp Municipal Val Rose, Rue du Val Rose, 41320 Mennetou-sur-Cher [02 54 98 11 02 or 02 54 98 01 19 (Mairie)]** Site sp fr D976/D2076 fr Villefranche (sm white sp); site on R in SW side of vill of Mennetou. To avoid narr bdge in town fr N76 onto A20, just outside town, turn imm R, site sp after L turn. Sm, pt shd; htd wc; chem disp; shwrs inc; el pnts (6A) €2; Indtte; snacks & shops adj; rest in town; playgrnd; htd pool adj; rv adj; dogs €0.20; adv bkg; quiet. "Delightful, well-kept site; friendly, helpful warden; excel, spotless san facs; excel Indtte; pretty, walled town 5 mins walk along canal; mkt Thurs; vg value; gem of a site." ♦ 13 May-5 Sep. € 6.50 2012*

VILLIERS LE MORHIER see Maintenon *4E2*

Champagne-Ardenne

Regional Introduction

Montagne de Reims

Welcome to Champagne-Ardenne Region

Celebrated worldwide for its sparkling wine which is still produced using traditional methods, Champagne-Ardenne is also famous for its small historical towns and cities.

The region also has many links with France's best-known sons and daughters - it was the home of Joan of Arc and the burial place of Charles de Gaulle. Visit the great monuments that they left behind and walk in the footsteps of the region's famous ancestral citizens.

Nature lovers will enjoy immersing themselves in the rolling landscapes, immense forests, deep gorges and vast rivers.

Local highlights

Within this region are the homes of world-renowned champagne houses and cellars. Explore the cavernous cellars beneath the streets of Reims and Châlons-en-Champagne.

The Elektricity Festival in March is a highlight, combining contemporary and urban music, for which Reims Cathedral provides a spectacular backdrop.

Major towns and cities

- Reims – a modern and lively former capital that has kept hold of its traditions.
- Chalons-en-Champagne – the city owes its name to the Gallic people of Chalons.
- Sedan – discover the Giant of Sedan, a fortress built nearly 600 years ago.
- Chaumont – built around a 10th-century castle overlooking the Suize and Marne valleys.

Regional attractions

- Cathédrale Notre-Dame, Reims – an impressive building where the kings of France were once crowned.
- Champagne cellar visits, Epernay – travel underground to see how the regions most famous export is matured.
- Maison de L'Outil, Troyes – museum specialising in extinct trades and tools.
- Palais du Tau, Reims – former palace of the Bishops of Reims.

Find out more

www.champagne-ardenne-tourism.com
Tel: (0)3 26 77 45 00 Reims Tourist Office
Tel: (0)7 81 11 46 09 Troyes Tourist Office

SITES IN CHAMPAGNE-ARDENNE

ANDELOT BLANCHEVILLE *6F1* (1km W Rural) *48.25220, 5.29901* **Camping du Moulin, 5 Rue du Moulin, 52700 Andelot-Blancheville [03 25 32 61 28 or 03 25 01 33 31 (Mairie); fax 03 25 03 77 54; mairie.andelot@wanadoo.fr; www.camping-andelot.com]** Fr N on D974 site sp on ent Andelot-Blancheville. Foll sp & turn L onto D147. Site on R in 1km. Med, hdg/mkd pitch, hdstg, shd; htd wc; chem disp; shwrs inc; el pnts (9A) €2 (poss rev pol); Indtte; shop 1km; tradsmn; snacks; bar; playgrnd; lake/rv fishing; games rm; wifi; TV rm; 10% statics; dogs free; phone; Eng spkn; quiet; red low ssn; CKE/CCI. "Peaceful, quiet site by rv; gd NH on journey S." ♦ 15 Jun-15 Sep. € 16.50 2009*

ARC EN BARROIS *6F1* (500m W Urban) *47.95052, 5.00523* **Camp Municipal Le Vieux Moulin, 52210 Arc-en-Barrois [03 25 02 51 33 (Mairie); fax 03 25 03 82 89; mairie.arc.en.barrois@wanadoo.fr]** Exit A5 junc 24 onto D10 S to Arc-en-Barrois; turn R onto D3 thro vill; site on L on o'skirts. Or fr D65 turn L onto D6 about 4km S of Châteauvillain; site on R on D3 at ent to vill, adj rv. Med, pt shd; htd wc; chem disp; mv service pnt; shwrs inc; el pnts (6A) inc; gas in vill; shops 500m; BBQ; sm playgrnd; tennis adj; TV; dogs €2.18; wifi; phone in vill; quiet; ccard not acc; CKE/CCI. "Attractive, peaceful, well-kept site by sm rv; adj vill sports field; basic, clean san facs but need update - excel hot shwrs; warden calls early eve; gd wildlife; beautiful vill; conv NH fr A5 or longer; w/ends poss noisy due to on-site funfair." 1 May - 30 Sep. € 17.00 2014*

ARCIS SUR AUBE *4E4* (300m N Urban) *48.53907, 4.14270* **Camping de l'Ile Cherlieu, Rue de Châlons, 10700 Arcis-sur-Aube [03 25 37 98 79; fax 03 25 37 91 29; camping-arcis@hermans.cx]** Fr A26 junc 21 foll sp to Arcis. Fr town cent take D677 dir Châlons-en-Champagne. Turn R after rv bdge, site sp. Med, mkd pitch, shd, wc (some cont); chem disp; shwrs inc; el pnts (10A) €3.50 (poss rev pol); Indtte (inc dryer); shop, rest, bar 500m; BBQ; playgrnd; rv adj; fishing; wifi; dogs €1.60; Eng spkn; poss cr w/end & noisy; no ccard acc; CKE/CCI. "Pleasant, well-kept site on island surrounded by rv; friendly, helpful Dutch owners; gd, clean san facs; popular NH, rec arr early." ♦ ltd 15 Apr-1 Oct. € 29.00 2014*

⊞ **ARCIS SUR AUBE** *4E4* (8km S Rural) *48.46696, 4.12633* **FFCC Camping La Barbuise, 10700 St Remy-sous-Barbuise [03 25 37 50 95 or 03 25 37 41 11; www.camping-ffcc.com]** Fr Arcis-sur-Aube, take D677 twd Voué; site on L bef vill of Voué, sp. Fr S exit A26 junc 21 onto D441 W; then onto D677 S twd Voué & as bef. Sm, pt sl, pt shd; wc; chem disp; mv service pnt; shwrs inc; el pnts (4A) inc (poss rev pol); tradsmn; shops 8km; sm bar (high ssn); BBQ; pool 8km; dogs (if on lead); phone; adv bkg; rd noise; red facs low ssn; ccard not acc; CKE/CCI. "Lovely, peaceful, spacious CL-type site; early arr rec; site yourself, owner calls eves (cash only); easy access & pitching for lge o'fits; charming owners; san facs basic but clean; elec poss unrel (2010); elec heaters not allowed; conv NH off A26 or sh stay." ♦ ltd € 13.50 2014*

ATTIGNY see Rethel *5C1*

AUBERIVE *6F1* (350m SE Rural) *47.78445, 5.06488* **Camp Municipal Les Charbonnières, 52160 Auberive [tel/fax 03 25 86 21 13 (Mairie); mairie.auberive@wanadoo.fr]** Leave A31 at junc 6 W twds Châtilion-sur-Seine on D428 for 12km, site on L bef vill. Site sp. Sm, mkd pitch, sl, pt shd; htd wc (some cont); chem disp (wc); shwrs inc; el pnts (6A) €1.60; Indry rm; shops in vill; rest in vill; playgrnd; phone; quiet; CKE/CCI. "Pleasant, clean, well-maintained site in wooded area; site yourself, friendly warden calls; ltd el pnts; attractive vill adj; music festival in abbey early Jul; gd." 15 Apr-1 Oct. € 7.40 2009*

BANNES see Langres *6F1*

BOURBONNE LES BAINS *6F2* (500m NW Urban) *47.95723, 5.74011* **Camping Le Montmorency, Rue du Stade, 52400 Bourbonne-les-Bains [03 25 90 08 64; fax 03 25 84 23 74; c.montmorency@wanadoo.fr; www.camping-montmorency.com]** Sp on ent town either way on D417. After exit D417, sp at 1st turn L at telephone box. Site adj to pool & stadium. Med, hdg/mkd pitch, pt sl, unshd; wc; mv service pnt; shwrs inc; el pnts (6-10A) €3.10-3.60; gas; Indry rm; shops 500m; snacks; playgrnd; pool adj; tennis; wifi; dogs €1.50; adv bkg; quiet; red low ssn. "Pleasant site; helpful warden; popular with visitors to spa cent; ok NH." 26 Mar-31 Oct. € 12.80 2011*

BOURG see Langres *6F1*

⊞ **BRAUCOURT** *6E1* (9km W Rural) *48.55754, 4.70629* **Camping Le Clos du Vieux Moulin, 33 Rue du Lac, 51290 Châtillon-sur-Broué [tel/fax 03 26 41 30 43; leclosduvieuxmoulin@wanadoo.fr; www.leclosduvieuxmoulin.fr]** Fr N take D13 fr Vitry-le-François. Turn R at sp for Châtillion-sur-Broué; site 100m on R. Fr S 2nd L fr Giffaumont (1km); site 100m on R. Med, hdg/mkd pitch, hdstg, pt sl, pt shd; htd wc; chem disp; baby facs; shwrs inc; el pnts (5A) €3.70; gas; Indtte; shops; tradsmn; rest 400m; snacks; bar; playgrnd; pool; lake 400m; watersports; birdwatching; 80% statics; dogs; phone; poss cr; quiet; ccard acc; red low ssn; CKE/CCI. "Busy high ssn; san facs need refurb (2010) & ltd low ssn; site poss unkempt (2010); grnd soft after rain." ♦ € 17.00 2013*

BRAUCOURT *6E1* (3km NW Rural) *48.55425, 4.79235* **FLOWER Camping Presqu'île de Champaubert, Lac du Der, 52290 Braucourt [03 25 04 13 20; fax 03 25 94 33 51; camping-de-braucourt@wanadoo.fr; www.lescampingsduder.com / www.flowercampings.com]** Fr St Dizier take D384 SW twd Montier-en-Der & Troyes. In Braucourt R onto D153 sp Presq'ile de Champaubert, site on L in 2km. Site situated on Lac du Der-Chantecoq. Lge, hdg/mkd pitch, shd; wc (some cont); chem disp; mv service pnt; serviced pitch; shwrs inc; el pnts (10A) €4 (rev pol); gas; Indtte; basic shop; tradsmn; rest, snacks; bar; playgrnd; htd pool; lake sw & sand beach nrby; watersports, boating, fishing, birdwatching; TV; dogs €1; poss cr; quiet; 60% statics; dogs; phone; quiet; ccard acc; red low ssn; CKE/CCI. "Beautiful lge beach; lge pitches; improved san facs; gates clsd 2230." ♦ 3 Apr-11 Sep. € 22.00 2009*

⊞ **BRIENNE LE CHATEAU** *6E1* (6km S Rural) *48.34835, 4.53265* **Camping Le Colombier, 8 Ave Jean-Lanez, 10500 Dienville [tel/fax 03 25 92 23 47; lecolombier10500@ wanadoo.fr; http://lecolombier10500.e-monsite.com]** On D443 S fr Brienne; in Dienville town cent turn L immed after church & bef bdge, site on R thro archway. Sm, hdg pitch, pt shd; htd wc; chem disp; mv service pnt; shwrs inc; el pnts (6A) €4; gas; lndry rm; shop 400m; rest; snacks (high ssn); bar; playgrnd; rv adj; lake 500m; watersports; dogs €2.50; Eng spkn; adv bkg; quiet. "Pretty rvside site - pitches away fr bdge quieter; rv view extra; some sm pitches; facs poss stretched high ssn & ltd low ssn; less pitch/site care low ssn; access poss diff lge o'fits if site busy; church clock strikes 24 hrs." ♦ ltd € 17.00 2010*

"That's changed – Should I let The Club know?"

If you find something on site that's different from the site entry, fill in a report and let us know. See www.caravanclub.co.uk/europereport.

BRIENNE LE CHATEAU *6E1* (6km S Rural) *48.34800, 4.5270* **Camping Le Tertre, Route de Radonvilliers, 10500 Dienville [tel/fax 03 25 92 26 50; campingdutertre@ wanadoo.fr; www.campingdutertre.fr]** On D443 S fr Brienne-le-Château; at Dienville turn R at rndabt onto D11; site on R in 200m, sp. NB Site opp Lake Amance harbour, foll sp 'Le Port'. Med, hdg/mkd pitch, hdstg, pt shd; wc; chem disp; mv service pnt; 50% serviced pitches; baby facs; shwrs inc; el pnts (6-10A) €4 (poss long lead req); gas; lndtte (inc dryer); shop; tradsmn; rest, snacks; bar; BBQ; playgrnd; htd pool; paddling pool; sand rv beach 200m; man-made lake with sailing, fishing; gym; games area; games rm; entmnt; internet; TV rm; 10% statics; dogs €1; phone; bus 500m; poss cr; Eng spkn; adv bkg; quiet; ccard acc; red low ssn/CKE/CCI. "Pleasant site 2 mins fr vill; excel site for all watersports & other activities; cycle tracks; vg." ♦ 1 Apr-15 Oct. € 23.60 2012*

BUZANCY *5C1* (1.5km SW Rural) *49.42647, 4.93891* **Camping La Samaritaine, 08240 [03 24 30 08 88; fax 03 24 30 29 39; info@campinglasamaritaine.com; www. campinglasamaritaine.com]** Fr Sedan take D977 dir Vouziers for 23km. Turn L onto D12, cont to end & turn L onto D947 for Buzancy. On ent Buzancy in 100m turn 2nd R immed after g'ge on R sp Camping Stade. Foll sp to site on L past football pitches. Med, hdg/mkd pitch, some hdstg, pt shd; wc; chem disp (wc); mv service pnt; 45% serviced pitches; mv service pnt; baby facs; shwrs inc; el pnts (10A) inc; lndtte; sm shop; tradsmn; rest 1.6km; snacks, bar high ssn; BBQ (gas/charcoal); playgrnd; lake sw & sand beach adj; fishing; horseriding nrby; tennis; library; games/TV rm; 10% statics; dogs €2.20; phone; Eng spkn; adv bkg; quiet; ccard not acc; red low ssn; CKE/CCI. "Beautiful area for walking/cycling; helpful, pleasant staff; excel facs, ltd low ssn." ♦ 29 Apr-20 Sep. € 18.50 2011*

CHARLEVILLE MEZIERES *5C1* (500m N Urban) *49.77813, 4.72245* **Camp Municipal Mont Olympe, Rue des Pâquis, 08000 Charleville-Mézières [03 24 33 23 60 or 03 24 32 44 80; fax 03 24 33 37 76; camping-charlevillemezieres@wandadoo.fr]** Fr N43/E44 head for Hôtel de Ville, with Hôtel de Ville on R, cont N along Ave des Arches, turn R at 'Gare' sp & cross rv bdge. At 'Gare' turn sharp L immed along Rue des Pâquis, site on L in 500m, visible fr rd. Well sp fr town cent. Med, hdg/mkd pitch, some hdstg, pt shd; htd wc (some cont); chem disp; mv service pnt; all serviced pitches; baby facs; fam bthrm; shwrs inc; el pnts (10A) €3.95; gas; lndtte (inc dryer); shops 500m; tradsmn; rest 300m; bar; BBQ; playgrnd; htd covrd pool adj; fishing & boating; wifi; TV/games rm; some statics; dogs €1.60; Eng spkn; quiet; ccard acc; CKE/CCI. "Lovely, spacious, well-kept site on Rv Meuse; lge pitches; v lge pitches extra; helpful staff; san facs req maintainence (2014); useful snack bar; easy walk to charming town; excel; NH for m'van's." 16 Apr-30 Sep. € 23.00 2014*

CHARLEVILLE MEZIERES *5C1* (12km N Urban) *49.87757, 4.74187* **Camp Municipal au Port à Diseur, Rue André Compain, 08800 Monthermé [03 24 53 01 21 / 03 24 53 00 09; fax 03 24 53 01 15]** Fr D988 at Revin turn E onto D1 TO Monthermé. Site is on D1 S of town. Site on R, 100m past supmkt on L. Med, hdg/ mkd pitch, pt sl, pt shd; wc (some cont); chem disp (wc); shwrs inc; el pnts (4-10A) inc; gas 100m; lndtte; shop 100m; rest, snacks, bar 1km; few statics; dogs; phone; poss cr; quiet but some rd noise; CKE/CCI. "Pleasant, rvside site in conv location; lge pitches; excel, clean san facs, poss stretched if site full; gd rvside walks; 20 min easy walk to Monthermé; gd cycling & walking; popular with fishermen & canoeists; excel site; some pitches adj rv; picturesque hilly wooded countryside." ♦ 13 Apr-30 Sep. € 15.50 2014*

CHAUMONT *6F1* (800m NW Urban) *48.11790, 5.13334* **Camp Municipal Parc Ste Marie, Rue des Tanneries, 52000 Chaumont [03 25 32 11 98 or 03 25 30 60 27 (Mairie); fax 03 25 30 59 50; sports@ville-chaumont.fr]** Site on Chaumont W by-pass joining N19 Troyes rd to N67 St Dizier rd. Do not try to app fr town cent. Exit A5 at exit 24, foll sp to town cntr, befr town foll sp to site. Sm, hdg/mkd pitch, pt sl, pt shd; wc (cont); chem disp; shwrs inc; el pnts (10A) inc (poss long lead req); shops 1km; tradsmn; snacks; playgrnd; 20% statics; dogs €1.50; poss cr; some traff noise; CKE/ CCI. "Rec arr early; care needed with steep access to some sl pitches; friendly warden; ent barrier under warden control at all times; gd NH." 2 May-30 Sep. € 14.25 2012*

CHESNE, LE *5C1* (2km NE Rural) *49.53166, 4.77430* **Camp Departmental du Lac de Bairon, 08390 Le Chesne [tel/fax 03 24 30 11 66; campinglacdebairon@cg08.fr]** Leave A203 exit Sedan, W on D764, in 500m L on D977 sp Vouziers. 2km bef Le Chesne R on D12, in 500m L on D312. Site 2km on L. Lge, mkd pitch, some hdstg, pt shd; htd wc; chem disp; mv service pnt; shwrs inc; el pnts (6-10A) €3-5; lndtte (inc dryer); shop 2km; tradsmn; snacks; bar; BBQ; playgrnd; tennis; cycle hire; watersports; entmnt; lake sw, sand beach, fishing, boat & canoe hire; TV rm; entmnt; 20% statics; dogs €1.20; phone; CKE/CCI. "Pleasant, quiet site; gd, clean san facs, but air of neglect (Sep 2010); poss diff site ent with lge o'fits; forest walks." ♦ 16 Mar-4 Nov. € 11.00 2010*

CLEFMONT *6F2* (500m E Rural) *48.09693, 5.50807* **Camp Municipal du Mont Clair, 52240 Clefmont [03 25 31 31 63]** Well sp on D74, site behind sm school. Sm, hdg pitch, pt shd; wc; chem disp; mv service pnt; shwrs inc; el pnts (6A) €1.50; tradsmn; BBQ; no statics; dogs; quiet; CKE/CCI. "Lovely, neat site with modern facs; vg." ♦ 15 Apr-15 Oct. € 8.00 2009*

CLEREY see Troyes *4E4*

DIENVILLE see Brienne Le Château *6E1*

DORMANS *3D4* (7km NE Rural) *49.10638, 3.73380* **Camping Rural (Nowack), 10 Rue de Bailly, 51700 Vandières [03 26 58 02 69 or 03 26 58 08 79; fax 03 26 58 39 62; champagne@nowack.fr; www.champagne-nowack.com]** Fr N3, turn N at Port Binson, over Rv Marne, then turn W onto D1 for 3km, then N into Vandières. Site on R about 50m fr start of Rue Bailly, sp 'Champagne Nowack' or 'Camping Nowack.' Sm, pt sl, pt shd; wc; shwrs inc; el pnts (6A) inc; Indtte; tradsmn; BBQ; playgrnd; pool 8km; fishing 1km; rv sw & boating 6km; tennis 2km; TV; adv bkg; ccard acc; CKE/CCI. "Charming, peaceful, CL-type site in orchard; friendly owners; lovely, well-kept modern san facs; fresh water tap beside chem disp (2011); site poss muddy when wet; poss grape pickers on site Sep; site pt of vineyard, champagne can be bought on site; excel value." 1 Apr-1 Nov. € 15.00 2013*

DOSCHES see Troyes *4E4*

DOUZY see Sedan *5C1*

⊞ **EAUX PUISEAUX** *4F4* (1km S Rural) *48.11696, 3.88317* **Camping à la Ferme des Haut Frênes (Lambert), 6 Voie de Puiseaux, 10130 Eaux-Puiseaux [03 25 42 15 04; fax 03 25 42 02 95; les.hauts.frenes@wanadoo.fr; www.les-hauts-frenes.com]** N fr St Florentin or S fr Troyes on N77. Ignore D374 but take next turning D111 in NW dir. Site in 2km; well sp. Long o'fits take care at ent gate. Med, hdg/mkd pitch, hdstg, pt shd; htd wc; own facs adv high ssn; chem disp; shwrs inc; el pnts (6-12A) €2-3 (poss some rev pol); gas; Indtte; shop 2km; tradsmn; rest 3km; snacks; BBQ; playgrnd; tennis 3km; TV & games rm; wifi; dogs €2; poss cr; Eng spkn; adv bkg; quiet; red long stay; CKE/CCI. "Well-kept, tidy farm site in beautiful setting; lge, level pitches; helpful, friendly owners; gd san facs; meals on request; loyalty card; cider museum in vill; conv m'way; excel NH en rte S; super v quiet site." ♦ € 15.00 2014*

ECLARON BRAUCOURT STE LIVIERE *6E1* (2km SW Rural) *48.57142, 4.84936* **Yelloh! Village en Champagne les Sources du Lac, 52290 Eclaron-Braucourt-Ste Livière [03 25 06 34 24; fax 03 25 06 96 47; info@yellohvillage-en-champagne.com; www.yellohvillage.co.uk]** S fr St Dizier on D2/D384 dir Troyes; site on R, 2km S of Eclaron-Braucourt-Ste Livière. Med, mkd pitch, pt shd; htd wc; chem disp; shwrs inc; el pnts (6A) inc; shop; tradsmn; rest, snacks; BBQ; pool; direct access to beach; watersports; fishing; cycle hire; games rm; entmnt; 40% statics; dogs; Eng spkn; poss cr; quiet; ccard acc; red low ssn; CKE/CCI. "Wooded site nr Lake Der; sm pitches; vg." 4 Apr-11 Sep. € 39.00 2009*

"I like to fill in the reports as I travel from site to site"

You'll find report forms at the back of this guide, or you can fill them in online at www.caravaclub.co.uk/europereport.

EPERNAY *3D4* (1km NW Urban) *49.05734, 3.95042* **Camp Municipal d'Epernay, Allées de Cumières, 51200 Epernay [03 26 55 32 14; fax 03 26 52 36 09; camping.epernay@free.fr; www.epernay.fr]** Fr Reims take D951 twd Epernay, cross rv & turn R at rndabt onto D301 sp Cumières (look for sp 'Stade Paul Chandon'), site sp. Site adj Stadium. Avoid town at early evening rush hour. Med, hdg/mkd pitch, pt shd; htd wc; chem disp; mv service pnt; shwrs inc; el pnts (5A) inc (poss long lead req); Indtte (inc dryer); tradsmn; supmkt; snacks; bar; BBQ; playgrnd; htd, covrd pool & waterslide 2km; fishing; canoeing; tennis; cycle hire; games area; wifi; dogs €1.80; phone; poss cr; Eng spkn; adv bkg; quiet but noisy tannoy; ccard acc; red long stay/low ssn/CKE/CCI. "Attractive, well-run site on Rv Marne in lovely location; generous pitches; friendly, helpful staff; gd spacious san facs; barrier open 0800-2100 & 0700-2200 high ssn; parking outsite; rec arr early; footpaths along rv into town; Mercier train tour with wine-tasting; site used by grape pickers; no twin-axles or c'vans over 6m acc; gd value; boulangerie and cafe nearby." ♦ 27 Apr-1 Oct. € 25.00 2014*

See advertisement

FISMES *3D4* (800m W Urban) *49.30944, 3.67138* **Camp Municipal de Fismes, Allée des Missions, 51170 Fismes [03 26 48 10 26; fax 03 26 48 82 25; contact@fismes.fr; www.fismes.fr]** Fr Reims NW on N31. At Fismes do not ent town, but stay on N31 dir Soissons. Site on L down little lane at end of sports stadium wall. Or exit A4 junc 22 sp Soissons & Fismes & as bef. Sm, hdstg, unshd; wc; chem disp; baby facs; shwrs; el pnts (12A) €3.50 (poss rev pol); shop 250m; supmkt 250m; BBQ (gas & el); games area; horseriding 5km; dogs; train; no twin-axles; adv bkg; noisy due to busy rd; ccard not acc; CKE/CCI. "Vg site; gd, clean san facs; warden on site ltd hrs; gates locked 2200-0700; train to Reims nr; conv Laon, Epernay, Reims; mkt Sat am; v gd NH; site clean and tidy; some rd noise; excel." 1 May-15 Sep. € 13.00 2014*

FRONCLES BUXIERES *6E1* (500m N Urban) *48.3004, 5.1476* **Camp Municipal Les Deux Ponts, Rue des Ponts, 52320 Froncles-Buxières [03 25 02 38 35 or 03 25 02 31 21 (Mairie); fax 03 25 02 09 80; mairie.froncles@wanadoo.fr; www.tourisme-champagne-ardenne.com]** Fr Chaumont take N67 twd Joinville, ignore sp to Vouécourt but take R turn E on D253 sp Froncles. Site sp fr main rd. Sm, hdg pitch, pt shd; wc (some cont); chem disp (wc); shwrs; el pnts (6A) inc; shops in vill; rv fishing; dogs €1.05; adv bkg; quiet. "Pleasant situation; friendly; warden calls pm; san facs clean; gd." 15 Mar-15 Oct. € 11.30 2011*

⊞ **GERAUDOT** *6E1* (1km E Rural) *48.30268, 4.33752* **Camping Les Rives du Lac/L'Epine aux Moines, 10220 Géraudot [tel/fax 03 25 41 24 36; camping.lepineauxmoines@orange.fr; www.campinglesrivesdulac.com]** Exit A26 at junc 23 onto D619 to Lusigny-sur-Barse; foll sp Parc de la Forêt d'Orient. Turn N along lake to site. Or fr Troyes D960 E. At Rouilly head S on D43 sp Géraudot. Site 1km E of vill. Lge, hdg/mkd pitch, pt sl, pt shd; htd wc (mainly cont); chem disp; mv service pnt; shwrs inc; el pnts (6A) inc (poss rev pol & long lead req); lndtte; shop 8km; tradsmn; rest & snacks adj; bar; playgrnd; lake sw adj; boat hire; dogs €2; poss cr; adv bkg; quiet; red low ssn/CKE/CCI. "Nice, well-kept site in attractive area; clean san facs; poss mosquitoes; gd walking & cycle paths; nr bird observatory; lovely vill; conv NH." 1 Mar-31 Dec. € 24.00 2013*

⊞ **GIVET** *5B1* (500m N Urban) *50.14345, 4.82614* **Caravaning Municipal La Ballastière, 16 Rue Berthelot, 08600 Givet [03 24 42 30 20; fax 03 24 42 02 44; sa.mairiegivet@wanadoo.fr; www.tourisme-champagne-ardenne.com]** Site at N end of town on lake. Foll 'Caravaning' sp fr W end of rv bdge or Dinant rd. Med, some hdg pitch, mkd pitch; hdstg, pt shd; htd wc; chem disp; shwrs inc; el pnts (10A) inc; lndry rm; supmkt, rest, snacks, bar 1km; BBQ; playgrnd; pool adj; 70% statics (sep area); dogs €0.85; quiet; CKE/CCI. "Nr Rv Meuse; adj sports & watersports complex; picturesque town; walking dist to shops & rest; v gd; conv for River Meuse cycleway; fair nh." € 8.60 2014*

GIVRY EN ARGONNE *5D1* (200m S Rural) *48.94835, 4.88545* **Camp Municipal du Val d'Ante, Rue du Pont, 51330 Givry-en-Argonne [03 26 60 04 15 or 03 26 60 01 59 (Mairie); fax 03 26 60 18 22; mairie.givryenargonne@wanadoo.fr; www.mairie-givry-en-argonne.fr]** Exit A4 junc 29 at Ste Menéhould; S on D382 to Givry-en-Argonne; site sp on R on lakeside. Sm, pt sl, pt shd; wc (some cont); chem disp; shwrs inc; el pnts (6A) €2.10; shops 200m; playgrnd; shgl lake beach sw; boats for hire adj; dogs €1.20; poss cr; quiet; no ccard acc. "Attractive, basic site; clean san facs; warden calls am & pm; gd birdwatching." 1 May-31 Aug. € 12.40 2013*

GRANDPRE *5D1* (300m S Rural) *49.33924, 4.87314* **FFCC Camp Municipal, Rue André Bastide, 08250 Grandpré [03 24 30 50 71 or 03 24 30 52 18 (Mairie); mairiegrandpre@wanadoo.fr; www.sud-ardennes-tourisme.com]** Fr D946 in Grandpré turn S onto D6 at vill sq by church twd rv, site in 300m on rvside. Med, mkd pitch, pt shd; wc; mv service pnt; shwrs €0.60; el pnts (6-10A) €2.60-3.50; lndtte (inc dryer); shops, rest, bar 300m; playgrnd; fishing; dogs €0.70; poss cr; quiet. "Pleasant site; two ents to site: 1st to newer pt with new facs, 2nd to office & older part." 1 Apr-30 Sep. € 7.20 2011*

HAULME see Charleville Mézières *5C1*

HUMES JORQUENAY see Langres *6F1*

JOINVILLE *6E1* (6km E Rural) *48.43018, 5.23077* **Camp Municipal La Petite Suisse, Rue de Mélaire, 52230 Poissons [03 23 94 55 75 or 03 25 94 51 78 (Mairie); www.tourisme-hautemarne.com]** Fr N67 to Joinville 'Centre Ville'; then onto D60 dir Thonnance; after supmkt turn R onto D427 to Poissons; site on L as exit vill. Site sp in vill. Sm, pt sl, pt shd; htd wc (cont); own san; chem disp (wc); shwrs inc; el pnts (6A) inc; shop 1km; rest 6km, snacks, bar 1km; BBQ; 20% statics; dogs; quiet; CKE/CCI. "Delightful, peaceful, basic CL-type site in great location; warden calls eves or call at No 7 in same rd to pay; dated but immac san facs; easy to find." 1 May-15 Sep. 2012*

LANGRES *6F1* (6km NE Rural) *47.89505, 5.39510* **Camping Hautoreille, 6 Rue du Boutonnier, 52360 Bannes [tel/fax 03 25 84 83 40; campinghautoreille@orange.fr; www.campinghautoreille.com]** N fr Dijon on D974/D674 to Langres; foll rd around Langres to E; onto D74 NE to Bannes; site on R on ent vill. Or exit A31 junc 7 Langres Nord onto D619, then D74 NE to Bannes. Med, mkd pitch, some hdstg, pt sl, pt shd; htd wc; chem disp; mv service pnt; shwrs inc; el pnts (10A) €4; lndtte; shop & 5km; tradsmn; rest (summer only); snacks; bar; playgrnd; lake sw 2.5km; horseriding & tennis 5km; cycle hire; wifi; some statics; dogs €1; phone; poss cr; Eng spkn; adv bkg; quiet; ccard not acc; CKE/CCI. "Peaceful, clean, tidy site; basic facs, ltd low ssn & poss inadequate high ssn; pleasant owner; gd rest; site muddy when wet - parking on hdstg or owner will use tractor; on Sundays site yourself - recep opens 1700; gd NH." ♦ 2 Jan-30 Nov. € 24.40 2013*

CHAMPAGNE-ARDENNE

LANGRES *6F1* (5km E Rural) *47.87190, 5.38120* **Kawan Village Le Lac de la Liez, Rue des Voiliers, 52200 Peigney [03 25 90 27 79; fax 03 25 90 66 79; campingliez@gmail.com; www.campingliez.com]** Exit A31 at junc 7 (Langres Nord) onto DN19; at Langres turn L at traff lts onto D74 sp Vesoul, Mulhouse, Le Lac de la Liez; at rndabt go strt on sp Epinal, Nancy; after Champigny-lès-Langres cross over rlwy bdge & canal turning R onto D52 sp Peigney, Lac de la Liez; in 3km bear R onto D284 sp Langres Sud & Lac de la Liez; site on R in 800m. Well sp fr N & S. Lge, hdg/mkd pitch, some hdstg, terr, pt shd; htd wc; chem disp; mv service pnt; sauna; baby facs; shwrs inc; el pnts (10A) €5.50; Indtte (inc dryer); shop; tradsmn; rest, snacks; bar; BBQ; playgrnd; 2 pools (1 htd covrd); paddling pool; spa; lake sw & sand beach adj; fishing; watersports; tennis; boat & cycle hire; horseriding, golf 10km; wifi; entmnt; games/TV rm; 15% statics; dogs €3; no c'vans/m'vans over 10m; phone; poss v cr; Eng spkn; ccard acc; red low ssn; CKE/CCI. "Popular, well-run, secure site; lake views fr some pitches; various sized pitches; helpful, friendly staff; gd, clean san facs, poss ltd low ssn; blocks poss req some pitches; some sm pitches & narr access rds diff manoeuvre lge o'fits; vg rest; rec arr bef 1600 high ssn; gd walks & cycle rte by picturesque lake; interesting & historic town; vg NH; excel." ♦ 1 Apr-27 Sep. € 44.00 (CChq acc) SBS - J05 2014*

LANGRES *6F1* (5km S Rural) *47.81210, 5.32080* **Camping de la Croix d'Arles, 52200 Bourg [03 25 88 24 02; fax 09 72 40 75 49; croix.arles@yahoo.fr; www.croixdarles.fr]** Site is 4km S of Langres on W side of D674 (1km S of junc of D674 with D428). Site opp junc of D51 with D974. Fr Dijon poss no L turn off D974 - can pull into indust est N of site & return to site, but memb reported that L turn now poss (2011). Med, hdg/mkd pitch, ltd hdstg, pt sl, pt shd; wc; chem disp; mv service pnt; shwrs inc; el pnts (10A) €4 (poss rev pol) (long cable req); Indtte; shop; tradsmn; rest, snacks; bar; playgrnd; pool; statics; dogs free; phone; poss cr; Eng spkn; ccard acc; red low ssn; CKE/CCI. "Popular site, fills up quickly after 1600; friendly staff; some lovely secluded pitches in woodland; gd san facs; access poss diff lge o'fits; muddy after rain; unkempt low ssn; poss haphazard pitching when full; conv NH Langres historic town; sm rest on site." ♦ 15 Mar-31 Oct. € 28.00 2014*

LANGRES *6F1* (15.2km S Rural) *47.74036, 5.30727* **Camping du Lac, 14 rue Cototte, 52190 Villegusien le Lac [(07) 70 05 87 19; richard-emmanuel@hotmail.fr; www.tourisme-langres.com/camping-du-lac_02_03__-campings-en_HPACHA5280000010_fiche.htm]** Take N19, foll N19 to Ave du Capitaine Baudoin, then foll Ave du Général de Gaulle, foll D974 to D26 in Villegusien-le-Lac, cont on D26 to your dest, turn L onto D26, turn L, turn R, dest will be on your L. Med, mkd pitch, shd; htd wc; chem disp; mv service pnt; shwr; pt sl; child/baby facs; family bathrm; el pnts; Indtte; rest; snacks; bar; gas BBQ; playgrnd; tennis; pool; sw in lake; games rm; wifi; twin axles; adv bkg; pets welcome; fishing, beach with lifeguard; sailing; windsurfing, trekking; supmkt 2km. "V pleasant site in lovely setting, some slight rd noise." 15 Mar-15 Oct. € 20.00 2014*

LANGRES *6F1* (500m SW Urban) *47.86038, 5.32894* **Camp Municipal Navarre, 9 Blvd Maréchal de Lattre de Tassigny, 52200 Langres [03 25 87 37 92 or 06 10 74 10 16; fax 03 25 87 37 92; contact@campingnavarre.fr; www.camping-navarre-langres.fr]** App fr N or S on D619/D674, cont on main rd until lge rndabt at top of hill & go thro town arched gateway; site well sp fr there. NB Diff access for lge o'fits thro walled town but easy access fr D619. Med, pt sl, pt shd; htd wc; chem disp; shwrs inc; el pnts (10A) €3.10 (long lead req & poss rev pol); Indtte (inc dryer); Spar supmkt 500m; BBQ; playgrnd nr; wifi; dogs free; phone; poss cr w/end; Eng spkn; some rd noise; ccard not acc; red low ssn; CKE/CCI. "Well-situated, busy NH, gd views fr some pitches; on arr site self & see warden; rec arr bef 1630; helpful staff; excel, modern unisex san facs; lovely walk round citadel ramparts; delightful town; vg site, views and location; warden mulit-lingual and helpful; conv for shops, rest, Friday mkt, cathedral." ♦ ltd 15 Mar-2 Nov. € 20.50 2014*

MARCILLY LE HAYER *4E4* (300m W Rural) *48.34754, 3.62709* **Camp Municipal, Rue des Dolmens, 10292 Marcilly-le-Hayer [03 25 21 74 34 or 03 25 21 70 36 (Mairie)]** Fr N on D619 turn S at Romilly-sur-Seine onto D440 to Marcilly-le-Hayer. Fr S on D660 turn N onto D374 to Marcilly. Site sp on rvside. Sm, hdg/mkd pitch, pt shd; htd wc; chem disp; shwrs inc; el pnts (5-10A) €2-3; shop, rest, bar in vill; playgrnd; fishing; quiet. "Height barrier with phone no at office for entry; gd site." ♦ 1 Apr-31 Oct. 2010*

MAZURES, LES see Rocroi *5C1*

"We must tell The Club about that great site we found"

Get your site reports in by mid-August and we'll do our best to get your updates into the next edition.

MESNIL ST PERE *6F1* (1km NE Rural) *48.26329, 4.34633* **Kawan Village Camping Lac d'Orient, Rue du Lac, 10140 Mesnil-St Père [03 25 40 61 85 or 03 85 72 27 21 (LS); fax 03 25 70 96 87 or 03 85 72 66 07 (LS); info@camping-lacdorient.com; www.camping-lacdorient.com]** On D619 foll sps Lac de la Forêt d'Orient. Approx 10km fr Vendeuvre or 20km fr Troyes turn N on D43A, to Mesnil-St Père; site sp. Sp at ent to site: 'Camping Lac d'Orient' (with 'Kawan Village' in v sm lettering). Lge, pt sl, pt shd; wc (some cont); chem disp; mv service pnt; private san facs some pitches; baby facs; fam bthrm; shwrs inc; el pnts (10A) inc; Indtte (inc dryer); shop; tradsmn; rest 1km; snacks; bar; BBQ; playgrnd; 2 htd pools (1 covrd); paddling pool; jacuzzi; lake sw/shgl beach & watersports 500m; fishing; games area; tennis; games rm; wifi; entmnt; some statics; dogs €3; no c'vans/m'vans over 10m high ssn; phone; Eng spkn; adv bkg; quiet; ccard acc; red low ssn; CKE/CCI. "Peaceful site with mature trees; lge pitches; 1st class san facs; poss muddy when wet; conv Nigloland theme park & Champagne area; conv A26; excel spacious site; excel cycle rte; fantastic res over looking lake." ♦ 5 Apr-26 Sep. € 46.60 (CChq acc) SBS - J07 2014*

MONTHERME see Charleville Mézières *5C1*

MONTIGNY LE ROI *6F2* (1km N Rural) *48.00084, 5.49637* **Camping du Château, Rue Hubert Collot, 52140 Montigny-le-Roi [tel/fax 03 25 87 38 93; campingmontigny52@wanadoo.fr; www.campingduchateau.com]** Fr A31 junc 8 for Montigny-le-Roi. Site well sp in cent vill on D74. Med, terr, pt shd; htd wc; chem disp; mv service pnt; baby facs; shwrs inc; el pnts (5A) €3; Indry rm; shop; snacks; bar; BBQ; playgrnd; tennis; cycle hire; entmnt. "Modern facs; steep ent; rests & shops in vill." ♦ 15 Apr-30 Sep. € 14.00 2014*

MONTMIRAIL *3D4* (1km E Rural) *48.87299, 3.55147* **Camp Municipal Les Châtaigniers, Rue du Petit St Lazare, 51210 Montmirail [03 26 81 25 61; fax 03 26 81 14 27; mairie.montmirail@wanadoo.fr; www.montmirail.fr]** Site sp at junc of D933 & D373 at E o'skts of town. By sports stadium 150m twds town by Gendarmerie. Med, mkd pitch, pt shd; wc (cont); own san rec; shwrs inc; el pnts (20A) €4; shops 500m; playgrnd; pool 500m; tennis; golf; ccard not acc; CKE/CCI. "Peaceful, clean site approx 1 hr fr Paris; warm welcome, helpful warden; dated, clean san facs; call at warden's house L of ent for removal of barrier; barrier v nr main rd; fees collected pm (cash only); vg NH." 1 Apr- 31 Oct. € 9.50 2013*

NOGENT SUR SEINE *4E4* (500m NE Rural) *48.50365, 3.50889* **Camp Municipal, Rue Villiers-aux-Choux, 10400 Nogent-sur-Seine [tel/fax 03 25 39 76 67 or 03 25 39 42 00 (Mairie)]** Fr Troyes site sp fr D619 on app to town & fr S ring rd, Site on rvside. Med, mkd pitch, some hdstg, pt shd; htd wc; shwrs; mv service pnt; el pnts; shop 500m; rest 100m; playgrnd; htd pool adj; tennis; quiet. "Pleasant site; poss many long-stay residents; gd NH." 1 Apr-5 Oct. 2009*

PEIGNEY see Langres *6F1*

REIMS *3D4* (16km SE Rural) *49.16687, 4.21416* **Camp Municipal Val de Vesle, 8 Rue de Routoir, Courmelois, 51360 Val-de-Vesle [03 26 03 91 79; fax 03 26 03 91 79; valdevesle.camping@orange.fr; www.reims-tourism.com]** Fr Reims twd Châlons-en-Champagne on D944, turn L by camp sp on D326 to Val-de-Vesle, foll camp sp; look for tall grain silos by canal. NB do not turn L bef D326 due narr lane. Med, mkd pitch, shd; wc; chem disp; shwrs inc; el pnts (6-10A) €3 (long lead poss req); Indtte; shops 1km; tradsmn; BBQ; playgrnd; pool; rv fishing; dogs €1; poss v cr; adv bkg; some rlwy/rd noise (not a problem); ccard acc over €15; CKE/CCI. "Charming, well-kept, busy site amongst trees; popular NH, rec arrive early; informal pitching; friendly, helpful staff; new security gate, booking in req for code (2011); in sm vill (no shops); poss mosquito prob; cycle rte to Reims along canal; gd touring base." ♦ 1 Apr-15 Oct. € 17.45 2014*

RETHEL *5C1* (14km E Urban) *49.48234, 4.57589* **Camp Municipal Le Vallage, 38 Chemin de l'Assaut, 08130 Attigny [03 24 71 23 06 or 03 24 71 20 68; fax 03 24 71 94 00; mairie-d-attigny@wanadoo.fr]** E on D983 fr Rethel to Attigny; fr town cent take D987 twd Charleville; over rv bdge; 2nd turn on L; sp. Med, hdg/mkd pitch, hdstg, pt shd; wc; chem disp; shwrs inc; el pnts (10A) inc; Indry rm; shop 1km; tradsmn; pool & sports facs adj; playgrnd; fishing; tennis; 50% statics; dogs; phone; CKE/CCI. "Lovely quiet site; lge pitches; helpful staff; gd facs." 1 Apr-30 Sep. € 13.00 2010*

REVIN *5C1* (1km W Rural) *49.94260, 4.62756* **Camp Municipal Les Bateaux, Quai Edgar Quinet, 08500 Revin [03 24 40 15 65 or 03 24 40 19 59 (LS); fax 03 24 40 21 98; camping.les.bateaux-revin@wanadoo.fr; www.ville-revin.fr]** Fr Fumay take D988 to Revin, or fr Charleville take D989/988 (23km) or take rte D1 E fr Rocroi. On ent Revin turn L after narr bdge (1-way) over Rv Meuse. Fr cent of Revin foll sp Montherme; at Total g'ge R fork, then 1st L. At rv turn L, 500m to site, sp. Med, hdg/mkd pitch, pt shd; htd wc; chem disp; baby facs; shwrs; el pnts (6A) inc (poss rev pol); Indtte; shop; supmkt 1km; tradsmn; playgrnd; rv fishing; paragliding nrby; games rm; TV rm; 5% statics; dogs €0.95; adv bkg; quiet; red low ssn; CKE/CCI. "Peaceful, clean, rvside site; lge pitches; excel san facs; if office clsd site self & book in later; helpful warden; gd walks; excel." ♦ Easter-30 Oct. € 11.80 2010*

"I need an on-site restaurant"

We do our best to make sure site information is correct, but it is always best to check any must-have facilities are still available or will be open during your visit.

⊞ **ROCROI** *5C1* (3km SE Rural) *49.89446, 4.53770* **Camping La Murée, 35 Rue Catherine-de-Clèves, 08230 Bourg-Fidèle [tel/fax 03 24 54 24 45; campingdelamuree@wanadoo.fr; www.campingdelamuree.com]** Site sp fr Rocroi on R. Sm, some hdstg, mkd pitch, pt sl, pt shd; htd wc; chem disp; baby facs; shwrs inc; el pnts (10A) €4; Indtte; shops 3km; rest; bar; tradsmn; BBQ; playgrnd; lake sw 4km; 60% statics; dogs €1.50; some Eng spkn; quiet; ccard acc; twin axle c'vans; adv bkg; CKE/CCI;. "Two fishing lakes on site; pleasant site; gd sh stay/NH; gd san facs, new management helpful & friendly; gd rest; scenic location." ♦ ltd 15 Jan-30 Nov. € 19.00 2013*

ROCROI *5C1* (8km SE Rural) *49.87200, 4.60446* **Camp Départemental du Lac des Vieilles Forges, 08500 Les Mazures [03 24 40 17 31; fax 03 24 41 72 38; cmpingvieillesforges@cg08.fr]** Fr Rocroi take D1 & D988 for Les Mazures/Renwez. Turn R D40 at sp Les Vieilles Forges. Site on R nr lakeside. Lge, mkd pitch, hdstg, pt sl, shd; htd wc; mv service pnt; shwrs inc; el pnts (6-10A) €2.50-4.30; Indtte; shop; tradsmn; snacks; playgrnd; shgl beach & lake sw; boating, fishing; tennis; cycle hire; entmnt high ssn; TV; 20% statics; dogs €1; poss cr; adv bkg; quiet. "Attractive walks; lake views fr some pitches; vg site." ♦ 16 Mar-4 Nov. € 13.00 2009*

⊞ **ROMILLY SUR SEINE** *4E4* (4km W Rural) *48.5259, 3.6646* **Camping du Domaine de la Noue des Rois, Chemin des Brayes, 10100 St Hilaire-sous-Romilly [03 25 24 41 60; fax 03 25 24 34 18; contact@lanouedesrois.com; www.lanouedesrois.com]** Site sp fr D619, on rvside. Lge, mkd pitch, pt shd; htd wc; mv service pnt; baby facs; shwrs; el pnts (16A) €3.50-5; gas; Indtte; shop; tradsmn; rest; bar; playgrnd; htd, covrd pool; paddling pool; waterslide; fishing; sailing; watersports; tennis; games area; entmnt; 90% statics; dogs (on lead) €3.50; Eng spkn; adv bkg; quiet; ccard acc; red long stay/low ssn; CKE/CCI. "Gd situation in wooded area; conv Paris & Disneyland; ltd pitches/facs for tourers." ♦ € 32.00 2012*

STE MENEHOULD *5D1* (1km E Rural) *49.08937, 4.90969* **Camp Municipal de la Grelette, Chemin de l'Alleval, 51800 Ste Menéhould [06 73 91 98 83 (mob) or 03 26 60 80 21 (Mairie); fax 03 26 60 62 54; mairie@ste-menehould.fr; www.ste-menehould.fr]** Exit A4 junc 29 to Ste Menéhould; foll sp 'Centre Ville' thro town to Mairie & central sq on D3; then foll sp 'Piscine' & 'Camping' on D3; cont uphill with rlwy on R; turn R over narr rlwy bdge, then L to site in 200m. Sm, pt sl, pt shd; wc; shwrs inc; chem disp; el pnts (4A) €3.40; Indtte nryby; tradsmn; supmkt 500m; rest, snacks, bar 1km; dogs €1.05; poss cr; adv bkg; Eng spkn; no ccard acc; CKE/CCI. "Delightful site; helpful warden; recep 08.00-10.00 & 18.00-20.00, access to o'fits over 2m poss restricted at other times, confirm dep with warden; vg, clean but dated san facs(2014); interesting old town; under new ownership (2013); wel maintained site; new indoor pool opened nrby; conv for Reims & Verdun." 1 Apr-31 Oct. € 17.00 2014*

ST REMY SOUS BARBUISE see Arcis sur Aube *4E4*

SEDAN *5C1* (11km SE Rural) *49.66265, 5.04718* **Camp Municipal du Lac, Route de Mouzon, 08140 Douzy [03 24 26 31 19 or 03 24 26 31 48 (Mairie); fax 03 24 26 84 01; aubergedulac@free.fr; www.camping-douzy.com]** On N43 fr Sedan-Metz to Douzy. Turn R (S) at traff lts in Douzy & site in 500m on L. Clearly sp. Med, few hdstg, pt shd; wc; 60% serviced pitch; shwrs inc; el pnts (6A) €3 (poss rev pol); gas 1km; Indtte; shops 1km; tradsmn; rest adj; snacks; bar; playgrnd; shgl beach & lake sw adj; waterslides; tennis; dogs €1.50; poss cr; Eng spkn; adv bkg; some rd & light aircraft noise; red long stay; CKE/CCI. "Helpful staff; pitches mostly uneven; gd san facs; gd rest adj." ♦ 15 Apr-1 Oct. € 11.00 2011*

SEDAN *5C1* (1km W Urban) *49.69868, 4.93848* **Camp Municipal La Prairie, Prairie de Torcy, Blvd Fabert, 08200 Sedan [03 24 27 13 05 or 03 24 27 73 42; fax 03 24 22 14 78; christophe.lagnier@mairie-sedan.fr]** Fr A34(A203) exit junc 4 dir Sedan cent. Cont strt thro town & over rlwy bdge; in 500m cont over viaduct, site visible on R, turn R at next traff lts at end of viaduct, site 100m on R. Easy to find. Med, pt shd; no hdstg; wc (some cont); chem disp; mv service pnt; shwrs inc; el pnts (10A) €3.15; Indtte; shop 300m; rest, snacks & bar 500m; BBQ; sm playgrnd; pool 500m; dogs €1; no twin-axles; phone; poss cr; adv bkg; some traff noise; no ccard acc; red long stay; CKE/CCI. "Pleasant, peaceful site in lovely spot by rv; haphazard parking; rough/uneven grnd; friendly, helpful staff; san facs dated but clean; poss muddy when wet; pleasant walk to interesting town; mkt traders for fair mid-Sep; gd value; highly rec; local Patisserie comes to site." ♦ 1 Apr-30 Sep. € 6.00 2013*

SEZANNE *4E4* (500m NW Rural) *48.72115, 3.70247* **Camp Municipal, Route de Launat, 51120 Sézanne [tel/fax 03 26 80 57 00/ 03 26 80 57 00 (mob); campingdesezanne@wanadoo.fr]** W'bound on N4 Sézanne by-pass onto D373 & foll site sp. Fr E turn R at 1st junc on Sézanne bypass & foll sps 'Camping & Piscine'. Avoid town cent. Med, mainly sl, pt shd; serviced pitches; wc (some cont); shwrs inc; shop, el pnts (10A) inc; shop 500m; rest in town 1km; sm playgrnd; pool adj; waterslide; dogs €1.05; no ccard acc; CKE/CCI. "Nice, well-kept site, v busy high ssn; generous pitches, some v sl; helpful manager; excel, immac san facs; levelling blocks req some pitches; request gate opening/closing at back bungalow of 2 opp site; nice vill; vg; well run site; excel value." ♦ 1 Apr-30 Sep. € 14.00 2014*

SIGNY L'ABBAYE *5C1* (550m N Urban) *49.70123, 4.41971* **Camp Municipal de l'Abbaye, 08460 Signy-l'Abbaye [03 24 52 87 73; mairie-signy-l.abbaye@wanadoo.fr]** Take D985 N twd Belgium fr Rethel to Signy-l'Abbaye. Foll sp fr town cent to Stade & Camping. Site by sports stadium. Sm, some hdg/hdstg pitch, pt sl, pt shd; htd wc; chem disp; shwrs inc; el pnts (10A) €2.90 (poss rev pol); Indry rm; shops, rest 500m; playgrnd; sports cent adj; rv fishing adj; dogs €0.60; little Eng spkn; adv bkg; v quiet; CKE/CCI. "Lovely site in gd location; friendly warden; san facs excel (shared with public fr sports cent); strong awning pegs req on gravel hdg pitches, or can park on open grassed area." ♦ ltd 1 May-30 Sep. € 6.40 2009*

SOULAINES DHUYS *6E1* (500m N Rural) *48.37661, 4.73829* **Camping La Croix Badeau, 6 Rue Croix Badeau, 10200 Soulaines-Dhuys [03 25 27 05 43 or 03 26 82 35 31 (LS); responsable@croix-badeau.com; www.croix-badeau.com]** 500m N of junc D960 & D384, behind lge church of Soulaines-Dhuys, well sp. Sm, hdg/mkd pitch, hdstg, pt shd; wc (some cont); chem disp; shwrs inc; el pnts (10A) €2.50; Indtte; shop 500m; playgrnd; tennis; rv 300m; dogs €1; phone; Eng spkn; quiet; CKE/CCI. "Excel, clean site in interesting vill." 1 Apr-15 Oct. € 14.00 2012*

THONNANCE LES MOULINS *6E1* (2km W Rural) *48.40630, 5.27110* **Camping La Forge de Ste Marie, 52230 Thonnance-les-Moulins [03 25 94 42 00; fax 03 25 94 41 43; info@laforgedesaintemarie.com; www.laforgedesaintemarie.com / www.les-castels.com]** Fr N67 exit sp Joinville-Est, foll D60 NE sp Vaucouleurs. In 500m turn R onto D427 sp Poissons & Neufchâteau. Site on R in 11km. NB Swing wide at turn into site fr main c'way, not fr what appears to be a run in. Site ent narr. Lge, hdg/mkd pitch, pt sl, pt terr,pt shd; wc; chem disp; mv service pnt; serviced pitches; baby facs; shwrs inc; el pnts (6A) inc; gas; Indtte (inc dryer); shop; tradsmn; rest, snacks; bar; BBQ; htd, covrd pool; paddling pool; sm lake on site; boating; freshwater fishing; cycle hire; games area; wifi; entmnt; games/TV rm; 25% statics; dogs €2; no c'vans/m'vans over 8m; phone; Eng spkn; adv bkg; ccard acc; red low ssn; CKE/CCI. "Vg, well-kept, busy site; friendly, helpful owners; access poss diff to some terr pitches/sharp bends on site rds; muddy after rain; vg rest; mkt Fri; lovely spacious, well run site, beautiful area; swing wide at ent." ♦ 18 Apr- 3 Sep. € 36.00 (CChq acc) SBS - J04 2013*

TROYES *4E4* (2km NE Urban) *48.31150, 4.09630* **Camp Municipal de Troyes, 7 Rue Roger Salengro, 10150 Pont-Ste Marie [tel/fax 03 25 81 02 64; info@troyescamping.net; www.troyescamping.net]** Fr N exit A26 junc 22 onto D677. site on R opp stadium & adj Esso g'ge, just pass junc with D960. Fr S exit A26 junc 23 for Pont-Ste-Mairie. Pont-Ste-Marie & site 'municipal' well sp fr all dirs & in town. NB Queues form onto rd outside site, use Esso g'ge to turn if queue too long. Med, some hdg/mkd pitch, some hdstg, pt shd; htd wc; chem disp; mv service pnt; shwrs inc; el pnts (10A) (long lead poss req); gas; Indtte (inc dryer); sm shop; tradsmn; supmkt nrby; rest nrby; snacks; takeaway; BBQ; playgrnd; htd pool; cycle hire; games area; games rm; wifi; TV; dogs €1.15; bus opp; poss cr; Eng spkn; adv bkg; ccard acc; red low ssn/long stay; CKE/CCI. "Busy, popular, transit site in parkland - rec arr early; can be noisy at w/ends; vg pool; some lge pitches; some pitches soft when wet; diff access some pitches; twin-axles acc at recep's discretion; red facs low ssn; Troyes Cathedral, museums & old quarter worth visit; Lac d'Orient & Lac du Temple nrby; conv NH; Gd res by the rv bdge 3 min walk fr site ent; conv for m'way; pleasant friendly site; clean facs; excel snacks/rest; Stay 7 nights pay for 6." ♦ 4 Apr-15 Oct. € 29.00 2014*

TROYES *4E4* (16km E Rural) *48.28998, 4.28279* **Camping La Fromentelle, Ferme Fromentelle, 10220 Dosches [03 25 41 52 67; fax 03 25 40 78 38; www.tourisme-champagne-ardenne.com]** Exit A26 junc 23 onto D619 dir Bar-sur-Aube. In 8.5km turn L onto D1 sp Géraudot (take care bends). Site on L in 5km. Sm, mkd pitch, pt sl, pt shd; wc; chem disp; mv service pnt; shwrs inc; el pnts (6A) €3 (long lead poss req)(poss rev pol); BBQ; playgrnd; sand beach 5km; lake sw 5km; games area; dogs €1.50; adv bkg; quiet; CKE/CCI. "Beautiful farm/CL-type site in old orchard; well-kept & well-run; warm welcome, charming owner; v clean san facs; gd for birdwatching, sailing, watersports on lakes; excel cycle tracks; nr nature reserve, lakes & forest; conv A26; excel spacious pitches; gd facs." ♦ 30 Apr-15 Oct. € 15.00 2013*

TROYES *4E4* (10km SE Rural) *48.20106, 4.16620* **Le Base de Loisirs au Plan d'Eau 'Les Terres Rouges', 10390 Clérey [03 25 46 04 45; fax 03 25 46 05 86; terres-rouges@wanadoo.fr; www.les-terres-rouges.fr]** Exit A5 junc 21 onto D671 S dir Bar-sur-Seine & Dijon; site on R in 3.5km. Or SE fr Troyes on D671 dir Bar-sur-Seine, foll sp Clérey; then as bef. Site well sp. App over gravel track thro gravel quarry area. Sm, hdstg, pt shd; wc (1 cont); chem disp; shwrs €1; el pnts (5-10A) €3.20 (poss rev pol); shops 4km; tradsmn; rest, snacks; bar; playgrnd; lake sw; tennis; lakes for fishing, waterskiing, boating; 10% statics; dogs; phone; wifi €3 per day; adv bkg; quiet; no ccard acc; CKE/CCI. "Gd, basic NH; clean, v basic san facs; friendly, helpful owners; gate opens 0600; conv fr a'route to Calais." ♦ Easter-30 Sep. € 14.50 2013*

VAL DE VESLE see Reims *3D4*

VAL DE VESLE *3D4* (2km SW Rural) *49.16691, 4.21422* **Camping Municipal Val de Vesle, 8 rue du Routoir, 51360 Val-de-Vesle [03 26 03 91 79; valdevesle.camping@orange.fr]** Fr Reims, take N44. L at the 2nd Val-de-Vesle sign by grain Silo. Sm, hdstg, pt shd; htd wc; chem disp; shwrs; el pnts (8A); Indtte; BBQ; games area; dogs; Eng spkn; adv bkg; quiet; ccard acc. "Pleasant sm site with gd san facs; close to canal; gd NH; fishing." 1 Apr-15 Oct. € 17.45 2014*

VANDIERES see Dormans *3D4*

VITRY LE FRANCOIS *6E1* (4km SE Rural) *48.69673, 4.63039* **Aire Naturelle Camping Nature (Scherschell), 13 Rue de l'Evangile, 51300 Luxémont-et-Villotte [03 26 72 61 14 or 06 83 42 83 53 (mob); eric.scherschell@wanadoo.fr; www.camping-nature.net]** Fr Châlons sp on N44, site sp at E end of Vitry-le-François by-pass (N4); foll sp to R, then foll 3km to site. Fr S take exit for Vitry-le-François & pass lorry park; in approx 1km, turn L at rndabt; foll sp to Luxémont-et-Villotte; site in vill on R. Sm, some hdstg, pt sl, shd; wc; chem disp; mv service pnt; shwrs inc; el pnts (6A) inc (poss rev pol & long lead req); gas 2km; shop 6km; tradsmn high ssn; BBQ; playgrnd; lake sw 500m; fishing; dogs €1; poss cr; Eng spkn; adv bkg; quiet; no ccard acc; CKE/CCI. "Delightful, CL-type site; well-kept & immac; helpful, friendly owners; gd, clean unisex san facs; no twin-axles; nr canal & cycle paths; interesting area to visit; excel." 1 May-15 Oct. € 14.60 2014*

VITRY LE FRANCOIS *6E1* (2km W Urban) *48.73020, 4.58114* **Camp Municipal La Peupleraie, 6 Esplanade de Tauberbischofsheim, Quai des Fontaines, 51300 Vitry-le-François [03 26 74 20 47 or 03 26 74 20 47 (Mairie); fax 03 26 41 22 88; camping@vitry-le-francois.net; www.vitry-le-francois.net]** Fr N on N44 turn R onto N4 at island with lge stone triumphal arch (sp Paris) & cont on dual c'way for 300m; then immed after sharp L bend turn R thro lge parking area. Med, hdg pitch, pt shd; wc; shwrs inc; el pnts (5A) inc; gas; shops adj; rest, snacks, bar 500m; dogs €1.55; quiet, but some rd noise. "Delightful site; tight ent poss diff lge o'fits, no twin-axles; lge pitches; san facs dated & poss tired end of ssn (2011); interesting town in walking dist; vg NH." 1 May-15 Oct. € 13.00 2011*

"There aren't many sites open at this time of year"

If you're travelling outside peak season remember to call ahead to check site opening dates – even if the entry says 'open all year'.

VOUECOURT *6E1* (Rural) *48.26774, 5.13671* **Camp Municipal Rives de Marne, Rue de Verdun 52320 Vouécourt [03 25 01 39 58 or 03 25 02 44 46 (Mairie); fax 03 25 02 44 46; camping-vouecourt@wanadoo.fr]** N fr Chaumont on N67; sp to site in 17km; thro vill by Rv Marne; site on L bef main rv bdge, almost opp Mairie; well sp. Sm, mkd pitch; pt shd; wc (some cont); chem disp; shwr; el pnts (10A) €2.20 (poss rev pol); gas; shop 5km; rest 1km; tradsmn; playgrnd; fishing; adv bkg; CKE/CCI. "Lovely, peaceful, rvside site; gd sized pitches; friendly warden calls pm; clean, dated san facs; rv poss floods in winter; forest walks & cycling; popular NH; excel." 1 May-30 Sep. € 13.80 2013*

Corsica

Regional Introduction

Bastia

Welcome to Corsica

One of the most beautiful islands in the Mediterranean with superb beaches and picturesque hillside villages, Corsica is quite different from mainland France in its geography, people, culture and customs.

Mountains take up two-thirds of the island and, with over 200 beaches, Corsica offers plenty of pretty views and dramatic landscapes.

If you have the time and are looking to take in lots of sights the Corsica coast road is a great place to start. It runs for 370 miles around the edge of the island and passes by many interesting and important sites, making for a truly memorable trip.

Local highlights

Having so many port towns and villages, fresh seafood is popular here. The southernmost part of the island takes a lot of influence from Italian dishes. Wild boar is also a local delicacy – look out for sanglier on menus.

Each August, Ajaccio hosts the Napoleonic Festival, when locals dress in period costume to celebrate the birthday of Corsica's most-famous son.

Major towns and cities

- Bastia – a long-established port town with an attractive harbour.
- Corte – stunning scenery and an imposing citadel.
- Porto Vecchio – built on salt marshes, this town is very popular with tourists.
- Bonifacio – located on the island's southern tip, this town has an Italian feel with expensive restaurants.
- Calvi – an old port town that boasts traditional Corsican culture.

Regional attractions

- La citadelle de Bonifacio – a historical landmark that showcases the culture of the area.
- Gorges de la Restonica – these partly forested gorges are a popular place with hikers and cyclists.
- Escalier du Roi d'Aragon, Bonifacio – 187 steps carved into the limestone cliff.

Find out more

www.visit-corsica.com
Tel: (0)4 95 54 20 40 Bastia Tourist Office
Tel: (0)4 95 65 16 67 Calvi Tourist Office

ALERIA *10H2* (7km N Coastal) *42.16155, 9.55265* **Camping-Village Riva-Bella (Part Naturist), 20270 Aléria [04 95 38 81 10; fax 04 95 38 91 29; rivabella.corsica@gmail.com; www.rivabella-corsica.com]** Fr Bastia S on N198 for 60km, site sp to L. Poor rd access (2011). Med, pt shd; wc; mv service pnt; steam rm; sauna; shwrs; el pnts €4.30; Indtte; shop; tradsmn; rest, snacks; bar; playgrnd; sand beach adj; fishing; watersports; tennis; cycle hire; games area; fitness rm; spa treatments; wifi; entmnt; TV rm; 10% statics; dogs €3.50; naturist site 15 May-20 Sep, non-naturist rest of year - but always sm end beach avail for naturists; adv bkg; quiet; red low ssn/long stay; INF card. "Site untidy early ssn (2011); poss insect problem." ♦ € 36.00 2011*

ALGAJOLA *10G2* (800m E Coastal) *42.60844, 8.87409* **Camping de la Plage en Balagne, 20220 Algajola [tel/fax 04 95 60 71 76 or 06 09262638 (mob); campingalgajola@wanadoo.fr; www.camping-de-la-plage-en-balagne.com]** Site 6km W fr L'Ile-Rousse on N197 dir Algajola. On R opp Hotel Pascal Paoli bef Algajola. Med, pt shd; htd wc (some cont); chem disp; mv service pnt; shwrs inc; el pnts (6A) €4; Indtte; shop; rest, snacks; bar; playgrnd; sand beach adj; games area; gym; entmnt; some statics; dogs €1.50; tram; poss cr; adv bkg; quiet; ccard acc. "Poss v busy high ssn; san facs v tired early ssn (2011); rest, snacks & bar on beach - poss clsd low ssn; tram to I'lle-Rousse & Calvi fr site gd for touring inland; gd." 15 Mar-15 Nov. € 22.70 2011*

"That's changed – Should I let The Club know?"

If you find something on site that's different from the site entry, fill in a report and let us know. See www.caravanclub.co.uk/europereport.

BASTIA *10G2* (5km N Coastal) *42.74039, 9.45982* **Camping Les Orangers, Licciola, 20200 Miomo [06 12 53 73 33; fax 04 95 33 23 65; www.camping-lesorangers.com]** Foll main coast rd D80 N 4km fr ferry. Site well sp on L of rd. Sm, shd; wc; shwrs; el pnts; shop; tradsmn; rest, snacks; bar; sandy/shgl beach adj; TV; quiet; CKE/CCI. "Poss run down low ssn; friendly owners; vg rest; site ent tight for lge o'fits; no m'vans (2011); poss unrel opening dates." 1 Apr-30 Sep. 2012*

BASTIA *10G2* (11km S Coastal) *42.62922, 9.46835* **Camping San Damiano, Lido de la Marana, 20620 Biguglia [04 95 33 68 02; fax 04 95 30 84 10; san.damiano@wanadoo.fr; www.campingsandamiano.com]** S fr Bastia on N193 for 4km. Turn SE onto Lagoon Rd (sp Lido de Marana). Site on L in 7km. Lge, pt shd; wc; chem disp; baby facs; shwrs inc; el pnts (6A) €3.40; Indtte; shop; rest; playgrnd; pool; sandy beach adj; cycle path; games area; games rm; dogs €0.90; Eng spkn; ccard acc; red long stay'/low ssn; CKE/CCI. "San facs basic but clean." ♦ 1 Apr-31 Oct. € 22.00 2013*

BIGUGLIA see Bastia *10G2*

BONIFACIO *10H2* (15km N Coastal) *41.47326, 9.26318* **Camping Rondinara, Suartone, 20169 Bonifacio [04 95 70 43 15; fax 04 95 70 56 79; reception@rondinara.fr; www.rondinara.fr]** Fr Bonifacio take N198 dir Porte-Vecchio for 10km, then turn R onto D158 dir Suartone (lge camp sp at turning). Site in 5km. NB D158 single track, many bends & hills. Med, pt sl, pt shd; wc; mv service pnt; shwrs inc; el pnts (6A) €3.60; Indtte; shop; rest, snacks; bar; BBQ; playgrnd; pool; sand beach 400m; watersports; games area; games rm; some statics; dogs €2.60; poss cr; Eng spkn; no adv bkg; quiet; red low ssn; ccard acc; CKE/CCI. "Excel rest; idyllic location by bay; excel new san facs 2013; rd to campsite steep and narr in places; adv bkg for mkd pitches fr May." 15 May-30 Sep. € 41.30 2014*

BONIFACIO *10H2* (4km NE Rural) *41.39986, 9.20141* **Camping Pian del Fosse, Route de Sant' Amanza, 20169 Bonifacio [tel/fax 04 95 73 16 34; camping@piandelfosse.com; www.piandelfosse.com]** Leave Bonifacio on D58 dir Sant' Amanza, site on L in 4km. Sm, hdg/mkd pitch, terr, shd; wc; chem disp; mv service pnt; baby facs; shwrs inc; el pnts (4A) €3.80; Indtte; shop; tradsmn; snacks; BBQ; playgrnd; sand/shgl beach 3km; 20% statics; dogs €2.50; poss cr; Eng spkn; quiet; red snr citizens/long stay. "Pitches poss diff lge m'vans due o'hanging trees, vg; ccard acc." ♦ ltd Easter-15 Oct. € 41.50 2013*

BONIFACIO *10H2* (4km NE Rural) *41.41842, 9.17898* **Pertamina Village U Farniente, Route de Porto Vecchio, 20169 Bonifacio [04 95 73 05 47; fax 04 95 73 11 42; pertamina@wanadoo.fr; www.camping-pertamina.com]** Fr Bonifacio take RN198 N, site on R in 4km. Med, hdg/mkd pitch, pt sl, pt shd; wc (some cont); chem disp; mv service pnt; baby facs; shwrs inc; el pnts (6A) inc; gas; Indtte (inc dryer); shop; rest, snacks; bar; playgrnd; htd pool; paddling pool; waterslide; beach 3km; tennis; cycle hire; fitness rm; wifi; entmnt; TV rm; 50% statics; dogs; poss cr; adv bkg; ccard acc; CKE/CCI. "Access to pitches diff; excel." ♦ 1 Apr-15 Oct. € 33.00 (CChq acc) 2009*

CALVI *10G2* (1.8km SE Coastal) *42.55228, 8.76423* **Camping Paduella, Route de Bastia, 20260 Calvi [04 95 65 06 16 or 04 95 65 13 20; fax 04 95 31 43 99; camping.paduella@wanadoo.fr; www.campingpaduella.com]** On N197 fr Calvi; on R 200m after rndabt by Casino supmkt. Med, mkd pitch, pt sl, terr, pt shd; wc chem disp; baby facs; shwrs inc; el pnts (6A) €3.65; Indtte; shop/supmkt; snacks; bar; playgrnd; sand beach 300m; 25% statics; dogs; poss cr; Eng spkn; quiet; CKE/CCI. "Poss best site in Calvi; immac san facs but slippery when wet, espec ramp; vg." ♦ 15 May-15 Oct. € 21.00 2013*

CALVI *1G2* (22.5km SW Urban) *42.46451, 8.68012* **La Morsetta Camping, Route Calvi-Porta, 20260 Calvi [04 95 65 25 28; fax 04 95 65 25 29; info@lamorsetta.net; www.lamorsetta.net]** Drive via the D81 fr Calvi to Galeria. Then about 12 km via the D81b coastal rd dir Calvi. Take the direct rte D81b fr Calvi, 20 km. Med, pt shd; wc; shwrs; el pnts €3.20; rest; bar; wifi; dog €1.70. ♦ 1 May-15 Oct. € 46.60 2013*

CARGESE *10H2* (4km N Coastal) *42.1625, 8.59791* **Camping Le Torraccia, Bagghiuccia, 20130 Cargèse [tel/fax 04 95 26 42 39; contact@camping-torraccia.com; www.camping-torraccia.com]** N fr Cargèse twd Porto on D81 for 3km. Site on L. Med, terr, pt shd; wc; baby facs; shwrs inc; ltd el pnts (6A) €3.10; Indtte; shop; rest 4km; snacks; bar; playgrnd; pool; sand beach 1km; games area; internet; no adv bkg; red low ssn. "Nearest site to Porto without diff traffic conditions." 21 Apr-30 Sep. € 20.00 2013*

CERVIONE *10G2* (7km NE Coastal) *42.36326, 9.52978* **Camping Merendella, Moriani-Plage, 20230 San Nicolao [04 95 38 53 47; fax 04 95 38 44 01; merendella@orange.fr; www.merendella.com]** Site 44km S of Bastia at Moriani-Plage; foll N193 & N198 fr Bastia to Moriani Plage, on E (beach side) of N198, 700m after supmkt. Med, hdg/mkd pitch, shd; wc; chem disp; mv service pnt; shwrs inc; el pnts (5A) €5.10; Indtte; shop & supmkt 1km; rest, snacks; bar; playgrnd; htd, covrd pool; dir access to beach adj; tennis 500m; games area; games rm; TV rm; no dogs Jul/Aug; adv bkg; quiet; ccard acc; CKE/CCI. "Idyllic beachside pitches; friendly, helpful, efficient staff; easy access; excel." ♦ 1 Apr-31 Oct. € 26.00 2010*

CERVIONE *10G2* (6km SE Coastal) *42.32155, 9.54546* **Camping Calamar, Prunete, 20221 Cervione [04 95 38 03 54 or 04 95 34 08 44 (LS); fax 04 95 31 17 09; contact@campingcalamar.eu; www.campingcalamar.eu]** On N198 S fr Prunete for 6km. Turn L at x-rds, site in 500m beside beach, sp. Sm, pt shd; wc; shwrs inc; el pnts €2.50; Indtte; shop 500m; tradsmn; snacks; bar; BBQ; sand beach adj; sailing; watersports; games area; dogs free; Eng spkn; adv bkg; quiet; red low ssn. "Friendly owner; pleasant site with trees & shrubs; excel." 1 Apr- 19 Oct. € 19.20 2013*

GHISONACCIA *10H2* (4km E Coastal) *41.99850, 9.44220* **Camping Arinella Bianca, Route de la Mer, Bruschetto, 20240 Ghisonaccia [04 95 56 04 78; fax 04 95 56 12 54; arinella@arinellabianca.com; www.arinellabianca.com]** S fr Bastia on N193/N198 approx 70km to Ghisonaccia. At Ghisonaccia foll sp opp pharmacy to beach (plage) & Rte de la Mer. In 3km turn R at rndabt & site well sp. NB When towing keep to main, coastal rds. Lge, hdg/mkd pitch, shd; wc (some cont); chem disp; mv service pnt; baby facs; shwrs inc; el pnts (6A) €5.50 (poss rev pol); gas; Indtte (inc dryer); shop; tradsmn; rest, snacks; bar; BBQ; playgrnd; htd pool; paddling pool; sand beach adj; fishing; watersports; tennis; horseriding adj; cycle hire; games area; games rm; wifi; entmnt; TV rm; 45% statics; dogs €6; Eng spkn; adv bkg; red low ssn; ccard acc; CKE/CCI. "Clean, well-run site; attractive lake in cent; trees make access to pitches diff; helpful owner & staff." ♦ 16 Apr-30 Sep. € 38.00 2009*

LECCI *10H2* (8km S Rural) *41.67200, 9.30152* **Camping Mulinacciu, 20137 Lecci [04 95 71 47 48; fax 04 95 71 54 82; infos@campingmulinacciu@.com; www.camping-mulinacciu.com]** N fr Porto-Vecchio on N198 for approx 10km. Cross double bdge over Rv Oso & turn L onto unmade rd opp D668 dir San Ciprianu. Site sp down this rd. Med, some hdstg, pt shd; wc; baby facs; shwrs inc; el pnts (5A) €3.50; Indtte; shop; tradsmn; rest, snacks; bar; playgrnd; pool; paddling pool; waterslide; sand beach 7km; fishing; tennis; games area; games rm; wifi; entmnt; TV; some statics; dogs €2; phone; Eng spkn; quiet. "Access to rv; friendly owners." 15 Jun-15 Sep. € 22.00 2010*

OLMETO *10H2* (3km S Coastal) *41.69803, 8.89667* **Camping Vigna Maggiore, 20113 Olmeto-Plage [04 95 76 02 07; fax 04 95 74 62 02; contact@vignamaggiore.com; www.vignamaggiore.com]** Site is approx 5km N of Propriano at junc N196 & D157. Med, terr, pt shd; wc; chem disp; mv waste; shwrs inc; el pnts €3.60; Indtte; rest; bar; playgrnd; pool; sand beach 1km; games area; some statics; poss cr; no adv bkg; CKE/CCI. 1 Apr-30 Sep. € 21.00 2009*

PIANOTTOLI CALDARELLO *10H2* (3.5km SE Coastal) *41.47272, 9.04327* **Camping Kevano Plage, Route du bord de mer 20131 Pianottoli-Caldarello [04 95 71 83 22; fax 04 95 71 83 83; campingkevano@gmail.com; www.campingkevano.com]** Turn off N196 in Pianottoli at x-rds onto D122 for 1km. Turn R in Caldarello, site on L in 2km. Med, mkd pitch, pt sl, terr, pt shd; wc; chem disp; mv service pnt; shwrs inc; el pnts (4-6A) €2.50; Indtte; shop; tradsmn; pizzeria; rest, snacks; bar; playgrnd; sand beach 400m; entmnt; TV; some statics; dogs €1; phone; poss cr; Eng spkn; adv bkg rec high ssn; quiet; ccard acc; CKE/CCI. "Beautiful, family-run site in macchia amongst huge boulders; san facs tired but clean; no dogs on beach Jul/Aug." ♦ ltd 27 Apr-30 Sep. € 42.00 2013*

PIETRACORBARA *10G2* (4km SE Coastal) *42.83908, 9.4736* **Camping La Pietra, Marine de Pietracorbara, 20233 Pietracorbara [04 95 35 27 49; fax 04 95 35 28 57; lapietra@wanadoo.fr; www.la-pietra.com]** Fr Bastia on D80 N. In 20km ent vill & turn L onto D232. Site on R in 1km at marina beach. Well sp. Med, hdg/mkd pitch, shd; htd wc; mv service pnt; baby facs; shwrs inc; el pnts (20A) €3.50; Indtte; shop; tradsmn; rest on beach; bar; BBQ; playgrnd; pool; sand beach 600m; lake fishing; tennis; wifi; TV; dogs €2.50; bus nr; Eng spkn; red low ssn; ccard acc; CKE/CCI. "Generous pitches; helpful owners; excel facs; beautiful pool; gd rest." ♦ 20 Mar-4 Nov. € 28.70 2011*

PORTO *10G2* (1km E Rural) *42.26275, 8.71020* **Camping Sole e Vista, Rue d'Ota, 20150 Porto [04 95 26 15 71; fax 04 95 26 10 79; campingsporto@voila.fr; www.camping-sole-e-vista.com]** On D81 Ajaccio-Calvi rd, turn E onto D124. Ent thro Spar supmkt car park in Porto. NB rd fr Calvi diff for c'vans. Lge, mkd pitch, terr, pt sl, shd; wc; chem disp; mv service pnt; shwrs inc; el pnts (16A) €3.50; gas; Indtte; shop adj; tradmsn; snacks; bar; BBQ; playgrnd; shgl beach 1.5km; internet; TV rm; some statics; dogs; poss cr; Eng spkn; adv bkg; quiet; red CKE/CCI. "Vg; modern san facs." 1 Apr-15 Oct. € 22.50 2010*

PORTO POLLO *10H2* (500m E Coastal) *41.71126, 8.80485* **Camping Alfonsi-U-Casselo, 20140 Serra-di-Ferro [04 95 74 01 80; fax 04 95 74 07 67]** Turn W onto D157 off N196 Propriano-Olmeto rd sp Porto-Pollo. After narr rv bdge turn L on D757. Site in 4km on L bef Porto-Pollo vill. Med, mkd pitch, pt shd; wc; mv service pnt; shwrs; el pnts (10A) €3; Indtte; shop 800m; supmkt in vill; rest high ssn; snacks; bar; sand beach adj; no dogs; poss cr; no adv bkg; poss noisy; ccard acc; CKE/CCI. "Pleasant site in gd situation." ♦ 1 Jun-30 Oct. € 22.60 2009*

PORTO VECCHIO *10H2* (5km NE Coastal) *41.62273, 9.2997* **Camping Les Ilots d'Or, Ste Trinité, Route de Marina di Fiori, 20137 Porto-Vecchio [04 95 70 01 30 or 04 95 36 91 75; fax 04 95 70 01 30; info@campinglesilotsdor.com; www.campinglesilotsdor.com]** Turn E off N198 5km N of Porto-Vecchio at Ste Trinité twd San Ciprianu. In 1km fork R, site in 300m on L. Med, pt sl, pt terr, shd; wc (cont); shwrs inc; el pnts (6A) €3.50; gas; Indtte; shop; rest, snacks; bar; sand beach adj; poss cr; quiet. "Well-organised site; helpful family owners; many vg beaches in easy reach." 2 May- 30 Sep. € 22.00 2013*

PORTO VECCHIO *10H2* (2km S Rural) *41.57084, 9.27609* **Camping U-Stabiacciu, Route de Palombaggia, 20137 Porto-Vecchio [04 95 70 37 17; fax 04 95 70 62 59; stabiacciu@wanadoo.fr; www.stabiacciu.com]** Foll ring-rd N198 to S Porto-Vecchio, take 1st L sp Palombaggia. Site in 50m. Ramps at site ent. Med, shd; wc (some cont); mv service pnt; shwrs inc; el pnts (5A) €3 (long lead poss req); Indtte; shop in ssn; tradsmn; rest, snacks; bar; BBQ; playgrnd; jacuzzis; sand beach 4km; 3% statics; dogs; phone; Eng spkn; rd noise; ccard acc; CKE/CCI. "Excel beaches; sh stay only." 1 Apr-14 Oct. € 19.00 2009*

PORTO VECCHIO *10H2* (8km W Coastal) *41.59336, 9.35718* **Camping Club La Chiappa (Naturist), 20137 Porto-Vecchio [04 95 70 00 31; fax 04 95 70 07 70; chiappa@wanadoo.fr; www.chiappa.com]** On N198 fr Bastia heading S thro Porto-Vecchio. 2km S turn L to Pointe de la Chiappa & foll camp sp. Lge, pt shd; wc; chem disp; shwrs; el pnts inc; Indtte; sauna; shop; rest; bar; playgrnd; pool; watersports; private sand beach adj; tennis; horseriding; entmnt; TV rm; 10% statics; dogs €6; adv bkg; quiet; red low ssn. "Superb site in lovely setting in naturist reserve; excel beach; vg facs; gd rest." 14 May-8 Oct. € 37.00 2011*

PORTO VECCHIO *10H2* (14km W Rural) *41.61788, 9.21236* **Campsite U Furu (Naturist), Route de Muratello, 20137 Porto-Vecchio [04 95 70 10 83; fax 04 95 70 63 47; contact@u-furu.com; www.u-furu.com]** Fr N on N198 turn R at rndabt sp Muratello. Foll sp to U-Furu. Sm, mkd pitch, terr, pt shd; wc; chem disp; shwrs inc; el pnts (6A); gas; Indtte; shop; tradsmn; rest; snacks; bar; pool; sw rv adj; games area; entmnt; 10% statics; twin axles; Eng spkn; adv bkg; quiet; CCI. "Site on beautiful sm rv with rock pools and waterfalls; fabulous beaches within 40 mins; easy access to Ospedale area & Bavella Pass." 15 May-15 Oct. € 37.40 2014*

SAGONE *10H2* (2km N Rural) *42.13030, 8.70550* **Sagone Camping, Route de Vico, 20118 Sagone [04 95 28 04 15; sagone.camping@wanadoo.fr; www.camping-sagone.com]** Fr Sagone dir Cargèse then D70 dir Vico, site sp. Lge, mkd pitch, pt shd; wc; chem disp; mv service pnt; baby facs; shwrs inc; el pnts €4.50; Indtte (inc dryer); shop; rest, snacks; bar; BBQ; playgrnd; pool; beach 2km; tennis 100m; cycle hire; horseriding 1km; entmnt; TV rm; 10% statics; dogs €2.30; adv bkg; quiet. ♦ 1 May-30 Sep. € 25.70 (CChq acc) 2011*

ST FLORENT *10G2* (1km SW Coastal) *42.67394, 9.29205* **Camping U Pezzo, Route de la Roya, 20217 St Florent [tel/fax 04 95 37 01 65; contact@upezzo.com; www.upezzo.com]** Exit St Florent for L'Ile-Rousse on D81 then N199 Route de la Plage. After 2km sharp R immed after x-ing bdge. Med, terr, pt shd; wc; mv service pnt; baby facs; shwrs inc; el pnts (10A) €4; Indtte; shop; rest, snacks; bar; sand beach adj; fishing; sailing; windsurfing; waterslide; horseriding; mini-farm for children; dogs €3.50; adv bkg; quiet; red low ssn; CKE/CCI. "Pleasant site." 01 Apr-15 Oct. € 19.00 2013*

SERRA DI FERRO (CORSICA) see Porto Pollo *10H2*

SOLENZARA *10H2* (12km W Rural) *41.83495, 9.32144* **Camping U Ponte Grossu, Route de Bavella, 20145 Sari-Solenzara [04 95 48 26 61 or 06 64 79 80 46 (mob); info@upontegrossu.com; www.upontegrossu.com]** Fr N198, take D268 to U Ponte Grossu. Sm, mkd pitch, terr, pt shd; wc; chem disp; mv service pnt; shwrs inc; el pnts (6A); rest; snacks; bar; rv adj; dogs; adv bkg; red low ssn; CCI. "Site alongside rv; canyoning; rafting; access to fab mountain areas; vg." ♦ ltd 1 May-20 Sep. € 25.00 2014*

VENACO *10G2* (3km E Rural) *42.22388, 9.19364* **Camping La Ferme de Peridundellu, 20231 Venaco [tel/fax 04 95 47 09 89 / 06 12 95 51 65 (mob); campingvenaco@wanadoo.fr; http://campingvenaco.monsite-orange.fr]** S on N200 fr Corte for 15km; R on D143; at bdge keep R twds Venaco; site on L in 1.5km on bend. Sm, pt sl, pt shd; htd wc; chem disp (wc); shwrs inc; el pnts (6-10A) €5.; Indtte; shop 2km; tradsmn; rest adj; snacks & bar 2km; quiet; CKE/CCI. "CL-type site; beautifully situated; gd walking country; friendly owner; highly rec." Apr-Sep. € 17.00 2013*

Côte d'Azur

Regional Introduction

Monaco

Welcome to Côte d'Azur

Part of the French Riviera, this region is best known for its elegant lifestyle.

Much of its popularity can be attributed to sunny, dry summers and mild winters that the region enjoys. The beaches are a real attraction, and the region's harbours make a great place to watch the world go by, look out for glamorous yachts and celebrities galore.

The perfumed streets of Grasse and the historical cobbles of Vence are exciting places to explore and offer many opportunities for you to enjoy a relaxing drink or meal one of the traditional boutique cafes.

Local highlights

The local speciality of Ratatouille is not to be missed – traditionally served as a side dish, it is now equally popular as a main. The best way to sample local produce is at one of the many traditional markets found in the harbour towns.

One of the most famous events of this region is Cannes Film Festival. This prestigious celebration sees the rich and famous flock to the area.

Major towns and cities

- Grasse – seen as the world's perfume capital.
- Cannes – a busy tourist destination.
- Vence – a medieval walled village set in a hillside.
- Nice – the natural beauty of the area attracts many artists.

Regional attractions

- Castle Hill, Nice – beautiful sweeping views of the city, Alps and Mediterranean.
- Cathédrale Orthodoxe Russe St-Nicolas, Nice – a Russian cathedral with stunning architecture.
- Promenade Le Corbusier – stunning views out to sea and within walking distance to Monaco.
- Monaco – soak up the local culture with a visit to this sovereign city-state.

Find out more

www.cotedazur-tourisme.com

Tel: (0)4 92 99 84 22 Cannes Tourist Office
Tel: (0)8 92 70 74 07 Nice Tourist Office

ADRETS DE L'ESTEREL, LES see Napoule, La *10F4*

ANTIBES *10E4* (3km N Coastal) *43.61009, 7.12473* **Camping le Logis de la Brague, 1221 Route de Nice, 06600 Antinbes [04 93 33 54 72; contact@camping-logisbrague.com; www.camping-logisbrague.com]** N fr Antibes on D6007 Route de Nice; site on L in 2km, just after sm rv brdge. Med, pt shd; wc; chem disp; mv service pnt; shwrs inc; el pnts (6A) €4.50 (poss rev pol); shops 3km; rest; bar; BBQ; pebble beach 250m; dogs €2; bus & train 250m; poss cr; rd & rlwy noise; ccard not acc; red low ssn. "Basic site; access to beach across busy main rd & under rlwy; helpful owner; gd." 2 May-30 Sep. € 22.00 2011*

> "I need an on-site restaurant"
>
> We do our best to make sure site information is correct, but it is always best to check any must-have facilities are still available or will be open during your visit.

ANTIBES *10E4* (3.5km N Coastal) *43.61101, 7.11675* **Camping Antipolis, Ave du Pylone, La Brague, 06600 Antibes [04 93 33 93 99; fax 04 92 91 02 00; contact@camping-antipolis.com; www.camping-antipolis.com]** Exit A8 at Biot dir Marineland. In 800m turn R & foll site sp. Lge, mkd pitch, hdstg, unshd; wc (some cont); chem disp; shwrs; el pnts (10A) inc; gas; lndtte (inc dryer); shop; tradsmn; rest, snacks; bar; BBQ; playgrnd; 2 pools (1 htd); paddling pool; shgl beach 800m; tennis; cycle hire; games area; wifi; entmnt; 30% statics; no dogs; phone; train 1km; no c'vans over 6m; adv bkg; quiet; ccard acc; CKE/CCI. "Situated beside m'way, but pitches away fr rd; sm pitches bet statics; walk to beach along busy rds & across dual c'way; excel pool complex & activities; some pitches private san facs; knocking in pegs diff due lge sized gravel; unshd due severe pruning (2010)." ♦ 2 Apr-26 Sep. € 29.00 (CChq acc) 2010*

ANTIBES *10E4* (3.5km N Coastal) *43.61270, 7.12522* **Camping Les Embruns, 63 Route de Biot, Quartier de la Brague, 06600 Antibes [04 93 33 33 35; fax 04 93 74 46 70; contact@campingembruns-antibes.com; www.campingembruns-antibes.com]** Fr Antibes take D6007 sp Nice, after 3.5km at rndabt with palm trees turn inland into Route de Biot; site sp on L. Sm, pt shd; wc; baby facs; shwrs inc; el pnts (5) €3; lndtte; snacks; bar; shop; shgl beach adj; fishing & watersports adj; cycle hire; tennis; TV; dogs €3; bus & metro adj; adv bkg; poss noise fr adj rd & rlwy, aslo fr adj amusement park; ccard acc; red low ssn. "Lovely, well-run site; helpful owner; walking dist beach, bus & metro; sm pitches; no turning space - not suitable lge o'fits; some pitches waterlogged in wet weather; gd." 11 Apr-31 Oct. € 24.00 2011*

AURIBEAU SUR SIAGNE see Grasse *10E4*

BAR SUR LOUP, LE see Grasse *10E4*

CAGNES SUR MER *10E4* (3km N Rural) *43.69018, 7.15643* **Camping Le Todos, 159 Vallon-des-Vaux, 06800 Cagnes-sur-Mer [04 93 31 20 05; fax 04 92 12 81 66; info@letodos.fr; www.letodos.fr]** Fr Aix on A8 exit junc 47 & foll dir Cagnes-sur-Mer/Nice on D6007 (do not foll sp 'Centre Ville'). After 1st traff lts beside racecourse strt on for 2km, then turn L dir Val Fleuri, site in 3km. Fr Nice take D6098 coast rd dir Cannes. Shortly after Cagnes turn R opp Le Port & foll sp Camping. Turn R then L at traff lts, site on L in 3km opp Camping Green Park. Med, mkd pitch, some terr, pt shd; wc; chem disp; mv service pnt; shwrs inc; el pnts (6-10A) €4.10-5.70; lndtte; tradsmn; shop; rest, snacks, bar at adj Camping Green Park; BBQ (gas/elec); playgrnd; pool & use of htd pool at Green Park; sand beach 4.5km; tennis 400m; cycle hire; games area; internet; TV; mainly statics; dogs €5; poss cr; adv bkg; quiet; red low ssn. "Owners also own Camping Green Park - some facs shared; v ltd touring pitches." ♦ ltd 22 Mar-12 Oct. € 36.00 2009*

CAGNES SUR MER *10E4* (3.5km N Rural) *43.68717, 7.15589* **Camping Le Val Fleuri, 139 Vallon-des-Vaux, 06800 Cagnes-sur-Mer [tel/fax 04 93 31 21 74; valfleur2@wanadoo.fr; www.campingvalfleuri.fr]** Fr Nice take D6007 W twd Cannes. On app Cagnes turn R & foll sp Camping; site on R after 3km, well sp. NB 3.3m height restriction on this rte. Sm, terr, pt shd; wc (some cont); shwrs; el pnts (3-10A) €4 shop 3km; tradsmn; rest; shgl beach 4km; playgrnd; htd pool; wifi; entmnt; dogs €1.50; poss cr; Eng spkn; adv bkg; red low ssn. "Gd, improving site, divided by rd (not busy); some sm pitches; helpful, friendly owners; gd; bus to Nice." 5 Apr - 27 Sept. € 34.30 2014*

> "Satellite navigation makes touring much easier"
>
> Remember most sat navs don't know if you're towing or in a larger vehicle – always use yours alongside maps and site directions.

CAGNES SUR MER *10E4* (2km S Coastal) *43.63128, 7.12993* **Camping Parc des Maurettes, 730 Ave du Docteur Lefebvre, 06270 Villeneuve-Loubet [04 93 20 91 91; fax 04 93 73 77 20; info@parcdesmaurettes.com; www.parcdesmaurettes.com]** Fr Nice exit A8 junc 47, turn L onto D6007 dir Antibes; foll sp Intermarché, then R into Rue des Maurettes; site in 250m. N fr Cannes on A8 exit Villeneuve-Loubet-Plage junc 46; foll D241 over D6007 & rwly line, U-turn back over rwly line, then R onto D6007 dir Antibes as above. NB Site on steep cliff with narr winding rds packed with trees; diff ent. Med, mkd pitch, terr, pt shd; htd wc; chem disp; mv service pnt; some serviced pitches; shwrs inc; el pnts (3-10A) €5.30; gas; lndtte; shops adj; snacks; playgrnd; jacuzzi; shgl beach 500m; wifi; sat TV; dogs €4; train Nice 400m; poss cr; Eng spkn; adv bkg rec high ssn; quiet; ccard acc; red long stay; CKE/CCI. "Well-kept site; variable pitch size/price." ♦ 10 Jan-15 Nov. € 44.30 2014*

⊞ **CAGNES SUR MER** *10E4* (7km S Rural) *43.62027, 7.12583* **Camping La Vieille Ferme, 296 Blvd des Groules, 06270 Villeneuve-Loubet-Plage [04 93 33 41 44; fax 04 93 33 37 28; info@vieilleferme.com; www.vieilleferme.com]** Fr W (Cannes) take Antibes exit 44 fr A8, foll D35 dir Antibes 'Centre Ville'. At lge junc turn onto D6007, Ave de Nice, twd Biot & Villeneuve-Loubet sp Nice (rlwy line on R). Just after Marineland turn L onto Blvd des Groules. Fr E (Nice) leave A8 at junc 47 to join D6007 twd Antibes, take 3rd turning after Intermarché supmkt; site well sp fr D6007. Med, hdg/mkd pitch, pt terr, pt sl, pt shd; htd wc; chem disp; mv service pnt; serviced pitches; baby facs; shwrs inc; el pnts (2A-10A) €3 - €7; gas; Indtte (inc dryer); tradsmn; supmkt 800m; snacks; BBQ (gas/elec); playgrnd; htd covrd pool; paddling pool; shgl beach 1km (across busy rd & rlwy); games rm; wifi; games/TV rm; 40% statics; dogs €2.50; no c'vans/m'vans over 8m; bus, train nrby; Eng spkn; adv bkg; some aircraft & rd noise; ccard acc; red long stay/low ssn. "Peaceful, well-kept family-run site; well-drained pitches, some lge; san facs need refurb (2010); beach not suitable children & non-swimmers; excel pool; gd walking, cycling & dog walking as lge park adj; vg value low ssn; excel." ♦ € 28.00 SBS - C22 2013*

> "There aren't many sites open at this time of year"
>
> If you're travelling outside peak season remember to call ahead to check site opening dates – even if the entry says 'open all year'.

CAGNES SUR MER *10E4* (4km SW Rural) *43.66001, 7.1000* **Parc Saint James Le Sourire, Route de Grasse, 06270 Villeneuve-Loubet [04 93 20 96 11; fax 04 93 22 07 52; lesourire@camping-parcsaintjames.com; www.camping-parcsaintjames.com]** Exit A8 at junc 47; take D2 to Villeneuve; at rndbt take D2085 sp Grasse. Site on L in 2km. Sp Le Sourire. Med, hdg pitch, hdstg, pt shd; htd wc; shwrs inc; el pnts (6A) inc; Indtte; tradsmn; rest; bar; playgrnd; htd pools; shgl beach 5km; tennis, golf & horseriding nr; games area; entmnt; 70% statics; dogs €5; Eng spkn; adv bkg; ccard acc; red long stay/low ssn. "Site shabby & poorly maintained; park in visitors' car park bef registering; conv Nice, Cannes & beaches." ♦ 7 Apr-29 Sep. € 40.00 2013*

CAGNES SUR MER *10E4* (1km NW Urban) *43.67159, 7.13845* **Camping Le Colombier, 35 Chemin de Ste Colombe, 06800 Cagnes-sur-Mer [tel/fax 04 93 73 12 77; campinglecolombier06@wanadoo.fr; www.campinglecolombier.com]** N fr Cagnes cent foll 1-way system dir Vence. Half way up hill turn R at rndabt dir Cagnes-sur-Mer & R at next island. Site on L 300m, sp fr town cent. Sm, hdg/mkd pitch, pt shd; htd wc; chem disp; mv service pnt; shwrs inc; el pnts (2-16A) €2-8; Indry rm; shop 400m; rest 800m; snacks; bar; no BBQ; playgrnd, sm pool adj; TV; beach 2.5km; cycle hire; some statics; no dogs Jul/Aug; phone; Eng spkn; quiet; red long stay/low ssn/CKE/CCI. "Friendly, family-run site." 30 Apr-1 Sep. € 22.20 2013*

> "That's changed – Should I let The Club know?"
>
> If you find something on site that's different from the site entry, fill in a report and let us know. See www.caravanclub.co.uk/europereport.

CAGNES SUR MER *10E4* (4km NW Rural) *43.68449, 7.07297* **Camping Le Vallon Rouge, Route de Gréolières, 06480 La Colle-sur-Loup [04 93 32 86 12 or 06 82 90 93 05 (mob); fax 04 93 32 80 09; info@auvallonrouge.com; www.auvallonrouge.com]** Exit A8 junc 47 onto D6007 dir Nice then D2 to Villeneuve-Loubet. Foll sp Villeneuve-Loubet over rv & thro sh tunnel to rndabt. Turn L at rndabt & foll sps for D6 La Colle-sur-Loup; after La Colle-sur-Loup site on R in 2.5km. NB Lge o'fits park in lay-by & ask at recep bef tackling steep, winding downhill ent driveway. NB Ask recep for code for rear gate on leaving. Med, mkd pitch, hdstg, shd; wc; chem disp; mv service pnt; baby facs; shwrs inc; solarium; el pnts (10A) inc; Indtte (inc dryer); sm shop; tradsmn; rest, snacks; bar; BBQ (gas/elec); playgrnd; pool; paddling pool; sand/shgl beach 9km; fishing; cycle hire; games area; wifi; entmnt; games/TV rm; 40% statics; dogs €3.50; adv bkg; ccard acc; red low ssn; CKE/CCI. "On banks of Rv Loup; conv Nice, Cannes, St Paul-de-Vence & Grasse; steep drop fr pitches down to shallow rv; Sat mkt; vg site." ♦ 3 Apr-26 Sep. € 35.50 2010*

CAGNES SUR MER *10E4* (4km NW Rural) *43.68272, 7.08391* **Camping Les Pinèdes, Route de Pont de Pierre, 06480 La Colle-sur-Loup [04 93 32 98 94; fax 04 93 32 50 20; info@lespinedes.com; www.lespinedes.com]** Exit A8 junc 47; take D6007 dir Nice, then D2 sp Villeneuve-Loubet; turn R at rndabt sp Villeneuve-Loubet & cross rv bdge; go thro sh tunnel, other side is Cagnes-sur-Mer & rndabt; turn L onto D6 to Colle-sur-Loup; site on R sh dist after Colle-sur-Loup. NB Take 2nd turning into site (1st leads to rest). Lge, hdg/mkd pitch, hdstg, pt sl, terr, pt shd; wc; chem disp; mv service pnt; serviced pitches; shwrs inc; el pnts (6-10A) €4.60-5.90 (poss rev pol); lndtte; shop (high ssn) & 1.5km; tradsmn; rest, snacks; bar; BBQ (gas/elec); playgrnd; htd pool; paddling pool; solarium; sand beach 13km; rv fishing & sw adj; tennis, horseriding adj; archery; games area; wifi; entmnt; games/TV rm; 20% statics; dogs €3.60; no c'vans over 6m (excluding towbar) & m'vans over 8m high ssn; no twin axle c'vans; Eng spkn; adv bkg; quiet; ccard acc over €50; red long stay/low ssn/CKE/CCI. "Excel, family-run site set in pine & oak trees; helpful & friendly; spacious pitches; steep access to pitches - poss diff lge o'fits, help avail; adequate san facs; gd rest at site ent; highly rec; vg site has everything you need; spacious pitches; excel pool." 22 Mar-29 Sep. € 53.00 SBS - C30 2014*

See advert on previous page

CANNES *10F4* (3km NE Urban) *43.55610, 6.96060* **Camping Parc Bellevue, 67 Ave Maurice Chevalier, 06150 Cannes [04 93 47 28 97; fax 04 93 48 66 25; contact@parcbellevue.com; www.parcbellevue.com]** A8 exit junc 41 twd Cannes. Foll N7 & at junc controlled by traff lts, get in L lane. Turn L & in 100m turn L across dual c'way, foll sp for site. Site in 400m on L after sports complex - steep ramp at ent. Lge, mkd pitch, pt shd; wc; chem disp; baby facs; shwrs; el pnts (6A) €4; gas; lndtte; shops; rest, snacks; bar; htd pool; sandy beach 1.5km; wifi; entmnt; sat TV; many statics; dogs; phone; bus/train nr; poss cr; Eng spkn; adv bkg; rd noise; red low ssn; CKE/CCI. "Site on 2 levels; gd security; gd san facs; some pitches long way fr facs; many steps to gd pool; helpful; conv beaches & A8; green oasis in busy area; gd bus to prom; no m'van facs; rec use Sat Nav; not rec in wet weather; no hdstg; o'fits have to be towed off pitches in bad weather." ♦ ltd 1 Apr-30 Sep. € 17.50 (CChq acc) 2013*

CANNES *10F4* (4km NW Urban) *43.56469, 6.97765* **Ranch Camping, L'Aubarède, Chemin de St Joseph, 06110 Le Cannet [04 93 46 00 11; fax 04 93 46 44 30; www.leranchcamping.fr]** Exit A8 at junc 42 Le Cannet. Foll sp L'Aubarède & then La Bocca. Site well sp via D9. Med, hdg pitch, pt sl, terr, pt shd; htd wc (some cont); baby facs; shwrs inc; el pnts (6A) inc; lndtte (inc dryer); shop; tradsmn; playgrnd; htd, covrd pool; sand beach 2km; games area; wifi; 10% statics; dogs €1; bus; adv bkg summer ssn ess by March; some rd noise; quiet. "Conv location; pitches at cent or top of site quieter; vg, modern san facs; gd." ♦ 1 Apr-30 Oct. € 25.00 2009*

COLLE SUR LOUP, LA see Cagnes sur Mer *10E4*

GRASSE *10E4* (8km NE Rural) *43.70230, 6.99515* **FFCC Camping des Gorges du Loup, Chemin des Vergers, 06620 Le Bar-sur-Loup [04 93 42 45 06; info@lesgorgesduloup.com; www.lesgorgesduloup.com]** E fr Gasse on D2085 sp Chateauneuf-Grasse; in 4km turn L onto D2210 to Le Bar-sur-Loup. Site well sp. Med, mkd pitch, some hdstg, terr, pt shd; wc (some cont); chem disp; shwrs inc; el pnts (6-10A) €3.50-5.50 (poss rev pol); gas; lndtte; ice: shop; tradsmn; playgrnd; pool; shgl beach; table tennis,bowls, basket ball;TV rm; 20% statics; dogs €3; phone; bus 1km; Eng spkn; adv bkg; quiet; ccard not acc; red low ssn; CKE/CCI. "Peaceful, well-kept site with superb views; helpful, pleasant owners; clean san facs; steep access rds; owner will site c'van; gd hilly cycling; highly rec." 6 Apr-21 Sep. € 27.00 2013*

GRASSE *10E4* (5.5km SE Urban) *43.63507, 6.94859* **Camping Caravaning La Paoute, 160 Route de Cannes, 06130 Grasse [04 93 09 11 42; fax 04 93 40 06 40; camppaoute@hotmail.com; www.campinglapaoute.com]** Sp fr Grasse town cent on Route de Cannes (secondary rd to Cannes, NOT D6185), a 10 min drive. Med, hdg/mkd pitch, sl, terr, pt shd; wc; chem disp; mv service pnt; shwrs inc; el pnts (10A) €4; lndtte (inc dryer); tradsmn; supmkt nr; snacks; bar; playgrnd; htd pool; games rm; wifi; 15% statics; dogs; bus 500m; poss cr; red low ssn/ long stay; CKE/CCI. "Gd site; m'vans acc out of ssn but adv bkg req." 1 Apr-30 Sep. € 21.00 2010*

GRASSE *10E4* (8km S Rural) *43.60650, 6.90216* **Camping Le Parc des Monges, 635 Chemin du Gabre, 06810 Auribeau-sur-Siagne [tel/fax 04 93 60 91 71; contact@parcdesmonges.fr; www.parcdesmonges.com]** Exit A8 junc 40 or 41 onto D6007 dir Grasse; then onto D109 becoming D9; foll sp to Auribeau-sur-Siagne; site on rd to Le Gabre. Med, hdg pitch, shd; htd wc (some cont); chem disp; mv service pnt; baby facs; fam bthrm; shwrs inc; el pnts (4-10A) €3.50-5.50; gas 2km; lndtte (inc dryer); ice; shop 600m; tradsmn; rest, snacks & bar 2km; playgrnd; htd pool; rv sw adj; fishing nrby; activities & entmnt; 7% statics; dogs €2.50; phone; bus adj; poss cr; Eng spkn; adv bkg; quiet; ccard acc; red low ssn; CKE/CCI. "Vg site by Rv Siagne; rv not accessible fr site; watch out for branches when manoeurvering." ♦ 4 Apr-26 Sep. € 23.00 2012*

⊞ **GRASSE** *10E4* (8km NW Rural) *43.69088, 6.86450* **Camping Parc des Arboins, 755 Route Napoléon, 06460 St Vallier-de-Thiey [04 93 42 63 89; fax 04 93 09 61 54; contact@parc-des-arboins.com]** N fr Cannes on D6085 foll sp thro Grasse for Digne; approx 1.5km bef vill of St Vallier-de-Thiey, site located on R of rd. Med, mkd pitch, hdstg, shd; htd wc; mv service pnt; shwrs; el pnts (3-15A) €3-4; gas; lndtte (inc dryer); shop; supmkt 1.5km; rest, snacks; bar; playgrnd; htd pool; paddling pool; sand beach 30km; tennis 1.5km; golf 10km; games area; entmnt; TV rm; 95% statics; dogs €1.20; adv bkg; quiet but poss rd noise; CKE/CCI. "Lovely position on hillside; ltd touring pitches; ltd space to manoeuvre; 'quaint' san facs (own san rec); vg rest adj." € 20.50 2010*

⊞ **NAPOULE, LA** *10F4* (2km N Coastal) *43.53913, 6.94273* **Camping Les Cigales, 505 Ave de la Mer, Quartier d'Etang, 06210 Mandelieu-la-Napoule [04 93 49 23 53; fax 04 93 49 30 45; campingcigales@wanadoo.fr; www.lescigales.com]** Take Mandelieu exit junc 40 fr A8 & turn R twice in Mandelieu cent into Ave des Ecureuils, sp Campings. Pass under a'route & in 1km turn L at T-junc into Ave de la Mer. Site in 50m on L. Or on DN7 fr Fréjus turn R at rndabt with fountains app Mandelieu. Or fr coast rd turn inland at bdge over Rv La Siagne into Blvd de la Mer & site in 1km on R. Med, hdg/mkd pitch, hdstg, shd; htd wc; chem disp; mv service pnt; baby facs; shwrs inc; el pnts (6A) €5.50; Indtte; shop 1.5km; rest, snacks; bar; playgrnd; pool; sand beach 800m; solarium; dir access to rv; fishing, sailing & other waterports 800m; wifi; entmnt; 50% statics; dogs €1.50; bus adj; poss cr; Eng spkn; adv bkg; some noise fr rd, rlwy, aircraft; ccard acc; red low ssn/long stay. "Excel location; ltd facs low ssn; gd pool; conv local transport; excel." ♦ € 41.00 2010*

"I like to fill in the reports as I travel from site to site"

You'll find report forms at the back of this guide, or you can fill them in online at www.caravaclub.co.uk/europereport.

NAPOULE, LA *10F4* (2km N Urban) *43.53507, 6.94258* **Camping Les Pruniers, 18 Rue de la Pinéa, 06210 Mandelieu-la-Napoule [04 93 49 99 23; fax 04 93 49 37 45; contact@bungalow-camping.com; www.bungalow-camping.com]** Fr A8 exit junc 40 & turn R twice in Mandelieu cent into Blvd des Ecureuils sp 'Sofitel Royal Casino'. Pass under a'route & in 1km turn L at T-junc into Ave de la Mer. At rndabt bear R & next R sp Pierre-Vacances. Turn R in 50m, site at end of rd. On DN7 fr Fréjus, turn R at rndabt with fountains app Mandelieu. Fr coast rd take slip rd for Mandelieu. Sm, mkd pitch, hdstg; shd; wc; chem disp; mv service pnt; shwrs inc; el pnts (5-20A) €4; Indtte; shop (high ssn) & 1.2km; snacks, bar in vill; playgrnd; htd pool; paddling pool; sand beach 500m; sea & rv fishing; wifi; entmnt; 60% statics (sep area); dogs €1.50; no twin-axle c'vans & max length c'van 6m, m'van 7m; poss cr; Eng spkn; adv bkg; quiet; red low ssn; ccard acc; red low ssn; CKE/CCI. "Delightful, peaceful site on rv opp marina; dated, clean san facs; excel base for area; easy cycling to beach & Cannes." 1 Apr-15 Oct. € 37.00 2010*

NAPOULE, LA *10F4* (3km N Urban/Coastal) *43.5234, 6.9308* **Camping Coté Mer (Formaly Camping de la Ferme), Blvd du Bon Puits, 06210 Mandelieu-la-Napoule [04 93 49 94 19; fax 04 93 49 18 52; info@campingcotemer.fr; www.campingdelaferme.com]** Fr A8 exit junc 40 & turn L in Mandelieu cent sp Fréjus; 200m after rndabt with palm tree centre, fork R into Ave Maréchal Juin & strt into Blvd du Bon Puits. Avoid La Napoule vill when towing. Med, shd; wc; shwrs €0.50; el pnts (10A) inc; gas; Indtte; shops; rest, snacks; bar; sand beach 700m; some statics; dogs €4.; poss v cr; adv bkg; quiet; red low ssn. "Nice atmosphere; some pitches v sm; friendly, helpful staff; dated but clean facs; pleasant sm bar & rest." ♦ 25 Mar-1 Oct. € 36.00 2013*

⊞ **NAPOULE, LA** *10F4* (5km N Urban/Coastal) *43.52547, 6.93354* **Camping L'Argentière, 264 Blvd du Bon-Puits, 06210 Mandelieu-la-Napoule [tel/fax 04 93 49 95 04; www.campingdelargentiere.com]** Fr A8 turn L in Mandelieu cent (sp Fréjus). At rndabt with fountains take 2nd exit, at next rndabt take 2nd exit to L of BP stn, at next rndabt take 2nd exit, site on R in 150m. Avoid La Napoule vill when towing. Med, hdg/mkd pitch, hdstg, pt shd; wc; chem disp; mv service pnt; shwrs inc; el pnts (10A) €3.20; Indtte; shop; hypmkt 1km; rest, snacks; bar; sand beach 800m; fishing; entmnt; TV rm; 80% statics; dogs €3; bus; Eng spkn; adv bkg ess in ssn; poss cr; quiet; CKE/CCI. "Clean san facs; lovely local beaches, conv to town." € 31.00 2012*

OPIO see Grasse *10E4*

PEGOMAS see Cannes *10F4*

PUGET THENIERS *10E4* (2km NW Rural) *43.95801, 6.85980* **Camping L'Origan (Naturist), 2160 Route de Savé, 06260 Puget-Théniers [04 93 05 06 00; fax 04 93 05 09 34; origan@wanadoo.fr; www.origan-village.com]** On N202 fr Entrevaux (dir Nice) at Puget-Théniers, immed turn L at rlwy x-ing (sp), site approx 1km up track. Med, hdg/mkd pitch, hdstg, pt sl, terr, pt shd; htd wc; sauna; shwrs inc; el pnts (6A) €4; gas 2km; Indtte; shop; tradsmn; rest, snacks; bar; BBQ; playgrnd; htd pool; paddling pool; waterslide; fishing; tennis; archery; wifi; TV rm; 50% statics; dogs €2.50; phone; train to Nice; adv bkg; Eng spkn; ccard acc; red low ssn; INF card. "Sm pitches not suitable o'fits over 6m; hilly site but pitches level; facs run down early ssn (2009); interesting area; great views; ent noise poss high ssn." ♦ Easter-3 Oct. € 38.00 2014*

ROQUETTE SUR SIAGNE, LA see Cannes *10F4*

ST LAURENT DU VAR see Cagnes sur Mer *10E4*

ST VALLIER DE THIEY see Grasse *10E4*

"We must tell The Club about that great site we found"

Get your site reports in by mid-August and we'll do our best to get your updates into the next edition.

SOLLIES PONT *10F3* (1.5km SE Rural) *43.18519, 6.06324* **Camping à la Ferme Le Petit Réal (Cambray), Le Cros de Castel, 1095 Chemin de Sauvebonne, 8310 Solliès-Pont [04 94 28 94 80; mireille.cambray@wanadoo.fr; http://cambray.pagesperso-orange.fr]** Exit A57 junc 8 onto D97 dir Solliès-Pont; in 500m turn L at 2nd rndabt onto D58; cont thro Solliès-Pont on D58 dir Le Crau & Hyères; site on L in 2km. Sm, hdg/mkd pitch, pt shd; wc; chem disp (septic tank friendly chemicals only); shwrs inc; el pnts (2-3A) €1.90-2.40; farm fruit & veg shop nrby; table tennis; quiet. "Quiet site bet orchards with mountain view; clean modern san facs; chem disp at mv service pnt at Casino supmkt in 2km; conv A57; vg." ♦ ltd 1 Apr-30 Sep. € 10.60 2011*

SOSPEL *10E4* (4km NW Rural) *43.89702, 7.41685* **Camping Domaine Ste Madeleine, Route de Moulinet, 06380 Sospel [04 93 04 10 48; fax 04 93 04 18 37; camp@camping-sainte-madeleine.com; www.camping-sainte-madeleine.com]** Take D2566 fr Sospel NW to Turini & site 4km on L; sp fr town. Rd to site fr Menton steep with many hairpins. Med, mkd pitch, pt sl, pt terr, shd; wc; chem disp; mv service pnt; shwrs €0.50; el pnts (10A) €2.90; gas; Indtte; pool; beach 20km; rv 3km; dogs €1.50; Eng spkn; adv bkg rec high ssn; quiet; 10% red low ssn; CKE/CCI. "Friendly, busy site; gd facs; gd pool but has no shallow end; stunning scenery." 31 Marr-29 Sep. € 21.00 2011*

"I need an on-site restaurant"

We do our best to make sure site information is correct, but it is always best to check any must-have facilities are still available or will be open during your visit.

TENDE *10E4* (9km S Rural) *44.00746, 7.55448* **Camp Municipal, Quartier Barnabin, 06540 Fontan [04 93 04 55 86]** Site is on D6204 200m N of Fontan on rvside. Sm, pt sl, pt shd; wc (some cont); shwrs inc; el pnts; Indtte; shop, rest, snacks, bar 200m; playgrnd; dogs; phone; adv bkg; some rd noise; CKE/CCI. "Pleasant site nr scenic vill of Saorge; site yourself if recep shut (ltd open hrs)." 15 Jun-15 Sep. 2009*

"Satellite navigation makes touring much easier"

Remember most sat navs don't know if you're towing or in a larger vehicle – always use yours alongside maps and site directions.

VENCE *10E4* (3km W Rural) *43.7117, 7.0905* **Camping Domaine La Bergerie, 1330 Chemin de la Sine, 06140 Vence [04 93 58 09 36; fax 04 93 59 80 44; info@camping-domainedelabergerie.com; www.camping-domainedelabergerie.com]** Fr A8 exit junc 47 & foll sp Vence thro Cagnes-sur-Mer. Take detour to W around Vence foll sp Grasse/Tourrettes-sur-Loup. At rndabt beyond viaduct take last exit, foll site sp S thro La Sine town; long, narr rd to site, up driveway on R. Lge, mkd pitch, hdstg, pt sl, shd; wc; chem disp; mv service pnt; baby facs; shwrs inc; el pnts (5A); gas; Indtte; shop on site & 5km; tradsmn; rest, snacks; bar; BBQ (gas only); playgrnd; pool; paddling pool; lake fishing; tennis; games area; dogs; poss cr; Eng spkn; adv bkg; quiet; ccard acc; red long stay/low ssn; CKE/CCI. "Shady site; helpful staff; clean san facs; no twin-axles or c'vans over 5m; gd dog walks; Vence lovely & excel touring base." ♦ 25 Mar-15 Oct. € 27.00 (CChq acc) 2014*

See advertisement

"There aren't many sites open at this time of year"

If you're travelling outside peak season remember to call ahead to check site opening dates – even if the entry says 'open all year'.

VENCE *10E4* (6km W Rural) *43.69958, 7.00785* **Camping Les Rives du Loup, Route de la Colle, 06140 Tourrettes-sur-Loup [04 93 24 15 65; fax 04 93 24 53 70; info@rivesduloup.com; www.rivesduloup.com]** Exit A8 junc 47 at Cagnes-sur-Mer. Foll sp La Colle-sur-Loup, then Bar-sur-Loup (D6). Site in Gorges-du-Loup valley, 3km bef Pont-du-Loup. Sm, pt shd; wc; baby facs; shwrs inc; el pnts (5A) €3.50 (poss rev pol); Indtte; shop; rest, snacks; bar; playgrnd; pool; fishing; tennis; guided walks; horseriding 5km; wifi; 60% statics; dogs €3.50; adv bkg; quiet. "Many activities avail; beautiful location; cramped pitches." 1 Apr-30 Sep. € 29.50 2013*

VILLENEUVE LOUBET see Cagnes sur Mer *10E4*

Franche-Comté

Regional Introduction

Besançon

Welcome to Franche-Comté

Sharing a border with Switzerland, this region has plenty of natural beauty and a rich history.

With stunning mountains, vast parks and dense woodlands, Franche-Comté offers countless leisure and sporting activities that will keep the whole family busy for an entire trip. In winter, the gentle slopes of the Jura mountains are perfect for cross-country skiing.

This is also a place in which to take time out from modern life – relax by the picturesque lakes, take a leisurely stroll through the towns and cities and sample the locally-produced cheeses along the way.

Local highlights

The region's signature cuisine is based around smoked meats, including Morteau and Montbéliard sausages. Tuyé chimneys used for smoking hams and sausage are still a feature in many of the region's traditional farmhouses.

Music lovers can visit one of France's oldest and most prestigious classical events, the Besançon International Music Festival in September.

Major towns and cities

- Belfort – enjoys a prime location at the foot of the Vosges Mountains.
- Besançon – the capital and principal city of the region.
- Lons-le-Saunier – famous for its salt wells and known as the city of salt.
- Vesoul – an medieval town built at the base of la Motte hill.

Regional attractions

- Musée de l'Aventure Peugeot, Sochaux – discover more about this famous car manufacturer.
- Royal Saltworks, Arc-et-Senans – learn about history of salt production in the region.
- Reculee de Baume les Messieurs – a beautiful valley which cuts through a limestone plateau.
- La Citadelle de Besançon – a UNESCO listed fort housing three museums.

Find out more

www.franche-comte.org

Tel: (0)3 84 55 90 90 Belfort Tourist Office
Tel: (0)3 81 80 92 55 Besançon Tourist Office

SITES IN FRANCHE-COMTÉ

ARBOIS *6H2* (1.5km E Urban) *46.90331, 5.78691* **Camp Municipal Les Vignes, 5 Rue de la Piscine, 39600 Arbois [03 84 66 14 12 or 03 84 25 26 19; fax 03 84 25 14 12; campinglesvignes@hotmail.fr; http://alexandrachti.wix.com/camping-les-vignes]** Fr N or S, ent town & at rndabt in cent foll camp sp on D107 dir Mesnay. Site adj stadium & pool. NB Steep slopes to terr & narr ent unsuitable lge o'fits. Med, some hdg pitch/mkd pitch, some hdstg, pt sl, terr, pt shd; wc; chem disp; mv service pnt; shwrs inc; el pnts (10A) inc; gas; lndtte; shop & 1km; rest, snacks; bar; playgrnd; htd pool adj; tennis; fishing 1km; entmnt; wifi; TV; dogs €2.50; twin-axles €45; poss cr; Eng spkn; adv bkg; quiet; ccard acc; red low ssn; CKE/CCI. "Beautiful setting; clean san facs but poss stretched high ssn; site clsd 2200-0800 low ssn; ltd facs low ssn; pitches on lower tier mostly sloping; pleasant sm town, home of Louis Pasteur; Roman salt works, grottoes nr; lge fair 1st w/end in Sep; excel." ♦ 16 Apr-2 Oct. € 20.00 2013*

BAUME LES DAMES *6G2* (500m S Rural) *47.34050, 6.35752* **Comping du Complex Touristique (Domaine d'Aucroix), Quai du Canal, 25110 Baume-les-Dames [03 81 84 38 89; fax 03 81 80 29 53; www.domainedaucroix.fr]** Fr D683 in Baume-les-Dames turn S onto D50, cross canal & turn W. Site sp. Sm, some hdstg, pt shd; wc; chem disp; shwrs; el pnts (16A) inc; lndtte; some statics; dogs €3; quiet; red low ssn. "Peaceful site; gd nh/long stay, v conv fr m/way." 1 May-30 Sep. € 17.00 2013*

BAUME LES DAMES *6G2* (5km S Rural) *47.32506, 6.36127* **Camping L'Ile, 1 Rue de Pontarlier, 25110 Pont-les-Moulins [03 81 84 15 23; info@campingdelile.fr; www.campingdelile.fr]** S fr Baume-les-Dames on D50, site on L on ent Pont-les-Moulins. Sm, pt shd; wc (some cont); chem disp; mv service pnt; shwrs inc; el pnts (6A) €2.50; gas; lndtte; shops 5km; bread 100m; rest & bar 500m; playgrnd; pool 6km; 10% statics; dogs free; Eng spkn; adv bkg; rd noise; red long stay; CKE/CCI. "Tidy, basic site in pleasant setting by Rv Cusancin; helpful, friendly owner; clean, basic facs; gd." 1 May-7 Sep. € 11.50 2009*

BAUME LES MESSIEURS see Lons le Saunier *6H2*

BELFORT *6G3* (1.5km N Urban) *47.65335, 6.86445* **FFCC Camping de l'Etang des Forges, 11 Rue du Général Béthouart, 90000 Belfort [03 84 22 54 92; fax 03 84 22 76 55; contact@camping-belfort.com; www.camping-belfort.com]** Exit A36 junc 13; go thro cent of Belfort; then foll sp Offemont on D13, then site sp. Or fr W on N19 site well sp. Med, hdg/mkd pitch, pt shd; htd wc (some cont); chem disp; mv service pnt; baby facs; shwrs inc; el pnts (6A) €3.50; lndtte (inc dryer); shop 500m; tradsmn; rest 1km; snacks, bar high ssn; BBQ; playgrnd; pool; fishing & watersports adj; archery; wifi; entmnt; TV rm; 5% statics; dogs €2; bus; extra for twin-axles; Eng spkn; adv bkg; quiet; ccard acc; red low ssn/long stay; CKE/CCI. "Pleasant,well-kept, basic site; some lovely pitches; friendly; modern, unisex san facs but needs updating (2014); lovely walk around lake fr site ent; cycle paths; conv for Corbusier's chapel at Ronchamp." ♦ 7 Apr-30 Sep. € 29.50 (CChq acc) 2014*

BESANCON *6G2* (5km NE Rural) *47.26472, 6.07255* **Camping de Besancon - La Plage, 12 Route de Belfort, 25220 Chalezeule [03 81 88 04 26; fax 03 81 50 54 62; contact@campingdebesancon.com; www.campingdebesancon.com]** Exit A36 junc 4 S; foll sp Montbéliard & Roulons onto D683; site in 1.5km on R, 200m after rlwy bdge; well sp fr D683. Fr Belfort 2.65m height restriction; foll sp to Chalezeule & 300m after supmkt turn L to rejoin D683, site in 200m on rvside. Med, mkd pitch, terr, pt shd; htd wc; chem disp; mv service pnt; baby facs; shwrs inc; el pnts (6A) €3.95 (poss rev pol); lndtte (inc dryer); supmkt 1km; rest 500m; snacks; BBQ; playgrnd; htd pool adj; rv adj; kayaking; 50% statics; dogs €1.35; bus to city; poss cr; Eng spkn; quiet but some rd & rlwy noise; ccard acc; red low ssn; CKE/CCI. "Helpful staff; excel modern san facs (2014); twin-axles extra; access to opp side of dual c'way under sm tunnel, suggest going to rndabt to make the turn." ♦ 1 Apr-30 Sep. € 28.50 2014*

BONLIEU *6H2* (1km E Rural) *46.59689, 5.87163* **Camping L'Abbaye, 2 Route du Lac, 39130 Bonlieu [03 84 25 57 04; fax 03 84 25 50 82; camping.abbaye@wanadoo.fr; www.camping-abbaye.com]** Fr W on D678 thro Bonlieu twd St Laurent-en-Grandvaux. In 1km turn R at sp for Lac de Bonlieu & site. Site 1km bef lake. Steep ent. Med, hdg/mkd pitch, pt sl, terr, pt shd; wc; chem disp; baby facs; shwrs inc; el pnts (6A) €3.80 (poss rev pol); lndtte (inc dryer); shop & 4km; tradsmn; rest, snacks; bar; BBQ; playgrnd; games area; no statics; dogs €1; adv bkg; quiet, some rd noise w/end; ccard acc; CKE/CCI. "Pleasant, peaceful site in attractive area; lge pitches, blocks req for most; modern san facs; access to disabled facs fr upper terr; bar/rest open low ssn; gd walks; gd dog walks." ♦ 1 May-30 Sep. € 14.50 2011*

BONNAL *6G2* (3.5km N Rural) *47.50777, 6.35583* **Camping Le Val de Bonnal, 1 Chemin du Moulin, 25680 Bonnal [03 81 86 90 87; fax 03 81 86 03 92; www.camping-valdebonnal.com / www.les-castels.com]** Fr N on D9 fr Vesoul or Villersexel to Esprels, turn S onto D49 sp 'Val de Bonnal'. Fr S exit A36 junc 5 & turn N onto D50 sp Rougemont, site sp to N of Rougemont. Lge, mkd pitch, pt shd; wc; chem disp; mv service pnt; baby facs; shwrs inc; el pnts (5-10A) inc (poss rev pol); gas; lndtte (inc dryer); sm shop; rest, snacks; bar; BBQ; playgrnd; pool; waterslide; paddling pool; lake sw & sand beach adj; fishing; watersports; canoe, cycle hire; gym; golf 6km; wifi; entmnt; games/TV rm; 40% statics; dogs €2; twin-axles acc (rec check in adv); poss cr; Eng spkn; adv bkg; quiet; ccard acc; red low ssn; CKE/CCI. "Attractive, busy site; lge accessible pitches; excel welcome; modern, clean san facs; gd child activities; ltd facs low ssn; tour ops." ♦ 7 May-6 Sep. € 48.40 SBS - J01 2011*

CHAMPAGNE SUR LOUE see Quingey *6H2*

FRANCHE-COMTÉ

CHAMPAGNOLE *6H2* (1km NW Urban) *46.74680, 5.89919* **Camp Municipal de Boÿse, 20 Rue Georges Vallerey, 39300 Champagnole [03 84 52 00 32; fax 03 84 52 01 16; camping.boyse@wanadoo.fr; www.camping.champagnole.com]** Turn W onto D5, N of town off D5 to Dijon. Look for sp. Site adj to sw pool. Lge, mkd pitch, pt sl, pt shd; wc; chem disp; mv service pnt; baby facs; shwrs inc; el pnts (5A) €3.20; Indtte; shops & supmkt 1km; tradsmn; rest, snacks; bar; htd sw pools adj; dogs €2; phone; adv bkg; no admissions 1200-1400; quiet; ccard acc; red low ssn; CKE/CCI. "Spacious, well-kept site; friendly warden; gd san facs, inc dog washing area; vg rest; direct access to Rv Ain; pleasant town; gd touring base." ♦ 1 Jun-15 Sep. € 14.40 2010*

CHILLY LE VIGNOBLE see Lons le Saunier *6H2*

CLAIRVAUX LES LACS *6H2* (1.2km SE Rural) *46.56431, 5.7562* **Yelloh! Village Le Fayolan, Chemin de Langard, 39130 Clairvaux-les-Lacs [03 84 25 88 52; fax 03 84 25 26 20; fayolan@odesia.eu; www.campinglefayolan.fr / www.yellohvillage.co.uk]** Fr town foll campsite sp, last site along lane adj to lake. V lge, hdg/mkd pitch, terr, pt shd; wc; serviced pitches; chem disp; sauna; some serviced pitches; shwrs inc; el pnts (6A) inc (poss rev pol); gas; Indtte; shop; rest, snacks; bar; playgrnd; htd pools (1 covrd); waterslide; sand lake beach adj; games rm; tennis 1km; cycle hire; entmnt; TV; 16% statics; dogs €4; extra for twin axles; Eng spkn; adv bkg rec; quiet; ccard acc; red low ssn; CKE/CCI. "Excel, clean site; extra for lakeside pitches high ssn; pleasant sm town in easy walking dist; lovely area." ♦ 6 May-4 Sep. € 38.00 2011*

CLAIRVAUX LES LACS *6H2* (1km S Rural) *46.56761, 5.75480* **Camping La Grisière et Europe Vacances, Chemin Langard, 39130 Clairvaux-les-Lacs [03 84 25 80 48; fax 03 84 25 22 34; bailly@la-grisiere.com; www.la-grisiere.com]** Turn S off D678 in Clairvaux opp church onto D118; fork R in 500m & foll site sps to lake. Sp in vill. Camping La Grisière ent after Camping Les Lacs. V lge, mkd pitch, pt sl, pt shd; htd wc (some cont); chem disp; mv service pnt; baby facs; shwrs inc; el pnts (6-10A) €2.60; Indry rm; shop; tradsmn; snacks; bar; BBQ; playgrnd; lake sw & beach adj; rv sw 5km; fishing; watersports; cycle & canoe hire; tennis 1km; wifi; TV; 5% statics; dogs €1; phone; bus 700m; Eng spkn; no adv bkg; quiet; ccard acc; red low ssn; CKE/CCI. "Lovely views in beautiful area; lge pitches; excel site; quiet; few facs." ♦ 1 May-30 Sep. € 28.00 2014*

CLAIRVAUX LES LACS *6H2* (10km SW Rural) *46.52311, 5.67350* **Camping de Surchauffant, Pont de la Pyle, 39270 La Tour-du-Meix [03 84 25 41 08; fax 03 84 35 56 88; info@camping-surchauffant.fr; www.camping-surchauffant.fr]** Fr Clairvaux S on D27 or D49 to D470. Foll sp Lac de Vouglans, site sp. Med, mkd pitch, pt sl, pt shd; wc; chem disp; mv service pnt; shwrs inc; el pnts (6A) €3; Indtte; shops adj; rest, snacks; bar; BBQ; playgrnd; pool; paddling pool; dir access to lake 120m; sailing; watersports; entmnt; TV rm; some statics; dogs €1.60; Eng spkn; adv bkg; quiet; ccard acc; red low ssn. "Vg facs; lovely location; hiking trails." ♦ 22 Apr-19 Sep. € 19.00 2010*

"That's changed – Should I let The Club know?"

If you find something on site that's different from the site entry, fill in a report and let us know. See www.caravanclub.co.uk/europereport.

CLAIRVAUX LES LACS *6H2* (7km W Rural) *46.59976, 5.68824* **Camping Beauregard, 2 Grande Rue, 39130 Mesnois [tel/fax 03 84 48 32 51; reception@juracampingbeauregard.com; www.juracampingbeauregard.com]** S fr Lons-le-Saunier on D52/D678, about 1km bef Pont-de-Poitte turn L on D151. Site 1km on L opp rd junc to Pont-de-Poitte. Lge, hdg/mkd pitch, hdstg, pt sl, terr, pt shd; htd wc (some cont); chem disp; baby facs; shwrs inc; el pnts (6A) €4 (poss long lead req); gas; Indtte; shop 1km; tradsmn; rest; playgrnd; htd pool high ssn; sand beach 800m; kayaking nr; tennis; cycle hire; games rm; 10% statics; dogs €2.20; poss cr; Eng spkn; adv bkg; quiet. "Super site, clean & well-run; different sized pitches; excel san facs, ltd low ssn; excel rest; poss muddy when wet; new indoor pool with jacuzzi and sauna (2012), extremely gd quality." ♦ 1 Apr-30 Sep. € 25.50 2012*

See advertisement

CROMARY see Rioz *6G2*

DOLE *6H2* (300m E Rural) *47.08937, 5.50339* **FFCC Camping Le Pasquier, 18 Chemin Victor et Georges Thévenot, 39100 Dole [03 84 72 02 61; fax 03 84 79 23 44; camping-pasquier@wanadoo.fr / lola@camping-le-pasquier.com; www.camping-le-pasquier.com]** Fr A39 foll sp dir Dole & Le Pasquier. Fr all dir foll sp 'Centre ville' then foll site name sp & 'Stade Camping' in town; well sp. Site on rvside private rd. Narr app. Lge, hdg/mkd pitch, pt shd; htd wc; chem disp; mv service pnt; shwrs inc; el pnts (10A) inc (rev pol); Indry rm; shop & 1km; tradsmn; snacks; bar; playgrnd; pool; aqua park 2km; dir access rv 500m; fishing; entmnt; wifi; 10% statics; dogs €1.50; extra for twin-axle c'vans; poss cr; Eng spkn; quiet; ccard acc; red long stay/low ssn; CKE/CCI. "Generous pitches; friendly recep; gd clean san facs; pleasant pool; walk along rv (otters!) into Dole; poss mosquito problem; mkt Tues, Thur, Sat; gd NH." 15 Mar-25 Oct. € 27.60 2014*

DOLE *6H2* (8km SE Rural) *47.01660, 5.48160* **FFCC Camping Les Bords de Loue, 39100 Parcey [03 84 71 03 82; fax 03 84 71 03 42; contact@jura-camping.fr; www.jura-camping.fr]** Leave A39 at junc 6 onto D905 dir Chalon-sur-Saône. Turn L (SE) at rndabt after going under A39 & in 6km turn R into vill of Parcey at 'Camping' sp. Lge, pt shd; wc; chem disp; 10% serviced pitches; shwrs inc; el pnts (6A) inc; Indtte; tradsmn; rest, snacks; bar; BBQ; playgrnd; paddling pool; beach adj; pool; fishing; boating; shops 7km; 20% statics; dogs €2, must keep on lead; phone; wi-fi; poss cr; Eng spkn; adv bkg; poss some noise when busy; ccard acc; red low ssn; CKE/CCI. "Pleasant site." ♦ 14 May-15 Sep. € 28.00 2013*

DOUCIER *6H2* (3km N Rural) *46.67755, 5.78080* **Camping La Pergola, 1 Rue des Vernois, Lac de Chalain, 39130 Marigny [03 84 25 70 03; fax 03 84 25 75 96; contact@lapergola.com; www.lapergola.com / www.les-castels.com]** Fr D471 Lons-le-Saunier to Champagnole rd, turn S on D27 twd Marigny, site on L in 6km on N shore of Lac de Chalain. Lge, hdg/mkd pitch, pt sl, terr, pt shd; wc; chem disp; baby facs; some serviced pitches; shwrs inc; baby facs; el pnts (12A) inc; gas; Indtte (inc dryer); shop; rest, snacks; bar; BBQ; playgrnd; htd pool; paddling pool; lake sand beach adj; fishing; games rm; games area; wifi; entmnt; TV; 50% statics; dogs €4; phone; poss cr; Eng spkn; adv bkg; red long stay; ccard acc; CKE/CCI. "Popular, busy site; beautiful gorges nrby; superb san facs; naturist beach on lake 500m; some sm pitches." ♦ 28 Apri--9 Sep. € 38.00 (CChq acc) 2011*

DOUCIER *6H2* (6km N Rural) *46.71221, 5.79709* **Camping du Gît, Monnet-le-Bourg, 39300 Montigny-sur-l'Ain [03 84 51 21 17 or 03 84 37 87 58 (LS); christian.olivier22@wanadoo.fr; www.campingdugit.com]** W fr Champagnole on D471 foll sp Monnet-la-Ville, foll camp sp thro vill, turn L at x-rds to church; site immed afterwards on R behind church in Monnet-la-Ville (also known as Monnet-le-Bourg). Med, mkd pitch, pt sl, pt shd; wc; chem disp; shwrs inc; el pnts (5A) €2.50; Indtte; supmkt 800m; rest, snacks; bar; playgrnd; lake sw 4km; sports area; fishing, kayaking 1.5km; dogs €1.50; adv bkg; quiet; CKE/CCI. "Peaceful site; beautiful views; lge pitches; gd san facs." ♦ 1 Jun-31 Aug. € 12.00 2012*

DOUCIER *6H2* (8km N Rural) *46.72383, 5.78463* **Camping Le Bivouac, Route du Lac de Chalain, 39300 Pont-du-Navoy [03 84 51 26 95; fax 03 84 51 29 70; campinglebivouac-jura@orange.fr; www.bivouac-jura.com]** D471 to Pont-du-Navoy, S over bdge & immed fork R onto D27; 2nd site on R. Med, mkd pitch, pt shd; htd wc; chem disp; shwrs inc; el pnts (16A) €2.80 (poss rev pol/no earth); Indtte; shops 1km; tradsmn; rest, snacks; bar; playgrnd; rv adj; lake sw 6km; TV; 20% statics; dogs €0.50; adv bkg; quiet; ccard acc; CKE/CCI. "In beautiful countryside; new owner (2011); ltd san facs." 1 Mar-5 Oct. € 12.20 2011*

DOUCIER *6H2* (3km NE Rural) *46.66361, 5.81333* **Camping Domaine de Chalain, 39130 Doucier [03 84 25 78 78; chalain@chalain.com; www.chalain.com]** Fr Lons-le-Saunier take D39 E. In Doucier, site sp to L. Fr Champagnole take D471 for 11km, L onto D27 at Pont-du-Navoy to Doucier & foll sp to site. V lge, pt shd; wc (some cont); mv service pnt; chem disp; sauna; shwrs inc; el pnts (7A) €3; gas; Indtte; shops; rest, snacks; bar; htd, covrd pools; waterslide & aquatic cent; lake sw adj; boating; fishing; watersports; cycle hire; tennis; horseriding; games area; entmnt; internet; statics; dogs €2; poss cr; adv bkg ess. "Extra for lakeside pitches; famous caves Grottes des Beaume adj; vg site." 29 Apr-21 Sep. € 33.00 (3 persons) 2009*

DOUCIER *6H2* (1.5km S Rural) *46.65260, 5.72119* **Kawan Village Domaine de l'Epinette, 15 Rue de l'Epinette, 39130 Châtillon-sur-Ain [03 84 25 71 44; fax 03 84 25 71 25; contact@domaine-epinette.com; www.domaine-epinette.com]** Exit A39 junc 7 to Poligny, then N5 to Champagnole & D471 W. Turn S onto D27 to Lac de Chalain then D39 to Châtillon. Med, mkd pitch, mainly sl, terr, pt shd; wc (some cont); chem disp; shwrs inc; el pnts (12A) inc; Indtte (inc dryer); shop; tradsmn; rest 1km; snacks; bar; BBQ; playgrnd; htd pool; paddling pool; rv sw & fishing; canoeing, kayaking & horseriding 3km; games rm; wifi; TV; 30% statics; dogs €2; phone; adv bkg; quiet. "Gd base for Jura area; vg." ♦ 2 Jun-11 Sep. € 27.00 (CChq acc) 2011*

ECRILLE *4H2* (2.7km WNW Rural) *46.50973, 5.62042* **Camping La Faz, 4 Pont de Vaux 39270 Ecrille [03 08 25 40 27 06 22 48 10 63 (mob); camping.la.faz@sft.fr; www.jura-camping-lafaz.com]** Fr Stye at the rndabt (the only rndabt onmain rd thro Stye) take dir Geneva, then 50 meters down on R is Ecrille. Site is 1.5km fr Stye. El pnts €3.10; dog €1.40. "Excel." 27 Apr-30 Sep. € 16.45 2013*

GRAY *6G2* (1km E Rural) *47.45207, 5.59999* **Camp Municipal Longue Rive, Rue de la Plage, 70100 Gray [03 84 64 90 44; fax 03 84 65 46 26; tourisme-gray@wanadoo.fr; www.ville-gray.fr]** S on D67 to Gray. cross rv bdge, L at rndabt, after 300m sp La Plage. Well sp fr all rtes. Med, hdg/mkd pitch, pt shd; wc (mainly cont); mv service pnt; shwrs inc; el pnts (10A) €2.45; gas; Indtte; shop 1.5km; rest, bar, & pool opp; playgrnd; boating & fishing; tennis; dogs €0.85; poss cr; Eng spkn; poss noisy; ccard not acc; CKE/CCI. "Lovely setting on Rv Saône; friendly recep; basic facs, poss stretched high ssn; twin-axles extra charge; many pitches waterlogged early ssn; several Bastide vills within cycling dist; NH only." 15 Apr-30 Sep. € 12.00 2011*

HUANNE MONTMARTIN see Baume les Dames *6G2*

ISLE SUR LE DOUBS, L' *6G2 (400m N Rural) 47.45288, 6.58338* **Camping Les Lûmes, 10 Rue des Lûmes, 25250 L'Isle-sur-le-Doubs [tel/fax 03 81 92 73 05; contact@les-lumes.com; www.les-lumes.com]** Well sp fr town edge on D683 bef rv bdge. Med, pt shd; wc; chem disp; shwrs; el pnts (10A) €3.30 (long lead req & poss rev pol; shop; tradsmn; playgrnd; rv sw; 20% statics; dogs €1.20; poss cr; Eng spkn; adv bkg; CKE/CCI. "Busy site; san facs need upgrade & up steps; gd." 1 May-30 Sep. € 11.70 2009*

LODS see Ornans *6G2*

LONGCHAUMOIS see Morez *9A3*

LONS LE SAUNIER *6H2 (1km NE Rural) 46.68437, 5.56843* **Camping La Marjorie, 640 Blvd de l'Europe, 39000 Lons-le-Saunier [03 84 24 26 94; fax 03 84 24 08 40; info@camping-marjorie.com; www.camping-marjorie.com]** Site clearly sp in town on D1083 twd Besançon. Fr N bear R dir 'Piscine', cross under D1083 to site. Lge, hdg pitch, some hdstg, pt sl, pt shd; wc; baby facs; chem disp; shwrs inc; el pnts (10A) inc (poss rev pol); gas; Indtte; shop; tradsmn; rest; bar; playgrnd; 2 htd pools (1 covrd) & aquatic cent adj; games area; golf 8km; wifi; entmnt; dogs €2.50; phone; Eng spkn; rd noise; ccard accs; red low ssn; twin-axles extra; CKE/CCI. "Lovely site in beautiful area; conv location; lge pitches; welcoming, friendly, helpful owners; excel, spotless san facs; 20 mins walk to interesting old town; ideal touring base; rec; excel; by busy main rd; well run." ♦ 1 Apr-15 Oct. € 30.00 2014*

LONS LE SAUNIER *6H2 (8km SW Rural) 46.65854, 5.49934* **Camp Municipal, Grande Rue, 39570 Chilly-le-Vignoble [03 84 43 09 34 or 03 84 43 09 32 (Mairie); fax 03 84 47 34 09; mairie.chillylevignoble@wanadoo.fr; www.ville-lons-le-saunier.fr]** Fr A39 exit junc 8 onto D678. After approx 5km turn R to Courlans & Chilly-le-Vignoble. Site sp 2km. Med, pt shd; wc (most cont); shwrs inc; el pnts (6A) inc; supmkt 3km; tradsmn; rest, snacks; playgrnd; games rm; golf nrby; quiet; CKE/CCI. "V pleasant site in quiet vill; warm welcome, friendly staff; ent for c'vans fr 1530 only; gd." 1 Jun-15 Sep. € 13.60 2010*

LUXEUIL LES BAINS *6F2 (500m N Rural) 47.82315, 6.38200* **FFCC Camping du Domaine de Chatigny, 14 Rue Grammont, 70300 Luxeuil-les-Bains [03 84 93 97 97; fax 03 84 40 56 44; camping.lechatigny@chainethermale.fr; www.camping.luxeuil.fr]** N fr Vesoul on N57; turn L at rndabt into Luxeuil-les-Bains; foll Camping sp. Vehicular access fr Rue Ste Anne. Med, pt hdg/mkd pitch, hdstg, terr, pt shd; htd wc; chem disp; mv service pnt; baby facs; shwrs inc; el pnts (16A) €3.50-4.50; gas; Indtte (inc dryer); shop; supmkt 100m; tradsmn; rest, snacks; bar; BBQ; playgrnd; pool; indoor tennis court; wifi; TV rm; 20% statics; dogs €1.70; bus 300m; no twin-axles; Eng spkn; adv bkg; quiet; ccard acc; red low ssn/long stay; CKE/CCI. "New (2009), high standard site; gd." 1 Mar-31 Oct. € 18.00 2014*

⊞ **MAICHE** *6G3 (1km S Rural) 47.24705, 6.79952* **Camp Municipal St Michel, 23 Rue St Michel, 25120 Maîche [03 81 64 12 56 or 03 81 64 03 01 (Mairie); fax 03 81 64 12 56; contact@mairie-maiche.fr; www.mairie-maiche.fr]** Fr S turn R off D437 onto D442. App on D464 L on o'skts of town. Sp fr both dir. Med, sl, terr, pt shd; htd wc; chem disp; shwrs inc; el pnts (5A) €4.46; Indtte; shops 1km; playgrnd; pool adj; games area; games rm; a few statics; dogs; phone; site clsd 3rd week Nov & Dec; adv bkg; rd noise. "Attractive, neat, well-run site with views; clean facs; phone ahead low ssn to check open; gd walks in woods." ♦ € 15.62 2013*

MAICHE *6G3 (10km SW Rural) 47.16304, 6.72469* **Camp Municipal Les Sorbiers, Rue Foch, 25210 Le Russey [03 81 43 72 35]** On D437 Maîche-Morteau, 1st R after vill church, site sp on L in 250m. Med, hdstg, pt shd; htd wc (men cont); chem disp; shwrs; el pnts (10A); gas; Indtte; shop 1km; rest, snacks, bar 500m; playgrnd; tennis; games rm; 20% statics; adv bkg; quiet; ccard not acc. "Excel, scenic cent; high altitude, poss cold nights." 15 Jun-15 Sep. 2009*

MALBUISSON *6H2 (2km S Rural) 46.77449, 6.27370* **Camping du Lac, 10 Rue du Lac, 25160 Labergement-Ste Marie [03 81 69 31 24; camping.lac.remoray@wanadoo.fr; www.camping-lac-remoray.com]** Exit N57/E23 junc 2 onto D437 thro Malbuisson to Labergement. Site sp to R of D437 after x-ing Rv Doubs. Med, mkd pitch, pt shd; wc; chem disp; mv service pnt; baby facs; shwrs inc; el pnts (6A) €3.50; gas; Indtte; tradsmn; rest, snacks; bar; playgrnd; lake beach adj; fishing; walking; cycling; sports area; tennis nrby; internet; TV; 5% statics in sep area; dogs €1.50; phone; Eng spkn; adv bkg; quiet; ccard acc; red low ssn; CKE/CCI. "Roomy site by Lake Remoray with forest views; kind & helpful owner; clean san facs; vill 500m with gd shops; excel." ♦ 1 May-30 Sep. € 21.00 2014*

MALBUISSON *6H2 (1.4km SW Urban) 46.79176, 6.29257* **Camping Les Fuvettes, 24 Route de la Plage et des Perrières, 25160 Malbuisson [03 81 69 31 50; fax 03 81 69 70 46; les-fuvettes@wanadoo.fr; www.camping-fuvettes.com]** Site 19km S of Pontarlier on N57 & D437 to Malbuisson, thro town, R down rd to Plage. Lge, pt sl, pt shd; htd wc (some cont); shwrs inc; el pnts (4-6A) €3.60-4; gas; Indtte (inc dryer); shop; rest, snacks; bar; playgrnd; shgl beach for lake sw; fishing; boating; games rm; 30% statics; dogs €1,50; poss cr; quiet; CKE/CCI. "Popular, lakeside, family site; mkd walks/cycle paths in adj woods; petting zoo (llamas etc) nrby." 1 Apr-30 Sep. € 34.30 2014*

MARIGNY see Doucier *6H2*

MARNAY (HAUTE SAONE) *6G2* (500m SE Urban) *47.28975, 5.77628* **Camp Municipal Vert Lagon, Route de Besançon, 70150 Marnay [03 84 31 71 41 or 03 84 31 73 16; sidmarnay@wanadoo.fr; www.camping-vertlagon.com]** Fr N stay on D67 Marnay by-pass; ignore old camping sp into town. Proceed to S of town on by-pass then turn L at junc. Bef bdge in 1km take gravel rd on S side, round under bdge to site (app thro town fr N v narr). Med, some hdg/mkd pitch, pt shd; wc; chem disp; mv service pnt; baby facs; shwrs inc; el pnts (10A) €4; Indtte; shops & rest 500m; snacks (high ssn); BBQ; playgrnd; fishing; canoeing; 40% statics; dogs €1; poss cr; adv bkg; quiet; ccard acc; red low ssn; CKE/CCI. "Pleasant, popular, family site by Rv Ognon; gd san facs; lake adj; tree-top walks; gd." 1 May-30 Sep. € 13.40 (CChq acc) 2009*

MELISEY *6F2* (2.5km N Rural) *47.77560, 6.58020* **Camping La Pierre, Route de Melay, 70270 Melisey [03 84 63 23 08 or 03 84 22 11 10; www.office-tourisme-melisey.fr]** Fr Lure on D486 to Melisey, L in vill onto D293 sp Melay. Site on L in 2.5km. Med, hdg/mkd pitch, hdstg, pt shd; wc; chem disp; mv service pnt; baby facs; shwrs inc; el pnts (6A)€2.60; Indry rm; rest 2km; shop 2km; bbq; playgrnd; pool (3km); games area; games rm; tv rm; 40% statics; dogs; phone; quiet; adv bkg; CKE/CCI. "V quiet, well-kept site; site yourself, warden calls; local c'van club organises reg social events and visitors are invited; gd site; conv Rochamp Courbusier Chapel; not suitable for lge units; all facs vg; peaceful." ♦ 1 May-30 Sep. € 16.30 2014*

MELISEY *6F2* (500m E Rural) *47.75484, 6.58683* **Camping La Bergereine, 17bis Route des Vosges, 70270 Mélisey [tel/fax 06 23 36 87 16 (mob); isabelle.schweizer0704@orange.fr]** Fr Lure (or by-pass) take D486 dir Le Thillot; site sp. Sm, pt shd; wc; chem disp; shwrs; el pnts inc; gas; leisure cent & pool 500m; fishing in adj rv; 25% statics; adv bkg; v quiet; CKE/CCI. "Ok NH; simple farm site; attractive scenery; improvd san block." 1 Apr-30 Sep. € 8.00 2014*

MELISEY *6F2* (7km E Rural) *47.75525, 6.65273* **Camping La Broche, Le Voluet, 70270 Fresse [tel/fax 03 84 63 31 40; www.camping-broche.com]** Fr Lure head NE on D486 twd Melisey. Fr Mélisey stay on D486 twd Le Thillot, in 2.5km turn R onto D97 dir Plancher-les-Mines. In approx 5.5km site sp on R in Fresse. Sm, mkd pitch, pt sl, terr, pt shd; wc; chem disp; shwrs inc; el pnts (10A) €2.50; Indtte; ice; shop 200m; BBQ; playgrnd; lake sw & fishing adj; games area; games rm; some statics; dogs €1; phone; poss cr; adv bkg; quiet apart fr double-chiming church bells; CKE/CCI. "Secluded, relaxing site in attractive setting in regional park; friendly owner; conv Rte of 1000 lakes; great site." ♦ 1 Apr-15 Oct. € 9.00 2010*

MENETRUX EN JOUX see Doucier *6H2*

MESNOIS see Clairvaux les Lacs *6H2*

MONTBARREY *6H2* (1km SW Rural) *47.01230, 5.63161* **FLOWER Camping Les Trois Ours, 28 Rue du Pont, 39380 Montbarrey [03 84 81 50 45; h.rabbe@orange.fr; www.camping-les3ours-jura.com / www.flowercampings.com]** Exit A39 junc onto D905 E; 1km after Mont-sur-Vaudrey on D472 turn L dir Montbarrey. Cross rv, site on L at rvside on edge of vill. Med, hdg/mkd pitch, shd; htd wc; chem disp; mv service pnt; baby facs; shwrs inc; el pnts (10A) inc; Indtte; shop 3km; rest, snacks; bar; BBQ; playgrnd; pool; games rm; wifi; TV; 10% statics; dogs; phone; bus; Eng spkn; adv bkg; quiet; ccard acc. "Improvements planned; vg walking/cycling fr site; excel menu in rest." ♦ 15 Apr-30 Sep. € 33.80 2014*

MOREZ *9A3* (3km N Rural) *46.54218, 6.01907* **Camp Municipal La Bucle, 15 Route Germain Paget, Les Pontets, 39400 Morbier [tel/fax 03 84 33 48 55; info.bucle@wanadoo.fr]** Fr N on N5 look for sps 10km after St Laurent. Pass supmkt & lge car pk on R, take sharp L turn after L bend in rd. Fr S turn R 50m past bdge. Med, some hdstg, pt sl, pt terr, unshd; wc; shwrs inc; el pnts (10A) €2.30; Indtte; shops 1km; pool; dogs €0.60; quiet; red low ssn; gd NH. "Lovely site & town; site poss unkempt." 1 Jun-10 Sep. € 14.50 2009*

MOREZ *9A3* (9km S Rural) *46.48368, 5.94885* **Camping Le Baptaillard, 39400 Longchaumois [03 84 60 62 34; camping-lebaptaillard@orange.fr; www.haut-jura.com]** Foll D69 S, site sp on R. Med, mkd pitch, pt sl, pt shd; htd wc; chem disp; shwrs inc; el pnts (6A) €2.50; Indtte; shop; rest, snacks, bar 3km; playgrnd; paddling pool; fishing 3km; tennis; skiing; games rm; wifi; some statics; adv bkg ess winter; quiet. "Beautiful CL-type site; views; lge pitches; friendly staff." 1 Jan-30 Sep, 1 Dec-31 Dec. € 30.45 2014*

MORTEAU *6H2* (750m SW Urban) *47.05304, 6.59908* **Camping Le Cul de la Lune, Rue du Pont Rouge, 25500 Morteau [03 81 67 17 52 or 03 81 67 18 53; fax 03 81 67 62 34; otsi.morteau@wanadoo.fr; www.morteau.org]** Fr Besançon take N57 E then D461. In Morteau foll sps to Pontarlier then 'Toutes Directions'. Site on R over rlwy/rv bdge sp Montlebon (D48). Clearly sp thro'out town. Across rv bdge. Sm, pt shd; wc (some cont); shwrs inc; el pnts (10A) €3; shops 300m; tradsmn; rv sw, fishing & boating; cycling; dogs €1.50; poss v cr; adv bkg; noise fr rd & rlwy; red low ssn. "Beautiful location on rv bank; gd modern san facs; pt of site v wet after heavy rain; poss v cold at nights (altitude)." 1 Jun-10 Sep. € 15.00 2010*

MOUCHARD *6H2* (4km NE Rural) *47.00358, 5.82366* **Camping Les Radeliers, 1 Rue Edgar Faure, 39600 Port-Lesney [03 84 73 81 44; camp.portlesney@aliceadsl.fr; www.camping-les-radeliers.com]** N fr Arbois on N83, cross junc with D472 & turn L in 1.5km sp Port-Lesney. Site sp. Med, mkd pitch, pt shd; wc; chem disp; shwrs inc; el pnts (13A) €4; Indtte; shop 300m; rest opp & 200m; snacks; bar 200m; playgrnd (for use by vill); sand/shgl beach & rv sw adj; canoeing; kayak hire; canyoning; 2% statics; dogs €2; bus & phone adj; poss cr; Eng spkn; adv bkg; quiet; twin-axles extra; red low ssn; CKE/CCI. "Tranquil site in delightful rvside setting; helpful staff; poss youth groups high ssn; gd walking & cycling; Salt Mine Museum in Salins-les-Bains worth visit; plenty rvside pitches." ♦ ltd 1 May-30 Sep. € 14.00 2014*

FRANCHE-COMTÉ

ORNANS *6G2* (1km E Rural) *47.10064, 6.16036* **Camping La Roche d'Ully, Allée de la Tour de Peiltz, 25290 Ornans [03 81 57 17 79; contact@larochedully.com; www.camping-larochedully.com]** Fr Ornans foll blue sps to site nr rvside. Med, mkd pitch, unshd; htd wc; chem disp; mv service pnt; baby facs; sauna; shwrs; el pnts (10A) €4; Indtte (inc dryer); shop; tradsmn; rest, snacks; bar; BBQ; playgrnd; 2 pools (1 htd, covrd); paddling pool; rv fishing; canoeing; cycle hire; games area; wifi; 20% statics; dogs €3; adv bkg; quiet; ccard acc; red low ssn. "Pleasant, family-run site in gd location; Popular with students; some noise in ssn." ♦ 1 Apr-15 Oct. € 21.00 (CChq acc) 2012*

ORNANS *6G2* (11km SE Rural) *47.04132, 6.26024* **Camp Municipal Le Champaloux, 25930 Lods [03 81 60 90 11 (Mairie) or 06 72 54 51 41 (mob); fax 03 81 60 93 86; mairie.lods@wanadoo.fr; www.camping-champaloux.fr]** Fr Ornans SE on D67. In Lods turn R across Rv Loue. Site in 150m beside rv. Or N fr Pontarlier on N57/E23 to St Gorgon then W on D67 to Lods. Med, pt shd, hdstg; wc; chem disp; mv service pnt; shwrs inc; el pnts (6A) €2.80; shop 1km; playgrnd; fishing; quiet. "Lovely, peaceful site by rv; on disused rlwy stn in attractive area; site yourself, office opens 1830-2000; friendly, helpful warden; clean, adequate san facs; dog shwr; vg rest 200m; woodland walks; excel." 15 Jun-30 Sep. € 12.40 2012*

ORNANS *6G2* (1km S Rural) *47.10070, 6.12795* **Camping Domaine Le Chanet, 9 Chemin de Chanet, 25290 Ornans [03 81 62 23 44; fax 03 81 62 13 97; contact@lechanet.com; www.lechanet.com]** Fr Besançon take D67 25km to Ornans. In Ornans at rndabt cont to town cent. Take 1st R, cross Rv Loue then turn R. Foll sp to site in 1km. Look for R turn after school. Med, hdg pitch, steep sl & terr, pt shd; htd wc; chem disp; mv service pnt; baby facs; shwrs inc; el pnts (3-10A) €3-3.50; Indtte; shop; tradsmn; snacks; bar; BBQ; sm playgrnd; htd pool 500m; rv 1km; games area; many statics; dogs €1.50; phone; poss cr; adv bkg; quiet; red low ssn. "Picturesque site; sm pitches; facs poss stretched in ssn." ♦ 28 Mar-25 Oct. € 17.40 2009*

OUNANS *6H2* (1km N Rural) *47.00290, 5.66550* **Kawan Village La Plage Blanche, 3 Rue de la Plage, 39380 Ounans [03 84 37 69 63; fax 03 84 37 60 21; reservation@la-plage-blanche.com; www.la-plage-blanche.com]** Exit A39 junc 6 sp Dole Centre. Foll N5 SE for 18km dir Pontarlier. After passing Souvans, turn L on D472 sp Mont-sous-Vaudrey. Foll sp to Ounans. Site well sp in vill. Lge, mkd pitch, hdstg, pt shd; wc; chem disp; mv service pnt; shwrs inc; el pnts (6A) €4 (poss rev pol); gas 1km; Indtte (inc dryer); shop 1km; supmkt 4km; tradsmn; rest, snacks; bar; playgrnd; pool; paddling pool; shgl rv beach & sw 500m; trout & carp fishing lake; canoeing; cycle hire; horseriding; wifi; entmnt; TV rm; 1% statics; dogs €2; Eng spkn; adv bkg rec (bkg fee); quiet; red low ssn; ccard acc; CKE/CCI. "Superb rvside pitches; friendly recep; excel san facs, recently updated (2013); gd rest; excel." ♦ 1 May-29 Sep. € 24.00 SBS - J02 2013*

PARCEY see Dole *6H2*

PATORNAY see Clairvaux les Lacs *6H2*

PESMES *6G2* (500m S Rural) *47.27612, 5.56451* **Camp Municipal La Colombière, Route de Dole, 70140 Pesmes [03 84 31 20 15; fax 03 84 31 20 54; campcolombiere@aol.com]** On D475 halfway bet Gray & Dole. S fr Pesmes immed on L after x-ing rv bdge. N fr Dole, site sp on R immed bef rest at rv bdge. Med, some hdg pitch, pt shd; wc; chem disp (wc); shwrs; el pnts (6-10A) €2.30-3.60; Indtte; shop 500m; rest adj; snacks; bar; cycle hire; dogs €1.20; phone; Eng spkn; adv bkg rec high ssn; some rd noise; no ccard acc. "Picturesque vill; helpful, friendly staff; gd san facs; vg; No twin axles." 1 May-31 Oct. € 12.60 2012*

POLIGNY *6H2* (1km SW Rural) *46.83455, 5.69840* **Camp Communautaire de la Croix du Dan, 39800 Poligny [03 84 37 01 35; fax 03 84 73 77 59; cccgrimont@wanadoo.fr; www.ville-poligny.fr]** Fr SW on N83 turn R at rndabt sp 'Centre'; site on R immed bef town sp Poligny. Fr N & NW take D905 into & thro town cent (no L turn on N83 S of Poligny), then foll sp Lons-Le Saunier. Site on L bef sportsgrnd - look for m'van sp. Do not overshoot ent, as diff to see. N5 fr E not rec as steep & hairpins. Med, mkd pitch, pt shd; wc (mainly cont); chem disp; shwrs inc; el pnts (10A) €6.40; Indtte; shops 1km; tradsmn; playgrnd; no statics; dogs; phone; poss cr; Eng spkn; quiet; CKE/CCI. "Excel, clean, tidy site; helpful warden; gates open 24hrs; twin-axles extra; pretty town." ♦ ltd 15 Jun-20 Sep. € 7.45 2009*

PONT DU NAVOY see Doucier *6H2*

PONT LES MOULINS see Baume les Dames *6G2*

PONTARLIER *6H2* (1km SE Rural) *46.90024, 6.37425* **FFCC Camping Le Larmont, Rue du Toulombief, 25300 Pontarlier [03 81 46 23 33; lelarmont.pontarlier@wanadoo.fr; www.camping-pontarlier.fr]** Leave N57 at Pontarlier Gare & foll site sp. Site uphill, turning nr Nestlé factory. Med, some hdstg, terr, unshd; htd wc; chem disp; mv service pnt; shwrs inc; el pnts (10A) €4; gas; Indtte; sm shop; Spar supmkt 1km; tradsmn; snacks; bar; playgrnd; pool 2km; horseriding adj; skiing winter; wifi; 10-20% statics; dogs €1; Eng spkn; adv bkg; red low ssn/CKE/CCI. "Friendly; easy access; clean san facs; ltd pitches for awnings; site self out of office hrs; well-behaved zebra on site; excel; horse riding next to site; rec." ♦ ltd 1 Jan - 15 Nov 15 Dec - 31 Dec. € 25.30 2014*

PONTARLIER *6H2* (12km S Rural) *46.81176, 6.30326* **Camp Municipal, 8 Rue du Port, 25160 St Point-Lac [03 81 69 61 64 or 03 81 69 62 08 (Mairie); fax 03 81 69 65 74; camping-saintpointlac@wanadoo.fr; www.camping-saintpointlac.com]** Exit Pontarlier S on N57 dir Lausanne, turn R on D437 dir Malbuisson; in 6km turn R onto D129 thro Les Grangettes to St Point-Lac. Site sp on L. Med, mkd pitch, hdstg, pt shd; htd wc; chem disp; mv service pnt; chem disp; shwrs inc; el pnts (16A) €4.50; Indtte (inc dryer); shop; rest 300m; snacks; bar; BBQ; playgrnd; lake beach adj; games area; entmnt; 5% statics; dogs €1.50; poss cr; Eng spkn; adv bkg rec high ssn; quiet; ccard acc; red low ssn; CKE/CCI. "Well-kept lakeside site in beautiful position; sm pitches; no twin-axles; friendly staff; vg san facs; m'van o'night area with facs opp; gd fishing, walking, birdwatching; excel." ♦ 1 May-30 Sep. € 10.50 2010*

PORT SUR SAONE *6F2* (800m S Rural) *47.68056, 6.03937* **Camp Municipal Parc de la Maladière, 70170 Port-sur-Saône [03 84 78 18 00 (Mairie); fax 03 84 78 18 09; serviceculturel@gmail.com; www.ville-port-sur-saone.fr]** Take D619 SE fr Langres or NW fr Vesoul. Site sp in vill bet rv & canal off D6 at municipal bathing area. Med, hdg pitch, pt shd; wc (mainly cont); own san facs; chem disp; shwrs inc; el pnts (6A) €3 (poss rev pol); Indtte; shops 800m; tradsmn high ssn; rest, bar adj; playgrnd; pool adj; fishing; tennis; adv bkg; ccard acc; quiet; CKE/CCI. "Peaceful site on island; rvside cycle path; gd walks; gd sh stay/NH." ♦ ltd 15 May-15 Sep. € 10.00 2013*

"I need an on-site restaurant"

We do our best to make sure site information is correct, but it is always best to check any must-have facilities are still available or will be open during your visit.

QUINGEY *6H2* (200m E Urban) *47.10431, 5.88821* **Camp Municipal Les Promenades, Bord de la Loue, 25440 Quingey [03 81 63 74 01 or 03 81 63 63 25 (Mairie); fax 03 81 63 63 25; www.campingquingey.fr]** Site sp off N83 by-pass, then in Quingey. Thro vill, immed on L after bdge over Rv Loue. Sm, pt shd; wc; chem disp; shwrs inc; el pnts (6A) €3; Indtte; shop; snacks; rest; playgrnd; fishing, sailing; canoeing, tennis, cycle hire & archery adj; dogs €1; quiet but some daytime rd noise. "Run down, neglected (Sep 10)." ♦ 1 May-30 Sep. € 11.20 2010*

QUINGEY *6H2* (8.5km SW Rural) *47.04080, 5.81560* **FFCC Camp Municipal La Louve, Rue du Pont, 39600 Champagne-sur-Loue [tel/fax 03 84 37 69 12; camping.champagne@valdamau.com; http://camping_champagne.monsite-orange.fr/]** Fr Quingey on D17 sp Lombard & in approx 4km turn L sp Champagne-sur-Loue, Buffard (still D17). Site on L after bdge. Sm, shd; wc (some cont); mv service pnt; shwrs inc; el pnts (10A) €2.50; shops 2km; tradsmn; rest 1km; BBQ; playgrnd; fishing; dogs €1; adv bkg; quiet; CKE/CCI. "Well-kept, peaceful site in beautiful situation on rv; open plan - all grass, poss diff for m'vans if wet; used by groups canoeists; site yourself; office 0800-0900 & 1830-1930; vg." ♦ 1 Apr-30 Sep. € 7.00 2010*

RIOZ *6G2* (850m E Rural) *47.42525, 6.07524* **Camp Municipal du Lac, Rue de la Faïencerie, 70190 Rioz [03 84 91 91 59, 03 84 91 84 84 (Mairie) or 06 33 78 63 75 (mob); fax 03 84 91 90 45; mairiederioz@wanadoo.fr; www.rioz.fr]** Site sp off D15. Med, some hdg pitch, some hdstg, pt shd; htd wc; baby facs; shwrs inc; el pnts (16A) €2.50; gas; shops 500m; rests in vill; playgrnd; pool adj; dogs €1.50; quiet, but some rd noise. "Site yourself, warden calls; some lge pitches; gd facs; footpath to vill shops." 1 Apr-30 Sep. € 10.40 2011*

ROCHEFORT SUR NENON see Dole *6H2*

RUSSEY, LE see Maîche *6G3*

ST CLAUDE *9A3* (2km SE Rural) *46.37153, 5.87171* **Camp Municipal du Martinet, 12 le Martinet, 39200 St Claude [tel/fax 03 84 45 00 40 or 03 84 41 42 62 (LS); contact@camping-saint-claude.fr; www.camping-saint-claude.fr]** On ent town foll 1-way, under bdge mkd 4.1m high, then take R turn 'Centre Ville' lane to next traff lts. Turn R then immed L sp Genève, turn R 300m after Fiat g'ge onto D290, site on R. Med, pt shd; wc (cont); chem disp; shwrs inc; el pnts (5A) €2.30; gas; ldntte; shops 1km; rest; htd pool adj; tennis; fishing; poss cr; adv bkg; quiet; red low ssn; CKE/CCI; "Warden calls am & pm only low ssn; ltd facs low ssn; excel walking; v attractive town; poss funfair on site in Jun - no prob; gd." 1 Apr-30 Sep. € 20.40 2013*

ST LAURENT EN GRANDVAUX *6H2* (500m SE Rural) *46.57645, 5.96214* **Camp Municipal Le Champs de Mars, 8 Rue du Camping, 39150 St Laurent-en-Grandvaux [03 84 60 19 30 or 06 03 61 06 61; fax 03 84 60 19 72; champmars.camping@wanadoo.fr / champmars.camping@orange.fr; www.st-laurent39.fr]** E thro St Laurent on N5 twd Morez, site on R, sp 'Caravaneige' at ent. Med, mkd pitch, hdstg, pt sl, pt shd; htd wc; chem disp; mv service pnt; shwrs inc; some serviced pitches; el pnts (4-10A) €5-6.40; Indry (inc dryer); shops & supmkt in vill; playgrnd; TV rm; 20% statics; dogs; phone; adv bkg; quiet; red low ssn; CKE/CCI; "Gd site; peaceful low ssn; gd NH; friendly staff." ♦ 15 Dec- 1 Oct. € 26.25 2014*

ST POINT LAC see Pontarlier *6H2*

SALINS LES BAINS *6H2* (500m N Rural) *46.94650, 5.87896* **Camp Municipal, 39110 Salins-les-Bains [03 84 37 92 70; campingsalins.kanak.fr; www.salinscamping.com]** SE fr Besançon on N83. At Mouchard take D472 E to Salins. Turn L at rndabt at N of Salins, well sp nr old stn. If app fr E take 2nd exit fr rndabt (blind app). Sm, pt shd; wc; shwrs inc; el pnts (10A) €3.10; Indry rm; supmkt 500m; playgrnd; htd pool adj; 10% statics; adv bkg; quiet but some rd noise at 1 end & primary school at other; "Well-run site; clean, modern san facs; excel touring base N Jura; not often visited by British; far end of site quieter; gd NH; barrier locked 1000-0700." ♦ 31 Mar-1 Oct. € 13.40 2013*

TOUR DU MEIX, LA see Clairvaux les Lacs *6H2*

⊞ **VESOUL** *6G2* (1.5km W Rural) *47.63026, 6.12858* **Camping International du Lac, Ave des Rives du Lac, 70000 Vesoul [03 84 76 22 86; camping_dulac@yahoo.fr; www.camping-vesoul.com]** 2km fr D619, sp fr W end of by-pass, pass indus est to lge lake on W o'skts. Ent opp Peugeot/Citroën factory on lakeside. Lge, mkd pitch, pt shd; htd wc; mv service pnt; baby facs; shwrs inc; el pnts (6A) €3; gas; Indtte; shops 2km; rest; bar; playgrnd; pool, paddling pool, waterslides 300m; fishing; tennis; games area; some statics; dogs €2; site clsd mid-Dec to early Jan; adv bkg; ccard acc; red CKE/CCI. "Super site screened fr indus est by trees; gd size pitches but poss soft after rain; excel aqua park nr; gd cycle rtes; v gd." ♦ € 18.00 2014*

VUILLAFANS see Ornans *6G2*

Languedoc-Roussillon

Regional Introduction

Carcassonne

Welcome to Languedoc-Roussillon

Found in the central region of southern France, this area benefits from the warm Mediterranean weather, but has a quieter coastline than neighbouring Provence. A largely unspoilt area, it feels very traditionally French and enjoys a slower pace of life.

The towns and villages of Languedoc-Roussillon are some of the most beautiful in France, with historical buildings and fortified ancient battlements more than a thousand years old.

Local highlights

Languedoc-Roussillon cuisine is rich in seafood and wine. A local delicacy is traditional bouillabaisse (fish stew) which is made from the day's fresh catch and complemented by a cool glass of white wine.

Try one of the indoor markets for the latest in seasonal produce. Olives and olive oil are also a local speciality.

History fans will love Carcassonne's annual Medieval Festival, with historical reenactments and performances set against the town's ancient architecture.

Major towns and cities

- Montpellier – the regional capital, with a historical centre.
- Nimes – an old city with narrow streets and ancient Roman remains.
- Perpignan – a 10th-century medieval town with a strong Catalonian influence.
- Carcassonne – a UNESCO listed fortified town, with an impressive gothic cathedral.

Regional attractions

- Château de Quéribus – one of the best-preserved castles in the region.
- Grotte de Demoiselles, Ganges – a spectacular limestone cave system.
- Jardins de La Fontaine, Nimes – an 18th-century formal garden filled with water architecture and impressive statues.
- Gorges de Galamus – breathtaking canyons which can be enjoyed by car or on foot.

Find out more

www.destination-languedoc.co.uk

Tel: (0)4 67 60 60 60 Montpellier Tourist Office
Tel: (0)4 68 10 24 30 Carcassonne Tourist Office

⊞ **AGDE** *10F1* (2km NE Rural) *43.38720, 3.48156* **Camping Les Chalets du Rec de Rieu, Ave de Pomérols, 34510 Florensac [04 67 77 94 64; ortiz.freddy@wanadoo.fr; http://freddy.ortiz.pagesperso-orange.fr/]** Leave Florensac on D18 dir Pomérols & Montpellier; site on L in 2km. Sm, mkd pitch, pt shd; htd wc; chem disp; shwrs; el pnts (5A) inc; Indtte; shop; tradsmn; snacks; bar; BBQ; sm above-grnd pool; adv bkg; quiet; CKE/CCI. "Welcoming owner; vg." ♦ ltd € 15.00 2009*

AGDE *10F1* (3km SE Coastal) *43.27949, 3.48114* **Camping Le Rochelongue, Chemin des Ronciers, Route de Rochelongue, 34300 Le Cap d'Agde [04 67 21 25 51; fax 04 67 94 04 23; le.rochelongue@wanadoo.fr; www.camping-le-rochelongue.fr]** Exit A9 junc 34 sp Agde. Foll D612 to Le Cap d'Agde then thro Rochelongue. Site on L just bef rndabt. Med, mkd pitch, hdstg, pt shd; wc (cont); chem disp (wc); mv service pnt; baby facs; shwrs inc; el pnts (6A) inc; gas; Indtte; shop; rest; takeaway; snacks; bar; BBQ; playgrnd; htd pool; conv store; table tennis; sand beach 500m; cycle hire; golf 1.5km; internet; entmnt; 50% statics; dogs €4; phone; poss cr; Eng spkn; adv bkg; poss noisy high ssn; CKE/CCI. "Friendly, well-kept site; sh walk to vill & beach." ♦ 29 Mar- 28 Oct. € 47.00 2013*

AGDE *10F1* (5km SE Coastal) *43.29645, 3.52255* **Centre Hélio-Marin René Oltra (Naturist), 1 Rue des Néréïdes, 34307 Le Cap-d'Agde [04 67 01 06 36 or 04 67 01 06 37; fax 04 67 01 22 38; infos@chm-reneoltra.fr; www.chm-reneoltra.fr]** S fr m'way A9 Agde-Pézenas junc on N312/D612 for 14km to Cap d'Agde turn-off; foll Camping Naturist sp to site on E side of Le Cap-d'Agde. V lge, hdg/mkd pitch, pt shd; all serviced pitches; wc (some cont); mv service pnt; chem disp; shwrs inc; el pnts (5A) inc; gas 1km; Indtte; shop; tradsmn; rest; bar; pool; sand beach adj; bus adj; 50% statics; dogs €3.40; poss cr high ssn; Eng spkn; adv bkg rec; quiet; ccard acc; red low ssn; INF card. "Naturist area in Cap-d'Agde has all facs; lovely beach; gd size pitches; friendly atmosphere; modern san facs; gd family facs; excel; great location; gd public transport & walking." ♦ 15 Mar-14 Oct. € 42.00 2014*

AGDE *10F1* (1km S Rural) *43.29657, 3.47714* **Kawan Village Les Champs Blancs, Route de Rochelongue, 34300 Agde [04 67 94 23 42; fax 04 67 94 87 81; champs-blancs@wanadoo.fr; www.champs-blancs.fr]** Exit fr A9 & foll sps to Agde (not Le Cap d'Agde). Thro cent of Agde foll sps to campsite & Rochelongue. Site on R after bdge over dual c'way. V lge, hdg pitch, shd; wc; chem disp; mv service pnt; private san facs some pitches (extra charge); shwrs inc; el pnts (10A) inc (poss rev pol); gas; Indtte (inc dryer); shop, rest, snacks, bar adj; playgrnd; 2 htd pools; waterslide; sand beach 2km; tennis; games area; golf 2km; wifi; 10% statics; dogs €2; adv bkg; quiet; CKE/CCI. "Friendly site; excel san facs; hot water to shwrs only; vg." ♦ 4 Apr-29 Sep. € 43.00 (CChq acc) 2010*

AGDE *10F1* (4km S Coastal) *43.28856, 3.44266* **Camping de la Tamarissière, 4 Rue du Commandant Malet, 34300 Agde [04 67 94 79 46; fax 04 67 94 78 23; contact@camping-tamarissiere.com; www.camping-tamarissiere.com]** At Agde bdge take D32E on R bank of Rv Hérault to La Tamarissière; sp. V lge, mkd pitch, pt sl, shd; wc; shwrs; el pnts (6A) €4.20; Indtte; shop; rest, snacks; bar; playgrnd; sand beach adj; games area; cycle hire; entmnt; harbour nr for boat owners; 5% statics; dogs €3.20; poss cr; adv bkg; quiet; ccard acc; red long stay/low ssn; CKE/CCI. "Sandy site under pines; ferry across rv; ltd facs on site & in vill; lge areas flood after heavy rain; gate shut 2200-0700." ♦ 15 Apr-15 Sep. € 22.50 2009*

AGDE *10F1* (2km SW Coastal) *43.29343, 3.45295* **Camping La Pepinière, 3 Route du Grau, 34300 Agde [04 67 94 10 94; lapepiniere@free.fr; www.campinglapepiniere.com]** S fr Agde on D32 dir Le Grau d'Agde; Blvd de St Christ is pt of D32; 500m after passing under D612, D32 becomes Route du Grau. Site sp on L. Med, mkd pitch, pt shd; wc; chem disp; mv service pnt; shwrs inc; el pnts (6A) €4.50; Indtte; shop; tradsmn; snacks; bar; BBQ; playgrnd; htd pool; games area; entmnt; wifi; TV; 30% statics; dogs €3.50; phone; poss cr; ccard acc; quiet; red low ssn; CKE/CCI. "Friendly staff; vg cycle paths; attractive area; vg." 1 Apr-15 Oct. € 19.50 2011*

AGDE *10F1* (2km SW Rural) *43.29806, 3.45639* **Camping Le Neptune, 46 Boulevard du St Christ, 34300 Agde [04 67 94 23 94; fax 04 67 94 48 77; info@campingleneptune.com; www.campingleneptune.com]** Fr A9 exit junc 34 onto N312, then E on D612. Foll sp Grau d'Agde after x-ing bdge. Site on D32E on E bank of Rv Hérault on 1-way system. Lge, hdg/mkd pitch, pt shd; wc (some cont); chem disp; baby facs; fam bthrm; shwrs inc; el pnts (6-10A) inc; gas; Indtte; shop & bar in ssn; hypmkt 3km; rest 2km; bar; BBQ; playgrnd; htd pool; paddling pool; sand beach 2km; tennis; games area; wifi; entmnt; TV; 40% statics; dogs €3 (no Pitbulls or Rottweillers); phone; bus 2km; poss cr; Eng spkn; adv bkg rec; quiet; ccard acc; red low ssn; CKE/CCI. "Peaceful, pleasant, clean site; helpful owners; modern facs, ltd low ssn; liable to flood after heavy rain; easy rvside walk/cycle to vill; gd cycleways; rv cruises; boat launch/slipway 500m; v popular site." ♦ 6 Apr-5 Oct. € 48.00 2014*

AGDE *10F1* (3km SW Coastal) *43.29440, 3.45010* **Camping Les Romarins, Le Grau d'Agde, 34300 Agde [04 67 94 18 59; fax 04 67 26 58 80; contact@romarins.com; www.romarins.com]** Fr Agde take rd to Grau d'Agde, site at ent to Grau d'Agde adj Rv Hérault. Med, mkd pitch, hdstg, pt shd; wc; chem disp; mv service pnt; baby facs; shwrs inc; el pnts (10A) inc; Indtte (inc dryer); shop 500m; rest, snacks; bar; BBQ; playgrnd; htd pool; sand beach 1km; games area; cycle hire; entmnt; wifi; 25% statics; dogs €3.30; bus; twin axles; poss cr; Eng spkn; adv bkg; quiet; CKE/CCI. "Pleasant town with many bars, rests; shops; helpful owner; excel site." ♦ ltd 29 May-4 Oct. € 44.00 (CChq acc) 2014*

AIGUES MORTES **See also sites listed under La Grande Motte and Le Grau-du-Roi.**

AIGUES MORTES *10F2* (5km N Rural) *43.61130, 4.21010* **Camping Fleur de Camargue, 30220 St Laurent-d'Aigouze [04 66 88 15 42; fax 04 66 88 10 21; contact@fleur-de-camargue.com; www.fleur-de-camargue.com]** Exit A9 junc 26 onto D6313/D979 dir Aigues-Mortes; turn L into St Laurent d'Aigouze; cont thro St Laurent onto D46; site on R in 2.5km. Or N fr Aigues-Mortes at junc with D58 over high-level bdge onto D46, site 2.5km on L on D46. NB Do not go thro St Laurent-d'Aigouze cent, v narr & one-way. Med, mkd pitch, pt shd; wc; chem disp; mv service pnt; shwrs inc; el pnts (10A) €4; gas; lndtte; shops 2km; tradsmn; rest, snacks & bar; playgrnd; htd pool; paddling pool; sand beach 11km; rv & fishing 3km; wifi; entmnt; TV rm; 40% statics; dogs €4; phone; adv bkg; quiet; ccard acc; red low ssn; CKE/CCI. "Peaceful, relaxing site; lge pitches; pleasant owners; gd clean san facs; gd pool; site floods easily; gd." ♦ 6Apr-20 Sep. € 26.00 2014*

"Satellite navigation makes touring much easier"

Remember most sat navs don't know if you're towing or in a larger vehicle – always use yours alongside maps and site directions.

AIGUES MORTES *10F2* (3km NE Rural) *43.57314, 4.21836* **Camping à la Ferme (Loup), Le Mas de Plaisance, 30220 Aigues-Mortes [04 66 53 92 84 or 06 22 20 92 37 (mob); info@ot-aiguesmortes.fr; www.ot-aiguesmortes.fr]** Site sp in Aigues-Mortes or foll D58 E dir Stes Maries-de-la-Mer, then sharp R along farm rd (v narr & potholed) at end of rv bdge. NB Fr town narr rd with much traff calming & sharp bends. Either way for v sm o'fits only. Sm, pt shd; wc; chem disp; mv service pnt; shwrs inc; el pnts inc; lndry rm; tradsmn; BBQ; quiet; CKE/CCI. "Excel sm site; superb san facs; helpful owners; rec not to use water at m'van service point as off irrigation system - other water points avail; video security at gate." 1 Apr-30 Sep. € 22.00 2014*

AIGUES MORTES *10F2* (3.5km W Rural) *43.56300, 4.15910* **Yelloh! Village La Petite Camargue, 30220 Aigues-Mortes [04 66 53 98 98; fax 04 66 53 98 80; info@yellohvillage-petite-camargue.fr; www.yellohvillage-petite-camargue.com / www.yellohvillage.co.uk]** Heading S on N979 turn L onto D62 bef Aigues-Mortes & go over canal bdge twd Montpellier; site on R in 3km; sp. V lge, mkd pitch, pt shd; wc; chem disp; mv service pnt; some serviced pitch; baby facs; jaccuzi; shwrs inc; el pnts (10A) inc; lndtte (inc dryer); shop; rest, snacks; bar; BBQ (charcoal/gas); playgrnd; pool; paddling pool; sand beach 3km; horseriding; cycle hire; tennis; games area; games rm; wifi; entmnt; TV; 50% statics; dogs €4; no c'vans/m'vans over 7m; bus to beach high ssn; Eng spkn; adv bkg; ccard acc; red low ssn; CKE/CCI. "Lively, busy, well-run, youth-oriented commercial site with many sports facs; clean san facs, poss stretched high ssn; excel pool complex; some sm pitches; take care o'head branches; gd cycling; mkt Wed & Sun." ♦ 26 Apr-15 Sep. € 44.00 2011*

AIGUEZE see Pont St Esprit *9D2*

AIRES, LES see Lamalou les Bains *10F1*

ALES *10E1* (6km S Rural) *44.07912, 4.09700* **Camping Mas Cauvy (Maurin-Daumet), Chemin du Mas Cauvy, 30380 St Christol-lès-Alès [tel/fax 04 66 60 78 24; maurin.helene@wanadoo.fr; http://fermemascauvy.free.fr]** Fr Alès S on N110/D6110 S sp Montpellier. At S end of Christol-lès-Alès (shortly after stone needle) take 2nd L into Rue de Mas Rouge; foll sp to site in 1.5km. NB Sps fr main rd diff to see. Sm, pt terr, pt shd; wc; chem disp (wc); shwrs inc; el pnts (6A) €3; gas 1.5km; lndtte; shop 1.5km; tradsmn; rest & snacks; 1.5km; BBQ; playgrnd; pool; tennis 3km; bus (1km); dogs €2; poss cr; adv bkg; quiet; red low ssn/CKE/CCI. "Attractive, CL-type site with lovely views; friendly, helpful owner; book early for shd pitch; excel." 1 Apr-30 Sep. € 15.00 2010*

⊞ **ALET LES BAINS** *8G4* (300m W Rural) *42.99490, 2.25525* **Camping Val d'Aleth, Ave Nicolas Pavillon, 11580 Alet-les-Bains [04 68 69 90 40; fax 04 68 69 94 60; camping@valdaleth.com; www.valdaleth.com]** Fr Limoux S on D118 twd Quillan; in approx 8km ignore 1st L turn over Aude bdge into vill but take alt rte for heavy vehicles. Immed after x-ing rv, turn L in front of casino & ent town fr S; site sp on L. Sm, hdg/mkd pitch, hdstg, pt sl, shd; htd wc; chem disp; mv service pnt; baby facs; shwrs inc; el pnts (4-10A) €2.75-4; gas; lndtte (inc dryer); shop; rest nrby; BBQ (gas only); playgrnd; pool 1km; rv adj (no sw); cycle hire; wifi; 25% statics; dogs €1.55; phone; poss cr; adv bkg; Eng spkn; rd & train noise, church bells daytime; ccard acc; red low ssn/long stay; CKE/CCI. "Rvside site in attractive, medieval vill; sm pitches (lge o'fits need to book); friendly British owner; gd clean san facs; v few facs in vill; poss unkempt early ssn; conv Carcassonne & Cathar country - scenic." ♦ € 25.00 2014*

"There aren't many sites open at this time of year"

If you're travelling outside peak season remember to call ahead to check site opening dates – even if the entry says 'open all year'.

ALLEGRE LES FUMADES *10E2* (2km NE Rural) *44.2089, 4.25665* **Camping Le Château de Boisson, 30500 Allègre-les-Fumades [04 66 24 85 61 or 04 66 24 82 21; fax 04 66 24 80 14; reception@chateaudeboisson.com; www.chateaudeboisson.com / www.les-castels.com]** Fr Alès NE on D904, turn R after Les Mages onto D132, then L onto D16 for Boisson. Fr A7 take exit 19 Pont l'Esprit, turn S on N86 to Bagnols-sur-Cèze & then D6 W. Bef Vallérargues turn R onto D979 Lussan, then D37 & D16 to Boisson. Lge, hdg/mkd pitch, pt sl, shd; wc; chem disp; mv service pnt; baby facs; shwrs inc; el pnts (6A) inc; gas; lndtte (inc dryer); shop; tradsmn; rest, snacks; bar; BBQ (gas & elec); playgrnd; 2 pools (1 htd & covrd); paddling pool; tennis; cycle hire; games rm; wifi; entmnt; 80% statics; dogs €5 (no dogs 9 Jul-20 Aug); phone; no c'vans/m'vans over 7m high ssn; poss cr; Eng spkn; adv bkg; quiet; ccard acc; red low ssn/long stay. "Vg, well-run, peaceful site; gd sized pitches, poss some v sm; helpful staff; excel san facs; excel rest & facs; superb pool complex." ♦ 12 Apr-27 Sep. € 39.00 SBS - C34 2011*

ALLEGRE LES FUMADES *10E2* (2km S Rural) *44.18538, 4.22918* **Camping Le Domaine des Fumades, 30500 Allègre-les-Fumades [04 66 24 80 78; fax 04 66 24 82 42; fumades@franceloc.fr; www.domaine-des-fumades.com / www.campings-franceloc.fr]** Take Bollène exit fr A7 m'way, foll sps to Bagnols-sur-Cèze, take D6 twd Alès; 10km bef Alès turn R sp Allègre-les-Fumades on D7 to site in 5km. Easy to find fr Alès ring rd. Med, mkd pitch, pt shd; wc; chem disp; baby facs; shwrs inc; el pnts (6A) €4; gas; Indtte (inc dryer); shop; tradsmn; rest, snacks; bar; playgrnd; 2 pools (1 htd, covrd); paddling pool; waterslide; tennis; games rm; golf & watersports nr; wifi; entmnt; some statics; dogs €5; adv bkg. "Pleasant location; friendly staff; beautiful, well-run site." ♦ 10 Apr-19 Sep. € 28.00 2010*

AMELIE LES BAINS PALALDA see Ceret *8H4*

ANDUZE *10E1* (5km E Rural) *44.03585, 4.02390* **Kawan Village Domaine de Gaujac, 2406 Chemin de la Madeleine, 30140 Boisset-et-Gaujac [04 66 61 67 57; fax 04 66 60 53 90; contact@domaine-de-gaujac.com; www.domaine-de-gaujac.com]** S fr Alès on D6110 & turn R onto D910A dir Anduze. At Bagard (3km bef Anduze) turn L at mini rndabt onto D246 dir Boisset-et-Gaujac. At next rndbt turn R, then immed L. Foll vill & camping sp. Lge, some hdstg, pt terr, shd; htd wc (some cont); chem disp; mv service pnt; some serviced pitches; shwrs inc; baby facs; el pnts (4-6A) €4-4.50; gas; Indtte (inc dryer); shop; rest, snacks; bar; BBQ; playgrnd; 1 htd pool; paddling pool; rv adj; fishing; tennis; cycle hire; games area; games rm; wifi; entmnt; TV; 30% statics; dogs €2.50; Eng spkn; adv bkg rec high ssn; quiet, but noisy until late in café area high ssn; red low ssn. "Tranquil site; friendly, helpful family owners; clean san facs; pitches poss unkempt; Trabuc caves, Tarn gorges nrby." ♦ 1 Apr-20 Sep. € 21.00 (CChq acc) 2009*

ANDUZE *10E1* (1.5km SE Rural) *44.03824, 3.99454* **Camping Le Bel Eté, 1870 Route de Nîmes, 30140 Anduze [tel/fax 04 66 61 76 04; contact@camping-bel-ete.com; www.camping-bel-ete.com]** S fr Alès on D6110; W on D910A to Anduze. In Anduze take D907 SE twds Nîmes. Site on L, 200m after rlwy bdge. Med, mkd pitch, pt shd; wc; chem disp; serviced pitches; shwrs inc; el pnts (6A) €4.50; gas; Indtte; shop 1.5km; tradsmn; rest; playgrnd; pool; rv adj; 10% statics; dogs €1.50; phone; adv bkg ess; quiet but some rd noise; ccard acc; CKE/CCI. "Delightful, well-kept site in superb location; vg facs but ltd low ssn; helpful owner; gd base for Cévennes area; Thurs mkt." ♦ 8 May-17 Sep. € 33.50 2012*

ANDUZE *10E1* (5km SW Rural) *44.02733, 4.02736* **Camping Le Fief, 195 Chemin du Plan d'Eau, 30140 Massillargues-Attuech [04 66 61 81 71; fax 04 66 61 87 80; lefief@wanadoo.fr; www.campinglefiefdanduze.com]** Leave Anduze S on D982 dir Nîmes; site on L on leaving Attuech; sp. Med, mkd pitch, some hdstg, shd; wc; chem disp; baby facs; sauna; shwrs inc; el pnts (6A) €3 (poss no earth); Indtte; shops; tradsmn; rest, snacks; bar; playgrnd; pool; paddling pool; spa; rv sw adj, shgl beach; wifi; 10% statics; dogs €2.10; phone; poss cr; adv bkg; quiet; ccard acc; CKE/CCI. "Clean facs; gd for cycling." 1 Apr-30 Sep. € 19.00 2010*

ANDUZE *10E1* (13.5km W Rural) *44.04364, 3.88109* **Camping La Pommeraie, Route de Lassalle, 30140 Thoiras [04 66 85 20 52; fax 04 66 85 20 53; info@la-pommeraie.fr; www.la-pommeraie.fr]** Fr Alès take D6110, & D910A to Anduze, over bdge, R onto D907. In 6km L under rlwy onto D57, site on L 2.5km bef Lasalle. Med, shd; wc; baby facs; shwrs; el pnts (6A) €4.50; gas; Indtte; shop; rest, snacks; bar; cooking facs; playgrnd; 2 pools; rv & beach adj; tennis; games area; entmnt; TV rm; some statics; dogs €2-5.50 (high ssn); adv bkg; quiet; red low ssn. 13 Apr-29 Sep. € 39.00 2014*

ANDUZE *10E1* (1.4km NW Rural) *44.06430, 3.97694* **Camping Castel Rose, 30140 Anduze [04 66 61 80 15; castelrose@wanadoo.fr; www.castelrose.com]** Fr Alès S on D6110 & W on N910A to Anduze. Foll sp Camping L'Arche. Lge, shd; wc; shwrs inc; el pnts (6-10A) €3.20-4; gas; Indtte; shop; rest, snacks; bar; pool; fishing; boating; wifi; entmnt; TV; dogs €2; poss cr; Eng spkn; adv bkg rec high ssn. "Excel site by rv; friendly, helpful owners; attractive countryside; gd cent touring Cévennes." 1 Apr-28 Sep. € 43.00 2014*

ANDUZE *10E1* (2km NW Rural) *44.06785, 3.97336* **Camping L'Arche, Quartier de Labahou, 30140 Anduze [04 66 61 74 08; fax 04 66 61 88 94; contact@camping-arche.fr; www.camping-arche.fr]** Fr Alès S on D6110/D910A to Anduze. On D907, sp on R. Access poss dff lge o'fits/m'vans. Lge, mkd pitch, shd; htd wc; chem disp; mv service pnt; baby facs; shwrs inc; el pnts (10A) €2; gas; lndtte; shop; tradsmn; rest, snacks; bar; BBQ; playgrnd; pool; waterslide; wifi; entmnt; TV; some statics; dogs €3.80; Eng spkn; adv bkg; quiet; red long stay; CKE/CCI. "Well-run site; gd san facs; beautiful area; bamboo gardens worth visit; 24hr security patrols." ♦ 1 Apr-30 Sep. € 28.50 2009*

ANDUZE *10E1* (4km NW Rural) *44.07814, 3.96533* **Camping Cévennes-Provence, Corbès-Thoiras, 30140 Anduze [04 66 61 73 10; fax 04 66 61 60 74; marais@camping-cevennes-provence.fr; www.camping-cevennes-provence.fr]** Fr Anduze D907 & D284 along rvside after bdge, site sp. Diff ent espec for lge o'fits. Lge, mkd pitch, terr, shd; htd wc (some cont); chem disp; some serviced pitches; mv service pnt; baby facs; shwrs inc; el pnts (3-15A) inc; gas; lndtte (inc dryer); shop; tradsmn; rest, snacks; bar; BBQ; playgrnd; discovery park; shgl beach & rv sw adj; fishing; tennis; games area; games rm; wifi; entmnt; TV; some statics; dogs €2.90; Eng spkn; adv bkg; quiet; red low ssn; CKE/CCI. "Variable pitch sizes; direct access to private rv beach; helpful recep; gd walking; dog walks & dog shwrs; gd touring base; vg site." ♦ 20 Mar-2 Oct. € 27.00 2010*

See advert on previous page

ANIANE *10E1* (1.5km SW Rural) *43.67550, 3.56542* **Camping La Source St Pierre (Naturist), 1 Route de Gignac, 34150 Aniane [tel/fax 04 67 57 76 95; campingstpierre@hotmail.com; www.campingstpierre.com]** Exit A750 at Gignac onto D32 dir Aniane; site on L in 2.5km (bef Aniane). Med, pt shd; wc (some cont); chem disp; shwrs inc; el pnts (5-10A) €3.30-3.90; gas; lndtte; tradsmn; rest, snacks; bar; BBQ (sep area); playgrnd; rv adj; canoe & kayak hire; wifi; dogs € 2.50; phone; Eng spkn; quiet; ccard acc; red low ssn; CKE/CCI. "Friendly site - many regs; vg rv bathing & rv sports; excel." ♦ ltd 1 May-30 Sep. € 19.50 2009*

ARGELES SUR MER *10G1* (1km N Coastal) *42.55726, 3.02893* **Camping de Pujol, Ave de la Retirada, Route du Tamariguer, 66700 Argelès-sur-Mer [04 68 81 00 25; fax 04 68 81 21 21; www.campingdepujol.com]** Fr Perpignan on D914 exit junc 10 dir Argelès. L off slip rd foll sp Pujol, site on R - wide ent. Lge, mkd pitch, pt shd; wc (some cont); chem disp; mv service pnt; baby facs; shwrs inc; el pnts (3-6A) €4; gas 2km; lndtte (inc dryer); shop; rest, snacks; bar; playgrnd; pool; paddling pool; sand beach 1km; car wash; entmnt; 30% statics; dogs free; phone; poss cr; Eng spkn; adv bkg rec high ssn; quiet but poss noisy disco; CKE/CCI. "Vg san facs but poss cold water shwrs only low ssn; pool poss cr high ssn; excel cycling." ♦ ltd 1 Jun-30 Sep. € 25.00 2011*

ARGELES SUR MER *10G1* (1km N Rural) *42.57158, 3.02607* **Camping Les Galets, Route de Taxo-à la Mer, Plage Nord, 66701 Argelès-sur-Mer [04 68 81 08 12; fax 04 68 81 68 76; lesgalets@campinglesgalets.fr; www.campmed.com]** Fr Perpignan take D914 dir Elne, Argelès, 4km after Elne pass Municipal Camping on L, sp listing many camp sites. Lge, pt shd; wc; mv service pnt; baby facs; shwrs inc; el pnts (10A) inc; gas; lndtte; shop; rest, snacks; bar; playgrnd; htd pool; paddling pool; sand beach 1.5km; fishing, sailing & windsurfing 1.5km; rv sw 3km; equestrian cent nr; games area; wifi; entmnt; TV rm; 90% statics; dogs €4; poss cr; adv bkg rec all year; quiet; red low ssn. "Ltd touring pitches; gd for families." ♦ 1 Apr-30 Sep. € 37.50 2010*

ARGELES SUR MER *10G1* (1km N Coastal) *42.56320, 3.03498* **Camping Les Marsouins, Ave de la Retirada, 66702 Argelès-sur-Mer [04 68 81 14 81; fax 04 68 95 93 58; marsouin@campmed.com; www.campmed.com]** Fr Perpignan take exit 10 fr D914 & foll sp for Argelès until Shell petrol stn on R. Take next L just bef rv into Allée Ferdinand Buisson to T-junc, turn L at next rndabt dir Plage-Nord. Take 2nd R at next rndabt, site on L opp Spanish war memorial. V lge, hdg/mkd pitch, shd; wc; chem disp; mv service pnt; shwrs inc; el pnts (5A) inc; gas; lndtte (inc dryer); shops; lge supmkt 3km; rest, snacks; bar; BBQ (gas/elec); playgrnd; htd pool; sand beach 800m; sailing & windsurfing 1km; cycle hire; games area; games rm; entmnt; internet; 20% statics; dogs €3; poss cr; Eng spkn; adv bkg; ccard acc; red low ssn. "Lovely, well-kept, well-run site; clean san facs; busy rd to beach, but worth it; many sm coves; gd area for cycling; TO on site; excel." ♦ 16 Apr-24 Sep. € 43.00 2012*

ARGELES SUR MER *10G1* (2km N Rural) *42.5724, 3.02171* **Camping Le Dauphin, Route de Taxo à la Mer, 66701 Argelès-sur-Mer [04 68 81 17 54; fax 04 68 95 82 60; info@campingledauphin.com; www.campingledauphin.com]** Fr Perpignan take D914 sp Elne & Argelès-sur-Mer. 4km after Elne, sp on L to Taxo d'Avall, turn L, site 2km on R. Lge, hdg/mkd pitch, pt shd; wc; chem disp; private bthrms avail some pitches - extra charge; baby facs; shwrs inc; el pnts (10A) inc; gas; lndtte; shop; rest, snacks; bar; BBQ (gas/elec); playgrnd; 2 pools; paddling pool; waterslides; sand beach 3km; fishing; sailing; windsurfing; tennis; games area; games rm; internet; entmnt; TV rm; 80% statics; dogs €4; Eng spkn; adv bkg; ccard acc; red low ssn. "Gd for families; superb pool area; helpful staff; excel facs; free transport to beach high ssn; vg site." ♦ 14 May-17 Sep. € 43.00 2011*

ARGELES SUR MER *10G1* (2km N Coastal) *42.55775, 3.03140* **Camping Paris Roussillon, Ave de la Retirada 1939, Quartier Pujol, 66700 Argelès-sur-Mer [04 68 81 19 71; fax 04 68 81 68 77; contact@parisroussillon.com; www.parisroussillon.com / www.campings-franceloc.fr]** Fr Perpignan, take D914, junc 10 twds Pujol. Site 2km on R. Lge, mkd pitch, shd; wc; chem disp; shwrs inc; baby facs; el pnts (6A) inc; lndtte; shop 1km; rest, snacks; bar; BBQ; playgrnd; pool; waterslide; paddling pool; beach 1.5km; tennis; games area; wifi; some statics; dogs €2.50; Eng spkn; quiet; red low ssn. "Satisfactory site." ♦ 3 Apr-26 Sep. € 30.00 2010*

ARGELES SUR MER *10G1* (2km NE Coastal) *42.54819, 3.03617* **Camping du Stade, 8 Ave du 8 Mai 1945, 66702 Argelès-sur-Mer [04 68 81 04 40; info@campingdustade.com; www.campingdustade.com]** S on D914 thro traff lts at Argelès; turn L after 400m at clearly mkd turn sp 'A la Plage'. Site 800m on L. Lge, shd; wc; baby facs; shwrs inc; el pnts (6A) inc; lndtte; supmkt 500m; rest, snacks; bar; playgrnd; sand beach 800m; sports complex adj; entmnt; TV rm; some statics; dogs €2; poss cr; adv bkg rec high ssn; quiet; red low ssn. "Lge pitches; gd walking area; mountain views; friendly owners." 1 Apr-30 Sep. € 24.50 2010*

ARGELES SUR MER *10G1* (2km NE Coastal) *42.57245, 3.04115* **Camping La Marende, Chemin de la Salanque, 66702 Argelès-sur-Mer [tel/fax 04 68 81 03 88; info@marende.com; www.marende.com]** Fr Perpignan S on D914 exit junc 10 Argelès-sur-Mer; foll sp Plage Nord; after 2km at rndabt turn L sp St Cyprian; at next rndabt turn R sp Plages Nord & Sud; site on L in 800m. L onto unmade rd. V lge, hdg/mkd pitch, shd; wc; chem disp; some serviced pitches; mv service pnt; baby facs; shwrs inc; el pnts (6-10A) inc; gas; lndtte; shop; rest & snacks (high ssn); bar; BBQ (el/gas); playgrnd; pool & paddling pool; jacuzzi; games area; sand beach adj; aquarobics, scuba-diving lessons Jul & Aug; internet; TV; 12% statics; dogs €2.50; phone; poss cr; Eng spkn; quiet; adv bkg; ccard acc; CKE/CCI. "Beautiful site; lge pitches; friendly, helpful family owners; 1st class facs; excel pool; many static tents high ssn; gd area for cycling & walking; v quiet Sept." ♦ 26 Apr-27 Sep. € 26.00 2012*

ARGELES SUR MER *10G1* (2km NE Coastal) *42.56728, 3.04425* **Camping Le Roussillonnais, Blvd de la Mer, 66700 Argelès-sur-Mer [04 68 81 10 42; fax 04 68 95 96 11; contact@le-roussillonnais.com; www.le-roussillonnais.com]** S fr Perpignan on D914 thro Elne to Argelès-sur-Mer, turn L in Argelès-sur-Mer foll coast rd & site on R in 1.5km. V lge, hdg/mkd pitch, pt shd; wc (some cont); chem disp; mv service pnt; baby facs; shwrs inc; el pnts (6A) €3.80; gas; lndtte; shop; rest, snacks; bar; playgrnd; sand beach 500m; boating; watersports; tennis; games area; entmnt; some statics; dogs €1.50; shuttle bus to beach; poss cr; Eng spkn; adv bkg; quiet; ccard acc; CKE/CCI. "Site open all yr for m'vans; ltd facs low ssn." 20 Apr-27 Sep. € 22.50 2009*

ARGELES SUR MER *10G1* (2km NE Coastal) *42.55583, 3.04222* **Camping Les Pins, Ave du Tech, Zone des Pins, 66700 Argelès-sur-Mer [04 68 81 10 46; fax 04 68 81 35 06; camping@les-pins.com; www.les-pins.com]** Exit D914 junc 10, foll sp Pujols & Plage-Nord, site sp. Lge, pt shd; hdg pitch; mkd pitch; wc; chem disp; mv service pnt; baby facs; shwrs inc; el pnts (6A) inc; gas; lndtte; shop; snacks; playgrnd; pool; games area; child entmnt; wifi; sand beach 200m; statics; dogs €4; CC/CCI acc; Eng spkn; adv bkg (ess Jul/Aug); quiet; ccard acc. "Cent for beach; pleasant, helpful, clean san facs; quiet peaceful site." ♦ 12 Apr-28 Sep. € 57.00 2014*

ARGELES SUR MER *10G1* (2.7km NE Coastal) *42.55147, 3.04444* **Campsite Comanges, Avenue du Général de Gaulle, 66701 Argelés-sur-Mer [04 68 81 15 62; fax 04 68 95 87 74; infos@campingcomanges.com; www.campingcomanges.com]** A9 exit Perpignan-sud, D914 dir Argeles to exit 10. At 2nd rndabt foll Argeles, les plages then foll signs to Cent Plage. Med, hdg pitch, pt shd; wc; chem disp; mv service pnt; baby facs; shwr; el pnts(10A); lndtte(inc dryer); playgrnd; beach 0.5km; wifi; 20% statics; Eng spkn. "Gd cycling nrby; vg site." 14 Apr-1 Oct. € 46.00 2014*

ARGELES SUR MER *10G1* (3km NE Coastal) *42.55682, 3.04082* **Camping Beauséjour, Ave de Tech, Argelès-Plage, 66700 Argelès-sur-Mer [04 68 81 10 63; fax 04 68 95 75 08; contact@camping-lebeausejour.com; www.camping-lebeausejour.com]** Fr Perpignan, foll D914 to Argelès-sur-Mer. Turn L after Champion supmkt & Shell g'ge; foll sp to Plage Nord. At coast rd turn R to Argelès-Plage cent. Site on R shortly after supmkt. Lge, mkd pitch, shd; wc; chem disp; baby facs; shwrs inc; el pnts (6A) inc; lndtte; shop adj; rest, snacks; playgrnd; 2 pools (1 htd, covrd); paddling pool; waterslide; jacuzzi; sand beach 300m; wifi; entmnt; 50% statics; dogs €3 (not acc Jul-Aug); phone; poss cr; Eng spkn; adv bkg rec; CKE/CCI. ♦ ltd 1 May-30 Sep. € 38.00 (3 persons) 2010*

ARGELES SUR MER *10G1* (3.5km NE Coastal) *42.57543, 3.0431* **Camping Le Soleil, Route du Littoral, Plage-Nord, 66700 Argelès-sur-Mer [04 68 81 14 48 or 04 68 95 94 62 (LS); fax 04 68 81 44 34; camping.lesoleil@wanadoo.fr; www.campmed.com]** Exit D914 junc 10 & foll sp Argelès Plage-Nord. Turn L onto D81 to site. Site sp among others. V lge, mkd pitch, pt shd; wc (some cont); chem disp; mv service pnt; baby facs; shwrs inc; el pnts (6A) €3.70; gas; lndtte; shop; tradsmn; rest, snacks; bar; no BBQ; playgrnd; pool; paddling pool; sand beach adj; rv fishing adj; tennis; cycle hire; horseriding; games area; wifi; entmnt; TV; 50% statics; no dogs; phone; Eng spkn; adv bkg (ess Aug); noisy nr disco; ccard acc; red low ssn. "Lovely views; excel site for partially-sighted & handicapped; rec visit to Collioure; vg." ♦ 16 May-30 Sep. € 32.50 2009*

ARGELES SUR MER *10G1* (1km E Coastal) *42.54993, 3.04183* **Camping Europe, Ave du Général de Gaulle, 66700 Argelès-sur-Mer [04 68 81 08 10; fax 04 68 95 71 84; camping.europe@wanadoo.fr; www.camping-europe.net]** Fr Perpignan take D914 to Argelès-sur-Mer. Exit junc 12 to Argelès. At rndabt take last exit L to Argelès Ville. At next rndabt turn R, site on L after Dyneff g'ge 50m fr 'Tropical Golf'. Med, mkd pitch, shd; wc; chem disp; baby facs; shwrs inc; el pnts (10A) €4.10; gas; lndtte; shop; tradsmn; rest, snacks; bar; BBQ; playgrnd; pool 800m; sand beach 300m; wifi; 10% statics; dogs €2.15; phone; bus adj; poss cr; Eng spkn; adv bkg; quiet; red low ssn; CKE/CCI. "Friendly, secure, family-run site; shady pitches; helpful staff; clean, modern, unisex san facs; cycling nrby." 3 Apr-25 Sep. € 20.00 2010*

ARGELES SUR MER *10G1* (2km E Urban/Coastal) *42.55317, 3.04375* **Camping La Chapelle, Ave du Tech, 66702 Argelès-sur-Mer [04 68 81 28 14; fax 04 68 95 83 82; contact@camping-la-chapelle.com; www.camping-la-chapelle.com]** Fr A9 exit junc 42 onto D900/D914 to Argelès-sur-Mer. At junc 10 cont thro Argelès vill & foll sp Argelès-Plage. In 2.5km turn L at rndabt, bear L at Office de Tourisme, site immed L. Lge, hdg/mkd pitch, shd; wc (mainly cont); baby facs; shwrs inc; el pnts (6A) €6.50; Indtte; shop; rest, snacks, bar 100m; playgrnd; pool 2km; beach 200m; tennis 200m; wifi; entmnt; 30% statics; dogs €4; poss cr; Eng spkn; adv bkg; quiet; red low ssn; CKE/CCI. "Narr site rds poss diff lge o'fits; ltd facs low ssn; gd." ♦ 17 Apr-25 Sep. € 30.00 2010*

ARGELES SUR MER *10G1* (4km SE Coastal) *42.53413, 3.06826* **Camping Les Criques de Porteils, Corniche de Collioure, 66701 Argelès-sur-Mer [04 68 81 12 73; fax 04 68 95 85 76; contactcdp@lescriques.com; www.lescriques.com]** Fr N on A9/E15 take exit junc 42 onto D914 Argelès-sur-Mer. Fr S exit junc 43 onto D914. At exit 13 leave D914 sp Collioure & foll site sp. Site by Hôtel du Golfe 1.5km fr Collioure. Lge, hdg/mkd pitch, pt sl, terr, pt shd; htd wc (some cont); chem disp; mv service pnt; baby facs; shwrs inc; el pnts (5A) €6; gas; Indtte (inc dryer); shop; rest, snacks; bar; playgrnd; htd pool; sand/shgl beach adj; fishing; watersports; scuba-diving; tennis; games rm; games area; wifi; TV rm; 15% statics; dogs €4; phone; Eng spkn; adv bkg; quiet; red low ssn/CKE/CCI. "Excel, well-run site; variable size pitches - not all suitable for lge o'fits; splendid views fr many terr pitches; steps to beach; clean, modern, well kept san facs; exposed, poss v windy; gd walks; v challenging walk to Collioure but stunning." ♦ 29 Mar-25 Oct. € 77.00 2014*

ARGELES SUR MER *10G1* (4.5km SE Coastal) *42.53147, 3.07167* **Camping Les Amandiers, Route des Campings, 66190 Collioure [04 68 81 14 69; fax 04 68 81 09 95; contact@camping-les-amandiers.com; www.camping-les-amandiers.com]** On D914 SE fr Perpignan, leave at junc 13 sp Collioure. After rndabt foll rd to Collioure. Climb coastal rd; site on L, steep descent, not rec lge o'fits. Med, mkd pitch, pt sl, terr, shd; htd wc (some cont); chem disp; mv service pnt; shwrs inc; el pnts (10A) inc; Indtte; gas; sm shop; tradsmn; sm rest, bar high ssn; sm playgrnd; shgl beach 200m; 10% statics; dogs €3; poss cr; Eng spkn; adv bkg; (rec high ssn); some rlwy noise; ccard not acc; CKE/CCI. "Site access v diff, espec for lge/med o'fits, manhandling prob req - rec investigation bef ent; sm pitches; facs stretched high ssn; many trees - dusty site; steep site rds; friendly, helpful owners; Collioure historic port; gd." ♦ 1 Apr-30 Sep. € 45.40 (CChq acc) 2013*

ARGELES SUR MER *10G1* (2.5km SW Rural) *42.53999, 2.99515* **Camping Le Romarin, Route de Sorède, Chemin des Vignes,66702 Argelès-sur-Mer [04 68 81 02 63; fax 04 68 81 57 43; contact@camping-romarin.com; www.camping-romarin.com]** S fr Perpignon on D914; at rndabt junc with D618 foll sp St André on minor rd; in 500m L & immed L & foll sp to site. Or fr A9 exit junc 43; foll D618 to rndabt junc with D914; then as above. Med, pt sl, shd; wc (some cont); shwrs inc; el pnts (6A) €2-3.50; gas; Indtte; shop; rest, snacks; bar; playgrnd; pool; waterslide; beach 4km; sports activities; entmnt; some statics; dogs €3 (not acc Jul/Aug); train 2km; Eng spkn; adv bkg; quiet; red low ssn. "Pleasant site; conv Spanish border." 15 May-30 Sep. € 32.50 2009*

ARGELES SUR MER *10G1* (8km W Urban) *42.52667, 2.93515* **Camp Municipal Le Vivier, 31 Rue du Stade, 66740 Laroque-des-Albères [04 68 89 00 93 or 04 68 95 49 97; fax 04 68 95 42 58; tourisme@laroque-des-alberes.fr; www.laroque-des-alberes.fr]** D2 fr Argelès-sur-Mer to Laroque-des-Albères; foll sp in cent of vill. Site on rvside. Lge, mkd pitch, pt sl, pt shd; wc; chem disp; shwrs inc; el pnts (6A) €4; Indtte; shop 300m; BBQ; playgrnd; 5% statics; dogs €4; bus 300m; adv bkg; quiet; CKE/CCI. "Peaceful, simple site on edge Pyrenees, pleasant vill; vg." ♦ 15 Jun-15 Sep. € 24.00 2009*

ARGELES SUR MER *10G1* (8km W Rural) *42.52366, 2.94446* **Camping Les Albères, 66740 Laroque-des-Albères [04 68 89 23 64; fax 04 68 89 14 30; contact@camping-des-alberes.com; www.camping-des-alberes.com]** Fr A9 exit junc 43 onto D618 dir Argelès-sur-Mer/Port Vendres. Turn R onto D50 to Laroque-des-Albères. In vill at T-junc turn L, then turn R at rndabt & foll sp to site on D11. Lge, mkd pitch, terr, pt shd; wc; chem disp; mv service pnt; baby facs; shwrs inc; el pnts (6A) €5; Indtte; shop; rest, snacks; bar; BBQ (gas only); playgrnd; pool (high ssn); sand beach 8km; tennis; entmnt; wifi; TV rm; 5% statics; dogs €3.50; phone; quiet; poss cr; red low ssn; CKE/CCI. "Attractive, peaceful site under slopes of Pyrenees; friendly owners; gd san facs; gd walking area; excel." ♦ ltd 2 Apr-15 Oct. € 24.00 2011*

ARGELES SUR MER *10G1* (3km NW Rural) *42.57018, 3.01239* **Camping Etoile d'Or, Chemin de la Gabarre, Route de Taxo à la Mer, 66701 Argelès-sur-Mer [04 68 81 04 34; fax 04 68 81 57 05; info@aletoiledor.com; www.aletoiledor.com]** Fr D914 exit junc 10 dir Taxo-Plage. Site in 1km on R. Lge, hdg/mkd pitch, pt shd; wc; chem disp; baby facs; shwrs inc; el pnts (6A) inc; gas; Indtte (inc dryer); shop; tradsmn; rest, snacks; bar; BBQ (elec/gas); playgrnd; pool complex; paddling pool; waterslide; sand beach 2.5km; tennis; fitness rm; games area; games rm; wifi; entmnt; TV rm; 45% statics; dogs €3; Eng spkn; adv bkg; quiet; ccard acc; red long stay. "Welcoming site; gd for families; bus to beach fr site." ♦ 15 May-15 Sep. € 35.00 2011*

ARLES SUR TECH *8H4* (500m W Urban) *42.45783, 2.62563* **Camping du RiuFerrer, 66150 Arles-sur-Tech [04 68 39 11 06; fax 04 68 39 12 09; pascal.larreur@campingduriuferrer; www.campingduriuferrer.fr]** Take D115 fr Le Boulou thro Arles-sur-Tech (v narr but poss). Twd town exit just bef rv bdge, turn R. Foll sp 500m to site. Ent across narr footbdge. O'fits width across axle over 2.19m ask for guidance to rear ent. Med, mkd pitch, hdstg, pt sl, shd; wc (some cont); chem disp; shwrs inc; el pnts (10A) €3; gas; Indtte; snacks, bar in ssn; shops 500m; tradsmn; playgrnd; pool, tennis, games area adj; poss cr; adv bkg; 20% statics; dogs €1; quiet; ccard not acc; red low ssn/long stay; Eng spkn; red CKE/CCI. "Helpful owner; some sm pitches diff for manoeuvring; beautiful area; vg." ♦ 1 Mar-15 Oct. € 14.00 2010*

AVIGNON *10E2* (2km N Rural) *43.97063, 4.79928* **Camp Municipal de la Laune, Chemin St Honoré, 30400 Villeneuve-lès-Avignon [tel/fax 04 90 25 76 06 or 04 90 25 61 33; campingdelalaune@wanadoo.fr; www.camping-villeneuvelezavignon.com]** Fr Avignon, take N100 twd Nîmes over rv bdge. At W end of 2nd pt of rv bdge, turn R onto N980 sp Villeneuve-lès-Avignon. Site is 3km on R just past town battlements on L. Adj sports complex. Med, hdg/mkd pitch, hdstg, shd; wc; chem disp; mv service pnt; shwrs inc; el pnts (6A) €3.10 (poss rev pol); Indtte; shop; snacks; bar; pool & sports complex adj (free to campers); wifi in vill sq; dogs €1.50; phone; bus; Eng spkn; quiet; ccard acc; red low ssn; CKE/CCI. "Lovely, peaceful well-run site; gd, clean facs; helpful staff; excel security; sports facs adj; gd walks/cycle rides; in walking dist of Villeneuve-lès-Avignon with fort & abbey; gd bus to Avignon; vg local mkt; poss rlwy noise at night." ♦ ltd 1 Apr-15 Oct. € 34.00 2014*

⊞ **AVIGNON** *10E2* (12km W Rural) *43.95155, 4.66451* **Camping Le Bois des Ecureuils, 947 Chemin De La Beaume, 30390 Domazan [tel/fax 04 66 57 10 03; infos@boisdesecureuils.com; www.boisdesecureuils.com]** Exit A9/E15 at Remoulins junc 23 twd Avignon on N100. Site on R in 6km. Fr S on N7 foll sp for Nîmes onto N100. Go over 2 lge rndabts, site about 6km on L at rndabt. Sm, mkd pitch, all hdstg, shd; wc (some cont); chem disp (wc); baby facs; shwrs inc; el pnts (6A) inc; gas; Indtte; shop; rest adj; snacks, bar high ssn; BBQ; playgrnd; htd pool; entmnt; TV; 5% statics; dogs €1.70; phone; poss cr; Eng spkn; adv bkg (rec high ssn); quiet but some rd noise; red low ssn CKE/CCI. "Ideal for touring Avignon & Pont du Gard; friendly owners; clean facs; steel awning pegs ess; many long-stay residents low ssn." € 20.00 2013*

AVIGNON *10E2* (5km NW Rural) *43.99573, 4.81843* **Campéole Camping L'Ile des Papes, Quartier l'Islon, 30400 Villeneuve-lès-Avignon [04 90 15 15 90; fax 04 90 15 15 91; ile-des-papes@campeole.com; www.avignon-camping.com / www.campeole.com]** Fr A9 exit sp Roquemaure; head S on D980. Site adj to rv 2km NW of city. Fr D907 (A7) exit Avignon Nord, twds Avignon cent & cross bdge twds Villeneuve. Turn off after x-ing rv bef x-ing canal. Site bet rv & canal. Lge, pt shd; wc; shwrs; el pnts (6A) €4; Indtte; cooking facs; rest; supmkt; playgrnd; pool; archery; lake fishing adj; hiking; entmt; TV; statics 35%; dogs €3.50; adv bkg; quiet but some rlwy noise; Eng spkn; red low ssn; ccard acc; red low ssn/CKE/CCI. "Lovely area; well-run site; pleasant staff; lge pitches; gd site rest." ♦ 27 Mar-6 Nov. € 25.00 (CChq acc) 2012*

AXAT *8G4* (2km E Rural) *42.80775, 2.25408* **Camping de la Crémade, 11140 Axat [tel/fax 04 68 20 50 64; www.lacremade.com]** S fr Quillan on D117, cont 1km beyond junc with D118 twd Perpignan. Turn R into site, sp, narr access. Med, hdg pitch, pt sl, pt shd; wc; chem disp; shwrs inc; el pnts (6A) €2.50; Indtte; shop & 3km; BBQ; playgrnd; games rm; 5% statics; dogs €1; Eng spkn; adv bkg; quiet; CKE/CCI. "Pleasant, well-maintained site in beautiful location; few level pitches; gd san facs; conv for gorges in Aude Valley." ♦ 1 May-24 Sep. € 15.50 2014*

BAGNOLS SUR CEZE *10E2* (1.5km N Rural) *44.17585, 4.63540* **Camping La Coquille, Route de Carmignan, 30200 Bagnols-sur-Cèze [04 66 89 03 05; fax 04 66 89 59 86; jose.gimeno@free.fr; www.campinglacoquille.com]** Head N fr Bagnols-sur-Cèze over rv bdge turn R at Total stn, site 2km on RH side. Sm, pt shd; wc (cont); chem disp; shwrs inc; el pnts (4-6A) €4-4.50; gas in town; Indtte; rest; shop 2.5km; pool; canoe hire; fishing; dogs; adv bkg rec high ssn; CKE/CCI;ccard acc; "Site under military aircraft flightpath, otherwise gd, friendly, family-run site." 24 Apr-15 Sep. € 34.00 2013*

BAGNOLS SUR CEZE *10E2* (2km NE Rural) *44.17358, 4.63694* **Camping Les Genêts d'Or, Chemin de Carmigan, 30200 Bagnols-sur-Cèze [tel/fax 04 66 89 58 67; info@camping.genets-dor.com; www.camping-genets-dor.com]** N fr Bagnols on N86 over rv bdge, turn R into D360 immed after Total stn. Foll sp to site on rv. Med, mkd pitch, some hdstg, pt sl, pt shd; htd wc; chem disp; baby facs; shwrs inc; el pnts (6A) €5 (poss rev pol); gas; Indtte (inc dryer); shop; tradsmn; rest, snacks; bar; playgrnd; htd pool; paddling pool; canoeing, fishing 2km; games area; games rm; wifi; entmnt; some statics; no dogs Jul/Aug; poss cr; Eng spkn; adv bkg ess; quiet; ccard acc. "Excel, clean site; welcoming Dutch owners; gd pool; wildlife in rv; gd rest; highly rec." ♦ 20 Apr-20 Sep. € 25.00 2013*

"I like to fill in the reports as I travel from site to site"

You'll find report forms at the back of this guide, or you can fill them in online at www.caravaclub.co.uk/europereport.

BAGNOLS SUR CEZE *10E2* (8km NW Rural) *44.18865, 4.52448* **Camping Les Cascades, Route de Donnat, 30200 La Roque-sur-Cèze [04 66 82 72 97; fax 04 66 82 68 51; infos@campinglescascades.com; www.campinglescascades.com]** Fr Bagnols take D6 W twd Alès. After 4km turn N on D143 & foll sp to La Roque-sur-Cèze. Site on R in 7km. App fr N not rec. Long narr bdge (2.3m). Med, pt sl, pt shd; htd wc (cont); chem disp; mv service pnt; baby facs; shwrs inc; el pnts (6-10A) €4.10-4.30; gas; Indtte (inc dryer); shop; tradsmn; supmkt 6km; rest, snacks; bar; BBQ; playgrnd; htd pool; shgl beach & rv adj; tennis; fishing; boating; wifi; entmnt; TV; dogs €1.85; poss cr; adv bkg; quiet. "Tranquil site; modern san facs." 19 Apr-13 Oct. € 44.00 (CChq acc) 2013*

BALARUC LES BAINS *10F1* (300m NE Coastal) *43.44084, 3.68320* **Camp Municipal du Pech d'Ay, Ave de la Gare, 34540 Balaruc-les-Bains [04 67 48 50 34; pechday@mairie-balaruc-les-bains.fr; www.herault-tourisme.com]** Exit N113 to Balaruc-les-Bains; foll sp Centre Commercial & then head for prom. Site on prom. Lge, mkd pitch, pt sl, pt shd; htd wc; chem disp; mv service pnt; shwrs; el pnts (10A) €3.40; Indtte in town; shops, rest & bar adj; playgrnd; shgle beaches nrby; bus; poss cr; Eng spkn; adv bkg rec (even low ssn); poss noisy; CKE/CCI. "Delightful holiday resort; busy site all ssn, rec arr early; vg, clean san facs poss stretched peak times; many gd rests adj; thermal baths in vill; bus to Sète." ♦ 20 Apr-14 Dec. € 16.00 2013*

BALARUC LES BAINS *10F1* (500m NE Coastal) *43.45344, 3.68802* **Camping Les Vignes, 34540 Balaruc-les-Bains [04 67 48 04 93; fax 04 67 18 74 32; camping.lesvignes@free.fr; www.camping-lesvignes.com]** Fr N113 take D2 sp Sète, turn W sp Balurac-les-Bains, after 2nd rndabt turn R, well sp in 100m on R. Med, hdg/mkd pitch, pt shd; wc (some cont); chem disp; mv service pnt; shwrs inc; el pnts (6-10A) €3-3.50; Indtte; shops 1km; snacks; bar; playgrnd; pool; shgl beach 1km; sand beach 7km; fishing, horseriding & tennis nr; 30% statics; dogs €2.50; poss cr; adv bkg rec high ssn; quiet; ccard acc; CKE/CCI. "Gd touring base; narr site rds tight for long o'fits; Sète worth a visit." ♦ ltd 1 Apr-31 Oct. € 18.50 2009*

BANYULS SUR MER *10H1* (700m S Rural) *42.47665, 3.11904* **Camp Municipal La Pinède, Ave Guy Malé, 66650 Banyuls-sur-Mer [04 68 88 32 13; fax 04 68 88 32 48; camp.banyuls@banyuls-sur-mer.com; www.camping-banyuls-sur-mer.com]** On D914 foll sp to Banyuls-sur-Mer; turn R at camping sp at cent of sea-front by town hall; foll sp to site. Lge, hdg/mkd pitch, pt sl, pt terr; pt shd; wc; chem disp; mv service pnt; shwrs; el pnts (4-13A) €2-3; Indtte; snacks; supmkt 100m; playgrnd; shgl beach 1km; dogs; Eng spkn; quiet; ccard acc; red low ssn; CKE/CCI. "Busy, friendly site; spacious pitches, some with sea view; narr site rds; vg, clean facs." ♦ 26 Mar-15 Nov. € 13.00 2011*

BARCARES, LE *10G1* (1.5km S Coastal) *42.77607, 3.02435* **Camping L'Oasis, Route de St Laurent, 66423 Le Barcarès [04 68 86 12 43; fax 04 68 86 46 83; info@camping-oasis.com; www.camping-oasis.com]** Fr N exit A9/E15 junc 40 Leucate onto D627 & D83 twd Le Barcarès. Exit junc 9 onto D81 dir Canet-Plage. Take 1st exit then turn L onto D90 sp Le Barcarès, site sp on L in approx 800m. Lge, shd; wc (some cont); chem disp; baby facs; shwrs; el pnts (10A) inc; Indtte (inc dryer); supmkt; rest, snacks; bar; BBQ; playgrnd; 3 pools; waterslide; sand beach 1km; tennis; games area; wifi; entmnt; TV; dogs €4.50; red low ssn; CKE/CCI. "Ltd facs low ssn." ♦ 24 Apr-18 Sep. € 35.00 (CChq acc) 2010*

BARCARES, LE *10G1* (2km S Coastal) *42.77570, 3.02300* **Camping California, Route de St Laurent, 66420 Le Barcarès [tel/fax 04 68 86 16 08; camping-california@orange.fr; www.camping-california.fr]** Exit A9 junc 41 onto D627 sp Leucate. Ignore sp Le Barcarès & Port Barcarès; exit junc 9 sp Canet onto D81; then at D90 intersection turn R dir St Laurent-de-la-Salangue & go under D81; site on L (after Les Tamaris). Lge, hdg/mkd pitch, shd; wc; chem disp; baby facs; shwrs inc; el pnts (10A) inc (poos rev pol); Indtte (inc dryer); supmkt 1km; shop; rest, snacks; bar; BBQ (gas/elec only); playgrnd; htd pool; waterslide; paddling pool; sand beach 1.5km; watersports 1km; tennis; games area; wifi; entmnt; games/TV rm; 20% statics; dogs €5; Eng spkn; adv bkg; poss v busy/noisy high ssn; ccard acc; red low ssn/long stay; CKE/CCI. "Vg recep; various pitch sizes, some poss diff; friendly, helpful owners; excel, modern san facs, ltd low ssn; mosquito repellant useful; busy rd thro site; highly rec." ♦ 1 May-27 Sep. € 36.00 SBS - C02 2011*

⊞ **BARCARES, LE** *10G1* (1km SW Coastal) *42.77462, 3.02207* **Camping L'Europe, Route de St Laurent, 66420 Le Barcarès [04 68 86 15 36; fax 04 68 86 47 88; reception@europe-camping.com; www.europe-camping.com]** Exit A9 at Perpignan N & take D83 sp Le Barcarès. After 9km turn R on D81 sp Canet Plage, L on D90 sp Le Barcarès. Site on R. Lge, hdg/mkd pitch, shd; wc; shwrs inc; el pnts (16A) €4.50; gas; Indtte; shop & 2km; rest, snacks; bar; playgrnd; 2 pools high ssn; waterslides; rv & beach 500m; tennis; archery; entmnt; disco; 50% statics; dogs €8; Eng spkn; adv bkg; poss noisy; red long stay/low ssn; CKE/CCI. "Gd location; tidy pitches, all have individual san facs (tired early ssn 2010); ltd facs low ssn; gd cycle rte to beach & shops; gd winter NH." ♦ ltd € 43.00 2010*

BARCARES, LE *10G1* (1km SW Coastal) *42.78094, 3.02267* **Yelloh! Village Le Pré Catalan, Route de St Laurent, 66420 Le Barcarès [04 68 86 12 60; fax 04 68 86 40 17; info@precatalan.com; www.precatalan.com / www.yellohvillage.co.uk]** Exit A9 junc 41 onto D83; app Le Barcarès turn R onto D81, then L onto D90 to Le Barcarès, site sp. Lge, shd; wc; shwrs inc; el pnts (6A) €4; gas; shop; rest, snacks; bar; playgrnd; htd pool; paddling pool; sand beach 1km; tennis; games area; games rm; wifi; entmnt; TV; dogs €3; phone; quiet; adv bkg. 14 May-17 Sep. € 32.00 2012*

BARJAC (GARD) *9D2* (3km S Rural) *44.26685, 4.35170* **Domaine de la Sablière (Naturist), 30430 St Privat-de-Champclos [04 66 24 51 16; fax 04 66 24 58 69; contact@villagesabliere.com; www.villagesabliere.com]** Exit A7 junc 19 onto D994/N86 to Pont-St Esprit; then take D6086 N; in 2km turn L onto D901 dir Barjac; 3km bef Barjac, nr St Privat-de-Champclos, turn L onto D266; in 2km turn L onto unclassified rd & foll site sp. NB Steep ent. Lge, hdg/mkd pitch, some hdstg, pt sl, shd; wc; chem disp; mv service pnt; sauna; baby facs; shwrs; el pnts (10A) €5.20; gas; Indtte (inc dryer); shop; rest, snacks; bar; BBQ; playgrnd; 2 pools (1 htd, covrd); paddling pool; rv & beach; fishing; canoeing; tennis; games area; games rm; beauty treatment cent; wifi; entmnt; TV rm; 40% statics; dogs €2.70; bus; sep car park; Eng spkn; adv bkg; quiet; ccard acc; red low ssn. "Helpful owners; excel facs; steep rds, narr bends & sm pitches - poss diff access lge o'fits; site shop gd value; risk of flooding after heavy rain; gd shopping & excel local mkt; many naturist trails in forest." 1 Apr-2 Oct. € 34.80 (CChq acc) 2011*

BARJAC (GARD) *9D2* (9km S Rural) *44.26738, 4.37041* **Naturissimo La Génèse (Naturist), Route de la Génèse, 30430 Méjannes-le-Clap [04 66 24 51 73 or 04 66 24 51 82; fax 04 66 24 50 38; info@lagenese.com; www.lagenese.com]** Fr A7 exit junc 19, take dir Bagnols-sur-Cèze (D994 & N86) then in Bagnols head twd Alès on D6. Exit twd Lusanne onto D979 & foll sp for Méjannes-le-Clap. Site on banks of Rv Cèze. Lge, hdg/mkd pitch, pt sl, shd; wc; chem disp; shwrs inc; el pnts (6A) inc; gas; Indtte; shop & 5km; rest, snacks; bar; playgrnd; htd pool; fishing; sailing; canoe & cycle hire; tennis; archery; entmnt; TV rm; 10% statics; dogs €4; phone; adv bkg; quiet; ccard acc; red low ssn; INF card. "Excel site; gd rest & shop." 1 Apr-30 Sep. € 25.55 (CChq acc) 2010*

BARJAC (LOZERE) see Mende *9D1*

BEDARIEUX *10F1* (8km N Rural) *43.67313, 3.17265* **FFCC Camping La Sieste, 34260 La Tour-sur-Orb [04 67 23 72 96; fax 04 67 23 75 38; campinglasieste@orange.fr; http://campinglasieste.pagesperso-orange.fr]** Fr Bédarieux, take D35 N twd Lodève; site 3km N of La Tour-sur-Orbe at sm vill of Vereilles. Med, pt shd; wc; chem disp; shwrs inc; el pnts (4-10A) €2.40-5.20; Indtte; shop; tradsmn; rest; bar; BBQ; pool open June; dogs €3; phone; adv bkg; Eng spkn; quiet; poss v cr; ccard acc; red low ssn/CKE/CCI. "Well-kept site; charming owners; immac pool; unspoilt countryside; excel." ♦ 1 May-31 Aug. € 16.00 2011*

⊞ **BELCAIRE** *8G4* (4km SW Rural) *42.79207, 1.92477* **Camping Les Sapins, Ternairols, 11340 Camurac [04 68 20 38 11; info@lessapins-camurac.com; www.lessapins-camurac.com]** Easiest app fr N - at Bélesta on D117 turn S onto D16/D29/D613 to Belcaire then cont to Camurac, site 1km SE of vill. Or take D613 fr Ax-les-Thermes (1st 10km over Col de Chioula diff climb - gd power/weight ratio). Site sp in vill of Camurac & visible fr rd. App rd fairly steep for sh dist. Med, mkd pitch; pt sl, pt shd; htd wc; chem disp; shwrs inc; el pnts (10A) €3; Indtte (inc dryer); shop 5km; tradsmn; rest & adj; snacks; bar; BBQ (gas, elec); playgrnd; pool; paddling pool; horseriding; mountain biking; winter sports; games area; wifi; entmnt; TV; 33% statics; dogs €2; poss cr; Eng spkn; adv bkg; quiet; ccard acc; red low ssn; site clsd 1 Nov-15 Dec; CKE/CCI. "Lovely, peaceful site in beautiful surroundings; welcoming Dutch owners; excel walking; in Cathar region; vg." ♦ ltd € 20.00 2011*

BELCAIRE *8G4* (300m W Rural) *42.81598, 1.95098* **Les Chalets Du Lac (formerly Camp Municipal La Mousquière/Le Lac), 4 Chemin Lac, 11340 Belcaire [04 68 20 39 47; fax 04 68 20 39 48; chaletsdulac@gmail.com; www.camping-pyrenees-cathare.fr]** Site on D613 bet Ax-les-Thermes & Quillan. Sm, mkd pitch, pt sl, shd; wc; chem disp; shwrs inc; el pnts (10A) €2; gas 1km; Indtte; lake sw adj; tennis & horseriding nrby; dogs; phone; quiet; ccard not acc; CKE/CCI. "Site by lake; site yourself, warden calls; gd cent for walking; historic vill of Montaillou nr; excel; conv for Georges de la Frau." ♦ ltd 1 Jun-30 Sep. € 14.00 2014*

BESSEGES see St Ambroix *9D2*

BEZIERS *10F1* (8km NE Rural) *43.36254, 3.31924* **FFCC Aire Naturelle Domaine de Clairac (Philippon), Route de Bessan, 34500 Béziers [04 67 76 78 97 or 06 11 19 98 13 (mob); fax 04 67 76 78 98; camping.clairac@free.fr; www.campingclairac.com]** Exit A9 junc 35 Béziers Est; after toll take dir 'Centre Ville'; at 1st & 2nd rndabts foll sp Pézenas onto N9; in 5km turn R to Domaine de Clairac. Sm, pt shd; wc; chem disp; shwrs inc; el pnts (6A) €3; Indtte; tradsmn; snacks; bar; BBQ; playgrnd; htd pool; dogs; Eng spkn; quiet. "Friendly, helpful Swedish owner; gd." ♦ 1 Apr-30 Sep. € 15.00 2009*

BEZIERS *10F1* (10km NE Rural) *43.39849, 3.37338* **Camping Le Rebau, 34290 Montblanc [04 67 98 50 78; fax 04 67 98 68 63; gilbert@camping-lerebau.fr; www.camping-lerebau.fr]** NE on N9 fr Béziers-Montpellier, turn R onto D18. Site sp, narr ent 2.50m. Lge, hdg/mkd pitch, hdstg, pt shd; wc; chem disp; baby facs; shwrs inc; el pnts (5A) €4.50; gas 2km; Indtte; shop in vill; snacks & bar high ssn; playgrnd; pool; wifi; entmnt; TV; 10% statics; dogs €2.80; phone; bus 1km; poss cr; Eng spkn; adv bkg; quiet; red low ssn; CKE/CCI. "Gd site; tight ent & manoeuvring onto pitches; some facs old, but modern shwrs; ltd facs low ssn, but clean; helpful owner; gd pool; gd touring base; low ssn phone ahead to check open." 1 May-31 Aug. € 19.50 2012*

BEZIERS *10F1* (6km SE Urban) *43.3169, 3.2842* **Camping Les Berges du Canal, Promenade des Vernets, 34420 Villeneuve-les-Béziers [04 67 39 36 09; fax 04 67 39 82 07; contact@lesbergesducanal.fr; www.lesbergesducanal.fr]** Fr A9 exit junc 35 & foll sp for Agde. Exit 1st rndabt for D612 dir Béziers then 1st L onto D37 sp Villneuve-les-Béziers. Foll site sp to site adj canal. Med, hdg/mkd pitch, shd; wc; chem disp; mv service pnt; baby facs; shwrs inc; el pnts (16a) €2.50 (poss rev pol); Indtte; shop; rest, snacks; wifi; playgrnd; htd pool; beach 10km; cycle hire; 45% statics; dogs €3; poss cr; Eng spkn; adv bkg; CKE/CCI. "Pleasant site; facs clean but poss stretched in ssn; some pitches tight lge o'fits; pleasant stroll along canal." 15 Mar-18 Oct. € 42.00 (CChq acc) 2014*

⊞ **BEZIERS** *10F1* (7km SW Rural) *43.31864, 3.14276* **Camping Les Peupliers, 7 Promenade de l'Ancien Stade, 34440 Colombiers [tel/fax 04 67 37 05 26; contact@camping-colombiers.com; www.camping-colombiers.com]** SW fr Béziers on D609 (N9) turn R on D162E & foll sp to site using heavy vehicle rte. Cross canal bdge & fork R; turn R & site on L. Easier ent fr D11 (Béziers-Capestang) avoiding narr vill streets, turn L at rndabt at end of dual c'way sp Colombiers; in 1km at rlwy bdge, go strt on; in 100m turn L (bef canal bdge) where rd turns sharp R. Med, mkd pitch, pt shd; wc; chem disp; mv service pnt; fam bthrm; shwrs inc; el pnts (10A) €3.50 (inc in high ssn) (poss rev pol); gas; Indtte (inc dryer); shop, rest 1km; snacks; bar; BBQ; playgrnd; pool; sand beach 15km; wifi; 25% statics; dogs €3; adv bkg; quiet, some rlwy noise; red low ssn/long stay; CKE/CCI. "Nr Canal du Midi away fr busy beach sites; modern san facs; no twin-axles; excel walking & cycling; pleasant sm vill, conv NH." ♦ € 33.00 2014*

BIZANET see Narbonne *10F1*

BIZE MINERVOIS *8F4* (300m SW Urban) *43.31584, 2.87070* **Camping La Cesse, Esplanade Champs de Foire, 11120 Bize-Minervois [tel/fax 04 68 46 14 40; marieange.lurqui@gmail.com; www.audetourisme.com]** Exit N fr D5/D11 Béziers-Carcassonne rd onto D26 to Bize-Minervois (D26 is 800m to E of D607); site in 1.8km on L, just bef rv bdge in S of vill. Sm, mkd pitch, pt shd; wc; chem disp (wc); shwrs inc; el pnts (5A) €2.30; Indtte; shops, rest & snacks nrby; BBQ; rv 400m; dogs €1.20; phone; poss cr; adv bkg; quiet; red low ssn; CKE/CCI. "Peaceful, relaxing site; in need of TLC but some maintenance works in progress (2011)." 1 May-30 Sep. € 11.40 2011*

BOULOU, LE *8G4* (2km N Rural) *42.54157, 2.83431* **Camping Le Mas Llinas, 66165 Le Boulou [04 68 83 25 46; info@camping-mas-llinas.com; www.camping-mas-llinas.com]** Fr Perpignan, take D900 S; 1km N of Le Boulou turn R at Intermarché supmkt 100m to mini rndabt, turn L & foll sp to Mas-Llinas to site in 2km. Or fr A9 exit 43 & foll sp Perpignan thro Le Boulou. L at rndabt adj Leclerc supmkt, site well sp. Med, terr, pt shd; htd wc; shwrs inc; chem disp; el pnts (5-10A) €4.10-5.20; gas; lndtte; shops adj; tradsmn; snacks; BBQ; playgrnd; pool; paddling pool; cycle hire; games area; games rm; TV rm; some statics; dogs €2.20; phone; adv bkg; Eng spkn; quiet; red low ssn; CKE/CCI. "Friendly, welcoming owners; peaceful, scenic site; beware poss high winds on high pitches; ltd water points at top levels; ltd facs low ssn; facs clean; gd sized pitches; golden orioles on site." ♦ ltd 1 Feb-30 Nov. € 19.00 2013*

“We must tell The Club about that great site we found”

Get your site reports in by mid-August and we'll do our best to get your updates into the next edition.

⊞ **BOULOU, LE** *8G4* (1km SE Rural) *42.52088, 2.84509* **Camping Les Oliviers, Route d'Argelès-sur-Mer, 66160 Le Boulou [04 68 83 12 86 or 06 15 43 99 89; fax 04 68 87 60 08; infos@lesoliviers.com; www.lesoliviers.com]** Exit A9 junc 43 at Le Boulou. Foll sp onto D618 twds Argelès-sur-Mer. Site on R in 1km, well sp fr D618. Med, mkd pitch, pt shd; htd wc; chem disp; mv service pnt; shwrs inc; el pnts (6-10A) €3.50; gas 1km; lndtte; shop 1km; tradsmn; bar; playgrnd; shgl beach 12km; 40% statics; dogs €1.50; site clsd mid-Dec to mid-Jan; poss cr; adv bkg; quiet; red low ssn; CKE/CCI. "Helpful, friendly owner; san facs basic but adequate, poss stretched peak ssn; dog-friendly; conv juncs of A9 & N9; popular NH en rte Spain." ♦ ltd € 18.00 2009*

BOULOU, LE *8G4* (1.8km S Urban) *42.50964, 2.82680* **Camping L'Olivette, Route du Perthus, 66160 Le Boulou [04 68 83 48 08; fax 04 68 87 46 00; info@camping-olivette.fr; www.camping-olivette.fr]** D900 twd Spanish border, site on R - v busy rd. Med, hdg/mkd pitch; pt sl, pt shd; wc; baby facs; shwrs inc; el pnts (10A) €2.50; lndtte; shops; snacks; bar; many statics; dogs €1.60; poss cr; Eng spkn; some rd noise. "Conv for Salvador Dali Museum & ruins at Empurias; security gate; poss tired pitches; clean san facs; helpful owners; gd NH." 15 Mar-31 Oct. € 14.50 2009*

BOULOU, LE *8G4* (5km S Rural) *42.49083, 2.79777* **Camping Les Pins/Le Congo, Route de Céret, 66480 Maureillas-las-Illas [04 68 83 23 21; fax 04 68 83 45 64; lespinslecongo@hotmail.fr; www.camping-lespinslecongo.com]** Fr Le Boulou take D900 S, fork R after 2km onto D618 dir Céret. Site on L 500m after Maureillas. Med, hdg pitch, shd; htd wc (cont); chem disp (wc); shwrs inc; el pnts (10A) €3.50; gas; lndtte; shop 500m; tradsmn; rest, snacks; BBQ; playgrnd; pool; sand beach 20km; 10% statics; dogs; phone; adv bkg; Eng spkn; ccard acc. "Shabby and expensive, shwrs OK (2010)." ♦ 1 Feb-30 Nov. € 23.00 2012*

BOULOU, LE *8G4* (4km SW Rural) *42.50664, 2.79502* **Camping de la Vallée/Les Deux Rivières, Route de Maureillas, 66490 St Jean-Pla-de-Corts [04 68 83 23 20; fax 04 68 83 07 94; campingdelavallee@yahoo.fr; www.campingdelavallee.com]** Exit A9 at Le Boulou. Turn W on D115. Turn L after 3km at rndabt, into St Jean-Pla-de-Corts, thro vill, over bdge, site on L. Med, mkd pitch, pt shd, htd wc; chem disp; mv service pnt; baby facs; shwrs inc; el pnts (5A) €4; gas 800m; lndtte; shop 800m; tradsmn; rest, snacks; bar; playgrnd; pool; sand beach 20km; lake sw & fishing 1km; archery; internet; entmnt; TV; 50% statics (sep area); dogs €2.50; phone; bus adj; poss cr; Eng spkn; adv bkg; quiet; ccard acc; red long stay/low ssn; CKE/CCI. "Lovely well-kept site; easy access lge pitches; friendly, helpful owners with gd local info; excel san facs; conv NH fr A9 or longer; highly rec." ♦ 1 Apr-31 Oct. € 17.00 2011*

BOULOU, LE *8G4* (5km SW Rural) *42.47853, 2.80399* **Camping La Clapère (Naturist), Route de Las Illas, 66400 Maureillas-las-Illas [04 68 83 36 04; fax 04 68 83 34 44; clapere@nordnet.fr; www.clapere.com]** Exit Le Boulou S on D900 twd Le Perthus; after 3km take N618 twd Maureillas, D13 for 2km twd Las Illas. Lge, terr, pt shd; wc; chem disp; sauna; shwrs inc; el pnts (6-10A) €5-8; lndtte; shop; rest, snacks; bar; playgrnd; pool; paddling pool; rv adj; fishing; tennis; archery; cycle hire; games area; entmnt; TV; dogs €3; poss cr; Eng spkn; adv bkg; quiet. "Excel with easy access for c'vans; INF card req or may be purchased; vg for children; friendly recep." ♦ 1 May-30 Sep. € 25.00 2010*

⊞ **BOULOU, LE** *8G4* (4km W Rural) *42.50908, 2.78429* **FFCC Camping Les Casteillets, 66490 St Jean Pla-de-Corts [04 68 83 26 83; fax 04 68 83 39 67; jc@campinglescasteillets.com; www.campinglescasteillets.com]** Exit A9 at Le Boulou; turn W on D115; after 3km turn L immed after St Jean-Pla-de-Corts; site sp on R in 400m. NB Narr app last 200m. Med, mkd pitch, pt shd; wc; chem disp; some serviced pitches; shwrs inc; el pnts (6A) €3.30 (poss rev pol); gas; lndtte; shop; rest, snacks; bar; playgrnd; pool; tennis; sand beach 20km; games area; internet; entmnt; TV; 10% statics; poss cr; Eng spkn; adv bkg ess high ssn; quiet; red low ssn/long stay. "Lovely, friendly, scenic site; lge pitches; conv for touring & en rte NE Spain." ♦ € 18.00 2009*

“I need an on-site restaurant”

We do our best to make sure site information is correct, but it is always best to check any must-have facilities are still available or will be open during your visit.

⊞ **BOURG MADAME** *8H4* (200m N Urban) *42.43531, 1.94469* **Camping Le Sègre, 8 Ave du Puymorens, 66760 Bourg-Madame [04 68 04 65 87; fax 04 68 04 91 82; camping.lesegre@free.fr]** N on N20 site on R immed under rlwy bdge. Med, pt shd; wc; shwrs inc; el pnts (3-6A); lndtte; shops adj; playgrnd; pool & sports cent 3km; site clsd Oct; some statics; dogs; poss cr; some rd & rlwy noise. "Ltd touring pitches in winter, rec arr early." ♦ 2009*

⊞ **BOURG MADAME** *8H4* (6km NW Rural) *42.45979, 1.91075* **Camping Le Robinson, 25 Ave Gare Internationale, 66760 Enveitg [tel/fax 04 68 04 80 38 or 06 11 81 25 46 (mob); lerobinson-cerdagne@wanadoo.fr; www.robinson-cerdagne.com]** Fr Bourg-Madame, take N20 N twd Foix. Thro vill of Enveitg & turn L down Chemin de la Gare & L at camping sp. Lge, mkd pitch, pt sl, shd; wc; chem disp; baby facs; shwrs inc; el pnts (4-13A) €3-9; gas; lndtte; shops adj; tradsmn; rest adj; snacks; BBQ; playgrnd; pool; games rm; entmnt; TV rm; some statics; dogs €1.50; phone; adv bkg; quiet. "Beautiful setting; winter sports cent; conv Barcelona, Andorra; conv scenic rte train (Train Jaune); new management; new shower block (excel)." ♦ € 18.50 2013*

BOUZIGUES see Meze *10F1*

BRISSAC see Ganges *10E1*

BROUSSES ET VILLARET *8F4* (500m S Rural) *43.33932, 2.25201* **Camping Le Martinet Rouge, 11390 Brousses-et-Villaret [tel/fax 04 68 26 51 98 / 06 91 34 41 60 (mob); camping.lemartinetrouge@orange.fr; www.camping-martinet.co.uk]** Fr D118 Mazamet-Carcassonne, turn R 3km after Cuxac-Carbades onto D103; turn L in Brousses & foll sp. Med, hdg pitch,pt shd, pt sl, shd; wc; chem disp; mv service pnt; baby facs; shwrs; el pnts (6-10A); lndtte (inc dryer); shop; tradsmn; rest; snacks; bar; playgrnd; pool; waterslide; paddling pool; games area; entmnt; trout-fishing; horseriding; canoeing; wifi; tv rm; 20% statics; dogs €2; phone; bus; Eng spkn; adv bkg; quiet; CKE/CCI. "Helpful owners, great for walking or mountain biking; cather castles, abbeys & churchs, Canal du Midi; forest, lakes, rv & caverns; excel site." ♦ ltd 27 Apr-15 Sep. € 38.00 2014*

CAMURAC see Belcaire *8G4*

CANET EN ROUSSILLON see Canet Plage *10G1*

CANET PLAGE *10G1* (3km N Coastal) *42.70808, 3.03332* **Camping Le Brasilia, 2 Ave des Anneux du Roussillon, 66140 Canet-en-Roussillon [04 68 80 23 82; fax 04 68 73 32 97; contact@brasilia.fr; www.brasilia.fr / www.yellohvillage.co.uk]** Exit A9 junc 41 sp Perpignan Nord & Rivesaltes onto D83 dir Le Barcarès & Canet for 10km; then take D81 dir Canet for 10km until lge rndabt which goes under D617 (do not foll sp to Canet to R) - cont round rndabt & foll sp Ste Marie-le-Mer (to go back the way you came). Then take 1st R sp Le Brasilia. V lge, hdg/mkd pitch, pt shd, wc (some cont); chem disp; all serviced pitch; mv service pnt; baby facs; shwrs inc; el pnts (10A) inc; gas; lndtte (inc dryer); supmkt; tradsmn; rest, snacks; bar; BBQ (gas/elec); playgrnd; htd pool high ssn; paddling pool; direct access to sand beach 150m; fishing; tennis; cycle hire; archery; wifi; entmnt; games/TV rm; 35% statics; dogs €4; twin-axles acc (rec check in adv); bus to Canet; Eng spkn; quiet but poss noisy entmnt; ccard acc; red low ssn; CKE/CCI. "Excel, well-run, well laid-out site; gd sized pitches; friendly staff; immac san facs; excel facs, espec for families/children/teenagers; in Jul & Aug identity card for pool - passport size photo needed; rvside walk adj; conv day trips to Andorra; daily mkt in Canet except Mon." ♦ 12 Apr-4 Oct. € 54.00 SBS - C01 2011*

CANET PLAGE *10G1* (4km N Coastal) *42.73897, 3.03355* **Camp Municipal de la Plage, Ave de Las-Illas, 66470 Ste Marie-Plage [04 68 80 68 59; fax 04 68 73 14 70; contact@camping-municipal-de-la-plage.com; www.camping-municipal-de-la-plage.com]** Exit A9 junc 41 onto D83, then D81 to Ste Marie-Plage. Look for sm red sp, site adj Camping La Palais de la Mer. Lge, hdg pitch, pt shd; wc; chem disp; mv service pnt; baby facs; shwrs; el pnts (6A) inc; lndtte; shop; rest, snacks; bar; BBQ; playgrnd; pool; paddling pool; sand beach adj; games area; games rm; cycle hire; TV; 30% statics; dogs €2.40; poss cr; Eng spkn; adv bkg; quiet; CKE/CCI. "Direct access to beach; v busy high ssn." ♦ ltd 1 Mar-31 Oct. € 32.00 2010*

CANET PLAGE *10G1* (4km NE Coastal) *42.72724, 3.03377* **Camping La Pergola, 66140 Ste Marie la Mer [02 51 20 41 94; contact@camp-atlantique.com; www.campinglapergola.com]** S fr Narbonne, exit N9 at Salses & foll D11 to St Marie-sur-Mer. St Marie-Plage beach for St Marie-sur-Mer. Site not sp but on D12 to coast. Lge, pt shd; wc (cont); shwrs inc; gas; shops; el pnts; sand beach 500m; adv bkg; quiet. Apr-Sep. € 12.00 2012*

"Satellite navigation makes touring much easier"

Remember most sat navs don't know if you're towing or in a larger vehicle – always use yours alongside maps and site directions.

CANET PLAGE *10G1* (500m S Coastal) *42.67540, 3.03120* **Camping Club Mar Estang, Route de St Cyprien, 66140 Canet-Plage [04 68 80 35 53; fax 04 68 73 32 94; contact@marestang.com; www.marestang.com]** Exit A9 junc 41 Perpignan Nord dir Canet, then foll sp St Cyprien, site sp. Site on D81A bet Canet-Plage & St Cyprien-Plage. V lge, mkd pitch, hdstg, pt shd; wc; chem disp; mv service pnt; baby facs; shwrs inc; el pnts (6A) €7; gas; lndtte; shop; tradsmn; rest, snacks; bar; playgrnd; htd pool; paddling pool; waterslide; private sand beach adj; tennis; cycle hire; fitness rm; TV rm; 50% statics; dogs €4; Eng spkn; adv bkg; quiet; ccard acc; red low ssn/long stay/CKE/CCI. "Conv Spanish border & Pyrenees; gd birdwatching." ♦ 26 Apr-14 Sep. € 80.00 2014*

CANET PLAGE *10G1* (4km W Rural) *42.68914, 2.99877* **FFCC Camping Les Fontaines, Route de St Nazaire, 66140 Canet-en-Roussillon [tel/fax 04 68 80 22 57 or 06 77 90 14 91 (mob); campinglesfontaines@wanadoo.fr; www.camping-les-fontaines.com]** Take D11 fr Canet dir St Nazaire; site sp on L in 1.5km. Easy access. Lge, hdg/mkd pitch, unshd; wc; chem disp; mv service pnt; baby facs; fam bathrm; shwrs inc; el pnts (10A) €3.50; gas 2km; lndtte (inc dryer); shop & 1km; tradsmn; snacks; bar; BBQ (gas/elec); playgrnd; pool; paddling pool; sand beach 2.5km; games area; wifi; entmnt; 30% statics; dogs €3.50; bus; phone; Eng spkn; adv bkg; quiet. "Pitches lge; conv Etang de Canet et St Nazaire nature reserve with flamingos; excel; relaxed atmosphere; friendly staff." 1 May-30 Sep. € 30.00 2013*

CANET PLAGE *10G1* (4km W Urban) *42.70114, 2.99850* **Kawan Village Ma Prairie, 1 Ave des Coteaux, 66140 Canet-en-Roussillon [04 68 73 26 17; fax 04 68 73 28 82; ma.prairie@wanadoo.fr; www.maprairie.com]** Leave A9/ E15 at junc 41, sp Perpignan Centre/Canet-en-Roussillon. Take D83, then D81 until Canet-en-Roussillon. At rndabt, take D617 dir Perpignan & in about 500m leave at exit 5. Take D11 dir St Nazaire, pass under bdge & at rndabt turn R. Site on L. Lge, hdg pitch, shd; wc; chem disp; mv service pnt; baby facs; serviced pitches; shwrs inc; el pnts (10A) inc; gas; Indtte (inc dryer); supmkt adj; tradsmn; rest, snacks; bar; BBQ (gas/ elec); playgrnd; pool; paddling pool; waterslide; sand beach 3km; waterskiing; sailing; canoeing; wifi; entmnt; games/ TV rm; 20% statics; dogs €5; c'vans/m'vans 7.50m & over by request; bus to town nr; poss cr; Eng spkn; adv bkg ess Aug; quiet; rd noise some pitches; ccard acc; red low ssn; CKE/ CCI. "Peaceful, popular site; friendly, helpful owners; reg bus to beach (Jul/Aug); daily mkt Perpignan; gd." ♦ 12 Apr-19 Sep. € 50.00 (CChq acc) SBS - C05 2014*

See advertisement

"There aren't many sites open at this time of year"

If you're travelling outside peak season remember to call ahead to check site opening dates – even if the entry says 'open all year'.

CANOURGUE, LA *9D1* (2km E Rural) *44.40789, 3.24178* **Camping Le Val d'Urugne, Route des Gorges-du-Tarn, 48500 La Canourgue [04 66 32 84 00; fax 04 66 32 88 14; lozereleisure@wanadoo.fr; www.lozereleisure.com]** Exit A75 junc 40 dir La Canourgue; thro vill dir Gorges-du-Tarn. In 2km site on R 600m after golf clubhouse. Sm, hdg pitch, pt sl, pt shd; wc; chem disp; mv service pnt; shwrs inc; el pnts (6A) €3.50; Indtte; shop (high ssn) & 2km; tradsmn; rest, snacks, bar at golf club; TV rm; some statics adj; dogs €2; Eng spkn; adv bkg; quiet; ccard acc; red low ssn; CKE/CCI. "Vg site; golf adj; conv A75 & Gorges-du-Tarn; low ssn stop at golf club for key to site; site poss tired end of ssn." ♦ ltd 1 May-30 Sep. € 16.40 2014*

CANOURGUE, LA *9D1* (7.4km W Rural) *44.43638, 3.1475* **Municipal la Vallèe, Miége Rivière 48500 Canilhac [04 66 32 91 14 or 04 66 32 80 05; commune.canilhac@ wanadoo.fr]** Leave A75 at junc 40. Take D988 W, sp St Laurent d'Olt. Site on L at level x-ing after 10 mins. Sm, hdg pitch, pt shd; wc; chem disp; mv service pnt; baby facs; shwr; el pnts (16A) €3; Indtte; shop; tradsmn; snack; bar; BBQ; playgrnd; htd pool; paddling pool; rv 0.1km; games rm; fishing; wifi; tv; 10% statics; dogs €1; phone; adv bkg; quiet; CCI. "Sm shop; supermkt 5km; next to rv (sw not allowed);horse riding, golf, canoeing, paint-balling & quad biking nrby; conv for Gorges du Tarn & Aubrac. St laurent d'Olt worth a visit." ♦ ltd 15 Jun-15 Sep. € 15.00 2014*

CAPESTANG *10F1* (500m W Urban) *43.32759, 3.03865* **Camp Municipal de Tounel, 1 Rue Georges Brassens, Ave de la République, 34310 Capestang [04 67 93 34 23 (TO) or 06 07 97 52 09 (mob); oacinfocapestang@orange.fr; www.ville-capestang.fr]** Fr Béziers on D11, turn R twd vill of Capestang, approx 1km after passing supmkt. Site on L in leisure park opp Gendamarie. Med, hdg pitch, pt shd; wc (cont); chem disp; shwrs; el pnts (6A) €3; Indtte; shops, rest 500m; playgrnd; fishing; tennis; cycle hire; internet; dogs free; rd noise. "300m fr Canal de Midi; excel walks or cycle rides; lovely rest in vill; low ssn site yourself, fees collected; facs poss tired low ssn; poss diff access to pitches for long o'fits; ltd el pnts; poss resident workers; NH only." ♦ 1 May-30 Sep. € 15.00 2014*

CARCASSONNE *8F4* (5km N Rural) *43.25999, 2.36509* **FFCC Camping Das Pinhiers, Chemin du Pont Neuf, 11620 Villemoustaussou [04 68 47 81 90; fax 04 68 71 43 39; campingdaspinhiers@wanadoo.fr; www.camping-carcassonne.net]** Exit A6 junc 23 Carcassonne Ouest & foll sp Mazamet on D118; R at rndabt with filling stn; turn R & foll camping sp. Med, hdg pitch, pt sl, shd; wc; chem disp; mv service pnt; shwrs inc; el pnts (10A) inc; shop (high ssn) & 1km; rest, snacks; bar; playgrnd; pool; 10% statics; no twin-axles; dogs €3; bus 1 km; Eng spkn; adv bkg; quiet; ccard acc; red low ssn; CKE/CCI. "Diff to pitch lge vans due hdg pitches & sl; san facs basic & stretched high ssn; general area rather run down (2009); office clsd noon-2pm." ♦ ltd 1 Mar-31 Oct. € 24.00 2014*

CARCASSONNE *8F4* (10km NE Rural) *43.28305, 2.44166* **Camping Le Moulin de Ste Anne, Chemin de Ste Anne, 11600 Villegly-en-Minervois [04 68 72 20 80; fax 04 68 72 27 15; campingstanne@wanadoo.fr; www.moulindesainteanne.com]** Leave A61 junc 23 Carcassone Ouest dir Mazamet; after approx 14km onto D620 to Villegly, site sp at ent to vill. NB Turning R off D620 hidden by trees, then over narr bdge; long o'fits need wide swing in. Med, hdg/mkd pitch, pt sl, terr, unshd; htd wc; chem disp (wc); mv service pnt; baby facs; shwrs inc; el pnts (10A) inc; Indtte; shop 300m; tradsmn; snacks; bar; BBQ; playgrnd; htd pool; sand beach 60km; games area; wifi; 25% statics; dogs €3.50; poss cr; adv bkg; Eng spkn; quiet; ccard acc; min 3 nights high ssn; red long stay/low ssn; CKE/CCI. "Pretty, clean site; lge pitches; friendly, helpful owner; ltd san facs; pitches poss diff/muddy in wet; gd touring base; poss local youths congregate on motorbikes nrby in eve; vg." ♦ 1 Mar-29 Oct. € 23.00 2010*

CARCASSONNE *8F4* (6km E Rural) *43.20700, 2.44258* **FFCC Camping à l'Ombre des Micocouliers, Chemin de la Lande, 11800 Trèbes [04 68 78 61 75; fax 04 68 78 88 77; infos@campingmicocouliers.com; www.campingmicocouliers.com]** Fr Carcassonne, take D6113 E for 6km to Trèbes; go under rlway bdge; fork L onto D610; turn R immed bef rv bdge; site on L in 200m. Fr W foll D6113 thro Trebes; at rndabt at E of town take last exit to L sp Sports Centre, site on R. Med, mkd pitch, shd; wc; chem disp; mv service pnt; shwrs (up steps); el pnts (6A) €3; Indtte; shop in ssn; rest in ssn; snacks; BBQ; htd, covrd pool nr,entmnt; rv fishing; TV; no statics; dogs €1.50; phone; poss cr; some Eng spkn; red low ssn; CKE/CCI. "Pleasant, sandy site by rv; well shd; friendly & helpful staff; gd, clean but dated san facs, 1 block up 15 steps; ltd el pnts; Trèbes in walking dist; vg cycling, 13 km cycle to Carcassonne along canal; gd base Canal du Midi; can be noisy fr local youths on mbikes; walk into town needs care with busy rd; lovely site; adv to arr early as popular site." ♦ 1 Apr-30 Sep. € 35.00 2014*

CARCASSONNE *8F4* (10km E Rural) *43.21498, 2.47031* **Camping La Commanderie, 6 Chemin Eglise,11800 Rustiques [04 68 78 67 63 or 06 25 28 35 80 (m); contact@campinglacommanderie.com; www.campinglacommanderie.com]** Fr Carcassonne take D6113/D610 E to Trèbes (approx 8km); at Trèbes take D610 & after 2km L onto D906, then L onto D206; site on R; foll sp 'Rustiques'. Or fr A61 ext junc 24 onto D6113 to Trèbes & then as bef. Sm, mkd pitch, pt sl, pt shd, htd wc; chem disp; shwrs inc; el pnts (6A) inc; Indtte; shop 1km; tradsmn; rest, snacks; bar; playgrnd; pool; wifi; 10% statics; dogs €2; phone; quiet; adv bkg; Eng spkn; quiet; ccard acc; red low ssn; CKE/CCI. "Pleasant, helpful owner & staff; modern san facs; patron sells own wines; gd cycling along canal fr Trèbes; conv A61; gd NH en rte Spain; superb refurbished pool; excel; quiet relaxing site; excellent site improving year on year, running track and 12 fitness machines added this year." 1 Apr-15 Oct. € 23.00 2014*

CARCASSONNE *8F4* (2km SE Rural) *43.19994, 2.35271* **Camping d la Cité, Route de St Hilaire, 11000 Carcassonne [04 68 10 01 00; fax 04 68 47 33 13; campingdelacite@carcassonne.fr; www.camping-delacite-carcassonne.com]** Fr N & W exit Carcassonne by D6113 twd Narbonne; cross rv & turn S on D104; foll sp. Fr S (D118) take D104 to E & foll sp. Fr E (D6113) take D342 S to D104; foll sp. Or exit A61 junc 23; at rndabt in 900m turn R onto D6161 sp Limoux; at traff lts in 1km turn L onto D118 sp La Cité; at rndabt in 700m turn R over rv for D104; in 600m turn L at rndabt onto D104 sp Camping La Cité; site on L in 1.4km. Or exit A61 junc 24 to D6113 sp Carcassonne; stay on rd until sp La Cité; cont to sp Camping La Cité. NB Site (La Cité) well sp fr all dirs & easy access fr A61 junc 23. Lge, hdg/mkd pitch, pt shd; wc (some cont); chem disp; mv service pnt; shwrs inc; el pnts (10A) inc (poss rev pol); Indry rm; shops 1.5km; tradsmn; rest, snacks; bar; playgrnd; pool (high ssn); tennis; wifi; entmnt; some statics; dogs €3.50; Eng spkn; adv bkg (rec high ssn - min 7 days); quiet with some rd noise; ccard acc; red low ssn; CKE/CCI. "Delightful, well-kept site in gd location adj woods; popular - rec arr bef 1600; mixed pitch sizes & types; friendly, helpful staff; san facs need refurb & stretched high ssn, poss irreg cleaning low ssn (2009); ltd water & waste water pnts; many leisure facs; parking area for waiting if office clsd, 1200-1400 low ssn; pleasant, well-lit walk along rv to La Cité; muddy after rain; no twin-axles; gd facs; high ssn o'spill area without el pnts; excel site for visiting Carcassonne; excel location for old & new city. " ♦ 02 Apr-13 Oct. € 30.50 2014*

⊞ **CARCASSONNE** *8F4* (5km S Rural) *43.17938, 2.37024* **Camping à l'Ombre des Oliviers, Ave du Stade, 11570 Cazilhac [tel/fax 04 68 79 65 08 or 06 81 54 96 00 (mob); florian.romo@wanadoo.fr; www.alombredesoliviers.com]** Fr N & W exit Carcassonne by D6113 dir Narbonne. Cross rv & turn S onto D104, then D142/D56 to Cazilhac, site sp. Sm, pt shd; wc; baby facs; shwrs inc; el pnts (6-10A) €3 (poss rev pol); Indry rm; supmkt in vill; bar; BBQ; playgrnd; pool; tennis; games area; TV; 10% statics; dogs €2; site clsd 1st week Jan; poss v cr; adv bkg; quiet; red low ssn. "Site in pleasant position; if office clsd phone owner on mob, or site yourself; helpful owners; v ltd facs low ssn; insufficient san facs when site full & ltd other facs; few water pnts; pitches poss muddy/soft when wet; bus to old city nrby." € 22.00 2013*

CARCASSONNE *8F4* (7km S Rural) *43.1588, 2.2930* **Airotel Camping Grand Sud, Route de Limoux, 11250 Preixan [04 68 26 88 18; fax 04 68 26 85 07; sudfrance@wanadoo.fr; www.camping-grandsud.com]** A61 exit junc 23 at Carcassonne Ouest onto D118 dir Limoux. Site visible fr rd on lakeside at end of dual c'way section. Lge, hdg/mkd pitch, hdstg, pt shd; wc; chem disp; mv service pnt; baby facs; shwrs inc; el pnts (6A) inc (poss rev pol); Indtte (inc dryer); shop; tradsmn; rest, snacks; bar; BBQ; playgrnd; htd pool; waterslide; private access to rv; fishing; boating; horseriding; tennis; games area; games rm; wifi; entmnt; TV; 50% statics; dogs €4; adv bkg; quiet; ccard acc; red low ssn; CKE/CCI. "Pleasant, attractive site by lake; easy access A61; friendly, helpful owners; gd rest; wild fowl reserve; conv Carcassonne; gd walking; excel." 1 Apr-15 Sep. € 30.00 2010*

CARCASSONNE *8F4* (12km SW Rural) *43.12410, 2.26080* **Yelloh! Village Domaine d'Arnauteille, 11250 Montclar [04 68 26 84 53; fax 04 68 26 91 10; info@arnauteille.com; www.arnauteille.com / www.yellohvillage.co.uk]** Fr Carcassonne take D118 S twd Limoux. Turn R bef end of sm section dual c'way (not 1st section) & foll sp to Montclar. Site approx 2.5km on L. NB Site app along single track - site ent steep & narr & sp v insignificant on gatepost & driveway appears to be to private house. V lge, hdg/mkd pitch, pt sl, terr, pt shd; htd wc; chem disp; mv service pnt; some serviced pitches; baby facs; fam bthrm; shwrs inc; el pnts (6-10A) inc; gas; lndtte; shop; tradsmn; rest, snacks; bar; playgrnd; pool; waterpark; horseriding, fishing 2km; golf 14km; games rm; games area; entmnt; internet; TV rm; 70% statics; dogs €4; Eng spkn; adv bkg; v quiet; ccard acc; red low ssn; CKE/CCI. "Vg site but huge & impersonal; wonderful views; helpful staff; superb pool complex & facs; excel rest; steep site rds; siting poss diff in wet weather; site muddy after rain." ♦ 9 Apr-25 Sep. € 39.00 2010*

CARCASSONNE *8F4* (15km NW Rural) *43.29861, 2.22277* **Camping de Montolieu, L'Olivier, 11170 Montolieu [04 68 76 95 01 or 06 31 90 31 92 (mob); nicole@camping-de-montolieu.com; www.camping-de-montolieu.com]** Fr D6113 4km W Carcassonne, take D629 twd Montolieu; site on R in 2.5km after Moussoulens. Sp fr D6113, approx 5km dist. App thro Montolieu not rec. Sm, hdg/mkd pitch, pt shd; wc; chem disp; shwrs inc; el pnts (5A) inc; gas; lndtte; shops 1.5km; tradsmn; rest, snacks, bar 100m; BBQ; pool 100m; games area; games rm; wifi; few statics; dogs €2.50; phone; adv bkg; some rd noise; red low ssn; CKE/CCI. "Well-run site in lovely countryside; manoeuvring tight; excel facs; conv Carcassonne; highly rec." ♦ 15 Mar-31 Oct. € 18.00 2014*

CASTELNAUDARY *8F4* (4km E Rural) *43.31723, 2.01582* **FFCC Camping à la Ferme Domaine de la Capelle (Sabatte), St Papoul, 11400 St Martin-Lalande [04 68 94 91 90; lacapelle2@orange.fr; www.wmaker.net/lacapelle/]** Fr D6113 Castelnaudary/Carcasonne, take D103 E & foll sp to St Papoul & site in 2km. Well sp. NB Ent poss awkward lge o'fits. Sm, hdg/mkd pitch, pt sl, pt shd; htd wc; chem disp (wc); shwrs inc; el pnts (4A) €2.50; lndtte (inc dryer); shop 2km; tradsmn; BBQ; no statics; dogs €1; phone; Eng spkn; quiet; CKE/CCI. "Delightful, peaceful, spacious CL-type site; friendly, helpful owner; vg san facs, poss stretched when site full; ltd el pnts; gd walking; nr St Papoul Cathar vill with abbey; ideal NH for Spain; excel; close to ind site, noisy; gd cycling." 1 Apr-30 Sep. € 14.50 2012*

CAUNES MINERVOIS *8F4* (1km S Rural) *43.32380, 2.52592* **Camp Municipal Les Courtals, Ave du Stade, 11160 Caunes-Minervois [04 68 78 46 58; mairie.de.caunes@wanadoo.fr; www.caunesminervois.com]** Sp fr D620 at stadium & adj rv. Sm, pt shd; wc; mv service pnt; shwrs; el pnts (4A) inc; shops adj; tradsmn; playgrnd; pool 6km; games area; rv adj; phone; quiet. "Pleasantly situated site; office opens 1800; gate locked 2100; site self, warden calls; interesting town." 15 Jan-15 Dec. € 12.00 2014*

CAYLAR, LE *10E1* (4km SW Rural) *43.83629, 3.29045* **Camping Mas de Messier, St Félix-de-l'Héras, 34520 Le Caylar [tel/fax 04 67 44 52 63; info@masdemessier.com; www.masdemessier.com]** Fr N exit A75 junc 49 onto D9 thro Le Caylar. Turn R sp St Félix & foll sp St Félix-de-l'Héras; at x-rds in St Félix turn R, site in 1km on L. Fr S exit A75 junc 50; foll sp to St Félix-de-l'Héras; at x-rds turn R & as bef. Sm, hdg pitch, pt sl, pt shd; wc; chem disp; mv service pnt; shwrs; el pnts (6A) €3; lndtte; shop 4km; tradsmn; playgrnd; pool; wifi; dogs free; adv bkg, ess high ssn; quiet; Eng spkn; red low ssn; CKE/CCI. "Excel views fr some pitches; friendly, helpful Dutch owner; facs fair; access unsuitable lge o'fits; meals avail some eves; gd walking." ♦ ltd 11 Apr-15 Oct. € 17.00 2014*

CENDRAS see Alés *10E1*

CERET *8H4* (7km N Rural) *42.54833, 2.75361* **Camp Municipal Al Comu, Route de Fourques, 66300 Llauro [04 68 39 42 08; alcomu@wanadoo.fr]** Fr N on A9 exit junc 43. Take D115 dir Céret. Bef bdge R onto D615 to Llauro. Site on L after vill. Sm, mkd pitch, hdstg, terr, pt shd; wc; chem disp; baby facs; fam bthrm; shwrs inc; el pnts (16A) €2.75; lndtte; shop in vill; tradsmn; BBQ; playgrnd; pool 10km; lake sw 6km; dogs; Eng spkn; quiet; red low ssn; CKE/CCI. "Attractive setting in lower Pyrenees; gd views; friendly, helpful owners live on site; vg." ♦ ltd 1 Apr-31 Oct. € 13.50 2010*

CERET *8H4* (500m E Urban) *42.48421, 2.75871* **Camp Municipal Bosquet de Nogarède, Ave d'Espagne, 66400 Céret [04 68 87 26 72; www.tourisme-pyreneesorientales.com]** Exit A9 junc 43 onto D115 twd Céret, then foll sp Maureillas D618. Site clearly sp 500m fr cent Céret. Med, mkd pitch, terr, shd; wc; chem disp; shwrs inc; el pnts (6A) inc; gas 1km; lndtte; shop 1km; rest, snacks; bar 1km; BBQ; playgrnd; htd, covrd pool, tennis 400m; 10% statics; dogs; phone; poss cr; some rd noise; CKE/CCI. "Attractive town with modern art museum; san facs fair; gd NH." ♦ ltd 1 Apr-31 Oct. € 15.00 2011*

⊞ **CERET** *8H4* (1km E Rural) *42.48981, 2.76305* **Camping Les Cerisiers, Mas de la Toure, 66400 Céret [04 68 87 00 08 or 06 78 04 60 32 (mob); fax 04 68 88 14 87; camping.lescerisiers@club-internet.fr; www.campingcerisiers.com]** Exit A9 junc 43 onto D115, turn off for cent of Céret. Site is on D618 approx 800m E of Céret twd Maureillas, sp. Tight ascent for lge o'fits. Med, mkd pitch, shd; wc; chem disp; baby facs; fam bthrm; shwrs inc; el pnts (4A); gas; lndtte; shop, rest, snacks, bar 1km; playgrnd; pool 600m; lake sw 2km; sand beach 28km; entmnt; TV; 60% statics; dogs; phone; site clsd Jan; quiet; CKE/CCI. "Site in cherry orchard; gd size pitches; facs dated & ltd low ssn; footpath to attractive vill with modern art gallery; conv Andorra, Perpignan, Collioure." ♦ € 18.00 2014*

CERET *8H4* (8km SW Rural) *42.47879, 2.67418* **Camp Municipal Can Day, Rue des Lledoners, Ave Beausoleil, 66112 Amélie-les-Bains-Palalda [04 68 39 22 37; fax 04 68 39 06 46; www.amelie-les-bains.com]** S fr Céret on D115, site sp on N edge of vill. Med, hdg/mkd pitch, pt shd; htd wc; mv service pnt; shwrs; el pnts inc; playgrnd; fishing nr; dogs €1; quiet. ♦ 1 Feb-1 Dec. € 10.30 2010*

CESSERAS see Olonzac *8F4*

CHANAC *9D1* (500m S Urban) *44.46519, 3.34670* **Camp Municipal La Vignogue, Rue de Plaisance, 48230 Chanac [04 66 48 24 09 or 06 82 93 60 68 (mob); gites-camping-chanac@orange.fr; www.chanac.fr]** Exit A75 junc 39.1 onto N88 to Chanac; site well sp in vill. Sm, mkd pitch, pt sl, pt shd; htd wc (some cont); chem disp; shwrs inc; el pnts (6A) inc; Indtte; shops, rest, bar 500m; BBQ; pool adj; wifi; some statics; dogs €1; Eng spkn; adv bkg; quiet. "Excel; rec arr early (bef 1800)." ♦ ltd 15 Apr-30 Sep. € 10.50 2011*

CHATEAURENARD see Avignon *10E2*

⊞ **CLERMONT L'HERAULT** *10F1* (5km NW Rural) *43.64491, 3.38982* **Camp Municipal du Lac du Salagou, 34800 Clermont-l'Hérault [04 67 96 13 13; fax 04 67 96 32 12; contact@le-salagou.fr; www.le-salagou.fr]** Fr N9 S take D909 to Clermont-l'Hérault, foll sp to Lac du Salagou 1.5km after town sp. Fr by-pass foll sp Bédarieux. Well sp. Lge, mkd pitch, pt sl, pt shd; htd wc (winter poss all cont); chem disp; mv service pnt; shwrs inc; el pnts (5-10A) €2.90-3.40; Indtte; shops 4km; tradsmn; rest, snacks; BBQ; playgrnd; shgl beach & lake 300m; fishing; watersports; entmnt; TV; many statics; dogs €1.70; phone; poss cr; adv bkg; noise fr disco some nights; red low ssn; CKE/CCI;Eng spkn; "Unique location; poss muddy low ssn & poss windy; facs dated; gd undeveloped beaches around lake; beautiful scenery." ♦ € 16.00 2013*

COLLET DE DEZE, LE *9D1* (7km W Rural) *44.23016, 3.86326* **Domaine Naturiste La Combe Ferrière (Naturist), 48160 St Michel-de-Dèze [04 66 45 52 43; info@la-combe.com; www.la-combe.com]** Fr Alès N on N106 twd Florac. Just after Le Collet-de-Dèze take D13 L for 10km to Col de Pendédis, then keep R & in 20m turn R bet 2 houses. Site on L in 2km. Do not app fr St Michel-de-Dèze as rd unsuitable. Sm, pt sl, pt shd; wc; baby facs; sauna; shwrs inc; el pnts (6A) €3.05; Indtte; tradsmn; rest; bar; BBQ; playgrnd; pool; games area; cycle hire; no statics; dogs free; poss cr; Eng spkn; adv bkg; quiet; INF card. "Ltd pitches for m'vans - rec phone ahead; site rds narr & winding but passable with care; friendly Dutch owners; recep on opp side of public rd to site (must dress to cross); gd." 15 May-15 Sep. € 18.00 2010*

COLLIAS see Remoulins *10E2*

COLLIOURE see Argeles sur Mer *10G1*

CREISSAN *10F1* (270m N Urban) *43.37550, 3.00909* **Camp Municipal Les Oliviers, 34370 Creissan [04 67 93 81 85 or 04 67 93 75 41 (Mairie); fax 04 67 93 85 28; mairie@creissan.com; www.creissan.com]** Fr D612 foll sp Creissan & site. Sm, mkd pitch, pt shd; shwrs inc; el pnts €3; Indtte; shop, rest, bar in vill; BBQ; playgrnd; pool adj; tennis; entmnt; adv bkg; quiet. "Pleasant site located in housing estate (30 pitches); helpful & friendly; key req to immac san facs - warden's hrs ltd (2009); excel." 1 Apr-30 Sep. € 10.00 2009*

CRESPIAN *10E1* (450m S Rural) *43.87850, 4.09590* **Kawan Village Le Mas de Reilhe, 30260 Crespian [04 66 77 82 12; fax 04 66 80 26 50; info@camping-mas-de-reilhe.fr; www.camping-mas-de-reilhe.fr]** Exit A9 at Nîmes Ouest N onto N106 dir Alès for 5km. Fork R, then L over bdge onto D999 dir Le Vigan. Foll rd for 24km, R at x-rds onto D6110 to site on R just on ent Crespian. Take care - ent on a bend on busy rd. Med, mkd pitch, pt sl, terr, pt shd; htd wc; chem disp; mv service pnt; baby facs; shwrs inc; el pnts (10A) inc; Indtte (inc dryer); sm shop; rest, snacks; bar; BBQ (gas/elec); playgrnd; htd pool; paddling pool; table tennis; fishing & horseriding 10km; games area; games rm; wifi; entmnt; TV; dogs €3; no c'vans/m'vans over 7.50m; poss cr; Eng spkn; quiet but poss some rd noise; ccard acc; red low ssn/long stay; CKE/CCI. "Quiet, relaxing & lovely site; friendly staff; clean, modern excel san facs; wine-tasting adj; conv Nîmes, Uzès & Cévennes National Park; excel." ♦ 26 Apr-13 Sep. € 42.00 (CChq acc) SBS - C10 2014*

DOMAZAN see Avignon *10E2*

DURBAN CORBIERES *8G4* (500m N Rural) *43.00017, 2.81977* **Camping Municipal De Durban-Corbieres, Lespazo, 11360 Durhan-Corbieres [04 68 45 06 81; fax 04 68 45 38 16; mairiededurham@orange.fr]** Fr A61 take exit 25, foll D611 S across to Durban Corbieres. Site sp on R on entering Vill. Sm, hdg pitch, pt sl, pt shd; wc; shwrs inc; el pnts (10A); BBQ; pool 0.5km; sandy beach 20km; 10% statics; dogs; bus 0.5km; twin axles; poss cr; adv bkg; quiet; CCI. "Tranquil site surrounded by rugged hills; Cathar castle in vill; vg." ♦ 15 Jun-15 Sep. € 11.00 2014*

ELNE *10G1* (1km E Coastal) *42.60695, 2.99098* **Camping Le Florida, Route Latour-Bas-Elne, 66200 Elne [04 68 37 80 88; fax 04 68 37 80 76; info@campingleflorida.com; www.campingleflorida.com]** Exit A9 junc 42 Perpignan-Sud onto D914 dir Argelès-sur-Mer. Exit D914 junc 7 onto D11 dir Elne Centre, then D40 sp St Cyprien to Latour-Bas-Elne, site sp. Lge, mkd pitch, pt shd; wc; chem disp; mv service pnt; baby facs; shwrs inc; el pnts (5A) €4; Indtte (inc dryer); shop adj; rest 400m; snacks; bar; BBQ; playgrnd; pool; paddling pool; sand beach 4km; tennis; games area; games rm; wifi; entmnt; TV; 70% statics; dogs; phone; Eng spkn; adv bkg; quiet; ccard acc; red low ssn; CKE/CCI. "Excel site; bus to beach high ssn." ♦ 4 Apr-8 Nov. € 28.00 2010*

ELNE *10G1* (4km S Rural) *42.57570, 2.96514* **Kawan Village Le Haras, Domaine St Galdric, 66900 Palau-del-Vidre [04 68 22 14 50; fax 04 68 37 98 93; haras8@wanadoo.fr; www.camping-le-haras.com]** Exit A9 junc 42 sp Perpignan S dir Argelès-sur-Mer on D900 (N9) & then D914; then exit D914 junc 9 onto D11 to Palau-del-Vidre. Site on L at ent to vill immed after low & narr rlwy bdge. Med, shd; wc; chem disp; mv service pnt; baby facs; shwrs inc; el pnts (10A) €5.; Indtte (inc dryer); supmkt 6km; tradsmn; rest, snacks & bar high ssn; BBQ (gas/elec only); playgrnd; pool; paddling pool; sand beach 6km; fishing 50m; tennis 1km; archery; wifi; entmnt; games/ TV rm; some statics; dogs €4; no c'vans/m'vans over 7m high ssn; poss cr; Eng spkn; adv bkg; some rlwy noise; ccard acc; red low ssn; CKE/CCI. "Peaceful, well-kept, family-owned site in wooded parkland; helpful, friendly warden; san facs poss red low ssn; gd rest & pool; 5 mins walk to delightful vill; rds around site poss liable to flood in winter; many walks in area; Collioure worth visit; conv Spanish border; excel." ♦ 1 Apr-29 Sep. € 31.50 (CChq acc) SBS - C26 2013*

ENVEITG see Bourg Madame *8H4*

ERR see Bourg Madame *8H4*

ESTAGEL *8G4* (3km W Rural) *42.76566, 2.66583* **Camping La Tourèze, Route d'Estagel, 66720 Latour-de-France [tel/fax 04 68 29 16 10; camping.latoureze@wanadoo.fr; http://campinglatoureze.monsite-orange.fr/]** Fr D117 at Estagel turn S onto D612 then R onto D17 to Latour. Site on R on ent to vill. Med, mkd pitch, shd; wc; chem disp; mv service pnt; baby facs; shwrs inc; el pnts (10A) €3.50; Indtte; tradsmn; shop, rest, bar 500m; playgrnd; htd pool 3km; rv sw adj; 13% statics; dogs €3; phone; Eng spkn; adv bkg; quiet; ccard acc; red low ssn/long stay. "Pretty vill & wine 'cave' in walking dist; rec visit Rv Agly barrage nrby; helpful staff; excel." 3 Apr-16 Oct. € 15.80 2014*

ESTAVAR see Bourg Madame *8H4*

FANJEAUX *8F4* (2.5km S Rural) *43.18070, 2.03301* **FFCC Camping à la Ferme Les Brugues (Vialaret), 11270 Fanjeaux [04 68 24 77 37; fax 04 68 24 60 21; lesbrugues@free.fr; http://lesbrugues.free.fr]** Exit A61 junc 22 onto D4/ D119 (dir Mirepoix) to Fanjeaux; cont on D119 dir Mirepoix; at top of hill turn L onto D102 sp La Courtète (past rest La Table Cathare & fuel stn) & in 100m turn R to site in 2.5km. Site well sp fr Fanjeaux. Sm, hdg/mkd pitch, pt sl, terr, shd; wc; chem disp; shwrs inc; el pnts (10A) inc (rev pol); Indtte (inc dryer); shop 2km; tradsmn; rest, bar 2.5km; playgrnd; games rm; wifi; few statics; dogs; Eng spkn; adv bkg; quiet; CKE/CCI. "Delightful, peaceful, 'off the beaten track' site adj sm lake; care req sm children; well-kept; v lge pitches, some o'looking lake; friendly, helpful owners; gd clean san facs; many walks; beautful countryside; excel touring base; rec." ♦ 1 Jun-30 Sep. € 14.00 2014*

FITOU see Leucate Plage *10G1*

FLEURY D'AUDE see Narbonne *10F1*

FLORAC *9D1* (1km N Rural) *44.33569, 3.59002* **FFCC Camp Municipal Le Pont du Tarn, Route de Pont de Montvert, 48400 Florac [04 66 45 18 26 or 04 66 45 17 96 (LS); fax 04 66 45 26 43; contact@camping-florac.com; www.camping-florac.com]** Exit Florac N on N106 & turn R in 500m by by-pass on D998; site on L in 300m. Lge, pt shd, mkd hdg pitch; htd wc (some cont); chem disp; mv service pnt; shwrs inc; el pnts (10A) €4.20; Indtte; supmkt 2km; tradsmn; rest, snacks, bar 2km; BBQ (no gas); playgrnd; pool; rv fishing & sw adj; wifi; 60% statics; dogs €2; phone; poss v cr; some Eng spkn; adv bkg rec; quiet; red low ssn; CKE/CCI. "Nice, well-kept, well-run site in beautiful area; clean san facs, but insufficient (2011); no twin-axles; 20 min walk to town; gd touring base; lge pitches; lge mkt Thurs; vg value; excel site on rv." ♦ 29 Mar-3 Nov. € 31.50 2014*

FLORAC *9D1* (2.5km NE Rural) *44.34528, 3.61008* **FFCC Camping Chantemerle, La Pontèze, 48400 Bédouès [04 66 45 19 66 or 06 73 86 53 16 (mob); chante-merle@wanadoo.fr; www.camping-chantemerle.com]** Exit Florac N on N106; in 500m turn R onto D998; in 2.5km site on L, past Bédouès vill cent. Med, mkd pitch, pt sl, pt shd; wc; chem disp (wc); shwrs inc; el pnts (6A) €2.80; Indry rm; sm shop; tradsmn; snacks; playgrnd; rv sw adj; games rm; wifi; 10% statics; dogs €1.50; poss cr; Eng spkn; quiet; red low ssn; CKE/CCI. "Lovely location; helpful owner; gd walking; conv Gorges du Tarn, Cévennes National Park; vg; water and el pnts now avail on lower pitches; excel site." 1 Apr-12 Nov. € 24.00 2014*

FLORAC *9D1* (4km NE Rural) *44.34433, 3.60533* **Camping Chon du Tarn, 48400 Bédouès [04 66 45 09 14; fax 04 66 45 22 91; info@camping-chondutarn.com; www.camping-chondutarn.com]** Exit Florac N on N106, turn R in 500m onto D998 (sp Pont de Monvert), site on L in 3km in vill. Med, mkd pitch, pt sl, terr, pt shd; wc; chem disp; mv service pnt; shwrs inc; el pnts (6A) €2 (poss rev pol); gas; Indtte; shop & 4km; rest & bar adj; playgrnd; rv sw & sand beach; games area; dogs €1; adv bkg; quiet; ccard not acc; red low ssn; CKE/CCI. "Beautiful rvside site with views; helpful staff; clean dated san facs, ltd low ssn; conv Tarn Gorges, Causses & Cévennes National Park; excel." ♦ 1 Apr-15 Oct. € 11.00 2010*

FLORENSAC see Agde *10F1*

FONTES *10F1* (800m N Rural) *43.54734, 3.37999* **FFCC Camping L'Evasion, Route de Cabrières, 34320 Fontès [04 67 25 32 00; fax 04 67 25 31 96; campingevasion34@yahoo.fr; http://camping.evasion.free.fr]** Fr A75 exit junc 59 (Pézenas). At rndabt take D124 to Lézignan-la-Cèbe then fork L, cont on D124 to Fontès. In vill foll sp to site. Sm, hdg/ mkd pitch, pt sl, pt shd; wc; chem disp; mv service pnt; baby facs; shwrs inc; el pnts (6A) €3; gas; Indtte; rest, snacks; bar; BBQ; playgrnd; pool; beach 30km; wifi; 75% statics; dogs €2.80; phone; adv bkg; quiet; CKE/CCI. "Excel san facs; touring pitches amongst statics (long-term residents)." ♦ ltd 1 Apr-30 Oct. € 12.00 (CChq acc) 2010*

⊞ **FONTES** *10F1* (3km E Rural) *43.54491, 3.41743* **Camping Les Clairettes, Route de Péret, 34320 Fontès [04 67 25 01 31; fax 04 67 25 38 64; www.campinglesclairettes.net]** Sp on D609. Turn onto D128 sp Adissan, Fontès. Fr A75 exit junc 58. Foll sp for Adissan & site. Med, hdg/mkd pitch, pt shd; wc; chem disp; serviced pitches; shwrs inc; el pnts (6A); gas; Indtte; sm shop, snacks, bar in ssn; rest 4km; BBQ; playgrnd; pool; entmnt; TV; 50% statics; adv bkg; red low ssn. "V quiet; friendly owners; ltd facs low ssn; nice site; no m'van drive-over drain. Convly nr m'way but away fr coastal crowds." ♦ ltd € 23.00 2014*

FRONTIGNAN *10F1* (5km NE Urban) *43.49173, 3.77932* **Camping L'Europe, 31 Route de Frontignan, 34110 Vic-la-Gardiole [08 25 00 20 30 or 04 67 18 02 61 (LS); resa@village-center.com; www.village-center.com]** Exit A9 junc 32 & foll sp D612 dir Sète; in 10km turn L onto D14 to Vic-la-Gardiole. Lge, pt shd; wc; baby facs; shwrs inc; el pnts (6A) inc; Indtte; shop; rest, snacks; bar; BBQ (charcoal); snacks; bar; playgrnd; 2 pools; paddling pool; waterslide; aqua gym; beach 5km (free shuttle); archery; games area; games rm; wifi; entmnt; some statics; dogs; adv bkg; red low ssn. 1 May-5 Sep. € 34.00 2010*

FRONTIGNAN *10F1* (1km S Coastal) *43.42998, 3.75968* **Camping Méditerranée, 11 Ave des Vacances, Quartier L'Entrée, 34110 Frontignan-Plage [04 99 04 92 32 / 06 49 39 03 79 l/s; camping-mediterranee@orange.fr; www.camping-mediterranee34.com]** 3km fr Sète on D612 to Montpellier, turn R at rlwy bdge, in approx 1km L at x-rds to site. Or on D129 fr Frontignan to Frontignan-Plage site on R 100m past reclamation area. Med, pt shd; wc; shwrs inc; el pnts (6A) €3.50; Indtte; shop adj; tradsmn; rest, snacks; bar; playgrnd; sand beach 100m; tennis; lake 500m; games area; entmnt; dogs €1.50; bus adj; adv bkg rec high ssn; quiet but some rlwy & rd noise; red low ssn." 30 Mar-29 Sep. € 17.00 (3 persons) 2013*

FRONTIGNAN *10F1* (6km S Coastal) *43.44970, 3.80540* **Camping Les Tamaris, 140 Ave d'Ingril, 34110 Frontignan-Plage [04 67 43 44 77 or 04 78 04 67 92 (LS); fax 04 67 18 97 90; les-tamaris@wanadoo.fr; www.les-tamaris.fr]** Fr A9/E15 exit junc 32 St Jean-de-Védas & foll sp Sète. At next rndbt foll sp Sète N112. After approx 8km turn L sp Vic-la-Gardiole onto D114. Cross rlwy & Canal du Rhône. Pass Les Aresquiers-Plages & turn L in 500m, site sp on L in 500m. Fr N on D613, take N300 to Sète; then N112 to Frontignan-Plage. Lge, hdg/mkd pitch, hdstg, pt shd; htd wc; chem disp; mv service pnt; baby facs; shwrs inc; el pnts (10A) inc (poss rev pol); Indtte (inc dryer); shop; tradsmn; rest, snacks; bar; BBQ; playgrnd; pool; paddling pool; sand beach adj; watersports; lake fishing; cycle hire; horseriding nrby; archery; weights rm; wifi; entmnt; games/TV rm; many statics; dogs €3; phone; poss cr; adv bkg rec; quiet; ccard acc; red long stay/low ssn; CKE/CCI. "Popular, family-run site; direct access to beach; sm pitches; friendly, helpful staff; gd clean san facs; vg for families; excel pool; late arr area; gd rest; lovely town; mkt Thu & Sat am; excel." ♦ 24 Apr-25 Sep. € 48.00 2011*

FUILLA see Vernet les Bains *8G4*

GALLARGUES LE MONTUEUX see Lunel *10E2*

⊞ **GANGES** *10E1* (7km E Rural) *43.92630, 3.78951* **Camp Municipal Le Grillon, Place de l'Eglise, 34190 Montoulieu [04 67 73 30 75; camping@montoulieu.fr; http://camping.montoulieu.fr/]** Fr Ganges take D999 E. At La Cadière-et-Cambo turn R onto D195 (site sp). Site on R in 3km. Sm, some hdg pitch, some hdstg, pt sl, pt shd; wc; mv service pnt; baby facs; shwrs inc; el pnts (6A) inc; Indtte (inc dryer); shop 6km; rest; bar; playgrnd; pool; 40% statics; dogs; quiet. "Gd cent for outdoor activities; gd, modern facs; useful winter NH; fairly isolated." ♦ ltd € 18.50 2014*

GIGNAC *10F1* (1km NE Rural) *43.66192, 3.55887* **Camp Municipal La Meuse, Route d'Aniane, 34150 Gignac [04 67 57 92 97; contact@campingdelameuse.com; www.campinglameuse.fr]** Exit A75 onto A750 sp Montpellier & Gignac. Exit sp Gignac Cent at rndabt & foll D32 sp Aniane. Site sp to L 600m past Aldi supmkt. Med, hdg/mkd pitch, pt shd; wc; mv service pnt; shwrs inc; el pnts (16A) €2.50; gas 1km; Indtte; shop 1km; bar; tennis; ltd wifi; dogs €1.70; Eng spkn; adv bkg; quiet; ccard acc; red long stay; CKE/CCI. "Pleasant, clean site; easy access; lge pitches; warden connects/disconnects el pnts; poss flooding on some pitches in heavy rain; gd cycling; unrel opening low ssn; rec." ♦ ltd 1 Jun-30 Sep. € 13.50 2010*

GIGNAC *10F1* (1.5km W Rural) *43.65395, 3.54056* **Camping du Pont, 730 Blvd du Moulin, 34150 Gignac [tel/fax 04 67 57 52 40; conto34@free.fr; www.campingdupont.com]** Foll sp fr town cent. Sm, pt shd; wc (some cont); chem disp; shwrs inc; el pnts (6A) €2.70; Indtte; shop; tradsmn; rest, snacks; BBQ; playgrnd; pool; fishing; tennis adj; games rm; entmnt; 20% statics; dogs €2; adv bkg; quiet; red low ssn. "Friendly welcome." ♦ 1 Apr-30 Sep. € 22.00 2010*

GIGNAC *10F1* (5km W Rural) *43.64056, 3.49521* **Camping Le Septimanien, Route de Cambous, 34725 St André-de-Sangonis [04 67 57 84 23; fax 04 67 57 54 78; info@camping-leseptimanien.com; www.camping-leseptimanien.com]** Exit A75 junc 57. At rndabt on E side of a'route take D128 to Brignac. In Brignac turn L at T-junc, then fork R on D4 twd St André-de-Sangonis. Site on R in 3km. Med, hdg pitch, pt shd; wc; chem disp; shwrs inc; el pnts (5A) inc; gas; Indtte; shop & 1km; tradsmn; rest, snacks; bar; playgrnd; pool; paddling pool; entmnt; 15% statics; dogs €2.15; phone; adv bkg; quiet; ccard acc; CKE/CCI. "Well-organised site; vg sh stay/NH." ♦ ltd 29 Apr-25 Sep. € 22.50 2009*

GOUDARGUES *10E2* (1km NE Rural) *44.22056, 4.47884* **Camping Les Amarines, La Vérune Cornillon, 30630 Goudargues [04 66 82 24 92; fax 04 66 82 38 64; contact@campinglesamarines.com; www.campinglesamarines.com]** Fr D928 foll sp onto D23 & site between Cornillon & Goudargues. Med, hdg/mkd pitch, shd; htd wc; baby facs; shwrs inc; el pnts (6A) €3.50; Indtte; tradsmn; snacks; bar; playgrnd; htd pool; rv fishing; entmnt; statics; dogs €2.20; adv bkg; quiet; red low ssn. "Lge pitches; site liable to flood after heavy rain; excel." ♦ 1 Apr-10 Oct. € 20.00 2010*

GRANDE MOTTE, LA *10F1* (700m W Coastal/Urban) *43.56334, 4.07275* **Camping Le Garden, Ave de la Petite Motte, 34280 La Grande-Motte [04 67 56 50 09; fax 04 67 56 25 69; jc.mandel@wanadoo.fr; www.legarden.fr]** Fr La Grande Motte W on D59, site sp. Lge, hdg/mkd pitch, hdstg, pt shd; htd wc; chem disp; mv service pnt; baby facs; fam bthrm; shwrs inc; el pnts (10A) inc; gas; Indtte; shop; rest, snacks; bar; BBQ (gas); pool; paddling pool; sand beach 300m; entmnt; 30% statics; dogs €2; phone; bus; poss cr; Eng spkn; adv bkg; ccard acc; red low ssn (30-40%); CKE/CCI. "Easy access to beach, town & bus; some soft sand on pitches; highly rec." 1 Apr-15 Oct. € 39.50 (3 persons) 2009*

GRANDE MOTTE, LA *10F1* (2km W Coastal) *43.56703, 4.07576* **Camp Intercommunal Les Cigales, Allée des Pins, 34280 La Grande-Motte [tel/fax 04 67 56 50 85; camping.lescigales@wanadoo.fr; www.sivom-etang-or.fr]** Ent La Grande-Motte fr D62. Turn R at 1st traff lts; 1st on R to site. Lge, mkd pitch, pt shd; htd wc (cont); shwrs inc; el pnts (10A) inc; Indtte; shop 200m; snacks; bar; playgrnd; sand beach 900m; quiet; red low ssn. "Spacious, well-organised site; quiet low ssn & ltd facs; pleasant seaside town." 3 Apr-3 Oct. € 20.00 2010*

GRANDE MOTTE, LA *10F1* (2km NW Coastal) *43.56440, 4.07528* **FFCC Camping La Petite Motte à La Grande-Motte, 195 Allée des Peupliers, 34280 La Grande-Motte [04 67 56 54 75; fax 04 67 29 92 58; camping.lagrandemotte@ffcc.fr; www.camping-lapetitemotte.com]** Exit A9 for Lunel or Montpellier Est to La Grande Motte, site sp on D59 & D62 coast rd. Lge, shd, wc; shwrs; mv service pnt; el pnts (4A) €4.50; Indtte (no dryer); shop; rest, snacks; bar; playgrnd; sand beach 700m; tennis, horseriding, golf & water sports nrby; games area; entmnt; wifi; 10% statics; twin-axles extra; dogs €4; poss cr; adv bkg; m'van o'night area; red low ssn/long stay/CKE/CCI. "Walk to beach thro ave of trees & footbdge over rds; helpful staff; clean modern san facs; cycle rtes nrby; vg." 29 Mar-30 Sep. € 19.50 (CChq acc) 2014*

GRAU DU ROI, LE *10F2* (1km N Coastal) *43.55450, 4.10720* **Camping Le Boucanet, Route de Carnon, 30240 Le Grau-du-Roi [04 66 51 41 48; fax 04 66 51 41 87; contact@campingboucanet.fr; www.campingboucanet.fr / www.campings-franceloc.fr]** Fr A9 fr N exit junc 26, fr S exit junc 29 Montpellier Airport dir Aigues-Mortes. Fr Aigues-Mortes take D62/D62A to Le Grau-du-Roi, twd La Grande-Motte. Site clearly sp off rndabt after area called Le Boucanet (on L). Lge, hdg/mkd pitch, some hdstg, pt shd; wc (some cont); chem disp; mv service pnt; shwrs inc; el pnts (6A) inc; gas; Indtte; shop; tradsmn; rest, snacks; bar; no BBQs; playgrnd; htd pool & paddling pool; dir access to sand beach adj; surf school; tennis; horseriding; golf 2km; creche; entmnt; 50% statics; no dogs; Eng spkn; adv bkg; quiet; ccard acc; red low ssn/ long stay; CKE/CCI. "Excel, popular site; some sm pitches poss diff lge o'fits; some pitches sandy; m'van parking on rd opp site; no waiting area outside site." ♦ 10 Apr-3 Oct. € 40.00 2010*

GRAU DU ROI, LE *10F2* (1km S Coastal) *43.52186, 4.14979* **Camping Les Jardins de Tivoli, Route de l'Espiguette, 30240 Le Grau du Roi [04 66 53 97 00; fax 04 66 51 09 81; contact@lesjardinsdetivoli.com; www.lesjardinsdetivoli.com]** Fr A9 take exit 26 to Aigues-Mortes. Then foll D979 twds Le Grau-du-Roi, Port Camargue & Espiguette. Site sp. Lge, hdg/mkd pitch, shd; wc; shwrs inc; individ san facs all pitches; el pnts (6-10A) inc; gas; Indtte; shop; rest, snacks; bar; gas; BBQ (gas); playgrnd; 3 pools; paddling pool; waterslides; sand beach 600m; tennis; sports activities; cycle hire; entmnt; TV; 20% statics; dogs €8; phone; adv bkg; ccard acc; red low ssn; CKE/CCI. "Excel site; superb individ san facs; lge pitches." ♦ 1 Apr-30 Sep. € 57.00 (4 persons) 2010*

GRAU DU ROI, LE *10F2* (4km SW Coastal) *43.50609, 4.12975* **Camping L'Espiguette, Route de l'Espiguette, 30240 Le Grau-du-Roi [04 66 51 43 92; fax 04 66 53 25 71; reception@campingespiguette.fr; www.campingespiguette.fr]** Fr A9 exit junc 26 onto D979 S to Aigues-Mortes & La Grande-Motte. Foll sps to Port Camargue & L'Espiguette & site sp on R fr rndabt; access via L bank of Le Grau-du-Roi; 3km fr Port Camargue & lighthouse. NB Caution on app due to height barrier. V lge, mkd pitch, pt shd; wc; mv service pnt; baby facs; shwrs inc; el pnts (5A) inc; gas; Indtte (inc dryer); shops; rest, snacks; bar; playgrnd; water park/play pool; waterslides into shallow sea water; sand beach adj & access to naturist beach 3km; cycle hire; games area; gym; wifi; entmnt; 10% statics; dogs €3.50; adv bkg; quiet; ccard acc; red long stay/low ssn; CKE/CCI. "Vg family site; beautiful beach adj; some pitches on sand; many facs high ssn; helpful staff; clean san facs; gd security." ♦ 27 Mar-3 Nov. € 36.00 2011*

GRUISSAN *10F1* (5km NE Coastal) *43.1358, 3.1424* **Camping Les Ayguades, Ave de la Jonque, 11430 Gruissan [04 68 49 81 59; fax 04 68 49 05 64; loisirs-vacances-languedoc@wanadoo.fr; www.loisirs-vacances-languedoc.com]** Exit A9 junc 37 onto D168/D32 sp Gruissan. In 10km turn L at island sp Les Ayguades, foll site sp. Lge, hdg/mkd pitch, unshd; htd wc; chem disp; mv service pnt; baby facs; shwrs inc; el pnts (6A) inc; Indtte; shop; rest; bar; playgrnd; sand beach adj; entmnt; TV; 75% statics; dogs €2.50; Eng spkn; adv bkg; quiet; ccard acc; CKE/CCI. "Pleasant site; extensive cycle network, 6 night min stay high ssn." ♦ 1 Apr-4 Nov. € 31.00 2012*

ISPAGNAC *9D1* (1km W Rural) *44.37232, 3.53035* **FFCC Camp Municipal Le Pré Morjal, 48320 Ispagnac [04 66 45 43 57; lepremorjal@gmail.com; www.campingdupremorjal.com]** On D907B 500m W of town, turn L off D907B & then 200m on R, sp. Med, hdg pitch, pt shd; htd wc; chem disp; mv service pnt; baby facs; shwrs inc; el pnts (10-16A) €3; Indtte; shops 200m; rest, snacks; BBQ area; playgrnd; pool 50m inc; paddling pool; rv sw 200m; games area; games rm; wifi; TV; dogs €1.20; quiet; red low ssn. "Lovely family site; gd sized pitches on rocky base, poss muddy when wet; friendly staff; gd rvside walks; vg base for Tarn & Joute Gorges; early ssn poss unkempt & irreg cleaning of san facs (2010)." ♦ 29 Mar-11 Nov. € 29.00 2014*

LAGRASSE *8F4* (1km NE Rural) *43.09516, 2.61893* **Camp Municipal de Boucocers, Route de Ribaute, 11220 Lagrasse [04 68 43 10 05 or 04 68 43 15 18; fax 04 68 43 10 41; mairielagrasse@wanadoo.fr; www.audetourisme.com]** 1km on D212 fr Lagrasse to Fabrezan (N). Sm, hdstg, pt sl, pt shd; wc; chem disp; mv service pnt; shwrs inc; el pnts (15A) €2.80; shops, rest 500m; rv sw 1km; dogs €2.10; phone; adv bkg; CKE/CCI. "At cent of 'off-the-beaten-track' beautiful touring area; helpful warden; simple but gd san facs; gd walking; path down to lagrasse centre; o'looks superb medieval town; rec arr early." ♦ ltd 15 Mar-15 Oct. € 15.00 2014*

LAMALOU LES BAINS *10F1* (400m NE Rural) *43.60074, 3.08314* **Camp Municipal Le Verdale, Blvd de Mourcairol, 34240 Lamalou-les-Bains [04 67 95 86 89 or 04 67 95 27 37 (LS); fax 04 67 95 64 52; camping@mairielamalou.fr; www.ot-lamaloulesbains.fr]** S fr Bédarieux on D908 twds Lamalou. Turn N off D908 at traff lts into Lamalou. At 2nd rndbt turn E foll sp to site on NE side of town. Med, mkd pitch, pt shd; htd wc; mv service pnt; shwrs; el pnts (6A) €2.30; supmkt, shop, pool, tennis & golf in town; games area; 30% statics; dogs; phone; poss cr; adv bkg rec. "Well-kept, popular site; bkg rec even low ssn; sm pitches; friendly, helpful warden; clean san facs; site popular with visitors to thermal baths nrby; easy walk to town & shops." ♦ 1 Mar-31 Oct. € 14.30 2011*

LAMALOU LES BAINS *10F1* (2km SE Rural) *43.57631, 3.06842* **Camping Domaine de Gatinié, Route de Gatinié, 34600 Les Aires [04 67 95 71 95 or 04 67 28 41 69 (LS); fax 04 67 95 65 73; gatinie@wanadoo.fr; www.domainegatinie.com]** Fr D908 fr Lamalou-les-Bains or Hérépian dir Poujol-sur-Orb, site sp. Fr D160 cross rv to D908 then as above. Med, hdg/mkd pitch, pt sl, pt shd; wc (some cont); chem disp; baby facs; shwrs inc; el pnts (6A) inc; Indtte; tradsmn; rest, snacks; bar; BBQ; playgrnd; pool; paddling pool; rv sw 100m; canoeing; fishing; games area; golf, horseriding, tennis 2km; entmnt; some statics; dogs €2; Eng spkn; adv bkg; quiet; red low ssn/long stay/CKE/CCI. "Beautiful, peaceful situation; many leisure activities; vg; helpful staff, leafy pleasant site in a lovely area." ♦ 1 Apr-31 Oct. € 19.00 2014*

LANGOGNE *9D1* (1km S Rural) *44.72781, 3.86466* **Camp Municipal de l'Allier, 9 Route de St Alban-en-Montagne, 48300 Langogne [04 66 69 28 98 or 04 66 69 10 33 (Mairie)]** Fr Le Puy take N88 dir Mende. At Langogne over rv bdge & 1st L. Foll sp, site in 1km. Med, mkd pitch, pt sl, pt shd; wc (some cont); chem disp (wc); shwrs inc; el pnts (6A) €2.50; Indtte; shops 500m; rest, snacks; bar; pool 500m; phone; poss cr; quiet; adv bkg; CKE/CCI. "Gd walking area; lake for sailing 2km; 2 san facs blocks - 1 modern; close to walking rtes." ♦ 15 May-15 Sep. € 6.65 2010*

LANGOGNE *9D1* (2km W Rural) *44.73180, 3.83995* **Camping Les Terrasses du Lac, 48300 Naussac [04 66 69 29 62; fax 04 66 69 24 78; info@naussac.com; www.naussac.com]** S fr Le Puy-en-Velay on N88. At Langogne take D26 to lakeside, site sp. Lge, terr, pt shd; wc; chem disp; mv service pnt; baby facs; shwrs; el pnts (6A) €2.50; Indtte (inc dryer); shop 2km; rest, snacks; bar; BBQ; playgrnd; pool; paddling pool; lake sw & sand beach adj; watersports adj; sailing school; games area; cycle hire; golf 1km, horseriding 3km; wifi; entmnt; TV rm; 10% statics; dogs €3.30; phone; Eng spkn; adv bkg; quiet; red low ssn; CKE/CCI. "Vg views; steep hill bet recep & pitches; vg cycling & walking." ♦ 15 Apr-30 Sep. € 18.60 2014*

LAROQUE DES ALBERES see Argelès sur Mer *10G1*

LATTES see Montpellier *10F1*

⊞ **LAUBERT** *9D1* (300m W Rural) *44.58262, 3.63552* **Camp Municipal La Pontière, 48170 Laubert [04 66 47 71 37; fax 04 66 47 73 08; pms.laubert@wanadoo.fr]** Site on N side of N88 in hamlet of Laubert. 7% hill descent fr Laubert to Mende. Sm, sl, pt shd; wc; shwrs inc; el pnts inc; Indtte; snacks; bar; playgrnd; quiet. "Peaceful; site at 1000m - can be chilly." ♦ € 10.50 2010*

⊞ **LAURENS** *10F1* (1km S Rural) *43.53620, 3.18583* **Camping L'Oliveraie, Chemin de Bédarieux, 34480 Laurens [04 67 90 24 36; fax 04 67 90 11 20; oliveraie@free.fr; www.oliveraie.com]** Clearly sp on D909 Béziers to Bédarieux rd. Sp reads Loisirs de L'Oliveraie. Med, mkd pitch, hdstg, terr, pt shd; htd wc; chem disp; baby facs; sauna high ssn; shwrs inc; el pnts (10A) €3.20-4.60 (poss rev pol); Indtte; shop high ssn; tradsmn; rest & bar high ssn; snacks; playgrnd; pool high ssn; games rm; wifi; beach 30km; TV rm; 30% statics; dogs free, €2 (high ssn); phone; adv bkg; quiet; red low ssn; ccard acc; site clsd 15 Dec-15 Jan; CKE/CCI. "Helpful staff; gd, clean san facs (2011); site becoming tatty (2011); in wine-producing area; gd winter NH." ♦ € 28.00 2014*

LEUCATE PLAGE *10G1* (200m S Coastal) *42.90316, 3.05178* **Camp Municipal du Cap Leucate, Chemin de Mouret, 11370 Leucate-Plage [04 68 40 01 37; fax 04 68 40 18 34; cap.leucate@wanadoo.fr; www.mairie-leucate.fr/capleucate]** Exit A9 junc 40 onto D627 thro Leucate vill to Leucate-Plage approx 9km. Site sp. Lge, hdg pitch, shd; wc (some cont); chem disp; mv service pnt; baby facs; fam bthrm; shwrs inc; el pnts (6A) €2.10 long lead req; Indtte; shop 200m; tradsmn; rest, snacks, bar 300m; BBQ; playgrnd; htd pool 100m; sand beach 100m; games area; entmnt; TV; 60% statics; dogs €2; phone; adv bkg; quiet; red low ssn; CKE/CCI. "Nice, spacious, sandy site in gd position; popular with surfers; m'van area outside; gd NH; immac new san facs (2012)." 1 Feb-30 Nov. € 18.50 2013*

LEUCATE PLAGE *10G1* (6km W Coastal) *42.91405, 2.99796* **Camping Le Fun, Domaine des Bergeries, 11510 Fitou [04 68 45 71 97; contact@lefun-camping.com; www.camping-lefun.com]** Exit A9 junc 40 dir Perpignan, site sp. Med, mkd pitch, pt shd; htd wc; chem disp; shwrs inc; el pnts (6A) €4; Indry rm; ltd shop; tradsmn; sm bar; BBQ (communal only); playgrnd; pool; paddling pool; windsurfing; tennis; games area; horseriding; wifi; 20% statics; dogs €4; Eng spkn; adv bkg; quiet; ccard acc; red low ssn; CKE/CCI. "Site in windy, rather isolated position & popular with windsurfers; clean, adequate san facs; gd." ♦ 1 Apr-13 Nov. € 20.00 2011*

LEZIGNAN CORBIERES *8F4* (10km S Rural) *43.11727, 2.73609* **Camping Le Pinada, Rue des Rousillous, 11200 Villerouge-la-Crémade [04 68 43 32 29; contact@camping-le-pinada.com; www.camping-le-pinada.com]** Fr Lézignan-Corbières on D611 S, pass airfield & fork L thro Ferrals-les-Corbières (steep, narr) on D106. Site sp & on L after 4km. Alt rte to avoid narr rd thro Ferrals: exit A61 junc 25 & foll D611 thro Fabrezan. At T-junc turn L onto D613 & after 2km turn L onto D106. Site on R after Villerouge-la-Crémade. Med, hdg/mkd pitch, pt sl, terr, shd; wc; chem disp (wc); baby facs; shwrs inc; el pnts (6A) €5; Indtte; shop; tradsmn; snacks; bar; playgrnd; pool; rv sw & fishing 3km; tennis; games area; entmnt; TV rm; 25% statics; dogs €2; poss cr; Eng spkn; adv bkg, bkg fee; quiet; ccard not acc; CKE/CCI. "Friendly owners; gd base for Carcassonne & Med coast; well-run site; dated san facs; excel." ♦ 1 Mar-30 Oct. € 18.50 2012*

LEZIGNAN CORBIERES *8F4* (500m NW Urban) *43.20475, 2.75255* **Camp Municipal de la Pinède, Ave Gaston Bonheur, 11200 Lézignan-Corbières [tel/fax 04 68 27 05 08; reception@campinglapinede.fr; www.campinglapinede.fr]** On D6113 fr Carcassonne to Narbonne on N of rd; foll 'Piscine' & 'Restaurant Le Patio' sp. Med, all hdg/hdstg pitch, pt sl, terr, pt shd; wc; chem disp; mv service pnt; shwrs inc; el pnts (6A) inc; gas; wifi; Indtte; shop 1km; rest, snacks; bar; BBQ (gas only); htd pool adj; tennis; 5% statics; dogs €2.10; adv bkg; quiet; ccard not acc; red low ssn/CKE/CCI. "Well-run, clean, popular site; helpful, friendly staff; gd san facs; gd m'van facs; some pitches diff due high kerb; no c'vans/m'vans over 5m; superb pool; mkt Wed; gd touring base or NH." ♦ 1 Mar-30 Oct. € 24.50 2014*

LIMOUX *8G4* (200m SE Urban) *43.04734, 2.22280* **Camp Municipal du Breilh, Ave Salvador Allende, 11300 Limoux [04 68 31 13 63; fax 04 68 31 18 43; limoux@limoux.fr]** Fr D118 cross bdge to E side of Rv Aude, then S on D129 Ave de Corbières & foll site sp. Not well sp on ent town fr N. Sm, pt sl; wc; shwrs; el pnts (6A) €2.90; shops adj; pool, tennis adj; fishing; boating; quiet but some rd noise. "Basic rvside site; pleasant town; suitable sh stay; staff exceptionally kind & helpful; san facs poor." 1 Jun-30 Sep. € 15.00 2014*

LLAURO see Ceret *8H4*

LODEVE *10E1* (5km NE Rural) *43.76110, 3.36000* **Camping des Sources, Chemin d'Aubaygues, 34700 Soubès [tel/fax 04 67 44 32 02 or 06 86 38 91 31 (mob); camping-sources@orange.fr; www.camping-sources.com]** Exit A75 junc 52 to Soubès; then 1st R dir Fozières; foll sp. Sm, terr, pt shd; wc; chem disp; shwrs inc; el pnts (6A) inc; Indtte; tradsmn; shop 1km; snacks; playgrnd; children pool; rv sw, sailing & fishing adj; dogs €3; adv bkg rec high ssn; quiet; ccard acc; red low ssn; CKE/CCI. "Peaceful site with relaxed atmosphere; helpful, pleasant owner; immac facs; not suitable lge o'fits as app rd v narr & some pitches sm; lovely bar/rest; excel." ♦ 29 Mar-11 Nov. € 20.00 2009*

⊞ **LODEVE** *10E1* (6km SE Rural) *43.69198, 3.35030* **Camping Les Peupliers, Les Casseaux, 34700 Le Bosc [tel/fax 04 67 44 38 08; contact@camping-les-peupliers-salagou.com; www.camping-les-peupliers-salagou.com]** Take exit 54 on A75; sp Le Bosc. Med, mkd pitch, pt sl, terr, pt shd; wc; shwrs inc; el pnts (5A) €2; gas; shop 4km; tradsmn Jul-Aug; snacks; bar; playgrnd; pool; sand beach 40km; lake 5km; 90% statics; dogs €1; Eng spkn; adv bkg; some rd noise; CKE/CCI. "Friendly staff; ltd facs low ssn; recep clsd low ssn, phone ahead; windsurfing Lac du Salagou; easy access fr m'way; conv winter NH." ♦ ltd € 20.00 2011*

LODEVE *10E1* (9km S Rural) *43.67182, 3.35429* **Camp Municipal Les Vailhés, Le Puech, Lac du Salagou, 34702 Lodève [04 67 44 25 98 or 04 67 44 86 00 (LS); fax 04 67 44 65 97; camping@lodevoisetlarzac.fr]** Fr N exit A75 junc 54 onto D148 dir Octon & Lac du Salagou. Foll site sp. Fr S exit A75 junc 55. Lge, hdg/mkd pitch, terr, pt shd; wc; chem disp; shwrs inc; el pnts (16A) inc; Indtte; tradsmn; BBQ; playgrnd; lake sw & beach; fishing; watersports; 20% statics; dogs; poss cr; Eng spkn; quiet; CKE/CCI. "Peaceful, remote site by lake; pleasant staff; no facs nrby; excel walks; gd." ♦ 1 Apr-30 Sep. € 17.50 2010*

LODEVE *10E1* (5km W Rural) *43.73631, 3.26443* **Camping Domaine de Lambeyran (Naturist), Lambeyran, 34700 Lodève [04 67 44 13 99; fax 04 67 44 09 91; lambeyran@wanadoo.fr; www.lambeyran.com]** Fr N or S on N9 take sliprd to Lodève. Leave town on D35 W twd Bédarieux. In 2km take 2nd R, sp L'Ambeyran & St Martin. Foll sp 3.7km up winding hill to site. Lge, hdg/mkd pitch, terr, pt sl, pt shd; wc; chem disp; shwrs inc; el pnts (6A) €4.20; gas; Indtte; shop & supmkt 4km, rest, snacks, bar high ssn; BBQ; playgrnd; pool; sailing, windsurfing 10km; 5% statics; dogs; phone; Eng spkn; adv bkg; quiet; ccard acc; red low ssn/long stay; CKE/CCI. "Superb location with views; lge pitches; gd walking, inc on site; gates clsd 2000; Lac du Salagou with sports facs 12km." 15 May-15 Sep. € 24.40 2010*

LUNEL *10E2* (2km NE Rural) *43.69000, 4.14800* **FFCC Camping du Pont de Lunel, Chemin du Mas de Viala, 34400 Lunel [04 67 71 10 22; contact@campingdupontdelunel.com; www.camping-du-pontdelunel.com]** Fr N on N113, cross Rv Vidourle & turn R at rndbt onto D34. Site on R in 400m. Sm, hdg/mkd pitch, shd; wc; mv service pnt; shwrs; el pnts (5A) inc; Indtte; shops adj; rest, snacks; bar; BBQ; playgrnd; pool 4km; sand beach 12km; games area; entmnt; dogs €1.50; adv bkg. "Pleasant, family-run site." 15 Mar-15 Sep. € 17.00 2009*

LUNEL *10E2* (5km NE Rural) *43.71675, 4.16704* **Camping Les Amandiers, Clos de Manset, 30660 Gallargues-le-Montueux [04 66 35 28 02; fax 04 66 51 48 57; camping-lesamandiers@orange.fr; www.camping-lesamandiers.com]** Exit A9 at junc 26 Gallargues/Les Plages. Turn R after toll, site in 2km. Med, mkd pitch, pt shd; wc; chem disp; mv service pnt; baby facs; shwrs inc; el pnts (16A) €4; gas; Indtte; shops adj; snacks; bar; playgrnd; pool; sand beach 15km; fishing 800m; tennis; games area; entmnt; TV; 20% statics; dogs €2.50; adv bkg; quiet; ccard acc; CKE/CCI. "Conv NH en rte to Spain; gd touring area." ♦ 30 Apr-1 Sep. € 18.00 2009*

LUNEL *10E2* (2km S Rural) *43.65666, 4.14111* **Camping Le Bon Port, 383 Chemin de Mas St Angé, 34400 Lunel [04 67 71 15 65; fax 04 67 83 60 27; contact@campingbonport.com; www.campingbonport.com]** Exit A9 junc 27 S dir La Grande Motte, D61. Site sp on L. Lge, hdg/mkd pitch, pt shd; wc; baby facs; shwrs inc; el pnts (5A) €4; Indtte; shop; tradsmn; rest, snacks; bar; BBQ (gas); playgrnd; pool; paddling pool; waterslide; games area; wifi; entmnt; TV rm; 30% statics; dogs €3.50; adv bkg; quiet. ♦ 1 Apr-30 Sep. € 26.00 (CChq acc) 2010*

MALENE, LA *9D1* (200m W Rural) *44.30120, 3.31923* **FFCC Camp Municipal Le Pradet, 48210 La Malène [04 66 48 58 55 or 04 66 48 51 16 (LS); fax 04 66 48 58 51; la.malene.mairie@wanadoo.fr]** W fr La Malène on D907B dir Les Vignes. Site on L in 200m. Well sp. Sm, mkd pitch, some hdstg, pt sl, pt shd; wc (some cont); chem disp; mv service pnt; shwrs inc; el pnts (10A) €2.50; Indtte; shops, rest, snacks & bar 200m; BBQ; playgrnd; rv sw & fishing; dogs €0.30; phone; poss cr; adv bkg; quiet; ccard acc; red low ssn; CKE/CCI. "Kayak hire; boat trips fr vill; helpful warden; excel." 1 Apr-30 Sep. € 13.00 2014*

⊞ **MARSEILLAN PLAGE** *10F1* (1km NE Coastal) *43.32158, 3.55932* **Camping Le Paradou, 2 Impasse Ronsard, 34340 Marseillan-Plage [tel/fax 06 15 49 09 90 / 04 67 21 90 10 ls; info@paradou.com; www.paradou.com]** Exit A9 junc 34 or 35 onto N113/N312 dir Agde & Sète. Fr Agde foll sp Sète to Marseillan-Plage. Site well sp on N112. Med, hdg pitch, pt shd; htd wc; chem disp; mv service pnt; baby facs; shwrs inc; el pnts (10A) €3.50; gas; Indtte; shop 1km; tradsmn; rest, bar 1km; snacks; playgrnd; dir access sand beach adj; 15% statics; dogs €1.50; phone; wifi; bus 1km; poss cr; CKE/CCI. "Gd area for cycling; ltd pitches avail for long o'fits; Gd clean facs, maybe stretched in ssn; superb san facs; cycle rte to Sete; highly rec." ♦ ltd € 29.00 2014*

MARSEILLAN PLAGE *10F1* (500m SW Coastal) *43.30648, 3.53924* **Camping Europ 2000, 960 Ave des Campings, 34340 Marseillan-Plage [tel/fax 04 67 21 92 85; contact@camping-europ2000.com; www.camping-europ2000.com]** Fr cent of Marseillan-Plage S on coast rd D51e, site on L. Med, hdg/mkd pitch, hdstg, pt shd; wc; chem disp; mv service pnt; shwrs inc; el pnts (10A) €3.50; gas; Indtte; shop & 500m; tradsmn; snacks; BBQ; playgrnd; sand beach adj; games area; 10% statics; dogs €2; phone; poss cr; Eng spkn; adv bkg; quiet; red low ssn CKE/CCI. "Easy access to beach; friendly, helpful owner; gd family-run site." ♦ 1 Apr-20 Oct. € 28.00 2009*

MARSEILLAN PLAGE *10F1* (500m SW Coastal) *43.31036, 3.54601* **Camping La Plage, 69 Chemin du Pairollet, 34340 Marseillan-Plage [04 67 21 92 54; fax 04 67 01 63 57; info@laplage-camping.net; www.laplage-camping.net]** On D612 fr Agde to Sète, turn R at rndabt dir Marseillan-Plage. Foll sp for site at 2nd rndabt. Site on L in 150m. Med, hdg pitch, pt shd; wc; chem disp; mv service pnt; shwrs inc; child/baby facs; el pnts (10A) inc; gas; Indtte (inc dryer); rest, snacks; bar; BBQ; playgrnd; direct access to sand beach adj; watersports; games area; entmnt; TV; 1% statics; dogs €4; phone; extra for beach front pitches; poss cr; Eng spkn; adv bkg; quiet; ccard acc, CKE/CCI. "Excel, popular, family-run site; superb beach; sm pitches; gd, friendly atmosphere." ♦ 15 Mar-6 Nov. € 34.00 2010*

MARSEILLAN PLAGE *10F1* (650m SW Coastal/Urban) *43.31365, 3.54779* **Camping Beauregard Plage, 250 Chemin de l'Airette, 34340 Marseillan-Plage [04 67 77 15 45; fax 04 67 01 21 78; reception@camping-beauregard-plage.com; www.camping-beauregard-plage.com]** On N112 Agde-Sète rd, turn S at rndabt to Marseillan-Plage onto D51 & foll camping sp thro town. Site immed on leaving town cent. Lge, hdg pitch, pt shd; wc; chem disp; mv service pnt; baby facs; shwrs inc; el pnts (6A) inc; Indtte; shop, rest & bar adj; rest-bar high ssn; playgrnd; sand beach adj; wifi; entmnt; TV rm; 5% statics; dogs €2 (allowed low ssn only); Eng spkn; adv bkg; poss cr; quiet; red low ssn. "Superb sand beach sheltered by dunes; some pitches soft & sandy; excel for beach holiday." ♦ 30 Mar-15 Oct. € 35.50 2013*

MARSEILLAN PLAGE *10F1* (1km SW Coastal) *43.31275, 3.54638* **Camping La Créole, 74 Ave des Campings, 34340 Marseillan-Plage [04 67 21 92 69; fax 04 67 26 58 16; campinglacreole@wanadoo.fr; www.campinglacreole.com]** Fr Agde-Sète rd N112, turn S at rndabt onto D51 & foll sp thro town. Narr ent easily missed among lger sites. Med, hdg/mkd pitch, hdstg, pt shd; wc; chem disp; mv service pnt; baby facs; shwrs inc; el pnts (6A) €3.50; Indtte; shop; rest, snacks, bar adj; playgrnd; sand beach adj; tennis 1km; games area; entmnt; 10% statics; dogs €3; phone; adv bkg; min stay 7 nights Jul-Aug; quiet; red low ssn; CKE/CCI. "Vg, well-kept site; dir access to excel beach; naturist beach 600m." ♦ 1 Apr-15 Oct. € 34.50 2012*

MARSEILLAN PLAGE *10F1* (1km SW Coastal) *43.30586, 3.53788* **Camping Les Sirènes, 1078 Ave des Campings, 34340 Marseillan-Plage [tel/fax 04 67 21 92 83]** On N112 Agde-Sète rd, turn S onto D51 at rndabt, & foll sps in town. Site at end of rd thro lge area of camp sites. V lge, hdg/mkd pitch, hdstg, pt shd; wc; chem disp; shwrs inc; el pnts (10A) inc; gas 300m; Indtte; shop 100m; tradsmn; playgrnd; pool complex; waterslides; sand beach adj; watersports; tennis 1km; cycle hire; horseriding; games area; games rm; entmnt; sat TV; no statics; dogs €2.80; Eng spkn; quiet; red low ssn; CKE/CCI. "Vg site in excel location; gd facs; seaside town nr with all facs; excel beach." ♦ 15 May-15 Sep. € 40.00 2010*

MARVEJOLS *9D1* (1km NE Rural) *44.55077, 3.30440* **Camping Village Le Coulagnet, Quartier de l'Empery, 48100 Marvejols [04 66 32 03 69]** Exit A75 junc 38 onto D900 & N9. Foll E ring rd onto D999, cont over rv & foll sp to site; no R turn into site, cont 500m to Aire de Retournement, & turn L into site. Foll sp 'VVF', camping pt of same complex. NB U-turn bef ent impossible long o'fits; nasty speed humps on app rd. Sm, hdg pitch, pt shd; wc; shwrs inc; el pnts (5A) inc (poss rev pol); Indtte (inc dryer); shop & 1km; BBQ (sep area); playgrnd; pool; rv adj; tennis; games area; games rm; TV rm; 50% statics; no dogs; phone; Eng spkn; adv bkg; quiet; ccard acc. "Well equiped site; san facs immac; sep area for tourers; interesting walled town; excel; ent too tight to make u-turn." ♦ 15 May-15 Sep. € 26.00 2014*

MAURY see St Paul de Fenouillet *8G4*

MEJANNES LE CLAP see Barjac (Gard) *9D2*

⊞ **MENDE** *9D1* (2km S Rural) *44.51409, 3.47363* **Camping Tivoli, Route des Gorges du Tarn, 48000 Mende [tel/fax 04 66 65 00 38; camping.tivoli0601@orange.fr; www.camping-tivoli.com]** Sp fr N88, turn R 300m downhill (narr but easy rd). Site adj Rv Lot. Med, pt shd; wc (some cont); chem disp; mv service pnt; shwrs inc; el pnts (6A) inc; Indtte; shop; hypmkt 1km; bar; playgrnd; pool; rv fishing; TV rm; some statics; dogs €1; quiet but rd noise; adv bkg. "Gd site nr town at back of indust est; v narr ent with little rm to park." € 19.00 2009*

"We must tell The Club about that great site we found"

Get your site reports in by mid-August and we'll do our best to get your updates into the next edition.

MENDE *9D1* (8km SW Rural) *44.50104, 3.40717* **Camping Le Clos des Peupliers, 48000 Barjac [04 66 47 01 16; leclosdespeupliers@wanadoo.fr]** Exit A75 junc 39 onto N88 dir Mende; turn off N88 N onto D42 sp Barjac; then turn almost immed turn R; rd goes thro sh narr but not diff tunnel (max height 3.4m). Site immed after tunnel, on S side of N88 adj Rv Lot. Med, mkd pitch, pt shd; wc; chem disp; shwrs inc; el pnts (6-10A) €2.50-3; Indtte; rest 300m; snacks; playgrnd; rv fishing adj; TV; dogs €1.30; quiet. "Pleasant rvside site; poss unkempt low ssn; helpful warden; basic, clean facs, ltd low ssn; gd walks." ♦ 1 May-15 Sep. € 9.00 2010*

MEYRUEIS *10E1* (3km N Rural) *44.19633, 3.45724* **FFCC Camping La Cascade, Salvinsac, 48150 Meyrueis [04 66 45 45 45 or 06 85 84 07 15 (mob); fax 04 66 45 48 48; contact@camping-la-cascade.com; www.camping-la-cascade.com]** N of Meyrueis on D996, on R. NB Do not app fr N - narr rd. Rec app fr Millau dir only. Sm, mkd pitch, pt sl, terr, pt shd; wc; chem disp; mv service pnt; baby facs; shwrs inc; el pnts (10A) €3; gas; Indtte; shop; tradsmn; BBQ; playgrnd; canoeing; fishing; horseriding; walking; 20% statics; dogs; poss cr; Eng spkn; adv bkg; ccard acc. "Friendly owners." ♦ 1 Apr-5 Nov. € 16.00 2010*

MEYRUEIS *10E1* (1km NE Rural) *44.18590, 3.43856* **Camping Le Pré de Charlet, Route de Florac, 48150 Meyrueis [04 66 45 63 65; fax 04 66 45 63 24; lepredecharlet@gmail.com; www.camping-lepredecharlet.com]** Exit Meyrueis on rd to Florac (D996). Site on R on bank of Rv Jonte. Med, mkd pitch, pt sl, terr, pt shd, pt sl; wc (some cont); chem disp; mv service pnt; baby facs; shwrs inc; el pnts (16A) inc; gas; Indtte; shop & 11km; tradsmn; bar; BBQ; playgrnd; pool 400m; rv fishing; phone; adv bkg; phone; quiet; ccard acc; red low ssn;CKE/CCI. "Friendly owner; excel walking area; not suitable lge o'fits; conv Les Gorges de la Jonte; excel." ♦ ltd 15 Apr-15 Oct. € 15.00 2010*

MEYRUEIS *10E1* (500m E Rural) *44.18075, 3.43540* **Camping Le Champ d'Ayres, Route de la Brèze, 48150 Meyrueis [tel/fax 04 66 45 60 51; campinglechampdayres@wanadoo.fr; www.campinglechampdayres.com]** Fr W on D907 dir Gorges de la Jonte into Meyrueis. Foll sp Château d'Ayres & site. Med, hdg/mkd pitch, pt sl, pt shd; wc (some cont); chem disp; mv service pnt; baby facs; fam bthrm; shwrs inc; el pnts (6A) €3; Indtte; shop; tradsmn; snacks; bar; BBQ; playgrnd; htd pool; cycle hire; games area; games rm; wifi; 15% statics; dogs €1; phone; poss cr; Eng spkn; adv bkg; red low ssn; ccard acc;CKE/CCI. "Helpful owners; rec." ♦ 11 Apr-19 Sep. € 26.50 2012*

MEYRUEIS *10E1* (800m NW Rural) *44.18580, 3.41977* **Kawan Village Le Capelan, Route de Jonte, 48150 Meyrueis [tel/fax 04 66 45 60 50; camping.le.capelan@wanadoo.fr; www.campingcapelan.com]** Site sp on D996 on banks of Rv Jonte. Med, mkd pitch, shd; wc; chem disp; mv service pnt; baby facs; fam bthrm; shwrs inc; el pnts (4-10A) €3; gas; Indtte (inc dryer); shop; tradsmn; supmkt 500m; BBQ; rest 1km; snacks; bar; BBQ; playgrnd; htd pool; paddling pool; fishing; tennis 1km; games rm; games area; rock climbing; wifi; entmnt; TV rm; 70% statics; Eng spkn; adv bkg; quiet; red low ssn; ccard acc;CKE/CCI. "Gd, scenic, rvside site; conv touring Gorges du Tarn & Cévennes National Park." ♦ 1 May-17 Sep. € 22.00 (CChq acc) 2010*

MEZE *10F1* (1km N Coastal) *43.43019, 3.61070* **Kawan Village Beau Rivage, 113 Route Nationale, 34140 Mèze [04 67 43 81 48; fax 04 67 43 66 70; reception@camping-beaurivage.fr; www.camping-beaurivage.fr]** Fr Mèze cent foll D613 dir Montpellier, site on R 100m past rndabt on leaving town; well sp. Lge, mkd pitch, pt shd; wc; chem disp; mv service pnt; baby facs; shwrs inc; el pnts (3-6A) inc; Indtte; shop; supmkt 200m; rest, snacks; bar; BBQ; playgrnd; htd pool; paddling pool; sand beach 700m; fishing; sailing; tennis 900m; fitness rm; wifi; entmnt; TV rm; 50% statics; phone; dogs €6; poss cr; Eng spkn; adv bkg; quiet but rd noise; ccard acc; red low ssn;CKE/CCI. "Well equipped site; trees & narr access rds poss diff lge o'fits; vg modern san facs; lovely pool; pitches poss worn end of ssn; poor security - rear of site open to public car park; diff exit onto busy coast rd; conv Sète & Noilly Prat distillery; vg; excel site; close to town with gd mkt, marina and rest." ♦ 10 Apr-17 Sep. € 40.00 2013*

MEZE *10F1* (2km N Rural) *43.44541, 3.61595* **Camp Municipal Loupian, Route de Mèze, 34140 Loupian [04 67 43 57 67 / 04 67 43 82 07 (ls); camping@loupian.fr; www.loupian.fr]** Fr Mèze tak D613 & turn L at 1st Loupian sp, then foll sp for site. Med, hdg/mkd pitch, pt shd; wc; chem disp; baby facs; shwrs; el pnts (6A) €3; Indtte; takeaway; snacks; bar; BBQ; playgrnd; sand beach 3km; tennis; entmnt; dogs €1; phone; poss cr; Eng spkn; adv bkg; quiet; red low ssn;CKE/CCI. "Pleasant site in popular area; plenty shd; friendly, helpful staff; vg san facs; gd beaches; excel fisherman's rest; gd rests at Mèze & Bouzigues; superb cycling on old rlwy rte fr site to Mèze (Voie Verte); rec; cent to main attractions." ♦ ltd 4 Apr-19 Oct. € 14.00 2014*

MEZE *10F1* (5.5km NE Coastal) *43.45070, 3.66562* **Camping Lou Labech, Chemin du Stade, 34140 Bouzigues [04 67 78 30 38; fax 04 67 78 35 46; contact@lou-labech.fr; www.lou-labech.fr]** Exit A9 junc 33 onto D660/D613 S to Bouzigues; site sp. Pt of Chemin du Stade borders sea. Sm, hdstg, terr, pt shd; wc; chem disp; baby facs; shwrs; el pnts (5A) £3; Indtte; tradsmn; rest 800m; bar; BBQ (charcoal sep area); playgrnd; wifi; TV; dogs free; poss cr; Eng spkn; quiet; red low ssn. "Delightful site; friendly, helpful staff; Bouzigues lovely vill." ♦ ltd Apr-Oct. € 21.00 2009*

⊞ **MILLAS** *8G4* (3km W Rural) *42.69067, 2.65785* **FLOWER Camping La Garenne, 66170 Néfiach [04 68 57 15 76; fax 04 68 57 37 42; camping.lagarenne.nefiach@wanadoo.fr; www.camping-lagarenne.fr / www.flowercampings.com]** Fr Millas on R of D916, sp. Med, shd; htd wc (some cont); chem disp; baby facs; shwrs inc; el pnts (10A) €5; gas; Indtte; shop; snacks; bar; BBQ; playgrnd; pool high ssn; tennis 500m; games area; entmnt; wifi; 50% statics; dogs free; adv bkg rec high ssn; slight rd noise & poss noisy disco; red low ssn. "Friendly owners; gd facs." ♦ € 20.00 2011*

MONS LA TRIVALLE *10F1* (2.5km SE Rural) *43.56247, 2.97306* **Camp Municipal de Tarassac, 34390 Mons-la-Trivalle [04 67 97 72 64; communedemonslatrivalle@orange.fr]** Fr D908 turn S onto D14, sp Béziers; site off D14 on Rv Orb. Lge, mkd pitch, hdstg, pt sl, shd; wc (some cont); shwrs inc; el pnts; Indtte; tradsmn; rest, snacks; bar; shop; playgrnd; rv sw & fishing adj; playgrnd; dogs; phone; 10% statics; poss cr; quiet. "Fair sh stay; watersports cent adj; pitches bounded by boulders; beautiful area; site a bit unkept; v natural enviroment; vg." € 14.50 2012*

MONT LOUIS *8G4* (3.5km N Rural) *42.51971, 2.09713* **Camping Rural du Pla de Barrès, Route des Bouillouses, 66210 La Llagonne [04 68 04 26 04 or 04 68 04 21 97 (TO); otmontlouis@wanadoo.fr; www.mont-louis.net/camping.htm]** Leave Mont-Louis N dir La Llagonne & Formiguères; 800m after rndabt (D118 junc with D618) turn L onto D60 & foll sp Lac des Bouillouses. Site sp on L at top of hill; cont for 1km. Lge, pt shd; wc (cont); shwrs; el pnts (6A) €3.50; playgrnd; paddling pool; rv sw adj; fishing; dogs €1; quiet; red low ssn. "Most of site in pine forest; v busy high ssn; modern san facs; grnd poss rocky & boggy; poss mosquitoes; beautiful area." ♦ 15 Jun-15 Sep. € 10.60 2010*

MONT LOUIS *8G4* (5km W Rural) *42.50636, 2.04671* **Camping Huttopia Font-Romeu, Route de Mont-Louis, 66120 Font-Romeu [04 68 30 09 32; fax 04 68 04 56 39; fontromeu@huttopia.com; www.huttopia.com]** W fr Mont-Louis on D618. Site on L bef Font-Romeu, opp stadium. Fr Aix-les-Thermes or Puigcerdà turn E at Ur up longish hill, thro town to site on R at o'skts. Lge, sl, pt shd; htd wc; shwrs; el pnts (6-10A) €4.20-6.20; Indtte; shop; rest, bar (w/ends); htd pool; paddling pool; tennis 500m; horserieing 1km; internet; entmnt; some statics; dogs €3.50; phone; adv bkg; quiet. "Gd cent for mountain walks; site at 1800m altitude." 19 Jun-13 Sep. € 22.00 SBS - D29 2013*

MONTAGNAC *10F1* (500m E Rural) *43.48200, 3.48893* **Camp Municipal La Piboule, 9 Chemin de la Piboule, 34530 Montagnac [04 67 24 01 31]** Exit A75 junc 59 Pézenas onto D613 E to Montagnac. Site sp to E of Montagnac. Narr app rds & parked cars unsuitable/v diff lge o'fits. Best app fr E on D5. Med, hdg/mkd pitch, pt sl, pt shd; wc (cont); shwrs inc; el pnts (10A) €3.20; Indry; shop, rest, snacks, bar 800m; playgrnd; phone; CKE/CCI. "Clean san facs; sh walk to pretty vill; diff lge o'fits." 15 May-31 Oct. € 10.00 2009*

MONTAGNAC *10F1* (4km SE Rural) *43.45175, 3.51600* **Camping Domaine St Martin-du-Pin, 34530 Montagnac [04 67 24 00 37; fax 04 67 24 47 50; www.saint-martin-du-pin.com]** Exit A75 junc 59 onto D113 to Montagnac; 2km past Montagnac turn R immed past picnic site at end of dual c'way, site sp. Sm, hdg pitch, pt sl, pt shd; wc; chem disp; mv service pnt; baby facs; shwrs inc; el pnts €3.50; Indtte; shop 4km; tradsmn; BBQ; playgrnd; pool; games area; few statics; no dogs; Eng spkn; adv bkg advised; quiet; CKE/CCI. "Delightful, relaxing site; lge pitches, blocks req on most; clean facs; gd touring base; beautiful views." ♦ 1 Mar-12 Oct. € 23.00 2014*

MONTBLANC see Béziers *10F1*

MONTCLAR (AUDE) see Carcassonne *8F4*

MONTFERRAND *8F4* (2km N Rural) *43.3902, 1.8277* **FFCC Domaine St Laurent, Les Touzets, 11320 Montferrand [04 68 60 15 80 or 06 76 60 58 42 (mob); info@camping-carcassonne-toulouse.com; campingsaintlaurent@orange.fr; www.camping-carcassonne-toulouse.com]** S fr Toulouse on N113/D1113 past Villefranche-de-Lauragais. Turn L onto D43 for 4.2km; then R to St Laurent. Or turn L onto D218 bypassing Montferrand & cont directly to St Laurent; turn L at church. Site well sp. Sm, some hdg pitch, pt shd; wc; chem disp; sauna; shwrs inc; el pnts (6A) inc; Indtte; shop; rest, snacks; bar; playgrnd; pool; tennis; archery; cycle hire; games rm; entmnt; TV rm; some statics; dogs €2; Eng spkn; adv bkg; quiet; ccard not acc; red low ssn. "Attractive, peaceful, well-kept site; clean san facs; friendly owners; gd views; woodland walks." 1 Apr-30 Oct. € 22.00 2012*

*Last year of report

LANGUEDOC-ROUSSILLON

MONTFERRAND *8F4* (6km SE Rural) *43.31451, 1.80246* **Camping Le Cathare, Château de la Barthe, 11410 Belflou [04 68 60 32 49; fax 04 68 60 37 90; info@auberge-lecathare.com; www.auberge-lecathare.com]** Fr Villefranche-de-Lauragais on N113/D6113, foll D622 sp Toulouse/Carcassonne over rlwy, canal, then immed L on D625 for 7km. Thro St Michel-de-Lanes then take D33 to Belflou; foll sp to Le Cathare. Sm, mkd pitch, pt shd; wc (some cont); chem disp; shwrs inc; el pnts (3-10A) €3-7.50; shops 12km; tradsmn; rest in ferme auberge; snacks, bar 4km; lake sw 3km; sand/shgl beach; some statics; dogs €1.20; v quiet; CKE/CCI. "Poss long walk to basic san facs - sh timer for lts & might prefer to use your own facs; Cent Nautique on lake; dramatic position o'looking lake." 15 Apr-1 Nov. € 18.00 2012*

MONTFRIN *10E2* (500m NW Urban) *43.87980, 4.58917* **Camping Belle Rive, Cours Antelme, 30490 Montfrin [tel/fax 04 66 57 20 79 or 06 20 89 57 04 (mob); fredbissiere@hotmail.fr; www.campingbellerive.fr]** Fr Pont-du-Gard on D986 dir Beaucaire. Or on D2 SW fr Avignon. Well sp in vill; by rv & sw pool. Med, mkd pitch, pt shd; wc; chem disp; mv service pnt; shwrs inc; el pnts (10A) €3 (poss rev pol); Indtte; rest 500m; snacks; bar; BBQ; playgrnd; pool adj; rv fishing; canoeing; tennis nrby; games area; games rm; wifi; entmnt; TV; 20% statics; dogs €1; no twin-axles; Eng spkn; adv bkg; quiet; red low ssn; CKE/CCI. "Peaceful, informal site in woodland by Rv Gardon; spacious & uncrowded; welcoming owner; friendly & laid back; nr interesting vill with bullring; conv Avignon, Arles, Nimes; vg." ♦ ltd 1 May-15 Sep. € 15.50 2010*

MONTPELLIER *10F1* (8km N Rural) *43.65135, 3.89630* **Camping Le Plein Air des Chênes, Route de Castelnau, 34830 Clapiers [04 67 02 02 53; fax 04 67 59 42 19; contact@pleinairdeschenes.net; www.pleinairdeschenes.net]** Exit A9 junc 28 onto N113/D65 twd Montpellier. Leave at junc with D21 sp Jacou & Teyran, site sp on L. NB Site ent/exit v narr & no place to stop when leaving. Med, mkd pitch, pt sl, terr, pt shd; wc (some cont); shwrs inc; private san facs some pitches (extra charge); el pnts (10A) inc; gas; Indtte; shops 800m; rest, snacks; bar; playgrnd; pool; paddling pool; waterslides; sand beach 16km; tennis; games area; horseriding; wifi; 60% statics; dogs €6; quiet; red long stay/low ssn. "Vg site; site rds tight for lge o'fits; pitches muddy in wet." ♦ 1 Mar-31 Dec. € 45.50 2011*

MONTPELLIER *10F1* (6km SE Rural) *43.57611, 3.92583* **FFCC Camping Le Parc, Route de Mauguio, 34970 Lattes [04 67 65 85 67; fax 04 67 20 20 58; camping-le-parc@wanadoo.fr; www.leparccamping.com]** Exit A9 junc 29 for airport onto D66. In about 4km turn R onto D172 sp Lattes & campings, cross over D21. Site ent in 200m on R. Med, hdg pitch, shd; wc; chem disp; shwrs inc; el pnts (10A) inc; gas; Indtte; sm shop; huge shopping cent 1km; tradsmn; snacks high ssn; playgrnd; pool; sand beach 4km; wifi; 15% statics; dogs €3; Eng spkn; adv bkg (dep); quiet; CKE/CCI. "Friendly, helpful owners; lge pitches but dusty; gd facs, excel pool & snack bar; conv Cévennes mountains & Mediterranean beaches; hiking & mountain biking; barrier locked 2200." ♦ 3 Apr-31 Oct. € 26.00 2009*

MOSTUEJOULS see Peyreleau *10E1*

NARBONNE *10F1* (10km N Rural) *43.26009, 2.95552* **Camp Municipal, Rue de la Cave Coopérative, 11590 Sallèles-d'Aude [04 68 46 68 46 (Mairie); fax 04 68 46 91 00; ot.sallelesdaude@wanadoo.fr; www.salleles-daude.com]** Fr A9/E15 exit junc 36 onto D64 N & in approx 4km turn L to join D11 W. Cont on this rd for approx 18km, then turn L onto D13 S to Ouveillan. In vill, turn R onto D418 SW to Sallèles-d'Aude. Site in vill. NB Nr Canal du Midi some narr app rds. Sm, hdg/mkd pitch, pt shd; wc; chem disp; el pnts €2.50; shops 1km; BBQ; no statics; dogs; adv bkg; quiet. "Clean site nr canal; 16 pitches; warden calls am; phone warden bef pitching; site not maintained but nice." 1 May-30 Sep. € 16.00 2014*

"I need an on-site restaurant"

We do our best to make sure site information is correct, but it is always best to check any must-have facilities are still available or will be open during your visit.

NARBONNE *10F1* (10.5km NE Rural) *43.23821, 3.11063* **Camp Municipal Les Sablous, Ave de Coursan, 11110 Salles-d'Aude [04 68 33 61 73 (Mairie); mairie-salles-daude@wanadoo.fr]** Fr Narbonne on D6009; at Coursan turn R onto D1118 sp Salles-d'Aude, site sp in 5km on W edge of vill. Med, mkd pitch, pt shd; wc (cont); chem disp (wc); shwrs inc; Indry rm; shop adj; BBQ; playgrnd; dogs free; quiet; CKE/CCI. "No twin-axle c'vans; site ent diff for lge o'fits; fair NH." 1 Jul-31 Aug. 2010*

NARBONNE *10F1* (6km S Rural) *43.13662, 3.02595* **Les Mimosas Village Camping, Chaussée de Mandirac, 11100 Narbonne [04 68 49 03 72; fax 04 68 49 39 45; info@lesmimosas.com; www.lesmimosas.co.uk]** Leave A9 junc 38 at Narbonne Sud & at rndabt foll sp La Nautique. Turn L opp ent to Camping La Nautique & foll sp Mandirac & site. Lge, hdg/mkd pitch, hdstg, pt shd; htd wc; chem disp; mv service pnt; baby facs; fam bthrm; sauna; some serviced pitches; shwrs inc; el pnts (6A) inc; gas; Indtte (inc dryer); shop; rest, snacks; bar; BBQ (gas/elec); playgrnds; lge htd pool complex; paddling pool; waterslides; jacuzzi; sand beach 6km; watersports; rv fishing adj; fishing lake 300m; tennis; cycle hire; horseriding adj; gym; cycle hire; games area; games rm; wifi; entmnt; TV rm; 6% statics; dogs €4; lge o'fits rec phone in adv high ssn; adv bkg; Eng spkn; quiet; ccard acc; red low ssn/long stay; CKE/CCI. "Attractive site with lge pitches; gd choice of pitches; friendly, helpful staff; vg san facs, poss ltd low ssn; excel pool complex; vg for children; excel touring base in historic area; gd birdwatching; cycle path to Narbonne." ♦ 12 Apr-31 Oct. € 41.00 SBS - C35 2011*

See advert on next page

NARBONNE *10F1* (4km SW Urban) *43.14702, 3.00424* **Camping La Nautique, Chemin de la Nautique,11100 Narbonne [04 68 90 48 19; fax 04 68 90 73 39; info@campinglanautique.com; www.campinglanautique.com]** Exit junc 38 fr A9 at Narbonne Sud. After toll take last rndabt exit & foll sp La Nautique. Site on R 2.5km fr A9 exit. Lge, hdg/mkd pitch, some hdstg, pt shd; chem disp; mv service pnt; individual san facs (wc, shwr) on each pitch inc; el pnts (10A) inc; gas; Indtte; shop & 3km; tradsmn; rest, snacks & bar high ssn; BBQ (elec only); playgrnd; htd pool; waterslide; paddling pool; canoeing; windsurfing; sand beach 10km; tennis; entmnt; wifi; 30% statics; dogs €6; Eng spkn; adv bkg; quiet with some rd noise; ccard acc; red low ssn/long stay; CKE/CCI. "Excel, well-run site; helpful, friendly Dutch owners; excel, clean facs; caution - hot water v hot; some pitches lge but narr; steel pegs req; pitches sheltered but some muddy after heavy rain; excel rest; many sports activities avail; cycle trips; gd walks nrby; highly rec." ♦ 1 Mar-30 Oct. € 60.00 SBS - C07 2014*

> "Satellite navigation makes touring much easier"
>
> Remember most sat navs don't know if you're towing or in a larger vehicle – always use yours alongside maps and site directions.

⊞ **NARBONNE** *10F1* (12km SW Rural) *43.16296, 2.89186* **Camping La Figurotta, Route de Narbonne, 11200 Bizanet [04 68 45 16 26 or 06 88 16 12 30 (mob); fax 04 68 48 98 22; info@figurotta.eu; www.figurotta.eu]** Exit A9 at Narbonne Sud onto slip rd N9/D6113 twd Lézignan-Corbières; in 3km at new rndabt head L twd D613 & then D224 sp Bizanet & site. App fr W not rec due narr D rds. Sm, mkd pitch, hdstg, pt sl, pt terr, shd; htd wc; chem disp; shwrs free; el pnts (4-6A) €2.50-3.50 (poss long lead req); gas; Indtte; sm shop & 2km; tradsmn; rest, snacks; bar; playgrnd; sm pool; sand beach 20km; games area; 5% statics; dogs €3 (sm dogs only); phone; Eng spkn; adv bkg; rd noise; red long stay/low ssn/CKE/CCI. "Pleasant, simple, well-run, scenic site; friendly & helpful; gd pool; gusty & stony site - steel pegs req; excel drainage; gd NH en rte Spain; vg; dated facs but beautifully clean." ♦ ltd € 34.00 2013*

NARBONNE PLAGE *10F1* (8km NE Coastal) *43.20592, 3.21056* **Camping La Grande Cosse (Naturist), St Pierre-sur-Mer, 11560 Fleury-d'Aude [04 68 33 61 87; fax 04 68 33 32 23; contact@grandecosse.com; www.grandecosse.com]** Exit A9 junc 37 & foll sp Narbonne-Plage. Cont thro Narbonne-Plage to St Pierre-sur-Mer, pass municipal site & turn R twd L'Oustalet, site sp. Lge, hdg/mkd pitch, pt shd; wc; serviced pitches; chem disp; mv service pnt; shwrs inc; el pnts (8A) €4; gas; Indtte; shop; rest, snacks; bar high ssn; playgrnd; htd pool; sand beach 300m; tennis; games area; games rm; gym; entmnt; boat hire; fishing; TV rm; 20% statics; dogs €6-9 (high ssn); phone; poss cr Aug; Eng spkn; adv bkg; red long stay/low ssn; ACSI; ccard acc; INF card req. "Excel, well-run site; gd pitches; helpful, friendly staff; excel san facs; naturist walk to lovely beach thro lagoons & dunes (poss flooded early ssn); mosquitoes poss problem Jun-Sep; flood risk after heavy rain; gd mkt St Pierre-sur-Mer; access rds can be diff, v narr." ♦ 5 Apr-5 Oct. € 60.00 (CChq acc) 2014*

NASBINALS *9D1* (1km N Rural) *44.67016, 3.04036* **Camp Municipal, Route de St Urcize, 48260 Nasbinals [02 46 32 51 87 or 04 66 32 50 17; mairie.nasbinals@laposte.net; www.mairie-nasbinals.info]** Fr A75 exit 36 to Aumont-Aubrac, then W on D987 to Nasbinals. Turn R onto D12, site sp. Med, pt sl, pt shd; htd wc; chem disp; mv service pnt; shwrs inc; el pnts (16A) €3; shop, rest in vill; BBQ; dogs; quiet; red CKE/CCI."Lovely loc gd views, no shd, facs inadequate peak ssn." ♦ ltd 15 May-30 Sep. € 8.40 2012*

⊞ **NIMES** *10E2* (4km S Rural) *43.78776, 4.35196* **Camp Municipal Domaine de la Bastide, route de Générac, 30900 Nîmes [04 66 62 05 82; fax 04 66 62 05 83; immocamp@wanadoo.fr; www.camping-nimes.com]** Fr A9 exit junc 25 onto A54 dir Arles; in 2km exit A54 junc 1 onto D42 sp St Gilles; in 1.5km (at 2nd rndabt) turn R onto D135; in 2.5km at rndabt turn R onto D13; site on L. Or N fr Montpellier on N113/D6113 to Nimes; at Périphique Sud turn S onto D13 sp Générac; site on R 500m after rndabt junc with D613. Site well sp fr town cent. Lge, hdg/mkd pitch, hdstg, shd; htd wc; chem disp; mv service pnt; baby facs; shwrs inc; el pnts (10A) inc; gas; Indtte; shop; tradsmn; hypmkt nr; rest, snacks; bar; playgrnd; games area; wifi; TV rm; 10% statics; dogs €2.70; phone; bus; Eng spkn; adv bkg; quiet - some rd noise; red low ssn; CKE/CCI. "Excel, well-run site; lge pitches; friendly, helpful recep; Nîmes 20 mins by bus fr site; gd site." ♦ ltd € 30.00 2014*

OCTON *10F1* (2 km NE Rural) *43.65948, 3.32052* **Camping Le Village du Bosc (Naturist), Chemin de Ricazouls, 34800 Octon [04 67 96 07 37; fax 04 67 96 35 75; www.villagedubosc.net]** Exit 54 or 55 fr N9/A75 dir Octon onto D148, foll sp to Ricazouls/site. Med, terr, pt shd; wc; chem disp; shwrs; el pnts (10A)inc; rest, snacks; bar; shop; lndtte; playgrnd; htd pool; lake sw; watersports; 20% statics; dogs €3 (restricted area only); poss cr; adv bkg; red long stay; INF card. "Lovely, quiet site with wooded walks; friendly owners; clean facs; tight turns on terr access for lge o'fits; Octon vill pretty." ♦ ltd 27 Apr-30 Sep. € 29.00 2013*

OCTON *10F1* (600m SE Rural) *43.65100, 3.30877* **Camping Le Mas des Carles, 34800 Octon [04 67 96 32 33]** Leave A75 at junc 54, foll sp for Octon, 100m after vill sp turn L & foll white site sp keeping L. Ent on L opp tel kiosk (sharp turn). Sm, some hdg/mkd pitch, pt sl, terr, pt shd, pt shd; wc; chem disp; shwrs inc; el pnts (6-10A) inc; lndtte; lndry rm; shop 500m; rest adj; playgrnd; pool; boating/watersports in lake 800m; 30% statics; dogs; phone; poss cr; adv bkg; quiet; ccard not acc; CKE/CCI. "Pleasant site with views; helpful owner; facs a little tired (2006); take care low branches on pitches; Lac de Salagou with abandoned vill of Celles 1km." 1 Apr-10 Oct. € 21.40 2012*

OLARGUES *8F4* (400m N Rural) *43.55798, 2.91440* **Camp Municipal Le Baoüs, 34390 Olargues [04 67 97 71 50; otsi.olargues@wanadoo.fr; www.olargues.org]** Take D908 W fr Bédarieux, site immed bef ent Olargues. Site sp over sm bdge on L. At end of bdge turn R to site. Last 50m rough track & narr turn into site. Sm, pt shd; wc (cont); chem disp; shwrs inc; el pnts (6A); shop 300m; playgrnd; canoeing; cycle hire; internet; adv bkg Jul/Aug; quiet. "Helpful warden; hill climb to services block; site poss flooded by Rv Jaur in spring; sh walk to amazing hilltop vill." 1 Jul-15 Sep. 2014*

OLONZAC *8F4* (6km N Rural) *43.3408, 2.7056* **Camping Le Mas de Lignières (Naturist), Montcélèbre, 34210 Cesseras-en-Minervois [tel/fax 04 68 91 24 86; lemas1@wanadoo.fr; www.lemasdelignieres.com]** Fr Olonzac go N on D182 thro Cesseras & cont N dir Fauzan. Look for R turn to Montcélèbre - site on R behind lge, clsd brown gates (intercom) - not easy to find. Care needed thro Cesseras. Sm, hdg/mkd pitch, hdstg, pt sl, pt shd; wc (some cont); chem disp; baby facs; fam bthrm; shwrs inc; el pnts (6A) inc; gas; lndtte; sm shop & 2km; tradsmn; covrd pool; tennis; TV rm; 5% statics; dogs €1.50; phone; poss cr; adv bkg; red 10 days; quiet; ccard acc; INF card ess & avail at site. "Well-run, scenic site in remote location; lge pitches; fair san facs; nearest supmkt in La Redorte (10km); vg walks." ♦ ltd 26 Apr-30 Sep. € 25.50 2009*

OLONZAC *8F4* (9km E Rural) *43.28372, 2.82688* **FFCC Camping Les Auberges, 11120 Pouzols-Minervois [tel/fax 04 68 46 26 50; vero.pradal@neuf.fr; www.camping-lesauberges.fr]** Fr D5 site 500m S of vill of Pouzols-Minervois. Sm, mkd pitch, pt shd; wc; chem disp (wc); shwrs inc; el pnts (5A) €3.50; gas adj; lndtte; shop adj; tradsmn; playgrnd; pool; 30% statics; dogs; poss cr; Eng spkn; adv bkg rec; quiet; CKE/CCI. "V popular site; friendly owners; sm Sat mkt at 'cave' opp." 15 Mar-15 Nov. € 16.00 2012*

PALAU DEL VIDRE see Elne *10G1*

⊞ **PALAVAS LES FLOTS** *10F1* (500m N Coastal) *43.53000, 3.92400* **Aire Communale/Camping-Car Halte, Base Fluviale Paul Riquer, 34250 Palavas-les-Flots [04 67 07 73 45 or 04 67 07 73 48; fax 04 67 50 61 04]** Fr Montpellier on D986 to Palavas. On ent town at 1st rndabt 'Europe' foll sp Base Fluviale & site sp. Med, mkd pitch, hdstg, pt shd; wc; chem disp; mv service pnt; shwrs inc; el pnts (16A) €2; lndtte; shop, rest, snacks, bar adj; sand beach 500m; phone; bus 200m; poss cr; some rd noise; ccard acc; CKE/CCI. "M'vans only; special elec cable req - obtain fr recep (dep); some pitches on marina quay; conv Montpellier, Camargue; 3 night max stay." € 10.00 2012*

PALAVAS LES FLOTS *10F1* (1km NE Coastal) *43.53346, 3.94820* **Camping Montpellier Plage, 95 Ave St Maurice, 34250 Palavas-les-Flots [04 67 68 00 91; fax 04 67 68 10 69; www.camping-montpellier-plage.com]** Site on D21ES on o'skts of vill twd Carnon. V Lge, pt mkd pitch, pt shd; wc (some cont); chem disp; shwrs inc; mv service pnt; el pnts (4A) inc; gas; lndtte; shops; tradsmn; rest, snacks; bar; BBQ; playgrnd; pool with spa facs; paddling pool; sand beach adj; games area; 50% statics; dogs; bus high ssn; poss cr; Eng spkn; adv bking; noisy; red low ssn; CKE/CCI. "Gd location; basic san facs, but lge pitches & friendliness of site outweigh this; gd security; poss somewhat unkempt; easy walk into Palavas - interesting sm port; flamingoes on adjoining lake; gd." ♦ 16 Apr-18 Sep. € 36.00 2011*

PALAVAS LES FLOTS *10F1* (2km E Urban/Coastal) *43.53867, 3.96076* **Camping Les Roquilles, 267b Ave St Maurice, 34250 Palavas-les-Flots [04 67 68 03 47; fax 04 67 68 54 98; roquilles@wanadoo.fr; www.camping-les-roquilles.fr]** Exit A9 junc 30 onto D986 dir Palavas. In Palavas foll sp Carnon-Plage on D62, site sp. V lge, mkd pitch, hdstg, pt shd; wc (mainly cont); chem disp; mv service pnt; serviced pitches; shwrs inc; el pnts (6A) €3.90; gas 100m; lndtte; rest, snacks; bar; playgrnd; 3 pools (1 htd); waterslide; sand beach 100m; entmnt; TV; 30% statics; no dogs; phone; bus; poss cr; Eng spkn; adv bkg; poss noisy high ssn; ccard acc; red low ssn/long stay; CKE/CCI. "Excel pizza bar on site." 15 Apr-15 Sep. € 49.00 2014*

PALAVAS LES FLOTS *10F1* (1.5km SW Coastal) *43.51972, 3.90959* **Camping Palavas, Route de Maguelone, 34250 Palavas-Les-Flots [04 67 68 01 28 or 06 62 42 34 43 (mob); www.palavas-camping.fr]** Exit A9 junc 30 onto D986 dir Palavas-Les-Flots; cross bdge; turn R at rndabt, foll sp Maguelone; sit on L in 1km. Lge, hdg/mkd pitch, hdstg, pt shd; wc; chem disp; m'van water refill; baby facs; shwrs inc; el pnts (6A) inc; lndtte; supmkt; rest, snacks; bar; playgrnd; pool; paddling pool; spa pool; beach adj; games area; games rm; infant club; 30% statics; dogs €2.50; phone adj; bus 1.5km; poss cr; Eng spkn; w/end disco noise some pitches; red low ssn. "Great views; gd pool area; sep car park; vg." 16 Apr-15 Sep. € 38.00 2009*

PALME, LA see Sigean *10G1*

PERPIGNAN *8G4* (4.5km NE Coastal) *42.73027, 2.92224* **Rouissillon Camping Catalan, Route de Bompas, 66000 Perpignan [04 68 63 16 92; camping.catalan@free.fr; http://camping-catalan.com]** Fr Perpignan N on D1, Bompas rd. Site on R bef rndabt. Med, shd; wc; serviced pitches; shwrs; el pnts (10A) €3.90; Indtte; shop 500m; rest, snacks; bar; pool; playgrnd; beach 10km; entmnt; TV; 60% statics; dogs €3; poss cr; adv bkg; CKE/CCI. "Pool deep, no shallow end." 15 Mar-31 Oct. € 19.00 2010*

PERPIGNAN *8G4* (6km S Rural) *42.63754, 2.89819* **Camping Les Rives du Lac, Chemin de la Serre, 66180 Villeneuve-de-la-Raho [04 68 55 83 51; fax 04 68 55 86 37; camping.villeneuveraho@wanadoo.fr]** Fr A9 exit Perpignan Sud, dir Porte d'Espagne. In 3km turn R onto N9 dir Le Boulou. In 1km after Auchan supmkt take slip rd to N91 dir Villeneuve-de-la-Raho. In 2km rd becomes D39, turn R to site, site on L in 1km. Beware ford on D39 in v wet weather (usually dry). Med, mkd pitch, pt sl, hdstg, pt shd; htd wc; chem disp; mv service pnt; shwrs inc; el pnts (6A) inc; Indtte; shop; supmkt 3km; rest, snacks; bar; BBQ (elec/gas); playgrnd; htd pool; lake sw, beach, fishing & watersports 1.5km; tennis 2km; some statics; dogs €1.60; phone; Eng spkn; adv bkg; poss noise fr adj picnic area w/ends; red low ssn; ccard acc; CKE/CCI. "Lakeside site with views; poor san facs & insufficient for site size; busy cycling/jogging path adj; conv trips to Spain; busy public beach nr." ♦ 15 Mar-15 Nov. € 17.50 2014*

PEYRELEAU *10E1* (1km N Rural) *44.19126, 3.20470* **Camp Municipal de Brouillet, 48150 Le Rozier [05 65 62 63 98; fax 05 65 62 60 83; contact@campinglerozier.com; www.camping-lerozier.com]** Fr Millau take D809 N to Aguessac, onto D907; in Le Rozier, x bdge over Rv Tarn onto D996 & in 200m (opp church); take rd on R to site; sp. Lge, mkd pitch, pt shd; wc (some cont); chem disp (wc); baby facs; shwrs inc; el pnts (6A) €3.50; Indtte; shop 200m; playgrnd; htd pool; poss cr; adv bkg rec high ssn; quiet; red low ssn; CKE/CCI. "V pleasant, busy, spacious site adj rv; friendly recep; vg for m'vans; poss facs stretched & unclean; gd base for Tarn Gorges; gd area walking & birdwatching." ♦ ltd 1 Apr-20 Sep. € 15.70 2012*

PEZENAS *10F1* (1km NE Urban) *43.46618, 3.42397* **Camping St Christol, Chemin de St Christol, 34120 Pézenas [04 67 98 09 00 or 06 11 39 59 17 (mob); fax 04 67 98 89 61; info@campingsaintchristol.com; www.campingsaintchristol.com]** Exit A75 junc 59 Pézenas N onto N9 by-pass for town cent; turn R immed bef bdge; sp on R in 200m. NB app rds narr. Med, hdg/mkd pitch, hdstg, shd; wc (some cont); chem disp (wc); baby facs; shwrs inc; el pnts (10A) €3.40; gas; Indtte; shop; tradsmn; rest, snacks; BBQ area; playgrnd; pool; fishing; games rm; entmnt; TV; some statics; dogs €1.70; poss cr; adv bkg rec Jul/Aug; quiet; ccard acc; red low ssn; CKE/CCI. "Friendly, lively site; lge gravel pitches but hard & dusty; poss diff to manoeuvre due trees; san facs reasonable (2009); historic town." ♦ 15 Apr-15 Sep. € 18.00 2009*

PEZENAS *10F1* (6km S Rural) *43.38776, 3.42298* **Camping Le Pin Parasol, Le Causse, 34630 St Thibéry [tel/fax 04 67 77 84 29; camping-pin-parasol@wanadoo.fr; www.campinglepinparasol.com]** Fr A9 exit junc 34 onto D13 & foll Pézenas sps; in 2.5km turn R to St Thibéry & site 150m on R. Med, mkd pitch, pt shd; wc; mv service pnt; shwrs inc; el pnts (10A) €5; supmkt 300m; tradsmn; rest, snacks; BBQ; playgrnd; pool; paddling pool; sand beach 10km; tennis 1km; games rm; rv sw 1km; fishing; entmnt; TV; 30% statics; dogs €4; sep car park; poss cr; adv bkg; rd noise; ccard not acc; red low ssn; CKE/CCI. "Vg site; vg san facs; lovely pool; gd value takeaway; stone quarry & indus units nrby (not a problem); site poss dusty low ssn; interesting vill." ♦ 1 Apr-30 Oct. € 19.00 2010*

PEZENAS *10F1* (500m SW Urban) *43.45419, 3.41573* **Campotel Municipal de Castelsec, Chemin de Castelsec, 34120 Pézenas [04 67 98 04 02; fax 04 67 98 35 40; contact@camping-pezenas.com; www.camping-gites-herault.com]** Fr Béziers take N9 to Pézenas; foll Centre Ville sps fr rndabt at edge of town onto Route de Béziers; in 600m at next rndabt (at junc with D13) go strt over into Ave de Verdun; in 400m take 1st L after McDonalds & pharmacy at ent to Carrefour supmkt; foll Campotel sps; site on L in 300m. Sm, mkd pitch, pt sl, pt terr, pt shd; wc; chem disp (wc); shwrs inc; el pnts (10A) €2.90; Indtte; shops 500m; playgrnd; pool 1km; tennis adj; TV; 30% statics; dogs €1.40; adv bkg; quiet; rd noise some pitches; red low ssn; CKE/CCI. "Great little site; friendly staff; clean, dated san facs; some pitches unsuitable lge o'fits; easy walk/cycle to interesting town; toy museum worth visit; vg." ♦ 1 Apr-30 Oct. € 16.00 2014*

PONT ST ESPRIT *9D2* (5km W Rural) *44.27306, 4.57944* **Camping Les Oliviers, Chemin de Tête Grosse, 30130 St Paulet-de-Caisson [04 66 82 14 13; info@camping-lesoliviers.net; www.camping-lesoliviers.net]** Exit A7 junc 19 & foll D994 to Pont-St Esprit, then sp to St Paulet-de-Caisson. Turn R into vill & foll sp to St Julien-de-Peyrolas on D343, site sp 1.5km off narr rd - unsuitable lge o'fits. Sm, hdg/mkd pitch, terr, pt shd; wc; chem disp; shwrs inc; el pnts (4A) €3; Indtte; shops 2km; tradsmn; rest, snacks; bar; pool; playgrnd; rv sw 5km; dogs free; Eng spkn; adv bkg; quiet; CKE/CCI. "Ardèche, Roman sites nr; helpful Dutch owners; painting tuition; ltd water points & long way fr lower levels; v attractive vill; gd cent for walking, cycling & driving." 1 Apr-30 Sep. € 35.00 2014*

⊞ **PONT ST ESPRIT** *9D2* (7km NW Rural) *44.29808, 4.56535* **Camping Les Cigales, 30760 Aiguèze [04 66 82 18 52; fax 04 66 82 25 20; www.camping-cigales.fr]** N fr Pont-St Esprit on D6086 take D901 NW twd Barjac & D141 to St Martin-d'Ardèche. Site on L bef rv bdge. Avoid app fr St Martin-d'Ardèche over narr suspension bdge. Care at ent. Sm, mkd pitch, shd; wc; mv service pnt; shwrs inc; el pnts (4-10A) €3.13-5.88; gas; Indtte; shops, rest 500m; tradsmn; BBQ; htd pool; rv sw 500m; wifi; 25% statics; dogs €2; poss cr; adv bkg; rd noise; ccard not acc; CKE/CCI. "Helpful owner; easy walk to St Martin-d'Ardèche." € 18.00 2011*

PONT ST ESPRIT *9D2* (8km NW Rural) *44.28950, 4.58923* **Camping Le Peyrolais, Route de Barjac, 30760 St Julien-de-Peyrolas [04 66 82 14 94; fax 04 66 82 31 70; contact@camping-lepeyrolais.com; www.camping-lepeyrolais.com]** N fr Pont-St. Esprit on D6086 turn L onto D901 sp Barjac. In 2.5km turn R at site sp, site in 500m up narr track on bank of Rv Ardèche. Med, mkd pitch, pt shd; wc; chem disp; mv waste; shwrs inc; el pnts (3-10A) €2.30-3.80; Indtte; shop & 3km; tradsmn; rest; bar; playgrnd; rv sw adj; fishing; kayaking; cycle & canoe hire; games area; hiking; horseriding; wifi; entmnt; TV rm; dogs €2; phone; poss cr; adv bkg; quiet; ccard acc; CKE/CCI. "Attractive, well-maintained site in beautiful location; clean facs; friendly owners; vg; great site." ♦ 1 Apr-30 Sep. € 32.00 2014*

PONTET, LE see Avignon *10E2*

PORT LA NOUVELLE *10G1* (2km S Coastal) *42.99817, 3.04825* **Camping Côte Vermeille, Chemin des Vignes, 11210 Port-la-Nouvelle [04 68 48 05 80; fax 04 68 27 53 03; infos@camping-cote-vermeille.com; www.campings-franceloc.fr]** Fr N exit A9 junc 39 onto D6139 then D6009 twd La Palme. In 9km turn L onto D709, site in 6km. V lge, mkd pitch, pt shd; wc; chem disp; mv service pnt; el pnts (6A) €4; Indtte; shop; supmkt 3km; rest, snacks; bar; playgrnd; pool; paddling pool; waterslide; sand beach 200m; wifi; entmnt; TV; some statics; adv bkg; CKE/CCI. "Superb pool complex." ♦ 4 Apr-27 Sep. € 26.00 2009*

⊞ **PORT VENDRES** *10G1* (500m W Urban) *42.51775, 3.11314* **Aire Communale des Tamarins, Route de la Jetée, 66660 Port-Vendres [04 68 82 07 54]** Fr D914 at Port-Vendres at Banyuls side of town turn N on D86B sp Port de Commerce & Aire de Camping-Cars. Foll sp to site on R in 700m. Sm, hdstg, pt shd; chem disp; mv service pnt; wc (pt cont); own san; no el pnts (2009); gas 1km; shop 1km; rest 500m; snacks, bar 1km; playgrnd adj; shgl beach 100m; red low ssn. "NH, m'vans only; walking dist rlwy stn; poss cr even low ssn; a bit run down (Jun 2009)." € 8.50 2009*

PORTIRAGNES PLAGE *10F1* (1km N Coastal) *43.28003, 3.36396* **Camping Les Sablons, Plage-Est, 34420 Portiragnes-Plage [04 67 90 90 55; fax 04 67 90 82 91; les.sablons@wanadoo.fr; www.les-sablons.com]** Fr A9 exit Béziers Est junc 35 onto N112. Then take D37 S to Portiragnes-Plage & foll sp. V lge, mkd pitch, shd; wc; chem disp; mv service pnt; baby facs; shwrs inc; el pnts (6A) inc; gas; Indtte; shop; rest, snacks; bar; BBQ; playgrnd; 2 htd pools; waterslide; sand beach adj; diving; boating; fishing; tennis; games area; cycle hire; entmnt; 50% statics; dogs €4; phone; poss cr; Eng spkn; adv bkg; ccard acc; quiet. "Gd site on beach; modern san facs; nightly disco but quiet after midnight." ♦ ltd 1 Apr-30 Sep. € 46.00 2012*

See advertisement

PORTIRAGNES PLAGE *10F1* (2km NE Coastal) *43.29138, 3.37333* **Camping Les Mimosas, Port Cassafières, 34420 Portiragnes-Plage [04 67 90 92 92; fax 04 67 90 85 39; info@mimosas.fr or les.mimosas.portiragnes@wanadoo.fr; www.mimosas.com]** Exit A9 junc 35 Béziers Est & take N112 sp Vias, Agde. After 3km at rndabt foll sp Portiragnes & cont along side of Canal du Midi. Cross canal, site sp. Lge, mkd pitch, hdstg, pt shd; wc; chem disp; mv service pnt; private san facs avail; baby facs; sauna; shwrs inc; el pnts (6-10A) €4; gas; Indtte (inc dryer); shop; supmkt; tradsmn; rest, snacks; bar; BBQ (gas); playgrnd; pools; paddling pool; waterslides; jacuzzi; sand beach 1km; cycle hire; games area; games rm; fitness rm; internet; entmnt; 50% statics; dogs €5.50; Eng spkn; adv bkg; quiet; ccard acc; red low ssn; CKE/CCI. "Excel touring base in interesting area; friendly welcome; superb water park; 4 star site; gd for families." ♦ 26 May-5 Sep. € 42.00 2011*

See advertisement

"There aren't many sites open at this time of year"

If you're travelling outside peak season remember to call ahead to check site opening dates – even if the entry says 'open all year'.

⊞ **PRADES** *8G4* (500m N Urban) *42.62141, 2.42272* **Camp Municipal Plaine St Martin, Chemin du Gaz, 66500 Prades [04 68 96 29 83 or 06 86 38 54 17 (mob); prades.conflent@wanadoo.fr; www.leconflent.net/camping]** Site sp on ent town on N116 fr both dirs. (Or foll sp 'Piscine' - site 200m fr municipal sw pool). Med, hdg/mkd pitch, pt sl, shd; wc (some cont); chem disp; 50% serviced pitches; shwrs inc; el pnts (6-10A) €3.50; gas 500m; Indtte; shop, rest, snacks & bar 500m; playgrnd; htd, covrd pool nrby; fishing; 30% statics; dogs €1.45; phone; poss cr; adv bkg; quiet; ccard acc; CKE/CCI. "Pleasant site with many trees; lge pitches; facs old but clean; poss unkempt low ssn; excel touring base; music festival in Jul; mkt Tues; NH." € 11.50 2011*

PRADES *8G4* (10km NE Urban) *42.64269, 2.53367* **Camping Lac De Vinca (formerly Municipal Les Escoumes), Rue des Escoumes, 66320 Vinça [04 68 05 84 78 or 06 09 01 00 40 (mob); campinglesescoumes@orange.fr; www.camping-lac-de-vinca.com/EN]** Fr Perpignan take N116 W twd Andorra. 10km E of Prades in vill of Vinça take 1st L foll camp sps to site (400m). Vinca 32km W of Perpignan. Med, mkd pitch, pt sl, pt shd; wc; chem disp; mv service pnt; shwrs inc; el pnts (6-10A) €3; gas; Indtte (inc dryer); shops 1km; supmkt at Prades; rest, bar in vill; private sand beach & lake sw; fishing; wifi; cycle hire; 20% statics; dogs €3.50; poss cr; Eng spkn; quiet. "Beautiful, quiet site; helpful staff." ♦ ltd 1 Apr-31 Oct. € 20.60 2014*

PRADES *8G4* (7km E Rural) *42.61722, 2.50111* **Camping Le Canigou, 66320 Espira-de-Conflent [04 68 05 85 40; fax 04 68 05 86 20; canigou@yahoo.com; www.canigou-espira.com]** On N116 Andorra-Perpignan, 2km after Marquixanes, R at sm site sp also sp 'Espira-de-Conflent'. Or, fr Perpignan on N116, turn L 7km bef Prades onto D25 & foll sp for 3.5km. Med, hdg/mkd pitch, pl sl, terr, shd; wc; chem disp; mv service pnt; shwrs inc; el pnts (6A) inc; Indtte; shop; tradsmn; rest, snacks; bar; playgrnd; rv pool; lake & watersports 5km; 5% statics; dogs €1.50; Eng spkn; adv bkg; quiet; red long stay/low ssn; ccard acc; CKE/CCI. "Beautiful rvside site; youth groups in summer; some noise; narr site rds not rec for lge o'fits." ♦ ltd 1 Feb-31 Oct. € 24.00 2009*

PRADES *8G4* (2km SW Rural) *42.60308, 2.39841* **Camping Bellevue, 18 Rue Bellevue, 66500 Ria-Sirach [tel/fax 04 68 96 48 96; camping.bellevue@free.fr; www.camping-bellevue-riasirach.com]** W on N116 fr Perpignan, thro Prades. In 1km at far edge of vill of Ria, turn L on D26A & foll sps to site. Access steep. Med, mkd pitch, pt sl, terr, shd; wc; baby facs; shwrs inc; el pnts (3-6A) €5.90-6.80; Indtte; shop 500m; bar; playgrnd; rv sw & fishing 500m; dogs €1; adv bkg; quiet; red CKE/CCI. "Peaceful with gd views." ♦ 1 Apr-30 Sep. € 10.00 2009*

PRADES *8G4* (5km W Rural) *42.58019, 2.35057* **Camping Mas de Lastourg, Serdinya, 66500 Villefranche-de-Conflent [04 68 05 35 25; maslastourg@aol.com; www.camping-lastourg.com]** W fr Prades on N116. Site on L of main rd 2km after Villefranche, turn L 100m after start of dual c'way. Med, hdg/mkd pitch, pt shd; wc; chem disp (wc); baby facs; shwrs inc; el pnts (6-10A) €4; Indtte; sm shop & 2km; tradsmn; rest, snacks; bar; BBQ; playgrnd; sm pool; a few statics; dogs €1; phone; poss cr; Eng spkn; adv bkg; quiet but some rd/rlwy noise; ccard acc; red low ssn; CKE/CCI. "Lovely site; helpful owners; easy access; gd pitches; conv 'Little Yellow Train'; phone ahead to check open low ssn; excel." ♦ 1 Apr-30 Sep. € 19.00 2011*

PRATS DE MOLLO LA PRESTE *8H4* (11km E Rural) *42.38892, 2.60620* **Camp Municipal Verte Rive, Chemin de l'Ile, 66260 St Laurent-de-Cerdans [04 68 39 54 64 or 04 68 39 50 04 (Mairie); fax 04 68 39 59 59; contact@ville-saint-laurent-de-cerdans.fr; www.ville-saint-laurent-de-cerdans.fr]** Fr Le Boulou, take D115 twd Prats-de-Mollo, turn L on D3 twd St Laurent. Site 4km fr Spanish border. Med, mkd pitch, pt sl, pt shd; htd wc; shwrs inc; el pnts (5A) €2.75; Indtte; shop 1.5km; BBQ; playgrnd; htd pool adj; some statics; poss cr; adv bkg; CKE/CCI. "Conv NH." ♦ 1 Jun-31 Oct. € 8.00 2010*

PRATS DE MOLLO LA PRESTE *8H4* (12km E Rural) *42.41200, 2.61800* **Camping Domaine Le Clols (Naturist), 66260 St Laurent-de-Cerdans [04 68 39 51 68; info@leclols.com; www.leclols.com]** Fr A9 at Le Boulou take D115 dir Prats-de-Mollo; 6km past Arles-sur-Tech take D3 on L sp St Laurent-de-Cerdans; at La Forge-del-Mitg turn sharp L sp Le Clols; site on R in 3km (narr, winding rd). Sm, pt sl, pt shd; wc (some cont); chem disp (wc); shwrs inc; el pnts (5-10A) €3-3.95; gas; Indtte; shop; snacks; playgrnd; pool; TV; some statics; dogs €2; adv bkg; quiet; red 10+ days; CKE/CCI. "Gd views; friendly British owners; gd walks fr site." ♦ ltd 1 May-30 Sep. € 24.00 2013*

PREIXAN see Carcassonne *8F4*

PREMIAN see St Pons de Thomières *8F4*

PUIVERT *8G4* (500m S Rural) *42.91596, 2.0441* **Camping de Puivert, Fontclaire, 11230 Puivert [04 68 20 00 58 or 06 22 45 15 74 (mob); fax 04 68 20 82 29; camping-de-puivert@orange.fr]** Take D117 W fr Quillan dir Lavelanet for 16km; at Puivert turn L onto D16; site in 500m by lake; well sp. Or E fr Foix on D117 for 45km; at Puivert turn R onto D16 & as bef. Med, hdg pitch, hdstg, terr, pt shd; wc; chem disp; mv service pnt; shwrs inc; el pnts (16A) €3; Indtte; shop & 500m; rests 500m; snacks; bar; BBQ sep area; lake sw & fishing adj; entmnt; internet; dogs; quiet; red low ssn. "Attractive area; lge pitches, some lakeside, some hill views; dated san facs but adequate & clean; museum in vill; chateau nrby; vg." 24 Apr-27 Sep. € 12.00 2014*

QUILLAN *8G4* (1.4km W Urban) *42.87358, 2.17565* **FFCC Camp Municipal La Sapinette, 21 Ave René Delpech, 11500 Quillan [04 68 20 13 52; fax 04 68 20 27 80; contact@camping-la-sapinette.com; www.camping-la-sapinette.com]** Foll D118 fr Carcassonne to Quillan; turn R at 2nd traff lts in town cent; site sp in town. Med, hdg/mkd pitch, some hdstg, sl, terr, pt shd; htd wc; chem disp; mv service pnt; shwrs inc; el pnts (6A) €3.10; Indtte; shops 400m; tradsmn; playgrnd; pool; leisure cent 500m in town; wifi; TV; 25% statics in sep area; dogs €1.60; poss cr; adv bkg; quiet; ccard acc; red low ssn/CKE/CCI. "Gd touring base; sm pitches, some level; early arr rec; helpful staff; gd san facs; excel pool; site poss tired end ssn; mkt Wed & Sat; vet adj; highly rec." 1 Apr-30 Oct. € 19.00 2012*

"That's changed – Should I let The Club know?"

If you find something on site that's different from the site entry, fill in a report and let us know. See www.caravanclub.co.uk/europereport.

REMOULINS *10E2* (1.5km S Rural) *43.92655, 4.56445* **Camping Domaine de la Soubeyranne, Route de Beaucaire, 30210 Remoulins [04 66 37 03 21; fax 04 66 37 14 65; soubeyranne@franceloc.fr; www.soubeyranne.com / www.campings-franceloc.fr]** Exit A9 for Remoulins onto D986. On D6086 Remoulins to Nîmes rd turn L after x-ing bdge fr Remoulins. Site on L in 1km. Lge, hdg pitch, shd; wc; chem disp; baby facs; shwrs inc; el pnts (6A) €4.70; gas; Indtte; shop; rest, snacks; bar; BBQ; playgrnd; htd, covrd pool; paddling pool; fishing; tennis; TV rm; some statics; dogs €5; adv bkg; some rd & rlwy noise; CKE/CCI. "Gd site." 4 Apr-27 Sep. € 26.50 2009*

REMOULINS *10E2* (2km NW Rural) *43.94805, 4.54583* **Camping La Sousta, Ave du Pont de Gard, 30210 Remoulins [04 66 37 12 80; fax 04 66 37 23 69; info@lasousta.fr; www.lasousta.fr]** Fr A9 exit Remoulins, foll sp for Nîmes, then sp 'Pont du Gard par Rive Droite' thro town. Immed over rv bdge turn R sp 'Pont du Gard etc'; site on R 800m fr Pont du Gard. Lge, mkd pitch, hdstg,pt sl, shd; wc; chem disp; mv service pnt; baby facs; shwrs inc; el pnts (6A) €3; gas; Indtte (inc dryer); shop; tradsmn; rest adj; snacks; bar; BBQ in sep area; playgrnd; pool; tennis; rv sw adj; watersports; fishing; cycle hire; wifi €4 ; entmnt; TV; 20% statics; dogs €2; poss cr; Eng spkn; adv bkg; quiet; ccard acc; red low ssn; CKE/CCI. "Friendly, helpful staff; poss diff lge o'fits due trees; excel touring base; in walking dist Pont-du-Gard; set in lovely woodland with plenty of shd; vg; can be dry & dusty in Jul & Aug; bar & rest open in ls; sw pool clsd until 5th May." ♦ 1 Mar-31 Oct. € 37.00 2014*

REMOULINS *10E2* (4km NW Rural) *43.95594, 4.51588* **Camping International Les Gorges du Gardon, Chemin de la Barque Vieille, Route d'Uzès, 30210 Vers-Pont-du-Gard [04 66 22 81 81; fax 04 66 22 90 12; camping.international@wanadoo.fr; www.le-camping-international.com]** Exit A9 junc 23 Remoulins & head NW twd Uzès on D981. Pass turn for Pont-du-Gard & site on L in 1.5km. Or fr E on N100 turn N onto D6086 then D19A to Pont-du-Gard (avoiding Remoulins cent). Lge, hdg/mkd pitch, pt shd; wc; chem disp; mv service pnt; baby facs; shwrs inc; el pnts (6A) inc; gas; lndtte; shop; tradsmn; rest, snacks; bar; playgrnd; htd pool; rv sw & private beach adj; boating; fishing; tennis; games area; games rm; entmnt; internet; TV rm; 10% statics; dogs €2; no twin-axles or o'fits over 5m; Eng spkn; adv bkg; quiet; ccard acc; red low ssn/long stay; CKE/CCI. "Beautiful location; many sm pitches - some lge pitches to back of site; friendly, cheerful owners; excel san facs, ltd low ssn; beavers in rv; site poss subject to flooding & evacuation; superb; conv for the Pont du Gard, thoroughly rec staying several nights, unique site." ♦ 15 Mar-30 Sep. € 29.00 2014*

REMOULINS *10E2* (7km NW Rural) *43.95788, 4.48716* **Camping Le Barralet, 30210 Collias [04 66 22 84 52 or 06 11 56 01 21 (mob); fax 04 66 22 89 17; camping@barralet.fr; www.camping-barralet.com]** W off A9 on D981 to Uzès; thro Remoulins; foll camp sp; turn S on D112 D3 to Collias; sp in 4km on L past quarry on bend; turn L up narr rd & site in 50m on R. Med, pt shd; wc; shwrs inc; el pnts €4 (adaptors avail); lndtte; shop; rest, snacks; bar; pool; playgrnd; fishing & canoe/kayak hire adj; tennis nr; games area; 30% statics; dogs €2; phone; quiet; ccard acc; CKE/CCI. "Gd location; gd rvside walks & cycling; sm pitches; poss lge youth groups use activity cent." ♦ 1 Apr-20 Sep. € 19.00 2010*

> "I like to fill in the reports as I travel from site to site"
>
> You'll find report forms at the back of this guide, or you can fill them in online at www.caravaclub.co.uk/europereport.

ROQUEBRUN *10F1* (300m SE Rural) *43.49775, 3.02834* **Camping Campotel Le Nice de Roquebrun, Rue du Temps Libre, 34460 Roquebrun [04 67 89 61 99 or 04 67 89 79 97; fax 04 67 89 78 15; camping-campotel@wanadoo.fr; www.camping-lenice.com]** N112 to St Chinian & take D20 dir Cessenon-sur-Orb, turn L onto D14 twd Roquebrun; site on L bef bdge over rv. Narr app rd. Sm, mkd pitch, some hdstg, pt sl, terr, pt shd; wc (some cont); chem disp; mv service pnt; shwrs inc; el pnts (6A) €2.50; lndtte; shops, rest, snacks, bar 1km; playgrnd; rv sw & shgl beach adj; rv sw, fishing, sailing, canoe hire adj; tennis; entmnt; 15% statics; dogs €1.30; phone; poss cr; adv bkg; quiet; ccard acc; CKE/CCI. "Excel cent for walking & cycling; beautiful scenery; ltd touring pitches; some gd, modern san facs; not suitable for lge o'fits; need key for WC block; off clsd Sundays low ssn." 15 Mar-15 Nov. € 14.00 2012*

ROZIER, LE see Peyreleau *10E1*

ST ALBAN SUR LIMAGNOLE see St Chély d'Apcher *9D1*

ST AMBROIX *9D2* (3km S Rural) *44.23748, 4.20163* **Camping Beau Rivage, Route de Uzès, Le Moulinet, 30500 St Ambroix [04 66 24 10 17; marc@camping-beau-rivage.fr; www.camping-beau-rivage.fr]** N on D904, after Les Mages in 5km. Camping sp on R. Foll sp approx 2-3km. Site off D37 twd Le Moulinet. Med, hdg/mkd pitch, pt sl, terr, pt sl, shd; wc (some cont); chem disp; shwrs inc; el pnts (6A); €3.50; gas; lndtte; shop 1km; tradsmn; rest, snacks 2km; bar 1km; playgrnd; pool; paddling pool; canoeing; wifi; no statics; dogs; poss cr; adv bkg; quiet; red low ssn; CKE/CCI. "Lovely location." ♦ ltd 1 May-1 Sep. € 20.00 2009*

ST AMBROIX *9D2* (200m W Rural) *44.26234, 4.19598* **Camping Le Clos, Place de l'Eglise, 30500 St Ambroix [04 66 24 10 08 or 06 07 54 57 66 (mob); fax 04 66 60 25 62; campingleclos@wanadoo.fr; www.camping-le-clos.fr]** Fr S on D904, in St Amboix turn L immed bef church. Site in 300m. Foll intn'l camping sp. Sm, mkd pitch, pt shd; wc; chem disp; shwrs inc; el pnts (3-10A) €2.70-5; lndtte; snacks; bar; playgrnd; pool; paddling pool; fishing; sailing; cycle hire; TV rm; 20% statics; dogs €2; adv bkg; quiet; red low ssn. "Well-kept san facs; access poss diff for lge o'fits." ♦ 1 Apr-31 Oct. € 17.50 2010*

ST CHELY D'APCHER *9D1* (8km E Rural) *44.77506, 3.37203* **FFCC Camping Le Galier, Route de St Chély, 48120 St Alban-sur-Limagnole [04 66 31 58 80; fax 04 66 31 41 83; accueil@campinglegalier.fr; www.campinglegalier.fr]** Exit A75 junc 34 onto D806, then E on D987 for 3km. Site 1.5km SW of St Alban on rvside. Sm, mkd pitch, pt sl; htd wc (some cont); chem disp; shwrs inc; el pnts (6A) €3.70; lndtte; shop 1.5km; snacks; bar; BBQ; playgrnd; pool; paddling pool; games rm; tennis 800m; wifi; some statics; dogs €1.60; poss cr; Eng spk; adv bkg; quiet; red low ssn/CKE/CCI. "Lovely setting by rv; friendly owners; clean san facs - stretched high ssn, ltd low ssn; gd walking, fishing; vg NH." ♦ 1 Mar-15 Oct. € 14.50 (3 persons) 2010*

ST CHINIAN *10F1* (2.4km W Rural) *43.42082, 2.93395* **Camp Municipal Les Terrasses, Route de St Pons, 34360 St Chinian [04 67 38 28 28 (Mairie); fax 04 67 38 28 29; mairie@saintchinian.fr]** On main Béziers-St Pons rd, D612, heading W on o'skts of St Chinian. Site on L. Med, terr, unshd; wc; shwrs inc; el pnts €2.15; shops 1km; poss cr; quiet. "Attractive site with gd views; sm pitches; diff access some pitches." 7 Jul-31 Aug. € 7.50 2009*

ST CYPRIEN PLAGE *10G1* (1.5km SW Urban/Coastal) *42.61851, 3.01582* **Chadotel Camping Le Roussillon, Chemin de la Mer, 66750 St Cyprien [04 68 21 06 45 or 02 51 33 05 05 (LS); fax 02 51 33 94 04; chadotel@wanadoo.fr; www.chadotel.com]** Exit A9 junc 42 Perpignan Sud onto D914 to Elne, D40 to St Cyprien. Site sp. Lge, hdg/mkd pitch, unshd; htd wc; baby facs; shwrs inc; el pnts (6A) inc; gas; lndtte; shop; snacks; bar; BBQ (gas); playgrnd; htd pool; waterslide; sand beach 1km; cycle hire; games rm; TV rm; entmnt; bus to beach; dogs €3; Eng spkn; adv bkg; red long stay/low ssn; ccard acc. "Vg family site; gd touring base." ♦ 7 Apr-22 Sep. € 32.50 2011*

ST CYPRIEN PLAGE *10G1* (3km W Rural) *42.62360, 3.00094* **Camp Municipal Bosc d'en Roug, 66750 St Cyprien [04 68 21 07 95; fax 04 68 21 55 43; www.camping-saint-cyprien.com]** Exit A9 junc 42 & foll sp Argelès-sur-Mer on D914. Turn off onto D40 dir Elne & foll sp St Cyprien. Site sp. V lge, mkd pitch, pt shd; wc; chem disp (wc only); mv waste; shwrs inc; (10A) inc; gas; lndtte; shop; rest, snacks; bar; playgrnd; htd pool; sand beach 3km; entmnt; 50% statics; dogs €2; phone; poss cr; Eng spkn; adv bkg; quiet; red low ssn. "Gd shady site in pleasant location on edge well-kept vill; helpful, friendly staff; gd rest & entmnt; no twin-axles." ♦ 9 Apr-17 Sep. € 25.00 2011*

STE ENIMIE *9D1* (6km E Rural) *44.33777, 3.47583* **Camping Del Ron, 48320 Blajoux [tel/fax 04 66 48 54 71; camping.delron@orange.fr; www.campingdelron.com]** E fr Ste Enimie on D907b dir Ispagnac, site on R by Rv Tarn after Prades. Med, hdg pitch, terr, pt shd; wc; shwrs inc; el pnts €3.80; lndtte; shop 300m; rest, snacks; bar; BBQ; playgrnd; htd pool; games area; rv sw & beach adj; fishing; canoe hire; wifi; 10% statics; dogs €0.60; adv bkg; quiet. "In Tarn Gorge with magnificent views; peaceful, espec low ssn; friendly owners; vg." ♦ 1 May-30 Sep. € 17.00 2009*

STE ENIMIE *9D1* (1.5km SW Rural) *44.35378, 3.40155* **Camp Couderc, Route de Millau, 48210 Ste Enimie [04 66 48 50 53; fax 04 66 48 58 59; campingcouderc@orange.fr; www.campingcouderc.fr]** Leave Ste Eminie on D907B in dir Millau, site on L bank of Rv Tarn. Med, mkd pitch, pt sl, terr, pt shd; wc; chem disp; mv service pnt; baby facs; shwrs inc; el pnts (6A) €3; gas; shop; snacks; bar; playgrnd; pool; canoeing; dogs free; Eng spkn; quiet; red low ssn; CKE/CCI. "Rd along gorge narr & twisting; busy, friendly, lovely site; gd modern facs." ♦ 1 Apr-30 Sep. € 18.00 2009*

ST GEORGES DE LEVEJAC see Vignes, Les *9D1*

ST GILLES *10E2* (300m SW Urban) *43.67569, 4.42946* **Camping de la Chicanette, Rue de la Chicanette, 30800 St Gilles [04 66 87 28 32; fax 04 66 87 49 85; camping.la.chicanette@libertysurf.fr; www.campinglachicanette.fr]** Site on D6572 W fr Arles, sp in cent of town, behind Auberge de la Chicanette. Narr app rd, tight turn to ent. Med, hdg pitch, pt shd; wc; chem disp; shwrs inc; el pnts (6A) €3 (rev pol); lndtte; shop adj; snacks; bar; playgrnd; pool; entmnt; 20% statics; dogs €2; poss cr; quiet; red low ssn; CKE/CCI. "Useful site; sm pitches; facs poss stretched high ssn; site poss unkempt low ssn; interesting old town; bus to Nîmes; mkt Sun." 1 Apr-30 Oct. € 20.00 2011*

ST JEAN DE CEYRARGUES see Alès *10E1*

ST JEAN DU GARD *10E1* (1.3km N Rural) *44.11346, 3.89208* **Camping Les Sources, Route du Mialet, 30270 St Jean-du-Gard [04 66 85 38 03; fax 04 66 85 16 09; camping-des-sources@wanadoo.fr; www.camping-des-sources.fr]** Fr Alès take D907 twd Anduze & St Jean-du-Gard. At St Jean turn R at traff lts on D983 (dir Florac), then R on D160 & foll camp sp. NB: Do not enter town cent when towing - narr rds. Med, hdg pitch, terr, shd; htd wc (some cont); chem disp; shwrs inc; el pnts (6A) inc; gas; shop; tradsmn; snacks; bar; playgrnd; pool; dogs €2.50; Eng spkn; adv bkg ess Jul/Aug; quiet. "Lovely, well laid-out site; pitches sm, not rec for lge o'fits; friendly, helpful family owners; modern san facs, ltd low ssn; conv National Park of Cévennes." ♦ 1 Apr-30 Sep. € 24.00 2010*

ST JEAN DU GARD *10E1* (3.6km W Rural) *44.11250, 3.85320* **Camping Mas de La Cam, Route de St André-de-Valborgne, 30270 St Jean-du-Gard [04 66 85 12 02; fax 04 66 75 32 07; camping@masdelacam.fr]** On S side of D 907, 1.1km W of W end of town by-pass, W of sp Camping les Baigneurs on non-Corniche rd to Florac. NB: Due to acute angle of slip rd off D907, if app fr W on D907 must go 500m past slip rd & make U-turn at layby opp D907-D9 junc. Slip rd sh but v narr; turn L after x-ing rv, L twd tennis court. Med, hdg/mkd pitch, pt sl, shd; wc; shwrs; el pnts (6A) €4.50; lndtte; rest, snacks; shops 1.3km; playgrnd; TV rm; entmnt; pool; tennis; cycle hire; quiet; red low ssn. "Excel site; friendly owners." Easter-30 Sep. € 16.00 2013*

See advertisement

ST JULIEN DE PEYROLAS see Pont St Esprit *9D2*

ST LAURENT DE CERDANS see Prats de Mollo la Preste *8H4*

ST MARCEL D'ARDECHE see Pont St Esprit *9D2*

ST MARTIN D'ARDECHE see Pont St Esprit *9D2*

ST MARTIN DE LONDRES *10E1* (2km E Rural) *43.79180, 3.73911* **FFCC Camping Le Pic St-Loup, 34380 St Martin-de-Londres [04 67 55 00 53; fax 04 67 55 00 04; depelchinp@aol.com]** Fr Ganges take D986 S. In St Martin turn L onto D122, site sp. Med, some hdg/mkd pitch, pt sl, pt shd; wc; chem disp; shwrs inc; el pnts (6A) inc; gas; Indtte; shop; rest, snacks; bar; playgrnd; htd covrd pool; 10% statics; poss cr; adv bkg; quiet but some rd noise; ccard not acc; red long stay; CKE/CCI. "Friendly, helpful owner; some pitches sm for van, awning & car; lger pitches on lower terr; dated san facs; excel pool; lower field muddy when wet." 1 Apr-30 Sep. € 20.00 2009*

ST MICHEL DE DEZE see Collet-de-Dèze, Le *9D1*

ST PAUL DE FENOUILLET *8G4* (7km E Rural) *42.80811, 2.6058* **Camping Le Maurynate, La Caunette Basse, 66460 Maury [04 68 67 11 01; lemaurynate@orange.fr; www.lemaurynate.fr]** W fr St-Paul-de-Fenouillet on D117 to Maury in 6km; cont past Maury on D117; site on L in 1km, just bef level x-ing. Sm, hdg/mkd pitch, pt shd; htd wc; chem disp; mv service pnt; baby facs; shwrs inc; el pnts (10A) €3.50; Indtte; sm shop; BBQ; playgrnd; dogs €2.00; Eng spkn; adv bkg; quiet, some rd noise; CKE/CCI. "Vg site; prehistoric history region." 1 Apr-31 Aug. € 24.70 2013*

ST PAUL DE FENOUILLET *8G4* (7km E Rural) *42.80782, 2.60579* **Camping Le Maurynate (Formerly Municipal Les Oliviers), 66460 Maury [04 68 67 11 01; fax 04 68 59 08 74; lemaurynate@orange.fr; www.lemaurynate.fr]** Heading W on D117. Site immed after level x-ing on R 500m bef Maury. Sm, mkd pitch, shd; wc (cont); shwrs inc; el pnts; shop, rest, bar 1km; playgrnd; CKE/CCI. "Some rd noise fr level x-ing; immac san facs." 1 Apr-30 Aug. € 16.50 2012*

⊞ **ST PAUL DE FENOUILLET** *8G4* (400m S Rural) *42.80762, 2.50235* **Camping de l'Agly, Ave 16 Août 1944, 66220 St Paul-de-Fenouillet [04 68 59 09 09; fax 04 68 59 11 04; contact@camping-agly.com; www.camping-agly.com]** Heading W on D117; turn L at traff lts in St Paul; site on R in 200m, well sp. Sm, hdg/mkd pitch, pt sl, pt shd; wc; chem disp; shwrs inc; el pnts (16A) €4.35; gas & supmkt 500m; pool 1km; rv sw 500m; quiet; red low ssn; site clsd Jan; dogs; CKE/CCI. "Vg site; friendly warden; mountain scenery; gd climbing & cycling; conv for Château's Payrepertuse & Quéribus." ♦ € 15.00 2014*

ST PONS DE THOMIERES *8F4* (8km NE Rural) *43.52181, 2.83027* **Camp Municipal Les Terrasses du Jaur, Chemin de Notre Dame, 34390 Prémian [04 67 97 27 85 or 04 67 97 06 40 (Mairie); mairie-de-premian@orange.fr; http://camping-premian.fr]** Go E on D908 fr St Pons-de-Thomières twd Olargues for 8km. Imposs to turn R over rv to site, cont on D908, turn round & app fr E, turn L into site. Sm, hdg pitch, pt sl, terr, pt shd; wc; chem disp; shwrs inc; el pnts (10A) €1.80; Indtte; shop; BBQ; fishing 100m; quiet; 30% statics; adv bkg; CKE/CCI. "Gd, scenic site; clean san facs; poss pitching all year with ltd facs; cycle path nr; town rather run down." 26 May-15 Oct. € 8.50 2009*

> "I need an on-site restaurant"
>
> We do our best to make sure site information is correct, but it is always best to check any must-have facilities are still available or will be open during your visit.

ST PONS DE THOMIERES *8F4* (2km E Rural) *43.49055, 2.78527* **Camping Village Les Cerisiers du Jaur, Les Marbrières-du-Jaur, Route de Bédarieux, 34220 St Pons-de-Thomières [04 67 95 30 33; fax 04 67 28 09 96; info@cerisierdujaur.com; www.cerisierdujaur.com]** Fr Castres on D612 to St Pons; go thro town cent under rlwy bdge; turn L onto D908 sp Olargues. Site on R in 500m. Med, hdg/mkd pitch, terr, pt shd; wc; chem disp; mv service pnt; baby facs; shwrs inc; el pnts (10A) €4; Indtte; ltd shop; tradsmn; rest 1km; snacks; BBQ; playgrnd; pool; cycle hire; games area; wifi; dogs €1.50; phone; poss cr; Eng spkn; quiet; ccard acc; red low ssn; CKE/CCI. "Excel site nr Rv Jaur; welcoming, friendly, helpful owner; vg san facs; cycle rte fr site; an oasis!; hot water not v hot; expensive in LS." ♦ 29 Mar-26 Oct. € 24.00 2013*

ST QUENTIN LA POTERIE see Uzès *10E2*

ST ROME DE DOLAN see Severac le Château *9D1*

ST THIBERY see Pézenas *10F1*

SALLELES D'AUDE see Narbonne *10F1*

SALLES D'AUDE see Narbonne *10F1*

⊞ **SALSES LE CHATEAU** *10G1* (1km N Rural) *42.84420, 2.92778* **FFCC Camp International du Roussillon, 66600 Salses-le-Château [04 68 38 60 72; fax 04 68 52 75 46; camping-roussillon@orange.fr; www.camping-roussillon.com]** Fr N on A9 exit junc 40 on D6009/D900 dir Perpignan; site on R, N of town. Fr S exit A9 junc 41. Site has hotel, rest & camping. Med, hdg pitch, hdstg, pt shd; wc; chem disp; shwrs inc; el pnts (5-6A) €3 (poss rev pol); gas; Indtte; shops 2km; tradsmn; rest, snacks; pizza adj low ssn; bar; BBQ (no elec); playgrnd; pool; 40% statics; dogs €3; phone; Eng spkn; adv bkg; some rd & rlwy noise; red long stay; ccard acc; CKE/CCI. "Helpful, friendly owners; red facs low ssn & poss unkempt pitches; gd access for lge m'vans; mosquitoes; popular NH." ♦ ltd € 22.00 2009*

LANGUEDOC-ROUSSILLON

SALVETAT SUR AGOUT, LA *8F4* (4km N Rural) *43.62739, 2.67919* **Camping Goudal, Route de Lacaune, La Gâche, 34330 La Salvetat-sur-Agout [04 67 97 60 44; fax 04 67 97 62 68; info@goudal.com; www.goudal.com]** Fr St Pons-de-Thomières take D907 N dir Lacaune. Go thro La Salvetat, site sp. Med, mkd pitch, pt sl, terr, pt shd; wc; chem disp; mv service pnt; baby facs; shwrs inc; el pnts (4-6A) €4; gas; Indtte; shop; rest high ssn; BBQ; playgrnd; entmnt; some statics; dogs €2; poss cr; Eng spkn; adv bkg; quiet; CKE/CCI. "Friendly Dutch owners; spacious site in woodland; vg." 1 May-30 Sep. € 17.35 2009*

SALVETAT SUR AGOUT, LA *8F4* (10km E Rural) *43.60653, 2.77940* **Camping Le Pioch, 34330 Fraisse-sur-Agout [04 67 97 61 72; www.lepioch.com]** Fr Salvetat take D14 E twd Fraisse-sur-Agout. In 6km look for sp on L (2km bef Fraise). Site is up narr, steep rd but with passing places. Med, pt sl, pt shd; wc; shwrs inc; el pnts (6A) €2.50; gas; Indtte; shop; tradsmn; rest, snacks; bar; BBQ; playgrnd; dogs €1.50; Eng spkn; adv bkg; quiet; CKE/CCI. "Excel walking area; views fr site." 1 May-30 Sep. € 12.50 2009*

SAUVIAN see Valras Plage *10F1*

SERIGNAN PLAGE *10F1* (500m W Coastal) *43.26715, 3.33051* **Camping Village Domaine de Beauséjour, La Maïre, 34410 Sérignan-Plage [04 67 39 50 93; fax 04 67 32 01 96; info@camping-beausejour.com; www.camping-beausejour.com]** Fr A9/E15, exit Béziers Est junc 35 onto D64 S. In 4km turn L onto D37E to Sérignan-Plage. Site on R just bef shops. Lge, hdg/mkd pitch, pt shd; wc; chem disp; mv service pnt; shwrs inc; el pnts (10A) inc; gas; Indtte (inc dryer); shop; tradsmn; hypmkt nr; rest, snacks; bar; BBQ; playgrnd; htd pool; paddling pool; waterslide; sand beach adj; games rm; entmnt; TV; 50% statics; dogs €3.50; poss cr; Eng spkn; adv bkg; quiet; ccard acc; red long stay/low ssn; CKE/CCI. "Vg site; excel beach; excel facs; weekly mkts in vill." ♦ 1 Apr-30 Sep. € 42.00 2010*

SERIGNAN PLAGE *10F1* (1km W Coastal) *43.26398, 3.3210* **Yelloh! Village Le Sérignan Plage, Les Orpelières, 34410 Sérignan-Plage [04 67 32 35 33; fax 04 67 32 26 36; info@leserignanplage.com; www.leserignanplage.com / www.yellohvillage.co.uk]** Exit A9 junc 35. After toll turn L at traff lts onto N112 & at 1st rndabt strt on to D64. In 5km turn L onto D37E Sérignan-Plage, turn R on narr 1-way rd to site. Adj to Camping Sérignan-Plage Nature (Naturist site). V lge, hdg/mkd pitch, pt shd; wc (some cont); chem disp; mv service pnt; baby facs; shwrs inc; el pnts (5A) inc; gas; Indtte (inc dryer); shop; hypmkt 6km; rest, snacks; bar; BBQ; playgrnd; 2 pools (1 htd, covrd); paddling pool; Club Nautique - sw, sailing & water-ski tuition on private beach; tennis; horseriding; wifi; entmnt; TV; many statics; dogs €4; use of naturist private beach & facs adj; poss v cr; Eng spkn; adv bkg; poss noisy; red low ssn; no ccard acc; CKE/CCI. "Busy, even low ssn: excel pool; some tourers amongst statics & sm sep touring area." 21 Apr-2 Oct. € 48.00 2010*

SERIGNAN PLAGE *10F1* (1.6km W Coastal) *43.26308, 3.31976* **Camping Le Sérignan-Plage Nature (Naturist), Les Orpelière, 34410 Sérignan-Plage [04 67 32 09 61; fax 04 67 32 26 36; info@leserignannature.com; www.leserignannature.com]** Exit A9 junc 36 Beziers Est onto D64. At Sérignan town turn L on D37E to Sérignan-Plage. After 4km turn R on single-lane dual c'way. At T-junc turn L & immed L again in 50m to site. Lge, mkd pitch, pt shd; wc (some cont); chem disp; mv service pnt; baby facs; shwrs inc; el pnts (5A) inc (poss rev pol); gas; Indtte (with dryer); shop; rest, snacks; bar; BBQ; playgrnd; pool complex; sand beach; golf 15km; beauty cent; cycle hire; wifi; TV rm; 75% statics; dogs €4; poss cr; Eng spkn; adv bkg rec; quiet, but some noise fr disco (quiet by 2330); red long stay/low ssn; CKE/CCI. "Lovely, clean site & facs; helpful staff; Cmp Le Sérignan Plage (non-naturist) adj with use of same private beach & facs; pool also shared - for naturists' use 1000-1200 only; cycle rtes adj; excel." 21 Apr-2 Oct. € 47.00 2010*

SERIGNAN PLAGE *10F1* (5km W Rural) *43.26965, 3.28631* **FFCC Camping Le Paradis, Route de Valras-Plage, 34410 Sérignan [tel/fax 04 67 32 24 03; www.camping-leparadis.com]** Exit A9 junc 35 Béziers Est onto D64 dir Valras-Plage. Site on L on rndabt at S end of Sérignan by-pass, 1.5km S of Sérignan. Med, mkd pitch, pt shd; wc; chem disp; shwrs; el pnts (6A) inc; gas; Indtte; shop; supmkt opp; rest, snacks & bar high ssn; snacks; playgrnd; pool (high ssn); sand beach 2km; no dogs; poss cr; Eng spkn; adv bkg rec; quiet except for twice weekly disco (high ssn only) to 0030 & some rd noise; red low ssn/CKE/CCI. "Excel, well-kept, family-run site; immac san facs; nr gd beaches; vg value low ssn; el pnts poss no earth." ♦ 1 Apr-30 Sep. € 33.50 2012*

See advert on next page

SETE *10F1* (11km SW Coastal) *43.34194, 3.58440* **Camping Le Castellas, Cours Gambetta, 34200 Sète [04 67 51 63 00; fax 04 67 51 63 01; www.le-castellas.com www.village-center.com]** On D612/N112 bet Agde and Sète. Foll sp for 'Plages-Agde'. Lge, hdg pitch, pt shd; wc; chem disp; shwrs inc; el pnts (6A) inc; gas; Indtte; shop; rest, snacks; bar; playgrnd; 2 htd pools; sand beach 150m (across busy rd); tennis; games area; cycle hire; entmnt; dogs €3; poss cr; Eng spkn; adv bkg; rd & rlwy noise; red low ssn/long stay; CKE/CCI. "Bull-fighting in ssn; superb beach; twin-axles welcome." ♦ 06 Apr -29 Sep. € 59.00 (CChq acc) 2013*

SEVERAC LE CHATEAU *9D1* (15km SE Rural) *44.27302, 3.21538* **Camp Municipal, 48500 St Rome-de-Dolan [tel/fax 04 66 44 03 81 or 04 66 48 83 59; mairie-stromededolan@wanadoo.fr; www.saint-rome-de-dolan.com]** Exit A75 junc 42 to Sévérac, then take D995 fr Séverac-le-Château then E thro Le Massegros to St Rome-de-Dolan. Site on R at ent to vill, sp. NB Rec not to use GPS. Sm, pt sl, pt terr, pt shd; wc; chem disp; shwrs inc; el pnts (6A) €2.20; Indtte; shop 5km; tradsmn; rest, snacks, bar 5km; BBQ; playgrnd; rv sw 5km; dogs €0.80; phone 50m; Eng spkn; adv bkg; quiet; CKE/CCI. "Simple, well-kept, well-run site in beautiful location nr Gorges du Tarn; fantastic views some pitches; friendly, helpful warden; clean san facs; some pitches sm & need mover; bird watching, inc vultures; walking; highly rec." ♦ 1 May-30 Sep. € 12.00 2011*

⊞ **SIGEAN** *10G1* (5km N Rural) *43.06633, 2.94100* **Camping La Grange Neuve, 17 La Grange Neuve Nord, 11130 Sigean [tel/fax 04 68 48 58 70; info@camping-sigean.com; www.camping-sigean.com]** Exit junc 39 fr A9; pass over A9 (fr N) then 1st R sp La Réserve Africaine. Do not go into Sigean. Med, hdg/mkd pitch, hdstg, pt sl, terr, pt shd; wc; chem disp; mv service pnt; shwrs inc; el pnts (6A) €4; Indtte; shop; rest; snacks, bar; playgrnd; pool; waterslide; sand beach 5km; wifi; TV rm; 5% statics; dogs €3; poss cr; adv bkg; quiet but some rd noise; red low ssn; CKE/CCI. "Easy access; gd san facs; excel pool; ltd facs low ssn; phone ahead to check open low ssn; gd NH." ♦ € 18.00 2011*

SIGEAN *10G1* (8km SE Rural) *42.95800, 2.99586* **Camping Le Clapotis (Naturist), 11480 La Palme [04 68 48 15 40; info@leclapotis.com; www.leclapotis.com]** On D6009 S fr Narbonne turn L 8km S of Sigean. After 350m turn R at camping sp. Site in 150m. Final app rd narr but negotiable for lge vans. Lge, mkd pitch, pt shd; wc (cont); shwrs inc; el pnts (4A) €4; gas; rest & bar in ssn; pool; sm lake beach; tennis; games area; internet; many statics; dogs €2; poss cr; Eng spkn; adv bkg; quiet; red low ssn; Naturists INF card req; ccard acc; red low ssn. "Pleasant, basic, friendly site; sm pitches; helpful owners; san facs dated but clean; gd pool; poss strong winds - gd windsurfing; La Palme vill 15 mins walk." 15 Mar-15 Oct. € 22.00 (CChq acc) 2009*

SOMMIERES *10E1* (2km SE Rural) *43.77550, 4.09280* **Camping Domaine de Massereau, 1990 Route d'Aubais, 30250 Sommières [04 66 53 11 20 or 06 03 31 27 21 (mob); fax 04 11 71 50 20; camping@massereau.com; www.massereau.com]** Exit A9 junc 26 at Gallargues, foll sp Sommières; site sp on D12. NB Danger of grounding at ent fr D12. Use this rte 24/7 - 03/08 (due to festival in Sommières). Otherwise exit A9 junc 27 onto D34 to Sommières, foll sps to "Centre Historique" dir Aubias; cross bdge (sharp turn) & turn R onto D12; site on L in 3km. Med, hdg/mkd pitch; pt sl, pt shd; wc (some cont); chem disp; mv service pnt; baby facs; serviced pitch; sauna; jaccuzi; shwrs inc; el pnts (16A) inc; gas; Indtte; shop; tradsmn; rest, snacks; bar; BBQ (gas); playgrnd; pool; waterslide; paddling pool; rv sw 500m; horseriding & canoeing nrby; tennis; cycle hire; running track; trampoline; games area; games rm; wifi; entmnt; TV; 50% statics; dogs €3.90; no c'vans/m'vans over 7m high ssn; phone; poss cr; Eng spkn; adv bkg; quiet; ccard acc; red low ssn; CKE/CCI. "Lovely, tranquil, well-run site adj vineyard; lge pitches, some uneven; pleasant, cheerful staff; modern san facs; narr site rds, sl/uneven pitches & trees diff lge o'fits; tight ents, diff without mover; excel; pool not htd." ♦ 12 Apr-1 Nov. € 63.00 SBS - C33 2014*

See advert below

SOMMIERES *10E1* (6km SE Urban) *43.77052, 4.12592* **Camping L'Olivier, 112 Route de Congénies Junas, 30250 Sommieres [04 66 80 39 52 or 04 66 80 98 05; www.campinglolivier.fr]** Fr Nîmes, take D40 twd Sommieres. At Congenies take D140 L to Junas, site sp in vill. Sm, pt sl, pt shd; wc; chem disp; shwrs inc; shops 500m; el pnts (6A) €5, poss inc on certain pitches; snack; pool; ; games area; fishing; tennis; dog €3; ping pong; mini golf; tennis; trampoline; wifi; quiet; adv bkg; "Entmnt Thur eve; excel home made pizzas; v friendly, helpful owners." 29 Mar-19 Oct. € 16.00 2013*

SOMMIERES *10E1* (500m NW Urban) *43.78672, 4.08702* **Camp Municipal Le Garanel, 110 Rue Eugène Rouché, 30250 Sommières [tel/fax 04 66 80 33 49; campingmunicipal.sommieres@wanadoo.fr; www.sommieres.fr]** Fr S on A9 exit junc 27 N & foll D34 then take D610 twd Sommières. By-pass town on D610, over rv bdge; turn R for D40, Rue Condamine. After L turn for Nîmes pull out to make sharp R turn sp 'Camping Arena' (easy to miss this R turn). At T-junc turn R, site thro car park. Fr N on D610 turn L at 4th junc sp 'Ville Vieille' & site adj rv. Site sp fr D610 fr N. NB Narr streets nr site. Sm, hdg/mkd pitch, pt shd; htd wc (some cont); chem disp; mv service pnt; shwrs inc; el pnts (10A) inc; Indtte; shops, rest, snacks 300m; tradsmn; bar 200m; BBQ; pool; beach 25km; tennis adj; dogs €2; bus 500m; twin-axle restrictions; poss cr; Eng spkn; adv bkg; quiet but noise fr vill car park; CKE/CCI. "Well-kept site in great location nr medieval town cent; some open views; friendly, helpful warden; well-kept, dated facs; nice sm pool; poss some workers' statics low ssn; rv walks; Voie Verte cycle rte; interesting town & area; site subject to flooding at any time; mkt Sat." 1 Apr-30 Sep. € 15.65 2014*

SOREDE see Argelès sur Mer *10G1*

SOUBES see Lodève *10E1*

TAUTAVEL see Estagel *8G4*

TORREILLES PLAGE *10G1* (850m N Coastal) *42.76750, 3.02972* **Camping Sunêlia Les Tropiques, Blvd de la Méditerranée, 66440 Torreilles-Plage [04 68 28 05 09; fax 04 68 28 48 90; contact@campinglestropiques.com; www.campinglestropiques.com]** Exit A9 junc 41 onto D83 E dir Le Barcarès, then D81 dir Canet-Plage. At 1st rndabt turn L onto D11 sp Torreilles-Plage, site sp. Lge, hdg/mkd pitch, shd; wc; chem disp; mv service pnt; baby facs; shwrs inc; el pnts (6A) inc; gas; Indtte; shops; rest, snacks; bar; 2 playgrnds; 2 pools; paddling pool; waterslide; sand beach 400m; tennis; cycle hire; games area; gym; internet; entmnt; TV rm; 80% statics; dogs €4; poss cr; Eng spkn; ccard acc; red low ssn/long stay/CKE/CCI. "Vg family site; excel leisure & san facs." ♦ 9 Apr-1 Oct. € 48.50 2011*

TORREILLES PLAGE *10G1* (1km N Coastal) *42.76760, 3.02820* **Camping Le Calypso, Blvd de la Plage, 66440 Torreilles-Plage [04 68 28 09 47; fax 04 68 28 24 76; info@camping-calypso.com; www.camping-calypso.com]** Take D617 fr Perpignan sp Canet-Plage & D81 to St Laurent. 1.7km prior to St Laurent on R hand side of rd. 2nd site on L on way to beach. Lge, mkd pitch, shd; wc; chem disp; baby facs; shwrs; private san facs avail; el pnts (6A) inc; gas; Indtte; supmkt; rest, snacks; bar; playgrnd; htd pool complex; sand beach 300m; games area; games rm; cycle hire; wifi; entmnt; TV; 40% statics; dogs €4; poss cr; adv bkg rec high ssn; quiet; ccard acc. "Trips to vineyards; many activities; superb pool complex." ♦ 1 Apr-30 Sep. € 37.00 2009*

TORREILLES PLAGE *10G1* (1.4km NW Coastal) *42.76640, 3.02606* **Chadotel Camping Le Trivoly, Blvd des Plages, 66440 Torreilles-Plage [04 68 28 20 28 or 02 51 33 05 05 (LS); fax 04 68 28 16 48; chadotel@wanadoo.fr; www.chadotel.com]** Torreilles-Plage is sp fr D81, site in vill cent. Lge, hdg/mkd pitch, pt shd; wc; serviced pitches; shwrs inc; el pnts (6A) inc; gas; Indtte; shop; snacks; bar; playgrnd; htd pool; waterslide; sand beach 800m; tennis; cycle hire; watersports; games rm; wifi; TV rm; entmnt; dogs €3.20; Eng spkn; adv bkg; quiet; ccard acc; red long stay. "Gd walking in Pyrenees; vg." ♦ 7 Apr-22 Sep. € 32.50 2011*

TREBES see Carcassonne *8F4*

UZES *10E2* (800m N Rural) *44.02231, 4.42087* **Camping La Paillotte, Quartier de Grézac, 30700 Uzès [04 66 22 38 55; fax 04 66 22 26 66; campinglapaillote@orange.fr; www.lapailloteuzes.monsite-orange.fr]** Exit A9 junc 23 sp Remoulins. Fr Remoulins take D981 to Uzès. Aim for town cent 1-way ring rd. Site sp clearly. Narr rds for 800m passing cemetery. Med, hdg/mkd pitch, terr, shd; wc; shwrs inc; el pnts (10A) inc; gas; Indtte; shop; tradsmn; rest high ssn; snacks; bar; playgrnd; pool; paddling pool; cycle hire; games area; games rm; entmnt; some statics; adv bkg; quiet; CKE/CCI. "Facs clean but water temperature poss variable; nice rest." 20 Mar-30 Sep. € 35.00 2013*

UZES *10E2* (2km E Rural) *44.03202, 4.45557* **Camping Le Moulin Neuf, 30700 St Quentin-la-Poterie [04 66 22 17 21; fax 04 66 22 91 82; lemoulinneuf@yahoo.fr; www.le-moulin-neuf.fr]** N fr Uzès on D982; after 3km turn L onto D5; in 1.5km fork R, keeping on D5; in 200m turn R onto D405 (Chemin du Moulin Neuf); site on L in 500m. Med, mkd pitch, pt shd; wc; chem disp; mv service pnt; shwrs inc; el pnts (5A) €3.50; Indtte; shop on site & 2km; snacks; bar; playgrnd; htd pool; fishing; tennis; cycle hire; horseriding; 10% statics; dogs €1.50; o'night m'van area; poss cr; v quiet. "Site off beaten track; busy high ssn, rec phone in adv; conv touring base; barrier clsd 2230-0700; poss mosquito problem; Uzès a lovely town; wonderful helpful staff." ♦ 1 Apr-22 Sep. € 28.00 2014*

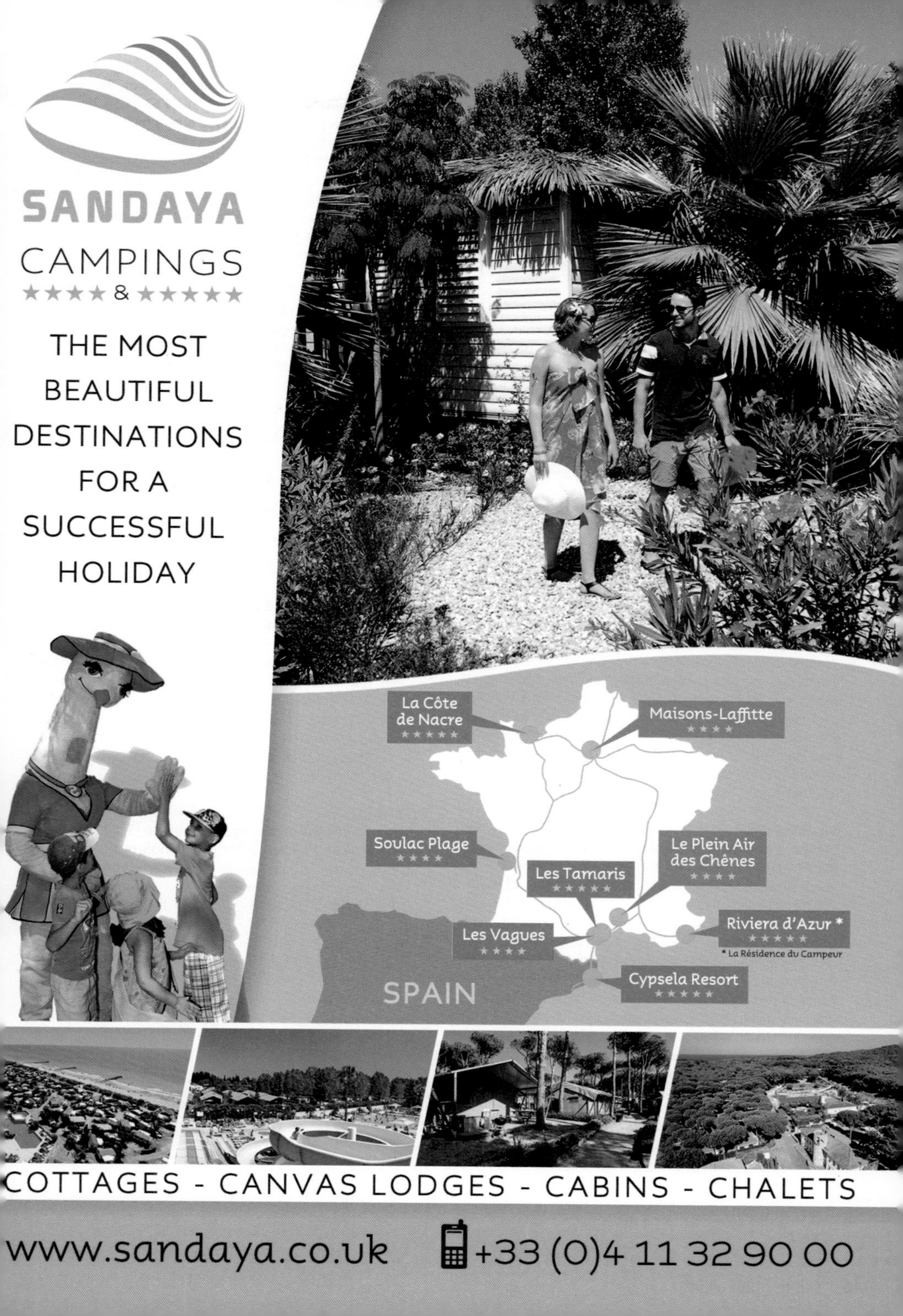
SANDAYA
CAMPINGS
★★★★ & ★★★★★
THE MOST BEAUTIFUL DESTINATIONS FOR A SUCCESSFUL HOLIDAY
La Côte de Nacre
Maisons-Laffitte
Soulac Plage
Le Plein Air des Chênes
Les Tamaris
Riviera d'Azur *
Les Vagues
* La Résidence du Campeur
Cypsela Resort
SPAIN
COTTAGES - CANVAS LODGES - CABINS - CHALETS
www.sandaya.co.uk
+33 (0)4 11 32 90 00

UZES *10E2* (3km SW Rural) *43.99843, 4.38424* **Camping Le Mas de Rey, Route d'Anduze, 30700 Arpaillargues [tel/fax 04 66 22 18 27; info@campingmasderey.com; www.campingmasderey.com]** Sp fr Uzès. Exit by D982 sp Anduze. After 2.5km cross narr bdge, turn L in 100m on site app rd. Med, hdg/mkd pitch, hdstg, pt sl, pt shd; wc; chem disp; fam bthrm; shwrs inc; el pnts (10A) €4 (rev pol); Indtte; shop on site & 3km; tradsmn; rest, snacks; bar; BBQ; playgrnd; pool; TV rm; dogs €2; phone; poss cr; Eng spkn; adv bkg; quiet; red low ssn/snr citizens; CKE/CCI. "Clean, comfortable, busy site; helpful Dutch owners; some v lge pitches; gd for sm children; excel cycling; Uzès interesting." ♦ 1 Apr-15 Oct. € 45.00 2014*

VALRAS PLAGE *10F1* (500m N Urban/Coastal) *43.25416, 3.28861* **Camping Le Levant, Ave Charles Cauquil, 34350 Valras-Plage [04 67 32 04 45; camping.dulevant@free.fr; www.campingdulevant.com]** Exit A9 junc 35 onto D64 twd Valras-Plage. At rndabt junc with D19, turn L into Ave Charles Cauquil, site sp. Med, hdg mkd pitch, pt shd; htd wc; chem disp; mv service pnt; baby facs; shwrs inc; el pnts (10A) inc; Indtte; ltd shop; tradsmn; snacks; bar; BBQ; playgrnd; htd pool; paddling pool; sand beach 800m; games area; games rm; wifi; 40% statics; dogs €4; Eng spkn; adv bkg; quiet; red low ssn; CKE/CCI. "Well-cared for, family-run site; friendly & helpul; gd san facs; vg early ssn; excel." 16 Apr-18 Sep. € 35.00 2011*

VALRAS PLAGE *10F1* (1km N Coastal) *43.25670, 3.28480* **Camping Les Sables du Midi (formerly L'Occitanie), Chemin de Querelles, 34350 Valras-Plage [04 67 32 33 86; www.siblu.fr/lessablesdumidi]** Fr A9/E15 exit junc 35 at Béziers Est & join D64 sp Valras-Plage. Site is immed on L after rndabt at ent to Valras-Plage Est. Lge, hdg/mkd pitch, hdstg, pt sl, shd; htd wc; chem disp; mv service pnt; baby facs; shwrs inc; el pnts (5A) inc (poss rev pol); Indtte; shop 1km; tradsmn; rest, snacks; bar; BBQ (gas/charcoal only); playgrnd; pool; paddling pool; waterslide; sand beach 1km; sailing; fishing; games area; wifi; entmnt; games/TV rm; 75% statics; no dogs; c'van/m'van max 7m Jul/Aug; poss cr; Eng spkn; adv bkg; quiet; ccard acc; red low ssn/long stay; CKE/CCI. "Lively town; mkt Mon & Fri am." ♦ 1 Jun-11 Sep. € 48.00 2009*

VALRAS PLAGE *10F1* (3km SW Coastal) *43.23750, 3.26166* **Camping Domaine de la Yole, 34350 Valras-Plage [04 67 37 33 87; fax 04 67 37 44 89; infocamping@layolewineresort.com; www.campinglayole.com]** Leave A9/E15 at Béziers-Ouest junc 36; foll D64 twd coast dir Valras-Plage, then Valras-Plage-Ouest & site sp. V lge, hdg/mkd pitch, hdstg, shd; wc (some cont); chem disp; mv service pnt; baby facs; shwrs inc; el pnts (4A) inc; gas; Indtte (inc dryer); supmkt; rest, snacks; bar; BBQ (charcoal/gas); playgrnd; 2 pools; paddling pool; waterslide; sand beach 400m; tennis; cycle hire; horseriding 3km; games area; games rm; wifi; entmnt; TV; tour ops statics; dogs €4.50 (not on beach); poss cr; Eng spkn; adv bkg; quiet but some rd noise; ccard acc; red low ssn; CKE/CCI. "Lovely, excel site; v busy high ssn; some gd sized pitches with plenty of shd - book ahead high ssn; gd for all age groups; mkt Mon & Fri; lge clean sw pool complex; site extremely lge; gd beach in 15 mins walk." ♦ 26 Apr-20 Sep. € 63.00 SBS - C03 2014*

VALRAS PLAGE *10F1* (3km SW Coastal) *43.23101, 3.25330* **Camping Les Vagues, Chemin des Montilles, 34350 Vendres-Plage [04 67 37 33 12; fax 04 67 37 50 36; contact@lesvagues.net; www.sandaya.fr]** Exit A9 junc 36 onto D64 to Valras-Plage then Vendres-Plage. Site sp. Lge, pt shd; wc; baby facs; shwrs inc; el pnts (10A) inc; Indtte (inc dryer); shop; rest, snacks; bar; playgrnd; htd pool complex inc wave machine; paddling pool; waterslides; jacuzzi; sand beach 400m; games area; horseriding 5km; wifi; entmnt; TV rm; 75% statics; dogs €7; adv bkg; red low ssn. "Recep helpful; clean san facs; excel." ♦ 1 Apr-30 Sep. € 51.00 2010*

VALRAS PLAGE *10F1* (3km W Coastal) *43.23502, 3.26845* **Camping La Plage et du Bord de Mer, Route de Vendres, 34350 Valras Plage [04 67 37 34 38; fax 04 67 37 33 74; contact@camping-plage-mediterranee.com; www.camping-plage-mediterranee.com]** Leave A9 at Junc 9 onto D64. Foll signs for Valras Plage Ouest. Site on R, past La Yole. Lge, mkd pitch, pt shd; wc; chem disp; mv service pnt; baby facs; fam bthrm; shwr; el pnts (6A) inc; Indtte (inc dryer); shop; rest; snack; bar; BBQ; cooking facs; playgrnd; htd pool; waterslide; paddling pool; beach adj; games area; games rm; bike hire; tennis; entmnt; wifi; 20% statics; dogs €4.50; phone; twin axles; Eng spkn; adv bkg; no ccard; CCI. "Excel site; watersports mkt Mon & Fri (am)." ♦ 28 Apr-21 Sep. € 54.00 2014*

VALRAS PLAGE *10F1* (5km NW Rural) *43.29273, 3.26710* **Camping La Gabinelle, 7 Rue de la Grille, 34410 Sauvian [04 67 39 50 87 or 04 67 32 30 79; info@lagabinelle.com; www.lagabinelle.com]** Exit A9 at Béziers Ouest, turn R twd beaches sp S to Sauvian on D19. Site 500m on L thro town. Med, pt shd; wc; chem disp; shwrs inc; el pnts (5A) €3; Indtte; shops, rest, snacks adj; bar; playgrnd; pool; sand beach 5km; fishing 1km; canoeing 2km; tennis; games area; games rm; entmnt; TV; dogs €3.50; adv bkg; quiet, but poss noise fr bar; red low ssn/long stay. "Friendly; suitable lge m'vans; low ssn ltd san facs & poss unkempt; sh walk to delightful old vill." ♦ 12 Apr-12 Sep. € 19.00 2009*

VAUVERT *10E2* (5km SE Rural) *43.65440, 4.29610* **FLOWER Camping Le Mas de Mourgues, Gallician, 30600 Vauvert [tel/fax 04 66 73 30 88; info@masdemourgues.com; www.masdemourgues.com / www.flowercampings.com]** Exit A9 junc 26 onto D6313/D6572. Site on L at x-rds with D779 sp to Gallician & Stes Marie-de-la-Mer. Med, mkd pitch, pt shd; wc; chem disp; mv service pnt; shwrs inc; el pnts (6A) inc; Indtte; shop; snacks; BBQ; pool; games area; internet; 15% statics; dogs €3; phone; Eng spkn; adv bkg; rd & farming noise; ccard acc; red low ssn; CKE/CCI. "Enthusiastic, helpful British owners; some diff, long narr pitches; grnd stony; clean facs but poss stretched high ssn; excel pool; excel cycling; vg site." ♦ 15 Mar-31 Oct. € 31.00 2013*

VEDENE see Avignon *10E2*

VERNET LES BAINS *8G4* (1km N Rural) *42.55506, 2.37756* **Camping L'Eau Vive, Chemin de St Saturnin, 66820 Vernet-les-Bains [04 68 05 54 14; fax 04 68 05 78 14; contact@leauvive-camping.com; www.leauvive-camping.com]** On app to town cent on D116 turn R over rv & site 1st R 1km at end of rd. Med, mkd pitch, terr, pt shd; wc; chem disp; serviced pitch; mv service pnt; shwrs inc; el pnts (6-10A) €3-4.50; Indtte; shop 1km; tradsmn; rest, snacks; bar; BBQ; playgrnd; pool; waterslide; tennis 500m; games area; TV rm; 40% statics; dogs €2; Eng spkn; quiet; red low ssn. "Beautiful area; friendly owners; gd walking; site rec." ♦ 29 Apr-30 Sep. € 22.00 2010*

VERNET LES BAINS *8G4* (2km N Rural) *42.56598, 2.38864* **Camping Las Closes, Route de Fillois, 66820 Corneilla-de-Conflent [04 68 05 66 48 or 06 81 85 14 46 (mob); www.las-closes.fr]** Exit N116 at Villefranche-de-Conflent onto D116 dir Vernet-Les-Bains; in 2km turn L into Corneilla-de-Conflent. Foll sp, site approx 1km. Med, mkd pitch, pt sl, terr, pt shd; wc (some cont); chem disp; shwrs inc; el pnts (10A) €3.20; Indtte; shop 500m; playgrnd; pool; wifi; dogs free; phone; adv bkg; CKE/CCI. "Beautiful views; helpful owners; interesting area." ♦ 1 Apr-30 Oct. € 11.80 2010*

"There aren't many sites open at this time of year"

If you're travelling outside peak season remember to call ahead to check site opening dates – even if the entry says 'open all year'.

VERNET LES BAINS *8G4* (3km S Rural) *42.53330, 2.39847* **Domaine-St-Martin, 6 Boulevard de la Cascade 66820 Casteil [04 68 05 52 09; info@domainestmartin.com]** Fr Prade to Villefranche on N116. Twd Vernet-les-Bains/Casteil at rndabt. Sp to campsite. Med, mkd pitch, hdstg, terr, shd; wc; chem disp; baby facs; shwrs inc; el pnts (10A); Indtte (inc dryer); shop 3km; tradsmn; rest; bar; BBQ; cooking facs; playgrnd; pool; games rm; wifi; tv rm; 20% statics; dogs; phone; bus adj, train 6km; Eng spkn; adv bkg; quiet; CCI. "Mountain hiking/biking; Grottoes 6km; Abbey in vill; friendly, helpful staff; excel rest; vg." ♦ ltd 1 Apr-31 Oct. € 35.50 2014*

VERNET LES BAINS *8G4* (3km NW Rural) *42.56255, 2.36050* **Camping Le Rotja, Ave de la Rotja, 66820 Fuilla [tel/fax 04 68 96 52 75; info@camping-lerotja.com; www.camping-lerotja.com]** Take N116 fr Prades dir Mont-Louis, 500m after Villefranche-de-Conflens turn L onto D6 sp Fuilla; in 3km just bef church, turn R at sp to site. D6 narr but passing places. Sm, mkd pitch, pt sl, terr, pt shd; htd wc; chem disp; baby facs; shwrs inc; el pnts (10A) €3.25; gas; Indtte; shop 2km; rest 100m; snacks; BBQ (gas); playgrnd; pool; rv adj; 10% statics; dogs €2; phone; Eng spkn; adv bkg; quiet; ccard acc; red long stay; CKE/CCI. "Peaceful site; views of Mount Canigou; friendly Dutch owners; gd hiking." ♦ 1 Apr-31 Oct. € 20.25 2010*

VERS PONT DU GARD see Remoulins *10E2*

VIAS *10F1* (3km S Coastal) *43.29800, 3.41750* **Camping Les Salisses, Route de la Mer, 34450 Vias-Plage [04 67 21 64 07; fax 04 67 21 76 51; info@salisses.com; www.salisses.com]** Turn S off D612 (Agde-Béziers rd) in Vias & foll sp to Vias-Plage. Cross Canal du Midi bdge & site on R. Lge, mkd pitch, pt shd; wc; chem disp; sauna; steam rm; baby facs; shwrs inc; el pnts (6A) inc; gas; Indtte (inc dryer); shop; rest, snacks; bar; BBQ; playgrnd; 3 pools (1 htd, covrd); waterslide; sand beach 1km; tennis; cycle hire; games area;; wifi; entmnt; TV rm; 80% statics; dogs €3.50; quiet; ccard acc. "Vg family hols; interesting town & mkt in Agde; sm pitches." ♦ 16 Apr-17 Sep. € 42.00 (CChq acc) 2012*

VIAS *10F1* (3km S Coastal) *43.29083, 3.41783* **Yelloh! Village Le Club Farret, Farinette-Plage, 34450 Vias-Plage [04 67 21 64 45; fax 04 67 21 70 49; farret@wanadoo.fr; www.camping-farret.com / www.yellohvillage.co.uk]** Fr A9, exit Agde junc 34. Foll sp Vias-Plage on D137. Sp fr cent of Vias-Plage on L, immed after Gendarmerie. V lge, mkd pitch, pt shd; wc; chem disp; mv service pnt; baby facs; shwrs inc; el pnts (6A) inc; gas; Indtte; shop; rest, snacks; bar; playgrnd; htd pool; sand beach adj; watersports; tennis; cycle hire; fitness rm; games area; games rm; entmnt; TV; some statics; dogs €4; Eng spkn; adv bkg; quiet; ccard acc; red low ssn; CKE/CCI. "Excel facs, entmnt; excursions; gd security." ♦ 29 Mar-29 Sep. € 52.00 2011*

VIAS *10F1* (5km SW Coastal) *43.29708, 3.42072* **Camping La Carabasse, Route de Farinette, 34450 Vias-Plage [04 67 21 64 01; fax 04 67 21 76 87; lacarabasse@siblu.fr; www.lacarabasse.fr]** Fr S on A9 exit 34 & take 1st exit onto N312 sp Vias & Agde. After 8km take RH lane twd Béziers on D612. Branch R to Vias-Plage & at rndabt foll sp for Vias-Plage on D137. Site 1km on L. V lge, hdg/mkd pitch, pt shd; htd wc; chem disp; baby facs; shwrs inc; some pitches with individual san facs; el pnts (6A) inc (poss rev pol); gas; Indtte; shop; rest, snacks; bar; BBQ; playgrnd; 2 htd pools; waterslide; sand beach 800m; tennis; watersports; golf 10km; entmnt; TV; 80% statics; no dogs; Eng spkn; adv bkg ess; quiet but poss noisy high ssn; red low ssn; CKE/CCI. "Vg local produce inc wines; organised activities; pitches poss tight med/lge o'fits due trees; many excel facs - vg for young families." ♦ 4 Apr-19 Sep. 2009*

VIAS *10F1* (5km SW Coastal) *43.29093, 3.40383* **Camping Les Flots Bleus, Côte Ouest, 34450 Vias-Plage [04 67 21 64 80; fax 04 67 01 78 12; campinglesflotsbleus@wanadoo.fr; www.camping-flotsbleus.com]** Fr D612 at Vias, take D137 sp Vias-Plage. After x-ing Canal du Midi turn R sp Côte Ouest, site sp. Lge, some hdg/mkd pitch, hdstg, pt shd; wc (some cont); chem disp; mv service pnt; baby facs; shwrs inc; el pnts (6A) inc; Indtte; shop; tradsmn; rest, snacks; bar; playgrnd; htd pool complex; waterslide; sand beach adj; games area; cycle hire; entmnt; 50% statics; dogs €3.50; adv bkg; quiet; red low ssn; CKE/CCI. "Facs clean but poss stretched high ssn; gd." 7 Apr-16 Sep. € 32.00 2009*

VIAS *10F1* (3km W Rural) *43.31222, 3.36320* **Camping Sunêlia Le Domaine de la Dragonnière, 34450 Vias [04 67 01 03 10; fax 04 67 21 73 39; contact@dragonniere.com; www.dragonniere.com]** Exit A9 junc 35 onto D64 twd Valras-Plage, then D612 dir Agde & Vias. Site on R bef Vias. Or exit junc 34 onto D612A. At Vias turn R onto D612 sp Béziers, site on L. NB Take care high speed humps at sh intervals. V lge, hdg/mkd pitch, pt shd; wc; chem disp; mv service pnt; sauna; shwrs inc; el pnts (16A) inc; gas; Indtte (inc dryer); shop; tradsmn; rest, snacks; bar; BBQ; playgrnd; htd pool complex; paddling pool; sand beach 3km (free shuttle high ssn); tennis; games area; cycle hire; wifi; entmnt; TV rm; 80% statics; dogs €5; phone; poss cr; Eng spkn; adv bkg; traff & aircraft noise; ccard acc; red low ssn; CKE/CCI. "Vg site in botanical reserve; excel for children & teenagers high ssn; Canal du Midi nrby; opp Béziers airport; site poss flooded after heavy rain; touring pitches have individual shower block on pitch (new 2014); v busy at w/ends." ♦ 4 Apr-2 Nov. € 79.40 (3 persons) 2010*

VIGAN, LE (GARD) *10E1* (2km E Rural) *43.99141, 3.63760* **Camping Le Val de l'Arre, Route du Pont de la Croix, 30120 Le Vigan [04 67 81 02 77 or 06 82 31 79 72 (mob); fax 04 67 81 71 23; valdelarre@wanadoo.fr; www.valdelarre.com]** E fr Le Vigan on D999. Turn R at 1st rndabt over bdge. Turn L immed after bdge; site in 400m, well sp. Height limit 3.5m. Med, mkd pitch, pt sl, pt shd; wc (some cont); chem disp; shwrs inc; el pnts inc (10A) €3.50 (poss rev pol); gas & 2km; Indtte; tradsmn; shop on site & 2km; rest, snacks; playgrnd; htd pool; fishing 4km; entmnt; games rm; TV; dogs €2; phone; Eng spkn; adv bkg; some rd noise; ccard acc; red low ssn; CKE/CCI. "Peaceful, well-run rvside site; friendly, helpful owners; gd touring base; rec for nature lovers." ♦ 1 Apr-30 Sep. € 18.00 2011*

See advertisement

VIGAN, LE (GARD) *10E1* (7km S Rural) *43.92896, 3.59061* **Camp Municipal, 30120 Montdardier [04 67 81 52 16 or 04 67 81 52 46 (Mairie); fax 04 67 81 53 22]** Fr D999 in Le Vigan turn S onto D48 dir Aveze to Montdardier in 5km; site on W of D48. Site sp (sm brown) in Mondardier. NB D48 narr & steep with hairpins - not rec lge o'fits. Sm, pt sl, pt shd; htd wc; shwrs; el pnts (6A) €1-1.50; shop 300m; playgrnd; dogs; poss cr; quiet; adv bkg. "Warden calls." 1 May-31 Oct. € 10.00 2009*

VIGNES, LES *9D1* (4.5km N Rural) *44.36207, 3.23135* **Aire Naturelle de Camping à la Ferme (Bonnal), Le Bouquet, 48500 St Georges-de-Lévéjac [04 66 48 81 82; campingbonnal@orange.fr; www.cardoule.com/lebouquet]** Exit A75 junc 42 onto D955 to Le Massegros; turn L onto D32 sp La Canourgue; at next x-rds turn L to Le Bouquet. Site sp at x-rds. Sm, pt sl, pt shd; wc; chem disp (wc); shwrs inc; el pnts (10A); wifi; dogs; phone; adv bkg; quiet. "Site is lge field on a farm; v peaceful, nr Gorge du Tarn; all basic facs; owners helpful." ♦ 1 May-30 Sep. 2009*

VILLARDONNEL see Carcassonne *8F4*

VILLEFORT (LOZERE) *9D1* (3.4km N Rural) *44.46133, 3.92736* **Camping du Lac, Morangiès, 48800 Pourcharesses [04 66 46 81 27 or 06 84 12 11 18 (mob); fax 04 66 69 77 49; contact@camping-lac-cevennes.com; www.camping-lac-cevennes.com]** Well sp on D906 nr Villefort dir Pourcharesses. Steep access rd. Med, hdg/mkd pitch, terr, pt shd; wc; chem disp (wc); baby facs; shwrs inc; el pnts €1.50; Indtte; tradsmn; playgrnd; pool; lake sw; some statics; dogs €1.50; poss cr; Eng spkn; adv bkg, ess high ssn. "Diff access to terr (with view) for lge o'fits, but worth effort; excel." 1 May-30 Sep. € 12.50 2009*

VILLEFORT (LOZERE) *9D1* (600m S Rural) *44.43536, 3.93323* **Les Sédariès (formerly Municipal), Ave des Cévennes, 48800 Villefort [04 66 46 84 33; fax 04 66 46 89 66; http://sedaries.villefort-cevennes.com/]** On D906 heading S fr Villefort twd Alès. Sm, terr, pt shd; wc; chem disp (wc); shwrs inc; el pnts (6A) €2; Indtte; shops, rest, bar in town; BBQ; sm pool, lake sw, fishing 2km; dogs €1; phone; poss cr; quiet; CKE/CCI. "Attractive, scenic site; bureau clsd 1000-1830; privately owned now (2014); not many touring places." 1 Jun-30 Sep. € 15.00 2014*

VILLEFRANCHE DE CONFLENT see Prades *8G4*

VILLENEUVE DE LA RAHO see Perpignan *8G4*

VILLEROUGE LA CREMADE see Lezignan Corbieres *8F4*

Limousin

Regional Introduction

Limoges

Welcome to Limousin

From the picturesque old city of Limoges to themany quaint hamlets, Limousin is a place yet to be discovered by many and is one of the few remaining places you can experience authentic France.

The scenery offers breathtaking valleys, forested mountains and rolling countryside, but as the population and towns are smaller then other regions, the atmosphere is more relaxed and in keeping with traditional ways.

Discover hidden streams and take a swim in the still lakes that make up this rural region.

Local highlights

The Limousin cow is renowned for its prize-winning quality, high-grade meat, which is shipped around the world.

Also try Clafoutis, a traditional cherry batter cake that can also be made with apples.

If you're visiting in August be sure to visit the 'Festival Internationale de la Dentelle' in Tulle, celebrating the town's famous lace production.

Major towns and cities

- Limoges – the regional capital, a city of art and history.
- Guéret – a small market town that has grown little in the last century.
- Tulle – famous for its lace-making.
- Bellac – a small market town with a long history based around leather-tanning.

Regional attractions

- Musée National de la Porcelaine – an extensive collection of ceramics, earthenware and porcelain.
- Parc Zoologique du Reynou – great for a day out, plenty to see and park areas for picnics.
- Oradour-sur-Glane old town – this site of a WWII massacre has been left as a very moving memorial to the victims.
- Chapelle Saint-Aurélien – a tiny and stunning chapel with intricate architecture.

Find out more

www.tourismelimousin.com

Tel: (0)5 55 11 05 90 Limousin Tourist Board

AIXE SUR VIENNE *7B3* (750m NE Rural) *45.79887, 1.13928* **Camp Municipal Les Grèves, Ave des Grèves, 87700 Aixe-sur-Vienne [06 73 67 23 48; fax 05 55 70 43 00; camping@mairie-aixesurvienne.fr; www.mairie-aixesurvienne.fr]** SW fr Limoges for approx 13km, on N21 twds Périgueux, cross bdge over Rv Vienne & in about 600m turn to R (site sp) by rv. Steep down hill app & U-turn into site - take care gate posts! Med, shd; wc (some cont); chem disp; mv service pnt; shwrs inc; el pnts (10A) €2.50 (poss rev pol); Indtte; tradsmn; shops, rest, snacks & bar 300m; playgrnd; pool adj; fishing; quiet; poss cr; adv bkg; dogs free; red long stay. "Pleasant, clean site by rv; spacious pitches; helpful, friendly warden; gd san facs, but ltd low ssn; conv Limoges area & Vienne valley; several chateaux in easy reach; no twin-axles; vg." ♦ 1 Jun-30 Sep. € 19.00 2013*

AMBAZAC *7B3* (1.8km NE Rural) *45.97158, 1.41315* **Camping L'Ecrin Nature (Formerly Camp Municipal de Jonas), 87240 Ambazac [06 52 92 71 65 or 05 55 56 60 25; contact@campinglecrinature.com; www.campinglecrinature.com]** Fr A20 foll sp to Ambazac; site on D914. Med, hdg/mkd pitch, pt sl, terr, pt shd; htd wc (few cont); chem disp; mv service pnt; shwrs inc; el pnts (10A) €2.05; shop & 2km; playgrnd; lake fishing, shgl beach adj (sw not allowed); wifi; quiet. "Excel waterside site with lovely views; v friendly new owners, improving site; san facs clean, updated 2013; ctr for mountain biking & walking; vg site." 12 Apr-31 Oct. € 14.50 2014*

"That's changed – Should I let The Club know?"

If you find something on site that's different from the site entry, fill in a report and let us know. See www.caravanclub.co.uk/europereport.

ARGENTAT *7C4* (10km N Rural) *45.16601, 1.97861* **Camp Municipal La Croix de Brunal, Route de Freygnac, 19320 St Martin-la-Méanne [05 55 29 11 91 or 05 55 29 12 75 (Mairie); fax 05 55 29 28 48]** Fr Argentat take D18 to St Martin-la-Méanne. Site well sp on ent to vill. Sm, hdg/mkd pitch, pt shd; wc; shwrs inc; el pnts (5A); gas, Indtte; shop, rest, snacks, bar 1km; BBQ; htd pool 1km; sand beach 15km; rv sw 8km; tennis 1km; games area; some statics; dogs; phone; quiet. "Simple site; warden calls am & pm; gd walking; fishing, horseriding, watersports within 15km." ♦ ltd 1 Jul-31 Aug. 2009*

ARGENTAT *7C4* (1km NE Urban) *45.10205, 1.94390* **Camp Municipal Le Longour, Route d'Egletons, 19400 Argentat [05 55 28 13 84; fax 05 55 28 81 26; camping@argentat.fr; www.argentat.fr]** Fr cent of Argentat head N dir Egletons on D18. Med, pt shd; wc; chem disp; shwrs inc; el pnts (10A) €3.20; Indtte; shops 1km; tradsmn; playgrnd; htd pool & sports complex adj; tennis; fishing; dogs €1.30; phone; wifi; Ccard acc; poss cr; quiet; red low ssn. "Efficiently run, clean site; pleasant rvside walk to old quay & cafés; gd touring base; excel; beautiful town." 1 Jun-31 Aug. € 19.70 2014*

ARGENTAT *7C4* (4km NE Rural) *45.11151, 1.95908* **Camping Château de Gibanel, 19400 Argentat (Correza) [05 55 28 10 11; fax 05 55 28 81 62; contact@camping-gibanel.com; www.camping-gibanel.com]** Exit Argentat on D18 twd Egletons & fork R on lakeside past hydro-elec dam. Sp fr all dir. Site in grnds of sm castle on N bank of Rv Dordogne. App rd narr but satisfactory. Lge, mkd pitch, pt sl, pt shd; wc (some cont); chem disp; child/baby facs; fam bthrm; shwrs inc; el pnts (10A) €3.70; gas; Indtte; shop; tradsmn; rest, snacks; bar; BBQ; playgrnd; pool; paddling pool; lake sw; boating; fishing; games area; games rm; entmnt; TV; 15% statics; dogs €2 (free low ssn); Eng spkn; adv bkg; quiet; red low ssn; ccard acc; CKE/CCI. "Excel, well-managed site in idyllic location; helpful owner; gd san facs; various pitch sizes; lovely sm town; excel." ♦ ltd 31 May-7 Sep. € 24.00 2013*

ARGENTAT *7C4* (3km SW Rural) *45.07686, 1.92945* **Camping Europe, Le Chambon, 19400 Monceaux-sur-Dordogne [05 55 28 07 70; fax 05 55 28 19 60; camping-europe@wanadoo.fr; www.camping-europe.fr]** Fr Argentat take D12 twd Beaulieu-sur-Dordogne. Site 2km fr D1120. Ent on L by awkward RH bend in Le Chambon. Med, hdg/mkd pitch, pt sl, pt shd; wc; chem disp; mv service pnt; shwrs inc; el pnts (5A) €3.10; gas; Indtte; shops 1km; tradsmn; rest 500m; snacks 1km; playgrnd; pool; paddling pool; rv sw & sand beach; canoeing; fishing; tennis; games area; wifi; entmnt; some statics; dogs €1.60; phone; poss cr; quiet. "Lovely rvside site; interesting town." 5 Apr-8 Nov. € 17.40 2010*

ARGENTAT *7C4* (9km SW Rural) *45.04583, 1.88388* **Camping Le Vaurette, 19400 Monceaux-sur-Dordogne [05 55 28 09 67; fax 05 55 28 81 14; info@vaurette.com; www.vaurette.com]** SW fr Tulle on D1120; fr Argentat SW on D12 sp Beaulieu; site sp on banks of Rv Dordogne. Med, mkd pitch, pt shd; wc; chem disp; mv service pnt; baby facs; shwrs inc; el pnts (6A) €3.30; gas; Indtte; shop; snacks; bar; BBQ; playgrnd; htd pool; shgl beach & rv sw adj; tennis; badminton; fishing; canoe expeditions; games area; games rm; wifi; TV rm; statics; dogs €3.50; Eng spkn; adv bkg; quiet; ccard acc; red low ssn; CKE/CCI. "Lovely setting; helpful, friendly owners; many sports avail." ♦ 1 May 21 Sep. € 23.50 2009*

AUBAZINES *7C3* (4km E Rural) *45.18620, 1.70730* **Campéole Camping Le Coiroux, Parc Touristique du Coiroux, 19190 Aubazines [05 55 27 21 96; fax 05 55 27 19 16; coiroux@campeole.com; www.camping-coiroux.com / www.campeole.com]** Fr Brive-La-Gaillarde take N89 NE twd Tulle. At Cornil turn R onto D48 & foll sp. Site in 8km - long, fairly steep climb. Med, pt hdg/mkd pitch, pt shd; wc; chem disp; mv service pnt; baby facs; shwrs inc; el pnts (5A); gas; Indtte; shop; rest, snacks; bar; playgrnd; htd pool; paddling pool; lake sw & sand beach; fishing; boating; tennis; golf; cycle hire; entmnt; TV rm; 50% statics; dogs; poss cr; Eng spkn; adv bkg; quiet; red low ssn; CKE/CCI. "Excel, wooded site." ♦ 15 Mar-15 Oct. € 25.00 (CChq acc) 2011*

⊞ **AUBUSSON** *7B4* (10km N Rural) *46.02133, 2.17052* **Camping La Perle, Fourneaux, 23200 St Médard-la-Rochette [05 55 83 01 25; fax 05 55 83 34 18; info@camping-laperle.nl; www.camping-laperle.nl]** On D942 N fr Aubusson dir Guéret; site on R bef Fourneaux. Sm, hdg/mkd pitch, some hdstg, terr, pt shd; wc; shwrs inc; el pnts (10A) poss rev pol €3.50; Indtte; shops 10km; tradsmn; rest; bar; BBQ; playgrnd; htd pool; cycle hire; wifi; TV rm; some statics; dogs; Eng spkn; adv bkg; quiet; red low ssn; CKE/CCI. "Site ever improving (2011); various sized pitches; Dutch owners; tapestry museum in Aubusson & other historical attractions; vg site." € 18.50 2013*

AUBUSSON *7B4* (1.5km S Urban) *45.94652, 2.17608* **Camp Municipal La Croix Blanche, Route de Felletin, 23200 Aubusson [05 55 66 18 00]** Site on D982 on banks of Rv Creuse; sp fr all dir. NB Do not drive thro town cent to site - narr main street with iron pillars. Med, shd; wc (some cont); shwrs inc; el pnts (6A) €2.20; Indry rm; tradsmn; snacks; playgrnd; pool 1km; wifi; phone; adv bkg; quiet but some rd noise; CKE/CCI. "Vg site in pleasant location by rv; excel shwrs; park on site rds if pitches waterlogged; conv tapestry factories." 1 Apr-30 Sep. € 10.20 2010*

AUBUSSON *7B4* (5km S Rural) *45.91939, 2.17044* **Camping des Combes, Les Combes, 23500 Felletin [05 55 66 77 29 or 07799 138014 (UK); info@campingdescombes-creuse-france.co.uk; www.campingdescombes-creuse-france.co.uk]** Fr Aubusson on D982 to Felletin, when in Felletin & immed bef rlwy line, turn R at cemetery. Foll camping sp approx 4km. Sm, hdg/mkd pitch, pt shd; wc; chem disp; mv service pnt; shwrs inc; el pnts (10A) €2 (long lead poss req); Indtte; shop & 6km; tradsmn; rest, snacks, bar 6km; playgrnd; fishing; boating; no statics; no dogs; phone; adv bkg; quiet. "Peaceful, British-owned site on edge Lake Combes; ideal touring base; vg; spotless." ♦ 1 Mar-30 Sep. € 20.00 2013*

BEAULIEU SUR DORDOGNE *7C4* (3km N Rural) *45.00911, 1.85059* **Aire Naturelle La Berge Ombragée (Lissajoux), Valeyran, 19120 Brivezac [05 55 91 01 17 or 06 08 40 78 69 (mob); contact@berge-ombragee.com; / www.berge-ombragee.com]** N fr Beauliew-sur-Dordogne on D940; in 500m turn R onto D12; site on R in 2km. Office down on rv bank. NB Front wheel drive tow cars may find diff on gravel hill leading up fr office. Sm, pt sl, pt shd; wc; chem disp; mv service pnt; shws inc; el pnts (6A) €3; sm shop; snacks; BBQ area; playgrnd; rv sw adj; canoeing; wifi; dogs €0.30; CKE/CCI. "CL-type site; friendly; canoeing fr site; gd." 15 Apr-15 Oct. € 17.00 2012*

BEAULIEU SUR DORDOGNE *7C4* (5km N Rural) *45.02167, 1.83960* **Camping la Champagne, La Champagne, 19120 Brivezac [05 87 06 01 21 or 06 70 78 65 63 (mob); info@campinglachampagne.com; www.campinglachampagne.com]** Fr Beaulieu-sur-Dordogne take D940, sp Tulle. R onto D12, sp Argentat. R onto D136. R again after bdge. Site 600m on R. Sm, mkd pitch, terr, pt shd; wc; chem disp; mv service pnt; shwrs; en pnts (6A) €3; Indtte; snacks; BBQ; sw rv adj; wifi; dogs €2.50; phone; twin axles; Eng spkn; adv bkg; quiet; red low ssn; CCI. "Aire Naturella (max 25 vans); fishing; canoeing; horseriding nrby; peaceful, spacious rvside location; Dutch owners." ♦ 1 May-30 Sep. € 16.00 2014*

BEAULIEU SUR DORDOGNE *7C4* (250m E Urban) *44.97950, 1.84040* **FLOWER Camping des Iles, Blvd Rodolphe-de-Turenne, 19120 Beaulieu-sur-Dordogne [05 55 91 02 65; fax 05 55 91 05 19; info@campingdesiles.fr; www.campingdesiles.fr / www.flowercampings.com]** Exit A20 junc 52 ont D158/D38 dir Collonges-la-Rouge; cont on D38 & turn R onto D940 to Beaulieu-sur-Dordogne; site sp fr o'skts of town. Or on D940 N fr Bretenoux, turn R in Beaulieu town sq, site about 200m on island in Rv Dordogne. NB 3m height limit at ent. Med, mkd pitch, shd; htd wc; chem disp; baby facs; fam bthrm; shwrs inc; el pnts (10A) inc (poss long lead req); Indtte; shops 500m; rest, snacks; bar; BBQ (gas); playgrnd; pool; rv & fishing; canoeing; cycle hire; games area; games rm; wifi; entmnt; 15% statics; dogs €2; poss cr; Eng spkn; adv bkg rec; quiet; red long stay/low ssn. "Delightful, wooded site; pitches by rv excel (extra charge); plenty shd; friendly owners; gd clean san facs, ltd low ssn; attractive medieval town; gd value; highly rec." 23 Apr-24 Sep. € 25.00 2014*

⊞ **BELLAC** *7A3* (700m N Urban) *46.12744, 1.05052* **Camp Municipal Les Rochettes, Rue des Rochettes, 87300 Bellac [05 55 68 13 27; camping.bellac@wanadoo.fr; www.camping-limousin.com]** On N147 ent Bellac fr Poitiers take sharp L at 1st traff lts onto D675. Cont to rndabt & turn L. Foll sp, site on L in 400m adj football pitch. Fr Limoges on N147 take R at 3rd traff lts after ent Bellac onto D675 then foll sp as above. NB Sl ent to site. Med, mkd pitch, pt sl, pt shd, terr; htd wc; own san; mv service pnt; shwrs inc; el pnts (10A) €2.50 (long lead poss req); gas; shops 500m; supmkt 1km; bar 500m; playgrnd; pool & waterslide 1km; games area; dogs €1.10; quiet; ccard not acc; red long stay/low ssn. "Spacious site but poss diff if wet; coded barrier clsd 2000-0800; san facs run down/dirty (June 2010); phone ahead to check open low ssn; NH only with own san." € 10.30 2010*

⊞ **BELLAC** *7A3* (9km SE Rural) *46.05718, 0.97766* **Camping Fonclaire, 87300 Blond [tel/fax 05 55 60 88 26; fontclair@neuf.fr; www.limousin-gites.com]** Fr Bellac take D675 S dir St Junien. Site on L in approx 7km, 2km bef Mortemart. Sm, some hdstg, pt shd, wc; chem disp; shwrs inc; (own san facs Nov-Mar) el pnts (6A) €3 (poss long lead req); gas 1km; Indtte; shop 4km; rest & bar 2km; sm htd pool; lake sw; fishing; golf 2km; horseriding 3km; no statics; dogs; phone 2km; Eng spkn; adv bkg; quiet; ccard not acc; CKE/CCI. "Lovely & peaceful, spacious CL-type site in lovely location; welcoming, helpful British owners; gd facs; gd hdstg in wet; nr Oradour-sur-Glane martyr vill; conv Futuroscope; gd cycling; gd; v quiet rural location." ♦ ltd € 17.00 2014*

⊞ **BESSINES SUR GARTEMPE** *7A3* (4km N Rural) *46.14777, 1.36505* **Camp Municipal, 87250 Morterolles-sur-Semme [05 55 76 05 09 (Mairie) or 05 55 76 09 28 (LS) or; fax 05 55 76 68 45; ot.bessines@wanadoo.fr]** S on A20 take exit 23.1 sp Châteauponsac. Take 1st turn R, site on L in vill of Morterolles by stadium. N on A20 take exit 24.2 sp Bessines, turn under a'route & take 1st R sp Châteauponsac to Morterolles in 3km. Sm, mkd pitch, pt shd; htd wc; shwrs inc; el pnts (10A) inc (poss rev pol); Indry rm; playgrnd; covrd pool 200m; cycle hire; dogs; poss cr; Eng spkn; quiet; CKE/CCI. "Delightful farm site nr Limoges; gd san facs; helpful warden; poss travellers; conv A20, excel NH; excel in all respects." ♦ ltd € 10.00 2013*

BESSINES SUR GARTEMPE *7A3* (1.5km SW Urban) *46.10013, 1.35423* **Camp Municipal Lac de Sagnat, Route de St Pardoux, 87250 Bessines-sur-Gartempe [05 55 76 17 69 or 05 55 76 05 09 (Mairie); fax 05 55 76 01 24; ot.bessines@wanadoo.fr; www.tourisme-bessines87.fr]** Exit A20 junc 24 sp Bessines-sur-Gartempe onto D220; then D27 sp lake. Foll sp to Bellevue Restaurant. At rest, turn R foll site sp. Well sp fr junc 24. Med, hdg/mkd pitch, pt sl, terr, pt shd; wc; chem disp (wc); shwrs inc; el pnts (6A) inc; lndtte; shops 1km; tradsmn high ssn; rest 500m; snacks high ssn; playgrnd adj; sand beach & lake sw adj; TV rm; Eng spkn; poss cr; quiet. "Pretty site with lake views; peaceful location; friendly staff; gd, clean san facs; poss unkempt low ssn (Jun 2009); hotel for meals nrby; conv NH A20." ♦ 15 Jun-15 Sep. € 18.70 2012*

BONNAC LA COTE *7B3* (1km S Rural) *45.93238, 1.28977* **Camping Le Château de Leychoisier, 1 Route de Leychoisier, 87270 Bonnac-la-Côte [tel/fax 05 55 39 93 43; contact@leychoisier.com; www.leychoisier.com]** Fr S on A20 exit junc 27 & L at T-junc onto D220. At rndabt take 3rd exit then 1st L onto D97. At mini-rndabt in Bonnac take 2nd exit, site on L in 1km. Fr N exit A20 junc 27, turn R at T-junc onto D97, then as above. Med, hdg, mkd pitch, sl, pt shd; wc; chem disp; mv service pnt; baby facs; shwrs inc; el pnts (10A) inc; lndtte (inc dryer); ltd shop; tradsmn; rest, snacks; bar; BBQ (gas/charcoal); playgrnd; pool; tennis; fishing; wifi; games rm/TV; dogs €3; phone; no c'vans/m'vans over 20m; twin axles; poss cr; Eng spkn; adv bkg; ccard acc; red low ssn; CKE/CCI. "Peaceful site in grnds of chateau; lge pitches; welcoming, friendly & helpful staff; clean san facs; excel rest; extra for m'vans; blocks req some pitches; rallies welcome; conv NH nr m'way; excel; ccard not acc for 1 night stay; access for lge o'fits diff; gd rest/pool area." ♦ 15 Apr-19 Sep. € 45.00 SBS - L11 2014*

See advertisement

BOURGANEUF *7B4* (5km E Rural) *45.94684, 1.81331* **Aire Naturelle Les Quatre Saisons, Chignat, 23250 Soubrebost [05 55 64 23 35; les4saisons0314@orange.fr; www.les-4-saisons.com]** Fr Bourganeuf take D8 sp Lac de Vassivière; in 3.5km turn L (on bend) onto D37 thro Chignat & foll sp to site. White gates at site ent. Well sp. NB Ent fr narr lane, turn sharp R up incline to site. Lge o'fits may req assistance fr owners, check in adv. Sm, pt sl, terr, pt shd; wc; shwrs; chem disp in Bourgneuf; el pnts (3A) €4; lndtte (inc dryer); tradsmn; rest; BBQ; games rm; wifi; 2 statics; dogs €2; poss cr; Eng spkn; adv bkg; quiet; CKE/CCI. "Lovely, peaceful, wooded site; friendly, helpful British owners; B&B, meals & produce avail; gd walking; vg." ♦ 1 Apr-1 Oct. € 13.00 2011*

BOUSSAC *7A4* (2km NE Rural) *46.37192, 2.20036* **Camping du Château de Poinsouze, Route de la Châtre, 23600 Boussac-Bourg [05 55 65 02 21; fax 05 55 65 86 49; info.camping-de.poinsouze@orange.fr; www.camping-de-poinsouze.com]** Fr junc 10 on A71/E11 by-pass Montluçon via N145 dir Guéret; in 22km turn L onto D917 to Boussac; cont on D917 dir La Châtre; site 3km on L. Or fr Guéret on N145, exit Gouzon, at rndabt take D997 to Boussac, then as above. Med, mkd pitch, pt sl, unshd; wc; chem disp; mv service pnt; serviced pitch; baby facs; shwrs inc; el pnts (6-20A) inc (poss rev pol); lndtte (inc dryer); shop & 3km; tradsmn; rest, snacks; bar; BBQ; playgrnd; pool; paddling pool; waterslide; lake fishing; horseriding 5km; golf 20km; cycle hire; games area; wifi; entmnt; games/TV rm; 10% statics; dogs €3 (not acc mid-July to mid Aug; no c'vans/m'vans over 15m; Eng spkn; adv bkg ess high ssn; quiet; ccard acc; red low ssn; CKE/CCI. "Peaceful, relaxed site by lake in chateau grnds; well-kept & well-run; lge pitches, some sl; welcoming, helpful owners; superb san facs; excel rest & snacks; gd for young children; gd walking." ♦ 15 May-15 Sep

15 May-15 Sep. € 41.00 SBS - L16 2013*

See advert on next page

BOUSSAC *7A4* (2km W Rural) *46.34938, 2.18662* **Camping Creuse-Nature (Naturist), Route de Bétête, 23600 Boussac [05 55 65 18 01; fax 05 55 65 81 40; creuse-nature@wanadoo.fr; www.creuse-nature.com]** Fr Boussac take D917 N twd La Châtre. In 500m turn L (W) on D15 sp Bétête. Site on R in 2.5km, clearly sp. Med, hdg/mkd pitch, pt sl, pt shd; wc; shwrs; el pnts (10A) €4.50 (poss long lead req); Indtte; sm shop; rest, snacks; bar; playgrnd; 2 htd pools (1 covrd); paddling pool; fishing; games area; entmnt; some statics; dogs €5.50; Eng spkn; adv bkg; v quiet; ccard acc; red low ssn. "Excel site in lovely area; great pitches; charming & helpful owners; clean facs; easy walk to town & interesting château; great location." ♦ 5 Apr-31 Oct. € 41.50 2014*

⊞ **BRIVE LA GAILLARDE** *7C3* (8km S Rural) *45.10049, 1.52423* **FFCC Camping à la Ferme (Delmas), Malfarges, 19600 Noailles [tel/fax 05 55 85 81 33]** Fr A20/E9 take exit 52 sp Noailles; in vill take 1st R across yellow paving at vill café/shop (to avoid steep dangerous hill); turn R at T-junc, site on L. Sp fr m'way. NB All vill streets have 3,500kg limit. Sm, mkd pitch, terr, pt shd; wc; chem disp; mv service pnt; shwrs inc; el pnts (5A) €2.70-5.30 (poss rev pol); shop 500m; farm meals & produce; fishing 200m; dogs €2.60; few statics; adv bkg; quiet; CKE/CCI. "Conv NH/sh stay adj A20; friendly, helpful farmer; if owner not around choose a pitch; basic san facs; parking on terr poss awkward; fly problem in hot weather; strict silence after 2200; excel." € 16.00 2014*

⊞ **BRIVE LA GAILLARDE** *7C3* (6km SW Rural) *45.09975, 1.45115* **Camping Intercommunal La Prairie, 19600 Lissac-sur-Couze [05 55 85 37 97; fax 05 55 85 37 11; lecausse.correzien@wanadoo.fr; www.caussecorrezien.fr]** A20 exit 51; D1089 to Larche; L onto D19 sp Lissac; take 1st L after St Cernin-de-Larche onto D59 round N side of Lac de Causse, sharp R down hill then bear L over dam; R to site in 2km. Site sp as 'Camping Nautica'. Med, mkd pitch, hdstg, terr, pt shd; wc; serviced pitches; shwrs inc; el pnts (16A) €2; gas 4km; Indtte; shop; snacks; bar; playgrnd; pool; lake sw; boating; windsurfing; 5% statics; dogs €3; quiet; Eng spkn; adv bkg; no ccard acc; red low ssn; CKE/CCI. "Beautiful site in idyllic setting o'looking lake; friendly recep; clean san facs; recep poss clsd Tues & Sun - site inaccessible when recep clsd, phone ahead rec; many outdoor activities." ♦ € 18.60 2014*

BRIVE LA GAILLARDE *7C3* (10km SW Rural) *45.06942, 1.43060* **Camping La Magaudie, La Magaudie Ouest, 19600 Chartrier-Ferrière [tel/fax 05 55 85 26 06; camping@lamagaudie.com; www.lamagaudie.com]** Exit A20 junc 53 onto D920/D19 dir Chasteaux. After rlwy bdge take 2nd L to Chartrier & foll blue sps to site. NB Diff app climbing up narr lane with no passing spaces for 1km. Sm, mkd pitch, sl, pt shd; htd wc; chem disp; shwrs inc; el pnts (10A) €3.50; Indtte; shop 2km; tradsmn; rest, snacks; bar; gas BBQ; playgrnd; pool; lake sw 3km; 5% statics; dogs €1.25; Eng spkn; adv bkg; quiet; red low ssn; CKE/CCI. "Dutch owners; vg site & facs but v ltd low ssn; rec arr early high ssn." ♦ 15 Apr-1 Nov. € 22.40 2014*

BRIVEZAC see Beaulieu sur Dordogne *7C4*

BUGEAT *7B4* (3km NW Rural) *45.60608, 1.88446* **Camp Municipal Puy de Veix, 19170 Viam [05 55 95 52 05 (Mairie); fax 05 55 95 21 86; viam.mairie@wanadoo.fr; www.viam.correze.net]** Fr Bugeat NW on D979; in 4km L onto D160; foll sp to Viam. Sm, mkd pitch, pt sl, terr, pt shd; wc; chem disp; mv service pnt; el pnts (6-10A) €2.60; Indtte (inc dryer); shop 4km; tradsmn; rest 500m; BBQ; playgrnd; lake sw & sand beach adj; fishing; games area; dogs €0.50; phone; poss cr; Eng spkn; adv bkg; quiet; CKE/CCI. "On lakeside; beautiful views; peaceful; mainly sm pitches; vg." ♦ 1 Jun-30 Sep. € 7.40 2011*

BUJALEUF see St Léonard de Noblat *7B3*

⊞ **BUSSIERE POITEVINE** *7A3* (500m SW Urban) *46.23282, 0.90242* **Camp Municipal La Croix de L'Hozanne, 87320 Bussière-Poitevine [05 55 60 08 17; fax 05 55 68 40 72]** NW fr Bellac on N147, 8km after St Bonnet-de-Bellac turn R onto D4 sp Bussière-Poitevine. Site 500m on R opp water tower. Sm, hdg pitch, pt shd; htd wc (some cont); shwrs inc; el pnts (10-15A) €1.90-2.80; shops, rest & bar 500m; snacks; playgrnd; CKE/CCI. "Pleasant site in attractive town; old but clean facs; grass pitches poss water-logged in winter but can pitch in rd; ltd facs low ssn; gd NH/sh stay." € 6.00 2009*

CHALARD, LE see St Yrieix la Perche *7B3*

⊞ **CHALUS** *7B3* (9km NW Rural) *45.71540, 0.91956* **Camping Parc Verger, Le Halte, 87150 Champagnac-la-Rivière, Limousin [05 55 01 22 83 or 06 04 09 05 20 (mob); pvbureau@parcverger.com; www.parcverger.com]** N fr Châlus on D901; in 9km turn L onto D75 sp Champagnac-la-Rivière; site on L in 150m. Sm, some mkd pitch, hdstg, unshd; htd wc; chem disp; mv service pnt; shwrs inc; el pnts (16A) inc; gas 1km; lndtte (inc dryer); shop 1km; tradsmn; rest, snacks & bar 1km; BBQ; no playgrnd (2009); sm pool; lake sw & sand beach 10km; wifi; dogs; bus 150m; Eng spkn; adv bkg; v quiet; ccard acc; red grass pitch; red long stay; CKE/CCI. "Lovely site; welcoming, friendly, helpful British owners; lge pitches suitable for RVs; gd clean san facs, poss stretched high ssn; gd mkd walks nrby; 15km-long walk/cycle path adj (old rwly track); excel local vet; excel area for walking." ♦ € 22.00 2013*

CHAPELLE TAILLEFERT, LA see Guéret *7A4*

⊞ **CHATEAUPONSAC** *7A3* (200m SW Rural) *46.13163, 1.27083* **Camp Municipal La Gartempe - Le Ventenat, Ave de Ventenat, 87290 Châteauponsac [05 55 76 55 33 or 05 55 76 31 55 (Mairie); fax 05 55 76 98 05; camping-chateauponsac@orange.fr]** Fr N exit A20 junc 23.1 sp Châteauponsac; go thro vill, well sp on L on rvside. Fr S exit A20 junc 24 sp Châteauponsac & then as above. Sm, hdg/mkd pitch, terr, pt shd; htd wc; chem disp; shwrs inc; el pnts (6A) €3 (poss rev pol); lndtte; supmkt 500m; rest, snacks, bar (Jul-Aug); playgrnd; pool; kayaking; lake 10km; archery; children's activites; adj to holiday bungalows/gites; dogs €1; poss cr; Eng spkn; poss noise fr parties in rest; adv bkg; red low ssn; CKE/CCI. "Pleasant site; gd san facs; pitches muddy in wet; not suitable lge m'vans; activities down steep hill by rv; low ssn warden visits eves only; new helpful owners (2014); nice vill." € 26.00 2014*

CHENERAILLES *7A4* (2km SW Rural) *46.10337, 2.16059* **Camp Municpal La Forêt, 23130 Chénérailles [05 55 62 38 26 or 05 55 62 37 22; fax 05 55 62 95 55; mairie.chenerailles@wanadoo.fr]** SW fr Chénérailles on D55; site in 2km on R. Sm, mkd pitch, pt sl, pt shd; wc (some cont); chem disp (wc); shwrs inc; el pnts (10A) €2.30; lndtte; shop, rest, bar 2km; BBQ; playgrnd; lake sw adj; dogs €0.60; Eng spkn; adv bkg; CKE/CCI. "Sand beach on lake adj; warden on site am & pm." ♦ ltd 15 Jun-15 Sep. € 7.35 2010*

CLERGOUX *7C4* (300m E Rural) *45.27871, 1.96566* **FFCC Camping La Petite Rivière, 19320 Clergoux [05 55 27 68 50; jcbakker@xs4all.nl; www.compumess.nl/lapetiteriviere]** Exit A89 junc 21 onto D1089. Go E until next rndabt, turn R & after approx 5km turn L onto D978 to Clergoux. Site on R just bef W end of vill. Or fr Tulle on D978 site in approx 20km, sp. Sm, mkd pitch, pt sl, pt shd; wc; chem disp; mv service pnt; baby facs; shwrs inc; el pnts (6A) €2.25; lndtte; tradsmn; lake sw & sand beach 1.5km; 20% statics; dogs €1.30; Eng spkn; adv bkg; quiet; red low ssn; CKE/CCI. "Helpful Dutch owner; 25 mkd walks in area; excel." 1 Apr-15 Sep. € 10.20 2009*

COGNAC LA FORET *7B3* (1.5km W Rural) *45.82494, 0.99674* **Camping des Alouettes, Les Alouettes, 87310 Cognac-la-Forêt [05 55 03 26 93; info@camping-des-alouttes.com; www.camping-des-alouettes.com]** Fr Aixe-sur-Vienne on D10, site W of Cognac-la-Forêt on D10, sp to L. Med, hdg pitch;pt sl; pt shd; wc; chem disp; shwrs inc; el pnts (10A) €3; lndtte; shop 1km; tradsmn; rest, snacks; bar; BBQ; playgrnd; pool & paddling pool; lake sw & sand beach 1km; tennis 700m; wifi; 10% statics; dogs €1; Eng spkn; adv bkg; quiet; red low ssn; CKE/CCI. "Beautiful location; friendly owners; conv war vill Oradour-sur-Glane & Richard Lion Heart sites; vg site & facs; excel, peaceful, relaxing site; new san block (2014); lge pitches." ♦ 1 Apr-30 Sep. € 27.00 2014*

COMPREIGNAC *7B3* (6km N Rural) *46.03282, 1.29559* **Camping Santrop, Lac de St-Pardoux, 87640 Razès [05 55 71 08 08 or 05 55 71 04 40 (LS); fax 05 55 71 23 93; lacsaintpardoux@wanadoo.fr; www.lac-saint-pardoux.com]** N fr Limoges on A20, exit junc 25 Razès, sp Lac de St Pardoux; foll sp 4km to site. Lge, hdg pitch, pt sl, shd; wc; baby facs; shwrs inc; el pnts (16A) €3.80; lndtte (inc dryer); shop; rest; bar; playgrnd; pool; waterslide; lake adj; watersports; games area; entmnt; TV rm; dogs €1.10; poss cr; Eng spkn; poss noisy. "Popular, busy site on lake beach; random pitching under trees in woodland; gd rest on lakeside; poss late night noise fr revellers on beach; pitches unkempt & site tired end ssn (2009)." 1 May-20 Sep. € 16.40 2009*

CORMAC see St Sulpice les Feuilles *7A3*

CROZANT *7A3* (350m S Rural) *46.38890, 1.61893* **Camp Municipal Fontbonne, Le Bourg, 23160 Crozant [05 55 89 80 12; fax 05 55 89 83 80; mairie-crozant@wanadoo.fr]** Fr A20 exit junc 20 onto D36 to Eguzon-Chantôme; turn R on D913 & after 11km turn L on D30 to Crozant. Site sp. Sm, mkd pitch, some hdstg, pt sl, pt shd; wc; shwrs inc; el pnts (6A) inc; lndry rm; shops, rest, snacks, bar 500m; BBQ; playgrnd; lake sw 7km; dogs €0.50; adv bkg; quiet; ccard not acc. "Attractive vill on Lake Chambon; rvside walk." 1 May-30 Sep. € 9.20 2010*

DONZENAC *7C3* (1.5km S Rural) *45.21978, 1.51784* **FFCC Camping La Rivière, Route d'Ussac, 19270 Donzenac [tel/fax 05 55 85 63 95; info@campingdonzenac.com; www.campinglariviere.jimdo.com]** Fr N exit A20 at junc 47 (do not use junc 48); take exit at rndabt dir Donzenac D920. In 3km on ent Donzenac keep on D920 & go down hill to rndabt. Take 2nd exit D170 sp Uzzac, site on R in 500m. NB Avoid app thro Donzenac as narr & diff for lge o'fits. Fr S exit junc 49 to Ussac. Med, mkd pitch, pt shd; wc; chem disp; mv service pnt; shwrs inc; el pnts (10A) €3.10; gas; lndtte (inc dryer); sm shop & 1km; snacks; bar; playgrnd; htd pool Jul/Aug; rv adj; fishing 5km; cycle hire; tennis; games area; games rm; wifi; TV rm; dogs €1.10; adv bkg rec high ssn; red low ssn. "Excel facs." ♦ 1 May-30 Sep. € 29.30 2014*

DUN LE PALESTEL *7A3* (1.5km N Rural) *46.31698, 1.66545* **Camp Municipal de la Forêt, Route d'Argenton, 23800 Dun-le-Palestel [05 55 89 01 30; mairie-dunlepalestel@orange.fr; www.mairie-dunlepalestel.fr]** Exit N145 N midway bet La Souterraine & Guéret onto D5 to Dun-le-Palestel; turn L onto D951; in 200m to R onto D913; site sp to R in1.5km. Site sp in town. Sm, mkd pitch, pt sl, pt shd; wc; shwrs inc; el pnts €2.30; shop 1 km; BBQ; rest, snacks & bar 800m; playgrnd; dogs; phone; quiet. "Pretty site with lovely views; gates kept locked; phone numbers listed at gate or call at Mairie 08.30-1200 & 1330-1630 (-1800 Tues & Thur); worth the trouble; vg." ♦ 15 Jun-15 Sep. € 5.60 2011*

⊞ **EGLETONS** *7C4* (2km NE Rural) *45.41852, 2.06431* **Camping du Lac, 10 Le Pont, 19300 Egletons [tel/fax 05 55 93 14 75; campingegletons@orange.fr; www.camping-egletons.com]** Fr Egletons on D1089 for approx 2km, site 300m past Hôtel Ibis on opp site of rd. Med, mkd pitch, terr, pt shd; wc; chem disp; baby facs; fam bthrm; shwrs inc; el pnts (4-8A) €2.90-3.80; gas; Indtte; shops 2km; tradsmn; rest, snacks; bar; lake sw, fishing & watersports 300m; playgrnd; entmnt; TV; 30% statics; dogs €1.30; phone; Eng spkn; quiet; red low ssn; CKE/CCI. "Lovely, wooded site in attractive area; lge pitches; friendly owners; vg." € 12.00 2011*

EVAUX LES BAINS *7A4* (400m NE Rural) *46.17841, 2.49009* **Camp Municipal Ouche-de-Budelle, Bois du Chez, 23110 Evaux-les-Bains [05 55 65 55 82 or 05 55 65 50 20 (Mairie)]** Fr N on D993/D996 sp 'International'. Also site sp fr other dirs. Sm, hdg/mkd pitch, pt sl, pt shd; wc (some cont); chem disp (wc); shwrs inc; el pnts (10A) €3.20; Indtte; shops 400m; playgrnd; pool, tennis 200m; 10% statics; dogs €0.70; quiet. "Well-kept, well-run site; friendly; gd facs; site rds a bit narr & manoeuvring poss diff due hedges; Evaux attractive, interesting health spa; gd." ♦ ltd Mar-Oct. € 6.60 2011*

EYMOUTIERS *7B4* (8km N Rural) *45.80560, 1.84342* **Camp Municipal Les Peyrades, Auphelle, Lac de Vassivière, 87470 Peyrat-le-Château [06 11 22 07 06 (mob) or 05 55 69 48 75 (Mairie); peyrat-tourisme@wanadoo.fr; www.peyrat-tourisme.com]** Fr Peyrat E on D13, at 5km sharp R onto D222 & foll sp for Lac de Vassivière. At wide junc turn L, site on R. Med, pt sl, pt shd; wc cont; shwrs inc; el pnts (5A) €2.50; Indtte; shop, rest, snacks, bar adj; BBQ; lake sw adj; sand beach adj; dogs; phone; poss v cr; adv bkg; quiet. "Helpful warden; some pitches o'look lake." 1 May-30 Sep. € 8.70 2009*

EYMOUTIERS *7B4* (8km N Rural) *45.82584, 1.76599* **Camp Municipal Moulin de l'Eau, 87470 Peyrat-le-Château [05 55 69 41 01 or 05 55 69 48 75; peyrat-tourisme@wanadoo.fr]** 1.5km N of Peyrat on D940 to Bourganeuf, site on L immed bef bdge. Med, pt sl, pt terr, pt shd; wc; shwrs; el pnts (6A); shops 2km; fishing; dogs; no adv bkg; quiet; CKE/CCI. "Pleasant site; beautiful area; pay at Mairie in town." 15 Jun-15 Sep. 2009*

EYMOUTIERS *7B4* (1km S Rural) *45.73061, 1.75249* **Camp Municipal, St Pierre-Château, 87120 Eymoutiers [05 55 69 10 21; fax 05 55 69 27 19; mairie-eymoutiers@wanadoo.fr; www.mairie-eymoutiers.fr]** On E of D940 S fr Eymoutiers site sp on R. Diff sharp bend bef ent. Sm, pt sl, terr, pt shd; wc; shwrs; el pnts (6A) €2 (long lead poss req); shops 2km; adv bkg; quiet. "Gd views; clean site; site yourself, warden calls; attractive town & area; excel value; v gd san facs; rec." 1 Jun-30 Sep. € 9.00 2012*

"I like to fill in the reports as I travel from site to site"

You'll find report forms at the back of this guide, or you can fill them in online at www.caravaclub.co.uk/europereport.

EYMOUTIERS *7B4* (10km W Rural) *45.71633, 1.60127* **FFCC Camping Le Cheyenne, Ave Michel Sinibaldi, 87130 Châteauneuf-la-Forêt [05 55 69 39 29; contact@camping-le-cheyenne.com; www.camping-le-cheyenne.com]** Fr Limoges E on D979 for approx 33km. Turn R at Lattée onto D15 & in 4km foll sp to site. Med, hdg/mkd pitch, pt shd; htd wc; chem disp; mv service pnt; shwrs inc; el pnts (6A) €3; Indtte; tradsmn; rest, snacks; bar; playgrnd; lake sw & fishing adj; tennis; wifi; some statics; dogs €1; phone; Eng spkn. "Lovely position by lake & woods but also nr town; gd size pitches; reasonable facs; poss unkempt/untidy low ssn (2006); factory on 24hr shift gives cont backgrnd hum, but not obtrusive; gd walks; gd." 1 Apr-31 Oct. € 12.00 2011*

EYMOUTIERS *7B4* (5.2km NW Rural) *45.75069, 1.69194* **Domaine des Monts de Bussy (Naturist), Bussy-Varache, 87120 Eymoutiers [05 55 69 68 20; montsdebussy@wanadoo.fr; www.montsdebussy.net]** Exit A20 junc 35 onto D979 dir Eymoutiers; in approx 40km, just bef Eymoutiers, turn L onto D129A sp Bussy; pass thro Bussy, in 2km; then 300m after vill turn R onto sm rd leading to site. Sm, pt sl, unshd; wc; chem disp; shwrs inc; el pnts €4; Indtte; sm bar; htd pool; dogs €3.50; Eng spkn; quiet; ccard not acc; red low ssn; CKE/CCI. "Lovely quiet site with views; lge pitches; friendly owners; v clean san facs; lovely pool; in Millevaches en Limousin national park; excel." 21 May-31 Oct. € 23.00 2011*

FELLETIN see Aubusson *7B4*

⊞ **FLEURAT** *7A4* (500m E Rural) *46.24027, 1.68666* **Camping Les Boueix, Les Boueix, 23320 Fleurat [09 63 61 23 80; info@campinglesboueix.com; www.campinglesboueix.com]** Fr N145 N onto D5 to Fleurat. Foll sp La Boueix & site. Sm, pt hdg/mkd pitch, sl, pt shd; wc; chem disp; shwrs inc; el pnts (13A) €3.50 (€5 winter); shops, rest, snacks & bar 6km; BBQ; fishing; dogs €1.50; Eng spkn; adv bkg; quiet; no ccard acc; CKE/CCI. "Beautiful, quiet & relaxing CL-type site; lge pitches with views; welcoming, helpful British owners; vg san facs; sl poss diff m'vans; well-stocked fishing lake nrby; lovely walks; ideal for beautiful Creuse Valley; rallies welcome; conv A20; highly rec." € 16.00 2014*

GOUZON *7A4* (300m SW Urban) *46.18785, 2.23913* **Camp Municipal de la Voueize, 1 Ave de la Marche, 23230 Gouzon [tel/fax 05 55 81 73 22; camping-gouzon@orange.fr; www.camping-lavoueize.fr]** On E62/N145 Guéret/Montluçon exit at sp for Gouzon. In cent of vill bear R past church & site is sp on edge of Rv Voueize. Sm, pt shd; wc; chem disp; shwrs inc; el pnts (10A) inc (poss rev pol); gas adj; lndry rm; shop, rest, bar in vill; playgrnd; fishing; cycle hire; golf 2km; birdwatching on lake 8km; dogs €0.50; adv bkg; quiet. "Lovely aspect; friendly recep; clean site; facs poss tired high ssn; gd walking & cycling rtes; gd NH; snacks/bar Jul & Aug only; big trees; adj rv; san facs tired." 1 May-16 Oct. € 12.00 2014*

GUERET *7A4* (8km S Rural) *46.10257, 1.83528* **Camp Municipal Le Gué Levard, 5 Rue Gué Levard, 23000 La Chapelle-Taillefert [05 55 51 09 20 or 05 55 52 36 17 (Mairie); www.ot-gueret.fr]** Take junc 48 fr N145 sp Tulle/Bourganeuf (D33 thro Guéret); S on D940 fr Guéret, turn off at site sp. Foll sp thro vill, well sp. Sm, hdstg, sl, terr, pt shd; wc; chem disp; mv service pnt; shwrs inc; el pnts (16A) €2.50; Indtte €6 (inc dryer); BBQ (sep area); playgrnd; fishing in Rv Gartempe; sports facs nr; 20% statics; dogs; quiet; adv bkg; ccard not acc; CKE/CCI. "Attractive, peaceful, well-kept site hidden away; vg san facs; site yourself, warden calls 1900; all pitches sl so m'van levelling diff; trout stream runs thro site; gd auberge in vill; gd walking; phone ahead to check open low ssn; excel little site." ♦ ltd 1 Apr-1 Nov. € 11.00 2014*

GUERET *7A4* (3km W Rural) *46.16387, 1.85882* **Camp du Plan d'Eau de Courtille (Formerly Municipal), Rue Georges Aullon, 23000 Guéret [05 55 81 92 24]** Fr W on N145 take D942 to town cent; then take D914 W; take L turn bef lake sp; site in 1.5km along lakeside rd with speed humps. Site sp. Med, hdg/mkd pitch, pt sl, pt shd; wc (some cont); chem disp; mv service pnt; baby facs; shwrs inc; el pnts (10A) inc; shops 2km; rest, bar 500m; BBQ; playgrnd; pool 1.5km; sand beach & lake sw; watersports; dogs; phone; poss cr; no adv bkg; quiet; CKE/CCI; "Pleasant scenery; well-managed site; narr ent to pitches; mkd walks nrby; poss noisy w/end." ♦ 1 Apr-5 Nov. € 18.00 2012*

LADIGNAC LE LONG see St Yrieix la Perche *7B3*

LAGUENNE see Tulle *7C4*

LIMOGES *7B3* (10km N Rural) *45.52142, 1.16326* **Camping Uzurat Sarl Generation Activities, 40 Ave d'Uzurat, 87280 Limoges [tel/fax 05 55 38 49 43; contact@campinglimoges.fr; www.campinglimoges.fr]** Fr N twd Limoges on A20 take exit 30 sp Limoges Nord Zone Industrielle, Lac d'Uzurat; foll sp to Lac d'Uzarat & site. Fr S twd Limoges on A20 exit junc 31 & foll sp as above. Well sp fr A20. Lge, hdstg, pt shd; htd wc (some cont); chem disp; mv service pnt; serviced pitches; baby facs; shwrs inc; el pnts (10A) €3.60; Indtte; hypmkt 500m; playgrnd adj; lake fishing; wifi; some statics; dogs €1.50; bus; phone; m'van o'night area; Eng spkn; quiet but some rd noise; ccard acc; red low ssn/long stay; CKE/CCI. "Lovely site by lake; gd sized pitches; friendly & helpful staff; clean modern san facs; pitch on chippings - awnings diff; poss red opening dates - phone ahead low ssn; poss mkt traders; conv martyr vill Oradour-sur-Glane; gd touring base; conv m'way; popular NH." ♦ 15 Mar-31 Oct. € 25.00 2013*

LUSSAC LES EGLISES *7A3* (300m E Rural) *46.34372, 1.17942* **Camp Municipal Les Forges, Ave François de Bourdelle, 87360 Lussac-les-Eglises [05 55 68 29 44 or 06 43 20 01 19 (mob)]** Exit A20 junc 22 onto D912 W sp St Sulpice-les-Feuilles. Cont on D912 dir Lussac-les-Eglises, site on R just bef vill. Sm, hdg pitch, pt shd; wc; chem disp; mv service pnt; shwrs inc; el pnts (10A) €1.60; shop, rest, bar 300m; BBQ; fishing adj; dogs; quiet. "Excel, CL-type site; basic, clean facs; warden calls evening." 1 Apr-30 Sep. € 6.50 2010*

MAGNAC BOURG *7B3* (Urban) *45.61965, 1.42864* **FFCC Camp Municipal Les Ecureuils, 87380 Magnac-Bourg [05 55 00 80 28 (Mairie); fax 05 55 00 49 09; mairie.magnac-bourg@wanadoo.fr; www.tourismelimousin.com]** Leave A20 at junc 41 sp Magnac-Bourg; foll sps to site in vill. Site behind town hall. Sm, pt sl, some hdg pitch, pt shd; wc; mv service pnt; shwrs inc; el pnts (16A) €3.10; supmkt, petrol & rest nr; playgrnd; fishing 2km; dogs; CKE/CCI. "Quiet, peaceful site; old but clean san facs; site yourself, warden calls at 1600 or see when avail on door of Mairie; mkt Sat am; gd NH." 15 May-15 Sep. € 10.20 2011*

MARCILLAC LA CROISSILLE *7C4* (2km SW Rural) *45.26896, 2.00838* **Camp Municipal Le Lac, 28 Route du Viaduc, 19320 Marcillac-la-Croisille [tel/fax 05 55 27 81 38 or 05 55 27 82 05 (Mairie); campingdulac19@wanadoo.fr; www.campingdulac19.com]** S fr Egletons on D16 & D18. Site sp at S end of vill at intersection with D978. Lge, pt sl, shd, wc; shwrs; el pnts (6A) €2.80; Indtte; shops 2km; snacks; playgrnd; lake & sand beach adj; tennis adj; entmnt; TV; some statics; dogs €0.90; adv bkg; quiet; red low ssn. "Spacious park like setting." 1 Jun-1 Oct. € 11.50 2012*

⊞ **MASSERET** *7B3* (9km N Rural) *45.61142, 1.50110* **Camping de Montréal, Rue du Petit Moulin, 87380 St Germain-les-Belles [05 55 71 86 20; fax 05 55 71 00 83; contact@campingdemontreal.com; www.campingdemontreal.com]** S fr Limoges on A20; exit junc 42 onto D7B to St Germain-les-Belles; turn R onto D216; site on L in 500m. Site sp in vill. NB Care needed due narr rds. Med, hdg/mkd pitch, terr, pt shd; htd wc; chem disp; mv service pnt; shwrs inc; el pnts (10A) €3; Indtte (inc dryer); sm shop 1km; tradmn; rest, snacks, bar; BBQ; playgrnd; htd pool; lake sw adj; fishing; watersports; tennis; cycle hire 1km; wifi; entmnt; 12% statics; dogs €2.60; phone; poss cr; Eng spkn; adv bkg; quiet; ccard acc; red low ssn; CKE/CCI. "Peaceful site in attractive setting o'looking lake; excel san facs; conv A20; a gem of a site." ♦ € 22.00 (CChq acc) 2014*

MASSERET *7B3* (5km E Rural) *45.53880, 1.57790* **Camping Domaine des Forges (formerly Camping Plan l'Eau), Complexe Touristique Bourg, 19510 Lamongerie [05 55 73 44 57; fax 05 55 73 49 69; www.domaine-des-forges.fr]** Exit A20 at junc 43 sp Masseret & foll sp Lamongerie. At rndabt turn R, site sp. Site ent bet 2 lge stone pillars. Med, sl, shd; wc; chem disp; shwrs; el pnts (5A) €2.30 (poss long lead req some pitches); Indtte; sm shop; rest, snacks; playgrnd; lake beach & sw; fishing; tennis; golf nrby; fitness course thro woods & round lake; TV; poss cr; ccard acc; quiet. "Pleasant situation; clean facs; gd NH & longer." ♦ 1 Apr-30 Sep. € 19.00 2014*

MERINCHAL *7B4* (S Urban) *45.91513, 2.48813* **Camp Municipal La Mothe, Château de Mérinchal, 23420 Mérinchal [05 55 67 25 56 (TO); fax 05 55 67 23 71; tourisme.merinchal@wanadoo.fr]** E fr Pontaumur on D941twds Aubusson. R onto D27 to Mérinchal. Site in vill. Sm, pt sl, pt shd; wc; shwrs inc; el pnts €2; Indtte; shop, rest, bar nr; playgrnd; TV; fishing 500m; quiet. "Excel site in chateau grnds but poss clsd w/end if weddings etc in chateau - phone ahead to check." ♦ 1 Apr-30 Oct. € 8.50 2010*

MEYMAC *7B4* (500m NE Rural) *45.54075, 2.15533* **Camping Municipal La Garenne, Blvd de la Garenne, 19250 Meymac [05 55 95 22 80; fax 05 55 95 66 12]** Fr Meymac take D30 dir Sornac. Site ent on R appears to be via a car park, sp. Med, mkd pitch, terr, pt sl, pt shd; htd wc (some cont); shwrs inc; shops 1km; el pnts (10A) €2.75; Indtte; shop, rest, snacks, bar 500m; BBQ; playgrnd; some statics; dogs €0.70; quiet;CKE/CCI. "Lge pitches; site in wooded area; gd walking." ♦ 15 May-15 Sep. € 8.80 2010*

MEYSSAC *7C3* (2km NE Rural) *45.06150, 1.66402* **Intercommunal Moulin de Valane, Route de Collonges-la-Rouge, 19500 Meyssac [05 55 25 41 59; fax 05 55 84 07 28; mairie@meyssac.fr; www.meyssac.fr]** Well sp on D38 bet Meyssac & Collonges-la-Rouge. Med, mkd pitch, pt sl, pt shd; wc; chem disp; shwrs; el pnts (10A) €2.80; Indtte; shop; rest, snacks; bar; playgrnd; pool; tennis; many statics; adv bkg;CKE/CCI. "Within walking dist of attractive vill; quiet at night; vg san facs; rec." ♦ 1 May-30 Sep. € 13.00 2012*

MONCEAUX SUR DORDOGNE see Argentat *7C4*

⊞ **MONTBOUCHER** *7B4* (1.5km N Rural) *45.96144, 1.67940* **Camping La Chassagne (C J Camping), 23400 Montboucher [05 55 64 22 87; cjcamping@aliceadsl.fr; www.cjcamping.com]** W fr Bourganeuf on D941 for approx 5km, turn R at Elan g'ge sp Montboucher. Take 1st R sp Les Martys, go thro vill & up hill, turn L (sm house on L). Take next L & after La Chassagne vill sp foll 2 L-hand bends. Site on next R-hand bend. Sm, hdg, sl, pt shd; htd wc; chem disp; fam bthrm; shwrs inc; el pnts (10A) inc; Indtte; shops & rest 5km; fishing, tennis & golf 5km; dogs; adv bkg; quiet; CKE/CCI. "Well-kept CL-type site in beautiful area; friendly, helpful British owners; clean facs; levelling blocks req; excel touring base; adv bkg rec; mv service pnt in vill; excel." € 12.00 2010*

> **"Satellite navigation makes touring much easier"**
>
> Remember most sat navs don't know if you're towing or in a larger vehicle – always use yours alongside maps and site directions.

NEUVIC (CORREZE) *7C4* (4km N Rural) *45.38245, 2.22901* **Camping Domaine de Mialaret, Route d'Egletons, 19160 Neuvic [05 55 46 02 50; fax 05 55 46 02 65; info@lemialaret.com; www.lemialaret.com]** Fr N on A89 exit 23 twds St Angel then D171 to Neuvic or foll sp fr Neuvic on D991. Med, some hdg pitch, pt sl, pt shd; htd wc; chem disp; mv service pnt; baby facs; shwrs inc; el pnts (10A) €3-4; Indtte; shop; tradsmn; rest in chateau fr May; snacks high ssn; bar; playgrnd; pool; 2 carp fishing pools; watersports nrby; mini-farm; mountain bike rtes; walking tours; games rm; wifi; entmnt; TV rm; 30% statics (sep area); dogs free; phone; bus 4km; poss cr; quiet; adv bkg; Eng spkn; red long stay/low ssn; CKE/CCI. "Excel site in grnds of chateau; charming owner, friendly staff; facs ltd low ssn; blocks req most pitches; children's mini-zoo & rare sheep breeds nrby." 26 Apr-5 Oct. € 42.60 2014*

NEUVIC (CORREZE) *7C4* (4km N Rural) *45.41034, 2.28469* **Camping Le Soustran, Pellachal, 19160 Neuvic [05 55 95 03 71 or 06 47 94 89 34 (mob); info@lesoustran.com; www.lesoustran.com]** N fr Neuvic on D982 dir Ussel for 4km; site on L 300m after bdge. Ent steepish & rough. Med, mkd pitch, terr, pt shd; wc; chem disp; shwrs inc; el pnts (6A) €3; Indtte; snacks; bar; BBQ; playgrnd; lake sw 300m; TV rm; dogs €1; Eng spkn; quiet; CKE/CCI. "No twin-axles." ♦ ltd 1 May-15 Sep. € 16.00 2010*

NEUVIC (CORREZE) *7C4* (5km NE Rural) **Camping à la Ferme Chez Père Jules (Van Boshuysen), Prentegarde, 19160 Liginiac [tel/fax 05 55 95 84 49; rob_ykie@hotmail.com]** Exit A89 junc 23 onto D979 dir Bort-les-Orgues; in 5km (just after La Serre) turn R onto D982; in 10km turn L to Liginiac; cont thro vill & then turn R uphill onto D20. Site sp to R in 1.5km. Sm, pt sl, pt shd; wc; chem disp; shwrs inc; el pnts (4A) inc; Indtte; shop 1.5km; sm rest; bar; BBQ; playgrnd; pool; lake sw 2km; 5% statics; dogs; Eng spkn; adv bkg; quiet; CKE/CCI. "Beautiful CL-type site; helpful Dutch owners; rallies welcome; mv service pnt in Liginiac; vg; highly rec." 1 Apr-30 Sep. € 15.00 2012*

LIMOUSIN

⊞ **NEUVIC (CORREZE)** *7C4* (7km NW Rural) *45.42721, 2.20419* **Camping Le Vianon, Les Plaines, 19160 Palisse [05 55 95 87 22; fax 05 55 95 98 45; camping.vianon@wanadoo.fr; www.levianon.com]** Fr Neuvic take D47 twd Pallisse. Site well sp. Med, mkd pitch, pt sl, pt shd; htd wc; chem disp; mv service pnt; baby facs; shwrs inc; el pnts (16A) €3.50; Indtte; shops; tradsmn; rest, snacks; bar; BBQ; playgrnd; pool; lake fishing; sports activities; tennis; entmnt; internet; TV rm; 15% statics; dogs €2; poss cr; Eng spkn; adv bkg; quiet; red 7+ days; CKE/CCI. "Woodland walks; friendly Dutch owners; vg rest & bar; clean facs." ♦ ltd € 25.85 2009*

NEXON *7B3* (1km SW Rural) *45.67104, 1.18059* **Camp Municipal de l'Etang de la Lande, 87800 Nexon [05 55 58 35 44 or 05 55 58 10 19 (Mairie); fax 05 55 58 33 50; campingdelalande.nexon@orange.fr; www.nexon.fr]** S fr Limoges on D704, take D15 W twd Nexon. Exit Nexon by D11 sp Ladignac-le-Long & Camping, site 3km S at junc with D17. Med, mkd pitch, sl, pt shd; htd wc; shwrs; el pnts (5-10A); Indtte; shop; bar; rest, supmkt 1km; playgrnd; lake sw adj; cycle hire; entmnt; TV rm; Eng spkn; quiet. "Excel base for Limoges; site open to adj leisure park." 1 Jun-30 Sep. € 10.00 2013*

NOAILLES see Brive la Gaillarde *7C3*

PEYRAT LE CHATEAU see Eymoutiers *7B4*

PIERRE BUFFIERE *7B3* (1.5km S Rural) *45.68937, 1.37101* **Camp Intercommunal Chabanas, 87260 Pierre-Buffière [tel/fax 05 55 00 96 43]** Approx 20km S of Limoges on A20, take exit 40 onto D420 S bound; site on L in 500m. Foll sps for 'Stade-Chabanas'. Med, hdg/mkd pitch (all grass gd size), pt sl, pt shd; wc; chem disp (wc); shwrs inc; el pnts (10A) inc (poss rev pol); Indtte; shop & snacks 2 km; playgrnd; fishing; dogs €0.80; phone; adv bkg; quiet but some rlwy noise; red low ssn; CKE/CCI. "Clean, quiet site; helpful staff; excel san facs; some pitches diff for lge o'fits; no twin-axles; warden on site 1600-2200, but gate poss locked all day low ssn (code issued); phone ahead; conv Limoges; excel NH fr A20." ♦ 15 May-30 Sep. € 16.00 2014*

PRESSIGNAC see Rochechouart *7B3*

ROCHECHOUART *7B3* (1km S Rural) *45.81498, 0.82208* **Camping de la Météorite, Boischenu, 87600 Rochechouart [05 55 03 65 96; fax 05 55 05 97 62; campingdelameteorite@orange.fr; www.campingmeteorite.fr]** S fr Rochechouart on D675. Turn R onto D10 them immed L by lake into park. Site ent at far end of park by snack bar. Med, mkd pitch, pt sl, terr, shd; wc; chem disp; mv service pnt; shwrs inc; el pnts (10A) €3 (poss long lead req); gas; sm shop & 3km; tradsmn; rest adj; BBQ; playgrnd; htd pool; cycle hire; games area; games rm; entmnt; internet; TV; 10% statics; dogs free; phone; poss cr; Eng spkn; adv bkg; quiet; ccard acc; red low ssn. "Delightful, wooded site; renovated (2009); helpful owner; clean, modern san facs; gd pool (unfenced 2009); some v steep (10ft) terraces with no retaining walls (2009)." ♦ ltd Easter-30 Sep. € 18.00 (CChq acc) 2010*

ROYERE DE VASSIVIERE *7B4* (6km S Rural) *45.79303, 1.90458* **Camping La Presqu'île, Broussas, 23460 Royère-de-Vassivière [05 55 64 78 98; fax 05 55 64 76 78; presquile.camping@free.fr; http://presquile.camping@free.fr]** Fr Royère-de-Vassivière S on D3 for 6km, turn R onto D34 dir Broussas, site 500m after Broussas. Med, hdg/mkd pitch, terr, shd; wc; chem disp; mv service pnt; shwrs inc; el pnts (10A) €3.10; Indtte (inc dryer); shop; tradsmn; rest, snacks, bar 500m; BBQ; playgrnd; lake sw & beach; fishing; games area; entmnt; 12% statics; dogs free; poss cr; Eng spkn; adv bkg; quiet; red low ssn; CKE/CCI. "Vg site; gd walking/cycling rtes around lake." 6 Jun-7 Sep. € 12.40 2010*

ROYERE DE VASSIVIERE *7B4* (6km SW Rural) *45.78869, 1.89855* **Camping Les Terrasses du Lac, Vauveix, 23460 Royère-de-Vassivière [05 55 64 76 77; fax 05 55 64 76 78; lesterrasses.camping@free.fr; http://lesterrasses.camping.free.fr]** Fr Eymoutiers take D43 for approx 10km then take D36 to Vauveix & foll sp. Med, hdg/mkd pitch, terr, pt shd; htd wc; chem disp; shwrs inc; el pnts (10A) €3.10 (poss rev pol); Indtte; rest, bar 300m; snacks 500m; sand beach, sw & watersports adj; horseriding; walking; cycling; TV rm; dogs free; phone 50m; quiet; CKE/CCI. "Helpful staff; lovely setting." ♦ 1 Apr-15 Oct. € 14.50 2010*

ST BRICE SUR VIENNE see St Junien *7B3*

ST GERMAIN LES BELLES see Masseret *7B3*

ST JUNIEN *7B3* (1km N Urban) *45.89616, 0.89979* **Camp Municipal de la Glane, Allée des Pommiers, Ave Corot, 87200 St Junien [05 55 02 34 86 or 06 74 09 85 88 (mob); fax 05 55 02 34 88; camping@saint-junien.fr; www.mairie-saint-junien.fr]** Fr Limoges take D941/N141 W to St Junien. Or 9km NE Rochechouart on D675. Site in town, well sp adj stadium & pool. Med, hdg pitch, pt sl, pt shd; wc; chem disp; mv service pnt; baby facs; shwrs inc; el pnts (10A) €3.47; Indtte; BBQ; playgrnd; htd pool 300m; rv fishing 200m; 6% statics; dogs; phone; adv bkg; quiet; CKE/CCI. "Modern san facs; many sloping pitches, some boggy after rain; vg." ♦ ltd 15 May-15 Sep. € 7.04 2010*

ST JUNIEN *7B3* (4km E Rural) *45.88078, 0.96539* **FFCC Camp Municipal de Chambery, 87200 St Brice-sur-Vienne [05 55 02 18 13; fax 05 55 02 93 36; mairiest-brice@wanadoo.fr; www.tourismelimousin.com]** Fr St Junien take D32 E sp St Brice & St Victurnien; on leaving St Brice on D32 turn L & foll sp; site on L in 500m, on E edge of vill. Or app on D32 fr E, turn R onto C2 bef St Brice-sur-Vienne town sign, sp 'Campings & Gite Rural'. Sm, hdg/mkd pitch, hdstg, pt sl, pt shd; htd wc; serviced pitches; shwrs inc; el pnts (10A) €3.40; Indtte; shop in vill; playgrnd; rv nr; dogs; adv bkg; CKE/CCI; "Peaceful, clean site in park; spacious pitches o'look lake & countryside; site yourself, office open 1hr am & pm; barrier clsd 2200-0700; conv Oradour-sur-Glane; excel; beautiful location; excel san facs; each pitch has own tap & drain." ♦ 1 May-15 Sep. € 10.00 2014*

ST LEONARD DE NOBLAT *7B3* (12km N Rural) *45.94311, 1.51459* **Camp Municipal du Pont du Dognon, 87240 St Laurent-les-Eglises [05 55 56 57 25; fax 05 55 56 55 17; mairie-st-laurent-les-eglises@wanadoo.fr]** Take D941 fr St Léonard-de-Noblat; after 1.5km turn L (N) on D19 thro Le Châtenet-en-Dognon. Site in approx 4km, bef St Laurent-les-Eglises. Med, mkd pitch, terr, pt shd; htd wc; shwrs inc; el pnts (5A) €2.62; gas; Indtte; shop & 3km; rest, snacks; BBQ; pool; shgl beach; canoeing; tennis; cycle hire; entmnt; dogs €0.90; adv bkg; quiet. "Vg site." 15 Apr-15 Oct. € 11.25 2009*

ST LEONARD DE NOBLAT *7B3* (2km S Rural) *45.82300, 1.49200* **Camping de Beaufort, 87400 St Léonard-de-Noblat [05 55 56 02 79; info@campingdebeaufort.com; www.campingdebeaufort.com]** Leave A20 S-bound at junc 34 dir St Léonard, onto D941. In 18km on ent St Léonard, 300m after x-ing Rv Vienne, fork R (sp). Site on R in 2km. Med, hdg pitch, pt sl, pt shd; htd wc; chem disp (wc); shwrs inc; el pnts (15A) €3-4; Indtte; shop & 4km; tradsmn; bar; playgrnd; fishing; dogs €1.50; phone; poss cr; adv bkg; ccard acc; CKE/CCI. ♦ Easter-30 Sep. € 13.00 2012*

ST MARTIAL ENTRAYGUES see Argentat *7C4*

ST MATHIEU *7B3* (3km E Rural) *45.71413, 0.78835* **Camp Municipal du Lac, Les Champs, 87440 St Mathieu [05 55 00 34 30 (Mairie); fax 05 55 48 80 62]** On D699 heading E in dir of Limoges 1.8km fr vill turn on L (N). Sp fr vill cent. Med, hdg/mkd pitch, terr, pt shd; wc; baby facs; shwrs €1; el pnts €3; Indtte; shops 3km; rest adj; playgrnd; lake sw & beach; windsurfing; pedalos; dog €3.50; quiet. "Attractive, well-kept site; pleasant situation on lakeside; lge pitches; site yourself, warden calls; beautiful lake with lots of activities." 1 May-30 Sep. € 19.60 2014*

ST PARDOUX *7A3* (3km S Rural) *46.04955, 1.27893* **Campsite Fréaudour, Site de Freaudour 87250 St Pardoux [05 55 76 57 22; camping.freaudour@orange.fr]** Fr A20 dir Limonges, take exit 25, onto D219. Cont onto D44 thro Razes & foll signs to Lac De Saint-Pardoux. Turn R onto D103A to Freaudour. Med, mkd pitch, pt shd; wc; chem disp; shwr; el pnts (6A); Indtte (inc dryer); shop; snack; bar; BBQ; playgrnd; pool; games area; wifi; tv rm; 20% statics; dogs; Eng spkn; adv bkg. "Fair site." 1 Apr-27 Oct. € 28.00 2014*

ST PRIVAT *7C4* (400m N Rural) *45.14382, 2.09938* **Camping du Chanaux, Rue du Queyrel, 19220 St Privat [tel/fax 05 55 28 28 77 (Mairie); francois-michel.perrier@wanadoo.fr; www.saint-privat-19.fr/camping]** Fr Argentat on D980 for 17km dir Pleaux & Mauriac, rd steep & winding in parts. Sm; wc; chem disp; mv service pnt; el pnts (10A) €3; shops, rests in vill; sm lake adj; some statics. 1 May-31 Oct. € 6.20 2009*

ST SEBASTIEN *7A3* (1km SW Rural) *46.38871, 1.52249* **Camp Municipal La Garenne, Route de la Garenne, 23160 St Sébastien [05 55 63 50 39; fax 05 55 63 44 62]** Exit A20 junc 20 & foll sp dir La Souterraine on D5. In 4km turn L to St Sébastien. On ent vill turn R, R again, site on L just after equestrian cent. Sm, mkd pitch, pt sl, terr, pt shd; wc; shwrs inc; el pnts €2.90; shop, rest 500m; dogs; quiet. "Gd NH nr A20; gd touring base." 15 Apr-15 Oct. € 4.00 2010*

ST SULPICE LES FEUILLES *7A3* (5km NW Rural) *46.33187, 1.31137* **Camping du Lac de Mondon, Mondon, 87160 Cromac [05 55 76 83 99 or 05 55 76 93 34; camping-mondon@orange.fr; www.campingdemondon.com]** Exit A20 junc 22 onto D912 to St Sulpice-les-Feuilles; cont on D912 for 3km until junc with D2; foll sp to Cromac on D105, site sp. Med, hgd/mkd pitch, hdstg, pt sl, pt shd; htd wc; chem disp; mv service pnt; baby facs; shwrs inc; el pnts (10A) €3.20; Indtte (inc dryer); sm shop & shop 6km; tradsmn; rest, snacks; bar; BBQ (gas); playgrnd; htd pool; paddling pool; waterslide; tennis; games area; games rm; wifi; entmnt; dogs €1; Eng spkn; adv bkg; quiet; red low ssn/long stay; CKE/CCI. "Gd cycling; gd touring base; vg." ♦ 17 Apr-3 Oct. € 13.00 2010*

ST YRIEIX LA PERCHE *7B3* (1.7km N Rural) *45.52793, 1.20021* **Camping Plan d'Eau d'Arfeuille, 87500 St Yrieix-la-Perche [05 55 75 08 75; fax 05 55 75 26 08; camping@saint-yrieix.fr]** Site well sp on L on D704 fr St Yrieix-la-Perche N dir Limoges. Fr other dirs look for sp 'Porcelaine Village' - site in same rd. Med, hdg pitch, terr, pt shd; htd wc; chem disp; mv service pnt; baby facs; shwrs; el pnts (10A) inc; Indtte (inc dryer); rest; bar; playgrnd; pool; waterslide; lake sw & beach adj; fishing; canoeing; games area; entmnt; adv bkg; quiet. "Pleasant situation; friendly staff." 15 Apr-15 Sep. € 12.40 2010*

"There aren't many sites open at this time of year"

If you're travelling outside peak season remember to call ahead to check site opening dates – even if the entry says 'open all year'.

⊞ **ST YRIEIX LA PERCHE** *7B3* (8km W Rural) *45.55460, 1.11867* **FFCC Camping Les Vigères, 87500 Le Chalard [05 55 09 37 22; fax 05 55 09 93 39; infovigeres@aol.com; www.lesvigeres.com]** Take N20 to Limoges then N704 to St Yrieix. In St Yrieix turn W on D901 to Châlus. 1st vill is Le Chalard & site is 1km after vill. Sm, hdg/mkd pitch, pt shd; wc; chem disp; shwrs inc; el pnts (3-10A) €3-4; Indtte; shops 2km; BBQ; playgrnd; pool; lake sw & sand beach adj; fishing; library; adv bkg; v quiet; 10% red low ssn; CKE/CCI. "Vg, peaceful site; welcoming British owners; clean san facs, ltd low ssn (htd extension planned 2010); poss unkempt low ssn; historic area; rec." ♦ € 14.50 2009*

ST YRIEIX LA PERCHE *7B3* (12km NW Rural) *45.59175, 1.11131* **Camp Municipal de Bel Air, 87500 Ladignac-le-Long [05 55 09 39 82 or 05 55 09 30 02 (Mairie); fax 05 55 09 39 80; camping-ladignac@wanadoo.fr; www.ladignac.com]** Exit Limoges S on N21 to Châlus. Turn E on D901 sp St Yrieix to Ladignac. Turn N to lakes at sp. Site on R. Med, pt shd, hdg pitch; wc; chem disp; mv service pnt; shwrs inc; el pnts (6A) €3.70; Indtte; shop & 1km; tradsmn; playgrnd; lake sw 500m; games/TV rm; 10% statics; dogs €1.10; phone; no twin-axles; Eng spkn; adv bkg; quiet; red low ssn; CKE/CCI. "Beautiful lakeside site; spacious pitches; clean san facs; barrier with card operation - early ssn apply to Mairie in vill sq for card; cycling; walking; excel." 1 Jun-30 Sep. € 11.50 2011*

SALLES LAVAUGUYON, LES see Rochechouart *7B3*

LIMOUSIN

SEILHAC *7C4* (4km SW Rural) *45.35018, 1.64642* **Camp Municipal du Pilard, La Barthe, 19700 Lagraulière [05 55 73 71 04; fax 05 55 73 25 28; mairie.lagrauliere@wanadoo.fr; www.lagrauliere.correze.net]** Exit A20 junc 46 onto D34 to Lagraulière, site sp. NB Lge o'fits rec take D44 & D167E fr Seilhac. Sm, mkd pitch, pt shd; wc; chem disp (wc); shwrs inc; el pnts (3-6A) €3 (poss rev pol); gas 2km, shop 700m; rest, snacks & bar 1km; BBQ; playgrnd; htd pool adj; tennis; dogs €1; phone adj; Eng spkn; quiet; CKE/CCI. "Quiet, clean site nr pleasant interesting vill; warden calls; mkts on Thurs." ♦ ltd 15 Jun-15 Sep. € 10.00 2014*

SEILHAC *7C4* (2.5km NW Rural) *45.37750, 1.70227* **Camp Municipal Le Lac de Bournazel, 19700 Seilhac [05 55 27 05 65; fax 04 73 93 71 00]** Fr Seilhac W on D1120 for 1.5km turn R at rndabt for 1km, clearly sp. Lge, mkd pitch, terr, pt shd; wc; chem disp; mv service pnt; baby facs; shwrs inc; el pnts (6-10A) €3.05; Indtte; shop in ssn; rest, bar; snacks 100m; BBQ; playgrnd; lakeside beach & sw adj; 25% statics; dogs €1.10; Eng spkn; adv bkg; CKE/CCI. "Clean site with public access; lge pitches." 1 Apr-30 Sep. € 13.85 2009*

SOUBREBOST see Bourganeuf *7B4*

⊞ **SOUTERRAINE, LA** *7A3* (2km NE Rural) *46.24368, 1.50606* **Camping Suisse Océan, Etang-du-Cheix, 23300 La Souterraine [05 55 63 33 32 or 05 55 63 59 71; fax 05 55 63 21 82]** Fr N145/E62 take D72 sp La Souterraine. Strt over 1st rndabt, at 2nd rndabt turn R, then L to L'Etang de Cheix. Fr N exit A20 junc 22 onto D912 sp La Souterraine; at T-junc turn L & foll outer rd D912b; at rndabt turn L to Etang-du-Cheix; in 50m turn L to site. Sp fr D912b. Sm, hdg/mkd pitch, hdstg, pt sl, terr, pt shd; htd wc (some cont); chem disp; mv service pnt; shwrs inc; el pnts (10A) €3.50; Indtte; sm shop & 2km; tradsmn; rest, snacks; bar; playgrnd; sand lake beach, fishing, sailing adj; diving (summer); tennis; 10% statics; dogs €1.20; poss cr; Eng spkn; adv bkg; quiet but night noise fr factory nrby; CKE/CCI. "Superb location by lake; lge pitches; sl rds on site could grnd lge o'fits - walk site bef pitching; san facs in portacabin; ltd facs low ssn inc el pnts & inadequate when site full; pleasant sm town; mkt Thur & Sat; site fair." ♦ € 15.30 2012*

SOUTERRAINE, LA *7A3* (6km E Rural) *46.24534, 1.59083* **Camp Municipal Etang de la Cazine, 23300 Noth [tel/fax 05 55 63 31 17; mairiedenoth@wanadoo.fr]** Exit A20 junc 23 onto N145 dir Guéret; turn L on D49 sp Noth. Site opp lake. Sm, pt shd, mkd pitch, pt sl; wc; chem disp; mv service pnt; shwrs inc; el pnts (16A) €3; ltd snacks; bar; playgrnd; dog €1.50; lake fishing & sw adj; quiet; CKE/CCI. "Gd touring base; gd; san facs portacabins; excel NH and sh stay; rural location." 31 Mar-7 Nov. € 16.00 2013*

SOUTERRAINE, LA *7A3* (10km S Rural) *46.15129, 1.51059* **Camp Municipal, 23290 St Pierre-de-Fursac [05 55 63 65 69 or 05 55 63 61 28 (Mairie); fax 05 55 63 68 20; www.communes-fursac.fr]** Exit A20 at junc 23.1 onto D1 S twd St Pierre-de-Fursac. Site on L at ent to vill dir 'Stade'. Sm, mkd pitch, pt sl, pt shd; wc; shwrs inc; el pnts (6A) €2 (poss rev pol); shop 500m; playgrnd; phone; quiet. "Pleasant, well-kept site o'looking vill; san facs basic but clean; fine NH; gd." ♦ ltd 15 Jun-15 Sep. € 8.00 2013*

TREIGNAC *7B4* (4.5km N Rural) *45.56023, 1.81369* **Camping La Plage, Lac des Barriousses, 19260 Treignac [05 55 98 08 54; fax 05 55 98 16 47; camping.laplage@flowercampings.com; www.laplagecamping.com]** On D940 opp Lac des Barriousses. Med, mkd pitch, pt sl, terr, shd; htd wc; chem disp; mv service pnt; shwrs inc; el pnts (6A) €2.80; Indtte; sm shop on site & 4.5km; rest 500m; snacks; lake sw, boating, fishing adj; 5% statics; dogs €1.20; poss cr; adv bkg; quiet; CKE/CCI. "Beautiful area & outlook; friendly; facs unclean low ssn." ♦ 30 Mar-29 Sep. € 22.70 2013*

TREIGNAC *7B4* (10km SE Rural) *45.50262, 1.86911* **Camping Le Fayard (Naturist), Cors, 19260 Veix [05 55 94 00 20 or 0031 113301245 (N'lands); veen514@zonnet.nl; www.le-fayard.com]** Fr Treignac take D16 dir Lestards. 1km after Lestards take D32 S & in 2km turn R dir Cors, site sp. Sm, mkd pitch, pt sl, pt shd; wc; chem disp; baby facs; fam bthrm; shwrs inc; el pts (6A) €3.50; Indtte; shop 7km; tradsmn; rest 10km; bar; playgrnd; htd pool; games area; dogs €2; adv bkg; quiet; CKE/CCI. "Friendly Dutch owners; relaxing site in National Park of Limousin." ♦ 1 May-19 Sep. € 16.00 2012*

TREIGNAC *7B4* (10km NW Rural) *45.57956, 1.70852* **Camp Municipal Le Merle/Badinage, 19370 Chamberet [05 55 98 30 12 (Mairie); fax 05 55 98 79 34; mairie.chamberet@wanadoo.fr; www.chamberet-correze.net]** S fr Eymoutiers on D30 or N fr Treignac on D16. In Chamberet foll sp Camping Badinage, opp lake take rd up past some houses, site 250m at end. Sm, mkd pitch, hdstg, pt sl, terr, shd; wc; chem disp (wc); mv service pnt at stadium; shwrs inc; el pnts (6A) €1.50; gas 1km; Indtte (inc dryers); shop, rest & bar 1km; BBQ; playgrnd; pool & lake sw 250m; cycle hire; dogs; quiet; CKE/CCI. "Peaceful site; pay at Camping du Bois Combet opp (tel 05 55 98 96 83); vg." ♦ ltd 15 Jun-15 Sep. € 10.00 2009*

TROCHE see Uzerche *7B3*

TULLE *7C4* (3km NE Rural) *45.28330, 1.78673* **Camp Municipal Bourbacoup, Ave du Lieutenant-Colonel Faro, 19000 Tulle [05 55 26 75 97; fax 05 55 21 73 62]** Fr Tulle, take D1120 NW dir Limoges. Turn R onto D23 & foll site sp. Med, mkd pitch, pt shd; wc (some cont); shwrs inc; el pnts inc; supmkt 3km; rest, bar 1km; pool 1km; rv adj; dogs; quiet. "Pretty site beside stream; easy cycle ride to town; dated but clean san facs." ♦ 1 Jul-31 Aug. € 11.30 2010*

TULLE *7C4* (12km NE Rural) *45.39658, 1.86223* **Camping L'Etang de Ruffaud, 19800 St Priest-de-Gimel [06 81 85 83 27 or 05 55 21 32 81; dominique.dorme@gmail.com; www.campingdeletang.sitew.com]** Sp on D1089 Tulle-Clermont-Ferrand rd & 3km S of this rd. Med, pt shd, pt sl; wc; chem disp; shwrs; el pnts (10A); gas; Indtte (inc dryer); tradsmn; rest; snack; BBQ; playgrnd; shgl beach adj; rv fishing; boating; windsurfing; cycle hire; tennis; TV rm; entmnt; dogs; phone; quiet; Eng spkn; adv bkg; CKE/CCI. "Vg site; canoe/pedalo hire; set in woodland next to lake; owner runs rest with reasonably priced menu; beautiful location; Gimel Cascades 4km." ♦ ltd 15 May-30 Sep. € 18.80 2014*

TULLE *7C4* (4km SE Rural) *45.24992, 1.78948* **Camping Le Pré du Moulin, 19150 Laguenne [tel/fax 05 55 26 21 96; camping@lepredumoulin.com; www.lepredumoulin.com]** Exit Tulle on D1120 twd Aurillac, pass ATAC commercial cent on R, cross bdge & 1st L to camp site. Last 1km on unmade rd, but not diff. Sm, pt sl, pt shd; wc; chem disp; shwrs inc; el pnts (6A) €2.50; gas; Indtte; shops 2km; tradsmn; snacks; pool; rv fishing adj; cycle hire; €1.50; adv bkg rec high ssn; quiet; red low ssn; CKE/CCI. "Attractive, peaceful, well-kept British-owned site; steep climb to adequate san facs." 1 Apr-1 Oct. € 16.00 2010*

UZERCHE *7B3* (8km NE Rural) *45.45200, 1.65056* **Camping Aimée Porcher (Naturist), 19140 Pingrieux Eyburie [05 55 73 20 97 or 06 01 11 51 90; aimeeporcher@hotmail.com; www.aimee-porcher.com]** Fr Uzerche take D3 NE to Eyburie & in Eyburie turn R at site sp (Cheyron/Pingrieux). In 1km turn L at site sp; site at end of narr lane. Sm, mkd pitch, terr, pt shd; wc; chem disp; shwrs inc; baby facs; el pnts (6A) (poss long lead req); Indtte; tradsmn; snacks; bar; BBQ; playgrnd; lake sw adj; games area; no statics; dogs; adv bkg; quiet; red long stay; INF card; wifi. "Beautiful views; wonderful location; INF not req; new san facs in lower meadow 2013; spacious pitches; basic; site rd steep in places; superb." ♦ 20 May-6 Sep. € 23.00 2014*

UZERCHE *7B3* (200m SE Rural) *45.42148, 1.56592* **Camp Municipal La Minoterie, Route de la Minoterie, 19140 Uzerche [tel/fax 05 55 73 12 75; nicolas@uzerche.fr; http://camping.uzerche.fr]** Fr N exit A20 at junc 44 for Uzerche on D920; proceed thro tunnel & cross town bdge. Site clearly sp on ent to town on rvside. Steep app rd & sharp bend. NB Narr app rd used by lorries fr nrby quarry. Site well sp. NB Steep exit. Sm, mkd pitch, pt sl, shd; wc; chem disp; shwrs inc; el pnts (10A) €2.90; Indtte; shops 200m; tradsmn; BBQ; playgrnd; fishing; kayak hire; white water sports cent; rock-climbing; tennis; games rm; TV rm; Eng spkn; quiet; CKE/CCI. "Lovely pitches on rv's edge; helpful warden; clean san facs; not suitable lge o'fits or lge m'vans; sh walk along rv to beautiful old vill; gd local walks; poss risk of flooding; v quiet end of ssn with ltd pitches; conv NH; excel." 1 May-2 Oct. € 13.30 2014*

UZERCHE *7B3* (9km SW Rural) *45.36861, 1.53849* **Camp Municipal du Lac du Pontcharal, 19410 Vigeois [05 55 98 90 86 or 05 55 98 91 93 (Mairie); fax 05 55 98 99 79; mairievigeois@wanadoo.fr; www.vigeois.com]** Fr A20 exit 45 onto D3 to Vegeois then D7. Site is 2.5km SE of Vigeois. Med, pt sl, shd; wc; chem disp; shwrs inc; el pnts (15A) €3.50 (poss rev pol); gas; Indtte; shop; rest, snacks; bar; playgrnd; lake sw & beach; fishing; watersports; games area; tennis 2km; entmnt; TV; dogs €0.90; adv bkg; quiet. "Delightful, well-kept site in picturesque setting; excel san facs." ♦ 1 Jun-15 Sep. € 10.70 2012*

UZERCHE *7B3* (9km SW Rural) *45.40833, 1.47898* **FFCC Camping à la Ferme Domaine Vert (Broeks), Les Magnes, 19230 Troche [tel/fax 05 55 73 59 89; www.ledomainevert.nl]** Exit A20 junc 45 onto D3 to Vigeois, 2km after Vigeois turn R onto D50 sp Lubersac. After 5km (ignore sp to Troche) foll site sp to R. NB Narr, twisty rds, not suitable lge o'fits. Sm, pt sl, pt shd; wc; shwrs; Indry rm; el pnts €2.50 (poss rev pol); meals avail; fishing 4km; canoeing nr, lake sw; wifi; dogs €1.50; Eng spkn; quiet; red CKE/CCI. "Popular, peaceful, well-kept farm site; many pitches v sl; welcoming, friendly Dutch owners; adv bkg ess high ssn; lovely lake; vg." 1 Apr-1 Oct. € 17.00 2010*

UZERCHE *7B3* (12km SW Rural) *45.34632, 1.51493* **Aire Naturelle du Bois Coutal (Veysseix), Perpezac-le-Noir, 19410 Vigeois [05 55 73 71 93; fax 05 55 73 27 66; boiscoutal@wanadoo.fr]** Exit A20/E09 S fr Uzerche at junc 46 onto D920 N & foll sp Perpezac le-Noir. Go thro Perpezac on D156 N dir Vigeois & foll site sp. Site in 4km. Sm, sl, pt shd; wc; chem disp; shwrs inc; el pnts inc (6A) €2.50; Indtte; shop, rest, snacks, bar 3km; playgrnd; pool; games rm; entmnt; few statics; dogs; poss cr; Eng spkn; adv bkg; v quiet. "Friendly, helpful owner; clean facs; gd NH." 15 Apt-15 Oct. € 9.00 2009*

VEIX see Treignac *7B4*

VIGEOIS see Uzerche *7B3*

Lorraine

Regional Introduction

Place Stanislas, Nancy

Welcome to Lorraine

A region with a growing tourism industry, Lorraine is particularly appreciated for its architecture and beautiful landscapes.

It has also hosted a number of famous battles and wars, most notably during WWI. Verdun's battlefields still show signs of bomb and grenade damage to remind visitors of the terrible struggles that took place.

There are many museums and monuments in the region's old cities and towns. With its blend of French and German cultures and its rich history, this region has a lot to offer.

Local highlights

Possibly the most famous dish from this region is Quiche Lorraine, created in the 16th-century. Regional cuisine is German influenced, such as Potée Lorraine (Lorraine hotpot), a speciality made from smoked meats.

Every two years Chambley Bussières Aerodrome hosts Europe's largest hot air balloon festival, and the 10 day event is a spectacular sight to behold.

Major towns and cities

- Metz – the region's capital city, boasting gothic architecture, festivals and concerts.
- Nancy – a pretty city full of museums and Art Nouveau heritage featuring 3 UNESCO listed squares.
- Thionville – found on the bank of the River Moselle, with lots of historical sights.
- Verdun – famous for battles including during WWI, it has many museums of remembrance.

Regional attractions

- Place Stanislas, Nancy – admire the golden gates, magnificent statues and fountains.
- Verdun Battlefield – read the stories and tour the bunkers of this humbling place.
- Cathédrale of St Stephen, Metz – one of the tallest cathedrals in France, known for an extensive use of stained glass.
- Joan of Arc's birthplace – visit the village of Domrémy-la-Pucelle to learn about her life.

Find out more

www.tourism-lorraine.com
Tel: (0)3 83 35 22 41 Nancy Tourist Office
Tel: (0)3 29 84 55 55 Verdun Tourist Office

ANOULD see Corcieux *6F3*

BACCARAT *6E2* (1km SE Rural) *48.44360, 6.74360* **Camp Municipal Pré de Hon, 54120 Baccarat [03 83 76 35 35 or 03 83 75 13 37 (LS); fax 03 83 75 36 76; info-baccarat@orange.fr; www.ot-baccarat.fr]** Fr Baccarat cent opp town hall take D158 S past church twd Lachapelle. Site in 500m down lane on L. Sm, pt shd, wc; chem disp; shwrs; el pnts (10A); shop 200m; pool nr; bus 400m; poss cr; adv bkg; quiet, some rd noise; CKE/CCI. "Pleasant, quiet rvside site; pleasant, helpful warden, if absent site yourself; vg san facs; rvside walk to interesting town; gd NH." ♦ ltd 30 Apr-10 Oct. € 9.40 2013*

BAERENTHAL *5D3* (500m N Rural) *48.98170, 7.51230* **Camp Municipal Ramstein-Plage, Rue de Ramstein, 57230 Baerenthal [tel/fax 03 87 06 50 73; camping.ramstein@wanadoo.fr; www.baerenthal.eu]** Fr N62 turn onto D36 sp Baerenthal, site sp on lakeside. Lge, hdg/mkd pitch, pt sl, pt shd; htd wc; chem disp; mv service pnt; baby facs; shwrs inc; el pnts (12A) €3.50; Indtte; shop 1km; rest, snacks; bar; playgrnd; htd pool; lake sw, sand beach adj; tennis; games area; entmnt; 80% statics (sep area); dogs €1.90; m'van o'night area; poss cr; Eng spkn; adv bkg; quiet. "Attractive location in important ecological area; generous pitches; modern san facs; gd walks; birdwatching; conv Maginot Line; excel." ♦ ltd 1 Apr-30 Sep. € 28.00 2013*

BAN DE SAPT see Raon l'Etape *6E3*

BAR LE DUC *6E1* (1km E Urban) *48.77433, 5.17415* **FFCC Camp Municipal du Château de Marbeaumont, Rue du Stade, off Rue de St Mihiel, 55000 Bar-le-Duc [03 29 79 17 33 (TO) or 03 29 79 11 13 (LS)); fax 03 29 79 21 95; barleduc.tourisme@wanadoo.fr; www.tourisme-barleduc.com]** Fr town cent foll Camping sps. Rue de St Mihiel is pt of D1916 dir Verdun. Fr NW on D994/D694 or fr SE on N1135, at rndabt turn E onto D1916 sp Metz, Verdun & St Mihiel. In 200m turn L into Rue du Stade sp Camping. Site on L in 100m. Sm, pt shd; wc; chem disp; shwrs inc; el pnts (6A) €3 (poss long lead req); Indtte (inc dryer); shops adj; no twin-axles; some rd noise. "Barrier clsd 1100-1500; delightful site in grnds of chateau; friendly & helpful warden; clean, modern san facs; check gate opening times; lovely walk into historic town; gd NH; vg site." 1 May-15 Oct. € 12.00 2014*

BAYON *6E2* (500m NW Rural) *48.47898, 6.30645* **Camp Municipal du Passetemps, Rue de la Moselle, 54290 Bayon [tel/fax 03 83 72 45 60 or 03 83 72 51 52 (Mairie)]** Fr N57 N fr Charmes or S fr Nancy; turn onto D9 sp Bayon; in 2.5km strt on at x-rds & over bdge; site on L in 500m by Rv Moselle. Med, pt shd; wc (some cont); chem disp; shwrs €0.90; el pnts (8A) inc; rest 500m; playgrnd; rv & sports facs adj; 50% statics; quiet. "Rv adj liable to dry out & also flood - care in wet weather; barrier clsd 2200-0700." 15 Apr-15 Oct. € 12.00 2009*

BLAMONT *6E3* (1km E Rural) *48.58890, 6.85051* **Camp Municipal de la Vezouze, Route de Cirey, 54450 Blâmont [03 83 76 28 28 (Mairie) or 06 07 70 27 39 (mob); fax 03 83 76 28 32; www.tourisme-meurtheetmoselle.fr]** Fr Sarrebourg on N4 dir Blâmont; foll sps Town Cent, then turn L onto D74/ D993 dir Cirey-sous-Vezouze & foll sp for site. Sm, pt shd; wc; shwrs inc; el pnts (16A) €2; shop, rest, snacks, bar 300m; playgrnd; sports area; sw, fishing adj; dogs €1; quiet. "Gd rvside site; gd walking, cycling." 15 May-15 Sep. € 12.00 2011*

⊞ **BRESSE, LA** *6F3* (3.2km E Rural) *47.99878, 6.91831* **FFCC Camp Municipal Le Haut des Bluches, 5 Route des Planches, 88250 La Bresse [03 29 25 64 80; fax 03 29 25 78 03; hautdesbluches@labresse.fr; www.domainehautdesbluches.labresse.fr]** Leave La Bresse on D34 Rte de la Schlucht. Site on R in 3km. Med, mkd pitch, terr, pt shd; htd wc; chem disp; mv service pnt; child/baby facs; shwrs inc; el pnts (4-13A) €2-4.80; Indtte; shop; tradsmn; rest, snacks; bar; BBQ; playgrnd; pool in vill; games area; games rm; internet; TV; 10% statics; dogs free; NH area for m'vans; site clsd early Nov-mid Dec; Eng spkn; adv bkg; red low ssn; ccard acc; red low ssn/CKE/CCI. "Excel site in attractive setting; excel san facs; gd walks fr site; conv winter sports." ♦ € 12.80 2009*

"That's changed – Should I let The Club know?"

If you find something on site that's different from the site entry, fill in a report and let us know. See www.caravanclub.co.uk/europereport.

BRIEY *5D2* (1km NW Rural) *49.25153, 5.92992* **Camping Intercommunal Plan d'Eau de la Sangsue, 54150 Briey [03 82 20 96 22; fax 03 82 46 19 47; maisondutourisme@ccpb54.fr; www.cc-paysdebriey.fr]** Exit A4 junc 33 to Briey, site sp. Access rd v steep & narr with bends & rough surface. Exit also diff due steep rd. Sm, hdstg, terr; wc; chem disp; shwrs inc; el pnts (16A) €1.50; snacks; playgrnd; dogs €0.50; CKE/CCI. "Gd site adj lake; gd walks; suitable m'vans only due steep access." 1 May-31 Oct. € 7.00 2010*

BRUYERES *6E2* (6km S Rural) *48.17870, 6.74309* **Camping Domaine des Messires, 1 La Feigne, 88600 Herpelmont [03 29 58 56 29 or 0031 321 331456 (N'lands); fax 03 29 51 62 86; mail@domainedesmessires.com; www.domainedesmessires.com]** SE fr Bruyères on D423; at Laveline turn R sp Herpelmont & foll site sp. Site 1.5km N of Herpelmont. Med, pt shd; wc; mv service pnt; chem disp; serviced pitches; baby facs; shwrs inc; el pnts (6A) inc; gas; Indtte (inc dryer); shop; tradsmn; rest, snacks; bar; BBQ; playgrnd; lake sw; fishing; boating; games rm; wifi; child entmnt; TV; dogs €4; Eng spkn; adv bkg; quiet; ccard acc; red low ssn/long stay; CKE/CCI. "Attractive, peaceful, lakeside site; gd touring base Alsace & Vosges; friendly, helpful staff." ♦ 23 Apr-18 Sep. € 25.50 2010*

LORRAINE

BULGNEVILLE *6F2* (750m SE Rural) *48.19828, 5.84554* **Camping Porte des Voges, La Grande Tranchée, Route de Contrexéville, 88140 Bulgnéville [03 29 09 12 00; fax 03 29 09 15 71; camping.portedesvosges@wanadoo.fr; www.camping-portedesvosges.com]** Exit A31 junc 9; at 1st rndabt foll sp Bulgnéville onto D164; in 2km turn R onto D14; site on L in 200m. Site sp. NB Foll site sp, ignore m'van sp. Med, pt hdstg, pt sl, pt shd; wc; chem disp; baby facs; shwrs inc; el pnts (10A) €3; Indry rm; shop 2km; tradsmn; takeaway; playgrnd; games area; wifi; dogs €2; phone; Eng spkn; quiet; ccard acc. "Lge pitches; clean san facs; conv NH fr A31; poss closes 22 Sept, phone ahead; excel NH; rec." ♦ 14 Apr-30 Sep. € 16.00 2011*

BURTONCOURT *5D2* (1km W Rural) *49.22485, 6.39929* **FFCC Camping La Croix du Bois Sacker, 57220 Burtoncourt [tel/fax 03 87 35 74 08; camping.croixsacker@wanadoo.fr; www.campingcroixsacker.com]** Exit A4 junc 37 sp Argancy; at rndabt foll sp Malroy; at 2nd rndabt foll sp Chieuilles & cont to Vany; then take D3 for 12km dir Bouzonville; turn R onto D53A to Burtoncourt. Lge, hdg/mkd pitch, some hdstg, terr, pt shd; wc (mainly cont); mv service pnt; shwrs €1; el pnts (6A) inc; gas; Indtte; shop; tradsmn; rest, snacks 1km; bar; playgrnd; games area; fishing; tennis; wifi; entmnt; TV; some statics; dogs €1.70; phone; bus 300m; Eng spkn; adv bkg; quiet; CKE/CCI. "Lovely, wooded site in beautiful location; lge pitches; pleasant, friendly owners; clean san facs; forest walks; gd security; gd NH or sh stay en rte Alsace/Germany; conv Maginot Line; excel." ♦ 1 Apr-20 Oct. € 16.00 2010*

CELLES SUR PLAINE see Raon l'Etape *6E3*

CHARMES *6E2* (500m NE Rural) *48.37706, 6.28974* **Camp Municipal Les Iles, 20 Rue de l'Ecluse, 88130 Charmes [tel/fax 03 29 38 87 71 or 03 29 38 85 85; andre.michel63@wanadoo.fr; www.ville-charmes.fr]** Exit N57 for Charmes, site well sp on Rv Moselle. Do not confuse with sp for 'Camping Cars'. Med, mkd pitch, pt shd; wc; chem disp; mv service pnt; shwrs inc; el pnts (10A) €3.55; gas; Indtte; shop 300m; tradsmn; rest, snacks; bar; BBQ; playgrnd; fishing; kayak hire; wifi; dogs; phone; Eng spkn; adv bkg; quiet; red long stay; CKE/CCI. "Lovely site bet rv & canal; lge pitches; friendly staff; footpath to town; m'van o'night area in town; vg value; gd; v lge pitches." ♦ 1 Apr-30 Sep. € 19.30 2013*

CHARNY-SUR-MEUSE see Verdun *5D1*

CHAUMARD *4H4* (400m W Rural) *47.14428, 3.90658* **Camp Municipal Les Iles, 58120 Chaumard [03 86 78 03 00; fax 03 86 78 05 83]** Fr Château-Chinon take D944 dir Pannecière-Chaumard; in 500m turn R onto D37 to Corancy; then D12 to Chaumard; foll camping sp, then turn L into site 100m after cemetary. Sm, hdg pitch, hdstg, pt shd; wc (some cont); chem disp (wc); shwrs; el pnts; lake sw adj; fishing; bus 250m. "Access poss diff lge o'fits." 2009*

CORCIEUX *6F3* (8km NE Urban) *48.18436, 6.95784* **Camping Les Acacias, 191 Rue Léonard de Vinci, 88650 Anould [03 29 57 11 06; contact@acaciascamp.com; www.acaciascamp.com]** Site in vill of Anould sp fr all dir; just off main rd. (Annexe Camping Nature Les Acacias 800m fr this site open 15 Jun-15 Sep, terr in woods). Med, pt shd; wc (some cont); chem disp; mv service pnt; baby facs; shwrs inc; el pnts (6-10A) €3.50-6; gas; Indtte (inc dryer); shops 500m; supmkt 2km; rest, snacks; sm bar; playgrnd; sm, htd pool; rv fishing nrby; games rm; tennis & karting 2km; cycle trails; 10% statics; dogs €1; poss cr; Eng spkn; adv bkg; quiet; CKE/CCI; wifi. "Gd standard site; helpful owners; gd, clean san facs; excel." ♦ 15 Jun-15 Sep. € 20.80 2014*

CORCIEUX *6F3* (600m E Rural) *48.16826, 6.89006* **Camping Le Clos de la Chaume, 21 Rue d'Alsace, 88430 Corcieux [tel/fax 03 29 50 76 76 or 06 85 19 62 55 (mob); info@camping-closdelachaume.com; www.camping-closdelachaume.com]** Take D145 fr St Dié, then D8 thro Anould & bear R onto D60. Site in 3km on R at ent to vill. Med, hdg/mkd pitch, hdstg, pt shd; wc; chem disp; mv service pnt; some serviced pitches; fam bthrm; baby facs; shwrs inc; el pnts (8-10A) €3.50 ; gas; Indtte (inc dryer); shop, rest, snacks & bar 600m; BBQ; playgrnd; pool; sand beach & lake sw 12km; fishing; cycle hire 800m; games area; games rm; wifi €5; TV; 15% statics; dogs €1.70; twin-axles acc (rec check in adv); phone; Eng spkn; adv bkg; quiet; ccard acc; red low ssn/long stay/CKE/CCI. "Lovely, peaceful site in beautiful area; stream runs thro; friendly & helpful owners; san facs poss stetched high ssn; conv Gérardmer & Alsace wine rte; excel; acess rd vg; highly rec." ♦ 26 Apr-19 Sep. € 31.00 SBS - J08 2013*

See advertisement

CORCIEUX *6F3* (1km E Rural) *48.16631, 6.89366* **Camping au Mica, 8 Route de Gérardmer, 88430 Corcieux [tel/fax 03 29 50 70 07; info@campingaumica.com; www.campingaumica.com]** S fr fr St Dié on D415 to Arnould; at rndabt turn R onto D8; in 3km (at La Plafond) turn R onto D60 sp Corcieux; site on L in 3km. Med, hdg/mkd pitch,pt shd; wc (some cont); chem disp; mv service pnt; baby facs; serviced pitches; shwrs inc; el pnts (6A) €3.50; gas; Indtte (inc dryer); shop; tradsmn; BBQ; playgrnd; pool 150m; rv fishing adj; games area; games rm; wifi; TV; some statics; dogs €1; phone; bus; poss cr; Eng spkn; adv bkg; quiet; red low ssn/long stay; ccard acc; CKE/CCI. "Peaceful site on edge of vill; nice scenery; generous pitches; friendly Dutch owners; gd clean san facs; walking rtes in beautiful National Park; a v pleasant stay; excel." ♦ ltd 24 Apr-15 Sep. € 13.00 2011*

CORNY SUR MOSELLE *5D2* (650m N Rural) *49.03768, 6.05736* **Camping Le Pâquis, rue de la Moselle, 57680 Corny-sur-Moselle [03 87 52 03 59 or 03 87 60 68 67; fax 03 87 52 05 78; campinglepaquis@orange.fr; http://campinglepaquis.free.fr]** SW fr Metz on D657; site sp on ent to vill. Or S on A31 take junc 29 Féy & turn R onto D66 into Corny-sur-Moselle; at rndabt in vill turn R & foll sp. Site 300m on L. Lge, pt shd; htd wc; chem disp; shwrs inc; el pnts (6A) inc (long cable poss req); Indtte; shops 1km; tradsmn; snacks; bar; playgrnd; sm lake; rv sw adj; games rm; entmnt; TV; dogs €1.30; poss cr; adv bkg; poss rlwy noise; ccard acc; opening dates vary according to public holidays; CKE/CCI. "Gd, well-run site on Rv Moselle; friendly, helpful owners; rec arr early for quieter pitch at far end site; many pitches long, drive-thro so no need unhitch; pleasant." 1 May-30 Sep. € 20.00 2013*

DUN SUR MEUSE *5C1* (10km SE Rural) *49.32071, 5.26589* **Camping Le Brouzel, 55110 Sivry-sur-Meuse [03 29 85 86 45]** On D964 11km S of Dun twd Verdun, site sp in vill of Sivry. Sm, some hdstg, unshd; wc (cont); chem disp; shwrs inc; gas; el pnts (6A) €3.15; shop adj; rest, snacks; bar; playgrnd; games area; dir access to rv; fishing; sailing 2km; 80% statics; dogs; Eng spkn; adv bkg; quiet. "Clean site; friendly owner; gd san facs." 1 Apr-1 Oct. € 10.40 2009*

DUN SUR MEUSE *5C1* (10km S Rural) *49.32112, 5.08136* **Camping La Gabrielle, Ferme de la Gabrielle, 55110 Romagne-sous-Montfaucon [03 29 85 11 79; info@lagabrielle.nl; www.lagabrielle.nl]** Site is on D998, 800m beyond end of Romagne. Well sp. Sm, pt sl, pt shd; wc; chem disp (wc); shwrs inc; el pnts (6A) €2 (rev pol); playgrnd; TV; 10% statics; dogs €1; Eng spkn; adv bkg; quiet; CKE/CCI. "Restful site in pretty setting; friendly Dutch owners; meals by arrangement; nr WW1 monuments; gd." ♦ 1 Apr-1 Nov. € 12.00 2011*

EPINAL *6F2* (1km E Urban) *48.17930, 6.46780* **Camping Parc du Château, 37 Rue du Petit Chaperon Rouge, 88000 Epinal [03 29 34 43 65 or 03 29 82 49 41 (LS); fax 03 29 31 05 12; parcduchateau@orange.fr]** Sp fr town cent. Or fr N57 by-pass take exit sp Razimont, site sp in 1km. Med, hdg/mkd pitch, some hdstg, terr, pt shd; htd wc (some cont); chem disp; mv service pnt; shwrs inc; el pnts (6-10A) €5-6; gas; Indtte; shop; snacks; BBQ; playgrnd; pool; lake sw 8km; tennis; TV; 20% statics; dogs €3; Eng spkn; adv bkg; quiet but stadium adj; ccard acc; red low ssn/long stay; CKE/CCI. "Lge pitches; ltd facs low ssn;walk thro park to town; helpful new owners who have improved site." ♦ 1 Apr-30 Sep. € 18.00 2013*

EPINAL *6F2* (8km W Rural) *48.16701, 6.35975* **Kawan Village Club Lac de Bouzey, 19 Rue du Lac, 88390 Sanchey [03 29 82 49 41; fax 03 29 64 28 03; lacdebouzey@orange.fr; www.lacdebouzey.com]** Fr Epinal take D460 sp Darney. In vill of Bouzey turn L at camp sp. Site in few metres, by reservoir. Lge, hdg/mkd pitch, some hdstg, pt sl, terr, pt shd; htd wc (some cont); chem disp; mv service pnt; baby facs; shwrs inc; el pnts (10A) €7; gas; Indtte (inc dryer); shop; tradsmn; rest, snacks; bar; BBQ; playgrnd; htd pool; paddling pool; sand beach & lake adj; fishing; games area; cycle hire; horseriding; wifi; entmnt; TV rm; 15% statics; dogs €4; phone; adv bkg; Eng spkn; quiet; ccard acc; red low ssn/long stay; CKE/CCI. "Excel site; sloping slightly but pitches fairly level; ACSI discount in LS; gd cycling area; nice cycle ride to Epinal." ♦ 1 Feb-31 Dec. € 49.00 (CChq acc) 2014*

FONTENOY LE CHATEAU *6F2* (2km S Rural) *47.95637, 6.21157* **Camping Le Fontenoy, Route de la Vierge, 88240 Fontenoy-le-Château [03 29 36 34 74 or 06 84 48 51 48 (mob); marliesfontenoy@hotmail.com; www.campingfontenoy.com]** SE fr Bains-les-Bains on D434 to Fontenoy-le-Château (6km). In cent of vill turn L onto D40 for 2km to site. Med, mkd pitch, pt shd; wc; chem disp; shwrs inc, el pnts (4A) €2.25; Indtte; tradsmn; rest, snacks; bar; playgrnd; pool 5km; 10% statics; dogs €0.60; poss cr; Eng spkn; adv bkg; quiet, ccard not acc; red long stay; CKE/CCI. "Attractive site; lovely area." 15 Apr-30 Sep. € 11.55 2009*

GERARDMER See also sites listed under Corcieux, Granges-sur-Vologne, La Bresse and Le Tholy.

⊞ **GERARDMER** *6F3* (3km E Rural) *48.07826, 6.94261* **Camp Municipal du Domaine de Longemer, 121 Route de la Plage, 88400 Xonrupt-Longemer [03 29 63 07 30; fax 03 29 63 27 10; camping.dudomaine@wanadoo.fr]** Fr W thro Gérardmer on D417. immed after sp Xonrupt-Longemer turn R & cont thro vill. Site 1st one; turn L over bdge. App fr E (Colmar), turn L opp hotel Auberge du Lac. Site on both sides of rd. V lge, pt shd; htd wc; mv service pnt; shwrs inc; el pnts (6A) €3; shop; rest, snacks; bar; playgrnd; lake sw; fishing; x-country skiing; 10% statics; phone; poss cr; quiet; red long stay; CKE/CCI. "Attractive, clean lakeside site; gd walking." € 10.80 2009*

GERARDMER *6F3* (6km E Rural) *48.06755, 6.94830* **FFCC Camping Les Jonquilles, Route du Lac, 88400 Xonrupt-Longemer [03 29 63 34 01; fax 03 29 60 09 28; info@camping-jonquilles.com; www.camping-jonquilles.com]** Sp off D417 SE of Xonrupt-Longemer. Fr W thro Gérardmer on D417 (sp Colmar) in approx 1km over bdge & turn R at T-junc (still on D417). After 3km turn R opp hotel Auberge du Lac & almost immed R round W end of lake for 500m to T-junc, turn L, site on S bank 1km. Lge, mkd pitch, pt sl, unshd; wc (some cont); chem disp; mv service pnt; baby facs; shwrs inc; el pnts (6-10A) €3.30-5.20; gas; Indtte; shop; rest, snacks; bar; playgrnd; lake beach & sw adj; fishing; sailing; TV;wifi; few statics; dogs €1.50; phone; bus 1km; Eng spkn; adv bkg; quiet but some noise fr entmnt at night; ccard acc; red low ssn; CKE/CCI. "Friendly, well-maintained, family-run site; gd views; poss uneven pitches; excel for Haute Vosges region; great lakeside site." ♦ 20 Apr-6 Oct. € 23.85 2014*

LORRAINE

GERARDMER *6F3* (1.5km SW) *48.06472, 6.85388* **Camping de Ramberchamp, 21 Chemin du Tour du Lac, 88400 Gérardmer [03 29 63 03 82; fax 03 29 63 26 09; info@camping-de-ramberchamp.com; www.camping-de-ramberchamp.com]** S bank of Lake Gérardmer. Fr W turn R off D417, 1km bef Gérardmer. Fr E thro cent of town foll sps to La Bresse, fork R onto D69, sp Vagney. Foll lakeside rd & camping sps. Lge, pt hdg/mkd pitch, pt shd; htd wc; chem disp; shwrs inc;baby facs; el pnts (4A) €3.50; Indtte; shop 1km; tradsmn; rest, snacks; BBQ; playgrnd; lake sw; fishing; TV; dogs €1; poss cr; Eng spkn; quiet; ccard acc; CKE/CCI. "Comfortable site in excel location; friendly staff; some sm pitches; easy-going walks; walk along lake to town; games for children, giant chessboard, mini golf; excel, stunning area; reception open from 0830 to 2030, sanfacs stretched when busy, access rds thro site very narrow for lge o'fits, superb location at edge of lake." 4 Apr-30 Sep. € 20.40 2014*

GERARDMER *6F3* (1.5km SW Rural) *48.0636, 6.8561* **Camping Les Sapins, 18 Chemin de Sapois, 88400 Gérardmer [tel/fax 03 29 63 15 01 or 06 37 35 36 20 (mob); les.sapins@camping-gerardmer.com; www.camping-gerardmer.com]** On S side of lake 150m up C17 rd sp Col de Sapois. Med, pt shd; wc; mv service pnt; shwrs inc; el pnts (4-6A) €3-4.70; sm shop; rest, snacks; bar; BBQ; playgrnd; lake with beach 200m; fishing & watersports adj; games area; TV rm; 10% statics; dogs €1.20; adv bkg rec; quiet; red low ssn. "Well-kept site in lovely area; lge pitches but o'looked by sports stadium; no lake views; walk along lake into pretty town, easy walk to vibrant town, friendly owner." 1 Apr-10 Oct. € 19.60 2014*

GONDREXANGE see Héming *6E3*

GRANGES SUR VOLOGNE *6F3* (5km S Rural) *48.12123, 6.82857* **Camping La Sténiole, 1 Le Haut Rain, 88640 Granges-sur-Vologne [03 29 51 43 75; steniole@wanadoo.fr; www.steniole.com]** D423 fr Gérardmer NW to Granges-sur-Vologne & foll sp. Well sp. Med, hdg pitch, terr, pt shd; wc (some cont); chem disp; shwrs inc; el pnts (4-10A) €3-5; gas; Indtte; shop; supmkt 3km; tradsmn; rest, snacks; bar; BBQ; playgrnd; lake sw & shgl beach adj; fishing, tennis; walking rte; horseriding 4km; games rm; TV rm; 10% statics; dogs €1; Eng spkn; adv bkg rec high ssn; quiet; CKE/CCI. "Pleasant, wooded, relaxing site; vg rest." 15 Apr-30 Oct. € 11.00 2009*

HEMING *6E3* (5km SW Rural) *48.69130, 6.92769* **Camping Les Mouettes, 4 Rue de Diane Capelle, 57142 Gondrexange [03 87 25 06 01; www.otsi-gondrexange.pagesperso-orange.fr]** Exit Héming on N4 Strasbourg-Nancy. Foll sp Gondrexange & site sp. App fr W on D955 turn to site sp on L about 1km bef Héming. Lge, mkd pitch, pt sl, unshd; htd wc; chem disp; mv service pnt; shwrs inc; el pnts (10A) inc (rev pol); Indtte; shop, rest, snacks, bar 200m; playgrnd; lake beach, sw, fishing & sailing adj; tennis; cycle hire; dog €1.50; 60% statics; phone; poss cr; quiet; CKE/CCI. "Pleasant site by lake; poss noisy w/end; basic facs but clean." 1 Apr-30 Sep. € 18.40 2013*

HENRIDORFF see Phalsbourg *5D3*

HERPELMONT see Bruyères *6E2*

HEUDICOURT SOUS LES COTES *5D2* (1km NE Rural) *48.94111, 5.71704* **Camp Municipal Heudicourt, Les Passons Madine 2, 55210 Heudicourt-sous-les-Côtes [03 29 89 36 08; fax 03 29 89 35 60; contact@lacmadine.com; www.lacmadine.com]** Fr St Mihiel, take D901 NE to Chaillon. Turn R on D133 to Heudicourt. Bear L out of vill, still on D133 & after 1km turn R to Nonsard. Site on R in 1.5km at N end of Lake Madine. Lge, mkd pitch, pt sl, pt shd; wc (mainly cont); shwrs inc; el pnts £4; Indtte; shop; rest; lake sw adj; watersports; fishing; many statics; dogs €1; CKE/CCI. "Gd location by Lake Madine." 1 Apr-31 Oct. € 15.00 2011*

JAULNY *5D2* (500m S Rural) *48.96578, 5.88524* **Camping La Pelouse, 54470 Jaulny [tel/fax 03 83 81 91 67; info@campingdelapelouse.com; www.campingdelapelouse.com]** SW fr Metz on D657, cross rv at Corny-sur-Moselle onto D6/D1; in 1.5km turn R onto D952 dir Waville & Thiaucourt-Regniéville; in 6km turn L onto D28 dir Thiaucourt-Regniéville; cont on D28 to Jaulny; site sp to L in Jaulny. Med, sl, pt shd; wc; chem disp; shwrs inc; el pnts (6A) €4; Indtte; tradsmn; rest; bar; BBQ; playgrnd; htd pool; rv sw 100m; fishing; many statics; dogs €2; rlwy noise, TGV trains pass nrby; CKE/CCI. "Vg site; friendly owner and staff; basic san facs, poss stretched high ssn; no fresh or waste water facs for m'vans; conv NH." 1 Apr-30 Sep. € 20.60 2012*

"I like to fill in the reports as I travel from site to site"

You'll find report forms at the back of this guide, or you can fill them in online at www.caravaclub.co.uk/europereport.

LIGNY EN BARROIS *6E1* (500m W Rural) *48.68615, 5.31666* **Camp Municipal Chartel, Rue des Etats-Unis, 55500 Ligny-en-Barrois [03 29 77 09 36 or 03 29 78 02 22 (Mairie)]** If app fr E, leave N4 at Ligny-en-Barrois N exit, turn S twd town; in approx 500m turn R at junc (bef rd narr); foll sm sp, site 500m on L. If app fr W, leave N4 at exit W of town onto N135 (Rue des Etats-Unis); site sp on R. Sm, hdstg, terr, pt shd; wc (some cont), own san facs; chem disp (wc); shwrs; el pnts inc; shop 500m; playgrnd; pool 1km; rv sw & fishing 500m; dogs; rd noise; Eng spkn; CKE/CCI. "Poss diff lge o'fits; modern san facs; further modernisation planned (2010); gd NH; great site and location." 1 Jun-30 Sep. € 10.65 2012*

LIVERDUN see Nancy *6E2*

LUNEVILLE *6E2* (1km NE Urban) *48.59650, 6.49871* **Camping Les Bosquets, 63 Quai des petit , 54300 Lunéville [03 83 74 05 00; fax 03 83 74 16 27; camping@cc-lunevillois.fr; www.cc-lunevillois.fr]** Exit N333 Lunéville by-pass sp 'Lunéville-Château' & foll sp to Lunéville. Fr traff lts in sq in front of chateau, take rd to L of chateau (Quai des Bosquets). At sm rndabt do not ent site on R but cont round rndabt to L to yard opp warden's house. Warden will open barrier. Sm, mkd pitch, terr, pt shd; wc; chem disp; shwrs inc; el pnts (10-15A) €2.55; Indtte; shops 500m; tradsmn; pool 200m; playgrnd nrby; internet; dogs; rd noise; CKE/CCI. "Friendly staff; rec visit adj chateau gardens; rd noise on bottom pitches; vg." ♦ 20 Apr-30 Sep. € 13.80 2014*

MANDRES AUX QUATRE TOURS *5D2* (2km S Rural) *48.82739, 5.78936* **Camp Municipal Orée de la Forêt de la Reine, Route Forêt de la Reine, 54470 Mandres-aux-Quatre-Tours [03 83 23 17 31; mandres.54470@wandoo.fr]** On D958 Commercy to Pont-à-Mousson, sp as Camping Mandres. Turn R at sp in Beaumont & foll sp to vill Mandres-aux-Quatre-Tours. Sm, pt mkd/hdg pitch, pt shd; wc; chem disp (wc); shwrs inc; el pnts (10A) €2.20 (poss long lead req); tradsmn; playgrnd; tennis; watersports, sailing 500m; horseriding adj; some statics; dogs; quiet; red long stay; CKE/CCI. "Gd, peaceful site; site yourself; basic san facs; site poss muddy when wet; gd birdwatching, walking, cycling; popular NH." 1 Apr-31 Oct. € 11.00 2011*

MARVILLE *5C1* (1km N Rural) *49.46294, 5.45859* **Camp Syndicat Mixte de la Vallée de l'Othain, 55600 Marville [03 29 88 19 06 or 03 29 88 15 15; fax 03 29 88 14 60; marville.accueil@wanadoo.fr]** Sp on D643 on app Marville fr both dirs. Med, hdg pitch, pt shd; wc (some cont); shwrs; el pnts (3A); Indtte; sm shop; snacks; rest; playgrnd; htd covrd pool adj; entmnt; 20% statics; quiet; CKE/CCI. "Easy access adj lake; gd NH." 1 Feb-30 Nov. 2012*

METZ *5D2* (500m NW Urban) *49.12402, 6.16917* **Camp Municipal Metz-Plage, Allée de Metz-Plage, 57000 Metz [03 87 68 26 48; fax 03 87 38 03 89; campingmetz@mairie-metz.fr; www.mairie-metz.fr]** Fr W exit A31 junc 33 Metz-Nord/Pontiffroy exit; cross rv brdges Pont Canal & Pont des Morts; then immed turn L into Allée de Metz-Plage; site in 200m (or after leaving A31 at junc 33, at rndabt turn R & foll sps). Fr E foll 'Autres Directions' over A31 & Rv Moselle, then as above. Lge, mkd pitch, hdstg, pt sl, pt shd; wc; chem disp; mv service pnt; baby facs; shwrs inc; el pnts (10A) inc (poss rev pol); Indtte; shop, snacks; playgrnd; pool adj; rv fishing adj; wifi; dogs €0.50; twin-axles & vehicles over 3,500 kg extra; poss cr; Eng spkn; adv bkg; traff noise fr rv bdge at far end; ccard acc;CKE/CCI. "Spacious, well-situated on rv with views; some gd sized pitches; helpful staff; poss long walk to san facs; rv unfenced; facs stretched if site full; early arr ess high ssn; vg; fac's need updating; wifi in designated areas." ♦ 18 Apr-1 Oct. € 23.00 2014*

MONTMEDY *5C1* (500m NW Urban) *49.52126, 5.36090* **Camp Municipal La Citadelle, Rue Vauban, 55600 Montmédy [03 29 80 10 40 (Mairie); fax 03 29 80 12 98; mairie.montmedy@wanadoo.fr; www.montmedy.fr]** Fr D643 foll sp to Montmédy cent & foll site sp. Steep app. Sm, hdg pitch, pt sl, pt shd; wc; chem disp; shwrs inc; el pnts (5-10A) €2.80-3.97; Indry facs; shops 1km; tradsmn; playgrnd; dogs €1.90; phone; quiet; red long stay/low ssn; CKE/CCI. "Warden calls am & pm; facs clean, ltd low ssn; nr Montmedy Haut fortified town; 10A hook-up not avail high ssn; vg." 1 May-30 Sep. € 12.00 2014*

NANCY *6E2* (6km SW Rural) *48.65730, 6.14028* **Campéole Le Brabois, 2301 Ave Paul Muller, 54600 Villers-lès-Nancy [03 83 27 18 28; fax 03 83 40 06 43; brabois@campeole.com; www.camping-brabois.com / www.campeole.com]** Fr A33 exit junc 2b sp Brabois onto D974 dir Nancy; after 400m turn L at 2nd traff lts; at slip rd after 2nd further traff lts turn R on slip rd & site on R; site well sp. Lge, mkd pitch, pt shd; htd wc; chem disp; mv service pnt; shwrs inc; el pnts (5-15A) €4.10-5.25 (poss rev pol)(ask for pitch with 15A if req); gas; Indtte; shop; tradsmn; supmkt & petrol 2km; rest; snacks (high ssn); bar; BBQ; playgrnd; games area; TV; dogs €2.60; bus adj (tickets fr recep); poss cr; Eng spkn; adv bkg; quiet; ccard acc; red low ssn; CKE/CCI. "Popular, well-run site; mostly lge pitches, but some sm, all grass; helpful staff; gd, clean, all new san facs; no twin-axle c'vans over 5.50m (m'vans OK); interesting town; rec arr early; vg NH; excel; ltd wifi coverage." ♦ 1 Apr-14 Oct. € 32.80 (CChq acc) SBS - J03 2014*

NANCY *6E2* (10km NW Rural) *48.74733, 6.05700* **Camping Les Boucles de la Moselle, Ave Eugène Lerebourg, 54460 Liverdun [03 83 24 43 78 or 06 03 27 69 71 (mob); fax 03 83 24 89 47; francis.iung@orange.fr]** Fr A31 exit junc 22 to Frouard. In Frouard bear L onto D90 to Liverdun; cross rv bdge (sp Liverdun); under rlwy bdge L at traff lts, thro town, fork L & foll sp to site by on rvside by sports area. Do not turn L at site exit when towing. Lge, pt shd; htd wc; baby facs; shwrs (0730-1000) inc; el pnts (6A) €3.20; Indtte; shop & 1.5km; rest, snacks; bar; playgrnd; pool; entmnt; some statics; dogs €1.20; quiet except rlwy noise; ccard not acc; CKE/CCI. "Lovely site & area; helpful staff; Nancy worth visit; new owners 2012." 1 May-30 Sep. € 11.00 2012*

NEUFCHATEAU *6E2* (10km N Rural) *48.44364, 5.67616* **Camp Municipal, Chemin de Santilles, Rue Principale, 88630 Domrémy-la-Pucelle [03 29 06 90 70; fax 03 29 94 33 77; mairie.domremylapucelle@packsurfwifi.com; www.tourisme-lorraine.fr]** Take D164 fr Neufchâteau, site in cent of Domrémy vill, clear sp by stadium, nr Rv Meuse. Sm, pt shd; wc; shwrs €0.90; el pnts (16A) €2.80; shops, rest & bar 1km N or 4km S; tennis; quiet. "Site yourself, warden calls (not Sun); nr birthplace of Joan of Arc." 1 Jun-31 Aug. € 6.35 2011*

PHALSBOURG *5D3* (2km N Rural) *48.78300, 7.25020* **FFCC Camping de Bouleaux (CC de F), 5 Rue des Trois Journeaux, 57370 Vilsberg [03 87 24 18 72; fax 03 87 24 46 52; info@campinglesbouleaux.fr; www.campinglesbouleaux.fr / www.campingclub.asso.fr]** Fr A4 exit junc 44 dir Phalsbourg. At x-rds turn L sp D661 Sarreguemines. Site on R in 2km. NB Site ent off steep descent on D661. Lge o'fits take care leaving site & turning L - watch rear overhangs. Lge, pt shd; wc; chem disp; mv service pnt; baby facs; shwrs inc; el pnts (6A) inc; Indtte; shop; tradsmn; BBQ; playgrnd; 15% statics; dogs €2; phone; bus 2km; Eng spkn; adv bkg; quiet; red low ssn; CKE/CCI. "Peaceful, well-kept site; welcoming, helpful Dutch owners; barrier clsd 1930; gd facs; access to some pitches poss diff, some uneven; conv m'way & NH to/fr Germany/Austria; gd NH." ♦ 1 Apr-31 Oct. € 23.50 2013*

PHALSBOURG *5D3* (6km SW Rural) *48.71922, 7.22643* **Camping du Plan Incliné, Hoffmuhl, 57820 Henridorff [tel/fax 03 87 25 30 13 or 06 71 21 86 91 (mob); campingplanincline@wanadoo.fr; www.campingplanincline.fr]** Exit A4 at junc 44. In Phalsbourg take D38 twds Lutzelbourg; turn R onto D98 dir Arzviller & foll sp to Henridorff & site on R adj rv (narr ent). Med, some hdg/hdstg pitches, pt shd; wc; chem disp; shwrs inc; el pnts (6A) €3; gas; Indtte; shop 2km; tradsmn; rest, snacks; bar; playgrnd; pool high ssn (spring water); rv sw, fishing & boating adj; entmnt; 60% statics; dogs €1; phone; wifi; Eng spkn; adv bkg; rlwy noise & some rd & boat noise; red long stay; ccard not acc; CKE/CCI. "In wooded valley; friendly, helpful owner; vg rest; grnd soft when wet; cycle path to Strasbourg; adj to unique canal; poss dif entry for lge units." ♦ 29 Mar-18 Oct. € 23.00 2014*

PLOMBIERES LES BAINS *6F2* (10km S Rural) *47.92460, 6.47545* **Camp Municipal Le Val d'Ajol, Rue des Oeuvres, 88340 Le Val-d'Ajol [03 29 66 55 17; camping@valdajol.fr; www.valdajol.fr]** Fr N on N57 after Plombières-les-Bains turn onto D20 sp Le Val-d'Ajol. Site sps in vill. Sm, hdg pitch, pt shd; wc; chem disp; shwrs inc; el pnts (6A) €2.50; Indte; shop 1km; htd, covrd pool adj; wifi; TV; dogs; phone; adv bkg; quiet; CKE/CCI. "Excel site; excel, clean san facs; vg touring base." ♦ 15 Apr-30 Sep. € 13.00 2012*

"I need an on-site restaurant"

We do our best to make sure site information is correct, but it is always best to check any must-have facilities are still available or will be open during your visit.

PLOMBIERES LES BAINS *6F2* (2km W Rural) *47.96731, 6.44656* **Camping de l'Hermitage, 54 Rue du Boulot, 88370 Plombières-les-Bains [03 29 30 01 87; fax 03 29 30 04 01; contact@hermitage-camping.com; www.hermitage-camping.com]** Fr Plombières-les-Bains take D63 N dir Epinal; site sp. Med, hgd/mkd pitch, terr, pt shd; htd wc; chem disp; baby facs; fam bthrm; shwrs inc; gas; el pnts (4-10A) €3.20-5.30; Indtte; tradsmn; snacks; BBQ; playgrnd; pool; games area; games rm; TV; 10% statics; dogs €1.60; phone; no twin-axles; poss cr; Eng spkn; adv bkg; quiet; red low ssn/CKE/CCI. "Gd, unisex san facs; vg." 1 Apr-15 Oct. € 14.00 2011*

RAON L'ETAPE *6E3* (10km NE Rural) *48.45490, 6.94722* **Camping des Lacs, 88110 Celles-sur-Plaine [03 29 41 28 00; fax 03 29 41 18 69; camping@paysdeslacs.com; www.paysdeslacs.com/camping]** Fr Raon-l'Etape turn onto D392A to Celles-sur-Plaine, site sp. Med, hdg/mkd pitch, hdstg, pt sl, pt shd; htd wc (some cont); solarium; chem disp; shwrs inc; el pnts (4-10A) inc; Indtte; shop; tradsmn; snacks; bar; playgrnd; htd pool; sand beach & lake sw 400m; fishing; windsurfing; tennis; 10% statics; dogs €1.50; Eng spkn; adv bkg; quiet; ccard acc; red low ssn/long stay; CKE/CCI. "Poss unkempt & facs unclean low ssn, otherwise vg." ♦ 1 Apr-31 Oct. € 23.00 2010*

RAON L'ETAPE *6E3* (10km E Rural) *48.35281, 6.98903* **Camping des 7 Hameaux, 1 La Fontenelle, 88210 Ban-de-Sapt [03 29 58 95 75; camping7hameaux@wanadoo.fr; http://camping7hameaux.monsite-orange.fr]** Fr St Dié NE on D49 to St Jean-d'Ormont (turn R after cathedral in St Dié). Then D32 sp 'Saales' to Ban-de-Sapt. Turn L onto D49 to La Fontenelle. Site on R 1km past sp to military cemetery. Or fr N59 take D424 sp Senones. In 3.3km in Moyenmoutiers turn R onto D37 sp Ban-de-Sapt. In 6.1km join D49. site on L in 1.3km. Sm, pt sl; wc; chem disp; shwrs €1; el pnts (6A) €2.50; rest, bar & shop 1km; tradsmn; pool 10km; quiet; adv bkg; ccard not acc; CKE/CCI. "Walks, cycle rtes; farm produce; friendly; vg." 1 Apr-31 Oct. € 8.00 2010*

RAON L'ETAPE *6E3* (3.7km SE Rural) *48.39474, 6.86232* **Camping Vosgina, 1 Rue la Cheville, 88420 Moyenmoutier [tel/fax 03 29 41 47 63; info@camping-vosgina.com; http://camping-vosgina.com]** On N59 St Dié-Lunéville rd, take exit mkd Senones, Moyenmoutier. At rndabt take rd twd St Blaise & foll camping sp. Site is on minor rd parallel with N59 bet Moyenmoutier & Raon. Med, hdg pitch, terr, pt shd; wc; chem disp; shwrs inc; el pnts (4-10A) €3-6; gas; Indtte; sm shop & 3km; tradsmn; snacks; bar; wifi; tv rm; 20% statics; dogs €1.50; Eng spkn; adv bkg; quiet but some rd noise; ccard acc; CKE/CCI. "Gd site for quiet holiday in a non-touristy area of Alsace; friendly recep; lovely countryside; many cycle/walking rtes in area; barrier clsd 2200-0700; park like setting; beautifully maintained; friendly Swiss owners; excel for sh stay or NH." 1 Apr-31 Oct. € 13.00 2014*

REHAUPAL see Tholy, Le *6F3*

REMIREMONT *6F2* (8km SE Rural) *47.94799, 6.63296* **Camping Le Pont de Maxonchamp, 3 Rue du Camping, 88360 Rupt-sur-Moselle [03 29 24 30 65 or 03 84 49 38 72; olivierleduc88@orange.fr; www.camping-vosges-88.com]** Fr Remiremont SE on N66/E51; site clearly sp to L; also visible 300m down lane. Sm, pt shd; wc; chem disp; shwrs €1; el pnts (10A) €3; shop 3km; playgrnd; rv sw adj; 20% statics; dogs €0.50; poss cr; quiet; CKE/CCI. "Attractive rvside site; if recep clsd site yourself; recep open eves; vg." ♦ 1 Apr-15 Oct. € 9.00 2011*

REVIGNY SUR ORNAIN *5D1* (250m S Urban) *48.82663, 4.98412* **Camp Municipal du Moulin des Gravières, Rue du Stade, 55800 Revigny-sur-Ornain [tel/fax 03 29 78 73 34 or 03 29 70 50 55 (Mairie); contact@ot-revigny-ornain.fr; www.ot-revigny-ornain.fr]** N fr Bar-le-Duc on D994 to Revigny-sur-Ornain; fr town cent take D995 twd Vitry-le-François. Site on R, sp. Sm, hdg/mkd pitch, pt shd; wc; chem disp; mv service pnt; baby facs; shwrs inc; el pnts (6A) €2.70; Indtte (inc dryer); supmkt 500m; snacks; playgrnd; tennis & cycle hire in town; TV rm; 3 statics; dogs; Eng spkn; adv bkg; v quiet; ccard not acc; CKE/CCI. "Pleasant, well-kept site; lge pitches; vg, modern facs; trout stream runs thro site; gd cycling along canal; mkt Wed adj; highly rec; excel site, beautifully kept; park like setting." ♦ 29 Mar-7 Oct. € 13.00 2014*

ROMAGNE SOUS MONTFAUCON see Dun sur Meuse *5C1*

RUPT SUR MOSELLE see Remiremont *6F2*

⊞ **ST AVOLD** *5D2* (1km N Urban) *49.10772, 6.70924* **FFCC Camping Le Felsberg, Centre International de Séjour, Rue en Verrerie, 57500 St Avold [03 87 92 75 05; fax 03 87 92 20 69; cis.stavold@wanadoo.fr]** Fr N on A4 exit junc 39 onto D633 to St Avold, stay in L hand lane at 2nd traff lts & turn L; pass under D603 for 2km & turn R. Site well sp in & around town; app up steep incline. Sm, hdg/mkd pitch, hdstg, pt sl, pt shd; wc; chem disp; mv service pnt; shwrs inc; el pnts (6-10A) €3-5; Indtte; tradsmn; hypmkt 1.5km; rest, bar high ssn; playgrnd; 50% statics; dogs €1; poss cr; adv bkg; ccard acc; red long stay; CKE/CCI. "German border 10km; sm pitches; gd facs; coal mine & archaeological park nrby worth visit; awkward, heavy duty security gate at site ent; conv NH nr m'way; gd." ♦ ltd € 14.00 2012*

⊞ **ST MAURICE SUR MOSELLE** *6F3* (4.5km NE Urban) *47.88888, 6.85758* **Kawan Village Domaine de Champé, 14 Rue des Champs Navés, 88540 Bussang [03 29 61 61 51; fax 03 29 61 56 90; info@domaine-de-champe.com; www.domaine-de-champe.com]** Fr N66/E512 in Bussang, site sp fr town sq. Opp Avia filling stn. Med, hdg/mkd pitch, pt sl, pt terr, pt shd; htd wc (some cont); chem disp; mv service pnt; baby facs; sauna; shwrs; el pnts (6-10A) €5-6; Indtte (inc dryer); shop 500m; tradmsn; rest, snacks; bar; BBQ; playgrnd; htd pool; paddling pool; waterslide; rv 1km; tennis; cycle hire; fitness rm; games area; games rm; wifi; entmnt; TV; 10% statics; dogs €3; phone; bus 1km; poss cr; Eng spkn; quiet; adv bkg; ccard acc; red low ssn; CKE/CCI. "Excel site behind hospital grnds; lovely views; welcoming, helpful owners; dated but clean unisex san facs; vg rest; excel walks, cycle path." ♦ ltd € 25.00 (CChq acc) 2012*

ST MIHIEL *5D2* (1km NW Rural) *48.90209, 5.53978* **Camping Base de Plein Air, 1Chemin du Gué Rappeau, 55300 St Mihiel [03 29 89 11 70 / 06 75 10 18 94 (mob); fax 03 29 89 07 18; base.de.plein.air@wanadoo.fr; www.tourisme-lorraine.fr]** Site on W bank of rv. Sp app St Mihiel. Fr town cent take rd sp Bar-le-Duc (D901) 1st R after rv bdge. Med, mkd pitch, pt shd; htd wc (mainly cont); chem disp; mv service pnt; shwrs inc; el pnts (10A) €2.60; Indtte; shops, rest, bar 1km; tradsmn; playgrnd; htd pool 1km; canoeing & sailing; games area; TV; 10% statics; bus 1km; adv bkg; quiet; CKE/CCI; "Site developed as youth cent; facs clean but tired; pleasant scenery; lge pitches; v friendly." 1 Apr-1 Nov. € 9.00 2013*

SANCHEY see Epinal *6F2*

SAVERNE *6E3* (25km SW Rural) *48.64830, 7.25222* **Camping du Rocher, 57850 Dabo [tel/fax 03 87 07 47 51; ot-dabo@claranet.fr; www.ot-dabo.fr]** Fr Saverne take D132 to Lutzelbourg, then D98 to Haselbourg & D45 to Dabo. Go thro vill; site sp on R in 2km. Sm, mkd pitch, pt shd; wc; shwrs €1.50; el pnts (6-10A) €2-3.30; shop 2km; playgrnd; cycling; fishing; quiet; "Site yourself, warden calls; fair sh stay/NH." ♦ ltd Easter-1 Nov. € 11.00 2013*

SIERCK LES BAINS *5C2* (1.7km W Rural) *49.44544, 6.34899* **Camp Municipal les Tilleuls, Allée des Tilleuls, 57480 Sierck-les-Bains [03 82 83 72 39; camping@siercklesbains.fr; www.siercklesbains.fr]** Fr S on D654 turn L onto D64 sp Contz. Fr Schengen (Lux) turn L immed bef Moselle Bdge sp Contz. Well sp on banks of Moselle. Sm, hdg/mkd pitch, pt shd; wc; chem disp; mv service pnt; shwrs; el pnts (16A); BBQ; playgrnd; bike hire; Eng spkn; adv bkg; CKE/CCI. "Excel site." ♦ ltd 1 May-15 Oct. € 14.00 2014*

SIVRY SUR MEUSE see Dun sur Meuse *5C1*

⊞ **STENAY** *5C1* (250m W Urban) *49.49083, 5.18333* **Port de Plaisance - Motor Caravan Parking Area, Rue du Port, 55700 Stenay [03 29 80 64 22 or 03 29 74 87 54; fax 03 29 80 62 59; otsistenayaccueil@orange.fr]** Off D947 fr town cent. Foll sp to rv port. NB M'vans only. Sm, hdstg; mv service pnt; shwrs inc; el pnts (6A) inc; shop 600m; rest 300m; quiet. "Adj to rv; excel san facs; NH only." ♦ ltd € 8.00 2013*

"Satellite navigation makes touring much easier"

Remember most sat navs don't know if you're towing or in a larger vehicle – always use yours alongside maps and site directions.

⊞ **THILLOT, LE** *6F3* (1km NW Rural) *47.88893, 6.75683* **Camp Municipal du Clos de Chaume, 36 Rue de la Chaume, 88160 Le Thillot [03 29 25 10 30; fax 03 29 25 25 87; campingmunicipal@ville-lethillot88.fr; www.ville-lethillot88.fr]** Site sp on N o'skts of town N on N66, on R behind sports cent. Med, pt sl, pt shd; htd wc; shwrs inc; el pnts (6A) €1.80; gas; Indtte; shops 1km; playgrnd; pool & tennis adj; few statics; adv bkg; quiet. "Attractive, well-maintained site; friendly staff; vg san facs; excel touring base." € 6.00 2012*

THIONVILLE *5C2* (500m NE Urban) *49.36127, 6.17534* **Camp Municipal, 6 Rue du Parc, 57100 Thionville [03 82 53 83 75; fax 03 82 53 91 27; camping.municipal@mairie-thionville.fr]** Exit A31 at sp Thionville Cent; foll sp 'Centre Ville'; foll site sp dir Manom. Sm, mkd pitch, some hdstg, pt shd; wc; chem disp; mv service pnt; shwrs inc; el pnts (3-10A) €2.40-4.65; shop 250m; rest snacks, bar 250m; playgrnd; pool 1km; boating; fishing; dogs €1.20; poss cr; Eng spkn; adv bkg; quiet; red long stay; CKE/CCI. "Well-kept site; some rvside pitches which can be noisy in eve; friendly warden; gd san facs; rec arr early high ssn; 5 min walk thro lovely adj park to town; vg; walk alongside rv as adj." ♦ 1 May-30 Sep. € 14.40 2014*

THOLY, LE *6F3* (6km N Rural) *48.12005, 6.73181* **Camping Le Barba, 45 Le Village, 88640 Rehaupal [03 29 66 35 57; barba@campingdubarba.com; www.campingdubarba.com]** Fr Gérardmer on D417 after 8km site sp on R 2km bef Le Tholy. Foll sp to Rehaupal, site on R on ent to vill. Sm, mkd pitch, pt shd; wc; chem disp; shwrs inc; el pnts (3-10A) €2.80-5.50; gas; Indtte; shop adj; tradsmn; rest; some statics; dogs €1; Eng spkn; quiet. "Friendly owner; scenic site; vg walking." 1 May-26 Sep. € 8.40 2010*

"There aren't many sites open at this time of year"

If you're travelling outside peak season remember to call ahead to check site opening dates – even if the entry says 'open all year'.

THOLY, LE *6F3* (1.3km NW Rural) *48.08897, 6.72869* **Camping de Noirrupt, 15 Chemin de L'Etang, 88530 Le Tholy [03 29 61 81 27; fax 03 29 61 83 05; info@jpvacances.com; www.jpvacances.com]** Fr Gérardmer, take D417 W, turn R in Le Tholy up hill onto D11. Site on L on secondary rd to Epinal & sp. Med, terr, pt shd; wc (some cont); chem disp; baby facs; sauna; shwrs inc; el pnts (2-6A) €3-5; gas; Indtte; shops 1km; snacks; bar; BBQ; htd pool; tennis; entmnt; TV rm; some statics; dogs €1.50; poss cr; some rd noise; red long stay. "Pleasant, well laid-out site in lovely area; sm pitches; vg." 15 Apr-15 Oct. € 20.30 2009*

TOUL *6E2* (7km E Rural) *48.65281, 5.99260* **Camping de Villey-le-Sec, 34 Rue de la Gare, 54840 Villey-le-Sec [tel/fax 03 83 63 64 28; info@campingvilleylesec.com; www.campingvilleylesec.com]** Exit Toul E on D909 or exit A31 junc 15 ondo D400 (W, in dir Hôpital Jeanne d'Arc); at rndabt turn L onto D909 to Villey-le-Sec; in vill site S by Rv Moselle, sp. V steep app rd. Med, hdg/mkd pitch, hdstg, pt shd; wc; chem disp; mv service pnt; baby facs; shwrs inc; el pnts (6-10A) €3.70-4.50; gas; Indtte; shop; hypmkt nr; rest, snacks; bar; BBQ; playgrnd; games area; dogs €1.80; phone; Eng spkn; no adv bkg; quiet; ccard acc; red long stay/low ssn. "Peaceful, well-kept site on rvside; lovely location; lge pitches; friendly; vg san facs, poss stretched; gd cycle paths; popular NH, ess arr bef 1800 high ssn." ♦ 1 Apr-15 Oct. € 27.00 2014*

VAL D'AJOL, LE see Plombières les Bains *6F2*

VARENNES EN ARGONNE *5D1* (350m N Rural) *49.22935, 5.03424* **Camp Municipal Le Pâquis, Rue St Jean, 55270 Varennes-en-Argonne [03 29 80 71 01 (Mairie); fax 03 29 80 71 43; mairievarennesenargonne@wanadoo.fr]** On D946 Vouziers/Clermont-en-Argonne rd; sp by bdge in vill, on banks of Rv Aire, 200m N of bdge. NB Ignore sp by bdge to Camping Lac Vert (not nr). Med, pt shd; wc; shwrs inc; el pnts (3-6A) €2.90; Indtte; shops adj; BBQ; playgrnd; rv fishing; dog €0.40; Eng spkn; quiet. "Pleasant site with gd facs; gd (hilly) cycle ride taking in US WWI cemetary." 06 Apr-12 Oct. € 8.00 2014*

VERDUN *5D1* (1km SW Urban) *49.15428, 5.36598* **Camping Les Breuils, 8 Allée des Breuils, 55100 Verdun [03 29 86 15 31; fax 03 29 86 75 76; contact@camping-lesbreuils.com; www.camping-lesbreuils.com]** Fr W (Paris) on A4/E50, exit junc 30 onto D1916/D603/D330; cont over rndabt junc with D34 onto D330; at next rndabt in 100m turn R into Allée des Breuils. Or fr E (Metz) exit junc 31 onto D964/D330; cont on D330 past junc with D34A; at rndabt in 150m turn L into Allée des Breuils. Site sp nr Citadel. Avoid Verdun town cent due to 1-way rds. Allée des Breuils runs parallel to D34 on E side of rwly. Site well sp fr D603 & all other dirs. Steepish ent. Lge, hdg/mkd pitch, some hdstg, pt sl, pt shd; wc; chem disp; mv service pnt; baby facs; shwrs inc; el pnts (6A) €4.55 (poss some rev pol); gas; Indtte; sm shop on site & 3km; tradsmn, rest, snacks & bar (high ssn); playgrnd; pool; waterslide; cycle hire; fishing; sports cent; wifi; dogs €2.10; phone; poss cr; Eng spkn; adv bkg rec high ssn; little rlwy noise; ccard acc; red low ssn/long stay; CKE/CCI. "Pleasant, clean, well-kept, busy site; grass pitches beside lge pond, some lge; poss long walk to water taps; some site rds tight for lge o'fits; gd pool; poss lge youth groups Sept; interesting historial town; cycle rtes around WWI battlefields; easy walk to Citadel with WWI museum; excel; gd rest; friendly staff; san block a little tired, poss stretched if site full, otherwise vg; bus tours fr site." ♦ ltd 15 Mar - 15 Oct. € 30.00 2014*

VERDUN *5D1* (6km NW Rural) *49.20998, 5.36567* **FFCC Camp Municipal sous Le Moulin, 55100 Charny-sur-Meuse [03 29 84 28 35 or 03 29 86 67 06 (LS); fax 03 29 84 67 99; mairie.charny.sur.meuse@wanadoo.fr; www.charny-sur-meuse.fr]** N fr Verdun on D964; turn L onto D115 to Charny-sur-Meuse; site sp. Med, pt sl, pt shd; wc (all cont) (own san rec); mv service pnt; shwrs inc; el pnts (6A) €2.50; fishing; dogs €1; CKE/CCI. "CL-type site; open pitches round lake; facs adequate; useful touring base; conv WWI sites; gd." 1 May-30 Sep. € 7.00 2011*

VILLERS LES NANCY see Nancy *6E2*

VITTEL *6F2* (1km NE Urban) *48.20762, 5.95531* **Camping de Vittel, 270 Rue Claude Bassot, 88800 Vittel [03 29 08 02 71; aquadis1@wanadoo.fr; www.aquadis-loisirs.com]** Fr Chaumont/Dijon at traff lts take Epinal/Nancy rd into Place Gen de Gaulle; turn L over bdge & foll sp. Fr Epinal turn R over bdge at Place Gen de Gaulle & foll sp. Med, hdg/mkd pitch, hdstg, pt shd; htd wc (mainly cont); chem disp; shwrs inc; el pnts (6A) inc; Indtte; shop 1km; tradsmn; pool. Tennis 2km; dogs €3.10; poss cr; Eng spkn; adv bkg; quiet; CKE/CCI. "Interesting town; on Tour de France rte; walking & cycling rtes; san facs unclean." 3 Apr-17 Oct. € 16.20 (CChq acc) 2010*

VOLSTROFF *5D2* (1.5km SE Rural) *49.29772, 6.26989* **FFCC Camp du Centre de Loisirs et Culture de Volstroff, Route de Luttange, 57940 Volstroff [03 82 56 93 40; fax 03 82 50 39 90; campingvol@aol.com; www.campingvol.com]** Exit A31 junc 37.2 E onto D918; in 5km at end vill of Stuckange turn R sp Volstroff, Luttange. Go thro Volstroff, site in R in 3km. Med, hdg/mkd pitch, hdstg, pt sl, shd; wc (some cont); chem disp; mv service pnt; baby facs; shwrs inc; el pnts (8A) €2.30; gas; Indtte (inc dryer); shop; rest, snacks; bar; playgrnd; pool; lake sw adj; waterslide; watersports; horseriding; tennis; cycle hire; wifi; entmnt; dogs; phone; Eng spkn; adv bkg; poss cr; ccard acc; red low ssn; CKE/CCI. "Lovely lake adj site; many facs for children; excel." ♦ 11 Apr-25 Oct. € 18.00 (4 persons) 2009*

XONRUPT LONGEMER see Gérardmer *6F3*

Midi-Pyrénées

Regional Introduction

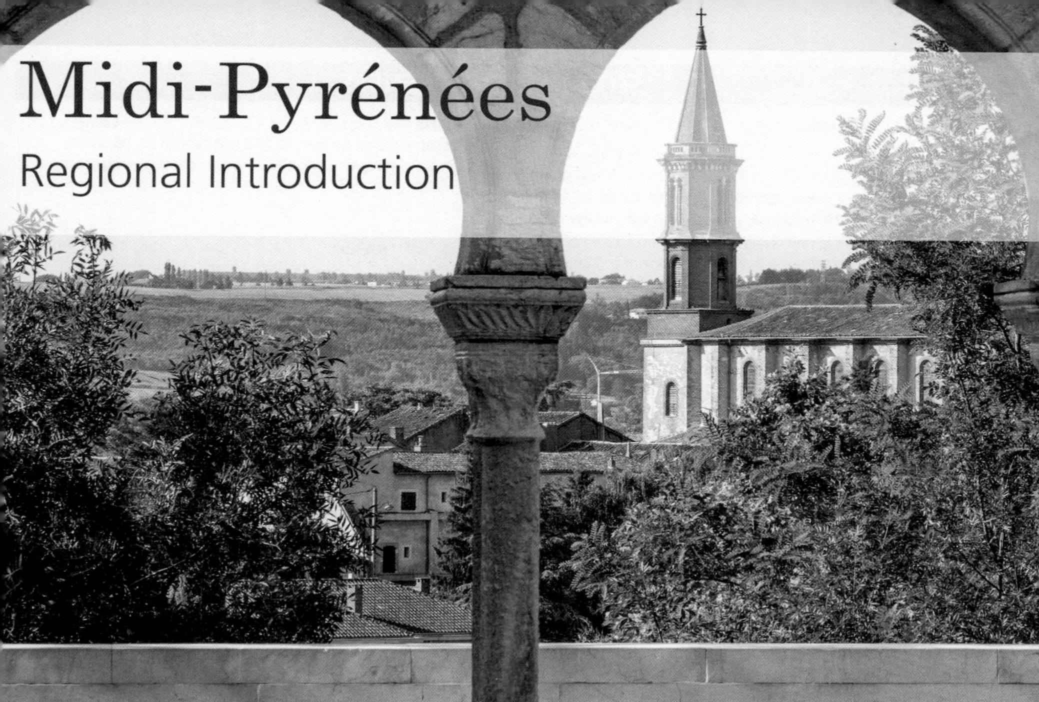

Albi

Welcome to Midi-Pyrénées

Taking up much of south-west France, Midi-Pyrénées offers a wealth of unspoilt countryside and wide open spaces. Colourful buildings in historical towns, vineyards, rivers and canals make up the landscape of this region and, with the Pyrénées as a backdrop, there are some stunning photo opportunities.

A must see is the Millau Viaduct that spans the valley of the River Tarn and is currently the tallest bridge in the world. It is also ranked as one of the great engineering achievements of all time.

Local highlights

With both French and Spanish influences the cuisine in Midi-Pyrénées is famous for its rich and spicy flavours. Roquefort cheese is one of the best known in the area. Made of sheep milk, this blue cheese is aged in the natural Combalou caves of Roquefort-sur-Soulzon.

Cordes-sur-Ciel hosts the Grand Falconer's Medieval Festival in July, where for two days the whole town comes alive with music and street performers.

Major towns and cities

- Toulouse – a beautiful metropolis with a village feel.
- Albi – there are many significant cultural and medieval sites to see within this city.
- Cordes-sur-Ciel – a fortified and historical hillside town.
- Lourdes – a small market town lying in the foothills of the Pyrénées.
- Roquefort – produces a famous blue cheese.

Regional attractions

- Sanctuary of Our Lady of Lourdes – a peaceful atmosphere and stunning architecture.
- Grotte du Pech-Merle, Cabrerets – stunning caves containing prehistoric paintings.
- Château de Montsegur – walk and explore the castle and surrounding village.
- Théâtre du Capitole, Toulouse – a grand opera house with impressive art and architecture.

Find out more

www.tourism-midi-pyrenees.co.uk

Tel: (0)5 61 13 55 55 Midi-Pyrénées Tourist Board

AGUESSAC see Millau *10E1*

⊞ **AIGNAN** *8E2* (600m S Rural) *43.69290, 0.07528* **Camping Le Domaine du Castex, 32290 Aignan [05 62 09 25 13; fax 05 62 09 24 79; info@gers-vacances.com; www.gers-vacances.com]** Fr N on D924/N124 turn S on D20 thro Aignan onto D48; in 500m g'ge on R, immed after turn L; site sp. Fr S on D935 turn E at Monplaisir onto D3/D48 to Aignan; site on R bef vill. Sm, hdg/mkd pitch, hdstg, pt shd; wc; chem disp; mv service pnt; shwrs inc; el pnts (10A) €3; Indtte; shop 500m; tradsmn; rest, snacks; bar; BBQ; playgrnd; pool; lake sw 4km; tennis & squash adj; games area; TV rm; 4% statics; dogs €4; phone; poss cr; Eng spkn; adv bkg; quiet; red low ssn; ccard acc; CKE/CCI. "Lovely site in grnds of medieval farmhouse; helpful Dutch owners; modern san facs; excel pool & rest; gd touring cent for Bastide vills; mkt Mon; phone ahead low ssn; vg." ♦ ltd € 16.00 2009*

⊞ **AIRE SUR L'ADOUR** *8E2* (9km E Rural) *43.69699, -0.13803* **Camping Le Lahount, Hameau de Lahount, 32400 Lelin-Lapujolle [tel/fax 05 62 69 64 09 or 06 81 52 39 15 (mob); camping.de.lahount@wanadoo.fr; www.campingdelahount.fr]** SE fr Aire-sur-l'Adour on D935, turn L in St Germé dir Lelin-Lapujolle. In 1.5km turn L, site on R, sp. Med, mkd pitch, terr, pt shd; wc; mv service pnt; baby facs; shwrs inc; el pnts (10A) inc; Indtte; shop; rest, snacks; bar; BBQ; playgrnd; pool; paddling pool; lake fishing; games area; cycle hire; entmnt; 60% statics; dogs €1; phone; adv bkg; ccard acc; CKE/CCI. "Ltd facs low ssn; pitches soft when wet; barrier at ent awkward for long o'fits; suitable sm o'fits only; poss contract workers & site unkempt low ssn." € 16.00 2010*

ALBAN *8E4* (1km NW Rural) *43.89386, 2.45416* **Camp Municipal La Franquèze, 81250 Alban [05 63 55 91 87 or 05 63 55 82 09 (Mairie); fax 05 63 55 01 97; mairie.alban@wanadoo.fr]** W of Albi on D999 turn L at ent to Alban. Site 300m on R, sp. Sm, hdg pitch, terr, pt sl, pt shd; wc; shwrs; el pnts (6A) €2.10; Indtte; playgrnd; rv fishing; adv bkg; quiet; CKE/CCI. "Beautiful area, conv Tarn Valley; vg; water taps scarce; gd hilltop site with views." 1 Jun-30 Sep. € 14.00 2014*

ALBI *8E4* (1.5km E Urban) *43.93485, 2.16213* **Albirondack Park, Camping Lodge & Spa (formerly Camping Caussels), 31 Allée de la Piscine, 81000 Albi [05 63 60 37 06 or 06 84 04 23 13 (mob); fax 05 31 60 51 86; albirondack@orange.fr; www.albirondack.fr]** Fr Albi ring rd/bypass exit sp Lacause/St Juéry (do not turn twd Millau). Strt over & foll sp Géant-Casino hypmkt & 'Centre Ville', then foll camping/piscine sp. Med, mkd pitch, pt sl, pt shd; htd wc; chem disp; mv service pnt; shwrs inc; el pnts (10A) €5.70; Indtte; supmkts adj; rest, snacks; BBQ; playgrnd; htd pool; spa; some statics; dogs €5; bus; adv bkg; quiet; red low ssn/CKE/CCI. "Vg site in conv position; pitches unlevelled - soft in wet & some poss diff lge o'fits due trees (2009); gd walk by rv to town cent; Albi Cathedral; Toulouse Lautrec exhibitions; spa & pool inc; excel rest; excel clean modern facs." ♦ ltd 1 Jan-31 Oct, 1 Dec-31Dec. € 45.20 2014*

ALBIES see Cabannes, Les *8G3*

ALBINE *8F4* (1km SW Rural) *43.45406, 2.52706* **Camping L'Estap Albine, Le Suc, 81240 Albine [05 63 98 34 74; campinglestap@orange.fr; www.campinglestap.com]** Fr Mazamet on D612 dir Béziers for approx 12km; turn R onto D88 sp Albine. On app to vill turn R at sp 'Camping du Lac'. Site in 1km. Sm, hdg/mkd pitch, hdstg, terr, pt shd; wc; chem disp; baby facs; shwrs inc; el pnts (6A) €4.; gas; Indtte; shop 1km; tradsmn; snacks; bar; BBQ (gas); playgrnd; pool; fishing; games area; dogs €2; poss cr; Eng spkn; adv bkg; quiet; ccard acc; CKE/CCI. "Well-kept, clean site; superb views; facs adequate; excel touring base; poss diff lge o'fits due sm pitches & steep access; vg; new friendly French owners." ♦ 30 Mar-31 Nov. € 32.40 2013*

ALLIAT see Tarascon sur Ariege *8G3*

AMBIALET *8E4* (500m SE Rural) *43.94181, 2.38686* **Camping La Mise à l'Eau, Fédusse, 81430 Ambialet [05 63 79 58 29; fax 05 63 79 58 09; contact@camping-ambialet.com; www.camping-ambialet.com]** Fr Albi E on D999; in 15km, after Villefranche-d'Albigeois, turn L onto D74 to Ambialet; turn R at junc; in 100m bear L; site on L. NB Sharp turn, turning pnt avail down rd. Sm, mkd pitch, pt shd; wc; shwrs; el pnts (6-10A) €2.15; Indtte; shops, rest & bar 500m; snacks; dogs €1.50; playgrnd; pool; kayaking; poss cr; adv bkg; some rd noise; ccard not acc; CKE/CCI. "Easy walk to pretty vill; clean facs; excel." ♦ ltd; pretty rvside site." 15 Jun-30 Sep. € 12.00 2011*

ARGELES GAZOST *8G2* (500m N Rural) *43.01218, -0.09709* **Camping Sunêlia Les Trois Vallées, Ave des Pyrénées, 65400 Argelès-Gazost [05 62 90 35 47; fax 05 62 90 35 48; 3-vallees@wanadoo.fr; www.l3v.fr]** S fr Lourdes on D821, turn R at rndabt sp Argelès-Gazost on D821A. Site off next rndabt on R. Lge, mkd pitch, pt shd; htd wc; chem disp; sauna; shwrs inc; el pnts (6A) inc (poss rev pol); Indtte; supmkt opp; tradsmn; bar; playgrnd; htd pool; waterslide; games rm; cycle hire; games area; golf 11km; wifi; entmnt; TV rm; 30% statics; dogs €2; poss cr; adv bkg ess high ssn; some rd noise nr site ent; ccard acc; red low ssn. "Excel touring base; views of Pyrenees; conv Lourdes; interesting area; red facs low ssn." ♦ 11 Mar-2 Nov. € 34.00 2010*

ARGELES GAZOST *8G2* (1km N Rural) *43.01725, -0.09670* **Camping La Bergerie, 54 Ave des Pyrénées, 65400 Ayzac-Ost [tel/fax 05 62 97 59 99; info@camping-labergerie.com; www.camping-labergerie.com]** Sp off D821. Sm, pt shd; wc; shwrs inc; el pnts (2-6A) €1.80-5.40; Indtte; rest, bar 100m; BBQ; playgrnd; htd pool; games area; entmnt; some statics; dogs €1; Eng spkn; adv bkg; quiet; ccard acc; red low ssn. "Clean, friendly site." ♦ 1 May-30 Sep. € 16.50 2009*

ARGELES GAZOST *8G2* (2km N Rural) *43.01885, -0.09167* **Camping Aire Naturelle Bellevue (Hourcastagnou), 24 Chemin de la Plaine, 65400 Ayzac-Ost [tel/fax 05 62 97 58 81; camping.bellevue65@wanadoo.fr]** Fr Lourdes S on D821, foll sp for Ayzac-Ost then sp for 'Camping La Bergerie' but cont past ent for 200m. Site on R behind farm buildings. Sm, pt shd; wc; chem disp; mv service pnt; shwrs inc; el pnts (6A) inc; Indtte; shop, rest, snacks, bar 1km; tradsmn; playgrnd; fishing 300m; 2% statics; dogs €1; phone; quiet; CKE/CCI. "Surrounded by fields; gd san facs block; site poss muddy; gd." ♦ 1 Jun-30 Sep. € 12.36 2011*

ARGELES GAZOST *8G2* (4km N Rural) *43.03560, -0.07086* **Camping Soleil du Pibeste, 65400 Agos-Vidalos [06 72 32 17 04 / 06 08 22 26 74; info@campingpibeste.com; www.campingpibeste.com]** On D821, S of Lourdes. Exit at rndabt sp Agos-Vidalos, site on R on ent vill. Med, terr, pt shd; htd wc; chem disp; mv service pnt; shwrs inc; el pnts (6-10A) €4-6; gas; Indtte; shops adj; Indtte; tradsmn; rest, snacks; bar; playgrnd; sm pool; rv 500m; entmnt; TV; 10% statics; dogs €8; bus; Eng spkn; adv bkg rec high ssn; some rd noise; CKE/CCI. "Open outlook with views; beautiful area; warm welcome; guided mountain walks; excel, v friendly family-run site; san facs need updating (2014)." ♦ ltd 1 May-1 Oct. € 54.00 2014*

ARGELES GAZOST *8G2* (5km N Rural) *42.98120, -0.06535* **Camping Le Viscos, 16 Route de Préchac, 65400 Beaucens [05 62 97 05 45; domaineviscos@orange.fr]** Fr Lourdes S twd Argelès-Gasost on D821. Cont twd Luz & Gavarnie to L of Argelès town, & turn L within 500m, sp Beaucens. Turn R to D13, site 2.5km on L. Med, pt sl, shd; wc; chem disp; shwrs inc; el pnts (2-10A) €2-4.50 (rev pol); gas; Indtte; shops 5km; tradsmn high ssn; snacks; BBQ; playgrnd; pool 4km; lake fishing 500m; dogs €1; quiet; adv bkg ess Jul-Aug; red long stay; ccard not acc; CKE/CCI. "Delightful site; landscaped grnds; excel, clean san facs; gd rests in area." 1 May-15 Oct. € 23.00 2014*

ARGELES GAZOST *8G2* (1km S Rural) *42.98670, -0.08854* **Camping Les Frênes, 46 Route des Vallées, 65400 Lau-Balagnas [05 62 97 25 12; fax 05 62 97 01 41; http://campinglesfrenes.fr]** Site on R of D821 twd S. Med, pt terr, pt shd; htd wc; chem disp; baby facs; shwrs inc; el pnts (10A); gas; Indtte; shop 100m; BBQ; playgrnd; pool; rv & fishing 1km; entmnt; TV; some statics; adv bkg rec; quiet; red long stay. ♦ 15 Dec-15 Oct. € 18.25 2009*

⊞ **ARGELES GAZOST** *8G2* (2km S Rural) *42.98826, -0.08923* **Kawan Village Le Lavedan, 44 Route des Vallées, 65400 Lau-Balagnas [05 62 97 18 84; fax 05 62 97 55 56; contact@lavedan.com; www.lavedan.com]** Fr Lourdes S on D821 dir Argelès-Gazost/Cauterets; 2km after Argelès on D921 site on R after vill of Lau-Balagnas. Med, mkd pitch, shd; htd wc; chem disp; baby facs; shwrs inc; el pnts (3A) €3 (poss rev pol; extra for 10A); gas; Indtte (inc dryer); shops 2km; rest, snacks; bar; BBQ; playgrnd; htd, covrd pool; paddling pool; wifi; entmnt; games/TV rm; many statics; dogs €2.50; phone; poss cr; Eng spkn; adv bkg; rd noise if pitched adj to rd & poss noise fr entmnt in café; ccard acc; red low ssn; CKE/CCI. "In beautiful valley; friendly, relaxed staff; clean modern san facs; excel cycle rte to Lourdes; vg." ♦ ltd € 24.00 (CChq acc) 2010*

ARGELES GAZOST *8G2* (2.5km S Rural) *42.9871, -0.1061* **Camping du Lac, 29 Chemin d'Azun, 65400 Arcizans-Avant [tel/fax 05 62 97 01 88; campinglac@campinglac65.fr; www.campinglac65.fr]** Fr Lourdes S thro Argelès-Gazost on D821 & D921. At 3rd rndabt take exit for St Savin/Arcizans-Avant. Cont thro St Savin vill & foll camp sp; site on L just thro Arcizans-Avant vill. NB: Dir rte to Arcizans-Avant prohibited to c'vans. Med, hdg/mkd pitch, pt sl, pt shd; wc; chem disp; baby facs; shwrs inc; el pnts (5-10A) €4.30-5; gas; Indtte; shop; tradsmn; rest 500m; snacks; playgrnd; htd pool; games rm; cycle hire; TV rm; wifi; dogs €2.50; Eng spkn; adv bkg; quiet; red low ssn; CKE/CCI. "Excel, peaceful, scenic & attractive site; mountain views; gd size pitches; clean san facs; gd for touring." ♦ 20 May-20 Sep. € 42.00 2014*

ARGELES GAZOST *8G2* (10km SW Rural) *42.94139, -0.17714* **Camping Pyrénées Natura, Route du Lac, 65400 Estaing [05 62 97 45 44; fax 05 62 97 45 81; info@camping-pyrenees-natura.com; www.camping-pyrenees-natura.com]** Fr Lourdes take D821 to Argelès Gazost; fr Argelès foll sp Col d'Aubisque & Val d'Azun onto D918; after approx 7.5km turn L onto D13 to Bun; after Bun cross rv & turn R onto D103 twd Estaing; site in 3km - rd narr. NB Rd fr Col d'Aubisque steep, narr & not suitable c'vans or lge m'vans. Med, hdg/mkd pitch, terr, pt shd; htd wc; chem disp; mv service pnt; baby facs; sauna; shwrs inc; el pnts (3-10A) €2-5 (poss rev pol); gas; Indtte (inc dryer); basics shop; tradsmn; snacks; bar; BBQ with legs; pool 4km; solarium; games area; internet; games/TV rm; 20% statics; dogs €3; no c'vans/m'vans over 7.50m high ssn; Eng spkn; adv bkg; quiet; ccard acc; red low ssn; CKE/CCI. "Superb, peaceful, well-kept, scenic site; friendly, helpful owners; clean unisex san facs; vg takeaway; gd for young families; no plastic grnd-sheets allowed; adj National Park; birdwatching area; excel; home cooked food at bar; vg site, one of the best ever visited." ♦ 10 Apr-14 Oct. € 38.40 SBS - D22 2013*

⊞ **ARREAU** *8G2* (7km N Rural) *42.97176, 0.37710* **Camp Municipal d'Esplantats, 65410 Sarrancolin [05 62 98 79 20 or 06 78 12 40 10 (mob); camping.esplantats.sarrancolin@wanadoo.fr; www.camping-esplantats.com]** Site on E side of D929 at N end of vill; ent by Total petrol stn, sp. Med, mkd pitch, pt shd; htd wc; mv service pnt; shwrs inc; el pnts (2-8A) €2.50-5.60 (long lead poss req); Indtte; shops, rest in vill; pool; some statics; dogs €2; quiet. "Site on rv bank; warden calls am & pm; clean san facs." ♦ € 10.40 2009*

ARREAU *8G2* (12km SE Rural) *42.79631, 0.40674* **FLOWER Camping Pène Blanche, 65510 Loudenvielle [05 62 55 68 85; fax 05 62 99 98 20; info@peneblanche.com; www.peneblanche.com / www.flowercampings.com]** S fr Arreau on D618 in dir of Avajan. Take D25 thro Genos. Site on W of D25 just bef turn over bdge to Loudenvielle. Avoid app fr E over Col de Peyresourde. Med, some mkd pitch, terr, pt shd; htd wc; chem disp; shwrs inc; el pnts (5-10A) €3.15-7; Indtte; shop 500m; rest, snacks; bar; BBQ; playgrnd; htd pool opp; lake 1km; 20% statics; dogs €1.90; clsd Nov; adv bkg; ccard acc. "Lge sports complex opp; quiet low ssn." ♦ 3 Apr-4 Nov. € 21.50 2010*

ARRENS MARSOUS *8G2* (800m E Rural) *42.9613, -0.2034* **Camping La Hèche, 54 Route d'Azun, 65400 Arrens-Marsous [05 62 97 02 64; laheche@free.fr; www.campinglaheche.com]** Fr Argelès-Gazost foll D918. Site on L immed bef Arrens. If towing c'van do not app fr Col d'Aubisque. Lge, mkd pitch, pt shd; htd wc; baby facs; shwrs inc; el pnts (3A) €2.70; gas; Indtte (inc dryer); shop; tradsmn; playgrnd; pool in vill high ssn; waterslide; tennis; games area; TV; 10% statics; dogs €0.50; phone; no adv bkg; quiet; CKE/CCI. "Beautiful location; gd san facs." ♦ 1 Jun-30 Sep. € 12.50-17.65 2013*

⊞ **ARTIGAT** *8F3* (700m NE Urban) *43.13776, 1.44407* **Camping Les Eychecadous, 09130 Artigat [(033) 05 61 68 98 24; campingartigat@hotmail.fr; www.camping-artigat.com]** Fr Toulouse take A64 S, take exit 28 twrds Capens. Marquefave, St. Sulpice. Turn L onto D10, at rndabt take 2nd exit onto D622, turn L sp Av. Antonin Triqué, cont twrds Lombardi on D622, go thro 1 rndabt, turn R sp Rue de la République/ D622 cont on D622, to Av. Des Pyrénées/ D4 cont onto D919 cont thro 3 rndabts then L onto Chemin du Comté then L twrds Les Eychecadous, then R, then L to site. Sm, mkd pitch, pt shd; wc; chem disp; mv service pnt; child/ baby facs; shwrs; el pnts (10A); tradsmn; rest, snacks, bar; BBQ; playgrnd; pool; entmnt; tv rm; wifi; ccard not acc; CKE/ CCI; dogs; few statics; twin axles; adv bkg. "V gd site on edge of Lèze; warm welcome; fishing, boating, & horse riding." ♦ € 12.00 2012*

ASCOU see Ax les Thermes *8G4*

ASPET *8G3* (1km SW Rural) *43.00969, 0.79665* **Camp Municipal Le Cagire, 31160 Aspet [05 61 88 51 55; fax 05 61 88 44 03; camping.aspet@wanadoo.fr]** Exit A64 at junc 18 St Gaudens & take D5 S. In 14km, site sp on R in vill of Aspet. Sp 'Camping, Stade.' Sm, mkd pitch, shd; wc; chem disp (wc); shwrs; el pnts (6A) €2.50; Indtte; shop, rest, snacks, bar 500m; pool, tennis 300m; games area; 30% statics; dogs €0.50; quiet; adv bkg; CKE/CCI. "Pleasant, well kept site nr lively, sm town; rec arr bef 1800 hrs high ssn; basic facs; some pitches muddy when wet." 1 Apr-30 Sep. € 8.30 2009*

ASTON see Cabannes, Les *8G3*

AUCH *8F3* (8km N Rural) *43.7128, 0.5646* **Kawan Village Le Talouch, Au Cassou, 32810 Roquelaure [05 62 65 52 43; fax 05 62 65 53 68; info@camping-talouch.com; www.camping-talouch.com]** Head W on N124 fr Auch, then N on D148 for 7km to site. Med, mkd pitch, pt shd; wc; chem disp; mv service pnt; baby facs; steam rm; sauna; shwrs; el pnts (6A) inc; gas; Indtte (inc dryer); shop; rest, snacks; bar; BBQ; playgrnd; 2 pools (1 htd, covrd pool); paddling pool; tennis; golf driving range; games area; wifi; entmnt; TV rm; 15% statics; dogs €2.40; Eng spkn; adv bkg; quiet; red low ssn; CKE/CCI. "Well-kept site; set in lovely countryside with lge grassed pitches, maintained to high standard; friendly Dutch owners who spk excel Eng; recreational facs superb for all age groups; gd walking & nature trails; poss liable to flooding." ♦ 1 Apr-30 Sep. € 33.40 2012*

AUCH *8F3* (1.5km SW Rural) *43.63664, 0.58858* **Camp Municipal d'Ile St Martin, Rue de Mouzon, Parc des Sports, 32000 Auch [05 62 05 00 22; frederic.estave@mairie-auch.fr]** Fr S on N21 approx 750m after business area, turn R at traff lts into Rue Général de Gaulle which runs into Rue du Mouzon, site in 500m adj rv. NB There is also a Parc des Sports on N side of Auch. Med, hdg pitch, hdstg, unshd; wc; shwrs inc; el pnts (6A) inc; shops 300m; pool 250m; few statics; poss cr; quiet but some rd noise. "Basic site with no shd; sm pitches; san facs dated but clean; facs up stairs; rec arr bef 1700; lovely walk along rv to town." 15 Apr-15 Oct. € 9.70 2010*

AUCUN *8F2* (700m E Rural) *42.97338, -0.18496* **Camping Azun Nature, 1 Route des Poueyes, 65400 [05 62 97 45 05; azun.nature@wanadoo.fr; www.camping-azun-nature.com]** Fr Toulouse- A64 exit Tarbes west. Fr Bordeaux or Bayonne- A64 Exit Soumoulou. Fr Lourdes- drive twd Argeles-Gazost, take exit Aubisque col-Val d'Azun; Fr town cent of Argeles-Gazost go twd Aubisque col, Soulor col; Cross Arras-en-Lavedan, go on twd Aucun vill, turn L sp Las Poueyes, site ent 100m on R bet barns. Sm, mkd pitch, pt shd; wc; chem disp; child/baby facs; shwrs inc; el pnts (3-6A) €2.50-3.50; Indtte; shop; tradsmn; BBQ; playgrnd; pool 3km; games area; games rm; wifi; TV rm; 50% statics; dogs free; adv bkg; CKE/ CCI; "Stunning setting; ideal walking & cycling area; gd for exploring the Pyrenees, visits to Lourdes; well maintained; friendly, helpful owner." ♦ 01 May-30 Sep. € 15.00 2013*

AUGIREIN *8G3* (300m E Rural) *42.93151, 0.91917* **Camping La Vie en Vert, 09800 Augirein [05 61 96 82 66; fax 05 61 04 73 00; daffis@lavieenvert.com; www.lavieenvert.com]** Fr St Girons on D618 twd Castillon. On app Castillon turn R foll sp to Luchon. 1km after vill Orgibet turn L into vill of Augirein. Site on L over bdge. Sm, hdg/mkd pitch, pt shd; wc; baby facs; shwrs inc; el pnts (3-10A) €3-5; Indtte; shop; tradsmn; rest in vill; BBQ; playgrnd; dogs €1; Eng spkn; adv bkg; quiet; red long stay; CKE/CCI. "Charming owners who own bar/café in vill; excel little site." ♦ 15 May-15 Sep. € 15.00 2009*

⊞ **AULUS LES BAINS** *8G3* (500m NW Rural) *42.79402, 1.33197* **Camp Municipal Le Coulédous, 09140 Aulus-les-Bains [05 61 66 43 56; campinglecouledous@orange.fr; www.couledous.com]** Take D618 fr St Girons. After 13km cross rv; turn R onto D3 sp Aulus-les-Bains. On app to Oust turn L onto D32, site approx 17km on R at ent to vill on rvside. Med, mkd pitch, hdstg, sl, pt shd; htd wc; chem disp; mv service pnt; shwrs inc; el pnts (6-10A) €4.50-6.50; Indtte; shop 500m; bar 300m, playgrnd; some statics; dogs €1; site clsd mid-Nov to mid-Dec; poss cr; Eng spkn; adv bkg; quiet; CKE/ CCI. "Gd walking & skiing (16km); sm spa in vill; excel." ♦ € 14.50 2010*

⊞ **AX LES THERMES** *8G4* (4km SE Rural) *42.70245, 1.88345* **Camp Municipal Les Ioules, 09110 Orlu [05 61 64 21 70; fax 05 61 64 64 23; camping.orlu@orange.fr]** On N20 S foll sp for Spain thro town cent. On exit town turn L immed bef bdge sp Orlu. Site on R in 3km. Med, mkd pitch, pt shd; htd wc; mv service pnt; shwrs inc; el pnts (6A) €3.95; gas; Indtte; shop 3km; rest, snacks, bar 500m; playgrnd; pool high ssn; rv adj; fishing; games area; entmnt; 30% statics; dogs €2; phone; poss cr; adv bkg; quiet; CKE/CCI. "Gd, friendly, scenic site; poss floods in bad weather; excel walks; conv Andorra or Spain." ♦ € 13.30 2010*

⊞ **AX LES THERMES** *8G4* (1km NW Rural) *42.72870, 1.82541* **Camping Sunêlia Le Malazéou, 09110 Ax-les-Thermes [05 61 64 69 14; fax 05 61 64 05 60; camping.malazeou@wanadoo.fr; www.campingmalazeou.com]** Sp on N20 to Foix. Lge, hdg pitch, pt sl, shd; htd wc (some cont); chem disp; mv service pnt; baby facs; shwrs inc; el pnts (6A) inc; gas; Indry rm; shop & 1km; tradsmn; playgrnd; 70% statics; dogs €3; train 500m; site poss clsd Nov; Eng spkn; adv bkg; quiet but some rd noise; red low ssn; CKE/CCI. "Pleasant site by rv; lovely scenery; gd fishing; gd heated san facs; rvside walk to town; gd." ♦ ltd € 37.00 2013*

⊞ **AX LES THERMES** *8G4* (8km NW Rural) *42.75880, 1.76319* **Camp Municipal Le Castella, 09250 Luzenac [05 61 64 47 53; fax 05 61 64 40 59; campinglecastella@orange.fr; www.campingcastella.com]** Site on W of N20 bet Ax-les-Thermes & Foix. Med, mkd pitch, terr, pt shd; htd wc; shwrs inc; el pnts (4-10A) €3-5.95; Indtte; shop, bar 300m; playgrnd; pool in ssn; fishing; tennis; archery; entmnt; 70% statics; quiet; ccard acc; red low ssn. "Mountain views; gd walking; prehistoric caves at Niaux; barrier locked until 0900 when office opens." ♦ € 13.20 2010*

BAGNERES DE BIGORRE *8F2* (9km NE Rural) *43.11196, 0.04931* **Aire Naturelle Le Cerf Volant (Dhom), 7 Cami de la Géline, 65380 Orincles [tel/fax 05 62 42 99 32; lecerfvolant1@yahoo.fr]** Fr Bagnères-de-Bigorre on D935; turn L onto D937 dir Lourdes; site on L opp D407. Single track app rd for 150m. Sm, pt shd; wc; chem disp; shwrs inc; el pnts (15A) €2.30; Indtte; tradsmn; playgrnd; no statics; dogs free; poss cr; no ccard acc; CKE/CCI. "Farm site - produce sold Jul-Aug; conv Lourdes & touring Pyrenees; gd, clean site." ♦ 15 May-15 Oct. € 7.70 2010*

BAGNERES DE BIGORRE *8F2* (1km E Urban) *43.07158, 0.15692* **Camping Les Fruitiers, 9 Rue de Toulouse, 65200 Bagnères-de-Bigorre [tel/fax 05 62 95 25 97; daniellevillemur@wanadoo.fr; www.camping-les-fruitiers.com]** NE fr town cent on D938 dir Toulouse; in 500m turn L at traff lits at x-rds onto D8; site on R in 50m. Site well sp on app; take care on final app to ent. Med, mkd pitch, pt sl, pt shd; htd wc; chem disp; baby facs; shwrs inc; el pnts (4-6A) €3.40-5; Indtte; shops 200m; rest 300m; snacks 200m; playgrnd; pool 200m; tennis; dogs €1; phone; bus; poss cr; adv bkg; quiet/some traff noise; ccard acc; CKE/CCI. "Lovely, well-kept site; helpful staff; excel facs; sharp bends on site rds & o'hanging trees poss diff lge o'fits; attractive town with thermal baths; gd touring base; vg mkt; vg." ♦ Apr-Oct. € 12.60 2011*

"We must tell The Club about that great site we found"

Get your site reports in by mid-August and we'll do our best to get your updates into the next edition.

BAGNERES DE BIGORRE *8F2* (3km E Rural) *43.08180, 0.15139* **Camping Le Monlôo, 6 Route de la Plaine, 65200 Bagnères-de-Bigorre [tel/fax 05 62 95 19 65; campingmonloo@yahoo.com; www.lemonloo.com]** Fr A64 exit junc 14 onto D20/D938 to Bagnères-de-Bigorre. At traff lts on ent turn R onto D8, site on R in 1km, sp at ent. Fr Tarbes (N) on D935 turn L at 1st rndabt, L again over old rlwy line, site on R. Med, sl, pt shd; wc; chem disp; mv service pnt; shwrs inc; el pnts (10A) €5.20; Indtte; shop 1km; playgrnd; pool (high ssn); waterslide; tennis; entmnt; wifi; TV; 30% statics; phone; dogs €1.50; Eng spkn; adv bkg; quiet; ccard acc; red low ssn; CKE/CCI. "Pleasant, peaceful, scenic site; spacious & well-kept site; friendly, welcoming, helpful owners; ltd water points; gd facs, poss stretched high ssn; pleasant town; conv Pyrenean mountain passes; nice views of Pyrenees." ♦ 1 Jan-19 Oct, 10 Nov-31 Dec. € 30.75 (3 persons) 2013*

See advertisement

BARBOTAN LES THERMES *8E2* (1km S Rural) *43.94027, -0.04557* **Camping Le Lac de l'Uby, Cazaubon, 32150 Barbotan-les-Thermes [05 62 09 53 91; fax 05 62 09 56 97; balia-vacances@wanadoo.fr; www.camping-uby.com]** Fr Eauze take D626/N524 sp Cazaubon, immed bef Cazaubon turn R sp Barbotan. Site on R in 2km. Lge, mkd pitch, some hdstg, pt shd; htd wc; chem disp; el pnts (5-10A) €6; Indtte; shop & 2km; cooking facs; playgrnd; pool; lake sw & beach 300m; fishing; sailing; windsurfing; tennis; games area; cycle hire; entmnt; some statics; dogs €1.80; adv bkg rec; ccard acc; red low ssn; CKE/CCI. "Gd, well-kept, well-run site; interesting Bastide towns nrby." ♦ 15 Mar-30 Nov. € 16.00 2009*

BAREGES see Luz St Sauveur *8G2*

BASSOUES *8F2* (600m NE Rural) *43.57972, 0.25560* **Camp Municipal St Fris, 32320 Bassoues [05 62 70 90 47 (Mairie); www.bassoues.net]** W fr Montesquiou on D943; site on L 200m after junc with D35 (immed after rugby stadium & bef ent to Bassoues). Sm, mkd pitch, pt sl, pt shd; wc; shwrs inc; el pnts €2.20; shop, rest & bar 1km; BBQ; games area; dogs; no twin-axles; adv bkg; quiet, but some traff noise; CKE/CCI. "Site next to delightful sm lake; various pitch sizes; warm welcome; barrier closes access, warden visits 0830-1000 & 1700-2000; Bassoues an interesting Bastide town; excel." ♦ ltd 1 Jun-30 Sep. € 11.50 2011*

BASTIDE DE SEROU, LA *8G3* (1km S Rural) *43.00150, 1.44472* **Camping L'Arize, Route de Nescus, 09240 La Bastide-de-Sérou [05 61 65 81 51; fax 05 61 65 83 34; mail@camping-arize.com; www.camping-arize.com]** Fr Foix on D117 on ent La Bastide-de-Sérou turn L at TO/ Gendarmerie on D15 sp Nescus, site 1km on R. Med, hdg/mkd pitch, pt shd; wc; chem disp; mv service pnt; baby facs; serviced pitch; shwrs inc; el pnts (6A) inc (poss rev pol); gas; Indtte (inc dryer); shop & 2km; tradsmn; rest 5km; snacks; playgrnd; pool; lake sw 5km; fishing; cycle hire; golf 5km; horseriding adj; golf nr; wifi; entmnt; 10% statics; dogs €2; poss cr; Eng spkn; adv bkg; ccard acc; CKE/CCI. "Pleasant, scenic site on bank Rv Arize; modern facs; gd mkd walking/cycle rtes." ♦ ltd 8 Mar-12 Nov. € 35.20 2013*

BEAUCENS see Argelès Gazost *8G2*

BEAUMONT DE LOMAGNE *8E3* (800m E Urban) *43.88406, 0.99800* **Village de Loisirs Le Lomagnol (formerly Municipal Le Lac), Ave du Lac, 82500 Beaumont-de-Lomagne [05 63 26 12 00; fax 05 63 65 60 22; villagedeloisirslelomagnol@wanadoo.fr; www.villagelelomagnol.fr]** On SE of D928 at E end of vill. Sp 'Centre de Loisirs, Plan d'Eau'. Med, mkd pitch, pt shd; wc; chem disp; baby facs; sauna; shwrs inc; el pnts (10A) inc (poss long lead req); Indtte; shop; rest, snacks; bar; playgrnd; pool; waterslide; jacuzzi; lake sw; fishing; canoe & cycle hire; tennis; golf; 25% statics; dogs €2; poss cr; quiet; red low ssn. "Gd quality, modern site; interesting old town; mkt Sat." ♦ 1 Apr-30 Oct. € 17.00 2010*

BEDUER see Figeac *7D4*

BELMONT SUR RANCE *8E4* (500m W Rural) *43.81777, 2.75108* **Camping Val Fleuri du Rance, Route de Lacaune, 12370 Belmont-sur-Rance [05 65 99 04 76 or 06 88 42 28 78 (mob); marjandejong@wanadoo.fr; www.campinglevalfleuri.com]** On D32 on ent vill fr SW; on L side of rd on sh unmade service rd. NB diff ent/exit to/fr S. Sm, hdg/mkd pitch, pt shd; wc; chem disp; shwrs inc; el pnts (6A) €3.50; gas; Indry rm; shop 500m; rest; pool 500m; rv fishing; tennis; wifi; some statics; dogs €1.50; Eng spkn; adv bkg; quiet; red low ssn; CKE/CCI. "Attractive valley setting; helpful Dutch owners; attractive sm town; v welcoming." ♦ ltd 1 Apr-30 Sep. € 14.00 2014*

BERAUT see Condom *8E2*

BEZ, LE see Brassac *8F4*

BOISSE PENCHOT see Decazeville *7D4*

BOULOGNE SUR GESSE *8F3* (6km NE Rural) *43.33135, 0.68046* **Camping Le Canard Fou, Laron, 31350 Lunax [05 61 88 26 06]** Fr Boulogne-sur-Gesse N on D632 sp Toulouse. In 6km turn L sp Lunax, foll site sp for 1km. Turn L at x-rds, site 300m on R. Sm, pt sl, pt shd; wc; chem disp (wc); shwrs inc; el pnts (9A) inc; gas; Indtte; shop 6km; BBQ; pool 6km; reservoir adj; some statics; phone 800m; Eng spkn; adv bkg; quiet. "Peaceful CL-type site; friendly owners; san facs clean but open to elements; breakfast & eve meals avail; perfect site for walking, cycling; rec phone ahead as ltd touring pitches." ♦ 15 Mar-15 Dec. € 11.00 (4 persons) 2009*

BOULOGNE SUR GESSE *8F3* (1.3km SE Rural) *43.28323, 0.65544* **Camp Municipal du Lac, Ave du Lac, 31350 Boulogne-sur-Gesse [05 61 88 20 54; fax 05 61 88 62 16; villagevacancesboulogne@wanadoo.fr; www.ville-boulogne-sur-gesse.fr]** Fr Boulogne-sur-Gesse, take D633 for 1km. Foll sp, turn L to site. Lake (watersports cent) adj ent. Lge, mkd pitch, pt sl, pt shd; wc (some cont); chem disp; shwrs inc; el pnts (10A) €3.70; gas; shops 1km; rest; bar; playgrnd; htd pool 300m; boating; fishing; tennis; golf; entmnt; 90% statics; dogs €1; phone; Eng spkn; quiet. "High kerbs poss diff lge o'fits; clean facs; phone ahead to check open early ssn." ♦ 1 Apr-30 Sep. € 10.30 2009*

BRASSAC *8F4* (11km SE Rural) *43.59700, 2.60732* **Camping Le Rouquié, Lac de la Raviège, 81260 Lamontélarie [05 63 70 98 06; fax 05 63 50 49 58; camping.rouquie@wanadoo.fr; www.campingrouquie.fr]** Fr Brassac take D62 to N side of Lac de la Raviège; site on lakeside. Med, mkd pitch, terr, pt shd; wc; chem disp; baby facs; shwrs; el pnts (3-6A) €4; Indtte (inc dryer); shop; tradsmn; snacks; bar; BBQ; playgrnd; lake sw; fishing; sailing & watersports adj; games area; cycle hire; entmnt; TV; 50% statics; dogs; adv bkg; poss cr; quiet; ccard acc; CKE/CCI. "Ltd facs low ssn; gd lake views; Site needs TLC." 15 Apr-31 Oct. € 25.00 2014*

BRASSAC *8F4* (5km S Rural) *43.60835, 2.47148* **FFCC Camping Le Plô, Le Bourg, 81260 Le Bez [tel/fax 05 63 74 00 82; info@leplo.com; www.leplo.com]** Fr Castres on D622 to Brassac; then D53 S to Le Bez, site sp W of Le Bez. Med, mkd pitch,terr, pt shd; wc; chem disp; fam bthrm; shwrs inc; el pnts (6A) €3; Indtte; shop 5km; snacks; BBQ; playgrnd; sm freestanding pool; cycle hire; games area; games rm; wifi; dogs €1.50; Eng spkn; adv bkg; quiet; red low ssn; CKE/CCI. "Lovely location; well-equipped site; excel, clean san facs; friendly, helpful Dutch owners; beautiful, historical area with National Park; much wildlife; cafés & gd rest nrby; vg." ♦ 1 May-30 Sep. € 25.50 (CChq acc) 2014*

BRENGUES *7D4* (1.5km N Rural) *44.58683, 1.83738* **Camping Le Moulin Vieux, Route de Figeac, 46320 Brengues [05 65 40 00 41; fax 05 65 40 05 65; contact@camping-lemoulinvieux.com; www.brengues.com]** Fr Figeac on D13, in 6km L onto D41. In approx 17km site well sp on L bef Brengues vill. Med, shd; wc; chem disp; shwrs inc; el pnts (10A) €2.60; Indtte; shop; snacks; bar; playgrnd; pool; entmnt; some statics; adv bkg; some rd noise; ccard acc; red low ssn; CKE/CCI. "Beautiful site; helpful owners; facs stretched high ssn; poss scruffy/unkempt early ssn (2009); excel." ♦ 1 Jul-30 Sep. € 13.00 2009*

BRENGUES *7D4* (500m S Rural) *44.57509, 1.83261* **Camp Municipal de Brengues, 46320 Brengues [tel/fax 05 65 40 06 82 or 05 65 40 05 71 (Mairie)]** W fr Figeac on D13. After 6km turn L onto D41. After 17km, turn L at x-rds with D38, site ent 100m on R bef bdge over Rv Célé. Sm, mkd pitch, pt shd; wc; shwrs €2; el pnts (10A) inc (rev pol); Indtte; shop 300m; rest; bar; playgrnd; tennis; CKE/CCI. "Warden visits." 1 Jun-30 Sep. € 11.25 2009*

BRETENOUX *7C4* (150m N Urban) *44.91650, 1.83816* **Camping La Bourgnatelle, 46130 Bretenoux [05 65 10 89 04; fax 05 65 10 89 18; contact@dordogne_vacances.fr; www.dordogne-vacances.fr]** In town 100m fr D940. Lge, pt shd; wc; mv service pnt; shwrs inc; el pnts (5-10A) €3; Indtte; shops adj; rest, snacks; playgrnd; pool; rv & fishing; canoe hire; entmnt; dogs €1.50; adv bkg; quiet; red low ssn. "Lovely site along banks of Rv Cère; clean site; gd fishing; lovely town MD Tues." 19 Apr-31 Nov. € 33.45 2014*

BRETENOUX *7C4* (4km W Rural) *44.91937, 1.80262* **Camping Les Chalets sur La Dordogne, Pont de Puybrun, 46130 Girac [05 65 10 93 33; contact@camping-leschalets.com; www.camping-leschalets.com]** Fr Bretenoux on D803 dir Puybrun. Site on L on rvside - sp on rd barrier easily missed. Sm, mkd pitch, shd; wc; chem disp; shwrs inc; el pnts (6A) inc; Indtte; shop; tradsmn; rest, snacks; bar; playgrnd; pool; rv & shgl beach adj; canoeing; TV rm; 20% statics; dogs €1.50; Eng spkn; quiet; ccard acc. "Gd, clean family site; helpful owners." ♦ 10 Apr-30 Sep. € 18.30 2009*

BROMMAT *7D4* (300m E Rural) *44.83083, 2.68638* **Camping Municipale, Le Bourg, 12600 Brommat [05 65 66 00 96; fax 05 65 66 22 84; mairie-de.brommat@wanadoo.fr; www.brommat.fr]** Fr D98, cross rv bdge, cont uphill to Mairie. Turn R in front of Mairie and cont strt on. Campsite on R. Sm, hdg pitch, pt shd; chem disp; shwr; el pnts (6A); sw 0.2km; lake 10km; tennis 2km; tv rm; dogs; bus 50m; fishing; adv bkg; quiet; CCI." Beautiful adj walk; vg." ♦ ltd 15 May-15 Sept. € 13.00 2014*

⊞ **CABANNES, LES** *8G3* (2km SE Rural) *42.77444, 1.70328* **Camp Municipal La Coume, 09310 Albiès [tel/fax 05 61 64 98 99; camping.albies@wanadoo.fr]** Site sp fr N20 in vill. Med, hdg pitch, pt sl, terr, pt shd; htd wc; chem disp (wc); shwrs inc; el pnts (5-10A) €1.75-2.70; Indtte; shop, rest in vill; BBQ; Rv Ariège 100m; fishing; games area; some statics; quiet. "Gd san facs." ♦ € 7.80 2009*

CABANNES, LES *8G3* (2km SW Rural) *42.77269, 1.67172* **FFCC Camping Le Pas de l'Ours, Les Gesquis, 09310 Aston [05 61 64 90 33; fax 05 61 64 90 32; contact@lepasdelours.fr; www.campingariege.fr]** S on N20, after Tarascon-sur-Ariège turn R sp Plateau de Beille/Les Cabannes. Pass thro Aulos, site well sp. Sm, hdg/mkd pitch, pt sl, pt shd; htd wc; chem disp; baby facs; shwrs inc; el pnts (6A) €4; Indtte (inc dryer); shop, rest 2km; snacks; bar; BBQ; playgrnd; pool adj; tennis; cycle hire; games area; wifi; entmnt; TV rm; 50% statics; dogs €2; phone; Eng spkn; adv bkg; quiet; ccard acc; red low ssn; CKE/CCI. "Attractive site surrounded by mountains; v clean san facs; not suitable lge o'fits; helpful owners; gd touring base; access poss diff for lge o'fits." ♦ ltd 26 May-15 Sep. € 32.00 2013*

CABRERETS *7D3* (1km NE Rural) *44.50771, 1.66234* **Camping Cantal, 46330 Cabrerets [05 65 31 26 61; fax 05 65 31 20 47]** Fr Cahors take D653 E for approx 15km bef turning R onto D662 E thro Vers & St Géry. Turn L onto D41 to Cabrerets. Site 1km after vill on R. Sm, pt sl, pt shd; wc; chem disp (wc); 50% serviced pitch; shwrs inc; el pnts €2.50; rv canoeing nrby; quiet; CKE/CCI. "Superb situation; v interesting vill; peaceful site; warden calls; grnd slightly bumpy; excel san facs; not suitable lge o'fits; conv Pech Merle; excel." 1 Apr-15 Oct. € 9.00 2014*

CABRERETS *7D3* (7km NE Rural) *44.52609, 1.71944* **Camping Mas de Nadal (Naturist), 46330 Sauliac-sur-Célé [05 65 31 20 51; fax 05 65 31 20 57; info@masdenadal.com; www.masdenadal.com]** Fr Cahors take D653 E. After 35km turn R onto D40 S, sp Blars. Fr Blars cont S for 2km to site ent on R. Sm, mkd pitch, pt sl, pt shd; wc; shwrs inc; el pnts (3-9A) €4; Indtte; shops 2km; tradsmn; rest; bar; playgrnd; pool; canoe hire; games area; phone; dogs €4.50; poss cr; Eng spkn; adv bkg; quiet; CKE/CCI/INF card req. "Secluded wooded hillside; ltd rough pitches not suitable lge o'fits; rec phone ahead to check avail; suitable for m'vans." 1 Apr-30 Sep. € 21.00 2009*

CAHORS *7D3* (8km N Rural) *44.52585, 1.46048* **Camping Les Graves, 46090 St Pierre-Lafeuille [tel/fax 05 65 36 83 12; infos@camping-lesgraves.com; www.camping-lesgraves.com]** Leave A20 at junc 57 Cahors Nord onto D820. Foll sp St Pierre-Lafeuille; at N end of vill, site is opp L'Atrium wine cave. Med, hdg pitch, sl, pt shd; wc, chem disp; mv service pnt; shwrs inc; el pnts (6-10A) €2.50-3.50 (poss rev pol); Indtte; shop 10km; tradsmn; rest, snacks; bar; playgrnd; pool; cycle hire; 5% statics; dogs €1.50; Eng spkn; adv bkg rec high ssn; rd noise; ccard acc; red low ssn/CKE/CCI. "Clean, scenic site; lge pitches; poss clsd during/after wet weather due boggy grnd; disabled facs over stony rd & grass; ltd facs low ssn; conv A20; nice quiet, clean site." ♦ 1 Apr-31 Oct. € 19.00 2014*

CAHORS *7D3* (1.5km E Urban) *44.46318, 1.44226* **Camping Rivière de Cabessut, Rue de la Rivière, 46000 Cahors [05 65 30 06 30; fax 05 65 23 99 46; contact@cabessut.com; www.cabessut.com]** Fr N or S on D820, at S end Cahors by-pass take D911 sp Rodez. At traff lts by bdge do not cross rv but bear R on D911. In 1km at site sp turn L. Site on E bank of Rv Lot, well sp fr town. 1.8km to site fr bdge (Pont Cabessut). Med, hdg/mkd pitch, pt shd; wc; chem disp; mv service pnt; some serviced pitches; baby facs; shwrs inc; el pnts (10A) €2 (poss rev pol); gas; lndtte; shop; hypmkt 1.5km; tradsmn; snacks; bar; BBQ (gas only); playgrnd; pool; rv adj; wifi; 5% statics; dogs €2; phone; bus to Cahors 600m; poss cr; adv bkg rec - ess high ssn; quiet; CKE/CCI. "Lovely, well-run site by rv; beautiful area; pleasant, mostly lge pitches, sm pitches diff access when site full; gd for children; walk to town by rv 1.8km; food mkt Wed, full mkt Sat; excel new san facs (2012); well maintained site, helpful, commited owners." ♦ 1 Apr-30 Sep. € 30.25 2014*

⊞ **CAHORS** *7D3* (13km W Rural) *44.47968, 1.35906* **Camping de L'écluse, Lieu dit Le Payras, 46140 Douelle [09 84 45 33 78; antinea.loisirs@orange.fr; www.tourisme-lot.com/en]** Fr N foll D820 past D811 junc, over rv lot bdge, immed take D8 on R, sp Pradines Douelle. In Douelle cont thro vill, take R sp Antinea Campings. Take R sp Camping, park outside barrier, walk to Antinea (by rv). Sm, mkd pitch, level, pt shd; wc (some cont); shwrs inc; el pnts (6A) €1.50; BBQ; sw rv 0.5km; dogs; twin axles; quiet. "Quiet rvside site by disused lock; basic but clean facs; level pitches but uneven & long grass; check in at Antinea Bar; barrier open on req; gd rvside walk into Douelle; attractive vill; fair." € 13.50 2014*

CAJARC *7D4* (6.4km NE Rural) *44.50612, 1.89667* **Camping Les Cournoulises, 46160 Montbrun [06 15 53 00 58 (mob); lescournoulises@sfr.fr; http://lescournoulises.perso.sfr.fr]** Fr Cahors foll D662 or fr Figeac D19. Foll D622 along N bank of R Lot for 6km. Site well sp on app. Sm, mkd pitch, pt shd; wc; chem disp (wc); mv service pnt nrby; shwrs inc; el pnts (6A) €3; lndtte; tradsmn; café; shops, rest, snacks & bar 6km; BBQ sep area (charcoal); playgrnd; htd pool 6km; direct acces to rv; canoe hire; fishing; paragliding; trekking; pool & tennis nrby; games area; dogs €0.50; phone adj; bus adj ; twin axles; Eng spkn; adv bkg; quiet; ccard not acc; red long stay; CKE/CCI. "Lge pitches; teepee & trapper tents on site (for hire); many attractions within 30km radius; fishing rods avail; friendly, helpful owner; excel; beautiful site; spotless facs; wonderful; highly rec ." ♦ ltd 1 Apr-10 Oct. € 13.90 2014*

CAJARC *7D4* (300m SW Urban) *44.48374, 1.83928* **Camp Municipal Le Terriol, Rue Le Terriol, 46160 Cajarc [05 65 40 72 74 or 05 65 40 65 20 (Mairie); fax 05 65 40 39 05; mairie.cajarc@wanadoo.fr; www.cajarc.fr]** Fr Cahors dir Cajarc on D662 on L foll sp to site. Sm, hdg/mkd pitch, some hdstg, pt shd; wc (cont); chem disp; baby facs; fam bthrm; shwrs inc; el pnts (10A) inc (poss rev pol); lndtte; shop, rest, bar in vill; BBQ; playgrnd; pool & tennis 500m; dogs; phone; no twin-axles; Eng spkn; adv bkg; some rd noise; CKE/CCI. "Gd sized pitches; clean, basic facs; lovely sm town on Rv Lot." 1 May-30 Sep. € 14.50 2013*

CAJARC *7D4* (6km SW Rural) *44.46630, 1.75077* **Camp Municipal Le Grand Pré, 46330 Cénevières [05 65 30 22 65 or 05 65 31 28 16 (Marie); fax 05 65 31 37 00; mairie.cenevieres@wanadoo.fr]** Fr Villefranche on D911 twd Cahors turn R onto D24 at Limogne for Cénevières. Foll sp. Fr St Cirq-Lapopie on D24 thro vill & over rlwy. Sm, hdg/mkd pitch, pt shd; wc; chem disp (wc); mv service pnt; shwrs inc; el pnts (10A) inc; lndtte; shop, rest, snacks, bar 1km; BBQ; rv sw; dogs; bus; phone; quiet. "Peaceful site by rv; wonderful views of cliffs; vg san facs; site self & warden calls pm; excel highly rec." 1 Jun-30 Sep. € 12.40 2012*

CAJARC *7D4* (6km W Rural) *44.4735, 1.7835* **Camping Ruisseau de Treil, 46160 Larnagol [05 65 31 23 39; fax 05 65 31 23 27; contact@lotcamping.com; www.lotcamping.com]** Exit A20 junc 57 onto D49 sp St Michel; in 4km turn R onto D653; after 5.5km in Vers at mini-rndabt turn L onto D662; site on L immed after leaving Larnagol. Or fr Figeac foll D19 thro Cajarc. At top of hill leaving Cajarc turn R onto D662 sp Cahors & Larnagol. Site sp on R 300m bef Larnagol on blind bend. Sm, mkd pitch, pt sl, pt shd; wc; chem disp; baby facs; shwrs inc; el pnts (6A) €3.60; lndtte; tradsmn; rest, snacks; bar; BBQ; playgrnd; 2 pools; rv sw, fishing, canoeing adj; horseriding; cycle hire; library; TV rm; 4% statics; dogs €3.90; poss cr; adv bkg; quiet; red low ssn/snr citizen; CKE/CCI. "Beautiful, spacious, peaceful site in lovely area; well-run; friendly, helpful British owners; clean san facs but ltd when site full; lge pitches poss uneven; many long-stay/returning campers; guided walks; vg touring base; excel." ♦ ltd 10 May-14 Sep. € 32.60 2014*

CAMON see Mirepoix (Ariege) *8F4*

CAMPAN see Bagnères de Bigorre *8F2*

CAMPOURIEZ see Entraygues sur Truyère *7D4*

CANET DE SALARS see Pont de Salars *7D4*

CAPVERN see Lannemezan *8F2*

CARENNAC *7C4* (1km SE Rural) *44.90985, 1.74070* **Camping L'Eau Vive, Route de St Céré, 46100 Carennac [05 65 10 97 39; fax 05 55 28 12 12; info@dordogne-soleil.com; www.dordogne-soleil.com]** Exit A20 junc 53 or 54 onto D803/D840 to Martel; then D803 to Bétaille in 10km; turn R onto D20 dir Carennac; in 3km cross rv; in 300m turn L onto D30; site on L in 400m. Med, hdg/mkd pitch, pt shd; wc (cont); chem disp; mv service pnt; baby facs; shwrs inc; el pnts (6A) €3.20; gas; lndtte (inc dryer); sm shop & 1km; tradsmn; snacks; bar; BBQ; playgrnd; pool; paddling pool; rv sw, shgl beach adj; white water rafting; canoeing; fishing; horseriding nrby; tennis; cycle hire (cycle rtes fr site); games area; games rm; wifi; entmnt; TV; 20% statics; dogs €2.20; phone; Eng spkn; adv bkg; quiet; ccard not acc; red low ssn; CKE/CCI. "Direct access to rv; friendly, helpful staff; ideal for rallies; vg." ♦ 30 Apr-15 Oct. € 19.80 2011*

CARLUCET *7D3* (1.5km NW Rural) *44.72880, 1.59692* **Camping Château de Lacomté Country Club, 46500 Carlucet [05 65 38 75 46; fax 05 65 33 17 68; lacomte2@wanadoo.fr; www.campingchateaulacomte.com]** Exit A20 junc 56 onto D802. In 2km take D807 & then turn L onto D32 to Carlucet. In approx 1.6km turn L & foll site sp for 4.8km. App rd narr with no passing places. Or fr Gramat SW on D677/D807. After approx 14km turn R onto D32 sp Carlucet, foll site sp. NB Take care Sat Nav dirs (2011). Med, hdg pitch, some hdstg, pt sl, terr, pt shd; wc; chem disp; all serviced pitches; shwrs; el pnts (10A) inc; gas 7km; Indtte; sm shop & 12km; rest, snacks; bar; BBQ; pool; tennis; table tennis; golf 9km; boat trips; wifi; entmnt; 5% statics; dogs €4; c'vans/m'vans over 8.50m by request high ssn; poss cr; adv bkg; quiet; ccard acc; red low ssn/CKE/CCI. "British-owned site in attractive area; adults-only; some pitches gd size, others sm & diff long o'fits; some pitches too sm for car, c'van & awning; levelling blocks req some pitches; 'freedom' pitches for m'vanners inc use of sm car, bookable daily; conv Rocamadour & Lot, & A20; excel walking in area." ♦ 15 May-15 Sep. € 35.00 2011*

CASSAGNABERE TOURNAS *8F3* (450m S Rural) *43.22583, 0.78920* **Camping Pré Fixe, 31420 Cassagnabère-Tournas [05 61 98 71 00 or 06 48 23 46 79 (mob); camping@instudio4.com; www.instudio4.com/pre-fixe]** Exit A64 at junc 21 onto D635 dir Aurignac. Cont thro vill on D635 sp Cassagnabère for 8km, sp in vill. Sm, hdg/mkd pitch, terr, pt shd; wc (some cont); chem disp; mv service pnt; baby facs; shwrs inc; el pnts (6-10A) €4; gas; Indtte; shop 500m; tradsmn; rest, snacks; bar; BBQ; playgrnd; pool; entmnt; TV rm; 10% statics; no dogs; phone; Eng spkn; adv bkg; quiet; CKE/CCI. "Friendly owners; beautiful landscape; gd touring base; excel." ♦ 15 Apr-30 Sep. € 18.00 2009*

CASTELFRANC *7D3* (6km SE Rural) *44.48095, 1.28160* **Camp Municipal L'Eau Berge de Caix, 46140 Luzech [05 65 30 72 32 (Mairie); fax 05 65 30 76 80; commune.luzech@wanadoo.fr; www.ville-luzech.fr]** Fr Cahors take D811 NW, turn L onto D8 foll sp to Luzech; cross both bdges in Luzech; site on R in 1km on D8; do not foll camp sp on D88 to Sauzac. Sm, pt shd; wc (cont); sauna; shwrs inc; el pnts (6-10A) (rev pol); shops 1km; bar; playgrnd; dogs; some rd noise; red low ssn. "Peaceful site on Rv Lot; rv not suitable for sw, sluice gates of dam upstream liable to be opened, causing rv to rise sharply; warden visits am & pm - arrange for barrier to be open; peaceful site." 1 May-30 Sep. 2009*

CASTELNAU MAGNOAC *8F2* (2km SE Rural) *43.26610, 0.52140* **Camping L'Eglantière (Naturist), 65230 Aries-Espénan [05 62 99 83 64 or 05 62 39 88 00; fax 05 62 39 81 44; infos@leglantiere.com; www.leglantiere.com]** Fr Castelnau-Magnoac take D929 S sp Lannemezan; in 2.5km L on D9 sp Monléon; in 1km L on unclass rd for 500m; L at T-junc & foll L'Eglantiere sp to site; app fr D632 not rec. Lge, hdg/mkd pitch, some hdstg, pt sl, pt shd; wc; chem disp; mv service pnt; serviced pitch; sauna; shwrs inc; el pnts (16A) €5.20 (rev pol); gas; Indtte (inc dryer); shop; tradsmn; rest, snacks; bar; BBQ; playgrnd; htd pool; paddling pool; fishing; canoeing; archery; cycle hire; golf nrby; wifi; 15% statics; dogs €4.20; adv bkg; Eng spkn; quiet; various pitch prices; ccard acc; red low ssn; CKE/CCI. "Beautiful, relaxing site on rv; helpful staff; pitches poss soft after rain; plenty naturist walks; conv Pyrenees." ♦ 1 Apr-25 Sep. € 34.00 (CChq acc) 2009*

CASTIES LABRANDE *8F3* (1.5km W Rural) *43.32502, 0.99046* **Camping Le Casties, Le Bas de Lebrande, 31430 Casties-Labrande [05 61 90 81 11; fax 05 61 90 81 10; lecasties@wanadoo.fr; www.camping-lecasties.com]** S fr Toulouse, exit A64 junc 26 onto D626; after Pouy-de-Touges turn L onto & foll camping sp. Med, hdg pitch, pt shd; wc; chem disp; shwrs inc; el pnts (5A) €1; Indtte; tradsmn; snacks; bar; BBQ; playgrnd; pool; paddling pool; fishing; tennis; 10% statics; dogs €1; phone; Eng spkn; adv bkg; quiet; ccard acc; CKE/CCI. "Remote; lge hdg pitches; staff friendly & helpful; value for money; lovely pool; excel; new vg san facs (2013);v peaceful; sm farm for children." ♦ ltd 1 May-30 Sep. € 12.50 2014*

CASTRES *8F4* (2km NE Urban) *43.62054, 2.25401* **Camping de Gourjade, Ave de Roquecourbe, 81100 Castres [tel/fax 05 63 59 33 51; contact@campingdegourjade.net; www.campingdegourjade.net]** Leave Castres NE on D89 sp Rocquecourbe; site on R in 2km. Well sp. Ave de Roquecourbe is pt of D89. Med, hdg pitch, pt terr, pt shd; wc unisex; chem disp; mv service pnt; shwrs; el pnts (6-10A) inc (poss rev pol); gas; Indtte; shop (ltd) in ssn; supmkt 1.5km; rest adj; BBQ; playgrnd; pool; 9 hole golf course adj; cycling; boat fr site to town; wifi; 5% statics; dogs €2; bus; quiet; ccard acc; red low ssn; CKE/CCI. "Lovely site in beautiful park on Rv Agout; lge pitches; helpful staff; gd, tired clean san facs; some lower pitches sl & poss soft; extra charge twin-axles; gd security; poss groups workers low ssn; leisure cent adj; vg cycling; highly rec; rest open evenings only; well run; excel for long or sh stay." ♦ 1 Apr-30 Sep. € 20.00 2014*

CAUSSADE *8E3* (750m NE Urban) *44.16582, 1.54446* **Camp Municipal de la Piboulette, Rue de la Piboulette, 82300 Caussade [05 63 93 09 07; secretariat@mairie-caussade.com; www.mairie-caussade.fr]** S on D820 fr Cahors (40km), turn L off D820 on ent Caussade onto D17 (Rte de Puylaroque). About 750m turn L (sp), site on R in 100m; lge grass stadium. Med, mkd pitch, pt shd; wc (some cont); chem disp; serviced pitches; shwrs inc; el pnts (6A) €1.90; Indtte; shop 500m; tradsmn; playgrnd; sports cent adj; pool on far side of stadium; dogs €1.25; adv bkg; quiet; CKE/CCI. "Pleasant site adj lake; spacious, mostly shd pitches; pleasant warden; excel, clean san facs, poss tired low ssn; gates locked 2100 low ssn; easy 15 min walk to town; gd walks; gd cycling round lake; conv A20 & Gorges de l'Aveyron; vg mkt Mon; excel value; vg." ♦ 1 May-30 Sep. € 9.00 2012*

⊞ **CAUSSADE** *8E3* (7km NE Rural) *44.18273, 1.60305* **Camping de Bois Redon, 10 Chemin de Bonnet, 82240 Septfonds [05 63 64 92 49 / 06 78 35 79 97 (Mob); info@campingdeboisredon.com; www.campingdeboisredon.com]** Exit A20 junc 59 to Caussade, then onto D926 to Septfonds (narr rds); after rndabt turn 3rd L; site sp. Site in 2km. One-way system when leaving site. Sm, mkd pitch, pt sl, pt shd; wc; chem disp; baby facs; shwrs inc; el pnts (10A) €3.50; Indtte; shop; tradsmn; snacks; bar; playgrnd; pool; cycle hire; 10% statics; dogs €2; Eng spkn; adv bkg (dep); quiet; red low ssn; CKE/CCI. "Well-shd, spacious site in ancient oak forest with walks; charming Dutch owners; immac facs; Septfonds nr with all facs; new shwrs (2013/14); enthusiastic owners continually making improvements; excel site." ♦ ltd € 32.00 2014*

CAUSSADE *8E3* (10km NE Rural) *44.21700, 1.61297* **Camping Le Clos de la Lère, Clergue, Route de Septfonds, 82240 Cayriech [05 63 31 20 41; contact@camping-leclosdelalere.com; www.camping-leclosdelalere.com]** Take D17 fr Caussade. Turn R at junc with D103 (sp Cayriech/ Septfonds). In Cayriech vill turn R at T-junc by church, site on R in 200m. Foll sp only for Camping Le Clos de la Lère. Fr Septfonds turn N off D926, site in 5.3km on L just bef Cayriech sp. Sm, hdg/mkd pitch, hdstg, pt shd; htd wc; chem disp; mv service pnt; baby facs; shwrs inc; el pnts (6A) inc; gas; Indtte; shop & 4km; tradsmn; snacks; no BBQ; playgrnd; pool; few statics; dogs €2; adv bkg; quiet; ccard acc; red low ssn/ long stay; CKE/CCI. "Attractive tidy site; site being sold (2011), phone ahead for new opening dates; helpful staff; clean san facs; ltd low ssn; excel games facs; rec arr bef dark; excel NH." ♦ 1 Mar-15 Nov. € 19.50 2011*

CAUSSADE *8E3* (10km NW Rural) *44.24323, 1.47735* **Camping Le Faillal, 46 Blvd Pasteur, 82270 Montpezat-de-Quercy [05 63 02 07 08; fax 04 73 93 71 00; lefaillal@ wanadoo.fr; http://www.revea-camping.fr]** N on D820, turn L onto D20, site clearly sp on R in 2km. (Do not take D38 bef D20 fr S). Med, hdg pitch, pt sl, terr, pt shd; wc; chem disp; shwrs inc; el pnts (4-6A) €3.50; Indtte; shops 200m; playgrnd; pool; tennis adj; games area; few statics; dogs €1.50; phone; adv bkg; quiet; red low ssn/CKE/CCI. "Pretty, well-kept site; friendly, helpful staff; gd, clean san facs, poss ltd; super pool; many pitches unavail after heavy rain; old town a 'must'; rec pay night bef dep; excel." ♦ 3 Apr-10 Oct. € 27.00 (CChq acc) 2014*

⊞ **CAUTERETS** *8G2* (500m N Urban) *42.89402, -0.11255* **Camping Les Glères, 19 Route de Pierrefitte, 65110 Cauterets [05 62 92 55 34; fax 05 62 92 03 53; camping-les-gleres@wanadoo.fr; www.gleres.com]** Fr N on D920 ent town; site on R with sharp turn but sp. Narr ent (take care long o'fits). Med, hdg/mkd pitch, hdstg, pt shd; htd wc; chem disp; mv service pnt nr; some serviced pitches; shwrs inc; el pnts (6A) inc; gas; Indtte; rest, snacks, bar, shop, pool 500m; playgrnd; 10% statics; dogs €1.10; phone; site clsd 21 Oct-30 Nov; Eng spkn; quiet; red low ssn; CKE/CCI. "Conv town cent; gd walking area with cable car 500m; superb san facs; friendly & helpful; tight access to pitches; municipal m'van site adj; excel." € 21.00 2010*

CAUTERETS *8G2* (1km N Rural) *42.90254, -0.10605* **Camping Le Péguère, Route de Pierrefitte, 65110 Cauterets [tel/fax 05 62 92 52 91 or 06 28 27 37 24 (mob); campingpeguere@ wanadoo.fr; www.campingpeguere.com]** Fr Lourdes on N21 foll sp for Cauterets. On app Cauterets site on R immed after rv bdge. Med, pt sl, pt shd; wc; mv service pnt; shwrs inc; el pnts (6A) inc; Indtte; tradsmn; snacks; playgrnd; rv fishing adj; entmnt; TV rm; some statics; dogs €0.85; adv bkg; quiet; ccard acc; red low ssn; CKE/CCI. "Spacious rvside site in beautiful setting; clean facs; stunning views; ideal base for walking in Pyrenees; rec." ♦ 30 Apr-30 Sep. € 13.50 2010*

CAUTERETS *8G2* (2.5km NE Rural) *42.91092, -0.09934* **Camping GR10, Route de Pierrefitte, 65110 Cauterets [06 70 72 05 02 or 06 20 30 25 85 (LS); contact@ gr10camping.com; www.gr10camping.com]** N fr Cauterets on D920; site in 2.5km on R. Med, mkd pitch, terr, shd; htd wc; chem disp; shwrs inc; el pnts €4; Indtte; supmkt nrby; playgrnd; htd pool; tennis; canyoning (guide on site); games area; games rm; TV; 25% statics; dogs €1.30; poss cr; Eng spkn; quiet. "Pretty site; excel." 25 Jun- 1 Sep. € 20.00 2014*

CAYLUS *8E4* (500m E Rural) *44.23368, 1.77636* **FFCC Camping de la Bonnette, 672 route de la Bonnette, 82160 Caylus [tel/fax 05 63 65 70 20; info@campingbonnette. com; www.campingbonnette.com]** Fr A20 exit junc 59 dir Caylus; thro Caylus to g'ge on L. Turn R in 1km over next crossrds & foll site sps to site on R in 1km. Med, hdg/mkd pitch, pt shd; wc; chem disp; mv service pnt; baby facs; shwrs inc; el pnts (10A) €3.50; Indtte (inc dryer); shop 1km; tradsmn; bar & rest; BBQ; playgrnd; pool; games area; wifi; entmnt; some statics; dogs €1.50; Eng spkn; adv bkg (rec high ssn); quiet; red 7 days. "Nice, tidy, scenic site on edge of medieval vill - worth a visit; friendly owner; pitches in groups of 4, not v private." ♦ 29 Mar-4 Oct. € 19.00 2014*

CAYRIECH see Caussade *8E3*

CAZALS *7D3* (600m W Rural) *44.64186, 1.22179* **Camp Municipal du Plan d'Eau, La Cayré, 46250 Cazals [05 65 22 84 45 or 05 65 22 82 84 (Mairie); fax 05 65 22 87 15; mairiecazals@wanadoo.fr]** Fr Frayssinet-le-Gélat N on D673 dir Gourdon; site on L immed after ent Cazals. Ent just past red/white 'No Entry' sp. Med, mkd pitch, pt shd; wc; mv service pnt; shwrs; el pnts; Indtte; shops 500m; rest; bar; playgrnd; lake sw; entmnt; some statics; poss cr; quiet. "Basic, clean facs; friendly warden; tractor/machinery museum nrby." 1 May-30 Sep. € 9.80 2009*

CENEVIERES see Cajarc *7D4*

COMPEYRE see Millau *10E1*

CONDOM *8E2* (4km NE Rural) *43.97491, 0.42038* **Camping à la Ferme (Rogalle), Guinland, 32100 Condom [05 62 28 17 85; rogalle.guinland@wanadoo.fr; http:// campingdeguinland.monsite-orange.fr]** NE fr Condom on D931, turn R onto D41. Pass water tower on R, site ent on L at bottom of hill just bef sm lake on R. Sm, shd; wc; chem disp; shwrs inc; el pnts (6-10A) €2.50; shop, rest etc 4km; BBQ; playgrnd; tennis & canoe hire nrby; 10% statics; dogs; quiet. "Vg CL-type site in pine grove; gd views; friendly owner; clean facs." 1 Apr-30 Oct. € 12.00 2011*

⊞ **CONDOM** *8E2* (7.4km SE Rural) *43.92929, 0.42698* **Camping à la Ferme (Vignaux), Bordeneuve, 32100 Béraut [05 62 28 08 41]** E fr Condom on D7 to Caussens; far end of vill turn R on D204, sp St Orens; in 1.2km turn R sp Béraut, bear R at fork, site on L in 400m. Also sp fr D654. Sm, pt sl, pt shd; wc; chem disp; shwrs inc; el pnts (12A) €2.50 (long lead poss req); Indtte; shops 2.5km; adv bkg; quiet. "Peaceful & secluded CL-type site; friendly owners; basic san facs; waymarked trails nr; phone ahead to check open low ssn - poss not open until Apr." € 12.00 2012*

CONDOM *8E2* (1.5km SW Rural) *43.94813, 0.36435* **Camp Municipal de l'Argenté, Chemin de l'Argenté, Gauge, 32100 Condom [tel/fax 05 62 28 17 32; camping.municipal@condom.org; www.condom.org/index.php/camping-municipal]** Fr Condom, take D931 twd Eauze; site ent on L opp municipal sports grnd. Med, mkd pitch, pt shd, wc; chem disp; baby facs; shwrs inc; el pnts (6A) €3.60; shop 500m; tradsmn; rest & bar adj; playgrnd; pool 200m; fishing; tennis adj; dogs €1.30; phone; red low ssn. "Pleasant, spacious, well-kept site adj rv; lge pitches; well shd; friendly staff; excel san facs but ltd low ssn; levelling blocks useful; no twin-axles; lots for older children to do; interesting, unspoilt town nr pilgrim rte; rec visit Armagnac distilleries; excel." 1 Apr-30 Sep. € 20.00 2013*

CONDOM *8E2* (2km SW Rural) *43.93638, 0.35711* **Camping La Ferme de Laillon (Danto), Route d'Eauze, 32100 Condom [tel/fax 05 62 28 19 71 or 06 07 69 14 19 (mob); dominique.danto1@free.fr; http://calaf32.free.fr/laillon]** Site sp fr D931 dir Vopillon. Bumpy lane to site. Sm, pt sl, shd; wc; chem disp; shwrs inc; el pnts inc; Indtte; farm produce; playgrnd; some statics; dogs; Eng spkn; quiet. "Delightful, wooded site; helpful owner; pleasant area." 21 Mar-19 Dec. € 9.20 2010*

CONQUES *7D4* (8km E Rural) *44.55948, 2.46184* **Camping L'Etang du Camp, 12320 Sénergues [05 65 46 01 95; info@etangducamp.fr; www.etangducamp.fr]** Fr S on D901 dir Conques; at St Cyprien turn R onto D46 sp Sénergues; foll sp Sénergues up hill for 6km; 2nd L at the top; foll Camping sp. Med, hdg/mkd pitch, pt shd; wc; chem disp; mv service pnt; baby facs; fam bthrm; shwrs inc; el pnts (6A) €3.50; Indtte; ice; sm shop; supmkt 3km; rest, bar 6km; tradsmn; BBQ (charcoal); playgrnd; htd pool 6km; fishing in private lake; cycle hire; canoeing nrby; cycle hire; games area; games rm; wifi; dogs €1.50; some statics; Eng spkn; adv bkg; quiet; red low ssn; 10% red CKE/CCI . "Well-situated, well-kept site; quiet & relaxing; warm welcome, British owners; modern, clean san facs; gd base for touring, walking & cycling; conv Conques; highly rec; excel." ♦ 1 Apr-30 Sep. € 25.50 2013*

CONQUES *7D4* (1km W Rural) *44.60041, 2.39461* **Camping Beau Rivage, 12320 Conques [05 65 69 82 23 or 05 65 72 89 29 (LS); fax 05 67 72 89 29; camping.conques@wanadoo.fr; www.campingconques.com]** Site on D901 Rodez-Aurillac rd on Rv Dourdou. Med, mkd pitch, pt sl, pt shd; wc (some cont); mv service pnt; shwrs inc; el pnts (6-10A) €3.50; gas; Indry rm; shop; tradsmn; rest, snacks; bar; playgrnd; pool; fishing; rv adj; some statics; dogs €1.50; adv bkg; quiet; red low ssn; CKE/CCI. "Gd position by rv bank; sm pitches; some modern san facs, others dated; tight for lge o'fits due trees & narr pathways; poss run down low ssn; gd." ♦ 1 Apr-30 Sep. € 17.50 2010*

CONQUES *7D4* (5km NW Rural) *44.62222, 2.36101* **Camping Du Moulin, Les Passes, 12320 Grand-Vabre [tel/fax 05 65 72 87 28 or 06 82 88 53 33 (mob); campingdumoulin12@orange.fr; www.grand-vabre.fr]** N fr Conques on D901, site sp on banks Rv Dourdou. Sm, mkd pitch, terr, shd; wc; mv service pnt; shwrs; el pnts (10A) €2; tradsmn; snacks; bar; playgrnd; htd pool; tennis 1km; games area; TV rm; mainly statics; poss cr; quiet. "Pleasant rvside site; gd, modern san facs; gd." 1 Apr-31 Oct. € 16.00 2012*

CORDES SUR CIEL *8E4* (5km SE Rural) *44.04158, 2.01722* **Camping Redon, Livers-Cazelles, 81170 Cordes-sur-Ciel [tel/fax 05 63 56 14 64; info@campredon.com; www.campredon.com]** Off D600 Albi to Cordes rd. Exit on D107 to E. Site sp. Sm, hdg pitch, pt sl, pt shd; wc; chem disp; mv service pnt; baby facs; shwrs inc; el pnts (6-16A) €4.25; gas; Indtte; shops 5km; tradsmn; ltd shop; rest, snacks; bar; sm playgrnd; pool; wifi; TV rm; dogs €2.25; phone; bus 1km; poss cr; Eng spkn; adv bkg; quiet; red long stay/low ssn/CKE/CCI. "Well-kept, well-run site; views fr some pitches; friendly, helpful Dutch owner; excel facs, poss stretched high ssn; ecological septic tank - environmentally friendly liquid sold on site; conv Bastides in area; highly rec." ♦ 1 Apr-1 Nov. € 29.00 2014*

"I need an on-site restaurant"

We do our best to make sure site information is correct, but it is always best to check any must-have facilities are still available or will be open during your visit.

CORDES SUR CIEL *8E4* (2km W Rural) *44.06681, 1.92408* **Camping Le Garissou, Les Cabannes, 81170 Cordes-sur-Ciel [05 63 56 27 14; fax 05 63 56 26 95; aquadis1@orange.fr; www.aquadis-loisirs.com/domaine-du-garissou]** Take D600 fr Cordes thro Les Cabanes; site sp on L at bottom of hill, 1.5km after Les Cabanes. Med, mkd pitch, terr, pt shd; wc; shwrs inc; el pnts (6A) inc; Indtte; sm shop; playgrnd; pool complex adj; dogs €1.50; quiet; red low ssn. "Hilltop site; excel views; clean facs." 11 Mar-10 Nov. € 14.00 (CChq acc) 2013*

CRAYSSAC *7D3* (500m SW Rural) *44.50694, 1.32416* **Campéole Camping Les Reflets du Quercy, Mas de Bastide, 46150 Crayssac [05 65 30 00 27; fax 05 17 47 50 80; reflets-du-quercy@campeole.com; www.camping-lot.info / www.campeole.com]** Take D911 W fr Cahors; 1km after steep winding climb foll camp sp on L sp Luzech for 1km. NB: D9 to Crayssac not rec. Med, hdg pitch, hdstg, pt sl, pt shd; htd wc; chem disp; mv service pnt; baby facs; shwrs inc; el pnts (10A) €4.10; gas; Indtte (inc dryer); shop; tradsmn; rest; bar; BBQ; playgrnd; pool; paddling pool; fishing, canoeing nr; tennis; horseriding nr; games area; wifi; entmnt; games/TV rm; 60% statics; dogs €2.60; Eng spkn; adv bkg; quiet; ccard acc; red low ssn; CKE/CCI. "Beautiful touring & walking area; pleasant, helpful staff." ♦ 3 Apr-19 Sep. € 20.00 (CChq acc) 2009*

⊞ **DECAZEVILLE** *7D4* (3km NW Rural) *44.58819, 2.22145* **FFCC Camping Le Roquelongue, 12300 Boisse-Penchot [tel/fax 05 65 63 39 67; info@camping-roquelongue.com; www.camping-roquelongue.com]** Fr D963 N fr Decazeville turn W onto D140 & D42 to Boisse-Penchot. Rte via D21 not rec (steep hill & acute turn). Site mid-way bet Boisse-Penchot & Livinhac-le-Haut on D42. Med, hdg/mkd pitch, pt shd; wc; chem disp; shwrs inc; el pnts (6-10A) 3.60-4.30; gas; Indtte; shop; tradsmn; supmkt 5km; snacks; bar; playgrnd; htd pool; fishing; canoeing; tennis; cycle hire; entmnt; internet; 10% statics; dogs free; phone; adv bkg; quiet; CKE/CCI. "Direct access Rv Lot; pitches gd size; san facs clean; no twin-axles; excel base for Lot Valley." ♦ ltd € 15.80 2009*

⊞ **DEYME** *8F3* (500m NE Rural) *43.48672, 1.5322* **Camping Les Violettes, Porte de Toulouse, 31450 Deyme [05 61 81 72 07; fax 05 61 27 17 31; campinglesviolettes@wanadoo.fr]** SE fr Toulouse to Carcassonne on N113, sp on L, 12km fr Toulouse (after passing Deyme sp). Med, mkd pitch, hdstg, pt shd; htd wc; mv service pnt; shwrs inc; el pnts (6A) €4; Indtte; shop; rest, snacks; bar; BBQ; playgrnd; TV; 60% statics; dogs €0.70; poss cr; quiet but rd noise; CKE/CCI. "Helpful, friendly staff; facs run down (Jun 2009); poss muddy when wet; 800m fr Canal du Midi & 10km fr Space City; Park & Ride 2.5km & metro to Toulouse." € 13.00 2012*

"There aren't many sites open at this time of year"

If you're travelling outside peak season remember to call ahead to check site opening dates – even if the entry says 'open all year'.

DURAVEL see Puy l'Evêque *7D3*

⊞ **DURFORT** *8F3* (1km S Rural) *43.19206, 1.45685* **FFCC Camping Le Bourdieu, 09130 Durfort [05 61 67 30 17; fax 05 61 67 29 00; contact@lebourdieu.net; www.lebourdieu.com]** Exit Pamiers NW on D119; in 6km turn R onto D626 to St Martin-d'Oydes in 6km; cont on D626 for another 4km; turn R onto D14; in 200m turn R onto sm rd sp Durfort; almost immed turn R again; site in 200m. Sm, some hdstg, pt shd; htd wc; baby facs; fam bthrm; shwrs inc; el pnts (6A) inc; Indtte (inc dryer); shop; tradsmn; snacks; bar; BBQ; playgrnd; pool; games area; wifi; entmnt; TV; dogs €1; adv bkg; red low ssn. € 21.00 (CChq acc) 2010*

ENTRAYGUES SUR TRUYERE *7D4* (4km NE Rural) *44.67777, 2.58279* **Camping Le Lauradiol (Formaly Municipal), Banhars, 12460 Campouriez [05 65 44 53 95; fax 05 65 44 81 37; info@camping-lelauradiol.com; www.camping-lelauradiol.com]** On D34, sp on rvside. Sm, hdg/mkd pitch, pt shd; wc; el pnts (6A) inc; Indtte; shop 5km; htd pool; paddling pool; rv adj; tennis; some statics; dogs €2; quiet; CKE/CCI. "Beautiful setting & walks; excel; Power mover needed for lge o'fits to access pitches; beautiful site; v friendly helpful staff; a real gem." ♦ 1 Jul-31 Aug. € 17.50 2013*

ENTRAYGUES SUR TRUYERE *7D4* (1.6km S Rural) *44.64218, 2.56406* **Camping Le Val de Saures (formerly Municipal), 12140 Entraygues-sur-Truyère [05 65 44 56 92; fax 05 65 44 27 21; info@camping-valdesaures.com; www.camping-valdesaures.com]** Fr town cent take D920 (twds Espalion) & in 200m turn R over narr rv bdge and then R onto D904. In 200m fork R onto new rd and thro sports complex to site. Med, mkd pitch, pt shd; wc; shwrs; el pnts (6A) €3.50; Indtte; shops in town; playgrnd; pool adj; entmnt; some statics; dogs €1.50; Eng spkn; quiet; ccard acc; red low ssn. "Pleasant, friendly, gd site; in great situation; footbdge to town over rv; vg, well-kept san facs; recep clsd Sun & pm Mon low ssn; gd touring base." ♦ 1 May-30 Sep. € 29.00 2014*

ESPALION *7D4* (300m E Urban) *44.52176, 2.77098* **Camping Roc de l'Arche, 12500 Espalion [tel/fax 05 65 44 06 79; info@rocdelarche.com; www.rocdelarche.com]** Sp in town off D920 & D921. Site on S banks of Rv Lot 300m fr bdge in town. Med, hdg/mkd pitch, pt shd; wc; mv service pnt; baby facs; shwrs inc; el pnts (6-10A); Indtte; shops 250m; snacks; BBQ; playgrnd; pool adj inc; tennis; fishing; canoeing; dogs €0.50; poss cr; adv bkg; quiet; red low ssn. "Well-kept site; gd sized pitches, water pnts to each; service rds narr; friendly, helpful warden; clean, modern san facs; excel." 12 May - 6 Sept. € 32.10 (CChq acc) 2014*

ESPALION *7D4* (4km E Rural) *44.51376, 2.81849* **Camping Belle Rive, Rue de Terral, 12500 St Côme-d'Olt [05 65 44 05 85; bellerive12@voila.fr]** Fr Espalion take D987 E to St Côme-d'Olt; thro vill to rndabt; turn R and foll sp. Med, pt shd; wc (some cont0; mv service pnt; shwrs inc; el pnts (6-10A) inc (poss rev pol & long lead may be req); Indtte; shop, rest in vill; 10% statics; dogs €0.70; wifi; poss cr; Eng spkn; quiet. "Pleasant rvside site; friendly, helpful owner; delightful medieval vill; excel." 1 May-30 Sep. € 13.30 2014*

ESTAING (HAUTES PYRENEES) see Argelès Gazost *8G2*

"Satellite navigation makes touring much easier"

Remember most sat navs don't know if you're towing or in a larger vehicle – always use yours alongside maps and site directions.

ESTANG *8E2* (500m E Rural) *43.86493, -0.10321* **Camping Les Lacs de Courtès, Courtès, 32240 Estang [05 62 09 61 98; fax 05 62 09 63 13; contact@lacsdecourtes.com; www.lacsdecourtes.com]** W fr Eauze site sp fr D30. Fr Mont-de-Marsan D932 take D1 to Villeneuve-de-Marsan, then D1/D30 to Estang. Med, mkd pitch, pt shd; wc; chem disp; mv service pnt; el pnts (6A) €3; Indtte (inc dryer); tradsmn; shop 300m; supmkt 5km; rest 300m; snacks; bar; playgrnd; htd pool; paddling pool; lake fishing; tennis; games area; internet; entmnt; TV rm; some statics; dogs €3; area for m'vans open all yr; adv bkg; quiet. "Gd family site." ♦ 1 Apr-31 Oct. € 24.50 (CChq acc) 2011*

FIGEAC *7D4* (1.5km E Rural) *44.60989, 2.05015* **Camping Caravanning Domaine Du Surgie, Domaine du Surgié, 46100 Figeac [05 61 64 88 54; fax 05 61 64 89 17; contact@marc-montmija.com; www.domainedusurgie.com]** Fr Figeac foll sp Rodez (on D840 S) to site by Rv Célé adj leisure complex. Foll sps 'Base Loisirs de Surgie'. Narr ent, light controlled. Or appr fr E on D840, immed after passing under rlwy arch a v sharp R turn into narr rd (keep R thro traff lts); site on L in 700m. NB Recep at beginning of rd to leisure cent & camping. Med, hdg/mkd pitch, pt shd, wc; chem disp; mv service pnt; shwrs inc; el pnts (10A) inc; gas 1km; Indtte; shop; rest, snacks; bar; playgrnd; htd pool & waterslide adj; boating; tennis; cycle hire; entmnt; 30% statics; dogs €2.50; Eng spkn; adv bkg; quiet; red low ssn/long stay. Ent clsd 1200 -1600 low ssn. "Excel pool complex adj (free to campers); peaceful low ssn; pleasant 2km walk or car park just outside town; adj rv unfenced; mkt Sat; vg." ♦ 1 Apr-30 Sept. € 35.80 2014*

FIGEAC *7D4* (7km SE Urban) *44.57328, 2.07296* **Camp Municipal Les Rives d'Olt, Blvd Paul-Ramadier, 12700 Capdenac-Gare [05 65 80 88 87 or 05 65 80 22 22 (Mairie); camping.capdenac@wanadoo.fr]** Fr Figeac on D840 dir Rodez; at Capdenac turn R onto D994 over rv bdge; immed after x-ing rv bdge turn R onto D86. Site in 200m on R by rv. Med, hdg/mkd pitch, shd; wc; chem disp; mv service pnt; shwrs inc; el pnts (9A) €2.90; gas adj; lndtte; shop, rest, snacks, bar adj; playgrnd; pool 1km; tennis adj; TV rm; 5% statics; dogs; quiet, a little rd noise; CKE/CCI. "Site beside Rv Lot; ent clsd 1200-1600 low ssn; gd fishing, walking & cycling." ♦ 10 Apr-30 Sep. € 11.00 2010*

FIGEAC *7D4* (7km SW Rural) *44.57833, 1.93750* **FFCC Camping de Pech-Ibert, Route de Cajarc, 46100 Béduer [05 65 40 05 85; fax 05 65 40 08 33; contact@camping-pech-ibert.com; www.camping-pech-ibert.com]** SW fr Figeac on D662/D19 twds Cajarc. Site well sp on R after Béduer. Sm, pt shd; htd wc; chem disp; mv service pnt; baby facs; shwrs inc; el pnts (16A) €3.50 (poss rev pol); snacks high ssn; BBQ; playgrnd; pool; fishing & sw 1km; tennis; cycle hire; a few statics; dogs €2; Eng spkn; adv bkg ess high ssn; quiet; red low ssn; CKE/CCI. "Peaceful, relaxing site on pilgrimage rte; pleasant, helpful owners; gd clean san facs; gd walking fr site (mkd trails); Sat mkt Figeac; excel; rock pegs req." ♦ 15 Mar-15 Nov. € 16.00 2014*

⊞ **FOIX** *8G3* (2km N Rural) *42.98911, 1.61565* **Camping du Lac, Quartier Labarre, 09000 Foix [05 61 65 11 58; fax 05 61 05 32 62; camping-du-lac@wanadoo.fr; www.campingdulac.com]** Fr N on N20 foll sp for 'Centre Ville', site on R in 2km. Fr S onto on N20 thro tunnel & take 1st exit N of Foix & foll sp 'Centre Ville', then as above. Site opp Chausson building materials store. Lge, mkd pitch, pt shd; wc; chem disp; mv service pnt; baby facs; shwrs inc; baby facs; el pnts (6A) inc; lndtte; supmkt adj; tradsmn; rest, snacks; bar; BBQ; playgrnd; pool; paddling pool; lake fishing adj; boating; windsurfing; tennis; wifi; entmnt; TV; 30% statics; dogs €1.50; bus to Foix adj (not Sun); Eng spkn; poss cr; adv bkg rec high ssn; quiet but some rd (N20) noise; ccard acc; red low ssn; CKE/CCI. "Busy site w/end; quiet, spacious pitches on L of camp; modern san facs, poss stretched high ssn; site & facs poss uncared for early ssn (2011); gates clsd 2300-0700; pleasant town; NH only low ssn." ♦ € 39.00 (CChq acc) 2014*

FOIX *8G3* (4km S Urban) *42.93081, 1.63883* **FFCC Camping Roucateille, 15 Rue du Pradal, 09330 Montgaillard [tel/fax 05 61 64 05 92; info@roucateille.com; www.camping-roucateille.com]** Fr N exit N20 junc 11, fr S exit N20 junc 12; foll sp Montgaillard; site sp fr main rd thro vill. NB Swing wide at ent - sharp turn. Med, hdg/mkd pitch, shd; wc; chem disp; mv service pnt; shwrs inc; el pnts (4-10A) €2.50-4.90; lndtte; shops & hypmkt 2km; rest, snacks & bar 3km; BBQ; playgrnd; pool 3km; wifi; 25% statics in sep area; dogs free; poss cr; some Eng spkn; adv bkg; quiet; ccard acc; red low ssn/long stay; CKE/CCI. "Lovely, picturesque, informal site; clean & well cared for; charming, helpful young owners; excel facs; care needed to avoid trees; garden produce in ssn; gd touring base; gd cycling; Forges de Pyène eco-museum worth visit; excel; historical area; nr stream with cherry orchard behind." ♦ ltd 1 May-30 Sep. € 24.00 2014*

⊞ **FOIX** *8G3* (5km NW Rural) *42.97151, 1.57243* **Camp Municipal de Rieutort, 09000 Cos [05 61 65 39 79 or 06 71 18 10 38 (mob); bernard.blazy09@orange.fr; http://camping-municipal-cos09.fr]** Fr Foix take D117 dir Tarbes. Foll sp Cos onto D617, site on L in 3km. NB Narr app rds. Sm, pt sl, pt shd; htd wc (some cont); chem disp; 25% serviced pitches; baby facs; fam bthrm; shwrs inc; el pnts (5A) €1.80; lndtte; shop 5km; rest, snacks, bar 5km; playgrnd; pool; tennis; dogs; quiet; CKE/CCI. "Pleasant site amongst trees with gd views; friendly, helpful warden; gd san facs, ltd low ssn; sm step into disabled facs; no c'vans over 6m." ♦ € 10.00 2011*

⊞ **FUMEL** *7D3* (4km E Rural) *44.48925, 1.02048* **Aire Naturelle Le Valenty (Baillargues), Rue de Chantegrue 46700 Soturac, Lot [05 65 36 59 50 or 06 72 57 69 80 (mob); campingdevalenty@gmail.com]** Fr Fumel take D911/811 dir Cahors. Thro Soturac, site immed on L outside vill. Sm, terr, pt shd; wc; shwrs inc; el pnts (4-10A) €2.50; gas 3km; lndtte; shops, snacks, bar 2.5km; tradsmn; rest 1km; playgrnd; pool; minigolf; pony rides; games rm; 20% statics; dogs €1; bus 200m; Eng spkn; adv bkg; quiet; CKE/CCI. "Delightful CL-type site; helpful owners; tranquil but secure; organic produce for sale; poss not open low ssn - phone ahead." € 13.00 2013*

FUMEL *7D3* (8km E Rural) *44.49810, 1.06670* **Camping Le Ch'Timi, La Roque, 46700 Touzac [05 65 36 52 36; fax 05 65 36 53 23; info@campinglechtimi.com; www.campinglechtimi.com]** Exit N20-E9 junc 57 onto D820 dir Cahors; turn R at rndabt onto D811 sp Villeneuve-sur-Lot; in Duravel take 3rd exit at rndabt onto D58, sp Vire-sur-Lot; in 2.5km cross bdge & turn R at rndabt onto D8, sp Touzac; site on R on rvside, on hill, in about 1.5km. Well sp. NB D8 not suitable lge c'vans or m'vans. Med, mkd pitch, pt sl, pt shd; wc; baby facs; shwrs inc, chem disp; el pnts (6A) inc; gas; lndtte; shop & 700m; tradsmn; rest, snacks; bar; BBQ (charcoal/gas); playgrnd; pool; paddling pool; canoeing & fishing 100m; cycle hire; tennis; archery; games area; wifi; entmnt; games/TV rm; 20% statics; dogs €1.75; no c'vans/m'vans over 7m high ssn; poss cr; Eng spkn; adv bkg; quiet; ccard acc; red low ssn; CKE/CCI. "Site in gd position; friendly, helpful Dutch owners; clean facs, ltd low ssn; rv nr site, down steep steps; access some pitches poss diff lge o'fits; gd local rests; wine-tasting tours; mkt Puy l'Evêque Tue; Wonderful stay, everyone friendly; rec." ♦ 1 Apr-30 Sep. € 22.80 SBS - D05 2014*

FUMEL *7D3* (10km E Rural) *44.48023, 1.05204* **Camping Le Clos Bouyssac, 46700 Touzac [05 65 36 52 21; fax 05 65 24 68 51; camping.leclosbouyssac@wanadoo.fr; www.campingbytheriver.eu]** Fr Fumel on D911/D811, turn R to Touzac. Cross bdge over Rv Lot, turn R in vill to site in 2km on rvside. Site sp. Med, mkd pitch, terr, shd; wc; chem disp; mv service pnt; baby facs; shwrs inc; el pnts (10A) €3.50; gas; lndtte; shop 8km; snacks; bar; BBQ; playgrnd; pool; paddling pool; fishing; canoe hire; games area; games rm; wifi; entmnt; TV rm; 15% statics; dogs €1.75; phone; poss cr; Eng spkn; adv bkg; quiet; ccard acc; red low ssn/CKE/CCI. "Pleasant, tranquil site on S bank of Rv Lot; friendly, welcoming British/Dutch owners; recent refurbs; gd, clean facs; plenty of activities high ssn, inc wine-tasting; vg cycling; guided walks; vg wine area; gd." 1 Apr-30 Sep. € 17.00 2011*

GAILLAC *8E4* (8km N Rural) *43.98373, 1.91432* **Camp Municipal au Village, Route de Cordes, 81140 Cahuzac-sur-Vère [05 63 33 91 94 or 05 63 33 90 18 (Mairie); fax 05 63 33 94 03; mairie.cahuzacsurvere@wandoo.fr]** Fr Gaillac, take D922 N twd Cordes. Site on L of rd, clearly sp thro vill of Cahuzac. Sm, pt sl, pt shd; wc; shwrs; el pnts (3A) inc (rev pol); shops, rest, snacks, bar nr; playgrnd; pool; tennis; games area; cycle hire; phone; adv bkg; quiet. "Gd, clean site; call warden on arr; barrier at entry - poss to remove post to ease entry." 1 Jul-31 Aug. € 11.05 2010*

"There aren't many sites open at this time of year"

If you're travelling outside peak season remember to call ahead to check site opening dates – even if the entry says 'open all year'.

GAILLAC *8E4* (2km W Urban) *43.89674, 1.88522* **FFCC Camping des Sources, 9 Ave Guynemer, 81600 Gaillac [05 63 57 18 30; fax 05 49 52 28 58; camping-gaillac@orange.fr; www.camping-gaillac.fr]** Exit A68 junc 9 onto D999 then in 3.5km at rndabt turn onto D968 dir Gaillac. In 100m turn R immed past Leclerc petrol stn, then L by Aldi. Site 200m on R, well sp fr town cent. Med, hdg/mkd pitch, hdstg, terr, pt shd; htd wc; chem disp; mv service pnt; chem disp (wc); baby facs; shwrs inc; el pnts (10A) €3; Indtte (inc dryer); shop 500m; tradsmn; snacks; bar; playgrnd; pool; entmnt; TV; 10% statics; dogs €2; quiet; ccard acc (over €15); CKE/CCI. "Peaceful, clean & tidy site; friendly, helpful staff; gd, modern san facs; steep walk to recep & bar but san facs at pitch level; purpose-made dog-walk area; gd touring base Tarn & Albi region & circular tour Bastides; cent of wine area; not suitable lge o'fits; gd." ♦ ltd 1 Apr-31 Oct. € 14.50 2014*

GARIN see Luchon *8G3*

GAUDONVILLE see St Clar *8E3*

GAVARNIE *8G2* (2km N Rural) *42.75896, 0.00069* **Camping Le Pain de Sucre, quartier Couret, 65120 Gavarnie [tel/fax 05 62 92 47 55 or 06 75 30 64 22 (mob); camping-gavarnie@wanadoo.fr or info@camping-gavarnie.com; www.camping-gavarnie.com]** N of Gavarnie, across rv by sm bdge; clearly visible & sp fr rd. Med, pt shd; wc; mv service pnt; shwrs inc; el pnts (2-10A) €2.30-6.50 (long lead poss req); Indtte; shops, rest, snacks, bar 3km; BBQ; playgrnd; dogs €2.15; quiet; ccard acc. "Gd base for walking; gd facs; access to national park; vg; gd clean san facs; fantastic view of Cirque." ♦ 1 Jun-30 Sep & 15 Dec-15 Apr. € 24.40 2013*

GAVARNIE *8G2* (500m S Rural) *42.72802, -0.00744* **Camping La Bergerie (Rivière Sacaze), Chemin du Cirque , 65120 Gavarnie [05 62 92 48 41 or 06 85 12 68 47 (mob); www.camping-gavarnie-labergerie.com]** Site at S end of Gavarnie on rd to Cirque de Gavarnie in Pyrenees National Park. Sm, pt sl, unshd; wc; chem disp (wc); baby facs; shwrs €2; no el pnts; Indtte (inc dryer); shop & rest 500m; snacks; bar; dogs; Eng spkn; quiet; CKE/CCI. "V sm site by rv with views; no el pnts; gd san facs; 1hr walk to Cirque de Gavarnie." 20 Jun-20 Sep. € 14.60 2011*

GIROUSSENS *8E4* (2km SE Rural) *43.75478, 1.80461* **FFCC Aire Naturelle La Rigaudié (Gaben/Noual), 81500 Giroussens [05 63 41 67 20; bernard.gaben@wanadoo.fr or marienoual@live.fr; www.larigaudie.com]** Exit A68 junc 7 onto D12 to Giroussens; pass vill & cont on D831 sp Lavaur; in 3km turn L; site in 500m. Sm, pt shd; wc; chem disp; shwrs inc; el pns (6A) €2.50; Indtte; shop 3km; tradsmn; BBQ; playgrnd; sm pool; games area; dogs free; adv bkg; quiet. "Delightful aire naturelle - attractive & spacious; pt grassy field, pt woodland; many places of interest; a real find; excel." 1 May-30 Sep. € 9.60 2011*

GONDRIN *8E2* (500m SE Rural) *43.88214, 0.23895* **FFCC Camping Domaine Le Pardaillan, Rue du Pardaillon, 32330 Gondrin-en-Armagnac [05 62 29 16 69; camplepardaillan@wanadoo.fr; www.camping-le-pardaillan.com]** Fr Condom take D931 S for 12km to Gondrin. Site clearly sp. Med, hdg/mkd pitch, hdstg, pt shd; htd wc; chem disp; mv service pnt; baby facs; shwrs inc; el pnts (6-10A) inc; gas; Indtte (inc dryer); shop; tradsmn; rest, snacks; bar; playgrnd; paddling pool; lake sw adj; games rm; wifi; entmnt; TV rm; many statics; dogs €3.50; phone; poss cr; Eng spkn; adv bkg; CKE/CCI. "Excel site; lovely region; red facs & NH only low ssn; highly rec." ♦ 1 Apr-15 Oct. € 22.00 2010*

GONDRIN *8E2* (2km S Rural) *43.86936, 0.25844* **Camping La Brouquère, Betbézé, 32330 Gondrin [05 62 29 19 44; camping@brouquere.com; www.brouquere.com]** Fr Condom S on D931; pass thro Gondrin & turn S onto D113 dir Courrensan; site sp in 2km. Sm, mkd pitch, pt sl, sp shd; wc; chem disp; fam bthrm; shwrs inc; el pnts (10A) €2.50; Indtte; tradsmn; bar; BBQ; playgrnd; pool 2km; cycle hire; wifi; TV; dogs €1; Eng spkn; adv bkg; quiet; red low ssn. "V quiet, CL-type site; friendly Dutch owners; immac san facs; wine-tasting; local produce, inc Armagnac; excel." 30 Apr-1 Oct. € 15.30 2011*

GOURDON *7D3* (4km E Rural) *44.77304, 1.44097* **Camping Le Rêve, 46300 Le Vigan [05 65 41 25 20; fax 05 65 41 68 52; info@campinglereve.com; www.campinglereve.com]** On D820, 3km S of Payrac. R onto D673, sp Le Vigan & Gourdon. After 2km turn R onto sm lane, foll camp sp for 2.5km. Med, pt shd; wc; chem disp; baby facs; shwrs inc; el pnts (6A) €2.90; gas; Indtte; sm shop & 4km; bar; playgrnd; htd pool & paddling pool; games area; cycle hire; entmnt; TV rm; dogs €0.90; Eng spkn; adv bkg ess Jun-mid Aug; v quiet; red long stay/low ssn; ccard not acc; CKE/CCI. "Welcoming, helpful Dutch owners; poss variable voltage (2010); gd walking; excel." ♦ 1 May-21 Sep. € 18.00 2011*

GOURDON *7D3* (11km S Rural) *44.64954, 1.43508* **Camp Municipal Le Moulin Vieux, 46310 St Germain-du-Bel-Air [05 65 31 00 71 or 05 65 31 02 12; contact@camping-moulin-vieux-lot.com; www.camping-moulin-vieux-lot.com]** W fr D820 Cahors-Souillac rd on D23 sp St Germain-du-Bel Air. On ent vill turn R at camping sp. After 150m turn R & foll narr rd, over sm bdge then immed turn L for site. Lge, shd; wc; chem disp; shwrs; el pnts (6-16A) €3-5; gas; Indtte; rest; shops 1km; pool adj; playgrnd; lake sw & fishing; entmnt; some statics; dogs €2; quiet. "Excel, clean site; friendly recep & helpful warden; vg walks in valley; highly rec." 1 Apr-15 Sep. € 13.00 2009*

GOURDON *7D3* (2km SW Rural) *44.72214, 1.37381* **Aire Naturelle Le Paradis (Jardin), La Peyrugue, 46300 Gourdon [tel/fax 05 65 41 65 01 / 06 72 76 32 60 (mob); contact@campingleparadis.com; www.campingleparadis.com]** S on D673 Gourdon/Fumel rd, after Intermarché supmkt on L, turn L onto track sp site. If full, overflow area avail - 2 hookups. Sm, pt sl, terr, pt shd; wc; shwrs inc; el pnts (6A) €2; Indtte; supmkt adj; rest; some statics; dogs €2; quiet; adv bkg; red low ssn. "Gd welcome; facs poss stretched if full; farm produce; delightful site; no entmnt; excel san facs." 1 May-31 Aug. € 14.00 2014*

GOURDON *7D3* (1.5km NW Rural) *44.74637, 1.37700* **Camping Domaine La Quercy, Ecoute S'il Pleut, 46300 Gourdon [05 65 41 06 19; fax 05 65 41 31 62; domainequercy@orange.fr; www.domainequercy.com]** Fr N site on R of D704 1.5km bef Gourdon. Sp fr Gourdon. Med, mkd pitch, some hdstg, terr, pt sl, pt shd; wc; chem disp; mv service pnt; baby facs; fam bthrm; shwrs inc; el pnts (6A) €3.50; Indtte (inc dryer); shop & 4km; tradsmn; rest, snacks; bar; BBQ; entmnt; cooking facs; playgrnd; pool; waterslides; paddling pool; bowling; volleyball; badminton; football; lake beach adj; fishing; sailing, watersports 200m; tennis; games area; games rm; wifi; TV; 30% statics; dogs €2.50; ACSI; phone; no twin-axles; poss cr; Eng spkn; adv bkg rec high ssn; quiet; ccard acc; red low ssn. "Gd leisure facs - gd for families; gd san facs; Gourdon attractive town; vg." ♦ 17 Apr-25 Sep. € 24.45 2013*

⊞ **GRAMAT** *7D4* (7km SE Rural) *44.74767, 1.79954* **Camping Le Teulière, L'Hôpital Beaulieu, 46500 Issendolus [05 65 40 86 71; fax 05 65 33 40 89; laparro.mcv@free.fr; http://laparro.mcv.free.fr]** Site on R on D840 at L'Hôpital, clearly sp. Access fr ent narr & tight corners, not for underpowered. Sm, pt sl, pt shd; wc; shwrs inc; el pnts (20A) €2.65 (poss rev pol); Indtte; shop; rest, snacks; bar; BBQ; playgrnd; pool; tennis; fishing; TV; some statics; poss cr; adv bkg; quiet. "Conv Rocamadour; basic san facs; ltd facs low ssn; site rds unmade, steep & narr - gd traction req; pitches muddy when wet." € 8.00 2009*

GUDAS *8G3* (2km S Rural) *42.99269, 1.67830* **Camping Mille Fleurs (Naturist), Le Tuillier, 09120 Gudas [tel/fax 05 61 60 77 56; info@camping-millefleurs.com; www.camping-millefleurs.com]** App Foix on the N20 fr Toulouse foll sp Foix-Tarbes. Pass Camping du lac on R, cont approx 2.2km, at traff lghts turn L sp D1 Laroque d'Olmes, Lieurac, l'Herm). Foll D1 for 6.5km until junc D13 (Care req, sharp bend). Turn L sp Col de Py, Mirepoix, cont past quarry, L fork (sp Gudas, Varhilles). After 2km sp Millefleurs, le Tuilier, turn L over bdge. Site in approx 2km bef Gudas. Sm, hdg/mkd pitch, terr, pt sl, shd; wc; chem disp; shwrs inc; baby facs; fam bthrm; sauna; el pnts (6-10A) €3.75; gas 10km; shop 8km; tradsmn; rest; bar; BBQ; pool; games rm; wifi; dogs €2.25; phone; twin axles; Eng spkn; adv bkg rec high ssn; quiet; red low ssn; INF card req. "Excel, scenic, beautiful, peaceful site; lovely owners; gd pitches; clean facs; gd base Andorra, Toulouse & Carcassonne." ♦ 1 Apr-1 Nov. € 30.00 2014*

L'ISLE JOURDAIN *8F3* (500m NW Urban) *43.61569, 1.07839* **Camping Municipal du Pont Tourné, 32600 L'Isle Jourdain [05 62 07 25 44; fax 05 62 07 24 81]** Exit N124 to town centre. Site well sp. Med, mkd pitch, shd; wc; chem disp; mv service pnt; shwrs; el pnts (10A); Indtte sinks; BBQ; dogs; twin axles; adv bkg; quiet; CCI. "Sports ctr adj to site; shops 300m; vg." 6 Jul-1 Sep. € 12.00 2014*

ISSENDOLUS see Gramat *7D4*

LACAUNE *8E4* (5km E Rural) *43.69280, 2.73790* **Camping Domaine Le Clôt, Les Vidals, 81230 Lacaune [tel/fax 05 63 37 03 59; campingleclot@orange.fr; www.pageloisirs.com/le-clot]** Fr Castres to Lacaune on D622. Cont on D622 past Lacaune then turn R onto unclassified rd to Les Vidals. Site sp 500m on L after Les Vidals. Sm, terr, pt shd; htd wc; chem disp; shwrs inc; el pnts (6-10A) €3.25-4; Indtte; shop 5km; rest, snacks; playgrnd; lake sw, fishing, sailing, windsurfing 12km; dogs €1.50; Eng spkn; quiet; CKE/CCI. "Excel site; modern, immac san facs; gd views; gd walking in Monts de Lacaune; friendly Dutch owner; site rd steep & narr; vg rest." ♦ 16 Feb-14 Dec. € 21.40 2013*

LAGUEPIE *8E4* (1km E Rural) *44.14780, 1.97892* **Camp Municipal Les Tilleuls, 82250 Laguépie [05 63 30 22 32 or 05 63 30 20 81 (Mairie); mairie.laguepie@info82.com; www.camping-les-tilleuls.com]** Exit Cordes on D922 N to Laguépie; turn R at bdge, still on D922 sp Villefranche; site sp to R in 500m; tight turn into narr lane. NB App thro Laguépie poss diff lge o'fits. Med, pt terr, pt shd; wc (some cont); shwrs inc; el pnts (10A) €2.70; shops 1km; bar/café adj; playgrnd; rv sw; canoe hire; fishing; tennis; games area; TV; 44% statics; dogs; phone; adv bkg; quiet. "Attractive setting on Rv Viaur; friendly welcome; excel playgrnd; gd touring base; conv Aveyron gorges." ♦ May-Oct. € 14.00 2014*

LAGUIOLE *7D4* (500m NE Rural) *44.68158, 2.85440* **Camp Municipal Les Monts D'Aubrac, 12210 Laguiole [05 65 44 39 72 or 05 65 51 26 30 (LS); fax 05 65 51 26 31; http://campinglesmontsdaubraclaguiole.jimdo.com]** E of Laguiole on D15 at top of hill. Fr S on D921 turn R at rndabt bef ent to town. Site sp. Med, hdg/mkd pitch, pt sl, pt shd; wc; chem disp; mv service pnt; shwrs inc; el pnts (16A) inc; Indtte; shops, rest, snacks & bar 500m; dogs; phone; quiet; CKE/CCI. "Clean & well cared for site; pleasant vill." 15 May-15 Sep. € 10.00 2014*

LAISSAC *7D4* (3km SE Rural) *44.36525, 2.85090* **FLOWER Camping La Grange de Monteillac, Chemin de Monteillac, 12310 Sévérac-l'Eglise [05 65 70 21 00 or 06 87 46 90 83 (mob); fax 05 65 70 21 01; info@le-grange-de-monteillac.com; www.la-grange-de-monteillac.com / www.flowercampings.com]** Fr A75, at junc 42, go W on N88 twds Rodez; after approx 22km; bef Laissac; turn L twds Sévérac-l'Eglise; site sp. Med, hdg/mkd pitch, pt sl, terr, unshd; wc; chem disp (wc); mv service pnt; shwrs inc; el pnts (6A) inc (long lead poss req); Indtte (inc dryer); rest, bar & shops high ssn; playgrnd; pool; paddling pool; tennis; horseriding; cycle hire; wifi; entmnt; TV; some statics; dogs €1.50; phone; Eng spkn; adv bkg rec high ssn; quiet; CKE/CCI. "Beautiful, excel site." ♦ 7 May-15 Sep. € 42.00 2014*

LAMONTELARIE see Brassac *8F4*

LANNE *8F2* (1km NW Rural) *43.17067, 0.00186* **Camping La Bergerie, 79 Rue des Chênes, 65380 Lanne [tel/fax 05 62 45 40 05; camping-la-bergerie@orange.com; www.camping-la-bergerie.com]** Fr Lourdes take N21 N dir Tarbes; turn R onto D16 (Rue des Chênes) dir Lanne; site on R in 200m. Med, mkd pitch, shd; htd wc; shwrs; el pnts (10A) €3 (poss rev pol); gas; shop; snacks & bar (high ssn); playgrnd; pool high ssn; tennis; dogs €1.20; bus 200m; Eng spkn; adv bkg; quiet but some rd noise & aircraft noise at night; red low ssn; CKE/CCI. "Well-run site; friendly owners; gd san facs; poss unkempt low ssn; poss flooding wet weather." ♦ 15 Mar-15 Oct. € 15.60 2011*

LANNEMEZAN *8F2* (6km W Rural) *43.10544, 0.32333* **FFCC Camping Les Craouès, Rue du 8 Mai 1945, 65130 Capvern [05 62 39 02 54; camping-les-craoues@orange.fr; www.camping-les-craoues.net]** Exit A64 junc 15. At rndabt at ent to Capvern foll sp Capvern Village. Site also sp fr Lannemezan on D817. Med, mkd pitch, some hdstg, pt sl, shd; wc (some cont); mv service pnt; baby facs; shwrs inc; el pnts (6-8A) €4-5; gas; Indtte (inc dryer); shops 500m; BBQ; playgrnd; pool; paddling pool; games area; games rm; dogs €1; poss cr; adv bkg; red low ssn. "Basic site; scruffy overall (low ssn report); NH only." ♦ 1 May-15 Oct. € 13.40 2010*

LARNAGOL see Cajarc *7D4*

LAVELANET *8G4* (1km SW Urban) *42.92340, 1.84477* **Camping Le Pré Cathare, Rue Jacquard, 09300 Lavelanet [tel/fax 05 61 01 55 54; leprecathare@orange.fr; www.campinglavelanet.com]** Fr Lavelanet, take D117 twd Foix & foll sp. Adj 'piscine'. Med, hdg/mkd pitch, pt shd; htd wc; chem disp; shwrs; el pnts (10A) €3; Indtte; shops 1km; tradsmn; snacks; BBQ; playgrnd; pool adj; tennis 800m; games area; rv 4km; entmnt; TV rm; some statics; dogs €1; adv bkg; quiet; CKE/CCI. "Gd sized pitches, some with mountain views; excel san facs; poss open in winter with adv bkg; gates locked 2200; quiet town; vg." ♦ 1 April-31 Oct. € 26.60 2013*

LAVIT *8E3* (500m NE Urban) *43.96212, 0.92409* **Camp Municipal Le Bertranon, Route d'Asques, 82120 Lavit [05 63 94 05 54; fax 05 63 94 11 10; mairie-lavit-de-lomagne@info82.com; www.tourisme-en-lomagne.com]** Fr N, exit A62 junc 8 onto D953 S; in 5km turn L onto D3 sp Lavit; on ent town turn L onto D15; Rte d'Asques is 3rd turning on L. Site adj stadium. Well sp on o'skts. Sm, hdg pitch, pt shd; wc; chem disp (wc); shwrs inc; el pnts (6A) €2.30; shops, rest & snacks nrby; playgrnd; 5% statics; dogs €1; bus 500m; no twin-axles; quiet. "Under-used site - quiet even high ssn; lge pitches; pay at Mairie (not open w/end); clean, dated san facs; gd." ♦ 15 Jun-30 Sep. € 8.00 2010*

LECTOURE *8E3* (2.5km SE Rural) *43.91260, 0.64500* **Yelloh! Village Le Lac des Trois Vallées, 32700 Lectoure [05 62 68 82 33; fax 05 62 68 88 82; contact@lacdes3vallees.fr; www.lacdes3vallees.fr / www.yellohvillage.co.uk]** Site sp fr N21, on lake bet Lectour & Fleurance. App fr N, look for & foll sps to L after leaving Lectoure; take this rd for 2.4km & site on L. NB Narr app rd with steep gradient. Lge, hdg/mkd pitch, pt sl, pt shd; wc; chem disp; mv service pnt; baby facs; shwrs inc; el pnts (10A) inc; Indtte (inc dryer); shop; bar; rest, snacks; bar; BBQ (gas/charcoal only); playgrnd; htd pool; paddling pool; waterslides; lake sw; fishing; watersports; canoeing; horseriding 6km; tennis; skateboard course; games area; fitness rm; wifi; entmnt; games/TV rm; 60% statics; dogs €4; no c'vans/m'vans over 7m high ssn; poss cr; adv bkg; quiet (some disco noise); ccard acc; red low ssn. "Excel lake pool; busy site - ideal for teenagers; generous pitch size but some poss diff lge o'fits due terr; modern san facs; excursions to Pau, Lourdes, Andorra; conv A62; mkt Tue Fleurance." ♦ 1 Jun-11 Sep. € 47.00 2010*

LERAN *8G4* (2km E Rural) *42.98368, 1.93516* **Camping La Régate, Route du Lac, 09600 Léran [tel/fax 05 61 03 09 17; campinglaregate@gmail.com; www.campinglaregate.com]** Fr Lavelanet go N on D625, turn R onto D28 & cont to Léran. Site sp fr vill. Ent easily missed - rd past it is dead end. Med, hdg/mkd pitch, terr, shd; wc; chem disp; baby facs; shwrs; el pnts (8A) €3.70; Indtte; shop 2km; tradsmn; rest adj; bar; BBQ; playgrnd; pool adj; lake adj; watersports; leisure cent nr; cycle hire & pony trekking nrby; entmnt; 10% statics; dogs €1; phone; quiet; adv bkg; ccard acc. "Conv Montségur chateau; clean san facs; gd location; mkd walking & cycle rtes around adj lake." 30 Mar-26 Oct. € 33.60 2014*

LIMOGNE EN QUERCY *7D4* (600m W Rural) *44.39571, 1.76396* **Camp Municipal Bel-Air, 46260 Limogne-en-Quercy [05 65 24 32 75; fax 05 65 24 73 59; camping.bel-air@orange.fr]** E fr Cahors on D911 just bef Limogne vill. W fr Villefranche on D911 just past vill; 3 ents about 50m apart. Sm, mkd pitch, sl, shd; wc; shwrs inc; el pnts (6A) inc; Indtte; shops & bar 600m; pool; quiet; adv bkg rec high ssn. "Friendly welcome; if warden absent, site yourself; pleasant vill." 1 Apr-1 Oct. € 18.00 2014*

LIMOGNE EN QUERCY *7D4* (6km NW Rural) *44.42344, 1.69609* **Camping Lalbrade (Naturist), Lalbrade, 46260 Lugagnac [05 65 31 52 35 or 06 20 05 98 57 (mob); fax 05 65 24 36 21; lalbrade@orange.fr; http://lalbrade.free.fr/]** Fr D911 Cahors to Villefranche-de-Rouergue rd; at Limogne-en-Quercy take D40 sp Lugagnac (narr rd); site sp after Lugagnac; 2km of single-track ent rd. Diff to find. Sm, pt shd; wc (some cont); shwrs inc; el pnts (6-10A) €3-4; pool; dogs €3; Eng spkn; quiet. "In interesting area; gd walking within site boundaries." ♦ 3 Apr-26 Sep. € 24.00 2010*

LOUDENVIELLE see Arreau *8G2*

LOUPIAC see Payrac *7D3*

LOURDES *8F2* (1km N Urban) *43.11425, -0.03661* **Caravaning Plein-Soleil, Route de Tarbes, 65100 Lourdes [05 62 94 40 93; fax 05 62 94 51 20; camping.plein.soleil@wanadoo.fr; www.camping-pleinsoleil.com]** Fr N site sp on N21. Turn R imm opp aquarium sp. Sm, terr, pt shd; htd wc; chem disp; shwrs inc; el pnts (4A) inc; Indtte; snacks; playgrnd; pool; dogs; poss cr; Eng spkn; adv bkg; poss noise fr adj builders' yard; red low ssn; CKE/CCI. "Pleasant site; helpful staff; gd san facs; gd security; ltd access lge o'fits; muddy when wet; conv hypmkt." Easter-10 Oct. € 19.00 2011*

LOURDES *8F2* (2km N Urban) *43.11569, -0.03225* **FFCC Camping Le Moulin du Monge, 28 Ave Jean Moulin, 65100 Lourdes [05 62 94 28 15; fax 05 62 42 20 54; camping.moulin.monge@wanadoo.fr; www.camping-lourdes.com]** Fr N on N21 fr Tarbes, past airport & on app to Lourdes turn L sp 'Zone Indust du Monge'. Site on L of rd in 100m immed bef rlwy bdge. Med, pt shd; htd wc; mv service pnt; sauna; shwrs inc; el pnts (4A) inc; Indtte (inc dryer); shop & farm produce; playgrnd; htd, covrd pool; some statics; some rd & rlwy noise. "Pleasant site." 1 Apr-10 Oct. € 18.30 2010*

LOURDES *8F2* (1km NE Urban) *43.10247, -0.02789* **Camping de Sarsan, 4 Ave Jean Moulin, 65100 Lourdes [tel/fax 05 62 94 43 09; camping.sarsan@wanadoo.fr; www.lourdes-camping.com]** Fr N on N21 past airport, on app to Lourdes turn L sp 'Zone Indust du Monge'. Pass Cmp Le Moulin du Monge & foll site sp for approx 2km. Site on L immed after x-rds. Med, pt sl, pt shd; wc; chem disp; mv service pnt; shwrs inc; el pnts (4-10A) pos rev pol. €2.50-4.60; Indtte; sm shop; supmkt nr; pool; games area; games rm; TV; wifi; some statics; dogs free; adv bkg; quiet; ccard not acc. "Easy 25min walk to town cent." 15 Apr-15 Oct. € 13.20 2012*

LOURDES *8F2* (2.1km E Rural) *43.09316, -0.02091* **Camping du Ruisseau Blanc, Route de Bagnères-Anclades, 65100 Lourdes [05 62 42 94 83 or 05 62 42 98 19 (LS); fax 05 62 42 94 62; www.camping-lourdes-ruisseau-blanc.com]** Exit Lourdes on D937 twd Bagnères & foll sp. Site has 2 ents. C'vans ignore 1st sp for site on R & cont on D937 foll next sp. Med, mkd pitch, some hdstg, pt shd; wc (mainly cont); chem disp; mv service pnt; shwrs; el pnts (6A) €2; Indtte (inc dryer); shop; playgrnd; games area; TV rm; dogs €0.50; "Gd views; beautiful site but facs poss stretched high ssn." 20 Mar-10 Oct. € 8.20 2010*

LOURDES *8F2* (2.5km W Urban) *43.09773, -0.06986* **Camp du Loup, Route de la Forêt, 65100 Lourdes [tel/fax 05 62 94 23 60; www.camping-du-loup-lourdes.com]** Fr N on N21 exit onto D914 to Lourdes; on ent Lourdes turn L off D914 under rlwy brdge dir Centre Ville & hospital; in 100m turn R onto Rue de Pau sp St Pé & Bétharram; in 1km turn L over rv brdge; site on R in 300m. Site sp. Sm, pt shd; wc; chem disp; mv service pnt; shwrs €1; el pnts (6A) €3; Indtte (inc dryer); shop 1km; tradsmn; playgrnd; rv 300m; dogs €1; poss cr; adv bkg ess; quiet; CKE/CCI. "Excel CL-type site; basic facs; friendly, helpful host; gd atmosphere; gd security; adv bkg rec high ssn; rvside walk to shrine." ♦ 1 May-10 Oct. € 12.00 2011*

LOURDES *8F2* (3km W Rural) *43.09561, -0.07463* **Camping La Forêt, Route de la Forêt, 65100 Lourdes [05 62 94 04 38; fax 05 62 42 14 86; campingdelaforet65@orange.fr; www.campingdelaforet.fr]** Fr N on N21 exit onto D914 to Lourdes; on ent Lourdes turn L off D914 under rlwy brdge dir Centre Ville & hospital; in 100m turn R onto Rue de Pau sp St Pé & Bétharram; in 1km turn L over rv brdge; site in 1km. Med, mkd pitch, pt shd; wc; mv service pnt; shwrs €1; el pnts (3-10A) €2.60-7.60; gas; Indtte (inc dryer); shop; rest, snacks; bar; playgrnd; few statics; dogs €1.30; poss cr; Eng spkn; adv bkg; quiet; ccard acc; CKE/CCI. "Lovely site; helpful owners; conv town cent & grotto (1km); poss open outside stated dates - adv bkg req; ideal site to visit Lourdes." 29 Mar-31 Oct. € 27.20 2014*

LOURDES *8F2* (4km W Rural) *43.10461, -0.06782* **Camping d'Arrouach, 9 Rue des Trois Archanges, Biscaye, 65100 Lourdes [05 62 42 11 43; fax 05 62 42 05 27; camping.arrouach@wanadoo.fr; www.camping-arrouach.com]** Fr Lourdes take D940 twd Pau. As you leave Lourdes take L fork D937 (sp) Bétharram. Site on R 200m. Med, hdg/mkd pitch, hdstg, pt sl, pt shd; wc; chem disp; mv service pnt; shwrs inc; el pnts (3-6A) €2.50-5; gas; Indtte; shop 2km; tradsmn; bar; BBQ; playgrnd; wifi; 10% statics; dogs; phone; poss cr; adv bkg; quiet; red long stay;CKE/CCI. "Pleasant, elevated site with views; poss flooding in v wet weather; clean san facs; easy access parking for Lourdes via Rte de Pau." ♦ 15 Mar-31 Dec. € 12.40 2010*

LOURDES *8F2* (2km NW Rural) *43.10972, -0.06242* **Camping Theil, 23 Chemin de St Pauly, 65100 Lourdes [tel/fax 05 62 94 24 59 or 06 86 65 80 24 (mob)]** Sp at junc D940 and D937, site 500m fr junc, nr stadium. Sm, pt shd; wc; chem disp; shwrs inc; el pnts €1; shop 1km; pool 1.5km; some statics; dogs €1; adv bkg; quiet. "Gd site but san facs in poor condition; 30 min walk to grotto or easy drive." 15 Mar-31 Oct. € 12.00 2011*

LOURES BAROUSSE see Montréjeau *8F3*

LUCHON *8G3* (2km N Rural) *42.80806, 0.59667* **Camping Pradelongue, 31110 Moustajon [05 61 79 86 44; fax 05 61 79 18 64; camping-pradelongue@wanadoo.fr; www.camping-pradelongue.com]** Site is on D125c on W of D125 main rd fr Luchon. Ent at Moustajon/Antignac going S. Site adj Intermarché; sp. Lge, hdg/mkd pitch, pt shd; wc; chem disp; mv service pnt; baby facs; shwrs inc; el pnts (2-10A) €2-4; Indtte; shop 100m; BBQ; playgrnd; htd pool; games area; wifi; 10% statics; dogs €2; Eng spkn; adv bkg; quiet; ccard acc; red low ssn; CKE/CCI. "Excel, well-run site; mountain views; gd sized pitches; friendly, helpful owners; rec." ♦ 1 Apr-30 Sep. € 18.00 2010*

LUCHON *8G3* (1km NE Rural) *42.79472, 0.60826* **Camping La Lanette/Arome Vanille, 31110 Montauban-de-Luchon [05 61 79 00 38; info@camping-aromevanille.com; www.camping-aromevanille.com]** Exit A64 junc 17 at Montréjeau onto D825/N125/D33/D125; at end of new section of D125 turn L at rndabt sp Luzet-de-Luchon; turn R in vill; site on R in 1km. Lge, hdg/mkd pitch, pt shd; htd wc; baby facs; shwrs inc; el pnts (6-10A) €4-5; gas; Indtte; rest, snacks; bar; playgrnd; games area; child entmnt; 30% statics; dogs €3; poss cr; adv bkg; quiet; ccard acc; red low ssn; CKE/CCI. "Vg site; high level hiking rtes 20-30 mins by car." 1 Apr-30 Oct. € 15.00 2009*

LUCHON *8G3* (7km W Rural) *42.80902, 0.51978* **Camping Les Frênes, 31110 Garin [05 61 79 88 44]** Fr Bagnères-de-Luchon take D618 W dir Arreau. Turn R in vill of Garin to site. Sm, terr, pt shd; wc; chem disp (wc); shwrs inc; el pnts (3A) inc; shop nr; rest 1km; playgrnd; 30% statics; dogs €1; quiet. "Basic site; conv for Lac d'Oô & mountain walking." 1 Apr-30 Nov. € 16.00 2010*

LUGAGNAC see Limogne en Quercy *7D4*

LUZ ST SAUVEUR *8G2* (1.5km N Rural) *42.88285, -0.01354* **Camping International, 50 Ave de Barège, 65120 Esquièze-Sère [05 62 92 82 02; fax 05 62 92 96 87; camping.international.luz@wanadoo.fr; www.international-camping.fr]** On E side of D921, clearly sp. Ave de Barège is pt of D921. Lge, hdg/mkd pitch, pt sl, pt shd; htd wc; chem disp; mv service pnt; baby facs; shwrs inc; el pnts (2-6A) €2-5; Indtte (inc dryer); shop; supmkt 800m; tradsmn; rest 1km; snacks; bar; playgrnd; htd pool; paddling pool; waterslide; tennis; horseriding; skiing; games area; games rm; wifi; entmnt; TV; 10% statics; dogs free; phone; poss cr; Eng spkn; adv bkg; quiet, some rd noise; red low ssn; CKE/CCI. "Beautiful views fr site; friendly, helpful owners; vg clean san facs, ltd low ssn; gd walking; gd base for cycling inc Col du Tourmalet; mkt Mon; vg; Excel modern san facs." ♦ 20 May-30 Sep. € 41.00 2013*

LUZ ST SAUVEUR *8G2* (500m E Rural) *42.87362, 0.00293* **Camping Le Bergons, Route de Barèges, 65120 Esterre [05 62 92 90 77; info@camping-bergons.com; www.camping-bergons.com]** On D918 to Col du Tourmalet, site on R. Med, mkd pitch, pt sl, terr, pt shd; htd wc; shwrs inc; chem disp; el pnts (2-6A) €2.10-5; gas; Indtte; shops adj; tradsmn; BBQ; playgrnd; pool 500m; 10% statics; dogs €0.80; phone; rd noise; red long stay/low ssn; CKE/CCI. "Well-kept site; friendly, helpful owner; gd san facs; levelling blocks poss req; v tight ent for lge o'fits; excel walking; Donjon des Aigles at Beaucens worth visit; mkt Mon; vg." ♦ 2 May-26 Oct. € 20.35 2014*

⊞ **LUZ ST SAUVEUR** *8G2* (8km E Rural) *42.89451, 0.05741* **Camping La Ribère, Route de Labatsus, 65120 Barèges [tel/fax 05 62 92 69 01 or 06 80 01 29 51 (mob); contact@laribere.com; www.laribere.com]** On N side of rd D918 on edge of Barèges, site sp as 'Camping Caraveneige'. Phone kiosk at ent. Sm, pt sl, pt shd; htd wc ltd; chem disp; shwrs inc; el pnts (2-6A) €2-6; Indtte (inc dryer); shop; tradsmn; rest adj; wifi; some statics; dogs €0.95; site clsd end Oct-mid Dec; poss cr; quiet. "Conv, attractive site; gd facs; magnificent views; Site clsd for refurb until Jun 15." ♦ € 23.00 2013*

"I like to fill in the reports as I travel from site to site"

You'll find report forms at the back of this guide, or you can fill them in online at www.caravaclub.co.uk/europereport.

⊞ **LUZ ST SAUVEUR** *8G2* (2km NW Rural) *42.88218, -0.02270* **FFCC Camping Le Pyrénévasion, Route de Luz-Andiden 65120 Sazos [05 62 92 91 54; fax 05 62 92 98 34; camping-pyrenevasion@wanadoo.fr; www.campingpyrenevasion.com]** Fr Lourdes S on D921 twd Gavarnie. Shortly bef Luz-St Sauveur after petrol stn & campsites sp, take R fork onto D12 sp Sazos. Cont thro vill & turn R sp Luz-Andiden, then immed R again sp Sazos (D12) & Luz-Andiden. Cont uphill, site on R just after Sazon sp. Med, hdg/mkd pitch, pt shd; htd wc; chem disp; baby facs; shwrs inc; el pnts (3A) inc; gas; Indtte; shop 200m; rest; tradsmn; snacks; bar; BBQ (gas/elec/charcoal); playgrnd; pool; paddling pool; fishing; games rm; wifi; 60% statics; dogs €2.50; no c'vans/m'vans over 7.50m high ssn; poss cr; Eng spkn; quiet; site clsd 20 Oct-19 Nov; red low ssn. "Fair site in mountains; long, steep trek to/fr shops." ♦ € 25.50 2011*

See advertisement

LUZECH see Castelfranc *7D3*

LUZENAC see Ax les Thermes *8G4*

MARCIAC *8F2* (1.5km NW Rural) *43.53228, 0.16633* **FFCC Camping du Lac, Bezines, 32230 Marciac [tel/fax 05 62 08 21 19; camping.marciac@wanadoo.fr; www.camping-marciac.com]** E fr Maubourguet take D943 to Marciac. Take D3 to lake dir Plaisance. At lake turn R & R again at sp. Site on L in 200m. Fr N exit A62 at junc 3 & foll D932 sp Pau to Aire-sur-Adour then E on D935 & D3 & foll sp. Med, mkd pitch, some hdstg, pt sl, pt shd; wc chem disp; mv service pnt; baby facs; shwrs inc; el pnts (6A) inc; gas; lndtte; shop & 800m; tradsmn; rest 300m; snacks; bar; BBQ; playgrnd; pool; lake adj; wifi; 8% statics; dogs €1.50; phone; adv bkg; red long stay/low ssn; ccard acc; CKE/CCI. "Friendly British owners; peaceful site; lge pitches with easy access; interesting old town; jazz festival 1st 2 weeks Aug (extra charge); Wed mkt." ♦ 20 Mar-17 Oct. € 25.00 2013*

MARCILLAC VALLON *7D4* (300m NW Urban) *44.47721, 2.45575* **Camp Municipal Le Cambou, 24 Ave Gustave Bessières, 12330 Marcillac-Vallon [05 65 71 74 96 or 06 62 39 19 37 (mob); mairie-marcillacvallon@wanadoo.fr; www.tourisme-aveyron.com]** App Marcillac-Vallon fr N on D901; on ent town, site on L immed after x-ing rv bdge. Sm, hdg/mkd pitch, pt sl, pt shd; htd wc; chem disp; shwrs inc; el pnts (6A) €2.30; shops nrby; tennis nrby; dogs; some statics; quiet. "Otters in sm rv; NH only." 1 Jul-31 Aug. € 9.00 2011*

MARTEL *7C3* (5km SE Rural) *44.88538, 1.59929* **Camping du Port, 46600 Creysse [05 65 32 20 82 or 05 65 32 27 59; fax 05 65 38 78 21; contact@campingduport.com; www.campingduport.com]** Exit A20 at Junc 55 foll D803 to Le Pigeon, then take D15 to Saint Sozy, then D114 to Creysse then foll signs to site. Med, pt sl, pt shd by rv; wc (some cont); shwrs inc; el pnts (6A) inc; lndtte; shops in Martel; rest in Creysse; playgrnd; pool; canoe & cycle hire; dogs €1.50; adv bkg; quiet. "Lovely grnds; gd access to rv; friendly; v peaceful low ssn; ltd facs low ssn; Creysse beautiful vill." 1 May-20 Sep. € 26.40 2013*

MARTEL *7C3* (6km SW Rural) *44.87604, 1.57707* **FFCC Camping La Plage, Rive Gauche de la Dordogne, 46200 Meyronne [05 65 32 23 26 or 06 32 02 82 82 (LS); contact@camping-laplage.com; www.camping-laplage.com]** W fr Souillac on D803 dir Martel; in 3km at Le Pigeon Bas turn R onto D15 sp St Sozy; cont past St Sozy; in 1km cross Rv Dordogne & site immed on R. Med, pt shd; wc; chem disp (wc); baby facs; shwrs inc; el pnts (6A) €3; gas 500m; lndtte; tradsmn; snacks; BBQ; playgrnd; pool; rv sw adj; canoeing; horseriding; rock climbing; games area; internet; dogs €0.50; poss cr; Eng spkn; adv bkg; some rd noise; ccard acc; CKE/CCI. "Excel site by rv; Rocamadour 14km; caves of Padirc 18km." ♦ 16 Jun-15 Sep. € 12.40 2011*

MARTRES TOLOSANE *8F3* (1.5km S Rural) *43.19060, 1.01840* **Camping Le Moulin, 31220 Martres-Tolosane [05 61 98 86 40; fax 05 61 98 66 90; info@domainelemoulin.com; www.domainelemoulin.com]** Exit A64 junc 22 (fr N or S) & foll camping sps. Site sp adj Rv Garonne. Med, hdg pitch, pt sl, pt shd; wc; chem disp; mv service pnt; baby facs; shwrs inc; el pnts (6-10A) €4-6; gas; lndtte; shops 1.5km; snacks; bar; BBQ; playgrnd; htd pool; paddling pool; rv fishing adj; tennis; cycle hire; games area; games rm; wifi; entmnt; TV; 20% statics; dogs €2.50; Eng spkn; adv bkg rec high ssn; quiet; red long stay; red low ssn; ccard acc; CKE/CCI. "Excel, well-maintained site; friendly welcome; gd, modern san facs; water on all pitches; gd touring base for Spain, Lourdes, etc." ♦ 31 Mar-5 Oct. € 23.00 SBS - D28 2012*

MARTRES TOLOSANE *8F3* (7km SW Rural) *43.13447, 0.93240* **Camp Municipal, Route de St Girons, 31360 St Martory [05 61 90 44 93 or 05 61 98 14 65; cccsm@wanadoo.fr; www.petitespyrenees.com]** Leave A64 at junc 20. Turn N onto D117 twd St Martory. In 1km turn L (sp) soon after Gendarmerie. Sm, hdg pitch, pt shd; htd wc (some cont); chem disp (wc); shwrs inc; el pnts €2.50; dogs €1.50; quiet; CKE/CCI. ♦ 15 Jun-15 Sep. € 10.00 2010*

MASSEUBE *8F3* (2km E Rural) *43.42748, 0.61142* **Camping Aux Mêmes, 32149 Bellegarde [tel/fax 05 62 66 91 45; info@camping-gascony.co.uk; www.gascogne-camping.fr]** Fr Masseube take D27 E dir Simorre & Bellegarde; in 2.5km turn L (having past sports stadium & driven up hill thro trees); site is 1st farm on R in 300m. Site sp. Sm, pt sl, unshd; wc; chem disp; shwrs inc; el pnts (6A) €3; lndtte (inc dryer); shop; snacks; bar; BBQ; playgrnd; pool; water sports, fishing, canoeing, windsufing & sailing nrby; tennis & golf nrby; cycle hire; games rm; wifi; TV; dogs; Eng spkn; adv bkg; quiet; excel." ♦ 1 Apr-1 Sep. € 22.00 2014*

MASSEUBE *8F3* (12km NE Rural) *43.50199, 0.68585* **Camping Domaine Naturiste du Moulin de Faget (Naturist), Au Grange, 32450 Faget-Abbatial [05 62 65 49 09; fax 05 62 66 29 21; info@moulin-faget.com; www.moulin-faget.com]** Fr Masseube D929 for 7 km; in Seissan R on D104 sp Faget-Abbatial; in 8.5km R at T-junc onto D40; site sp on L in 300m; at top of track after 500m. Sm, pt sl, unshd; wc; chem disp (wc); shwrs inc; el pnts (6A) €3.50; lndtte; tradsmn; rest; bar; lake adj; games area; cycle hire; 10% statics; no dogs; B & B avail all yr; Eng spkn; adv bkg; quiet; CKE/CCI. "Extremely quiet & secluded site in beautiful area; no play facs for children; friendly, helpful Dutch owners; modern san facs; gd walking, cycling; attractive vill nrby; excel." ♦ ltd 1 May-1 Oct. € 22.00 2009*

MASSEUBE *8F3* (400m E Rural) *43.42914, 0.58516* **Camping Berges du Gers, Route de Simorre, 32140 Masseube [05 62 66 01 75; camping.masseube@orange.fr; www.camping-masseube-lesbergesdugers.fr]** S fr Auch on D929 to Masseube; turn L onto D27 dir Simorre; site on L in 500m. Med, shd; wc; chem disp; shwrs inc; el pnts (6A) €3; gas 500m; lndtte; shop 500m; tradsmn; rest, snacks & bar 500m; BBQ; playgrnd; htd pool adj; access to rv; tennis; cycle hire; games area; games rm; entmnt; wifi; TV; 10% statics; dogs free; phone adj; Eng spkn; adv bkg; quiet; ccard acc; red low ssn; CKE/CCI. "Well-run site in pleasant setting; security barrier; vg." ♦ ltd 1 May 31 Oct. € 12.00 2011*

MAUBOURGUET *8F2* (700m SW Urban) *43.46657, 0.03199* **Camp Municipal de l'Echez, Rue Jean Clos Pucheu, 65700 Maubourguet [05 62 96 37 44 or 06 12 90 14 55 (mob); camping.maubourguet@yahoo.fr]** On D935 (NW of Tarbes), sp in Maubourguet, on bank of Rv Echez. Sm, pt shd; wc; shwrs inc; mv service pnt; el pnts; shops 200m; lndtte; playgrnd; TV; rv fishing 300m; quiet. "Pleasantly situated; pleasant country town." 1 Jun-15 Sep. € 11.00 2009*

MAUROUX see St Clar *8E3*

MAZAMET *8F4* (1.5km E Urban) *43.49634, 2.39075* **FFCC Camp Municipal de la Lauze, Chemin de la Lauze, 81200 Mazamet [tel/fax 05 63 61 24 69; camping.mazamet@imsnet.fr; www.camping-mazamet.com]** Exit Mazamet dir St Pons on D612, site on R past rugby grnd. Med, hdstg, pt sl, pt shd; wc (mainly cont); chem disp; mv service pnt; baby facs; shwrs inc; el pnts (15A) €3.50; lndtte; BBQ; htd pool adj; tennis; dogs; poss cr; adv bkg; some rd noise; red long stay/CKE/CCI. "Well-kept site in 2 adj parts, 1 flat & other sl; office thro gateway - warden needed for access; san facs excel; gd touring base 'Black Mountain' region." ♦ 1 Jun-30 Sep. € 16.00 2014*

⊞ **MERENS LES VALS** *8G4* (1km W Rural) *42.64633, 1.83083* **Camp Municipal Ville de Bau, Ville de Bau, 09110 Mérens-les-Vals [05 61 02 85 40 or 05 61 64 33 77; fax 05 61 64 03 83; camping.merens@wanadoo.fr; http://merenslesvals.fr]** Fr Ax-les-Thermes on N20 sp Andorra past Mérens-les-Vals turn R nr start of dual c'way sp Camp Municipal. Site on R in 800m. Med, hdg pitch; htd wc (some cont); shwrs inc; el pnts (6-10A) €3.20-5.20 (poss rev pol); lndtte (inc dryer); shop; bar; BBQ; playgrnd; pool 8km; 20% statics; dogs €0.70; poss cr; quiet; ccard acc; CKE/CCI. "Excel site; gd clean san facs; gd walks fr site; conv Andorra, Tunnel de Puymorens." € 15.20 2012*

"I need an on-site restaurant"

We do our best to make sure site information is correct, but it is always best to check any must-have facilities are still available or will be open during your visit.

MILLAU *10E1* (1km NE Urban) *44.10500, 3.08833* **Camping du Viaduc, Millau-Cureplat, 121 Ave du Millau-Plage, 12100 Millau [05 65 60 15 75; fax 05 65 61 36 51; info@camping-du-viaduc.com; www.camping-du-viaduc.com]** Exit Millau on N991 (sp Nant) over Rv Tarn via Cureplat bdge. At rndabt take D187 dir Paulhe, 1st campsite on L. Lge, hdg/mkd pitch, shd; htd wc; chem disp; some serviced pitches (extra charge); baby facs; shwrs inc; el pnts (6A) €4 (poss long lead req); gas; lndtte (inc dryer); shop high ssn; rest, snacks; bar; BBQ; playgrnd; htd pool; paddling pool; rv sw & private sand beach; wifi; entmnt; 20% statics; dogs €3; Eng spkn; some rd noise; ccard acc; red low ssn/long stay/CKE/CCI. "Peaceful, well-run site; helpful, welcoming staff; excel, clean san facs; barrier clsd 2200-0700; many sports & activities in area; conv for gorges & viaduct tours; quiet low ssn; super site." ♦ 25 Apr-14 Sep. € 51.00 2014*

MILLAU *10E1* (1km NE Urban) *44.11044, 3.08712* **Camping Larribal, Ave de Millau Plage, 12100 Millau [05 65 59 08 04; camping.larribal@wanadoo.fr; www.campinglarribal.com]** Exit Millau on D991 (sp Nant), cross rv & at rndabt take 3rd exit, site on L. Med, mkd pitch, shd; htd wc; chem disp; shwrs inc; el pnts (6A) €3; gas; lndtte; shop; tradsmn; playgrnd; rv sw adj; shgl beach; TV; 5% statics; dogs €1; phone; adv bkg; quiet but poss noise fr stadium across rv; red low ssn/long stay; CKE/CCI. "Peaceful, well-kept site on Rv Tarn; friendly, helpful staff; excel, clean san facs; lge o'fits poss diff access; high m'vans poss diff under trees; gd access to gorges; severe tree fluff in May; excel." ♦ 23 Apr-30 Sep. € 13.80 2011*

MILLAU *10E1* (1km NE Rural) *44.10640, 3.08800* **Camping Les Erables, Route de Millau-Plage, 12100 Millau [tel/fax 05 65 59 15 13; camping-les-erables@orange.fr; www.campingleserables.fr]** Exit Millau on D991 (sp Nant) over Rv Tarn bdge; take L at island sp to Millau-Plage & site on L immed after Camping du Viaduc & bef Camping Larribal. On ent Millau fr N or S foll sps 'Campings'. Med, hdg/mkd pitch, shd; htd wc; chem disp; baby facs; shwrs inc; el pnts (10A) €3 (rev pol); lndtte (inc dryer); shop; snacks high ssn; bar; BBQ; playgrnd; rv sw, canoeing adj; wifi; entmnt; TV; dogs €1.20; phone; Eng spkn; adv bkg; some rd noise & fr nrby sites; ccard acc; red low ssn; CKE/CCI. "Peaceful, well-kept site on banks of Rv Tarn; lge shd pitches; friendly, helpful owners; excel modern san facs; some pitches poss diff lge o'fits; excel walking; beavers nrby; Millau Viaduct Vistor Cent a must; excel." ♦ 5 Apr-30 Sep. € 29.00 2014*

MILLAU *10E1* (2km NE Urban) *44.10240, 3.09100* **Camping Indigo Millau, Ave de l'Aigoual, 12100 Millau [tel/fax 05 65 61 18 83; millau@camping-indigo.com; www.camping-cotesud.fr]** Fr N exit A75 junc 45 to Millau. Turn L at 2nd traff island sp 'Camping'. Site on R over bdge in 200m. Fr S exit A75 junc 47 onto D809 & cross rv on by-pass, turn R at 1st traff island sp Nant on D991, cross bdge, site on R in 200m, sp. Site a S confluence of Rv Dourbie & Rv Tarn. Med, mkd pitch, pt sl, shd; wc; chem disp; shwrs inc; el pnts (5A) €3.50; gas; lndtte; shop; snacks; playgrnd; pool; rv sw adj; fishing, canoe hire & hang-gliding nrby; some statics; dogs €1.50; Eng spkn; adv bkg; red low ssn; CKE/CCI. "Excel site; gd san facs; pleasant, helpful owner; conv Tarn Gorges; lge mkt Fri." 1 Apr-30 Sep. € 20.50 2012*

MILLAU *10E1* (6km NE Rural) *44.15188, 3.09899* **Camping La Belle Etoile (formerly Camping d'Aguessac), Chemin des Prades, 12520 Aguessac [05 65 72 91 07 ou 06 72 23 10 56 (mob); fax 05 65 59 08 72; contact@camping-labelleetoile.fr; http://camping-labelleetoile.fr]** Site on N907 in vill; ent on R v soon after level x-ing when app fr Millau. Alt app fr J44.1 on A75 via D29, unmade rd fr A75 to Aguessa. Med, mkd pitch, pt shd; wc; chem disp; shwrs inc; el pnts (6A) inc; gas; lndtte; shops adj; bar; rv adj; fishing; canoeing; games area; sports grnd adj; wifi; entmnt; dogs €2; quiet; red long low ssn; CKE/CCI. "Nice, spacious, clean rvside site; gd position with mountain views; gd sized pitches; helpful & friendly staff; public footpath thro site along rv to picturesque vill; poss youth groups high ssn; excel touring base; vg location." ♦ 15 May-20 Sep. € 16.00 2012*

MILLAU *10E1* (8.5km NE Rural) *44.16861, 3.11944* **Camping Les Cerisiers, Pailhas, 12520 Compeyre [05 65 59 87 96 or 05 65 59 10 35 (LS); contact@campinglescerisiers.com; www.campinglescerisiers.com]** Fr Millau N on D809 for 4km, then D907 to Pailhas; site at exit to vill on R. Med, mkd pitch, pt shd; wc; chem disp; shwrs inc; el pnts (6A) €3; lndry rm; shop; tradsmn; snacks; playgrnd; private beach on Rv Tarn; pool 3km; rock climbing; canoeing, mountain biking, paragliding & horseriding nrby; games rm; wifi; entmnt; 5% statics; dogs €1.50; phone; poss cr; Eng spkn; adv bkg; quiet; ccard acc; red low ssn; CKE/CCI. "Vg, clean site; helpful staff; birdwatching; Millau tourist train; conv Tarn gorges." ♦ ltd 1 May-15 Sep. € 15.00 2011*

MILLAU *10E1* (1km E Urban) *44.10287, 3.08732* **Camping des Deux Rivières, 61 Ave de l'Aigoual, 12100 Millau [05 65 60 00 27 or 06 07 08 41 41 (mob); fax 05 65 60 76 78; camping.deux-rivieres@orange.fr / camp2rivieres@yahoo.fr; www.camping-des-deux-rivieres.fr]** Fr N on D911 foll sp for Montpellier down to rv. At rndabt by bdge turn L over bdge, site immed on L well sp. Fr S on D992 3rd bdge, sp camping. Sm, mkd pitch, shd; htd wc (50% cont); chem disp; mv service pnt; shwrs inc; el pnts (8-10A) €3. (poss long lead req); gas; lndry rm; shops adj; tradsmn; snacks; playgrnd; fishing;dog €1.50; phone; wifi; poss cr; quiet; ccard not acc; red low ssn; CKE/CCI. "Basic site in gd situation by rv; friendly, helpful owners; gd san facs; gd base for touring gorges." 1 Apr-29 Oct. € 29.00 2014*

MILLAU *10E1* (1km E Rural) *44.10166, 3.09611* **Camping Les Rivages, Ave de l'Aigoual, 12100 Millau [05 65 61 01 07 or 06 10 75 65 94 (mob); fax 05 65 59 03 56; info@campinglesrivages.com; www.campinglesrivages.com]** Fr Millau take D991 dir Nant (sp Gorges de la Dourbie & Campings). Cross Rv Tarn & cont on this rd, site is 500m after bdge on R. Lge, pt shd; htd wc (some cont); chem disp (wc); mv service pnt; serviced pitches (additional charge); baby facs; shwrs inc; el pnts (10A) inc (poss rev pol); lndtte (inc dryer); shop; supmkt 2km; tradsmn; rest, snacks; bar; BBQ (on legs only); playgrnd; 2 pools; spa; rv sw adj - shingle beach; tennis & squash; fishing; canoeing nr; hang-gliding; games area; wifi; entmnt; games/TV rm; 10% statics; dogs €4; twin-axles acc (rec check in avd); phone; poss cr; Eng spkn; adv bkg; quiet; ccard acc over €30; red low ssn/long stay; CKE/CCI. "Pleasant, busy, scenic site - esp rv/side pitches; helpful & friendly staff; immac, clean san facs; vg rest/snack bar - home cooked & inexpensive; gd security; views of Millau viaduct; easy access to town; mkt Wed & Fri; pleasant cycle ride along rvbank." ♦ 15 Apr-30 Sep. € 49.00 SBS - D20 2014*

MILLAU *10E1* (2.5km E Rural) *44.10029, 3.11099* **FFCC Camping St Lambert, Ave de l'Aigoual, 12100 Millau [05 65 60 00 48; camping.saintlambert@orange.fr; www.campingsaintlambert.fr]** Fr N on either D809 or D11 foll dir D992 St Affrique/Albi. Turn L at rndabt over bdge onto D991 dir Nant. Site on R, sp. Fr S on D992 turn R at rndabt & dir as above. Med, mkd pitch, shd; wc (some cont); chem disp; mv service pnt; shwrs inc; el pnts (6A) €2.80; gas; lndtte; shop; bar; playgrnd; sm pool; sand/shgl beach & rv sw adj; wifi; 10% statics; dogs €1; poss cr; adv bkg; quiet; ccard acc; red low ssn; CKE/CCI. "Spacious, gd site; gd low ssn; owners pleasant & helpful; twin-axles not acc; lovely area." 1 May-30 Sep. € 26.70 2014*

MIRANDE *8F2* (1km NE Rural) *43.55235, 0.31371* **Camping Pouylebon (Devroome), Pouylebon, 32320 Montesquiou [05 62 66 72 10; campingpouylebon2@wanadoo.fr; http://campingpouylebon.pagesperso-orange.fr]** Exit N21 NW at Mirande onto D159; in 10km, at Pouylebon, turn R onto D216; in 900m site on R, 600m down track. Sm, pt sl, pt shd; wc; chem disp; shwrs inc; el pnts (6A) €2.85; lndtte; sm shop & 12km; snacks; bar; BBQ; playgrnd; pool; tennis, fishing & horseriding nr; games area; games rm; wifi; TV rm; dogs free; poss cr; Eng spkn; adv bkg; ccard not acc; red low ssn. "Rural retreat; charming, Dutch owners; meals on request; excel." 15 Apr-15 Oct. € 26.00 2013*

MIRANDE *8F2* (500m E Rural) *43.51432, 0.40990* **Camp Municipal L'Ile du Pont, Au Batardeau, 32300 Mirande [05 62 66 64 11; fax 05 62 66 69 86; info@camping-gers.com; www.camping-gers.com]** On N21 Auch-Tarbes, foll sp to site on island in Rv Grande Baise. Med, pt shd; htd wc (some cont); chem disp; mv service pnt; baby facs; shwrs inc; el pnts (6-10A) inc; lndtte (inc dryer); tradsmn; rest, snacks; bar; BBQ; playgrnd; pool; waterslides; canoeing; sailing; windsurfing; fishing; cycle hire; tennis; games rm; entmnt; 20% statics; dogs €1; adv bkg rec; quiet; red low ssn; ccard not acc; CKE/CCI. "Excel site; helpful staff." 15 May-15 Sep. € 17.60 2010*

"Satellite navigation makes touring much easier"

Remember most sat navs don't know if you're towing or in a larger vehicle – always use yours alongside maps and site directions.

MIRANDE *8F2* (10km NW Rural) *43.56500, 0.31972* **Camping Château Le Haget, Route de Mielan, 32320 Montesquiou [05 62 70 95 80; fax 05 62 70 94 83; info@lehaget.com; www.lehaget.com]** SW fr Mirande on N21 for 9km. At Renault g'ge turn R onto D16, then immed R onto D34 sp Montesquiou. Site on L in 11km. Rec do not use D943 fr Auch. Med, hdg/mkd pitch, pt sl, pt shd; htd wc (some cont); chem disp; shwrs inc; el pnts (10A) €4; lndtte; rest, snacks; bar; playgrnd; pool; games area; games rm; 60% statics; dogs €3; Eng spkn; adv bkg; quiet; cc acc; CKE/CCI. "Wooded site full of wildlife & flowers; lge pitches, but poss access problems for lge o'fits; excel rest." 1 May-30 Sep. € 20.00 (3 persons) 2011*

MIREPOIX (ARIEGE) *8F4* (1km E Rural) *43.08871, 1.88585* **Camping Les Nysades, Route de Limoux, 09500 Mirepoix [05 61 60 28 63; fax 05 61 68 89 48; campinglesnysades@orange.fr; www.camping-mirepoix-ariege.com]** E fr Pamiers on D119 to Mirepoix. Site well sp on D626. Med, hdg/mkd pitch, shd; wc; chem disp; shwrs; el pnts (6A) €3.50; shops 1km; pool; fishing 1km; tennis; some statics; dogs €2; quiet; red low ssn. "Lge pitches; gd san facs; interesting medieval town; mkt Mon; gd little site, walks along rv; Barrier open 0700-2300, if warden not on site he will collect fees later."♦ 16 Apri-31 Oct. € 15.00 2012*

MOISSAC *8E3* (1.5km S Rural) *44.09664, 1.08878* **Camping De L'Ile du Bidounet, St Benoît, 82200 Moissac [tel/fax 05 63 32 52 52; info@camping-moissac.com; www.camping-moissac.com]** Exit A62 at junc 9 at Castelsarrasin onto N113 dir Moissac, site sp. Or fr N on N113 cross Rv Tarn, turn L at 1st rndabt & foll camp sp, site on L by rv. NB Height restriction 3.05m for tunnel at ent & tight turn lge o'fits. Med, hdg/mkd pitch, some hdstg, shd; wc (some cont); chem disp; mv service pnt; baby facs; shwrs inc; el pnts (6A) €3.10; gas 2km; lndtte; shop, rest & snacks 2km; tradsmn; bar; BBQ; playgrnd; pool (high ssn); fishing; watersports; boat & canoe hire; cycle hire; wifi; entmnt; 10% statics; dogs €1.50; phone; Eng spkn; adv bkg; quiet; ccard acc; red low ssn/long stay; CKE/CCI. "Excel rvside site in lovely area; extra for twin-axles; pitches tight lge o'fits; helpful staff; basic, clean san facs; conv lovely town & abbey; gd fishing; walking/cycling; vg cycle track by canal." ♦ 1 Apr-30 Sep. € 15.80 2012*

See advertisement

MOLIERES (TARN ET GARONNE) *8E3* (1.5km E Rural) *44.18480, 1.38790* **Camping Domaine des Merlanes, 82220 Molières [05 63 67 64 05; fax 05 63 24 28 96; simone@domaine-de-merlanes.com; www.domaine-de-merlanes.com]** Fr N on N20, exit on D20 to Montpezat-de-Quercy & Molières; sp in vill. Sm, terr, pt shd; wc; chem disp; baby facs; shwrs; el pnts (6A) inc; tradsmn; rest; bar; playgrnd; htd pool; 10% statics; dogs €3; poss cr; Eng spkn; quiet; red low ssn; ccard acc; CKE/CCI. "Pleasant, Dutch owners; clean, well-kept site; excel children's facs; adv bkg ess high ssn; excel." 25 Apr-5 Sep. € 32.80 2009*

MONFORT *8E3* (100m N Urban) *43.79628, 0.82315* **Camp Municipal de Monfort, 32120 Monfort [tel/fax 05 62 06 83 26 (Mairie); mairiemonfort@orange.fr]** SE fr Fleurance on D654 to Monfort, then foll sp to 'Centre Ville' & camping sp. Town has narr rds so foll sp & v narr app rd. Sm, hdg pitch, pt sl, pt shd; wc; chem disp (wc); shwrs inc, el pnts (5A) €1.50; shop, rest & bar 200m; BBQ; playgrnd; no twin-axles; dogs €0.50; quiet; ccard not acc; CKE/CCI. "Well-kept, scenic, CL-type site on ramparts of attractive Bastide vill; pitch yourself, warden calls am & pm; ltd pitches big enough for c'van; long walk to waste disposal; excel; pitches well prepd and solid." 1 May-15 Oct. € 9.50 2013*

MONTCABRIER *7D3* (2km NE Rural) *44.54865, 1.08229* **Camping Le Moulin de Laborde, 46700 Montcabrier [05 65 24 62 06; fax 05 65 36 51 33; moulindelaborde@wanadoo.fr; www.moulindelaborde.com]** Fr Fumel take D673 NE & site 1km past Montcabrier on L. Med, hdg pitch, pt shd; wc; chem disp; baby facs; shwrs inc; el pnts (6A) €3; gas; lndtte; shop; tradsmn; rest, snacks; bar; playgrnd; pool; sm lake; games area; cycle hire; wifi; entmnt; TV rm; no dogs; phone; poss cr; Eng spkn; adv bkg; quiet, but some noise fr rd & local quarry; ccard not acc; red low ssn. "Pleasant, peaceful site; friendly owners; gd facs; gd rest; many attractions & activities nrby; vg." ♦ 22 Apr-8 Sep. € 23.70 2011*

"There aren't many sites open at this time of year"

If you're travelling outside peak season remember to call ahead to check site opening dates – even if the entry says 'open all year'.

MONTECH *8E3* (1km E Rural) *43.96608, 1.24003* **Camping de Montech (Formerly Camping Paradis), Chemin de la Pierre, 82700 Montech [05 63 31 14 29; fax 05 62 65 68 69; contact@camping-montech.fr; www.camping-montech.fr]** Exit A20 junc 65 Montauban Sud onto D928 dir Auch. In Montech turn R just bef canal, site well sp. Lge, hdg/mkd pitch, unshd; wc; chem disp; mv service pnt; shwrs inc; el pnts (16A) €4; lndtte; shop high ssn; rest, snacks; bar; BBQ; playgrnd; pool; lake fishing nr; games area; entmnt; 60% statics; dogs €2.80; extra for twin-axles; Eng spkn; adv bkg; CKE/CCI. "Gd cycle paths." 1 Apr-30 Oct. € 23.00 2014*

MONTESQUIOU see Mirande *8F2*

MONTESQUIOU *8F2* (350m W Rural) *43.57705, 0.29111* **Camping l'Anjou, L'Anjou 32320 Montesquiou [05 62 70 95 24; clemens.van-voorst@orange.fr; www.camping-anjou.com]** Campsite is bet Montesquiou & Bassoues on the D943. Site is well mkd. A sm lane leads to site ent. Sm, hdg pitch, mkd pitch, hdstg, pt sl, pt shd; wc; chem disp; mv service pnt; baby facs; shwr; el pnts (6A); lndtte (inc dryer); snack; bar; BBQ; playgrnd; mini farm; pool; paddling pool; games area; wifi; 50% statics; dogs; Eng spkn; adv bkg; CCI. "Excel." ♦ ltd 15 Apr-15 Oct. € 24.40 2014*

MONTESTRUC SUR GERS *8E3* (2km NE Rural) *43.79257, 0.64291* **Camping en Saubis (Daguzan), Route de Céran, 32390 Montestruc-sur-Gers [05 62 62 26 12; contact@chambresdhotesgers.com; www.chambresdhotesgers.com]** S fr Fleurance on N21; after Montestruc-sur-Gers (immed past level x-ing) turn L onto D240; then turn R onto D251 for 1.5km, take R fork. Farm ent on L in 500m with conifer drive, site on L 50m. Sm, shd; wc; chem disp (wc); shwrs inc; el pnts (6A) €2.50 (long cable poss req); shops 2km; BBQ; playgrnd; golf 4km; 2 statics; dogs; poss cr; quiet. "Gd CL-type site with gd facs; peaceful farm with pleasant walks; friendly farmer." 15 Apr-15 Oct. € 6.50 2010*

MONTFAUCON *7D3* (2km N Rural) *44.69197, 1.53480* **Kawan Village Domaine de la Faurie, 46240 Séniergues [05 65 21 14 36; fax 05 65 31 11 17; contact@camping-lafaurie.com; www.camping-lafaurie.com]** Fr N20 turn E onto D2 sp Montfaucon, or fr A20 exit junc 56. In 5km site sp. Rd to site (off D2) is 500m long, single-track with passing places & steep but passable. Well sp fr A20. Med, mkd pitch, pt sl, terr; pt shd; htd wc; chem disp; mv service pnt; baby facs; shwrs inc; el pnts (6-10A) €4.50-6.70; lndtte (inc dryer); shop; rest; playgrnd; htd pool; paddling pool; cycle hire; games area; wifi; TV rm; 30% statics; dogs €3; twin axles; Eng spkn; adv bkg; quiet; ccard acc; red low ssn. "Superb, pretty site with great views; quiet & peaceful; lge pitches; excel facs & rest; gd touring base; poss intermittent elec supply some pitches (2010); many walks; conv A20; award winning site." ♦ 5 Apr-30 Sep. € 39.80 (CChq acc) 2014*

See advertisement

MONTGAILLARD see Foix *8G3*

MONTGEARD see Villefranche de Lauragais *8F3*

MONTPEZAT DE QUERCY see Caussade *8E3*

⊞ **MONTREJEAU** *8F3* (1.5km N Rural) *43.09234, 0.55457* **Camping Midi-Pyrénées, Chemin de Loubet, 31210 Montréjeau [05 61 95 86 79; fax 05 61 95 90 67; camping-midi-pyrenees@wanadoo.fr; www.campingmidipyrenees.com]** Exit A64 junc 17 onto A645; in 500m at rndabt turn R onto D817 dir Montréjeau; in 3km turn R onto D34; in 800m (having passed Carrefour Supmkt) do not turn R onto D34 sp Cugeron, but in 50m turn R onto D34D (diff turn off curve to lane behind cemetry); in 200m turn L into Chemin de Loubet; site on R in 300m. Site well sp. Med, hdstg, pt sl, some terr, pt shd; htd wc; mv service pnt; shwrs inc; el pnts (6A) €3.20; rest, snacks; bar; playgrnd; htd pool; rv & lake 2km; wifi; entmnt; 70% statics; dogs €1; extra for twin-axles; quiet; CKE/CCI. "Gd site; excel views Pyrenees; gd welcome; gd modern san facs; excel infinity pool." € 12.00 2011*

MIDI-PYRÉNÉES

"That's changed – Should I let The Club know?"

If you find something on site that's different from the site entry, fill in a report and let us know. See www.caravanclub.co.uk/europereport.

MONTREJEAU *8F3* (7km S Rural) *43.02864, 0.57852* **Camping Es Pibous, Chemin de St Just, 31510 St Bertrand-de-Comminges [05 61 94 98 20 or 05 61 88 31 42; fax 05 61 95 63 83; contact@es-pibous.fr; www.es-pibous.fr]** Turn S fr D817 onto D825 sp Bagnères-de-Luchon & Espagne. Foll past 'Super U' to lge rndabt & turn R sp St Bertrand-de-Comminges/Valcabrère then at 1st traff lts turn R & foll sp for St Bertrand & site. Or exit A64 junc 17 onto A645 sp Bagnères-de-Luchon to lge rndabt, then as above. Med, hdg/mkd pitch, pt shd; htd wc; chem disp; mv service pnt; baby facs; shwrs inc; el pnts (6A) €3.70; gas; lndtte; shop; rest, bar 300m; playgrnd; pool; fishing, tennis 3km; TV; 20% statics; dogs; poss cr; adv bkg; quiet; ccard acc; red low ssn. "Peaceful, friendly site; pitches among trees; clean dated san facs, ltd low ssn; lndtte is owner's washing machine, not always avail (2010); gd touring area nr mountains; picturesque town in walking dist." ♦ 1 Mar-30 Sep. € 12.00 2010*

MONTREJEAU *8F3* (8km S Rural) *43.02898, 0.60859* **Camp Municipal Bords de Garonne, Chemin du Camping, 65370 Loures-Barousse [05 62 99 29 29 or 05 62 99 21 28 (Mairie)]** Exit A64 junc 17 onto A645 by-passing Montréjeau. Or fr Montréjeau take D825 sp Luchon & 'Espagne'. In 5km cont onto D33. Site on R in 3km, visible fr rd. Med, shd; htd wc (some cont); chem disp (wc); mv service pnt; shwrs; el pnts (10A) inc; shop 500m; rest, bar 400m; shops 500m; 80% statics; adv bkg; some Eng spkn; quiet but some rd noise; CKE/CCI. "Pleasant site; touring pitches on rvside; friendly, helpful staff; clean san facs; barrier clsd 12 noon Sat until Mon am low ssn, ring/visit Hotel de Ville nrby for barrier code; easy walk to vill; ideal as NH to/fr Spain." ♦ 15 Feb-15 Nov. € 11.50 2011*

MONTREJEAU *8F3* (1km W Rural) *43.08624, 0.55414* **Camping Essi Les Hortensias, Route de Tarbes, 31210 Montréjeau [05 61 95 74 43]** Fr St Gaudens on D817, R at foot of steep hill, sp 'Tarbes Poids Lourds' to avoid Montréjeau cent. Site on L in 1km. On W o'skirts of town, well sp on rd to Tarbes. Sm, pt shd; wc; chem disp; shwrs; el pnts (15A) inc; shops 1km; BBQ; pool 1km; playgrnd; some rd noise; ccard not acc; CKE/CCI. "Gd NH; no twin-axles." 1 Apr-31 Oct. € 11.50 2010*

MONTRICOUX *8E3* (500m W Rural) *44.07660, 1.61103* **FFCC Camping Le Clos Lalande, Route de Bioule, 82800 Montricoux [tel/fax 05 63 24 18 89; contact@camping-lecloslalande.com; www.camping-lecloslalande.com]** Fr A20 exit junc 59 to Caussade; fr Caussade take D964 to Montricoux, where site well sp. Med, hdg/mkd pitch, pt shd; wc; chem disp; mv service pnt; baby facs; shwrs inc; el pnts (6A) €3.60; Indtte; shop 1km; tradsmn; snacks; bar & 1km; BBQ; playgrnd; pool; rv & shgl beach 400m; fishing; watersports; tennis; cycle & canoe hire; games area; wifi; TV rm; 10% statics; dogs €2.50; phone; bus 400m; poss full; some Eng spkn; adv bkg (rec high ssn); CKE/CCI. "Peaceful, quiet, well-kept site by rv at mouth of Aveyron gorges; beautiful area, inc Bastide vills; great family site; friendly, helpful owners; mkt Weds; easy walk to town; highly rec." ♦ 29 Mar-28 Sep. € 33.00 2014*

NAGES see Lacaune *8E4*

NAJAC *8E4* (1.7km W Rural) *44.22011, 1.96985* **Camping Le Païsserou, 12270 Najac [05 65 29 73 96; fax 05 65 29 72 29; info@camping-le-paisserou.com; www.camping-le-paisserou.com]** Take D922 fr Villefranche-de-Rouergue. Turn R on D39 at La Fouillade to Najac. Site by rv, sp in vill. Or fr A20 exit junc 59 onto D926. At Caylus take D84 to Najac. All appr v steep. Med, hdg pitch, shd; wc; chem disp; shwrs inc; el pnts €3; Indtte; shops & rest in vill; tradsmn; snacks; bar; htd, covrd pool adj (free); tennis adj; some statics; dogs €1.50; phone; poss cr; Eng spkn; adv bkg; quiet; red low ssn; CKE/CCI. "Conv for Aveyron gorges; friendly owners; ltd facs low ssn; lovely vill; unrel opening low ssn, phone ahead; Site yourself if recep clsd, avail pitches listed." 30 Apr-1 Oct. € 23.00 2012*

NANT *10E1* (2km N Rural) *44.03578, 3.29008* **Camping Le Roc Qui Parle, Les Cuns, 12230 Nant [tel/fax 05 65 62 22 05; contact@camping-roc-qui-parle-aveyron.fr; www.camping-roc-qui-parle-aveyron.fr]** Fr Millau take D991E to site passing Val de Cantobre. Fr La Cavalerie take D999E to Nant & at T-junc on o'skts of Nant turn N; Millau & Les Cuns approx 2km; site on R. NB Steep decent into site. Med, hdg/mkd pitch, pt sl, pt shd; wc; serviced pitches; chem disp; mv service pnt; shwrs inc; el pnts (10A) €3.30; Indtte; shop; BBQ; playgrnd; rv sw & fishing on site; wifi; dogs free; adv bkg; quiet; no ccard acc; CKE/CCI. "Excel, well-run site in magnificent surroundings; lge pitches with views; warm welcome, friendly & helpful; excel facs; rv walk; rec." ♦ ltd 1 Apr-30 Sep. € 25.20 2014*

NANT *10E1* (4km N Rural) *44.04550, 3.30170* **RCN Camping Le Val de Cantobre, Domaine de Vellas, 12230 Nant [05 65 58 43 00 or 06 80 44 40 63 (mob); fax 05 65 62 10 36; cantobre@rcn.fr; www.rcn-valdecantobre.fr]** Exit A75 junc 47 (La Cavalerie/Nant); foll sp D999 E dir La Cavalerie/Nant for 12 km. At Nant at T-junc turn L onto D991 sp Val de Cantobre. Site on R in 4km. NB Steep access rd, care req. Rec park in parking area at ent to site & walk down drive to recep. Lge, mkd pitch, hdstg, terr, pt shd; wc (some cont); chem disp; mv service pnt; baby facs; shwrs inc; el pnts (6A) inc; gas; Indtte (inc dryer); shop; rest, snacks; bar; BBQ; playgrnd; htd pool; paddling pool; waterslide; tennis; cycle hire; games area; games rm; wifi; entmnt; games/TV rm; some tour op statics & tents; dogs €7; no c'vans/m'vans over 7m high ssn; no twin-axles; poss cr; Eng spkn; adv bkg ess; quiet; ccard acc; red low ssn. "Busy, popular, Dutch-owned site; in gd position - views fr most pitches; helpful, welcoming staff; clean, modern san facs but long walk fr some pitches; steep site rds & many steps; mkt Tue (July/Aug only); excel." ♦ 6 Apr-29 Sep. € 45.65 (CChq acc) 2011*

See advert on next page

NANT *10E1* (7km E Rural) *44.01117, 3.20457* **Camping La Dourbie, Route de Nant, 12230 Saint-Jean-du-Bruel, Aveyron [05 65 46 06 40; fax 05 65 46 06 50; info@camping-la-dourbie.com; www.camping-la-dourbie.com]** Fr A75 take exit 47, twrds La cavalerie, Nat, St-Eulalie-de-Cernon. At rndabt take 3rd exit onto D999, go thro next rndabt, turn R cont D999 to site. Med, hdg pitch, pt shd; wc; shwrs; el pnts (6,10, 16A) €2.-€4; mv service pnt; chem disp; Indtte; rest; bar; BBQ; dogs - 1 per pitch, leashed; htd pool; spa; playgrnd; wifi; canoeing; bungee jumping; paragliding; "Excel site, such a lot to do and see." ♦ 12 Apr-29 Sept. € 19.00 2013*

NANT *10E1* (1km S Rural) *44.01698, 3.30125* **Camping Les Deux Vallées, 12230 Nant [05 65 62 26 89 or 05 65 62 10 40; fax 05 65 62 17 23; www.lesdeuxvallees.com]** Exit A75 junc 47 onto D999 for 14km to Nant; site sp. Med, mkd pitch, pt shd; wc (some cont); own san; chem disp; mv service pnt; some serviced pitches; shwrs inc; el pnts (6A) €2 (poss rev pol); Indtte; tradsmn; rest, snacks; bar; shop 1km; pool 500m; playgrnd; entmnt; rv fishing; TV; dogs €1; phone; quiet; adv bkg; CKE/CCI. "Peaceful, well-kept, scenic site; friendly; clean, modern san facs; 15 mins walk fr vill cent; gd walking; rec." ♦ 1 Apr-28 Oct. € 25.00 2012*

NANT *10E1* (2.5km S Rural) *44.01319, 3.32032* **Camping Castelnau (Gely), 12230 Nant [05 65 62 25 15; isaetdom@aliceadsl.fr; www.campingcastelnau.free.fr]** Fr Nant take D999 E twds Le Vigan; site is sp on L in 2.5km. Last 200m rough rd. Sm, pt shd; wc; chem disp (wc); shwrs inc; el pnts (11A) €2.50 (poss long lead req); Indtte; shop, rest, snacks, bar 2.5km; playgrnd; pool 3km; sw & fishing nr; some statics; dogs free; poss cr; adv bkg; quiet; ccard not acc; CKE/CCI. "Spacious CL-type site; lovely location; clean facs; conv Roquefort." ♦ 1 Apr-31 Oct. € 8.00 2009*

NANT *10E1* (500m SW Rural) *44.02105, 3.29390* **Camping Les Vernèdes, Route St Martin-Le Bourg, 12230 Nant [05 65 62 15 19]** Site sp fr vill cent. Sm, shd; wc (some cont); chem disp; shwrs inc; el pnts (10A) inc (long lead req); gas 500m; Indtte; BBQ; playgrnd; dogs; Eng spkn; adv bkg; quiet; CKE/CCI. "Orchard site set in beautiful location; pleasant stroll to Nant cent; gd trout rest adj; gd touring base; v helpful owners; excel and great site to stay on." 1 Mar-31 Oct. € 11.50 2014*

NAUCELLE *8E4* (1km S Rural) *44.18818, 2.34825* **FLOWER Camping du Lac de Bonnefon (FFCC), L'Etang de Bonnefon, 12800 Naucelle [05 65 69 33 20; fax 05 65 69 33 20; camping-du-lac-de-bonnefon@wanadoo.fr; www.camping-du-lac-de-bonnefon.com / www.flowercampings.com]** N fr Carmaux turn L off N88 Albi-Rodez rd at Naucelle Gare onto D997, sp Naucelle Centre. Site sp in 2km. Med, mkd pitch, pt sl, pt shd; htd wc; chem disp; mv service pnt; shwrs inc; el pnts (6A) €4.20; Indtte; shop 1.5km; rest, snacks; bar, playgrnd; htd pool; wifi; TV; many statics; dogs €2.50; poss cr; quiet; red low ssn; CKE/CCI. "Pleasant, clean site adj lge fishing lake; gd san facs; conv Sauveterre-de-Rouergue." ♦ 1 Apr-15 Oct. € 19.70 2009*

ORINCLES see Bagneres de Bigorre *8F2*

OUST *8G3* (2km N Rural) *42.89343, 1.21381* **Camp Municipal La Claire, Rue La Palere, 09140 Soueix-Rogalle [05 61 66 84 88; campinglaclaire@orange.fr; http://haut-couserans.ingenie.fr]** S fr St Girons on D618; in 13km, just bef rndabt, turn R onto D32 (thro rock arch) to Soueix-Rogalle; turn L at vill sq; site in 100m, just after x-ing rv bdge. NB Narr ent, rec park in sq & walk down first. Sm, pt shd; htd wc (some cont); shwrs inc; el pnts (10A) €3 (poss long lead req); Indtte; shop 1.5km; rest 200m; playgrnd; paddling pool; fishing; 10% statics; dogs €1; phone; quiet; CKE/CCI. "Pleasant, well-maintained, rvside site; lge pitches; basic san facs." 1 Mar-31 Oct. € 10.00 2011*

OUST *8G3* (9km SE Rural) *42.81105, 1.25558* **Camping Le Montagnou, Route de Guzet, 09140 Le Trein-d'Ustou [05 61 66 94 97; campinglemontagnou@wanadoo.fr; www.lemontagnou.co.uk]** Fr St Girons S on D618 & D3 to Oust. Fr Oust SE on D3 & D8 thro Seix & at Pont de la Taule turn L onto D8 twd Le Trein-d'Ustou. Site on L just bef vill, sp. Med, hdg pitch, pt shd; htd wc; chem disp; shwrs inc; el pnts (6-10A) €3.50-5.50; Indry rm; mini shop, tradsmn & snacks (Jul/Aug); rest nr; BBQ; playgrnd; fishing; rv sw 3km; tennis; skiing 9km; wifi; 30% statics; dogs €1.50; phone; poss cr; adv bkg; quiet; ccard acc; red low ssn; CKE/CCI. "Well-situated, well-run rvside site; mountain views; gd sized pitches; friendly British owners; gd walking; highly rec." ♦ 1 Mar-1 Dec. € 16.20 2010*

OUST *8G3* (600m S Rural) *42.87042, 1.21947* **Camping Les Quatre Saisons, Route d'Aulus-les-Bains, 09140 Oust [05 61 96 55 55; camping.ariege@gmail.com; www.camping4saisons.com]** Take D618 S fr St Girons; then D3 to Oust; on N o'skts of town turn L (sp Aulus) onto D32; in 1km site on R nr Rv Garbet. Med, hdg pitch, pt shd; htd wc; chem disp; shwrs inc; el pnts (5-10A) €2.80-5.60; Indtte; shop 200m; bar; playgrnd; pool; games area; TV; 25% statics; dogs €1.50; phone; Eng spkn; adv bkg rec; quiet; ccard acc; red low ssn; CKE/CCI. "In beautiful, unspoilt area; friendly site; footpath to vill; excel." 7 Mar-30 Sep. € 17.50 2012*

⊞ **OUST** *8G3* (2.5km S Rural) *42.87085, 1.20663* **Camping Le Haut Salat, La Campagne-d'en Bas, 09140 Seix [05 61 66 81 78 or 06 82 16 00 36; info@camping-haut-salat.com; www.camping-haut-salat.com]** Take D618 S fr St Girons, at Oust take D3 twds Seix. Site well sp just N of vill nr rv. Med, hdg/mkd pitch, pt shd; htd wc; baby facs; shwrs inc; el pnts (5-10A) €2 (long lead req); lndtte (inc dryer); shops 500m; bar; BBQ; htd pool; fishing; games area; games rm; wifi; entmnt; TV; 85% statics; dogs free; clsd 24 Dec-1 Jan; adv bkg; quiet; CKE/CCI. "Gd facs; gd walking area; pitches poss not open winter, phone ahead." € 16.50 2011*

PAMIERS *8F3* (800m N Rural) *43.12490, 1.60195* **Kawan Village L'Apamée, Route de St Girons, 09100 Pamiers [tel/fax 05 61 60 06 89; campingapamee@orange.fr; http://lapamee.com]** Fr N on D820 at traff lts turn R & cross narr bdge over Rv Ariège, Pont du Jeu-du-Mail, site sp. Med, mkd pitch, some hdstg, shd; htd wc; chem disp; mv service pnt; baby facs; shwrs inc; el pnts (10A) inc; lndtte (inc dryer); shop 800m; tradsmn; rest, snacks; bar; BBQ; playgrnd; htd pool; rv fishing; tennis 100m; games area; games rm; cycle hire; wifi; TV rm; 5% statics; dogs €2; phone; o'night area for m'vans; adv bkg; quiet but rd noise; red low ssn; CKE/CCI. "Clean, modern facs; helpful staff; poss unkempt & ltd facs early ssn; excel." ♦ 1 Apr-15 Nov. € 24.00 (CChq acc) 2010*

PAMPELONNE *8E4* (2km NE Rural) *44.12685, 2.25681* **Camping Thuriès, 81190 Pampelonne [05 63 76 44 01; fax 05 63 76 92 78; campthuries@wanadoo.fr]** N fr Carmaux on N88 turn L onto D78 sp Pampelonne. Site sp & 2km fr town over narr bdge; steep, winding rd. Or S fr Rodez on N88 turn R onto D17 sp Pampelonne. Site bef rv bdge on L. Sm, mkd pitch, shd; htd wc; chem disp; mv service pnt; shwrs inc; el pnts (6A) inc; lndtte; shop & 3km; tradsmn; rest, snacks 3km; dogs; phone; poss cr; Eng spkn; quiet; CKE/CCI. "Pleasant site; conv Albi & Rodez." 15 Jun-1 Sep. € 15.70 2009*

⊞ **PAYRAC** *7D3* (1km N Rural) *44.80574, 1.47479* **Camping Panoramic, Route de Loupiac, 46350 Payrac-en-Quercy [05 65 37 98 45; fax 05 65 37 91 65; info@campingpanoramic.com; www.campingpanoramic.com]** N fr Payrac on D820, turn L onto D147 sp Loupiac (200m after 'end of village' sp), site 300m on R. Sm, pt sl, hdstg, pt shd; htd wc; chem disp; baby facs; shwrs inc; el pnts (5A) €3 (poss rev pol); gas; lndtte; shop 1km; tradsmn; rest high ssn; snacks; bar; BBQ; playgrnd; pool 400m; rv sw 5km; canoe hire; cycle hire; wifi; entmnt; TV rm; 10% statics; phone; poss cr; Eng spkn; adv bkg; quiet; CKE/CCI. "Well-run, clean site; OK san facs - poss inadequate if site full; poss muddy in bad weather but hdstg avail; friendly, helpful Dutch owner; gd walking; excel winter NH." ♦ € 11.00 2013*

PAYRAC *7D3* (6km N Rural) *44.82182, 1.46801* **Camping Chez Francis (Gatignol), 46350 Loupiac [05 65 37 64 87; francis.gatignol@wanadoo.fr; http://chez.francis.pagesperso-orange.fr]** Fr N or S on D820, sp 'A la Ferme'. Sm, sl, pt shd; wc; chem disp (wc); shwrs inc; el pnts (4A) €2 (long lead poss req); lndtte; shops 2km; tradsmn; bar; playgrnd; pool; fishing; boating; tennis; golf 3km; TV; some statics; sm dogs; poss cr; Eng spkn; adv bkg; quiet. "Pleasant site; friendly owner; mkd ent for c'vans poss diff long o'fits - rec use ent for tents if gd power/weight ratio." 1 May-31 Oct. € 11.00 2010*

PAYRAC *7D3* (6km N Rural) *44.83527, 1.46008* **Camping Les Hirondelles, Al Pech, 46350 Loupiac [05 65 37 66 25; fax 05 65 37 66 65; camp.les-hirondelles@orange.fr; www.les-hirondelles.com]** Fr Souillac foll D820 for about 12km. Site on R bef dual c'way. Sm, hdg/mkd pitch, pt sl, shd; htd wc; chem disp; baby facs; shwrs inc; el pnts (6A) inc (poss rev pol); gas; lndtte (inc dryer); shop; tradsmn; rest, snacks; bar; playgrnd; htd pool; paddling pool; cycle hire; games area; wifi; entmnt; TV; 40% statics; dogs €2.50; phone; poss cr w/end; Eng spkn; adv bkg; quiet; CKE/CCI. "Vg friendly, helpful owners; clean site; gd views fr some pitches; excel." ♦ 1 Apr-15 Sep. € 23.20 2012*

PAYRAC *7D3* (500m S Rural) *44.78936, 1.47299* **FLOWER Camping Les Pins, 46350 Payrac-en-Quercy [05 65 37 96 32; fax 05 65 37 91 08; info@les-pins-camping.com; www.les-pins-camping.com / www.flowercampings.com]** Exit A20 junc 55 onto D804 dir Souillac; in 2.4km at next rndbt take 3rd exit onto D820; cont for 16km thro Payrac; site on R in 800m - tight R-hand turn. Med, hdg/mkd pitch, hdstg, terr, pt shd; wc; chem disp; mv service pnt; serviced pitches; shwrs inc; el pnts (10A) inc; gas 1km; lndtte; shop; rest, snacks; bar; BBQ; playgrnd; 2 htd pools; waterslide; paddling pool; tennis; wifi; entmnt; games/TV rm; many statics; dogs €3; no c'vans/m'vans over 7m high ssn; some rd & disco noise; adv bkg; Eng spkn; rd noise; ccard acc; red low ssn/long stay; CKE/CCI. "Lovely, well-kept site in interesting area; gd sized pitches; welcoming, friendly owners; clean san facs; vg pool; many pitches shd with high firs; trees make access to some pitches diff; gd for young children; peaceful site low ssn; boggy in wet." ♦ 18 Apr-7 Sep. € 31.00 SBS - D25 2011*

PAYRAC *7D3* (5km NW Rural) *44.80805, 1.41027* **Camping Les Grands Chênes (Naturist), Le Peyronnet, 46350 Lamothe-Fénelon [tel/fax 05 65 41 68 79; camping@les-grands-chenes.com; www.les-grands-chenes.com]** Fr N exit A20 junc 55 onto D820 dir Payrac; turn R onto minor rd to Lamothe-Fénelon; site on D12, sp in vill. Or fr N on D820 turn R in Payrac onto D36 (best rte). Fr S exit junc 56 onto D801, then turn R onto D820 to Payrac. Access rds narr fr Payrac. Sm, mkd pitch, pt sl, pt shd; wc; chem disp; baby facs; shwrs inc; el pnts (6A) €3 (long lead poss req); lndtte; shop; tradsmn; rest 6km; snacks; bar; playgrnd; pool; games area; canoe hire, golf, horseriding nrby; 2% statics; dogs €1.50; poss cr; little Eng spkn; adv bkg; quiet; INF card req; red low ssn. "Charming, peaceful site in woodland; lovely location; attractive, unusual architecture on site; friendly staff; excel san facs; cycling rte on old rlwy; close to Rv Dordogne; excel." ♦ ltd 16 May-12 Sep. € 21.80 2009*

PEYRELEAU *10E1* (1km N Rural) *44.19111, 3.20486* **Camping Les Peupliers, 48150 Le Rozier [05 65 62 60 85 or 06 74 37 79 72 (mob); peupliers12@orange.fr; www.camping-lespeupliers.com]** Fr Millau take D809 N to Aguessac, turn R onto D907 to Le Rozier. Cross bdge over Rv Tarn onto D996 & take rd on R to site; sp. Sm, mkd pitch, pt shd; wc; chem disp; shwrs inc; el pnts (6A) €2.50; lndry rm; shop, rest, bar 300m; tradsmn; snacks; BBQ; playgrnd; wifi; dogs free; bus 300m; Eng spkn; adv bkg rec high ssn; quiet; CKE/CCI. "Lovely, friendly, little site on Rv Jonte; gd base for walking etc." € 9.00 2009*

PEYRELEAU *10E1* (1km W Rural) *44.19470, 3.20210* **Camping Saint Pal, Route des Gorges du Tarn, 12720 Mostuéjouls [tel/fax 05 65 62 64 46 or 05 65 58 79 82 (LS); saintpal@orange.fr; www.campingsaintpal.com]** Exit A75 exit junc 44.1 onto D29 to Aguessac then L onto D907 to Mostuéjouls. Or fr Millau take D809 N to Aguessac, turn R onto D907 to Mostuéjouls. Site in 10km 500m fr Rozier bdge. Med, hdg/mkd pitch, shd; wc (some cont); chem disp; mv service pnt; baby facs; fam bthrm; shwrs; el pnts (6A) €3.20; gas; lndtte; shop & 1km; tradsmn; snacks, bar high ssn; BBQ; playgrnd; pool; rv sw & beach adj; games rm; organised walks; TV; 20% statics; dogs €2; phone; poss cr; Eng spkn; adv bkg; quiet; ccard acc; red low ssn/CKE/CCI. "Excel site & facs; gd walks, canoeing, fishing & birdwatching, beavers on rv bank opp; poss diff for lge o'fits." ♦ 1 May-30 Sep. € 27.50 2012*

PEYRELEAU *10E1* (1.2km NW Rural) *44.19810, 3.19442* **FFCC Camping Les Bords du Tarn, 12720 Mostuéjouls [05 65 62 62 94; lesbordsdutarn@orange.fr; www.campinglesbordsdutarn.com]** Exit A75 junc 44.1 onto D29 to Aguessac; turn L onto D907 dir Le Rozier & Peyreleau; site on R 1km bef Le Rozier. NB Do not use exit 44 fr A75 (as Sat Nav might instruct). Med, mkd pitch, pt sl, pt shd; wc; chem disp; baby facs; shwrs inc; el pnts (10A) €3.50; lndtte; sm shop & 1.2km; rest & 1.2km; snacks; bar; BBQ (charcoal/gas); playgrnd; htd pool; rv sw adj, pebble beach; canoe hire; climbing; paragliding; cycling; fishing; tennis; games rm; ltd wifi; entmnt; 10% statics; dogs €2; phone; poss cr; Eng spkn; adv bkg; quiet; ccard acc; red low ssn; CKE/CCI. "Site in beautiful area by rv; some v lge pitches; gd for rv sports; modern san facs; gd walking; conv Gorges du Tarn & Gorges de la Jonte; excel ." ♦ ltd 7 May-12 Sep. € 39.80 2014*

PIERREFORT *7C4* (7km SW Rural) *44.85405, 2.77060* **FLOWER Camping La Source Aveyron, Presqu'ile de Laussac, 12600 Thérondels [05 65 66 27 10; fax 05 65 66 21 00; info@camping-la-source.com; www.camping-la-source.com / www.flowercampings.com]** Fr A75 at St Flour, take D921 to Les Ternes, then D990 thro Pierrefort. Approx 2km after Pierrefort, turn L onto D34. Go thro Paulhenc, site on L after approx 7km. Med, mkd pitch, terr, pt shd; wc; chem disp; mv service pnt; baby facs; shwrs inc; el pnts (6A) inc; gas; lndtte (inc dryer); shop; tradsmn; rest, snacks; bar; playgrnd; htd pool; paddling pool; waterslide; lake sw & beach adj; fishing; watersports; boat hire; tennis; games area; wifi; entmnt; TV; dogs €1.70; 35% statics; quiet; adv bkg rec high ssn; ccard acc; red low ssn/long stay; CKE/CCI. "Excel lakeside site; poss diff lge o'fits due lge trees." ♦ 27 May-9 Sep. € 28.50 (CChq acc) 2011*

PLAISANCE *8F2* (100m Urban) *43.92511, 2.54616* **Camping Municipal Le Moulin De L'Horte, 12550 Plaisance [05 65 99 72 07 or 05 65 99 75 07; mairie.plaisance12@laposte.net; www.plaisance12.com/camping htm]** Fr D999 Albi-Millau, exit at D127 to Plaisance. R onto D77. Site on R after bdge. Sm, mkd pitch, pt shd; wc; shwrs inc; el pnts (6A); gas; lndtte (inc dryer); BBQ; pool; sw adj; games rm; tv rm; wifi; 10% statics; dogs; phone; twin axles; Eng spkn; adv bkg; quiet. " Vg, great quiet site with rv adj to swim in; excel rest & café nrby 0.2km; sm town but v pleasant." 15 Jun-15 Sep. € 12.00 2014*

PLAISANCE (GERS) *8F2* (500m E Rural) *43.60805, 0.05370* **Camping de l'Arros, Allée de Ormeaux, 32160 Plaisance [05 62 69 30 28; infos@plaisance-evasion.com; www.plaisance-evasion.com]** N fr Tarbes on D935, approx 25 km N of Maubourguet turn R onto D946 to Plaisance. Foll sp to site on o'skts of town. Sm, mkd pitch, some hdstg, pt sl, pt shd; wc (some cont); chem disp; baby facs; shwrs inc; el pnts (6A) inc; lndtte (inc dryer); shops 500m; tradsmn; rest, snacks; bar; BBQ (gas only); playgrnd; pool; cycle hire; games rm; wifi; entmnt; TV; 40% statics; dogs €2; phone; adv bkg ess high ssn; red low ssn; ccard acc; CKE/CCI. "Close to rv; canoes avail." ♦ ltd 1 Apr-30 Sep. € 22.20 2010*

PONT DE SALARS *7D4* (1.5km N Rural) *44.29150, 2.72571* **Parc Camping du Lac, 12290 Pont-de-Salars [05 65 46 84 86; fax 05 65 46 60 39; camping.du.lac@wanadoo.fr; www.camping-du-lac.fr.st]** Fr Rodez on D911 La Primaube-Millau rd, turn L bef ent Pont-de-Salars. Site sp. Lge, mkd pitch, pt sl, terr, pt shd; wc (some cont); chem disp; baby facs; shwrs inc; el pnts (3-6A) €2.50-3.50; gas; lndtte; shop & 1km; tradsmn; rest, snacks; bar; BBQ; playgrnd; pool; paddling pool; lake sw; sailing; fishing; entmnt; TV; 90% statics; no dogs; phone; poss cr; adv bkg; noisy nr entmnt area; ccard acc; red low ssn. "Beautiful situation; poor for c'vans, OK m'vans; diff lge o'fits; blocks req; site poss unclean end of ssn." ♦ ltd 1 Jun-30 Sep. € 17.00 2009*

PONT DE SALARS *7D4* (4km N Rural) *44.30471, 2.73526* **FLOWER Camping Les Terrasses du Lac, Route du Vibal, 12290 Pont-de-Salars [05 65 46 88 18 or 06 72 89 84 34 (mob); fax 05 65 46 85 38; campinglesterrasses@orange.fr; www.campinglesterrasses.com / www.flowercampings.com]** Fr Rodez S on N2088 to La Primaube. Turn L in La Primaube onto D911 for Pont-de-Salars. Turn L onto D523 by timberyard to Le Vibal & foll sp to site approx 4km fr vill cent. Or fr A75 exit junc 44.1 dir Pont-de-Salars, turn R onto D523 then as above. Lge, hdg pitch, terr, pt shd; wc; chem disp; mv service pnt; some serviced pitches; baby facs; shwrs inc; el pnts (6A) €4; gas; lndtte (inc dryer); shop; tradsmn; rest, snacks; bar; BBQ; playgrnd; htd pool; paddling pool; sand beach & lake sw adj; boating; fishing; games area; games rm; wifi; entmnt; TV; 30% statics; dogs €2; phone; Eng spkn; adv bkg; quiet; ccard acc; red low ssn/long stay; CKE/CCI. "Well laid-out site o'looking lake; gd touring base; vg." ♦ 1 Apr-30 Sep. € 23.50 2010*

PONT DE SALARS *7D4* (7km SE Rural) *44.21420, 2.76660* **Camping Le Caussanel, Lac de Pareloup, 12290 Canet-de-Salars [05 65 46 85 19; fax 05 65 46 89 85; info@lecaussanel.com; www.lecaussanel.com / www.les-castels.com]** Exit A75 junc 44.1 onto D911 dir Pont-de-Salars, then D993 Salles-Curan & D538 Canet-de-Salars, dir Lac de Pareloup. In 6km fork R to Le Caussanel: in 100m fork L to site. Fr N88 exit at La Primaube then D911 to Pont-de-Salars, then as above. Lge, mkd pitch, hdstg, pt sl, terr, pt shd; wc; mv service pnt; chem disp; baby facs; shwrs inc; el pnts (5A) inc; lndtte (inc dryer) shop or 10km; tradsmn; rest, snacks; bar; BBQ; playgrnd; htd pool; paddling pool; waterslide; fishing; windsurfing & sailing; lake fishing; tennis; boat & cycle hire; games rm; wifi; entmnt; 20% statics; dogs €3.90; Eng spkn; adv bkg; quiet; red low ssn; CKE/CCI. "Beautiful situation, views over lake; friendly owner; vg." ♦ 23 May-17 Sep. € 33.00 (CChq acc) 2009*

MIDI-PYRÉNÉES

PONT DE SALARS *7D4* (8km S Rural) *44.21500, 2.77777* **Camping Soleil Levant, Lac de Pareloup, 12290 Canet-de-Salars [05 65 46 03 65; contact@camping-soleil-levant.com; www.camping-soleil-levant.com]** Exit A75 junc 44.1 onto D911 to Pont-de-Salars, then S on D993 dir Salles-Curan. Site in 8km bef bdge on L. Lge, mkd pitch, terr, pt sl, pt shd; htd wc (some cont); chem disp; baby facs; fam bthrm; shwrs inc; el pnts (6A) inc; gas; Indtte (inc dryer); shop 4km; tradsmn; snacks; bar; BBQ; playgrnd; lake sw & sand/shgl beach adj; fishing; watersports; tennis; games area; games rm; wifi; entmnt; TV rm; 10% statics; dogs €2; Eng spkn; adv bkg; quiet; ccard acc; red low ssn/CKE/CCI. "Lovely lakeside site; excel san facs." ♦ 1 May-30 Sep. € 25.00 2011*

PUY L'EVEQUE *7D3* (2.5km S Rural) *44.47780, 1.14214* **FFCC Village-Camping Les Vignes, Le Méoure, Le Cayrou, 46700 Puy-l'Evêque [tel/fax 05 65 30 81 72; contact@camping-lesvignes.fr; www.camping-lesvignes.fr]** App fr E on D911 dir Villeneuve-sur-Lot, just bef ent Puy-l'Evêque turn L, foll sp for 3km. Site adj Rv Lot. Avoid town cent while towing. Med, shd; wc; baby facs; shwrs; el pnts; (10A) €2.90; gas; Indtte; shops 3km; tradsmn; snacks; bar; playgrnd; pool; tennis; games area; fishing; cycle hire; entmnt high ssn; TV; dogs €1.50; quiet; red over 55s/low ssn. "Lovely, peaceful site in beautiful countryside; well-kept; warm welcome, friendly owners; gd san facs." 1 Apr-30 Sep. € 18.00 2012*

"We must tell The Club about that great site we found"

Get your site reports in by mid-August and we'll do our best to get your updates into the next edition.

PUY L'EVEQUE *7D3* (6km W Rural) *44.49636, 1.08220* **Club de Vacances Duravel, Route de Vire, 46700 Duravel [05 65 24 65 06; fax 05 65 24 64 96; info@clubdevacances.eu; www.clubdevacances.eu]** Fr D811 Puy-l'Evêque to Fumel rd at Duravel town cent, opp Mairie turn S onto D58 sp Vire-sur-Lot. Site in 2.5km. Lge, hdg/mkd pitch, pt sl, pt shd; wc (some cont); chem disp; mv service pnt; shwrs inc; el pnts (10A) €4; gas; Indtte (inc dryer); shop; tradsmn; rest, snacks; bar; playgrnd; 2 pools (1 htd); paddling pool; waterslide; beach nr; tennis; games area; canoeing; fishing; cycle hire; wifi; entmnt; 12% statics; dogs; poss cr; Eng spkn; adv bkg; quiet; 10% red low ssn; ccard acc; CKE/CCI. "Vg, lively site in lovely situation by rv; friendly staff; excel facs; lovely pools; entmnt in Dutch; all sps on site in Dutch - enquire at recep for info in Eng." ♦ ltd 24 Apr-30 Sep. € 26.50 2010*

PUYSSEGUR *8E3* (200m N Rural) *43.75064, 1.06065* **FFCC Camping Namasté, 31480 Puysségur [tel/fax 05 61 85 77 84; camping.namaste@free.fr; http://camping.namaste.free.fr]** Fr Toulouse NW on N224/D1 sp Cadours; at Puysségur in 30km foll Camping Namasté sp. (Puysségur is 1km NE of Cadours). Sm, pt shd; wc; baby facs; shwrs; sauna; el pnts (4-10A) €3-5; Indtte; shop; rest, snacks; bar; BBQ; playgrnd; pool; paddling pool; fishing; cycle hire; games area; games rm; wifi; entmnt; some statics; dogs €1.50; quiet; red low ssn. ♦ 1 May - 15 Oct. € 40.50 2014*

RABASTENS *8E3* (2km NW Rural) *43.83090, 1.69805* **Camp Municipal des Auzerals, Route de Grazac, 81800 Rabastens [05 63 33 70 36 or 06 23 81 85 69 (mob); fax 05 63 33 64 05; mairie.rabastens@libertysurf.fr]** Exit A68 junc 7 onto D12. In Rabastens town cent foll sp dir Grazac, site sp. Sm, hdg/mkd pitch, pt sl, terr, pt shd; wc (mainly cont); chem disp; shwrs inc; el pnts (10A) inc; Indtte; shop 2km; rest 2km; playgrnd; pool adj high ssn; quiet; adv bkg ess high ssn; CKE/CCI. "Attractive lakeside site; facs old but clean; office 0900-1200 & 1500-1900, otherwise height barrier in place; conv m'way NH; highly rec; gd hedges around plots." 1 Apr-30 Sep. € 11.20 2014*

REALMONT *8E4* (2km SW Rural) *43.77092, 2.16336* **Camp Municipal La Batisse, Route Graulhet, 81120 Réalmont [05 63 55 50 41 or 05 63 45 50 68; fax 05 63 55 65 62; camping-realmont@wanadoo.fr; www.realmont.fr]** On D612 fr Albi heading S thro Réalmont. On exit Réalmont turn R on D631 where site sp. Site 1.5km on L on Rv Dadou. Sm, pt shd; wc; shwrs; el pnts (3A) inc; gas; shops, rest, snacks, bar 2km; playgrnd; rv adj; fishing; some statics; quiet. "Pleasant, peaceful, well-kept site in rv valley; friendly, pleasant warden; dated but clean san facs; nr Albi-Castres cycle rte; excel value; mkt Wed; gd." 1 Apr-30 Sep. € 11.50 2014*

REVEL *8F4* (500m E Urban) *43.45454, 2.01515* **Camp Municipal Le Moulin du Roy, Tuilerie de Chazottes, off Ave de Sorèze, 31250 Revel [05 61 83 32 47 or 05 62 18 71 40 (Mairie); mairie@mairie-revel.fr; www.tourisme-revel.com]** Fr Revel ring rd take D1/D85 dir Sorèze, site sp. Med, hdg pitch, pt shd; mv service pnt; shwrs inc; el pnts €320; shop 500m; supmkt 1km; playgrnd; htd pool adj; lake sw & beach 2.5km; tennis adj; dogs €0.90; phone; bus; Eng spkn; daytime heavy traff noise; red CKE/CCI. "Pleasant, immac site; helpful staff; Sat mkt; vg." 2 Jun-7 Sep. € 10.20 2014*

REVEL *8F4* (5.5km E Urban) *43.45446, 2.06953* **Camping St Martin, Les Vigariés, 81540 Sorèze [05 63 50 20 19; fax 05 63 73 28 99; campingsaintmartin@gmail.com; www.campingsaintmartin.com]** Fr Revel take D85 sp Sorèze; site sp on N side of vill; turn L at traff lts; site on R in 100m. Sm, hdg/mkd pitch, some hdstg, pt shd; wc; chem disp; mv service pnt; shwrs inc; el pnts (10A) €3.60; Indtte; sm shop & rest 500m; snacks; bar; BBQ; playgrnd; pool; lake sw 3km; tennis; games rm; wifi; entmnt; TV; 20% statics; dogs €1.50; quiet; CKE/CCI. "Vg, well-kept site; friendly staff; excel san facs; fascinating medieval town; nr Bassin de St Ferréol; excel mkt in Revel; rec; poss noisy at w/end." ♦ 1 Apr-30 Sep. € 30.80 2013*

RISCLE *8E2* (500m N Urban) *43.66324, -0.08180* **FFCC Camp Municipal Le Pont de l'Adour, Allée du Camping, 32400 Riscle [05 67 36 00 08; fax 05 62 69 72 45; camping.dupontdeladour@wanadoo.fr; www.camping-adour.new.fr]** On ent Riscle fr N on D935, site on L immed after x-ing Rv Adour. Med, hdg pitch, pt shd; wc (some cont); chem disp; mv service pnt; shwrs inc; el pnts (6A) inc; Indtte; shop; rest, snacks; pool adj; paddling pool; playgrnd; fishing; tennis; games area; entmnt; TV; dogs €1.50; quiet; red low ssn;CKE/CCI. "V quiet low ssn." ♦ 1 Apr-15 Oct. € 15.50 2010*

RIVIERE SUR TARN *10E1* (2km E Rural) *44.19100, 3.15675* **FLOWER Camping Le Peyrelade, Route des Gorges du Tarn, 12640 Rivière-sur-Tarn [05 65 62 62 54; fax 05 65 62 65 61; campingpeyrelade@orange.fr; www.campingpeyrelade.com / www.flowercampings.com]** Exit A75 junc 44.1 to Aguessac, then take D907 N thro Rivière-sur-Tarn to site in 2km. Fr Millau drive N on N9 to Aguessac, then onto D907 thro Rivière-sur-Tarn, & site sp on R. Lge, hdg/mkd pitch, terr, shd; wc; chem disp; mv service pnt; baby facs; shwrs inc; el pnts (6A) €4; gas; Indtte (inc dryer); shop; tradsmn; rest, snacks; bar; BBQ; cooking facs; playgrnd; htd pool; rv beach & sw adj; canoeing; games rm; cycle hire 100m; wifi; entmnt; TV; dogs €2; phone; bus; adv bkg; quiet; ccard acc; red low ssn;CKE/CCI. "Excel touring base in interesting area; rvside pitches extra charge." ♦ 16 May-12 Sep. € 27.00 2010*

"I need an on-site restaurant"

We do our best to make sure site information is correct, but it is always best to check any must-have facilities are still available or will be open during your visit.

RIVIERE SUR TARN *10E1* (2.5km E Rural) *44.20083, 3.15944* **Camping du Moulin de la Galinière, Boyne, 12640 Rivière-sur-Tarn [05 65 62 65 60 or 06 08 28 49 07 (mob); moulindelagaliniere@orange.fr; www.moulindelagaliniere.com]** Exit A75 junc 44.1 La Gamasse onto D29 & foll sp Gorges du Tarn. Site ent bef Boyne vill, other side of bdge to Camping Le Pont, bef R turn. Site on bank Rv Tarn. Med, pt shd; wc; baby facs; shwrs inc; el pnts (6A) €3; Indtte; shops adj; tradsmn; rest, snacks; playgrnd; shgl beach; rv sw & fishing; wifi; TV; dogs €1; quiet. "Excel, clean facs, poss tired low ssn; pleasant owners." 1 Apr-30 Sep. € 14.00 2010*

RIVIERE SUR TARN *10E1* (2.5km E Rural) *44.20319, 3.15806* **FFCC Camping Le Pont, Boyne, 12640 Rivière-sur-Tarn [05 65 62 61 12; nicolas.garlenq@orange.fr; www.campinglepont.com]** Fr Millau head N on N9, R after 7km onto D907 sp Gorges du Tarn, site in 9km on R on ent to vill. Sm, pt shd; wc (some cont); chem disp; mv service pnt; shwrs inc; el pnts (8A) €2.50; Indtte; shops, rest adj; playgrnd; sw pool 2km; rv sw & fishing adj; dogs €1; quiet;CKE/CCI. "Gd base for Tarn gorges; canoeing & climbing nrby; facs dated but clean; helpful owner; excel." 1 Apr-30 Sep. € 14.00 2012*

RIVIERE SUR TARN *10E1* (250m SE Rural) *44.18680, 3.13650* **Camping Le Papillon, Les Canals, 12640 La Cresse [tel/fax 05 65 59 08 42; info@campinglepapillon.com; www.campinglepapillon.com]** Fr N on A75 exit junc 44.1 onto D29 to Aguessac; then turn L onto D547/D907; in 3km turn R sp La Cresse on D187. Site sp. Rivière-sur-Tarn on W bank of rv, site on E bank; Rivière-sur-Tarn 2km by rd. Rec app fr S. Sm, hdg/mkd pitch, terr, shd, pt shd; htd wc; chem disp; baby facs; fam bthrm; shwrs inc; el pnts (10A) €3; gas; Indtte; ice; tradsmn; rest, snacks; bar; BBQ (not charcoal); playgrnd; rv sw 150m; TV; 5% statics; dogs €2; Eng spkn; adv bkg; quiet; red long stay/low ssn;CKE/CCI. "Pleasant site, amazing views; new helpful Dutch owner (2009); excel facs; rec." 25 Apr-12 Sep. € 18.50 2009*

RIVIERE SUR TARN *10E1* (400m SW Rural) *44.18530, 3.13060* **Camping Les Peupliers, Rue de la Combe, 12640 Rivière-sur-Tarn [05 65 59 85 17; fax 05 65 61 09 03; lespeupliers12640@orange.fr; www.campinglespeupliers.fr]** Heading N on N9 turn R dir Aguessac onto D907 twd Rivière-sur-Tarn. Site on R bef vill. Or fr A75 exit junc 44.1 sp Aguessac/Gorges du Tarn. In Aguessac, foll sp Rivière-sur-Tarn for 5km, site clearly sp. Med, hdg/mkd pitch, some hdstg, pt shd; wc (some cont); chem disp; mv service pnt; baby facs; fam bthrm; shwrs inc; el pt (6A) inc; gas; Indtte (inc dryer); shop 200m; tradsmn; rest; snacks, bar; BBQ; supmkt; playgrnd; htd pool; paddling pool; waterslide; rv sw & shgl beach adj; fishing; canoeing; watersports; horseriding; games area; wifi; entmnt; TV rm; tennis; some statics; dogs €3; Eng spkn; adv bkg; quiet; ccard acc; red low ssn; CKE/CCI. "Lovely rural site alongside rv Tarn; friendly staff and owners; beautiful scenery; kayaking avail; adv bkg rec high ssn; excel site for gorges." ♦ 1 Apr-30 Sep. € 35.00 (CChq acc) 2013*

ROCAMADOUR *7D3* (1km E Rural) *44.80427, 1.62755* **FFCC Le Relais du Campeur, L'Hospitalet, 46500 Rocamadour [05 65 33 63 28; fax 05 65 10 68 21; lerelaiducampeur@orange.fr; www.lerelaisducampeur.com]** Fr S exit D820 (Brive-la-Gaillarde to Cahors) at Payrac; R on D673, 21km to L'Hospitalet. Fr N exit D820 at Cressensac for D840 to Figeac & Rodez; turn R at D673; site at x-rds after 4km; site behind grocer's shop on L. Avoid app fr W thro Rocamadour (acute hair-pin & rd 2.2m wide). Med, pt sl, pt shd; wc (some cont); chem disp; mv service pnt; baby facs; shwrs inc; el pnts (10A) €3; gas; Indtte (inc dryer); shop nrby; tradsmn; sm rest; BBQ; playgrnd; pool; cycling; wifi; dogs €2; Eng spkn; adv bkg; quiet; ccard acc; red low ssn. "Busy site, even low ssn; great location; friendly staff; vg san facs; excel." 1 Apr-31 Oct. € 15.00 2011*

ROCAMADOUR *7D3* (7km E Rural) *44.81805, 1.68638* **Campsite Padimadour, La Châtaigneraie-Varagne, 46500 Rocamadour [05 65 33 72 11; camping@padimadour.fr; www.padimadour.fr]** Fr N of A20, take exit 54 dir Gramat D840. Turn L onto Pounou. Sharp L onto La Chataigneraie after Pounou. Sm, mkd pitch, pt sl, pt shd; htd wc; chem disp; mv service pnt; baby facs; fam bthrm; shwrs inc; el pnts; Indtte (inc dryer); shop; snacks; bar; BBQ; pool; games area; games rm; entmnt; internet; wifi; 30% statics; dogs; phone; poss cr; Eng spkn; adv bkg; quiet; ccard acc; red low ssn; CCI. "Excel & clean san facs & pool; helpful, friendly owners; homemade pizza's in high ssn; highly rec." ♦ 30 Apr-12 Oct. € 38.00 2014*

ROCAMADOUR *7D3* (1km NW Rural) *44.81040, 1.61615* **FFCC Camping Ferme Branche, Route de Souillac, Les Campagnes, 46500 Rocamadour [05 65 33 63 37; campingfermebranche@yahoo.fr; www.campingfermebranche.com]** Site on D247, 1km N of Rocamadour. Sm, pt shd; wc; (some cont); mv service pnt; shwrs inc; el pnts (6A) €2; Indtte; shop 1km; BBQ; playgrnd; dogs free; phone; quiet. "Lovely, open, spacious site; gd, clean facs; gd for dogs; nr chateau; facs stretched in ssn; friendly owner; great site for price." 1 Apr-15 Nov. € 10.60 2014*

MIDI-PYRÉNÉES

RODEZ *7D4* (1km NE Urban) *44.35323, 2.58708* **Camp Municipal Layoule, 12000 Rodez [05 65 67 09 52; fax 05 65 67 11 43; contact@mairie-rodez.fr; www.mairie-rodez.fr]** Clearly sp in Rodez town cent & all app rds. Access at bottom steep hill thro residential area. Med, hdg/mkd pitch, hdstg, pt shd; wc (poss cont only low ssn); chem disp; mv service pnt; shwrs inc; el pnts (6A) inc; lndry rm; shop 1km; tradsmn; playgrnd; pool, golf, tennis nrby; no statics; no dogs; phone; quiet;CKE/CCI. "Site by lake & rv; gd sized pitches; helpful warden; clean facs; steep walk to historic town; gates clsd 2000-0700; ent is down steep twisty rds & exit is up the same hill; interesting wild life; gd walks & cycling; excel NH." ♦ 1 Jun-30 Sep. € 18.00 (3 persons) 2014*

ROMIEU, LA *8E2* (300m NE Rural) *43.98299, 0.50183* **Kawan Village Le Camp de Florence, 32480 La Romieu [05 62 28 15 58; fax 05 62 28 20 04; info@lecampdeflorence.com; www.lecampdeflorence.com]** Take D931 N fr Condom & turn R onto D41, where La Romieu sp next to radio mast. Go thro La Romieu & turn L at sp just bef leaving vill. Lge, hdg pitch, some hdstg, pt shd; wc; chem disp; mv service pnt; baby facs; shwrs inc; el pnts (10A) inc (poss rev pol); lndtte (inc dryer); shops in vill; tradsmn; rest in 16thC farmhouse; snacks; bar; BBQ; playgrnd; pool; paddling pool; waterslide; jacuzzi; leisure complex 500m; tennis; cycle hire; games area; archery; wifi; entmnt; TV/games rm; many statics; dogs €2.30; twin-axles acc (rec check in adv); Eng spkn; adv bkg ess; quiet; ccard acc; red low ssn; CKE/CCI. "Peaceful, Dutch-run site in pleasant location; gd sized pitches, most with views; welcoming, helpful staff; gd clean san facs; gd rest; poss muddy when wet; some noise fr disco, ask for pitch away fr bar; gd pool but take care sl ent; gd cycling; historic 11thC vill; mkt Wed Condom." ♦ 1 Apr-9 Oct. € 37.50 SBS - D19 2013*

See advertisement

ROQUELAURE see Auch *8F3*

ROQUES see Toulouse *8F3*

ST AFFRIQUE *8E4* (1km E Urban) *43.95025, 2.89248* **Camp Municipal, Parc des Sports, La Capelle Basse, 12400 St Affrique [05 65 98 20 00; fax 05 65 49 02 29]** Site on D99 Albi-Millau rd to St Affrique sp fr all dir in E end of town. Nr stn & sports complex. Med, pt shd; wc (some cont); shwrs; el pnts €2.75; shop 1km; rest, snacks & bar 1km; pool; rv fishing & sw; tennis; adv bkg; quiet. "Gd clean facs; NH." 14 Jun-13 Sep. € 12.30 2012*

ST ANTONIN NOBLE VAL *8E4* (1.5km N Rural) *44.1595, 1.7564* **FFCC Camp Municipal Le Ponget, Route de Caylus, 82140 St Antonin-Noble-Val [05 63 68 21 13 or 05 63 30 60 23 (Mairie); camping-leponget@wanadoo.fr]** Fr Caylus take D19 S to St Antonin; site on R, well sp. Sm, hdg pitch, pt shd; htd wc; mv service pnt; shwrs inc; el pnts (3-6A) €2.50-3.70; gas; lndtte; shops, rest, snacks, bar 1km; playgrnd; sw 1km; dogs €1.20; phone; quiet; ccard not acc; CKE/CCI. "Well-kept site adj sports field; modern san facs; poss diff lge o'fits; gd walking; v gd friendly site; excel mkt Sun; discount for 7 days." ♦ 2 May-30 Sep. € 11.70 2011*

ST ANTONIN NOBLE VAL *8E4* (6km N Rural) *44.19265, 1.69570* **FFCC Camping Les Trois Cantons, Vivens, 82140 St Antonin-Noble-Val [05 63 31 98 57; fax 05 63 31 25 93; info@3cantons.fr; www.3cantons.fr]** Fr Caussade take D926 dir Villefranche (do not take D5 or D19 sp St Antonin.) Site is on C5, sp. Fr St Antonin foll dir Caylus on D19. Just outside vill, after sm bdge where rd turns to R, turn L up hill. Foll this rd for 6km - narr rd. NB Hill steep & continuous. Med, mkd pitch, hdstg, pt sl, pt shd; htd wc (some cont); chem disp; mv service pnt; baby facs; shwrs inc; el pnts (6A) €4.75; gas; lndtte (inc dryer); shop; supmkt 8km; BBQ; playgrnd; htd, covrd pool; rv sw 8km; tennis; cycle hire; horseriding nr; canoeing; wifi; entmnt; TV rm; dogs €2; poss cr; Eng spkn; adv bkg; quiet; ccard acc; red low ssn; CKE/CCI. "Peaceful, clean, well-managed, family site in oak forest; unspoilt region; helpful Dutch owners; gravel pitches muddy in wet; gd." ♦ 16 Apr-30 Sep. € 22.00 2010*

ST ANTONIN NOBLE VAL *8E4* (1km E Rural) *44.15192, 1.77152* **FLOWER Camping des Gorges de L'Aveyron, Marsac Bas, 82140 St Antonin-Noble-Val [05 63 30 69 76; fax 05 63 30 67 61; info@camping-gorges-aveyron.com; www.camping-gorges-aveyron.com / www.flowercampings.com]** Fr Caussade on D926 dir Caylus for approx 5km; after Septfords take D5 then D958 to St Antonin-Noble-Val; on ent to vill cont over rv & L thro tunnel onto D115 dir Féneyrols & Cordes-sur-Ciel. Site in 1.5km on L. Med, hdg pitch, pt shd; wc; chem disp; mv service pnt; baby facs; shwrs inc; el pnts (6A) inc (poss rev pol); Indtte (inc dryer); shops; tradsmn; snacks; bar; playgrnd; pool; fishing rv adj; canoeing; cycle hire; wifi; 15% statics; dogs €2.50; poss cr; adv bkg; quiet; red long stay/low ssn; CKE/CCI. "Neat, tidy site; lge, shady pitches; friendly owners; gd san facs; gd walking & cycling; supmkt & fuel W of St Antonin." ♦ 18 Apr-28 Sep. € 37.00 2010*

ST BERTRAND DE COMMINGES see Montréjeau *8F3*

ST CERE *7C4* (500 SE Urban) *44.85792, 1.89761* **Camping Le Soulhol, Quai Salesses, 46400 St Céré [tel/fax 05 65 38 12 37; info@campinglesoulhol.com; www.campinglesoulhol.com]** Fr S on D940 twds St Céré turn onto D48 (Leyme); in 300m turn L (sp not easily seen); site in 200m. Site sp fr all dirs to St Céré. Lge, pt shd; wc; chem disp; mv service pnt; baby facs; shwrs; el pnts (10A) €3.60 (dated electrics); gas; Indtte; sm shop, tradsmn (high ssn); shops, rests in town 1km; snacks; pool; tennis; cycles hire (1 hr free); Eng library; internet; entmnt; TV rm; 10% statics; dogs €2; phone; quiet; red low ssn; ccard not acc; red low ssn/long stay; CKE/CCI. "Excel, spacious site; lge pitches; friendly, helpful staff; gd clean san facs; far end of site bet 2 rvs v quiet; poss flooding after heavy rain; mkt alt Weds." ♦ 1 May-20 Sep. € 15.50 2011*

"Satellite navigation makes touring much easier"

Remember most sat navs don't know if you're towing or in a larger vehicle – always use yours alongside maps and site directions.

ST CIRQ LAPOPIE *7D3* (2km N Rural) *44.46926, 1.68135* **Camping La Plage, Porte Roques, 46330 St Cirq-Lapopie [05 65 30 29 51; fax 05 65 30 23 33; camping-laplage@wanadoo.fr; www.campingplage.com]** Exit Cahors on D653, in Vers take D662 sp Cajarc. In 20km turn R at Tour-de-Faure over narr bdge, sp St Cirq-Lapopie, site 100m on R beside Rv Lot. Med, mkd pitch, shd; wc; baby facs; shwrs inc; el pnts (6-16A) €4-5; Indtte; shop; rest, snacks; bar; BBQ; playgrnd; pool; canoeing; watersports; wifi; entmnt; 5% statics; dogs €2; Eng spkn; adv bkg; quiet; red low ssn; CKE/CCI. "Pleasant, clean & tidy rvside site; v shady; low ssn site yourself, pay later; friendly, helpful owner; gd walking; excel." ♦ 1 Apr-15 Oct. € 18.80 2012*

ST CIRQ LAPOPIE *7D3* (2.5km S Rural) *44.44871, 1.67468* **FFCC Camping La Truffière, Route de Concots, 46330 St Cirq-Lapopie [05 65 30 20 22; fax 05 65 30 20 27; contact@camping-truffiere.com; www.camping-truffiere.com]** Take D911, Cahors to Villefranche rd; in 20km turn N onto D42 at Concots dir St Cirq for 8km - site clearly sp. NB Do not app fr St Cirq-Lapopie. Med, pt sl, terr, shd; htd wc; chem disp; mv service pnt; baby facs; shwrs inc; el pnts (10A) €4; Indtte (inc dryer); ltd shop & 4km; rest, snacks; bar; playgrnd; htd pool; paddling pool; fishing 3km; cycle hire; entmnt; TV; dogs €1.50; phone; Eng spkn; adv bkg; quiet; ccard acc; red low ssn; CKE/CCI. "Well-kept site in gd location; friendly owners; excel but dated san facs (2014), ltd low ssn; most pitches in forest clearings; muddy when wet; lovely pool; gd; 2m fr fairytale vill of St Cirq Lapopie, a must see; site 11m fr nearest supmkt." ♦ 12 Apr-28 Sep. € 33.00 (CChq acc) 2014*

"There aren't many sites open at this time of year"

If you're travelling outside peak season remember to call ahead to check site opening dates – even if the entry says 'open all year'.

ST CIRQ LAPOPIE *7D3* (7km W Rural) *44.46991, 1.58701* **Camp Municipal, 46330 St Géry [05 65 31 40 08 (Mairie); fax 05 65 31 45 65; mairiestgery@wanadoo.fr]** Fr St Cirq foll N side Rv Lot on D662. Thro St Géry & after rlwy x-ing turn R bef petrol stn. Sp. Sm, pt sl, shd; wc (cont); el pnts (10A) €2.50 (poss long lead req); shop 2km; rv & fishing adj; quiet. "Clean facs; warden calls eve." 15 Jun-15 Sep. € 7.50 2010*

ST CLAR *8E3* (4km NE Rural) *43.89797, 0.81114* **Camping Les Roches (Naturist), Le Nèri, 32380 Mauroux [tel/fax 05 62 66 30 18; campinglesroches@wanadoo.fr; www.campinglesroches.net]** Fr Fleurance take D953 to St Clar then D167 for 3km to site on L. Well sp on D167. Sm, hdg pitch, pt sl, pt shd; wc; chem disp; mv service pnt; sauna; shwrs; el pnts (6A) €4; Indtte; shops; tradsmn; rest, snacks; bar; pool; lake fishing; entmnt; TV rm; some statics; dogs €1.80; phone; Eng spkn; adv bkg; quiet; red low ssn/long stay; INF card. "Beautiful site in remote location; pleasant, helpful owners; gd sized pitches; gd walking; excel." ♦ ltd 1 May-15 Sep. € 18.50 2009*

ST CYPRIEN SUR DOURDOU see Conques *7D4*

ST GAUDENS *8F3* (1km W Rural) *43.11000, 0.70839* **Camp Municipal Belvédère des Pyrénées, Rue des Chanteurs du Comminges, 31800 St Gaudens [05 62 00 16 03; www.st-gaudens.com]** Foll camping sp fr St Gaudens town cent on D817 dir Tarbes. Site ent at top of hill on N side. Last rd sp is 'Belvédère'. Med, pt shd; htd wc; mv service pnt; shwrs inc; el pnts (4-13A) €3.50-6.00; gas; rest nrby; playgrnd; dogs €1.50; no adv bkg; some rd noise; ccard not acc. "Pleasant site; facs clean; gates clsd 1200-1500 & 2300-0700." 1 Jun-30 Sep. € 15.00 2013*

ST GENIEZ D'OLT *9D1* (750m NE Rural) *44.46861, 2.98166* **Campéole Camping La Boissière, Route de la Cascade, 12130 St Geniez-d'Olt [05 65 70 40 43; fax 05 65 47 56 39; boissiere@campeole.com; www.campeole.com]** Exit A75 junc 40 onto D998 dir St Laurent-d'Olt. Then foll sp St Geniez-d'Olt via D988/D45/D202/D45 to St Martin-de-Lenne. At T-junc turn R & foll site sp. Lge, hdg/mkd pitch, hdstg, pt sl, pt shd; htd wc; chem disp; baby facs; shwrs inc; el pnts (6A) €4.10; Indtte (inc dryer); shop; supmkt nr; tradsmn; rest, snacks; bar; BBQ; playgrnd; htd pool; paddling pool; tennis adj; fishing & canoeing nrby; games area; games rm; wifi; entmnt; 40% statics; dogs €2.80; phone; Eng spkn; adv bkg; quiet; ccard acc; red low ssn/CKE/CCI. "Lovely, tranquil site in Lot Valley; gd pool; sh walk into lovely town; gd cycling." ♦ 17 Apr-19 Sep. € 18.00 (CChq acc) 2010*

ST GENIEZ D'OLT *9D1* (500m W Rural) *44.46210, 2.96240* **Kawan Village Marmotel, La Salle, 12130 St Geniez-d'Olt [05 65 70 46 51; info@marmotel.com; www.marmotel.com]** Exit A75 at junc 41 onto D37 dir Campagnac. Then onto D202, D45 & D988. Site situated on W of vill by Rv Lot on D19. Lge, hdg pitch, pt shd; wc; chem disp; mv service pnt; some pitches with individual san facs; baby facs; sauna; shwrs inc; el pnts (10A) inc; gas; Indtte (inc dryer); shop 500m; tradsmn; rest, snacks; bar; BBQ; playgrnd; htd pool; paddling pool; waterslide; lake fishing; tennis; games area; cycle hire; wifi; entmnt; TV rm; some statics; dogs €2; Eng spkn; adv bkg; quiet; red low ssn; ccard acc; CKE/CCI. "Highly rec; some pitches poss tight lge o'fits; poss muddy when wet; gd pool & rest." ♦ 1 May-24 Sep. € 31.00 2011*

ST GERY see St Cirq Lapopie *7D3*

ST GIRONS *8G3* (3km N Rural) *43.00731, 1.18409* **Camping Audinac Les Bains, 09200 Montjoie-en-Couserans [tel/fax 05 61 66 44 50; accueil@audinac.com; www.audinac.com]** E fr St Girons take D117 twd Foix; after 2km uphill turn L onto D627; foll sp. Med, terr, pt shd; htd wc; chem disp (wc); mv service pnt; shwrs inc; el pnts (10A) €3.50; gas; Indtte (inc dryer); shops 5km; tradsmn; rest in ssn; playgrnd; pool high ssn; statics; dogs €1; no twin-axles; Eng spkn; adv bkg ess; quiet; ccard acc; red low ssn; CKE/CCI. "Spacious, attractive, well-kept site; facs ltd low ssn." ♦ 1 May-30 Sep. € 16.00 2010*

⊞ **ST GIRONS** *8G3* (2km SE Rural) *42.97400, 1.16582* **FFCC Camping Parc de Palétès, Route de Lacourt, 09200 St Girons [05 61 66 06 79 or 06 07 02 40 24 (mob); fax 05 61 66 76 86; contacts@parcdepaletes.com; www.parcdepaletes.com]** Fr S loop of D117 in St Girons at rndabt take D3 dir Lacourt (D3 runs parallel to D618 on E of rv & starts as Ave des Evadés de France); site sp on L in 1.5km. Note: D618 runs on W side of rv - cannot cross it bef Lacourt. Sm, pt sl, pt shd; wc; chem disp; mv service pnt; shwrs inc; el pnts (10A) €4; gas; lndry rm; shop; tradsmn; rest, snacks; bar; BBQ; playgrnd; pool; wifi; dogs €1.50; bus; phone; poss cr; Eng spkn; adv bkg; quiet; red low ssn; m'vans all year, c'vans 1 Jun-30 Sep; CKE/CCI. "Gd site." ♦ € 17.00 2009*

⊞ **ST LARY SOULAN** *8G2* (4km NE Rural) *42.84482, 0.33836* **Camping Le Lustou, 89 Chemin d'Agos, 65170 Vielle-Aure [05 62 39 40 64; fax 05 62 39 40 72; contact@lustou.com; www.lustou.com]** Exit A64 junc 16 & head S on D929. Thro Arreau & Guchen turn R onto D19 dir Vielle-Aure. Site on R just bef Agos. Med, hdg pitch, pt sl, pt shd; htd wc; chem disp; baby facs; shwrs inc; el pnts (6-10A) €6.80; gas; Indtte; shop 2km; snacks; bar; BBQ; playgrnd; sports area; fishing, canoeing, tennis nrby; wifi; TV rm; 5% statics; dogs €1.80; phone; adv bkg; quiet; CKE/CCI. "Organised walks in mountains by owner; excel skiing; immac facs; communal meals organised weekly; excel site." ♦ € 24.00 2014*

ST PANTALEON *7D3* (4km NE Rural) *44.36760, 1.30634* **Camping des Arcades, Moulin de St Martiel, 46800 St Pantaléon [05 65 22 92 27 or 06 80 43 19 82 (mob); fax 05 65 31 98 89; info@des-arcades.com; www.des-arcades.com]** Fr N20 3km S of Cahors take D653 sp Montcuq, after 17km site in hamlet of St Martial on L. Med, mkd pitch, pt sl, pt shd; wc; chem disp; shwrs inc; el pnts (6A) €4; Indtte; sm shop; tradsmn; rest, snacks; bar; BBQ; playgrnd; htd pool; paddling pool; lake sw & fishing adj; wifi; 5% statics; dogs €1.50; Eng spkn; adv bkg; quiet; red low ssn; ccard acc; CKE/CCI. "Vg Dutch-owned site with restored 13thC windmill; sm lake; clean facs." ♦ 23 Apr-30 Sep. € 20.00 2012*

ST PARTHEM see Decazeville *7D4*

ST PIERRE LAFEUILLE see Cahors *7D3*

ST PONS DE THOMIERES *8F4* (11km W Rural) *43.47776, 2.65768* **Camp Municipal de Cabanes, Route de St Pons, 81270 Labastide-Rouairoux [05 63 98 49 74 or 05 63 98 07 58; tourisme@labastide-rouairoux.com; www.labastide-rouairoux.com]** E fr Labastide-Rouairoux twd St Pons on D612. Site adj D612 immed after leaving Labastide vill. Sm, hdg/mkd pitch, terr, pt shd; wc; chem disp; shwrs; el pnts inc; shop 1km; tradsmn; adv bkg; some rd noise; CKE/CCI. "Lovely site; poss diff lge o'fits due to terr; sans block small." 15 Jun-15 Sep. € 11.00 2014*

⊞ **ST ROME DE TARN** *8E4* (300m N Rural) *44.05302, 2.89978* **Camping de la Cascade des Naisses, Route du Pont, 12490 St Rome-de-Tarn [05 65 62 56 59; fax 05 65 62 58 62; contact@camping-cascade-aveyron.com; www.camping-cascade-aveyron.com]** Fr Millau take D992 to St Georges-de-Luzençon, turn R onto D73 & foll sp to St Rome. In St Rome turn R along Ave du Pont-du-Tarn, site sp. Diff, steep app for sm/underpowered car+c'van o'fits. Med, hdg/mkd pitch, hdstg, terr, pt shd; htd wc; own san; chem disp; mv service pnt; baby facs; shwrs inc; el pnts (6A) inc; Indtte (inc dryer); shop; rest; bar; playgrnd; pool; paddling pool; rv fishing, boating; tennis; cycle hire; wifi; entmnt; 40% statics; dogs €6; Eng spkn; adv bkg; quiet; red low ssn; CKE/CCI. "Lovely rvside pitches; pleasant vill; friendly, helpful staff; each level has a wc but steep walk to shwr block; owners will site vans; conv Millau viaduct; excel tranquil, scenic site." ♦ € 27.40 2010*

ST VICTOR ET MELVIEU see St Rome de Tarn *8E4*

SALIES DU SALAT *8F3* (2km S Rural) *43.07621, 0.94683* **Complex Touristique de la Justale, Chemin de St Jean, 31260 Mane [05 61 90 68 18; fax 05 61 97 40 18; contact@village-vacances-mane.fr; www.village-vacances-mane.fr]** Fr A64 exit 20 onto D117, turn R in vill at sp 'Village de Vacances'. Site on R in approx 500m. Sm, pt shd; wc; chem disp; mv service pnt; shwrs inc; el pnts (6A) €3.60 (poss rev pol); Indtte; shops 500m; playgrnd; pool; fishing; tennis; horseriding; internet; TV rm; dogs €1.20; phone' adv bkg. "Lovely, peaceful site; lge pitches; helpful staff; excel facs; sinage poss diff to follow." 1 Apr-31 Oct. € 11.80 2013*

SALLES CURAN *8E4* (3km N Rural) *44.20167, 2.77705* **Camping Beau Rivage, Route des Vernhes, 12410 Salles-Curan [05 65 46 33 32; fax 05 65 46 33 96; camping-beau-rivage@orange.fr; www.beau-rivage.fr]** Fr Rodez D911 turn S onto the D993 sp Salles Curan.Foll rd for approx 7km; turn R after lake bdge to site on R in approx 1.5km. Med, pt shd; wc; chem disp; shwrs inc; el pnts (6A) inc; Indtte; shop; rest; playgrnd; pool; shgl beach & lake; fishing; watersports nrby; horseriding nrby; games rm; TV; quiet; dogs €3.90; adv bkg."Excel site on lake location; lovely area, gd walks & lots of activities nrby." Jun-Sep. € 35.00 2013*

SALLES CURAN *8E4* (2km NW Rural) *44.18933, 2.76693* **Camping Les Genêts, Lac de Pareloup, 12410 Salles-Curan [05 65 46 35 34; fax 05 65 78 00 72; contact@camping-les-genets.fr; www.camping-les-genets.fr]** Fr D911 Rodez-Millau rd take D993 S for approx 9km, then R onto D577, site sp on R by lake. Lge, pt sl, shd; wc; mv service pnt; baby facs; fam bthrm; shwrs; el pnts (6A) inc; Indtte (inc dryer); shop; rest, snacks; pizzeria; bar; htd pool; paddling pool; lake sw & beach; sailing; fishing; cycle hire; games area; wifi; entmnt; 40% statics; dogs €4; adv bkg; red long stay/low ssn. "Beautiful area; ltd facs low ssn." ♦ 17 May-13 Sep. € 34.00 (CChq acc) SBS - D07 2013*

See advertisement

SAULIAC SUR CELE see Cabrerets *7D3*

SENERGUES see Conques *7D4*

SERIGNAC *7D3* (5km W Rural) *44.43103, 1.06902* **Camping Le Clos Barrat (Naturist), 46700 Sérignac [05 65 31 97 93; fax 05 65 31 91 17; contact@leclosbarrat.com; www.leclosbarrat.fr]** Fr Fumel by-pass turn S on D139 to Montayral, rd cont but becomes D4. Site sp bet Mauroux & St Matré. Med, pt shd, mkd pitch; wc; chem disp; shwrs inc; el pnts (6A) inc; gas; Indtte; shop; tradsmn; rest, snacks; playgrnd; pool; paddling pool; wifi; entmnt; TV; some statics; dogs €1.60; quiet; ccard acc. "Nr Rv Lot; INF card req - can be bought on site; helpful staff; excel." 1 May-25 Sep. € 23.00 2010*

SEVERAC LE CHATEAU *9D1* (1km SE Urban) *44.31841, 3.06412* **FFCC Camping Les Calquières, Ave Jean Moulin, 12150 Sévérac-le-Château [05 65 47 64 82; contact@camping-calquieres.com; www.camping-calquieres.com]** Exit A75 junc 42 sp Sévérac & Rodez; foll 'Camping' sps to avoid narr town rds. Med, hdg pitch, pt shd; wc (some cont); 50% serviced pitches; shwrs inc; el pnts (6A) €3.40; (poss long lead & rev pol); Indry rm; shop 250m; tradsmn; rest, snacks; bar; playgrnd; htd, covrd pool; games area; fishing; tennis; wifi; some statics; dogs €1.50; adv bkg; quiet, but poss noise fr sports facs adj; red long stay/low ssn; CKE/CCI. "Lovely, spacious site with gd views; lge pitches; friendly owners; vg clean san facs; if office clsd site self; gd touring base; conv A75; busy NH, espec w/end; gd for main holiday stay." ♦ 1 Apr-14 Oct. € 34.40 2014*

See advert on next page

SOUILLAC *7C3* (7km SE Rural) *44.87716, 1.57361* **Camping Les Borgnes, 46200 St Sozy [tel/fax 05 65 32 21 48; info@campinglesborgnes.fr; www.campinglesborgnes.fr]** Exit A20 junc 55; foll sp Martel on D803; in 5km turn R onto D15 to St Sozy; site just bef rv bdge. Med, pt shd; wc (some cont); chem disp; mv service pnt; shwrs inc; el pnts €3; gas; Indtte; shop nr; tradsmn; rest, snacks; bar; supmkt 2km; rest 2km; BBQ; playgrnd; pool; paddling pool; rv sw adj; canoe hire; 60% statics; dogs €1; phone; Eng spkn; adv bkg; quiet, some rd noise; ccard acc; red CKE/CCI. "Helpful British owners; gd." ♦ ltd 1 May-30 Sep. € 12.00 2013*

SOUILLAC *7C3* (1km S Rural) *44.88197, 1.48253* **Camp Municipal du Pont de Lanzac, 46200 Lanzac [05 65 37 02 58; fax 05 65 37 02 31; mairie.lanzac@wanadoo.fr; www.lanzac.fr]** S on D820 thro Souillac; immed after x-ing Rv Dordogne site visible on R of D820. Sm, shd; wc (mainly cont); chem disp; shwrs inc; el pnts (6A) €3; gas; shops 1km; tradsmn; rest, snacks; playgrnd; rv sw; fishing; canoe hire; TV; some statics; dogs; adv bkg; CKE/CCI. "Gd site in lovely location; free-style pitching; helpful warden; clean, basic san facs; easy stroll into Souillac along rv; unrel opening dates - phone ahead; gd NH." ♦ July-Aug. € 11.00 2014*

"That's changed – Should I let The Club know?"

If you find something on site that's different from the site entry, fill in a report and let us know. See www.caravanclub.co.uk/europereport.

SOUILLAC *7C3* (5km S Rural) *44.86602, 1.49715* **Camping Verte Rive, 46200 Pinsac [05 65 37 85 96 or 06 65 37 85 96 (mob); fax 05 65 32 67 69; camping-laverterive@orange.fr; www.location-dordogne-chalet.com]** Fr Souillac S on D820. Turn L immed bef Dordogne rv bdge on D43 to Pinsac. Site on R in 2km on rvside. Med, hdg/mkd pitch, shd; wc (some cont); chem disp; baby facs; shwrs inc; el pnts (10A) €4.; gas; lndtte; shop & 1km; rest, snacks; bar; playgrnd; pool; canoeing; games rm; 20% statics; dogs €2; poss cr; Eng spkn; adv bkg ess high ssn; quiet; ccard acc; red low ssn; CKE/CCI. "Pleasant, peaceful, wooded site on Rv Dordogne; gd san facs; poss mosquitoes by rv; gd pool; excel." ♦ 1 Apr-15 Sep. € 31.00 2013*

⊞ **SOUILLAC** *7C3* (300m SW Urban) *44.89150, 1.47654* **Aire Communale, Rue de la Pomme, 46200 Souillac [05 65 32 71 00]** Take D820 to Souillac cent then D804/D703 dir Sarlat. In 200m turn L, site ent on R at Parking Baillot. Sm, hdstg, unshd; chem disp; wc; water & el pnts €2; shop, rest 300m; free parking for m'vans only. "Rec arr early; ltd hdstg." 2010*

SOUILLAC *7C3* (1km W Urban) *44.88895, 1.47418* **FLOWER Camping Les Ondines, Ave de Sarlat, 46200 Souillac [05 65 37 86 44 or 06 33 54 32 00; fax 05 65 32 61 15; camping.les.ondines@flowercampings.com; www.camping-lesondines.com / www.flowercampings.com]** Turn W off D820 in cent Souillac onto D804/D703 sp Sarlat. In 200m turn L at sp into narr rd. Ent 400m on R adj rv. Lge, mkd pitch, pt sl, pt shd; wc; chem disp; shwrs inc; el pnts (5A) inc; lndtte; shop; rest 1km; BBQ; playgrnd; htd pool & aquatic park nrby; tennis; fishing; canoeing; tennis; horseriding; entmnt; wifi; some statics; dogs €2; phone; Eng spkn; quiet; red low ssn; CKE/CCI. "Gd touring base nr rv; helpful staff; clean facs; conv NH Rocamadour & caves; easy access fr D820; vg." ♦ 1 May-28 Sep. € 34.40 2014*

SOUILLAC *7C3* (7km NW Rural) *44.93599, 1.43743* **Camping La Draille, La Draille, 46200 Souillac [05 65 32 65 01; fax 05 65 37 06 20; la.draille@wanadoo.fr; www.ladraille.com]** Leave Souillac on D15 sp Salignac-Evvigues; at Bourzoles in 6km take D165; site sp in 500m on L. Med, hdg pitch, pt sl, pt shd; wc; chem disp; baby facs; shwrs inc; el pnts (4A) €4.; lndtte; shop; rest, snacks; bar; BBQ; pool; 25% statics; dogs €3; phone; poss cr; Eng spkn; adv bkg; quiet; ccard acc; CKE/CCI. "Lovely location; friendly; gd walks; highly rec." ♦ 27 Apr- 5 Oct. € 26.00 2013*

SOUILLAC *7C3* (8km NW Rural) *44.94510, 1.44140* **Domaine de la Paille Basse, 46200 Souillac [05 65 37 85 48; fax 05 65 37 09 58; info@lapaillebasse.com; www.lapaillebasse.com / www.les-castels.com]** Exit Souillac by D15 sp Salignac, turn onto D165 at Bourzolles foll sp to site in 3km. NB Narr app, few passing places. Lge, hdg pitch, terr, pt shd; wc; chem disp; mv service pnt; shwrs inc; el pnts (3-10A) €4-6; gas; lndtte (inc dryer); shop; rest, snacks; bar; BBQ; playgrnd; pool; paddling pool; waterslide; tennis; cycle hire; games area; golf 5km; organised outdoor activities; wifi; entmnt; TV/cinema rm; dogs €4; adv bkg; quiet; ccard acc; red low ssn. "Excel site in remote location; friendly, helpful staff; clean facs; some shwrs unisex; restored medieval vill." ♦ 15 May-14 Sep. € 24.80 (CChq acc) SBS - D06 2009*

TARASCON SUR ARIEGE *8G3* (4km N Rural) *42.87910, 1.62829* **Camping du Lac, 1 Promenade du Camping, 09400 Mercus-Garrabet [tel/fax 05 61 05 90 61 or 06 86 07 24 18 (mob); info@campinglac.com; www.campinglac.com]** N20 S fr Foix, after 10km exit Mercus over N20 sp, cross rlwy line. At T-junc turn R thro Mercus, site of R over level x-ing. Tight bend into site off long, narr ent drive. Med, hdg/mkd pitch, terr, shd; wc (some cont); chem disp; baby facs; shwrs inc; el pnts (6-10A) €3.40-4.90; Indtte; shop; tradsmn; supmkt 4km; rest, bar 1km; BBQ; htd pool; rv & lake sw, fishing & watersports adj; games rm; 20% statics; dogs €2; phone; some Eng spkn; adv bkg (fee); some rd & rlwy noise; red long stay: CKE/CCI. "Clean facs; friendly owners; sm pitches; steep entry rd with tight turn to get thro barrier; 60km Andorra; a real find!" ♦ ltd 11 Apr-19 Sep. € 26.00 2014*

TARASCON SUR ARIEGE *8G3* (600m SE Rural) *42.83981, 1.61215* **Kawan Village Le Pré-Lombard, Route d'Ussat, 09400 Tarascon-sur-Ariège [05 61 05 61 94; fax 05 61 05 78 93; leprelombard@wanadoo.fr; www.prelombard.com]** Travelling S twd Andorra join N20 to Tarascon. Approx 17km S of Foix after 3 rndabts & x-ing a bdge, at 4th rndabt turn L, after rlwy on D618 foll site sp. This rte avoids cent of Tarascon. Lge, hdg/mkd pitch, pt shd; htd wc; chem disp; mv service pnt; shwrs inc; el pnts (10A) inc; gas; Indtte (inc dryer); shop; rest, snacks; bar; BBQ; playgrnd; htd pool; paddling pool; kayaking, rv fishing & sw adj; canyoning & climbing nrby; tennis; cycle hire; archery; wifi; entmnt; games/TV rm; 50% statics; dogs €4; no c'vans/m'vans over 6m; Eng spkn; adv bkg rec high ssn; ccard acc; red low ssn; CKE/CCI. "Busy, well-run, family site in lovely location by rv; spacious pitches; helpful owner; gd san facs, poss stretched high ssn; plenty for teenagers to do; gd base for exploring area; excel winter NH en rte to Spain; poss rallies low ssn; excel." ♦ 15 Mar-15 Oct. € 36.00 2013*

TARASCON SUR ARIEGE *8G3* (3km SW Rural) *42.81311, 1.58908* **Camping Les Grottes, Dumaines de la Hille, 09400 Alliat [05 61 05 88 21; fax 05 61 03 89 91; info@campingdesgrottes.com; www.campingdesgrottes.com]** S fr Foix on N20 dir Andorra, turn R onto D8 just past Tarascon-sur-Ariège sp Niaux/Vicdessos. Site on R in 2km. Med, hdg/mkd pitch, hdstg, pt shd; wc (some cont); chem disp; mv service pnt; shwrs inc; el pnts (6-10A) €2; Indtte (inc dryer); shop; rest nrby; snacks; bar; playgrnd; htd pool; paddling pool; waterslide; games area; entmnt; TV; 20% statics; dogs €2; phone; adv bkg; quiet. "Lovely, peaceful site in valley; ideal NH for Andorra or long stay; prehistoric cave paintings nr; excel." 1 Mar-1 Nov. € 25.00 (CChq acc) 2010*

⊞ **TARASCON SUR ARIEGE** *8G3* (1.5km NW Rural) *42.85606, 1.58861* **Camping Le Sédour, Florac, 09400 Surba [05 61 05 87 28; fax 05 61 01 49 33; info@campinglesedour.com; www.campinglesedour.com]** Fr rndbt 1km N of Tarascon take 1st R sp Massat. Turn R in 100m, site on L in Surba vill. Med, hdg/mkd pitch, pt sl, pt shd; wc; chem disp; some serviced pitches; shwrs inc; el pnts (10A) inc; Indtte (inc dryer); supmkt 1km; tradsmn; rest, bar 300m; playgrnd; 60% statics; dogs €2; poss cr; some Eng spkn; adv bkg; quiet; red long stay; CKE/CCI. "Friendly, helpful owners; gd facs; poss diff access lge o'fits; conv for Ariège valleys & prehistoric park; mountain views." ♦ € 20.00 2009*

THERONDELS see Pierrefort *7C4*

⊞ **TOULOUSE** *8F3* (5km N Urban) *43.65569, 1.41585* **Camping Toulouse Le Rupé, 21 Chemin du Pont de Rupé, 31000 Toulouse [05 61 70 07 35; fax 05 61 70 93 17; campinglerupe31@wanadoo.fr; www.camping-toulouse.com]** N fr Toulouse on D820, sp. Poss tricky app fr N for long vans, suggest cont past Pont de Rupé traff lts to next rndabt & double back to turn. Fr S on ring rd exit junc 33A (after junc 12), turn immed R & foll sp. Lge, hdg/mkd pitch, hdstg, pt shd; htd wc (some cont); chem disp; mv service pnt; baby facs; shwrs inc; el pnts (10A) €4; Indtte (inc dryer); shop; tradsmn; rest, snacks; bar; playgrnd; lake fishing; games rm; wifi; TV; 50% statics; dogs €1.50; phone; bus; poss cr (esp public hols); Eng spkn; no adv bkg; ccard acc; CKE/CCI "If site clsd 1200-1500, park in layby just bef site & use speakerphone; gd clean san facs; rock pegs poss req; itinerant camp opp but no probs, site security excel; conv Airbus factory tours; space theme park 10km; well maintained." € 36.20 2014*

TREIN D'USTOU, LE see Oust *8G3*

TRIE SUR BAISE *8F2* (2.5km NE Rural) *43.34400, 0.36970* **Camping Fontrailles, Le Quartier Lanorbe, 65220 Fontrailles [05 62 35 62 52; detm.paddon@orange.fr; www.fontraillescamping.com]** Fr N on N21 leave Mirande & turn L (S) at end of town sp Trie-sur-Baïse onto D939; after St Michel look out for silos on R after 7km, site sp. Fr S at Miélan turn onto D3/D17 sp Trie-sur-Baïse to Fontrailles. Sm, pt sl, pt shd; wc; chem disp (wc); shwrs inc; el pnts (9A) €2.50; shop, rest, snacks & bar 3km; BBQ; playgrnd; pool; tennis; fishing; wifi; dogs; Eng spkn; adv bkg; quiet; red long stay; CKE/CCI. "Delightful, well-kept CL-type site in orchard; friendly, helpful British owners; excel pool & tennis nrby; gd walking; conv Lourdes, Pyrenees & Spain; mkt Trie-sur-Baïse Tues; Excel site; beautiful views." 1 Jul-30 Sep. € 17.00 2012*

USTOU see Oust *8G3*

⊞ **VARILHES** *8G3* (400m NE Urban) *43.04714, 1.63096* **FFCC Camp Municipal du Parc du Château, Ave de 8 Mai 1945, 09120 Varilhes [05 61 67 42 84 or 05 61 60 55 54 (TO); campingdevarilhes@orange.fr; www.campingdevarilhes.com]** Exit N20/E9 at sp Varilhes. Turn N in town on D624. Site 250m on L (sp) just bef leisure cent adj Rv Ariège. Med, mkd pitch, terr, pt shd; htd wc; mv service pnt; baby facs; shwrs inc; el pnts (5-10A) €5.90-6.40; Indtte; shops adj & 200m; tradsmn; rest 200m; snacks; bar 300m; playgrnd; pool adj; rv fishing adj; games area; wifi; 20% statics; dogs; adv bkg; quiet. ♦ € 18.00 2012*

⊞ **VARILHES** *8G3* (3km NW Rural) *43.06258, 1.62101* **FFCC Camping Les Mijeannes, Route de Ferriès, 09120 Rieux-de-Pelleport [05 61 60 82 23; fax 05 61 67 74 80; lesmijeannes@wanadoo.fr; www.campinglesmijeannes.com]** Exit N20 sp Varilhes; on app Varilhes cent join 1-way system; 1st R at Hôtel de Ville; over rv bdge; foll camp sps; site 2km on R. Med, hdg pitch, pt shd; htd wc; mv service pnt; chem disp; shwrs inc; el pnts (10A) €4.60; tradsmn; bar; BBQ; playgrnd; pool; volley; badminton; fishing; kids club; entmnt; games area; TV; wifi; dogs €1.10; some Eng spkn; adv bkg; quiet; red low ssn; CKE/CCI; ACSI; "Peaceful site by rv - on island formed by rv; helpful owner; gd size pitches; excel san facs; weekly theme nights high ssn; excel." € 32.80 2014*

VAYRAC *7C4* (3.5km S Rural) *44.93462, 1.67981* **FFCC Camping Les Granges, Les Granges-de-Mezel, 46110 Vayrac [05 65 32 46 58; fax 05 65 32 57 94; info@les-granges.com; www.les-granges.com]** App Vayrac on D803; turn S at sq in town sp "Campings"; site in 3.5km on banks of Rv Dordogne. Sp in Vayrac. Alt rte fr D803 in St Denis-les-Martel on D80 S - shorter on narr rds; site sp. Lge, pt shd; wc; shwrs; el pnts (10A) €4; gas; Indtte; shop; rest, snacks; bar; playgrnd; pool; paddling pool; fishing; canoeing; cycling; games area; entmnt; TV; dogs €1.60; adv bkg; quiet; red low ssn. "Vg children's amenities; facs fair; poss mosquitoes." 8 May-20 Sep. € 20.20 2012*

VERDUN SUR GARONNE *8E3* (300m NE Rural) *43.85789, 1.24124* **FFCC Camping Le Grand Gravier, Chemin des Allées, 82600 Verdun-sur-Garonne [05 63 64 32 44 or 05 63 26 30 64 (LS); camping@garonne-gascogne.com; www.garonne-gascogne.com]** Exit A20/E09 at junc 68 onto A72 & exit junc 10 onto D820 S to Grisolles. At rndabt turn R onto D813 NW for 3km, then L at rndabt onto D6 W sp Verdun-sur-Garonne. Cross rv bdge; site sharp R in 200m. Med, hdg pitch, pt shd; wc (mainly cont); mv service pnt; shwrs inc; el pnts (6A) €2.80; shop 1km; BBQ; playgrnd; rv fishing; tennis; games rm; 30% statics; dogs €1; adv bkg; quiet; red long stay; CKE/CCI. "Pleasant, interesting site; next to fast flowing rv, poss floods in wet weather; gd facs." 22 May-5 Sep. € 9.40 2010*

VERS *7D3* (200m S Rural) *44.48442, 1.55380* **Camp Municipal de l'Arquette, 46090 Vers [05 65 31 42 59 (Mairie) or 06 33 65 06 23 (mob); mairie-vers@wanadoo.fr; www.commune-de-vers.net]** Fr Cahors foll D653 on N side Rv Lot to Vers; in vill turn R over bdge onto D662 sp St Cirq-Lapopie; turn R in 100m, foll site sp. Use this rte to avoid low bdge 2.9m. Med, mkd pitch, shd; wc; chem disp; mv service pnt; shwrs inc; el pnts (10A) €4 (rev pol); Indry rm; shop & rest 200m; playgrnd adj; dogs €1.50; phone; poss cr; Eng spkn; adv bkg; ccard not acc; CKE/CCI. "Attractive rvside site; friendly staff; excel san facs; gd walks; poss flood risk; poss noisy youth groups w/ends; conv Pech-Merle cave paintings." 1 May-30 Sep. € 12.00 2009*

⊞ **VILLEFRANCHE DE LAURAGAIS** *8F3* (8km SW Rural) *43.35498, 1.64862* **Camping Le Lac de la Thésauque, Nailloux, 31560 Montgeard [05 61 81 34 67; fax 05 61 81 00 12; camping@thesauque.com; www.camping-thesauque.com]** Fr S exit A61 at Villefrance-de-Lauragais junc 20 onto D622, foll sp Auterive then Lac after Gardouch vill, site sp. Fr N turn off A61 at 1st junc after tolls S of Toulouse onto A66 (sp Foix). Leave A66 at junc 1 & foll sp Nailloux. Turn L on ent vill onto D662 & in 2km turn R onto D25 & immed R to site, sp. Med, mkd pitch, hdstg, terr, pt shd; htd wc; chem disp; shwrs inc; el pnts (10A) inc; Indtte; shop; rest, snacks; bar; BBQ; playgrnd; pool; fishing; boating; tennis; wifi; 70% statics; dogs; poss cr; ccard acc; red low ssn; CKE/CCI. "Scenic, peaceful location; conv NH for A61; helpful owners; ltd facs low ssn; gd security; steep app to sm terr pitches poss diff lge o'fits; facs basic but adequate." ♦ € 28.50 2014*

VILLEFRANCHE DE ROUERGUE *7D4* (9km SE Rural) *44.26695, 2.11575* **Camping Le Muret, 12200 St Salvadou [05 65 81 80 69 or 05 65 29 84 87; info@lemuret.com; www.lemuret.com]** Fr Villefranche on D911 twd Millau, R on D905A sp camping & foll camping sp 7km. Sm, hdg/mkd pitch, shd; wc; shwrs inc; el pnts (16A) €4.50; gas & ice at farm; Indtte; shops 9km; tradsmn; rest, snacks; bar; lake adj; fishing; dogs €2; phone; adv bkg; v quiet; red long stay; CKE/CCI. "Lovely setting; gd sized pitches; san facs need refurb (owners aware)." ♦ 5 Apr-22 Oct. € 26.00 2012*

VILLEFRANCHE DE ROUERGUE *7D4* (1km SW Urban) *44.34207, 2.02731* **FFCC Camping du Rouergue, 35 Ave de Fondies, Le Teulel, 12200 Villefranche-de-Rouergue [tel/fax 05 65 45 16 24; campingrouergue@wanadoo.fr; www.campingdurouergue.com]** Best app fr N on D922, then D47 dir Monteils & Najac; avoid 1-way system in town; ent thro sports stadium. Site well sp. Med, hdg/mkd pitch, hdstg, shd; wc (some cont); chem disp; mv service pnt; baby facs; serviced pitches; shwrs inc; el pnts (16A) €3.50; Indtte; shop; tradsmn; rest, snacks; bar; playgrnd; pool; sports stadium adj; tennis 1km; wifi; entmnt; TV rm; 15% statics; dogs €1; bus high ssn; extra for twin-axles; Eng spkn; adv bkg (30% dep); quiet; ccard acc; red low ssn/long stay/CKE/CCI. "Well-kept, peaceful site; easy access; lge pitches; pleasant, friendly owner; excel clean san facs; pool v sm; gd security; easy walk/cycle to town; m'van services outside site; rec; v hot water, gd supply; excel." ♦ 12 Apr-30 Sep. € 23.75 2014*

Nord Pas-de-Calais

Regional Introduction

Lille

Welcome to Nord Pas-de-Calais

Located at the northernmost point of France, Nord Pas-de-Calais is famous for the large continental ports along its coastline.

Many military cemeteries and memorials can be found in this region due to its historical links with WWI and II. Monuments in memory of the men and women who fought for their countries have been maintained in peaceful areas for visitors.

Whether passing through en-route to the rest of France or Europe, or staying to soak up its history, this area will not disappoint with its many landmarks and sights.

Local highlights

The region is notable for rearing turkeys and chickens, for growing chicory and for its seafood.

Nord Pas-de-Calais beers are also renowned throughout France. The local beer is called Biére du Nord – it is made using traditional recipes and accompanies many local dishes.

Berck-sur-Mer is home to the annual International Kite Festival in April, where you sit on the sand dunes and watch the huge variety of kite flying displays.

Major towns and cities

- Arras – filled with historical squares and a magnificent town hall.
- Calais – a popular port used as a gateway to France.
- Dunkirk– famous for the beach landings in WWII, there is lots of maritime history here.
- Lille – lively markets and elegant shops line the streets of this cultural city.

Regional attractions

- Town Hall, Calais – a truly stunning piece of architecture.
- La Coupole – secret military base constructed by the German army.
- Grande Place, Lille – main square where the 17th-century Vielle Bourse is located.
- Musée d'Art et d'Industrie, St Étienne – an old municipal pool and baths which have been converted into a museum.

Find out more

www.northernfrance-tourism.com

Tel: (0)3 21 51 26 95 Arras Tourist Office
Tel: (0)3 21 96 62 40 Calais Tourist Office

AIRE SUR LA LYS *3A3* (2km NE Urban) *50.64390, 2.40630* **Camp Municipal de la Lys, Bassin des Quatre Faces, Rue de Fort Gassion, 62120 Aire-sur-la-Lys [03 21 95 40 40; fax 03 21 95 40 41; camping@ville-airesurlalys.fr; www.ville-airesurlalys.fr]** Fr town cent, find main sq & exit to R of town hall. Thro traff lts turn R into narr lane just bef rv bdge dir of Hazebrouck. Site poorly sp. Sm, hdg/mkd pitch, hdstg, pt shd; htd wc; chem disp (wc); shwrs inc; some el pnts (6A) €2.10; quiet; 95% statics. "Ltd touring pitches; ltd but clean san facs; not suitable lge o'fits; rec for NH only; v welcoming; waterside pitches; vg NH; easy walk to town." 1 Apr-31 Oct. € 10.50 2014*

AMBLETEUSE see Wimereux *3A2*

ANDRES *3A3* (2km S Rural) *50.83865, 1.97612* **Camping St Louis, 223 Rue Leulène, 62610 Autingues [03 21 35 46 83; fax 03 21 00 19 78; campingstlouis@sfr.fr; www.campingstlouis.com]** Fr Calais S on D943 to Ardres; fr Ardres take D224 S twd Licques, after 2km turn L on D227; site well sp in 100m. Or fr junc 2 off A26 onto D943 dir Ardres. Turn L just after Total g'ge on R on app to Ardres. Well sp. If app fr S via Boulogne avoid Nabringhen & Licques as narr, steep hill with bends. NB Mkt Thurs am - avoid R turn when leaving site. Med, hdg/mkd pitch, pt shd; wc; chem disp; mv service pnt; baby facs; shwrs inc; el pnts (6A) inc (long lead poss req; poss rev pol); gas; lndtte; sm shop & 1km; supmkt 3km; tradsmn; rest, snacks; bar; BBQ; playgrnd; lake 1km; games rm; wifi; entmnt; 70% statics; dogs free; phone; poss cr; Eng spkn; adv bkg ess high ssn; quiet, but some rwly noise & poss music w/end fr bar; ccard acc; CKE/CCI. "Peaceful, well-kept, well-run, busy site; conv Dunkerque, Calais ferries; some gd sized pitches; gd welcome & friendly; clean san facs poss stretched high ssn; ltd touring pitches - phone ahead to check avail high ssn; early dep/late arr area; automatic exit barrier; barrier opens 0600 high ssn; gd rest; vg vet in Ardres; v gd, conv NH; shwrs v hot, no temp control; lovely clean site; new owners." ♦ 19 Mar-21 Oct. € 26.00 2014*

ARDRES *3A3* (500m N Urban) *50.85726, 1.97551* **Camping Ardresien, 64 Rue Basse, 62610 Ardres [03 21 82 82 32]** Fr St Omer on D943 to Ardres, strt on at lights in town onto D231; site 500m on R - easy to o'shoot; v narr ent, not suitable twin-axles. Sm, hdg pitch, pt shd; wc; shwrs; el pnts (16A) inc; 95% statics; dogs free; poss cr; CKE/CCI. "Basic site; friendly staff; walk to lakes at rear of site; ltd touring pitches; conv Calais & local vet; NH only." 1 May-30 Sep. € 11.00 2011*

ARDRES *3A3* (9km NE Rural) *50.88147, 2.08618* **Camp Municipal Les Pyramides, Rue Nord Boutillier, 62370 Audruicq [03 21 35 59 17 or 03 21 46 06 60 (Mairie)]** Fr Calais take A16 dir Dunkerque, after 8km exit S at junc 21 onto D219 to Audruicq; foll camp sp. Fr Ardres NE on D224 to Audruicq. Site on NE side of Audruicq nr canal. Med, hdg pitch, unshd; wc; chem disp; shwrs inc; el pnts (6A); gas; lndtte; tradsmn; playgrnd; 80% statics; dogs; no ccard acc; quiet; CKE/CCI. "Conv Calais; few sm pitches for tourers; rec phone ahead." ♦ ltd 1 Apr-30 Sep. 2013*

ARDRES *3A3* (8km SE Rural) *50.80867, 2.05569* **Hôtel Bal Caravaning, 500 Rue du Vieux Château, 62890 Tournehem-sur-la-Hem [03 21 35 65 90; fax 03 21 35 18 57; hotelbal@yahoo.fr; www.hotel-bal.com]** Fr S on A26 leave at exit 2; turn R onto D217 then R onto D943 dir St Omer. Turn R in Nordausques onto D218 (approx 1km), pass under A26, site is 1km on L - ent thro Bal Parc Hotel gates. Fr N or S on D943, turn R or L in Nordausques, then as above. Med, hdg/mkd pitch, hdstg, pt sl, pt shd; htd wc (in hotel in winter); chem disp; shwrs inc; el pnts (10A) inc (poss rev pol); gas; tradsmn; rest, snacks & bar in adj hotel; playgrnd; sports grnd & leisure cent adj; tennis; entmnt; wifi; 80% statics; poss cr; Eng spkn; adv bkg; quiet; ccard acc; red low ssn/CKE/CCI. "Tidy area for tourers, but few touring pitches; gd rest & bar; san facs refurbed (2010); 25km Cité Europe mall; gd NH." ♦ 1 Apr-31 Oct. € 20.00 2014*

"I like to fill in the reports as I travel from site to site"

You'll find report forms at the back of this guide, or you can fill them in online at www.caravaclub.co.uk/europereport.

ARDRES *3A3* (9km SE Rural) *50.82193, 2.07577* **Camping Le Relax, 318 Route de Gravelines, 62890 Nordausques [tel/fax 03 21 35 63 77; camping.le.relax@cegetel.net]** Fr N on D943 in vill 25km S of Calais at beginning of vill, turn L at sp. Site 200m on R. Or fr S on A26, leave at junc 2 & take D943 S for 1km into Nordausques, then as above. NB Ent diff, beware low o'hanging roof on recep. Med, hdg pitch, pt shd; wc; chem disp; shwrs €1.50; el pnts (6A) €2.20 (poss rev pol); lndry rm; shop 200m; tradsmn; snacks; playgrnd; 90% statics; poss cr; adv bkg ess; quiet, but rd noise; CKE/CCI. "Obliging owner; sm pitches & sharp access, not suitable lge o'fits; basic san facs, poss tired high ssn; conv A26, Calais & war sites; NH only." 1 Apr-30 Sep. € 13.40 2014*

⊞ **ARMENTIERES** *3A3* (3km E Rural) *50.68774, 2.93279* **Camping L'Image, 140 Rue Brune, 59116 Houplines [03 20 35 69 42 or 06 81 61 56 82 (mob); fax 03 20 87 21 53; campimage@wanadoo.fr; www.campingimage.com]** Exit A25 junc 8 sp Armentières, onto D945 N twd Houplines; pass on R Chemin du Pilori in 1.8km; then pass on R Hameau de L'Hépinette in 2.2km; turn R into Rue Brune in 3km; site in 1km on R. Ent not v clearly sp. Med, hdg pitch, shd; htd wc; chem disp; mv service pnt; serviced pitches; shwrs inc; el pnts (6-10A) inc (take care electrics, poss prob 2011); lndtte; shop high ssn & 4km; snacks; playgrnd; tennis; games area; wifi; entmnt; 90% statics; poss cr; adv bkg; quiet; CKE/CCI. "Mainly statics, adv bkg rec; friendly, helpful staff; dated san facs, poss unclean & unkempt (2011); pitches exposed & poss v windy; gd NH prior to ferry." € 19.00 2013*

ARRAS *3B3* (12km SE Rural) *50.27347, 2.94852* **Camping La Paille Haute, 145 Rue de Seilly, 62156 Boiry-Notre-Dame [03 21 48 15 40; fax 03 21 22 07 24; lapaillehaute@wanadoo.fr; www.la-paille-haute.com]** Fr Calais take A26/A1 twd Paris, exit junc 15 onto D939 twd Cambrai; in 3km take D34 NE to Boiry-Notre-Dame & foll camp sp. Fr D950 Douai-Arras rd, at Fresnes turn S onto D43, foll sp to Boiry in 7km, site well sp in vill. Med, pt hdg pitch, hdstg, terr, pt shd; wc; chem disp; mv service pnt; baby facs; shwrs inc; el pnts (6A) €4. (poss rev pol); lndtte (inc dryer); rest & snacks high ssn; bar; BBQ; playgrnd; htd pool; paddling pool; lake fishing; tennis; games rm; wifi; entmnt; 60% statics in sep area; dogs; site open w/ends in winter; poss cr; Eng spkn; quiet; red long stay/low ssn; ccard acc; CKE/CCI. "Popular NH; useful & reliable; pretty site with views; rec arr early; lge pitches; friendly, helpful owner; gd for children; facs poss stretched high ssn but clean and adquate; Calais over 1hr; conv WW1 sites & A26; gd reg used site; gd for long stay; peaceful vill; facs outdated & tired (2014); pitches muddy in wet weather."
♦ 01 Apr -31 Oct. € 32.50 2014*

See advertisement

AUBENCHEUL AU BAC *3B4* (2km W Rural) *50.26134, 3.14042* **Camping aux Roubaisiens, Rue de l'Abbeye, 62860 Oisy-le-Verger [03 21 59 51 54; lagep@hotmail.fr]** Fr Cambrai take D643 NW twd Douai. In 10km immed turn L (W) twd Oisy-le-Verger, site sp in vill. Sm, pt shd; wc; own san rec; chem disp; shwrs; el pnts (6A) €2; lndtte (inc dryer); shop; playgrnd; fishing; 95% statics; quiet. "Fine as NH/sh stay; helpful owner; gd shop." 1 Apr-15 Oct. € 8.40 2010*

AUDRUICQ see Ardres *3A3*

AUXI LE CHATEAU *3B3* (500m NW Rural) *50.2341, 2.1058* **Camp Municipal des Peupliers, 22 Rue du Cheval, 62390 Auxi-le-Château [03 21 41 10 79; fax 03 21 04 10 22; www.ville-auxilechateau.fr]** Fr S on D925, turn N onto D933 at Bernaville to Auxi-le-Château; turn W onto D941; then turn R in 300m into Rue du Cheval; site sp on R in 500m by football stadium. Or take D928 S fr Hesdin; in 11km take D119 to Auxi-le-Château. Med, hdg pitch; unshd; wc; chem disp; shwrs inc; el pnts (3-6A) €1.85; lndtte; shops, rest, snacks & bar 500m; playgrnd; fishing; sailing; dir access to rv; 80% statics; poss cr; adv bkg; quiet; ccard acc; "Easy walk into town." 1 Apr-30 Sep. € 9.00 2013*

BAILLEUL *3A3* (3km N Rural) *50.76160, 2.74956* **Camping Les Saules (Notteau), 453 Route du Mont Noir, 59270 Bailleul [03 28 49 13 75]** N fr Lille on A25 exit junc 10 & head N into Bailleul cent; in town at traff lts turn R onto D23/N375; in 2km just bef Belgian border turn L onto D223. Site on L in 300m. Sm, hdstg, pt shd; wc; chem disp; shwrs inc; el pnts (6A) €2.84; farm shop; BBQ; playgrnd; 90% statics; dogs; Eng spkn; quiet but some rd noise; CKE/CCI. "Farm site; friendly owner; clean san facs; conv Calais, Dunkerque & WW1 sites; excel site, highly rec well kept and comfortable site; first class farm shop." 1 Apr-31 Oct. € 13.60 2014*

BAILLEUL *3A3* (4km N Rural) *50.77909, 2.73692* **Camping Domaine de la Sablière, Mont-Noir, 59270 St Jans-Cappel [03 28 49 46 34; fax 03 28 42 62 90]** Fr A25 exit junc 10, N on D10 thro Bailleul to St Jans-Cappel. Thro vill turn R at x-rds onto D318 to Mont-Noir. Site on R at top of hill. Med, hdg/mkd pitch, terr, shd; wc; chem disp; some serviced pitches; shwrs inc; el pnts (6A) inc; lndtte; shop, rest & bar 3km; bar; playgrnd; fishing 2km; tennis; mini-golf 100m; 80% statics; phone. "Well-kept site; new owners (2009); clean san facs; pitch access poss diff lge o'fits due steep gradients & tight turns; conv WW1 battlefields, Dunkerque & Calais; gd." 15 Mar-15 Oct. € 18.00 2009*

BAILLEUL *3A3* (8km NE Rural) *50.79397, 2.67311* **Camping Les 5 Chemins Verts, 689 Rue des 5 Chemins Verts, 59299 Boeschepe [tel/fax 03 28 49 42 37; camping5cheminsverts@orange.fr; www.camping-5-chemins-verts.fr]** Fr N exit A25 junc 13 onto D948 W; in 5km turn R onto D10 to Boeschepe; turn R in vill. Or fr S exit A25 at Bailleul; N onto D10 to Boeschepe; turn L in vill. Site sp. V narr app rds, not suitable lge o'fits. Med, pt sl, pt shd; wc (some cont); chem disp; fam bthrm; shwrs inc; gas; el pnts (5A) inc; gas; lndtte; tradsmn; rest, snacks; bar; BBQ; playgrnd; games area; games rm; wifi; entmnt; 98% statics; dogs; phone; some Eng spkn; adv bkg; ccard acc; CKE/CCI. "Pleasant site with well-kept gardens; just a few touring pitches; clean, roomy modern san facs up steps; gd rest; poss diff access to pitches due sl & overhanging branches, not suitable lge o'fits; lots of activities, a child-oriented site; fishing in pond with ducks; gd rests around Mont des Cats; conv WWI sites & Calais; gd."
♦ ltd 15 Mar-31 Oct. € 12.00 2011*

⊞ **BEAURAINVILLE** *3B3* (750m SE Rural) *50.41971, 1.91243* **Camp Municipal La Source, Rue des Etangs, 62990 Beaurainville [03 21 81 40 71 or 06 80 32 17 25 (mob); fax 03 21 90 02 88; campingbeaurainville@orange.fr; www.beaurainville.fr/tourisme/camping]** Fr Hesdin take D349 NW to Beaurainville. Site on R bef cent of town, sp. Med, mkd pitch, pt shd; htd wc; shwrs inc; el pnts (10A) €2.70 (poss rev pol); Indtte; shop 1km; bar; playgrnd; fishing; boating; games area; horseriding; wifi; 90% statics; dogs free; red long stay; CKE/CCI. "Ltd touring pitches; site poss clsd in winter - phone ahead; pleasant area with plenty wildlife; gd NH." ♦ € 12.00 2011*

BERCK *3B2* (4km E Rural) *50.41861, 1.60556* **Camping L'Orée du Bois, 251 Chemin Blanc, 62180 Rang-du-Fliers [03 21 84 28 51; fax 03 21 84 28 56; oree.du.bois@wanadoo.fr; www.oreedubois.fr]** Exit A6 junc 25 onto D140 & D917. Thro Rang-du-Fliers, turn R bef pharmacy into Chemin Blanc, site sp. V lge, hdg/mkd pitch, pt shd; wc (some cont); chem disp; mv service pnt; serviced pitches; shwrs inc; el pnts (6A) inc; gas; Indtte (inc dryer); shop adj; tradsmn; rest, snacks; bar; playgrnd; 2 pools (1 htd, covrd); paddling pool; tropical water park; sand beach 4km; tennis; games area; fishing lake; cycle hire; internet; entmnt; 80% statics; dogs €4; phone; Eng spkn; adv bkg; quiet; ccard acc; red low ssn/long stay/CKE/CCI. "Conv Le Touquet, Boulogne, Montreuil & Calais; peaceful site in woodland; ltd space for tourers; vg pools; pleasant, helpful owners; m'van pitches cramped." ♦ 30 Mar-31 Oct. € 47.00 2013*

BERGUES *3A3* (7km N Rural) *50.96500, 2.43300* **Aire de Camping-Car Municipal, 59380 Bergues** Exit A25 junc 16 twd Bergues (N) on D916 then R onto D110. When town ramparts appear on L turn L twd town ent arch. Turn R bef drawbdge, site in 200m. NB m'vans only. Med, all hdstg, unshd; no facs; own san; shop, rest, snacks, bar in town; BBQ; dogs; bus adj; quiet. "Only avail when all-weather, winter sports pitch adj not in use; no charge; gd views of town; clean & tidy; pleasant walks." 2009*

BERGUES *3A3* (500m NE Urban) *50.97248, 2.43420* **Camping Le Vauban, Blvd Vauban, 59380 Bergues [03 28 68 65 25; fax 03 28 63 52 60; cassiopee.tourisme@wanadoo.fr; http://campingvauban.free.fr]** Exit A16 junc 60 twd Bergues on D916. In 2km turn L onto D2 dir Coudekerque vill. In 2km turn R at rndabt onto D72 to Bergues, turn R immed bef canal, site strt on at foot of town ramparts. Med, hdg/mkd pitch, terr, pt shd; wc (cont); chem disp; mv service pnt; baby facs; fam bthrm; shwrs €1.30; el pnts (6A) inc (poss rev pol); Indtte; tradsmn; shop, rest, snacks & bar in town; playgrnd; pool nr; 60% statics; no twin-axles; dogs €1.05; poss cr; adv bkg; quiet; no ccard acc; red low ssn; CKE/CCI. "Pleasant site; sm pitches poss diff lge o'fits; ltd manoeuvring in site rds; friendly & helpful; basic, dated san facs, but improvements in hand (2011); gates clsd 2130-0700 & poss clsd 1230-1730; lovely fortified town; conv Dunkerque & Calais; NH only." ♦ ltd 1 Apr-31 Oct. € 16.00 2011*

⊞ **BERGUES** *3A3* (4km NE Rural) *50.97720, 2.50447* **FFCC Parc Les Résidences La Becque, 791 Rue de l'Est, 59380 Warhem [03 28 62 00 40; fax 03 28 62 05 65; www.residences-la-becque.com]** Exit A25 at junc 16 sp Bergues. At top of slip rd turn L D916 then turn R at rndabt onto D110; L in 4km to Warhem. Site well sp in vill. Med, hdg/mkd pitch, hdstg, pt shd, wc (cont); own san; shwrs €1.55; el pnts (6A) €2.50; gas; Indry rm; shop 1km; supmkt in Hoymille; playgrnd; rv fishing 2km; tennis; 99% statics; dogs €1.55; quiet. "Only 2 pitches for tourers; low ssn ltd office opening (clsd Mon & Fri) & access/exit diff (Jun 08) - not rec to arr on these days; otherwise last resort NH; clean facs." ♦ € 17.00 2009*

BOIRY NOTRE DAME see Arras *3B3*

⊞ **BOULOGNE SUR MER** *3A2* (6km E Rural) *50.75133, 1.72013* **Camping Manoir de Senlecques, 45 Rue de la Fontaine, 62126 Pernes lez Boulogne [03 21 30 09 85 or 06 16 76 75 22 (mob); isabelleansel@orange.fr; www.lemanoirdesenlecques.com]** Exit A16 junc 33 sp Wimille; at rndabt turn under m'way onto D233 (pt of rd is narr) to Pernes in 7km & site is on L 1km past vill. Alt rte for longer o'fits (rds wider): exit A16 onto N42 dir St Omer. Turn R for La Capelle, then L on D233E for Pernes; turn R at junc in vill. NB Foll sp 'Manoir de Senlecques' if no 'Camping' sp. Long o'fits take care at ent. Sm, some hdstg, pt shd; wc; chem disp; mv service pnt; shwrs; el pnts (6A) inc(some rev pol); Indtte; shop, supmkt 5km; rest in walking dist; BBQ; sand beach 6km; fishing; 10% statics; dogs; some Eng spkn; adv bkg; quiet; red CKE/CCI. "Beautiful area; site in manor house grnds; gite avail; conv NH; vet within 3km; conv Calais, Channel Tunnel & Nausica Seaworld." € 12.00 2013*

BOULOGNE SUR MER *3A2* (8km E Rural) *50.73111, 1.71582* **Camp Municipal Les Sapins, Route de Crémarest, 62360 La Capelle-lès-Boulogne [03 21 83 16 61]** Exit A16 junc 31 E onto N42 to La Capelle vill; cont to next rndabt & take sp Crémarest; site on L opp horse riding school. Sm, pt shd; wc; shwrs inc; el pnts (4-6A) €2.35-4.60 (poss rev pol); Indtte; hypmkt, rest, snacks & bar 2km; BBQ; playgrnd; sand beach 4km; bus 1km; poss cr; adv bkg; poss rd noise & fr horseriding school; no ccard acc; CKE/CCI. "Helpful warden; gd modern san facs but insufficient amount; office 0800-0900 & 1600-1700; gd NH for Calais; poss travellers." 15 Apr-15 Sep. € 17.00 2014*

⊞ **BOULOGNE SUR MER** *3A2* (16km E Rural) *50.73400, 1.82400* **Camping à la Ferme Le Bois Groult (Leclercq), 120 impasse du Bois Groult, 62142 Henneveux Le Plouy [03 21 33 32 16; leclercq.gilbert0643@orange.fr; www.leboisgroult.fr]** Take N42 fr Boulogne twd St Omer, take exit S dir Desvres (D127). Immed at rndabt foll sp Colembert. On ent Le Plouy turn R at the calvary & foll sp to site in 1km. Sm, hdstg, pt sl, pt shd; wc; shwrs; el pnts (6-10A) €5; shops 6km; dogs €1; adv bkg; quiet; ccard not acc. "Charming, well-kept, peaceful CL-type site; pleasant & helpful owner; no barrier; WWI places of interest; easy access fr N42; ideal NH to/fr ferry/tunnel; excel; new san facs (2013); excel site; v clean & tidy site." ♦ € 14.00 2014*

BOULOGNE SUR MER *3A2* (6km S Coastal) *50.67128, 1.57079* **FFCC Camp Municipal La Falaise, Rue Charles Cazin, 62224 Equihen-Plage [03 21 31 22 61; fax 03 21 80 54 01; camping.equihen.plage@orange.fr; www.camping-equihen-plage.fr]** Exit A16 junc 28 onto D901 dir Boulogne, then D940 S. Turn R to Condette then foll sp Equihen-Plage, site sp in vill. Access fr D901 via narr rds. Med, hdg pitch, sl, terr, pt shd; wc; chem disp; mv service pnt; shwrs inc; el pnts (10-16A) €4.90-5.40 (poss rev pol); Indtte; playgrnd; sand beach 200m; watersports; games rm; 85% statics (sep area); dogs €2.40; phone; adv bkg; ccard acc; red low ssn; CKE/CCI. "Pleasant, well-run site in excel location, but poss windy; excel clean facs; sl pitches poss diff long o'fits; steep rd to beach." 28 Mar - 12 Nov. € 19.00 2013*

BOULOGNE SUR MER *3A2* (7km S Urban) *50.67752, 1.64335* **Camping Les Cytises, Chemin Georges Ducrocq, 62360 Isques [tel/fax 03 21 31 11 10 / 06 62 91 72 71 (ls); campcytises@orange.fr; www.lescytises.fr]** S fr Boulogne on D901 to Isques; site 150m fr D901. Or on A16 exit junc 28 & foll sp Isques & camp sp. Med, hdg pitch, hdstg, terr, pt shd; htd wc; chem disp; mv service pnt; baby facs; shwrs inc; el pnts (6A) inc (poss rev pol); gas; Indtte; shop 400m; snacks; playgrnd; pool & sand beach 4km; rv adj; games area; games rm; 50% statics; dogs €1; Eng spkn; adv bkg; some rlwy noise; ccard acc; red low ssn; CKE/CCI. "Pleasant site; poss sm pitches; friendly staff; clean, modern san facs, ltd low ssn; barrier clsd 2300-0700; conv Channel Tunnel & 5 mins fr Nausicaá; poss unkempt low ssn; conv NH nr m'way; gd." ♦ 29 Mar-19 Oct. € 25.50 2014*

BRAY DUNES see Dunkerque *3A3*

BUYSSCHEURE see St Omer *3A3*

CALAIS *3A3* (8km E Rural) *50.98020, 2.01393* **Camping Les Petits Moulins, 1634 Rue des Petits Moulins, 62215 Oye-Plage [03 21 85 12 94]** Fr A16 junc 21 proceed to Oye-Plage. Strt thro traff lts & take 2nd L to site past derelict windmill. Sm, unshd; wc (own facs low ssn); chem disp (wc); shwrs inc; el pnts (10A) inc; shops 2km; sw beach 2km; 90% statics; dogs; poss cr; quiet. "Busy, well-kept CL-type site at end of statics site; open view; friendly, helpful owner; gd, basic san facs; ltd el pnts; poss run down low ssn; find pitch, book in house adj; ltd touring pitches; phone ahead; conv ferries; NH only." 15 Apr-30 Sep. € 12.00 2009*

⊞ **CALAIS** *3A3* (12km E Coastal) *50.99657, 2.05062* **Camping Clairette, 525 Route des Dunes, 62215 Oye-Plage [03 21 35 83 51 / 06 14 22 92 71 (mob); fax 03 21 35 83 51; www.campingclairette62.com]** Exit A16 junc 50 & foll sp Oye-Plage. At traff lts at D940 cont strt. At junc with D119 turn R then L, site on L in 2km. Foll sp 'Réserve Naturelle'. Med, hdg/mkd pitch, pt sl, unshd; htd wc; chem disp (wc); mv service pnt; shwrs inc; el pnts (10A) €4; gas 5km; Indtte; shops 5km; tradsmn; BBQ; sm playgrnd; htd, covrd pool 5km; beach 500m; 95% statics; dogs €1.40; clsd 16 Dec-14 Jan; poss cr; Eng spkn; adv bkg; quiet; ccard acc; CKE/CCI. "Ltd touring pitches, rec phone/email in adv; warm welcome; helpful owners; security barrier; nature reserve nrby; conv ferries; fair; san facs ok (2013)." € 14.80 2013*

⊞ **CALAIS** *3A3* (12km E Rural) *50.96613, 2.05270* **Camping Le Pont d'Oye, 308 Rue de la Rivière, 62215 Oye-Plage [06 21 85 65 25; ch.lavallee@laposte.net; www.campingdupontdoye.fr]** Exit A16 at junc 50 onto D219 to Oye-Plage; cross rv & immed turn R sp camping; foll rv; site on L. Sm, unshd hdg pitch; wc; chem disp (wc); child/baby facs; shwrs €1; el pnts (6A) €2.50; Snacks; Bar; BBQ; gas; Indtte; shop 2km; tradsmn; playgrnd; sandy beach 5km; dogs; wifi; 85% statics, Eng spkn, adv bkg; CKE/CCI. "Basic CL-type site; few touring pitches; grassed field for c'vans; friendly, helpful owners; san facs adj statics park - v dated but clean; conv ferries; NH only; new owner (2012); site improved." ♦ € 13.00 2013*

⊞ **CALAIS** *3A3* (1km SW Coastal) *50.96603, 1.84370* **Aire Communale, Plage de Calais, Ave Raymond Poincaré, 62100 Calais [03 21 97 89 79, 03 21 46 66 41 or 06 79 62 93 22 (mob); camping@marie-calais.fr]** A16 exit junc 43 dir Blériot-Plage/Calais cent & foll sp for beach (plage). Site nr harbour wall & Fort Risban. Well sp fr town cent. Med; wc (Jun-Sep); water; shop, rest nrby; obtain token/pass fr Camp Municipal adj; wc part-time (charge); warden calls to collect fee pm or pay at Camp Municipal; noise fr ferries; m'vans only. "Well-kept, busy site; gd NH to/fr ferries." € 7.00 2010*

CALAIS *3A3* (4km SW Coastal) *50.95677, 1.81101* **Camp du Fort Lapin, Route Provincial 940, 62231 Sangatte-Blériot Plage [tel/fax 03 21 97 67 77; campingdufortlapin@orange.fr; www.ville-sangatte.fr]** Fr E exit junc 43 fr A16 Calais cent, dir beach (Blériot-Plage). Turn L along coast onto D940 dir Sangatte; site on R in dunes shortly after water tower, opp sports cent; site sp fr D940. Fr S exit A16 junc 41 to Sangatte; at T-junc turn R onto D940; site on L just bef water tower. Med, mkd pitch, pt sl, unshd; wc (some cont); chem disp; baby facs; shwrs inc (poss clsd 2130); el pnts (10A) inc (poss rev pol); Indtte; shop 1km; rest, snacks; bar; BBQ; playgrnd; sand beach adj; 50% statics; dogs; phone; bus; poss cr; adv bkg; quiet; CKE/CCI. "Conv ferry; warden lives on site; rec arr bef 1700 high ssn; gates clsd 2300-0700; recep 0900-1200 & 1600-2000, barrier clsd when recep clsd; ltd parking outside espec w/end - phone ahead for access code; poss cr; gd bus service; basic, clean, adequate san facs (shwrs and Indry clsd after 21:00); conv Auchan & Cité Europe shops; poss youth groups high ssn; conv NH; close to beach; Clean tidy site; quite cr holiday site; lots of statics; adequate facs; grnd v well drained; easy cycle into Calais or walk along the promenade to the harbour ent." ♦ 1 Apr-31 Oct. € 20.75 2014*

CALAIS *3A3* (8km SW Rural) *50.91160, 1.75127* **Camping Les Epinettes, Impasse de Mont Pinet, 62231 Peuplingues [03 21 85 21 39; fax 03 21 85 26 95; lesepinettes@aol.com; www.lesepinettes.fr]** A16 fr Calais to Boulogne, exit junc 40 W on D243 sp Peuplingues, go thro vill & foll sp; site on L in 3km. Med, hdg pitch, pt sl, pt shd; wc; chem disp; shwrs €1; el pnts (4-6A) €2.80-3.80; Indtte; sm shop & 3km; hypmkt 5km; tradsmn; rest 1.5km; playgrnd; sand beach 3km; 80% statics; dogs €1.50; phone; wifi; Library; poss cr; adv bkg; quiet; ccard acc; CKE/CCI. "Pleasant, easy-going site; conv NH for ferries & tunnel; some pitches sm; san facs clean but insufficient for site size; when bureau clsd, site yourself - warden calls eve or call at cottage to pay; if arr late, park on grass verge outside main gate - use facs excl elec, pay half price; few touring pitches." 1 Apr-31 Oct. € 14.00 2014*

CALAIS *3A3* (5km W Coastal) *50.94610, 1.75798* **Camping des Noires Mottes (formerly Cassiopée), Rue Pierre Dupuy, 62231 Sangatte [tel/fax 03 21 82 04 75; campingdesnoiresmottes@orange.fr; www.ville-sangatte.fr]** Fr A16 exit junc 41 sp Sangatte onto D243, at T-junc in vill turn R then R again bef monument. Lge, hdg/mkd pitch, pt sl, pt shd; wc (some cont); chem disp; mv service pnt; shwrs inc (clsd 2130-0800); el pnts (10A) €4.10; Indtte; shop 200m; tradsmn; playgrnd; sand beach 500m; 90% statics; dogs €1.30; bus 500m; poss cr; some Eng spkn; adv bkg rec high ssn; ccard not acc; CKE/CCI. "Conv ferries & Eurotunnel; lge pitches; san facs clean but need update (2010); barrier - no arr bef office opens 1500 (1600 low ssn); san facs clsd o'night & poss 1200-1600; some pitches boggy when wet; windy spot; OK NH." ♦ ltd 01 Apr-31 Oct. € 16.00 2014*

CAMBRAI *3B4* (1km W Urban) *50.17533, 3.21534* **FFCC Camp Municipal Les Trois Clochers, 77 Rue Jean Goudé, 59400 Cambrai [03 27 70 91 64; camping@mairie-cambrai.fr; www.villedecambrai.com/decouverte.html]** Exit A2 junc 14; at rndabt after slip rd (with 6 exits) take D630 dir Cambrai; in 1km (by Buffalo Grill) turn L onto D630; in 200m turn L onto D939; in 100m turn L into Rue Jean Goudé. Or fr Cambrai W on D939; after x-ing rv bdge cont on D939 until traff lts in 300m; go strt over traff lts, then in 100m turn L into Rue Jean Goudé. Site sp fr all dirs on ent town. Sm, hdg pitch, unshd; htd wc; chem disp; mv service pnt; baby facs; shwrs inc; el pnts (5-8A) €2.50; shop, rest adj; Eng spkn; noise fr busy rd adj & early cockerel. "Beautiful, well-kept site; gd, spacious pitches; conv Calais; early arr rec high ssn; helpful, friendly manager; vg san facs but ltd & stretched when site full; interesting town; excel." ♦ 1 Apr-15 Oct. € 12.50 2014*

CAMIERS see Touquet Paris Plage, Le *3B2*

CAPELLE LES BOULOGNE, LA see Boulogne sur Mer *3A2*

CASSEL *3A3* (3km SW Rural) *50.79288, 2.43113* **Camping Le Val de Cassel, 1035 Route des Trois Rois, 59670 Zuytpeene [03 28 48 45 82; charley.chris@hotmail.fr; www.levaldecassel.skyrock.com]** S fr Cassel on D933, turn R onto D138 to Zuytpeene. Site adj church in vill. Sm, hdg pitch, pt shd; wc; chem disp; shwrs €1.50; el pnts (4A) €2-2.20; Indry rm; BBQ; playgrnd; tennis; games area; 90% statics; dogs €1; Eng spkn; adv bkg; quiet; CKE/CCI. "Site is single, narr lane cul-de-sac & only suitable sm o'fits; v few touring pitches; Cassel is unsuitable c'vans as main rd is cobbled, twisting & uneven for 1km; fair NH." 1 Apr-31 Oct. € 14.00 2011*

CONDETTE see Hardelot Plage *3A2*

DOUAI *3B4* (10km S Rural) *50.27374, 3.10565* **Camp Municipal Les Biselles, Chemin des Bisselles, 59151 Arleux [03 27 89 52 36 or 03 27 93 10 00; fax 03 27 94 37 38; office.tourisme@arleux.com]** Exit A2 junc 14 at Cambrai & take D643 twd Douai, after 5km turn W at Bugnicourt to Arleux. Site sp in vill adj canal La Sensée. Lge, hdg/mkd pitch, shd; wc (some cont); shwrs inc; el pnts €6.85; playgrnd; pool; rv fishing; tennis 200m; games area; 96% statics; dogs; phone; poss cr; adv bkg; quiet. "Very few touring pitches; basic san facs; gd cycling along canal." ♦ 1 Apr-31 Oct. € 14.00 2010*

DUNKERQUE *3A3* (3km NE Coastal) *51.05171, 2.42025* **Camp Municipal La Licorne, 1005 Blvd de l'Europe, 59240 Dunkerque [03 28 69 26 68; fax 03 28 69 56 21; campinglalicorne@ville-dunkerque.fr; www.campingdelalicorne.com]** Exot A16 junc 62 sp 'Malo'; at end of slip rd traff lts turn L sp Malo-les-Bains; in 2km (at 5th traff lts) turn R at camping sp; at 2nd traff lts past BP g'ge turn L. Site on L (cont strt to rndabt & return on opp side of dual c'way to ent). Lge, mkd pitch, pt sl, unshd; htd wc; chem disp; mv service pnt; shwrs; el pnts (10A) €4.25 (poss long lead); gas; Indtte; sm shop; supmkt 500m; rest, snacks; bar; playgrnd; pool in high ssn; sand beach adj; 50% statics; dogs €0.90; bus fr site ent; clsd 2200-0700; poss cr; Eng spkn; adv bkg; quiet; red low ssn; CKE/CCI. "Gd, secure NH for ferries - obtain gate code for early depart; pitches uneven; many site rd humps; promenade along sea front to town cent; site backs onto sand dunes & beach; poss windy; m'van o'night area." ♦ ltd 1 Apr-30 Nov. € 17.00 2014*

DUNKERQUE *3A3* (12km NE Coastal) *51.07600, 2.55524* **Camping Perroquet Plage, 59123 Bray-Dunes [03 28 58 37 37; fax 03 28 58 37 01; www.camping-perroquet.com]** On Dunkerque-Ostend D601, about 100m fr Belgian frontier, thro vill on D947; cont 1km to traff lts, R on D60 thro vill, past rlwy stn to site on L. NB Take care some speed humps. V lge, hdg pitch, hdstg, pt shd; htd wc; chem disp; sauna; shwrs €1; el pnts (4A) €4.50; Indtte (inc dryer); shop; rest, snacks; bar; playgrnd; sand beach adj; watersports; tennis; gym; wifi; entmnt; 85% statics; dogs €0.50; poss cr; adv bkg (ess high ssn); Eng spkn; CKE/CCI. "Busy, well-kept site; lge pitches; if parked nr site ent, v long walk to beach; lge bar & rest nr beach (long walk fr ent); gd san facs, poss far; many local attractions; conv NH for ferries; gd." ♦ 1 Apr-1 Oct. € 15.20 2012*

⊞ **DUNKERQUE** *3A3* (6km S Urban) *51.00340, 2.40670* **Camping Les Bois des Forts, 59380 Coudekerque [03 28 61 04 41 or 06 73 83 28 81 (mob); www.campings-nord.com]** Exit A16 junc 60 onto D916, in 2km turn L onto D2 dir Coudekerque. In 2km at rndabt turn L, site on R. Med, hdg pitch, unshd; wc; shwrs €1.50; el pnts (10A) inc; Indtte; bar; playgrnd; games area; 95% statics; quiet."gd NH close to ferry, basic san facs." € 13.00 2013*

⊞ **EMBRY** *3B3* (200m NW Rural) *50.49365, 1.96463* **Aire de Service Camping-Cars d'Embryère, 62990 Embry [03 21 86 77 61]** N fr Embry site is just off D108 dir Hucqueliers & Desvres. Sm, hdstg; wc; shwrs; el pnts; mv service pnt; el pnts £2; Indry sinks; picnic area & gardens; BBQ; m'vans only. "Modern, well-kept site; jetons fr ccard-operated dispenser for services; conv Boulogne & Calais." ♦ ltd € 6.00 2009*

EPERLECQUES see St Omer *3A3*

ESCALLES see Wissant *3A2*

ETAPLES *3B2* (2km N Rural) *50.53238, 1.6257* **Camp Municipal La Pinède, Rue de Boulogne, 62630 Etaples [tel/fax 03 21 94 34 51; www.etaples-tourisme.com]** Take D940 S fr Boulogne-sur-Mer for 25km, site on R after war cemetary & bef Atac supmkt. Or N fr Etaples for 2km on D940. Med, hdg pitch, terr, pt sl, pt shd; wc; mv service pnt; shwrs €0.70; el pnts (6A) €6; gas 500m; Indtte; rest, snacks & bar high ssn; shop high ssn 500m & 1km; playgrnd; beach 4km; rv 500m; some statics; dogs €2.80; phone; poss cr; adv bkg; some rd/rlwy noise; CKE/CCI. "No twin-axles; helpful warden; dated, tired san facs, ltd low ssn; war cemetery 200m; conv Calais; gd NH." ♦ 15 Feb-15 Nov. € 16.00 2012*

FOURMIES see Hirson *3C4*

GRAND FORT PHILIPPE see Gravelines *3A3*

GRAVELINES *3A3* (3km N Coastal) *51.00777, 2.11777* **Camping des Dunes, Rue Victor-Hugo, Plage de Petit-Fort-Philippe, 59820 Gravelines [03 28 23 09 80; fax 03 28 65 35 99; campingdesdunes@campingvpa.fr; www.camping-des-dunes.com]** E fr Calais on D940 foll sp to Gravelines. Heading W fr Dunkerque exit D601 E of Gravelines; turn R into Blvd de L'Europe & foll sp for Petit-Fort-Philippe & site. Site on both sides of rd. Lge, hdg/mkd pitch, hdstg, pt shd; htd wc; chem disp; shwrs inc; el pnts (10A) €4.05; Indtte (inc dryer); shop (high ssn); shop, rest, snacks & bar 1km; playgrnd; direct access to sand beach adj; entmnt; games rm; wifi; entmnt; TV; 10% statics; dogs €2.10; phone; bus; Eng spkn; adv bkg; ccard acc; red low ssn/CKE/CCI. "Site in 2 parts, various prices; gd site rds; helpful, friendly staff; poss uneven pitches & raised manhole covers; conv Dunkerque ferries (15km); adv bkg ess bank holidays; vg." ♦ 1 Apr-31 Oct. € 17.75 2012*

GRAVELINES *3A3* (3km W Coastal) *51.00250, 2.09694* **Camping de la Plage, 115 Rue du Maréchal-Foch, 59153 Grand-Fort-Philippe [03 28 65 31 95 or 03 28 23 09 80; fax 03 28 65 35 99; campingdelaplage@campingvpa.fr; www.camping-de-la-plage.info]** Exit A16 junc 51 dir Grand-Fort-Philippe; at o'skts of town turn R sp Camping ***; cont into town cent; foll rd along quayside; foll rd to L past lge crucifix; turn R at next x-rds; site on R. Med, hdg pitch, hdstg, terr, pt shd; htd wc; chem disp; mv service pnt; shwrs inc (clsd 10pm-8am); el pnts (10A) €3.70 (poss long lead req); Indtte; shop 3km; tradsmn; playgrnd; pool 3km; sand beach 500m; wifi; entmnt; 5% statics; dogs €2; Eng spkn; adv bkg; quiet; ccard acc; red low ssn/CKE/CCI. "Various pitch sizes; ltd el pnts; pleasant walk to sea front; night security guard; conv ferries; rec adv bkg." ♦ 1 Apr-31 Oct. € 21.00 2014*

GUINES *3A3* (2km N Rural) *50.88468, 1.87046* **La p'tite source, 3438 Route de Guînes, 62340 Hames-Boucres, Pas de Calais [06 18 53 02 69; ptitesource@gmail.com; www.camping-laptitesource.com]** Fr Calais take the national CD127 and the CD247. At the rndabt turn L and you are at the site. Med, hdg pitch numbered, pt shd; chem disp; mv service pnt; shwr inc; el pnts (16A) €2.50; gas; Indtte; rest, bar; BBQ; picnic area; bowling, pool table; karaoke; dances; fishing €12 pp per day; playgrnd; dogs; quiet. 1 Apr-30 Oct. € 19.00 2013*

GUINES *3A3* (2km W Rural) *50.86611, 1.85694* **Camping De La Bien Assise, Route D231 62340 Guînes [03 21 35 20 77; fax 03 21 36 79 20; castels@bien-assise.com; www.camping-la-bien-assise.com]** Fr Calais or Boulogne, leave A16 at junc 43; foll D305 then D127 to Guines; cont to junc with D231; turn R (across S of vill and cont to rndabt) site ent on L. Fr S (A26 or D943), take D231 to Guines. Lge, hdg/mkd pitch, pt sl, pt shd; htd wc (some cont); chem disp; mv service pnt; baby facs; shwrs inc; el pnts (6A) €5. (poss rev pol); gas; Indtte (inc dryer); shop; supmkt 4km; tradsmn; rest, snacks; bar; BBQ (charcoal/gas); playgrnd; 2 pools (1 htd, covrd); paddling pool; waterslide; beach 12km; tennis; cycle hire; horseriding 3km; golf nrby; wifi; entmnt; TV/games rm; 20% statics (tour ops); dogs €3; twin-axles acc (rec check in adv); v cr high ssn; Eng spkn; adv bkg, rec all times; rd & rlwy noise; some pitches; ccard acc; red long stay/low ssn; CKE/CCI. "Pleasant, busy site in grnds of chateau; well-kept & well-run; gd sized pitches with easy access; conv ferries - late arr area; pleasant, cheerful, helpful staff; clean san facs, stretched when site full; excel rest clsd in Jan; vg pool complex; grass pitches, some soft low ssn & boggy when wet; vet in Ardres (9km), site will book for you; even if notice says 'Complete' check availability for sh stay; mkt Fri; excel; vg site; shwrs falling below standard; excel rest; ACSI acc; gd modern facs; v popular o'night stop; san facs need refurb." ♦ 05 Apr-27 Sep. € 41.00 SBS - P05 2014*

GUINES *3A3* (1km NW Urban) *50.88562, 1.87080* **Camping La Belle Pêche, Route de Guînes, 62340 Hames-Boucres [03 21 35 21 07 or 06 18 53 02 69 (mob); fax 03 21 82 51 50; camping-belle-peche@wanadoo.fr; www.camping-belle-peche.com]** Fr Guînes foll sp Calais on D127; site on L in 1km. Med, hdg pitch, hdstg, pt shd; wc; chem disp; shwrs €1; el pnts (6A) €2.30; shop 500m, rest; bar; playgrnd; rv fishing; tennis; entmnt; 80% statics; Eng spkn; quiet; no cc. "Conv ferries; Eurotunnel 15 mins; some pitches flood in wet weather; NH only." 1 May-30 Oct. € 16.30 2011*

HARDELOT PLAGE *3A2* (3km NE Urban) *50.64661, 1.62539* **Caravaning du Château d'Hardelot, 21 Rue Nouvelle, 62360 Condette [tel/fax 03 21 87 59 59; contact@camping-caravaning-du-chateau.com; www.camping-caravaning-du-chateau.com]** Take D901 S fr Boulogne, R turn onto D940 dir Le Touquet; then R at rndabt on D113 to Condette; take 2nd turning to Château Camping, R at next rndabt & site 400m on R. Fr S leave A16 at exit 27 to Neufchâtel-Hardelot, take D940 twd Condette & turn L at 1st rndabt onto D113, then as above. Not well sp last 3km. Tight turn into site ent. Med, hdg/mkd pitch, pt sl, pt shd; wc; chem disp; mv service pnt; baby facs; shwrs inc; el pnts (10A) €4.70 (poss rev pol); Indtte; shop 500m; playgrnd; sand beach 3km; tennis 500m; sm multi-gym; horseriding; golf; games rm; child entmnt; wifi; 30% statics; dogs free; poss v cr; some Eng spkn; adv bkg (rec high ssn); some rd noise; no ccard acc; red low ssn; CKE/CCI. "Lovely, well-run, wooded site; busy high ssn; vg low ssn; sm pitches; helpful, friendly owners; clean, modern san facs; tight access some pitches; conv Calais (site barrier opens 0800)." ♦ ltd 1 Apr-31 Oct. € 21.30 2011*

HARDINGHEN *3A3* (500m SE Rural) *50.79462, 1.81369* **Camping à la Ferme Les Piloteries, Rue de l'Eglise, 62132 Hardinghen [03 21 85 01 85; lespiloteries@free.fr; http://lespiloteries.free.fr]** Fr N exit A16 junc 36 at Marquise onto D191 to Hardinghen; turn R onto D127 (where D191 turns sharp L); site in 1km (concealed ent). Sm, pt sl, pt shd; wc; chem disp (wc); shwrs €1; el pnts (6A) €2; BBQ; playgrnd; quiet. "Vg CL-type site; friendly owner." 16 Apr-2 Oct. € 7.40 2011*

HENNEVEUX see Boulogne sur Mer *3A2*

HESDIN *3B3* (6km SE Rural) *50.35979, 2.07116* **Camping Rural St Ladre, 66 Rue Principale, 62770 St Georges [03 21 04 83 34; fax 03 21 30 04 81; bd-martin@wanadoo.fr; http://martinbernard.monsite-orange.fr]** Fr Hesdin SE on D340 for 5.5km. Site on L after St Georges, ent narr lane next cottage on bend. Fr W on D939 or D349 foll sp Frévent, then St Georges. Sp to site poor. Sm, hdg/mkd pitch, pt shd; wc; chem disp; shwrs inc; el pnts (5A) €2.40; no statics; adv bkg; quiet; ccard not acc; CKE/CCI. "Pleasant, peaceful, CL-type site in orchard; basic facs but clean; welcoming, pleasant owner; conv Channel ports, Agincourt & Crécy; usual agricultural noises; gd rests in Hesdin." 1 May-30 Sep. € 8.50 2014*

HIRSON *3C4* (10km N Rural) *50.00585, 4.06195* **FFCC Camping Les Etangs des Moines, 100 rue des Etangs, 59610 Fourmies [tel/fax 03 27 60 04 32; contact@etangs-des-moines.fr]** Fr D1043 Hirson by-pass head N on D963 to Anor. Turn L onto D156 dir Fourmies, site sp on R on ent town. Site also well sp off D42 & thro Fourmies. Med, hdg pitch, hdstg, pt shd; wc; chem disp; mv service pnt; baby facs; shwrs; el pnts (10A) €3.30; Indtte (inc dryer); shop 1km; tradsmn; snacks; bar; BBQ; playgrnd; htd pool; 80% statics; dogs €1; no twin-axles; poss cr; Eng spkn; some rlwy noise; CKE/CCI. "Textile & eco museum in town; shwrs run down, other facs gd; vg." 1 Apr-7 Nov. € 20.00 2014*

HOUPLINES see Armentières *3A3*

ISQUES see Boulogne sur Mer *3A2*

LICQUES *3A3* (1km E Rural) *50.77974, 1.94766* **Camping Les Pommiers des Trois Pays, 273 Rue du Breuil, 62850 Licques [tel/fax 03 21 35 02 02; contact@pommiers-3pays.com; www.pommiers-3pays.com]** Fr Calais to Guînes on D127 then on D215 to Licques; take D191 fr vill & foll sp; site on L in 1km. Or exit A26 junc 2 onto D217 to Licques; turn L onto D215; cont strt on & site on L on far side of vill. NB sloping ent, long o'fits beware grounding. Med, hdg/mkd pitch, sl, pt shd; wc; chem disp; mv service pnt; baby facs; shwrs inc; el pnts (16A) €4.80; Indtte; shops 1km; rest, snacks; bar; BBQ; playgrnd; htd, covrd pool; sand beach, golf, sailing 25km; fishing 2km; games area; games rm; wifi; entmnt; TV rm; 65% statics; dogs €1; adv bkg; quiet; ccard acc; red long stay/low ssn. "Site v full early Jun, adv bkg rec; lge pitches; friendly, helpful owners; gd quality facs, ltd low ssn; gd beaches nr; gd walking; conv Calais/Dunkerque ferries; gd." ♦ 1 Apr-1 Nov. € 32.00 2013*

LICQUES *3A3* (2.5km E Rural) *50.77905, 1.95567* **Camping-Caravaning Le Canchy, Rue de Canchy, 62850 Licques [tel/fax 03 21 82 63 41; camping.lecanchy@wanadoo.fr; www.camping-lecanchy.com]** Fr Calais D127 to Guînes, then D215 sp Licques; site sp in vill on D191; site on L in 1km with narr app rd. Or fr Ardres take D224 to Liques then as above. Or A26 fr Calais exit junc 2 onto D217 dir Zouafques/Tournehem/Licques. Foll site sp in vill. Med, hdg/mkd pitch, pt shd; wc (some cont); chem disp; shwrs €0.50; el pnts (6A) €3.70; Indtte; shops 2km; snacks; bar; BBQ; playgrnd; fishing nrby; entmnt; 50% statics; Eng spkn; adv bkg; quiet; ccard acc; red CKE/CCI. "Busy site; friendly, helpful owners; dated san facs, ltd low ssn; gd walking/cycling; conv Calais & ferries; vg." 15 Mar-31 Oct. € 17.70 2012*

MARQUION *3B4* (2km N Rural) *50.22280, 3.10863* **FFCC Camping de l'Epinette, 7 Rue du Calvaire, 62860 Sauchy-Lestrée [03 21 59 50 13; epinette62@wanadoo.com; www.lepinette62.com]** Fr A26 exit junc 8 onto D939 to Marquion. On ent Marquion turn R at x-rds to Sauchy-Lestrée; on ent vill turn R at 1st T-junc & site on L in 100m. Fr Cambrai take D939 twd Arras, then as above. Sm, pt sl, pt shd; wc (own san rec); chem disp; shwrs €2; el pnts (6A) €3 (poss rev pol); gas; Indtte; shops 3km; playgrnd; games area; many statics; dogs free; adv bkg; quiet but some military aircraft noise; ccard not acc; CKE/CCI. "Charming, well-kept site in tranquil spot; sm CL-type area for tourers; helpful owner; clean simple but adequate facs, ltd low ssn; levelling blocks ess for m'vans; conv Calais/Dunkerque; WW1 cemetary nr; gd value; popular NH." 1 Apr-31 Oct. € 17.00 2013*

MARQUISE *3A3* (4km S Rural) *50.78316, 1.67035* **FFCC Camping L'Escale, 15 Route Nationale, 62250 Wacquinghen [tel/fax 03 21 32 00 69; camp-escale@wanadoo.fr; www.escale-camping.com]** Fr A16 S fr Calais exit junc 34. Fr A16 N fr Boulogne exit junc 33. Foll sp. Lge, pt shd; wc (cont); chem disp; mv service pnt; shwrs inc; el pnts (4A) €3.50 (poss rev pol); gas; Indtte; shop; supmkt 3km; rest, snacks; bar; playgrnd; entmnt; wifi; 90% statics; dogs; poss cr; quiet; ccard acc. "Pleasant site; open 24 hrs; conv NH nr ferries, Channel tunnel & WW2 coastal defences; o'fits staying 1 night pitch on meadow at front of site for ease of exit (but some noise fr m'way); m'van 'aire' open all yr; vg." ♦ 1 Apr-15 Oct. € 18.00 2011*

MAUBEUGE *3B4* (1km N Rural) *50.29545, 3.97696* **Camp Municipal du Clair de Lune, 212 Route de Mons, 59600 Maubeuge [03 27 62 25 48; fax 03 27 60 25 94; camping@ville-maubeuge.fr; www.ville-maubeuge.fr]** Fr Mons head S on N2 twd Maubeuge, site on L about 1.5km bef town cent, sp. Med, hdg/mkd pitch, some hdstg, pt sl, pt shd; htd wc; chem disp; baby facs; shwrs inc; el pnts (6A) inc (rev pol); Indry rm; shops 500m; hypmkt 1km; tradsmn; rest, snacks, bar 2km; BBQ; playgrnd; watersports 25km; cycle hire; games rm; internet; a few statics; dogs free; twin-axles acc (rec check in adv); phone adj; bus adj; adv bkg; some rd noise; ccard acc. "Attractive, wooded, well-kept site; busy but peaceful; spacious pitches - some asymmetric & pitching poss diff; friendly, helpful staff; excel, clean san facs; mkt Sat am; popular NH; excel; v clean & tidy; gd value; some rd noise during the day." ♦ 1 Apr-29 Sep. € 19.00 SBS - P07 2014*

⊞ **MONTREUIL** *3B3* (500m N Rural) *50.46853, 1.76280* **FFCC Camping La Fontaine des Clercs, 1 Rue de l'Eglise, 62170 Montreuil [tel/fax 03 21 06 07 28; desmarest.mi@wanadoo.fr; www.campinglafontainedesclercs.fr]** Fr N or S turn SW off D901 at rndabt onto D349 to Montreuil; turn R immed after rlwy x-ing (onto Rue des Préaux); in 120m turn R; site in 100m on R; sp on Rv Canche. Or take 2nd R ALMOST immed after (20m) rlwy-xing (onto Grande Ville Basse); in 50m fork R (Rue de l'Eglise); site in 200m on R. NB Poss difff access lge o'fits. Med, mkd pitch, hdstg, pt sl, terr, pt shd; htd wc; chem disp; mv service pnt; shwrs inc; el pnts (10A) €4; shops 500m; tradsmn; BBQ; pool 1.5km; rv adj; fishing; games rm; wifi; 60% statics; dogs €2; site clsd over New Year; adv bkg rec high ssn; quiet; no ccard acc; red low ssn; CKE/CCI. "Busy, basic site in beautiful spot; helpful owner; dated san facs (2010); steep & narr site rd with tight turns to terr pitches, some sm; not suitable lge o'fits; some generous pitches beside rv; vet in Montreuil; attractive, historic town - uphill walk; conv NH Le Touquet, beaches & ferry; san facs improving." € 23.40 2014*

NAMPONT ST MARTIN *3B3* (2km NE Rural) *50.37039, 1.77546* **Camping Auberge des Etangs, 91 Rue Vallée de l'Authie, 62870 Roussent [03 21 81 20 10; www.auberge-des-etangs.fr]** 11km S of Montreuil on D901, take D139E to Roussent, site on R in vill. Med, mkd pitch, pt sl, pt shd; wc; chem disp; shwrs inc; el pnts (6A) inc; gas; lndtte; shop; rest, snacks; playgrnd; rv fishing 2km; entmnt; TV; mostly statics; quiet but noise fr hotel (disco). "Ltd space for tourers; NH only." 1 Apr-30 Nov. € 21.00 2010*

NORDAUSQUES see Ardres *3A3*

OYE PLAGE see Calais *3A3*

PEUPLINGUES see Calais *3A3*

RANG DU FLIERS see Berck *3B2*

ST AMAND LES EAUX *3B4* (3.5km SE Rural) *50.43535, 3.46290* **FFCC Camping du Mont des Bruyères, 806 Rue Basly, 59230 St Amand-les-Eaux [tel/fax 03 27 48 56 87; info@campingmontdesbruyeres.com; www.campingmontdesbruyeres.com]** Exit A23 m'way at junc 5 or 6 onto ring rd D169, site sp. Fr N exit E42 junc 31 onto N52/N507 then D169. Avoid St Amand cent. Med, hdg/mkd pitch, pt sl, terr, shd; htd wc; mv service pnt; shwrs inc; el pnts (6A-10A) €4.20-6.30; lndtte; shop; tradsmn; bar; BBQ; playgrnd; wifi; pool 7km; 60% statics; dogs €1.50; adv bkg; quiet; red low ssn; CKE/CCI. "Attractive site on forest edge; most touring pitches under trees; access to some pitches diff due slopes; gd cycling; excel birdlife on site; fac gd & clean." 15 Mar-31 Oct. € 17.40 or €20.62 inc. 6A 2011*

ST AMAND LES EAUX *3B4* (7km NW Rural) *50.46313, 3.34428* **FFCC Camping La Gentilhommière, 905 Rue de Beaumetz, 59310 Saméon [tel/fax 03 20 61 54 03; campsameon@orange.fr; www.camping-lagentilhommiere.fr]** Fr A23 Paris-Lille, exit junc 3, sp St Amand, then L at rndabt foll sp Saméon. Site on R 300m. Med, hdg pitch, shd; htd wc; chem disp; shwrs inc; el pnts (3A) inc; gas; lndtte; shop 8km; tradsmn; snacks; bar; BBQ; playgrnd; fishing; 90% statics; dogs €0.80; poss cr; quiet; CKE/CCI. "Well-kept lovely site; 5 touring pitches only; charming owner; gd local rest; gd for Lille (park & ride fr a'route); 1km to train to Lille with Piscine Roubaix museum." ♦ 1 Apr-30 Oct. € 13.20 2011*

ST JANS CAPPEL see Bailleul *3A3*

ST OMER *3A3* (8km NE Rural) *50.80152, 2.33924* **Camping La Chaumière, 529 Langhemast Straete, 59285 Buysscheure [03 28 43 03 57; camping.lachaumiere@wanadoo.fr; www.campinglachaumiere.com]** Take D928 fr St Omer (see NOTE) twd Bergues & Watten & foll sp St Momelin. Stay on rd until Lederzeele & turn R onto D26 twds Cassel. After approx 2km turn R just bef rlwy bdge sp Buysscheure & site. Turn L after church, R, then site on L 500m. Single-track rd after church. NOTE on D928 fr St Omer height limit 3m; use adj level x-ing sp rte for vehicles over 3m. NB app fr Cassel diff, espec for wide or long o'fits; also rd thro Cassel cobbled & poss more diff to find. Sm, hdg/mkd pitch, hdstg; pt sl, unshd; wc; chem disp; mv service pnt; baby facs; shwrs inc; el pnts (6A) inc; lndry rm; shop 1km; rest, snacks; bar; BBQ; playgrnd; htd pool; paddling pool; fishing lake; cycle hire; archery; entmnt; wifi; TV; dogs €1; Eng spkn; adv bkg; quiet, but poss some rlwy noise; ccard not acc; red low ssn; CKE/CCI. "Lovely, well-kept site; friendly, family-run; conv ferries - but poss no exit bef 0800; gd sized pitches - some may req o'fit manhandling due hedges; gd san facs, ltd in number, stretched when site full; no arr bef 12 noon; close to WW1/WW2 sites; local vet; excel; friendly well kept site, gd bar and food; rest open only w/end in low ssn." ♦ 1 Apr-30 Sep. € 34.00 2014*

ST OMER *3A3* (10km E Rural) *50.73490, 2.37463* **FFCC Camping Le Bloem Straete, 1 Rue Bloemstraete, 59173 Renescure [03 28 49 85 65 / 06 80 21 28 46 (ls); lebloemstraete@yahoo.fr; www.lebloemstraete.fr]** E fr St Omer on D642 thro Renescure dir Hazebrouck; turn L (site sp) onto D406 Rue André Coo on bend on leaving Renescure; over level x-ing; site on L thro gates. Sm, hdg pitch, hdstg, pt shd; htd wc; chem disp (wc); shwrs inc; el pnts (2-6A) €2.50 (poss rev pol); lndtte; shop, rest, snack & bar 1km; playgrnd; tennis; games rm; wifi; 70% statics; dogs; poss cr; Eng spkn; quiet; adv bkg; CKE/CCI. "Conv Calais ferry & tourist sites; manoeuvring poss diff due high kerbs; m'van area; poss lack of maintenance early ssn (2011); v helpful owners, site clean and tidy; worth finding!; excel facs; easy access to ports." ♦ ltd 15 Apr-15 Oct. € 16.00 2013*

ST OMER *3A3* (3km SE Urban) *50.74612, 2.30566* **Camp Municipal Beauséjour, Rue Michelet, 62510 Arques [tel/fax 03 21 88 53 66; camping-arques@wanadoo.fr; www.ville-arques.fr]** Fr junc 4 of A26 foll sp Arques to town cent. Foll sp Hazebrouck. After x-ing canal site sp 'Camping ***' on L. NB Drive 25m bef correct turning to site. Site signs sm and easily missed. Med, hdg/mkd pitch, pt sh; wc; chem disp; mv service pnt; baby facs; shwrs (€0.50); el pnts (6A) €3 (poss rev pol); lndtte; shops, rest, snack & bar 1.5km; BBQ playgrnd; lake fishing; 80% statics; dogs; phone, wifi; Eng spkn; adv bkg; some noise fr rlwy & mill across lake; ccard acc; CKE/CCI. "Neat, tidy site; well-run; lge pitches but tight access; friendly, helpful warden; excel, clean facs; m'van o'night area adj (no el pnts); gd cycling along canal; lakes & nature park nrby; conv Cristal d'Arques; canal lift & preserved rlwy in town; Calais & Dunkerque 50 mins drive; useful NH; vg." ♦ 1 Apr-31 Oct. € 19.25 2014*

ST OMER *3A3* (12.8km SW Rural) *50.66938, 2.16490* **Camping du Moulin, 14 bis rue Bernard Chochoy, 62380 Remilly- Wirquin [tel/fax 03 21 93 05 99; www.campingdumoulin.ex-flash.com]** Fr A26 N or S take exit 3 sp St Omer; at rndabt take D342 sp Lumbres; in 2m at Setques turn L onto D211 sp Esquerdes; in 2m at Esquerdes turn R onto D192E to Crehem; at Crehem turn R on D192; site on L in 1m; sharp turn into site. Med, hdg, pt shd; wc; chem disp; shwrs; el pnts (3A) €2.50; lndtte (inc dryer); BBQ; playgrnd; games rm; 75% statics; dogs €1; phone; bus 45m; twin axles; adv bkg; quiet; CKE/CCI. "Rando rail 6km; horse riding 5km; gd walking country; rv fishing on site; golf 10mins away." ♦ 1 Jan-31 Nov. € 13.00 2014*

ST OMER *3A3* (10km NW Rural) *50.81890, 2.17870* **Kawan Village Château du Gandspette, 133 Rue du Gandspette, 62910 Eperlecques [03 21 93 43 93 or 03 21 12 89 08 (LS); fax 03 21 95 74 98; contact@chateau-gandspette.com; www.chateau-gandspette.com]** Fr Calais SE on A26/E15 exit junc 2 onto D943 foll sp Nordausques-St Omer. 1.5km after Nordausques turn L onto D221 twd Eperlecques; site 5km on L. Do not ent Eperlecques. (Larger o'fts should cont on D943 fr Nordausques to Tilques; at rndabt foll sp for Dunkerque (D300) then D221 dir Eperlecques, site on R. Med, hdg/mkd pitch, some hdstg, pt sl, pt shd; wc; chem disp; mv service pnt; baby facs; shwrs inc; el pnts (6A) €5.20 (some rev pol); gas; lndtte (inc dryer); supmkt 800m; tradsmn; rest (high ssn); snacks; bar; BBQ (charcoal/gas); playgrnd; 2 pools (1 htd); fishing 3km; horseriding & golf 5km; tennis; cycle hire; wifi; entmnt; games/TV rm; 15% statics; dogs €1; no c'vans/m'vans over 8m; phone; poss cr; Eng spkn; adv bkg; quiet; ccard acc; red low ssn; CKE/CCI. "Beautiful, well-kept, busy site; spacious, mainly sl pitches; charming, helpful owners; superb, clean san facs; vg pool & playgrnd; excel rest; site poss muddy in wet; conv NH for ferries - early dep catered for; poss poor security; gd for dogs; rec visit WW2 'Le Blockhaus' nr site; conv A26; highly rec; conv for Calais & for ferry to Dover; spectacular location." ♦ 1 Apr-30 Sep. € 43.00 (CChq acc) SBS - P08 2014*

SAUCHY LESTREE see Marquion *3B4*

STELLA PLAGE see Touquet Paris Plage, Le *6B2*

THIEMBRONNE *3A3* (500m NW Rural) *50.62114, 2.05424* **Camping Les Pommiers, 1 Route des Desvres, 62560 Thiembronne [tel/fax 03 21 39 50 19; campinglespommiers@orange.fr; www.camping-pommiers.com]** SW fr St Omer for 25km on D928 to Fauquembergues. NW on D158 for 4km past water tower. Site sp. Med, mkd pitch, sl, shd; wc; chem disp; shwrs €0.30; el pnts (6A) €2.60; lndtte (inc dryer); shop 1km; snacks; playgrnd; pool; games area; entmnt; TV; 75% statics; poss cr; adv bkg; quiet. ♦ 15 Mar-15 Oct. € 14.40 2009*

TORTEQUESNE see Douai *3B4*

⊞ **TOUQUET PARIS PLAGE, LE** *3B2* (5km N Rural) *50.55270, 1.61887* **Camping La Dune Blanche, Route d'Etaples, 62176 Camiers [03 21 09 78 48 or 06 86 15 69 32 (mob); fax 03 21 09 79 59; duneblanche@wanadoo.fr; www.lesdomaines.org]** Leave A16 junc 26 dir Etaples or junc 27 dir Neufchâtel onto D940 dir Etables, Le Touquet. Site well sp. Lge, mkd pitch, pt sl, shd; htd wc; chem disp; baby facs; shwrs inc; el pnts (6A) €6; gas; lndtte; shops 2km; tradsmn; bar; BBQ; playgrnd; sand beach 3km; entmnt; TV; 90% statics; dogs €2.50; phone; bus to beach at Ste Cécile; poss cr; adv bkg; quiet; red long stay; ccard acc; CKE/CCI. "Amongst trees; remote, quiet by rlwy line; staff friendly & helpful." ♦ € 17.55 2014*

TOUQUET PARIS PLAGE, LE *3B2* (1km S Coastal) *50.51091, 1.58867* **Camping Caravaning Municipal Stoneham, Ave François Godin, 62520 Le Touquet-Paris-Plage [03 21 05 16 55; fax 03 21 05 06 48; caravaning.stoneham@letouquet.com; www.letouquet.com]** Fr Etaples on D939; stay in L-hand lane at traff lts dir airport & cont strt on (Ave du Général de Gaulle); L at traff lts sp Golf (Ave du Golf); foll rd to rndabt; turn R onto Ave François Godin (site sp); at next rndabt site on R. Or cont another 500m along Ave du Général de Gaulle to x-rds; turn L into Ave Louis Quetelart; in 500m at T-junc turn L into Ave François Godin; site on L in 200m. Lge, hdg pitch, pt shd; wc; shwrs inc; el pnts (6A) inc (poss rev pol); lndtte; shops 1km; tradsmn; playgrnd; htd pool 2km; sand beach 1km; 95% statics; dogs €2; poss cr even low ssn; adv bkg rec; CKE/CCI. "Pleasant & well kept site; conv for town; helpful staff; excel facs; recep closes 1800 (low ssn 2010); m'van 'aires' nr harbour & equestrian cent; mkt Sat; walking & cycle paths to South Beach; town has many rest." 2 Feb-15 Nov. € 26.60 2014*

TOUQUET PARIS PLAGE, LE *3B2* (5km S Coastal) *50.47238, 1.57717* **Camp Municipal de la Mer, Cours des Champs Elysées, 62780 Stella-Plage [03 21 84 60 60; fax 03 21 09 58 36; info@campingdelamer.com; www.campingdelamer.com]** S fr Etaples on D940, in 4km turn R dir Stella-Plage; at lge rndabt by sea front turn L to site; sp at end of rd. Lge, unshd; wc; el pnts (10A) €5; lndtte; shops etc nrby; direct access to beach 200m; tennis nrby; aqualand, golf & horseriding in Le Touquet; some statics; dogs €0.90; quiet. "Interesting, sandy site sheltered by dunes; busy high ssn; san facs clean; v busy site, poss noisy." ♦ 14 Jun-9 Sep. € 16.60 2013*

TOUQUET PARIS PLAGE, LE *3B2* (6km S Coastal) *50.47343, 1.59178* **Camping La Forêt, 149 Blvd de Berck, 62780 Stella-Plage [03 21 94 75 01; info@laforetstella.fr; www.laforetstella.fr/uk/]** Exit A16 junc 26 onto D393 to Etaples; turn L onto D940 dir Berck; foll sp Stella-Plage. Blvd de Berck is turning S off D144 W to Stella-Plage. Med, hdg/mkd pitch, unshd; wc; baby facs; shwrs; el pnts €5; gas; Indtte (inc dryer); shop; tradsmn; playgrnd; fishing nrby; sandy beach 2km; tennis 900m; sailing; wind surfing; games area; games rm; entment; wifi; 90% statics; dogs €2.50; phone; bus adj; poss cr; Eng spkn; adv bkg; quiet; red low ssn. "Gd site; tourist attractions nrby; narr aves to pitches with tight corners; not suitable for lge o'fits; unisex facs; not a touring site." 1 Apr-30 Sep. € 27.00 2014*

TOURNEHEM SUR LA HEM see Ardres *3A3*

VILLERS SIRE NICOLE see Maubeuge *3B4*

WACQUINGHEN see Marquise *3A3*

"I need an on-site restaurant"

We do our best to make sure site information is correct, but it is always best to check any must-have facilities are still available or will be open during your visit.

WATTEN *3A3* (200m W Urban) *50.83353, 2.21005* **Camping Le Val Joly (Le Val Joli), Rue de Aa, 59143 Watten [tel/fax 03 21 88 23 26 or 03 21 88 24 75; www.campings-nord.com]** NW fr St Omer on D943; N of Tilques turn N onto D300; in 5km at rndabt turn R onto D207 sp Watten; at T-junc turn L onto D213; cross rv brdg & turn L in 500m at camping sp. Med, mkd pitch, pt shd; wc; chem disp; shwrs €2; el pnts (10A) €2.20-3.10; Indtte; shops adj; supmkt nr; tradmn; playgrnd; fishing & cycling along rv/canal; 90% statics; dogs; adv bkg; quiet but some rd & rlwy noise; ccard not acc. "Spacious, attractive, well-kept site; conv NH for ferries; welcoming, friendly, helpful owner; basic, clean san facs; secure gates, locked 2200-0700, but off rd parking; no site lighting (2010); few touring pitches - arr early or phone ahead high ssn; access to rv walk; glass works at Arques; vet nr; vg." 1 Apr-31 Oct. € 10.65 2013*

WIMEREUX *3A2* (1km S Coastal) *50.76131, 1.60769* **Camp Municipal L'Olympic, 49 Rue de la Libération, 62930 Wimereux [03 21 32 45 63; fax 03 21 83 68 94; camping.wimereux@orange.fr; www.ville-wimereux.fr]** A16 exit 32 & foll sp Wimereux Sud to vill; turn R at rndabt to site. Or N fr Boulogne on D940, at vill sp Wimereux & rndabt, turn R. Med, hdg/mkd pitch, pt sl, unshd; wc; chem disp; baby facs; shwrs inc; el pnts (6A) €4; BBQ; Indry rm; shop adj; tradsmn; rest; playgrnd; pool 4km; beach 800m; sailing; fishing; mainly statics; dogs €2; Eng spkn; some noise fr rds & rlwy; ccard acc; CKE/CCI. "Conv Boulogne; basic facs, stretched high ssn & poss irreg cleaning low ssn (2010); hot water runs out early; poss waterlogging after rain; gd vet in attractive seaside town; poor security, take care thieves at night (2009); useful NH only; off clsd 1300-1500." 17 Mar-19 Oct. € 23.50 2014*

⊞ **WIMEREUX** *3A2* (1.5km S Coastal) *50.75277, 1.60722* **Caravaning L'Eté Indien, Hameau de Honvault, 62930 Wimereux [03 21 30 23 50; fax 03 2191 20 46; ete.indien@wanadoo.fr; www.eteindien-wimereux.com]** Fr Calais on A16 exit junc 32 sp Wimereux Sud. Thro Terlincthun R after x-ing rlwy, site in 700m on R - narr, v rough rd. Med, pt sl, terr, unshd; wc; chem disp; mv service pnt; serviced pitches; baby facs; shwrs inc; el pnts (10A) inc; gas; Indtte (inc dryer); shop; snacks; bar; BBQ (gas); playgrnd; htd pool; paddling pool; sandy beach 1.5km; games area; games rm; wifi; entmnt; 90% statics; dogs €3; phone; poss cr; Eng spkn; adv bkg; some rlwy noise; red low ssn/long stay. "Conv A16, Calais ferries; rec low ssn phone to check site open; ltd touring pitches & poss steep; muddy & unpleasant in winter; rlwy runs along one side of site; NH only if desperate!; new sw pool and MV area; gd clean facs (2012); poor facs for waste water." ♦ € 39.00 2014*

WISSANT *3A2* (6km NE Coastal) *50.91226, 1.72054* **Camping Les Erables, 17 Rue du Château d'Eau, 62179 Escalles [03 21 85 25 36; boutroy.les-erables@wanadoo.fr; www.camping-les-erables.fr/]** Fr A16 take exit 40 onto D243 thro Peuplingues. Site sp to L on ent Escalles (on sharp R bend). Steep ent. Don't be put off by No Entry signs - 1-way system for c'vans on app rd. Sm, mkd pitch, hdstg, terr, unshd; htd wc; chem disp; mv service pnt; shws €1.20; private san facs extra; el pnts (6-10A) €3.50-€4.50; Indtte (inc dryer); shop 2km; tradsmn; rest & snacks 500m; BBQ; sand beach 2km; dogs; phone; poss cr/noisy at w/end; Eng spkn; adv bkg; CKE/CCI. "Lovely, well-kept open site with great views; family owned; spacious pitches but poss haphazard pitching; welcoming staff; immac, modern facs; gates open 0800-2200; 2 pitches for disabled visitors with san facs; coast walks; sh walk to vill; conv tunnel & ferries; gd site with view of Channel; excel grass pitch site; friendly helpful owners; popular site." ♦ 1 Apr-11 Nov. € 23.40 2014*

"Satellite navigation makes touring much easier"

Remember most sat navs don't know if you're towing or in a larger vehicle – always use yours alongside maps and site directions.

WISSANT *3A2* (4km E Rural) *50.88290, 1.70938* **Camping La Vallée, 901 Rue Principale, 62179 Hervelinghen [03 21 36 73 96 or 03 21 85 15 43; www.campingdelavallee.net]** Fr Calais exit A16 onto D244 & foll sp St Inglevert. Site on L at end Hervelinghen vill. Med, hdg/mkd pitch, pt shd; htd wc; chem disp; shwrs €1; el pnts (6A) €3.60 (poss rev pol); Indry rm; rest, snacks; bar; BBQ; playgrnd; sand/shgl beach 3km; games area; wifi; 75% statics; dogs €1; Eng spkn; no adv bkg - phone to check availability; quiet; CKE/CCI. "Family-run site; clean san facs; conv Calais, Cité Europe; gd walking in area." ♦ ltd 1 Apr-31 Oct. € 14.50 2013*

Normandy

Regional Introduction

Rouen

Welcome to Normandy

A fascinating area of France, dotted with historical war memorials and cemeteries commemorating some of the biggest battles of WWI and II.

For a more relaxing stay, there are an extraordinary number of parks and gardens open to the public. Explore these well-kept open spaces with a gentle stroll and take a picnic on the manicured lawns.

Renowned for its museums, monuments and concert halls, Normandy caters for all types of visitors looking to learn about the region's history and culture.

Local highlights

Famous for its dairy products of butter, milk, cream and cheese, the region is also renowned worldwide for its apples. Try authentic and traditional dishes made from these locally-sourced ingredients in one of the small eateries that can be found all over Normandy.

Every four years, visitors come to the prestigious L'Armada. The port of Rouen plays host to the finest and largest sailing ships, modern warships and many other vessels which come from all around the world and sail up the River Seine. Visitors can also enjoy concerts, fireworks and other entertainment.

Major towns and cities

- Rouen – in the heart of Normandy and home to many historical landmarks.
- Caen – founded in the 11th-century by William the Conqueror.
- Bayeux – a medieval town with cobbled streets, famous for its cathedral and tapestry.
- Camembert – traditional and picturesque village, famous for its cheese.

Regional attractions

- Claude Monet's House and Gardens, Giverny – beautiful gardens that inspired the impressionist's most famous works.
- Museum of the Battle of Normandy, Bayeux – details and accounts of the first 10 weeks after D-Day.
- Palais de la Bénédictine, Fécamp – housing a historical distillery and museum.
- Rue du Gros-Horloge, Rouen – an ancient cathedral, market place and clock tower.

Find out more

www.normandie-tourism.fr

Tel: (0)2 32 08 32 40 Rouen Tourist Office
Tel: (0)2 31 27 14 14 Caen Tourist Office

SITES IN NORMANDY

AGON COUTAINVILLE *1D4* (300m NE Urban/Coastal) *49.05163, -1.59136* **Camp Municipal Le Marais, Blvd Lebel-Jéhenne, 50230 Agon-Coutainville [02 33 47 05 20; martinetmarais@wanadoo.fr]** Fr Coutances take D44 to Agon-Coutainville. Site sp adj Hippodrome. Lge, unshd; wc; chem disp; shwrs inc; el pnts (5A) €3; Indtte; shops adj; tradsmn; playgrnd; sand beach 600m; sailing; fishing; dogs €3.10; adv bkg; quiet. ♦ 1 Jul-31 Aug. € 11.00 2010*

AGON COUTAINVILLE *1D4* (300m NE Urban/Coastal) *49.05105, -1.59112* **Camp Municipal Le Martinet, Blvd Lebel-Jéhenne, 50230 Agon-Coutainville [02 33 47 05 20; martinetmarais@wanadoo.fr; www.agoncoutainville.fr / www.coutainville.com]** Fr Coutances take D44 to Agon-Coutainville; site sp nr Hippodrome. Med, hdg/mkd pitch, pt shd; wc; mv service pnt; shwrs inc; el pnts (5A) €3.10; Indtte (inc dryer); shop 250m; tradsmn; BBQ; playgrnd; sand beach 600m; 55% statics; dogs €3.20; bus; poss cr; Eng spkn; adv bkg; ccard acc; CKE/CCI. "V pleasant site; ltd facs low ssn; horse racecourse adj; vg." ♦ 1 Apr-30 Oct. € 11.00 2010*

AGON COUTAINVILLE *1D4* (6km SE Rural) *48.99275, -1.52881* **Camp Municipal Les Gravelets, 3 Rue du Rey, 50590 Montmartin-sur-Mer [tel/fax 02 33 47 70 20; campgrav@chez.com; www.chez.com/campgrav]** Fr Coutances take D971 S twd Granville. Turn W at Hyenville to Montmartin-sur-Mer, site sp in vill. Med, mkd pitch, pt sl, terr, pt shd; wc; shwrs inc; el pnts (6A) €2; Indry rm; shop 300m; tradsmn; playgrnd; sand beach, fishing & sailing 2km; tennis adj; dogs €0.80; some statics; adv bkg; quiet; CKE/CCI. "Gd." ♦ 1 Apr-31 Oct. € 9.30 2010*

AIGLE, L' *4E2* (12km NW Rural) *48.78841, 0.46533* **Camp Municipal des Saints-Pères, 61550 St Evroult-Notre-Dame-du-Bois [06 78 33 04 94 (mob) or 02 33 34 93 12 (Mairie); catherine-matte@orange.fr]** Fr L'Aigle on D13, on ent vill site on L by lake. Sm, hdstg, terr, pt shd; wc; chem disp; mv service pnt; shwrs inc; el pnts (4-10A) €1.50-2.50; shop, rest, snacks, bar 500m; playgrnd; lake sw adj; watersports; fishing; dogs €0.20; no adv bkg; poss noisy; CKE/CCI. "Pleasant lakeside vill; facs gd & clean with hot water, ltd low ssn; quiet; walks; on edge of sm vill opp ruins of ancient abbey; friendly, helpful staff, but no Eng spkn." ♦ 1 Apr-30 Sep. € 14.00 2014*

ALENCON *4E1* (1km SW Rural) *48.42566, 0.07321* **Camp Municipal de Guéramé, 65 Rue de Guéramé, 61000 Alençon [tel/fax 02 33 26 34 95; camping.guerame@orange.fr; www.ville-alencon.fr]** Located nr town cent. Fr N on D38 take N12 W (Carrefour sp). In 5km take D1 L sp Condé-sur-Sarthe. At rndabt turn L sp Alençon then R immed after Carrefour supmkt, foll site sp. Site is sp fr D112 inner ring rd. Med, hdg pitches, hdstg, pt shd; htd wc (some cont); chem disp; mv service pnt; baby facs; shwrs inc; el pnts (5A) €3.10 (check el pnts carefully) (poss long lead req); Indtte (inc dryer); shop, snacks, bar adj; BBQ; playgrnd; pool complex 700m; tennis; rv fishing; canoeing; cycle hire; horseriding; wifi; entmnt; TV rm; dogs €1.90; poss cr; Eng spkn; adv bkg; quiet but w/end disco noise; no ccard acc; CKE/CCI. "Helpful warden; clean san facs; o'night area for m'vans; barrier/recep clsd 1800 low ssn; low ssn phone ahead to check site open; some pitches poss flood in heavy rain; rvside walk to town thro arboretum; peaceful site." ♦ 1 Apr-30 Sep. € 18.65 2014*

ANCTEVILLE see Coutances *1D4*

ANDELYS, LES *3D2* (1km S Rural) *49.23582, 1.40016* **FFCC Camping de L'Ile des Trois Rois, 1 rue Gilles Nicolle, 27700 Les Andelys [02 32 54 23 79; fax 02 32 51 14 54; campingtroisrois@aol.com; www.camping-troisrois.com]** Fr Rouen S on A13, exit junc 18 onto D135 & foll sp Les Andelys. Cross bdge over Rv Seine & turn immed R at rndabt, site on R on rvside. Site sp fr town cent. Lge, hdg/mkd pitch, some hdstg, pt shd; htd wc (some cont); chem disp; mv service pnt; shwrs inc; el pnts (10A) inc; gas; Indtte (inc dryer); snacks; bar; BBQ; playgrnd; htd pool; paddling pool; fishing; bowling alley; cycle hire; games rm; wifi; entmnt; TV rm; 50% statics; dogs €2.50; phone; poss cr; Eng spkn; quiet but some rd noise; ccard acc; red long stay/CKE/CCI. "Well-kept site on Rv Seine; extra lge pitches avail; friendly, helpful staff; ltd san facs which are dated but clean; gd security; conv Rouen, Evreux, Giverny; view ruins of Château Gaillard; nice place, nice people." ♦ 15 Mar-15 Nov. € 26.00 (CChq acc) 2014*

See advertisement

NORMANDY

ANET *3D2* (1km N Urban) *48.86278, 1.41552* **Camp Municipal Les Trillots, Chemin des Trillots, 27530 Ezy-sur-Eure [02 37 64 73 21 or 02 37 64 73 48 (Mairie)]** N fr Dreux on D928/D143. Site on N side of Rv Eure. Med, pt shd; htd wc; shwrs inc; el pnts (4A) inc; Indtte; supmkt nr; rest, snacks & bar 1km; BBQ; 95% statics; dogs; quiet. "Quiet site adj rvside walks; gd san facs; helpful warden; poss not suited to tourers; not rec." 1 Mar-15 Nov. € 13.00 2012*

ANNOVILLE *1D4* (1km SW Coastal) *48.95521, -1.54911* **Camp Municipal Les Peupliers, 177 Rue de la Libération, 50660 Annoville [02 33 47 67 73 or 02 33 47 67 (LS); campinglespeupliers@orange.fr]** N fr Granville on D971 to Bréhal then take D20 for approx 6km dir Annonville, turn L at Hameau Hébert, site sp on R. Med, mkd pitch, pt sl, unshd; wc; chem disp; baby facs; shwrs inc; el pnts €3; supmkt in Bréhal; snacks; playgrnd; sand beach 500m; 10% statics; dogs €1.20; Eng spkn; adv bkg; quiet; CKE/CCI. "Gd walking, birdwatching; gd site." 12 Jun-5 Sep. € 8.00 2010*

ARGENTAN *4E1* (500m SE Urban) *48.73991, -0.01668* **Camp Municipal du Parc de la Noé, 34 Rue de la Noé, 61200 Argentan [02 33 36 05 69; fax 02 33 39 96 61; camping@argentan.info; www.argentan.fr]** S fr Caen on D958 foll camping sp fr by-pass. At rndabt in town cent foll sp to Alencon (Boulevard Carnot). In 300m turn L and foll camping signs. NB. Site ent immed on R on entering Rue de la Noe. Sm, shd; htd wc; chem disp; mv service pnt; shwrs; el pnts (6A) €2.60; Indtte (inc dryer); shop 1km; playgrnd; pool 1km; rv & pond; games area; wifi; TV; few statics; poss cr; adv bkg ess high ssn; lake & park adj; quiet. "Superb, clean, tidy site adj town park; helpful warden; excel, clean san facs; gd touring base; lovely town; immac site run by efficient warden." ♦ 1 Apr-30 Sep. € 11.70 2014*

ARGENTAN *4E1* (2km S Rural) *48.71841, -0.01077* **FFCC Aire Naturelle du Val de Baize (Huet des Aunay), 18 Rue de Mauvaisville, 61200 Argentan [02 33 67 27 11; fax 02 33 35 39 16; mhuetdesaunay@orange.fr; www.normandiealaferme.com]** Take D958 fr Argentan twd Sées & Alençon; site clealy sp on D958 - turn R just bef leaving Argentan boundary. Site adj T-junc N of farm buildings. Sm, some hdstg, pt shd; wc; chem disp; mv service pnt; shwrs inc; el pnts (3-6A) €2.50-4.60; shops 1.5km; snacks; playgrnd; pool 2.5km; B&B; 10% statics; dogs; Eng spkn; adv bkg; quiet; ccard not acc; CKE/CCI. "Charming, well-kept site; lge pitches in orchard; clean but dated facs, ltd low ssn; friendly welcome; NH only; ring in advance to check opening dates." opening date unknown - closing 30 Sep. € 15.00 2014*

ARROMANCHES LES BAINS *3D1* (3km E Coastal) *49.33963, -0.58188* **Camp Municipal Quintefeuille, Ave Maurice Schumann, 14960 Asnelles [02 31 22 35 50; fax 02 31 21 99 45; campingquintefeuille@wanadoo.fr; www.arromanches.com/uk/camping_accueil.htm]** Site sp on D514, but visible fr vill sq in Asnelles. Med, mkd pitch, unshd; wc; chem disp; shwrs; el pnts; Indtte; shops adj; rest, snacks, bar 300m; playgrnd; sand beach 300m; fishing; tennis; games area; quiet. ♦ 1 Apr-2 Nov. € 14.50 2014*

ARROMANCHES LES BAINS *3D1* (450m W Urban/Coastal) *49.33793, -0.62647* **Camp Municipal, Ave de Verdun, 14117 Arromanches-les-Bains [02 31 22 36 78; fax 02 31 21 80 22; campingarromanches@wanadoo.fr]** App fr Bayeux on D516. Turn R on onto D65 on app to Arromanches to site on L. Med, pt sl, terr, pt shd; wc; shwrs inc; el pnts (10A) €3; gas; sand beach 500m; poss cr. "Conv Mulberry Harbour exhibition & invasion beaches; friendly warden; gd san facs; levelling blocks req most pitches; grnd soft when wet; sh stay pitches stony; water access diff for m'vans (2010); gd." 1 Apr-2 Nov. € 16.00 2014*

AUMALE *3C3* (500m W Rural) *49.76618, 1.74618* **Camp Municipal Le Grand Mail, Chemin du Grand Mail, 76390 Aumale [02 35 93 40 50 (Mairie); fax 02 35 93 86 79; communeaumale@wanadoo.fr; www.aumale.com]** Clearly sp in town; long steep climb to ent. Med, pt shd; wc; mv service pnt; shwrs €2.10; el pnts (6A) €2.40; Indtte; shops 1km; playgrnd; pool 1km; cycle hire €1; fishing 1km; dogs €2; noise fr rd. "Gd site; clean, modern san facs; conv Channel ports; steep slope fr town to site; gd NH." ♦ 01 Aprr-30 Sep. € 19.60 2014*

AUNAY SUR ODON *3D1* (500m NE Urban) *49.02530, -0.62515* **Camp Municipal La Closerie, Rue de Caen, 14260 Aunay-sur-Odon [02 31 77 32 46 or 07850 511893; fax 02 31 77 70 07; mairieaunaysurodon@orange.fr; www.aunaysurodon.fr]** Exit A84 junc 43 sp Villers-Bocage/Aunay & take D6 twd Aunay. In approx 3km bef Aunay town sp, turn L sp 'Zone Industrielle', in 200m turn R at rndabt. Site on R in 100m nr sports stadium. Sm, mkd pitch, pt sl, pt shd; wc; chem disp; mv service pnt; shwrs inc; el pnts €2.80; gas, shops 200m; games area; dogs €1.55; Eng spkn; quiet; CKE/CCI. "Delightful, attractive vill; Sat mkt; vet avail; conv NH for Caen ferry & gd touring base; helpful, welcoming warden." ♦ ltd 6 Jul - 31 Aug. € 7.50 2013*

AVRANCHES *2E4* (6km S Rural) *48.62092, -1.36556* **FFCC Camping Rural Avallonn (Martinet), La Caufetière, 50220 Céaux [02 33 68 39 47]** Fr Avranches on N175 exit La Buvette & W onto D43. Site in approx 2km. Sm, pt shd; wc; shwrs inc; el pnts (5A) €3.50; rest, snacks; playgrnd; pool; sand beach 20km; dogs; Eng spkn; adv bkg; quiet. "In apple orchard; friendly, helpful owners; clean, rustic san facs; goats & horses in pens on site; many activities, museums nrby; 10km fr Mont-St Michel; uneven grnd, steep & narr ent but gd NH." ♦ 15 Apr-30 Sep. € 14.00 2009*

AVRANCHES *2E4* (10km W Rural) *48.69663, -1.47434* **FFCC Camping La Pérame, 50530 Genêts [02 33 70 82 49; www.wix.com/campinglaperame/home]** Fr Avranches on N175; in 1km turn L on D911 thro Genêts. Turn R onto D35 immed after passing thro Genêts, site on R in 1km. Sm, pt shd; wc; shwrs inc; el pnts (10A) €3 (rev pol); tradsmn; farm produce; playgrnd; 60% statics; dogs €0.90; phone; poss cr; red low ssn; quiet; CKE/CCI. "CL-type site in apple orchard nr sm vill; pleasant owner; gd views of Mont-St Michel fr vill; poss ltd & unkempt low ssn; poss boggy after heavy rain; guided walks to Mont St Michel; rec." 1 May-30 Sep. € 12.50 2011*

BAGNOLES DE L'ORNE *4E1* (1.3km SW Urban) *48.54783, -0.41995* **Camp Municipal de la Vée, Avenue du President Coty, 61140 Bagnoles-de-l'Orne [02 33 37 87 45; fax 02 33 30 14 32; info@campingbagnolesdelorne.com; www.campingbagnolesdelorne.com]** Access fr D335 in vill of Bagnoles-Château. Or fr La Ferté-Macé on D916 for 6km sp Couterne. Well sp fr all dirs. Lge, hdg/mkd pitch, pt sl, pt shd; htd wc (some cont); chem disp; mv service pnt; baby facs; shwrs inc; el pnts (10A) €3.50 (poss rev pol); gas; Indtte; shop 1km; tradsmn; rest, snacks; bar; BBQ; playgrnd; htd pool 1.5km; rv & lake nrby; golf, archery, tennis & mini-golf nrby; wifi; TV; dogs €1.55; phone; free bus to town cent at site ent; poss cr; Eng spkn; no adv bkg; quiet; ccard acc; red low ssn; CKE/CCI. "Excel, well-kept, well-run site in vg location; vg, spotless facs; easy walk to beautiful thermal spa town & lake; forest walks; gd for dogs." ♦ 10 Mar-27 Oct. € 13.25 2012*

See advertisement

"There aren't many sites open at this time of year"

If you're travelling outside peak season remember to call ahead to check site opening dates – even if the entry says 'open all year'.

BALLEROY *1D4* (5km SW Rural) *49.15677, -0.92287* **Camping Domaine de Litteau, Le Perron, 14490 Litteau [02 31 22 22 08 or 05 56 07 90 17; domainedelitteau@siblu.fr; www.siblu.fr/litteau]** Fr St Lô, take D972 to Bayeux. After 14km, at La Malbreche, turn R onto D209 to Litteau. Site on L in approx 500m. Med, some hdg/mkd pitch, pt sl, unshd; wc; chem disp; baby facs; shwrs inc; el pnts (6A) inc; Indtte; shop & 4km; snacks; bar; playgrnd; htd covrd pool; lake fishing adj; sand beach 25km; horseriding; child entmnt; TV; 90% statics; dogs; phone; poss cr; Eng spkn; adv bkg; ccard acc; CKE/CCI. "Busy high ssn; forest adj; conv D-Day beaches, museums, Bayeux tapestry." 9 Apr-1 Nov. € 40.00 2009*

BARFLEUR *1C4* (500m NW Urban/Coastal) *49.67564, -1.26645* **Camp Municipal La Blanche Nef, 12 Chemin de la Masse, 50760 Gatteville-le-Phare [02 33 23 15 40; fax 02 33 23 95 14; lablanchenef@wanadoo.fr]** Foll main rd to harbour; half-way on L side of harbour & turn L at mkd gap in car pk; cross sm side-rd & foll site sp on sea wall; site visible on L in 300m. Site accessible only fr S (Barfleur). Med, pt sl, unshd; htd wc; chem disp; mv service pnt; shwrs inc; el pnts (6-10A); Indtte; shops 1km; tradsmn; snacks; bar; playgrnd; sand beach adj; internet; 45% statics; dogs €1.30; Eng spkn; quiet; adv bkg; ccard acc; red low ssn; CKE/CCI. "Gd sized pitches; vg facs; lovely site; sea views; gd beach; gd birdwatching, walking, cycling; m'vans all year; walking dist to fishing vill; exceptionally new & clean washing facs (2014)." ♦ Mid Feb-Mid Nov. € 15.00 2014*

⊞ **BARFLEUR** *1C4* (1km NW Coastal) *49.67971, -1.27364* **Camping La Ferme du Bord de Mer, 50760 Gatteville-le-Phare [02 33 54 01 77; fax 02 33 54 78 99; fdbm@caramail.com]** On D901 fr Cherbourg; on o'skts of Barfleur turn L onto D116 for Gatteville-Phare. Site on R in 1km. Sm, hdg/mkd pitch, pt sl, pt shd; wc; chem disp; shwrs inc; Indry rm; some serviced pitches; el pnts (3-10A) €2.60-4.40; gas; Indry rm; shop 1.5km; rest, snacks & bar high ssn or 1.5km; playgrnd; sm sand beach adj; entmnt; games rm; 25% statics; dogs €1.45; phone; poss cr; quiet; red low ssn. "CL-type site; sheltered beach; coastal path to vill & lighthouse; conv ferries (30 mins); Sep 2002 member reported high-strength poison against rodents in field adj site - no warning notices displayed, beware children or dogs; gd." ♦ ltd € 10.85 2009*

BARNEVILLE CARTERET *1C4* (3.5km SE Coastal) **Camping du Golf, Saint Jean de la Rivière, 50270 Barneville-Cartere [02 33 04 78 90; contact@camping-du-golf.fr; www.camping-du-golf.co.uk]** Fr Barneville-Carteret, turn W on D130, after 1.5km turn L. Site on R after 1.5km. Site well sp fr Barneville-Carteret. Med, mkd pitch, unshd; wc; shwrs inc; el pnts (6A) inc; shop; gas; rest, snacks; sandy beach 1km; covered, htd pool; playgrnd; entmnt; adv bkg; quiet. "Gd quiet site with clean facs." ♦ 1 Apr-30 Oct. € 30.00 2014*

See advert on next page

BARNEVILLE CARTERET *1C4* (2.5km S Coastal) *49.36383, -1.75386* **Yelloh! Village Les Vikings, 50270 St Jean-de-la-Rivière [02 33 53 84 13; contact@camping-lesvikings.com; www.camping-lesvikings.com / www.yellohvillage.co.uk]** Fr D650 foll sp dir St Jean-de-la-Rivière. Site well sp. Lge, mkd pitch, pt shd; wc; chem disp; baby facs; shwrs inc; el pnts (4A) inc (poss rev pol); lndtte (inc dryer); shop; rest, snacks; bar; BBQ; playgrnd; 2 htd pool (1 covrd); paddling pool; waterslide; sand beach 500m; games rm; games area; golf, tennis nr; wifi; entmnt high ssn; TV; 50% statics; dogs; Eng spkn; adv bkg; quiet; red low ssn; ccard acc; CKE/CCI. "Gd site; helpful owner; vg touring base; gd walking." ♦ 1 Apr-2 Oct. € 39.65 2010*

"That's changed – Should I let The Club know?"

If you find something on site that's different from the site entry, fill in a report and let us know. See www.caravanclub.co.uk/europereport.

BARNEVILLE CARTERET *1C4* (2.5km SW Coastal) *49.36758, -1.75773* **Camping Les Bosquets, Rue du Capitaine Quenault, 50270 Barneville-Plage [02 33 04 73 62; fax 02 33 04 35 82; lesbosquets@orange.fr; www.camping-lesbosquets.com]** Fr D650 at Barneville-Carteret turn S dir Barneville-Plage, site sp. Lge, terr, pt shd; wc; chem disp; shwrs inc; el pnts (10A) €3.80; lndtte; shop; bar; playgrnd; htd pool; paddling pool; sand beach 400m; horseriding nrby; games rm; TV; 50% statics; dogs €1.80; bus; poss cr; adv bkg; quiet; CKE/CCI. "Pleasant site; beach ideal for children." ♦ 1 Apr-15 Sep. € 17.40 2009*

BARNEVILLE CARTERET *1C4* (10km SW Coastal) *49.30323, 1.68825* **Camping L'Espérance, 36 Rue de la Gamburie, 50580 Denneville-Plage [02 33 07 12 71; fax 02 33 07 58 32; camping.esperance@wanadoo.fr; www.camping-esperance.fr]** S fr Cherbourg on D950 thro Barneville-Carteret; in 7km fork R & cont on D650 & then R onto D137 sp Denneville-Plage & camping. Med, hdg/mkd pitch, pt shd; wc; chem disp; shwrs inc; el pnts (4-6A) €2.90-3.80; gas; lndtte; shop; snacks; bar; playgrnd; htd pool; sand beach 300m; tennis; cycle hire; games rm; entmnt; 50% statics; dogs €2; phone; poss cr; Eng spkn; adv bkg; quiet; ccard acc; CKE/CCI. "Helpful owners." 1 Apr-30 Sep. € 21.00 2009*

BARNEVILLE CARTERET *1C4* (2.5km W Urban/Coastal) *49.38081, -1.78614* **FFCC Camping du Bocage, Rue du Bocage, Carteret, 50270 Barneville-Carteret [02 33 53 86 91; fax 02 33 04 35 98; www.barneville-carteret.fr]** Fr Cherbourg take D650 to Carteret, turn R onto D902, site by disused rlwy stn & nr TO. Med, hdg pitch, shd; wc (some cont); chem disp; baby facs; shwrs inc; el pnts (3-6A) €2.50-3; lndtte; shops adj; rest 200m; snacks; playgrnd; sand beach 500m; 40% statics; poss cr; adv bkg; quiet; red low ssn; CKE/CCI. "Pleasant seaside resort with excel beaches; well-kept site; pitches soft in wet weather." 1 Apr-30 Sep. € 21.80 2011*

BAUBIGNY see Barneville Carteret *1C4*

BAYEUX *3D1* (500m N Urban) *49.28392, -0.69760* **Camp Municipal des Bords de L'Aure, Blvd d'Eindhoven, 14400 Bayeux [tel/fax 02 31 92 08 43; campingmunicipal@mairie-bayeux.fr; www.mairie-bayeux.fr]** Site sp off Périphérique d'Eindhoven (Bayeux by-pass, D613). Fr W (Cherbourg) exit N13 junc 38, turn L over N13, then R onto D613 thro Vaucelles. At rndabt cont on D613 (3rd exit) Blvd d'Eindhoven. Site on R immed after traff lts, almost opp Briconaute DIY store. Fr E (Caen) on N13 exit junc 36 onto D613 N; foll ring rd across 2 rndabts, 4 traff lts, site on L opp Bayeux town sp. Lge, pt shd, some hdg pitch, some hdstg; wc (some cont); chem disp; mv service pnt; shwrs inc; el pnts (5A) €3.66 (poss rev pol); gas; lndtte; shop (Jul/Aug); playgrnd; indoor pool adj; sand beach 10km; dogs; phone; some; adv bkg ess high ssn; rd noise; 10% red 5+ days; CKE/CCI. "Gd, well-kept site; clean, basic san facs; avoid perimeter pitches (narr hdstgs & rd noise); no twin-axles; office open LS; gd footpath to town along stream; Bayeux festival 1st w/end July; conv ferries; lge mkt Sat." ♦ 15 Apr-31Oct. € 24.25 2014*

BAYEUX *3D1* (17.6km SE Rural) *49.15722, -0.76018* **Camping Caravaning Escapade, Rue de l'église, 14490 CAHAGNOLLES [02 31 21 63 59; escapadecamping@orange.fr; www.campinglescapade.net]** Fr Saint Paul du Varnay take D99 Cahagnolles on the L; foll rd for aprrox 2.5km; turn L & aft church campsite on R. Med, mkd pitch, pt shd; wc; chem disp; shwrs inc; el pnts (10A) €3.90; lndtte; bar/bistro; BBQ; pool (htd); lake; recep rm for events; wifi; dogs €2.70; adv bkg; ccard acc. "Lovely site; well looked after & cared for; clean san facs; friendly owners & staff; pt of Flower Campings chain." 1 Apr-15 Oct. € 35.00 (CChq acc) 2014*

BAYEUX *3D1* (7km SE Rural) *49.24840, -0.60245* **Camping Le Château de Martragny, 52 Hameau Saint-Léger, 14740 Martragny [02 31 80 21 40; fax 02 31 08 14 91; chateau.martragny@wanadoo.fr; www.chateau-martragny.com / www.chateau-martragny.fr]** Fr Caen going NW on N13 dir Bayeux/Cherbourg, leave at Martragny/Carcagny exit. Strt on & take 2nd R (past turn for Martragny/Creully) into site & chateau grnds. Fr Bayeux after leaving N13 (Martragny/Carcagny), go L over bdge to end of rd, turn L then take 2nd R into Chateau grnds. Lge, some mkd pitch, pt sl, pt shd; wc; chem disp; mv service pnt; baby facs; shwrs inc; el pnts (15A) €5 (long lead poss req, poss rev pol); gas; lndtte (inc dryer); shop; tradsmn; snacks; bar; BBQ; playgrnd; htd pool; paddling pool; sand beach 12km; fishing; tennis; horseriding 500m; wifi; entmnt; games/TV rm; dogs €0.50; no c'vans/m'vans over 8m; poss cr; Eng spkn; adv bkg; quiet; ccard acc; red low ssn; CKE/CCI. "Popular, attractive site on lawns of chateau; attractive area; relaxed atmosphere; friendly, helpful staff; new san facs (2013); gd rest; poss muddy when wet; conv cemetaries; D-Day beaches 15km; Sat mkt in Bayeux; conv Caen ferry; excel." ♦ 12 May-11 Sep. € 48.30 (CChq acc) SBS - N06 2014*

⊞ **BAYEUX** *3D1* (8km SE Rural) *49.25041, -0.59251* **Camping Le Manoir de l'Abbaye (Godfroy), 15 Rue de Creully, 14740 Martragny [tel/fax 02 31 80 25 95; yvette.godfroy@libertysurf.fr; http://godfroy.pagesperso-orange.fr]** Take N13 Bayeux, Caen dual c'way for 7km, fork R sp Martagny. Over dual c'way L at T-junc, then 1st R sp D82 Martragny & Creully site on R 500m. Sharp L steep turn into site. Sm, pt shd; wc unisex; chem disp; shwrs inc; el pnts (15A) €4.(poss rev pol); lndtte; tradsmn; dogs €2.30; Eng-spkn; adv bkg; red low ssn; CKE/CCI. "Peaceful, relaxing, well-kept site; lovely grnds; helpful, welcoming owners; steps to ltd san facs; meals & wine avail on request; winter storage; conv Ouistreham ferries; highly rec; wc, shwr, kitchen fac's in same rm; v restful; some elec hookups rev polarity." ♦ ltd € 16.00 2014*

BAYEUX *3D1* (9km NW Rural) *49.33120, -0.80240* **Camping Reine Mathilde, 14400 Etréham [02 31 21 76 55; fax 02 31 22 18 33; campingreinemathilde@gmail.com; www.camping-normandie-rm.fr]** NW fr Bayeux on D6 turn L to Etréham (D100); site 3km (sp). Or W fr Bayeux on N13 for 8km, exist junc 38. At x-rds 1.5km after vill of Tour-en-Bessin turn R on D206 to Etréham & bear L at church. Med, hdg/mkd pitch, pt shd; htd wc; chem disp; mv service pnt adj; baby facs; shwrs inc; el pnts (6A) €4.70; lndtte; sm shop & 4km; tradsmn; rest, snacks & pizza van (high ssn); bar; playgrnd; htd pool; paddling pool; sand beach 5km; cycle hire; fishing 1km; wifi; entmnt; TV; 15% statics; dogs €2.50; phone; Eng spkn; adv bkg; quiet; ccard not acc; red low ssn; CKE/CCI. "Well-kept, attractive site; lge, well spaced hdg pitches; app rds quite narr; friendly, helpful warden; gd, clean san facs; conv D-Day beaches etc; excel." ♦ 1 Apr-30 Sep. € 33.50 (CChq acc) 2014*

BAZINVAL see Blangy sur Bresle *3C2*

BEAUMONT HAGUE *1C4* (5km N Rural/Coastal) *49.70442, -1.84116* **Camp Municipal du Hable, 50440 Omonville-la-Rogue [tel/fax 02 33 52 86 15 or 02 33 01 86 00]** W fr Cherbourg on D901 to Beaumont-Hague; turn N onto D45 dir Omonville-la-Rogue. Med, hdg/mkd pitch, hdstg, pt shd; wc; chem disp; mv service pnt; shwrs €1; el pnts (5-10A) €2.95-4.80; lndtte; shop, gas adj; rest; bar; playgrnd; beach 100m; dogs €0.95; quiet; CKE/CCI. "In pretty vill with gd harbour; 30 mins fr Cherbourg; gd NH." 1 Apr-30 Sep. € 8.50 2009*

BEAUVOIR see Mont St Michel, Le *2E4*

BEC HELLOUIN, LE see Brionne *3D2*

BELLEME *4E2* (1km SW Urban) *48.37420, 0.55370* **Camp Municipal Le Val, Route de Mamers, 61130 Bellême [02 33 85 31 00 (Mairie) 06 07 11 27 39 (After 19h00); fax 02 33 83 58 85; mairie.bellame@wanadoo.fr; www.lepaysbellemois.com]** Fr Mortagne, take D938 S to Bellême; turn R ent town on D955 Alençon rd; site sp on L half-way down hill. Sm, hdg pitch, pt sl, pt shd; wc (some cont); chem disp (wc); shwrs inc; el pnts (8A) €2.65 (poss long lead req); shops 1km by footpath; supmkt 1km; playgrnd, pool, fishing; tennis adj; dogs €0.50; adv bkg rec high ssn. "Pretty, well-kept site; some pitches v sl; warden visits twice daily; gd san facs; poss long water hoses req; pitches poss soft when wet; steep walk to town." 15 Apr-15 Oct. € 14.50 2014*

BENOUVILLE see Ouistreham *3D1*

BERNAY *3D2* (1km S Urban) *49.08020, 0.58703* **Camp Municipal, Rue des Canadiens, 27300 Bernay [02 32 43 30 47; camping@bernay27.fr; www.ville-bernay27.fr]** Site sp fr S'most (Alençon) rndabt off Bernay by-pass D438; twd France Parc Exposition then 1st L & on R. Well sp. Sm, hdg/mkd pitch, pt shd; wc; chem disp; mv service pnt; shwrs inc; el pnts (10A) €3.65 (poss rev pol); lndry rm; shop 500m; tradsmn; rest, bar 1km; playgrnd; pool 300m; wifi; TV rm; dogs; phone; adv bkg; quiet; no ccard acc; CKE/CCI. "Well-kept site; well set-out pitches, diff sizes; helpful & friendly staff; gd clean facs; barrier clsd 2200-0700; conv NH A28; excel, lovely site; debit card acc." ♦ 1 May-30 Sep. € 15.60 2014*

BERNEVAL LE GRAND *3B2* (500m N Coastal) *49.96158, 1.1933* **FFCC Camp Municipal Le Val Boisé, 56 Ave Capitaine Porthéous, 76340 Berneval-le-Grand [02 35 85 29 18; camping-berneval@wanadoo.fr; http://bernevallegrand.fr/camping]** Fr Dieppe take D925 for 6km, turn L at Graincourt onto D54 past Silo on R. Site sp. Sm, mkd pitch, hdstg, terr, pt shd; wc; chem disp; mv service pnt; shwrs; el pnts (16A) €2.70; shop 2km; playgrnd; shgl beach 700m; entmnt; some statics; dogs €0.80; Eng spkn; adv bkg rec; quiet, but rd noise some pitches; CKE/CCI. "Lovely quiet spot; v hilly area, poss diff lge o'fits; gd." 1 Apr-1 Nov. € 9.40 2009*

BLANGY LE CHATEAU *3D1* (500m N Rural) *49.24670, 0.27370* **Camping Le Domaine du Lac, 14130 Blangy-le-Château [02 31 64 62 00; fax 02 31 65 03 46; info@domaine-du-lac.fr; www.domaine-du-lac.fr]** Fr Pont-l'Evêque & A13 S on D579 twd Lisieux. In 5km turn L onto D51 to Blangy where at fountain (rndabt) turn L, taking care. In 200m at end of vill turn L onto D140 Rte de Mesnil & site 200m on R. Site is 5km SE of Pont-l'Evêque. Med, mkd pitch, pt sl, pt shd; wc; chem disp; baby facs; shwrs inc; el pnts (6A) inc (long lead poss req); gas; lndtte; shop & 1km; rest, snacks; bar; BBQ; beach 22km; lake fishing; tennis; games rm; wifi; 70% statics; dogs; adv bkg; some rd noise; ccard acc; CKE/CCI. "Peaceful NH in lovely area; friendly British owner; poss uneven pitches; tired, access to pitches diff when wet; pretty vill; gd walks; conv Honfleur; 1hr to Le Havre ferry; NH only; mainly statics." 1 Apr-31 Oct. € 24.30 2013*

BLANGY LE CHATEAU *3D1* (3km SE Rural) *49.22525, 0.30438* **Camping Le Brévedent, 14130 Le Brévedent [02 31 64 72 88 or 02 31 64 21 50 (LS); contact@campinglebrevedent.com; www.campinglebrevedent.com]** Fr Pont l'Evêque & A13 go S on D579 twd Lisieux; after 5km turn L onto D51 twd Blangy-le-Château. In Blangy bear R at rndabt to stay on D51 & foll sp to Le Brévedent & Moyaux; site on L in just after le Breveden vill. Med, mkd pitch, pt sl, pt shd; htd wc; chem disp; mv service pnt; baby facs; shwrs inc; el pnts (10A) (poss long leads req, poss rev pol); lndtte (inc dryer); sm shop & 3km; tradsmn; rest, snacks; bar; BBQ; playgrnd; htd pool; paddling pool; sand beach 22km; lake fishing; tennis; games area; games rm; cycle hire; horseriding 2km; golf 11km; wifi; entmnt; TV; 10% statics in sep area; no dogs; no c'vans/m'vans over 8m; phone; poss cr; Eng spkn; adv bkg; quiet; ccard acc; red low ssn; CKE/CCI. "Pleasant, busy site with all amenities, around lake in grnds of chateau; welcoming, helpful staff; some modern san facs, ltd low ssn; gd pool; rallies welcome; excel." ♦ 3 May-12 Sep. € 44.30 SBS - N01 2014*

BLANGY SUR BRESLE *3C2* (2.5km E Rural) *49.92378, 1.65693* **Camping Aux Cygnes d'Opale (Formerly Municipal), Zone de Loisirs, 76340 Blangy-sur-Bresle [02 35 94 55 65 / 09 72 32 88 40; fax 09 72 32 88 41; contact@auxcygnesdopale.fr; www.auxcygnesdopale.fr]** Leave A28 at junc 5, R at T-junc onto D49, site on L in 800m. Med, mkd pitch, unshd; wc unisex; chem disp; shwrs inc (clsd 1130-1400 & 2100-0700); el pnts (5-10A) €3 (poss rev pol); lndry rm; supmkt 1km; rest, snacks, bar 2km; BBQ; playgrnd; tennis & mini-golf nrby; wifi; dogs €2; ccard not acc; adv bkg rec; CKE/CCI. "Attractive, well-kept site adj lakes; conv Calais, A28 & D928; gd san facs; adv bkg rec lge o'fits high ssn; no twin-axles; pleasant & helpful warden; rec wait for warden for pitching; poss waterlogged in wet (& entry refused); avoid during Int'l Petanque Competition 3rd w/end June on adj leisure cent; excel NH; new owners (2013), many improvements." ♦ 1 Apr-30 Oct. € 20.00 2014*

BOURG ACHARD *3D2* (1km W Rural) *49.35330, 0.80814* **Camping Le Clos Normand, 235 Route de Pont Audemer, 27310 Bourg-Achard [02 32 56 34 84 or 06 03 60 36 26 (mob); eric.tannay@wanadoo.fr; www.leclosnormand.eu]** 1km W of vill of Bourg-Achard, D675 Rouen-Pont Audemer or exit A13 at Bourg-Achard junc. Med, hdg/mkd pitch, pt sl, pt shd; wc; shwrs inc; el pnts (6A) €3.40 (poss rev pol & poss long lead req); gas; shop; supmkt nr; playgrnd; pool; paddling pool; 10% statics; dogs free; poss cr; adv bkg; some rd noise; ccard acc; red low ssn; CKE/CCI. "Vg, clean san facs; plenty hot water; many pitches uneven; gd." ♦ 1 Apr-30 Sep. € 16.00 2011*

BOURG DUN, LE see Veules les Roses *3C2*

BREHAL *1D4* (4km N Coastal) *48.90863, -1.56473* **FFCC Camp Intercommunal de la Vanlée, 50290 Bréhal [02 33 61 63 80; fax 02 33 61 87 18; contact@camping-vanlee.com; www.camping-vanlee.com]** Turn W off D971 onto D20 thro Bréhal to coast, then N. Site sp, nr 'route submersible'. Lge, mkd pitch, pt sl, unshd; wc; chem disp; mv service pnt; baby facs; shwrs inc; el pnts (6A) €3.80; lndtte; shop high ssn; supmkt nr; rest, snacks; bar; playgrnd; pool; paddling pool; sand beach adj; games area; entmnt; TV rm; dogs €2.60; poss cr; Eng spkn; ccard acc; quiet; CKE/CCI. "Beware soft sand when pitching." ♦ 1 May-30 Sep. € 14.00 2009*

BRETEUIL SUR L'ITON *4E2* (300m SSE Urban) *48.83175, 0.91258* **Camping Les Berges de l'Iton, 53 rue du Fourneau, 27160 Breteuil-sur-Iton [02 32 62 70 35 or 06 84 75 70 32 (mob); campinglesberges-de-liton@orange.fr; www.camping-breteuil-iton.com]** Fr Evreux take D830 twd Conches-en-Ouche. L onto D840 to Breteuil, then foll sp for site. Med, hdg pitch, mkd pitch, hdstg, pt sl, pt shd; htd wc; chem disp; mv service pnt; shwrs inc; el pnts (6-8A); gas; lndtte rm (inc dryer); tradsmn; snacks; bar; BBQ; playgrnd; pool 1km; wifi; 66% statics; dogs; adv bkg; INF; CCI. "Well kept, landscaped site; gd NH; mkt on Wednesdays; helpful staff; vg." 1 Apr-30 Sep. € 24.55 2014*

BRETTEVILLE see Cherbourg *1C4*

BREVEDENT, LE see Blangy le Château *3D1*

BREVILLE SUR MER see Granville *1D4*

BRIONNE *3D2* (500m N Urban) *49.20256, 0.71554* **Camp Municipal La Vallée, Rue Marcel Nogrette, 27800 Brionne [02 32 44 80 35; fax 02 32 46 25 61; www.ville-brionne.fr]** Fr D438 N or S on by-pass, turn N at D46 junc, pass Carrefour supmkt on L & take 1st R, site on L. Sm, hdg pitch, pt shd; wc; chem disp; mv service pnt; shwrs inc; el pnts (8A) €3.40; gas; lndtte; shop, rest etc nrby; BBQ; playgrnd; some statics; dogs; poss cr; quiet; CKE/CCI. "Excel site in lovely vill; gd san facs, poss ltd low ssn; no arr 1000 to 1600 barrier clsd; sh walk to supmkt." 30 Apr-30 Sep. € 15.20 2014*

BRIONNE *3D2* (5km N Rural) *49.23648, 0.72265* **FFCC Camp St Nicolas (Formaly Municipal), 15 Rue St Nicolas, 27800 Le Bec-Hellouin [tel/fax 02 32 44 83 55 or 02 32 44 86 40 (Mairie); campingstnicolas@orange.fr; www.lebechellouin.fr]** Exit A28 junc 13 onto D438 then take D581 to Malleville-sur-le-Bec; site on R 1km after Malleville. Well sp. Med, pt shd; htd wc; chem disp; mv service pnt ; shwrs inc; el pnts (10A) €3.50; Indtte; tradsmn (excel bakeries); rest, snacks, bar in vill; BBQ; playgrnd; tennis, horseriding nr; wifi; some statics; dog €1.50; poss cr; quiet; htd covrd pool CKE/CCI. "Attractive, peaceful, well-kept site in pleasant location; spacious pitches; friendly, helpful warden; vg, clean san facs; gate clsd 2200-0700; gd dog walks; vg cycling; attractive countryside; conv NH nr Calais; rec; delightful vill; rec dir in book." ♦ ltd 15 Mar-15 Oct. € 24.00 (CChq acc) 2014*

⊞ **BRIONNE** *3D2* (6km N Rural) *49.24174, 0.70339* **Camp Municipal Les Marronniers, Rue Louise Givon, 27290 Pont-Authou [02 32 42 75 06 or 06 27 25 21 45 (mob); fax 02 32 56 34 51; lesmarroniers27@orange.fr / campingmunicipaldesmarronniers@orange.fr; www.normandie-accueil.fr]** Heading S on D438 take D130 just bef Brionne sp Pont-Audemer (care req at bdge & rndabts). Site on L in approx 5km, well sp on o'skts of Pont-Authou; foll sp in vill. Med, mkd pitch, ltd hdstg, pt shd; htd wc; chem disp; mv service pnt; shwrs; el pnts (10A) €3.40 (poss rev pol); Indtte (inc dryer); shops 500m; tradsmn; rest & bar in vill; BBQ; playgrnd; fishing; cycle hire; 50% statics; dogs €1.35; adv bkg; quiet but rd noise; CKE/CCI. "Useful, clean stop nr Rouen & m'way; friendly recep; clean san facs; best pitches far side of lake; few hdstg; adv bkg rec; some statics unsightly; stream runs thro site; beautiful valley with many historic towns & vills; excel walking; gd NH; pretty but basic site." € 9.30 2014*

⊞ **BROGLIE** *3D2* (400m S Rural) *49.00684, 0.53067* **Aire de Camping-Car Broglie, Route de la Barre-en-Ouche, 27270 Broglie [02 32 44 60 58; mairie-broglie@wanadoo.fr]** Exit A28 junc 15 onto D49 E dir Broglie. Turn R in vill onto D6138 Rue des Canadiens, then L into Rue de la Victoire over rv, site on R in former rlwy yard, nr municipal library. Sm, mkd pitch, hdstg, pt shd; chem disp; mv service pnt; Indtte 200m; supmkt 800m; rest 200m; rest 400m; quiet. "M'vans only; gate secured at night; ideal NH." € 5.00 2013*

CABOURG *3D1* (8km SW Rural) *49.25210, -0.18823* **Camping Le Clos Tranquille, 17 Route de Troarn, 14810 Gonneville-en-Auge [02 31 24 21 36; fax 02 31 24 28 80; le.clos.tranquille@wanadoo.fr; www.campingleclostranquille.fr]** Fr Cabourg, take D513 twd Caen. 2km after Varaville turn R to Gonneville-en-Auge (by garden cent) D95A. Foll sp to vill, site ent on R after LH bend. Med, pt shd; wc; chem disp; el pnts (6-10A) €3.50-€5 (poss rev pol & long lead req); shwrs inc; gas; Indtte; tradsmn; snacks; shop; playgrnd; cycle hire; sand beach 5km; 12% statics; dogs €2; poss cr; Eng spkn; adv bkg; quiet; ccard acc; CKE/CCI. "Excel, quiet site, no bar and nothing within walking dist." 2 Apr-1 Oct. € 27.00 2013*

CABOURG *3D1* (1km W Coastal) *49.28166, -0.13795* **Camping La Pommeraie, Le Bas Cabourg, 14390 Cabourg [02 31 91 54 58 or 06 07 15 84 67; fax 02 31 91 66 57]** Take D513 fr Cabourg twd Caen. Site on L 1km after Bas-Cabourg sp. Med, pt shd; wc; shwrs €1; el pnts (5A) €4; gas; Indtte; shop; sand beach 800m; 90% statics; dogs; adv bkg; ccard acc. "Few touring pitches; mkt Sat." 1 Apr-30 Sep. € 18.00 2009*

CABOURG *3D1* (2km W Coastal) *49.28326, -0.17053* **Camping Les Peupliers, Allée des Pins, 14810 Merville-Franceville-Plage [tel/fax 02 31 24 05 07; contact@camping-peupliers.com; www.camping-peupliers.com]** Exit A13 to Cabourg onto D400, take D513 W, turn R sp Le Hôme, site sp, 2km E of Merville-Franceville. Med, pt sl, unshd; htd wc; chem disp; baby facs; shwrs inc; el pnts (10A) €5.50; Indtte; shop 2km; tradsmn; rest high ssn; snacks; bar; BBQ; playgrnd; htd pool; sand beach 300m; games area; tennis 2km; entmnt; TV; 50% statics; dogs €3.10; phone; poss cr; Eng spkn; adv bkg; ccard acc; red low ssn; CKE/CCI. "Pleasant, friendly, well-run, busy site; some lge pitches; clean, modern san facs; vg facs for children; conv ferries." ♦ 1 Apr-31 Oct. € 21.30 2009*

CABOURG *3D1* (6km W Coastal) *49.28319, -0.19098* **Camping Le Point du Jour, Route de Cabourg, 14810 Merville-Franceville-Plage [02 31 24 23 34; fax 02 31 24 15 54; contact@camping-lepointdujour.com; www.camping-lepointdujour.com]** Fr Ouistreham on D514 turn E at Bénouville onto D224, cross bdge onto D514, site on L dir Cabourg, 8km beyond Pegasus Bdge at far end of Merville. Or fr A13/D675 exit Dozulé dir Cabourg, then D514 to site. Med, hdg pitch, pt shd; htd wc; chem disp; mv service pnt; baby facs; shwrs inc; el pnts (10A) €5 (poss rev pol); gas; Indtte (inc dryer); shop; tradsmn; rest, snacks; bar; BBQ; playgrnd; htd, covrd pool; sand beach adj; games rm; wifi; entmnt; TV rm; 10% statics; dogs €3; bus; poss cr; adv bkg; quiet; ccard acc; red low ssn/long stay/CKE/CCI. "Excel site with sea views; direct access to Sword Beach (D-Day) & sand dunes; conv Pegasus Bdge; some pitches might be diff for lge o'fits." ♦ 1 Apr-2 Nov. € 45.00 SBS - N03 2014*

CABOURG *3D1* (6km W Coastal) *49.28296, -0.19072* **Camping Village Ariane, 100 Route de Cabourg, 14810 Merville-Franceville-Plage [02 31 24 52 52; fax 02 31 24 52 41; info@loisirs-ariane.com; www.camping-ariane.com]** Fr Ouistreham on D514 turn E at Bénouville onto D224, cross bdge onto D514 to site dir Cabourg. Or fr A13/D675 exit Dozulé dir Cabourg, then D514 to site. Lge, mkd pitch, pt shd; htd wc; chem disp; baby facs; fam bthrm; shwrs inc; el pnts (6-10A) €4; gas; Indtte; shop 500m; tradsmn; snacks; playgrnd; sand beach 300m; watersports & tennis nr; games area; games rm; wifi; entmnt; TV rm; 10% statics; dogs €3; Eng spkn; adv bkg; quiet; red long stay/low ssn; CKE/CCI. ♦ 1 Apr-5 Nov. € 19.20 2009*

CAEN *3D1* (14km N Coastal) *49.32551, -0.39010* **Yelloh! Village Côte de Nacre, 17 Rue du Général Moulton, 14750 St Aubin-sur-Mer [02 31 97 14 45; fax 02 31 97 22 11; camping-cote-de-nacre@wanadoo.fr; www.camping-cote-de-nacre.com / www.yellohvillage.co.uk]** Fr Caen on D7 dir Douvres-la-Délivrande, Langrune-sur-Mer & St Aubin. Site in St Aubin-sur-Mer on S side of D514; clearly sp on o'skts. Lge, hdg/mkd pitch, hdstg, unshd; htd wc; chem disp; mv service pnt; baby facs; sauna; shwrs inc; el pnts (10A) inc; Indtte (inc dryer); shop high ssn; tradsmn; rest, snacks; bar; BBQ; playgrnd; htd pools (1 covrd); paddling pool; waterslide; sand beach 500m; tennis 200m; cycle hire; games rm; wifi; entmnt; TV; 15% statics; dogs €4; quiet; phone; poss cr; Eng spkn; adv bkg rec; ccard acc; CKE/CCI."Ideal for families; lge pitches; conv Caen ferry, Normandy beaches, WW2 sites; helpful staff; excel modern san facs; poss waterlogging; gd cycle tracks along sea front low ssn; easy walk into quiet vill; vg; payment on arr, no refund for early dep." ♦ 29 Mar-22 Sep. € 58.20 2013*

⊞ **CANY BARVILLE** *3C2* (3km N Rural) *49.80375, 0.64960* **Camping Maupassant, 12 Route de la Folie, 76450 Vittefleur [tel/fax 02 35 97 97 14; campingmaupassant@orange.fr; www.camping-maupassant.com]** S fr St Valery-en-Caux on D925 dir Cany-Barville; site sp turning to R 700m bef Cany-Barville. Med, hdg/mkd pitch, hdstg, pt shd; htd wc; chem disp; mv service pnt; baby facs; shwrs €1.70; el pnts (6A) €3.30; gas; Indtte (inc dryer); shop, rest, snacks & bar 6km; BBQ (charcoal); some statics; dogs; phone; adv bkg; quiet; CKE/CCI. "Friendly staff; gd NH." 9 Mar-14 Dec. € 16.60 2013*

CANY BARVILLE *3C2* (500m S Urban) *49.78335, 0.64214* **Camp Municipal, Route de Barville, 76450 Cany-Barville [02 35 97 70 37; fax 02 35 97 72 32; camping@cany-barville.fr; www.cany-barville.fr]** Sp fr town cent, off D268 to S of town, adj stadium. Med, hdg/mkd pitch, hdstg, pt shd; htd wc; chem disp; mv service pnt; shwrs inc; el pnts (10A) €3.25 (poss rev pol); Indtte; shop 500m; playgrnd; pool 1km; lake 1.5km; 25% statics; dogs €1.35; adv bkg; poss noisy at w/ends & late evenings; ccard acc; red long stay; CKE/CCI. "Vg facs but poss stretched at high ssn; poss no check-in on Sun; within reach of Dieppe & Fécamp chateau; gd cycling; poss mkt traders on site." ♦ 1 Apr-30 Sep. € 14.00 2014*

CARENTAN *1D4* (600m NE Urban) *49.30988, -1.2388* **Camping Le Haut Dick, 30 Chemin du Grand-Bas Pays, 50500 Carentan [tel/fax 02 33 42 16 89; contact@camping-lehautdick.com; www.camping-lehautdick.com]** Exit N13 at Carentan; clearly sp in town cent, nr pool, on L bank of canal, close to marina.Foll sp to Port de Plaisance. Med, hdg/mkd pitch, pt shd; wc; chem disp; mv service pnt; shwrs inc; el pnts (6A) €4 (rev pol); gas; shop 500m; tradsmn; snacks; rest & bar 500m; BBQ; playgrnd; htd pool adj; crazy golf; sand beach 10km; cycle hire; games rm; 5% statics; dogs €1.50; phone; poss cr; adv bkg; quiet; ccard not acc; red low ssn; CKE/CCI. "Some pitches poss tight for lge o'fits; gd security; eve meals avail; gates locked 2200-0700; conv Cherbourg ferry & D-Day beaches; gd birdwatching & cycling; mkt Mon." ♦ 1 Apr-30 Sep. € 25.50 2012*

CARENTAN *1D4* (6km SE Rural) *49.27849, -1.16945* **FFCC Camping à la Ferme Le Clos Fleuri (Duval), 50620 Montmartin-en-Graignes [02 33 56 84 87]** On N13 by-pass Carantan going S; join N174; site on L in 4km. Sm, unshd; wc; shwrs inc; chem disp; el pnts inc; playgrnd; adv bkg; quiet. "Charming CL-type site, also B&B; pleasant owner; 1 hr fr Cherbourg." 15 Jun-15 Sep. 2010*

CAUDEBEC EN CAUX *3C2* (6km S Urban) *49.48373, 0.77247* **Camp Municipal du Parc, Rue Victor Hugo, 76940 La Mailleraye-sur-Seine [02 35 37 12 04; mairie-sg.lamaillerayesurseine@wanadoo.fr]** Fr N on D131/D490 turn E onto D65. Or fr S on D913. Site sp in cent of town close to rv bank. Sm, hdg pitch, pt sl, pt shd; wc; chem disp; shwrs; el pnts (6A) inc; shop, rest, bar 200m; playgrnd; poss cr; quiet. "Pleasant, tidy site; site yourself, warden calls; adequate, clean san facs; gd walking area; vg NH." 1 Apr-30 Sep. € 12.50 2011*

CAUDEBEC EN CAUX *3C2* (1.5km W Rural) *49.52303, 0.70606* **FFCC Camping Barre-y-Va, Route de Villequier, 76490 Caudebec-en-Caux [02 35 96 26 38 or 02 35 95 90 10 (Mairie); campingbarreyva@orange.fr; www.camping-barre-y-va.com]** Fr Caudebec take D81 W twd Villequier & site on R in 1.5km next to Rv Seine. Med, some hdstg, pt shd; wc (some cont); chem disp; shwrs inc; el pnts (10A) €4.30 (poss rev pol); Indtte (inc dryer); shop & 1.5km; tradsmn; rest, snacks; bar; playgrnd; pool 300m; rv fishing & boating adj; cycle hire; games area; games rm; wifi; TV; some statics; dogs €2.60; no twin-axles; phone; Eng spkn; noise fr rd, rv & nrby disco; red low ssn/CKE/CCI. "Popular, well-kept site in interesting area; basic, clean unisex san facs; san block ltd; ent awkward long o'fits; barrier clsd 2200-0700." ♦ 2 Apr-24 Oct. € 17.45 2010*

CEAUCE *4E1* (1km N Rural) *48.49812, -0.62481* **Camp Municipal de la Veillotière, Chemin de la Veillotière, 61330 Ceaucé [02 33 38 31 19; mairie-ceauce@wanadoo.fr]** S fr Domfront on D962 dir Mayenne, at rndabt in Ceaucé turn L. Site in 200m on R adj sm lake. Sm, hdg pitch, pt sl, pt shd; wc; chem disp; mv service pnt; shwrs inc; el pnts (5A) inc; shop; rest; bar 200m; playgrnd; fishing adj; quiet. "Well-kept site on edge vill; gd." ♦ ltd 1 May-30 Sep. € 10.00 2010*

CHERBOURG *1C4* (5km NE Urban/Coastal) *49.65405, -1.56675* **Camp Municipal Espace Loisirs de Collignon, Plage Collignon, 50110 Tourlaville [02 33 54 80 68; fax 02 33 20 53 03; camping-collignon@wanadoo.fr; www.mairie-tourlaville.fr]** Foll sp fr ferry terminal for Espace Loisirs Collignon or Tourlaville-Plage; site on D116; turn L at lge rndabt beyond Tourlaville boundary. Med, mkd pitch, unshd; wc; chem disp; shwrs inc; el pnts (10A) €3.75; gas; Indtte; shops 500m; rest 2km; bar 500m; covrd pool adj; sand beach adj; fishing, sw & watersports adj; games rm; entmnt; TV; 30% statics; dogs; poss cr; adv bkg (rec high ssn); poss noisy high ssn (youth groups); some rd noise; ccard acc; CKE/CCI. "Lge landscaped complex; generous pitches; poss poor security; conv ferries." ♦ 1 May-30 Sep. € 16.00 2009*

⊞ **CHERBOURG** *1C4* (10km E Coastal) *49.65703, -1.52645* **Camp Municipal Le Fort, 47 Route du Fort, 50110 Bretteville [02 33 22 27 60 or 02 33 88 78 20 (Mairie); mairie.bretttevilleensaire@orange.fr; www.brettevilleensaire.fr]** Immed exit car ferries in Cherbourg, turn L on D116. On leaving Bretteville turn sharp L at junc of D116 & D611, 1st turn R. App poss diff lge o'fits. Med, pt sl, unshd; wc; chem disp; shwrs; el pnts (10A) €2.50; shops 4km; BBQ; playgrnd; shgl beach adj; 90% statics; quiet. "Sep area tourers, sm pitches; some pitches view of coast; locked 2200-0700; poss diff in wet; some pitches diff lge o'fits; sh stay only." € 11.70 2010*

CHERBOURG *1C4* (10km E Coastal) *49.66720, -1.48772* **Camping L'Anse du Brick, 18 L'Anse du Brick, 50330 Maupertus-sur-Mer [02 33 54 33 57; fax 02 33 54 49 66; contact@adbcamping.com; www.anse-du-brick.com / www.les-castels.com]** At rndabt at port take 2nd exit sp Caen, Rennes & Mont St Michel; at 2nd rndabt take 3rd exit sp Caen & Mont St Michel (N13); at 3rd rndabt take 2nd exit onto dual c'way sp St Lô, Caen (N13), Bretteville-sur-Mer; exit on D116 & foll sp thro Bretteville-en-Saire (take care lge speed hump in Le Becquet); turn R for site just after R-hand blind bend & turning for Maupertus; up v steep incline. Med, hdg/mkd pitch, terr, sl, shd; wc; chem disp; mv service pnt; baby facs; serviced pitches; shwrs inc; el pnts (10A) inc (poss rev pol); gas; lndtte (inc dryer); shop & 3km; tradsmn; rest, snacks; bar; BBQ; playgrnd; htd pool; paddling pool; waterslide; sand beach adj (via bdge over coastal rd); tennis; cycle hire; archery; wifi; games/TV rm; dogs €6; no c'vans/m'vans over 8m; poss cr; adv bkg; quiet; ccard acc; red low ssn; CKE/CCI. "Attractive, well-kept site in beautiful setting; conv ferry; gd clean san facs; some pitches for lge o'fits; conv Landing Beaches, Barfleur, coastal nature reserve." ♦ 1 Apr-29 Sep. € 52.50 SBS - N14 2013*

⊞ **CHERBOURG** *1C4* (6km S Rural) *49.58951, -1.59433* **Camping Le Village Vert, 50470 Tollevast [02 33 43 00 78; fax 02 33 43 03 38; le-village-vert@wanadoo.fr; www.le-village-vert.com]** S'bound take N13 sp Caen out of town. Cont on N13 fr Auchan rndabt for approx 5km to D56 slip rd sp Delasse. Turn L at x-rds over N13 onto N13 sp Cherbourg. Site on R approx 3.5km, sp nr Auchan hypmkt. N'bound exit sp Tollevast & site. Lge, some hdstg, pt sl, pt shd; wc; chem disp; mv service pnt; shwrs inc; baby facs; el pnts (10A) €1.50 (check rev pol); gas; sm shop & 1km; tradsmn; rest 200m; playgrnd; tennis; golf & horseriding 2km; 95% statics (sep); dogs €2; Eng spkn; adv bkg; quiet but poss rd noise at front of site; ccard acc; red CKE/CCI. "Conv NH for ferries in woodland setting; ltd space for tourers but spacious pitches; friendly & efficient; poss waterlogged pitches in wet weather; poss travellers; office closes 1930, night arr area." ♦ € 13.00 2009*

⊞ **CHERBOURG** *1C4* (3km NW Urban/Coastal) *49.65576, -1.65257* **Camp Municipal de la Saline, Rue Jean Bart, 50120 Equeurdreville-Hainneville [02 33 93 88 33 or 02 33 53 96 00 (Mairie); fax 02 33 93 12 70; mairie-equeurdreville@dialoleane.com; www.equeurdreville.com]** Fr ferry terminal foll D901 & sp Beaumont-Hague. On dual c'way beside sea look out for site sp to L at traff lts. Med, hdg/mkd pitch, hdstg, pt sl, terr, pt shd; htd wc; chem disp; mv service pnt in 100m; shwrs inc; el pnts (10A) €4.56 lndry rm; shop, rest, snacks & bar 500m; sand beach adj; fishing; 50% statics; dogs €0.50; phone; rd noise; adv bkg; CKE/CCI. "Sea views; boules & skateboard park adj; aquatic cent 500m; cycle path to town; secured at night; gd NH." ♦ ltd € 9.00 2010*

CLECY *3D1* (1.4km E Rural) *48.91491, -0.47374* **FFCC Camping Les Rochers des Parcs, La Cour, 14570 Clécy [02 31 69 70 36; camping.normandie@gmail.com; www.camping-normandie-clecy.fr]** Fr Condé take D562 dir Caen; turn R onto D133a sp Clécy & Le Vey; do not take turning to Clécy cent but cont downhill, past museum on L & then over bdge; turn R in 150m at campsite sp; site on R. Med, mkd pitch, some hdstg, pt sl, pt shd; htd wc; mv service pnt; baby facs; shwrs inc; el pnts (6A) €3.50; lndtte (inc dryer); shop 1km; tradsmn; rest 1km; snacks; bar; BBQ; playgrnd; rv fishing; cycle hire; games area; wifi; some statics; dogs €1; phone; poss cr; Eng spkn; quiet; red long stay low ssn. "Lovely rvside situation; friendly, helpful owner; facs poss stretched high ssn & ltd low ssn; excel cent for walking." ♦ 1 Apr-30 Sep. € 17.50 (CChq acc) 2013*

CONDE SUR NOIREAU *3D1* (500m W Urban) *48.85146, -0.55703* **Camp Municipal du Stade, Rue de Vire, 14110 Condé-sur-Noireau [02 31 69 02 93; fax 02 31 59 15 51; www.conde-sur-noireau.com]** On D562 (Flers to Caen rd). In town, turn W on D512 twd Vire. After Zone Industrielle, sports complex on L, no L turn. Go 1 block further & foll lge white sp 'Espace Aquatique' to site. Site 500m on R in grnds of sports cent. Sm, pt shd; wc; chem disp; shwrs inc; el pnts (6-10A) inc; lndry rm; shops, rest, snacks, bar 300m; playgrnd; htd pool adj; tennis; dogs; quiet; CKE/CCI. "Well-kept clean site in grnds of leisure cent; gd size pitches; gd clean san facs; staff friendly & helpful; pleasant town; gd NH." 2 May-30 Sep. € 8.30 2013*

CORMEILLES *3D1* (4km E Rural) *49.24623, 0.44954* **Camping Les Pommiers (Desbois), La Febvrerie, 27260 St Sylvestre-de-Cormeilles [02 32 42 29 69; cmaraisc@aol.com; www.campinglespommiers.com]** Exit A13 junc 28 Beuzeville onto N175 then D27 S sp Epaignes & Bernay twds Lieurey. Cont on D27 for approx 15km & at rndabt with D139 at Epaignes strt on for 5.6km, turn R down narr lane D706 sp St Sylvestre, Camping. Site on R in 1.5km. Fr S on D27 turn L onto D810 at Lieurey & in approx 2km turn R to St Sylvestre. Sm, hdg pitch, pt shd; wc; chem disp (wc); shwrs inc; el pnts inc (6A) €2.50 (poss rev pol); lndry rm; shops 4km, rest, snacks, bar 4km; BBQ; playgrnd; some statics; dogs free; phone; poss cr; Eng spkn; adv bkg; quiet. "Pleasant, secluded, family-run site in orchard; friendly; san facs need refurb (2010)." 1 Apr-31 Oct. € 9.00 2010*

COURSEULLES SUR MER *3D1* (500m NE Coastal) *49.33417, -0.44433* **Camp Municipal Le Champ de Course, Ave de la Libération, 14470 Courseulles-sur-Mer [02 31 37 99 26 (Mairie); fax 02 31 37 96 37; camping.courseulles@wanadoo.fr; www.courseulles-sur-mer.com]** Fr N814 by-pass thro Caen, take exit 5 onto D7 & D404 dir Courseulles-sur-Mer. On ent to town, foll sp 'Campings' at 1st rndabt Site on D514 on R. Gd sp's for site. Lge, hdg/mkd pitch, unshd; wc; chem disp; mv service pnt; baby facs; shwrs inc; el pnts (10A) €4.50; lndtte; tradsmn; rest, snacks, bar adj; BBQ; playgrnd; pool adj; sand beach; games area; boat hire; tennis, mini-golf & horseriding nr; TV rm; 15% statics; dogs €1.90; phone; wifi; poss cr; Eng spkn; adv bkg; quiet; ccard acc; CKE/CCI. "Nice site adj beach; friendly staff; facs clean; early dep for ferry catered for; conv D-Day landing beach; gd dog walks; oyster beds & daily fish mkt; vg; excel modern & clean san facs; exit barriers open at 7am; supmkt 0.5 km." ♦ 1 Apr-30 Sep. € 25.00 2014*

COURSEULLES SUR MER *3D1* (2km E Coastal) *49.33225, -0.42820* **Camping Le Havre de Bernières, Chemin de Quintefeuille, 14990 Bernières-sur-Mer [02 31 96 67 09; fax 02 31 97 31 06; info@camping-normandie.com; www.camping-normandie.com]** W fr Ouistreham on D514 for 20km. Site well sp. Lge, mkd pitch, pt sl, pt shd; wc; chem disp; 50% serviced pitches; shwrs inc; el pnts (20A) €6; lndtte; shop; rest, snacks; bar; playgrnd; pool; sand beach adj; tennis; games area; entmnt; many statics; dogs €4.20; poss v cr; Eng spkn; adv bkg; poss noisy; red low ssn; CKE/CCI. "Gd beaches & watersports; conv Ouistreham ferries; busy site, poss untidy; inadequate san facs high ssn & poss unclean; pool unclean (8/09); when site cr c'vans poss need manhandling." ♦ 28 Mar-31 Oct. € 27.50 (CChq acc) 2009*

COURSEULLES SUR MER *3D1* (8km SW Rural) *49.28949, -0.52970* **Camp Municipal des Trois Rivières, Route de Tierceville, 14480 Creully [tel/fax 02 31 80 12 00 or 02 31 80 90 17; camping.creully@orange.fr; www.campingdes3rivieres.fr]** Fr Caen ring rd, exit junc 8 onto N13 dir Bayeux; in 15km turn R onto D82 to Creully; site on R 500m past cent of Creully. Med, hdg pitch, pt sl, pt shd; htd wc; chem disp (wc); shwrs inc; chem disp; el pnts (10A) €4.10 (long leads req, poss rev pol); lndtte; tradsmn; shops, rest, snacks, bar 1km; BBQ; playgrnd; pool 5km; games area; games rm; sand beach 5km; dogs €1.20; Eng spkn; adv bkg; quiet; ccard acc; CKE/CCI. "Well-kept, clean site; gd pitches; friendly, helpful warden; excel facs, stretched high ssn; conv D-Day beaches, Bayeux; barrier clsd 1500-1700; gd cycling; excel." ♦ 1 Apr-30 Sep. € 12.50 2014*

COURTILS see Mont St Michel, Le *2E4*

⊞ **COUTANCES** *1D4* (1km W Urban) *49.05172, -1.45927* **FFCC Camp Municipal Les Vignettes, 27 Rue de St Malo, 50200 Coutances [02 33 45 43 13; fax 02 33 45 74 98]** Fr N on D971 or D2 turn R onto Coutances by-pass, sp St Malo & Avranches. At rndabt turn L. Site 200m on R after Cositel ent. Fr S foll sp for Valognes or Cherbourg. Site in Coutances on L immed after Logis sp. Med, hdg/mkd pitch, pt sl, pt shd; wc (some cont); chem disp; mv service pnt; shwrs inc; ltd el pnts (6A) inc; shops 500m; snacks; bar; BBQ; playgrnd; htd pool adj; sports stadium adj; few statics; dogs €1.05; poss cr; some rd noise; CKE/CCI. "Pretty site; gd, clean san facs; friendly warden; access poss diff to some pitches; muddy when wet; gd NH for Cherbourg." € 12.40 2011*

⊞ **COUTANCES** *1D4* (6.5km NW Rural) *49.09951, -1.48421* **Camping La Renaudière Féret, 50200 Ancteville [02 33 45 57 53; service.clients@renaudiere-feret.com; www.renaudiere-feret.com]** N fr Coutances on D2; in 6.5km take 1st R after R turn for Servigny; site on R in 200m. App fr N on D2, take 1st L turn after L turn for Ancteville (site on rd bet turnings for Ancteville & Servigny). Sm, unshd; wc; chem disp; mv service pnt; fam bthrm; shwrs inc; el pnts (10-16A) inc; shops nrby; BBQ area; wifi; dogs; adv bkg; quiet; red long stay. CKE/CCI. "Tranquil, scenic farm site; British owners; conv NH or longer; vg." ♦ ltd € 15.00 2009*

CREULLY see Courseulles sur Mer *3D1*

⊞ **CRIEL SUR MER** *3B2* (2km N Coastal) *50.02568, 1.30855* **FFCC Camp Municipal Le Mont Joli Bois, 29 Rue de la Plage, 76910 Criel-sur-Mer [02 35 50 81 19 or 06 08 80 67 35 (mob); fax 02 35 50 22 37; contact@camping-montjolibois.fr; www.camping-montjolibois.fr]** Fr D925 take D222 into Criel cent. Turn R opp church into D126 for 1.6km to beach. Turn L then immed R & foll beach rd to site in 1.5km. Med, hdg/mkd pitch, pt sl, terr, pt shd; htd wc; chem disp; mv service pnt; shwrs inc; el pnts (4-6A) €3-4.60; lndtte; tradsmn; shops, rest, snacks, bar 2km; playgrnd; shgl beach 500m; TV rm; 50% statics; dogs €1.60; bus; poss cr; quiet; CKE/CCI. "Fair." ♦ ltd € 13.00 2013*

CRIEL SUR MER *3B2* (1.5km NW Coastal) *50.03048, 1.30815* **Camping Les Mouettes, Rue de la Plage, 76910 Criel-sur-Mer [tel/fax 02 35 86 70 73; contact@camping-lesmouettes.fr; www.camping-lesmouettes.fr]** Fr D925 take D222 thro Criel to coast, site sp. Care needed with narr, steep access. Sm, mkd pitch, terr, unshd; wc; chem disp; shwrs; el pnts (6A) €3.70; lndtte; shop; supmkt 5km; snacks; bar; BBQ; games area; games rm; TV; some statics; dogs €2; Eng spkn; adv bkg; quiet; red low ssn. "Pleasant, well-kept site; friendly, helpful owner; gd san facs; sea views; 3 min walk to Stoney Beach." 1 Apr-1 Nov. € 16.00 2014*

CRIQUETOT L'ESNEVAL see Etretat *3C1*

DEAUVILLE *3D1* (3km S Urban) *49.32903, 0.08593* **Camping La Vallée de Deauville, Ave de la Vallée, 14800 St Arnoult [02 31 88 58 17; fax 02 31 88 11 57; www.camping-deauville.com]** Fr Deauville take D27 dir Caen, turn R onto D278 to St Arnoult, foll site sp. Lge, hdg/mkd pitch, hdstg, pt shd; htd wc (some cont); baby facs; shwrs inc; el pnts (10A) €4; gas; Indtte; shop; tradsmn; rest, snacks; bar; playgrnd; htd pool; waterslide; sand beach 4km; fishing lake; games rm; wifi; entmnt; 80% statics; dogs €4; phone; Eng spkn; some rlwy noise; red low ssn; ccard acc; CKE/CCI. "Easy access to beaches & resorts; conv Le Havre using Pont de Normandie; lake walks & activities on site; excel san facs." ♦ 1 Apr-2 Nov. € 30.00 2011*

DENNEVILLE PLAGE see Barneville Carteret *1C4*

DIEPPE *3C2* (4km S Urban) *49.90040, 1.07472* **Camping Vitamin, 865 Chemin des Vertus, 76550 St Aubin-sur-Scie [02 35 82 11 11; camping-vitamin@wanadoo.fr; www.camping-vitamin.com]** Foll dir to Formule 1 & Hotel B&B. Lge, hdg pitch, unshd; wc; chem disp; mv service pnt; shwrs inc; el pnts (10A) inc; Indtte; shops 1km; bar; playgrnd; pool; shgl beach 2km; adv bkg; many statics; dogs €3; quiet; red low ssn; CKE/CCI. "Lovely, well-kept site; san facs immac; poss boggy in wet; conv ferries; excel; auto barrier for early dep." 1 Apr-15 Oct. € 26.00 2014*

DIEPPE *3C2* (5km S Rural) *49.87063, 1.14426* **Camping des 2 Rivières, 76880 Martigny [02 35 85 60 82; fax 02 35 85 95 16; www.camping-2-rivieres.com]** Martigny vill on D154 S fr Dieppe. If appr fr Dieppe, ent is on L bef vill sp. Med, pt shd; wc; el pnts €3.05; Indtte; shop; playgrnd; covrd pool, watersports, mountain biking, horseriding & Arques forest nrby; dogs €1.70; tax .55c pppn adv bkg; quiet. "Attractive, spacious site by lge lake; access poss diff long o'fits due parked vehicles; cycle paths; highly rec." 26 Mar-10 Oct. € 19.50 2013*

DIEPPE *3C2* (4km SW Rural) *49.89820, 1.05705* **Camping La Source, 63 Rue des Tisserands, Petit-Appeville, 76550 Hautot-sur-Mer [02 35 84 27 04; fax 02 35 82 25 02; info@camping-la-source.fr; www.camping-la-source.fr]** Fr Dieppe ferry terminal foll sp Paris, take D925 W dir Fécamp. In 2km at Petit Appeville turn L, site in 800m on rvside. NB 4m bdge bef ent & narr rd to site - not suitable v lge o'fits. Med, mkd pitch, pt shd; wc (some cont); chem disp; mv service pnt; shwrs inc; el pnts (10A) €4.20; Indtte (inc dryer); shop 3km; tradsmn; bar; playgrnd; htd pool; sand beach 3km; rv sw, fishing & boating adj; games area; games rm; cycle hire; golf 4km; wifi; entmnt; TV rm; few statics; dogs €2.20; some rlwy (daytime) & rd noise; adv bkg; quiet; ccard acc; red low ssn; CKE/CCI. "Lovely, well-kept site in attractive setting; some lge pitches; pleasant, vg, clean san facs; footpath to Le Plessis vill; gd cycling; excel NH for ferry." ♦ 15 Mar-15 Oct. € 38.00 (CChq acc) 2014*

DIEPPE *3C2* (4km SW Rural) *49.90886, 1.04069* **Camping Marqueval, 1210 Rue de la Mer, 76550 Pourville-sur-Mer [02 35 82 66 46; fax 02 34 00 02 82; contact@campinglemarqueval.com; www.campinglemarqueval.com]** Site well sp fr D75. Lge, hdg/mkd pitch, pt shd; htd wc; chem disp; mv service pnt; baby facs; shwrs; el pnts (6A) €2.50; Indtte (inc dryer); shop; rest, snacks; bar; BBQ; playgrnd; htd pool; paddling pool; spa; lake fishing; sand beach 1.2km; games rm; wifi; entmnt; TV; some statics; dogs €2; Eng spkn; adv bkg; quiet; ccard acc; red CKE/CCI. "Attractive, well-kept site; gd facs; vg family site." ♦ 21 Mar-15 Oct. € 21.50 2012*

DIEPPE *3C2* (6km SW Urban) *49.87297, 1.04497* **Camp Municipal du Colombier, 453 Rue Loucheur, 76550 Offranville [02 35 85 21 14; fax 02 35 04 52 67]** W fr Dieppe on D925, take L turn on D55 to Offranville, site clearly sp in vill to Parc du Colombier. NB Pt of site cul-de-sac, explore on foot bef towing in. Med, hdg/mkd pitch, pt shd; wc; chem disp; shwrs inc; el pnts (10A) €2.20 (poss rev pol); gas; Indtte; shop & supmkt 500m; rest; shgl beach 5km; many statics; ltd Eng spkn; CKE/CCI. "Pleasant setting in ornamental gardens; vg clean site & facs; helpful staff; gates clsd 2200-0700; ask warden how to operate in his absence; conv ferries; easy walk to town; rec." ♦ 1 Apr-15 Oct. € 22.20 2014*

DOMFRONT *4E1* (500m S Urban) *48.58808, -0.65045* **Camp Municipal Champ Passais, 4 Rue du Champ Passais, 61700 Domfront [02 33 37 37 66 or 02 33 38 92 24 (LS); fax 02 33 30 60 67; mairie-de-domfront@wanadoo.fr; http://camping-municipal-domfront.jimdo.com]** Fr N on D962 foll Laval sps into Domfront; then take D976 W dir Mont-St Michel; site turning in 400m on L; well sp bet old quarter & town cent. Fr S on D962 well sp fr edge of town. Sm, hdg/mkd pitch, hdstg, terr, pt shd; wc; chem disp; shwrs inc; el pnts (10A) €4; Indtte; shops, rest, snacks, bar 1km; playgrnd; rv fishing nr; TV rm; dogs €0.80; phone; Eng spkn; some rd noise; red low ssn; CKE/CCI. "Pleasant, well-kept terr site with views; helpful, charming staff; few shady pitches; gd security; sh, steep walk to medieval town; no twin-axles; vg; site still excel value, but showing signs of wear." ♦ 1 Apr-30 Sep. € 5.50 2014*

⊞ **DORCEAU** *4E2* (2km N Rural) *48.43717, 0.82742* **Camping Forest View, L'Espérance, 61110 Dorceau [tel/fax 02 33 83 78 55; peter@forestviewfrance.com; www.forestviewleisurebreaks.co.uk]** Fr D920 (ring rd) in Rémalard take D38 sp Bretoncelles; site in 4km on corner on L. Sm, pt sl, pt shd; wc; chem disp; shwrs inc; el pnts (10A) inc; lake fishing; painting workshops; wifi; dogs €1.40; some statics; adv bkg; quiet; red low ssn; CKE/CCI. "Simple, well-kept site in beautiful countryside; helpful, friendly British owners; gd touring base or NH; excel; evening meal avail with hosts, reasonable price." € 10.20 2013*

DUCEY see Pontaubault *2E4*

ESSAY *4E1* (550m S Rural) *48.53799, 0.24649* **FFCC Camp Municipal Les Charmilles, Route de Neuilly, 61500 Essay [02 33 28 40 52; fax 02 33 28 59 43; si-paysdessay@orange.fr]** Exit A28 junc 18 (Alençon Nord) onto D31 to Essay (sp L'Aigle); turn R in vill dir Neuilly-le-Bisson; site on R in 200m. Sm, hdg pitch, pt shd; wc; shwrs €1.60; el pnts (6A) €1.60; lndry rm; playgrnd; adv bkg; quiet. "Lge pitches, some diff to access; park, then find TO in vill to pay; historical vill; fair NH." 1 Apr-30 Sep. € 5.80 2009*

ETREHAM see Bayeux *3D1*

ETRETAT *3C1* (5km E Rural) *49.69880, 0.27580* **FFCC Camping de l'Aiguille Creuse, 24 Rue de l'Aiguille, 76790 Les Loges [02 35 29 52 10; fax 02 35 10 86 64; camping@aiguillecreuse.com; www.campingaiguillecreuse.com]** On S side of D940 in Les Loges; sp. Med, unshd; wc (some cont); chem disp; mv service pnt; shwrs inc; el pnts (10A) inc; lndtte (inc dryer); shops 500m; rest 3km; snacks; bar; BBQ; playgrnd; pool; beach 3km; tennis; games rm; wifi; TV; dogs €2.50; adv bkg; quiet. "Facs ltd low ssn." ♦ 1 Apr-30 Sep. € 21.80 (CChq acc) 2010*

ETRETAT *3C1* (1km SE Urban/Coastal) *49.70053, 0.21428* **Camp Municipal, 69 Rue Guy de Maupassant, 76790 Éetretat [tel/fax 02 35 27 07 67]** Fr Fécamp SW on D940 thro town cent of Etretat & site on L. Or fr Le Havre R at 2nd traff lts; site on L in 1km on D39. Med, mkd pitch, some hdstg, pt sl, pt shd; htd wc (some cont); chem disp; mv service pnt; shwrs inc; el pnts (6A) €6 (poss rev pol); gas; lndtte (inc dryer); shop 1km; BBQ; playgrnd; shgl beach 1km; no statics; phone; poss cr; no adv bkg; quiet; ccard acc; CKE/CCI. "Busy, well-kept site; lge pitches; conv Le Havre ferry; friendly & helpful staff; clean san facs; level walk to pleasant seaside resort, attractive beach nr; gd cliff top walks nr; m'van o'night area adj (no el pnts) open all yr; early arr high ssn rec; excel; lovely site." ♦ 1 Apr-15 Oct. € 23.60 2014*

ETRETAT *3C1* (3km S Rural) *49.68302, 0.21319* **Camping Les Tilleuls, Hameau de Grosse Mare, Impasse Dom-Filastre, 76790 Le Tilleul [tel/fax 02 35 27 11 61]** Fr Le Havre N on D940 18km to vill of Le Tilleul. Turn R after filling stn, site sp. Med, shd; wc (some cont); chem disp; shwrs €1.30; el pnts (4A) inc; lndtte; shop; snacks; BBQ; playgrnd; beach 3km; adv bkg; quiet. "Pleasant site; vg." 1 Apr-30 Sep. € 10.50 2010*

ETRETAT *3C1* (10km SW Rural) *49.62271, 0.24904* **Camping Le Beau Soleil, 41 Route de Turretot, 76280 Criquetot-l'Esneval [02 35 20 24 22; fax 02 35 20 82 09; le.beau.soleil@wanadoo.fr; www.campinglebeausoleil.com]** S fr Etretat on D39 to Criquetot-l'Esneval. Site is 3km SW of Criquetot-l'Esneval on D79 twd Turretot. Med, pt shd; wc; chem disp; mv service pnt; shwrs €1.10; el pnts (2-10A) €1.20-6; lndtte (inc dryer); bar; playgrnd; beach 8km; 70% statics; dogs €0.70; Eng spkn; CKE/CCI. "Pleasant site, friendly owners; conv Le Havre ferry." 1 Apr-30 Sep. € 8.50 2010*

EU *3B2* (300m W Rural) *50.05065, 1.40996* **Camp Municipal des Fontaines, Le Parc du Château, 76260 Eu [02 35 86 20 04; camping-du-chateau@ville-eu.fr; www.ville-eu.fr]** App fr Blangy on D1015 turn L at junc with D925 & foll camp sp to site in grnds of Hôtel de Ville (chateau). Fr Abbeville on D925 fork R at 1st rndabt in town S of rlwy then immed strt on over cobbled rd to chateau walls. Turn R at chateau walls into long, narr app rd thro trees. Med, some hdg pitch, hdstg, mainly terr, pt shd; wc; chem disp; shwrs inc; el pnts (6A) €5 (poss rev pol); gas; lndtte (inc dryer); shops 250m; shgl beach 3km; 10% statics; poss cr. "Louis-Philippe museum in chateau; clean san facs; easy uphill walk to town thro forest behind chateau; Eu worth visit, an alt to seaside towns nrby; vg Fri mkt." 1 Apr-31 Oct. € 9.20 2011*

FALAISE *3D1* (500m W Urban) *48.89545, -0.20476* **FFCC Camp Municipal du Château, 3 Rue du Val d'Ante, 14700 Falaise [02 31 90 16 55 or 02 31 90 30 90 (Mairie); fax 02 31 90 53 38; camping@falaise.fr; www.falaise.fr/tourisme/le-camping]** Fr N on N158, at rndabt on o'skirts of town, turn L into vill; at next rndabt by Super U go strt on; at 2nd mini-rndabt turn R; then sp on L after housing estate. Or fr S on D958, at 1st rndabt foll sp town cent & site. Cont down hill thro town then up hill to 1st rndabt, site sp, then sp on L after housing est. Med, hdg/mkd pitch, pt sl, terr, pt shd; wc (some cont); chem disp; mv service pnt; shwrs inc; el pnts (6-10A) €4.20; gas 500m; lndry rm; tradsmn; shops, rest, snacks, bar 500m; BBQ; playgrnd; htd pool in town; tennis; wifi; TV rm; sat TV some pitches; dogs €2.20; poss cr; some Eng spkn; adv bkg; quiet; ccard acc; red low ssn/long stay/CKE/CCI. "Lovely, peaceful, well-kept site in pleasant surroundings; pitches poss diff lge o'fits; clean san facs (lots of hot water) poss ltd low ssn & stretched high ssn & clsd 2200-0800; pitch self & pay later; uphill walk to town, birthplace of William the Conqueror; vet in Falaise; mkt Sat am; excel; clean well kept facs; easy walking dist to town." ♦ ltd 1 May-30 Sep. € 24.80 2014*

FECAMP *3C1* (6km SE Rural) *49.74041, 0.41660* **Camp Municipal Le Canada, 76400 Toussaint [02 35 29 78 34 or 02 35 27 56 77 (Mairie); fax 02 35 27 48 82; mairie.toussaint@wanadoo.fr; http://commune-de-toussaint.fr]** On D926 N of Toussaint (sharp turn at side of golf course). Med, hdg pitch, pt sl, shd; htd wc (some cont); shwrs inc; el pnts (4-10A) inc; lndtte; shop; BBQ; playgrnd; games area; 70% statics; dogs; quiet; CKE/CCI. "Lovely quiet site; helpful warden; clean san facs; gd." ♦ 15 Mar-15 Oct. € 12.00 2011*

FECAMP *3C1* (500m SW Coastal) *49.75712, 0.36200* **Camping Le Domaine de Renéville, Chemin de Nesmond, 76400 Fécamp [02 35 28 20 97 or 02 35 10 60 00; fax 02 35 29 57 68; reneville@aliceadsl.fr; www.campingdereneville.com]** Site off Etretat rd (D940) on o'skts of Fécamp; sp. NB Steep cliff site, access poss diff lge o'fits; narr bends. NB Lge o'fits best app fr dir Etretat & not Fécamp town. Lge, hdg/mkd pitch, terr, pt sl, shd; htd wc; chem disp; mv service pnt; shwrs inc; el pnts (6A) inc (poss long cable req; poss rev pol); lndtte (inc dryer); shop; tradsmn; snacks; rest & bar in town; playgrnd; pool adj; shgl beach 500m; 15% statics; phone; Eng spkn; adv bkg fr 1000 same day only - rec peak ssn; CKE/CCI. "Vg site with sea views; gd san facs - poss steep walk to reach; interesting town; sep m'van o'night area on harbour adj TO; highly rec." ♦ 1 Apr-15 Nov. € 18.50 2011*

FERMANVILLE see Cherbourg *1C4*

FIQUEFLEUR EQUAINVILLE see Honfleur *3C1*

FLERS *4E1* (3km E Urban) *48.75451, -0.54341* **Camping du Pays de Flers, 145 La Fouquerie 61100 Flers [02 33 65 35 00; camping.paysdeflers@wanadoo.fr; www.flers-agglomeration.fr]** Fr E on D924 thro town cent, site on L in 2 km. Fr W on D924 dir Centre Ville, site on R. Sm, pt shd; wc; chem disp; baby facs; shwr; el pnts (6A); tradsmn; BBQ; playgrnd; games area; bike hire; wifi; 15% statics; dogs; Eng spkn; quiet; CCI. "Easy walk to interesting town; excel." ♦ ltd 1 Apr-31 Oct. € 15.00 2014*

⊞ **FORGES LES EAUX** *3C2* (500m S Urban) *49.60597, 1.54262* **Aire de Service (M'vans only), Blvd Nicolas Thiessé, 76440 Forges-les-Eaux [02 35 90 52 10; officeforgesleseaux@wanadoo.fr; www.forgesleseaux-tourisme.fr]** Fr Forges-les-Eaux cent, take D921 S sp Lyons-la-Forêt. In 500m turn R foll sp, camp on L in 250m opp municipal site. Med, mkd pitch, hdstg, unshd; mv service pnt; water points; el pnts (poss rev pol). "No power, water etc Nov to Mar; max 2 nights; warden visits or pay at Municipal site opp; town cent easy walk; views of open countryside; excel." € 7.30 2014*

FORGES LES EAUX *3C2* (1km S Urban) *49.60603, 1.54302* **Camp Municipal La Minière, 3 Blvd Nicolas Thiese, 76440 Forges-les-Eaux [02 35 90 53 91; http://forgesleseaux-tourisme.fr]** Fr Forges-les-Eaux cent, take D921 S sp Lyons-la-Forêt. In 750m turn R foll sp, camp on R in 150m. NB 3,500kg limit in town all dirs. Med, hdg/mkd pitch, pt sl, pt shd; wc (some cont); mv service pnt opp; shwrs inc; el pnts (6A) €2.75 (rev pol); Indry rm; shops nr; htd pool in town; 85% statics (sep area); poss cr; quiet; CKE/CCI. "Well-presented site; lge pitches; friendly warden, warm welcome; basic, clean san facs; poss diff access some pitches; m'van o'night area opp; pleasant town with excel WWII Resistance Museum; gd local vet; useful NH." ♦ 15 Mar-15 Oct. € 14.00 2014*

FORT MOVILLE see Pont Audemer *3D2*

GACE *4E1* (200m E Urban) *48.79475, 0.29926* **Camp Municipal Le Pressoir, Ave de Tahiti, 61230 Gacé [02 33 35 50 24 or 02 33 35 50 18; fax 02 33 35 92 82; ville.gace@wanadoo.fr]** Exit A28 junc 16 onto D932/D438; in 2km turn R off D438 opp Intermarché onto D724; site immed on L. Foll sp. NB Take care corners on app if o'fit v long. Sm, hdg/mkd pitch, sl, pt shd; wc; chem disp (wc); mv service pnt in vill; shwrs inc; el pnts (6A) €2.50 (poss long lead req); Indry rm; supmkt & rest 100m; playgrnd; rv 500m; poss cr; no ccard acc; quiet, but church bells 7 am - midnight. "Clean, well-run site; rec early arr; san facs dated but clean; most pitches gd size, sm pitches poss diff for lge o'fits; pitches rather sl for m'van; twin-axles extra charge; warden calls am & pm; conv NH fr A28; nice site, well kept." 1 Jun-8 Sep. € 11.30 2013*

GENETS see Avranches *2E4*

GISORS *3D3* (7km SW Rural) *49.25639, 1.70174* **Camp Municipal de l'Aulnaie, Rue du Fond-de-l'Aulnaie, 27720 Dangu [02 32 55 43 42; contact@campingdelaulnaie-dangu.com; www.campingdelaulnaie-dangu.fr]** On ent Gisors fr all dirs, take ring rd & exit dir Vernon D10, then L onto D181 dir Dangu. Site on L bef Dangu. Site sp fr D10. NB speed humps. Lge, mkd pitch, pt shd; htd wc; chem disp; mv service pnt; shwrs inc; el pnts (10A) €2.80; gas; Indtte; tradsmn; rest, snacks, bar 800m; playgrnd; lake sw; fishing; 90% statics; dogs €2.60; poss cr; adv bkg; some rd noise; CKE/CCI. "Lakeside site; Gisors attractive town; conv Giverny & Gisors local attractions; beautiful site." ♦ ltd 1 Apr-31 Oct. € 13.70 2014*

GRANDCAMP MAISY *1C4* (500m W Coastal) *49.38814, -1.05204* **Camping Le Joncal, Le Petit Nice, 14450 Grandcamp-Maisy [02 31 22 61 44; fax 02 31 22 73 99; campingdujoncal@hotmail.fr; www.campingdujoncal.com]** Ent on Grandcamp port dock area; visible fr vill. Fr N13 take D199 sp Grandcamp-Maisy & foll Le Port & Camping sps. Lge, hdg/mkd pitch, pt shd; mv service pnt; wc; shops, rest adj; gas; el pnts (6-10A) €5.40-7.50; Indtte; shop; BBQ; sand beach adj; 80% statics; dogs €1.10; bus; no adv bkg; quiet. "Conv for D Day beaches; some pitches at water's edge; excel morning fish mkt close by; gd NH." ♦ 1 Apr-30 Sep. € 31.30 2014*

"Satellite navigation makes touring much easier"

Remember most sat navs don't know if you're towing or in a larger vehicle – always use yours alongside maps and site directions.

GRANVILLE *1D4* (6km NE Coastal) *48.86976, -1.56380* **Kawan Village La Route Blanche, 6 La Route Blanche, 50290 Bréville-sur-Mer [02 33 50 23 31; fax 02 33 50 26 47; larouteblanche@camping-breville.com; www.camping-breville.com]** Exit A84 junc 37 onto D924 dir Granville. Bef Granville turn L onto D971, then L onto D114 which joins D971e. Site on R bef golf club. Nr Bréville sm airfield. Lge, hdg/mkd pitch, hdstg, pt shd; htd wc (some male cont); chem disp; mv service pnt; baby facs; serviced pitches; shwrs inc; el pnts (6-10A) €4-5; gas; Indtte (inc dryer); shop; tradsmn; snacks; bar; BBQ; playgrnd; htd pools; paddling pool; waterpark; waterslide; sand beach 500m; sailing school; golf & tennis nr; games area; wifi; entmnt; TV rm; 40% statics; dogs €3; phone; poss cr; Eng spkn; adv bkg; quiet; ccard acc; red long stay/low ssn/CKE/CCI. "Pleasant, busy site with vg clean facs; staff friendly & helpful; disabled seatlift in pool; gd walking, cycling & beach; pleasant old walled town & harbour; vg." ♦ 1 Apr-1 Oct. € 36.00 (CChq acc) 2012*

GRANVILLE *1D4* (3.5km SE Rural) *48.79054, -1.52598* **Camping Angomesnil, 50380 St Pair-sur-Mer [02 33 51 64 33; info@angomesnil.com]** Take D973 SE fr Granville twd Avranches. At D154 exit to R sp Kairon-Bourg & site in 1km. Sm, hdg/mkd pitch, pt sl, pt shd; wc; chem disp; mv service pnt; shwrs inc; el pnts (6A) €3.10; Indtte; shops 3km; tradsmn; playgrnd; sand beach 3.5km; tennis; games rm; TV; no dogs; adv bkg; quiet. "Nice, quiet little site; roomy pitches; friendly, helpful owners; clean san facs; popular with Dutch." ♦ 20 Jun-10 Sep. € 13.70 2010*

GRANVILLE *1D4* (6km SE Rural) *48.79790, -1.5244* **Camping Le Château de Lez-Eaux, 50380 St Pair-sur-Mer [02 33 51 66 09; fax 02 33 51 92 02; bonjour@lez-eaux.com; www.lez-eaux.com / www.les-castels.com]** App site on D973 Granville to Avranches rd (not via St Pair). Fr rndabt at Intermarché cont for 2km, site sp on R. Lge, mkd pitch, pt sl, pt shd; htd wc; chem disp; mv service pnt; serviced pitches; baby facs; shwrs inc; el pnts (10-16A) inc; lndtte (inc dryer); shop & 4km; snacks; bar; BBQ; playgrnd; 2 pools (1 htd covrd); paddling pool; waterslide; children's indoor aqua park; sand beach 4km; lake fishing; tennis; cycle hire; boat hire 7km; horseriding 4km; games area; wifi; games/TV rm; 80% statics; dogs free; twin-axles acc (rec check in adv); poss cr; quiet; ccard acc; red low ssn; CKE/CCI. "Superb site in grnds of chateau; easy access; spacious pitches, various prices; helpful & friendly staff; clean, modern san facs; excel pool complex; gd for children; great for dogs; gd cycling & gd cycle rte to beach; gd touring base; conv Mont St Michel, Dol & landing beaches; mkt Thu St Pair; highly rec." ♦ 1 Apr-20 Sep. € 57.00 SBS - N02 2014*

See advertisement

GRANVILLE *1D4* (7km S Urban) *48.77783, -1.56618* **Camp Municipal du Docteur Lemonnier, Ave du Dr Lemonnier, 50610 Jullouville [02 33 51 42 60; mairiejullou@wanadoo.fr; www.jullouville.com]** S on D911 Granville-Avranches coast rd. On on ent Jullouville turn L in mkt sq. Ent in far L corner. Med, unshd; wc; mv service pnt; shwrs €0.80; el pnts (6A) inc; gas; lndtte; shop 200m; snacks; BBQ; playgrnd; sand beach 100m; 10% statics; dogs; poss cr high ssn; adv bkg; CKE/CCI. "Nice, clean, basic site." 8 Apr-30 Sep. € 17.70 2011*

⊞ **GROS THEIL, LE** *3D2* (3km SW Rural) *49.21207, 0.81533* **Camp de Salverte, Route de Brionne, 27370 Le Gros-Theil [02 32 35 51 34; fax 02 32 35 92 79; david.farah@wanadoo.fr; www.camping-salverte.com]** Fr Brionne take D26 E twd Le Gros-Thiel. After 10km turn R at Salverte, site sp. Lge, hdg pitch, terr, pt shd; htd wc; chem dist; baby facs; shwrs inc; el pnts (4A) inc (poss rev pol); el pnts (6A) inc; gas; lndry rm; shop; tradsmn; rest, snacks; bar; BBQ; playgrnd; covrd pool; tennis; games rm; entmnt; 90% statics; dogs; phone; adv bkg; quiet; ccard acc; CKE/CCI. "Conv NH Le Havre/Caen ferries; attractive site but v ltd facs low ssn; lge pitches; sm area for tourers diff when wet; excel." € 18.00 2011*

⊞ **HAMBYE** *1D4* (1.5km N Rural) *48.9600, -1.2600* **Camping aux Champs, 1 Rue de la Ripaudière, 50450 Hambye [02 33 90 06 98; michael.coles@wanadoo.fr; www.campingauxchamps.com]** Exit A84 junc 38 onto D999 to Percy; then turn L at town cent rndabt onto D58 to Hambye; at mkt sq proceed to junc, strt sp Le Guislain, past Mairie; site on R in 1.5 km on D51. Sm, some hdstg, unshd; htd wc; chem disp; fam bthrm; shwrs inc; el pnts (10A) €3; lndtte; shop, rest, snacks, bar 2km; adv bkg; red long stay; quiet; red long stay; adv bkg req low ssn (Nov-Mar) for full facs; CKE/CCI. "Peaceful, CL-type site; friendly, helpful British owners; adults only; excel, clean san facs; Hambye Abbey nrby; bell foundry at Villedieu-les-Poêls worth visit; conv ferry ports." € 12.00 2011*

HAUTOT SUR MER see Dieppe *3C2*

> "There aren't many sites open at this time of year"
>
> If you're travelling outside peak season remember to call ahead to check site opening dates – even if the entry says 'open all year'.

HAYE DU PUITS, LA *1D4* (1km N Rural) *49.29980, -1.54495* **Camping L'Etang des Haizes, 43 Rue Cauticotte, 50250 St Symphorien-le-Valois [02 33 46 01 16; fax 02 33 47 23 80; info@campingetangdeshaizes.com; www.campingetangdeshaizes.com]** Heading N fr La Haye-du-Puits on D900 under rlwy bdge & site 3rd on L, well sp. Med, hdg pitch, some hdstg, pt sl, pt shd; wc; chem disp; mv service pnt; baby facs; shwrs inc; el pnts (10A) €2-6; gas; lndtte; supmkt 1km; shop; tradsmn; rest, snacks; bar; playgrnd; htd pool; paddling pool; waterslide; fishing; cycle hire; games area; wifi; entmnt; TV rm; 50% statics (sep area); dogs €2; bus; phone; poss cr; Eng spkn; adv bkg rec; quiet; red low ssn; CKE/CCI. "Pretty, well-kept, well-run site in nature park; helpful, pleasant owners; ltd facs low ssn; barrier clsd 2300-0700; conv Cherbourg ferry (1hr)." ♦ 1 Apr-9 Oct. € 27.00 2009*

HAYE DU PUITS, LA *1D4* (6km N Urban) *49.38725, -1.52755* **FFCC Camp Municipal du Vieux Château, Ave de la Division-Leclerc, 50390 St Sauveur-le-Vicomte [02 33 41 72 04 or 02 33 21 50 44; fax 02 33 95 88 85; ot.ssv@wanadoo.fr; www.ville-saint-sauveur-le-vicomte.fr]** Fr Cherbourg on N13/D2 site on R after x-ing bdge at St Sauveur-le-Vicomte, sp. Med, mkd pitch, pt sl, pt shd; wc; chem disp; shwrs inc; el pnts (6A) €2.40 (poss rev pol); Indtte; shop 500m; tradsmn; rest adj; BBQ; playgrnd adj; pool, tennis 1km; games area; games rm; TV; dogs €1.15; phone; adv bkg; quiet; ccard acc; CKE/CCI. "Excel site in chateau grnds; friendly warden; gd clean facs; ideal 1st stop fr Cherbourg; office open until 2200 for late arr; barrier clsd 2200-0800; vg auberge opp; helpful warden; Eng not spkn; friendly town." 1 Jun-15 Sep. € 9.40 2013*

HAYE DU PUITS, LA *1D4* (2km SW Rural) *49.27292, -1.55896* **Camping La Bucaille, 50250 Montgardon [02 33 07 46 38; fax 09 62 15 99 39; info@labucaille.com; www.labucaille.com]** Fr Cherbourg S on N13 & D2 twd St Sauveur-le-Vicomte, then D900 to La Haye-du-Puits. Fr cent of La Haye turn onto D136 Rte de Bretteville-sur-Ay for approx 2km, site sp at L turn, site on L. Sm, pt sl, pt shd; wc; chem disp; shwrs inc; el pnts (16A) €5; shop, rest, snacks & bar 2km; BBQ; sand beach 4km; wifi; no statics; dogs free; adv bkg; quiet; width restriction 3m. "Pleasant quiet, 'hide-way' CL-type site; lge grassy pitches; friendly British owners; ideal for walking; excel." ♦ ltd 1 Apr-30 Sep. € 12.00 2013*

HEURTEAUVILLE see Bourg Achard *3D2*

HONFLEUR *3C1* (5km S Rural) *49.40083, 0.30638* **Camping Domaine Catinière, 910 Route de la Morelle, 27210 Fiquefleur-Equainville [02 32 57 63 51; fax 02 32 42 12 57; info@camping-catiniere.com; www.camping-catiniere.com]** Fr A29/Pont de Normandie (toll) bdge exit junc 3 sp Le Mans, pass under m'way onto D580/D180. In 3km go strt on at rndabt & in 100m bear R onto D22 dir Beuzeville; site sp on R in 500m. Sm, hdg/mkd pitch, pt shd; wc (some cont); chem disp; shwrs inc; baby facs; el pnts (4A) inc or (8-13A) €1.-1.50 (long lead poss req, poss rev pol); Indtte; sm shop; supmkt; tradsmn; snacks; bar; BBQ; playgrnd; htd pool; waterslide; rv fishing; games rm; wifi; entmnt; TV rm; 15% statics; dogs €2; no c'vans/m'vans over 8.50m; poss cr; Eng spkn; adv bkg rec high ssn & w/end; ccard acc only over €70; CKE/CCI. "Attractive, well-kept site; pleasant, helpful young owners; clean unisex san facs, stretched high ssn & ltd low ssn; some pitches quite sm; unfenced stream on far boundary; gd touring base; gd walks; easy parking for m'vans nr town; 20 mins to Le Havre ferry via Normandy bdge; conv A13; highly rec; friendly staff; gd NH; busy; lovely pool." ♦ 10 Apr-16 Sep. € 40.00 SBS - N16 2014*

See advertisement

HONFLEUR *3C1* (2.5km SW Rural) *49.39777, 0.20861* **Camping La Briquerie, 14600 Equemauville [02 31 89 28 32; fax 02 31 89 08 52; info@campinglabriquerie.com; www.campinglabriquerie.com]** Fr E ent town cent keeping harbour on R. Turn L onto D279 then in 2km turn R at rndabt at Intermarché. Site on R, N of water tower, E of Equemauville. Site well sp fr town cent. Fr S take D579 dir Honfleur Centre. At water tower on R turn L at Intermarché rndabt, site on R in 300m. Lge, hdg pitch, pt shd; wc; chem disp; mv service pnt; baby facs; fam bthrm; shwrs inc; el pnts (5-10A) €4-5 (poss rev pol); gas; Indtte; supmkt adj; rest, snacks & bar (high ssn); BBQ; playgrnd; 3 htd pools; waterslide; sand beach 2.5km; tennis, horseriding 500m; games rm; fitness rm; wifi; TV rm; entmnt; 50% statics; dogs €3; bus nr; poss cr; Eng spkn; adv bkg (fee for Jul/Aug); poss late noise high ssn; red low ssn; CKE/CCI. "Lge pitches; staff helpful; gd clean san facs; late/early ferry arr; local vets geared up for dog inspections, etc; gd; cash only." ♦ 1 Apr-30 Sep. € 46.80 2013*

HONFLEUR *3C1* (800m NW Coastal) *49.42445, 0.22753* **Camping du Phare, Blvd Charles V, 14600 Honfleur [02 31 89 10 26 / 02 13 24 22 12 (Cen Res); fax 02 31 93 06 05; vival-cabourg@wanadoo.fr / contact@campings-plage.fr; www.campings-plage.fr]** Fr N fr Pont de Normandie on D929 take D144; at ent to Honfleur keep harbour in R; turn R onto D513 sp Trouville-sur-Mer & Deauville (avoid town cent); fork L past old lighthouse to site entry thro parking area. Or fr E on D180; foll sp 'Centre Ville' then Vieux Bassin dir Trouville; at rectangular rndabt with fountain turn R sp Deauville & Trouville, then as above. Med, hdg pitch, pt shd; wc; chem disp; mv service pnt; shwrs €1.20; el pnts (2-10A) €4.10-5.90; gas; lndtte; shop 800m; tradsmn; rest 1km; snacks; bar; BBQ; playgrnd; htd, covrd pool nr; sand beach 100m; fishing; 10% statics; dogs €3; phone; poss v cr; Eng spkn; rd noise; no ccard acc; red low ssn; CKE/CCI. "Gd clean site in excel location; conv NH Le Havre ferry; busy high ssn, rec arr early; friendly owners; san facs dated but clean, ltd low ssn; barrier clsd 2200-0700; m'van pitches narr & adj busy rd; some soft, sandy pitches; easy walk to town/harbour; sep m'van Aire de Service nr harbour." 1 Apr-30 Sep. € 24.00 2014*

HOULGATE *3D1* (3.5km NE Coastal) *49.30699, -0.04382* **Camping Les Falaises, Route de la Corniche, 14510 Gonneville-sur-Mer [02 31 24 81 09; fax 02 31 28 04 11; camping.lesfalaises@voila.fr; www.lesfalaises.com]** Fr D513 take D163; site clearly sp close to Auberville. Lge, pt sl, pt shd, wc; chem disp (wc); shwrs inc; el pnts (4-6A) €3.90-4.60 (poss v long lead req); snacks; shop; gas; htd pool; playgrnd; 30% statics; dogs €2.50; poss cr. "Nice site, different areas sep by trees; most pitches sl & poss uneven; pleasant, helpful staff; gd, clean facs, red low ssn." ♦ 1 Apr-15 Oct. € 18.00 2009*

HOULGATE *3D1* (1km E Urban) *49.29223, -0.07428* **Camp Municipal des Chevaliers, Chemin des Chevaliers, 14510 Houlgate [02 31 24 37 93; camping-chevaliers.houlgate@orange.fr; www.ville-houlgate.fr]** Fr Deauville take D513 SW twds Houlgate; 500m after 'Houlgate' town sp, turn L & foll camping sps to site, 250m after Camping de la Vallée. Lge, mkd pitch, pt sl, pt terr, unshd; wc (some cont); shwrs inc; el pnts (6-10A) €3-5; tradsmn; sand beach, fishing & boating 800m; 70% statics; dogs €0.85; Eng spkn; adv bkg (rec high ssn); v quiet. "Well-kept site; pleasant warden; facs simple but adequate & clean; sep area for tourers nr ent; attractive town; excel." ♦ 1 Apr-30 Sep. € 13.75 2014*

HOULGATE *3D1* (1km E Coastal) *49.29390, -0.06820* **Camping Yelloh! Village La Vallée, 88 Rue de la Vallée, 14510 Houlgate [02 31 24 40 69; fax 02 31 24 42 42; camping.lavallee@wanadoo.fr; www.campinglavallee.com]** Exit junc 29 or 29a fr A13 onto D45 to Houlgate. Or fr Deauville take D513 W. Bef Houlgate sp, turn L & foll sp to site. Lge, hdg/mkd pitch, pt sl, terr, pt shd; htd wc; chem disp; mv service pnt; some serviced pitches; shwrs inc; el pnts (6A) inc; gas; lndtte (inc dryer); supmkt; tradsmn; rest, snacks; bar; playgrnd; 2 pools (1 htd, covrd); paddling pool; waterslide; sand beach 900m; lake fishing 2km; tennis; cycle hire; golf 1km; games rm; wifi; entmnt; TV rm; 30% statics; dogs €5; Eng spkn; adv bkg (fee); ccard acc; red low ssn; CKE/CCI. "Superb, busy site; friendly recep; clean san facs; some pitches poss sm for lge o'fits; sep area m'vans; 1,5km walk to sandy beach and town." ♦ ltd 1 Apr-15 Oct. € 48.80 2014*

See advertisement

IGOVILLE see Pont de l'Arche *3D2*

ISIGNY SUR MER *1D4 (500m NW Rural) 49.31872, -1.10825* **Camping Le Fanal, Rue du Fanal, 14230 Isigny-sur-Mer [02 31 21 33 20; fax 02 31 22 12 00; info@camping-lefanal.com]** Fr N13 exit into Isigny, site immed N of town. Foll sp to 'Stade' in town, (just after sq & church on narr rd just bef R turn). Med, hdg/mkd pitch, pt shd; wc; chem disp; mv service pnt; shwrs inc; el pnts (16A) inc (long cable poss req); lndtte; shop; snacks; bar; playgrnd; pool; aquapark; sand beach 10km; lake fishing adj; horseriding; tennis; games area; games rm; entmnt; TV; 50% statics; dogs €4; phone; adv bkg; quiet; ccard acc; red low ssn; CKE/CCI. "Friendly staff; poss boggy in wet weather; vg site." ♦ 1 Apr-30 Sep. € 30.50 2012*

JULLOUVILLE see Granville *1D4*

JUMIEGES *3C2 (1km E Rural) 49.43490, 0.82970* **Camping de la Forêt, Rue Mainberte, 76480 Jumièges [02 31 87 05 21 or 02 35 37 93 43; fax 02 31 87 09 67 or 02 35 37 76 48; info@campinglaforet.com; www.campinglaforet.com]** Exit A13 junc 25 onto D313/D490 N to Pont de Brotonne. Cross Pont de Brotonne & immed turn R onto D982 sp Le Trait. In Le Trait turn R onto D143 sp Yainville & Jumièges. In Jumièges turn L at x-rds after cemetary & church, site on R in 1km. NB M'vans under 3.5t & 3m height can take ferry fr Port Jumièges - if towing do not use Sat Nav dirs. Med, hdg/mkd pitch, pt shd; htd wc; chem disp; mv service pnt; baby facs; shwrs inc; el pnts (10A) €4.50 (poss rev pol); gas; lndtte (inc dryer); sm shop; tradsmn; snacks; rest & bar nr; BBQ (charcoal/gas/elec); playgrnd; htd pool; paddling pool; lake beach 2.5km; watersports; fishing; tennis; cycle hire; games area; wifi; games/TV rm; 30% statics; dogs free; no c'vans/m'vans over 7m high ssn; phone; bus to Rouen; poss cr; adv bkg; quiet; ccard accp red low ssn. "Nice site, well-situated in National Park; busy; some sm pitches; gd, clean san facs but poss stretched high ssn; interesting vill; conv Paris & Giverny; gd walking, cycling; ferries across Rv Seine; gd for dogs; children loved it." ♦ 1 Apr-30 Oct. € 23.00 (CChq acc) SBS - N15 2014*

JUMIEGES *3C2 (3km S Rural) 49.41164, 0.84624* **Camping Boucles de la Seine-Normande, Base de Plein Air du Parc de Brotonne, 76480 Jumièges [02 35 37 31 72; fax 02 35 37 99 97; jumieges@ucpa.asso.fr]** E fr Le Havre on N15; foll D131 S fr Yvetot by-pass twd Pont de Brotonne (toll). Bef bdge turn SE on D982, thro Le Trait. Turn S on D143 at Yainville for Jumièges. Cont thro Jumièges on D65, site well sp on R on lake in 3km. Fr S fr Bourg-Achard take D313 twd Pont de Brotonne; turn off after bdge on D982 as above. Med, hdg pitch, pt sl, shd; wc; chem disp; mv service pnt; shwrs inc; el pnts (6A) (check pol); lndtte; shops 3km; tradsmn; rest, snacks, bar 3km; playgrnd; lake sw adj; watersports; tennis; games area; archery; golf, 30% statics; dogs €1.05; barrier clsd 2200-0800; poss cr; adv bkg; quiet; red long stay; CKE/CCI. "Lovely area; helpful warden; lge pitches; poss travellers low ssn; san facs stretched high ssn; gd." ♦ ltd 1 Apr-31 Oct. 2009*

LESSAY *1D4 (6km SW Coastal) 49.19753, -1.60427* **Camp Municipal des Dunes, 832 Blvd de la Mer, 50710 Créances [02 33 46 31 86 or 02 22 17 25 61; fax 02 33 07 40 42; www.ville-creances.fr]** Turn W onto D72/D652 in Lessay, after 3km turn L on D650 at T-junc. After 1.5km turn R at rndabt on D394 sp 'Créances Plage' & site office opp seafront car pk. Med, mkd pitch, pt shd; wc; shwrs inc; el pnts (10A) €4; gas; lndtte; shop 3km; tradsmn; rest, snacks; bar; playgrnd; paddling pool; sand beach adj; games area; games rm; dogs €1.50; poss cr; adv bkg; quiet; CKE/CCI. ♦ ltd 27 Jun-6 Sep. € 12.50 2011*

⊞ **LILLEBONNE** *3C2 (4km W Rural) 49.53024, 0.49763* **Camping Hameau des Forges, 76170 St Antoine-la-Forêt [02 35 39 80 28 or 02 35 91 48 30]** Fr Le Havre take rd twds Tancarville bdge, D982 into Lillebonne, D81 W to site on R in 4km, sp (pt winding rd). Fr S over Tancarville bdge onto D910 sp Bolbec. At 2nd rndabt turn R onto D81, site 5km on L. NB Concealed ent by phone box. Med, pt shd; wc; chem disp; shwrs €1.20; el pnts (5A) inc; tradsmn; 90% statics; dogs; poss cr; adv bkg; quiet; no ccard acc; CKE/CCI. "Basic, clean site; staff welcoming & helpful; poss statics only low ssn & facs ltd; site muddy when wet; conv NH for Le Havre ferries late arr & early dep; Roman amphitheatre in town worth visit." € 10.40 2010*

LISIEUX *3D1 (2km N Rural) 49.16515, 0.22054* **Camp Municipal de La Vallée, 9 Rue de la Vallée, 14100 Lisieux [02 31 62 00 40 or 02 31 48 18 10 (LS); fax 02 31 48 18 11; tourisme@cclisieuxpaysdauge.fr; www.lisieux-tourisme.com]** N on D579 fr Lisieux twd Pont l'Evêque. Approx 500m N of Lisieux take L to Coquainvilliers onto D48 & foll sp for Camping (turn L back in Lisieux dir). Site on D48 parallel to main rd. Med, hdstg, pt shd; wc (some cont); chemp disp; shwrs inc; el pnts (6A) €2.50-4.50; gas; shop 1km; rest, snacks, bar 2km; htd pool, waterslide nrby; 20% statics; bus fr ent; poss cr; ccard not acc; rd noise; CKE/CCI. "Interesting town, childhood home of St Thérèse; helpful warden; v clean san facs; gd." 1 Apr-30 Sep. € 12.00 2010*

LISIEUX *3D1 (10km NE Rural) 49.18009, 0.33238* **Aire Naturalle Le Mont Criquet (Bernard), Clos du Mont Criquet, 14590 Ouilly-du-Houley [tel/fax 02 31 62 98 98 or 06 08 93 19 63 (mob); bernard.ocjh@orange.fr; http://rmc14.pagesperso-orange.fr]** Fr D613 turn N onto D137 to Ouilly-du-Houley; foll D137 after x-rds in vill by church; site sp. NB App narr single track rd - owner assists, just phone. Sm, pt sl, pt shd; wc; shwrs inc; el pnts (2-6A) €2.40; lndtte; tradsmn; BBQ; playgrnd; games area; 60% statics; dogs; poss cr; Eng spkn; adv bkg; quiet; CKE/CCI. "Beautiful site in orchard; helpful, knowledgeable owner; gd modern facs; m'vans not acc in periods wet weather." 30 Apr-14 Sep. € 9.00 2009*

LITTEAU see Balleroy *1D4*

NORMANDY

⊞ **LONGNY AU PERCHE** *4E2* (1km SW Rural) *48.51749, 0.74177* **FFCC Camping Monaco Parc, Route de Monceaux, 61290 Longny-au-Perche [02 33 73 59 59; fax 02 33 25 77 56; info@campingmonacoparc.com; www.campingmonacoparc.com]** Fr N on N12 take D918 to Longny, then D111 S to site, sp. Med, mkd pitch, some hdstg, pt shd; htd wc; chem disp; mv service pnt; baby facs; sauna; shwrs; el pnts; lndtte (inc dryer); shop; tradsmn; supmkt 2km; rest, snacks; bar; BBQ; playgrnd; htd, covrd pool; lake fishing; games area; fitness rm; entmnt; TV; 80% statics; adv bkg; quiet. "Conv NH to/fr Paris; ltd touring pitches." ♦ 2009*

LOUVIERS *3D2* (2km W Rural) *49.21490, 1.13279* **Camping Le Bel Air, Route de la Haye-Malherbe, Hameau de St-Lubin, 27400 Louviers [tel/fax 02 32 40 10 77; contact@camping-lebelair.fr; www.camping-lebelair.fr]** Site well sp in Louviers. Fr cent foll D81 W for 2.5km dir La Haye-Malherbe; twisting rd uphill; site on R. Or if travelling S leave A13 at junc 19 to Louviers & as bef. NB In town cent look for sm green sp after Ecole Communale (on L) & bef Jardin Public - a narr rd (1-way) & easy to miss. Med, hdg/mkd/hdstg pitch, shd; wc; chem disp; mv service pnt; shwrs inc; el pnts (6A) €4.90; gas; lndtte (with dryer); supmkt 2km; tradsmn; playgrnd; htd pool; bowling; wifi; 30% statics; dogs €2.50; poss cr; Eng spkn; adv bkg; quiet; ccard acc; red low ssn/CKE/CCI. "Access to pitches diff long o'fits, poss mover req; check barrier opening times; poss NH only (2013); gd site and dog walks on site." 15 Mar-15 Oct. € 23.20 2013*

LUC SUR MER see Ouistreham *3D1*

LYONS LA FORET *3D2* (500m NE Rural) *49.40334, 1.47954* **Camping Saint Paul, 27480 Lyons-la-Forêt [02 32 49 42 02; camping-saint-paul@orange.fr; www.camping-saint-paul.fr]** Fr Rouen E on N31/E46 for 33km; at La Feuillie, S on D921/321 for 8km; site on L at bottom of hill at ent to town adj Rv Lieure. Med, hdg/mkd pitch, pt shd; htd wc (cont); chem disp; shwrs inc; el pnts (6A) €2.50 (poss rev pol); lndtte; shops 1km; tradsmn; rest, snacks, bar 1km; playgrnd; pool adj inc; fishing; tennis; horseriding; poss cr; 50% statics; dogs €1; adv bkg; quiet; no ccard acc; red low ssn/CKE/CCI. "Pleasant, well-kept municipal site; helpful staff; Lyons-la-Forêt lovely town, conv Dieppe ferry; walking & cycling in forests; liable to flood after heavy rain; rec." 1 Apr-31 Oct. € 20.50 2010*

See advertisement

MAILLERAYE SUR SEINE, LA see Caudebec en Caux *3C2*

MARCHAINVILLE *4E2* (200m N Rural) *48.58617, 0.81360* **Camp Municipal Les Fosses, 61290 Marchainville [tel/fax 02 33 83 68 14 or 02 33 73 65 80 (Mairie); mairiemarchainville@wanadoo.fr]** Fr Verneuil-sur-Avre take D941 S to La Ferté-Vidame & at start of town turn R onto D4/D11 SW to Marchainville; site sp at x-rds in vill on D243. Sm, hdg/mkd pitch, pt sl, pt shd; wc; shwrs; el pnts (10A) €2.30; shop, rest, snacks, bar 8km; tennis; no statics; phone; adv bkg; quiet; CKE/CCI. "Clean, basic site; warden visits." ♦ ltd 1 Apr-30 Oct. € 5.60 2010*

MARTRAGNY see Bayeux *3D1*

MAUPERTUS SUR MER see Cherbourg *1C4*

MELE SUR SARTHE, LE *4E1* (500m SE Rural) *48.50831, 0.36298* **Camp Intercommunal La Prairie, La Bretèche, St Julien-Sarthe, 61170 Le Mêle-sur-Sarthe [02 33 27 18 74]** Turn off N12 onto D4; site sp in vill. Med, mkd pitch, pt shd; wc; chem disp; mv service pnt; shwrs; el pnts (6A) inc; lndtte; supmkt 300m; playgrnd; sand beach/lake 300m; sailing; tennis; adv bkg; CKE/CCI. "Pt of excel sports complex; vg." 1 May-30 Sep. € 13.80 2014*

MERVILLE FRANCEVILLE PLAGE see Cabourg *3D1*

MONT ST MICHEL, LE *2E4* (8km E Rural) *48.62820, -1.41450* **Camping St Michel, Route du Mont-St Michel, 50220 Courtils [02 33 70 96 90; fax 02 33 70 99 09; infos@campingsaintmichel.com; www.campingsaintmichel.com]** Fr E exit A84 junc 33 to N175. Take D43 coast rd fr Pontaubault twds Le Mont-St Michel. Site in vill of Courtils on L. Med, hdg/mkd pitch, some hdstg, pt sl, pt shd; htd wc; chem disp; mv service pnt; baby facs; shwrs inc; el pnts (6A) €3.50; gas; lndtte; shop; rest, snacks; bar; BBQ; playgrnd; htd pool; sand beach 8km; cycle hire; games rm; internet; entmnt; some statics; dogs €1; phone; bus adj; poss cr; Eng spkn; adv bkg; quiet; ccard acc; red low ssn; CKE/CCI. "Excel, flat site; helpful owner; excel modern san facs (unisex); cycle paths adj; gd NH for St Malo." ♦ 5 Feb-14 Nov. € 19.50 (CChq acc) 2010*

MONT ST MICHEL, LE *2E4* (2km S Rural) *48.61476, -1.50887* **Camping du Mont St Michel, 50150 Le Mont St Michel [02 33 60 22 10; fax 02 33 60 20 02; stmichel@le-mont-saint-michel.com; www.ot-montsaintmichel.com]** Located at junc of D976 (Pontorson/Le Mont St Michel) with D275, behind Hotel Vert. Lge, hdg/mkd pitch, pt shd; wc; chem disp; mv service pnt; shwrs inc; baby facs; el pnts (5A) €2.80 (poss long lead req); gas; lndtte (inc dryer); lge supmkt & rest adj; snacks; bar; playgrnd; sand beach 2km; fishing; cycle hire; TV; dogs; phone; adv bkg; Eng spkn; ccard acc; red low ssn/CKE/CCI. "Well-located, well-kept site; book in at hotel recep, friendly & helpful; excel san facs; no provision to fill Aquaroll etc; vg shady pitches behind hotel; poss noisy - lge m'van area on opp side D275 quieter, closes end Sep; some pitches diff due trees; poss muddy after heavy rain; gd walking & cycling; beach at 2km reported unsafe for sw (quicksand)." ♦ 5 Feb-12 Nov. € 15.00 2011*

MONT ST MICHEL, LE *2E4* (4km S Rural) *48.59622, -1.51244* **Camping aux Pommiers, 28 Route du Mont-St Michel, 50170 Beauvoir [tel/fax 02 33 60 11 36; pommiers@aol.com; www.camping-auxpommiers.com]** N fr Pontorson foll D976 sp Le Mont St Michel. Site 5km on R on ent vill of Beauvoir. Med, hdg/mkd pitch, hdstg, pt shd; htd wc (some cont); chem disp; mv service pnt; shwrs inc; el pnts (6A) €4; gas; lndtte; shop; supmkt 4km; tradsmn; snacks; bar; BBQ; playgrnd; htd pool; waterslide; sand/shgl beach 2km; tennis 900m; games area; games rm; cycle hire; wifi; entmnt; TV; 30% statics; dogs €1.20; Eng spkn; adv bkg; quiet; ccard acc; red low ssn/CKE/CCI. "Busy site, rec arr early; friendly, helpful staff & owner; tired clean facs; gd touring base; easy cycle ride to Mont St Michel or pleasant walk; excel site; modern; v highly rec." 30 Mar-11 Nov. € 34.85 2014*

MORTAIN *2E4* (8km S Rural) *48.57039, -0.94883* **Camping Les Taupinières, La Raisnais, 50140 Notre-Dame-du-Touchet [02 33 69 49 36 or 06 33 26 78 82 (mob); belinfrance@fsmail.net; www.lestaupinieres.com]** Fr Mortain S on D977 sp St Hilaire-du-Harcouët; shortly after rndabt take 2nd L at auberge to Notre-Dame-deTouchet. In vill turn L at PO, sp Le Teilleul D184, then 2nd R sp La Raisnais. Site at end of lane on R (haycart on front lawn). Sm, hdstg, pt sl, pt shd; wc; chem disp; shwrs inc; el pnts (10A) inc (poss long lead req); washing machine on request; NB no wc or shwrs Dec-Feb but water & el pnts all year; shop & rest 1km; htd pool 8km; DVD library; wifi; dogs; adv bkg; quiet. "Pleasant, tranquil, spacious CL-type site adj farm; lovely outlook; adults only; friendly, helpful British owners; well-kept, clean san facs; adv bkg rec; highly rec." 1 Mar-31 Oct. € 15.00 2014*

MORTAIN *2E4* (500m W Urban) *48.64808, -0.94350* **Camp Municipal Les Cascades, Place du Château, 50140 Mortain [02 33 79 30 30 (Mairie0; mairie.de.mortain@wanadoo.fr; www.ville-mortain.fr]** On D977 S fr Vire twd St Hilaire-du-Harcouët; site in cent of Mortain, sp to R. Sm, pt shd; wc; chem disp; mv service pnt; shwrs inc; el pnts (6A) inc; shop 200m; sm playgrnd; no statics; dogs; m'van parking area outside site; CKE/CCI. "Sm extra charge for twin-axles; gd san facs." ♦ Easter-30 Sep. € 10.00 2010*

MOYAUX *3D1* (3km NE Rural) *49.20860, 0.39230* **Camping Château Le Colombier, Le Val Séry, 14590 Moyaux [02 31 63 63 08; fax 02 31 61 50 17; mail@camping-lecolombier.com; www.camping-lecolombier.com]** Fr Pont de Normandie on A29, at junc with A13 branch R sp Caen. At junc with A132 branch R & foll sp Lisieux, D579. Turn L onto D51 sp Blangy-le-Château. Immed on leaving Moyaux turn L onto D143 & foll sp to site on R in 3km. Lge, mkd pitch, pt shd; wc; chem disp; mv service pnt; baby facs; shwrs inc; el pnts (10A) inc (poss lead req); gas; lndtte (inc dryer); sm shop; tradsmn; rest, snacks; bar; BBQ; playgrnd; htd pool; tennis; cycle hire; excursions; horseriding nr; games area; wifi; entmnt; games/TV rm; some static tents/tour ops; dogs free; no c'vans/m'vans over 7m high ssn; phone; Eng spkn; adv bkg; quiet; ccard acc; red long stay/low ssn; CKE/CCI. "Beautiful, peaceful, spacious site in chateau grnds; ltd san facs low ssn; lge pool, but no shade, seats or sunshades around; vg for children; gd shop & crêperie; shgl paths poss diff some wheelchairs/pushchairs; if dep bef 0800 must move to car park o'night; mkt Sun." ♦ ltd 1 May-14 Sep. € 36.00 SBS - N04 2013*

NEUFCHATEL EN BRAY *3C2* (900m NW Urban) *49.73781, 1.42803* **Camping Sainte Claire, 19 rue Grande Flandre, 76270 Neufchâtel-en-Bray [02 35 93 03 93 or 06 20 12 20 98 (mob); fancelot@wanadoo.fr; www.camping-sainte-claire.com]** Fr S exit A28 junc 9 onto D928 sp Neufchâtel; in 1km, at bottom hill, turn L into Rue de la Grande Flandre, following Leclerk supmkt sp; cont past supmkt for 400m to Rue Ste Claire. Or Fr N exit A28 junc 7 onto D928 dir Neufchâtel; in approx 5km turn R onto D1 for Dieppe & in 1km turn L at site sp. (NB Motorvan aire imm bef site ent - do not turn in by mistake as there are charges). Med, hdg/mkd pitch, hdstg, pt sl, terr, pt shd; wc; chem disp; mv service point; serviced pitches; baby facs; shwrs inc; el pnts (6-10A) €4-6; lndtte (inc dryer); sm shop; supmkt 400m; tradsmn; bar/rest, bar; BBQ; playgrnd; cycle hire; fishing; wifi; 30% statics; dogs free low ssn; phone; bus 400m; twin axles; poss cr; some Eng spkn; adv bkg; quiet; ccard acc; red long stay; CKE/CCI. "Beautiful, spacious, well-run, well-kept, busy site by rv; lge, med & sm pitches; not all pitches have 10A, poss 6A pitches better; friendly, helpful owner; excel clean san facs - poss long walk low ssn; wet rm for disabled; wheelchair access/easy walking; pleasant walk along cycle rte (old rlwy line) to town; Sat mkt; conv Le Havre/Dieppe ferries & A28; sep o'night area; some drive-thro pitches; gd value sh or long stay; popular NH; excel; nice site as always; Aire for m'vans now open; busy, efficient site; gd easy access fr a'route; ent tight for lge o'fits; best book for twin axles; excel rest." ♦ 1 Apr-24 Oct. € 22.40 2014*

NEUVE LYRE, LA *3D2* (350m W Urban) *48.90750, 0.74486* **Camp Municipal La Salle, Rue de l'Union, 27330 La Neuve-Lyre [02 32 60 14 98 or 02 32 30 50 01 (Mairie); fax 02 32 30 22 37; mairie.la-neuve-lyre@wanadoo.fr]** Fr NE on D830 into vill turn R at church (sp not visible), fr S (Rugles) foll sp. Well sp fr vill. Med, pt shd; wc (some cont) ltd; chem disp (wc); mv service pnt; shwrs €0.75; el pnts (5A) inc (poss long lead req); shops 500m; fishing; 40% statics; dogs; quiet; CKE/CCI. "Delightful, peaceful, clean site; site yourself, warden calls; excel sh stay/NH." ♦ 15 Mar-15 Oct. € 8.00 2014*

NORMANDY

NOLLEVAL *3C2* (200m N Rural) *49.49513, 1.48126* **Camp Municipal Le Clair-Ruissel, 9 Rue Marceau Fortin, 76780 Nolléval [tel/fax 02 35 90 83 26 or 02 35 90 83 47; mairie-nolleval@wanadoo.fr; www.normandie-tourisme.fr]** E fr Rouen on D31; in 29km at La Feuillie turn L onto D921 to Nolléval; at junc of D921 & D38 fork R onto D921; site on R in 200m. Site sp in vill. Sm, hdg/mkt pitch, pt shd; wc (some cont); chem disp (wc); shwrs inc; el pnts €3; shops, snacks & bar 500m; 50% statics; dogs; phone adj; quiet; adv bkg; CKE/CCI. "Vg site." 15 Mar-15 Oct. € 12.00 2011*

NOTRE DAME DU TOUCHET see Mortain *2E4*

OFFRANVILLE see Dieppe *3C2*

OMONVILLE LA ROGUE see Beaumont Hague *1C4*

ORBEC *3D1* (500m N Urban) *49.02829, 0.40857* **Camp Municipal Les Capucins, Rue des Frères Bigot, 14290 Orbec [02 31 32 76 22; camping.sivom@orange.fr]** Exit A28 junc 15 to Orbec; on ent town foll site sp. If app fr D519 or D819 steep drag up to site & care req down to town. Sm, pt shd; wc; chem disp; shwrs inc; el pnts (10A) €2; shops 800m; playgrnd; dogs free; quiet. "Well-kept site; site yourself if office clsd; san facs old but clean; no twin-axles; access easy for lge o'fits; delightful countryside; excel." 25 May-8 Sep. € 12.00 2014*

OUILLY DU HOULEY see Lisieux *3D1*

"We must tell The Club about that great site we found"

Get your site reports in by mid-August and we'll do our best to get your updates into the next edition.

OUISTREHAM *3D1* (1km S Urban) *49.26909, -0.25498* **Camp Municipal Les Pommiers, Rue de la Haie Breton, 14150 Ouistreham [02 31 97 12 66; fax 02 31 97 12 66; campinglespommiers14150@gmail.com; www.camping-pommiers-ouistreham.fr]** Fr ferry terminal foll sp Caen on D84 (Rue de l'Yser/Ave du Grand Large); in approx 1.5km site sp at rndabt; take 3rd exit. Lge, hdg pitch, pt shd; htd wc; chem disp; mv service pnt; shwrs inc; el pnts (10A) inc; gas; lndtte (inc dryer); shop; supmkt 500m; tradsmn; playgrnd; pool 1km; sand beach 1.8km; tennis; games area; 40% statics; dogs €1.10 poss cr; Eng spkn; no adv bkg; quiet, some rd noise; ccard acc; CKE/CCI. "V conv for late or early ferry (5 mins to terminal), site stays open for late Brittany ferry; busy high ssn; gd sized pitches; sandy soil; gates open 0700-2300 (dep out of hrs, by request); opens for late arr; staff pleasant & helpful; san facs clean but basic, stretched high ssn; no twin-axles; nice walk/cycle along canal to town; wonderful beaches; interesting area; mkt Thur; conv NH & longer; excel; British twin axle caravans acc; sep area for NH; gd for long stay; take away food and bread shop on site; conv NH without unhitching." 15 Feb-15 Dec. € 18.70 2014*

⊞ **OUISTREHAM** *3D1* (6km S Rural) *49.23838, -0.25763* **FFCC Camping des Capucines, rue de la Côte Fleurie,14860 Ranville [02 31 78 69 82; fax 02 31 78 16 94; campingdescapucines.14@orange.fr; www.calvados-tourisme.com]** App Caen fr E or W, take Blvd Péripherique Nord, then exit 3a sp Ouistreham car ferry (D515). In approx 8.5km turn R onto D514 sp Cabourg, cross Pegasus Bdge & foll sp Ranville across 2 rndabts; at x-rds in 500m turn L (at sm campsite sp); site in 300m on L. Fr Ouistreham foll D514 dir Caborg to Pegasus Bdge, then as above. Med, hdg/mkd pitch, terr, pt shd; htd wc; chem disp; mv service pnt; baby facs; shwrs inc; el pnts (10A) inc (poss rev pol); gas; lndtte; sm shop; supmkt 2km; rest, bar 1km; playgrnd; sand beach 3km; 60% statics; dogs €1.80; phone; bus 500m; poss cr; some Eng spkn; adv bkg if arr late; quiet; ccard acc; red low ssn/CKE/CCI. "Excel site in pleasant position; some pitches sm; helpful, friendly owner; gd clean san facs; barrier open 0600-2400 but if clsd low ssn use intercom at recep; conv ferries (if arr late fr ferry, phone in adv for pitch number & barrier code & use intercom at recep); take care o'hanging trees; conv Pegasus Bdge, museum & war cemetery; vg, quiet well run site; conv for ferry; hypermkt 4.8km." € 28.00 2014*

OUISTREHAM *3D1* (3km SW Urban) *49.24970, -0.27190* **Camping Les Hautes Coutures, avenue de la Côte de Nacre, 14970 Bénouville [02 31 44 73 08 or 06 07 25 26 90 (mob LS); fax 02 31 95 30 80; info@campinghautescoutures.com; www.campinghautescoutures.com]** Leave Ouistreham ferry & foll sp Caen & A13 over 2 rndabts. After 2nd rndabt join dual c'way. Leave at 1st exit (D35) sp St Aubin d'Arquenay & ZA de Bénouville. Turn R at end of slip rd, then L at T-junc; site in 200m uphill on R. Or fr Caen twd port on dual c'way, site has own exit shortly after Pegasus Memorial Bdge exit; site clearly visible on R of dual c'way. Lge, hdg pitch, pt sl & uneven, pt shd; htd wc; chem disp; mv service pnt; baby facs; shwrs inc; el pnts (10A) €5.50 (rev pol)(adaptors avail); lndtte (inc dryer); hypmkt at Hérouville; tradsmn; rest, snacks; bar; BBQ; playgrnd; htd, covrd pool; paddling pool; waterslide; jacuzzi; beach 2km; fishing; horseriding & windsurfing 1km; golf 4km; cycle hire; wifi; entmnt; games/TV rm; 30% statics; dogs €3; no c'vans/m'vans over 12m high ssn; poss cr; Eng spkn; adv bkg; ccard acc; red low ssn; CKE/CCI. "Busy, poss noisy holiday complex o'verlooking Caen Canal; friendly staff; sm pitches; access tight some pitches when busy; recep 0800-2000 high ssn, but staff will open for late ferry arr if req in adv; ltd el pnts (2009); cycle path to Caen; daily mkt in Ouistreham; conv NH; access to pitches diff as high kerbs, some pitches on steep slopes." ♦ 1 Apr-31 Oct. € 49.20 (CChq acc) 2013*

OUISTREHAM *3D1* (7km W Coastal) *49.2915, -0.3017* **Camping des Hautes Sentes, Chemin des Hautes Sentes, 14880 Hermanville [02 31 96 39 12; fax 02 31 96 92 98; leshautessentes@yahoo.fr; www.campingdeshautessentes.fr]** Well sp on D514 W fr Ouistreham. Med, hdg/mkd pitch, pt shd; wc; chem disp; shwrs inc; el pnts (6A) €2; lndtte; tradsmn; snacks; bar; playgrnd; beach 700m; games area; entmnt; TV rm; 90% statics; dogs €1.52; bus 400m; Eng spkn; quiet. "Friendly, pleasant site; clean facs; few tourist pitches." 1 Apr-30 Sep. € 16.70 2009*

OUISTREHAM *3D1* (12km NW Coastal) *49.31799, -0.35824* **Camp Municipal La Capricieuse, 2 Rue Brummel, 14530 Luc-sur-Mer [02 31 97 34 43; fax 02 31 97 43 64; info@campinglacapricieuse.com; www.campinglacapricieuse.com]** Fr ferry terminal turn R at 3rd traff lts (D514) into Ave du G. Leclerc. Cont to Luc-sur-Mer; 1st turn L after casino; site on R in 300m. Ave Lecuyer is sp & Rue Brummel is off that rd. Lge, hdg/mkd pitch, terr, pt shd; wc; mv service pnt; chem disp; shwrs inc; el pnts (6-10A) €4.65-6.25; gas; Indtte; shop 300m; tradsmn; playgrnd; sand beach adj; tennis; games rm; entmnt; excursions; wifi; TV rm; dogs €2.50; Eng spkn; adv bkg by wk only; quiet; ccard acc; red low ssn; CKE/CCI. "Excel location; some lge pitches with easy access; clean, ltd facs low ssn; conv beach & Luc-sur-Mer; conv WW2 beaches; excel site; conv for ferries." ♦ 1 Apr-30 Sep. € 26.40 2013*

⊞ **PERIERS** *1D4* (6km NE Rural) *49.21581, -1.35093* **Camping Le Clos Castel, 50500 Raids [02 33 17 23 61 or 07789 227484 (mob); lecloscastel@live.com; www.camping-france-normandy.com]** S fr Carentan on D791 to Raids; cont past vill on D791 for 300m; turn R to site, ent on R in 100m. Or N fr Periers on D791; turn L 300m bef Raids & then as bef. Site well sp. Sm, hdstg, unshd; wc; chem disp; shwrs inc; el pnts (6A) inc; shops 6km; tradsmn; bar; BBQ; dogs free; Eng spkn; adv bkg; ccard not acc. "New site (2011) also offering B&B accommotion; helpful British owners; conv D-day beaches; excel." € 15.00 2011*

PERIERS *1D4* (5km SE Rural) *49.16638, -1.34916* **FFCC Aire Naturelle Municipale Le Clos Vert, 50190 St Martin-d'Aubigny [02 33 46 57 03 or 02 33 07 73 92 (Mairie); fax 02 33 07 02 53; mairie-st-martin-daubigny@wanadoo.fr; www.gites-de-france-manche.com]** E fr Périers on D900 dir St Lô; in 4km turn R sp St Martin-d'Aubigny; site on L in 500m adj church. Sm, pt shd; wc; chem disp; shwrs inc; el pnts (6A) €2.50; Indry rm; shop 300m; rest & bar 500m; BBQ; playgrnd; fishing, tennis & golf 2km; quiet; CKE/CCI;"Charming, well-kept, useful site; facs basic but OK; easy 70km run to Cherbourg; no twin-axles; basic quiet site in vill, bar & res within walking dist." ♦ 15 Apr-15 Oct. € 7.50 2013*

PIEUX, LES *1C4* (3km SW Coastal) *49.49444, -1.84194* **Le Grand Large, 11 Route de Grand Large, 50340 Les Pieux [02 33 52 40 75; fax 02 33 52 58 20; info@legrandlarge.com; www.legrandlarge.com]** Fr ferry at 1st rndabt take 1st exit sp Centre Ville. Closer to town cent foll old N13 sp Caen. In about 1.5km branch R onto D900 then L onto D650 sp Carteret. Foll this rd past Les Pieux, cont on D650 to sp Super U. Turn R & foll site sp onto D517, then D117 for 3km until reaching beach rd to site, site on L in 2km. Lge, hdg/mkd pitch, pt shd; htd wc; chem disp; mv service pnt; baby facs; shwrs inc; el pnts (10A) €4.; gas; Indtte (inc dryer); shop; tradsmn; snacks high ssn; bar; BBQ; playgrnd; htd pool; paddling pool; sand beach adj; horseriding 4km; tennis; wifi; entmnt; games/TV rm; 40% statics; dogs free (1 per pitch); c'vans/m'vans over 8m by request; phone; poss cr; Eng spkn; adv bkg; quiet; ccard acc; red low ssn/long stay; "Well-run site; rec for families; dir access to superb lge beach; friendly staff; clean modern san facs; barrier clsd 2100-0900; conv Cherbourg ferries but arr not rec after dark due sm country lanes; outside pitches avail for early dep for ferries; mkt Fri." ♦ ltd 12 Apr-20 Sep. € 33.00 (CChq acc) SBS - N07 2013*

See advertisement

PIEUX, LES *1C4* (4km SW Coastal) *49.48022, -1.84216* **Camping Le Ranch, 50340 Le Rozel [02 33 10 07 10; fax 02 33 10 07 11; contact@camping-leranch.com; www.camping-leranch.com]** S fr Cherbourg on D650 & turn R to Les Pieux, then take D117 to Le Rozel. Turn L thro Rozel, foll sps to site. Site is on R at end rd. Med, pt sl, unshd; wc; chem disp; baby facs; shwrs inc; el pnts(10A) €4.50; Indtte; shop; rest, snacks; bar; playgrnd; htd pool; waterslide; sand beach adj; fishing; watersports; games area; wifi; entmnt; mostly statics; dogs €3.20; quiet; red low ssn/long stay; CKE/CCI. 1 Apr-30 Sep. € 46.60 2013*

PONT AUDEMER *3D2* (8km W Rural) *49.31433, 0.40344* **Camping La Lorie (Lehaye), 5 La Lorie, 27210 Fort-Moville [02 32 57 15 49]** Fr Pont-Audemer take D675 twrds Beauzeville. Then L onto D27. Take 3rd exit at rndabt to stay on D27. Then 3rd exit at next rndabt onto Haut Rue de Fort Moville; slight L then strt on; site on L. Sm, pt shd; wc; chem disp (wc); shwrs inc; el pnts (10A) inc; BBQ; rest, snacks, bar 2km; playgrnd; 10% statics; dogs; quiet; CKE/CCI. "CL-type site in attractive area; basic facs but clean; conv Le Havre, Honfleur; gd base." Easter-1 Nov. € 13.50 2012*

NORMANDY

PONT AUDEMER *3D2* (2km NW Rural) *49.36660, 0.48739* **Camp Municipal Risle-Seine Les Etangs, 19 Route des Etangs, 27500 Toutainville [02 32 42 46 65; fax 02 32 42 24 17; camping@ville-pont-audemer.fr; www.ville-pont-audemer.fr]** Fr Le Havre on A131/E05 cross rv at Pont de Normandie (toll). Take D580 & at junc 3 branch R & take 2nd exit onto D22 sp Beuzeville. At edge of Fiquefleur take D180, then D675 dir Pont-Audemer. In Toutainville foll site sp, turn L just bef A13 underpass, then immed R. Site approx 2km on R. Med, hdg/mkd pitch, pt shd; wc; chem disp; mv service pnt; serviced pitches; shwrs inc; el pnts (5-10A) €3.95; Indtte (inc dryer); shop 1.5km; tradsmn; snacks; bar; BBQ; playgrnd; htd pool & tennis 1.5km; fishing; canoeing, watersports; cycle hire; games area; wifi; games/TV rm; dogs free; bus; Eng spkn; adv bkg; quiet; red long stay/low ssn; ccard acc. "Lovely, well-run site; helpful warden; barrier clsd 2200-0830 but flexible for ferry; many leisure activities; poss school groups at w/end; vg for dogs; 1hr Le Havre ferry; Fri mkt Pont-Audemer; conv NH; excel; facs stretched low ssn; boggy when wet." ♦ 1 Apr-30 Oct. € 23.00 SBS - N13 2014*

See advertisement

PONT AUTHOU see Brionne *3D2*

PONT DE L'ARCHE *3D2* (300m N Urban) *49.3060, 1.1546* **Camp Municipal Eure et Seine, Quai Maréchal Foch, 27340 Pont-de-l'Arche [02 35 23 06 71 or 02 32 98 90 70 (Mairie); fax 02 32 98 90 89; campeure@orange.fr or campeure@pontdelarche.fr; www.pontdelarche.fr]** Fr Rouen S on D6015 turn 1st L after x-ing rv bdge, drive downhill then L under bdge & strt on for 300m, site on R. Restricted width on app. Or exit A13 junc 20 onto D321 to Pont-de-l'Arche; turn L at War Memorial onto Place du Souvenir; in 300m to R at rv; site on L in 200m. Med, mkd pitch, pt shd; wc; chem disp; shwrs inc; el pnts (6-10A) €5.70-630; Indtte; shop 200m; rest; bar; playgrnd; rv fishing adj; wifi; 4% statics; dogs €1.15; phone; poss v cr; adv bking; local rd noise; ccard acc; red long stay; CKE/CCI. "Pleasant, peaceful, clean rvside site in attractive medieval town; sm pitches; helpful warden; gd, modern san facs; recep 1000-1200 & 1600-2000; many shops clsd Wed pm; bus fr town to Rouen; popular NH & longer; Beautiful site nr Gothic church; excel; superb setting; v busy so arrive early or ring ahead." ♦ 1 Apr-30 Oct. € 15.60 2014*

⊞ **PONT DE L'ARCHE** *3D2* (10km S Rural) *49.22513, 1.22406* **FFCC Camping Le St Pierre, 1 Rue du Château, 27430 St Pierre-du-Vauvray [tel/fax 02 32 61 01 55; eliane.darcissac@wanadoo.fr; www.lecampingdesaintpierre.com]** Fr S exit A154 junc 3 or A13 junc 18 (Louviers) onto D6155 E until junc with D6015. Turn L & in 4km turn R to St Pierre. Fr N on D6015 after x-ing Rv Seine at Pont-de-l'Arche cont for approx 6km & turn L to St Pierre. Do not ent St Pierre fr E on D313 due low bdge under rlwy line. Med, hdg/mkd pitch, pt shd; wc; chem disp; shwrs inc; el pnts (6-10A) €2.80 (poss rev pol); Indry rm; shop 1km; BBQ; playgrnd; htd pool; 25% statics; dogs €1.20; site clsd 2 weeks at Xmas/New Year; Eng spkn; adv bkg rec; noise fr rlwy adj; CKE/CCI; "In grnds sm chateau; TGV rlwy line adj site; conv Giverny; friendly staff; ltd facs; site tired, expensive but OK for NH; not enough facs, scruffy and dirty." € 13.00 2013*

PONT D'OUILLY see Condé sur Noireau *3D1*

PONT FARCY *1D4* (500m N Rural) *47.46810, 4.35709* **Camp Municipal Pont-Farcy, Quai de la Vire, 14380 Pont-Farcy [02 31 68 32 06 or 02 31 68 86 48; pontfarcy@free.fr; www.pont-farcy.fr]** Leave A84 junc 39 onto D21 to Pont-Farcy; site on L at ent to vill. Med, hdg/mkd pitch, terr, pt shd; wc; chem disp; mv service pnt; shwrs inc; baby facs; el pnts (10A) €2.50; shop, rest & bar 500m; playgrnd; rv fishing & boating adj; tennis; cycle hire; 30% statics; dogs €1; phone; adv bkg; quiet; CKE/CCI. "Barrier poss locked periods during day but parking avail; helpful, friendly warden; clean facs; mosquitoes at dusk." ♦ 1 May-15 Sep. € 10.00 2014*

PONT L'EVEQUE *3D1* (500m NW Urban) *49.28486, 0.17573* **Camping du Stade, Rue de Beaumont, 14130 Pont l'Evêque [02 31 64 15 03 / 06 52 69 86 72; contact@campingdustade.fr; www.campingdustade.fr]** Fr town cent take D675 W twd Caen, turn R at traff lts bef town o'skts to site in 300m. Site sp on R in 300m on D118. Med, mkd pitch, pt shd; wc (some cont); chem disp; shwrs inc; el pnts (5A) €3 (poss rev pol); Indry rm; shops in town; tradsmn; playgrnd; beach 12km; rv fishing; tennis; 2% statics; quiet; ccard not acc; CKE/CCI. "Basic, clean site; friendly, helpful staff; dated san facs; no hdgs - poss noisy high ssn; trees round site are starling roosts - don't site o'fit underneath! (2010); mkt Mon; open flat level site; san facs dated (2014)." ♦ ltd 5 Apr-28 Sep. € 13.20 2014*

PONTAUBAULT *2E4* (Urban) *48.62983, -1.35205* **Camping La Vallée de la Sélune, 7 Rue Maréchal Leclerc, 50220 Pontaubault [tel/fax 02 33 60 39 00; campselune@wanadoo.fr; www.camping-manche.com]** Foll sp to Pontaubault (well sp fr all dirs). In vill head twd Avranches. Turn L immed bef bdge over Rv Sélune. In 100m turn L, site strt in 100m, well sp. Med, mkd pitch, pt sl, pt shd; wc; chem disp; shwrs inc; el pnts (10A) inc; Indtte; shop; tradsmn; supmkt 6km; snacks, bar high ssn; playgrnd; pool 7km; sand beach 10km; tennis adj; fishing adj; horseriding, cycling & golf nrby; wifi; 10% statics; dogs €1.30; poss cr; adv bkg rec; rd/rlwy noise; ccard acc; red long stay/CKE/CCI. "Relaxing, clean, tidy site; friendly British owner; vg, clean san facs; conv Mont St Michel & Cherbourg ferries; gd NH; pleasant site; friendly Yorkshire owner." ♦ 1 Apr-20 Oct. € 20.00 2013*

PONTAUBAULT *2E4* (4km E Rural) *48.61690, -1.29475* **Camp Municipal La Sélune, Rue de Boishue, 50220 Ducey [02 33 48 46 49 or 02 33 48 50 52; fax 02 33 48 87 59; ducey.tourisme@wanadoo.fr; www.ducey-tourisme.com]** Exit A84 junc 33 onto N176 E fr Pontaubault. In Ducey turn R onto D178 twd St Aubin-de-Terregatte. Ent at sports grnd in 200m. Sm, hdg pitch, pt sl, shd; wc; chem disp; shwrs inc; el pnts (5A) €1.85 (poss rev pol; poss long lead req); gas; Indtte; shop; rest, snacks, bar in vill; playgrnd; pool nr; sand beach 25km; tennis adj; 10% statics; dogs €1.30; phone; bus; poss cr; Eng spkn; adv bkg; quiet; CKE/CCI. "Well-maintained site; warden calls am & pm; poss travellers; excel; v clean facs; friendly, helpful owners." ♦ 1 Apr-30 Sep. € 17.50 2014*

PONTAUBAULT *2E4* (6km SW Coastal) *48.56583, -1.47111* **Campéole Camping St Grégoire, Le Haut Bourg, 50170 Servon [02 33 60 26 03; fax 02 33 60 68 65; saint-gregoire@campeole.com; www.camping-mont-saint-michel.com / www.campeole.com]** Foll N175 fr Pontaubault twd Pontorson. After 6km site sp on R twd Servon vill. Med, hdg/mkd pitch, some hdstg, pt shd; wc; chem disp; baby facs; shwrs; el pnts (6A) inc; Indtte (inc dryer); sm shop; tradsmn; BBQ; playgrnd; pool; games rm; wifi; TV; 30% statics; dogs €2.60; adv bkg; quiet but some rd noise on S side of site; ccard acc; red low ssn; CKE/CCI. "Conv ferries; useful stop en rte to Cherbourg." 5 Apr-21 Sep. € 35.20 (CChq acc) 2014*

PONTORSON *2E4* (400m NW Rural) *48.55805, -1.51444* **Kawan Village Haliotis, Chemin des Soupirs, 50170 Pontorson [02 33 68 11 59; fax 02 33 58 95 36; camping.haliotis@wanadoo.fr; www.camping-haliotis-mont-saint-michel.com]** Exit A84 junc 33 onto N175 dir Pontorson; foll sp Centre Ville/Mont-St-Michel. Site well sp. Lge, hdg/mkd pitch, pt sl, pt shd; htd wc; chem disp; mv service pnt; baby facs; sauna; shwrs inc; el pnts (10-16A) inc (poss rev pol); gas; Indtte; shop; supmkt 400m; tradsmn; rest 400m; snacks; bar; BBQ; playgrnd; htd pool; paddling pool; spa; rv fishing; boating; tennis; cycle hire; games area; games rm; library; wifi; 25% statics; dogs €2; phone; bus 400m; poss cr; Eng spkn; adv bkg rec; quiet, poss noise till late w/ends; ccard acc; red low ssn; CKE/CCI. "Popular, well-kept, busy site; lge pitches; friendly, helpful owners; immac, unisex san facs; lovely pool & bar; rvside walk to town; cycle rte/bus to Mont St Michel; highly rec; serviced pitches; pitches with private bathrooms avail." ♦ ltd 15 Mar-11 Nov. € 35.00 (CChq acc) 2014*

PORT EN BESSIN HUPPAIN *3D1* (600m W Coastal) *49.34693, -0.77095* **Camping Port'land, Chemin du Sémaphore, 14520 Port-en-Bessin [02 31 51 07 06; fax 02 31 51 76 49; campingportland@wanadoo.fr; www.camping-portland.com]** Site sp fr D514 W of Port-en-Bessin. Lge, hdg/mkd pitch, hdstg, pt shd; htd wc; chem disp; mv service pnt; shwrs inc; el pnts (6-10A) €5; gas 1km; Indtte; shop; tradsmn; rest, snacks; bar; BBQ; playgrnd; htd, covrd pool; waterslide; paddling pool; sand beach 4km; tennis 800m; games area; games rm; wifi; entmnt; TV; 30% statics; dogs €3; Eng spkn; adv bkg; ccard acc; red long stay/low ssn; CKE/CCI. "Pleasant site; friendly, helpful staff; vg san facs; extra charge lger pitches; excel touring base for landing beaches etc." ♦ 1 Apr-1 Nov. € 35.00 SBS - N09 2013*

POSES *3D2* (1.6km SE Urban) *49.29552, 1.24914* **Base de Loisirs, Rue du Souvenir French, 27740 Poses [02 32 59 13 13; campinggsmb@hotmail.fr; www.basedeloisirs-lery-poses.fr]** Fr Poses head NE on Rue du Bac twrd Rue das Masures, take 1st R onto Rue des Masures, turn R onto Rue du Roussillon, after 350 mtrs turn L onto Rue du Souvenir Francais, after 220 mtrs turn L and arrive at your dest Lge, pt shd; wc; chem disp; shwrs; el pnts (16A) mini golf; water ski; pedalo hire; canoe; catamaran; beaches; hiking; beach volleyball; table tennis; overlooking Rv Seine. "Good san facs, gravel rdway throughout site, site adj to the Rv Seine with direct access to the rvside, plenty of pitches for tourers, supmkt 5km." 1 Apr-31 Oct. € 14.10 2014*

POURVILLE SUR MER see Dieppe *3C2*

PUTANGES PONT ECREPIN *4E1* (1km W Rural) *48.76067, -0.24564* **Camp Municipal Le Val d'Orne, Le Friche, 61210 Putanges-Pont-Ecrepin [02 33 35 04 67 or 02 33 35 00 25 (Mairie); fax 02 33 35 49 50; mairie.putanges.61@wanadoo.fr; www.office-tourisme-putanges.com]** S fr Falaise on D909 to Putanges. Ent Putanges cross Rv L'Orne & ignore camping sp immed on L (Grand Rue). Go thro vill for approx 1km, turn L sp camping 200m. Site on R. Sm, hdg/mkd pitch, pt shd; wc; shwrs inc; el pnts (6-10A) €2.30-3.30; shops & rest 5 mins walk via rv bank; rv fishing; playgrnd; dogs €1.15; adv bkg; quiet. "Clean, well-run rvside site; site yourself, warden visits am & pm; ltd facs; gd." 1 Apr-30 Sep. € 7.50 2010*

QUETTEHOU *1C4* (2.5km E Urban/Coastal) *49.58520, -1.26858* **Camping La Gallouette, Rue de la Gallouette, 50550 St Vaast-la-Hougue [02 33 54 20 57; fax 02 33 54 16 71; contact@camping-lagallouette.fr; www.lagallouette.com]** E fr Quettehou on D1, site sp in St Vaast-la-Houge to S of town. Lge, hdg/mkd pitch, pt shd; wc; chem disp; mv service pnt; baby facs; shwrs; el pnts (6-10A) €3.80-4.60; gas; Indtte; shop; tradsmn; rest, snacks; bar; BBQ; playgrnd; htd pool (solar heating); sand beach 300m; games area; games rm; 10% statics; dogs €1.80; phone; poss cr; adv bkg; quiet; red low ssn; CKE/CCI. "Lovely friendly site; some lge pitches; gd range of facs; sh walk to interesting town; excel site." ♦ 1 Apr-30 Sep. € 37.00 2013*

*Last year of report

QUETTEHOU *1C4* (2km S Coastal) *49.57960, -1.30760* **Camping Le Rivage, 75 Rue Ste Marie, 50630 Quettehou [02 33 54 13 76; fax 02 33 43 10 42; camping.lerivage@wanadoo.fr; www.camping-lerivage.fr]** Fr Quettehou on D14, sp on L. Med, unshd; wc; shwrs inc; el pnts (6A) €4.30; Indtte (inc dryer); shop; snacks; bar; BBQ; playgrnd; htd pool; paddling pool; sand beach 400m; cycle hire; internet; entmnt; 50% statics; dogs €3; Eng spkn; adv bkg rec high ssn; quiet. "Gd clean site." 1 Apr-30 Sep. € 19.50 2010*

QUIBERVILLE PLAGE see Veules les Roses *3C2*

RAIDS see Periers *1D4*

RANVILLE see Ouistreham *3D1*

RAVENOVILLE PLAGE see Ste Mere Eglise *1C4*

"I need an on-site restaurant"

We do our best to make sure site information is correct, but it is always best to check any must-have facilities are still available or will be open during your visit.

⊞ **ROUEN** *3C2* (5km E Urban) *49.43154, 1.15387* **Camping L'Aubette, 23 Rue du Vert- Buisson, 76160 St Léger-du-Bourg-Denis [tel/fax 02 35 08 47 69; www.rouentourisme.com]** Fr Rouen E on N31 dir Darnétal & Beauvais; in 1km cont strt on onto D42/D138 dir St Léger-du-Bourg-Denis; in 400m turn L onto Rue du Vert Buisson; site on r in 800m just past stop sp. Site well sp as 'Camping' fr Rouen cent. Med, sl, terr, pt shd; wc (mainly cont); shwrs €1.60; el pnts (3-10A) €1.50-3; shops 400m; mainly statics; poss cr. "In attractive rv valley; conv city cent; conv bus to town; v ltd touring pitches; v basic site, gd NH." € 9.50 2014*

ST ARNOULT see Deauville *3D1*

ST AUBIN SUR MER see Caen *3D1*

ST EVROULT NOTRE DAME DU BOIS see Aigle, L' *4E2*

ST FRAIMBAULT see Domfront *4E1*

ST GEORGES DU VIEVRE *3D2* (2km E Rural) **Camping à la Ferme La Brettonnière (Séjourne), 27450 St Grégoire-du-Vièvre [02 32 42 82 67]** At traff lts on D130 in Pont Authou turn W onto D137 twd St Georges-du-Vièvre; after 7km turn L, sp Camping Rural; site in 1km. NB Steep rdway down & narr terrs poss unsuitable for c'vans. Sm, mkd pitch, terr, shd; wc; chem disp; shwrs inc; el pnts €4.20; shop 1km; playgrnd; pool 4km; adv bkg; quiet; CKE/CCI. "CL-type farm site; vg." Mar-Oct. € 15.30 2010*

ST GEORGES DU VIEVRE *3D2* (200m W Rural) *49.24248, 0.58040* **Camp Municipal du Vièvre, Route de Noards, 27450 St Georges-du-Vièvre [02 32 42 76 79 or 02 32 56 34 29 (LS); fax 02 32 57 52 90; camping.stgeorgesduvievre@wanadoo.fr; www.saintgeorgesduvievre.org]** Fr traff lts on D130 in Pont Authou turn W onto D137 to St Georges-du-Vièvre; in town sq at tourist info turn L uphill sp camping; site 200m on L. If app fr S on N138 at Bernay take D834 sp Le Havre to Lieurey. Turn R onto D137 to St Georges, then turn R at camping sp by sw pool. Sm, hdg pitch, pt shd; htd wc; chem disp; serviced pitches; shwrs inc; el pnts (5A) inc; gas 200m; Indtte; shops 200m; BBQ; playgrnd; pool 150m; tennis 50m; sw 100m; cycle hire; wifi at TO; dogs; Eng spkn; adv bkg (rec high ssn); quiet; CKE/CCI. "Peaceful; gd facs & pitches; well-run site; interesting area; gd cycling; vg." ♦ 1 Apr-30 Sep. € 13.30 2014*

ST HILAIRE DU HARCOUET *2E4* (1km W Urban) *48.58105, -1.09771* **FFCC Camp Municipal de la Sélune, 50600 St Hilaire-du-Harcouët [02 33 49 43 74 or 02 33 49 70 06; fax 02 33 49 59 40; info@st-hilaire.fr; www.st-hilaire.fr]** Sp on N side of N176 twd Mont St Michel/St Malo/Dinan, on W side of town; well sp. Med, hdg pitch, pt sl, pt shd; wc; chem disp; shwrs inc; el pnts (16A) €1.95; Indry rm; shops 1km; snacks 500m; playgrnd; pool 300m; wifi; dogs €0.70; red long stay/CKE/CCI. "Peaceful, beautifully maintained site; easy access; helpful, pleasant warden; superb san facs; gate locked 2200-0730; excel." 23 Apr-16 Sep. € 22.50 2014*

ST LEGER DU BOURG DENIS see Rouen *3C2*

"Satellite navigation makes touring much easier"

Remember most sat navs don't know if you're towing or in a larger vehicle – always use yours alongside maps and site directions.

STE MARIE DU MONT *1D4* (3km SE Coastal) *49.36564, -1.17721* **Camping La Baie des Veys, Le Grand Vey, 50480 Ste Marie-du-Mont [02 33 71 56 90 or 06 09 82 61 82 (mob); jerome.etasse@orange.fr; www.campinglabaiedesveys.com]** N of Carentan exit N13 onto D913 thro Ste Marie-du-Mont. At lge calvary 2km after vill, turn R onto D115 sp Le Grand Vey. Turn R at sea edge, site on R in 100m. Med, hdg/mkd pitch, pt shd; wc; chem disp (wc); shwrs inc; el pnts (6A) €3; Indtte; shop & 6km; snacks; bar; BBQ; htd pool; cycle hire; wifi; 10% statics; dogs free; Eng spkn; adv bkg; quiet. "Site beside salt flats; helpful, friendly owners; gd birdwatching, fishing; conv Utah Beach, D-Day museums etc." ♦ ltd 1 May-15 Sep. € 16.00 (CChq acc) 2010*

ST MARTIN DES BESACES *1D4* (1.2km W Rural) *49.00889, -0.85955* **Camping Le Puits, La Groudière, 14350 St Martin-des-Besaces Calvados [tel/fax 02 31 67 80 02; enquiries@lepuits.com; www.lepuits.com]** Fr Caen SW on A84 dir Rennes, Villers-Bocage & exit junc 41 to St Martin-des-Besaces. At traff lts in vill turn R & foll site sp, site on L at end of vill in 500m. Fr Cherbourg foll sp St Lô onto m'way. After Torini-sur-Vire at junc with A84 foll sp Caen & exit junc 41, then as above. Sm, hdg/mkd pitch, pt sl, pt shd; wc; chem disp; mv service pnt; shwrs inc; el pnts (6A) €5 (poss rev pol); gas; Indtte; shop 500m; tradsmn; rest 500m; snacks; bar; BBQ; sm playgrnd; pool 10km; sand beach 35km; lake adj; fishing; cycling; equestrian trails; entmnt; no statics; dogs €1.50; adv bkg; quiet, but some rd noise; red low ssn; ccard acc; CKE/CCI. "Pleasant CL-type orchard site; welcoming, helpful Irish owners; no arr bef 1400; lge pitches with garden; 'super' pitches extra cost; san facs v basic & inadequate if site full - little privacy; B&B in farmhouse; suitable for rallies up to 30 vans; c'van storage; war museum in vill; conv Caen ferries; excel." ♦ 1 Mar-31 Oct. € 29.00 2013*

ST MARTIN EN CAMPAGNE *3B2* (3km N Coastal) *49.96631, 1.20469* **Camping Domaine Les Goélands, Rue des Grèbes, 76370 St Martin-en-Campagne [02 35 83 82 90; fax 02 35 83 21 79; domainelesgoelands@orange.fr; www.lesdomaines.org]** Fr Dieppe foll D925 twd Le Tréport & Abbeville. Turn L at rndabt on D113 twd St Martin-en-Campagne. Cont thro vill to St Martin-Plage (approx 3km) & foll 'Camping' sp to site on L. Lge, hdg/mkd pitch, hdstg, pt sl, terr, pt shd; htd wc; 100% serviced pitches; chem disp; baby facs; shwrs inc; el pnts (16A) inc (poss rev pol); gas; Indtte; shop 1km; tradsmn; snacks (& in vill), bar high ssn; BBQ; playgrnd; htd pool & waterslide 1km; sand/shgl beach 500m; fishing; tennis; cycle hire; golf 20km; horseriding, archery 15km; TV; 40% statics; dogs €2; Eng spkn; adv bkg; quiet; ccard acc; red CKE/CCI. "Gd touring area; ltd recep hrs low ssn; no late arr area; poss resident workers low ssn; mkt Dieppe Sat; vg site." ♦ 1 Mar-8 Nov. € 25.50 2010*

STE MERE EGLISE *1C4* (9.5km NE Coastal) *49.46650, -1.23540* **Kawan Village Le Cormoran, 2 Rue du Cormoran, 50480 Ravenoville-Plage [02 33 41 33 94; fax 02 33 95 16 08; lecormoran@wanadoo.fr; www.lecormoran.com]** NE on D15 fr Ste Mère-Eglise to Ravenoville, turn L onto D14 then R back onto D15 to Ravenoville Plage. Turn R on D421, Rte d'Utah Beach, site on R in 1km. Or fr N13 sp C2 Fresville & ent Ste Mère-Eglise, then take D15. Lge, hdg/mkd pitch, some hdstg, unshd; wc; chem disp; mv service pnt; baby facs; sauna; shwrs inc; el pnts (6A) inc; gas; Indtte (inc dryer); shop; tradsmn; snacks; bar; BBQ (charcoal/gas); playgrnd; 2 htd pools (1 covrd); paddling pool; jacuzzi; sand beach adj (across main rd); tennis; cycle hire; horseriding; games area; archery; wifi; entmnt; TV/games rm; 60% statics; dogs €3; twin-axles acc (rec check in adv); poss cr; Eng spkn; adv bkg; quiet; ccard acc; red low ssn; CKE/CCI. "Popular, family-run site; lge pitches; warm welcome, helpful recep; well-kept san facs, poss tired end of ssn; poss v windy; vg children's facs; special pitches for early dep for ferry; m'van o'night area; excel." ♦ 5 Apr-27 Sep. € 33.00 (CChq acc) SBS - N12 2011*

STE MERE EGLISE *1C4* (500m E Urban) *49.41006, -1.31078* **Camp Municipal, 6 Rue due 505eme Airborne, 50480 Ste Mère-Eglise [02 33 41 35 22; fax 02 33 41 79 15; mairie-sme@wanadoo.fr; www.sainte-mere-eglise.info]** Fr Cherbourg S on N13 to cent of Ste Mère-Eglise (avoiding by-pass); at vill sq turn L on D17 to site, next adj sports grnd. Med, some hdstg, pt sl, pt shd, wc (some cont); chem disp (wc); shwrs inc; el pnts (12A) €4 (poss rev pol); gas 500m; Indtte; shop & bar 500m; rest, snacks, BBQ; playgrnd; sand beach 10km; tennis; cycle hire; 5% statics; games rm; dogs €1.50; phone; poss cr; little Eng spkn; adv bkg; CKE/CCI. "Nice, basic site; clean facs; friendly warden; if warden absent site yourself & pay later; conv ferries & D-Day beaches etc; gates open 6am for early dep; rec." ♦ 15 Mar-1 Oct. € 23.00 2011*

ST PAIR SUR MER see Granville *1D4*

ST PIERRE DU VAUVRAY see Pont de l'Arche *3D2*

ST PIERRE EN PORT *3C2* (500m N Coastal) *49.80943, 0.49354* **Les Falaises, 130 rue du Camping, 76540 St Pierre-en-Port [02 35 29 51 58; lesfalaises@cegetel.net]** Fr D925 turn onto D79 bet St Valery & Fecamp. Site sp in St Pierre. Med, open plan, grassy, unshd; wc; chem disp; mv service pnt; shwrs; el pnts (10A); Indtte; bar; beach 1.6km; playgrnd; games rm; 60% statics; dogs; CKE/CCI. "Cliff top site; path to beach steep with steps; narr app rd; facs dated but clean (2014); well kept site; takeaway snacks avail hg ssn only; v quiet, pleasant site; vg." ♦ ltd 1 Apr-5 Oct. € 28.00 2014*

ST SAUVEUR LE VICOMTE see Haye du Puits, La *1D4*

ST VAAST LA HOUGUE see Quettehou *1C4*

⊞ **ST VALERY EN CAUX** *3C2* (1.6km N Coastal) *49.86839, 0.71154* **Aire Communale, Quai d'Aval, Plage Ouest, 76460 St Valery-en-Caux [02 35 97 00 22 or 02 35 97 00 63 (TO); servicetourisme@ville-saint-valeryen-caux.fr]** Sp fr cent of St Valery-en-Caux along rv/seafront to harbour. Sm, chem disp; mv service pnt; water fill €4; Indtte, shops, rests nr; phone; free parking for 48 hrs. M'vans only. "M'vans only; rec arr early; low ssn free except Fri, Sat & Sun." € 4.00 2012*

⊞ **ST VALERY EN CAUX** *3C2* (1.5km SW Coastal) *49.85853, 0.70450* **Camp Municipal d'Etennemare, 21 Rue du Hameau Etennemare, 76460 St Valery-en-Caux [tel/fax 02 35 97 15 79; servicetourisme@ville-saint-valery-en-caux.fr]** Fr Dieppe on D925 foll camping sp on ent town. Med, mkd pitch, pt sl, pt shd; htd wc; chem disp; baby facs; shwrs inc; el pnts (6A) inc; Indtte; shop; tradsmn; rest 800m; playgrnd; htd pool & tennis in town; shgl beach; adv bkg; quiet; ccard acc; CKE/CCI. "Site poss clsd low ssn - phone to check; clean, tidy site." ♦ € 14.45 (CChq acc) 2010*

NORMANDY

SEES *4E1* (1 km S Urban) *48.59875, 0.17103* **Camp Municipal Le Clos Normand, Ave du 8 mai 1945, 61500 Sées [02 33 28 87 37 or 02 33 28 74 79 (LS); fax 02 33 28 18 13; tourisme@sees.fr; www.ville-sees.fr]** C'vans & lge m'vans best app fr S - twd rndabt at S end of by-pass (rec use this rndabt as other rtes diff & narr). Well sp. Narr ent. Sm, hdg pitch, pt shd; wc; chem disp; mv service pnt; shwrs inc; el pnts (4A) €2.50; gas; Indtte; supmkt opp; snacks & bar 100m; rest 500m; playgrnd; pool 2km; fishing; 10% statics; no twin axles; dogs €1.25; some Eng spkn; adv bkg; slight rd noise; CKE/CCI. "Spacious, well-cared for pitches; helpful, friendly warden; gd san facs, poss stretched if site full; excel mv service pnt; gates clsd 2100 (2000 low ssn)." ♦ 1 May-30 Sep. € 17.00 2014*

SERVON see Pontaubault *2E4*

⊞ **SURTAINVILLE** *1C4* (1km W Coastal) *49.46447, -1.82919* **Camp Municipal Les Mielles, 80 Route des Laguettes, 50270 Surtainville [tel/fax 02 33 04 31 04; camping.lesmielles@wanadoo.fr; www.surtainville.com]** S fr Cherbourg on D650, take D66 W thro Surtainville, site on R. Med, pt sl, unshd; htd wc (male cont); chem disp; shwrs inc; el pnts (4A) €2.50; Indtte; playgrnd; sand beach 100m; 30% statics; dogs €1; adv bkg; quiet; CKE/CCI. "Excel beach." ♦ ltd € 8.70 2009*

THURY HARCOURT *3D1* (500m NE Rural) *48.98930, -0.46966* **FFCC Camping Vallée du Traspy, Rue du Pont Benoît, 14220 Thury-Harcourt [02 31 79 61 80 or 02 31 52 53 54; fax 02 31 84 76 19]** App fr N on D562 fr Caen, take L fork into town after pool complex. In 100m turn L at Hôtel de la Poste, 1st L to site, clearly sp adj Rv Orne. Med, mkd pitch, terr, pt shd; wc (some cont); chem disp; mv service pnt; shwrs inc; el pnts (4A) inc; gas; Indtte; shop 1km; tradsmn; snacks; bar; BBQ; playgrnd; htd pool nr; rv adj & lake nrby; fishing; canoeing; entmnt; 20% statics; dogs €2.90; phone; poss cr; Eng spkn; adv bkg rec high ssn; quiet; CKE/CCI. "Friendly owners; well-maintained pitches; san facs need update; o'night area for m'vans; gd walking." ♦ 1 Apr-30 Sep. € 18.40 2011*

TORIGNI SUR VIRE *1D4* (1km S Rural) *49.02833, -0.97194* **Camping Le Lac des Charmilles, Route de Vire, 50160 Torigni-sur-Vire [02 33 56 91 74; fax 02 33 55 91 13; contact@camping-lacdescharmilles.com; www.camping-lacdescharmilles.com]** Exit A84 junc 40 onto D974 dir Torigni-sur-Vire/St Lô; site on R in 4km. Opp municipal stadium. Med, hdg/mkd pitch, hdstg, pt sl, pt shd; htd wc; chem disp; mv service pnt; baby facs; fam bthrm; shwrs inc; el pnts (16A) inc (long lead poss req); Indtte (inc dryer); shop; tradsmn; rest, snacks; bar; BBQ; playgrnd; htd pool; lake sw adj; cycle hire; games area; games rm; wifi; TV; 30% statics; dogs €2; phone; poss cr; Eng spkn; adv bkg; quiet; ccard acc; red low ssn; CKE/CCI. "Lovely, well-kept, well-laid out site; clean, modern san facs; interesting town; excel; excel shopping in the town within walking dist." ♦ 23 Mar-30 Sep. € 34.40 (CChq acc) 2014*

TOUQUES see Deauville *3D1*

TOURNIERES *1D4* (500m S Rural) *49.23017, -0.93256* **Camping Le Picard, 14330 Tournières [02 31 22 82 44; fax 02 31 51 70 28; paulpalmer@orange.fr; www.normandycampsite.com]** Fr Bayeux foll D5/D15 W to Tournières, 5km past Le Molay-Littry. Fr N13 Cherbourg-Bayeux, E of Carentan turn S onto N174 then E on D15 to Tournières. Site sp opp Tournières church. Sm, hdg pitch, pt shd; htd wc; chem disp; serviced pitches; shwrs inc; el pnts (10A) €4.30; shop 5km; tradsmn; rest, snacks; bar; playgrnd; htd pool; boating; fishing; wifi; some statics; no dogs; phone; adv bkg; quiet; ccard acc; CKE/CCI. "Delightful, British-owned site; conv Normandy beaches, Bayeux, Cherbourg ferry; helpful owners bake croissants & will do laundry; san facs need refurb/update; c'van storage; clean well maintained site; staff v helpful & friendly; nice fishing pool with Carp; home cooked food avail; themed evenings inc food." ♦ 31 Apr-1 Nov. € 21.00 2013*

TOUSSAINT see Fécamp *3C1*

TOUTAINVILLE see Pont Audemer *3D2*

TREPORT, LE *3B2* (1km N Urban) *50.05805, 1.38860* **Camp Municipal Les Boucaniers, Rue Pierre Mendès-France, 76470 Le Tréport [02 35 86 35 47; fax 02 27 28 04 10; camping@ville-le-treport.fr; www.ville-le-treport.fr]** Fr Eu take minor rd sp to Le Tréport under low bdge. On ent o'skts of Le Tréport, turn R at traff lts, camp ent 100m on R. Site nr stadium. Lge, hdstg, pt shd; htd wc; shwrs inc; el pnts (6A) €4.60; Indtte; shop; rest, snacks; bar; playgrnd; sand beach 2km; games rm; entmnt; wifi; TV; 10% statics; dogs €1.60; no adv bkg; quiet; red facs low ssn. "Busy, well-kept, well-run site; some lge pitches; gd, clean san facs; gd sep m'van area; lots to see in Le Tréport; m'van Aire de Service adj; gd value; excel; check elec lead is long enough bef unhitching." ♦ 28 Mar-30 Sep. € 23.00 2014*

TREPORT, LE *3B2* (1km S Coastal) *50.05311, 1.36623* **Camp International du Golf, 102 Route de Dieppe, 76470 Le Tréport [02 27 28 01 50; fax 02 27 28 01 51; evergreen2@wanadoo.fr]** Fr Dieppe, take D925 NE twd Le Tréport for 20km bef taking D940 sp Floques/Le Tréport. Site on L at top of hill on o'skts of Le Tréport. Foll sp. Lge, mkd pitch, shd; wc; chem disp; mv service pnt; 30% serviced pitches; shwrs inc; el pnts (5A) €4.60; shop 1km; rest, snacks, bar 500m; playgrnd; shgl beach 600m; fishing; sailing; windsurfing; 10% statics; dogs €3; poss cr; adv bkg; quiet; red low ssn; ccard acc; CKE/CCI. "Site neglected (2009); san facs need update; more suitable tents only; fairly steep hill down fr site to town." 1 Apr-20 Sep. € 15.00 2009*

TREVIERES *1D4* (1.4km NE Rural) *49.31308, -0.90578* **Camp Municipal Sous Les Pommiers, Rue du Pont de la Barre, 14710 Trévières [02 31 22 57 52 or 02 31 92 89 24; fax 02 31 22 19 49; mairie@ville-trevieres.fr]** Turn S off N13 onto D30 sp Trévières. Site on R on ent to vill. Med, hdg/mkd pitch, pt shd; wc (cont); chem disp; mv service pnt; shwrs inc; el pnts (10A) €3; Indtte; shops 500m; rest; playgrnd; sand beach 10km; rv fishing adj; wifi; poss cr; adv bkg rec high ssn; quiet; CKE/CCI. "Delightful site in apple orchard; lge pitches; vg san facs; conv D-Day beaches; excel site; sm town in walking dist." ♦ 1 Apr-30 Sep. € 14.30 2014*

TREVIERES *1D4* (3km NE Rural) *49.32530, -0.86480* **Camping La Roseraie d'Omaha, Rue de l'Eglise, 14710 Surrain [tel/fax 02 31 21 17 71; camping-laroseraie@orange.fr; www.camping-laroseraie.com]** Take N13 fr Bayeux twds Cherbourg. In approx 12km take D208 sp Surrain. Site sp in vill. Med, mkd pitch, pt sl, pt shd; wc; el pnts (6A) €4.60; Indtte; shop; snacks; playgrnd; htd pool; tennis; entmnt; 50% statics; dogs €2.50; Eng spkn; adv bkg; quiet. "Friendly recep; touring pitches bet statics; access rds restricted; conv Bayeux & D-Day Museums." ♦ 1 Apr-20 Sep. € 17.30 2009*

VALOGNES *1C4* (1km N Urban) *49.51154, -1.47534* **Camp Municipal Le Bocage, Rue Neuve, 50700 Valognes [02 33 95 82 03 or 06 10 84 59 33 (mob); environement@mairie-valognes.fr; www.mairie-valognes.fr]** Off N13 Cherbourg to Carentan take 1st exit to Valonges, turn L just past Champion at Lidl sp; site sp bef & in town. Fr Carentan dir, take 3rd R after 4th set traff lts. Sm, hdg/mkd pitch, hdstg, pt shd; wc; chem disp (wc); shwrs inc; el pnts (10A) €3.55 (poss rev pol); gas; supmkt 100m; rest, snacks, bar nr; dogs €0.66; poss cr; quiet; ccard not acc; CKE/CCI. "Super little site; clean san facs; friendly staff; conv Cherbourg ferries (17km) & town; poss travellers; warden calls 1900-2000, site self if office clsd; gates clsd 2200-0600; ideal NH; excel as always." ♦ 1 Apr-15 Oct. € 14.60 2012*

VERNON *3D2* (2km W Rural) *49.09625, 1.43851* **Camping Les Fosses Rouges, Chemin de Réanville, 27950 St Marcel [02 32 51 59 86 / 06 22 42 19 11 l/s; camping@cape27.fr; www.cape-tourisme.fr]** Exit A13/E5 junc 16 dir Vernon onto D181; in 2km at rndabt turn L onto D64e dir St Marcel; in 2km at 5-exit rndabt take 1st R onto Chemin de Réanville (D64) & foll camping sp. At 1st major bend to R, cont strt ahead, site on L in 50m. Med, mkd pitch, pt sl, pt shd; htd wc; chem disp; shwrs inc; el pnts (6-10A) €3.20-4.20; gas; shops 600m steep hill; BBQ; playgrnd; pool 4km; some statics; dogs €0.50; adv bkg; quiet; no ccard acc; CKE/CCI. "Well-kept, well-run scenic site; friendly, helpful owner; gd clean san facs; parking for m'vans at St Marcel - cont past site over rndabt for 900m, turn sharp L past hotel on R & parking on R; lovely little vill; conv Giverny, but access diff lge o'fits; gd size pitches; peaceful site." ♦ ltd 1 Mar-31 Oct. € 13.40 2014*

VEULES LES ROSES *3C2* (3.5km E Rural) *49.88351, 0.85188* **Camp Municipal Le Mesnil, Route de Sotteville, 76740 St Aubin-sur-Mer [tel/fax 02 35 83 02 83; lemesnil76@orange.fr; www.campinglemesnil.com]** On D68 2km W of St Aubin-sur-Mer. Med, hdg pitch, terr, unshd; mv service pnt; 30% statics; htd wc; shwrs inc; el pnts (10A) €3.70 (pos rev pol); Indtte; shop; tradsmn; playgrnd; sand beach 1.5km; wifi; ccard acc; CKE/CCI. ♦ 1 Apr-31 Oct. € 22.75 2012*

VEULES LES ROSES *3C2* (6km E Rural) *49.86083, 0.89079* **Camping Les Garennes de la Mer, 12 Route de Luneray, 76740 Le Bourg-Dun [02 35 83 10 44; camping_lesgarennesdelamer@hotmail.fr; www.lesgarennes.fr]** Fr Veules-les-Roses, take D925 twd Dieppe. Site sp in Le Bourg-Dun - 1km SE. Sm, mkd pitch, pt sl, pt shd; wc; shwrs inc; el pnts (16A) €4; gas; Indtte; shops 250m; supmkt 5km; tradsmn; shgl beach 3km, dog €1; 60% statics; Eng spkn; poss cr; adv bkg; quiet; ccard acc; CKE/CCI. "Well-kept site; vg san facs." ♦ ltd 1 Apr-15 Oct. € 26.30 2013*

VEULES LES ROSES *3C2* (10km E Coastal) *49.90558, 0.92787* **Camp Municipal de la Plage, 123 Rue de la Saâne, 76860 Quiberville-Plage [02 35 83 01 04 or 02 35 04 21 33 (Mairie); fax 02 35 85 10 25; campingplage3@wanadoo.fr]** Fr Dieppe on D75, site sp in Quiberville-Plage on D127. Lge, hdg/mkd pitch, unshd; wc; mv service pnt; shwrs; el pnts (6-10A) €4.10-4.80; Indtte; rest in vill; playgrnd; beach adj; tennis adj; games area; dogs €1.40; phone; adv bkg; quiet. "Conv Dieppe ferry; pleasant site." ♦ 1 Apr-31 Oct. € 19.30 2009*

VEULES LES ROSES *3C2* (300m S Coastal/Rural) *49.87586, 0.80314* **Camping Les Mouettes, 7 Ave Jean Moulin, 76980 Veules-les-Roses [02 35 97 61 98; fax 02 35 97 33 44; camping.les.mouettes0509@orange.fr]** On ent vill fr Dieppe on D925, turn R onto D68, site in 500m up hill (14%). Lge, hdg/mkd pitch, pt shd; htd wc; chem disp; mv service pnt; baby facs; shwrs inc; el pnts (6A) €4.70; gas; Indtte (inc dryer); sm shop; tradsmn; supmkt 8km; snacks; bar; BBQ; playgrnd; htd, covrd pool; paddling pool; shgl beach 800m; fitness rm; games area; games rm; wifi; entmnt; TV; 10% statics; dogs €2.00; adv bkg; Eng spkn; quiet; ccard acc; red long stay/low ssn/CKE/CCI. "Pleasant area; peaceful, well-kept site; vg." ♦ 1 Apr-4 Nov. € 20.80 2011*

VILLEDIEU LES POELES *1D4* (500m S Urban) *48.83638, -1.21694* **Camping Les Chevaliers, 2 Impasse Pré de la Rose, 50800 Villedieu-les-Poêles [02 33 61 02 44; fax 02 33 49 49 93; contact@camping-deschevaliers.com; www.camping-deschevaliers.com]** Exit A84 junc 38 onto D999 twd Villedieu, then R onto D975 & R onto D924 to avoid town cent. Foll sp fr car park on R after x-ing rv. Med, hdg/mkd pitch, hdstg, pt shd; htd wc; chem disp; mv service pnt; shwrs inc; baby facs; el pnts (6A) inc poss rev pol; Indtte (inc dryer); shop 500m; supmkt 2km; rest, snacks; bar; BBQ; playgrnd; htd pool; rv fishing; boating; tennis; games rm; wifi; entmnt; TV; dogs €1.50; phone; poss cr; Eng spkn; adv bkg; quiet; red low ssn; CKE/CCI. "Peaceful site; lge pitches but kerbs poss diff lger o'fits; gd, modern san facs; interesting historic town; avoid arr Tue am due mkt; conv A84 & Cherbourg ferry; vg; exceptional facs all new; well worth a visit to town; excel site; rest extended 2011; staff v helpful." ♦ ltd 23 Mar-30 Sep. € 34.40 2013*

VIMOUTIERS *3D1* (700m N Urban) *48.93236, 0.19646* **Camp Municipal La Campière, Ave Dr Dentu, 61120 Vimoutiers [02 33 39 18 86 (Mairie); fax 02 33 36 51 43; campingmunicipalvimoutiers@wanadoo.fr; www.vimoutiers.fr]** App Vimoutiers fr N on on D579/D979/D916, site on R 300m after passing junc with D16; turn R at flag poles (200m after Avia petrol stn). Or appr fr Gacé on D979 turn L at flag poles (on D916 just bef junc with D16). Site nr stadium & not well sp. Sm, hdg pitch, pt shd; htd wc; chem disp; shwrs inc; el pnts (6A) €2.40; Indry rm; shop 200m; rest, snacks 800m; playgrnd adj; pool & sports facs 2km; rv fishing, sw & boating 2km; tennis; cycle hire; 10% statics; dogs €1.50; poss cr; adv bkg; noise fr nrby factory; red low ssn; CKE/CCI. "Excel, well-maintained, pretty site at cent of Camembert cheese industry; helpful, friendly warden; vg, clean san facs; unrel opening dates - phone ahead low ssn; attractive town." ♦ 1 Apr-31 Oct. € 9.00 2011*

VITTEFLEUR see Cany Barville *3C2*

YPORT *3C1* (900m SE Rural) *49.73221, 0.32098* **Camp Municipal La Chenaie, Rue Henri-Simon, 76111 Yport [02 35 27 33 56]** Take D940 fr Fécamp SW, D211 to Yport to site. Med, pt shd; wc; shwrs; shops 500m; el pnts (4A); shgl beach 1km; many statics; poss cr; quiet. "Conv Le Havre." 2012*

YPORT *3C1* (300m SW Coastal/Rural) *49.73746, 0.30959* **Camping Le Rivage, Rue Hottières, 76111 Yport [tel/fax 02 35 27 33 78; contact@camping-lerivage.com; www.camping-lerivage.com]** Fr D940 bet Etretat & Fécamp take D11 2km NE of Les Loges, meeting up with D211 & head twd Yport. Site on D211. Or foll sp fr Yport. Med, pt sl, some hdstg, terr, unshd; wc; chem disp; shwrs; el pnts (6A) inc (poss long lead req); lndry rm; shops 1km; snacks; bar; BBQ; shgl beach 300m; games rm; TV rm; phone; adv bkg; quiet. "Well-situated, o'looking sea; steep descent to beach; san facs inadequate high ssn & long walk fr most pitches; rec stop at top of site & walk to recep bef pitching, as turning poss diff lge o'fits." 25 Mar-30 Sep. € 17.50 2012*

Paris Ile-de-France

Regional Introduction

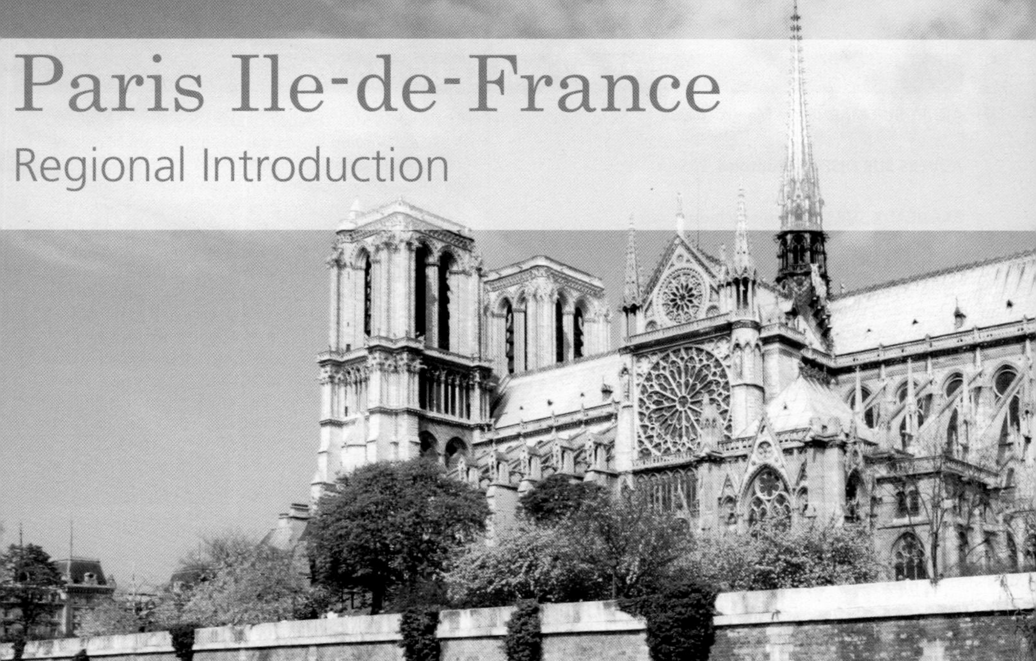

Notre Dame de Paris

Welcome to Paris Ile-de-France

A wealthy region surrounding the capital city of France, Paris Ile-de-France is full of famous landmarks, museums and artworks.

Paris, known as the 'City of Love' and the 'City of Lights', is renowned for its diverse culture and its not-to-be-missed gourmet delights. From small patisseries to some of the most expensive restaurants in the world, all palettes will be catered for.

Outside Paris and its large surrounding towns there are also natural highlights in the form of parks, forests and rivers.

Local highlights

There are lots of well-known cheeses from Ile-de-France. Two of the most widely recognised are Brie and Brie de Meaux. The latter can only be found in certain areas of the province and is widely eaten on canapés and enjoyed with a glass of wine.

Paris' 'Quartier d'été' is a summer festival offering shows, a circus and many other open-air performances in streets, gardens and parks across the city.

Major towns and cities

- Paris – the romantic capital city with many world-famous landmarks and museums.
- Fontainebleau – renowned for its large and scenic forest and historical château.
- Rueil-Malmaison – famous for connections to Napoléon's first wife Joséphine.
- Versailles – home of the magnificent Palace of Versailles and other historical sites.

Regional attractions

- Eiffel Tower, Paris – one of the most famous and iconic landmarks in the world.
- Albert Kahn Musée et Jardins, Boulogne-Billancourt – beautiful gardens, large glass greenhouse and museum.
- Château Fontainebleau – a grand palace that was once a favourite of Napoléon.
- Palace of Versailles – with the Hall of Mirrors and infamous history.

Find out more

www.visitparisregion.com

Tel: (0)1 49 52 42 63 Paris Tourist Office

Tel: (0)1 39 24 88 88 Versailles Tourist Office

ANNET SUR MARNE see Meaux *3D3*

AUVERS SUR OISE see Pontoise *3D3*

BAGNEAUX SUR LOING see Nemours *4F3*

BEAUMONT SUR OISE *3D3* (8km SW Rural) *49.12805, 2.18318* **Parc de Séjour de l'Etang, 10 Chemin des Belles Vues, 95690 Nesles-la-Vallée [01 34 70 62 89; campinparis@gmail.com; www.campinparis.com]** Fr D927 Méru-Pontoise rd, turn L onto D64 at sp L'Isle Adam. After passing thro Nesles-la-Vallée camp sp on L. Med, hdg pitch, pt shd; htd wc (cont); chem disp; serviced pitches (extra charge); shwrs inc; el pnts (3A) inc (rev pol); Indtte; shops 1km; playgrnd; lake fishing adj; dogs €2; Eng spkn; quiet; red CKE/CCI. "Lovely, peaceful, out-of-the way setting; spacious pitches; friendly, helpful staff; gd facs; conv day trips to Paris & Versailles; excel." 1 Apr-30 Sep. € 18.50 2010*

“That’s changed – Should I let The Club know?”

If you find something on site that’s different from the site entry, fill in a report and let us know. See www.caravanclub.co.uk/europereport.

⊞ **BONNIERES SUR SEINE** *3D2* (2km N Rural) *49.05804, 1.61224* **Camping Le Criquet, 42 Rue du Criquet, 78840 Freneuse [tel/fax 01 30 93 07 95; www.camping-le-criquet.fr]** Fr D915 at Bonnières to Freneuse on D37. Thro vill, site sp at end of vill past cemetary. Lge, pt shd; wc; chem disp; shwrs €3; el pnts (10A) €3; BBQ; playgrnd; games area; mainly statics; adv bkg; quiet. "V run down - san facs unclean & need refurb, pitches unkempt; Monet's garden 12km." € 12.30 2011*

BONNIERES SUR SEINE *3D2* (5km E Rural) *49.04646, 1.66256* **Camping Loisirs des Groux, 1 Chemin de L'ile, 78270 Mousseaux-sur-Seine [01 34 79 33 86; www.campingdesgroux.com]** Fr W exit A13 junc 15 onto D113 dir Bonnières. Cont thro Bonnières, turn L onto D37 Mousseaux/Base de Loisirs. Cont strt on D37/D124/D125 & then turn R & foll site sp. Fr E exit A13 junc 14 sp Bonnières & foll sp Zone Industrielle. At rndabt take D113 Bonnières, then as above. Med, hdg/mkd pitch, pt shd; wc (some cont); chem disp (wc); mv service pnt; shwrs inc; el pnts (10A) €2; Indtte; BBQ; leisure cent inc pool 500m; lake sw & beach 500m; games area; wifi; 90% statics; dogs; Eng spkn; adv bkg rec high ssn; quiet; ccard acc; CKE/CCI. "Conv Paris (65km), Versailles, Rouen, Giverny; lge pitches; friendly, helpful staff; basic, dated san facs; excel walks or cycling along Rv Seine; poss clsd earlier than published dates - phone ahead to check in low ssn; long winding track fr main rd; poor quality." ♦ 1 Apr-30 Nov. € 20.00 2014*

See advertisement

BOULANCOURT see Malesherbes *4E3*

BRAY SUR SEINE *4E4* (200m E Rural) *48.41425, 3.24623* **Camping La Peupleraie, Rue des Pâtures, 77480 Bray-sur-Seine [01 60 67 12 24; camping.lapeupleraie@wanadoo.fr; www.lapeupleraie.com]** Exit A5 at junc 18 onto D41, in 20km turn N to Bray. Turn L bef bdge, foll rd down under bdge, cont on rvside to site. Foll 'complex sportif' & camping sp. Lge, hdg/mkd pitch, pt shd; wc (cont); shwrs inc; el pnts (6A); Indtte; supmkt adj; snacks; playgrnd; pool adj; boating; tennis; 80% statics; dogs; adv bkg; quiet. "Diff to exit bef 0900 when office opens; clean site; helpful warden; site adapted for handicapped." ♦ 1 Apr-31 Oct. € 14.40 2009*

CHAMPIGNY SUR MARNE see Paris *3D3*

CREVECOEUR EN BRIE see Fontenay Trésigny *4E3*

DISNEYLAND PARIS see Meaux *3D3*

DOURDAN *4E3* (700m NE Urban) *48.52572, 2.02878* **Camping Les Petits Prés, 11 Rue Pierre Mendès France, 91410 Dourdan [01 64 59 64 83 or 01 60 81 14 17; fax 01 60 81 14 29; camping@mairie-dourdan.fr; www.mairie-dourdan.fr]** Exit A10 junc 10 dir Dourdan; foll by-pass sp Arpajon; after 5th rndabt site 200m on L. Med, mkd pitch, pt sl, unshd; htd wc; shwrs; el pnts (4A) €3.40; gas & supmkt 500m; rest 1km; playgrnd; pool 500m; poss cr; 75% statics; Eng spkn; adv bkg; poss noisy. "Gd NH; friendly welcome; clean dated san facs, ltd low ssn; town worth visit." 1 Apr-30 Sep. € 14.00 (3 persons) 2012*

⊞ **ETAMPES** *4E3* (3km S Rural) *48.41015, 2.14413* **FFCC Caravaning Le Vauvert, Route de Saclas, 91150 Ormoy-la-Rivière [01 64 94 21 39; fax 01 69 92 72 59]** Fr Etampes S on N20 take D49 sp Saclas. Site on L in approx 1.5km. NB acess on a loop to cross rd. Lge, hdg/mkd pitch, shd; htd wc (cont); chem disp; mv service pnt; shwrs inc; el pnts (10A) €4; gas; shop & hypmkt 3km; rest & 3km; snacks; bar; htd, covrd pool 2km; tennis; fishing; rv adj; games area; 90% statics; quiet; site clsd 16 Dec-14 Jan; red long stay; ccard acc; CKE/CCI. "If travelling in winter phone to check site open; few touring pitches; san facs in touring area clean, ltd low ssn & clsd winter; conv train to Paris; gd NH only." € 17.00 2010*

"I like to fill in the reports as I travel from site to site"

You'll find report forms at the back of this guide, or you can fill them in online at www.caravaclub.co.uk/europereport.

FERTE GAUCHER, LA *4E4* (700m E Rural) *48.77928, 3.31072* **FLOWER Camping La Ferté-Gaucher, Rue de Coutran, 77320 La Ferté-Gaucher [01 64 20 20 40; info@flowercampings-la-ferte-gaucher.com; www.flowercampings.com]** On D634 bet Coulommiers & Sézanne; site opp leisure cent. Lge, hdg/mkd pitch, pt shd; htd wc (some cont); chem disp (wc); shwrs inc; el pnts (10A) inc; gas; lndry rm; shop, rest, snacks, bar 700m; playgrnd; htd pool 100m; 30% statics; dogs; bus 500m; phone; adv bkg; quiet; ccard acc; red CKE/CCI. "Attractive parkland site by leisure cent; san facs dated but clean; gd touring base." ♦ 1 Mar-30 Nov. € 26.00 2010*

FONTAINEBLEAU *4E3* (5km NE Rural) *48.42215, 2.74872* **Camp Municipal Grange aux Dîmes, Rue de l'Abreuvoir/Rue de l'Eglise, 77210 Samoreau [01 64 23 72 25; fax 01 64 23 98 31; mairie-de-samoreau@wanadoo.fr; www.samoreau.fr]** Fr cent of Fontainebleau take D210 (dir Provins); in approx 4km at rndabt cross bdge over Rv Seine; take R at rndabt; site sp at end of rd thro Samoreau vill; site twd rv. Med, hdg/mkd pitch, pt sl, pt shd; htd wc; chem disp; mv service pnt; shwrs inc; el pnts (10A) inc (poss rev pol); lndtte; shop 250m; snacks & bar 100m; rest 500m; phone; bus; poss v cr; adv bkg; rlwy & barge noise; CKE/CCI. "Peaceful site in attractive location by Rv Seine; gd sized pitches; helpful staff; gd, immac san facs; adj vill hall poss noisy w/end; jazz festival late Jun; conv palace, Paris (by train) & Disneyland; clsd 2200-0700; excel." ♦ ltd 1 Mar-31 Oct. € 22.06 2012*

FONTAINEBLEAU *4E3* (10km S Rural) *48.33362, 2.75386* **Camping Le Parc du Gué, Route de Montigny, La Genevraye, 77690 Montigny-sur-Loing [01 64 45 87 79; fax 01 64 78 31 46; contact@camping-parcdugue.com; www.camping-parcdugue.com]** On D607 foll sp S to Montigny-sur-Loing, site sp. Lge, hdg/mkd pitch, pt shd; htd wc (some cont); chem disp; shwrs inc; el pnts (6A) €3.50; lndtte; tradsmn; BBQ; playgrnd; rv sw adj; watersports; kayaks; fishing; wifi; 10% statics; dogs €3.50; mkt Sat 2km; Eng spkn; adv bkg; quiet; ccard acc; red low ssn/CKE/CCI. "Beautiful, wooded country; excel walking & cycling." ♦ 15 Mar-30 Nov. € 16.00 2011*

FONTAINEBLEAU *4E3* (10km S Rural) *48.31740, 2.69650* **Camping Les Prés, Chemin des Prés, 77880 Grez-sur-Loing [tel/fax 01 64 45 72 75; camping-grez@wanadoo.fr; www.camping-grez-fontainebleau.info]** Fr Fontainebleau on D607 twd Nemours (S) for 8km; look for camping sps. At traff island turn L onto D40D, in 1km immed after x-ing bdge turn R; site on L. Do not tow into Grez-sur-Loing. Med, pt shd; wc; chem disp; shwrs inc; el pnts (5A) €3; gas; lndtte; shop; rest, bar 200m; snacks; playgrnd; htd, covrd pool 10km; fishing; canoe hire; cycle hire; wifi; mostly statics; dogs; phone; poss cr; Eng spkn; adv bkg; quiet but half touring pitches nr busy rd; ccard acc; red long stay; CKE/CCI. "In attractive area; helpful British owner; mainly statics; site poss unkempt/scruffy end of ssn; adequate NH (2010)." ♦ 20 Mar-11 Nov. € 10.60 2010*

FONTENAY TRESIGNY *4E3* (6km NE Rural) *48.75050, 2.89728* **Camping des Quatre Vents, 77610 Crèvecoeur-en-Brie [01 64 07 41 11; fax 01 64 07 45 07; f.george@free.fr; www.caravaning-4vents.fr]** At Calais take A26/E15 dir Arras; at Arras take A1/E15 dir Paris; next take A104 dir A4 Metz/Nancy/Marne-la-Vallée, then A4 dir Metz/Nancy, exit junc 13 onto D231 dir Provins; after rndabt with lge monument turn R dir Crèvecoeur-en-Brie & foll site sp. Site in 13km. Lge, hdg/mkd pitch, pt shd; htd wc; chem disp; mv service pnt; baby facs; serviced pitches; shwrs inc; el pnts (6A) inc; lndtte (inc dryer); shops 2km; tradsmn; snacks; BBQ; playgrnd; pool; horseriding; games area; games rm; wifi; TV; 50% statics sep area; dogs €3; no c'vans/m'vans over 10m high ssn; phone; poss cr; Eng spkn; adv bkg ess in ssn; quiet but some aircraft noise; ccard acc; CKE/CCI. "Friendly, well-run site; lge, well-kept pitches; welcoming, helpful staff; san facs spacious & clean; pleasant pool; conv Disneyland & Paris; poss muddy when wet; vg." ♦ 15 Mar-31 Oct. € 42.00 SBS - P09 2014*

FRENEUSE **see Bonnières sur Seine** *3D2*

GRANDE PAROISSE, LA **see Montereau Fault Yonne** *4E3*

GREZ SUR LOING **see Fontainebleau** *4E3*

JABLINES **see Meaux** *3D3*

MAISONS LAFFITTE **see Paris** *3D3*

⊞ **MALESHERBES** *4E3* (5km S Rural) *48.25659, 2.43574* **FFCC Camping Ile de Boulancourt, 6 Allée des Marronniers, 77760 Boulancourt [01 64 24 13 38; fax 01 64 24 10 43; info@camping-iledeboulancourt.com; www.camping-iledeboulancourt.com]** Exit A6 at junc 14 Ury & Fontainebleau. SW on D152 to Malesherbes; S on D410 for 5km into Boulancourt. Site sp fr D410 & in vill. Med, pt shd; htd wc (many cont); chem disp; mv service pnt; shwrs inc; el pnts (3-6A) €2.10; Indtte; shop 3km; rest; BBQ; playgrnd; pool nr; tennis; rv adj; fishing 3km; waterslide 5km; 90% statics; dogs €1; sep field for tourers; Eng spkn; quiet; red low ssn; CKE/CCI. "Attractive rv thro site; well-maintained facs, ltd low ssn; friendly, helpful staff; golf course in vill; chateau nr; excel." € 13.60 2009*

MARNE LA VALLEE see Meaux *3D3*

MEAUX *3D3* (4km NE Rural) *49.00301, 2.94139* **Camping Village Parisien, Route des Otages, 77910 Varreddes [01 64 34 80 80; fax 01 60 22 89 84; direction@villageparisien.com; www.villageparisien.com]** Fr Meaux foll sp on D405 dir Soissons then Varreddes, site sp on D121 dir Congis. Med, hdg/mkd pitch, pt shd; wc; chem disp; mv service pnt; baby facs; shwrs inc; el pnts (6A) €2; gas; Indtte (inc dryer); sm shop (high ssn); tradsmn; rest & snacks (high ssn); bar; BBQ; playgrnd; pool; paddling pool; waterslide; fishing; tennis; games area; cycle hire; golf 5km; games rm; wifi; entmnt; TV rm; 85% statics; dogs free; poss cr; Eng spkn; adv bkg; aircraft noise; ccard acc; red low ssn/long stay/CKE/CCI. "Conv Paris cent (drive to metro), Parc Astérix & Disneyland - tickets avail fr site; friendly, helpful staff; sm pitches; narr site rds; v busy, well-used site." 15 Mar-1 Nov. € 27.00 2009*

MEAUX *3D3* (10km SW Rural) *48.91333, 2.73416* **Camping L'International de Jablines, 77450 Jablines [01 60 26 09 37; fax 01 60 26 43 33; welcome@camping-jablines.com; www.camping-jablines.com]** Fr N on A1 then A104 exit Claye-Souilly. Fr E on A4 then A104 exit Meaux. Fr S on A6, A86, A4, A104 exit Meaux. Site well sp 'Base de Loisirs de Jablines'. Lge, mkd pitch, pt sl, pt shd; htd wc; chem disp; mv service pnt; baby facs; shwrs inc; el pnts (10A) inc; Indtte (inc dryer); shop; tradsmn; rest 500m; snacks; bar; BBQ; playgrnd; sand beach & lake sw 500m; fishing; sailing; windsurfing; tennis 500m; horseriding; cycle hire; internet; dogs €3; bus to Eurodisney; Eng spkn; adv bkg ess high ssn; quiet; red low ssn; ccard acc; CKE/CCI. "Clean, well-run, well-guarded site; vg pitches; pelasant staff; san facs poss tired high ssn; ideal for Disneyland (tickets for sale), Paris & Versaille." ♦ 31 Mar-29 Sep. € 28.00 (CChq acc) 2011*

See advertisement

⊞ **MEAUX** *3D3* (10km SW Urban) *48.87723, 2.78663* **Motor Caravan Park at Disneyland Paris, 77777 Marne-la-Vallée** Fr all dirs foll sp to Disneyland & foll sp to m'van (camping car) park. Easy to find. Lge, hdstg, unshd; htd wc; mv service pnt; shwrs inc; no el pnts; picnic area; rest etc in Disney Village; dogs; phone; bus, train adj; Eng spkn; quiet; ccard acc; m'vans only, many other sites nr Disneyland cater for car/c'van o'fits. € 13.00 2009*

MELUN *4E3* (3km S Rural) *48.52569, 2.66930* **Kawan Village La Belle Etoile, Quai Maréchal Joffre, 77000 Melun-La Rochette [01 64 39 48 12; fax 01 64 37 25 55; info@campinglabelleetoile.com; www.campinglabelleetoile.com]** On ent La Rochette on D606 fr Fontainbleu pass Total stn on L; turn immed R into Ave de la Seine & foll site sp; site on L in 500m. Lge, hdg/mkd pitch, hdstg, pt shd; htd wc; chem disp; mv service pnt; shwrs; el pnts (6A) €3.50 (poss rev pol); gas; Indtte (inc dryer); shop 1km; rests in vill; snacks (high ssn); bar; BBQ; playgrnd; htd pool; paddling pool; rv fishing; games area; golf 8km; wifi; TV rm; 10% statics; phone; some statics; dogs €1.50; bus to stn - train to Paris; Eng spkn; adv bkg; some rlwy & rv noise, v little at night; ccard acc; red low ssn; CKE/CCI. "Pretty site; helpful owners; gd san facs; gates locked 2300; conv Paris, Fontainebleau & Disneyland (tickets fr recep); sports complex nrby; gd walking & cycling in forest along rv/canal; mkt Melun Wed; vd value; gd." ♦ 26 Mar-2 Oct. € 19.50 (CChq acc) 2011*

MILLY LA FORET *4E3* (4km SE Rural) *48.39569, 2.50380* **Camping La Musardière, Route des Grandes Vallées, 91490 Milly-la-Forêt [01 64 98 91 91; fax 01 64 98 37 01; lamusardiere91@orange.fr]** Fr S exit A6 junc 14 onto D152 then D16 dir Milly; Rte des Grande Vallées is R turn 2km after Noisy-sur-Ecole (4km bef Milly). Look for 'Domain Regional' sps (not easy to read). Fr N exit A6 junc 13 onto D372 to Milly; exit Milly S on D16; Rte des Grandes Vallées turning to L in 1.5km. Site on L 1km along Rte des Grandes Vallées. Best app fr N. Lge, mkd pitch, hdstg, pt sl, pt shd; htd wc (some cont); chem disp; baby facs; fam bthrm; shwrs inc; el pnts (6A) inc; Indtte; shop 4km; tradsmn (w/end only low ssn); BBQ; playgrnd; htd pool/waterpark high ssn; paddling pool; cycle hire; 70% statics; dogs free; Eng spkn; adv bkg; ccard acc; red long stay; CKE/CCI. "Wooded site; excel pools; helpful, friendly staff; gd walks in nrby forest." ♦ 15 Feb-15 Nov. € 22.20 2011*

MONNERVILLE *4E3* (2km S Rural) *48.33256, 2.04702* **Camping Le Bois de la Justice, Méréville, 91930 Monnerville [01 64 95 05 34; fax 01 64 95 17 31; leboisdelajustice@gmail.com; www.campingleboisdelajustice.com]** Fr N20 S of Etampes, turn onto D18 at Monnerville, site well sp. Long narr app rd. Med, hdg/mkd pitch, pt sl, pt shd; htd wc; chem disp (wc); shwrs inc; el pnts (5A) €2.50; Indtte; tradsmn; snacks high ssn; bar; BBQ; cooking facs; playgrnd; htd pool high ssn; tennis; games area; TV rm; 50% statics; dogs €1; phone; Eng spkn; adv bkg; quiet; red low ssn; ccard acc. "Delightful woodland oasis in open countryside; beware caterpillars in spring (poisonous to dogs); friendly welcome; clean san facs; ideal for Chartres, Fontainebleau, Orléans, Paris or excel NH just off N20." ♦ 4 Feb-26 Nov. € 19.50 2012*

MONTEREAU FAULT YONNE *4E3* (3km W Rural) *48.37472, 2.90382* **Camping La Grande Paroisse, La Noue Notre-Dame, 77130 La Grande-Paroisse [01 60 57 02 02; fax 01 60 74 28 93; tourisme.cc2f@cc-deuxfleuves.fr; www.cc-deuxfleuves.fr]** Exit A5 junc 17 onto D210 then D605 S to Montereau. In Montereau take D39 W & foll sp La Grand-Paroisse & site on rvside. Med, hdg/mkd pitch, hdstg, pt shd; wc; chem disp; mv service pnt; shwrs; el pnts (4-13A) €3-6; shop; supmkt 2km; rest 5km; bar 2km; BBQ; playgrnd; pool 5km; sand beach 8km; sw & fishing adj; sailing, windsurfing & watersports; sailing school; games area; entmnt; 60% statics; dogs; adv bkg; quiet. "Well-situated site; conv Fontainebleau; excel fishing, walking & sailing; vg." ♦ 16 Mar-31 Oct. € 10.00 2009*

MORET SUR LOING *4E3* (2km NW Rural) *48.38333, 2.80194* **Camping Les Courtilles du Lido, Chemin du Passeur, 77250 Veneux-les-Sablons [01 60 70 46 05; fax 01 64 70 62 65; lescourtilles-dulido@wanadoo.fr; www.les-courtilles-du-lido.fr]** Use app fr N6 sp Veneux-les-Sablons & foll sp. 1km fr N6. Or fr Moret foll sp; long, tortuous rte; narr rds; 35m, 1-width tunnel. NB sp say 'Du Lido' only. Lge, mkd pitch, pt shd; wc; chem disp; mv service pnt; shwrs inc; el pnts (10A) €3; gas; Indtte; shops 1km; tradsmn; rest, snacks; bar; playgrnd; sm pool; tennis; wifi; 75% statics; dogs €1.50; poss cr; Eng spkn; adv bkg; rlwy noise at night; ccard acc; CKE/CCI. "Early arr rec; lge pitches; clean facs but poss insufficient high ssn; friendly owners; vg for children; lovely old town; conv Fontainebleau & train to Paris; excel." 9 Apr-20 Sep. € 16.50 2011*

MOUSSEAUX SUR SEINE see Bonnières sur Seine *3D2*

NEMOURS *4F3* (5km S Urban) *48.24073, 2.70389* **FFCC Camping de Pierre Le Sault, Chemin des Grèves, 77167 Bagneaux-sur-Loing [01 64 29 24 44; camping.bagneaux-sur-loing@orange.fr]** Well sp bef town fr both dir off D607. Med, hdg/mkd pitch, pt shd; wc; shwrs inc; el pnts (3-6A) €2-3.10; gas 2km; Indtte; shop 2km; tradsmn; playgrnd; tennis; 30% statics; poss cr; some Eng spkn; ent barrier clsd 2200-0700; no adv bkg; some rd noise; red low ssn; no ccard acc; CKE/CCI. "Lovely site by canal & rv; excel clean facs; site a bit run down, but pleasant." ♦ 1 Apr-31 Oct. € 16.40 2014*

NESLES LA VALLEE see Beaumont sur Oise *3D3*

NEUILLY SUR MARNE see Paris *3D3*

PARIS *3D3* (12km E Urban) *48.85385, 2.53794* **Camp Municipal La Haute Ile, Chemin de l'Ecluse, 93330 Neuilly-sur-Marne [01 43 08 21 21; fax 01 43 08 22 03; campingmunicipal.nsm@wandadoo.fr; www.tourisme93.com]** Fr Périphérique (Porte de Vincennes) foll N34 sp Vincennes. Shortly after passing Château de Vincennes on R, L at fork, sp Lagny. At next major x-rds sharp L (still N34) sp Chelles. Thro Neuilly-Plaisance to Neuilly-sur-Marne. In cent lge x-rds turn R sp N370 Marne-la-Vallée & A4 Paris. In 200m, bef rv bdge, foll Camp Municipal sp (no tent or c'van symbols on sp) turn L. Site at junc of rv & canal. Lge, mkd pitch, pt shd; wc (some cont); shwrs inc; el pnts (10A) inc (check rev pol); gas; Indtte adj; shop; rest adj; BBQ; playgrnd; rv fishing; 25% statics; dogs €2.85; bus/train 900m; poss cr; Eng spkn; adv bkg (rec high ssn); quiet. "Lovely location bet rv & canal (almost on an island); additional; wooden posts on pitches poss diff manoeuvring lge o'fits; some sm pitches; poss unkempt (2011); soft after rain; gd base & transport for Paris & Disney; gd dog walks adj; gd NH; san facs are run down." 1 Apr-30 Sep. € 25.00 2014*

⊞ **PARIS** *3D3* (15km SE Urban) *48.82963, 2.47720* **Camping Paris Est Le Tremblay, Blvd des Alliés, 94507 Champigny-sur-Marne [01 43 97 43 97; fax 01 48 89 07 94; champigny@campingparis.fr; www.campingchampigny.fr]** Rec rte for c'vans. Fr A4 (Paris-Reims) exit 5 sp Nogent/Champigny-sur-Marne. D45 dir Champigny to end of dual c'way at traff lts go R on N303 dir St Maur. Join N4 after 1km (traff lts) & take 2nd R (200m). Site sp. NB site also known as 'Camping de Champigny' or 'Camping International/IDF'. Med, hdg/mkd pitch, pt shd; htd wc (some cont); chem disp; mv service pnt; shwrs inc; el pnts (10A) inc; gas; Indtte (inc dryer); shop; rest, snacks; bar; games rm; internet; TV; playgrnd; 20% statics; dogs €2.60; adv bkg; some rd noise; red low ssn; ccard acc; CKE/CCI. "Vg site; easy parking nr metro or bus fr camp to rlwy stn direct to city & Disneyland; twin-axle c'vans book ahead or poss extra charge; take care to avoid grounding on kerb to pitches; clsd to cars 0200-0600." ♦ € 33.00 2011*

⊞ **PARIS** *3D3* (10km W Urban) *48.86843, 2.23471* **Camping Indigo Paris Bois de Boulogne, 2 Allée du Bord de l'Eau, 75016 Paris [01 45 24 30 00; fax 01 42 24 42 95; paris@camping-indigo.com; www.camping-indigo.com]** Site bet bdge of Puteaux & bdge of Suresnes. App fr A1: take Blvd Périphérique W to Bois de Boulogne exit at Porte Maillot; foll camp sp. App fr A6: Blvd Périphérique W to Porte Dauphine exit at Porte Maillot; foll camp sp. App fr Pont de Sèvres (A10, A11): on bdge take R lane & take 2nd rd R mkd Neuilly-sur-Seine; rd runs parallel to Seine; cont to site ent. App fr A13: after St Cloud Tunnel foll sp twd Paris; immed after x-ing Rv Seine, 1st R sp Bois de Boulogne; foll camp sps; traff lts at site ent. NB Sharp turn to site, poorly sp fr N - watch for lge 'Parking Borne de l'Eau 200m'. V lge, hdg/mkd pitch, hdstg, pt sl, pt shd; htd wc (some cont); chem disp; mv service pnt; baby facs; shwrs inc; el pnts (10A) inc; gas; Indtte; shop, rest & bar in ssn or 1km; pool 1km; TV; Metro Porte Maillot 4km; some statics; dogs €2; phone; bus to metro; extra €26 per night for twin-axles; poss cr; Eng spkn; adv bkg rec high ssn; rd noise; red low ssn; ccard acc; CKE/CCI. "Busy site in excel location; easy access A13; conv cent Paris; some v sm pitches; walk over Suresne bdge for shops, food mkt, supmkt etc; some tour ops on site; gd security; refurbished san facs (2014); vg." € 53.00 2014*

See advertisement

PARIS *3D3* (20km NW Urban) *48.94001, 2.14563* **Camping International Maisons Laffitte, Ile de la Commune, 1 Rue Johnson, 78600 Maisons-Laffitte [01 39 12 21 91; fax 01 39 12 70 50; maisonslaffitte@sandaya.fr; www.sandaya.fr]** Easy access fr A13 sp Poissy; take D308 to Maisons-Laffitte; foll site sp bef town cent. Fr A15 take N184 S fr Poissy, foll sp St Germain; approx 6km after x-ing Rv Seine & approx 300m after x-ing lge steel bdge, take L lane ready for L turn onto D308 to Maison-Laffitte; foll camp sp. Or D301 to St Denis, then A86 exit Bezons, then dir Poissy, Noailles, Sartrouville & Maisons-Laffitte. NB Narr app rd diff due parked cars & high kerbs. Lge, hdg/mkd pitch, pt shd; htd wc; chem disp; mv service pnt; shwrs inc; el pnts (6A) €3.20 (poss rev pol); gas; Indtte; sm shop; tradsmn; hypmkt 5km; rest, snacks; bar; no BBQ; playgrnd; games area; TV rm; 50% statics; dogs €2.60; RER stn 1km; poss cr; Eng spkn; adv bkg; some noise fr rlwy & rv traff; ccard acc; red low ssn; CKE/CCI. "V busy, popular site on island in Rv Seine; ideal for visiting Paris (20 min by RER), Disneyland & Versailles; mobilis ticket covers rlwy, metro & bus for day in Paris; friendly, helpful staff; poss ltd facs low ssn." ♦ 4 Apr-2 Nov. € 49.00 2014*

PONTOISE *3D3* (6km E Urban) *49.06514, 2.16425* **Camp Municipal Bellerive, Chemin de Bellerive, 95430 Auvers-sur-Oise [01 34 48 05 22; fax 01 30 36 70 30; www.auvers-sur-oise.com]** Exit N184 junc 7 sp Méry & Auvers-sur-Oise; in Méry foll sp to Auvers; immed on ent Auvers turn L sp Parking; foll rd (narr in places) to T-junc, turn L; foll Camping sp. Site 300m on L on rvside. Sm, shd; wc (some cont); chem disp (wc); shwrs inc; el pnts (6A) (poss rev pol); Indry rm; shop, rest, snacks & bar 1km; BBQ; adv bkg; quiet; CKE/CCI. "Easy access to Paris & Disneyland; sh walk to town where Van Gogh buried; gd." May-Oct. 2009*

RAMBOUILLET *4E3* (3km SE Rural) *48.6252, 1.84495* **Camping Huttopia Rambouillet, Route du Château d'Eau, 78120 Rambouillet [01 30 41 07 34; fax 01 30 41 00 17; rambouillet@huttopia.com; www.huttopia.com]** Fr N exit D910 at 'Rambouillet Eveuses' & foll sp to site in 2.5km. Fr S exit at 'Rambouillet Centre' & foll sp to site back onto D910 (in opp dir), exit 'Rambouillet Eveuses' as above. Avoid Rambouillet town cent. Lge, hdg pitch, pt shd; htd wc (some cont); mv service pnt; chem disp; baby facs; shwrs inc; el pnts (6-10A) €4.60-6.80 (poss rev pol); Indtte; shop; tradsmn, rest, snacks; bar; BBQ (gas/elec); playgrnd; fishing adj; some statics; dogs €4; phone; sep car park; Eng spkn; adv bkg (rec high ssn); quiet; ccard acc; red low ssn; CKE/CCI. "Excel, busy, wooded site; conv Paris by train - parking at stn 3km; gd cycling rtes; interesting town." ♦ 3 Apr-5 Nov. € 25.20 2009*

See advert on next page

⊞ **ST CHERON** *4E3* (3km SE Rural) *48.54435, 2.13840* **Camping Héliomonde (Naturist), La Petite Beauce, 91530 St Chéron [01 64 56 61 37; fax 01 64 56 51 30; helio@heliomonde.fr; www.heliomonde.fr]** N20 S to Arpajon; then D116 to St Chéron. Site bet Arpajon & Dourdan. Sp in town. Med, shd; htd wc (most cont); chem disp; mv service pnt; sauna; baby facs; shwrs inc; el pnts (10A) €3.80; Indtte (inc dryer); shop; supmkt 3km; rest, snacks; bar; BBQ; playgrnd; htd pool; paddling pool; tennis; games area; fitness rm; wifi; entmnt; TV; mainly statics; dogs €3; train (Paris) 2km; sep carpk; adv bkg; quiet; red low ssn. "Open site; vg facs but grnd condition left a lot to be desired (2011); gd rest; conv Versailles, Paris; gd." ♦ € 25.00 2011*

ST CHERON *4E3* (3.5km SE Rural) *48.54341, 2.13791* **Camping Le Parc des Roches, La Petite Beauce, 91530 St Chéron [01 64 56 65 50; fax 01 64 56 54 50; info@camping-parcdesroches.com; www.camping-parcdesroches.com]** N20 S to Arpajon; then D116 to St Chéron. Site bet Arpajon & Dourdan. Sp in town. Lge, hdg/mkd pitch, hdstg, pt shd; htd wc; chem disp; mv service pnt; baby facs; shwrs inc; el pnts (10A) €3; gas 200m; Indtte (inc dryer); shop 3km; tradsmn, rest, snacks; bar; BBQ; playgrnd; htd pool; paddling pool; tennis; solarium; games area; games rm; wifi; 70% statics; dogs €2; train 3km; Eng spkn; adv bkg; quiet but poss noisy high ssn; ccard acc; red low ssn; CKE/CCI. "Pleasant, wooded site; helpful, friendly owner; gd san facs; o'night pitches lge & nr ent; gd walking; great site; v conv for train to Paris." ♦ 1 Mar-15 Dec. € 27.00 (CChq acc) 2014*

SAMOREAU see Fontainebleau *4E3*

TOUQUIN *4E4* (2.5km W Rural) *48.73305, 3.04697* **Camping Les Etangs Fleuris, Route de la Couture, 77131 Touquin [01 64 04 16 36; fax 01 64 04 12 28; contact@etangs-fleuris.com; www.etangsfleuris.com]** On D231 fr Provins, turn R to Touquin. Turn sharp R in vill & foll sp to site on R in approx 2km. Or fr Coulommiers, take D402 SW twd Mauperthuis, after Mauperthuis L twd Touquin. Foll sp in vill. NB Beware two unmkd speed bumps on entering vill. Med, hdg/mkd pitch, hdstg, pt shd; htd wc; chem disp; mv service pnt; shwrs inc; el pnts (10A) inc; gas; Indtte (inc dryer); sm shop on site & 2.5km; tradsmn; snacks; bar; BBQ; playgrnd; htd pool; paddling pool; fishing; games area; games rm; wifi; entmnt; TV rm; 20% statics (inc tour ops); dogs €1.50; phone; adv bkg; quiet; ccard acc; red CKE/CCI; "Peaceful site; no twin-axle c'vans high ssn; conv Paris & Disneyland; helpful, supportive staff; no noise after 11pm." 5 Apr-15 Sep. € 31.00 2014*

VARREDDES see Meaux *3D3*

VERNEUIL SUR SEINE *3D3* (1.5km N Rural) *48.99567, 1.95681* **Camping-Caravaning 3* du Val de Seine, Chemin du Rouillard, 78480 Verneuil-sur-Seine [01 39 71 88 34 or 01 39 28 16 20; fax 01 39 71 18 60; vds78@orange.fr; www.vds78.com]** Exit A13 junc 8 & foll sp to Verneuil; site sp twd rvside. Med, mkd pitch, hdstg, pt shd; htd wc; shwrs inc; chem disp; mv service pnt; el pnts (6A) €4.25; Indtte; shop on site & 1km; rest, snacks; BBQ; playgrnd; lake sw & beach 600m; fishing; watersports; horseriding; games area; some statics; dogs €2; Paris 20 mins by train; Eng spkn; quiet; ccard acc; red low ssn. "V pleasant site adj Rv Seine; friendly, helpful staff; gd facs & activities; site and area run down." ♦ 15 Apr-30 Sep. € 17.50 2012*

VERSAILLES *4E3* (3km E Urban) *48.79455, 2.16038* **Camping Huttopia Versailles, 31 Rue Berthelot, Porchefontaine, 78000 Versailles [01 39 51 23 61; fax 01 39 53 68 29; versailles@huttopia.com; www.huttopia.com]** Foll sp to Château de Versailles; fr main ent take Ave de Paris dir Porchefontaine & turn R immed after twin gate lodges; sp. Narr access rd due parked cars & sharp bends. No sp rec use SatNav. Lge, mkd pitch, pt sl, terr, pt shd; htd wc; chem disp; mv service pnt; baby facs; shwrs inc; el pnts inc (6-10A) €4.60-6.80; gas; Indtte; shop 500m; tradsmen; rest, snacks; bar; BBQ; playgrnd; htd pool; games area; cycle hire; TV rm; 20% statics; dogs €4; bus 500m; Eng spkn; adv bkg; quiet; ccard acc; red low ssn/long stay; CKE/CCI. "Wooded site; sm, sl, uneven pitches poss diff lge o'fits; friendly, helpful staff; excel, clean san facs, stretched high ssn; conv Paris trains & Versailles Château." ♦ 3 Apr-4 Nov. € 45.00 2012*

⊞ **VILLEVAUDE** *3D3* (2km E Rural) *48.91258, 2.67025* **Camping Le Parc de Paris, Rue Adèle Claret, Montjay-la-Tour, 77410 Villevaudé [01 60 26 20 79; fax 01 60 27 02 75; info@campingleparc.fr; www.campingleparc.fr]** Fr N, A1 twds Paris, then A104 to Marne-la-Vallée, exit at junc 6B (Paris Bobigny), then D105 to Villevaudé, then to Montjay & site sp. Fr S exit A104 at junc 8 to Meaux & Villevaudé. Lge, hdg/mkd pitch, pt sl, pt shd; htd wc; serviced pitches; chem disp; mv service pnt; baby facs; shwrs inc; el pnts (10A) €5; Indtte (inc dryers); shop 5km; tradsmn; rest high ssn; snacks; bar; playgrnd; lake sw & sand beach 5km; tennis 200m; games area; games rm; wifi; entmnt; TV rm; 50% statics; dogs €6; phone; Eng spkn; adv bkg; ccard acc; red low ssn; CKE/CCI. "Conv Disneyland, Paris, Parc Astérix (Disney tickets fr recep); gd san facs; twin-axles acc if adv bkg; drive to local stn (10mins) & park free; shuttle service to Disneyland; gd sh stay; san facs tired, pitches sm and uneven." ♦ € 28.00 2013*

⊞ **VILLIERS SUR ORGE** *4E3* (600m SE Urban) *48.65527, 2.30409* **Camping Le Beau Village, 1 Voie des Prés, 91700 Villiers-sur-Orge [01 60 16 17 86; le-beau-village@wanadoo.fr; www.beau-village.com]** Rec app fr N20, exit sp La Ville-du-Bois & Carrefour. Take rd for Villiers-sur-Orge & turn R at traff lts with sm Renault g'ge. Site sp 200m on L. Care needed on app due to narr rds. Med, hdg pitch, pt shd, htd wc; chem disp; mv service pnt; shwrs inc; el pnts (10A) inc (poss rev pol); gas; Indtte; shops 700m; tradsmn; bar; playgrnd; kayaking; games rm; wifi; dogs €2; phone; train 700m; recep clsd w/ends Dec to Feb; poss cr; quiet; red low ssn. "Pleasant, well-run site; conv Paris; ltd space for lge o'fits." € 18.00 2009*

Pays de la Loire

Regional Introduction

Saumur

Welcome to Pays de la Loire

With many major attractions, Pays de la Loire is a great area to explore. Take in the stunning coastline, stroll around small traditional towns and villages, and see unspoilt landscapes and follow the Loire River as it runs through the region to the Atlantic Ocean.

The best way to explore the region's small towns is to walk the narrow streets – at each turn, you'll discover historic castles, cathedrals and half-timbered houses. Whilst taking in the sights stop at one of the vineyards and try some of the wine that the region is renowned for.

Local highlights

The area is noted for the variety and quality of the Loire Valley's wines. Book a tasting at one of the many local vineyards. The western town of Nantes has its own speciality, a well-known butter biscuit known as Petit Beurre – an ideal gift to take home.

Motoring enthusiasts should head to Le Mans, where the world-famous motor racing circuit hosts a variety of events, such as the 24 Hour race and Le Mans Classic.

Major towns and cities

- Nantes – the capital city of the region.
- Le Mans – home of the famous 24-Hours Le Mans motor race.
- Laval – a mix of medieval churches, bridges and remnants of city walls.
- Saumur – historic town surrounded by vineyards.

Regional attractions

- Cadre Noir, Saumur – the French National Riding School puts on fabulous performances with horses.
- Château d'Angers – an imposing and historical limestone fortress.
- Cathédrale de Saint-Pierre et Saint-Paul, Nantes – gothic cathedral and tombs.
- La Nuit des Chiméres– free lightshow projected on to Le Mans cathedral, summer months only.

Find out more

www.paysdeloire.co.uk

Tel: (0)8 92 46 40 44 Nantes Tourist Office
Tel: (0)2 43 49 46 46 Laval Tourist Office

AIGUILLON SUR MER, L' *7A1* (1km W Coastal) *46.33218, -1.31764* **Camp Municipal La Côte de Lumière, Place du Dr Pacaud, 85460 La Faute-sur-Mer [02 51 97 06 16; fax 02 51 27 12 21; camping.municipal.lafautesurmer@orange.fr; www.lafautesurmer.com]** On D46 E of La Tranche, thro town. Site bef bdge over rv. Lge, shd; wc (some cont); shwrs inc; el pnts (6A) inc; Indtte; shop; snacks; playgrnd; sand beach 600m; tennis; dogs; quiet; ccard acc; CKE/CCI. "Naturist beach adj; bird sanctuary, oyster/mussel beds adj; poss problem with insects; facs poss ltd & run down low ssn." ♦ 1 Apr-15 Oct. € 18.00 2009*

AIGUILLON SUR MER, L' *7A1* (1km W Coastal) *46.34349, -1.32006* **Camping Le Bel Air, 2, Route de Bel Air, 85460 L'Aiguillon-sur-Mer [02 51 56 44 05 or 02 54 77 33 08 (LS); fax 02 51 97 15 58; camping.belair@wanadoo.fr; www.camping-belair.com]** Fr La Roche-sur-Yon take D747 to La Tranche-sur-Mer via coast rd D46 to La Faute-sur-Mer. Cross bdge to L'Aiguillon-sur-Mer. Site 1km W of town on D44. Sp fr all dir. Lge, pt shd; wc; baby facs; shwrs; el pnts (3A) €3.50; Indtte; shop; rest, snacks; bar; BBQ; playgrnd; pool; waterslide; sand beach 800m; entmnt; cycle hire; pony trekking; archery; some statics; dogs €3.50; adv bkg; red low ssn. "Excel, clean, friendly site." 1 Apr-30 Sep. € 25.00 (CChq acc) 2010*

See advertisement

AIZENAY *2H4* (1.5km SE Rural) *46.73410, -1.58950* **FFCC Camping La Forêt, 1 Rue de la Clairière, 85190 Aizenay [tel/fax 02 51 34 78 12; info@camping-laforet.com; www.camping-laforet.com]** Exit Aizenay on D948 twd La Roche-sur-Yon. Site 1.5km on L. Med, hdg/mkd pitch, pt shd; wc; chem disp; mv service pnt; shwrs inc; el pnts (6A) €2.70; gas; Indtte; shop; tradsmn; rest 1.5km; snacks; bar; BBQ; wifi; playgrnd; htd pool; lake beach & sw 1km; tennis; cycle hire; 10% statics; dogs €1.30; phone; adv bkg; quiet; ccard acc; red low ssn/CKE/CCI. "Undergoing refurbishment 2013; new bar & ent." ♦ ltd Easter-30 Sep. € 18.00 2014*

AIZENAY *2H4* (6km NW Rural) *46.75282, -1.68645* **Camping Val de Vie, Rue du Stade, 85190 Maché [tel/fax 02 51 60 21 02; campingvaldevie@bbox.fr; www.campingvaldevie.fr]** Fr Aizenay on D948 dir Challans. After 5km turn L onto D40 to Maché. Fr vill cent cont twd Apremont. Sm, blue site sp 100m on L. Med, hdg/mkd pitch, pt sl, pt shd; wc; chem disp; 10% serviced pitches; baby facs; fam bthrm; shwrs inc; el pnts (6-10A) €3.30-4; gas; Indtte; shops 200m; BBQ; playgrnd; htd pool; sand beach 20km; tennis adj; lake 300m; fishing; boat hire; cycle hire; wifi; 10% statics; dogs €2.80; phone in vill; Eng spkn; adv bkg; quiet; red low ssn/long stay; CKE/CCI. "Lovely, peaceful, well-run site in pretty vill; new young owners upgrading facs & rds (2011); warm welcome; clean san facs; steel pegs useful; gd touring base; gd cycling; excel." ♦ 1Apr-30 Sep. € 20.00 2013*

ALLONNES see Saumur *4G1*

> "I need an on-site restaurant"
>
> We do our best to make sure site information is correct, but it is always best to check any must-have facilities are still available or will be open during your visit.

AMBRIERES LES VALLEES *4E1* (2km SW Rural) *48.39121, -0.61680* **Camping Le Parc de Vaux, 35 Rue des Colverts, 53300 Ambrières-les-Vallées [02 43 04 90 25; parcdevaux@camp-in-ouest.com; www.parcdevaux.com]** Fr S on D23 turn R at sp 'Parc de Loisirs de Vaux'. Site in approx 100m on bank Rv Varenne. Check in at Office de Tourisme bef site recep. Med, hdg/mkd pitch, some hdstg, terr, pt shd; wc; shwrs inc; el pnts (10A) €3.20 (poss long lead req) (poss rev pol); Indtte (inc dryer); shops 500m; tradsmn; rest; bar; BBQ; playgrnd; htd pool; waterslide; lake adj; canoe hire; fishing; tennis; cycle hire; games area; wifi; entmnt; TV rm; 40% statics; dogs €1.80; Eng spkn; adv bkg; quiet; red long stay/low ssn/CKE/CCI. "Excel site in beautiful surroundings; helpful recep; nice rvside site adj to leisure pool; vill 20 mins along rv." ♦ 9 Apr-30 Oct. € 14.80 (CChq acc) 2014*

ANCENIS *2G4* (12km E Rural) *47.36702, -1.01275* **Camping de l'Ile Batailleuse, St Florent-le-Vieil, 44370 Varades [02 40 96 70 20; contact@campingilebatailleuse.fr; http://ilebatailleuse.onlycamp.fr/en]** On Ancenis-Angers rd D723 turn S in Varades onto D752 to St Florent-le-Vieil. After x-ing 1st bdge over Rv Loire site on L on island immed bef 2nd bdge. Med, pt shd; wc; chem disp; shwrs inc; el pnts (10A) €2; shops 1km; rest 20m; playgrnd; pool 1km; tennis 1km; cycle hire; games area; dogs €1.20; poss cr; Eng spkn; wifi; quiet but poss rd noise; CKE/CCI. "Basic, clean site; main shwr facs up stone staircase; panoramic views of Rv Loire in town; gd cycle rtes along rv; new san facs (2014); v pleasant sites." ♦ 30 May-14 Sep. € 18.00 2014*

ANCENIS *2G4* (5km SW Rural) *47.34400, -1.20693* **Camp Municipal Beauregret, 49530 Drain [02 40 98 20 30 or 02 40 98 20 16 (Mairie); fax 02 40 98 23 29; mairie-sg.drain@wanadoo.fr]** Fr Ancenis take D763 S for 2km, turn R onto D751 & cont for 3km. Site on R bef vill of Drain on L. Sm, hdg pitch, pt shd; wc; chem disp; mv service pnt; shwrs inc; el pnts (6A) inc (poss rev pol); Indtte; shop nr; tradsmn; BBQ; playgrnd; lake nrby; games area; entmnt; TV rm; adv bkg; quiet. "Secluded, tranquil site; immac san facs up steps - ltd number; poss not suitable lge o'fits; warden calls am & pm; gd fishing; nice quiet site." ♦ 1 May-30 Sep. € 11.55 2013*

ANCENIS *2G4* (1km W Rural) *47.36201, -1.18721* **FFCC Camping de l'Ile Mouchet, La Davrays, 44150 Ancenis [02 40 83 08 43 or 06 83 52 73 44 (mob); fax 02 40 83 16 19; efberthelot@wanadoo.fr; www.camping-estivance.com]** Fr S, exit N249 at Vallet onto D763 to Ancenis; turn L immed after x-ing Rv Loire & foll sp; site on banks of rv. Or fr N, exit A11 junc 20 onto D923 to Ancenis; cont on D923 over rndabt; foll D923 along rv; in 400m, at next rndabt, do not cross rv but cont strt on onto D23; site sp to L in 700m. Med, mkd pitch, pt shd; htd wc; chem disp; mv service pnt; shwrs inc; el pnts (6-10A) €3.30; Indtte; gas; shops adj; rest, snacks, bar high ssn; playgrnd; pool; waterslide; tennis 50m; games rm; TV; 12% statics; dogs; Eng spkn; adv bkg; quiet; ccard acc; red low ssn/CKE/CCI. "Excel touring base; ltd facs low ssn; some steps; rvside walks; gd site with modern facs; worth a couple of nights." 2 Apr-23 Oct. € 14.00 2014*

ANDOUILLE see Laval *2F4*

⊞ **ANGERS** *4G1* (10km SE Rural) *47.44332, -0.40881* **Camping du Port Caroline, Rue du Pont Caroline, 49800 Brain-sur-l'Authion [02 41 80 42 18; info@campingduportcaroline.fr; www.campingduportcaroline.fr]** E fr Angers on D347 turn onto D113, site sp at ent to vill. Med, hdg/mkd pitch, hdstg, pt shd; htd wc; chem disp; shwrs inc; el pnts (10A) inc; Indtte; shop 300m; snacks; BBQ; playgrnd; htd pool; paddling pool; tennis, fishing nrby; games area adj; games rm; skateboarding; entmnt; TV rm; 5% statics; dogs €3; site clsd Feb; adv bkg; some rd & rlwy noise (& owls, woodpeckers); ccard acc. "Gd touring base; lge pitches." ♦ € 15.00 (CChq acc) 2010*

ANGERS *4G1* (5km S Urban) *47.42442, -0.52701* **Camping Hortus L'Ile du Château, Ave de la Boire Salée, 49130 Les Ponts-de-Cé [02 41 44 62 05; info@camping-hortus.com]** Fr Angers take D160 (sp Cholet) to Les Ponts-de-Cé. Foll sp 'Centre Ville' & turn R at rndabt in town opp Hôtel de Ville, & site on R in 200m on banks of Rv Loire. Med, hdg pitch, pt shd; wc; chem disp; mv service pnt; child/baby facs; shwrs inc; el pnts (10A) inc (poss rev pol); Indtte (inc dryer); shop; tradsmn; rest, snacks; BBQ; playgrnd; htd pool, waterslide adj; sand beach 500m; tennis; games area; games rm; golf 5km; internet; TV; 4% statics; dogs €2; phone; poss cr; Eng spkn; red low ssn; CKE/CCI. "Well-kept, scenic site; excel pool adj; gd touring base for chateaux, vineyards; gd dog walking; highly rec." ♦ 1 Apr-31 Oct. € 23.00 2014*

"Satellite navigation makes touring much easier"

Remember most sat navs don't know if you're towing or in a larger vehicle – always use yours alongside maps and site directions.

⊞ **ANGERS** *4G1* (6km SW Urban) *47.41878, -0.61160* **Camping Aire d'Accueil de Camping Cars, 25 Rue Chevrière, 49080 Bouchemaine [02 41 77 11 04 or 02 41 22 20 00 (Mairie); adm.generale@ville-bouchemaine.fr; www.ville-bouchemaine.fr]** Fr Angers take D160 S, at intersection with D112 W sp Bouchemaine. Cross Rv Maine via suspension bdge. At rndabt on W bank turn L, site on L in 100m dir La Pointe adj rv. Fr Château-Gontier take N162, then D106, then D102E. Bouchemaine well sp. Sm, hdstg, pt shd; wc; chem disp; mv service pnt; shwrs; el pnts (16A) €2.55 (poss rev pol); Indtte; shops 1km; tradsmn; rest 500m; pool 500m; games area; dogs; bus; phone; poss cr; adv bkg quiet; CKE/CCI. "M'vans & tents only; warden calls am & pm; free Oct-Apr but no el pnts; san facs upstairs; poss flooding nr rv; vg NH; automated access; excel cycling, track into Angers." € 11.00 2014*

ANGERS *4G1* (5km W Urban) *47.45387, -0.59463* **Camping du Lac de Maine, Ave du Lac de Maine, 49000 Angers [02 41 73 05 03; fax 02 41 73 02 20; camping@lacdemaine.fr; www.camping-angers.fr]** W fr Angers on D723, exit at 'Quartier du Lac de Maine' then foll sp to site & Bouchemaine. After 4 rndabts site on L; sp W of Rv Maine. Fr S on D160 or A87, turn onto D4 at Les Ponts-de-Cé. In 6km, cross Rv Maine to Bouchemaine & turn R to Pruniers dir Angers. Site on R at Pruniers town exit sp. Med, hdg/mkd pitch, hdstg, pt shd; htd wc; chem disp; mv service pnt; serviced pitches; baby facs; shwrs inc; el pnts (10A) €4.20 (rev pol); gas; Indtte (inc dryer); shop 1.5km; tradsmn; hypmkt 2km; rest, snacks & bar high ssn; BBQ; playgrnd; htd pool; paddling pool; jacuzzi; lake sw, sand beach 800m; fishing; boating; windsurfing 500m; tennis 800m; games area; cycle hire; wifi; TV rm; 10% statics; dogs €2.30; bus adj; phone; Eng spkn; adv bkg rec high ssn; quiet; ccard acc; twin-axles extra; red low ssn/long stay/CKE/CCI. "Excel, well-run site in leisure park; pitches narr, some suitable v l'ge o'fits; height barrier at ent 3.20m; conv Loire chateaux; pay 6 nights, stay 7." ♦ 25 Mar-10 Oct. € 29.70 (CChq acc) 2013*

APREMONT *2H4* (2km N Rural) *46.77848, -1.73394* **Camping Les Charmes, Route de la Roussière, 85220 Apremont [02 51 54 48 08 or 06 86 03 96 93 (mob); fax 02 51 55 98 85; contact@campinglescharmes.com; www.campinglescharmes.com]** Fr D948 Challans to Aizenay turn W onto D94 sp Commequiers; after 2km L, sp Les Charmes. Med, mkd pitch, pt shd; wc (some cont); chem disp; fam bthrm; shwrs inc; el pnts (6-10A) €3.30-4 (poss rev pol); gas; Indtte; shop; tradsmn; playgrnd; pool; lake sw with beach 3km; sand beach 18km; TV rm; 60% statics; dogs €2.80; poss cr; Eng spkn; adv bkg; quiet; ccard acc; red low ssn/long stay; CKE/CCI. "Beautiful, well-kept site; generous pitches but soft when wet; welcoming, helpful owners; excel, clean san facs; a great find; friendly recep." ♦ 1 Apr-12 Sep. € 19.30 2013*

ASSERAC *2G3* (5km NW Coastal) *47.44533, -2.44766* **Camping Le Moulin de l'Eclis, Pont Mahé, 44410 Assérac [02 40 01 76 69; fax 02 40 01 77 75; info@camping-moulin-de-leclis.fr; www.camping-moulin-de-leclis.fr]** Fr D774 turn N onto D83 to Assérac. Take D82 two coast to Pont Mahé, site sp. Lge, hdg/mkd pitch, pt shd; wc; chem disp; mv service pnt; baby facs; shwrs inc; el pnts (6-10A) €3.60-4; Indtte (inc dryer); shop high ssn & 5km; rest 100m; snacks; bar; BBQ (gas/elec); playgrnd; htd, covrd pool; paddling pool; waterslide; dir access to sand beach adj; watersports; sailing school; games area; cycle hire; wifi; entmnt; TV rm; 60% statics; dogs €3; phone; adv bkg; Eng spkn; quiet; ccard ac; red low ssn. "Excel family site; conv Guérande; vg touring base." ♦ 1 Apr-14 Nov. € 25.00 2010*

AVRILLE *7A1* (500m N Rural) *46.47641, -1.49373* **Camping Le Domaine des Forges, Rue des Forges, 85440 Avrillé [02 51 22 38 85; fax 02 51 90 98 70; contact@campingdomainedesforges.com; www.campingdomainedesforges.com / www.les-castels.com]** Fr N on D747 turn R at Moutiers-les-Mauxfaits onto D19 to Avrillé. In town cent cont strt & after sm rndabt foll yellow/white site sp. Turn R into Rue des Forges, site on R in 600m. Med, mkd pitch, pt shd; wc; chem disp; mv service pnt; baby facs; shwrs; el pnts (16A) inc; gas; Indtte (inc dryer); sm shop; snacks; bar; BBQ; playgrnd; 2 pools, 1 htd, covrd; paddling pool; lake fishing; sand beach 10km; tennis; cycle hire; fitness rm; games area; games rm; wifi; entmnt; TV; dogs €4; no c'vans/m'vans over 10m Apr-Oct; Eng spkn; adv bkg; ccard acc; red low ssn. "Attractive site in lovely location; spacious, well-kept pitches; helpful, friendly owner; gd, clean, modern san facs; lots of fish in lake; highly rec." ♦ 18 Apr-27 Sep. € 43.00 SBS - A43 2013*

AVRILLE *7A1* (1km S Rural) *46.45578, -1.48365* **Camping Les Mancellières, Route de Longeville-sur-Mer, 85440 Avrillé [02 51 90 35 97; fax 02 51 90 39 31; camping.mancellieres@wanadoo.fr; www.lesmancellieres.com]** Fr Avrillé take D105 S twd Longeville-sur-Mer. Site on L in 1.5km. Med, hdg/mkd pitch, pt sl; wc (some cont); chem disp; baby facs; shwrs inc; el pnts (6A) €3.90; gas; Indtte; shop; snacks; BBQ (charcoal/gas); playgrnd; htd pool; paddling pool; waterslide; beach 5km; fishing 2km; tennis 800m; cycle hire, horseriding 3km; games rm; entmnt; 30% statics; dogs €2; some Eng spkn; adv bkg; quiet; 30% red low ssn; ccard not acc. "Friendly owners; peaceful; ent gates set on angle & poss diff lge o'fits." ♦ 1 May-15 Sep. € 17.00 2009*

BARBATRE see Noirmoutier en l'Ile *2H3*

BATZ SUR MER see Croisic, Le *2G3*

BAUGE *4G1* (1km E Rural) *47.53889, -0.09637* **Camp Municipal du Pont des Fées, Chemin du Pont des Fées, 49150 Baugé [02 41 89 14 79 or 02 41 89 18 07 (Mairie); fax 02 41 84 12 19; camping@ville-bauge.fr; www.ville-bauge.fr]** Fr Saumur traveling N D347/D938 turn 1st R in Baugé onto D766. Foll camping sp to site by sm rv; ent bef rv bdge. Sm, hdg/mkd pitch, pt shd; wc; chem disp; mv service pnt; shwrs inc; el pnts (4A) €2.70; Indtte; shops 1km; BBQ; pools & tennis 150m; fishing; no twin-axles; phone; adv bkg; quiet; ccard acc. "Excel countryside; pleasant, well-kept site; obliging wardens." 15 May-15 Sep. € 9.40 2010*

BAULE, LA *2G3* (2km NE Rural) *47.29833, -2.35722* **Airotel Camping La Roseraie, 20 Ave Jean Sohier, Route du Golf, 44500 La Baule-Escoublac [02 40 60 46 66; fax 02 40 60 11 84; camping@laroseraie.com; www.laroseraie.com]** Take N171 fr St Nazaire to La Baule. In La Baule-Escoublac turn R at x-rds by church, site in 300m on R; sp fr La Baule cent. Lge, hdg/mkd pitch, some hdstg, pt shd; wc (some cont); chem disp; mv service pnt; baby facs; fam bthrm; shwrs inc; el pnts (6-10A) €5.50-€7.50; gas; Indtte (inc dryer); shop 400m; tradsmn; rest, snacks; bar; BBQ; playgrnd; htd, covrd pool; paddling pool; waterslide; sand beach 2km; fishing; watersports; tennis; games area; games rm; fitness rm; wifi; entmnt; TV rm; 80% statics; dogs €5; phone; Eng spkn; adv bkg; quiet but rd noise; ccard acc; red long stay/low ssn; CKE/CCI. "Gd site & facs; sm pitches; clean unisex san facs; ltd facs low ssn; easy walk into La Baule-Escoublac; excel beach nrby; vg." ♦ 1 Apr-25 Sep. € 40.00 (CChq acc) 2012*

> "There aren't many sites open at this time of year"
>
> If you're travelling outside peak season remember to call ahead to check site opening dates – even if the entry says 'open all year'.

BAULE, LA *2G3* (1km E Coastal) *47.28864, -2.37236* **Camping Le Bois d'Amour, Allée de Diane, 44500 La Baule [02 40 60 17 40 or 04 73 77 05 05 (LS); fax 04 73 73 05 06; contact@lesbalconsverts.com; www.lesbalconsverts.com]** Fr Ave du Bois d'Amour bear L & immed under rlwy bdge, turn R at traff lts. Ent to site on R. Lge, mkd pitch, shd; wc; chem disp; shwrs inc; el pnts (6A) inc; gas; Indtte; shop; rest; playgrnd; sand beach 800m; wifi; 50% statics; dogs €2; phone; bus & rlwy adj; no dogs high ssn; poss cr; Eng spkn; adv bkg; quiet, but some rd/rlwy noise at site perimeter; red low snn; CKE/CCI. "Useful NH, some pitches v sm; sm area for tourers." ♦ 1 Apr-3 Oct. € 25.00 (CChq acc) 2009*

BAULE, LA *2G3* (1km W Rural) *47.29372, -2.37916* **Camping Les Ajoncs d'Or, Chemin du Rocher, 44500 La Baule [02 40 60 33 29; fax 02 40 24 44 37; contact@ajoncs.com; www.ajoncs.com]** Fr D13 foll sp for La Baule cent & turn L at rndabt nr Champion supmkt, site sp. Lge, mkd pitch, pt shd; wc; chem disp; baby facs; shwrs; el pnts (6A) inc; Indtte; shop; supmkt 1km; rest, snacks; bar; playgrnd; sand beach 1.5km; games area; entmnt; TV; 25% statics; dogs €1; adv bkg; quiet; red low ssn. "Peaceful, well-run site; vg." ♦ 1 Apr-30 Sep. € 21.00 2010*

PAYS DE LA LOIRE

BEAUMONT SUR SARTHE *4F1* (500m E Rural) *48.22382, 0.13651* **FFCC Camp Municipal du Val de Sarthe, Rue de l'Abreuvoir, 72170 Beaumont-sur-Sarthe [02 43 97 01 93; camping-beaumontssarthe@orange.fr; www.ville-beaumont-sur-sarthe.fr]** Fr D338 Alençon-Le Mans, turn L at traff lts in cent of Beaumont & foll site sp twd E of town. Fr Le Mans on A28 exit 21 onto D6, R onto D338 & R at traff lts & foll sp. NB Narr, sloping app thro town rds with blind corners. Narr site access. Med, hdg/mkd pitch, pt shd; wc; chem disp; mv service pnt; shwrs inc; el pnts (6A) €3.20; (long cable poss req & poss rev pol); Indtte; shops & rest 500m; playgrnd; pool 500m; rv boating & fishing adj; dogs €0.50; poss cr w/end; adv bkg rec high ssn; ccard acc; CKE/CCI. "Beautiful, peaceful, well-run rvside site; lge pitches, some by rv; no twin-axles & poss no c'vans over 2,000 kg; barrier clsd 2200; easy walk to interesting, pretty town; mkt Tues; rec; nice clean site, pleasant & friendly; well maintained site." ♦ 1 May-30 Sep. € 15.60 2014*

BEAUMONT SUR SARTHE *4F1* (9.5km S Rural) *48.14267, 0.18428* **FFCC Camp Municipal Le Pont d'Orne, 72380 Montbizot [02 43 27 60 44 or 02 43 27 62 16 (LS); mairie.montbizot@wanadoo.fr]** Exit A28 junc 21 onto D47 to Montbizot; cont on D47, site 300m S of vill on L. Sm, hdg/mkd pitch, shd; wc; mv service pnt; shwrs inc; el pnts inc; snacks; bar; playgrnd. "Busy but quiet site with access to rv; excel facs; warden calls am/pm." 15 May-27 Sep. € 9.50 2011*

BEAUVOIR SUR MER *2H3* (4km E Rural) *46.89984, -1.98840* **Camp Municipal, 85230 St Gervais [02 51 68 73 14 (Mairie); fax 02 51 68 48 11]** On D948, 1km E of St Gervais on R. Sm, mkd pitch, pt shd; wc; chem disp; shwrs; el pnts (10A) €2.50; gas; Indry rm; shop; BBQ; quiet; CKE/CCI. "Facs basic but clean." ♦ 1 Apr-15 Sep. € 8.50 2009*

BEAUVOIR SUR MER *2H3* (4km E Rural) *46.92298, -1.99036* **Camping Le Fief d'Angibaud, 85230 St Gervais [02 51 68 43 08; camping.fief.angibaud@orange.fr; www.campinglefiefangibaud.com]** Fr Beauvoir-sur-Mer E on D948 to St Gervais turn L after PO/Mairie onto D59 twd Bouin (narr ent easy to miss); in 2km pass sm chapel; take 2nd rd on L; site on R after 500m. Sm, unshd; wc; chem disp; shwrs inc; el pnts (6-13A) €4-7; gas 4km; basic Indry rm; shops 2km; tradsmn; sand beach 5km; fishing/golf nrby; no statics; dogs €1.50; wifi; adv bkg rec high ssn; quiet; red long stay/CKE/CCI. "Excel, simple site adj farm; lge pitches; pleasant, helpful British owners; clean san facs but need update (2010); conv Ile de Noirmoutier; ferry to Ile d'Yeu, coastal resorts; free parking close to beach (blue flag); gd cycling area; vg value; gd for rallies." ♦ 1 Mar-31 Oct. € 17.50 2013*

BERNERIE EN RETZ, LA see Pornic *2G3*

BLAIN *2G4* (1km S Rural) *47.46782, -1.76787* **Camp Municipal Le Château, Route de St Nazaire, 44130 Blain [02 40 79 11 00; otsi.blain@free.fr; www.ville-blain.fr]** Fr N on N137 turn W onto N171; fr S on N137 turn W onto D164 to Blain. On app town, take L at rndabt on N171 dir St Nazaire/Bouvron. Immed after x-ing Brest-Nantes canal bdge, site on L adj to chateau. Sm, mkd pitch, pt shd; wc; shwrs inc; chem disp; mv service pnt; el pnts (10A) €2.40; Indry rm; shops 500m; tradsmn; rest, bar 500m; playgrnd; pool 1km; fishing; boating; dogs €1; phone adj; adv bkg; quiet but some rd noise; CKE/CCI. "Super, well-managed site; gd pitch size; helpful staff; immac san facs; chateau museum adj; no twin-axles; no access for vehicles after 2000 high ssn." ♦ 1 May-30 Sep. € 19.00 2014*

BOISSIERE DU MONTAIGU, LA see Montaigu *2H4*

BOUCHEMAINE see Angers *4G1*

BRAIN SUR L'AUTHION see Angers *4G1*

BRETIGNOLLES SUR MER *2H3* (2km N Coastal) *46.63024, -1.86048* **Camping Les Vagues, 85470 Bretignolles-sur-Mer [02 51 90 19 48 or 02 40 02 46 10; fax 02 40 02 49 88; lesvagues@free.fr; www.campinglesvagues.fr]** Well sp on D38. Lge, hdg pitch, pt shd; wc; chem disp; sauna; baby facs; shwrs; el pnts (6A) €4; Indtte (inc dryer); rest, snacks; bar; BBQ; playgrnd; 2 pools (1 htd, covrd); paddling pool; waterslide; sand beach 900m; games area; games rm; entmnt; TV; 50% statics; dogs €2.50; adv bkg; red low ssn; CKE/CCI. "Gd sized pool; close to town cent with shops & rests." ♦ 1 Apr-30 Sep. € 25.00 2009*

BRETIGNOLLES SUR MER *2H3* (1km E Urban) *46.63583, -1.85861* **Chadotel Camping La Trévillière, Route de Bellevue, 85470 Bretignolles-sur-Mer [02 51 90 09 65 or 02 51 33 05 05; fax 02 51 33 94 04; info@chadotel.com; www.chadotel.com]** S along D38 fr St Gilles Croix-de-Vie twd Olonne-sur-Mer, site is sp to L in Bretignolles-sur-Mer. Site 1km fr town cent nr football stadium. Sp fr town cent. Lge, hdg/mkd pitch, pt shd; wc; chem disp; mv service pnt; 50% serviced pitches; baby facs; shwrs inc; el pnts (6A) inc; gas; Indtte (inc dryer); shop; tradsmn; snacks; bar; BBQ (gas); playgrnd; htd, covrd pool; waterslide; paddling pool; sand beach 1.5km; fishing; watersports 3km; horseriding 5km; cycle hire; wifi; entmnt; games/TV rm; 70% statics; dogs €3.20; phone; no c'van/m'van over 8m high ssn; Eng spkn; adv bkg; ccard acc; red long stay/low ssn; CKE/CCI. "Friendly, family site; lge pitches; quiet low ssn; gd cycling area; salt marshes worth a visit; mkt Thu & Sun." ♦ 5 Apr-20 Sep. € 30.50 SBS - A26 2012*

BRETIGNOLLES SUR MER *2H3* (5km E Rural) *46.63502, -1.79735* **Camping L'Evasion, Route des Sables, 85220 Landevieille [tel/fax 02 51 22 90 14; contact@camping-levasion.fr; www.camping-levasion.fr]** Site sp in Landevieille. Med, hdg/mkd pitch, pt shd; wc (some cont); chem disp; baby facs; shwrs inc; el pnts (10A) inc; gas; Indtte (inc dryer); shop; supmkt 750m; rest, snacks; bar; BBQ; playgrnd; 3 htd pools; waterslides; jacuzzi; beach 5km; fishing lake; games area; wifi; entmnt; 75% statics; dogs; dog exercise area; phone; some Eng spkn; quiet except for bar/disco high ssn; ccard acc; CKE/CCI. "Vg." 1 Apr-15 Oct. € 25.00 2010*

BRETIGNOLLES SUR MER *2H3* (5km E Rural) *46.64021, -1.80708* **Camping L'Oree de l'Océan, Rue Capitaine de Mazenod, 85220 Landevieille [02 51 22 96 36; fax 02 51 22 29 09; info@camping-oreedelocean; www.camping-oreedelocean.com]** Take D12 fr La Mothe-Achard to St Julien-des-Landes & cont to x-rds bef La Chaize-Giraud. Turn L onto D32, take 1st R in Landevieille to site on L in 50m. Adj Mairie. Med, hdg/mkd pitch, pt sl, pt shd; wc; chem disp; shwrs inc; el pnts (10A) €4; Indtte; shops 500m; bar; playgrnd; htd pool; tennis; sand beach 5km; TV rm; phone; 95% statics; dogs €3; phone; poss cr; quiet; adv bkg; Eng spkn; 15% red 7+ days; ccard acc; CKE/CCI. "Gd, friendly, family site; many gd beaches & mkd cycle tracks nr; gd for NH." ♦ 1 Apr-30 Sep. € 23.00 2014*

BRETIGNOLLES SUR MER *2H3* (750m W Coastal) *46.62708, -1.86488* **Camping La Motine, 4 Rue des Morinières, 85470 Bretignolles-sur-Mer [02 51 90 04 02; fax 02 51 33 80 52; campinglamotine@wanadoo.fr; www.lamotine.com]** Foll sp fr D38 in Bretignolles-sur-Mer dir Plage de la Parée along Ave de la Plage, then turn R into Rue des Morinières. Med, hdg pitch, pt sl, pt shd; wc; chem disp; mv service pnt; serviced pitches; baby facs; shwrs inc; el pnts (6A) inc; Indtte; rest; bar; playgrnd; htd, covrd pool; sand beach 600m; 60% statics; dogs €3; adv bkg; quiet; ccard acc; CKE/CCI. "Unisex san facs low ssn; vg site." ♦ 1 Apr-30 Sep. € 27.00 2009*

BRETIGNOLLES SUR MER *2H3* (3.1km NW Coastal) *46.64868, -1.87811* **Camping La Haute Rivoire, Route des Rivoires, 85470 Bretignolles-sur-Mer [02 51 33 80 34 or 0207 193 6613 (UK); hauterivoire@gmail.com]** Fr St Gilles Croix-de-Vie take D38 S twd Les Sables. Cross bdge over Rv Jaunay. Turn L on D12 sp Chaize-Giraud. Site 2nd turning on R sp Chambres. Site in 400m. Take ent after barns. Sm, unshd; wc; chem disp; shwrs inc; el pnts (6A) €4.50 (poss rev pol); snacks; supmkt, shop 2km; pool; sand beach 2km; fishing, watersports, golf, horseriding nr; no dogs; sep car park adj; adv bkg req; red low ssn. "British-owned, adults-only, peaceful CL-type farm site; san facs v clean; twin-axles extra; phone bef arr to check open; payment on arr." 2010*

BRISSAC QUINCE *4G1* (2km NE Rural) *47.35944, -0.43388* **Campsite Sites & Paysages de l'Etang, Route de St Mathurin, 49320 Brissac-Quincé [02 41 91 70 61; fax 02 41 91 72 65; info@campingetang.com; www.campingetang.com]** Fr N on A11, exit junc 14 onto N260 passing E of Angers, following sp for Cholet/Poitiers. After x-ing Rv Loire, foll sp to Brissac-Quincé on D748. Foll sp for St Mathurin/Domaine de l'Etang on D55 to site. Med, hdg/mkd pitch, hdstg, pt shd; htd wc; mv service pnt; chem disp; baby facs; some serviced pitches (€3 extra charge); shwrs inc; el pnts (10A) inc; gas; Indtte (inc dryer); shop; tradsmn; rest, snacks; bar; BBQ (charcoal/gas); playgrnd; 2 pools (1 htd, covrd); paddling pool; waterslide; lake fishing; cycle hire; golf 8km; wifi; entmnt; games/TV rm; dogs €2.10-9.10; twin-axles acc (rec check in adv); Eng spkn; adv bkg; quiet; ccard acc; red long stay/low ssn; CKE/CCI. "Excel, well-cared for site amongst vineyards; lge pitches; staff pleasant & helpful; clean, modern facs; leisure facs gd for children; pleasant 15 min rvside walk to Brissac-Quincé; wine tasting; gd touring base Loire valley; mkt Thu." ♦ 26 Apr-13 Sep. € 41.70 SBS - L15 2014*

BRISSAC QUINCE *4G1* (1km S Rural) *47.33317, -0.43664* **Camping à la Ferme Domaine de la Belle Etoile, La Belle Etoile, 49320 Brissac-Quincé [06 62 32 99 40 (mob); www.domaine-belle-etoile.fr]** Take D748 S fr Angers dir Poitiers. At D761 rndabt cont on D748 sp N-D-d'Allençon. Site sp at 2nd turn on L in 500m. Sm, pt shd; wc; chem disp; shwrs €1; el pnts (5A) €3; Indtte; BBQ; playgrnd; quiet. "Vg CL-type site in vineyard with wine-tasting & farm produce; clean, modern facs; troglodyte caves, mushroom farms & château nrby." 1 Apr-1 Nov. € 8.30 2014*

BRULON *4F1* (500m SE Rural) *47.96275, -0.22773* **Camping Le Septentrion, Le Bord du Lac, 72350 Brûlon [02 43 95 68 96; fax 02 43 92 60 36; le.septentrion@wanadoo.fr; www.campingleseptentrion.com]** Exit A81 junc 1; foll D4 S to Brûlon; site sp on ent to town to L; turn on L down narr rd (Rue de Buet); then turn R in 300m. Site well sp. Sm, pt sl, shd; htd wc; mv service pnt; baby facs; shwrs inc; el pnts (6A) €3; Indtte; shop 600m; tradsmn; rest, snacks; bar; BBQ; playgrnd; htd pool (high ssn); lake sw; boating; fishing; cycle hire; games/TV rm; wifi; 50% statics; dogs €1.20; phone; adv bkg; quiet, but poss noise fr teepee cent adj; red long stay/low ssn. "Attractive, well-kept site; spacious pitches; welcoming staff; gd, clean san facs - unisex low ssn; poss a bit unkempt early ssn; gd cycling & walking area; excel." ♦ 3 Apr-30 Oct. € 13.50 2013*

CHAIZE GIRAUD, LA see Bretignolles sur Mer *2H3*

⊞ **CHALLANS** *2H4* (11km SE Rural) *46.81522, -1.77472* **Camping Domaine de Bellevue, Bellevue Du Ligneron, 85670 Saint Christophe du Ligneron [02 51 93 30 66 / 06 21 55 54 29 (mob); campingdebellevue85@orange.fr; www.vendee-camping-bellevue.com]** Fr S: On Route National D948 exit Saint Christophe du Lingeron; turn W in dir Saint Gilles Croix de Vie/Commequirers; at rndbt cont strt on; take 2nd R at Bellevue du Ligneron. Med, hdg pitch; wc; baby facs; shwrs (inc); el pnts (16) €4.00; Indtte; bar; take away; BBQ; pool (htd); fishing; cycle hire; games rm; wifi; 50% statics; dogs €3; adv bkg; Eng spkn; ccard acc; CKE/CCI. "Gd value for money, in lovely Vendee region; gd fishing on site; new site with friendly owners." ♦ € 17.00 2013*

See advert on next page

CHALONNES SUR LOIRE *2G4* (8km SE Rural) *47.32285, -0.71428* **Camp Municipal Les Patisseaux, Route de Chalonnes, 49290 Chaudefonds-sur-Layon [02 41 78 04 10 (Mairie); fax 02 41 78 66 89; mairie.chaudefondsurlayon@wanadoo.fr]** Fr Chalonnes on D961 S dir Cholet. Turn L onto D125. At narr rlwy bdge after 3km, foll sp to site on Rv Layon. Sm, hdg/mkd pitch, pt shd; wc; mv service pnt; shwrs; el pnts; shop, bar 500m; quiet. "V basic, clean site nr rv; lots of interest in area; reverse polarity; ltd san facs; lovely peaceful site." ♦ 1 May-31 Aug. € 9.25 2014*

PAYS DE LA LOIRE

CHALONNES SUR LOIRE *2G4* (9km SE Urban) *47.32803, -0.67134* **Camp Municipal du Layon, Rue Jean de Pontoise, 49190 St Aubin-de-Luigné [02 41 78 33 28 (Mairie); fax 02 41 78 68 55; mairie-sg.staubin@wanadoo.fr]** Exit N160 Angers-Chemillé at sp St Aubin or turn S off D751 at sp St Aubin. Site sp in vill. Sm, hdg/mkd pitch, pt shd; wc; mv service pnt in adj car pk with access to facs; shwrs inc; el pnts €4.90; shop 150m; playgrnd; rv adj; boat hire; quiet. "Pleasant, historic vill; warden calls 0800-0945 or pay at Mairie nrby; unsuitable lge o'fits due diff manoeuvring; san facs adequate; public footpath thro site; gd walking/cycling." ♦ 1 May-30 Sep. € 7.00 2009*

CHALONNES SUR LOIRE *2G4* (11km NW) *47.39211, -0.87082* **Camping La Promenade, Quai des Mariniers, 49570 Montjean-sur-Loire [02 41 39 02 68 or 06 26 32 60 28 (mob); contact@campinglapromenade.com; www.campinglapromenade.com]** Exit Angers on N23 twd Nantes. Exit 1km beyond St Germain-des-Prés dir Montjean-sur-Loire. Cross rv then R on D210 to site in 500m. Lge, hdg, mkd pitch; pt shd; wc; chem disp; mv service pnt; baby facs; shwrs inc; el pnts (10A) €4; gas; lndtte (inc dryer); shops adj; tradsmn; café; rest, snacks; bar; BBQ; playgrnd; htd pool; paddling pool; sand beach 600m; games area; entmnt; TV; wifi; 30% statics; dogs €2; twin axles; Eng spkn; adv bkg; quiet; ccard acc; CKE/CCI. "Friendly, young owners; interesting sculptures in vill & at Ecomusée; gd for Loire cycling; new san facs (2014) diff exit to R for lge vehicles; fishing nrby; vg." 1 Apr-30 Sep. € 27.00 2014*

⊞ **CHANTONNAY** *2H4* (12km NE Rural) *46.75168, -0.94568* **Camping La Baudonnière, Route des Salinières, 85110 Monsireigne [tel/fax 02 51 66 43 79; tombann1962@gmail.com; www.labaudonniere.com]** Fr Chantonnay take D960B NE dir St Prouant & Pouzauges. In St Prouant take D23 to Monsireigne. Foll rd downhill, cross sm rv & as rd starts to climb take 2nd L sp Reaumur; in 400m L onto Rue des Salinières. Site on L in 800m. Sm, pt sl, pt shd; wc; chem disp; shwrs inc; el pnts (10A) €4; lndtte (inc dryer); shops, rest, snacks, bar 3km; BBQ; playgrnd; pool, tennis 2km; lake 5km; games rm; no statics; dogs; Eng spkn; adv bkg; quiet. "V relaxing, peaceful, pretty CL-type site; welcoming, friendly, helpful Irish owners; excel san facs; conv Puy de Fou theme park; vg; v well kept site." ♦ € 22.00 2014*

CHANTONNAY *2H4* (7km NW Rural) *46.74516, -1.11817* **Camp Municipal La Rivière, 25 Rue du Stade, 85110 Ste Cécile [02 51 40 24 07; fax 02 51 40 25 59; mairiestececile85@wanadoo.fr; www.saintececile85.fr]** Fr Chantonnay NW on D137; in St Vincent-Sterlanges turn onto D39 to Ste Cécile (2.5km); site sp clearly fr main rd. Sm, hdg/mkd pitch, pt shd; wc; shwrs inc; el pnts (10A); lndtte; playgrnd; pool; paddling pool; rv fishing adj; tennis; statics; adv bkg rec high ssn; quiet. "Pt of larger complex of holiday bungalows; some facs dated & poor." 1 Jun-30 Sep. 2010*

"I like to fill in the reports as I travel from site to site"

You'll find report forms at the back of this guide, or you can fill them in online at www.caravaclub.co.uk/europereport.

CHAPELLE HERMIER, LA *2H4* (4km SW Rural) *46.66652, -1.75543* **Camping Le Pin Parasol, Châteaulong, 85220 La Chapelle-Hermier [02 51 34 64 72; fax 02 51 34 64 62; contact@campingpinparasol.fr; www.campingpinparasol.fr]** Exit A83 junc 4 onto D763/D937 dir La Roche-sur-Yon; turn R onto D948; at Aizenay turn R onto D6 twd St Gilles Croix-de-Vie; after 10km at x-rds turn L onto D21; in La Chapelle-Hermier foll D42 twds L'Aiguillon-sur-Vie; site sp in 4km. Lge, hdg/mkd pitch, pt sl, terr, unshd; wc; chem disp; mv service pnt; baby facs; shwrs inc; el pnts (16A) €4.50; gas; lndtte (inc dryer); sm shop; tradsmn; rest 500m nr lake; snacks; bar; BBQ; playgrnd & adventure zone; 2 pools (1 htd); paddling pool; waterslide; sand beach 12km; lake sw, boating, fishing, canoeing 200m; cycle hire; archery; fitness rm; tennis; games area; excursions; wifi; entmnt; games/TV rm; 70% statics; dogs €4.20; no c'vans/m'vans over 11m; poss v cr; Eng spkn; adv bkg; quiet; ccard acc (Visa only); red low ssn; CKE/CCI. "On banks of Lake Jaunay; access to lake down sm path; lge pitches; friendly staff; excel facs; lovely pools; away fr crowds but close to beaches; pleasant walks & cycle tracks around lake; beautiful site, v well kept." ♦ 18Apr-24 Sep. € 44.00 SBS - A36 2013*

CHARCHIGNE see Lassay les Châteaux *4E1*

CHARTRE SUR LE LOIR, LA *4F2* (500m W Rural) *47.73220, 0.57451* **Camping Le Vieux Moulin, Chemin des Bergivaux, 72340 La Chartre-sur-le Loir [02 43 44 41 18; bordduloir@orange.fr]** Sp fr D305 in town. Fr S exit A28 junc 27 onto D766 dir Beaumont-la-Ronce; then take D29 to La Chartre-sur-le Loir; go over rv, turn L immed after bdge. Fr N leave A20 at junc 24 & foll D304 to Chartre, site well sp on R bef bdge. Med, hdg/mkd pitch, pt shd; htd wc (some cont); chem disp; mv service pnt; baby facs; fam bthrm; shwrs inc; el pnts (5-10A) €4-5 (poss rev pol); gas 500m; Indtte; shop 500m; bar; BBQ; playgrnd; htd pool; rv fishing, cycle hire; wifi; TV; 20% statics; dogs €1.50; poss cr; Eng spkn; adv bkg rec high ssn; quiet; 15% red CC members; red low ssn; CKE/CCI. "Beautiful, well-kept rvside site; helpful, friendly staff; excel pool; gd for dogs; v lge m'vans acc; gd base for chateaux, forest & Loir Valley; excel." ♦ 27 Apr-15 Oct. € 24.00 2014*

"We must tell The Club about that great site we found"

Get your site reports in by mid-August and we'll do our best to get your updates into the next edition.

⊞ **CHATAIGNERAIE, LA** *2H4* (8km N Rural) *46.7325, -0.7425* **Camping Le Grand Fraigneau, Le Grand Fraigneau, 85700 Menomblet Vendée [02 51 51 68 21 / 06 42 68 48 12 (mob); info@legrandfraigneau.com; www.legrandfraigneau.com]** NE fr La Châtaigneraie on D938T to St Pierre-du-Chemin; turn L onto D49 to Menomblet; in 500m turn L to Le Grand Fraigneau. Site sp. Sm, pt shd; wc; fam bathrm; shwrs; el pnts (10A) €3; BBQ; pool (above grnd); lake sw & boating 9km; wifi; dogs free; Eng spkn; adv bkg; twin-axles acc; quiet; "CL-type site; friendly, helpful British owners; fenced pond; walks in lovely countryside; excel." ♦ ltd € 9.00 2013*

CHATEAU D'OLONNE see Sables d'Olonne, Les *7A1*

CHATEAU DU LOIR *4G1* (6km E Rural) *47.71250, 0.49930* **Camping du Lac des Varennes, Route de Port Gauthier, 72340 Marçon [02 43 44 13 72; fax 02 43 44 54 31; lacdesvarennes@camp-in-ouest.com; www.camp-in-ouest.com / www.lacdesvarennes.com]** Fr N on D338 fr Château-du-Loir dir Vendôme for 3km. Turn L onto D305 sp Marçon. In vill turn L onto D61 over bdge. Site on R by lake. Lge, hdg/mkd pitch, hdstg, pt shd; htd wc; chem disp; mv service pnt; baby facs; shwrs inc; el pnts (10A) €3.40 (poss rev pol, poss long lead req); Indtte (inc dryer); shop high ssn; tradsmn; rest, snacks; bar; BBQ; playgrnd; lake sw & sand beach adj; boat hire; watersports; tennis; cycle hire; horseriding; cycle hire; wifi; entmnt; 11% statics; dogs €1.80; Eng spkn; adv bkg rec; quiet; ccard acc; red long stay/low ssn; CKE/CCI. Low ssn office clsd 1200-1600. "Pretty site in lovely situation bet lake & rv; friendly, helpful staff; gd security; gd walks & cycling; san facs basic & unisex." ♦ 18 Apr-28 Sep. € 25.00 2014*

⊞ **CHATEAU GONTIER** *4F1* (1km N Urban) *47.83851, -0.69965* **Camping Le Parc, 15 Route de Laval, 53200 Château-Gontier [02 43 07 35 60; fax 02 43 70 38 94; camping.parc@cc-chateau-gontier.fr; www.sudmayenne.com]** App Château-Gontier fr N on N162, at 1st rndabt on bypass take 1st exit. Site on R in 250m. Sm, mkd pitch, sl, pt shd; htd wc; chem disp; mv service pnt; shwrs inc; el pnts (10A) inc (rev pol); Indtte; shops 1km; tradsmn; bar; playgrnd; pool 800m; fishing; tennis; entmnt; games rm; TV; 20% statics; dogs; quiet; ccard acc; red low ssn; CKE/CCI. "V pleasant site; most pitches sloping, some o'look rv; superb clean unisex san facs; rvside path to attractive town; mkt Thurs; excel site, gd pitches; superb clean san facs; helpful staff; lots of activity on rv to watch." ♦ € 12.00 2014*

⊞ **CHATEAU GONTIER** *4F1* (11km N Rural) *47.92109, -0.68334* **Camping Village Vacances et Pêche, Rue des Haies, 53170 Villiers-Charlemagne [02 43 07 71 68; fax 02 43 07 72 77; vvp.villiers.charlemagne@wanadoo.fr; www.villiers-charlemagne.mairie53.fr]** N fr Château-Gontier on N162; turn R onto D20 to Villiers-Charlemagne; site on R. Sm, pt shd; wc; chem disp; shwrs inc; el pnts (6A) inc; Indtte; BBQ; cooking facs; playgrnd; cycle hire; lake 200m; fishing; tennis; games rm; entmnt; dogs; wifi; 10% statics; twin axle acc; Eng spkn; CKE/CCI; red low ssn; "Sm wooded site in rural surroundings; each pitch has own san facs & kitchenette; site is amazing; helpful, friendly staff; v peaceful; well maintained." € 17.00 2013*

"I need an on-site restaurant"

We do our best to make sure site information is correct, but it is always best to check any must-have facilities are still available or will be open during your visit.

CHATEAUBRIANT *2F4* (1.5km S Urban) *47.70305, -1.37789* **Camp Municipal Les Briotais, Rue de Tugny, 44110 Châteaubriant [02 40 81 14 38 or 02 40 81 02 32; mairie.chateaubriant@wanadoo.fr]** App fr Nantes (D178) site sp on S end of town. Or fr Angers on D963/D163 foll sp at 1st rndabt; fr town cent, foll sps thro town. Sm, hdg pitch, pt shd; wc; mv service pnt; shwrs; el pnts €2.70; shops, rest, snacks, bar 1km; pool in town; games area; dogs; €0.35; quiet. "11thC chateau in town; site locked o'night; site on municipal playing field; gd NH." ♦ 2 May-30 Sep. € 6.00 2009*

CHATEAUNEUF SUR SARTHE *4G1* (400m S Rural) *47.67745, -0.48673* **Camp Municipal du Port, Rue de la Gare, 49330 Châteauneuf-sur-Sarthe [02 41 69 82 02 or 02 41 96 15 20; fax 02 41 96 15 29; tourismechateauneufsursarthe@wanadoo.fr; www.chateauneufsursarthe.fr]** Site clearly sp in vill, 18km E of Le Lion-d'Angers. Access to site fr bdge. Sm, pt shd; wc; chem disp; shwrs inc; el pnts (10A) €2.70 (long lead poss req); Indtte; shops & rest in vill; playgrnd; rv adj; fishing; sailing; v quiet but some rd noise; CKE/CCI. "Attractive area; lge pitches; clean facs but poss stretched high ssn; warden on site am & pm; v few elec points." 1 May-30 Sep. € 7.00 2013*

CHAUDEFONDS SUR LAYON see Chalonnes sur Loire *2G4*

CHEMILLE *2G4* (1km SW Rural) *47.20182, -0.73486* **FFCC Camping Coulvée, Route de Cholet, 49120 Chemillé [02 41 30 42 42 or 02 41 30 39 97 (Mairie); fax 02 41 30 39 00; camping-chemille-49@wanadoo.fr; www.camping-coulvee-chemille.com]** Fr Chemillé dir Cholet on D160, turn R in 1km. Sm, hdg pitch, terr, pt shd; wc; chem disp; mv service pnt; shwrs inc; el pnts (10A) €3.60; Indtte; tradsmn; bar; BBQ; playgrnd; sm sand beach; lake sw; pedalos; dogs €1.70; some Eng spkn; adv bkg; quiet; ccard not acc; red long stay; CKE/CCI. "Clean facs; helpful staff; gd pitches; poss unrel opening dates; mkt Thurs." ♦ 1 May-15 Sep. € 23.60 (CChq acc) 2012*

CHOLET *2H4* (5km SE Rural) *47.03699, -0.84171* **Camping Village Vacances Le Lac de Ribou, Allée Léon Mandin, 49300 Cholet [02 41 49 74 30; fax 02 41 58 21 22; info@lacderibou.com; www.lacderibou.com]** Fr Cholet ring rd foll sp Parc des Loisirs de Ribou. Sp fr Cholet. Lge, hdg/mkd pitch, hdstg, terr, pt shd; htd wc; chem disp; mv service pnt; serviced pitches; shwrs inc; el pnts (10A) €3.85 (long lead req); Indtte; tradsmn; shop; hypmkt 1.5km; rest, snacks; bar; BBQ; playgrnd; 2 htd pools; waterslides; lake sw & sand beach 500m; fishing; boating; windsurfing; skating; tennis; archery; golf nr; entmnt; TV rm; dogs €2.10; extra for twin-axles; poss cr; Eng spkn; adv bkg ess; quiet; ccard acc; 5% red CKE/CCI. "Excel touring area; excel site." ♦ 1 Apr-30 Sep. € 19.00 2009*

CHOLET *2H4* (8km SE Rural) *47.01915, -0.82976* **Camping du Verdon, Le Bois Neuf, Route du Verdon, 49280 La Tessoualle [02 41 49 74 61; fax 02 41 58 21 22; lacduverdon@cholet-sport-loisirs.fr; www.cholet-sports-loisirs.com]** Exit Cholet ring rd S onto D258 sp L Tessoualle; turn L bef La Tessoualle sp Barrage du Verdon dam. Site adj dam. Poss diff to app fr other rds. Sm, hdg pitch, pt shd; wc; chem disp; shwrs; el pnts (3-5A) €2.10-3.05 (long lead req some pitches, poss rev pol); shop; rest, snacks, bar adj; lake sw & beach; dogs €1; Eng spkn; adv bkg; quiet; CKE/CCI. "Peaceful location, lovely pitches; facs dated but clean; site yourself, warden calls; windsurfing on Lac du Verdon; excel walking, cycling." 1 Jul-31 Aug. € 9.85 2010*

CLISSON *2H4* (1.3km N Urban) *47.09582, -1.28216* **Camp Municipal du Vieux Moulin, Rue de la Fontaine Câlin, Route de Nantes, 44190 Clisson [02 40 54 44 48 or 02 40 54 02 95 (LS); camping@valleedeclisson.fr; www.mairie-clisson.com]** 1km NW of Clisson cent on main rd to Nantes, at rndabt. Look for old windmill nr ent on L of rd. Leclerc hypmkt on opp side of rd; site sp fr town cent. Narr ent. Sm, hdg pitch, pt sl, pt shd; wc; chem disp; shwrs inc; el pnts inc; hypmkt, rest, snacks & bar 500m; tradsmn; fishing, tennis, horseriding adj; boating; dogs €1.12; phone (card only); Eng spkn; adv bkg; quiet but some rd noise. "Gd municipal site; lge pitches; gd clean san facs; if office clsd pitch self, book in later; picturesque town 15 min walk; mkd walks; interesting old town with castle ruins; next to retail park." ♦ 6 Jul-13 Oct. € 17.00 2013*

COEX *2H4* (2.5km W Rural) *46.67679, -1.76899* **RCN Camping La Ferme du Latois, 85220 Coëx [02 51 54 67 30; fax 02 51 60 02 14; ferme@rcn.fr; www.rcn-campings.fr]** Exit D948 at Aizenay onto D6 dir St Gilles-Croix-de-Vie; at Coëx take D40 SW sp Brétignolles; site in 1.5km on L. Lge, pt shd; htd wc; chem disp; shwrs inc; el pnts inc (poss rev pol); Indry rm; shop; tradsmn; rest, snacks; bar; BBQ (gas); playgrnd; pool; lake fishing; cycle hire; games area; games rm; wifi; 20% statics; dogs €5; phone; Eng spkn; adv bkg; quiet; red low ssn. "Spacious pitches; cycle rtes adj; conv Lac du Jaunay & Lac du Gué-Gorand; excel." ♦ 11 Apr-10 Oct. € 45.40 2014*

See advertisement

CONNERRE *4F1* (8km SE Urban) *48.03945, 0.59302* **Camp Municipal La Piscine, 36 Rue du Parc, 72390 Dollon [02 43 93 42 23; fax 02 43 71 53 88; mairie.dollon@wanadoo.fr; www.tourisme-en-sarthe.com]** Fr Connerré take D302 sp Vibraye & Thorigné-sur-Dué. In Dollon foll 'La Piscine' sp to sports complex at E end of vill. Sm, hdstg, pt shd; wc; chem disp; shwrs; el pnts (10A) inc; gas; shops 300m; playgrnd; pool; tennis; fishing; adv bkg rec; quiet. "Popular site; pt of sports complex; rec arr early high ssn." 15 May-15 Sep. € 10.00 2011*

COULON *7A2* (6km W Rural) *46.33020, -0.67524* **Camping Le Relais du Pêcheur, 85420 Le Mazeau [02 51 52 93 23 or 02 51 52 91 14 (Mairie); fax 02 51 52 97 58]** Fr Fontenay-le-Comte take N148 SE. At Benet turn R onto D25 thro vill to Le Mazeau. Turn L in vill then R over canal bdge. Site on L in 500m. Med, hdg pitch, pt shd; wc (most cont); chem disp; shwrs inc; el pnts (16A) €3.50; Indtte; shop 500m; supmkt 5km; playgrnd; paddling pool; boat hire nrby; adv bkg; quiet; eng spkn; CKE/CCI. "Pleasant, clean site in delightful location; gd cyling & walks; facs need updating." ♦ ltd 1 Apr-30 Sep. € 11.50 2014*

COUTURES *4G1* (1km NE Rural) *47.37440, -0.34690* **Camping Parc de Montsabert, 49320 Coutures [02 41 57 91 63; fax 02 41 57 90 02; camping@parcdemontsabert.com; www.parcdemontsabert.com]** Easy access on R side of Rv Loire bet Angers & Saumur. Take D751 to Coutures & fr town cent foll sp for site. 1st R after 'Tabac' & foll rd to site (1st on R bef chateau). Med, hdg/mkd pitch, hdstg, pt sl, pt shd; htd wc; chem disp; 50% serviced pitches; child/baby facs; shwrs inc; el pnts (5-10A) inc; Indtte; shop 1.5km; tradsmn; rest, snacks; bar; playgrnd; htd, covrd pool; paddling pool with slide; tennis; games area; games rm; cycle hire; gym; entmnt; TV; 15% statics; dogs €4; phone; bus 1km; Eng spkn; adv bkg; quiet; ccard acc; CKE/CCI. "Ideal for chateaux & wine cellars; lge pitches." ♦ 12 Apr - 8 Sep. € 29.00 2010*

See advertisement

CRAON *2F4* (1.7km E Urban) *47.84819, -0.94409* **Camp Municipal du Mûrier, Rue Alain Gerbault, 53400 Craon [02 43 06 96 33 or 02 43 06 13 09 (Mairie); fax 02 43 06 39 20; contact@ville-craon53.fr; www.ville-craon53.fr]** Fr Laval take D771 S to Craon. Site sp fr town cent. Sm, hdg pitch, pt shd; wc; shwrs inc; el pnts (6A) €2.10; Indtte; snacks; playgrnd; pool 200m; tennis; wifi; entmnt; no twin-axles; adv bkg; quiet; red long stay. "Lge pitches; san facs poss stretched when site full; easy walk to town; office clsd Tues & Sun low ssn, when barrier key req (2010); local chateau gardens." 1 May-21 Sep. € 10.00 2010*

CROISIC, LE *2G3* (3.5km SE Coastal) *47.27888, -2.49138* **Flower Camping Les Paludiers, Rue Nicolas Appert, 44740 Batz-sur-Mer [02 40 23 85 84; fax 02 40 23 75 55; paludiers@flowercampings.com; www.camping-paludiers.com]** Fr Guérande take D774/D245 to Batz-sur-Mer. Thro Batz sp Le Croisic, site is opp windmill. Lge, hdg/mkd pitch, unshd; wc; mv service pnt; baby facs; shwrs; el pnts inc; Indtte (inc dryer); tradsmn; rest, snacks; bar; BBQ; playgrnd; htd pool; paddling pool; sand beach 100m; watersports; cycle hire; games area; games rm; wifi; TV rm; 50% statics; dogs €2.50-3.20; Eng spkn; adv bkg; quiet; ccard acc; red low ssn; CKE/CCI. "Vg, family site; helpful, friendly staff." ♦ 1 Apr-30 Sep. € 27.00 2009*

CROISIC, LE *2G3* (2km S Coastal) *47.29272, -2.52850* **Camping La Pierre Longue, Rue Henri Dunant, 44490 Le Croisic [02 40 23 13 44; fax 02 40 23 23 13; contact@campinglapierrelongue.com; www.campinglapierrelongue.com]** Turn L off Le Pouliguen-Le Croisic rd at g'ge at Le Croisic sp; foll camp sps. Lge, hdg/mkd pitch, pt shd; htd wc; chem disp; mv service pnt; baby facs; shwrs inc; el pnts (6-10A) inc; gas; Indtte; shop; rest, snacks; bar; BBQ; playgrnd; htd pool; sand beach 500m; entmnt; TV; 60% statics; phone; dogs; Eng spkn; adv bkg; quiet; ccard acc; red low ssn; CKE/CCI. "Lge pitches; warm welcome, helpful staff; excel, clean facs, unisex low ssn; excel beaches." ♦ 1 Mar-30 Nov. € 23.70 2011*

CROISIC, LE *2G3* (1km W Coastal) *47.29558, -2.53605* **Camping de l'Océan, 15 Route de la Maison Rouge, 44490 Le Croisic [02 40 23 07 69; fax 02 40 15 70 63; info@camping-ocean.com; www.camping-ocean.com]** Foll N171/D213 to Guérande. At junc take D774 to La Baule, Batz-sur-Mer, then D245 to Le Croisic. At rndabt foll site sp. Lge, hdg/mkd pitch, pt shd; wc; chem disp; mv service pnt; serviced pitches; baby facs; shwrs inc; el pnts (6A) €4-6; gas; Indtte; shop; rest, snacks; bar; BBQ; playgrnd; 2 htd pools, (1 covrd); waterslide; jacuzzi; shgl beach 150m; tennis; games area; fitness rm; wifi; entmnt; 30% statics; dogs €6.50; adv bkg; Eng spkn; quiet; red low ssn; ccard acc; red low ssn/CKE/CCI. "Interesting coast line nr La Baule; salt flats at ent to Le Croisic; pleasant walk to Guérande adj; excel pool complex." ♦ 3 Apr-30 Sep. € 40.00 2009*

CROISIC, LE *2G3* (2km W Coastal) *47.29415, -2.53846* **Camping Le Paradis, Chemin Turballo, 44490 Le Croisic [02 40 23 07 89; www.camping-paradis.com]** Fr La Baule take D245 to Le Croisic; on ent Le Croisic cont on D245 (R fork), which then becomes D45 coast rd; cont on coast rd anti-clockwise for approx 4km until site sp on L. Med, hdg/mkd pitch, pt shd; wc; chem disp; shwrs inc; el pnts (3-6A) €2.90-€3.60; gas; Indtte (inc dryer); shop 2km; tradsmn; rest, snacks; bar; BBQ; playgrnd; sand/shgl beach 500m; horseriding; golf adj; TV; 10% statics; dogs €2; phone; poss cr; adv bkg; quiet; red low ssn/long stay; CKE/CCI. "Beaches sm bet rocks; gd cycling; gd mkt; vg." ♦ ltd 1 May-30 Sep. € 16.00 2010*

DAMVIX see Maillezais *7A2*

DAON see Château Gontier *4F1*

DOLLON see Connerré *4F1*

DOUE LA FONTAINE *4G1* (1km N Rural) *47.20338, -0.28165* **Camp Municipal Le Douet, Rue des Blanchisseries, 49700 Doué-la-Fontaine [02 41 59 14 47 or 06 22 71 25 53 (mob); contact@camping-lesrivesdudouet.fr; www.camping-lesrivesdudouet.fr]** Fr Doué N on D761 twd Angers; site in sports grnd on o'skts of town; sp. Med, mkd pitch, pt shd; wc; chem disp; shwrs inc; el pnts (6A) inc; Indtte; shop 2km; rests nr; htd pool high ssn adj; tennis; wifi; few statics; poss cr; quiet but some factory noise at E end; no ccard acc; CKE/CCI. "Clean, well-run site; gd, flat pitches; helpful warden; gd san facs; lovely park & museum; conv zoo, rose gardens & Cadre Noir Equestrian Cent; poss itinerant workers low ssn; gd shd; shop will order bread; vg." ♦ ltd 1 Apr-15 Oct. € 21.50 2014*

DOUE LA FONTAINE *4G1* (2km SW Rural) *47.17390, -0.34750* **Camping La Vallée des Vignes, 49700 Concourson-sur-Layon [02 41 59 86 35; fax 02 44 84 46 95; info@campingvdv.com; www.campingvdv.com]** D960 fr Doué-la-Fontaine (dir Cholet) to Concourson-sur-Layon; site 1st R 250m after bdge on leaving Concourson-sur-Layon. Or fr Angers foll sp dir Cholet & Poitiers; then foll sp Doué-la-Fontaine. Med, mkd pitch, pt shd; htd wc; chem disp; serviced pitches; baby facs & fam bthrm; shwrs inc; el pnts (10A) €4; gas; Indtte; shop; tradsmn; rest, snacks; bar; BBQ; playgrnd; htd pool; paddling pool; lake sw 10km; cycle hire; entmnt; TV rm; 5% statics; dogs €3; bus; poss cr; Eng spkn; adv bkg; quiet, some rd noise; ccard acc; red long stay low ssn; ccard acc; CKE/CCI; wifi. "Peaceful site poss open all yr weather permitting - phone to check; friendly, helpful British owners; vg, clean, well-maintained facs; pool open & htd early ssn; some pitches diff lge o'fits due o'hanging trees; conv for Loire chateaux & Futuroscope." ♦ 1 May-30 Sep. € 38.00 2014*

DOUE LA FONTAINE *4G1* (8km W Rural) *47.19355, -0.37075* **Camping Les Grésillons, Chemin des Grésillons, 49700 St Georges-sur-Layon [02 41 50 02 32; fax 02 41 50 03 16; camping.gresillon@wanadoo.fr; www.camping-gresillons.com]** Fr Doué-la-Fontaine on D84, site sp. Sm, hdg pitch, hdstg, terr, pt shd; htd wc; chem disp; baby facs; shwrs inc; el pnts (6-10A) €2.90-3.50; Indtte; shop & 500m; rest; snacks, bar 500m; playgrnd; htd pool; rv fishing 200m; games area; entmnt; 28% statics; dogs free; Eng spkn; adv bkg; quiet; ccard acc; red long stay/CKE/CCI. "Delightful site in area of vineyards; friendly, helpful owner." ♦ 1 Apr-30 Sep. € 11.00 2009*

DOUE LA FONTAINE *4G1* (17.6km W Rural) *47.18032, -0.43574* **Camping KathyDave, Les Beauliers, 49540 La Fosse de Tigné [02 41 67 92 10 or 06 14 60 81 63 (mob); bookings@camping-kathydave.co.uk; www.camping-kathydave.co.uk]** Fr Doué-la-Fontaine on D84 to Tigne, turn S thro La Fosse-de-Tigné. Pass chateau, site sp on R. NB Tight turn in, access poss diff lge o'fits. Sm, mkd pitch, pt shd; htd wc; chem disp; shwrs inc; el pnts (8A) €3 (poss rev pol); Indtte; tradsmn; rest nr; BBQ (gas); wifi; dogs free; adv bkg; quiet; CKE/CCI. "Tranquil orchard site in picturesque area; welcoming, helpful British owners; gd san facs; some pitches restricted by trees; gd touring base; adults only preferred; phone ahead rec; excel; sm cl type site in an old orchard." 1 Jun-30 Sep. € 14.50 2014*

DURTAL *4G1* (200m W Urban) *47.67115, -0.23798* **Camping Les Portes de l'Anjou, 9 Rue du Camping, 49430 Durtal [02 41 76 31 80; lesportesdelanjou@camp-in-ouest.com; www.lesportesdelanjou.com]** Exit A11 junc 11 dir La Flèche, by-passing Durtal. At D323 turn R for Durtal, site on L at ent to town. Sps not readily visible, look out for 'Motor C'van Parking'. Med, hdg/mkd pitch, pt shd; wc (mainly cont); chem disp; baby facs; shwrs inc; el pnts (6A) €3.40; gas; Indtte (inc dryer); shops 500m; tradsmn; snacks; bar; playgrnd; htd pool; paddling pool; fishing; canoeing; games rm; wifi; entmnt; TV rm; 12% statics; dogs €2.50; Eng spkn; office clsd 12.30-3.30; adv bkg; quiet; ccard acc; red long stay/low ssn/CKE/CCI. "Site in need of TLC, in pleasant position on Rv Loir; helpful staff; interesting vill." ♦ 12 Apr-27 Oct. € 22.60 (CChq acc) 2013*

ECOMMOY *4F1* (400m NE Urban) *47.83367, 0.27985* **Camp Municipal Les Vaugeons, Rue de la Charité, 72220 Ecommoy [02 43 42 14 14 or 02 43 42 10 14 (Mairie); fax 02 43 42 62 80; mairie.ecommoy@wanadoo.fr]** Heading S on D338 foll sp. Turn E at 2nd traff lts in vill; sp Stade & Camping. Also just off A28. Med, pt sl, pt shd; well mkd, wc (some cont); chem disp; shwrs €1.30; el pnts (6A) €2.35; Indtte; shops 1km; playgrnd; tennis; poss cr; Eng spkn; adv bkg; quiet; ccard not acc; red low ssn; CKE/CCI. "Site full during Le Mans week (nr circuit); gd san facs; new arr no access when recep clsd, hours 0900-1130 & 1500-2030; coarse sand/grass surface." ♦ ltd 1 May-30 Sep. € 10.00 2014*

ECOMMOY *4F1* (4km SE Rural) *47.81564, 0.33358* **Camp Municipal Le Chesnaie, 72220 Marigné-Laillé [02 43 42 12 12 (Mairie); fax 02 43 42 61 23; mairie. marigne-laille@wanadoo.fr / mairie.marigne-laille. catherine@wanadoo.fr; www.tourisme-en-sarthe.com]** S on D338 Le Mans-Tours, turn E 3km after Ecommoy twds Marigné-Laillé. Site in 1.5km. Sm, pt shd, hdstg, mkd pitch; wc; shwrs; el pnts (10A) inc; shops 300m; playgrnd; pool 5km; lake & fishing adj; tennis; poss cr; v quiet; CKE/CCI. "Lovely site; clean, adequate san facs; pleasant warden; if height barrier down, use phone at ent; easy access A28; v warm welcome; basic site, but clean; pretty site, great NH." 1 May-30 Sep. € 8.00 2013*

ECOMMOY *4F1* (8km S Rural) *47.75641, 0.28780* **Camp Municipal Plan d'Eau du Fort des Salles, 72360 Mayet [02 43 46 68 72, 06 89 93 76 05 (mob) or 02 43 46 60 11 (Mairie); fax 02 43 46 07 61]** On D338 Le Mans-Tours rd turn W at St Hubert onto D13 to Mayet & site. Sp 'Camping Plan d'Eau'. Or exit A28 sp Ecommoy & then as above. Med, mkd pitch, pt shd; wc, chem disp; mv service pnt; shwrs inc; el pnts (10A); gas; lndtte; shops 500m; playgrnd; pool nrby; lake fishing; cycle hire; statics; quiet; CKE/ CCI. "Well-maintained, clean site; mkd walks nrby; recep open 0830-1130 & 1600-1900; arr only bet these times as no waiting area." ♦ ltd 1 Apr-15 Sep. 2009*

EPESSES, LES *2H4* (500m N Rural) *46.88920, -0.89950* **FFCC Camping La Bretèche, La Haute Bretèche, 85590 Les Epesses [02 51 57 33 34; fax 02 51 57 41 98; contact@ campinglabretache.com; www.camping-la-breteche.com]** Fr Les Herbiers foll D11 to Les Epesses. Turn N on D752, site sp on R by lake - sp fr cent Les Epesses. Med, hdg/mkd pitch, pt shd; wc, chem disp; mv service pnt; baby facs; shwrs inc; el pnts (10A) €3 (poss rev pol); lndtte (inc dryer); shop 1km; tradsmn; rest, snacks; bar; playgrnd; htd pool adj inc; fishing; tennis; horseriding; entmnt; TV; 30% statics; dogs €1.85; poss cr; Eng spkn; adv bkg; ccard acc; red low ssn; CKE/CCI. "Well-kept, well-run site; busy high ssn; helpful staff; plenty of attractions nr; events staged in park by lake high ssn; conv Puy du Fou; vg; no waste or water on site, long leads req." ♦ 1 Apr-30 Sep. € 22.00 2012*

ESSARTS, LES *2H4* (800m W Urban) *46.77285, -1.23558* **Camp Municipal Le Pâtis, Rue de la Piscine, 85140 Les Essarts [02 51 62 95 83 / 06 30 02 37 09 (mob); camping. lepatis@wanadoo.fr; www.ville-les-essarts85.fr]** Exit A83 junc 5 onto D160. On ent Les Essarts, foll sp to site. Site on L just off rd fr Les Essarts to Chauché. Med, mkd pitch, pt shd; htd wc; baby facs; shwrs inc; el pnts (6A) €2.80; lndtte; supmkt, rests in town; tradsmn; snacks; BBQ (gas/charcoal); playgrnd; 2 pools (1 Olympic size), paddling pool, tennis & sports cent adj; 40% statics; dogs €1.60; some statics; v quiet; ccard not acc; CKE/CCI. "Excel NH off A83; gd, clean san facs; warden resident." ♦ 15 Apr-15 Sep. € 18.70 2013*

EVRON *4F1* (7km SE Rural) *48.09423, -0.35642* **Camp Municipal La Croix Couverte, 10 Rue de la Croix Couverte, 53270 Ste Suzanne [02 43 01 41 61 or 02 43 01 40 10 (Mairie); fax 02 43 01 44 09]** Take D7 SW fr Evron sp Ste Suzanne. Site 800m S (downhill) after this sm fortified town. Sm, some hdg/mkd pitch, hdstg, pt shd; wc; shwrs inc; el pnts (3-5A) inc; shops 800m; playgrnd; htd pool adj; walking & horseriding adj; some statics; quiet; CKE/ CCI. "Simple, clean site in lovely area; sm pitches; site open to public for cycling & walking; pool v busy high ssn; unspoilt town & castle with historic Eng conns; excel NH - open all yr for m'vans." ♦ 1 May-30 Sep. € 10.00 2011*

"There aren't many sites open at this time of year"

If you're travelling outside peak season remember to call ahead to check site opening dates – even if the entry says 'open all year'.

⊞ **EVRON** *4F1* (300m W Urban) *48.15077, -0.41223* **Camp Municipal de la Zone Verte, Blvd du Maréchal Juin, 53600 Evron [02 43 01 65 36; fax 02 43 37 46 20; camping@ evron.fr; www.camping.evron.fr]** Site on ring rd 200 yards fr Super-U supmkt; clearly sp fr all rds into town. Med, some hdg pitch, pt shd; htd wc (some cont); chem disp; mv service pnt; shwrs inc; el pnts (6-10A) €1.60-2.45; lndtte; shops 1km; playgrnd; htd pool & sports complex adj; 50% statics; dogs €0.80; no twin-axles; adv bkg; quiet; red long stay. "Attractive, peaceful, comfortable, well-kept site with many flowers; gd, clean san facs; restricted recep hrs in winter - warden on site lunchtime & early eve only; poss maintenace issues early ssn (2011); no twin-axles; some worker's c'vans; highly rec for sh or long stay; excel; gd value." ♦ ltd € 12.45 2013*

FAUTE SUR MER, LA see Aiguillon sur Mer, L' *7A1*

FENOUILLER, LE see St Gilles Croix de Vie *2H3*

FLECHE, LA *4G1* (10km E Rural) *47.70230, 0.07330* **Camp Municipal La Chabotière, Place des Tilleuls, 72800 Luché-Pringé [02 43 45 10 00; fax 02 43 45 10 00; contact@ lachabotiere.com; www.lachabotiere.com / www. loir-valley.com]** SW fr Le Mans on D323 twd La Flèche. At Clermont-Créans turn L on D13 to Luché-Pringé. Site sp. Med, hdg/mkd pitch, pt sl, pt shd; wc (some cont); chem disp; mv service pnt; baby facs; shwrs; el pnts (10A) inc (poss rev pol); lndtte; shops 100m; playgrnd; pool adj high ssn; cycle hire; TV; 10% statics; dogs €1.50; phone; sep car park high ssn; poss cr; Eng spkn; adv bkg; quiet; red low ssn; CKE/CCI. "Lovely, well-kept site by Rv Loir; helpful, friendly warden; clean, modern facs; gd site for children; many cycle rtes; conv chateaux; nice vill nrby; avoid Le Mans motor bike week - poss many bikers on site; excel." ♦ 1 Apr-15 Oct. € 14.70 2011*

FLECHE, LA *4G1* (500m S Urban) *47.69514, -0.07936* **Camping de la Route d'Or, Allée du Camping, 72200 La Flèche [tel/fax 02 43 94 55 90; info@camping-laroutedor.com; www.camping-laroutedor.com / www.loir-valley.com]** Fr NW dir Laval D306, keep to W of town, leave S on D306 twd Bauge; site on L after x-ing rv; sp. Fr S take dir for A11 & Laval, site clearly sp on R on rvside. Lge, hdg/mkd pitch, some hdstg, pt shd; htd wc; chem disp; mv service pnt; shwrs inc; el pnts (10A) €3.80 (poss long lead req); gas; Indtte (inc dryer); shop 500m; supmkt nr; tradsmn; rest & bar nr; BBQ; playgrnd; htd pool; sand lake beach 2km; canoeing, fishing nr; tennis; games area; wifi; child entmnt; dogs €1; phone; Eng spkn; ccard acc; red low ssn; CKE/CCI. "Lovely, busy site in beautiful location by rv; well kept, run & maintained site; lge pitches; welcoming, helpful staff; facs ltd low ssn; ring for entry code if office clsd; no twin-axles; attractive, easy, sh walk across rv to attractive town; conv ferries; mkt Wed; rec; mkt Sun & Wed; defibrillator on site; new san fac's being built (2013)." ♦ 1 Mar-30 Oct. € 20.70 2014*

FONTENAY LE COMTE *7A2* (7km NE Rural) *46.52140, -0.76906* **FFCC Camping La Joletière, 85200 Mervent [02 51 00 26 87 or 06 14 23 71 31 (mob LS); fax 02 51 00 27 55; contact@campinglajoletiere.fr; www.campinglajoletiere.fr]** Fr Fontenay-le-Comte N on D938; after 6.5km, turn R onto D99; in 3km enter vill of Mervent; site on R. Or fr A83 exit junc 8 & take bypass to W of Fontenay-le-Comte. Med, hdg/mkd pitch, some hdstg, pt sl, pt shd; wc; mv service pnt; shwrs inc; el pnts (10A) €4.10 (rev pol); gas; Indtte; shop 1km; rest, snacks; bar; playgrnd; htd pool high ssn; sw 2km; fishing; boating/windsurfing 2km; forest walks 500m; 25% statics; dogs €1.70; poss cr; adv bkg; ccard acc. "Quiet & pleasant site; gd lge pitches; friendly owners; poss ltd facs low ssn; san facs old & unclean." ♦ 30 Mar - 26 Oct. € 15.00 2011*

"That's changed – Should I let The Club know?"

If you find something on site that's different from the site entry, fill in a report and let us know. See www.caravanclub.co.uk/europereport.

FONTENAY LE COMTE *7A2* (7km NE Rural) *46.52454, -0.76983* **FFCC Camping Le Chêne Tord, 34 Chemin du Chêne Tord, 85200 Mervent [02 51 00 20 63 or 06 43 17 73 70 (mob); fax 02 51 00 27 94; contact@camping-mervent.fr; www.camping-mervent.fr]** Exit A83 junc 8 & foll D938 N fr Fontenay-Le-Comte twd La Châtaigneraie for 6km to vill of Fourchaud. Turn E to Mervent on D99 & foll camp sps, sharp L turn immed bef vill at stone cross. Site is 500m W of Mervent. Sm, mkd pitch, pt sl, pt shd; htd wc; chem disp; shwrs inc; el pnts (6A) €3; gas; Indtte (inc dryer); shop 1km; rest, snacks, bar 1km; BBQ (gas only); rv/lake sw & fishing 2km; games area; 90% statics; dogs €1; phone; Eng spkn; adv bkg rec high ssn; v quiet; red low ssn; CKE/CCI. "Nice area; third of site forest adventure park - poss noisy high ssn; poss scruffy low ssn; welcoming & friendly; mainly statics; gd NH." 27 Mar-26 Nov. € 14.00 2009*

FRESNAY SUR SARTHE *4E1* (200m NW Rural) *48.28297, 0.0158* **Camp Municipal Le Sans Souci, Rue du Haut Ary, Ave Victor Hugo, 72130 Fresnay-sur-Sarthe [02 43 97 32 87; fax 02 43 33 75 72; regisseur@camping-fresnaysursarthe.fr; www.camping-fresnaysursarthe.fr]** Fr Alençon S on D338; in 14km at La Hutte turn R on D310 to Fresnay; sp in town on traff lts bef bdge; bear R imm after x-ing bdge, then sharp R, sp diff to see, if missed V diff for c'vans to turn fr opp dir. Fr Beaumont-sur-Sarthe NW on D39 to Fresnay. Med, hdg/mkd pitch, pt sl, terr, pt shd; wc; chem disp; shwrs inc; el pnts (6A) €3.20 (poss rev pol); Indtte (inc dryer); shops high ssn & 500m; htd pool adj inc; rv adj; fishing; canoe hire; cycle hire; wifi; entmnt; dogs €1.20; Eng spkn; adv bkg; quiet; CKE/CCI. "Pleasant, clean site adj Rv Sarthe; gd rvside pitches; 3 pitches for lge o'fits, mover rec; facs poss stretched high ssn; gd cycling; vg." ♦ 1 Apr-30 Sep. € 16.60 2013*

GENNES *4G1* (650m NE Rural) *47.34205, -0.22985* **Camping Au Bord de Loire, Ave des Cadets-de-Saumur, 49350 Gennes [02 41 38 04 67 or 02 41 38 07 30; fax 02 41 38 07 12; auborddeloire@free.fr; www.camping-auborddeloire.com]** At Rv Loire bdge cross S to Gennes on D751B. Site 200m on L. Ent to site thro bus terminus/car park on ent to Gennes. Med, pt sl, pt shd; wc; chem disp; shwrs inc; el pnts (10A) €3.40; Indtte; shop in vill; snacks; bar; BBQ; shop in vill; tradsmn; snacks; playgrnd; htd pool in vill; entmnt; 2% statics; dogs €1.60; quiet, but some rd noise; red long stay; wifi; CKE/CCI. "Delightful, relaxing, well-kept site by Rv Loire, spacious pitches, main san facs block up steps, vg; Loire cycle rte passes gate." 1 May-30 Sep. € 19.40 2014*

GIVRAND see St Gilles Croix de Vie *2H3*

⊞ **GIVRE, LE** *7A1* (1.5km S Rural) *46.44472, -1.39832* **Camping La Grisse, 85540 Le Givre [02 51 30 83 03; info@campinglagrisse.com; www.campinglagrisse.com]** Fr Luçon take D949 & turn L at junc with D747 (La Tranche rd). Turn L in 3km & foll sps. Sm, pt shd; wc; chem disp; shwrs inc; el pnts (16A) €4; Indtte; playgrnd; htd, covrd pool 10km; sand beach 10km; games area; some statics; dogs €2; Eng spkn; adv bkg; ccard not acc; CKE/CCI. "Peaceful, friendly, farm site; lge pitches; clean, modern facs; beautiful area/beach; gd for dogs." ♦ ltd € 21.00 2011*

GRAND'LANDES see Legé *2H4*

GUEMENE PENFAO *2G4* (1km SE Rural) *47.62575, -1.81857* **Camping L'Hermitage, 36 Ave du Paradis, 44290 Guémené-Penfao [02 40 79 23 48; fax 02 40 51 11 87; camping.hermitage@wanadoo.fr; www.campinglhermitage.com]** On D775 fr cent of Guémené-Penfao, dir Châteaubriant for 500m, turn R, site sp. Med, mkd pitch, hdstg, pt shd; wc; chem disp; mv service pnt; baby facs; shwrs inc; el pnts (6A) €3.50; gas; Indtte; shop 1.5km; tradsmn; rest, snacks; bar; BBQ; playgrnd; htd, covrd pool adj; paddling pool; waterslide; jacuzzi; rv sw & fishing 300m; canoeing; tennis; games area; games rm; cycle hire; entmnt; TV; 20% statics; dogs €2; phone; some Eng spkn; adv bkg; quiet; red low ssn; CKE/CCI. "Gd walking in area; excel site." ♦ 1 Apr-31 Oct. € 18.00 2013*

GUENROUET *2G3* (66m E Rural) *47.52215, -1.95008* **Camp Municipal St Clair, Route de Plessé, 44530 Guenrouet [tel/ fax 02 40 87 61 52 or 06 98 86 89 90; chabliny@wanadoo.fr; www.campingsaintclair.com]** S fr Redon take D164 dir Blain, turn R onto D2 to Guenrouet, over bdge & site directly on L after bdge. Med, hdg/mkd pitch, pt sl, pt shd; wc; chem disp; mv service pnt; 50% serviced pitches; shwrs inc; el pnts (10A) €3; gas 1km; shop & 1km; tradsmn; rest 100m; playgrnd; htd pool adj; waterslide; fishing; canoe hire; dogs €1.50; Eng spkn; quiet; CKE/CCI. "On banks of canal; special area for late arr; excel." ♦ 1 May-27 Sep. € 18.20 2009*

GUERANDE *2G3* (2km N Rural) *47.34954, -2.43170* **Camping La Fontaine, Kersavary, Route de St-Molf, 44350 Guérande [02 40 24 96 19 or 06 08 12 80 96 (mob); lafontaine.guerande@orange.fr; www.camping-lafontaine.com]** Fr Guérande take N774 N sp La Roche-Bernard; in 1 km, opp windmill, fork L onto D233 sp St-Molf; site on L in 500m. Med, mkd pitch, hdstg, pt shd; wc; chem disp; shwrs inc; el pnts (6A) €4; Indtte; snacks; shop, rest & bar 4km; playgrnd; sand beach 4km; statics sep; dogs €2; phone; adv bkg rec high ssn; quiet; red low ssn/CKE/CCI. "Pleasant, peaceful site; lge pitches; helpful staff; san facs dated but clean; gd." ♦ ltd 15 Mar-15 Nov. € 18.00 2011*

GUERANDE *2G3* (2km NE Rural) *47.34340, -2.41935* **Domaine de Bréhadou, Route de Bréhadour, 44350 Guérande [02 43 53 04 33; www.domainedebrehadour.com]** Exit N165 onto D774 to Guérande. After 20km at rndabt take 3rd exit onto D99E. Turn L twd Route de Bréhadour, take first R and site is on L. Lge, hdg pitch, pt shd; wc; mv service pnt; shwrs inc; el pnts (4A) €3-4.70; gas; Indtte; shop; rest, snacks; bar; BBQ; playgrnd; htd pool; sand beach 8km; tennis; golf; entmnt; 40% statics; dogs €3.70; Eng spkn; adv bkg; quiet; red low ssn; ccard acc; CKE/CCI. "Beautiful, quiet site; redeveloped for 2014." 28 May-18 Sep. € 40.80 (4 persons) 2013*

See advertisement

GUERANDE *2G3* (2km E Rural) *47.33352, -2.39060* **Camping Le Domaine de Léveno, Route de Sandun, 44350 Guérande [02 40 24 79 30; fax 02 40 62 01 23; contact@camping-leveno.com; www.camping-leveno.com]** Fr Guérande foll sps to L'Etang de Sandun. Lge, pt shd; wc; serviced pitches; shwrs; el pnts (6A) inc; gas; Indtte; shop; rest; snacks, bar; BBQ; playgrnd; htd, covrd pool; paddling pool; waterslide; sand beach 5km; tennis; games area; entmnt; TV rm; 90% statics; dogs €5; adv bkg; quiet; red low ssn. "Conv La Baule; site in lovely park; few touring pitches; pitches shabby (2010)." 3 Apr-30 Sep. € 35.00 2010*

GUERANDE *2G3* (3km S Urban/Rural) *47.29797, -2.39988* **Camping Trémondec, 48 Rue du Château Careil, 44350 Guérande [02 40 60 00 07; fax 02 40 60 91 10; camping.tremondec@wanadoo.fr; www.camping-tremondec.com]** Fr Nantes on N165/N171/D213 dir La Baule. Take D192 dir La Baule cent, turn W in 800m dir Brenave, Careil. Site sp. Med, hdg/mkd pitch, hdstg, pt sl, pt shd; wc; chem disp; mv service pnt; baby facs; shwrs inc; el pnts (16A) inc; Indtte (inc dryer); sm shop; tradsmn; supmkt 900m; rest, snacks, bar high ssn; BBQ; playgrnd; htd pool; sand beach 1.5km; cycle hire; games area; games rm; wifi; entmnt; TV rm; 50% statics; dogs €3; Eng spkn; adv bkg; quiet; ccard acc; red low ssn/long stay/ CKE/CCI. "Lovely beaches & coast; interesting walks thro salt marshes; cycle rtes; site poorly maintained (2014); uneven ground." ♦ 1 Apr-Nov. € 34.00 2014*

GUERANDE *2G3* (7km W Coastal) *47.32856, -2.49907* **Camp Municipal Les Chardons Bleus, Blvd de la Grande Falaise, 44420 La Turballe [02 40 62 80 60; fax 02 40 62 85 40; campingleschardonsbleus@mairielaturballe.fr; www.camping-laturballe.fr]** Foll D99 to La Turballe. Site well sp fr town cent along D92. Lge, hdg/mkd pitch, unshd; wc; chem disp; mv service pnt adj; shwrs inc; el pnts (6-10A) €3.35-4.50; (poss rev pol, long lead poss req); gas; Indtte; shop; tradsmn; rest, snacks; bar; playgrnd; htd pool; sand beach adj (pt naturist) & 2km; entmnt; dogs €2.55; wifi; phone; Eng spkn; ccard acc; red low ssn; CKE/CCI. "Well-run, well-kept site in great location; warm welcome; gd, clean san facs, poss stretched high ssn; ltd el pnts when full; variable opening dates - phone ahead to check early ssn; nature reserve adj with bird life; superb beach adj, walk along beach to pretty fishing port of La Turballe with rests." ♦ 30 Mar-29 Sep. € 18.00 2013*

GUERANDE *2G3* (7km NW Rural) *47.34252, -2.47159* **Camping Le Parc Ste Brigitte, Manoir de Bréhet, 44420 La Turballe [02 40 24 88 91; fax 02 40 15 65 72; saintebrigette@wanadoo.fr; www.campingsaintebrigitte.com]** Take D99 NW fr Guérande twd La Turballe thro vill of Clis. Sp on R in 900m. Lge, mkd pitch, shd; wc; chem disp; mv service pnt; serviced pitch; shwrs inc; baby facs; el pnts (6-10A) inc; gas; lndtte; shop; rest, snacks; bar; playgrnd; htd, covrd pool; sand beach 2km; fishing; cycle hire; entmnt; TV rm; some statics; dogs €1.50; phone; poss cr; adv bkg; poss noisy; ccard acc; CKE/CCI. "V peaceful; excel rest & bar; some sm pitches; poss unkempt low ssn; gd." ♦ 1 Apr-1 Oct. € 32.00 2014*

See advertisement

GUERANDE *2G3* (8km NW Coastal) *47.36045, -2.51473* **Camping Le Refuge, 56 Rue de Brandu, 44420 La Turballe [02 40 23 37 17; fax 02 40 11 85 10; info@tourisme-laturballe.fr; www.tourisme-laturballe.fr]** On D99 thro La Turballe twd Piriac. Ikm after SuperU supmkt turn R into Rue de Brandu. Site on R in 800m, sp. Lge, hdg pitch, shd; wc; chem disp (wc); mv service pnt; shwrs inc; el pnts (6A) €3.50; lndtte; shop 1km; tradsmn; BBQ (gas); playgrnd; sand beach 300m; fishing; sailing; tennis; no dogs; Eng spkn; adv bkg; quiet; CKE/CCI. "Excel, well-kept site; lge grassy pitches pt shd; easy access to gd beach; gd cycling area; excel site with lge pitches; friendly staff; town & shops 15 min walk; excel cycling area." ♦ 1 Jun-30 Sep. € 19.20 2013*

GUIERCHE, LA *4F1* (500m W Rural) *48.10863, 0.19244* **Camping Les Platanes, Les Boucheries, 72380 La Guierche [02 43 27 36 29]** N fr Le Mans on D338 turn R onto D149 at Trois Couleurs, thro Souillé. Turn R bef rlwy line, site on R in 300m. Sm, hdg pitch, pt shd; wc; shwrs inc; el pnts (6A) inc; lndtte; shop 500m; tradsmn; BBQ; playgrnd; dogs; train 500m; quiet; ccard not acc; CKE/CCI. "Pretty site; accommodating owners; basic facs; gd NH within easy reach Le Mans." Easter-30 Sep. € 20.00 2010*

HERBIGNAC *2G3* (300m E Rural) *47.44802, -2.31073* **Camp Le Ranrouet, 7 Allee des Pres Blancs, 44410 Herbignac [02 40 15 57 56; campingleranrouet@orange.fr; www.camping-parc-de-la-briere.com]** Site at intersection D774 & D33 on E edge of vill. Med, mkd pitch, pt shd; wc; chem disp; mv service pnt; shwrs; htd pool; el pnts (6A); lndtte; supmkt, bar adj; rest 1km; playgrnd; beach 10km; entmnt; TV; CKE/CCI. "Immac san facs; gd cent for Guérande." Easter-30 Oct. € 18.00 2014*

⊞ **HERIC** *2G4* (2km W Rural) *47.41329, -1.67050* **Camping La Pindière, La Denais, Route de la Fay-de-Bretagne, 44810 Héric [tel/fax 02 40 57 65 41; contact@camping-la-pindiere.com; www.camping-la-pindiere.com]** Exit N137 twd Héric at traff lts in town, leave town & turn W onto D16 (sp Camping). Site on L after rndabt supmkt, turn at sp Notre Dames-des-Landes. Med, hdg pitch, hdstg, pt shd; wc; chem disp; mv service pnt; baby facs; shwrs inc; el pnts (6-10A) €3.20-4.80; gas; lndtte; shop or 1.5km; tradsmn; rest; bar; playgrnd; htd pool; paddling pool; sports facs; tennis; horseriding 200m; TV; 80% statics; dogs €1.40; phone; Eng spkn; adv bkg rec, site poss clsd w/end low ssn; some noise fr rd on N side; red low ssn; CKE/CCI. "Pleasant site; lge, grass pitches, soft in wet weather; warm welcome; gd clean san facs; gd NH." ♦ € 14.00 2010*

JARD SUR MER *7A1* (1.2km NE Urban) *46.42064, -1.56967* **Chadotel Camping L'Océano d'Or, Rue Georges Clémenceau, 85520 Jard-sur-Mer [02 51 33 65 08 or 02 51 33 05 05 (LS); fax 02 51 33 94 04; chadotel@wanadoo.fr; www.chadotel.com]** D21 & D19 to Jard-sur-Mer. Site sp. Lge, hdg/mkd pitch, pt shd; htd wc; chem disp; baby facs; shwrs inc; el pnts (6A) inc; gas; lndtte; shop; snacks; bar; playgrnd; htd pool; waterslide; sand beach 900m; tennis; cycle hire; entmnt; dogs €3; adv bkg; quiet; red long stay/low ssn; CKE/CCI. "Vg; gd walking." ♦ 7 Apr-22 Sep. € 31.00 2011*

JARD SUR MER *7A1* (2km NE Rural) *46.42624, -1.56564* **Camping La Mouette Cendrée, Les Malécots, 85520 St Vincent-sur-Jard [02 51 33 59 04; fax 02 51 20 31 39; camping.mc@orange.fr; www.mouettecendree.com]** Fr Les Sables-d'Olonne take D949 SE to Talmont-St-Hilaire; then take D21 to Jard-sur-Mer; at rndabt stay on D21 (taking 2nd exit dir La Tranche-sur-Mer & Maison-de- Clemanceau); in 500m turn L onto D19 sp St Hilaire-la-Forêt & foll site sps. Site on L in 700m. Med, hdg/mkd pitch, pt shd; wc (some cont); chem disp; shwrs inc; el pnts (10A) inc; Indtte; supmkt nr; tradsmn; BBQ (gas/elec); playgrnd; pool; waterslide; paddling pool; sand beach 2km; fishing; windsurfing 2km; horseriding 500m; golf 10km; cycle hire; games rm; wifi; entmnt; 30% statics; dogs €3; no c'vans/m'vans over 7.50m high ssn; Eng spkn; adv bkg; ccard acc; red low ssn; CKE/CCI. "Busy site high ssn; gd pitches; welcoming, helpful owners; san facs poss stretched when site full; vg pool; gd woodland walks & cycle rtes nr; mkt Mon." ♦ 1 Apr-4 Oct. € 27.50 SBS - A20 2011*

JARD SUR MER *7A1* (1km E Coastal) *46.41433, -1.55181* **Camp Municipal du Pied Girard, 9 Rue de la Forêt, 85520 St Vincent-sur-Jard [tel/fax 02 51 33 65 11; camping.pg@wanadoo.fr]** Fr Talmont-St Hilaire take D21 S to Jard-sur-Mer & on to St Vincent-sur-Jard. Site sp fr edge of vill. Med, mkd pitch, sl, pt shd; wc; chem disp (wc); shwrs inc; el pnts (10A) inc; Indtte; shop & rest 1km; snacks & bar 500m; playgrnd; sand beach 500m; dogs; poss cr; adv bkg; ccard acc. "Vg site in pine wood; uneven pitches; gd clean san facs." 15 Apr-15 Sep. € 14.00 2009*

JARD SUR MER *7A1* (450m SE Coastal) *46.41088, -1.57269* **Chadotel Camping La Pomme de Pin, Rue Vincent Auriol, 85520 Jard-sur-Mer [02 51 33 43 85 or 02 51 33 05 05 (LS); fax 02 51 33 94 04; chadotel@wanadoo.fr; www.chadotel.com]** Foll sp fr town. Lge, hdg/mkd pitch, shd; htd wc; serviced pitches; baby facs; shwrs inc; el pnts (6A) inc; gas; Indtte; shop; snacks; bar; BBQ (gas); playgrnd; pool; waterslide; sand beach 150m; games rm; entmnt; TV rm; mainly statics; dogs €3; Eng spkn; adv bkg; quiet; ccard acc; CKE/CCI. "Well-maintained site; early arr rec; ltd facs low ssn; vg." ♦ 7 Apr-22 Sep. € 32.50 2011*

JARD SUR MER *7A1* (2km SE Coastal) *46.41980, -1.52580* **Chadotel Camping La Bolée d'Air, Route du Bouil, Route de Longeville, 85520 St Vincent-sur-Jard [02 51 90 36 05 or 02 51 33 05 05; fax 02 51 33 94 04; info@chadotel.com; www.chadotel.com]** Fr A11 junc 14 dir Angers. Take N160 to La Roche-sur-Yon & then D747 dir La Tranche-sur-Mer to Moutier-les-Mauxfaits. At Moutiers take D19 to St Hilaire-la-Forêt & then L to St Vincent-sur-Jard. In St Vincent turn L by church sp Longeville-sur-Mer, site on R in 1km. Lge, hdg/mkd pitch, pt shd; htd wc; chem disp (wc); serviced pitches; baby facs; sauna; jaccuzi; shwrs inc; el pnts (6A) inc; gas; Indtte; shop; snacks; bar; BBQ (charcoal/gas); playgrnd; 2 pools (1 htd covrd); paddling pool; waterslide; whirlpool; sand beach 900m; tennis; cycle hire; wifi; entmnt; games/TV rm; 25% statics; dogs €3.20; no c'vans/m'vans over 8m high ssn; Eng spkn; adv bkg; rd noise & poss fr late night entmnt; ccard acc; red long stay/low ssn; mkt Sun; CKE/CCI. "Popular, v busy site high ssn; access some pitches poss diff lge o'fits; excel." ♦ 5 Apr-19 Sep. € 30.00 SBS - A31 2011*

JARD SUR MER *7A1* (350m SW Coastal) *46.41092, -1.58099* **Camping Le Bosquet, Rue de l'Océan, 85520 Jard-sur-Mer [02 51 33 56 57 or 02 51 33 06 72; fax 02 51 33 03 69; info@campings-parfums-ete.com; www.campings-parfums-ete.com]** Exit D949 at Talmont St Hilaire onto D21 to Jard-sur-Mer. In town look for sp Port de Plaisance, pass Camping Les Ecureuils & La Ventouse on L & take 2nd rd, Rue de l'Ocean, to R. Sm, pt sl, shd; wc; baby facs; shwrs inc; el pnts (10A) €3; Indry rm; shops adj; playgrnd; pool 1.5km; sand beach; tennis adj; entmnt; 30% statics; dogs €1.50; Eng spkn; adv bkg; quiet. "Gd location nr harbour; picturesque boating cent with man-made harbour; few touring pitches." 1 Apr-30 Sep. € 14.00 2009*

JAVRON LES CHAPELLES *4E1* (1km SW Rural) **Camp Municipal, Route de Bagnoles, 53250 Javron-les-Chapelles [02 43 03 40 67; fax 02 43 03 43 43; col360@live.co.uk]** Foll sp fr town cent on N12 twds Mayenne. Sm, pt terr, unshd; wc; chem disp; shwrs inc; el pnts (10A) €5; shops 1km; rest 3km; snacks 3km; bar 3km; BBQ charcoal & gas; pool 10km; Eng spkn. "V gd site." Apr-Sep. € 15.00 2013*

LANDEVIEILLE see Bretignolles sur Mer *2H3*

⊞ **LASSAY LES CHATEAUX** *4E1* (2km N Rural) *48.45478, -0.47458* **Camping La Cloue, La Cloue, 53110 Ste Marie-du-Bois [02 43 00 10 80; cheryl_carter@hotmail.co.uk; www.lovecamping.co.uk/campsites/europe]** Fr D976 turn S onto D34. In 8km turn R at top of hill bef sm church & in 1km turn R bef junc to site. Sm, pt sl, pt shd; own san req; mv service pnt in vill car park; shop, rest, bar 2km; no statics; dogs €1; quiet; ccard not acc; CKE/CCI. "Fair, basic CL-type area for self-contained o'fits; British owners; conv Caen ferries." € 5.00 2009*

LAVAL *2F4* (10km N Rural) *48.17467, -0.78785* **Camp Municipal Le Pont, 53240 Andouillé [02 43 69 72 72 (Mairie); fax 02 43 68 77 77]** Fr Laval N on D31 dir Ernée. In 8km turn R onto D115 to Andouillé. Site on L bef hill to vill cent. Sm, hdg pitch, pt shd; wc; chem disp; shwrs inc; el pnts (3A) inc; Indtte; shops 300m; playgrnd; pool 10km; rv adj; poss cr; quiet; no ccard acc. "Pretty, busy, basic site; vg, clean san facs; warden on site am & pm; site liable to flood." 1 Apr-31 Oct. € 5.50 2009*

LAVAL *2F4* (4km W Rural) *48.06428, -0.83140* **Camp Municipal Le Moulin de Coupeau, 53940 St Berthevin [02 43 68 30 70; fax 02 43 69 20 88; office.tourisme@mairie-laval.fr; www.ville.saint-berthevin.fr]** Fr Laval W on D57 twd Rennes. Site sp at St Berthevin. Sm, hdg/mkd pitch, terr, pt shd; wc; shwrs inc; el pnts (10A) €1.60; shops 2km; rest in ssn; bar adj; BBQ; htd pool adj; paddling pool; 50% statics; dogs €1; bus; adv bkg; quiet; no ccard acc; CKE/CCI. "Attractive, well-kept site on hillside by rv; helpful staff; grnd v soft after heavy rain; poss itinerant workers; poss diff access lge o'fits." 25 Apr-27 Sep. € 9.70 2009*

⊞ **LE MANS** *4F1* (20km SW Urban) *47.88985, 0.03038* **Aire De Camping Car, Rue de La Port, Suze Sur Sarthe** Fr A11 Lemans-Angers take exit 9 twds Tours/Allonnes on A11.1, 1st exit on rndabt onto D309. Then take D233 to La Suze-sur-Sarthe. Turn L immed bef Rv brdg onto site. Sm, hdstg, pt shd; wc (cont); own san rec; chem disp; mv service pnt; el pnts (6A) inc; shops 0.2km; rest 0.2km; snacks 0.2km, bar 0.1km; dogs; bus/train. "Excel site; no c'vans allowed; on edge of rv bank with views; conv for Le Mans." € 5.00 2014*

"I like to fill in the reports as I travel from site to site"

You'll find report forms at the back of this guide, or you can fill them in online at www.caravaclub.co.uk/europereport.

LEGE *2H4* (7km S Rural) *46.82899, -1.59368* **Camp Municipal de la Petite Boulogne, 12 Rue du Stade, 85670 St Etienne-du-Bois [02 51 34 52 11 or 02 51 34 54 51; fax 02 51 34 54 10; la.petite.boulogne@wanadoo.fr; www.stetiennedubois-vendee.fr]** S fr Legé on D978 dir Aizenay. Turn E onto D94 twd St Etienne-du-Bois. Foll sp to site. Sm, mkd pitch, pt sl, terr, pt shd; wc; chem disp (wc); shwrs inc; el pnts (10A) €2.70; gas 7km; Indtte; shops 500m; bar in vill; pool; sand beach 30km; TV rm; dogs €2.10; Eng spkn; adv bkg; quiet; CKE/CCI. "Pleasant, clean site; helpful warden; san facs would be stretched if site full." ♦ 1 May-1 Oct. € 15.35 2014*

⊞ **LEGE** *2H4* (8km SW Rural) *46.82121, -1.64844* **Camp Municipal Les Blés d'Or, 10 rue de la Piscine, 85670 Grand'Landes [02 51 98 51 86; fax 02 51 98 53 24; mairiegrandlandes@wanadoo.fr; www.vendee-tourisme.com]** Take D753 fr Legé twd St Jean-de-Monts. In 4km turn S on D81 & foll sp. Fr S on D978, turn W sp Grand-Landes. 3km N of Palluau. Sm, pt sl, pt shd; wc; chem disp; shwrs inc; el pnts (16A) €2.30; gas; shop, rest & bar adj; playgrnd adj; 30% statics; Eng spkn; adv bkg; quiet; ccard not acc. "V pleasant site; ent barrier clsd 2000 (poss earlier); height barrier only, cars 24hr access; rec arr early; immac facs; pay at Mairie adj." € 10.00 2014*

LION D'ANGERS, LE *2G4* (500m N Rural) *47.63068, -0.71190* **Camp Municipal Les Frênes, Route de Château-Gontier, 49220 Le Lion-d'Angers [02 41 95 31 56; fax 02 41 95 34 87; mairie.lelionangers@wanadoo.fr; www.leliondangers.fr]** On N162 Laval-Angers rd, site on R bef bdge over Rv Oudon app Le Lion-d'Angers, easily missed. Med, mkd pitch, pt shd; wc; chem disp; shwrs inc; el pnts (10A) €2.75 ; Indry rm; shops adj; rest; BBQ; playgrnd; rv fishing adj; phone; no twin-axle vans; poss cr; Eng spkn; adv bkg; quiet but some rd noise; CKE/CCI. "Excel site; friendly staff; gd location; wc block up 2 flights steps; no m'vans; unrel opening dates - phone ahead." ♦ 18 May-1 Sep. € 6.40 2013*

LONGEVILLE SUR MER *7A1* (2km S Coastal) *46.40402, -1.50673* **Camp Le Petit Rocher, 1250 Ave du Dr Mathevet, 85560 Longeville-sur-Mer [02 51 90 31 57; fax 02 51 96 17 93; info@campinglepetitrocher.com; www.campinglepetitrocher.com]** Fr La Tranche-sur-Mer take D105 N. In 8km site clearly sp 'Le Rocher' at 3rd exit fr rndabt (Ave du Dr Mathevet). Site on R in 1km at beginning of beach rd. Lge, hdg/mkd pitch, pt sl, shd; wc; chem disp; shwrs inc; el pnts (6A) inc; gas; shops adj; rest & snacks nrby; playgrnd; sand beach 150m; games area; games rm; cycle hire; entmnt; some statics; dogs €3; adv bkg; quiet; CKE/CCI. "Gd beach holiday; gd facs." 1 May-20 Sep. € 23.00 2014*

See advertisement

LONGEVILLE SUR MER *7A1* (2km S Coastal) *46.39499, -1.48736* **Camping Le Sous-Bois, La Haute Saligotière, 85560 Longeville-sur-Mer [02 51 33 32 73 / 02 51 33 36 90 / 06 71 63 39 62 (mob)]** Sp fr D105 fr La Tranche-sur-Mer. Med, hdg pitch, shd; wc; chem disp; shwrs inc; el pnts (10A) €4. (poss rev pol); Indtte; shop; tradsmn; playgrnd; sand beach 1km; tennis; TV; 15% statics; dogs €1.60; phone; quiet; ccard not acc; CKE/CCI. "Nice, well-managed, family site; pleasant 1km woodland walk to beach; gd walks; cycle tracks; excel; great for cycling; lovely sandy beach." ♦ 1 Jun-30 Sep. € 19.00 2013*

LONGEVILLE SUR MER *7A1* (3km S Coastal) *46.38830, -1.48777* **Camping Les Clos des Pins, Les Conches, 85560 Longeville-sur-Mer [02 51 90 31 69; fax 02 51 90 30 68; info@campingclosdespins.com; www.campingclosdespins.com]** Fr La Tranche-sur-Mer take D105 coast rd N, turn L in Les Conches into Ave de la Plage, site on R in 1km. Med, mkd pitch, pt sl, shd; wc; chem disp; baby facs; shwrs inc; el pnts (6A) €4; gas; Indtte; shop; tradsmn; rest, snacks; bar; BBQ (gas/elec); playgrnd; htd pool; paddling pool; waterslide; sand beach 200m; watersports; cycle hire; games area; many activities; wifi; entmnt; 60% statics; dogs €3.30; phone; bus; Eng spkn; adv bkg; quiet; red low ssn/CKE/CCI. "Set among pine trees; some pitches in soft sand - adv bkg rec to ensure a suitable pitch; friendly, helpful staff; excel leisure facs; vg." ♦ 3 Apr-26 Sep. € 25.00 2009*

LUCHE PRINGE see Flèche, La *4G1*

LUCON *7A1* (11km E Rural) *46.46745, -1.02792* **Camp Municipal Le Vieux Chêne, Rue du Port, 85370 Nalliers [02 51 30 91 98 or 02 51 30 90 71; fax 02 51 30 94 06; nalliers.mairie@wanadoo.fr]** Fr Luçon E on D949 dir Fontenay-le-Comte; 500m after ent Nalliers turn R onto D10 (Rue de Brantome); after level x-ing cont strt on for 50m (leaving D10); then Rue du Port on L. Site sp on D949 but easy to miss. Sm, hdg/mkd pitch, pt shd; wc; chem disp; shwrs inc; el pnts (4-13A) €3.90; shop 500m; tradsmn; playgrnd; adv bkg; quiet; site yourself on lge pitch; CKE/CCI. "Excel, clean site; in low ssn contact Mairie for ent to site; vg NH; conv for rd to Bordeaux." 15 May-15 Sep. € 11.60 2013*

LUCON *7A1* (10km SW Rural) *46.41170, -1.26527* **Camping La Fraignaye, Rue de Beau Laurier, 85580 St Denis-du-Payré [tel/fax 02 51 27 21 36; camping.fraignaye@wanadoo.fr; www.camping-lafraignaye.com]** Fr A8 exit junc 7 onto D137 dir La Rochelle. Turn L after Ste Gemme onto D949 to Luçon, then take D746 to Triaize. Take D25 to St Denis-du-Payré, in vill turn L bef church & foll sp. Sm, mkd pitch, pt shd; wc; chem disp; shwrs inc; el pnts (6A) €3; gas; Indtte; shop & 7km; rest, snacks; bar; playgrnd; sand beach 12km; games rm; cycle hire; TV; 20% statics; dogs €1.50; phone; poss cr; Eng spkn; adv bkg; quiet; ccard acc; red long stay/low ssn. "Pleasant owner; nr nature reserve; site liable to flooding." ♦ 1 Apr-30 Sep. € 15.00 2010*

LUDE, LE *4G1* (1km NE Rural) *47.65094, 0.16221* **Camp Municipal au Bord du Loir, Route du Mans, 72800 Le Lude [02 43 94 67 70; fax 02 43 94 93 82; contact@camping-auborddulolr.fr; www.ville-lelude.fr / www.loir-valley.com]** Fr town cent take D305 (E); in 1km take D307 (N) sp 'Le Mans'; site immed on L. Well sp. Fr E on D305, avoid cent of Vaas, use HGV route. Med, hdg/mkd pitch, pt shd; wc; chem disp; mv service pnt; shwrs inc; el pnts (5A) €4; Indtte; shops 300m; tradsmn; rests 100m; snacks adj (high ssn); BBQ (gas only); playgrnd; tennis; beach 6km; pool; canoeing; fishing; cycling; entmnt; TV; dog; 10% statics; phone; poss cr; Eng spkn; adv bkg; poss traff noise far end of site; ccard acc; CKE/CCI. "Well-kept, well-run site; warm welcome, helpful staff; modern san facs; vg walk to town; Château du Lude & excel rest nrby; highly rec." ♦ 1 Apr-30 Sep. € 20.00 2013*

MACHE see Aizenay *2H4*

MACHECOUL *2H4* (500m SE Urban) *46.98987, -1.81562* **Camp Municipal La Rabine, Allée de la Rabine, 44270 Machecoul [tel/fax 02 40 02 30 48 / 06 08 49 22 88; camprabine@wanadoo.fr; www.camping-la-rabine.pagesperso-orange.fr]** Sp fr most dirs. Look out for prominent twin-spired church in cent; take sm one-way street that leads away fr spire end; site on R in 400m. Med, pt shd; wc; chem disp; shwrs €1; el pnts (4-13A) €2-3.20; Indtte; shops 500m; tradsmn; BBQ (gas only) playgrnd; pool adj; sand beach 14km; entmnt; dogs €0.90; wifi; adv bkg; quiet. "Pleasant site with lge pitches & gd facs; excel base for birdwatching & cycling over marshes; pleasant town; mkt Wed & Sat; lovely friendly well managed site, generous size pitches, excel facs." 1 Apr-30 Sep. € 10.80 2013*

MAILLE see Maillezais *7A2*

MAILLEZAIS *7A2* (350m S Rural) *46.36921, -0.74054* **Camp Municipal de l'Autize, Rue du Champ de Foire, 85420 Maillezais [02 51 00 70 79 or 06 31 43 21 33 (mob); fax 02 51 00 70 79; camping.lautize@orange.fr; www.maillezais.fr]** Fr Fontenay take D148 twd Niort; after 9km, turn R onto D15 to Maillezais; pass church in vill on L, site on R after 200m. Or fr A83, exit junc 9 onto D148, then D15 (do not use v minor rds, as poss directed by Sat Nav). Sm, hdg/mkd pitch, pt shd; wc; chem disp; shwrs inc; el pnts (4-13A) €3-5; Indtte; shops 200m; playgrnd; games area; games rm; TV; wifi; adv bkg; quiet; ccard not acc; red low ssn; CKE/CCI. "Lovely, clean site; spacious pitches, gd views fr some; friendly, helpful warden; excel, immac san facs; warden calls am & pm; some low branches (2010); twin-axles extra; excel mkd cycle paths; conv Marais Poitevin area & Venise Verte; nrby abbey worth a visit; vg NH fr A83; excel." ♦ 1 Apr-30 Sep. € 14.00 2014*

MAILLEZAIS *7A2* (6km S Rural) *46.31308, -0.73342* **FFCC Camping Les Conches, Route du Grand Port, 85420 Damvix [tel/fax 02 51 87 17 06; campingdesconches@orange.fr; http://campingdesconches.free.fr]** Fr Fontenay-le-Comte exit D148 at Benet then W on D25 thro Le Mazeau to sp on L for Damvix. Or exit A83 junc 8 then S on D938 & E on D25 dir Benet. Site 1km thro vill on R over bdge (sp). Med, mkd, shd; wc; chem disp; mv service pnt; shwrs; el pnts (6-10A) €3; Indtte; shops adj; rest adj; playgrnd; pool; tennis; golf; horseriding; rv fishing & boating adj; dogs €1; adv bkg rec; quiet but some noise fr disco opp high ssn; CKE/CCI. "Gd rest; friendly staff; gd cycling." 1 May-15 Oct. € 11.50 2010*

MAILLEZAIS *7A2* (5km SW Rural) *46.34037, -0.79640* **Camp Municipal La Petite Cabane, 85420 Maillé [02 51 87 07 52; contact@lesasterides.com]** Site is 500m W of Maillé, clearly sp. Sm, pt shd; wc; shwrs inc; el pnts (10) inc (poss rev pol); gas 500m; Indry rm; shops 500m; playgrnd; paddling pool; boat & canoe hire; adv bkg; quiet; CKE/CCI. "Site by canal in cent of Marais Poitevin National Park; diff access lge o'fits; gd cycle rtes." 1 Apr-30 Sep. € 11.50 2011*

MALICORNE SUR SARTHE *4F1* (800m N Urban) *47.81736, -0.08791* **Camp Municipal Porte Ste Marie, Route de Noyen, 72270 Malicorne-sur-Sarthe [02 43 94 80 14; fax 02 43 94 57 26; camping.malicorne@wanadoo.fr; www.ville-malicorne.fr]** Fr A11/E501 take D306 exit twds La Flèche. Turn E onto D23 twds Malicorne. Site across rv on W of town adj stadium. Med, pt shd; wc; chem disp; mv service pnt; baby facs; shwrs inc; el pnts (4-13A) €1.60-2.65; Indtte; shops, rest, bar 500m; BBQ; playgrnd; pool; tennis adj; dogs €0.65; poss cr; quiet; red low ssn; "Quiet position by rv; gd san facs; no access when recep clsd 1230-1430 & after 1930; poss noise (church bell); no waiting area; diff turning; gd." 1 Apr-30 Sep. € 9.20 2010*

MAMERS *4E1* (500m N Rural) *48.35778, 0.37181* **Camp Municipal du Saosnois, Route de Contilly, 72600 Mamers [02 43 97 68 30; fax 02 43 97 38 65; camping.mamers@free.fr; www.mairie-mamers.fr]** Fr W on D311, at rndabt at top of hill on circular rd, turn R (sp); then easy L (sp). Fr E on D311, strt thro rndabt (at Super U), ignore 1st camping sp, turn R at traff its & 2nd camping sp; at mini-rndabt turn L, sp Contilly; see lake & site. Sm, hdg pitch, hdstg, pt sl, terr, pt shd; htd wc; mv service pnt; shwrs inc; el pnts (10A) €3-4.20 (long lead poss req); Indtte; shop & 500m; snacks; pool 200m; lakeside beach; games area; TV rm; 30% statics; dogs €0.50; poss cr; adv bkg; quiet; CKE/CCI. "Well-kept, secure site; admittance low ssn 1700-1900 only; Mamers pretty; poss travellers." ♦ 3 Mar-3 Nov. € 12.00 2013*

MANS, LE *4F1* (8km N Rural) *48.07179, 0.18934* **FFCC Camping Le Vieux Moulin, 72190 Neuville-sur-Sarthe [02 43 25 31 82; fax 02 43 25 38 11; info@lemanscamping.net; www.lemanscamping.net]** Leave D338 6km N of Le Mans at St Saturnin; turn E onto D197 to Neuville & foll sp for 3km to site nr Rv Sarthe. Med, pt shd, hdg/mkd pitch, serviced pitch; wc (some cont); chem disp; mv service pnt; baby facs; shwrs inc; el pnts (10A) €3 (poss rev pol); gas; Indtte; sm shop (high ssn) & 500m; tradsmn; rest adj; playgrnd; sm htd pool; tennis; 5% statics; dogs €1; Eng spkn; adv bkg; quiet; ccard acc; red low ssn/CKE/CCI. "Open for Le Mans 24 hours race ssn only - phone to confirm opening dates; lge, grassy pitches; friendly, helpful owner; clean san facs; sm lake & watermill/rest adj; peaceful setting; gates clsd 2200-0730; highly rec." € 13.00 2009*

MANS, LE *4F1* (6km NE Rural) *48.01904, 0.27996* **Camping Le Pont Romain, Allée des Ormeaux, Lieu-dit La Châtaigneraie, 72530 Yvré-l'Evêque [02 43 82 25 39; contact@campinglepontromain.fr]** Fr Le Mans take D314 to Yvré-l'Evêque - but do not ent town; just after rv bdge take 1st L into Allée des Ormeaux; site on L in 800m. Or exit A28 junc 23 onto D314 dir 'Le Mans Centre'; site on R just bef Yvré-l'Evêque. Med, hdg/mkd pitch, hdstg, pt shd; htd wc; chem disp; mv service pnt; baby facs; shwrs inc; el pnts (16A) inc; Indtte (inc dryer); shop; rest, snacks; playgrnd; htd pool; games rm; wifi; TV rm; 10% statics; dogs €1; phone, bus to Le Mans 500m; sep car park; no twin-axles; poss cr; Eng spkn; adv bkg; red low ssn; CKE/CCI. "New site (2009); excel modern san facs but ltd number of toilets; conv Le Mans & m'way; vg." ♦ ltd 1 Mar-1 Nov. € 30.00 2014*

MANSIGNE *4F1* (500m N Rural) *47.75188, 0.13153* **Camping A Tou Vert La Plage, Route du Plessis, 72510 Mansigné [02 43 46 14 17; camping-mansigne@orange.fr; www.atouvert.com]** N fr Le Lude on D307 to Pontvallain. Take D13 E for 5km to Mansigné, thro vill & foll site sp. Lge, pt shd; wc; chem disp; shwrs inc; el pnts (10A) €3.70; Indtte (inc dryer); shop 200m; rest, snacks; bar; BBQ; htd pool; sand beach & lake sw adj; watersports; tennis; some statics; dogs €1.10; adv bkg; quiet; red long stay/low ssn; CKE/CCI. "Pleasant lakeside position; conv for Loir Valley & Le Mans 24-hr race; ltd facs & office hrs low ssn." ♦ 1 Apr-31 Oct. € 11.50 2010*

⊞ **MARANS** *7A1* (10km NE Rural) *46.38196, -0.97186* **Camping à la Ferme Le Pont Grenouilles (Berjonneau), 24 Rue du Port d'Aisne, 85450 Vouillé-les-Marais [02 51 52 53 96]** Fr N/S use D137 to Le Sableau N of Marans; at rndabt take D25A twds Vouille les Marais; site on L in 3.8km. Sm, pt shd; wc; shwrs inc; el pnts (3-6A); Indtte; playgrnd; quiet. "Friendly, helpful owners; peaceful site; toilet block old but clean; charming area; nightingales in Spring; gd NH or sh stay." € 12.50 2014*

MARCON see Château du Loir *4G1*

MAYENNE *4E1* (1km N Rural) *48.31350, -0.61296* **Camp Municipal du Gué St Léonard, 818 Rue de St Léonard, 53100 Mayenne [06 76 73 71 69; camping@paysdemayenne.fr; www.paysdemayenne-tourisme.fr]** Fr N, sp to E of D23 & well sp fr cent of Mayenne on rvside. Med, hdg/mkd pitch, pt shd; htd wc; chem disp; some serviced pitches; shwrs inc; el pnts (10A) €2.20; Indtte; shop (high ssn) & 1km; tradsman high ssn; snacks; rest 1km; BBQ; playgrnd; htd pool high ssn inc; rv fishing adj; 8% statics; phone; extra for twin-axles; adv bkg; some noise fr adj factory; red low ssn; CKE/CCI. "Peaceful, well-kept site by rv; pleasant location adj parkland walks; modern san facs with piping hot water; some pitches sm & access poss diff; vg value." ♦ 15 Mar-30 Sep. € 18.30 2014*

MAYET see Ecommoy *4F1*

MENITRE, LA see Rosiers sur Loire, Les *4G1*

MENOMBLET see Châtaigneraie, La *2H4*

MERVENT see Fontenay le Comte *7A2*

MESLAY DU MAINE *4F1* (2.5km NE Rural) *47.96409, -0.52979* **Camp Municipal La Chesnaie, St Denis-du-Maine, 53170 Meslay-du-Maine [02 43 98 48 08 or 02 43 64 10 45 (Mairie); fax 02 43 98 75 52; camping.lachesnaie@wanadoo.fr; www.paysmeslaygrez.fr]** Take D21 SE fr Laval to Meslay; turn L in cent of vill onto D152. Site on R in 2.5km. Med, hdg/mkd pitch, pt shd; wc (some cont); shwrs inc; el pnts (6A) €2.60 (poss long lead req); Indtte; shop & rest 2.5km; snacks; bar; playgrnd; lake adj; watersports, leisure cent adj; cycle hire; 10% statics; poss cr; adv bkg; ccard acc; CKE/CCI. "Excel clean & quiet site; san facs old but clean." ♦ Easter-30 Sep. € 9.40 2011*

MONSIREIGNE see Chantonnay *2H4*

MONTAIGU *2H4* (10km SE Rural) *46.93769, -1.21975* **Camping L'Eden, La Raillière, 85600 La Boissière-de-Montaigu [02 51 41 62 32; fax 02 51 41 56 07; contact@domaine-eden.fr; www.domaine-eden.fr]** Fr Montaigu S on D137, in 8km turn E on D62, thro Le Pont-Legé. Site sp on L off D62. Med, mkd pitch, shd; wc (some cont); shwrs inc; el pnts (10A) inc; gas; lndtte; shop & 4km; rest, snacks; bar; playgrnd; htd pool; tennis; entmnt; TV; 40% statics; dogs €2; poss cr; adv bkg; site poss open all year; red low ssn CKE/CCI. "Pleasant, quiet site in woodlands; clean facs; motor mover useful; excel." ♦ ltd 1 Mar-15 Nov. € 21.00 2009*

MONTBERT *2H4* (500m SE Rural) *47.05133, -1.47930* **Camping Le Relais des Garennes (Gendron), La Bauche Coiffée, 44140 Montbert [tel/fax 02 40 04 78 73; phgendron@wanadoo.fr; www.gites-de-france-44.fr/relais_garennes]** Fr Nantes on N937 dir La Roche, at Geneston turn L dir Montbert & foll site sp. Or fr Nantes on N137 dir La Rochelle turn R at Aigrefeuille-sur-Maine for Montbert. Sm, mkd pitch, pt shd; htd wc; chem disp; baby facs; fam bthrm; shwrs inc; el pnts (10A) €2.50; lndry rm; htd pool 1km; tennis, sports facs nrby; sm lake; lake fishing adj; dogs; Eng spkn; adv bkg; quiet; CKE/CCI. "Peaceful, picturesque site; lge pitches; friendly owners; immac facs, but no individual wash rms; rabbits & hens on site; toys for children; many attractions nrby; pleasant walk to town; gd value; highly rec." ♦ 1 Jun-30 Sep. € 8.50 2010*

MONTBIZOT see Beaumont sur Sarthe *4F1*

MONTJEAN SUR LOIRE see Chalonnes sur Loire *2G4*

"We must tell The Club about that great site we found"

Get your site reports in by mid-August and we'll do our best to get your updates into the next edition.

⊞ **MONTREUIL BELLAY** *4H1* (4km E Rural) *47.15263, -0.13599* **FFCC Camping Le Thouet, Les Côteaux-du-Chalet, route Bron 49260 Montreuil-Bellay [02 41 38 74 17 or 06 19 56 32 75 (mob); campinglethouet@alicepro.fr; www.campinglethouet.com]** Fr D347 N of Montreuil-Bellay take dir 'Centre Ville'; turn L immed bef rv bdge & foll sp to Les Côteaux-du-Chalet. Access via narr, rough rd for 1km. Med, pt shd; wc; chem disp; shwrs inc; el pnts (10A) €3; gas; shop 4km; tradsmn; bar; BBQ; playgrnd; pool; fishing; boating; dogs €2; phone; 5% statics; adv bkg; quiet; ccard acc; red low ssn; CKE/CCI. "Peaceful, spacious, British-owned site; lge area grass & woods surrounded by vineyards; pitches in open grass field; poss unkempt low ssn; gd walks; vill not easily accessed by foot; unguarded rv bank poss not suitable children; v lge pitches." ♦ € 26.00 2013*

MONTREUIL BELLAY *4H1* (1km W Urban) *47.13191, -0.15897* **Camping Les Nobis, Rue Georges Girouy, 49260 Montreuil-Bellay [02 41 52 33 66; fax 02 41 38 72 88; camping-les-nobis@orange.fr; www.campinglesnobis.com]** Fr S on D938 turn L immed on ent town boundary & foll rd for 1km to site; sp fr all dir. Fr N on D347 ignore 1st camping sp & cont on D347 to 2nd rndabt & foll sp. Fr NW on D761 turn R onto D347 sp Thouars to next rndabt, foll site sp. Lge, hdg/mkd pitch, pt shd; wc (some cont); chem disp; mv service pnt; shwrs inc; el pnts (10A) €3 (poss long cable req, rev pol); gas; lndtte; shop; tradsmn; rest, snacks; bar; playgrnd; htd pool; cycle hire; wifi; TV rm; 50% statics; dogs; phone; poss cr; Eng spkn; adv bkg; quiet; ccard acc; red long stay/low ssn; CKE/CCI. "Spacious site between castle & rv; gd, modern san facs; local chateaux & town worth exploring; 'aire de service' for m'vans adj; gd patissiere in town." ♦ 29 Mar-5 Oct. € 30.00 2014*

"I need an on-site restaurant"

We do our best to make sure site information is correct, but it is always best to check any must-have facilities are still available or will be open during your visit.

MONTSOREAU *4G1* (500m NE Rural) *47.21805, 0.05270* **Kawan Village L'Isle Verte, Ave de la Loire, 49730 Montsoreau [02 41 51 76 60 or 02 41 67 37 81; fax 02 41 51 08 83; isleverte@cvtloisirs.fr; www.campingisleverte.com]** At Saumur on S side of rv turn R immed bef bdge over Rv Loire; foll sp to Chinon & site. Fr N foll sp for Fontevraud & Chinon fr Rv Loire bdge; site on D947 in vill on banks of Loire opp 'Charcuterie' shop. Med, mkd pitch, pt shd; wc; chem disp; mv service pnt; baby facs; shwrs inc; el pnts (16A) €3.50 (poss long lead req); gas; lndtte (inc dryer); shops 200m; tradsmn; rest & in vill; snacks; bar; playgrnd; pool; paddling pool; rv fishing/watersports; tennis; car and cycle hire; games area; golf 13km; wifi; entmnt; TV rm: some statics; dogs €2; bus to Saumur; poss cr; Eng spkn; adv bkg rec high ssn; rd noise & poss disco noise; ccard acc; red low ssn; CKE/CCI. "Pleasant rvside site in beautiful situation; v busy high ssn; various sized/shaped pitches; adequate san facs, poss irreg cleaning low ssn; vg rest; barrier clsd 2200-0700; gd security; pleasant vill; gd; excel; helpful staff." ♦ 1 Apr-13 Oct. € 36.00 (CChq acc) 2014*

MOTHE ACHARD, LA *2H4* (5km NW Rural) *46.64107, -1.71046* **Camping Château de la Forêt, Rue de la Forêt, 85150 St Julien-des-Landes [02 51 46 62 11; fax 02 51 46 60 87; camping@domainelaforet.com; www.domainelaforet.com]** Take D12 fr La Mothe-Achard to St Julien. Turn R onto D55 at x-rds & site sp on L. Med, hdg/mkd pitch, pt shd; wc; all serviced pitches; shwrs inc; el pnts (6A) €4.20; gas; lndtte (inc dryer); shop & in vill; rest, snacks; bar; BBQ; playgrnd; 2 htd pools; games rm; sand beach 12km; lake fishing adj; cycle hire; tennis; wifi; entmnt; dogs €2.70; 60% statics; poss cr; adv bkg rec high ssn; quiet; red low ssn; CKE/CCI. "Pt of private chateau estate, popular with British visitors; gd for families; excel facs; gates clsd 2200-0800." 15 May-15 Sep. € 29.00 (3 persons) 2010*

"Satellite navigation makes touring much easier"

Remember most sat navs don't know if you're towing or in a larger vehicle – always use yours alongside maps and site directions.

MOTHE ACHARD, LA *2H4* (5km NW Rural) *46.65285, -1.74759* **Camping La Guyonnière, 85150 St Julien-des-Landes [02 51 46 62 59; fax 02 51 46 62 89; info@laguyonniere.com; www.laguyonniere.com]** Leave A83 junc 5 onto D160 W twd La Roche-sur-Yon. Foll ring rd N & cont on D160 twd Les Sables-d'Olonne. Leave dual c'way foll sp La Mothe-Achard, then take D12 thro St Julien-des-Landes twd La Chaize-Giraud. Site sp on R. Lge, hdg pitch, pt sl, pt shd; wc; chem disp; shwrs inc; el pnts (6A) €3.50 (long lead rec); gas; lndtte; shop; tradsmn; rest, snacks; bar; BBQ; playgrnd; 2 pools (1 htd, covrd); water park; waterslide; sand beach 10km; lake fishing, canoe hire, windsurfing 400m; cycle hire; internet; cab/sat TV rm; some statics; dogs €3; phone; Eng spkn; adv bkg; ccard acc; red low ssn. "V lge pitches; gd views; friendly owners; gd walking area." ♦ 26 Apr-28 Sep. € 23.50 (CChq acc) SBS - A12 2013*

See advert above

MOTHE ACHARD, LA *2H4* (6km NW Rural) *46.64469, -1.73346* **FLOWER Camping La Bretonnière, 85150 St Julien-des-Landes [02 51 46 62 44 or 06 14 18 26 42 (mob); fax 02 51 46 61 36; camp.la-bretonniere@wanadoo.fr; www.la-bretonniere.com / www.flowercampings.com]** Fr La Roche-sur-Yon take D160 to La Mothe-Achard, then D12 dir St Gilles-Croix-de-Vie. Site on R 2km after St Julien. Med, mkd pitch, pt sl, pt shd; wc (some cont); chem disp; mv service pnt; baby facs; shwrs inc; el pnts (6-12A) €2-4.50; lndtte; ice; shops 7km; tradsmn; bar 1km; BBQ; playgrnd; 2 pools, htd covrd; sand beach 12km; fishing; sailing & lake sw 2km; tennis; cycle hire; games area; games rm; wifi; entmnt; TV rm; 20% statics; dogs €2-5; Eng spkn; adv bkg; quiet; ccard acc; red low ssn; CKE/CCI. "Excel, friendly site adj dairy farm; lge pitches; 10 mins fr Bretignolles-sur-Mer sand dunes." ♦ ltd 1 Apr-15 Oct. € 27.00 2014*

See advert below

"There aren't many sites open at this time of year"

If you're travelling outside peak season remember to call ahead to check site opening dates – even if the entry says 'open all year'.

MOTHE ACHARD, LA *2H4* (7km NW Rural) *46.66280, -1.71380* **Camping La Garangeoire, 85150 St Julien-des-Landes [02 51 46 65 39; fax 02 51 46 69 85; info@garangeoire.com; www.camping-la-garangeoire.com / www.les-castels.com]** Site sp fr La Mothe-Achard. At La Mothe-Achard take D12 for 5km to St Julien, D21 for 2km to site. Or fr Aizenay W on D6 turn L dir La Chapelle-Hermier. Site on L, well sp. Lge, hdg/mkd pitch, pt sl, shd; wc; chem disp; mv service pnt; some serviced pitch; baby facs; fam bthrm; shwrs inc; el pnts (16A) inc (poss rev pol); gas; lndtte (inc dryer); shop; rest, snacks; bar; BBQ (gas/el); playgrnd; htd pool complex; paddling pool; waterslide; lake fishing; sand beach 12km; horseriding; tennis; cycle hire; games area; games rm; wifi; entmnt; 50% statics (tour ops); dogs €4; twin-axles acc (rec check in adv); phone; poss cr; Eng spkn; adv bkg (ess Aug); ccard acc; red low ssn; CKE/CCI. "Busy, well-run site set in chateau parkland; some v lge pitches; pleasant helpful owners; excel, clean facs; gd for families & all ages; pitches quiet - entmnt well away fr pitches; super site; gd site in every way." ♦ 19 Apr-19 Sep. € 37.00 SBS - A42 2012*

MOUCHAMPS *2H4* (1km SE Rural) *46.77493, -1.05510* **Camp Municipal Le Hameau du Petit Lay, Route de St Prouant, Chauvin, 85640 Mouchamps [tel/fax 02 51 66 25 72; wbm85640@mouchamps.com; www.lehameaudupetitlay.com]** Fr Chantonnay to D137 NW; 1km past St Vincent-Sterlanges turn R sp Mouchamps; turn R onto D113 sp St Prouant & camping; site on L in 1 km. Sm, hdg/mkd pitch, pt shd; wc, chem disp; shwrs inc; el pnts €2.50; lndtte; shop, rest, snacks & bar 1km; playgrnd adj; htd pool adj; quiet, but traff noise am; CKE/CCI. "Barrier clsd 2200-7000; vg." ♦ 15 Jun-15 Sep. € 10.80 2010*

MOULIHERNE see Vernantes *4G1*

MOUTIERS EN RETZ, LES see Pornic *2G3*

NALLIERS see Luçon *7A1*

⊞ **NANTES** *2G4* (3km N Urban) *47.24261, -1.55703* **Nantes Camping, 21 Blvd de Petit Port, 44300 Nantes [02 40 74 47 94; fax 02 40 74 23 06; nantes-camping@nge-nantes.fr; www.nantes-camping.fr]** Fr ring rd exit junc 39 sp Porte de la Chapelle & foll sp Centre Ville, Camping Petit Port or University when ent o'skts of Nantes. Site ent opp Hippodrome & nr racecourse & university; well sp. Take care tram lines. Lge, hdg/mkd pitch, some hdstg, pt shd; htd wc; serviced pitches; chem disp; mv service pnt; baby facs; shwrs inc; el pnts (16A) €5; gas; lndtte (inc dryer); sm shop; tradsmn; rest, snacks; bar; BBQ (charcoal only); playgrnd; htd, covrd pool & waterslide adj inc; cycle hire; entmnt; wifi €1; TV; 30% statics; dogs €3.10; bus & tram to city cent adj; twin-axles acc (extra charge); o'night m'van area; poss cr; Eng spkn; adv bkg (groups); quiet; ccard acc; red low ssn/long stay; CKE/CCI. "Well kept and maintained; excel san facs; tram stop next to site, easy access to Nantes centre; sw pool across the rd with discount; excel site, great location; ACSI red low ssn." ♦ € 31.20 (CChq acc) 2014*

⊞ **NANTES** *2G4* (6km E Rural) *47.25416, -1.45361* **Camping Belle Rivière, Route des Perrières, 44980 Ste Luce-sur-Loire [tel/fax 02 40 25 85 81; belleriviere@wanadoo.fr; www.camping-belleriviere.com]** Fr 'Nantes Périphérique Est' take exit 43 (at Porte d'Anjou) onto A811; exit A811 junc 24 dir Thouaré-sur-Loire on D68; at double rndabt by car showroom turn S & foll sp over rlwy bdge; site sp. Fr E via D68, thro Thouaré dir Ste Luce; at double rndabt by car showroom, S over rlwy bdge twd rv; site sp. Med, hdg/mkd pitch, hdstg, pt shd; wc (50% cont); chem disp; shwrs inc; el pnts (3-10A) €2.70-3.90 (extra charge in winter); gas; lndry rm; shops 3km; tradsmn; rest 3km, snacks; bar; BBQ; playgrnd; wifi; 50% statics; dogs €1.45; poss cr; Eng spkn; adv bkg; quiet; red low ssn/CKE/CCI. "Beautifully-kept site; helpful owners; gd clean san facs; rvside walks; conv Nantes Périphérique & city cent; gd touring base; excel." ♦ € 17.00 2014*

NANTES *2G4* (20km E Urban) *47.24930, -1.37118* **Camping Le Chêne, 44450 St Julien-de-Concelles [02 40 54 12 00; contact@campingduchene.fr; www.campingduchene.fr]** Fr Nantes, cross Rv Loire dir Poitiers; immed turn E sp St Sébastien; thro town onto D751 to Le Bout-des-Pont; turn S onto D57 sp Camping. Site on L immed after lake. Med, shd; wc; mv service pnt; shwrs €1; el pnts (10A) €2.60; shops 1.2km; rest; bar; BBQ; playgrnd; covered pool; tennis; cycle hire; golf; lake adj; fishing; sailing; windsurfing; wifi; dogs €1; adv bkg rec high ssn; rd noise. "Under new ownership (2013); v helpful staff." 1 Apr-31 Oct. € 16.00 2014*

NESMY see Roche sur Yon, La *2H4*

NEUVILLE SUR SARTHE see Mans, Le *4F1*

NOIRMOUTIER EN L'ILE *2H3* (2km E Coastal) *46.99769, -2.22331* **Camp Municipal Le Clair Matin, Les Sableaux, 85330 Noirmoutier-en-l'Ile [02 51 39 05 56; fax 02 51 39 74 36]** Ent Noirmoutier on D948 & foll sp to Les Sableaux. Site well sp. Med, mkd pitch, terr, pt shd; wc; mv service pnt; shwrs; el pnts (10A) €3.60; lndtte; shop; rest 500m; bar 150m; playgrnd; pool 2.5km; sand beach adj; fishing; dogs €1.20; adv bkg rec; quiet; red low ssn. "Excel site; gd clean san facs; excel cycle paths & beach fishing; lovely town." ♦ Easter-30 Oct. € 17.00 (3 persons) 2010*

NOIRMOUTIER EN L'ILE *2H3* (2km E Coastal) *46.99697, -2.22057* **Camping Indigo Noirmoutier La Vendette, Bois de la Chaize, 23 Rue des Sableaux, 85330 Noirmoutier-en-l'Ile [02 51 39 06 24; fax 02 51 35 97 63; noirmoutier@camping-indigo.com; www.camping-indigo.com]** Ent Noirmoutier on D948, strt on over bdge & foll sp for Bois-de-la-Chaize, then 'campings'. Lge, pt shd; wc (some cont); chem disp; mv service pnt; baby facs; shwrs inc; el pnts (10A) €4.80; lndtte (inc dryer); tradsmn; snacks; bar; playgrnd; sand beach adj; fishing; boat-launching; cycle hire; internet; some statics; dogs €4; phone; poss cr; adv bkg; quiet; red low ssn; CKE/CCI ess. "Peaceful site in pine forest nr salt water marshes; gd for children." 1 Apr-1 Oct. € 21.00 2010*

See advert on next page

PAYS DE LA LOIRE

NOIRMOUTIER EN L'ILE *2H3* (6.3km SE Coastal) *46.96659, -2.22027* **Domaine Les Moulins, 54 Rue des Moulins, 85680 La Guérinière [0251 39 51 38; fax 0251 39 57 97; moulins@originalcamping.com; www.domaine-les-moulins.com]** Cross to island on D38, sp to La Guérinière, imm turn L, site dir ahead. Lge, hdg, mkd, pt sl, pt shd pitch, htd WC, chem disp, mv service pnt, el pnts (10A) child/baby, facs, shwrs, Indtte, rest, bar, playgrnd, pool, beach, games area, games rm, wifi, 40% statics, dogs, adv bkg, quiet, ccard acc, red low ssn, CKE/CCI, ACSI card acc."Excel site, cycle hire 100m, shop adj." 1 Apri-30 Sept. € 67.00 2014*

NOIRMOUTIER EN L'ILE *2H3* (10km SE Coastal) *46.94503, -2.18542* **Camping du Midi, 17 Rue du Camping, 85630 Barbâtre [02 51 39 63 74; fax 02 51 39 58 63; camping-du-midi@wanadoo.fr; www.camping-du-midi.com]** Cross to island by Passage du Gois D948 (low tide - 2.5 hrs per day) or bdge D38. Turn L after 2.5km off dual c'way to Barbâtre. Site sp N thro vill. V lge, pt sl, shd; wc; baby facs; shwrs; el pnts (10A) €6; gas; Indtte; shop 400m; rest, snacks; bar; BBQ (gas/elec); htd pool; paddling pool; sand beach adj; tennis; games area; entmnt; dogs €3.90; poss cr; no adv bkg; quiet; ccard acc; red low ssn. "Gd site; sandy but firm pitches; no longer municiapal & many changed planned (2011); food, wine and pool only avail high ssn." ♦ 1 Apr-20 Sep. € 27.00 (3 persons) 2011*

NOIRMOUTIER EN L'ILE *2H3* (3.5km SW Coastal) *46.98609, -2.28790* **Camp Municipal La Bosse, 85740 L'Epine [02 51 39 01 07; campinglabosse@orange.fr]** Fr bdge take D38 to La Guérinière: turn W along D38 to L'Epine & foll camp sp to La Bosse. Lge, pt sl, unshd; wc; chem disp; shwrs inc; el pnts (5A) €2.50-3; Indtte; BBQ; playgrnd; sand beach, boat hire, sw & fishing 100m; entmnt; quiet; adv bkg. "Cheap & cheerful; many pitches sandy & v sl or uneven, others permanently occupied; poss windy; san facs adequate." ♦ 1 Apr-30 Sep. € 15.00 2009*

NOIRMOUTIER EN L'ILE *2H3* (8km W Coastal) *47.02409, -2.30374* **Camp Municipal La Pointe, L'Herbaudière, 85330 Noirmoutier-en-l'Ile [02 51 39 16 70; fax 02 51 39 74 15]** Fr bdge to island foll sp to Noirmoutier town, then to L'Herbaudière & port. At port turn L, 500m to site. Lge, mkd pitch, unshd; wc; chem disp; mv service pnt; shwrs inc; el pnts (10A) €3.65 (long leads poss req); gas; Indtte; shop; rest, snacks & bar in town; playgrnd; beach adj; wifi; dogs €1.60; adv bkg; quiet; ccard acc; red low ssn; CKE/CCI. "Excel site in beautiful location; peaceful; sea views some pitches; poss windy (exposed to sea on 3 sides); helpful staff; clean, adequate facs; grnd poss soft in some areas; gd cycle rtes on island; sh walk to fishing/pleasure harbour; rec; v busy." 18 Mar-15 Oct. € 19.00 2014*

NORT SUR ERDRE *2G4* (1km S Rural) *47.42770, -1.49877* **Camping Seasonova du Port Mulon - formaly Municipal, Rue des Mares Noires, 44390 Nort-sur-Erdre [02 36 81 00 01 / 02 40 72 23 57; fax 02 40 72 16 09; contact@camping-portmulon.com; www.camping-portmulon.com]** Sp fr all ents to town; foll 'Camping' & 'Hippodrome' sp. NB: C'vans banned fr town cent, look for diversion sp. Med, shd; wc; chem disp; shwrs inc; el pnts (6A) €2.40; Indtte (inc dryer); supmkt 1.5km; playgrnd; tennis; fishing; boating; dogs €0.90; adv bkg; quiet; CKE/CCI. "Delightful, spacious, under-used site; gd walking & cycling area, espec along Nantes canal & Rv Erdre; Barrier perm locked, access when warden on site only; new site rd & toilet block (2014); friendly staff." 5 Apr-15 Oct. € 24.00 (CChq acc) 2014*

NOTRE DAME DE RIEZ *2H3* (1km NE Rural) *46.75523, -1.89814* **Camping Domaine des Renardières, 13 Chemin de Chêne Vert, 85270 Notre-Dame-de-Riez [02 51 55 14 17 or 06 20 98 37 46 (mob); fax 02 51 54 96 13; caroline.raffin@free.fr; www.camping-renardieres.com]** On D38 to Notre-Dame-de-Riez. Thro vill, over rv & 1st L over rlwy to site in 1km. Med, pt shd; wc; chem disp; baby facs; shwrs inc; el pnts (6A) inc; gas; Indtte (inc dryer); tradsmn; rest, snacks; bar; BBQ; playgrnd; htd pool; sand beach 5km; wifi; entmnt; TV rm; 20% statics; dogs €3; phone; Eng spkn; adv bkg; quiet; 15% red low ssn; CKE/CCI. "Gd picturesque site; helpful owners; rec." ♦ ltd 1 Apr-2 Sep. € 20.00 2010*

NOZAY *2G4* (8km NW Rural) *47.59606, -1.71583* **Camp Municipal La Roche, 44170 Marsac-sur-Don [02 40 87 54 77 (Mairie); fax 02 40 87 51 29; mairie.marsacsurdon@wanadoo.fr]** Fr N137 turn W onto D124 to Marsac-sur-Don. Fr vill take D125 W dir Guénouvry, site sp. Sm, mkd pitch, pt sl, pt shd; htd wc; shwrs; el pnts €2.15; rest, bar nrby; playgrnd; fishing; games area; walking circuit; dogs €0.50; quiet; CKE/CCI. "Gd basic site." 1 May-30 Sep. € 5.00 2009*

OLONNE SUR MER see Sables d'Olonne, Les *7A1*

PAIMBOEUF *2G3* (850m W Urban/Coastal) *47.28907, -2.03964* **Camp Municipal de l'Estuaire, Quai Eole, 44560 Paimboeuf [02 40 27 84 53 or 06 46 41 60 93 (mob); camping-lestuaire@orange.fr; www.campinglestuaire.fr]** Fr St Nazaire on D77; turn L at rndabt imm after town sp; site on L in 300m. Med, pt shd; htd wc; shwrs inc; el pnts (10A) €3.85 (poss rev pol & poss long lead req); Indtte; supmkt 3km; bar; crêperie rest adj; playgrnd; pool; rv adj; cycle hire; wifi; entmnt; dogs €1.25; adv bkg; red low ssn; CKE/CCI. "Poss travellers." 4 Apr-30 Sep. € 11.50 2010*

"That's changed – Should I let The Club know?"

If you find something on site that's different from the site entry, fill in a report and let us know. See www.caravanclub.co.uk/europereport.

PIRIAC SUR MER *2G3* (3.5km E Coastal/Rural) *47.38705, -2.51021* **Camping Parc du Guibel, Route de Kerdrien, 44420 Piriac-sur-Mer [02 40 23 52 67; fax 02 40 15 50 24; camping@parcduguibel.com; www.parcduguibel.com]** Fr Guérande take D99 to La Turballe, D333 to St Sébastien. In St Sébastien turn R to Kerdrien over x-rds & site on R in approx 500m. Lge, mkd pitch, hdstg, pt sl, pt shd; wc (some cont); chem disp; mv service pnt; serviced pitches; shwrs inc; el pnts (3-10A) €2.90-4.30 (poss rev pol); gas; Indtte; shop; rest, snacks; bar; BBQ; playgrnd; htd pool high ssn; paddling pool; mini-waterslide; sand beach 1km; tennis; games area; cycle hire; entmnt; TV rm; 30% statics; dogs €2; phone; adv bkg; ccard acc; CKE/CCI. "Helpful owner; lovely, quiet location in woods; gd touring base; site split by rd; san facs need upgrade." ♦ 22 Mar-21 Sep. € 19.50 2012*

PIRIAC SUR MER *2G3* (1km S Rural) *47.37485, -2.53556* **Camping Armor-Héol, Route de Guérande, 44420 Piriac-sur-Mer [02 40 23 57 80; fax 02 40 23 59 42; armor-heol@wanadoo.fr; www.camping-armor-heol.com]** Fr Guérande on D90 & D33, site sp. Lge, hdg/mkd pitch, pt shd; wc; chem disp; baby facs; shwrs inc; el pnts (5A) €4 (poss rev pol); gas; Indtte; shops 1km; rest, snacks; bar; BBQ; playgrnd; htd, covrd pool; waterslide; sand beach 700m; tennis; games area; games rm; fitness rm; 60% statics; dogs €4; adv bkg; quiet. "Attractive, well-maintained site; lge pitches." 3 Apr-19 Sep. € 32.00 2010*

PLAINE SUR MER, LA see Pornic *2G3*

PONTCHATEAU *2G3* (4km W Rural) *47.44106, -2.15981* **Kawan Village Le Château du Deffay, Ste Reine-de-Bretagne, 44160 Pontchâteau [02 40 88 00 57; fax 02 40 01 66 55; info@camping-le-deffay.com; www.camping-le-deffay.com]** Leave N165 at junc 13 onto D33 twd Herbignac. Site on R approx 1.5km after Le Calvaire de la Madeleine x-rds, 270m past Chateau ent. Site sp fr by-pass. Lge, some hdg/mkd pitch, pt sl, pt terr, pt shd; wc; chem disp; mv service pnt; baby facs; shwrs inc; el pnts (6-10A) inc poss rev pol; Indtte (inc dryer); sm shop; rest, snacks; bar; BBQ (charcoal/gas); playgrnd; htd, covrd pool; paddling pool; lake fishing; tennis & free pedalos; cycle hire; golf 10km; wifi; entmnt; games/TV rm; 18% statics; dogs €1; Eng spkn; adv bkg; ccard acc (not in rest); red low ssn; CKE/CCI. "Excel site with trees in grnds of chateau by lake; friendly, welcoming staff; gd clean san facs; some pitches lakeside & not fenced; mkt Mon." ♦ 1 May-29 Sep. € 37.70 (CChq acc) SBS - B25 2014*

PONTS DE CE, LES see Angers *4G1*

PORNIC C'vans are prohibited in Pornic. If app fr E on D751 or fr SE on D213 remain on by-pass to N of Pornic & take D86 or D213 exit.

PORNIC *2G3* (700m N Urban) *47.12066, -2.10019* **Camping Bon Accueil, 8 Rue de St Père-en-Retz, 44210 Pornic [06 09 56 84 28 (mob); fax 02 40 82 87 45; bonaccueil44@wanadoo.fr; www.camping-bon-accueil.fr]** Fr D213 exit Pornic cent N on D86. Site on L in 300m. Sm, hdg/mkd pitch, pt sl, pt shd; wc; chem disp; mv service pnt; baby facs; shwrs inc; el pnts (6A) inc; Indtte (inc dryer); shop 1km; rest, snacks; bar; BBQ; playgrnd; sm htd pool; sand beach 1.5km; entmnt; 50% statics; dogs €0.80; phone; bus adj; poss cr; Eng spkn; adv bkg; quiet; cc acc; CKE/CCI. "Nearest site to Pornic cent; friendly, welcoming owner; some pitches poss tight for lge o'fits; facs old but clean; gd/fair." ♦ 1 Apr-30 Sep. € 19.60 2009*

"I like to fill in the reports as I travel from site to site"

You'll find report forms at the back of this guide, or you can fill them in online at www.caravaclub.co.uk/europereport.

PORNIC *2G3* (10km N Urban) *47.20315, -2.03716* **Camping du Grand Fay, Rue du Grand Fay, 44320 St Père-en-Retz [02 40 21 72 89; fax 02 40 82 40 27; legrandfay@aol.com; www.camping-grandfay.com]** Fr Mairie in cent St Père-en-Retz take D78 E twds Frossay. After 500m turn R into Rue des Sports, after 200m turn L into Rue du Grand Fay. Site on L in 200m adj sports cent. Med, mkd pitch, pt sl, pt shd; wc (some cont); shwrs inc; el pnts (6A) €3.80; Indry rm; tradsmn; supmkt nrby; playgrnd; htd pool; beach 8km; lake fishing adj; games area; some statics; dogs €2; quiet; red low ssn; CKE/CCI. "Pleasant site nr sandy beaches." ♦ 1 Apr-15 Oct. € 16.00 2010*

PORNIC *2G3* (2km E Rural) *47.11855, -2.06894* **Camping La Chênaie, 36 Rue du Patisseau, 44210 Pornic [02 40 82 07 31; fax 02 40 27 95 67; acceuil@campinglachenaie.com; www.campinglachenaie.com]** Fr Nantes on D751 to Pornic, at 1st rndabt turn R. Fr St Nazaire on D213, foll sp Nantes & Le Clion-sur-Mer to avoid Pornic cent. Lge, hdg/mkd pitch, hdstg, pt sl, terr, pt shd; wc; chem disp; mv service pnt; baby facs; shwrs inc; el pnts (10A) €5; Indtte (inc dryer); shop; tradsmn; rest, snacks; bar; BBQ; playgrnd; 2 pools (1 htd, covrd); paddling pool; waterslide; sand beach 2.5km; horseriding; golf; cycle hire; wifi; entmnt; 35% statics; dogs €4; Eng spkn; adv bkg; quiet; ccard acc; red low ssn/long stay; CKE/CCI. "Lge pitches; friendly site; gd walking; gd touring base." ♦ 30 Apr-13 Sep. € 37.00 2011*

"We must tell The Club about that great site we found"

Get your site reports in by mid-August and we'll do our best to get your updates into the next edition.

PORNIC *2G3* (4km E Rural) *47.11885, -2.07296* **Camping Le Patisseau, 29 Rue du Patisseau, 44210 Pornic [02 40 82 10 39; fax 02 40 82 22 81; contact@lepatisseau.com; www.lepatisseau.com]** Fr N or S on D213, take slip rd D751 Nantes. At rndabt take exit sp to Le Patisseau, foll sp. Med, hdg/mkd pitch, hdstg, pt sl, pt shd; htd wc; chem disp; mv service pnt; baby facs; fam bthrm; sauna; shwrs inc; el pnts (6A) inc; Indtte (inc dryer); shop; tradsmn; rest, snacks; bar; BBQ; playgrnd; 2 htd pools (1 htd, covrd); 2 htd paddling pools (1 covrd); 2 waterslides; sand beach 2.5km; jacuzzi; fitness rm; tennis 1km; cycle hire; games area; games rm; golf 2km; wifi; entmnt; TV; 35% statics; dogs €6; Eng spkn; adv bkg rec high ssn; quiet; ccard acc; red low ssn. "Excel, modern, family site; modern san facs block - lovely shwrs; 1hr walk on path fr back of site to Pornic." ♦ 7 Apr-12 Sep. € 42.00 2011*

See advertisement

PORNIC *2G3* (5km E Coastal) *47.09748, -2.0525* **Airotel Camping Village La Boutinardière, 23 Rue de la Plage de la Boutinard, 44210 Pornic [02 40 82 05 68; fax 02 40 82 49 01; info@laboutinardiere.com; www.camping-boutinardiere.com]** SW fr Nantes on D723; after abt 6km turn L on D751 sp Pornic; after abt 30km L at 2nd rndabt onto D13 sp la Bernerie en Retz; site rd on R after abt 3km in la Rogere abt 50mtrs bef rndabt; recep on R; park on gravel next to low walls on R. Lge, hdg pitch, pt sl, pt shd; wc; chem disp; mv service pnt; serviced pitches; baby facs; sauna; shwrs inc; el pnts (6-10A) €5-6 (poss rev pol); gas; Indtte; shop; supmkt; rest, snacks; bar; BBQ; playgrnd; 2 pools (1 htd, covrd); paddling pool; waterslide; jacuzzi; sand beach 200m; lake sw 3km; tennis; games rm; golf 5km; cycle hire; entmnt & activities; wifi; TV rm; 15% statics; dogs €5; bus nrby; poss cr; Eng spkn; adv bkg; quiet; red low ssn; ccard acc; red long stay/low ssn; CKE/CCI. "Excel family site; vg pool complex; v busy high ssn; Pornic interesting town." ♦ 1 Apr-30 Sep. € 62.00 2014*

PORNIC *2G3* (6km SE Rural/Coastal) *47.08450, -2.03650* **Camping Les Ecureuils, 24 Ave Gilbert Burlot, 44760 La Bernerie-en-Retz [02 40 82 76 95; fax 02 40 64 79 52; camping.les-ecureuils@wanadoo.fr; www.camping-les-ecureuils.com]** Fr Pornic take D13 S for 5km, then D66 for 1km; site sp. Lge, hdg pitch, pt sl, pt shd; wc; chem disp; baby facs; shwrs inc; el pnts (6-10A) €4; Indtte; shops 500m; snacks; bar; BBQ area; playgrnd; htd pool; paddling pool; waterslide; sand beach 350m; tennis; golf 5km; entmnt; children's club; 30% statics; dogs (up to 10kg only) €4; Eng spkn; adv bkg; quiet; ccard acc; red low ssn/CKE/CCI. "Excel." ♦ 10 Apr-19 Sep. € 30.00 2010*

PORNIC *2G3* (10km S Coastal) *47.07500, -2.00741* **Campsite Les Brillas, Le Bois des Treans, 44760 Les Moutiers-en-Retz [02 40 82 79 78; fax 02 40 64 79 60; info@campinglesbrillas.com; www.campinglesbrillas.com]** Fr Nantes ring rd, take D723 SW. Take exit D751 twd Pornic. Turn L on D66. Foll sp. Med, hdg pitch, mkd pitch; wc; chem disp; baby facs; en pnts inc (6A); Indtte (inc dryer); Eng spkn; quiet; red low ssn; CCI. "Sm coastal vill; easy walk to beach; vg." 11 Apr-12 Oct. € 38.30 2014*

PORNIC *2G3* (2km W Urban) *47.12219, -2.12780* **Camping Les Coeurés, 28 Rue des Coeurés, 44210 Ste Marie-sur-Mer [06 87 29 33 62 (mob); www.camping-pornic.com/les-coeures]** S fr St Nazaire on D213; turn R bef Pornic onto D286 to Ste Marie; turn R at rndabt onto D13, then 1st L. Site on L in 100m. Med, pt shd; wc (some cont); chem disp (wc); shwrs inc; el pnts (10A) €2.90; shop 300m; sand beach 3km; 10% statics; dogs €0.60; poss cr; quiet. "Excel site; san facs poss inadequate (early ssn 2010)." 1 May-30 Sep. € 11.70 2010*

> "I need an on-site restaurant"
>
> We do our best to make sure site information is correct, but it is always best to check any must-have facilities are still available or will be open during your visit.

PORNIC *2G3* (5km W Coastal) *47.11593, -2.15222* **Camping Domaine de la Madrague, Chemin de la Madrague, 44210 Ste Marie-sur-Mer [02 40 82 06 73; fax 02 51 74 11 93; madrague@franceloc.fr; www.madrague.net / www.campings-franceloc.fr]** Fr Pornic on D213 foll sp Ste Marie-sur-Mer. Foll D286 then R on D13. Turn L into Rue du Moulin Neuf, then R into Rue des Bougrenets. Cont on Rue Yves Ponceau, then Chemin de la Madrague to site. Lge, hdg/mkd pitch, pt sl, pt shd; htd wc; chem disp; mv service pnt; baby facs; fam bthrm; shwrs inc; el pnts (10A) €8; gas; Indtte; shop; tradsmn; rest, snacks; bar; playgrnd; htd pool; dir access to sand beach 500m; games area; wifi; entmnt; 80% statics; dogs €5; phone; bus; poss cr; adv bkg; quiet. "Clean, well-organised site; helpful staff; facs stretched high ssn; excel coastal path walks; gd for dog owners; sea views." ♦ 10 Apr-19 Sep. € 29.00 2009*

PORNIC *2G3* (5km W Rural) *47.14079, -2.15306* **FFCC Camping La Tabardière, 44770 La Plaine-sur-Mer [02 40 21 58 83; fax 02 40 21 02 68; info@camping-la-tabardiere.com; www.camping-la-tabardiere.com]** Take D13 NW out of Pornic sp Préfailles & La Plaine-sur-Mer. In about 5.5km turn R (nr water tower). Foll sps to site, about 1km fr main rd. NB C'vans not allowed in Pornic town cent, use by-pass. Lge, hdg/mkd pitch, hdstg, terr, pt shd; htd wc (some cont); chem disp; mv service pnt; baby facs; shwrs inc; el pnts (8A) €5; gas; Indtte (inc dryer); shop & 3km; tradsmn; snacks; bar; BBQ (gas/charcoal); playgrnd; 2 htd pools (1 covrd); paddling pool; waterslides; sand beach 3km; tennis; fishing 3km; horseriding 5km; multi-sport area; games rm; wifi; entmnt; TV rm; 40% statics; dogs €3.50; no c'vans/m'vans over 7.50m high ssn; Eng spkn; adv bkg; quiet; ccard acc; red low ssn; CKE/CCI. "Excel, peaceful site; vg facs for families; v clean unisex san facs; gates clsd 2230-0800; recep clsd lunchtime." ♦ 12 Apr-20 Sep. € 47.00 (CChq acc) SBS - B31 2014*

See advertisement

> "Satellite navigation makes touring much easier"
>
> Remember most sat navs don't know if you're towing or in a larger vehicle – always use yours alongside maps and site directions.

PORNIC *2G3* (8km W Coastal) *47.13261, -2.23138* **Camping Eléovic, Route de la Pointe St Gildas, 44770 Préfailles [02 40 21 61 60; fax 02 40 64 51 95; contact@camping-eleovic.com; www.camping-eleovic.com]** W fr Pornic on D13 to La Plaine-sur-Mer, turn S to Préfailles, cont twds Pointe-St Gildas 1km, L site sp. Med, hdg pitch, terr, pt shd; htd wc; chem disp; mv service pnt; serviced pitches; baby facs; shwrs inc; el pnts (6A) €4.90; Indtte; tradsmn; rest, snacks; bar; BBQ; htd, covrd pool; waterslide; playgrnd; sand beach adj; fishing; watersports; entmnt; TV; 20% statics; dogs €5; phone; Eng spkn; adv bkg; red low ssn/long stay/CKE/CCI; ccard acc. "Dir access to coast path; barrier clsd 2200-1000; vg." ♦ 3 Apr-26 Sep. € 31.00 2010*

PORNIC *2G3* (7km NW Coastal) *47.17614, -2.15462* **Camping Bel Essor, Rue de Tharon, 44730 St Michel-Chef-Chef [02 40 27 85 40 or 02 47 38 89 07 (LS); www.campingbelessor.com]** On D123 fr Pornic dir St Nazaire (Route Bleue) turn L sp Tharon-Plage. After 2nd rndabt take next turn R & keep R. Foll sps St Michel & site. Site on L after supmkt ent. Lge, mkd pitch, pt sl, pt shd; wc (some cont); chem disp (wc); shwrs inc; el pnts (6A) €4.20; Indtte; supmkt opp; tradsmn; snacks; bar; playgrnd; sand beach 400m; some statics; dogs €2; phone adj; poss cr in high ssn; Eng spkn; adv bkg; red low ssn; CKE/CCI. "Vg site; clean facs; helpful owners." ♦ 25 Apr-20 Sep. € 14.60 2009*

PORNIC *2G3* (8km NW Coastal) *47.17305, -2.15833* **Camping Clos Mer et Nature, 103 Rue Tharon, 44730 St Michel-Chef-Chef [02 40 27 85 71; fax 02 40 39 41 89; info@camping-clos-mer-nature.com; www.camping-clos-mer-nature.fr]** Take D213 fr Mindin. After 11km R on D77 sp St Michel-Chef-Chef 2nd R after cent of vill sp Tharon-Plage site on L after 1.5km. Lge, pt sl, pt shd; htd wc; mv service pnt; baby facs; shwrs inc; el pnts (6-10A) €3.50-4; Indtte; shop; supmkt 300m; snacks; playgrnd; pool; waterslide; sand beach 400m; fishing; sailing; windsurfing; tennis; cycle hire; games area; entmnt; some statics; dogs €3; o'night m'van area; adv bkg; quiet; red low ssn. "Lge pitches; vg, modern san facs; gd beaches." ♦ 1 Apr-17 Oct. € 20.00 2010*

"There aren't many sites open at this time of year"

If you're travelling outside peak season remember to call ahead to check site opening dates – even if the entry says 'open all year'.

PORNIC *2G3* (8km NW Coastal) *47.16007, -2.16274* **Camping Le Vieux Château, Ave du Vieux-Tharon, 44730 Tharon-Plage [02 40 27 83 47 or 06 23 46 06 60 (mob); camping.duvieuxchateau@wanadoo.fr; www.camping-duvieuxchateau.com]** Fr Pornic dir St Nazaire, turn W twd Tharon-Plage, site sp. Med, hdg/mkd pitch, terr, pt shd; wc; chem disp; shwrs inc; el pnts (6A) €4; Indtte; shop; tradsmn; snacks; bar; BBQ; playgrnd; htd pool; paddling pool; sand beach 500m; playgrnd; games rm; many statics; dogs €2; poss cr; Eng spkn; adv bkg; quiet; ccard acc; red long stay; CKE/CCI. ♦ 1 May-15 Sep. € 18.50 2009*

PORNIC *2G3* (10km NW Coastal) *47.15076, -2.19481* **Camping Bernier, 56 Rue de la Cormorane, 44770 La Plaine-sur-Mer [02 40 21 04 31 or 06 63 82 39 91 (mob); fax 02 40 21 08 12; www.camping-lebernier.com]** S fr St Nazaire bdge on D213 twd Pornic, turn R, S of St Michel-Chef-Chef on D96. Cont to junc, turn R, cont to x-rd, turn L. In 500m on R. Or thro La Plaine-sur-Mer on D13, turn R on leaving vill past g'ge twd Port Giraud. Site on L in 1km. Med, some hdg pitch, pt shd; wc; chem disp; some serviced pitches; shwrs inc; el pnts (6A) €3.60; Indtte; shop 300m; snacks; playgrnd; htd pool; sand beach 600m; some statics; dogs €2.80; adv bkg; quiet; 40-50% red low ssn; 5% red CKE/CCI. "Excel family site site nr gd beaches." ♦ 1 May-30 Sep. € 19.00 2009*

PORNICHET *2G3* (2km E Urban/Coastal) *47.25280, -2.31910* **Camping du Bugeau, 33 Ave des Loriettes, 44380 Pornichet [02 40 61 02 02 or 02 40 61 15 44 (LS); fax 02 40 61 22 75; info@campingdubugeau.com; www.campingdubugeau.com]** W fr St Nazaire on D92 then L at rndabt at St Marguerite by car showrm; site sp 2nd L, site 500m on L. Med, hdg/mkd pitch, pt shd; htd wc; chem disp; mv service pnt; shwrs inc; el pnts (5A) €4.50; Indtte; shop & 500m; tradsmn; snacks; BBQ; playgrnd; htd, covrd pool; sand beach & watersports 500m; tennis 500m; cycle hire 1km; TV; 30% statics; dogs €1; Eng spkn; adv bkg; ccard acc; red low ssn. "Gd touring site." ♦ 10 Apr-26 Sep. € 25.70 2010*

POUANCE *2F4* (1.5km N Rural) *47.74850, -1.17841* **Camp Muncipal La Roche Martin, 23 Rue des Etangs, 49420 Pouancé [02 41 92 43 97 or 02 41 92 41 08 (Mairie); fax 02 41 92 62 30]** Take D6 (sp St Aignan) N fr town. After level x-ing turn L onto D72 (sp La Guerche-de-Bretagne). In 300m, site on L. Sm, mkd pitch, pt terr, pt sl; wc; mv service pnt; shwrs; el pnts (10A); gas; shops 1km; rest, bar 100m; playgrnd; direct access to lake; watersports; tennis; games area; tennis; poss cr; adv bkg. "Well-kept, friendly site o'looking lge lake; noise fr rd & sailing school." 1 Apr-30 Sep. 2012*

PRE EN PAIL *4E1* (200m N Urban) *48.46094, -0.20140* **Camp Municipal Alain Gerbault, Rue des Troënes, 53140 Pré-en-Pail [02 43 03 04 28; camping.preenpail@wanadoo.fr]** Fr E on N12, turn R at major rndabt (sp D176 Domfront). Turn R twd sports cent & well sp fr there on N edge of vill. Sm, mkd pitch, pt shd; wc (some cont); chem disp; shwrs inc; el pnts (16A); shop 250m; rest, snacks; bar; playgrnd; htd pool adj; dogs €1.10; phone; CKE/CCI. "Pleasant wooded region; poss mkt traders on site; OK as touring base." 1 Apr-30 Sep. 2009*

PREFAILLES see Pornic *2G3*

⊞ **ROCHE SUR YON, LA** *2H4* (8.2km SW Rural) *46.62281, 1.44983* **Campilo, L'Auroire, 85430 Aubigny [02 51 31 68 45; accueil@campilo.com; www.campilo.com]** Take Rue du Maréchal Joffre, D248 Rue du Maréchal Lyautey and D747 to Les Gâts in Aubign, take Rue des Mésanges and Le Champt des Landes to La Guyonnière, turn R onto Les Gâts, turn L onto Route de l'Auroire, cont onto Rue des Mésanges, turn L onto Le Champt des Landes, take the 2nd R onto La Guyonnière. Med, mkd pt, sl, pt shd; chem disp; shwrs; el pnts (10A); Indtte (€4); tradsmn July/Aug; bar; BBQ; playgrnd; pool; bicycles; dogs (€3); Eng spkn. "Tow cars not allowed besides caravans sep car park; fishing lake on site; walks and cycling rtes; lge sports area; small gym; friendly staff; new san facs and pool." ♦ ltd € 18.90 2014*

ROCHE SUR YON, LA *2H4* (8km S Rural) *46.59340, -1.43839* **Camping La Venise du Bocage, Le Chaillot, 85310 Nesmy [tel/fax 02 51 98 01 20; contact@la-venise-du-bocage.com; www.la-venise-du-bocage.com]** Fr N take D747 dir La Tranche-sur-Mer. Take D36 twd Nesmy & site sp on R after 500m. Sm, mkd pitch, pt shd; wc (some cont); chem disp; baby facs; shwrs inc; el pnts (6-10A) €2.80-3.70; Indtte; ltd shop or 3km; rest & bar 3km; playgrnd; pool; tennis; horseriding, golf 3km; 25% statics; dogs €1.70; phone; poss cr; adv bkg; quiet; red low ssn. "Helpful, friendly owner; gd san facs; poss untidy end of ssn; poss barrier down & staff not avail to open for arr; NH only." ♦ 1 Apr-30 Sep. € 10.60 2009*

ROSIERS SUR LOIRE, LES *4G1* (1km N Rural) *47.35908, -0.22500* **FLOWER Camping Val de Loire, 6 Rue Ste Baudruche, 49350 Les Rosiers-sur-Loire [02 41 51 94 33; fax 02 41 51 89 13; contact@camping-valdeloire.com; www.camping-valdeloire.com / www.flowercampings.com]** Take D952 fr Saumur in dir Angers. Site on D59 1km N of vill cent on L dir Beaufort-en-Vallée. Med, hdg/mkd pitch, hdstg, pt shd; wc; chem disp; mv service pnt; baby facs; 50% serviced pitch; shwrs inc; el pnts (10A) €4.50; gas; lndtte; tradsmn; rest, snacks; bar; BBQ; playgrnd; htd pool; paddling pool; lake sw 15km; waterslide; tennis; games rm; internet; entmnt; TV rm; 15% statics; dogs €3; Eng spkn; adv bkg; quiet; red long stay/low ssn; CKE/CCI. "Close to Rv Loire; lge pitches; friendly, helpful staff; excel san facs; gd touring base for chateaux region; excel." ♦ 1 Apr-30 Sep. € 38.00 2014*

SABLE SUR SARTHE *4F1* (10km NE Rural) *47.86677, -0.20869* **Camp Municipal des Deux Rivières, 72430 Avoise [02 43 92 76 12; fax 02 43 95 62 48]** Fr Sablé take D309 twd Le Mans, after 10km thro vill of Parcé-sur-Sarthe, cont twds Le Mans & cross bdge over Rv Sarthe; sp for Avoise & camping sp on L. Site adj rv. Sm, hdg pitch, pt shd; wc; shwrs inc; el pnts inc (poss rev pol); gas; shops, rest, bar adj; playgrnd; BBQ; 10% statics; Eng spkn; adv bkg; quiet; CKE/CCI. "Vg, pleasant, clean site; off beaten track." 1 Jun-6 Sep. € 8.20 2009*

SABLE SUR SARTHE *4F1* (500m S Rural) *47.83101, -0.33177* **Camp Municipal de l'Hippodrome, Allée du Québec, 72300 Sable-sur-Sarthe [02 43 95 42 61; fax 02 43 92 74 82; camping@sablesursarthe.fr; www.tourisme.sablesursarthe.fr]** Sp in town (foll sm, white sp with c'van symbols or Hippodrome). Fr N on D306; at trff lts at junc with D309, go strt over & under rlwy brdg sp Centre Ville; foll camping sps. Med, hdg pitch, pt shd; wc; shwrs inc; el pnts (15A) €2.40; gas; BBQ; lndry rm; sm shop; tradsmn; snacks; playgrnd; pool; rv fishing; boat & cycle hire; canoeing; entmnt; TV rm; Eng spkn; quiet; ccard acc; red long stay/low ssn. "Excel site; gd, clean facs; helpful staff; some pitches diff for lge fits." ♦ 3 Apr-15 Oct. € 16.40 2014*

SABLES D'OLONNE, LES *7A1* (4km N Rural) *46.53320, -1.79379* **Camping Le Nid d'Eté, 2 Rue de la Vigne Verte, 85340 Olonne-sur-Mer [02 51 95 34 38; fax 02 51 95 34 64; info@leniddete.com; www.leniddete.com]** Fr Les Sables-d'Olonne take D32 N to Olonne-sur-Mer. L onto D80 twd St Gilles-Croix-de-Vie. Immed over rlwy bdge turn L, site on L. Med, pt hdg/mkd pitch, pt shd; wc; chem disp; baby facs; shwrs inc; el pnts (6A) €3.80; lndtte; shop & 2km; snacks; playgrnd; htd, covrd pool high ssn; beach 3km; entmnt; few statics; dogs €2.50; c'van winter storage; adv bkg; v quiet; red low ssn; CKE/CCI. "Pleasant site; excel." 4 Apr-26 Sep. € 23.80 2009*

See advertisement

SABLES D'OLONNE, LES *7A1* (5km N Coastal) *46.54613, -1.80591* **Camping La Loubine, 1 Route de la Mer, 85340 Olonne-sur-Mer [02 51 33 12 92; fax 02 51 33 12 71; info@la-loubine.fr; www.la-loubine.fr]** Fr Les Sables-d'Olonne take D32 N to Olonne-sur-Mer then D80 dir St Gilles-Croix-de-Vie for 3.5km; turn L at junc to Plage-de-Sauveterre; ent to site immed on L after turn. Lge, hdg/mkd pitch, pt sl, pt shd; wc; chem disp; serviced pitches; shwrs inc; el pnts (5A) €3.65; gas; lndtte; shop; rest, snacks; bar; playgrnd; 2 htd pools (1 covrd); sand beach 1.8km; tennis; entmnt; TV; 50% statics; no dogs; poss cr; Eng spkn; adv bkg; noise fr rd & nightclub; ccard acc; CKE/CCI. "Site lit & guarded at night; lge car park for late arr; excel." ♦ 4 Apr-30 Sep. € 27.00 2009*

See advert on next page

SABLES D'OLONNE, LES *7A1* (5km N Urban) *46.53166, -1.75843* **Camping Le Trianon, 95 Rue du Maréchal Joffre, 85340 Olonne-sur-Mer [02 51 23 61 61; fax 02 51 90 77 70; campingletrianon@wanadoo.fr; www.camping-le-trianon.com]** S on D160 La Roche-sur-Yon twd Les Sables-d'Olonne; at Pierre Levée turn R onto D80 sp Olonne-sur-Mer. Also sp fr D80 N. V lge, hdg/mkd pitch, pt shd, serviced pitches; htd wc; chem disp; shwrs inc; el pnts (6A) inc (extra for 10-16A); lndtte; shop; rest, snacks; bar; playgrnd; 2 pools (1 htd, covrd); waterslide; sand beach 5km; fishing & watersports 4km; tennis; golf; games area; entmnt; 40% statics; dogs €4.43; poss cr; adv bkg; quiet; red low ssn. "Pleasant situation; friendly, helpful staff; excel facs for families." ♦ 3 Apr-30 Oct. € 38.00 (CChq acc) 2011*

SABLES D'OLONNE, LES *7A1* (2km E Rural) *46.48098, -1.73146* **Camping Le Puits Rochais, 25 Rue de Bourdigal, 85180 Château-d'Olonne [02 51 21 09 69; fax 02 51 23 62 20; info@puitsrochais.com; www.puitsrochais.com]** Fr Les Sables-d'Olonne take D949 twd La Rochelle. Pass rndabt with lge hypermrkt 'Magasin Géant' & turn R at 1st traff lts at Mercedes g'ge, then 1st L to site. Med, hdg/mkd pitch, pt shd; wc; chem disp; baby facs; shwrs inc; el pnts (6-10A) inc; lndtte; shop; supmkt 1km; rest, snacks; bar; BBQ (gas); playgrnd; htd pool; paddling pool; waterslide; sand beach 2km; tennis; cycle hire; games area; games rm; internet; entmnt; TV; 60% statics; dogs €3.30; phone; adv bkg; quiet; ccard acc; red low ssn/CKE/CCI. "Friendly, welcoming site; gd for families; san facs gd but ltd." ♦ 19 Apr-30 Sep. € 46.00 2014*

SABLES D'OLONNE, LES *7A1* (600m SE Urban/Coastal) *46.49171, -1.76536* **Chadotel Camping Les Roses, Rue des Roses, 85100 Les Sables-d'Olonne [02 51 95 10 42 or 02 51 33 05 05 (LS); fax 02 51 33 94 04; chadotel@wanadoo.fr; www.chadotel.com]** Fr town cent foll dir Niort, turn down Blvd Ampère by Total petrol stn to Rue des Roses. Site opp take-away cafe & adj to hospital, lying bet D949 & sea front. Lge, hdg/mkd pitch, pt sl, pt shd; wc; chem disp; shwrs inc; el pnts (6A) inc (poss rev pol); gas 1.5km; lndtte; tradsmn; rest 500m; snacks (high ssn); bar; BBQ (gas); playgrnd; htd pool; waterslide; sand beach 500m; entmnt; cycle hire; games rm; wifi; TV rm; mostly statics; dogs €3.20; phone; poss cr; Eng spkn; adv bkg; ccard acc; red low ssn/long stay; CKE/CCI. "Conv for town & beach; close by harbour, shops, museums & salt marshes; san facs poss tired high ssn; shuttle buses; easy walk to beach and town cent; excel." ♦ 7 Apr-11 Nov. € 32.50 2011*

SABLES D'OLONNE, LES *7A1* (2km SE Urban) *46.47932, -1.74123* **Camping Les Fosses Rouges, La Pironnière, 8 Rue des Fosses Rouges, 85180 Château-d'Olonne [02 51 95 17 95; info@camping-lesfossesrouges.com; www.camping-lesfossesrouges.com]** Take D949 La Rochelle. At lge rndabt turn R, sp La Pironnière. Camp clearly sp on L in 1km. Lge, mkd pitch, shd; wc; shwrs inc; el pnts (10A) €3.60; gas; lndtte; shop & 500m; snacks; bar; playgrnd; htd pool; sand beach 1.5km; cycle hire; entmnt; internet; TV; 70% statics; dogs €1.60; poss cr; adv bkg; quiet; red low ssn. "Attractive site on o'skts fishing port; some pitches poss diff lge o'fits; gd pool." ♦ 8 Apr-30 Sep. € 19.00 2011*

SABLES D'OLONNE, LES *7A1* (4km SW Coastal) *46.51193, -1.81398* **Chadotel Camping La Dune des Sables, La Paracou, 85100 Les Sables-d'Olonne [02 51 32 31 21 or 02 51 33 05 05 (LS); fax 02 51 33 94 04; chadotel@wanadoo.fr; www.chadotel.com]** Foll D160 to Les Sables-d'Olonne. Fr town foll sps to La Chaume & Les Dunes. Lge, mkd pitch, pt sl, unshd; wc; serviced pitches; shwrs inc; el pnts (6A) inc; gas; lndtte; shop; snacks; bar; BBQ (gas); playgrnd; pool; waterslide; sand beach 100m; tennis; cycle hire; games rm; entmnt; wifi; 75% statics; dogs €3; Eng spkn; adv bkg rec high ssn; red low ssn/long stay; CKE/CCI. "Great for family beach holiday; helpful warden." ♦ 7 Apr-22 Sep. € 32.50 2011*

ST ANDRE DES EAUX see Baule, La *2G3*

ST AUBIN DE LUIGNE see Chalonnes sur Loire *2G4*

⊞ **ST BREVIN LES PINS** *2G3* (1km S Coastal) *47.23800, -2.17030* **Camping La Courance, 100-110 Ave Maréchal Foch, 44250 St Brévin-les-Pins [02 40 27 22 91; fax 02 40 27 24 59; info@campinglacourance.fr; www.campinglacourance.fr]** Take Ave Foch fr cent of St Brevin, site on R, clearly sp. Lge, pt sl, shd; htd wc; baby facs; shwrs inc; el pnts (5A) €5.40 (poss long lead req); gas; lndtte; shops 1km; rest, snacks; bar; beach adj; 90% statics; dogs €2.50; quiet; red low ssn. "Well-maintained; steep, poss slippery paths." € 17.20 2009*

⊞ **ST BREVIN LES PINS** *2G3* (2km S Coastal) *47.21375, -2.15409* **Camping Les Rochelets, Chemin des Grandes Rivières, 44250 St Brévin-les-Pins [tel/fax 02 40 27 40 25; info@rochelets.com; www.rochelets.com]** Fr N or S on D213 exit sp Les Rochelets, site sp. Lge, hdg/mkd pitch, pt shd; wc (some cont); shwrs; el pnts (6-10A) €5-6.50; lndtte; tradsmn; rest, snacks; bar; playgrnd; htd pool; beach 100m; cycle hire; games area; games rm; wifi; entmnt; 30% statics; dogs €4; adv bkg; quiet; ccard acc; red low ssn. "Gd site for families; lots of entmnt & activities in high ssn; great location." € 29.60 2014*

ST BREVIN LES PINS *2G3* (2.4km S Coastal) *47.23514, -2.16739* **Camping Sunêlia Le Fief, 57 Chemin du Fief, 44250 St Brévin-les-Pins [02 40 27 23 86; fax 02 40 64 46 19; camping@lefief.com; www.lefief.com]** Fr Nantes dir St Nazaire. After St Nazaire bdge S on D213. Pass Leclerc & exit sp St Brévin-l'Océan/La Courance. At rndabt foll sp Le Fief. Lge, mkd pitch, hdstg, pt shd; wc; chem disp; mv service pnt; baby facs; sauna; shwrs inc; el pnts (6A) €6; gas; Indtte (inc dryer); shop; tradsmn; rest, snacks; bar; BBQ (gas/charcoal); playgrnd; 2 pools (1 htd, covrd); paddling pool; waterslide; jacuzzi; sand beach 800m; waterpark & waterslide etc adj; tennis; games area; games rm; wellness cent; fitness rm; cycle hire nr; gym; wifi; entmnt; TV rm; 30% statics; dogs €11; Eng spkn; adv bkg; quiet; ccard acc; red low ssn/long stay/CKE/CCI. "Excel for families; vg leisure facs." ♦ 7 Apr-30 Sep. € 41.00 2011*

See advertisement

ST BREVIN LES PINS *2G3* (5km S Coastal) *47.20441, -2.15773* **Camping Les Pierres Couchées, Ave des Pierres Couchées, L'Ermitage, 44250 St Brévin-les-Pins [02 40 27 85 64; fax 02 40 64 97 03; www.siblu.com/lespierrescouchees]** Sp fr D213 in St Brévin-l'Ermitage. Lge, mkd pitch, terr, pt shd; htd wc (some cont); baby facs; shwrs inc; el pnts (10A); Indtte; shop & 3km; tradsmn; rest, snacks; bar; BBQ; playgrnd; htd pool; paddling pool; waterslide; sand beach 300m; tennis; games area; games rm; fitness rm; cycle hire; horseriding 300m; golf 12km; entmnt; TV; 75% statics; dogs; Eng spkn; adv bkg; quiet; ccard acc; red low ssn; CKE/CCI. "Vg facs for families; friendly, helpful staff." ♦ 4 Apr-26 Sep. € 28.00 2009*

ST CALAIS *4F2* (500m N Urban) *47.92691, 0.74413* **Camp Municipal du Lac, Rue du Lac, 72120 St Calais [02 43 35 04 81/ 02 43 63 15 15 (Town hall); camping.stcalais@orange.fr]** E fr Le Mans on D357 to St Calais; after sharp (90 degree) L/H bend away fr town cent take L/H lane for next junc in 100m; do not foll D357 bend to R but go strt ahead on D429; in 200m turn R onto sm rd sp 'Conflans/ Plan d'Eau'. Site on R after football grnd. Fr N exit A11 junc 5 onto D1 to St Calais; turn R onto D357 dir Le Mans; in 200m turn R onto D429 N; in 400 turn R into sm rd sp 'Confland/ Plan d'Eau to site; leave D357 at R angle bend by Champion supmkt; site in 100m. Site by lake on N edge of town, well sp fr cent. Ent easy to miss. Med, hdg/mkd pitch, pt shd; wc; chem disp; mv service pnt; shwrs inc; el pnts (6A) inc; Indry rm; shops 500m; tradsmn; supmkt nrby; snacks & bar adj; BBQ; playgrnd; pool adj; lake sw adj; some statics; dogs; poss cr; adv bkg; quiet; no ccard acc; CKE/CCI; "Delightful, well-kept site; friendly, helpful warden; spacious pitches, espec nr lake; easy rvside walk to town; gd touring base." ♦ 1 Apr-15 Oct. € 17.00 02 43 35 15 13 2013*

STE CECILE see Chantonnay *2H4*

ST DENIS DU PAYRE see Luçon *7A1*

⊞ **ST ETIENNE DE MONTLUC** *2G4* (200m N Rural) *47.28002, -1.77967* **Camp Municipal de la Coletterie, Rue de Tivoli, 44360 St Etienne-de-Montluc [02 40 86 97 44 or 02 40 86 80 26 (Mairie); campinglacoletterie@st-etienne-montluc.net; www.st-etienne-montluc.net]** Well sp fr N165 (E60) in both dirs. Sm, hdg/mkd pitch, pt sl, pt shd; htd wc; chem disp; shwrs inc; baby facs; el pnts (15A) €3.80; Indtte (inc dryer); shop, rest, bar 500m; playgrnd; fishing; games area; dogs €1.20; phone; adv bkg; quiet; CKE/CCI. "Vg; check open bef travelling." ♦ € 10.30 2013*

ST ETIENNE DU BOIS (VENDEE) see Legé *2H4*

ST GEORGES SUR LAYON see Doué la Fontaine *4G1*

ST GILLES CROIX DE VIE *2H3* (3km NE Rural) *46.71217, -1.90613* **Camping Aire Naturelle Le Petit Beauregard, Rue du Petit Beauregard, 85800 Le Fenouiller [02 51 55 07 98]** N fr Les Sables d'Olonne take D38 twd St Gilles Croix-de-Vie. Turn R onto D754 sp Le Fenouiller for 3km. Turn R; site well sp in 500m. Sm, mkd pitch, pt shd; wc; chem disp; shwrs inc; el pnts (6A) €3; lndtte; shop 1km; tradsmn; rest nr; BBQ; playgrnd; pool; sand beach 3km; few statics; dogs; quiet; Eng spkn; adv bkg; CKE/CCI. "Friendly, helpful owner; excel, clean san facs; gd beaches nrby; St Gilles busy & cr." ♦ 1 Apr-30 Sep. € 13.50 2009*

ST GILLES CROIX DE VIE *2H3* (3km NE Rural) *46.71201, -1.91457* **Camping Le Chatelier, Chemin des Etrivières, Route de Nantes, 85800 Le Fenouiller [tel/fax 02 28 10 50 75; www.domainelechatelier.fr]** Fr St Gilles-Croix-de-Vie D754 NE, sp to Le Fenouiller, site on L. Med, mkd pitch, pt shd; wc; chem disp; shwrs inc; baby facs; el pnts (6A) (rec long lead); gas; lndtte (inc dryer); tradsmn; shops 2km; snacks; bar; BBQ; playgrnd; htd pool high ssn; sand beach 3km; games area; wifi; entmnt adj; TV rm; 50% statics; dogs; quiet. "Friendly owners." ♦ Easter-15 Oct. 2010*

ST GILLES CROIX DE VIE *2H3* (5km E Rural) *46.69480, -1.85310* **Camping Europa, Le Bois Givrand, 85800 Givrand [02 51 55 32 68; contact@europacamp.com; www.europacamp.com]** App site fr 'Leclerc' rndabt at St Gilles-Croix-de-Vie, take D6 exit dir Coëx & Aizenay; at 1st & 2nd rndabts go strt on; at 3rd rndabt take 1st exit; site on R in 150m, opp boat builders. Lge, mkd pitch, pt shd; wc (mainly cont); chem disp; serviced pitches; baby facs; shwrs inc; el pnts (10A) inc; gas; lndtte; shop 3km; rest, snacks & bar high ssn; BBQ; playgrnd; pool complex; waterslide; whirlpool; covrd pool; paddling pool; sand beach 5km; rv fishing, boat hire adj; fishing, watersports, cycle hire & horseriding 5km; golf nr; tennis; wifi; entmnt; games/TV rm; 60% statics; dogs €2.70; no c'vans/m'vans over 10m; adv bkg; ccard acc; red low ssn. "Pleasant site; busy high ssn, quiet low ssn; facs poss stretched high ssn; vg." ♦ ltd 1 Apr-31 Oct. € 30.60 2011*

ST GILLES CROIX DE VIE *2H3* (8km E Rural) *46.69665, -1.83395* **Camping Le Pont Rouge, Ave Georges Clémenceau, 85220 St Révérend [tel/fax 02 51 54 68 50; camping.pontrouge@wanadoo.fr; www.camping-lepontrouge.com]** W fr Aizenay on D6 rd for St Gilles-Croix-de-Vie, turn R just past water tower into St Révérend. Foll sp to site. Med, hdg pitch, pt sl, pt shd; htd wc; chem disp; mv service pnt; baby facs; shwrs inc; el pnts (6A) €4 (poss long lead req); lndtte; shop 1km; tradsmn; rest 3km; snacks; playgrnd; htd pool; sand beach 8km; golf course with rest 3km; games area; entmnt; TV; 50% statics; dogs €3; poss cr; Eng spkn; adv bkg; quiet; red low ssn; CKE/CCI. "Attractive, secluded site; run by enthusiastic young couple; clean modern san facs, plenty hot water; working windmill (with tours) 1km; vg." ♦ 1 Apr-30 Sep. € 19.00 2011*

ST GILLES CROIX DE VIE *2H3* (3km SE Coastal) *46.66748, -1.90213* **Camping du Jaunay, 102 Route des Sables, 85800 Givrand [02 51 55 14 77; buro@campingduejaunay.com; www.campingdujaunay.com]** S fr St Gilles-Croix-de-Vie on D38 or B38B; site on R 200m after 2nd rndabt (1st rndabt joins D38 with D38b, 2nd rndabt 400m further on). Sm, mkd pitch, pt shd; htd wc; chem disp; shwrs inc; el pnts (6A) €3; lndtte; shop or 3km; tradsmn; rest, snacks; bar; BBQ; playgrnd; htd pool; canoe hire; fishing; sand beach 1.2km; TV; 30% statics; dogs €1.60; phone; adv bkg; red low ssn; CKE/CCI. "Vg site; lge pitches; friendly, helpful owner; vg cycle paths adj." Apr-Sep. € 14.00 2009*

ST GILLES CROIX DE VIE *2H3* (4km SE Rural) **Camping à la Ferme Petit Bois, 85800 Givrand [06 21 55 26 89 (mob)]** W fr Aizenay on D6 for 20km; turn L at rndabt sp Givrand; site on L in 1km. Sm, hdg/mkd pitch, shd; htd wc; chem disp; shwrs inc; el pnts (6A) €3; lndtte; shop 2km; BBQ; sand beach 4km; dogs free; poss cr; Eng spkn; quiet; CKE/CCI. "Well-kept site; lge pitches; friendly owner; site yourself, owners calls eves; many cycle tracks; gd access to coast; excel." 1 May-30 Sep. € 15.00 (3 persons) 2009*

ST GILLES CROIX DE VIE *2H3* (4km SE Coastal) *46.67095, -1.90874* **Camping Les Cyprès, 41 Rue du Pont du Jaunay, 85800 St Gilles-Croix-de-Vie [02 51 55 38 98; fax 02 51 54 98 94; contact@camping-lescypres85.com; www.campinglescypres.com]** Site on S end of St Gilles-Croix-de-Vie off D38, after rndabt sp Le Jaunay turn sharp L - hard to spot. Lge, hdg pitch, shd; wc; chem disp, mv service pnt, shwrs inc; el pnts (10A) €3; gas; Indtte; shop, tradsmn; rest, snacks; bar; playgrnd; htd, covrd pool & jacuzzi; sand beach 600m; 12% statics; dogs €3.30; rv 100m; Eng spkn; adv bkg €7.62 fee; quiet; ccard acc; red long stay/low ssn; CKE/CCI. "Excel for family hols; family-run site; red facs low ssn; footpath along rv to town cent; busy & noisy in high ssn." ♦ 9 Apr-28 Sep. € 42.70 2014*

See advert on previous page

ST GILLES CROIX DE VIE *2H3* (4km SE Urban/Coastal) *46.67113, -1.90356* **Chadotel Le Domaine de Beaulieu, Rue du Parc, Route des Sables-d'Olonne, 85800 Givrand [02 51 55 59 46 or 02 51 33 05 05 (LS); info@chadotel.com; www.chadotel.com]** S on D38 fr St Gilles Croix-de-Vie, site sp on L. Lge, hdg/mkd pitch, pt shd; wc; serviced pitches; baby facs; shwrs inc; el pnts (6A) inc (poss long lead req); gas; Indtte; shop; snacks; bar; BBQ (gas); playgrnd; 2 pools; waterslide; sand beach 1km; tennis; golf 5km; entmnt; wifi; TV; dogs €3.20; adv bkg; quiet; red long stay/low ssn; ccard acc; CKE/CCI. "Gd site for families; red facs low ssn; low trees poss diff; gd; excel value for money; lovely site; friendly, helpful Eng spkn staff." ♦ 5 Apr-20 Sep. € 39.00 2014*

ST GILLES CROIX DE VIE *2H3* (2km S Coastal) *46.67819, -1.91561* **Chadotel Camping Le Bahamas Beach, 168 Route des Sables, 85800 St Gilles-Croix-de-Vie [02 51 54 69 16 or 02 51 33 05 05 (LS); fax 02 51 33 94 04; chadotel@wanadoo.fr; www.chadotel.com]** S fr St Gilles-Croix-de-Vie on Rte des Sables (D38), sp. Lge, hdg/mkd pitch, unshd; wc; chem disp (wc); shwrs inc; el pnts (6A) €4.70; gas; Indtte; sm shop (high ssn) & 3km; tradsmn; rest, snacks & bar (high ssn); BBQ (gas); playgrnd; htd covrd pool; waterslide; sand beach 800m; watersports; excursions; cycle hire; games area; games rm; entmnt; wifi; TV rm; many statics; dogs €3; phone; poss cr; Eng spkn; adv bkg; quiet; red long stay/low ssn; ccard acc; CKE/CCI. "Gd for children; superb pool; san facs ltd low ssn; facs far fr some pitches; excel cycle rtes along coast." ♦ ltd 7 Apr-22 Sep. € 31.00 2011*

STE HERMINE *2H4* (11km NE Rural) *46.59555, -0.97247* **FFCC Camping Le Colombier (Naturist), 85210 St Martin-Lars [02 51 27 83 84; fax 02 51 27 87 29; lecolombier.nat@wanadoo.fr; www.lecolombier-naturisme.com]** Fr junc 7 of A83 take D137 N; 3km past Ste Hermine turn R onto D52 to Le Poteau; turn L onto D10 to St Martin-Lars; 150m past St Martin-Lars turn R sp Le Colombier. Site ent on L in 200m. Lge, hdg/mkd pitch, pt sl, pt shd; wc; chem disp; shwrs inc; sauna; jaccuzi; el pnts (16A) €4.50; gas; Indtte; shops 6km; tradsmn; rest, snacks; bar; playgrnd; pool; wifi; 50% statics; dogs €4.50; poss cr; Eng spkn; adv bkg; quiet; ccard acc; red low ssn. "Well-run site; diff areas diff character; lge pitches; friendly Dutch owners; san facs clean but tired (2010); gd walking in site grnds & local area; conv Mervent National Park; excel; gd facs." ♦ ltd 1 Apr-1 Oct. € 35.50 2014*

ST HILAIRE DE RIEZ *2H3* (6km N Rural) *46.76332, -1.95839* **Camping La Puerta del Sol, 7 Chemin des Hommeaux, 85270 St Hilaire-de-Riez [02 51 49 10 10; fax 02 51 49 84 84; info@campinglapuertadelsol.com; www.campinglapuertadelsol.com]** N on D38 fr Les Sables-d'Olonne; exit onto D69 sp Soullans, Challans, Le Pissot. At next rndabt take 3rd exit & foll lge sp to site. Site on R in 1.5km. Lge, hdg/mkd pitch, pt sl, pt shd; wc; chem disp; serviced pitches; baby facs; sauna; jaccuzi; shwrs inc; el pnts (10A) inc (poss rev pol); Indtte (inc dryer); shop; rest, snacks; bar; BBQ (gas/elec); playgrnd; htd pool; paddling pool; waterslide; sand beach 4.5km; watersports 5km; fishing 2km; tennis; horseriding; golf; cycle hire; games area; wifi; entmnt; games/TV rm; 50% statics; dogs €4; no c'vans/m'vans over 10m high ssn; Eng spkn; adv bkg; quiet; ccard acc; red low ssn; CKE/CCI. "Vg site; med sized pitches, some diff lge o'fits due odd shape; clean san facs; gd for families; gd touring base; lovely pools and playgrnd." ♦ 1 Apr-30 Sep. € 33.00 2012*

ST HILAIRE DE RIEZ *2H3* (1km E Coastal) *46.74458, -2.00423* **Camping La Ningle, 66 Chemin des Roselières, 85270 St Hilaire-de-Riez [02 51 54 07 11; fax 02 51 54 99 39; campingdelaningle@wanadoo.fr; www.campinglaningle.com]** Fr St Hilaire, take rd sp Sion-sur-l'Océan. At traff lts/rndabt, foll sp 'Autres Campings' until site sp is seen. Med, hdg/mkd pitch, pt shd, wc; chem disp; serviced pitches; shwrs inc; el pnts (10A) inc; gas; Indtte; shop; tradsmn; bar; playgrnd; pool; sand beach 1.5km; tennis; fitness rm; poss cr; adv bkg; dogs €2; Eng spkn; red low ssn; CKE/CCI. "Highly rec; friendly, helpful staff; gd sized pitches; well-maintained; excel." ♦ ltd 20 May-10 Sep. € 32.00 2009*

ST HILAIRE DE RIEZ *2H3* (5km NW Coastal) *46.73970, -1.98410* **Camping La Parée Préneau, 23 Ave de la Parée Préneau, 85270 St Hilaire-de-Riez [02 51 54 33 84; fax 02 51 55 29 57; contact@campinglapareepreneau.com; www.campinglapareepreneau.com]** Fr N on D38 a rndabt foll sp Sion-sur-l'Océan & St Hilaire-de-Riez cent. At next rndabt take 1st exit (petrol stn on R) & foll sp La Parée Préneau; site on L in 2km. Or fr S on D38, go thro St Gilles-Croix-de-Vie & pass St Hilaire-de-Riez; at rndabt turn L sp Sion-sur-l'Océan & St Hilaire-de-Riez cent, then as above. Lge, hdg pitch, pt sl, shd; wc (some cont); baby facs; shwrs inc; jaccuzi; el pnts (6A) inc; Indtte (inc dryer); supmkt nrby; tradsmn; bar; BBQ (charcoal/gas); playgrnd; 2 htd pools (1 covrd); paddling pool; jacuzzi; sand beach 1km; fishing 1km; windsurfing 5km; games area; wifi; entmnt; TV/games rm; dogs €3; no c'vans/m'vans over 7m high ssn; Eng spkn; adv bkg; ccard acc; red low ssn; CKE/CCI. "Simple, relaxed site; family-run; some pitches poss tight lge o'fits; unisex san facs, mixed reports; v quiet low ssn; mkt Thu & Sun; gd." ♦ 7 May-9 Sep. € 27.00 2011*

ST HILAIRE LA FORET *7A1* (4km SW Rural) *46.44836, -1.52860* **Camping Les Batardières, Rue des Bartardières, 85440 St Hilaire-la-Forêt [02 51 33 33 85]** Fr Sables d'Olonne take D949 twd Avrillé. 7km after Talmont-St-Hilaire fork R on D70 to St Hilaire-la-Forêt. In 3km turn R on ent vill. Site 70m on L. Med, hdg pitch, pt shd; wc; chem disp; serviced pitches; shwrs inc; el pnts (6A) €3.50; Indtte; shop adj; playgrnd; sand beach 5km; free tennis; cycling; no statics; dogs €1.50; adv bkg; quiet; CKE/CCI. "Excel; spacious pitches; clean facs; excel for families; rec." 9 April -22 Sept. € 20.00 2012*

ST HILAIRE LA FORET *7A1* (1km NW Rural) *46.44846, -1.52643* **Camping La Grand' Métairie, 8 Rue de la Vineuse-en-Plaine, 85440 St Hilaire-la-Forêt [02 51 33 32 38; fax 02 51 33 25 69; info@camping-grandmetairie.com; www.la-grand-metairie.com]** Fr D949 turn S onto D70, sp St Hilaire-la-Forêt, or fr Avrillé take D19. Site at ent to vill. Lge, hdg/mkd pitch, pt shd; wc; chem disp; serviced pitches; sauna; baby facs; shwrs inc; el pnts (10A) inc (poss rev pol); gas; Indtte (inc dryer); shop; tradsmn; rest, snacks; bar; BBQ; playgrnd; 2 htd pools (1 covrd); paddling pool; sand beach 3km; tennis; jacuzzi; fitness rm; games rm; games area; cycle hire; golf 15km; wifi; entmnt; TV; 80% statics; dogs €4; phone; poss cr; Eng spkn; adv bkg; quiet; ccard acc; red long stay/low ssn/CKE/CCI. "Gd base for beaches, La Rochelle & Ile de Ré; friendly, helpful owners; cycle rtes fr site; excel." ♦ 2 Apr-24 Sep. € 29.00 2011*

ST HILAIRE ST FLORENT see Saumur *4G1*

ST JEAN DE MONTS *2H3* (2km N Coastal) *46.80666, -2.09970* **Camping La Davière Plage, Route de Notre-Dame, 85160 St Jean-de-Monts [tel/fax 02 51 58 27 99; info@daviereplage.com; www.daviereplage.com]** Site on L off D38 Rte de Notre Dame fr St Jean & 2km W of Notre-Dame. Well sp. Med, hdg/mkd pitch, pt shd; wc; chem disp; shwrs; el pnts (10A) €3.90; gas; Indry rm; shops adj; tradsmn; rest, snacks; bar; playgrnd; sand beach, watersports 700m; sports area; entmnt; TV rm; dogs €3.35; red low ssn; CKE/CCI. "Gd family site close to amenities; mkd cycle & walking trails; o'night area for m'vans." 1 May-30 Sep. € 20.00 2010*

ST JEAN DE MONTS *2H3* (2km SE Urban) *46.78841, -2.03008* **Camping Le Bois Masson, 149 Rue des Sables, 85167 St Jean-de-Monts [02 51 58 62 62 or 05 56 07 90 17; fax 02 51 58 29 97; boismasson@siblu.fr; www.siblu.com/leboismasson]** Fr Challans pass thro Le Perrier to St Jean-de-Monts. At 1st rndabt take last exit dir Les Sables-d'Olonne. Foll Les Sables at next rndabts & at 4th rndabt turn R, site on R shortly after Camping Le Bois Dormant. V lge, hdg/mkd pitch, pt shd; htd wc; chem disp; baby facs; shwrs inc; el pnts (6A) inc; gas; Indtte; shop; rest, snacks; bar; BBQ (gas); playgrnd; 2 htd pools (1 covrd); waterslide; sand beach 2.5km; fishing, windsurfing, watersports nrby; entmnt; internet; TV; 4% statics; no dogs; Eng spkn; adv bkg; quiet; 20% red low ssn. "Excel, busy, popular, family site; narr access rds; mkt Sat." ♦ 4 Apr-20 Sep. 2009*

ST JEAN DE MONTS *2H3* (3km SE Coastal) *46.78160, -2.01810* **Camping Zagarella, Route des Sables, Le Puy Blanc, 85160 St Jean-de-Monts [02 51 58 19 82; fax 02 51 59 35 28; zagarella@zagarella.fr; www.zagarella.fr / www.campings-franceloc.fr]** On D38, S fr St Jean-de-Monts. Med, hdg/mkd pitch, pt shd; wc; chem disp; baby facs; shwrs inc; el pns (16A) inc; gas; Indtte (inc dryer); shop; tradsmn; rest, snacks; bar; playgrnd; htd pool; tennis; cycle hire; fitness rm; aqua gym; games rm; entmnt; children's club Jul/Aug; wifi; TV; 50% statics; dogs €3; phone; poss cr; Eng spkn; adv bkg; red low ssn; CKE/CCI. "Vg, clean site; gd pool." ♦ ltd 24 Apr-25 Sep. € 32.00 2010*

ST JEAN DE MONTS *2H3* (3.7km SE Urban/Coastal) *46.78087, -2.05397* **Campéole Camping Les Sirènes, Ave des Demoiselles, 85160 St Jean-de-Monts [02 51 58 01 31; fax 02 51 59 03 67; sirenes@campeole.com; www.vendee-camping.info / www.campeole.com]** Site in town cent; ent town on D753 fr Challans, turn R at junc, then 1st L at church. Take 2nd L (Ave des Demoiselles). Site on L. V lge, pt sl, shd; wc (some cont); chem disp; shwrs inc; el pnts (10A) €4.10; gas; Indtte; sm shop adj or 2km; rest, snacks; bar; playgrnd; pool; sand beach 500m; fishing, watersports 500m; cycle hire; games area; entmnt; dogs €2.50; adv bkg ess high ssn; quiet; red low ssn. "Vg site; sm unmkd pitches." ♦ 2 Apr-12 Sep. € 22.50 2010*

ST JEAN DE MONTS *2H3* (6km SE Coastal) *46.75638, -2.00749* **Camping La Yole, Chemin des Bosses, Orouët, 85160 St Jean-de-Monts [02 51 58 67 17; fax 02 51 59 05 35; contact@la-yole.com; www.la-yole.com]** Take D38 S fr St Jean-de-Monts dir Les Sable d'Olonne & Orouet. At Orouet turn R at L'Oasis rest dir Mouette; in 1.5km turn L at campsite sp; site on L. Situated bet D38 & coast, 1km fr Plage des Mouettes. On arr, park in carpark on R bef registering. Lge, hdg/mkd pitch, pt shd; wc; chem disp; serviced pitch; baby facs; jacuzzi; shwrs inc; el pnts (10A) inc; Indtte (inc dryer); shop; tradsmn; rest, snacks; bar; BBQ area (gas only); playgrnd; 2 pools (1 htd covrd); paddling pool; waterslide; jacuzzi; sand beach 2km; tennis; fishing; horseriding 3km; watersports 6km; wifi; entmnt; games/TV rm; many statics (tour ops); sm dogs €7; no c'vans/m'vans over 8m; poss cr; Eng spkn; adv bkg ess; ccard acc; red low ssn; CKE/CCI. "Busy, well-run site; san facs clean, not spacious; excel cycle paths; mkt Wed & Sat; vg." ♦ 11 Apr-24 Sep. € 34.00 (CChq acc) SBS - A23 2012*

See advertisement

ST JEAN DE MONTS *2H3* (1km W Coastal) *46.79931, -2.07378* **Camping Le Bois Joly, 46 Route de Notre Dame-de-Monts, 85165 St Jean-de-Monts [02 51 59 11 63; fax 02 51 69 11 06; contact@camping-leboisjoly.com; www.camping-leboisjoly.com]** N on D38 circular around St Jean-de-Monts; at rndabt past junc with D51 turn R dir Notre Dame-de-Monts, site on R in 300m. Lge, hdg/mkd pitch, pt shd; wc; chem disp; baby facs; sauna; shwrs inc; el pnts (6A) inc rev pol; lndtte; shops 1km; rest, snacks, bar high ssn; playgrnd; 2 pools (1 htd, covrd); waterslide; sand beach 1km; games area; wifi; entmnt; TV rm; 25% statics; dogs €3; phone; poss cr; Eng spkn; adv bkg; ccard acc; red low ssn; ACSI; CKE/CCI. "Ideal for families; gd san facs; lge pitches; coastal & inland cycleways nrby; excel." ♦ 13 Apr-29 Sep. € 34.00 2012*

ST JEAN DE MONTS *2H3* (1km NW Rural) *46.80083, -2.08013* **Camping La Buzelière, 79 Rue de Notre Dame, 85169 St Jean-de-Monts [02 51 58 64 80; fax 02 28 11 03 61; buzeliere@aol.com; www.buzeliere.com]** Take D38 fr St Jean-de-Monts to Notre Dame-de-Monts. Site on L. Med, hdg/mkd pitch, pt sl, pt shd; wc; chem disp; serviced pitch; baby facs; fam bthrm; shwrs inc; el pnts (10A) inc; gas; lndtte; shop 1km; tradsmn; snacks; bar; BBQ; playgrnd; htd pool; sand beach 1km; games area; games rm; TV; 20% statics; dogs €2.50; phone adj; Eng spkn; adv bkg; quiet; ccard acc; red low ssn; CKE/CCI. "Many sports inc golf nr; clean san facs; red facs low ssn; excel." ♦ 1 May-30 Sep. € 29.70 2012*

ST JEAN DE MONTS *2H3* (3.5km NW Urban/Coastal) *46.80825, -2.10461* **Camping Les Amiaux, 223 Rue de Notre-Dame-de-Monts, 85160 St Jean-de-Monts [02 51 58 22 22; fax 02 51 58 26 09; accueil@amiaux.fr; www.amiaux.fr]** Site on D38 mid-way bet St Jean-de-Monts & Notre-Dame-de-Monts. V lge, hdg/mkd pitch, pt shd; htd wc; chem disp; serviced pitches; baby facs; shwrs inc; el pnts (10A) inc; gas; lndtte; sm shop; rest, snacks; bar; BBQ (gas & elec); playgrnd; htd, covrd pool; waterslides; sand beach 700m; tennis; cycle hire; horseriding 2km; golf 4km; games area; games rm; wifi; entmnt; TV rm; 50% statics; dogs €2.50; Eng spkn; adv bkg; ccard acc; red low ssn; CKE/CCI. "Excel, family site; gd facs; conv Puy du Fou theme park; rec long stay." ♦ 3 May-30 Sep. € 26.50 2009*

ST JEAN DE MONTS *2H3* (6km NW Coastal) *46.81831, -2.13006* **Camping La Forêt, 190 Chemin de la Rive, 85160 St Jean-de-Monts [02 51 58 84 63; camping-la-foret@wanadoo.fr; www.hpa-laforet.com]** Fr St Jean-de-Monts, take D38 twd Notre-Dame-de-Monts for 6km, over rndabt then turn L (last turning bef Notre-Dame-de-Monts) sp Pont d'Yeu, then immed L, site on L in 200m, on parallel rd to main rd. Med, hdg/mkd pitch, pt shd; wc; chem disp; shwrs inc; el pnts (6A) €3.80; gas; lndtte; shop; tradsmn; snacks; pool; playgrnd; htd pool; sand beach 500m; horseriding nrby; TV; 30% statics; dogs €2.50; phone; poss cr; Eng spkn; adv bkg; quiet; Eng spkn; BBQ; CKE/CCI. "Friendly, helpful owners; clean san facs; not suitable twin-axles; some pitches diff c'vans; excel." ♦ ltd 2 May-20 Sep. € 27.00 2009*

ST JULIEN DES LANDES see Mothe Achard, La *2H4*

ST LAMBERT DU LATTAY *4G1* (600m SE Urban) *47.29954, -0.63012* **FFCC Camp Municipal La Coudraye, Rue de la Coudraye, 49190 St Lambert-du-Lattay [02 41 78 44 26 or 02 41 78 49 31; miche.rip@wanadoo.fr; www.saintlambertdulattay.fr]** Fr Angers on D160 thro vill cent dir Chemillé. Site sp on L adj wine museum in 200m. Poor sp fr N. Sm, hdg pitch, pt sl, pt shd; wc (some cont); chem disp; mv service pnt; shwrs inc; el pnts (10A) €2.65-4.70; gas; lndtte; playgrnd; rv 500m; fishing 50m; entmnt; dogs €0.80; adv bkg. "Lovely, quiet site; wine museums worth visiting; site yourself, warden calls am & pm; gd walking; fair NH." ♦ 1 Apr-31 Oct. € 7.80 2010*

ST LAURENT SUR SEVRE *2H4* (5km S Rural) *46.92452, -0.87406* **Camp Municipal La Vallée de Poupet, 85590 St Malô-du-Bois [02 51 92 31 45; fax 02 51 92 38 65; camping@valleedepoupet.com; www.valleedepoupet.com]** Fr N on N149 turn S onto D752 at La Trique. At St Malô-du-Bois (4km) foll sp for 4.5km. Fr S fr Mauléon on N149 turn L onto D11 twd Mallièvre; 4km after Mallièvre turn R onto D752. After 2.5km turn R & foll sp. Steep app to site. Med, mkd pitch, pt shd; wc; chem disp; mv service pnt; baby facs; shwrs inc; el pnts (6A) €2.80; lndtte; shops 2km; tradsmn; rest; bar 500m; playgrnd; htd, covrd pool; fishing; entmnt; 10% statics; dogs €1.50; phone adj; Eng spkn; adv bkg; quiet; CKE/CCI. "Excel rvside site." ♦ 15 May-15 Sep. € 18.00 2010*

ST LAURENT SUR SEVRE *2H4* (1km W Rural) *46.95790, -0.90290* **Camping Le Rouge Gorge, Route de la Verrie, 85290 St Laurent-sur-Sèvre [02 51 67 86 39; campinglerougegorge@wanadoo.fr; www.camping-lerougegorge-vendee.com]** Fr Cholet on N160 dir La Roche-sur-Yon; at Mortagne-sur-Sèvre take N149 to St Laurent-sur-Sèvre. In St Laurent foll sp La Verrie on D111. Site on R at top of hill. Or take 762 S fr Cholet to St Laurent. Site sp in town. Med, hdg/mkd pitch, pt sl, pt shd; htd wc; chem disp; mv service pnt; baby facs; shwrs inc; el pnts (4-13A) €2.95-4.10; lndtte (inc dryer); shop; snacks; bar; playgrnd; pool; paddling pool; rv & lake fishing 800m; games area; golf 15km; wifi; 30% statics; dogs €2; adv bkg; quiet; red low ssn; CKE/CCI. "Peaceful family site; woodland walks & mountain biking; attractive sm town; close to Puy du Fou Theme Park." ♦ 15 Mar-30 Sep. € 27.35 2013*

ST LEONARD DES BOIS *4E1* (190m N Rural) *48.35353, -0.07669* **Camp Municipal Les Alpes Mancelles, Le Bourg, 72130 St Léonard-des-Bois [02 43 33 81 79; fax 02 43 34 49 02; campalpesmancelles@free.fr; www.ot-alpes-mancelles.com]** SW of Alençon on D1/D121 to Gesvres; turn L onto D149 to St Léonard-des-Bois; site sp on Rv Sarthe. Or easy access fr Fresnay-sur-Sarthe N on D15/D112. Med, mkd pitch, pt sl, pt shd; wc; shwrs inc; el pnts (6A) inc (poss rev pol); lndry rm; shop, snacks & bar nrby; playgrnd; rv watersports; dogs €0.50; phone; CKE/CCI. "Pretty, well-run, basic site by rv; gd san facs; well-mkd walks; gd touring base; interesting vill; vg." 1 Apr-30 Sep. € 11.40 2009*

ST MALO DU BOIS see St Laurent sur Sèvre *2H4*

ST MARTIN LARS see Ste Hermine *2H4*

ST MICHEL CHEF CHEF see Pornic *2G3*

ST PHILBERT DE GRAND LIEU *2H4* (400m N Rural) *47.04202, -1.64021* **Camping La Boulogne, 1 Ave de Nantes, 44310 St Philbert-de-Grand-Lieu [32 40 78 88 79; fax 32 40 78 76 50; accueil@camping-la-boulogne.com; www.camping-la-boulogne.com]** Fr Nantes on A83 exit junc 1 or 2 onto D178 - D117 dir St Philbert; turn L onto D65 (Ave de Nantes) to St Philbert; site on R in 500m adj rv & sp. Or fr Machecoul take bypass to St Philbert & then D65 as narr rds thro town. Med, hdg/mkd pitch, pt shd; wc; chem disp; baby facs; shwrs inc; el pnts (6A) inc; lndtte; shops & supmkt 500m; tradsmn; bar; BBQ; playgrnd; htd, covrd pool 200m; lake adj; fishing; games area; wifi; entmnt; 10% statics; dogs €1; phone; bus adj; no twin-axles; Eng spkn; adv bkg; quiet; ccard acc; red low ssn; CKE/CCI. "Well-kept, secure site; new enthusiastic, helpful owners (2010); gd." ♦ 1 Apr-31 Oct. € 13.50 2011*

ST REVEREND see St Gilles Croix de Vie *2H3*

ST VINCENT SUR JARD see Jard sur Mer *7A1*

SANDUN see Guérande *2G3*

SAUMUR See also sites listed under Bourgueil, Coutures, Doué-la-Fontaine, Montsoreau, Les Rosiers-sur-Loire and Vernantes.

SAUMUR *4G1* (1km N Urban) *47.25990, -0.06440* **Flower Camping de L'Ile d'Offard, Rue de Verden, 49400 Saumur [02 41 40 30 00; fax 02 41 67 37 81; iledoffard@flowercampings.com; www.flowercampings.com]** Exit A85 junc 3 onto N347; ent town past rlwy stn & cross Rv Loire bdge; turn L immed over bdge & foll sp Chinon alongside rv. At rndabt turn L & take 1st L to site; foll sp. Site on island facing Saumur castle. Lge, hdg/mkd pitch, hdstg, pt sl, pt shd; htd wc; chem disp; mv service pnt; baby facs; shwrs inc; el pnts (10A) €4 (poss rev pol); gas; lndtte (inc dryer); shops in ssn; tradsmn; rest; snacks, bar; playgrnd; htd pool; paddling pool; jacuzzi; rv sw & fishing, boating adj; tennis; cycle hire; games area; wifi; entmnt; TV rm; 20% tour ops statics; dogs €1.50; poss cr; Eng spkn; adv bkg (non-refundable bkg fee); some rlwy noise; ccard acc; red low ssn/CKE/CCI. "Pleasant, busy, well-run site; ideal for children; hdstg pitches in winter; helpful staff; clean, unisex san facs, some need refurb & poss ltd low ssn; most pitches lge but some v sm pitches bet statics - lge o'fits check in advance; gd bar & rest; site recently became private - hedges & trees etc need attention (2011); can be muddy when wet; gd cycle rtes; nice rvside and bdge walk to town." ♦ ltd 2 Mar-16 Nov. € 26.00 2013*

SAUMUR *4G1* (7km NE Rural) *47.29937, -0.01218* **Camping Le Pô Doré, 49650 Allonnes [tel/fax 02 41 38 78 80 or 06 09 26 31 28 (mob); camping.du.po.dore@wanadoo.fr; www.camping-lepodore.com]** NE fr Saumur on N347 & turn R onto D10. Site 3km W of Allonnes on R. Med, hdg/mkd pitch, some hdstg; pt shd; wc; chem disp; mv service pnt; shwrs inc; el pnts (6-10A) €3-4 (poss rev pol); lndtte; tradsmn; rest, snacks; bar; playgrnd; htd pool; cycle hire; entmnt; 25% statics; dogs €1.50; phone; poss cr; some Eng spkn; some rlwy noise; ccard acc; red low ssn; CKE/CCI. "Gd, clean & tidy site; helpful staff; dirty, sandy soil; conv wine rtes, caves, museums & a'route; conv NH/sh stay." ♦ 12 Mar-15 Nov. € 19.00 2011*

SAUMUR *4G1* (6km E Rural) *47.24755, -0.00033* **Camping Domaine de la Brèche, 5 Impasse de la Brèche, 49730 Varennes-sur-Loire [02 41 51 22 92; fax 02 41 51 27 24; mail@etang-breche.com; www.domainedelabreche.com / www.les-castels.com]** Exit Saumur on N152 twd Tours & site sp fr either dir. Site on N side of rd (6km W of Varennes) app fr lge lay-by giving easy ent. Lge, hdg pitch, pt shd; wc; chem disp; mv service pnt; 20% serviced pitch; baby facs; shwrs inc; el pnts (10A) €3.50; gas; lndtte; shop; tradsmn; rest, snacks; bar; playgrnd; 2 htd pools (no shorts); waterslide; cycle hire; tennis; games rm; entmnt; internet; TV rm; 30% statics; dogs; phone; Eng spkn; adv bkg (ess Jul/Aug); quiet but rd noise in some areas; ccard acc; red low ssn; CKE/CCI. "Spacious site & pitches; well-organised; excel facs; auto barrier clsd 2300-0700; helpful staff; excel." ♦ 30 Apr-15 Sep. € 33.00 2009*

SAUMUR *4G1* (5km NW Rural) *47.29440, -0.14120* **Camping de Chantepie, Route de Chantepie, 49400 St Hilaire-St Florent [02 41 67 95 34; fax 02 41 67 95 85; info@campingchantepie.com; www.campingchantepie.com]** Fr Saumer take D751 on S bank of Rv Loire sp Gennes. Turn L 3km N of St Hilaire-St-Florent just bef lge sp for a supmkt & bef mushroom museum. Site sp. Or fr N after x-ing rv on N347, take turn sp St Hilaire-St-Florent & join D751 for Gennes; site is 3km N of St Hilaire-St Florent, well sp fr D751. NB Easy to miss turning. Lge, hdg/mkd pitch, pt shd; htd wc; chem disp; mv service pnt; baby facs; shwrs inc; el pnts (10A) inc (poss rev pol); gas; lndtte; shop; tradsmn; snacks; bar/café; BBQ; playgrnd; 2 pools (1 htd, covrd); paddling pool; rv beach 200m; fishing; tennis & golf 2km; horseriding, boating 5km; cycle hire; games rm; wifi; entmnt; games/TV rm; 10% statics; dogs €4; no c'vans/m'vans over 10m; Eng spkn; adv bkg; quiet; ccard acc; red low ssn; CKE/CCI. "Excel well-run site nr rv; well-spaced, lge pitches, some with rv views, ltd; access to some pitches diff lge o'fits; friendly, helpful staff; excel san facs, conv Loire cycle rte; mkt Sat Saumur; excel views, bar & rest; excel cycle track; tv recep may be diff due to many trees." ♦ 26 Apr-12 Sep. € 46.70 (CChq acc) SBS - L06 2014*

SAUMUR *4G1* (8km NW Rural) *47.30982, -0.14492* **Camping La Croix Rouge, Rue de la Croix Rouge, 49160 St Martin-de-la-Place [02 41 38 09 02 or 06 32 17 14 61 (mob); campinglacroixrouge@laposte.net; www.campinglacroixrouge.com]** Exit A85 junc 3 sp Saumur. Take slip rd immed bef bdge then L sp 'Angers Touristique'. Site on L at vill sp. Fr Saumur take D347 N across rv then turn L onto D952 dir Angers. At St Martin-de-la-Place foll sp for site. Med, mkd pitch, pt shd; wc; chem disp; mv service pnt; shwrs; el pnts (6-10A) €3.-4.; lndtte; shop 600m; sm rest, bar 200m; playgrnd; rv sw, sailing adj; dogs €1.50; bus 150m; Eng spkn; adv bkg; quiet; ccard/chq not acc; red low ssn/CKE/CCI. "Beautiful, tranquil site on Rv Loire; friendly, helpful owners; 26 steps to clean spacious san facs; disabled facs at grnd level; 2m high security fence by rv; barrier clsd 2200-0700; no twin-axles; conv Saumur; excel; v pleasant site." ♦ ltd 13 Apr-30 Sep. € 21.50 2014*

SAVENAY *2G3* (2km E Rural) *47.35651, -1.92136* **Camp Municipal du Lac de Savenay, Route du Lac, 44260 Savenay [tel/fax 02 40 58 31 76]** Site well sp in Savenay. Can avoid Savenay Town by turning off N165 SW of town on new rd, dir LAC. Med, mkd pitch, terr, pt shd; htd wc; shwrs inc; el pnts (10A) €2.07; gas adj; lndtte; tradsmn; snacks; sm playgrnd; pool adj; fishing; dog €1.20 quiet; "Vg, clean site in attractive lakeside park; lge pitches." ♦ 1 May-30 Sep. € 16.34 2014*

SEGRE *2F4* (7km NW Rural) *47.71003, -0.95165* **Camping Parc de St Blaise, 49520 Noyant-la-Gravoyère [02 41 61 93 09; fax 02 41 61 44 68; campingstblaise@orange.fr; www.campingsaintblaise.fr]** Fr Segré take D775 dir Pouancé to Noyant, site/park sp in vill on R. Sm, hdg pitch, terr, pt shd; wc; chem disp (wc); shwrs inc; el pnts (6A) inc; shop & 1km; tradsmn; rest; bar; playgrnd; lake sw adj; aquatic park; fishing; horseriding; entmnt; dogs; phone; CKE/CCI. "Clean, well-maintained site in leisure park; gd views; slate mine worth visit." ♦ 15 Jun-30 Sept. € 17.00 2014*

SILLE LE GUILLAUME *4F1* (3km N Rural) *48.20352, -0.12774* **Camping Indigo Les Mollières, Sillé-Plage, 72140 Sillé-le-Guillaume [02 43 20 16 12; molieres@camping-indigo.com; www.camping-indigo.com]** Fr Sillé-le-Guillaume take D5 N, D203 to site. Med, shd; htd wc; chem disp; mv service pnt; shwrs inc; el pnts (13A) inc; lndtte (inc dryer); shop; tradsmn; supmkt 2km; snacks; playgrnd; htd pool; padding pool; lake sw; fishing; watersports; cycle hire; games area; internet; some statics; dogs; quiet; ccard acc. "Site in pine forest." ♦ 1 Jun-11 Sep. € 13.30 2009*

SILLE LE GUILLAUME *4F1* (3km N Rural) *48.20928, -0.13444* **FFCC Camping La Forêt, Sillé-Plage, 72140 Sillé-le-Guillaume [02 43 20 11 04; fax 02 43 20 84 82; campingsilleplage@wanadoo.fr / info@campingsilleplage.com; www.campingsilleplage.com]** Exit Sillé on D304 sp Mayenne. After 2km at x-rds turn R; across next x-rds & turn L at next x-rds; sp Sillé-Plage; site on R in 500m, visible. Sp fr other dir. Med, pt shd; wc; mv service pnt; shwrs inc; el pnts (10A) €4.10; gas; shop; tradsmn; playgrnd; tennis; boating; lake sw; fishing; 40% statics; dogs €1.15; poss cr; rd noise; CKE/CCI. "Pleasant lakeside & forest scenery (some pitches amongst trees); highly rec." 31 Mar-31 Oct. € 17.80 2013*

SILLE LE GUILLAUME *4F1* (2km NW Rural) *48.18943, -0.14130* **Camping Les Tournesols, Route de Mayenne, Le Grez, 72140 Sillé-le-Guillaume [02 43 20 12 69 or 06 98 04 74 29 (mob); campinglestournesols@orange.fr; www.campinglestournesols.com]** Exit Sillé on D304/D35 sp Mayenne; in 2km at x-rds turn R; site in 150m on L, easily visible & sp. Med, hdg/mkd pitch, pt sl, pt shd; wc; chem disp; mv service pnt; shwrs inc; el pnts (6A) inc (poss long lead req); lndtte (inc dryer); shop; tradsmn; snacks; bar; BBQ (gas); playgrnd; rv/lake sw & canoeing 2km; fishing 1km; cycle hire; entmnt; internet; mini golf; bouncy castle; football; badminton; volley ball; jeux de boules; TV; wifi; 20% statics; dogs €2 rabies cert req'd; no twin-axles; Eng spkn; adv bkg; quiet; ccard acc; red long stay; CKE/CCI. "Beautiful site; friendly, new owners (2013); facs dated but spotless; pleasant town; conv Le Mans; gd; welcoming owner." ♦ 1 May-30 Sep. € 24.00 (CChq acc) 2014*

SILLE LE PHILIPPE *4F1* (2km SW Rural) *48.10880, 0.33730* **Camping Le Château de Chanteloup, Parc de l'Epau Sarl, 72460 Sillé-le-Philippe [02 43 27 51 07 or 02 43 89 66 47; fax 02 43 89 05 05; chanteloup.souffront@wanadoo.fr; www.chateau-de-chanteloup.com]** Leave A11/E50 at junc 7 Sp Le Mans Z1 Nord. After toll turn L onto N338. Foll this & turn L onto D313 sp Coulaines, Mamers & Ballon. Take D301 (at lge supmkt) & in approx 13km site is sp just after ent to Sillé-le-Philippe. Avoid cent Sillé-le-Philippe. Med, some mkd pitch, pt sl, pt shd; wc; chem disp; baby facs; shwrs inc; el pnts (10A) €4. (poss rev pol); gas; lndtte (inc dryer); ltd shop & 2km; tradsmn; rest high ssn; snacks; bar; BBQ; playgrnd; pool; paddling pool; lake fishing; horseriding & golf 10km; games area; wifi; entmnt; games/TV rm; dogs free; twin-axles & lge o'fits by request; sep o'night area with elec & water; poss v cr; Eng spkn; adv bkg; higher charge during Le Mans events; quiet; ccard acc; red low ssn; CKE/CCI. "Lovely, tranquil, spacious site in chateau grnds; pleasant, helpful staff; dated, clean san facs - poss far fr pitches; some pitches in wooded areas poss tight lge o'fits; gd rest; gd for Le Mans; rec; no facs to drain waste water fr m'van." ♦ 31 May-31 Aug. € 47.60 SBS - L13 2013*

SOULLANS *2H3* (500m NE Urban) *46.79840, -1.89647* **Camp Municipal Le Moulin Neuf, Rue St Christophe, 85300 Soullans [02 51 68 00 24 (Mairie); fax 02 51 68 88 66; camping-soullans@wanadoo.fr]** Fr Challans ring rd take D69 sp Soullans. Site sp on L just bef town cent. Med, hdg/mkd pitch, pt shd; wc (some cont); shwrs inc; el pnts (4A) inc; gas 500m; lndtte; shop 500m; playgrnd; beach 12km; tennis; phone adj; poss cr; adv bkg; quiet; CKE/CCI. "Simple site; lovely walks & cycling; no twin-axles; vg." 15 Jun-15 Sep. € 10.00 2011*

THARON PLAGE see Pornic *2G3*

THOUARCE *4G1* (500m SW Rural) *47.26524, -0.50747* **Camp Municipal de l'Ecluse, 18 Ave des Trois Ponts, 49380 Thouarcé [02 41 54 14 36 (Mairie); fax 02 41 54 09 11; mairie.thouarce@wanadoo.fr; www.thouarce.fr]** Exit A87 junc 24 onto D160/D55 dir Beaulieu-sur-Layon & Thouarcé. Site sp adj Rv Layon. Sm, pt shd; wc (cont for men); shwrs inc; el pnts €1.70; gas; shops 500m; supmkt 1km; playgrnd; htd, covrd pool, tennis nr; fishing; extra charge (€30+) for twin-axles; no adv bkg; quiet; CKE/CCI. 15 Apr-15 Sep. € 6.80 2009*

TRANCHE SUR MER, LA *7A1* (300m N Urban/Coastal) *46.34563, -1.44296* **Camp Municipal Le Vieux Moulin, Ave Maurice Samson, 85360 La Tranche-sur-Mer [tel/fax 02 51 28 93 48; campinglevieuxmoulin@latranchesurmer.fr; www.latranchesurmer.org]** On ent town foll sp for Gendarmerie, sp adj supmkt. Lge, mkd pitch, some hdstg, pt sl, pt shd; wc; chem disp; baby facs; shwrs inc; el pnts (6A) inc; lndry rm; shop 400m; sand beach 350m; 50% statics; dogs €2.60; poss cr; adv bkg (dep); quiet; CKE/CCI. "Ltd touring pitches - some sm; town cent & beach 5 mins walk." 14 Mar-11 Oct. € 20.00 2009*

TRANCHE SUR MER, LA *7A1* (2km NE Coastal) *46.39206, -1.40199* **Camping Le Clos Cottet, Route de la Tranche-sur-Mer, 85750 Angles [02 51 28 90 72; fax 02 51 28 90 50; contact@camping-clos-cottet.com; www.camping-clos-cottet.com]** Fr N on D747 twd La Tranche-sur-Mer, site is on R sp after passing Angles, sp. Lge, hdg/mkd pitch, some hdstg, pt shd; htd wc (some cont); chem disp; mv service pnt; serviced pitch; baby facs; shwrs inc; el pnts (5A) €4; gas; Indtte (inc dryer); shop; tradsmn; rest, snacks; bar; BBQ; playgrnd; 2 pools (1 htd, covrd); paddling pool; waterslide; jacuzzi; sand beach 4km (free bus high ssn); lake fishing; games area; games rm; fitness rm; wifi; entmnt; 60% statics; dogs €3; Eng spkn; adv bkg; quiet; red low ssn/CKE/CCI. "Excel family site; vg facs; helpful, friendly staff." ♦ 7 Apr-22 Sep. € 25.00 2011*

TRANCHE SUR MER, LA *7A1* (2.6km NE Rural) *46.36286, -1.41936* **Camping Les Blancs Chênes, Route de la Roche-sur-Yon, 85360 La Tranche-sur-Mer [02 51 30 41 70 or 02 51 27 37 80 (res); fax 02 51 28 84 09; info@camping-vagues.oceanes.com; www.camping-vagues-oceanes.com]** Site sp on rd D747. Lge, mkd pitch, pt shd; mv service pnt; wc; baby facs; shwrs inc; el pnts (6A) inc; gas; Indtte; shop; tradsmn; rest, snacks; bar; BBQ; playgrnd; htd, covrd pool; paddling pool; waterslide; sand beach 1.8km; tennis; games area; games rm; entmnt; statics; dogs; shuttle bus to beach; quiet; Eng spkn; adv bkg; ccard acc; red low ssn; CKE/CCI. "Superb pool complex." ♦ Easter-11 Sep. € 28.00 2010*

TRANCHE SUR MER, LA *7A1* (500m E Coastal) *46.34611, -1.43225* **Camping La Baie d'Aunis, 10 Rue de Pertuis-Breton, 85360 La Tranche-sur-Mer [02 51 27 47 36; fax 02 51 27 44 54; info@camping-baiedaunis.com; www.camping-baiedaunis.com]** Fr La Roche-sur-Yon on D747 to La Tranche-sur-Mer; at 1st rndabt turn R, at 2nd rndabt (by Super U) turn L, at 3rd rndabt turn R - (all sp Centre Ville); ahead at min-rndabt & site on L in 100m. Med, hdg/mkd pitch, hdstg, pt shd; htd wc; chem disp; mv service pnt; baby facs; shwrs inc; el pnts (10A) inc; gas; Indtte; shop 600m; tradsmn; rest, snacks; bar; BBQ; playgrnd; htd pool; sand beach adj; sailing; sea-fishing; watersports; tennis 500m; cycle hire adj; games rm; entmnt; TV; 10% statics; dogs (not Jul/Aug) €2.30; Eng spkn; adv bkg (ess Jul/Aug); quiet; ccard acc; red low ssn; CKE/CCI. "Vg, friendly site; helpful staff; excel san facs; excel rest; poss diff ent for lge o'fits; gd beaches, lovely area." ♦ 26 Apr-15 Sep. € 35.00 2013*

See advertisement

TRANCHE SUR MER, LA *7A1* (3km E Coastal) *46.34810, -1.38730* **Camping du Jard, 123 Blvd du Lattre de Tassigny, 85360 La Tranche-sur-Mer [02 51 27 43 79; fax 02 51 27 42 92; info@campingdujard.fr; www.campingdujard.fr]** Foll D747 S fr La Roche-sur-Yon twd La Tranche; at rndabt on o'skirts of La Tranche turn L onto D46 sp La Faute-sur-Mer; cont for approx 5km. At rndabt turn R sp La Faute-sur-Mer 'par la côte'; then R at next rndabt onto D46 sp La Tranche-sur-Mer 'par la côte' & La Grière-Plage (ignore all previous La Grière sps); site on R in 1km. Rough app rd. Lge, hdg/mkd pitch, pt shd; wc; chem disp; serviced pitch; baby facs; sauna; shwrs inc; el pnts (10A) inc; Indtte (inc dryer); shop; rest, snacks; bar; BBQ (charcoal/gas); playgrnd; 2 pools (1 htd, covrd); paddling pool; waterslide; sand beach 700m; tennis; games area; fitness cent; cycle hire; horseriding 10km; golf 20km; wifi; entmnt; games/TV rm; 75% statics (tour ops); no dogs; no c'vans over 8m high ssn; Eng spkn; adv bkg; rd noise; ccard acc; red low ssn/CKE/CCI. "Lovely, well-run, clean & tidy site; busy high ssn; gd sized pitches, some sm; gd, well-kept san facs; gd pool; superb beach across busy coastal rd; easy parking at other beaches; poss flooding in wet weather; mkt Tue & Sat." ♦ 17 May-12 Sep. € 36.00 SBS - A03 2011*

TRANCHE SUR MER, LA *7A1* (4km E Coastal) *46.34781, -1.38303* **Camping La Grande Vallée, 145 blvd de Lattre de Tassigny, 85360 La Tranche-sur-Mer [02 51 30 12 82; fax 02 51 30 12 82; c.lagrandevallee@orange.fr; www.campinglagrandevallee.com]** Fr La Roche Sur Yon on D747 to Latranche. At rndabt turn L onto D46, in 5km at rndabt turn R sp Le Gote L'Aiguillon. R at next rndabt. Site sp on R past Spar. Med, mkd pitch, pt shd; wc; chem disp; mv service pnt; baby facs; shwrs inc; el pnts (4-10A); Indtte; BBQ; snacks; bar; playgrnd; beach 700m; 10% statics; dogs; bus; Eng spkn; adv bkg; quiet; red for long stay; ccards acc. "Vg; rec long stay; cycle hire; coastal bus Jul-Aug; friendly young owners; booking fee for mid/high ssn." 1 Apr-30 Sep. € 30.00 2014*

TUFFE *4F1* (1km N Urban) *48.11866, 0.51148* **FFCC Camping du Lac, Route de Prévelles, 72160 Tuffé [02 43 93 88 34; fax 02 43 93 43 54; camping.tuffe@wanadoo.fr; www.camping.tuffe.fr]** Site on D33, sp. Med, hdg/mkd pitch, pt shd; htd wc; chem disp; mv service pnt; baby facs; fam bthrm; shwrs inc; el pnts (6A) €2.50; Indtte; snacks; bar; BBQ; playgrnd; fishing; TV; wifi; lake sw adj; 10% statics; dogs €2; Eng spkn; adv bkg; CKE/CCI. "Well-kept, pretty lakeside site; adj tourist train; clean san facs; friendly staff." ♦ 30 Mar-30 Sep. € 24.70 2013*

TURBALLE, LA see Guérande *2G3*

VARADES see Ancenis *2G4*

VARENNES SUR LOIRE see Saumur *4G1*

VERNANTES *4G1* (2km E Rural) *47.38996, 0.06797* **Camping Intercommunal de la Grande Pâture, Route de Vernoil, 49390 Vernantes [02 41 51 45 39; contact@camping-grande-pature.com; www.camping-grande-pature.com]** Fr Saumur on N147. Take D767 to Vernantes then D58 dir Vernoil. Site sp. Sm, pt shd; wc; mv service pnt; shwrs inc; el pnts (10A) €1.80; shop 200m; rest; BBQ; playgrnd; tennis, fishing adj; some statics; adv bkg; quiet; CKE/CCI. 15 Jun-30 Sep. € 8.00 2009*

VERNANTES *4G1* (4km E Rural) *47.38310, 0.10036* **Camping La Sirotière, La Sablonnière, 49390 Vernoil-le-Fourrier [02 41 67 29 32; ann.bullock@orange.fr]** Fr Vernantes foll sp Vernoil & Super U; at rndabt (Super U on L) strt over & at end vill (at Barthelemy sp on L) turn R sp La Sablonnière. Foll rd up hill & turn R 300m after 2nd x-rds sp, & foll long drive to site. If coming fr Noyant (N) on D767 do not use satnav after Noyant, but foll dirs above. Fr A85 exit junc 2 onto D53 to St Philbert & Vernantes, then as above. Sm, pt sl, pt shd; htd wc; chem disp; shwrs inc; el pnts (10A) inc; lndtte; shop on site & bar 1km; rest 2km; cycle hire; dogs by request; Eng spkn; adv bkg; quiet; no ccard acc. "Peaceful CL-type site; British owners; adults only; site yourself if no reply at bell; vg." 1 Mar-31 Dec. € 13.00 2009*

VERNANTES *4G1* (4km NW Rural) *47.43700, 0.00600* **Camping La Fortinerie, La Fortinerie, 49390 Mouliherne [02 41 67 59 76; north.john.a@gmail.com; www.lafortinerie.com]** Fr Vernantes take D58 dir Mouliherne; opp Château Loroux (Plaissance) turn L; at x-rds turn R, site over 1.5km on L. Sm, pt shd; wc; chem disp; mv service pnt; shwrs inc; el pnts (16A) €5 (poss rev pol); ice; shop 4km; rest & bar 3km; BBQ; no statics; dogs free (by arrangement); B&B avail; adv bkg; quiet. "Peaceful CL-type site; only sound is crickets!; lge pitches; helpful, friendly British owners; beautiful chateau town; conv Loire valley & vineyards; excel." ♦ ltd 1 May-30 Sep. € 10.00 2011*

VILLIERS CHARLEMAGNE see Chateau Gontier *4F1*

VOUILLE LES MARAIS see Marans *7A1*

YYVRE L'EVEQUE see Mans, Le *4F1*

ST DENIS D'OLERON (ILE D'OLERON) see Brée les Bains, La *7A1*

Picardy

Regional Introduction

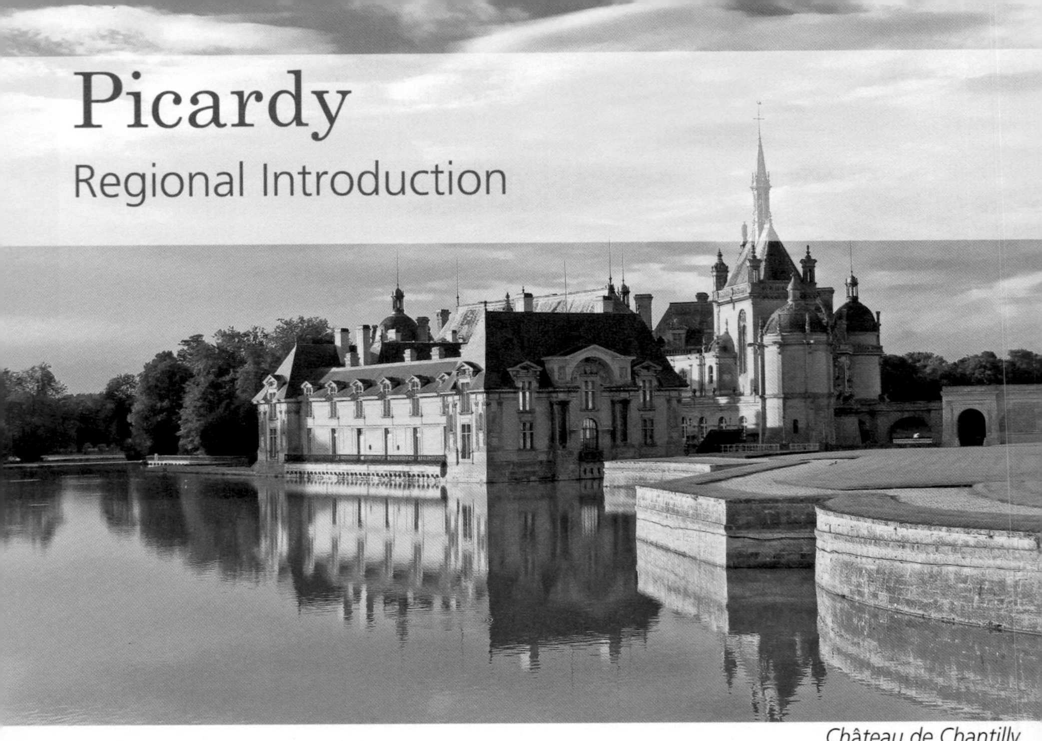

Château de Chantilly

Welcome to Picardy

With long sandy beaches, cliffs and coves of the Somme estuary in the West and vast pastures, agriculture and forests to the East, the landscape of Picardy is varied and picturesque.

Famously the location of the Battle of the Somme, the region has many museums and memorials to educate visitors and provide a place in which to remember those who fought for their countries.

The Bay of Somme is also popular with lovers of birds, since many species flock to the area for the expanses of open water and marshes which are ideal breeding grounds.

Local highlights

Markets in traditional Picardy towns are really popular and attract visitors looking for gourmet products like pâté de canard from Amiens or Flamiche leek pie.

April sees Picardy host the Festival of Birds and Nature, which makes the most of the excellent bird-watching opportunities of the Somme Bay.

Each June, Gerberay hosts its Rose Festival, when visitors get to see these beautiful flowers blossoming all over town.

Major towns and cities

- Amiens – famous for its cathedral and floating gardens.
- Abbeville – an important fort city located on the Somme River.
- Beauvais – known as the 'City of Tapestry Making'.
- Saint-Quentin – a town of architectural heritage on the banks of the Somme.
- Creil – steeped in history, the area includes a Neolithic site.

Regional attractions

- Château de Chantilly – a historical site, surrounded by forests and lakes.
- Musée d'Art et d'Archeologie, Senlis – a fascinating collection of art and Gallo-Roman artefacts, housed in a former Episcopal palace.
- Abbaye Saint-Jean-des-Vignes, Soissons – the remains of an impressive abbey, free to visit.
- Château du Coucy, Aisne – one of the largest defensive structures in France.

Find out more

www.picardietourisme.com
Tel: (0)3 22 22 33 66 Picardy Tourist Board

SITES IN PICARDY

ABBEVILLE *3B3* (14km SE Rural) *50.03416, 1.98383* **Camp Municipal La Peupleraie, 80510 Long [03 22 31 84 27 or 03 22 31 80 21; fax 03 22 31 82 39; bacquet.lionel@free.fr; www.long.fr]** Exit A16 at junc 21 for D1001 N then turn L at Ailly-le-Haut Clocher onto D32 for Long & foll sp. Med, mkd pitch, pt shd; wc (some cont); chem disp; shwrs inc; el pnts (6A) inc (caution - poss rev pol & poss other elec concerns) (long lead req); lndry rm; tradsmn; shop, rest, snacks, bar in vill; BBQ; playgrnd; fishing adj; 90% seasonal statics; dogs; phone adj; poss cr; adv bkg; ccard not acc; red long stay; CKE/CCI. "Pretty, busy site beside Rv Somme; gd san facs; gd walking/cycling by rv; site busy 1st week Sep - flea mkt in town; interesting area; old power stn museum; warden lives on site; conv en rte Calais; san facs v clean; quiet peaceful site; highly rec." 15 Mar-15 Nov. € 9.00 2013*

"I like to fill in the reports as I travel from site to site"

You'll find report forms at the back of this guide, or you can fill them in online at www.caravaclub.co.uk/europereport.

ABBEVILLE *3B3* (5km S Urban) *50.07826, 1.82378* **Camp Municipal du Marais-Talsac/Le Marais Communal, 62 Rue du Marais-Talsac, 80132 Mareuil-Caubert [03 22 31 62 37 or 03 22 24 11 46 (Mairie); fax 03 22 31 34 28; mairie.mareuilcaubert@wanadoo.fr]** Leave A28 at junc 3; at T-junc turn L onto D928; foll camping sp; in 4km turn sharp R onto D3 into Mareuil-Caubert; in 1km turn L thro housing est to site by stadium. Well sp. Med, mkd pitch, hdstg, pt shd; wc; chem disp; mv service pnt; shwrs inc; el pnts (6A) €2.90 (poss rev pol); shop & 5km; rest 5km; playgrnd; 25% statics; quiet; Eng spkn; CKE/CCI. "Well-kept, friendly site; sm pitches; helpful staff; clean dated facs, poss tired low ssn; no twin-axles or o'fits over 8m; hdstgs stony/loose gravel; gates clsd 2000-0800; interesting area; poss travellers low ssn (2010); vg NH Calais." 1 Apr-30 Sep. € 15.00 2014*

ABBEVILLE *3B3* (10km SW Rural) *50.08586, 1.71519* **Camping Le Clos Cacheleux, Rue des Sources, Route de Bouillancourt, 80132 Miannay [03 22 19 17 47; fax 03 22 31 35 33; raphael@camping-lecloscacheleux.fr; www.camping-lecloscacheleux.fr]** Fr A28 exit junc 2 onto D925 sp Cambron. In 5km at Miannay turn S onto D86 sp Bouillancourt. Site thro vill of R opp sister site Camping Le Val de Trie which is sp fr A28. Med, hdg/mkd pitch, pt sl pt shd; wc; chem disp; baby facs; fam bthrm; shwrs inc; el pnts (10A) inc (poss long lead req); gas; lndtte (inc dryer); shop; tradsmn; rest & 1km; snacks; bar; BBQ (charcoal/gas); playgrnd; htd, covrd pool adj; paddling pool adj; jacuzzi; sand beach 20km; fishing pond; tennis 3km; games area; games rm; farm animals; wifi; entmnt; TV rm; dogs €2.10; no c'vans/m'vans over 18m; some Eng spkn; adv bkg; quiet; ccard acc; red low ssn; CKE/CCI. "Pleasant, peaceful, wooded site; lge pitches; charming, helpful owner; excel facs; all services (inc shop, rest & pool) are on sister site 'Le Val de Trie' on opp side of rd, accessed via steep track 500m fr site ent; gd walking, cycling; gd for dogs." ♦ 15 Mar-14 Oct. € 26.00 SBS - P12 2014*

See advertisement

ABBEVILLE *3B3* (10km SW Rural) *50.08570, 1.71480* **Camping Le Val de Trie, 1 Rue des Sources, Bouillancourt-sous-Miannay, 80870 Moyenneville [03 22 31 48 88; fax 03 22 31 35 33; raphael@camping-levaldetrie.fr; www.camping-levaldetrie.fr]** Fr A28 exit junc 2 onto D925 sp Cambron. In 5km at Miannay turn S onto D86 sp Bouillancourt. Site thro vill on L. Site sp fr A28. NB Last pt of app narr with bends. Med, hdg/mkd pitch, hdstg, pt sl, shd; htd wc; chem disp; mv service pnt; baby facs; shwrs inc; el pnts (6A) €4.40; gas; lndtte (inc dryer); shop; tradsmn; rest, snacks; bar; BBQ; playgrnd; htd, covrd pool; paddling pool; lake fishing; games rm; wifi; entmnt; TV rm; 1% statics; dogs €2.10; phone; Eng spkn; adv bkg; quiet but poss noise nr generator for bouncy castle; ccard acc; red long stay/low ssn; CKE/CCI. "Beautiful, well-run site; well- shd; welcoming, helpful, conscientious owner; excel clean san facs, ltd low ssn; gd family site; woodland walks; interesting area; conv Calais." ♦ 1 Apr-15 Oct. € 27.00 (CChq acc) 2014*

See advertisement

ABBEVILLE *3B3* (7km NW Rural) *50.14166, 1.76237* **Camping Le Château des Tilleuls, Rue de la Baie, 80132 Port-le-Grand [03 22 24 07 75; fax 03 22 24 23 80; contact@chateaudestilleuls.com; www.chateaudestilleuls.com]** Fr N on A16 join A28 dir Rouen. At junc 1 take D40 dir St Valery-sur-Somme, site on R in approx 3km. Med, hdg/mkd pitch, hdstg, sl, terr, pt shd; htd wc; chem disp; mv service pnt; shwrs inc; el pnts (16A) €4; Indtte; shop & 5km; snacks; BBQ; playgrnd; htd pool; sand beach 7km; tennis; bike hire; games rm; wifi; TV rm; dogs free; adv bkg; quiet; ccard acc; red long stay; CKE/CCI. "Pleasant site; improvements in progress (2011); lge, v sloping pitches; find suitable pitch bef booking in; long uphill walk fr recep; unisex san facs; new pitches far fr ent; site being updated." ♦ 1 Mar-31 Dec. € 30.50 2013*

⊞ **ACY EN MULTIEN** *3D3* (700m SE Rural) *49.09842, 2.96144* **Caravaning L'Ancien Moulin (CC de F), 60620 Acy-en-Multien [tel/fax 03 44 87 21 28; ccdf_acy@cegetel.net; www.campingclub.asso.fr]** Exit N2 at Lévignen onto D332 S dir Betz; cont thro Betz to Acy-en-Multien; cont thro Acy on D332 dir Rosoy-en-Multien; site on R as leaving Acy. Med, mkd pitch, pt shd; htd wc; chem disp; shwrs inc; el pnts (6A) inc; Indtte; shops, rest, snacks, bar, playgrnd 1km; fishing; games area; games rm; entmnt; TV rm; 90% statics; dogs €2.20; adv bkg; quiet but poss aircraft noise; CKE/CCI. "Touring pitches by mill pool; helpful, friendly staff; clean, adequate san facs; recep 1400-1700; site tired & has seen better days (2011); mainly tired statics, many unoccupied (2011); 30km fr Disneyland Paris & conv other theme parks." ♦ € 24.00 2011*

AIZELLES *3C4* (500m N Rural) *49.49076, 3.80817* **Camping du Moulin (Merlo), 16 Rue du Moulin, 02820 Aizelles [03 23 22 41 18 or 06 14 20 47 43 (mob); magali.merlo@orange.fr; www.camping-du-moulin.fr]** Fr Laon take D1044 dir Reims; in 13km turn L on D88 to Aizelles; site sp in vill 'Camping à la Ferme'. Fr Reims on A26 exit junc 14 onto D925 then D1044 N. Turn R to Aizelles on D889 past Corbeny. Turn onto Rue du Moulin & site on R in 250m. Camping sp at church says 100m but allow 300m to see ent. NB Lge o'fits take care sharp R turn at ent to site. Sm, pt sl, pt shd; wc (cont); chem disp; shwrs €1; el pnts (6A) €3.60 inc (poss rev pol, poss long lead req); shop 2km; tradsmn; playgrnd; fishing 800m; 70% statics (not visible); poss cr; little Eng spkn; quiet but poss noisy w/end; ccard acc; red low ssn; CKE/CCI. "Attractive, well-kept CL-type farm site; friendly, helpful owners; basic san facs need update; gates clsd 2200-0700; wonderful well maintained site in a sm pretty vil; conv Calais 3 hrs." 15 Apr-15 Oct. € 23.00 2014*

ALBERT *3B3* (500m N Urban) *50.01136, 2.65556* **Camp Municipal du Vélodrome, Ave Henri Dunant, 80300 Albert [03 64 62 22 53; fax 03 22 74 38 30; campingalbert@laposte.net; www.ville-albert.fr]** Fr town cent take Rue Godin E adj to Basilica & foll sp for site. Easiest access fr Bapaume (N) twds Albert; turn R at camping sp on edge of town. Med, mkd pitch, unshd; wc; chem disp; mv service pnt; shwrs inc; el pnts (4-10A) €2.20-3.60 (rev pol); shop 1km open 7 days; fishing adj; 40% statics; dogs; poss cr in high ssn; Eng spkn; poss rwly noise; adv bkg; red long stay; CKE/CCI. "Pleasant, well-run, clean site; friendly, helpful warden; poss security prob; conv for Lille, Arras & Amien by train & for WW1 battlefields etc; facs basic but rates reasonable; well maintained clean site; if office close find pitch and inform warden later; gates clsd fairly early, will need entry code if late." ♦ 1 Apr-15 Oct. € 23.00 2014*

ALBERT *3B3* (5km NE Rural) *50.04141, 2.66868* **International Camping Bellevue, 25 Rue d'Albert, 80300 Authuille [03 22 74 59 29 / 06 71 96 88 78 (mob); fax 03 22 74 05 14; camping.bellevue0767@orange.fr; www.visit-somme.com]** Take D929 Albert to Bapaume rd; in 3km turn L at La Boiselle, foll sp to Aveluy cont to Authuille. Site on R in vill cent. Med, hdg pitch, pt sl, pt shd; wc; chem disp; shwrs; el pnts (5A) inc (rev pol); shop 7km; tradsmn; rest; playgrnd; rv fishing 500m; 80% statics; dogs €1; adv bkg; quiet, poss noisy at w/end; CKE/CCI. "Helpful owner; basic site - poss run down (5/2010); useful touring Somme WW1 battlefields; walking dist of Thiepval Ridge; gd NH; lovely site; excel rest in vill." 15 Mar-31 Oct. € 14.00 2013*

ALBERT *3B3* (10km SE Rural) *49.92943, 2.74891* **Camp Municipal Les Charnilles, Les Près Bana, 80340 Cappy [03 22 76 14 50, 06 45 19 60 63 (mob) or 03 22 76 02 13 (Mairie); fax 03 22 76 62 74; mariedecappy@wandoo.fr; http://picardietourisme.com]** Fr Albert S on D329 to Bray-sur-Somme; turn L in Bray onto D1; 100m after vill sp Cappy, turn R (opp D197 to Lille). Site in 500m at end of lane. Med, hdg/mkd pitch, hdstg, pt shd; htd wc; chem disp; shwrs €1.50; el pnts (6A) inc; Indry rm; shops 1km; tradsmn; dogs €0.10; Eng spkn; quiet; ccard not acc; CKE/CCI. "Lovely, clean, well-laid out site; friendly, helpful warden; immac san facs; ltd touring pitches; pretty vill on Rv Somme; conv A1." ♦ 1 Apr-31 Oct. € 15.50 2011*

ALBERT *3B3* (10km SW Rural) *49.91930, 2.57985* **FFCC Camping Les Puits Tournants, 6 Rue du Marais, 80800 Sailly-le-Sec [tel/fax 03 22 76 65 56; camping.puitstournant@wanadoo.fr; www.camping-les-puits-tournants.com]** Fr N exit A1 junc 14 onto D929 dir Amiens, at Albert take D42 S to Sailly-Laurette then turn R onto D233 to Sailly-le-Sec & foll sp. Or fr S exit junc 13 twd Albert onto D1029. At Lamotte-Warfusée R onto D42 to Sailly-Laurette, turn L to Sailley-le-Sec. Med, some hdg pitch, some hdstg, pt shd; htd wc; chem disp; mv service pnt; shwrs inc; el pnts (4A) €3; gas; Indtte; shop & 7km; tradsmn; rest 2km; BBQ; playgrnd; htd pool; paddling pool; lake sw; fishing; sports area; canoe & cycle hire; tennis 2km; horseriding 5km; TV rm; 60% statics; dogs; adv bkg; quiet; ccard acc. "Lovely family-run site; amiable staff; gd clean san facs; grass pitches muddy when wet; tight ent, lge o'fits poss diff; gd pool; walks by rv; excel." ♦ 1 Apr-31 Oct. € 18.00 (3 persons) (CChq acc) 2011*

AMIENS *3C3* (800mtrs N Rural) *49.97240, 2.30150* **FFCC Camping du Château, Rue du Château, 80260 Bertangles [tel/fax 09 51 66 32 60; camping@chateaubertangles.com; www.chateaubertangles.com]** Foll N25 N of Amiens; after 8km turn W on D97 to Bertangles. Well sp in vill. Sm, hdg pitch, pt shd; wc; chem disp; shwrs inc; el pnts (5A) €3.70 (poss rev pol); tradsmn; tabac/bar in vill; bus; poss cr; quiet but slight rd noise; ccard notacc; red long stay; CKE/CCI. "Pleasant, peaceful, well-kept site by chateau wall; busy high ssn - early arr rec (bef 1600); pleasant welcome; clean san facs; ltd recep hrs, pitch yourself; grnd soft when wet; Amiens attractive city; gd walks; conv a'routes & NH; excel; gd value." ♦ 19 Apr-9 Sep. € 26.30 2014*

AMIENS *3B3* (32km N Rural) *50.13813, 2.36842* **Camping Familial Au Bord De l'Authie, Route d'Albert 80600 Authieule [03 22 32 56 13 or 06 74 59 92 65 (mob); contact@campingauborddelauthie.com; www.campingauborddelauthie.com]** Fr Amiens N25 twd Rue de Longpré, turn R at Doullens onto D938. After 2.6 km site on R. Sm, mkd pitch, pt sl, terr, shd; wc; chem disp; mv service pnt; fam bthrm; shwr inc; el pnts (6A); Indtte (inc dryer); shop; snack bar; rest; BBQ; entmnt; wifi; 80% statics; dogs; Eng spkn; adv bkg; quiet; CCI. ♦ 1 Feb-1 Dec. € 13.00 2014*

AMIENS *3C3* (8km NW Urban) *49.92091, 2.25883* **Camping Parc des Cygnes, 111 Ave des Cygnes, 80080 Amiens-Longpré [03 22 43 29 28; fax 03 22 43 59 42; camping.amiens@wanadoo.fr; www.parcdescygnes.com]** Exit A16 junc 20 twds Amiens onto ring rd Rocade Nord exit junc 40. At 1st rndabt foll sp Amiens, Longpré D412; foll sp Parc de Loisirs & site. Med, mkd pitches, ltd shd; htd wc; chem disp; mv service pnt; baby facs; shwrs inc; el pnts (10A) inc on most pitches (poss long lead req); gas; Indtte (inc dryer); sm shop; snacks; bar; BBQ; playgrnd; fishing nrby; kayaking; cycle hire; games rm; wifi; TV; dogs €2.40; no c'vans/m'vans over 11m high ssn; bus to city adj; adv bkg rec; quiet; ccard acc; red low ssn. "Peaceful, well-kept, secure site in parkland; leisure park adj; lge pitches; helpful, welcoming staff; gd, clean san facs, ltd low ssn; ring bell by recep if office clsd; access to grass pitches off hard areas - m'vans can keep driving wheels on in wet weather; gd canal-side cycling/walk to city; Amiens cathedral worth visit; longer leads req for some pitches; conv Somme battlefields; excel; rec; 50% of pitches have el pnts; san facs need updating." ♦ 1 Apr-14 Oct. € 38.00 SBS - P11 2014*

ATTICHY *3C4* (500m SW Rural) *49.40664, 3.05295* **Camping De l'Aigrette (Formaly Camp municipal Fleury), 22 Rue Fontaine-Aubier, 60350 Attichy [03 44 42 15 97 or 06 62 83 79 35 (mob); fax 09 72 42 38 20; contact@campingdelaigrette.com; www.campingdelaigrette.com]** Fr Compiègne E on N31. After 16km turn L at traff lts sp Attichy & site. Over iron bdge & turn R to site on lakeside. Med, hdg pitch, pt shd; htd wc; chem disp; mv service pnt; shwrs inc; el pnts (10A) €2; shop 1km; tradsmn; rests in town; BBQ; playgrnd; pool; fishing; 80% statics; dogs €0.50; wifi; poss cr; quiet; ccard not acc; site clsd 25 Dec - 31 Jan; CKE/CCI. "Attractive, clean site in pleasant vill; many w/end statics, few touring pitches; helpful wardens live on site; modern san facs, stretched high ssn; gd security; excel NH low ssn; excel site." ♦ 1 Mar-30 Nov. € 20.80 2014*

AUTHUILLE see Albert *3B3*

⊞ **BEAUVAIS** *3C3* (15.7km E Rural) *49.40506, 2.25803* **Camping de la Trye, Rue de Trye, 60510 Bresles [03 44 07 80 95 or 06 10 40 30 29 (mob); www.camping-de-la-trye.com]** Exit N31 (Beauvais to Clermont) at Bresles; foll site sp. Med, hdg/mkd pitch, pt sl; wc; chem disp; mv service pnt; shwrs inc; el pnts (6A) inc; Indtte (inc dryer); tradsmn; playgrnd; pony rides; cycle hire; trampoline; entmnt; wifi; dogs; ccard acc; CKE/CCI. "New Dutch owners, improving site (2011); cycle & walking rtes; theme parks nrby; largely a holiday chalet/static site with ltd no of touring pitches; fair NH/sh stay." € 25.00 2014*

⊞ **BERNY RIVIERE** *3C4* (1.5km S Rural) *49.40603, 3.12860* **Camping La Croix du Vieux Pont, Rue de la Fabrique, 02290 Berny-Rivière [03 23 55 50 02; fax 03 23 55 05 13; info@la-croix-du-vieux-pont.com; www.la-croix-du-vieux-pont.com]** On N31 bet Soissons & Compiègne. At site sp turn onto D13, then at Vic-sur-Aisne take next R, R again then L onto D91. Foll sp to site on o'skts of Berny. V lge, hdg pitch, hdstg, pt shd; htd wc; chem disp; mv service pnt; some serviced pitch; baby facs; shwrs inc; el pnts (6A) €2.50 (poss rev pol, no earth & ltd supply); gas; Indtte (inc dryer); supmkt; tradsmn; rest, snacks; bar; playgrnd; 4 htd pools (2 covrd); waterslide; lake beach & sw; fishing; boating; tennis; games rm; horseriding; archery; golf; cycle hire; beauty cent; gym; wifi; entmnt; TV rm; many tour op statics high ssn; dogs; poss cr; Eng spkn; adv bkg rec; quiet; ccard acc; CKE/CCI. "Pleasant, well-run, clean site; busy low ssn; lge pitches, some rvside; excel for families or older couples; friendly, helpful staff; vg san facs, ltd low ssn; some sh stay pitches up steep bank; some pitches worn/uneven end of ssn (2010); some pitches liable to flood; site open all yr but no services Nov-Mar; excel." ♦ € 22.50 2010*

⊞ **BERNY RIVIERE** *3C4* (2km W Rural) *49.39280, 3.15161* **Camping La Halte de Mainville, 18 Chemin du Routy, 02290 Ressons-le-Long [03 23 74 26 69; fax 03 23 74 03 60; lahaltedemainville@wanadoo.fr; www.lahaltedemainville.com]** Fr Soissons W on N31 dir Compiègne, in approx 8km look for site sp on L. Clearly sp. Lge, hdg/mkd pitch, pt shd; htd wc; chem disp; shwrs inc; el pnts (6A) €3 (poss rev pol); Indtte; shop 4km; tradsmn; playgrnd; htd pool; paddling pool; fishing; tennis; 60% statics; dogs; phone; Eng spkn; adv bkg rec; quiet but poss some rd noise; no ccard acc; red CKE/CCI. "Pleasant, clean, conv NH; friendly staff; 1 hr fr Disneyland; vg." € 16.00 2010*

BERTANGLES see Amiens *3C3*

⊞ **BOURG ET COMIN** *3D4* (500m NE Rural) *49.39871, 3.66072* **Camping de la Pointe, 5 Rue de Moulins, 02160 Bourg-et-Comin [03 23 25 87 52; fax 03 23 25 06 02; michel.pennec@9online.fr; www.tourisme-paysdelaon.com]** Leave A26/E17 at junc 14 & turn W along D925 dir Soissons for 15km. Site on R on ent vill. Sm, hdg pitch, pt shd; htd wc; chem disp; mv service pnt; shwrs inc; el pnts (6A) €3.20; Indtte; baker 500m; tradsmn; crêperie adj; rest; bar 500m; BBQ; playgrnd; htd, covrd pool; internet; dogs €2; phone; bus 500m; adv bkg; quiet; CKE/CCI. "CL-type site in orchard; narr ent & access to pitches poss diff lge o'fits; most pitches sm & not suitable lge o'fits; el pnts poss not working (2010); gd rest; gd walking area; 10 mins fr Parc Nautique de l'Ailette with watersports; conv Aisne Valley." € 12.60 2011*

CARLEPONT see Noyon *3C3*

PICARDY

CAYEUX SUR MER *3B2* (2km NE Coastal) *50.19765, 1.51675* **Camping Le Bois de Pins, Rue Guillaume-le-Conquérant, Brighton, 80410 Cayeux-sur-Mer [tel/fax 03 22 26 71 04; info@campingleboisdepins.com; www.campingleboisdepins.com]** Take D940 out of St Valery to Cayeux, then D102 NE for 2km & foll sp. Lge, mkd pitch, terr, pt shd; htd wc; shwrs; chem disp; mv service pnt; el pnts (6-10A) inc; lndtte; shop; tradsmn; BBQ; playgrnd; beach 500m; sailing & fishing adj; cycle hire; horseriding; games rm; 50% statics; dogs €2; adv bkg; quiet; red low ssn/CKE/CCI. "Friendly, clean, busy site; attractive sm town; gd cycling & birdwatching area; gd." ♦ 1 Apr-1 Nov. € 28.50 (3 persons) 2011*

CAYEUX SUR MER *3B2* (3km NE Coastal) *50.20291, 1.52641* **Camping Les Galets de la Mollière, Rue Faidherbe, 80410 La Mollière-d'Aval [03 22 26 61 85; fax 03 22 26 65 68; info@campinglesgaletsdelamolliere.com; www.campinglesgaletsdelamolliere.com]** Fr Cayeux-sur-Mer take D102 N along coast for 3km. Site on R. Lge, mkd pitch, pt shd; wc; chem disp; mv service pnt; baby facs; shwrs inc; el pnts (6A) inc; gas; lndtte (inc dryer); shop; snacks; bar; BBQ; playgrnd; htd pool; paddling pool; sand beach 500m; games area; games rm; wifi; 25% statics; dogs €3; phone adj; quiet; red low ssn; CKE/CCI. "Spacious, much improved, wooded site with lge pitches; barrier clsd 2300-0700; pleasant staff." 1 Apr-1 Nov. € 31.00 (3 persons) 2011*

⊞ **CHANTILLY** *3D3* (5km W Rural) *49.21225, 2.40270* **Camping L'Abbatiale, 39 Rue Salvador Allendé, 60340 St Leu-d'Esserent [tel/fax 03 44 56 38 76; contact@camping-abbatiale.fr; http://campingabbatiale.wix.com/campingabbatiale]** S twds Paris on A1 exit Senlis; cont W fr Senlis on D924/D44 thro Chantilly x-ing Rv Oise to St Leu-d'Esserent; cont on D44, x-ing D603 which becomes Rue Salvador Allendé in 700m; foll site sps; avoid rv x-ing on D17 fr SW; v narr bdge. Sm, hdg/mkd pitch, hdstg, pt shd; htd wc; chem disp; mv service pnt; shwrs; el pnts (3A) €2.50; lndtte (inc dryer); shop 2km; rest 2km; BBQ (sep area); playgrnd; sandy beach/sw 1km; games area; games rm; internet; wifi; dogs; phone; bus adj; twin axles; Eng spkn; adv bkg; quiet; ccard acc; red long stay. "Chantilly & chateau interesting; conv for Chantilly, Paris & L'oise Valley; gd walks nrby (woodland & rvside); v friendly family owned & managed; lge nbr of statics on site but does not detract from touring pitches nor impact on facs." € 17.50 2014*

CHANTILLY *3D3* (5km NW Rural) *49.22571, 2.42862* **Camping Campix, 60340 St Leu d'Esserent [03 44 56 08 48; fax 03 44 56 28 75; campix@orange.fr; www.campingcampix.com]** Exit A1 junc 8 to Senlis; cont W fr Senlis on D924 thro Chantilly, x-ing Rv Oise to St Leu-d'Esserent; leave town on D12 NW twd Cramoisy thro housing est; foll site sp for 1km, winding app. Med, mkd pitch, hdstg, terr, shd; htd wc; chem disp; mv service pnt; baby facs; shwrs inc; el pnts (6-10A) €3.50 (min 25m cable poss req); gas; lndtte (inc dryer); shop; tradsmn; rest, snacks; pizza delivery; BBQ; playgrnd; pool complex; sand beach & lake sw 1km; fishing; games rm; wifi; no statics; dogs €2; phone; Eng spkn; adv bkg; quiet; red long stay/low ssn; ccard acc; CKE/CCI. "Beautiful, peaceful site in former quarry - poss unguarded, vertical drops; helpful owner & friendly staff; wide variety of pitches - narr, steep access & o'hanging trees on some; conv Paris Parc Astérix & Disneyland (Astérix tickets fr recep); sh walk to vill; rec; facs inadequate hg ssn & outdated (2014); long elec leads maybe needed ." ♦ 7 Mar-30 Nov. € 25.00 (CChq acc) 2014*

CHARLY SUR MARNE *3D4* (500m S Urban) *48.97363, 3.28210* **Camp Municipal Les Illettes, Route de Pavant, 02310 Charly-sur-Marne [03 28 82 12 11 or 03 23 82 00 32 (Mairie); fax 03 23 82 13 99; mairie.charly@wanadoo.fr; www.charly-sur-marne.fr]** Exit A4 junc 18 onto D603 dir La Ferté; then take D402/D969 NE to Charly. Site sp in town. Sm, hdg pitch, pt shd; wc; chem disp; shwrs; el pnts (5-10A) €2-3; lndry rm; supmkt adj; dogs €2.50; quiet, but poss noise eves fr sports complex adj; no twin-axles; red long stay/low ssn. "Lovely, well-kept site; pleasant warden; 10 min walk to rv & rvside walks; conv for touring Champagne rte; rec arr early to secure pitch during grape harvest; excel." ♦ 1 Apr-30 Sep. € 14.50 2012*

CLERY SUR SOMME see Péronne *3C3*

CREVECOEUR LE GRAND *3C3* (10km SW Rural) *49.57569, 1.93899* **Camping du Vieux Moulin, 9 Rue Larris Boissy, 60690 Roy-Boissy [03 44 46 33 06]** Fr Marseille-en-Beauvasis SW onto D930 dir Gournay-en-Bray; in 1.5km site sp to R at Roy-Boissy. Sm, pt shd; wc; chem disp; shwrs inc; el pnts inc (poss rev pol); playgrnd; 90% statics; phone; v quiet. "Farm site in area with few sites; beautiful countryside; pitch yourself, owner calls eves; excel." ♦ 1 Apr-31 Oct. € 8.00 2009*

PICARDY

CROTOY, LE *3B2* (1.3km N Urban/Coastal) *50.22396, 1.61908* **Camping La Prairie, 2 Rue de Mayocq, 80550 Le Crotoy [tel/fax 03 22 27 02 65; info@camping-laprairie.fr; www.camping-laprairie.fr]** Fr S exit A16 at Abbeville onto D86/ D940 to Le Crotoy to rndabt at ent to town. Cont strt for 1.5km then 2nd L, site on L in 500m. Fr N exit A16 for Rue onto D32, then D940, then as above. Lge, hdg pitch, pt shd; wc (some cont); chem disp (wc); shwrs; el pnts (3A) inc; tradsmn; playgrnd; sand beach 400m; 90% statics; dogs €1; phone; poss cr; quiet. "Busy site; ltd pitches for tourers; conv beach & town; gd san facs; gd cycle paths; gd tourist train & bird walks; everything in walking dist." ♦ 1 Apr-30 Sep. € 25.00 2014*

CROTOY, LE *3B2* (1.5km N Rural) *50.22968, 1.64140* **Camping La Ferme de Tarteron, Route de Rue, 80550 Le Crotoy [03 22 27 06 75; fax 03 22 27 02 49; contact@letarteron.fr; www.letarteron.fr]** Fr A16 exit junc 24 onto D32, then D940 around Rue twd Le Crotoy. Pass D4 dir St Firmin site on L. Med, hdg/mkd pitch, pt shd; wc; chem disp; shwrs inc; el pnts (4-10A) €3.50-8; gas; shop; tradsmn; snacks; bar; playgrnd; htd pool; sand beach 1.5km; wifi; many statics; quiet. "Conv Marquenterre bird park & steam train fr Le Crotoy; v clean, basic san facs." 1 Apr-31 Oct. € 36.00 2014*

CROTOY, LE *3B2* (3km N Rural/Coastal) *50.23905, 1.63182* **Kawan Club Camping Le Ridin, Mayocq, 80550 Le Crotoy [03 22 27 03 22; fax 03 22 27 70 76; leridin@baiedesommepleinair.com; www.campingleridin.com]** Fr N exit A16 junc 24 dir Rue & Le Crotoy; at rndabt on D940 on app to Le Crotoy take D4 (due W) sp St Firmin; take 2nd rd to L, site sp. Or fr S exit A16 junc 23 onto D40/D940 to Le Crotoy; at rndabt cont strt over onto D4; in 800m turn R; site on R in 1km. NB Do not ent Le Crotoy town with c'van. Lge, hdg/mkd pitch, hdstg, unshd; htd wc; chem disp; mv service pnt; baby facs; fam bthrm; shwrs inc; el pnts (4-10A) €3-5.50; gas; lndtte (inc dryer); shop; supmkt 1km; tradsmn; rest, snacks; bar; playgrnd; htd pool; paddling pool; sand beach 1km; tennis 4km; cycle hire; fitness rm; games rm; golf 10km; wifi; entmnt; TV rm; 60% statics; dogs €2; poss cr; Eng spkn; adv bkg; quiet except noise fr adj gravel pit/lorries; ccard acc; red long stay/CKE/CCI. "Some sm, tight pitches bet statics; narr site rds not suitable lge o'fits; helpful staff; clean san facs, unisex low ssn; bird sanctuary at Marquenterre; Le Crotoy interesting town; vg site." ♦ 31 Mar-6 Nov. € 30.00 (CChq acc) 2012*

See advert on previous page

CROTOY, LE *3B2* (4km N Coastal) *50.24941, 1.61145* **Camping Les Aubépines, 800 Rue de la Maye, St Firmin, 80550 Le Crotoy [03 22 27 01 34; fax 03 22 27 13 66; lesaubepines@baiedesommepleinair.com; www.baiedesommepleinair.com]** Exit A16 junc 23 to Le Crotoy via D40 & D940; then foll sp St Firmin; site sp. Or exit A16 junc 24 onto D32 dir Rue; by-pass Rue but take D4 to St Firmin; after church look for site sp. Site on rd to beach on W of D4. Med, hdg/mkd pitch, pt shd; htd wc; chem disp; baby facs; shwrs inc; el pnts (3-10A) €3-8 (poss long lead req); gas; lndtte (inc dryer); sm shop & 4km; tradsmn; BBQ; playgrnd; htd pool; paddling pool; sand beach 1km; horseriding; cycle hire; games rm; internet; entmnt; 40% statics; dogs €2; phone; poss cr; Eng spkn; adv bkg; quiet; ccard acc; red low ssn; CKE/CCI. "Peaceful, popular, well-run site; tourers sited with statics; lovely pool; gd cycling & walking; check office opening hrs for early dep; Marquenterre ornithological park 3km; steam train 3km; excel." ♦ 1 Apr-6 Nov. € 21.50 2011*

See advert on previous page

"I need an on-site restaurant"

We do our best to make sure site information is correct, but it is always best to check any must-have facilities are still available or will be open during your visit.

CROTOY, LE *3B2* (4km N Coastal) *50.24959, 1.61207* **Les 3 Sablières, 1850, Rue de la Maye, 80550 St. Firmin les Crotoy [03 22 27 01 33; fax 03 22 27 10 06; contact@camping-les-trois-sablieres.com; www.camping-les-trois-sablieres.com]** Fr Calais foll sp for RUE & then St Firmin Crotoy. Med, mkd pitch, hdstg; wc; chem disp; mv service pnt; baby facs; shwrs inc; el pnts (6A) €4.50; lndtte (inc dryer); shop; bar; BBQ; playgrnd; htd pool; fitness rm; sauna & solarium; games rm; TV; statics; dogs €2.10; ccard acc. "V nice site with clean facs; lovely atmosphere in gd location; cycle tracks start fr campsite; would rec." € 24.00 2011*

See advertisement

PICARDY

CUVILLY *3C3* (1.5km N Rural) *49.56750, 2.70790* **Camping de Sorel, 24 Rue St Claude, 60490 Orvillers-Sorel [03 44 85 02 74; fax 03 44 42 11 65; contact@aestiva.fr; www.camping-sorel.com]** Exit A1/E15 at junc 12 (Roye) S'bound or 11 (Ressons) N'bound. Site on E of D1017. Med, mkd pitch, pt shd; htd wc; chem disp; mv service pnt; baby facs; shwrs inc; el pnts (10A) €3; Indtte; shop; tradsmn; rest, snacks; bar; BBQ; playgrnd; rv fishing 10km; games area; wifi; TV rm; 50% statics; poss cr; quiet; red low ssn. "Pleasant situation; conv NH A1 & Calais; friendly staff; facs need updating (2014); rec early arr in ssn; busy at w/end; 30 mins Parc Astérix; plenty to visit." ♦ 1 Feb-15 Dec. € 32.00 (CChq acc) 2014*

ETREAUPONT see Vervins *3C4*

“Satellite navigation makes touring much easier”

Remember most sat navs don't know if you're towing or in a larger vehicle – always use yours alongside maps and site directions.

FERE, LA *3C4* (400m N Urban) *49.66554, 3.36205* **Camp Municipal du Marais de la Fontaine, Rue Vauban, 02800 La Fère [03 23 56 82 94; fax 03 23 56 40 04]** S on D1044 (St Quentin to Laon); R onto D338; turn E at rndabt; ignore 1st camping sp; turn N at next rndabt; site sp. Or Exit A26 junc 12 onto D1032 SW; in 2km turn R onto D35; in 4km pass under D1044; in 400m turn R; in 800m turn R at traff lts; foll over bdge to sports complex. Sm, hdg/mkd pitch, pt shd; wc; chem disp (wc); shwrs inc; el pnts (15A) €3; shop; tradsmn; rest, snacks & bar 1km; BBQ; htd, covrd pool adj; dogs €1.20; adv bkg rec; rd & rlwy noise; red long stay; CKE/CCI. "Well-kept site adj leisure cent; conv Calais, 2hrs 30mins; clean san facs; pitching awkward due sm pitches & narr site rds; warden lives adj site - on arr open double gates & ring doorbell to register; gates shut 2200-0700 - no vehicle/person access; avoid 1st w/end June as Wine & Food Festival held on site; conv A26; gd NH." ♦ ltd 1 Apr-30 Sep. € 14.00 2013*

FEUILLERES *3C3* (350m W Rural) *49.94851, 2.84364* **Camping du Château et de l'Oseraie, 12 Rue du Château, 80200 Feuillères [03 22 83 17 59 or 06 16 97 93 42 (mob) (LS); fax 03 22 83 04 14; jsg-bred@wanadoo.fr; www.camping-chateau-oseraie.com]** Fr A1/E15 exit 13.1 Maurepas onto D938 dir Albert & then L onto D146; R at staggered x-rds in Feuillères (by church) & site on R in 500m. Med, hdg/mkd pitch, hdstg, pt shd; wc; chem disp; mv service pnt; shwrs €1.20; el pnts (6A) inc (poss rev pol); gas; Indtte; tradsmn; supmkt 10km; snacks; bar; BBQ; playgrnd; htd pool; fishing; tennis; games area; games rm; wifi; entmnt high ssn; 10% statics; dogs €1.20; no twin-axles; Eng spkn; slight rlwy noise; adv bkg rec high ssn; ccard acc; red long stay; CKE/CCI. "Excel, well-kept, well-run site; gd sized pitches; friendly staff; clean san facs; conv A1 a'route, WW1 battlefields & Disneyland Paris." ♦ 29 Mar-31 Oct. € 19.20 2013*

FOREST MONTIERS see Rue

FORT MAHON PLAGE *3B2* (1km E Rural) *50.33230, 1.57990* **Airotel Camping Le Royon, 1271 Route de Quend, 80120 Fort-Mahon Plage [03 22 23 40 30; fax 03 22 23 65 15; info@campingleroyon.com; www.campingleroyon.com]** Exit A16 at junc 24 Forest-Montiers onto D32 to Rue, then dir Quend & Fort-Mahon-Plage, site sp. Lge, hdg/mkd pitch, pt shd; wc (some cont); mv service pnt; chem disp; baby facs; shwrs inc; el pnts (6A) inc; gas; Indtte (inc dryer); shop; tradsmn; snacks; bar; playgrnd; htd, covrd pool; paddling pool; sand beach 2km; games area; sailing, fishing, golf nr; cycle hire; wifi; entmnt; 90% statics; dogs €3; phone; poss cr; Eng spkn; adv bkg; ccard acc; red low ssn/long stay/CKE/CCI. "Modern san facs; med sized pitches, but access poss diff due parked cars; conv Mercanterre nature reserve." ♦ 12 Mar-1 Nov. € 31.00 (3 persons) 2011*

FORT MAHON PLAGE *3B2* (8km S Rural) *50.31950, 1.60583* **FLOWER Camping Les Vertes Feuilles, 25 Route de la Plage, Monchaux, 80120 Quend Plage-les-Pins [03 22 23 55 12; fax 03 22 19 07 52; lesvertesfeuilles@baiedesommepleinair.com; www.baiedesommepleinair.com / www.flowercampings.com]** Exit A16 junc 24 onto D32/D940 N. Turn W dir Quend onto D32, site sp. Med, hdg/mkd pitch, hdstg, pt shd; htd wc; chem disp; baby facs; shwrs inc; el pnts (4-10A) €3.50-6.50; gas; Indtte (inc dryer); shop; tradsmn; snacks; BBQ; playgrnd; htd, covrd pool; paddling pool; sand beach 4km; tennis 6km; cycle hire; games area; games rm; wifi; entmnt; TV rm; 40% statics; dogs €2; poss cr; Eng spkn; adv bkg; quiet; ccard acc; red low ssn. "Pleasant, family site." ♦ 1 Apr-7 Nov. € 24.50 2010*

GAMACHES *3B2* (1km NW Rural) *49.99397, 1.54366* **Camping Domaine Les Marguerites, Rue Antonin Gombert, 80220 Gamaches [tel/fax 03 22 30 89 51; domainelesmarguerites@orange.fr]** A28 exit 5 onto D1015 dir Eu & Le Treport to Gamaches in 8km. Site sp fr town, 200m fr stadium. Lge, mkd pitch, hdstg, pt shd; wc (cont); chem disp; shwrs inc; el pnts (6-10A) inc; Indtte; tradsmn; rest, snacks; bar; BBQ; playgrnd; pool; paddling pool; rv adj; games area; 75% statics; dogs; poss cr; quiet; adv bkg; red long stay/CKE/CCI. "Nr forest of Eu & Somme coast; gd fishing, riding." ♦ ltd 21 Mar-15 Sep. € 19.50 2010*

GUIGNICOURT *3C4* (500m SE Urban) *49.43209, 3.97035* **Camping au Bord de l'Aisne (Formaly Municipal), 14b Rue des Godins, 02190 Guignicourt [tel/fax 03 23 79 74 58; campingguignicourt@orange.fr; www.camping-aisne-picardie.fr]** Exit A26 junc 14 onto D925 to Guignicourt; after passing under rlway bdge cont on D925 for 800m; then turn R at Peugeot g'ge down narr rd to site (12% descent at ent & ramp). Site sp in vill on rv bank. Med, hdg/mkd pitch, pt shd; htd wc (some cont); chem disp; mv service pnt; shwrs; el pnts (6-10A) €3-5.30 (poss rev pol, poss long cable req); sm supmkt & shops in vill; tradsmn; rest 600m; pizzeria; snacks; bar; BBQ; playgrnd; htd covrd pool; fishing; wifi; 20% statics; dogs €1.60; phone; train 500m; poss cr; some Eng spkn; adv bkg; quiet; ccard acc; red long stay; CKE/CCI. "Pretty, well-kept site in beautiful setting on banks of rv; popular NH, conv A26; well-guarded; friendly, helpful staff; poss muddy when wet; pleasant town; excel touring base Reims, Epernay; easy access despite gradient; excel; v clean refurbished facs." ♦ 1 Apr-30 Oct. € 30.00 SBS - P02 2014*

GUISE *3C4* (500m SE Urban) *49.89488, 3.63372* **FFCC Camping de la Vallée de l'Oise, 33 Rue du Camping, 02120 Guise [03 23 61 14 86; fax 03 23 61 21 07]** Foll Vervin sp in town & camp clearly sp fr all dirs in town. Lge, pt shd; wc (some cont); shwrs inc; el pnts (3-6A) €3-5 (rev pol); lndry rm; shops 500m; tradsmn; playgrnd; rv fishing & canoe hire adj; cycle hire; games rm; TV; entmnt; 50% statics; dogs; some Eng spkn; adv bkg; v quiet; red low ssn; CKE/CCI. "Spacious, beautifully kept, friendly site; busy w/ends; gd san facs; barrier always open, warden not always on site; if arr late, pitch & pay next morning; interesting old town; gd value." 15 Apr-15 Oct. € 13.00 2013*

GUISE *3C4* (6km NW Rural) *49.92709, 3.57768* **Camp Muncipal de Bovalon, 02120 Vadencourt [tel/fax 03 23 61 07 03 (Mairie); www.vadencourt.com]** Exit Guise NW on D960 dir Bohain-en-Vermandois; in 6km turn R onto D69; site on R in 1km just bef Vadencourt. Or exit D66 S at Vadencourt onto D69; site on L in 150m, just after rv bdg. Site sp in Vadencourt off D66. Sm, hdg pitch, pt shd; wc (some cont); chem disp (wc); shwrs inc; el pnts (6A) €5; shops & bar 250m; dogs €0.45; quiet, but some rd noise daytime; CKE/CCI. "Site by Rv Oise in pleasant area; height barrier, but call mob number on noticeboard or contact Café du Centre; gd; can't rec due to crowding by travellers (2012)." ♦ ltd 1 May-30 Sep. € 9.50 2012*

LAON *3C4* (2.5km W Rural) *49.56190, 3.59583* **Camp La Chênaie (formerly Municipal), Allée de la Chênaie, 02000 Laon [03 23 20 25 56/ 03 23 22 85 81 (ls); fax 03 23 22 85 85 (ls); contact-camping-laon@gmail.com; www.ville-laon.fr]** Exit A26 junc 13 onto N2 sp Laon; in 10km at junc with D1044 (4th rndabt) turn sp Semilly/Laon, then L at next rndabt into site rd. Site well sp. Med, hdg/mkd pitch, pt shd; htd wc; chem disp; mv service pnt; baby facs; shwrs inc; el pnts (10A) €3.40 (poss rev pol); lndry rm; v ltd shop & 1km; tradsmn; BBQ; playgrnd; fishing lake 50m (no sw); dogs €2; phone; poss cr; Eng spkn; adv bkg; quiet with some rd noise; ccard not acc; red long stay; CKE/CCI. "Peaceful, pleasant site in gd location; popular NH; well-mkd pitches - lgest at end of site rd; extremely helpful staff; no twin-axles; if travelling Sept phone to check site open; m'van parking nr cathedral; vg; woodland glades; gd NH; site now privately owned (2014) upgraded with new excel facs." ♦ 1 May-30 Sep. € 21.00 2014*

LONG see Abbeville *3B3*

MERS LES BAINS *3B2* (1.5km NE Rural) *50.07730, 1.41540* **Camping Le Rompval, Lieudit Blengues, 154 Rue André Dumont, 80350 Mers-les-Bains [02 35 84 43 21 or 06 50 02 79 57 (mob); lerompval@baiedesommepleinair.com; www.campinglerompval.com]** Fr Calais on A16, exit junc 23 at Abbeville onto A28. In 5km exit junc 2 onto D925 dir Friville-Escarbotin, Le Tréport. In approx 20km at rndabt junc with D19 foll sp Ault & at next rndabt take D940 twd Mers-les-Bains. In St Quentin-la-Motte turn R, site on R, sp. Fr S on A28 exit junc 5 onto D1015 to Mers-les-Bains & foll sp Blengues & site. Med, hdg/mkd pitch, hdstg, unshd; htd wc; chem disp; mv service pnt; baby facs; fam bathrm; shwrs inc; el pnts (6-13A) €4-6.50; gas; lndtte (inc dryer); shop; supmkt 2km; tradsmn; snacks; bar; BBQ; playgrnd; htd, covrd pool; paddling pool; sand beach 2.5km; tennis 3km; cycle hire; games area; games/TV rm; library; wifi; entmnt; 25% statics; dogs €3; Eng spkn; adv bkg; quiet; ccard acc; red long stay/low ssn/CKE/CCI. "Vg site; gd facs." ♦ 29 Mar-11 Nov. € 22.50 (CChq acc) 2014*

See advert on page 466

MIANNAY see Abbeville *3B3*

MOYENNEVILLE see Abbeville *3B3*

NAMPONT ST MARTIN *3B3* (3km W Rural) *50.33595, 1.71230* **La Ferme des Aulnes, 1 Rue du Marais, Fresne-sur-Authie, 80120 Nampont-St Martin [03 22 29 22 69 or 06 22 41 86 54 (mob LS); fax 03 22 29 39 43; contact@fermedesaulnes.com; www.fermedesaulnes.com]** D901 S fr Montreuil 13km thro Nampont-St Firmin to Nampont-St Martin; turn R in vill onto D485; site in 3km; sp fr D901. Med, some hdg pitch, pt sl, pt shd; htd wc; chem disp; mv service pnt; baby facs; shwrs inc; el pnts (6-10A) €6-12; lndtte (inc dryer); shop 5km; tradsmn, rest, snacks, bar high ssn; BBQ (not elec); playgrnd; htd, covrd pool; sand beach 12km; archery; golf 1km; games area; wifi; entmnt; TV & cinema rm; mostly statics; dogs €4; poss cr; adv bkg; quiet; CKE/CCI. "Attractive site nr Calais; some pitches sm, some v sl; friendly staff; clsd 2200-0800." ♦ 4 Apr-31 Oct. € 21.00 (3 persons) (CChq acc) SBS - P13 2013*

See advertisement

PICARDY

NOUVION EN THIERACHE, LE *3B4* (1.2km S Rural) *50.00538, 3.78292* **Camp Municipal du Lac de Condé, Promenade Henri d'Orléans, Rue de Guise (Le Lac), 02170 Le Nouvion-en-Thiérache [03 23 98 98 58; fax 03 23 98 94 90; camping-lacdeconde@orange.fr; www.camping-thierache.com]** Sp fr cent of Le Nouvion fr D1043 on D26, dir Guise opp chateau. Med, hdg/mkd pitch, some hdstg, pt sl, pt shd; wc; chem disp; shwrs inc; el pnts (4-8A) €3.20-3.90; Indtte (inc dryer); shop 1km; tradsmn; rest, snacks, bar 1km; BBQ; playgrnd; htd pool adj; tennis, canoe hire, horseriding nrby; 70% statics; dogs €0.80; phone; ccard acc; red long stay/CKE/CCI. "Beautiful, spacious, lakeside site; busy even low ssn - rec phone ahead; gd sized pitches; warm welcome, staff helpful; gd san facs; gd for families; some pitches not suitable m'vans due slope; muddy when wet; walk around lake; conv NH; excel." ♦ 1 Apr-30 Sep. € 9.00 2013*

⊞ **NOYON** *3C3* (4.5km E Rural) *49.58882, 3.04370* **FFCC Camping L'Etang du Moulin, 54 Rue du Moulin, 60400 Salency [03 44 09 99 81; fax 03 44 43 06 78]** Take D1032 fr Noyon dir Chauny. On ent Salency turn L & foll site sp. Site in 1km. Sm, pt sl, shd; htd wc; chem disp; mv service pnt; shwrs €2; el pnts (10A) €1.60; gas; shop, rest 4km; tradsmn; bar; BBQ; playgrnd; pool 3km; fishing; tennis; 60% statics; dogs €1; quiet; CKE/CCI. "Site unclean (Jan 2009)." ♦ € 14.30 2009*

NOYON *3C3* (8km S Rural) *49.50667, 3.01765* **FFCC Camping Les Araucarias, 870 Rue du Général Leclerc, 60170 Carlepont [03 44 75 27 39; fax 03 44 38 12 51; camping-les-araucarias@wanadoo.fr; www.camping-les-araucarias.com]** Fr S, fr A1 exit junc 9 or 10 for Compiègne. There take D130 sp Tracy-le-Val & Carlepont. Site on L 100m fr Carlepont vill sp. Or fr N on D934 Noyon-Soissons rd take D130 dir Carlepont & Tracy-le-Val. Site on R after vill on SW twd Compiegne - not well sp. Sm, mkd pitch, pt sl, pt shd; htd wc; chem disp; mv service pnt; baby facs; shwrs inc; el pnts (6-10A) €3 (poss rev pol); gas; Indtte; shop, rest, bar 1km; BBQ; playgrnd; mainly statics; dogs €1; poss cr; Eng spkn; adv bkg; quiet; CKE/CCI. "Secluded site, previously an arboretum; close Parc Astérix & La Mer-de-Sable (theme park); 85km Disneyland; san facs poss scruffy low ssn; vg." ♦ ltd 21 Mar-21 Dec. € 10.00 2010*

OURSEL MAISON see Crèvecoeur le Grand *3C3*

PERONNE *3C3* (300m NE Urban) *49.93424, 2.94140* **Camp Municipal du Brochet, Rue Georges Clémenceau, 80200 Péronne [03 22 84 02 35; fax 03 22 73 31 01; peter.v.gent@orange.fr]** Fr N on D1017 turn R into town. L at lights & L immed after footbdge. 1st R & site on L. Well sp fr all dirs. Go to town cent then foll 'Intn'l Camping Site' sps. Sm, hdstg, pt sl, terr, pt shd; wc; chem disp; mv service pnt; el pnts (16A) inc; Indtte; shops & rest 500m; playgrnd; bus 500m; dogs free; phone; poss cr; Eng spkn; adv bkg; quiet; CKE/CCI. "Pleasant, basic site nr park & attractive town; grass pitches soft when wet; rec arr early high ssn; conv WW1 museum; NH, vg." 1 Apr-1 Oct. € 19.60 2014*

PERONNE *3C3* (1km S Rural) *49.91805, 2.93227* **Camping du Port de Plaisance, Route de Paris, 80200 Péronne [03 22 84 19 31; fax 03 22 73 36 37; contact@camping-plaisance.com; www.camping-plaisance.com]** Exit A1/E15 junc 13 dir Peronne on D1029 to D1017. Site on L o'looking canal. Well sp fr all dirs. Med, mkd pitch, pt shd; htd wc; chem disp; mv service pnt; shwrs inc; el pnts (6-10A) €4.30-7.95 (some rev pol & long lead poss req); Indtte; sm shop; tradsmn; supmkt nr; snacks high ssn; rest nr; bar; playgrnd; htd pool high ssn; jacuzzi; fishing; wifi; dogs €1.30; poss v cr; Eng spkn; poss some rd noise; red low ssn/long stay; ccard acc. "Pleasant, site; popular NH; helpful staff & owners; san facs clean; gd play park & pool; gates locked 2200-0800 - when clsd, park outside; vg rest adj; rec visit to war museum in Péronne castle; popular with ralliers; no twin-axles; facs need upgrading (2013); vg site, pleasant situation nr a canal; gd size pitches; gd dog walk along canal; hypmkt 3km." ♦ 1 Mar-31 Oct. € 31.20 (3 persons) 2014*

PERONNE *3C3* (2km NW Rural) *49.94409, 2.90826* **Camping La Tortille, L'Orgibet, 80200 Cléry-sur-Somme [03 22 83 17 59 or 03 22 84 10 45 (LS); fax 03 22 83 04 14; jsg-bred@wanadoo.fr]** Exit A1/E15 junc 13.1 onto D938 to Cléry, dir Péronne. Site sp on rvside in 5km. Med, hdg pitch, hdstg, pt shd; wc; shwrs €1.20; el pnts (10A) €3.60; shop 4km; BBQ; playgrnd; rv fishing; games area; 80% statics; dogs €1.30; adv bkg; quiet; red long stay; CKE/CCI; "Peaceful site; sm pitches, poss bet statics; clean modern san facs; conv for A1 m'way; some h/s." ♦ 1 Apr-31 Oct. € 18.90 2014*

> "There aren't many sites open at this time of year"
>
> If you're travelling outside peak season remember to call ahead to check site opening dates – even if the entry says 'open all year'.

PICQUIGNY *3C3* (400m E Urban) *49.9445, 2.1458* **Camp Municipal, 66 Rue du Marais, 80310 Picquigny [03 22 51 25 83 or 03 22 51 40 31 (Mairie); fax 03 22 51 30 98; http://picquigny.free.fr]** Site sp fr town cent. Med, unshd; wc; chem disp; shwrs inc; el pnts (10A) inc; Indry rm; shop nr; playgrnd; rv & fishing; mainly statics; dogs; quiet; occasional noise fr rlwy line; adv bkg rec high ssn; "Pleasant, well laid out site; modern san facs; some shd pitches bet statics; WW1 war cemetery nr town." 1 Apr-31 Oct. € 17.00 2014*

PIERREFONDS *3D3* (500m N Urban) *49.35427, 2.97564* **Camp Municipal de Batigny, 34 Rue de l'Armistice, 60350 Pierrefonds [03 44 42 80 83 / 09 71 20 42 08 (mob); fax 03 44 42 87 73; camping-de-pierrefonds@orange.fr]** Take D973 fr Compiegne; after 14km site on L adj sp for Pierrefonds at ent to vill. Med, hdg pitch, pt shd; htd wc; chem disp; mv service pnt; 90% serviced pitches; shwrs inc; el pnts (10A) €2.80 (poss rev pol); Indtte; shops 800m; rest in vill; dog €1; poss cr; adv bkg; rd noise; ccard not acc; red long stay; CKE/CCI; "Attractive, well-run, busy site; tight pitches for lge o'fits; clean san facs; poss unkempt low ssn; site yourself if recep clsd; cycle paths; nr Armistice train & museum; gd site; walking dist to vill." 6 Apr-30 Sep. € 18.80 2014*

POIX DE PICARDIE *3C3* (300m SW Rural) *49.77621, 1.97467* **Camp Municipal Le Bois des Pêcheurs, Route de Forges-les-Eaux, 80290 Poix-de-Picardie [03 22 90 11 71 or 03 22 90 32 90 (Mairie); fax 03 22 90 32 91; camping@ville-poix-de-picardie.fr; www.ville-poix-de-picardie.fr]** Fr town cent on D901 dir Beauvais, in 100m turn R onto D919 opp Citroën agent sp Camping; site on R in 500m. Fr Beauvais, turn L at bottom of steep hill opp Citroën agent; site in 500m on R. Med, hdg/mkd pitch, hdstg, pt shd; wc; chem disp; shwrs inc; el pnts (10A) €4 (poss long lead req); gas 300m; Indtte; shops, supmkt adj; rest, bar 500m; BBQ; playgrnd; htd, covrd pool 800m; rv & fishing adj; tennis 800m; games rm; cycle hire; wifi; TV; dogs €1.50; poss cr; Eng spkn; adv bkg; quiet; ccard not acc; red long stay; CKE/CCI. "Pleasant, peaceful, tidy site in delightful area; clean san facs; gd touring base; vg walking & cycling; train to Amiens; mkt Sun; rec." ♦ 1 Apr-30 Sep. € 20.00 2014*

PORT LE GRAND see Abbeville *3B3*

QUEND PLAGE LES PINS see Fort Mahon Plage *3B2*

RUE *3B2* (7km N Rural) *50.31367, 1.69472* **Kawan Village Le Val d'Authie, 20 Route de Vercourt, 80120 Villers-sur-Authie [03 22 29 92 47; fax 03 22 29 92 20; camping@valdauthie.fr; www.valdauthie.fr]** Best access via Rue or via D85/D485 fr D1001. Rd fr Vron to Villers-sur-Authie is narr single track across fields. Alt Exit 24 on A16 twrds Vron, foll sp Camping Vercourt thro town. Lge, hdg/mkd pitch, pt sl, pt shd; htd wc; chem disp; mv service pnt; sauna; steam rm; shwrs inc; baby facs; el pnts (6-10A) €5-8 (rev pol); gas; Indtte (inc dryer); shop; tradsmn; rest, snacks; bar; playgrnd; htd, covrd pool; paddling pool; sand beach 10km; tennis; games area; games rm; fitness rm; wifi; entmnt; TV rm; 60% statics; dogs €1.50; phone; poss cr; Eng spkn; adv bkg; quiet but poss noise fr chalets/statics; ccard acc; red low ssn; CKE/CCI. "Set in pleasant countryside; helpful, friendly owners; clean, unisex facs & spacious shwrs; sm sep area for tourers, but many touring pitches bet statics (2009); poss diff for lge o'fits; gd pool; v cr & noisy high ssn; excel." ♦ 1 Apr-9 Oct. € 25.00 (3 persons) (CChq acc) 2012*

RUE *3B2* (4km SE Rural) *50.25278, 1.71224* **Camping de la Mottelette, Ferme de la Mottelette, 80120 Forest-Montiers [03 22 28 32 33 or 06 72 85 73 77 (mob); contact@la-mottelette.com; www.la-mottelette.com]** Exit A16 junc 24 onto D32 dir Rue & L Crotoy; at rndabt junc with D235 cont on D32; site on L in 1.5km. Site sp on leaving A16. Sm, hdg/mkd pitch, unshd; wc; chem disp; baby facs; el pnts (6A) €4; Indtte (inc dryer); supmkt 4km; tradsmn; BBQ; playgrnd; games area; games rm; 20% statics; dogs €1; poss cr; Eng spkn; adv bkg; quiet; CKE/CCI. "Basic, clean site on working farm; welcoming, friendly owners; mkt Sat; conv A16; gd touring base or NH; vg. ♦ ltd 1 Apr-31 Oct. € 14.00 2014*

SAILLY LE SEC see Albert *3B3*

ST LEU D'ESSERENT see Chantilly *3D3*

"That's changed – Should I let The Club know?"

If you find something on site that's different from the site entry, fill in a report and let us know. See www.caravanclub.co.uk/europereport.

ST QUENTIN *3C4* (3.2km NE Urban) *49.85536, 3.31033* **Camp Municipal, 91 Blvd Jean Bouin, 02100 St Quentin [03 23 06 94 05 / 03 23 06 94 21; auberge.camping@ville-saint-quentin.fr; www.campingmunicipaldesaint-quentin]** Fr all app rds foll sp Centre Ville/Auberge de Jeunesse (c'van on sign). Poss diff to find - foll canal rd. Sp 'Terrain de Camping'. Press intercom at barrier for ent. Poorly sp - easy to drive past. Sm, mkd pitch, hdstg, pt shd; htd wc (most cont); chem disp; shwrs inc; el pnts (6A) €4.10; supmkt 1km; pool adj; dogs free; bus adj; quiet; ccard acc; CKE/CCI. "Lovely little site by canal; usefully placed; secure; easy access to lge, gritty pitches; helpful warden; clean modern san facs; gates clsd 2200-0700; pleasant canal walk adj; poss travellers; vg." ♦ 1 Jun-30 Sep. € 13.00 2013*

ST QUENTIN *3C4* (10km SW Urban) *49.78222, 3.21333* **Camping du Vivier aux Carpes, 10 Rue Charles Voyeux, 02790 Seraucourt-le-Grand [03 23 60 50 10; fax 03 23 60 51 69; contact@camping-picardie.com; www.camping-picardie.com]** Fr A26 take exit 11 St Quentin/ Soissons; S 4km on D1 dir Tergnier/Soissons. Fork R onto D8 to Essigny-le-Grand & in vill foll camping sp W to Seraucourt. Fr St Quentin, S 10km on D930 to Roupy, E on D32 5km to Seraucourt-le-Grand. Site N of Seraucourt on D321. Narr ent fr rd unsuitable lge o'fits. Med, hdg/mkd pitch, some hdstg, pt shd; wc; chem disp; mv service pnt; baby facs; shwrs inc; el pnts (10A) inc (poss rev pol); gas; Indtte; shop & supmkt 200m; tradsmn; snacks; BBQ; playgrnd; pool nr; angling; golf, tennis, horseriding adj; games rm; wifi; 30% statics; dogs €1.50; c'van storage; Eng spkn; adv bkg; quiet; CKE/CCI. "Delightful, lovely, well-run site; busy, even low ssn - rec arr early; ltd hdstg; peaceful low ssn; gd, lge pitches; narr site rds; friendly, helpful staff; pitches by lake poss boggy when wet; poss flooding; mkd footpaths round lakes; vg angling; mosquito probs; Disneyland 90 mins; conv Channel ports; warn staff night bef if v early dep; excel; facs stretched but clean & gd; lovely cycle rte along canal to St Quentin; nice bistro in vill." ♦ 1 Mar-30 Oct. € 28.50 SBS - P14 2014*

ST QUENTIN EN TOURMONT *3B2* (500m S Rural) *50.26895, 1.60263* **Camping Le Champ Neuf, 8 Rue du Champ Neuf, 80120 St Quentin-en-Tourmont [03 22 25 07 94; fax 03 22 25 09 87; campinglechampneuf@orange.fr; www.camping-lechampneuf.com]** Exit D1001 or A16 onto D32 to Rue, take D940 around Rue & foll sp St Quentin-en-Tourmont, Parc Ornithologique & Domaine du Marquenterre to site. Site sp fr D204. Lge, hdg/mkd pitch, pt shd; htd wc; chem disp; mv service pnt; baby facs; shwrs inc; el pnts (5-10A) inc; Indtte (inc dryer); shop; tradsmn; snacks; bar; BBQ; playgrnd; htd, covrd pool complex; paddling pool; beach 2km; games area; cycle hire; horseriding 500m; wifi; entmnt high ssn; many statics; dogs €1.50; phone; adv bkg; quiet; ccard acc. "Excel Ornithological Park nrby; well-kept, pleasant site; friendly, helpful owner; gd cycle paths." ♦ 1 Apr-1 Nov. € 30.00 2011*

See advert on previous page

ST QUENTIN EN TOURMONT *3B2* (1km S Rural) *50.26978, 1.59855* **Camping des Crocs, 2 Chemin des Garennes, 80120 St Quentin-en-Tourmont [03 22 25 73 33; fax 03 22 25 75 17; contact@campingdescrocs.com; www.campingdescrocs.com]** Exit D1001 or A16 onto D32 to Rue. When W of Rue turn off onto D4 heading W. In 2km turn R onto D204 & foll sp Le Bout des Crocs, then Parc Ornithologique. Site on R. Med, hdg/mkd pitch, unshd; wc; chem disp; baby facs; shwrs €1; el pnts (6A) €3; Indtte; tradsmn; playgrnd; TV rm; 80% statics; dogs €0.50; CKE/CCI. "V quiet site; nr Marquenterre bird reserve; immac facs, but poss long walk; cycle tracks to beach & inland; mosquitoes poss problem; vg." 1 Apr-1 Nov. € 14.00 2009*

ST VALERY SUR SOMME *3B2* (2km S Rural) *50.15333, 1.63583* **Camping Le Domaine du Château de Drancourt, 80230 Estréboeuf [03 22 26 93 45; fax 03 22 26 85 87; chateau.drancourt@wanadoo.fr; www.chateau-drancourt.com / www.les-castels.com]** Exit A28/E402 junc 1 at Abbeville onto D40 twd Noyelles-sur-Mer. At rndabt with D940 turn L sp St Valery-sur-Somme. At next rndabt go strt over dir Le Tréport, then at next rndabt at junc with D48 take last exit (sp Estréboeuf), turn immed L & foll sps to site. NB.1-way system at recep area. Lge, some hdg/mkd pitch, pt sl, pt shd; wc; chem disp; mv service pnt; baby facs; shwrs inc; el pnts (10A) inc (poss rev pol); gas; Indtte; shop; rest, snacks; bar; BBQ; playgrnd; 2 htd pools (1 covrd); paddling pool; fishing adj; golf driving range; watersports 2km; sand beach 8km; horseriding 12km; tennis; games hall; cycle hire; entmnt; 80% statics; dogs €4.50; poss cr & noisy; Eng spkn; adv bkg; ccard acc; red low ssn; CKE/CCI. "Conv, busy, popular NH in grnds of chateau; friendly staff; facs poss stretched when site full; red facs low ssn; bird sanctuary in estuary nrby; gd." ♦ 30 Mar-15 Sep. € 48.50 2013*

ST VALERY SUR SOMME *3B2* (1km SW Urban/Coastal) *50.18331, 1.61786* **Camping Le Walric, Route d'Eu, 80230 St Valery-sur-Somme [03 22 26 81 97; fax 03 22 60 77 26; info@campinglewalric.com; www.campinglewalric.com]** Ringrd round St Valery D940 dir Le Tréport. Cont to 3rd rndabt (1st rndabt Carrefour supmkt on L) 3km & take 1st exit (R) sp St Valery & Cap Hornu D3. Site on R in 2km at ent to town sp. Lge, hdg/mkd pitch, some hdstg, pt shd; wc; chem disp; mv service pnt; baby facs; shwrs inc; el pnts (6A) inc; gas; Indtte (inc dryer); shop; tradsmn; bar; BBQ; playgrnd; htd pool; paddling pool; beaches nr; fishing; boat & cycle hire; tennis; games area; games rm; wifi; entmnt high ssn; 70% statics; dogs €3; phone; Eng spkn; adv bkg; quiet; ccard acc; red low ssn/long stay; CKE/CCI. "Well-kept, well-run, busy site in excel location; clean dated san facs; cycle rtes, canal track; steam train; delightful medieval town; mkt Sun; excel; easy to find." ♦ 1 Apr-1 Nov. € 41.00 (3 persons) 2014*

ST VALERY SUR SOMME *3B2* (3km SW Rural) *50.17632, 1.58969* **Camping de la Baie, Routhiaville, 80230 Pendé [03 22 60 72 72; contact@campingdelabaie.eu; www.campingdelabaie.net]** Just off D940 twd Tréport, well sp. Sm, hdg pitch; wc (some cont); chem disp; shwrs inc; el pnts (6A) €4; Indtte; shop 2km; tradsmn; playgrnd; 95% statics; adv bkg; quiet; red low ssn; CKE/CCI. "Well-run, clean, tidy site & san facs; friendly, helpful owners; low trees in places need care; cycle rte to St Valery; adequate NH." 27 Mar-16 Oct. € 15.50 2013*

ST VALERY SUR SOMME *3B2* (1km W Urban) *50.18447, 1.62263* **Camping de la Croix l'Abbé, Place de la Croix l'Abbé, 80230 St Valery-sur-Somme [03 22 60 81 46; w.a.georges@wanadoo.fr]** Ringrd round St Valery D940 dir Le Tréport. Cont to 2nd rndabt (1st rndabt Champion supmkt on L) 3km & take exit sp St Valery & Cap Hornu D3. Site 250m beyond Camping Le Walric. Lge, hdg/mkd pitch, pt sl, unshd; wc (some cont); chem disp; shwrs inc; el pnts (10A) inc; shop 1km; tradsmn; rest, snacks; bar; playgrnd; htd, covrd pool; sand/shgl beach 1km TV rm; 85% statics; bus adj; poss cr; Eng spkn; quiet. "San facs needs updating (2014); gd location for walk to town; sh stay/NH only." 1 Apr-30 Nov. € 20.00 2014*

SERAUCOURT LE GRAND see St Quentin *3C4*

SOISSONS *3D4* (1km N Urban) *49.39295, 3.32701* **Camp Municipal du Mail, 14 Ave du Mail, 02200 Soissons [03 23 74 52 69; fax 03 23 75 05 21; campingdumail@gmail.com; www.tourisme-soissons.fr]** Fr N on D1; foll town cent sp to 1st rndabt; turn R, cross rv & immed R into Ave du Mail. Foll sp 'Camping Piscine'. Site well sp beside sw pool. Rd humps & tight ent on last 500m of access rd. (Poss to avoid tight ent by going 150m to rndabt & returning). Or fr S on D1, turn R sp Centre Ville along Ave de Château-Thiery; at 3rd rndabt turn R into Rue du Général Leclerc to Place de la Republique; cont strt over into Blvd Gambette for 500m, then turn L into Ave de l'Aisne, leading into Ave du Petit Mail; then as above. Med, hdg/mkd pitch, hdstg, pt shd; htd wc; chem disp; mv service pnt; shwrs inc; el pnts (6A) inc (poss rev pol); lndtte (inc dryer); shop; rest, snacks; bar 1km; BBQ; playgrnd; pool adj; cycle hire; wifi; 5% statics; dogs €1; phone; poss cr; quiet; ccard acc; clsd 1 Jan & 25 Dec; CKE/CCI. "Pleasant, excel, clean & well-run site in interesting area; gd sized pitches, some nr rv; poss muddy, park on site rds in winter; m'van pitches all hdstg; helpful, friendly staff; gd clean, modern unisex san facs; rvside walks/cycling; gate clsd 2200-0700; lge mkt Wed & Sat; vg winter NH; conv for town (15mins)."
♦ € 18.00 2 Jan-24 Dec, 26 Dec-31 Dec 2014*

VADENCOURT see Guise *3C4*

VERVINS *3C4* (7km N Rural) *49.90676, 3.91977* **FFCC Camping du Val d'Oise, 3 Rue du Mont d'Origny, 02580 Etréaupont [03 23 97 48 04; www.evasion-aisne.com]** Site to E of Etréaupont off N2, Mons-Reims rd. Site adj football pitch on banks of Rv Oise. Well sp fr main rd. Sm, hdg/mkd pitch, pt shd; wc (some cont); shwrs inc; el pnts (6A) €3.30 (poss rev pol); shops 500m; tradsmn; playgrnd; tennis; sports field adj; rv & fishing adj; dogs €0.30; quiet. "Pretty, tidy site; warm welcome; v clean san facs; site self if recep clsd; no twin-axles; conv rte to Zeebrugge ferry (approx 200km); gd walking & cycling; gd." 1 Apr-31 Oct. € 19.25 2013*

VILLERS SUR AUTHIE see Rue *3B2*

⊞ **VRAIGNES EN VERMANDOIS** *3C4* (90m N Rural) *49.88777, 3.06488* **Camping des Hortensias, 22 Rue Basse, 80240 Vraignes-en-Vermandois [03 22 85 64 68; campinghortensias@free.fr; www.campinghortensias.com]** Fr N on A1/E15 take exit 13 onto D1029 sp St Quentin; strt rd 16km until rndabt, take D15 (Vraignes) exit; site sp 1st on R in vill. Or fr S & A26, take junc 10 onto D1029 sp Péronne; after 15km at rndabt take D15 as bef. Sm, hdg pitch, hdstg, pt shd; htd wc; chem disp; shwrs €1.20; el pnts (4-8A) €2.50-4.50 (poss long lead req); lndtte; shop 2km; tradsmn; snacks & bar 1.5km; BBQ; a few statics; dogs €1.30; quiet; red long stay; CKE/CCI. "Lovely farm site; sm pitches, poss muddy when wet; helpful, friendly owners; vg, clean san facs; conv for Somme battlefields & m'way; excel." € 18.00 2014*

Poitou-Charentes

Regional Introduction

Poitiers

Welcome to Poitou-Charentes

Poitou-Charentes is renowned for having one of the most pleasant climates in France. It is an area with many sights and attractions. The famous and unique Marais Poitevin, a large area of marshland which connects the Poitou and the Vendée, offers boating, angling and walking opportunities. The historic port of La Rochelle boasts fine restaurants and plenty of appeal.

As you travel through the diverse countryside you'll see sunflower fields, elegant châteaux, historic towns and sandy beaches - these combine to make Poitou-Charentes a region that is well worth investigating.

Local highlights

The region is most famous for the strong but smooth spirit, Cognac. With its long coastline, it's not surprising that seafood is very popular here. Make sure you try the ultra-fresh oysters of Marannes-Oléron that are sought after all over France.

La Rochelle is host to the famous Les Francofolies music festival, which promotes French music and is held annually in July.

Major towns and cities

- Cognac – famous for the spirit of the same name.
- La Rochelle – a lively city with maritime connections.
- Poitiers – picturesque streets full of historical and religious architecture.
- Rochefort – home to a unique transporter bridge and known for its breweries.
- Saintes – a small town with Celtic origins found on the banks of the Charente River.

Regional attractions

- Towers of La Rochelle – fortified landmarks looking out to the Atlantic.
- Monolithic Church of Saint-Jean, Aubeterre, – a church carved into a cave.
- Cordouan Lighthouse – an impressive lighthouse near the Gironde estuary.
- Château de La Roche Courbon – a castle and gardens built in the 15th century.

Find out more

www.visit-poitou-charentes.com
Tel: (0)5 49 50 10 50 Poitou-Charentes Tourist Board

AIGREFEUILLE D'AUNIS *7A1* (2km N Rural) *46.14621, -0.94571* **Camp Municipal de la Garenne, Route de la Mazurie, 17220 St Christophe [05 46 35 51 79 or 05 46 35 16 15 (LS); fax 05 46 35 64 29; saintchristophe@mairie17.com]** Fr Aigrefeuille-d'Aunis take D112 2.5km N to vill of St Christophe, site sp. Sm, hdg, mkd pitch, pt shd; wc; chem disp; mv service pnt; shwrs inc; el pnts (4A) €2.50; Indry rm; shop 250m; playgrnd; lake fishing 3km; tennis; horseriding; dogs €0.85; quiet; CKE/CCI. "V clean site in sm vill; unrel opening dates, phone ahead low ssn." ♦ 15 Mar-15 Oct. € 23.00 2012*

AIRVAULT *4H1* (1km N Rural) *46.83200, -0.14690* **Camping de Courte Vallée, 8 Rue de Courte Vallée, 79600 Airvault [tel/fax 05 49 64 70 65; camping@caravanningfrance.com; www.caravanningfrance.com]** Fr N, S or W leave D938 sp Parthenay to Thouars rd at La Maucarrière twd Airvault & foll Ige sp to site. Site on D121 twd Availles-Thouarsais. NB If app fr NE or E c'vans not permitted thro Airvault - watch carefully for sp R at Gendarmerie. Well sp fr all dirs. Sm, hdg/mkd pitch, some hdstg, pt sl, pt shd; wc; chem disp; mv service pnt; shwrs inc; el pnts (8A) inc (poss long lead req); gas; Indtte (inc dryer); shop; tradsmn; rest, snacks; bar; BBQ; playgrnd; htd pool; fishing; cycle hire; c'van storage; wifi; games/TV rm; 8% statics; dogs €1.50; twin-axles acc (rec check in adv); adv bkg; quiet; ccard acc; red low ssn/long stay; CKE/CCI. "Peaceful, popular, well-kept site; pleasant, helpful British owners; excel, clean & vg facs, poss stretched high ssn; conv Futuroscope & Puy du Fou theme park; mkt Sat." ♦ 1 Apr-15 Oct. € 43.00 SBS - L14 2014*

ANGOULEME *7B2* (15km N Rural) *45.78194, 0.11915* **FFCC Camp Municipal Les Platanes, 16330 Montignac-Charente [05 45 39 89 16 or 05 45 39 70 09 (Mairie); fax 05 45 22 26 71; www.campings-poitou-charentes.com]** Fr N, on N10, turn W on D11 then N on D737 thro vill onto D15. Narr rds on app, site on R by Rv Charente. Med, pt shd; wc (some cont); chem disp; shwrs inc; el pnts (10A) €4.40 (poss rev pol); gas 2km; Indry rm; shop 800m; rest, snacks in vill; bar; rv & fishing adj; canoeing; direct access to rv; dogs; poss cr; quiet; 25% red 16 days; ccard not acc; CKE/CCI. "Pleasant, basic, grassy, under-used site in gd position; friendly staff; warden calls am & pm; excel clean facs; many trees; no twin-axles; poss travellers; site open to public at one end; pleasant vill." ♦ 1 Jun-30 Aug. € 9.75 2011*

ANGOULEME *7B2* (11km SW Rural) *45.60773, 0.02365* **Camping Le Nizour, 2 Route de la Charente, 16440 Sireuil [05 45 90 56 27 or 06 87 54 64 05 (mob); fax 05 45 90 92 67; contact@campingdunizour.com; www.campingdunizour.com]** SW fr Angouleme on N10; in 11km exit N10 at junc with D7 sp Sireuil; cont on D7 for 3km; site on R just after x-ing rv. Site 1.5km bef Sireuil & sp in town. Sm, pt shd; wc; chem disp; shwrs inc; el pnts €3.20; Indtte; shop 1.5km; rest, snacks; bar; playgrnd; pool; 5% statics, sep area; dogs € 1.30; poss cr; quiet. "Pleasant, well-run site nr Rv Charente; conv NH fr N10 & longer stay." 15 Apr-Sep. € 15.25 2009*

ANGOULEME *7B2* (10km NW Rural) *45.79761, 0.06284* **Camping Marco de Bignac (formerly Les Sablons), Chemin de la Résistance, 16170 Bignac [05 45 21 78 41; fax 05 45 21 52 37; info@marcodebignac.com; www.marcodebignac.com]** Fr N10 approx 14km N Angoulême take exit La Touche & foll D11 W thro Vars; at Basse turn R onto D117 & foll sp in Bignac. Med, mkd pitch, pt shd; htd wc; chem disp; shwrs inc; child/baby facs; fam bthrm; el pnts (3-6A) €2-3; Indtte; shop or 10km; tradsmn; rest, snacks; bar; BBQ; playgrnd; pool high ssn; lake adj; fishing; watersports; tennis; pets corner; tennis; games area; games rm; wifi; few statics; dogs free; phone; bus adj; Eng spkn; adv bkg; quiet; ccard acc; red low ssn/long stay; CKE/CCI. "Attractive, peaceful, tidy, lakeside site; worth long drive; scenic area; Ige pitches; welcoming, helpful British owners; clean san facs; gd rest; pleasant walk round lake; ideal for Angoulême Circuit des Remparts; vg." ♦ ltd 1 Apr-31 Oct. € 35.00 2014*

ANGOULINS SUR MER **see Rochelle, La** *7A1*

ARCHIAC *7B2* (400m W Urban) *45.52322, -0.30452* **Camp Municipal, Rue des Voituriers, 17520 Archiac [05 46 49 10 46 or 05 46 49 10 82 (Mairie); fax 05 46 49 84 09; archiacmairie@free.fr]** Site sp fr D731 100m past sw pool. Sm, mkd pitch, terr, pt sl, pt shd; wc; mv service pnt; shwrs inc; el pnts (5A) €3.50; Indtte; tradsmn; shops 400m; 2 pools adj; tennis; games rm; dogs €0.85; quiet. "Spacious site; gates locked when warden absent but access details displayed; vg pool adj; rec." 15 Jun-15 Sep. € 6.80 2010*

ARGENTON LES VALLEES *4H1* (500m N Rural) *46.9877, -0.4504* **Camp Municipal du Lac d'Hautibus, Rue de la Sablière, 79150 Argenton-les-Vallées [05 49 65 95 08 or 05 49 65 70 22 (Mairie); fax 05 49 65 70 84; mairie-argenton-chateau@cegetel.net; www.campings-poitou-charentes.com]** Fr E or W on D759, site well sp in town, on lakeside. Med, hdg pitch, pt sl, terr; wc (some cont); chem disp; mv service pnt; shwrs inc; el pnts (6A) €2.50; Indtte; shops in town; playgrnd; pool 100m; lake sw 500m; tennis 100m; games rm; some statics; Eng spkn; quiet; CKE/CCI. "Beautifully-situated, well-kept site; interesting, quiet town; excel." ♦ 1 Apr-30 Sep. € 8.80 2011*

ARS EN RE (ILE DE RE) *7A1* (400m S Coastal) *46.20395, -1.52014* **FFCC Camping du Soleil, 57 Route de la Grange, 17590 Ars-en-Ré [05 46 29 40 62; fax 05 46 29 41 74; contact@campdusoleil.com; www.campdusoleil.com]** On ent Ars-en-Ré on D735, pass Citroën g'ge & in 700m take 3rd L dir Plage de la Grange. Site sp. Med, hdg/mkd pitch, shd; wc; chem disp; mv service pnt; baby facs; fam bthrm; shwrs inc; el pnts (4-10A) €3.70-4.90; Indtte; shop; rest, snacks; bar; BBQ (gas/elec); playgrnd; htd pool; paddling pool; sand beach 400m; tennis; games area; cycle hire; wifi; TV rm; 35% statics; dogs €3.20; phone; adv bkg; red low ssn; CKE/CCI. "Pleasant, pretty site with pines & bamboo; helpful, friendly staff; gd pool; gd cycling & walking." ♦ 15 Mar-15 Nov. € 34.00 (3 persons) 2011*

ARS EN RE (ILE DE RE) *7A1* (300m NW Coastal) *46.21130, -1.53017* **Airotel Camping Le Cormoran, Route de Radia, 17590 Ars-en-Ré [05 46 29 46 04; fax 05 46 29 29 36; info@cormoran.com; www.cormoran.com]** Fr La Rochelle take D735 onto Ile-de-Ré, site sp fr Ars-en-Ré. Med, hdg/mkd pitch, hdstg, pt shd; wc; chem disp; mv service pnt; baby facs; sauna; shwrs inc; el pnts (10A) €5; Indtte; shop 800m; tradsmn; rest, snacks; bar; playgrnd; htd pool; beach 500m; tennis; cycle hire; games area; games rm; golf 10km; entmnt; some statics; dogs €5.50; Eng spkn; adv bkg; quiet; ccard acc; red low ssn; CKE/CCI. "Delightful vill; vg site." ♦ 1 Apr-30 Sep. € 40.00 (3 persons) 2012*

See advertisement

AUBETERRE SUR DRONNE *7C2* (200m E Rural) *45.26975, 0.17566* **Camp Municipal, Route de Ribérac, 16390 Aubeterre-sur-Dronne [05 45 98 60 17 or 06 87 29 18 36 (mob); camping.aubeterre-sur-dronne@orange.fr; www.camping-aubeterre.fr]** On D2 fr Chalais, take D17 around S end of town. Turn R over rv & site on R adj sports grnd. Med, pt shd; wc (cont); chem disp (wc); mv service pnt; shwrs inc; el pnts (10A) €2.50; shop 250m; rest in town; snacks; bar; playgrnd; beach & rv adj; fishing & boating adj; tennis adj; cycle hire; wifi; some statics; dogs €1; poss cr; Eng spkn; quiet. "Excel site; gd for children; friendly staff; picturesque town; conv touring Périgord." 1 May-30 Sep. € 17.85 2013*

AUNAC see Mansle *7B2*

AVAILLES LIMOUZINE see Pressac *7A3*

AVAILLES LIMOUZINE *7A3* (7km E Rural) *46.12342, 0.65975* **FFCC Camp Municipal Le Parc, 86460 Availles-Limouzine [05 49 48 51 22; fax 05 49 48 66 76; camping.leparc@wanadoo.fr; www.campingleparc.monsite-orange.fr]** Fr Confolens N on D948 & turn R on D34 to Availles-Limouzine. Site on Rv Vienne by town bdge. Med, pt shd; wc; chem disp; mv service pnt; shwrs inc; el pnts (10A) inc; gas; shops 750m; playgrnd; lge paddling pool; dogs €2.65; poss cr; Eng spkn; adv bkg; quiet; CKE/CCI. "Attractive, well-run site in beautiful position; rv views; vg playgrnd; barrier clsd 2200-0800; poss scruffy low ssn; vg value; permanent warden." ♦ 1 May-30 Sep. € 17.40 2013*

AVANTON see Poitiers *7A2*

AZAY SUR THOUET see Parthenay *4H1*

BAIGNES STE RADEGONDE *7B2* (500m SW Rural) *45.38187, -0.23862* **FFCC Camp Municipal, Le Plein, 16360 Baignes-Ste-Radegonde [05 45 78 79 96 or 05 45 78 40 04 (Mairie); fax 05 45 78 47 41; point.i@live.fr; www.baignes-sainte-radegonde.fr]** Fr N10 turn W onto D2 to Baignes; site well sp on rvside. Sm, pt shd; wc; baby facs; shwrs inc; chem disp in vill; el pnts (5A) €2; Indtte; shops 100m; pool & tennis nrby; adv bkg; quiet; ccard acc; red CKE/CCI. "Warden calls pm; gd san facs; attractive sm town; gd." 1 May-19 Sep. € 10.00 2010*

BENON see Courçon *7A2*

BIGNAC see Angoulême *7B2*

BONNES see Chauvigny *7A3*

"I like to fill in the reports as I travel from site to site"

You'll find report forms at the back of this guide, or you can fill them in online at www.caravaclub.co.uk/europereport.

BREE LES BAINS, LA (ILE D'OLERON) *7A1* (500m NW Coastal) *46.01861, -1.35446* **Camp Municipal Le Planginot, Allée du Gai Séjour, 17840 La Brée-les-Bains [05 46 47 82 18; fax 05 46 75 90 74; camping.planginot@orange.fr; www.leplanginot.com]** N fr St Pierre d'Oléron on D734, turn R for La Brée on D273, site sp (if sp diff to see - foll 'plage' sp). Lge, mkd pitch, pt shd; htd wc; chem disp; mv service pnt; shwrs inc ltd hot water; el pnts (10A) €3.60; Indtte; snacks; rest in high ssn; playgrnd; beach adj; dogs €2; Eng spkn; adv bkg; quiet; red low ssn; 15% statics; "Well-kept site in quiet location; friendly, helpful staff; immac san facs; gd cycling; daily mkt nrby; excel value low ssn; excel." ♦ 15 Mar-15 Oct. € 13.20 2012*

BREE LES BAINS, LA (ILE D'OLERON) *7A1* (3km NW Coastal) *46.03855, -1.37521* **Camp Municipal, 10 Blvd d'Antioche, 17650 St Denis-d'Oléron [05 46 47 85 62; camping-municipal-st-denis-doleron@wanadoo.fr; www.st-denis-oleron.com]** Clear sp fr D734 in St Denis-d'Oléron town cent. 300m fr port. Lge, mkd pitch, pt sl, pt shd; htd wc; chem disp; mv service pnt; shwrs inc; el pnts (6A) €3.95; gas; Indtte; shop; rest nrby; snacks; playgrnd; sand beach adj; fishing; tennis; dogs €2.55; phone; poss cr; Eng spkn; quiet; CKE/CCI. "Some sea views; gd facs; some pitches v soft; ideal for beach holiday with children; gd." 15 Mar-30 Sep. € 13.40 (3 persons) 2010*

BREE LES BAINS, LA (ILE D'OLERON) *7A1* (1km N Coastal) *46.02027, -1.35762* **Camping Antioche d'Oléron, 17840 La Brée-Les-Bains [05 46 47 92 00; fax 05 46 47 82 22; info@camping-antiochedoleron.com; www.camping-antiochedoleron.com]** Go over bdge on D26 onto D734; turn R after St Georges onto D273E1 dir La Brees-les-Baines; turn L at T junc; campsite sp. Med, mkd pitch; wc; chem disp; mv service pnt; serviced pitches; shwrs inc; el pnts (10A) €5.50; rest; bar; playgrnd; pool; jacuzzi; paddling pool; cycle hire (high ssn); games rm; wifi; Eng spkn. "Gd site; entmnt in summer months; v gd pool." 2 Apr-24 Sep. € 31.80 2011*

See advertisement

BRESSUIRE *4H1* (1km S Rural) *46.82981, -0.50326* **Camping Le Puy Rond, Allee du Puy Rond, Cornet, 79300 Bressuire [05 49 72 43 22 or 06 85 60 37 26 (mob); puyrondcamping@gmail.com; www.puyrondcamping.com]** Fr N149 foll site sp on rte 'Poids Lourds' to site on D38. Fr 'Centre Ville' foll sp for Fontenay-Le-Comte; turn R 100m after overhead bdge & go across junc to site. Well sp. Sm, mkd pitch, pt sl, pt terr, pt shd; htd wc; chem disp (wc); mv service pnt; baby facs; shwrs inc; el pnts (10A) €3.50; gas 1.50m; Indtte; shop & 1.5km; tradsmn; snacks; rest, bar 1.5km; BBQ; playgrnd; pool; fishing 1km; 15% statics; dogs €1.50; bus 2km; adv bkg; quiet; red low ssn/long stay; ccard acc; CKE/CCI. "Gd touring base, poss tired early ssn; friendly British owners; basic, clean san facs; adv bkg ess for twin-axles; winter storage avail." ♦ 1 Apr-31 Oct. € 36.00 2014*

BRIOUX SUR BOUTONNE see Melle *7A2*

CELLES SUR BELLE see Melle *7A2*

CHALANDRAY *4H1* (750m N Rural) *46.66728, -0.00214* **Camping du Bois de St Hilaire, Rue de la Gare, 86190 Chalandray [tel/fax 05 49 60 20 84 or 01246 852823 (UK); acceuil@camping-st-hilaire.com; www.camping-st-hilaire.com]** Foll N149 bet Parthenay & Vouille; at xrds in vill, turn N into Rue de la Gare (D24); site 750m on R over rlwy line. Sm, mkd pitch, pt shd; wc; chem disp; shwrs inc; el pnts (10A) €3.95; Indtte; shop; rest, snacks, bar in vill; BBQ; playgrnd; pool; tennis; games rm; TV rm; dogs free; bus 750m; c'van storage; adv bkg; ccard acc; quiet; CKE/CCI. "Friendly, helpful British owners; situated in mature forest area, sh walk fr vill; 20 mins fr Futuroscope; lge pitches; excel, clean site & pool; poss muddy in wet weather." ♦ 1 May-30 Sep. € 23.25 2013*

CHASSENEUIL DU POITOU see Jaunay Clan *4H1*

⊞ **CHASSENEUIL SUR BONNIEURE** *7B3* (9km E Rural) *45.83283, 0.55811* **Camping Le Paradis, Mareuil, 16270 Mazières [tel/fax 05 45 84 92 06 / 078 66 49 67 41 (mob); info@le-paradis-camping.com; www.le-paradis-camping.com]** Fr Limoges W on N141 twd Angoulême, turn L at 1st traff lts in Roumazières-Loubert D161. Site sp in 2km at t-junc. Sm, hdg/mkd pitch, hdstg, pt shd; wc; chem disp; mv service pnt; fam bthrm; shwrs inc; el pnts (10-16A) €5.50-8.50; gas 3km; Indtte; shop; tradsmn; rest, snacks & bar 1km; BBQ; playgrnd; lake sw & watersports 5km; fishing nrby; tennis nr; games area; 20% statics; dogs free; phone; bus 1km; adv bkg rec; quiet; CKE/CCI. "Clean, tranquil site; gd sized pitches; vg, immac san facs; welcoming British owners, helpful & friendly; gd touring base; adv bkg rec lge o'fits; excel; min €30 for 1 night stays. " ♦ ltd € 17.50 2013*

CHASSENEUIL SUR BONNIEURE *7B3* (650km W Urban) *45.82389, 0.44415* **Camp Municipal Les Charmilles, Rue des Ecoles, 16260 Chasseneuil-sur-Bonnieure [05 45 39 55 36; jctelemaque@free.fr]** On N141 Angoulême-Limoges leave by-pass sp Chasseneuil. In town turn L onto D27 sp Mémorial de la Résistance. Turn R at camping sp, site ahead. Med, hdg/mkd pitch, pt shd; wc; chem disp; shwrs inc; el pnts (10A) inc; Indtte; gas 200m; shop; supmkt 100m; rest, snacks, bar 50m; playgrnd; htd, covrd pool adj; dogs; quiet. "Warden calls pm or key fr Mairie; diff to ent/leave site without key to bollard; gd san facs; vg value." ♦ ltd Easter-30 Sep. € 9.00 2009*

CHATEAU D'OLERON, LE (ILE D'OLERON) *7B1* (1km W Coastal) *45.88207, -1.20648* **Camping Airotel Oléron, Domaine de Montravail, 17480 Le Château-d'Oléron [05 46 47 61 82; fax 05 46 47 79 67; info@camping-airotel-oleron.com; www.camping-airotel-oleron.com]** Clearly sp fr D734 after x-ing bdge. Not well sp fr N of island. Ent to site thro stables & horseriding cent. Med, mkd pitch, pt shd; wc; shwrs inc; el pnts (8-10A) €3.90 (poss rev pol); gas; Indtte; shop & 500m; snacks; bar; BBQ; playgrnd; htd pool; sand beach 1km; fishing; tennis; equestrian centre; games area; cycle hire; some statics; dogs €3; poss cr; Eng spkn; adv bkg; quiet; red low ssn/CKE/CCI. "Gd site but poss unkempt early ssn; sparse water points; easy walk to town." ♦ 1 Apr-31 Oct. € 22.50 2010*

See advertisement

CHATEAU D'OLERON, LE (ILE D'OLERON) *7B1* (850m NW Urban/Coastal) *45.88970, -1.20028* **Camping Les Remparts, Blvd Philippe-Daste, 17480 Le Château-d'Oléron [05 46 47 61 93; fax 05 46 47 73 65; camping@les-remparts.com; www.les-remparts.com]** Fr cent Le Château-d'Oléron take D734 dir Dolus d'Oléron rd. After x-ing ramparts/moat turn R at next rndabt, site on R. Lge, pt sl, pt shd; wc (mainly cont); mv service pnt; shwrs inc; el pnts (5A) €3.90; Indtte; shop nrby; tradsmn; rest, snacks, bar nrby; playgrnd; sand beach adj; some statics; dogs €2; phone; quiet; red low ssn/long stay. "Pleasant site for NH/sh stay." 1 Mar-30 Nov. € 17.50 (3 persons) 2009*

"We must tell The Club about that great site we found"

Get your site reports in by mid-August and we'll do our best to get your updates into the next edition.

CHATEAU D'OLERON, LE (ILE D'OLERON) *7B1* (2.5km NW Coastal) *45.90415, -1.21525* **Camping La Brande, Route des Huîtres, 17480 Le Château-d'Oléron [05 46 47 62 37; fax 05 46 47 71 70; info@camping-labrande.com; www.camping-labrande.com / www.campings-oleron.com]** Cross bdge on D26, turn R & go thro Le Château-d'Oléron. Foll Rte des Huîtres to La Gaconnière to site. Lge, shd; wc; mv service pnt; baby facs; sauna; steam rm; shwrs inc; el pnts (6-10A) €4-6; gas; Indtte (inc dryer); shop; tradsmn; rest in ssn; snacks; bar; BBQ; playgrnd; 3 pools (1 htd, covrd); waterslide; sand beach 300m; tennis; cycle hire; games area; golf 6km; wifi; entmnt; TV rm; 60% statics; dogs €3; sep car park; Eng spkn; adv bkg; ccard acc; red low ssn; CKE/CCI. "Pleasant owners; pitches at far end adj oyster farm - some noise fr pumps & poss mosquitoes; 10 min cycle ride into town; v gd." ♦ 31 Mar-11 Nov. € 39.00 2013*

See advertisement

CHÂTEAU LARCHER see Vivonne *7A2*

CHATELAILLON PLAGE *7A1* (2km N Urban) *46.08632, -1.09489* **Camping L'Océan, Ave d'Angoulins, 17340 Châtelaillon-Plage [05 46 56 87 97; www.campingocean17.com]** Fr La Rochelle take D602 to Châtelaillon-Plage, site sp on L in 300m (after passing g'ge & L'Abbaye camp site). Med, hdg/mkd pitch, san fan; wc (some cont); chem disp (wc); baby facs; shwrs inc; el pnts (10A) €5.00; Indry rm; tradsmn; ice; shops, rest, snacks & bar 1km; BBQ; pool complex; waterslide; sand beach 500m; dogs €2; bus; park & ride 400m; phone; poss cr; some Eng spkn; occasional noise fr rlwy & clay pigeon range; ccard acc; red low ssn. "Very nice site, no statics and gd cycle rtes." ♦ 18 May- 23 Sep. € 25.50 2013*

"I need an on-site restaurant"

We do our best to make sure site information is correct, but it is always best to check any must-have facilities are still available or will be open during your visit.

CHATELAILLON PLAGE *7A1* (2.5km SE Coastal) *46.05491, -1.08331* **Camping Port Punay, Les Boucholeurs, Allée Bernard Moreau, 17340 Châtelaillon-Plage [05 46 56 01 53; fax 05 46 56 86 44; contact@camping-port-punay.com; www.camping-port-punay.com]** Fr N exit D137 La Rochell-Rochefort rd onto D109; strt on at 1st rndabt, L at 2nd rndabt; then cont for 2.8km to end (harbour); turn L, keep R along narr one-way st; at next junc to L, site sp. Fr S exit D137 onto D203 sp Les Boucholeurs; at rndabt in 1km foll site sp to edge of Châtelaillon & turn R, foll sp. Site in 500m. Lge, pt shd; wc; baby facs; shwrs inc; el pnts (10A) €5; gas; Indtte; Indry rm; shops adj; rest, snacks; bar; playgrnd; pool; sand beach 500m; games area; cycle hire; wifi; entmnt; TV; 25% statics; dogs €2.50; poss cr; Eng spkn; adv bkg; quiet; red low ssn. "Busy but quiet site; immac san facs; friendly, energetic, helpful owners; steel pegs req; sm pitches; excel." 22 Apr-25 Sep. € 24.50 (3 persons) 2011*

See advertisement

CHAUVIGNY *7A3* (1km E Urban) *46.57072, 0.65326* **Camp Municipal de la Fontaine, Rue de la Fontaine, 86300 Chauvigny [tel/fax 05 49 46 31 94; camping-chauvigny@cg86.fr; www.chauvigny.fr]** N151 fr Poitiers to Chauvigny. Turn L in cent Chauvigny just bef gate.Site well sp fr Chauvigny. Med, pt shd; htd wc (some cont); chem disp; mv service pnt; baby facs; shwrs; el pnts (15A) inc; Indtte; shop 500m; tradsmn; BBQ; playgrnd; pool & tennis 1km; rv 1km; cycle hire; wifi; dogs €1.80; adv bkg; red low ssn; CKE/CCI. "Popular, well-kept, well-run site adj park & lake; views of castle; lge pitches; helpful, friendly staff; immac san facs; o'night area for m'vans; delightful walk to cent; mkts Tue, Thur & Sat; a real find; excel facs; gd value; old style elec plug/socket adaptor needed, poss rev pol; rec." ♦ 19 Apr-30 Sep. € 17.35 2014*

CHAUVIGNY *7A3* (7km NW Rural) *46.60189, 0.59838* **Camp Municipal, 13 Rue de la Varenne, 86300 Bonnes [05 49 56 44 34 or 05 49 56 40 17 (Mairie); fax 05 49 56 48 51; camping_bonnes86@hotmail.com]** Sp fr D951 & D749. Sp to site easily missed in vill. Site on rvside. Med, hdg pitch, pt shd; wc; chem disp; mv service pnt; shwrs inc; el pnts (15A) €2.70; Indtte; shop adj in vill; tradsmn; rest & bar 500m; pool adj; waterslide; playgrnd; rv & sand beach adj; tennis; dogs €1.05; poss cr; adv bkg; quiet; Eng spkn; dogs; CKE/CCI. "Friendly, helpful staff; clean & welcoming; vg pool; poss travellers." 15 May-15 Sep. € 9.70 2010*

⊞ **CHEF BOUTONNE** *7A2* (2km W Rural) *46.10767, -0.09342* **Camping Le Moulin, 1 Route de Niort, 79110 Chef-Boutonne [05 49 29 73 46; info@campingchef.com; www.campingchef.com]** Fr D950 to or fr Poitiers, turn E onto D740 to Chef-Boutonne, site on R. Fr N10 turn onto D948 to Sauzé-Vaussais then L onto D1 to Chef-Boutonne; then take D740 dir Brioux-sur-Boutonne; site on L. Sm, hdg/mkd pitch, ltd hdstg, pt shd; htd wc; chem disp; mv service pnt 1km; baby facs; fam bthrm; shwrs inc; el pnts (10A); Indry rm; ice; shop 2km; tradsmn; rest, snacks; bar; BBQ; playgrnd; pool; wifi; entmnt; 10% statics; dogs €1.20; bus 2km; poss cr; twin axles; Eng spkn; adv bkg; quiet; ccard acc; red long stay/low ssn; CKE/CCI. "Well-kept site; lge pitches; friendly, helpful British owners; gd rest; much bird life; conv Futuroscope & La Rochelle; vg; san facs refurbished (2014)." ♦ € 24.00 2014*

CHENAC ST SEURIN D'UZET see Cozes *7B1*

CIVRAY *7A2* (1km NE Urban) *46.15835, 0.30169* **Camping Les Aulnes, Les Coteaux de Roche, 86400 Civray [05 49 87 17 24 / 06 32 95 00 77 (mob); fax 05 49 87 17 24; campingaulnes@yahoo.fr; www.camping-les-aulnes.com]** Civray 9km E of N10 halfway bet Poitiers & Angoulême. Site outside town SE of junc of D1 & D148. Sp on D148 & on S by-pass. Avoid town cent narr rds. Med, pt sl, pt shd; wc (cont); chem disp (wc); shwrs; el pnts (6-10A) €3 (poss long lead req); lndtte; shop 500m; rest, snacks; bar; BBQ; playgrnd; htd pool 1km; rv sw & fishing adj; cycle hire; golf; few statics; dogs €1; Eng spkn; quiet; ccard acc; CKE/CCI. "Pleasant rvside site; old, but clean san facs, poss irreg cleaning low ssn; pitches soft when wet; vg rest; conv town cent; mkt Wed; vg." 1 Apr-15 Oct. € 7.50 2013*

COGNAC *7B2* (1.8km N Urban) *45.69858, -0.33260* **Aire Communautaire, Place de la Levade, Quartier St Jaques, 16700 Cognac [05 45 36 64 30; contact@cc-cognac.fr]** M'vans only. N fr Cognac, cross rv bdge & foll m'van sp on L. Opp Hennessy Cognac House. Chem disp, mv service pnt, el pnts; lndtte; shop; rest. "Free NH adj rv." 1 Jun-15 Sep. 2010*

COGNAC *7B2* (2.5km NE Rural) *45.70920, -0.31284* **Camping de Cognac, Blvd de Châtenay, 16100 Cognac [05 45 32 13 32; fax 05 45 32 15 82; contact@campingdecognac.com; www.campingdecognac.com]** Fr N141 foll 'Camping' sp to town cent. Turn R at 'Speedy' g'ge, site immed on R in 2km after x-ing rv. - foll sp 'Base de Plein Air'. Take care ent barrier. Med, hdg/mkd pitch, some hdstg, pt shd; wc (some cont); chem disp; mv service pnt; shwrs inc; el pnts (6A) inc (poss long leads req & poss rev pol); lndtte; shop high ssn & 2km; tradsmn; rest, snacks high ssn; bar; BBQ; playgrnd; pool; rv boating & fishing; games area; entmnt; 5% statics; dogs €1.50; bus; phone; poss cr; Eng spkn; adv bkg; rd noise; ccard acc; red long stay/low ssn; CKE/CCI. "Excel lge park with many facs; helpful staff; clean modern san facs; gates clsd 2200-0700 (1800 low ssn); night watchman high ssn; no twin axles; footpath to town; conv Cognac distilleries (vouchers fr site recep); cycle rte to town cent." ♦ 25 Apr-30 Sep. € 26.00 2014*

COGNAC *7B2* (10km E Rural) *45.67160, -0.22718* **Camping du Port, 16200 Bourg-Charente [06 03 98 60 19 (mob)]** Exit N141 onto D158 dir Bourg-Charente; turn L in 800m & site on R. Site sp fr D158. Chicane-type ent gates. Sm, pt sl, pt shd; wc (some cont); chem disp; mv service pnt; shwrs; el pnts (6A) €2.50; rest & shop 500m; fishing; tennis; dogs; ccard acc; red long stay; "Delightful site on banks of Rv Charante; friendly staff; facs basic but clean, poss stretched high ssn; site on 2 levels, lower one sl; gd walks & cycle path to Jarnac & Cognac; gd." 1 May-15 Sep. € 17.80 2013*

> **"Satellite navigation makes touring much easier"**
>
> Remember most sat navs don't know if you're towing or in a larger vehicle – always use yours alongside maps and site directions.

COGNAC *7B2* (14km E Urban) *45.67606, -0.17349* **FFCC Camping de l'Ile Madame, 16200 Jarnac [05 45 81 18 54 or 05 45 81 68 02; fax 05 45 81 24 98; camping.jarnac@wanadoo.fr; www.camping-jarnac.com]** Turn E at S end of rv bdge at S end of town. Fr Angoulême on N141, exit junc sp 'Jarnac Est'; foll sp Jarnac thro 1 rndabt into Jarnac; at traff lts (LH lane) turn L sp Tourist Info/Camping; cross rv brge & immed turn L to site. Lge, pt shd; wc; shwrs inc; el pnts (6-10A) €2.80 (rev pol); lndtte; shops & rest adj; playgrnd; pool inc; games area; golf, canoe & cycle hire nrby; entmnt; TV; dogs €0.50; poss cr; adv bkg; poss noise fr adj sports grnd & disco; red long stay; CKE/CCI. "Pleasant, well-run site; gd sized pitches; san facs clean but update needed; no twin-axles; easy walk into Jarnac with shops & rests; gd walks along rv; nr Courvoisier bottling plant." 1 Apr-30 Sep. € 13.60 2010*

⊞ **COGNAC** *7B2* (8km S Rural) *45.60148, -0.36067* **Camping Le Chiron (Chainier), 16130 Salles-d'Angles [05 45 83 72 79; fax 05 45 83 64 80; mchainier@voila.fr]** Fr Cognac D731 Barbezieux to Salles-d'Angles, R at bottom hill onto D48; then in 3km turn L onto D151; site on L in 500m (foll Chambres d'Hôtes sps). Sm, pt sl, pt shd; htd wc (1 cont); chem disp; shwrs inc; el pnts (10A) inc (rev pol); shop 3km; no dogs; Eng spkn; quiet; ccard not acc. "Vg; meals avail at farm; v basic; own san facs rec." € 12.00 2014*

CONFOLENS *7A3* (500m N Rural) *46.01905, 0.67531* **Camp Municipal des Ribières, Ave de St Germain, 16500 Confolens [05 45 85 35 27 or 05 45 84 01 97 (Mairie); fax 05 45 85 34 10; contact@mairieconfolens.com; www.mairieconfolens.com]** Fr N foll D951 dir Confolens turn L sp St Germain-de-Confolens, site on R in 7km at edge of town bet rd & rv. NB Diff app fr S thro vill. Med, mkd pitch, pt shd; wc (most cont); shwrs inc; gas; el pnts (16A) €2; Indry rm; shop 700m; tradsmn; BBQ; pool 200m; rv sw adj; fishing & boating; no statics; dogs; phone; m'van o'night area outside site; adv bkg (post only 2010); some rd noise; ccard & CKE/CCI not acc. "Interesting, pretty town; facs neglected & ltd low ssn; warden calls am & pm." ♦ 15 May-15 Sep. € 7.00 2009*

CONFOLENS *7A3* (7km S Rural) *45.96605, 0.70888* **Camp Municipal Moulin de la Cour, 16500 St Maurice-des-Lions [05 45 85 55 99; fax 05 45 85 52 89]** Fr Confolens take D948 S. In 6.5km turn L thro vill, site 700m, well sp. Sm, hdg/mkd pitch, terr, pt shd; wc (some cont); chem disp (wc); shwrs inc; el pnts (6A) €2; shop, rest, bar 500m; BBQ; adv bkg; quiet. "Pleasant site in quiet location; pitch yourself, warden calls pm; old, inadequate facs; height limitations when site clsd (see sp at ent to sports cent & site); ent thro stone pillars; site used by Boules Club & football; nr pretty vill with 12thC church & old houses; Confolens folk festival mid-Aug." 1 Jun-30 Sep. € 6.00 2009*

COUARDE SUR MER, LA (ILE DE RE) *7A1* (4km SE Coastal) *46.17733, -1.38629* **Campéole Camping Les Amis de la Plage, Ave Pas des Boeufs, 17580 Le Bois-Plage-en-Ré [tel/fax 05 46 09 24 01; contact@les-amis-de-la-plage.com; www.les-amis-de-la-plage.com / www.campeole.com]** Fr toll bdge fr La Rochelle foll D201 to Le Bois-Plage-en-Ré; on ent vill take 1st L sp 'Plage-des-Boeufs' & 'Municipal'. Site on R at end of rd. Lge, pt sl, pt shd; wc; chem disp (wc); mv service pnt; baby facs; shwrs inc; el pnts (10A) €4.10; Indtte; shops & mkt 1km; tradsmn; rest & snacks adj; BBQ; playgrnd; sand beach adj; pool adj; 5% statics; dogs €2; phone; bus 1km; poss cr; Eng spkn; quiet; ccard acc; red low ssn; CKE/CCI. "Friendly, easy-going site; pitches on sand/soil/dry grass; vg." 2 Apr-30 Sep. € 19.00 (3 persons) 2010*

COUARDE SUR MER, LA (ILE DE RE) *7A1* (4km SE Coastal) *46.17405, -1.37865* **Sunêlia Parc Club Interlude, 8 Route de Gros Jonc, 17580 Le Bois-Plage-en-Ré [05 46 09 18 22; fax 05 46 09 23 38; infos@interlude.fr; www.interlude.fr]** Fr toll bdge at La Rochelle foll D201 to Gros-Jonc. Turn L at rndabt at site sp. Site 400m on L. Lge, hdg/mkd pitch, hdstg, pt shd; htd wc; chem disp; mv service pnt; baby facs; fam bthrm; sauna; some serviced pitches; shwrs inc; el pnts (10A) inc; gas; Indtte (inc dryer); shop; rest, snacks; bar; BBQ; playgrnd; 2 pools (1 htd, covrd); sand beach; watersports; jacuzzi; solarium; tennis nr; games area; boat & cycle hire; fitness rm; wifi; TV rm; 45% statics; dogs €8; poss cr; Eng spkn; o'night area for m'vans; adv bkg ess; quiet; red low ssn. "Excel, well-run, clean, relaxing site; busy but not noisy; vg facs; some sm, sandy pitches - extra for lger; gd rest; nrby beaches excel; walk to great beach; gd atmosphere, entmnt and shop." ♦ 13 Apr-22 Sep. € 67.20 2013*

COUARDE SUR MER, LA (ILE DE RE) *7A1* (5km SE Coastal) *46.16793, -1.36351* **Camping Antioche, Route de Ste Marie, 17580 Le Bois-Plage-en-Ré [05 46 09 23 86; fax 05 46 09 43 34; camping.antioche@wanadoo.fr]** Fr toll bdge fr La Rochelle, at 1st rndabt take D201 sp Le Bois-Plage. In about 9km, site on L. Med, hdg/mkd pitch (sandy), pt sl, pt shd; wc; chem disp; mv service pnt; shwrs inc; el pnts (6A) inc; Indtte; shop & 3km; playgrnd; snacks; bar; BBQ; cooking facs; sand beach adj; entmnt; some statics; dogs €6; phone; poss cr; Eng spkn; adv bkg; ccard acc; red low ssn/long stay/CKE/CCI. "Lovely site with gd sized pitches; direct access to beach & cycle path; friendly staff; clean facs." ♦ 4 Apr-19 Sep. € 37.00 (3 persons) 2009*

COUARDE SUR MER, LA (ILE DE RE) *7A1* (500m W Urban/Coastal) *46.19348, -1.43427* **Camp Municipal Le Remondeau, 12 Route Petite Noue, 17670 La Couarde-sur-Mer [05 46 29 84 27; campingleremondeau@wanadoo.fr]** Fr toll bdge foll D735 to rndabt on W side of La Couarde-sur-Mer & take D201. Foll sp to site. Lge, pt sl, pt shd; htd wc; chem disp; mv service pnt; baby facs; shwrs inc; el pnts (10A) €3.70; Indtte (inc dryer); tradsmn; BBQ; playgrnd; sand beach adj; wifi; few statics; dogs; Eng spkn; no adv bkg; quiet; red long stay; CKE/CCI. "Vg site." ♦ ltd Easter-30 Oct. € 19.00 2010*

COUARDE SUR MER, LA (ILE DE RE) *7A1* (2.5km W Coastal) *46.20296, -1.45505* **Camping Le Bois Henri IV, Route d'Ars, 17670 La Couarde-sur-Mer [tel/fax 05 46 29 87 01; campingduboishenri4@aliceadsl.fr; www.campingduboishenri4.17-flash.com]** On D735 W fr La Couarde-sur-Mer, site ent bet 2 pedestrian x-ings - easy to miss. Med, hdg/mkd pitch, pt shd; wc; chem disp; mv service pnt; baby facs; shwrs inc; chem disp (wc); el pnts (5A) €4; Indtte (inc dryer); shop; BBQ (gas/elec); playgrnd; sand beach 200m; cycle hire; wifi; TV rm; 30% statics; dogs €2; poss cr; Eng spkn; adv bkg; quiet; red low ssn; CKE/CCI. "Busy site; long, sandy beaches; friendly owner; clean, dated san facs; birdwatching in salt marshes; 100km of flat cycling pathways; vg." ♦ ltd 1 Apr-30 Sep. € 22.00 2011*

COUARDE SUR MER, LA (ILE DE RE) *7A1* (800m NW Coastal) *46.20408, -1.46740* **Camping de l'Océan, 50 Route d'Ars, 17670 La Couarde-sur-Mer [05 46 29 87 70; fax 05 46 29 92 13; info@campingocean.com; www.campingocean.com]** Fr La Rochelle take D735 over bdge to Ile de Ré. Past St Martin-de-Re & La Couarde twd Ars-en-Ré. Site on R, 2.5km after La Couarde. Lge, hdg/mkd pitch, shd; htd wc; chem disp; mv service pnt; baby facs; fam bthrm; shwrs inc; el pnts (10A) €5.50; Indtte (inc dryer); shop; rest, snacks; bar; no BBQ; playgrnd; 2 pools (1 htd); paddling pool; sand beach adj; watersports; tennis; games area; cycle hire; horseriding 1.5km; golf 6km; wifi; entmnt; 40% statics; dogs €5; phone; poss cr; Eng spkn; adv bkg; rd noisy; ccard acc; red low ssn; CKE/CCI. "Popular site in superb location; some sm pitches with diff access; site rds & ent to pitches narr; gd, clean san facs; friendly staff; twin-axles not rec; recep clsd 1230-1400, if clsd, park in yard facing recep; gd walking & cycling; excel; toll fee to island €27.50." ♦ 16 Apr-18 Sep. € 49.00 (3 persons) 2012*

See advert on previous page

POITOU-CHARENTES

COUARDE SUR MER, LA (ILE DE RE) *7A1* (2km NW Coastal) *46.20473, -1.44470* **Camping La Tour des Prises, Route d'Ars D735, 17670 La Couarde-sur-Mer [05 46 29 84 82; fax 05 46 29 88 99; camping@lesprises.com; www.lesprises.com]** Fr toll bdge foll D735 or D201 to La Couarde, then Rte d'Ars for 1.8km to R turn; site sp & 200m on R. Med, hdg/mkd pitch, pt shd; htd wc (some cont); chem disp; mv service pnt; baby facs; shwrs inc; el pnts (16A) €5.50; Indtte; shop; tradsmn; snacks; playgrnd; htd, covrd pool; beach 600m; sailing school; games rm; cycle hire; wifi; 30% statics; dogs €4.; Eng spkn; adv bkg; quiet; ccard acc; red low ssn; CKE/CCI. "Excel, well-managed, clean site; lge individual pitches, mixed sizes; helpful owner & staff; excel pool; many cycle/walking tracks; beach 10 mins walk; ideal for families; lge o'fits drive cautiously, no one way; v busy; v friendly staff; cent located on Isle de Re; acc to cycle paths fr site gate." ♦ 5 Apr-28 Sep. € 47.20 (3 persons) 2014*

"There aren't many sites open at this time of year"

If you're travelling outside peak season remember to call ahead to check site opening dates – even if the entry says 'open all year'.

COUHE *7A2* (1km N Rural) *46.31254, 0.18216* **Camping Les Peupliers, 86700 Couhé [05 49 59 21 16; fax 05 49 37 92 09; info@lespeupliers.fr; www.lespeupliers.fr]** Site 35km S of Poitiers on N10 bis (old rd off by-pass); ent by bdge over Rv Dive. Fr N or S on N10 take N exit for Couhé. Site on R in 800m. Lge, hdg/mkd pitch, pt shd; wc; 30% serviced pitch; chem disp; mv service pnt; shwrs inc; el pnts (10A) €4.50; gas; Indtte (inc dryer); sm shop & 1.5km; tradsmn; rest, snacks; bar; BBQ; playgrnd; 2 htd pools & paddling pools high ssn; waterslides; jacuzzi; fishing; games area; games rm; wifi; entmnt; TV rm; some statics; dogs free; Eng spkn; adv bkg; quiet, poss some rd noise; ccard acc; red low ssn/long stay/CKE/CCI. "Beautiful, well-run & well-kept site; friendly, helpful staff; immac san facs; easy access fr N10; conv Futuroscope; excel." ♦ 2 May-30 Sep. € 26.50 2011*

See advertisement

⊞ **COUHE** *7A2* (8.5km SW Rural) *46.25652, 0.08892* **Camping La Grande Vigne, 11 Rue du Paradis, 79120 Messé [05 49 29 39 93 or 0800 073 8385; grande.vigne@orange.fr; www.grande-vigne.com]** Fr N10 exit at Chaunay onto D35/D55 sp Lezay, thro Vanzay & in approx 1.5km turn R onto C11. Site sp. Sm, pt shd; htd wc; chem disp (wc); shwrs inc; el pnts (10A) €3.50; Indtte (inc dryer); shop, rest 8km; tradsmn; bar 5km; BBQ; htd pool; cycle hire; games area; 2 gîtes to rent; wifi; dogs €0.75 (by prior agreement); twin axle acc; adv bkg; quiet; CKE/CCI. "Gd walking, cycling; gd birdwatching; British owners; friendly welcome; excel." ♦ ltd € 18.50 2013*

"That's changed – Should I let The Club know?"

If you find something on site that's different from the site entry, fill in a report and let us know. See www.caravanclub.co.uk/europereport.

COULON *7A2* (500m N Rural) *46.32739, -0.58437* **Camp Municipal La Niquière, Route de Benet, 79510 Coulon [05 49 35 81 19 or 05 49 35 90 26 (Mairie); fax 05 49 35 82 75; tourisme.coulon79@orange.fr; www.ville-coulon.fr]** Fr N148 at Benet take D1 to Coulon to site on L at ent to Coulon. Sm, pt shd; wc (some cont); chem disp (wc); shwrs inc; el pnts (10A) €3.10; gas; shops 1km; sports facs adj; boats for hire; dogs €0.50; poss cr. "Well-kept site; dated but clean san facs; ent only with barrier card - collect fr Mairie when site office clsd; 10 min walk to vill; gd NH." 1 Apr-30 Sep. € 7.80 2010*

COULON *7A2* (5km SE Rural) *46.31307, -0.53495* **Camping le Martin-Pêcheur, 155 av. Du Marais Poitevin, 79460 Magné [05 49 35 71 81; info@camping-le-martin-pecheur.com; www.camping-le-martin-pecheur.com]** Fr S take A10, exit 33 dir Marais Poitevin. Then Sansais, La Garette, Magne. Fr Nantes A83, exit 9 twds Marais Poitevin, Coulon & Magne. Med, hdg/ mkd pitch, pt shd; htd wc; mv service pnt; shwrs inc; baby fasc; el pnts (10A) inc; BBQ; Indtte; Indtte rm; shop; rest 500m; playgrnd; bus; Eng spkn; quiet; adv bkg; red 10 days; CKE/CCI. "Excel; beautiful area; interlaced with canals; gd walking & cycling; boats & gondolas for hire, with or without boatman; new facs (2014)." ♦ 1 May-28 Sep. € 27.50 2014*

COULON *7A2* (2km W Rural) *46.31444, -0.60888* **Camping La Venise Verte, 178 Route des Bords de Sèvre, 79510 Coulon [05 49 35 90 36; fax 05 49 35 04 69; accueil@camping-laveniseverte.fr; www.camping-la-venise-verte.com]** Exit A83 junc 9 onto D148 to Benet. Turn R at rndabt onto D25E sp Benet cent & foll sp for Coulon thro Benet. In Coulon turn R at traff lts onto D123 sp Le Vanneau-Irleau & Arcais. Cont for approx 3km with canal on L to site R bef canal bdge. Site sp. Med, mkd pitch, pt shd; wc; chem disp; mv service pnt; baby facs; shwrs inc; el pnts (10A) inc (poss rev pol); Indtte (inc dryer); tradsmn; rest, snacks, bar (high ssn); BBQ (charcoal/gas); playgrnd; pool; paddling pool; boating; fishing; canoe/cycle hire; games rm; wifi; entmnt; 25% statics; dogs €2; twin-axles acc (rec check in adv); phone; poss cr; adv bkg; poss noisy high ssn; ccard acc; red low ssn; ACSI; CKE/CCI. "Superb, peaceful site in park-like setting; helpful, v friendly owner; excel facs; gd rest; gd sized pitches, but some sm & diff due trees & posts; excel touring base for nature lovers; gd walking & cycle paths beside waterways; pretty town; lovely area; much revisited site; well placed pitches; gd facs; beautiful, tranquil location; highly rec." ♦ 1 Apr-30 Oct. € 39.60 SBS - A37 2013*

COURCON *7A2* (6km N Rural) *46.30089, -0.80782* **Camping du Port (Naturist), Rue du Port, 17170 La Ronde [05 46 41 65 58 or 06 26 06 72 37 (mob); camping.naturisteduport@orange.fr; www.camping-naturiste-du-port.com]** Fr Marans E on D114, bef Courçon head N on D116 dir Maillezais. Site on R after leaving vill of La Ronde. Sm, hdg/mkd pitch, hdstg, pt shd; wc; chem disp; shwrs inc; el pnts (6-10A) €3.50; gas; Indtte; shops adj; BBQ; playgrnd; pool high ssn; sand beach 30km; few statics; dogs €2; poss cr; adv bkg; quiet. "Excel, well looked-after site; helpful owner; facs clean; site poss open outside dates shown." ♦ 1 May-30 Sep. € 17.00 2009*

COURCON *7A2* (500m SE Rural) *46.24060, -0.80635* **Camp Municipal La Garenne, 12 Rue du Collège, 17170 Courçon [05 46 01 60 19 or 05 46 01 60 50 (Mairie); fax 05 46 01 63 59; mairie.courcon@mairie17.com]** Fr E on N11 turn N at La Laigne on D114 to Courçon. Site on L on app to vill. Fr W turn N onto D116 to Courçon. Sm, pt shd; wc; mv service pnt; shwrs; el pnts (3A) €3.50; Indtte; shops 500m; htd pool adj; rv sw 5km; fishing 5km; dogs €1.50; adv bkg rec high ssn; quiet. 1 Jul-31 Aug. € 8.80 2009*

COURCON *7A2* (5km S Urban) *46.20365, -0.81619* **Camp Municipal du Château, 17170 Benon [06 66 90 35 59 (mob) or 05 46 01 61 48 (Mairie); fax 05 46 01 01 19; mairie-benon@smic17.fr; mairie-benon@smic17.fr; www.tourisme-aunisverte.com]** Fr N11 turn S to Benon onto D116. On S side of Benon turn E onto D206 twd St Georges-du-Bois, site immed on R thro tall, narr, metal gateway; take wide sweep on ent (or use easier access at rear - foll wall round to L). Site also sp in Benon. Sm, pt sl, mainly shd; wc; chem disp; mv service pnt; shwrs inc; el pnts (10A) €2.50; Indtte; tradsmn; playgrnd; pool 6km; tennis; dogs €1; quiet; adv bkg; ccard acc; CKE/CCI. "Attractive site adj Mairie; immac & tidy; no lighting; oyster beds at Châtelaillon; gd cycling area; 20 mins La Rochelle; poss travellers." 15 May-30 Sep. € 9.40 2011*

COUX see Montendre *7C2*

COZES *7B1* (4km SW Rural) *45.54536, -0.88901* **Camping Fleur des Champs, Le Coudinier, 17120 Arces-sur-Gironde [05 46 90 40 11; fax 05 46 97 64 45; contact@campingfdc.com; www.campingfdc.com]** Site on D114 on R 1km fr Arces to Talmont. Sm, mkd pitch, pt sl, pt shd; wc; shwrs inc; el pnts (6A) €3.30; gas; tradsmn; Indtte; shop 1km; tradsmn; playgrnd; pool 4km; lake sw & beach; cycle hire; entmnt; wifi; 80% statics; dogs €1.70; quiet. "Pleasant, basic site; ideal for seaside holiday away fr typical coastal sites; clean, dated san facs, ltd if site full; NH/sh stay only." 1 Jun-15 Sep. € 9.50 2011*

COZES *7B1* (650m NW Urban) *45.58650, -0.83568* **Camp Municipal Le Sorlut, Rue de Stade, 17120 Cozes [05 46 90 75 99 or 05 46 90 90 97 (Mairie); fax 05 46 90 75 12]** Clearly sp in Cozes, 150m fr D730. Turn into app rd on R of Champion supmkt. Med, mkd pitch, pt shd; wc; chem disp; shwrs inc; el pnts (5A) €2.50; Indry rm; shops adj; supmkt 500m; playgrnd; pool; sand beach 6km; tennis; poss cr; quiet; CKE/CCI. "Pleasant site close to Royan; friendly, helpful warden; gd, clean san facs; poss unkempt low ssn; no twin-axles; popular with long stay British." 15 Apr-14 Oct. € 10.50 2010*

DAMPIERRE SUR BOUTONNE *7A2* (Rural) *46.06642, -0.41459* **Camp Municipal, 17470 Dampierre-sur-Boutonne [05 46 24 02 36 (Mairie); fax 05 46 33 95 49; dampierre-sur-boutonne@mairie17.com; www.aulnaytourisme.com]** S fr Niort on D150 twds St Jean-d'Angély; in vill of Tout-y-Faut turn E on D115 sp Dampierre; turn N in vill on D127 twds Rv Boutonne, site behind vill hall; well sp. Sm, hdg pitch, shd; wc (some cont); shwrs inc; el pnts (6A) €2; shop, rest, snacks, bar 500m; rv fishing; dogs €0.80; quiet. "Clean site; san facs outside camp boundary & wc's open to public; poss noisy, local youths congregate nrby; rec sh stay/NH only." 30 Apr-30 Sep. € 8.00 2009*

DANGE ST ROMAIN *4H2* (3km N Rural) *46.96944, 0.60399* **Camp Municipal, 8 Rue des Buxières, 86220 Les Ormes [05 49 85 61 30 (Mairie); fax 05 49 85 66 17; les-ormes@cg86.fr; www.tourisme-vienne.com]** Turn W off D910 in cent Les Ormes onto D1a sp Vellèches & Marigny-Marmande, foll site sp to site on rv. Sm, mkd pitch, pt sl, pt shd; wc; chem disp (wc); shwrs inc; el pnts (6A) inc; Indtte; shop; rest & bar 800m; playgrnd; tennis 100m; a few statics; dogs €1.20; quiet, but some rlwy noise; adv bkg; dogs; CKE/CCI. "Lovely, quiet setting on rv bank; helpful warden; clean basic modern san facs; poss travellers; quiet vill; chateau in walking dist; gd NH." 1 Apr-30 Sep. € 12.00 2011*

⊞ **DIENNE** *7A3* (800m NE Rural) *46.44613, 0.56023* **Camping Domaine de Dienné, 86410 Dienné [05 49 45 87 63; fax 05 49 54 17 96; info@domaine-de-dienne.fr; www.domaine-de-dienne.fr]** Fr Poitiers on N147/E62 S thro Fleuré & in 2.5km turn R to Dienné. Foll site sp. Med, pt shd; wc; sauna; shwrs; el pnts inc; Indtte; rest, snacks; playgrnd; 2 pools (1 htd, covrd); fishing; horseriding; games area; statics; site clsd 1-17 Jan; adv bkg; quiet. € 43.00 2009*

DISSAY see Jaunay Clan *4H1*

POITOU-CHARENTES

DOUHET, LE *7B2* (2km S Rural) *45.81080, -0.55288* **Camping La Roulerie, 17100 Le Douhet [05 46 96 40 07 or 06 75 24 91 96 (mob); www.camping-laroulerie.fr]** Fr Niort to Saintes, site on W side of D150 in vill of La Roulerie. Sm, some hdg/mkd pitch, some hdstdg, pt shd; wc; chem disp; mv service pnt; shwrs inc; el pnts (16A) €3.50; Indtte; shop; supmkt 9km; playgrnd; pool; games area; dog €1; some statics; Eng spkn; adv bkg; quiet but some rd noise; ccard not acc; CKE/CCI. "Sm pitches; full by early eve; friendly, helpful owner; gd san facs; vg value; gd NH." 1 May-15 Oct. € 9.00 2013*

ESNANDES see Rochelle, La *7A1*

EYMOUTHIERS see Montbron *7B3*

FLOTTE EN RE, LA see St Martin de Ré *7A1*

⊞ **FOURAS** *7A1* (500m NE Coastal) *45.99264, -1.08680* **Camp Municipal du Cadoret, Blvd de Chaterny, 17450 Fouras [05 46 82 19 19; fax 05 46 84 51 59; www.campings-fouras.com]** Fr Rochefort take N137, L onto D937 at Fouras, fork R at sp to site in 1km. At next rndabt take 3rd exit into Ave du Cadoret, then 1st R at next rndabt. Lge, hdg/mkd pitch, pt sl, pt shd; wc (some cont); chem disp; baby facs; shwrs inc; el pnts (6-10A) €3.40-5.20 (poss long lead req); gas; Indtte; shop 800m; rest; bar; htd pool; paddling pool; sand beach adj; pool; fishing; boating; tennis 1km; golf 5km; games area; wifi; entmnt; 50% statics (sep area); dogs €2.80; bus to La Rochelle, Rochefort, ferry to Ile d'Aix; poss cr; adv bkg; red low ssn; CKE/CCI. "Popular, well-kept site; vg location; well shd; lge pitches; clean san facs, unisex low ssn; coastal footpath; pleasant town; a favourite; highly rec; gd conv site; Eng spkn." ♦ € 38.30 2014*

⊞ **FOURAS** *7A1* (1km E Rural) *45.99023, -1.05184* **Camping Domaine Les Charmilles, Route de l'OcÃcan, 17450 Fouras [05 46 84 00 05; fax 05 46 84 02 84; info@domainedescharmilles.com; www.domainedescharmilles.com]** N fr Rochefort on N137, after 2km L onto D937. Site on L in 2km bef ent Fouras. Lge, hdg/mkd pitch, pt shd; htd wc; chem disp; mv service pnt; shwrs inc; el pnts (6A) €4; gas; Indtte; shop & 1km; tradsmn; snacks; bar; BBQ area; playgrnd; 3 pools (1 htd covrd); paddling pool; waterslides; sand beach 3km; cycle hire; games rm; wifi; entmnt; 20% statics; no dogs; bus to beach high ssn; poss cr; adv bkg; ccard acc; red long stay/low ssn; CKE/CCI. "Gd site; friendly staff; unisex facs." ♦ € 37.50 2013*

GEMOZAC *7B2* (400m W Urban) *45.56825, -0.68086* **Camp Municipal, 26 Rue Carnot, 17260 Gémozac [05 46 94 50 16; fax 05 46 94 16 25; gemozac@mairie17.com]** Exit A10 junc 36 (or turn W off off D137) onto D732 sp Gémozac. In 7km foll site sp. Turn L immed after Renault g'ge at end of vill. Sm, mkd pitch, pt shd; wc; chem disp; mv service pnt adj; baby facs; shwrs inc; el pnts (10A) inc (poss rev pol); Indtte; shop, pizzeria & snacks 500m; tradsmn; rest & bar 100m; BBQ; htd pool adj; dogs; Eng spkn; adv bkg; ccard not acc; quiet; CKE/CCI. "Excel site; pleasant sm town; no twin-axles." 15 Jun-31 Aug. 2009*

GICQ, LE see Matha *7B2*

GOUEX see Lussac Les Châteaux *7A3*

HOUMEAU, L' see Rochelle, La *7A1*

INGRANDES *4H2* (1km N Rural) *46.88700, 0.58800* **Camping Le Petit Trianon de St Ustre, 1 Rue du Moulin de St Ustre, 86220 Ingrandes-sur-Vienne [05 49 02 61 47; fax 05 49 02 68 81; petit-trianon@camp-in-ouest.com; www.petit-trianon.com / www.les-castels.com]** Leave A10/E5 at Châtellerault Nord exit 26 & foll sp Tours. Cross rv heading N on D910 twd Tours & Dangé-St Romain. At 2nd traff lts in Ingrandes (by church), turn R. Cross rlwy line & turn L at site sp in 300m. After 1.5km turn R at site sp, site at top of hill. NB Site ent narr, poss diff lge o'fits. Med, mkd pitch, pt sl, pt shd; wc; chem disp; mv service pnt; baby facs; shwrs inc; el pnts (10A) inc; gas; Indtte (inc dryer); shop; tradsmn; rest, snacks; bar; BBQ; playgrnd; htd pool; paddling pool; games area; cycle hire; tennis 1.5km; rv fishing 3km; horseriding 1km; wifi; entmnt; games/TV rm; dogs €2.10; quiet; some rlwy noise at night; Eng spkn; adv bkg; ccard acc; red low ssn; CKE/CCI. "Lovely site in chateau grnds; charming old buildings; gd sized pitches; friendly, helpful staff; excel facs." ♦ 18 Apr-20 Sep. € 30.30 SBS - L07 2010*

ISLE JOURDAIN, L' *7A3* (500m N Rural) *46.24065, 0.68502* **Camp Municipal du Lac de Chardes, Rue de Chardes, 86150 L'Isle-Jourdain [05 49 48 72 46 or 05 49 48 70 54 (Mairie); fax 05 49 48 84 19; isle-jourdain.mairie@wanadoo.fr]** Fr N147 in Lussac take D11 S to L'Isle-Jourdain. Site sp on R. Sm, mkd pitch, terr, pt shd; wc (some cont); shwrs inc; el pnts inc; Indtte; shops, rest, snacks, bar 700m; tradsmn; htd pool adj; sand beach & fishing 100m; tennis; dogs; adv bkg; quiet. "Lovely peaceful site nr rv; excel san facs; sh walk to Rv Vienne; site yourself, warden calls am & pm." ♦ 1 May-31 Aug. € 9.20 2009*

JARNAC see Cognac *7B2*

JAUNAY CLAN *4H1* (1km N Rural) *46.68302, 0.35851* **Camping La Croix du Sud, Route de Neuville, 86130 Jaunay-Clan [05 49 62 58 14 or 05 49 62 57 20; fax 05 49 62 57 20; camping@la-croix-du-sud.fr; www.la-croix-du-sud.fr]** On A10 fr N or S, take Futuroscope exit. Take last exit at rndabt sp Neuville & after 1.5km turn L onto D20/D62. Site on L immed after x-ing m'way. Also clearly sp fr D910 at traff lts in Jaunay-Clan. Lge, hdg/mkd pitch, pt shd, 20% serviced pitches; wc; chem disp; mv service pnt; shwrs inc; el pnts (10A) €3; gas; Indtte; shop & hypmkt 1km; tradsmn; rest, snacks; bar; playgrnd; pool; entmnt; 15% statics; dogs; Eng spkn; adv bkg; some rd noise & dogs barking; ccard acc; red low ssn/CKE/CCI. "Conv position & NH; clean, tidy site; 3km to Futuroscope - mini-bus fr site high ssn; 10km to Poitiers; san facs poss unclean; poss travellers." ♦ 1 Feb-11 Nov. € 10.70 2009*

JAUNAY CLAN *4H1* (6km NE Rural) *46.69807, 0.42619* **Camp Municipal du Parc, Rue du Parc 86130 Dissay [05 49 62 84 29 or 05 49 52 34 56 (Mairie); fax 05 49 62 58 72; accueil@dissay.fr; www.dissay.fr]** N on D910 Poitiers dir Châtellerault. At rndabt turn R on D15 sp Dissay. Turn R ent Dissay & site on R 50m. Sm, mkd pitch, shd; wc; chem disp; shwrs inc; el pnts (10A) €2.65 (poss rev pol); Indry rm; shop 100m; tradsmn; playgrnd; dogs; Eng spkn; quiet; CKE/CCI. "Friendly warden; clean modern facs; conv Futuroscope; 15thC chateau adj; gate locked 2200 but can request key; gd." ♦ 19 Jun-29 Aug. € 10.00 2013*

JAUNAY CLAN *4H1* (7km NE Rural) *46.72015, 0.45982* **FLOWER Camping Lac de St Cyr, 86130 St Cyr [05 49 62 57 22; fax 05 49 52 28 58; contact@campinglacdesaintcyr.com; www.campinglacdesaintcyr.com / www.flowercampings.com]** Fr A10 take Châtellerault Sud exit & take D910 dir Poitiers; at Beaumont turn L at traff lts for St Cyr; foll camp sp in leisure complex (Parc Loisirs) by lakeside - R turn for camping. Or fr S take Futuroscope exit to D910. Lge, hdg/mkd pitch, pt sl, pt shd; wc; chem disp; mv service pnt; serviced pitches; shwrs inc; el pnts (10A) inc (poss rev pol); gas; lndtte (inc dryer); shop; rest, snacks; bar; BBQ; playgrnd; sand beach & lake sw; watersports; canoeing; sailing; fishing; tennis; boat & cycle hire; fitness rm; games rm; games area; golf course adj; wifi; entmnt; TV rm; 15% statics; dogs €3; no c'vans/m'vans over 8m; poss cr; some Eng spkn; adv bkg; quiet, some rlwy sound; ccard acc; red low ssn/long stay; CKE/CCI. "Excel, well-kept site in leisure complex; lovely setting by lake; gd sized pitches; helpful recep; gd, clean san facs, poss stretched high ssn; gd rest; some pitches poss diff lge o'fits; rec long o'fits unhitch at barrier due R-angle turn; public access to site fr lakeside beach; Futuroscope approx 13km; highly rec; excel site; gd size pitches; friendly helpful staff." ♦ 1 Apr-29 Sep. € 24.00 SBS - L09 2013*

⊞ **JAUNAY CLAN** *4H1* (2km SE Urban) *46.66401, 0.39466* **Kawan Village Le Futuriste, Rue du Château, 86130 St Georges-les-Baillargeaux [05 49 52 47 52; fax 05 49 37 23 33; camping-le-futuriste@wanadoo.fr; www.camping-le-futuriste.fr]** On A10 fr N or S, take Futuroscope exit 28; fr toll booth at 1st rndabt take 2nd exit. Thro tech park twd St Georges. At rndabt under D910 take slip rd N onto D910. After 150m exit D910 onto D20, foll sp. At 1st rndabt bear R, over rlwy, cross sm rv & up hill, site on R. Med, hdg/mkd pitch, pt shd; htd wc; chem disp; mv service pnt; some serviced pitches; shwrs inc; el pnts (6A) €4.40 (check earth & poss rev pol); gas; lndtte (inc dryer); shop; hypmkt 2km; tradsmn; rest, snacks high ssn or 500m; bar; BBQ; playgrnd; 2 htd pools (1 covrd); waterslide; lake fishing; games area; games rm; entmnt; wifi; TV rm; some statics; dogs €2.50; poss cr; Eng spkn; adv bkg; quiet; ccard acc; red low ssn; CKE/CCI. "Lovely, busy, secure site; well-kept; friendly, helpful family owners; vg clean facs, ltd low ssn - facs block clsd 2200-0700; vg pool; vg for families; ideal touring base for Poitiers & Futuroscope (tickets fr recep); vg value, espec in winter; conv a'route; excel." ♦ € 35.50 (3 persons) (CChq acc) 2013*

See advertisement

JAUNAY CLAN *4H1* (4km SE Rural) *46.65464, 0.37786* **Camp Municipal Parc des Ecluzelles, Rue Leclanché, 86360 Chasseneuil-du-Poitou [05 49 62 58 85 / 05 49 52 77 19 (Ls); maire@mairie-chasseneuildupoitou.fr; www.ville-chasseneuil-du-poitou.fr]** Fr A10 or D910 N or Poitiers take Futuroscope exit 28/18. Take Chasseneuil rd, sp in town to site. Sm, mkd pitch, some hdstg, pt shd; wc; chem disp; mv service pnt; shwrs inc; el pnts (8A) inc; shop 1km; tradsmn; BBQ; playgrnd; htd pool adj inc; dogs; poss cr; no adv bkg; quiet; red low ssn. "Vg, clean site; lge pitches; conv Futuroscope; immac; v simple site with the v gd san facs, helpful staff; gd bus service into the city." ♦ 4 Apr-26 Sep. € 18.75 2013*

LINDOIS, LE see Montbron *7B3*

LOUDUN *4H1* (1km W Rural) *47.00379, 0.06337* **Camp Municipal de Beausoleil, Chemin de l'Etang, 86200 Loudun [05 49 98 14 22 / 05 49 98 15 38; fax 05 49 98 12 88; mairie@ville-loudun.fr; www.ville-loudun.fr]** On main rte fr Poitiers to Saumur/Le Mans; N on D347 around Loudun, foll sp; turn L just N of level x-ing, then on R approx 250m. Sm, hdg/mkd pitch, terr, pt shd; wc, chem disp; shwrs inc; el pnts (10A) €3.15; shop 1km; playgrnd; lake adj for fishing; bus adj; Eng spkn; quiet; CKE/CCI. "Beautiful, well-kept site; lge pitches; low ssn site yourself, warden calls am & pm; friendly & helpful; excel; long way fr the town." ♦ 15 May-31 Aug. € 10.40 2013*

LUSIGNAN *7A2* (500m NE Rural) *46.43712, 0.12369* **Camp Municipal de Vauchiron, Chemin de la Plage, 86600 Lusignan [05 49 43 30 08 or 05 49 43 31 48 (Mairie); fax 05 49 43 61 19; lusignan@cg86.fr; www.lusignan.fr]** Site sp fr D611, 22km SW of Poitiers; foll camp sp in Lusignan to rvside. Med, pt shd; wc; chem disp; baby facs; shwrs inc; el pnts (15A) €2.40 (poss rev pol); lndtte; shops 2km; tradsmn; snacks high ssn; bar 1km; BBQ; playgrnd; rv sw adj; fishing; boat hire; entmnt; wifi; dogs free; phone; no twin-axles; adv bkg; quiet; ccard acc; CKE/CCI. "Beautiful, peaceful site in spacious park; lge pitches; forest & rv walks adj; friendly, helpful resident warden; excel clean san facs; steep walk to historic town; highly rec." ♦ 15 Apr-30 Sep. € 16.35 2014*

POITOU-CHARENTES

LUSSAC LES CHATEAUX *7A3* (6km SW Rural) *46.36912, 0.69330* **Camp Municipal du Moulin Beau, 86320 Gouex [05 49 48 46 14; fax 05 48 84 50 01; www.tourisme-vienne.com]** Fr Lussac on N147/E62 dir Poitiers, cross rv bdge sp Poitiers & immed turn L on D25; foll sp to Gouex; site on L in 4km at sw pool/camping sp. Sm, pt shd; wc (some cont); chem disp; shwrs inc; el pnts (15A) €1.60 (check pol); bakery 500m in vill; pool 300m; v quiet; no ccard acc; CKE/CCI. "Excel site on bank Rv Vienne; facs clean but ltd; bollards at site ent, care needed if van over 7m or twin-axle; highly rec." 15 Jun-15 Sep. € 4.20 2012*

LUSSAC LES CHATEAUX *7A3* (11km SW Rural) *46.32231, 0.67384* **Camp Municipal du Renard, 86150 Queaux [05 49 48 48 32 or 05 49 48 48 08 (Mairie); fax 05 49 48 30 70; contact@queaux.fr; www.queaux.fr]** Fr Lussac cross rv bdge sp Poitiers & immed turn L. Foll sp to Gouex & Queaux. Site on D25 S of vill. Med, mkd pitch, pt sl, pt shd; wc; mv service pnt; shwrs inc; el pnts (6A) €2.50; tradsmn; shops, rest 500m; bar; playgrnd; paddling pool; quiet. "Lovely rvside site nr pleasant vill; manned high ssn or apply to Mairie." 15 Jun-15 Sep. € 5.50 2009*

LUSSAC LES CHATEAUX *7A3* (3km W Rural) *46.39636, 0.70531* **Camp Municipal Mauvillant, 86320 Lussac-les-Châteaux [tel/fax 05 49 48 03 32; www.tourisme-vienne.com]** W fr Lussac on N147/E62 dir Poitiers; in 1km (shortly bef bdge) turn L at Municipal sp & foll to site 800m on L. Site parallel to Rv Vienne. Exit L turn onto N147 can be diff for lge o'fits. Med, hdg/mkd pitch, hdstg, pt shd; wc (mainly cont); chem disp; baby facs; shwrs inc; el pnts (10A) inc; Indtte; BBQ; playgrnd; pool nr; rv 200m; dogs; Eng spkn; adv bkg; quiet; CKE/CCI. "Site nr rv; if office clsd site yourself & register later; height barrier - o'fits above 2m can't ent if office clsd; gd; NH only." 1 Jun-15 Oct. € 12.00 2011*

MANSLE *7B2* (350m NE Urban) *45.87841, 0.18175* **Camp Municipal Le Champion, Rue de Watlington, 16230 Mansle [05 45 20 31 41 or 05 45 22 20 43; fax 05 45 22 86 30; mairie.mansle@wanadoo.fr; www.mansle.fr]** N on N10 fr Angoulême, foll sp Mansle Ville. Leave N10 at exit to N of town, site rd on L, well sp. Rec ent/leave fr N as rte thro town diff due to parked cars. Site beside Rv Charente. Med, hdg pitch, pt shd; wc; chem disp; mv service pnt; shwrs inc; el pnts (16A) €2.80 (poss long lead req); gas in town; Indtte; shops 200m; rest; snacks, bar adj; BBQ; playgrnd; rv sw & boating adj; fishing; entmnt; 5% statics; phone; poss cr; quiet but some rd noise; adv bkg; phone 1km; Eng spkn; ccard not acc; CKE/CCI. "Popular, peaceful, well-kept NH nr N10; lge pitches, choose own; helpful warden; immac san facs; grnd poss boggy after heavy rain; mkt Tues, Fri am; great site in excel location; vg." ♦ 15 May-16 Sep. € 20.00 2014*

MANSLE *7B2* (8km NE Rural) *45.90904, 0.25247* **Camp Municipal Le Magnerit, Les Maisons Rouges, 16460 Aunac [05 45 22 24 38; fax 05 45 22 23 17; mairie.aunac@wanadoo.fr]** N on N10 fr Mansle, exit onto D27 to Bayers & Aunac. Site 1km SE vill, well sp. Sm, pt shd; wc; chem disp; shwrs; el pnts (8A) €2.50; shop 1km; playgrnd; rv sw adj; fishing; Eng spkn; quiet; CKE/CCI. "Peaceful, simple, CL-type site beside Rv Charente; ltd, dated facs but clean; warden visits; vg NH." 15 Jun-15 Sep. € 7.30 2010*

⊞ **MANSLE** *7B2* (10km SE Rural) *45.84137, 0.27319* **Camping Devezeau, 16230 St Angeau [05 45 94 63 09; cddevezeau@gmail.com; www.campingdevezeau.com]** N or S on N10 exit Mansle; in cent vill at traff lts foll sp twd La Rochefoucauld (D6); past Champion supmkt; over bdge; 1st R onto D6. In approx 9km at T-junc turn R, site sp. App down narr rd. Sm, some hdstg, pt sl, pt shd; wc; chem disp; shwrs inc; el pnts (10A) €2; gas; Indtte; shop 1.5km; tradsmn; supmkt in Mansle; rest 5km; snacks & bar; BBQ; playgrnd; pool; cycling; walking; canoeing; fishing; horseriding; 10% statics; dogs; phone 1km; Eng spkn; adv bkg; quiet; red low ssn; CKE/CCI. "Nice CL-type site; friendly British owners; dated san facs; traction diff in wet (4x4 avail); gd cycling country; phone ahead in winter." ♦ ltd € 22.00 2014*

"I like to fill in the reports as I travel from site to site"

You'll find report forms at the back of this guide, or you can fill them in online at www.caravaclub.co.uk/europereport.

MARANS *7A1* (2km N Rural) *46.31682, -0.99158* **Camp Municipal Le Bois Dinot, Route de Nantes, 17230 Marans [05 46 01 10 51; fax 05 46 66 02 65; campingmarans@orange.fr; www.ville-marans.fr]** Heading S, site on L of D137 bef ent Marans. Heading N, site is well sp on R 300m after supmkt on L. Lge, shd; wc; shwrs inc; el pnts (10A) €4; shops adj; rest, snacks, bar 200m; pool adj; fishing; boat hire; wifi; dogs €1.10; Eng spkn; poss cr; some rd noise; red long stay/low ssn; CKE/CCI. "Well-kept, wooded site; v helpful, efficient staff; quieter pitches at back of site; vg pool adj; poss mosquitoes; gd cycling; mkt Tues & Sat; excel; v clean san facs." 1 Apr-30 Sep. € 21.00 2014*

MARENNES *7B1* (5km SE Rural) *45.81083, -1.06027* **Camping Séquoia Parc, La Josephtrie, 17320 St Just-Luzac [05 46 85 55 55; fax 05 46 85 55 56; info@sequoiaparc.com; www.sequoiaparc.com / www.les-castels.com]** Fr A10/E05 m'way exit at Saintes, foll sp Royan (N150) turning off onto D728 twd Marennes & Ile d'Oléron; site sp to R off D728, just after leaving St Just-Luzac. Or fr Rochefort take D733 & D123 S; just bef Marennes turn L on D241 sp St Just-Luzac. Best ent to site fr D728, well sp fr each dir. Lge, hdg/mkd pitch, sl, unshd; wc; chem disp; mv service pnt; baby facs; shwrs inc; el pnts (6-10A) inc (poss rev pol); gas; Indtte (inc dryer); shop; rest, snacks; bar; BBQ; playgrnd; aquapark: 3 pools (2 htd), paddling pool; waterslides, waterjets & whirlpool; sand beach 6km; fishing 1.5km; watersports 3km; horseriding; tennis; cycle hire; games area; games rm; cash machine; wifi; entmnt; TV rm; 50% statics (tour ops); dogs €5; no c'vans/m'vans over 9m; barrier clsd 2230-0700; adv bkg; ccard acc; red long stay/low ssn; CKE/CCI. "High standard site; lge pitches; clean san facs; superb pools; excel free club for children." ♦ 12 May-9 Sep. € 48.00 2012*

See advert on next page

MARENNES *7B1* (10.5km SE Rural) *45.77324, -0.96301* **Camping Le Valerick, La Petite Mauvinière, 17600 St Sornin [tel/fax 05 46 85 15 95; camplevalerick@aol.com; www.marennes.fr]** Fr Marennes take D728 sp Saintes for 10km; L to St Sornin; site sp in vill. Fr Saintes D728 W for 26km; take 2nd R turn R in vill D118, site on L sp La Gripperie. Sm, mkd pitch, pt sl, pt shd; wc; chem disp (wc); shwrs inc; el pnts (4-6A) €3-€3.80 (poss rev pol); Indtte; shop; rest, snacks; bar; BBQ; playgrnd; sand beach 18km; entmnt; dogs €1.40; adv bkg; CKE/CCI. "Nice, friendly site; gd san facs; plenty of bird life - herons, storks etc; poss mosquito problem." 1 Apr-30 Sep. € 14.00 2010*

"We must tell The Club about that great site we found"

Get your site reports in by mid-August and we'll do our best to get your updates into the next edition.

MARENNES *7B1* (2km NW Coastal) *45.83139, -1.15092* **Camp Municipal La Giroflée, 17560 Bourcefranc-le-Chapus [05 46 85 06 43 or 05 46 85 02 02 (Mairie); fax 05 46 85 48 58; campinglagiroflee@orange.fr; www.bourcefranc-le-chapus.fr]** Fr Saintes on D728/D26 to Boucefranc, turn L at traff lts. Site on L after 1km (after sailing school) opp beach. Med, pt shd; wc (few cont); shwrs €0.80; el pnts (8A) €3; Indry rm; shops 2km; snacks; playgrnd; beach adj; poss cr; quiet. 1 May-30 Sep. € 7.65 2011*

MATHA *7B2* (5km S Rural) *45.83584, -0.30747* **Camping Le Relais de l'Etang, Route de Matha, La Verniouze, 17160 Thors [05 46 58 26 81 or 05 46 58 75 36 (LS); paysmatha@cc-matha.fr; www.paysdematha.com]** Fr Matha take D121 S twd Cognac. Site on L in 5km. Sm, hdg/mkd pitch, pt shd; wc (some cont); chem disp; shwrs inc; el pnts (10A) €2.60; Indtte; rest, snacks; bar; playgrnd; lake sw; dogs €1; adv bkg; quiet; CKE/CCI. "Gd for visiting Cognac." 15 May-30 Sep. € 5.80 2010*

MATHES, LES *7B1* (1km WSW Urban) *45.71517, -1.15520* **Camping Monplaisir, 26 avenue de la Palmyre, 17250 Les Mathes [05 46 22 50 31; camping-monplaisir@orange.fr; www.campingmonplaisirlesmathes.fr]** Fr Saujon take D14 to the o'skirts of Tremblade, avoid vill of Arvert & Etaule if towing caravan, rd surface poor & narr. At rndabt take D25 for a short distance & take L onto D268 twrds La Palmyre. Cont along D141 to o'skirts of Les Mathes, then L at rndabt. Site on L within approx 450m opp cycle hire. Med, hdg pitch, pt sl, pt shd; wc; chem disp; mv service pnt; baby facs; shwrs; el pnts €4.50; Indtte (inc dryer); shops 300m; tradsmn; rest 300m; snacks; bar 300m; BBQ (site BBQ also avail); playgrnd; pool; sandy beach 3.5km; games area; games rm; wifi; tv; dogs; poss cr; Eng spkn; quiet; ccard acc. "Cycle hire nrby; crazy golf & childrens car track on site; friendly family owned site; gd cycle tracks in area; zoo 4km; vg; v clean san facs; open mkt in vill most days." Apr-Sep. € 20.00 2014*

"I need an on-site restaurant"

We do our best to make sure site information is correct, but it is always best to check any must-have facilities are still available or will be open during your visit.

MATHES, LES *7B1* (2.5km N Rural) *45.72333, -1.17451* **Camping La Palombière, 1551 Route de la Fouasse, 17570 Les Mathes [05 46 22 69 25; fax 05 46 22 44 58; camping.lapalombiere@wanadoo.fr; www.camping-lapalombiere.com]** Fr La Tremblade bypass foll sp Dirée on D268; site on R in 5km just past Luna Park. Med, pt shd; htd wc; chem disp; mv service pnt; baby facs; fam bthrm; shwrs inc; el pnts (6-10A) €4.50-5.; gas; Indtte (inc dryer); ice; shop; tradsmn; rest, snacks; bar; BBQ; playgrnd; htd pool; sand beach 5km; games area; wifi; 10% statics; dogs €3; phone; bus; Eng spkn; quiet; ccard not acc; red low ssn; CKE/CCI. "Spacious, tranquil site under oaks & pines; lge pitches; palatial san facs; superb beaches 5km (some naturist); excel, spacious site, helpful staff; immac maintained." ♦ 1 Apr-20 Oct. € 40.40 2013*

MATHES, LES *7B1* (3.5km N Rural) *45.72980, -1.17929* **Camping L'Orée du Bois, 225 Route de la Bouverie, La Fouasse, 17570 Les Mathes [05 46 22 42 43; fax 05 46 22 54 76; info@camping-oree-du-bois.fr; www.camping-oree-du-bois.fr]** Fr A10 to Saintes, then dir Royan. Fr Royan take D25 thro St Palais & La Palmyre twd Phare de la Coubre. Cont 4km past Phare & turn R on D268 to La Fouasse. Site on R in 4km. Lge, hdg/mkd pitch, hdstg, pt shd; wc (some cont); private san facs some pitches; chem disp; mv service pnt; baby facs; shwrs inc; el pnts (6A) inc; gas; Indtte (inc dryer); shop; rest, snacks; bar; BBQ; playgrnd; 3 htd pools; waterslide; sand beach 4km; tennis; cycle hire; golf 20km; games area; games rm; wifi; entmnt; sat TV rm; 50% statics; dogs €3.60; Eng spkn; adv bkg rec high ssn; quiet; ccard acc; red low ssn/ CKE/CCI. "Well-kept site in pine wood; local beaches ideal for sw & surfing; helpful staff; excel pool area; zoo in La Palmyre worth visit; min stay 7 days high ssn; excel." ♦ 28 May-10 Sep. € 38.00 (CChq acc) 2011*

MATHES, LES *7B1* (1km SW Rural) *45.70256, -1.15638* **Camping Palmyre Loisirs, 28 Ave des Mathes, 17570 La Palmyre [05 46 23 67 66; www.palmyreloisirs.com]** S fr La Tremblade on D14; at Arvert take D141 SW thro Les Mathes; site on L of rd 1km fr Les Mathes. Lge, pt shd; wc; shwrs inc; el pnts (6A) inc; rest, snacks; bar; shop; sand beach 3km; pool; quiet; adv bkg; dogs €4.50. "Excel new san facs; new pool complex for 2015; pitches away fr bar/rest are quiet." Apr - Sept. € 51.50 2013*

See advertisement

"Satellite navigation makes touring much easier"

Remember most sat navs don't know if you're towing or in a larger vehicle – always use yours alongside maps and site directions.

MATHES, LES *7B1* (3km SW) *45.70133, -1.16613* **Camping Atlantique Parc, 26 Ave des Mathes, 17570 La Palmyre [05 46 02 17 17; fax 05 46 02 52 30; info@camping-atlantique-parc.com; www.camping-atlantique-parc.com]** Fr N150, in Saujon turn R onto D14 sp Les Mathes for 22km. At 3rd rndabt take 3rd exit sp D14 Ètaules. In Arvert turn L on D141 sp Les Mathes, La Palmyre Zoo. Foll D141 thro Les Mathes, at rndabt take 3rd exit onto Avenue des Mathes sp La Palmyre, site ent on L after1.5km, sp fr road. Lge, pt shd; wc; shwrs inc; el pnts (10A) €7 (poss rev pol); gas; Indtte; shop; snacks; bar; playgrnd; 2 pools (1 htd), waterslide; sand beach 2km; fishing & watersports 3km; TV rm; games rm; 80% statics; dogs €5; wifi. "€30 refundable deposit for card for barriers and san fac access; 1 dog per pitch; gd site, espec for families; gd san fac." Apr- Sep. € 49.00 2013*

See advertisement

MATHES, LES *7B1* (6km SW Coastal) *45.6974, -1.2286* **Camping Parc de la Côte Sauvage, Phare de la Coubre, 17570 La Palmyre [05 46 22 40 18 or 05 49 35 83 60; contact@parc-cote-sauvage.com; www.parc-cote-sauvage.com]** D25 fr Royan, thro La Palmyre, at rndabt foll sp 'Phare de la Coubre'. Turn L at junc sp as bef, turn L on R-hand bend. Ent nr lighthouse. Lge, mkd pitch, pt terr, pt shd; wc (some cont); chem disp; mv service pnt; baby facs; shwrs inc; el pnts (6-10A) €5; gas; Indtte; shop; rest/bar adj; snacks; playgrnd; pool complex; sand beach 500m - can be v windy; tennis; cycle hire adj; boating; surf school; entmnt; internet; TV; 25% statics; dogs €3 (not acc Jul/Aug); poss v cr (NH area); Eng spkn; no adv bkg; ccard acc; red low ssn; CKE/CCI. "Lge pitches." ♦ 1 May-15 Sep. € 63.00 2014*

MATHES, LES *7B1* (2km W Rural) *45.72826, -1.17593* **Camping La Pinède, La Palmyre, 17570 Les Mathes [05 46 22 45 13; fax 05 46 22 50 21; contact@campinglapinede.com; www.campinglapinede.com]** Fr La Tremblade, take D141 twd Les Mathes. Turn W after vill onto D141 E twd La Fouasse, foll sp. Site in 2km. Lge, mkd pitch, pt shd; wc; chem disp; shwrs inc; el pnts (5A) €6.90; Indtte; shop; rest, snacks; bar; BBQ; playgrnd; 2 pools (1 htd, covrd); waterslides; sand beach 4km; tennis; cycle hire; archery; games area; games rm; entmnt; mini-farm; 75% statics; dogs (sm only) €6.50; private san facs avail for extra charge; adv bkg; quiet. "Dir access to rv; excel for children." 1 May-20 Sep. € 39.00 2009*

See advertisement

MATHES, LES *7B1* (2km NW Rural) *45.73473, -1.17713* **Camping Atlantique Forêt, La Fouasse, 17570 Les Mathes [05 46 22 40 46 or 05 46 36 82 77 (LS); www.camping-atlantique-foret.com]** Fr La Tremblade by-pass, foll sp Diree (D268). Drive thro vill & cont for 2km. Site on L. Or fr La Palmyre on D141 twd Les Mathes; at rndabt take dir La Fouasse. Last site on R. Med, pt shd; wc (a few cont); chem disp; baby facs; shwrs inc; el pnts (6A) €4.50; gas; Indtte (inc dryer); shop; tradsmn; rest, snacks, bar 500m; BBQ (gas only); playgrnd; pool & tennis 300m; beach 4km; 2% statics; dogs free; phone; poss cr; Eng spkn; adv bkg; ccard not acc; quiet; CKE/CCI. "Pleasant, peaceful wooded site in beautiful area; spacious & well-run; friendly, family-owned; gd san facs; gd alt to nrby lge sites; excel for young children; cycle paths thro forest; great place to stay; excel." ♦ ltd 15 Jun-15 Sep. € 21.00 2011*

⊞ **MATHES, LES** *7B1* (2km NW Coastal) *45.72482, -1.17465* **Camping Naturiste Le Petit Dauphin (Naturist), 1696 Route de la Fouasse, 17570 Les Mathes [05 46 06 38 23 or 06 76 37 57 65 (mob); lepetitdauphin2 @wanadoo.fr; http://le-petit-dauphin.com]** Fr La Palmyre take D141E dir Les Mathes; in 2.5km foll D141E to L sp La Fouasse (D141 goes strt on to Les Mathes); site sp on R in 2km. Med, pt shd; wc; chem disp; mv service pnt; baby facs; fam bthrm; shwrs inc; el pnts (10A) €3; gas; Indtte (inc dryer); ice; shops 1.5km; rest, snacks; bar; BBQ; playgrnd; sand beach 5km; games rm; internet; 5% statics; dogs €1.50; poss cr; Eng spkn; adv bkg; quiet; red low ssn/long stay; CKE/CCI. "Family-run site; welcoming, friendly & helpful; conv lge naturise beach & zoo at La Palmyre; vg. ♦ ltd € 19.00 2009*

MATHES, LES *7B1* (2.5km NW Rural) *45.72098, -1.17165* **Camping La Clé des Champs, 1188 Route de la Fouasse, 17570 Les Mathes [05 46 22 40 53; fax 05 46 22 56 96; contact@la-cledeschamps.com; www.la-cledeschamps.com]** S of La Tremblade, take D141 twd La Palmyre, site sp. Lge, mkd pitch, pt shd; htd wc (some cont); chem disp; baby facs; shwrs; el pnts (6-10A) inc; gas; Indtte; shop; rest, snacks; bar; BBQ; playgrnd; htd, covrd pool; paddling pool; sand beach 3.5km; gym, jacuzzi & sauna; fishing & watersports 3km; cycle hire; games area; games rm; TV rm; entmnt; wifi; 30% statics; dogs €3.80; Eng spkn; adv bkg; ccard acc; quiet; red low ssn; CKE/CCI. "Well-equipped, busy site; many excel beaches in area; modern san facs; local oysters avail; Cognac region; Luna Park nrby." ♦ 30 Mar-15 Nov. € 40.00 2013*

See advert on next page

MATHES, LES *7B1* (3km NW Rural) *45.73229, -1.17655* **Camping L'Estanquet, 2596 Route de la Fouasse, 17570 Les Mathes [05 46 22 47 32 or 05 46 93 93 51 (LS); fax 05 46 22 51 46; contact@campinglestanquet.com; www.campinglestanquet.com]** Fr Royan take D25 to La Palmyre. Turn R in town cent onto D141 dir Les Mathes; cont on D141 passing racecourse on R; turn L bef Les Mathes along La Fouasse. Site in 2.5km on L. Lge, hdg pitch, pt shd; wc; chem disp; baby facs; shwrs inc; el pnts (10A) inc; gas; Indtte; shop; rest, snacks; bar; BBQ (gas only); playgrnd; pool; paddling pool; waterslide; sand beach 5km; fishing, windsurfing 5km; tennis; cycle hire; horseriding 1km; golf 9km; entmnt; games/TV rm; 85% statics; dogs €4; poss cr; adv bkg; quiet. ♦ 1 May-30 Sep. € 27.00 2010*

MAZIERES see Chasseneuil sur Bonnieure *7B3*

⊞ **MELLE** *7A2* (8km S Rural) *46.15127, -0.12022* **Camping La Maison de Puits, 14 Rue de Beauchamp, 79110 Tillou [05 49 07 20 28; mark.hall@sfr.fr; www.hallmarkholidays.eu]** Fr Niort on D948. At Melle foll sp Angoulême, R turn (to ring rd & avoids Melle cent). At Total stn rndabt turn R onto D948 dir Chef-Boutonne. In 3.5km turn R onto D737 sp Chef-Boutonne. After approx 5km at x-rds of D111 & D737, strt over & take 2nd turn R in 1km (sm sp to Tillou) along narr rd sp Tillou. In 1.6km site on L. Sm, sl, unshd; wc; chem disp; shwr; el pnts (6A) €3; BBQ; splash pool; adv bkg; quiet. "CL-type site in meadow/orchard (6 vans only); quiet & peaceful; friendly, helpful British owners - help with house-hunting avail; ring ahead to book; interesting area." € 12.00 2013*

MELLE *7A2* (10km SW Rural) *46.14421, -0.21983* **Camp Municipal, Rue des Merlonges, 79170 Brioux-sur-Boutonne [05 49 07 50 46; fax 05 49 07 27 27]** On ent Brioux fr Melle on D150 turn R immed over bdge; site on R in 100m. Sm, pt shd; wc; shwrs inc; el pnts (6A) €1.80; lndry rm; shops 300m; playgrnd adj; quiet, some rd noise. "Pleasant rural setting; tidy, well-cared for site; ltd facs but clean; choose own pitch & pay at Mairie on dep if no warden; vg sh stay/NH." 1 Apr-31 Oct. € 5.40 2013*

MELLE *7A2* (6km NW Rural) *46.25877, -0.21463* **Camp Municipal La Boissière, Route de Chizé, 79370 Celles-sur-Belle [06 76 31 22 76 or 05 49 79 80 17 (Mairie); fax 05 49 32 95 10; mairie-cellessurbelle@wanadoo.fr; www.ville-celles-sur-belle.com]** Fr Melle or Niort on D948. Exit by-pass into Celles & in town foll sp to Sports Complex & camping. Sm, pt sl, pt shd; htd wc (some cont); shwrs inc; el pnts (6A); gas, shop 500m; BBQ; playgrnd; pool adj; rv 200m; lake 400m; tennis; 20% statics; dogs €0.85; adv bkg rec high ssn. "Warden calls am & pm; quiet apart fr football grnd adj; gd NH."♦ 15 Apr-15 Oct. 2009*

MESCHERS SUR GIRONDE see Royan *7B1*

MESSE see Couhé *7A2*

MIRAMBEAU *7C2* (500m N Urban) *45.37822, -0.56874* **Camp Municipal Le Carrelet, 92 Ave de la République, 17150 Mirambeau [06 71 77 30 38; campingcarrelet@hotmail.fr; www.mirambeau-tourisme.fr]** Exit 37 fr A10 onto D730/D137 dir Mirambeau. Site opp Super U supmkt, behind TO. Sm, pt sl, pt shd; wc (cont); chem disp (wc); mv service pnt;; shwrs inc; el pnts (10A) €4.50 (poss rev pol); gas; lndtte; shops, rest adj; snacks; bar; mostly statics; dogs €1.50; phone; quiet. "Basic site; clean but tired facs; obliging warden; site yourself & warden calls evening; v muddy when wet; poss neglected low ssn; conv NH for A10." 1 Apr-31 Oct. € 19.00 2014*

⊞ **MIRAMBEAU** *7C2* (11km W Coastal) *45.38333, -0.72250* **Camping L'Estuaire, La Grange Godinet, 17150 St Thomas-de-Cônac [05 46 86 08 20; fax 05 46 86 09 18; info@lestuaire.com; www.lestuaire.com]** Exit A10 junc 37 Mirambeau onto D730 dir Royan. At St Ciers-du-Taillon foll sp St Thomas-de-Cônac, site sp. Lge, hdg/mkd pitch, unshd; htd wc; chem disp; mv service pnt; baby facs; shwrs inc; el pnts (5A) inc; lndtte (inc dryer); shop; tradsmn; rest, snacks; bar; BBQ; playgrnd; pool complex; padding pool; fishing; watersports nr; tennis; cycle hire; games area; gym; entmnt; TV rm; 60% statics; dogs €4; adv bkg; quiet. "Interesting area nr Gironde estuary; gd walking & cycling." ♦ € 20.00 (CChq acc) 2010*

MONTBRON *7B3* (11km NE Rural) *45.74042, 0.58678* **Camping de l'Etang, Les Geloux, 16310 Le Lindois [05 45 65 02 67; fax 05 45 65 08 96; www.campingdeletang.com]** Fr S take D16 N fr Montbron, in 9km turn R onto D13, in 3km turn R onto D27. Site sp in vill opp lake. Sm, hdg/mkd pitch, pt sl, pt shd; htd wc; chem disp; baby facs; shwrs inc; el pnts (16A) €4.50; gas inc; lndtte; sm shop; rest, snacks; bar; sm library; playgrnd; lake sw & fishing; beach adj; dogs €1.50; phone; Eng spkn; adv bkg rec high ssn; ccard acc; quiet; CKE/CCI. "Loads of wildlife in attractive surroundings; v pleasant & restful; gd quality rest; gd value; rec." 1 Apr-1 Nov. € 17.50 2013*

MONTBRON *7B3* (6km SE Rural) *45.65972, 0.55805* **Camping Les Gorges du Chambon, Le Chambon, 16220 Eymouthiers [05 45 70 71 70; fax 05 45 70 80 02; info@gorgesduchambon.fr; www.gorgesduchambon.fr / www.les-castels.com]** Fr N141 turn SE onto D6 at La Rochefoucauld; cont on D6 out of Montbron; after 5km turn L at La Tricherie onto D163; foll camp sp to site in approx 1.9km. NB Fr La Tricherie narr in places & some sharp bends. Med, mkd pitch, some hdstg, pt sl, pt shd; htd wc; chem disp; mv service pnt; baby facs; shwrs inc; el pnts (10A) inc; gas; lndtte (inc dryer); shop; tradsmn; rest, snacks; bar; BBQ (gas/charcoal only); playgrnd; pool; paddling pool; sand/shgl beach 15km; rv fishing; canoe hire; tennis; cycle hire; horseriding, golf nrby; games area; entmnt; internet; games/TV rm; 25% statics; no dogs; twin-axles; Eng spkn; adv bkg; quiet; ccard acc; red long stay/low ssn; CKE/CCI. "Beautiful, 'away fr it all', scenic site in grnds of old farm; welcoming, helpful & friendly staff; lge pitches but some sl; excel san facs; superb rest; gd mkd walks; birdwatching & wildlife; poss motorbike rally on site end June; excel." ♦ 19 Apr-13 Sep. € 45.00 SBS - D11 2012*

See advertisement

⊞ **MONTENDRE** *7C2* (5km N Rural) *45.33156, -0.39526* **The Vines Camping, Chez Penaud, 17130 Coux [05 46 48 95 55 or 06 42 45 34 99 (mob); barry.playford@orange.fr; www.vinescoux.com]** Exit A10 at Mirambeau onto D730 dir Montendre; then D19 dir Jonzac; then D253 dir Coux; do not turn into Coux vill but cont on D253; cross rlwy & then over x-rds; turn L at sp Chez Penaud; foll sps. NB D253 is long & winding. Sm, some hdstg, unshd; htd wc; chem disp; shwrs inc; el pnts (6A) inc; gas 4km; lndtte; shops etc 4km; BBQ; lake fishing & golf nrby; dogs; Eng spkn; adv bkg; quiet; red long stay. "Beautiful, well-kept, CL-type site; lge pitches; friendly British CC owners; gd touring base; wine tasting; vg." € 14.00 2011*

MONTIGNAC CHARENTE see Angoulême *7B2*

MONTLIEU LA GARDE *7C2* (8km N Rural) *45.30233, -0.23228* **Camp Municipal Bellevue, 17210 Chevanceaux [05 46 04 60 03 or 05 46 04 60 09 (Mairie)]** N fr Montlieu on N10 to Chevanceaux in 7km; site by church & primary school in vill. Sm, mkd pitch, pt sl, pt shd; wc; chem disp; shwrs inc; el pnts (6A) inc; shops, rest, bar in vill; snacks high ssn; BBQ (gas, elec); playgrnd; pool adj; tennis; quiet; CKE/CCI. "Peaceful, clean site in pleasant vill; lge pitches; warden visits am; no security; easy walk to vill; walking/cycling along disused rlwy; poss problems with local youths (2010); gd NH." 1 Apr-30 Oct. € 11.00 2010*

"There aren't many sites open at this time of year"

If you're travelling outside peak season remember to call ahead to check site opening dates – even if the entry says 'open all year'.

MONTLIEU LA GARDE *7C2* (1km NE Rural) *45.24849, -0.25097* **Camp Municipal des Lilas, Roch, 17210 Montlieu-la-Garde [05 46 04 44 12 (Mairie); fax 05 46 04 50 91; montlieulagarde@mairie17.com]** On L N10 sp Montlieu-la-Garde; take D730 into vill. Turn L at multiple sp on corner (diff to see) & in 1km turn R & foll site sp. Site along vill lane. Sm, pt sl, pt shd; wc; shwrs; el pnts inc; tradsmn; shop in vill; pool 1km; quiet, some rd noise. "Vg NH; clean san facs." 1 May-30 Sep. € 8.00 2010*

MONTMORILLON *7A3* (500m E Urban) *46.42035, 0.87554* **Camp Municipal de l'Allochon, 31 Ave Fernand Tribot, 86500 Montmorillon [05 49 91 02 33 or 05 49 91 13 99 (Mairie); fax 05 49 91 58 26; camping@ville-montmorillon.fr / montmorillon@cg86.fr; http://en.tourisme-vienne.com]** On D54 to Le Dorat, approx 400m SE fr main rd bdge over rv at S of town. Site on L. Fr S v sharp RH turn into site. Med, mkd pitch, terr, pt shd; htd wc (some cont); mv service pnt; shwrs inc; el pnts (6-10A) €1.80-4.75; lndtte; shop 1km; rest, snacks, bar 500m; BBQ; playgrnd; htd, covrd pool adj; fishing; games area; wifi; TV; dogs; poss cr; adv bkg; some rd noise; CKE/CCI. "Delightful, peaceful, well-kept site; lge pitches; friendly, hard-working warden; gd touring base; vg value; v clean facs; relaxing; rec." ♦ 1 Mar-31 Oct. € 11.50 2014*

MONTROLLET *7B3* (85m N Rural) *45.98316, 0.89702* **Camping Auberge La Marchadaine, Beaulieu, 16420 Montrollet [05 45 71 09 88 or 06 63 07 82 48 (mob); aubergedelamarchadaine@gmail.com; www.auberge-camping-16.com]** N fr St Junien on D675, turn W onto D2 to Montrollet. Auberge sp in vill. Sm, pt shd; wc; chem disp (wc); shwr; el pnts (6A) inc; gas; shop 4km; tradsmn; rest; bar; playgrnd; fishing; internet; dogs free; phone; Eng spkn; adv bkg; quiet; CKE/CCI. "Delightful CL-type site o'looking lake; vg rest." € 9.50 2010*

⊞ **MORTAGNE SUR GIRONDE** *7B2* (1km SW Coastal) *45.47600, -0.79400* **Aire Communale Le Port, 17120 Mortagne-sur-Gironde [05 46 90 63 15; fax 05 46 90 61 25; mairie-mortagne@smic17.fr]** Fr Royan take D730 dir Mirambeau for approx 28km. Turn R in Boutenac-Touvent onto D6 to Mortagne, then foll sp Le Port & Aire de Camping-Car. M'vans only. Sm, unshd; chem disp; mv service pnt; shwrs €1; el pnts (10A) inc; shop 500m; rest, snacks, bar 600m; dogs; poss v cr; quiet. "Car/c'vans poss acc; shwrs & mv service pnt 800m fr site; fees collected 0900; all pitches have views; excel." € 6.00 2013*

MOSNAC *7B2* (Rural) *45.50557, -0.52304* **Camp Municipal Les Bords de la Seugne, 34 Rue de la Seugne, 17240 Mosnac [05 46 70 48 45; fax 05 46 70 49 13; mosnac@ mairie17.com]** Fr Pons S on N137 for 4.5km; L on D134 to Mosnac; foll sp to site behind church. Sm, mkd pitch, pt shd; htd wc; shwrs inc; el pnts (6A) inc; gas; 10% statics; dogs free; Eng spkn; adv bkg; no ccard acc; quiet; red long stay; CKE/CCI. "Charming, clean, neat site in sm hamlet; site yourself, warden calls; helpful staff; excel, spotless san facs; conv Saintes, Cognac & Royan." 18 Apr-15 Oct. € 10.44 2014*

PALMYRE, LA see Mathes, Les *7B1*

PARTHENAY *4H1* (8km SE Rural) *46.63294, -0.13428* **Camping La Ferme Naturiste de l'Oliverie (Naturist), 79200 Saurais [05 49 94 61 05 or 06 87 91 64 53 (mob); info@oliverie.com; www.oliverie.com]** Fr Parthenay take D59 SE dir Vasles. After 8km in La Chapelle-Bertrand turn L to Saurais then turn L onto D22 twd La Ferrière-en-Parthenay. After 2km turn L at site sp. Site on R. Sm, pt sl, pt shd; wc; chem disp (wc); shwrs inc; el pnts (10A) €3.25; tradsmn; snacks; bar; playgrnd; pool; 1 gite & B&B; Eng spkn; adv bkg; quiet. "Ltd el pnts (16 for 25 pitches); 45km Futuroscope; excel." ♦ 24 Apr-30 Sep. € 20.00 (CChq acc) 2010*

PARTHENAY *4H1* (1km SW Urban) *46.64160, -0.26740* **Camping Flower du Bois Vert, 14 Rue Boisseau, Le Tallud, 79200 Parthenay [05 49 64 78 43; fax 05 49 95 96 68; campingboisvert@orange.fr; www.camping-boisvert.com]** Site on D743 to Niort. Sp fr N & S. Fr S 1km bef town turn L at sp La Roche-sur-Yon immed after rv bdge turn R; site on R in 500m. Med, hdg/mkd pitch, some hdstg, pt sl, pt shd; htd wc (some cont); chem disp; mv service pnt; baby facs; shwrs inc; el pnts (6 or 10A) inc; Indtte (inc dryer); shops 1km; tradsmn; rest, snacks; bar; BBQ; playgrnd; htd pool complex; paddling pool; boating; fishing; tennis; cycle hire; games rm; wifi; entmnt; TV; 10% statics; phone; poss cr; adv bkg; noisy nr main rd & bar; ccard not acc; red low ssn; CKE/CCI. "1 hr rvside walk to town; m'van o'night area adj; Wed mkt; gd NH to Spain; conv Futuroscope; new facs, plenty hot water; well spaced hdg grass pitches; excel facs." ♦ 4 Apr-31 Oct. € 39.50 2014*

PARTHENAY *4H1* (9km W Urban) *46.62214, -0.35139* **Camp Municipal Les Peupliers, 79130 Azay-sur-Thouet [05 49 95 37 13 (Mairie); fax 05 49 95 36 14; mairie-azaysurthouet@cc-parthenay.fr; www.tourisme-gatine.com]** Fr Parthenay take D949 dir Secondigny to Azay-sur-Thouet; turn L onto D139 dir St Pardoux; site on L in 200m. Site adj stadium on rvside. Sm, mkd pitch, pt shd; wc; shwrs inc; el pnts (10A) €3; shop 250m; BBQ; playgrnd; quiet. "Pleasant, peaceful site; barrier open 0900; clean dated san facs, poss inadequate number high ssn (2009)." 15 Jun-30 Sep. € 10.00 2013*

⊞ **PARTHENAY** *4H1* (10km W Rural) *46.65738, -0.34816* **FFCC Camping La Chagnée (Baudoin), 79450 St Aubin le Cloud [05 49 95 31 44 or 06 71 10 09 66 (mob); gerard.baudoin3@wanadoo.fr; www.cc-parthenay.fr/la-chagnee]** Fr Parthenay on D949BIS dir Secondigny. Turn R in Azay-sur-Thouet onto D139 dir St Aubin, site on R in 2km, look for 'Gîte' sp. Sm, hdg pitch, terr, pt shd; wc; chem disp (wc); mv service pnt; shwrs; el pnts €3; Indtte; shops 1km; pool 1km; fishing; dogs; Eng spkn; quiet; "Charming, CL-type organic farm site o'looking lake; friendly, helpful owners; clean facs; open all yr providing use own san in winter; maps loaned for walking; excel; m'vans only during period Nov-Mar; farmhouse meal avail weekly." ♦ € 14.50 2014*

PLEUVILLE see Pressac *7A3*

POITIERS For sites conv for Futuroscope, also see listings under Châtellerault and Jaunay Clan.

POITIERS *7A2* (10km N Rural) *46.65611, 0.30194* **Camping du Futur, 9 Rue des Bois, 86170 Avanton [05 49 54 09 67; contact@camping-du-futur.com; www.camping-du-futur.com]** Exit A10 junc 28. After toll take 1st exit at rndabt sp Avanton. Site well sp fr Avanton, but care needed thro Martigny & hotel complex. Med, hdg/mkd pitch, pt shd; wc; chem disp (wc); mv service pnt; shwrs inc; el pnts (6-10A) €3.50-3.80; Indtte; shop, rest & snacks 1km; tradsmn; bar; playgrnd; pool (high ssn); games area; games rm; wifi; TV; dogs €1.50; c'van storage; adv bkg; quiet; red low ssn; CKE/CCI. "Attractive, spacious site in rural setting; well-kept & well-run; helpful French owners; vg clean san facs, ltd early ssn; 5 mins Futuroscope & A10; ideal NH or longer; bread, pastries and breakfast can be ordered; mv service pnt; nr Futurscope attraction; ltd shd." ♦ 1 Apr-5 Nov. € 29.40 2014*

POITIERS *7A2* (4.5km S Rural) *46.54367, 0.33230* **Camp Municipal de St Benoît, 2 Rue de Passe Lourdain, 86280 St Benoît [05 49 88 48 55; tourisme@ville-saint-benoit.fr; www.ville-saint-benoit.fr]** Fr N or S turn W off D741 to St Benoît, site well sp. Med, mkd pitch, pt shd; wc; shwrs; el pnts (4A) €3; shops, rest, bar in vill; playgrnd; rv fishing & watersports adj; dogs €0.50; poss cr; adv bkg; rlwy noise adj; CKE/CCI. "Pleasant 10 min walk into vill; gd cheap bus service fr vill to Poitiers." 1 Jun-6 Sep. € 16.20 2014*

⊞ **PONS (CHARENTE MARITIME)** *7B2* (1km NE Rural) *45.59429, -0.53841* **Camping Les Moulins de la Vergne, 9 Route de Colombiers, 17800 Pons [tel/fax 05 46 90 50 84 or 05 46 49 11 49; uffelen@wanadoo.fr; www.moulinsdelavergne.nl]** Fr N on D137 take 1st exit Pons, turn L & foll yellow site sp. Fr S exit A10 junc 36 onto D732 & at 2nd rndabt take D137 N dir Saintes. In 4km turn R onto D125(E2) then R (S) onto D234, site sp on L. Fr town cent foll yellow sps in Pons - do not confuse with municipal site Le Paradis. NB c'vans not allowed thro Pons & should stay on by-pass. Med, mkd pitch, pt shd; htd wc; chem disp; shwrs inc; el pnts (10A) €3.50; Indtte; shops 1km; tradsmn; rest, snacks; bar; BBQ; playgrnd; pool; wifi; dogs €2; adv bkg; Eng spkn; rd noise; ccard acc; CKE/CCI. "Relaxed, friendly & helpful Dutch owners; clean san facs need update, ltd low ssn; excel rest; grass pitches soft in wet weather - park on site rds off ssn; no site lighting low ssn in touring area; site poss unkempt low ssn & poss mkt traders; conv touring base or NH; nr A10 en rte Spain; rest clsd Mon." ♦ € 25.30 2014*

PONS (CHARENTE MARITIME) *7B2* (500m W Urban) *45.57791, -0.55552* **Camp Municipal Le Paradis, 1 Ave de Poitou, 17800 Pons [05 46 91 36 72; fax 05 46 96 14 15; campingmunicipalpons@voila.fr; www.pons-ville.org]** Well sp fr town o'skts. Med, mkd pitch, pt shd; wc; mv service pnt; shwrs inc; el pnts (6-10A) inc (poss rev pol); shops adj; tradsmn; pool, waterslide 100m; rv fishing 200m; TV; wifi; dogs €1.76. "Excel site in attractive grnds; helpful super wardens; interesting town; conv for Saintes, Cognac, Royan; free wifi in snack bar." ♦ 1 May-30 Sep. € 21.00 2014*

⊞ **PONS (CHARENTE MARITIME)** *7B2* (2km W Rural) *45.56976, -0.57906* **FFCC Camping Chardon, 13 Route des Bernards,Chardon 17800 Pons [50 46 95 01 25 or 06 18 19 39 10 (mob); camping.chardon@gmail.com; www.camping-chardon.com]** Fr N or S on A10, exit junc 36 onto D732 (take care as heavy, fast traff). Site sp on R in 1km. Narr ent to rd. Or fr N or S on N137 take D732 twd Gémozac, site on L 2km fr Pons. Site lies to S of D732, bet N137 & A10. Sm, hdg pitch, pt shd; wc; chem disp; serviced pitch; shwrs; el pnts (10A) €3; gas 2km; Indtte; shops 1km; tradsmn; rest; pizzeria; bar; playgrnd; pool 1km; 75% statics; dogs €1.50; adv bkg; quiet; no ccard acc. "Excel basic, rustic site; friendly owners; basic, open-air san facs, ltd low ssn; vg rest; conv Cognac, Saintes & Royan; low ssn phone ahead to check if open; conv NH A10 or N137." ♦ ltd € 13.00 2013*

PONT L'ABBE D'ARNOULT *7B1* (500m E Urban) *45.82592, -0.86568* **Camping Parc de la Garenne, 24 Ave Bernard Chambenoit, 17250 Pont-l'Abbé-d'Arnoult [05 46 97 01 46 or 06 09 43 20 11 (mob); info@lagarenne.net; www.lagarenne.net]** N fr Saintes on N137. In 18km turn L onto D18 to Pont-l'Abbé-d'Arnoult. In town turn L, foll camp sp to site adj sw pool. Med, shd; wc; chem disp; mv service pnt 150m; baby facs; shwrs inc; el pnts (6A) €4.20; gas; Indtte (inc dryer); shop, rest, snacks & bar 500m; snacks; BBQ (elec only); playgrnd; pool adj; tennis; games area; wifi; entmnt; TV rm; 10% statics; dogs €3; phone; Eng spkn; adv bkg; quiet; CKE/CCI. "Well-run site; friendly; gd san facs; lack of maintenance early ssn (2011); gd." ♦ 1 May-15 Sep. € 21.00 2011*

PORT DES BARQUES see Rochefort *7B1*

⊞ **PRESSAC** *7A3* (6km SW Rural) *46.09696, 0.48081* **Camping Rural des Marronniers, La Bussière, 16490 Pleuville [05 45 31 03 45; ssmpooleman1@aliceadsl.fr; www.conkertreefarmcampsite.bravehost.com]** S fr Poitiers on D741 to Pressac; turn R onto D34 to Pleuville then turn onto D30 dir Charroux, site on L in 1.5km - look for sp La Bussière. Sm, pt sl, pt shd; htd wc; chem disp; fam bathrm; shwrs inc; el pnts (10A) €2.50; gas; Indtte; shop 1km; rest 8km; snacks; bar 1km; BBQ; playgrnd; pool; games rm; dogs; adv bkg; quiet. "British-owned, CL-type farm site; open field - chickens & ducks roaming; gd touring base; excel." ♦ ltd € 8.00 2010*

QUEAUX see Lussac les Châteaux *7A3*

ROCHE POSAY, LA *4H2* (1.5km N Rural) *46.79951, 0.80933* **Camping La Roche-Posay Vacances, Route de Lésigny. 86270 La Roche-Posay [05 49 86 21 23; info@larocheposay-vacances.com; www.larocheposay-vacances.com]** On A10 take exit 26 Châtellerault-Nord, La Roche-Posay; foll sp La Roche-Posay; foll the D725 to La Roche-Possay; at rndabt foll sp for 'Camping-Hippodrome'. Lge, hdg/mkd pitch, shd; htd wc; mv service pnt; shwrs inc; el pnts (16A) inc (check pol); gas; Indtte; shops 1km; rest, snacks; bar; BBQ (gas/elec); playgrnd; aquatic park; waterslides; htd, covrd pool; rv sw & fishing 1.5km; tennis; cycle hire; entmnt; 10% statics; dogs €1.50; poss cr; Eng spkn; adv bkg; quiet; red low ssn/long stay;CKE/CCI. "Excel, popular, well-maintained site; 1st class facs; barrier locks automatically 2300; parking avail outside; walk to town on busy rd with no pavement; spa town." ♦ 27 Apr-21 Sep. € 28.00 2011*

See advert on next page

⊞ **ROCHECHOUART** *7B3* (13km SW Rural) *45.73390, 0.68070* **Camping Chez Rambaud, 87440 Les Salles-Lavauguyon [05 55 00 08 90; fax 05 55 00 08 90; camping@chez-rambaud.com; www.chez-rambaud.com]** Fr Rochechouart on D675 then immed R onto D10 dir Videix & Verneuil; in 11km at Verneuil turn L to Les Salles-Lavauguyon. At Salles turn R at bottom of hill (leaving church on L) onto D34 sp Sauvagnac; in 300m turn L sp Chez Rambaud, site on L in 1km along narr rd. Sm, hdg/mkd pitch, some hdstg, sl, pt shd; htd wc; chem disp; shwrs inc; el pnts (10A) €3.50 (long lead poss req); Indtte; ice; shop, rest, bar 1.5km; supmkt 8km; BBQ; lake sw & sand beach 10km; horseriding & kayaking nrby; dogs €1.50; Eng spkn; adv bkg; quiet; no ccard acc;CKE/CCI. "Tranquil, CL-type site in National Park; views over wooded valley; enthusiastic, friendly & helpful British owners; excel, immac facs; levelling blocks poss req; some pitches inadequate for awnings; farm animals in pens on site; gd touring base; gd walking & cycling; easy walk to vill (1.5km); Richard The Lion Heart rte in vill; mkt in Rochechouart Sat; superb." ♦ ltd € 18.00 2012*

ROCHEFORT *7B1* (1.5km N Coastal) *45.94986, -0.99499* **Camping Le Bateau, Rue des Pêcheurs d'Islande, 17300 Rochefort [05 46 99 41 00; fax 05 46 99 91 65; lebateau@wanadoo.fr; www.campinglebateau.com]** Exit A837/E602 at junc 31 & take D733 dir Rochefort. At 1st rndabt by McDonalds, take D733 dir Royan. At next rndabt 1st R onto Rue des Pêcheurs d'Islande. Site at end of rd on L. Med, hdg pitch, pt shd; wc; chem disp; shwrs inc; el pnts (8A) €4; Indtte; shop; tradsmn; rest, snacks; bar; playgrnd; pool; waterslide; watersports; fishing; tennis; games rm; entmnt; 25% statics; dogs €1.70; quiet; red low ssn;CKE/CCI. "Sm pitches, a few o'look estuary; helpful staff; basic, clean san facs; poss scruffy low ssn - ducks & geese on site; no twin-axles; gd cycling, walking; mkt Tues & Sat; fishing lake; Lidl 10 mins walk; intersting town; friendly non-english speaking owners; site adj to rv." 1 Apr-1 Nov. € 22.50 2014*

"That's changed – Should I let The Club know?"

If you find something on site that's different from the site entry, fill in a report and let us know. See www.caravanclub.co.uk/europereport.

ROCHEFORT *7B1* (500m S Urban) *45.93013, -0.95826* **Camping Municipal Le Rayonnement, 3, Avenue de la Fosse Aux Mâts, 17300 Rochefort [05 46 82 67 70; camping.municipal@ville-rochefort.fr; www.ville-rochefort.fr/decouvrir/camping]** Exit E602 at junc 31 & take D733 dir Rochefort. At rndabt by McDonalds, take D733 dir Royan. Cont on D733. At rndabt with plane take 3rd exit onto Bd Edouard Pouzet. At rndabt take 3rd exit onto Bd de la Résistance, at next rndabt take 1st exit & then turn L onto ave de la Fosse aux Mâts. Site on L. Med, hdg pitch, hdstg, shd; wc; chem disp; mv service pnt; baby facs; shwrs inc; el pnts (15A) inc; Indtte; shop 100m; tradsmn; BBQ; playgrnd; games rm; cycle hire; entmnt; wifi;TV rm; 15% statics; dogs €1.05; phone; bus 100m; Eng spkn; adv bkg. "Bikes borrowed free of charge; rv Charente & its cycle path to the cent 800m away; v helpful staff; no c'vans over 6m; no twin-axles; san facs are renewed and v clean; Ecolabel campsite; vg; excel transporter bdge & access to town." ♦ 27 Feb-03 Dec. € 15.72 2014*

ROCHEFORT *7B1* (8km W Coastal) *45.94828, -1.09592* **Camp Municipal de la Garenne, Ave de l'Ile-Madame, 17730 Port-des-Barques [05 46 84 80 66 or 06 08 57 08 75 (mob); fax 05 46 84 98 33; camping@ville-portdesbarques.fr; www.camping-municipal-portdesbarques.com]** Fr Rochefort S on D773, cross Rv Charente bdge & take 1st exit sp Soubise & Ile Madame. Cont strt thro Port-des-Barques, site on L opp causeway to Ile-Madame. Lge, mkd pitch, unshd; wc; chem disp; mv service pnt; baby facs; shwrs inc; el pnts (10A) inc; Indtte; shop 1km; rest 500m; snacks; bar 1km; playgrnd; htd pool; sand/shgl beach adj; wifi; 25% statics; dogs €1.26; phone; bus adj; poss cr; adv bkg; quiet; ccard acc; red low ssn/long stay;CKE/CCI. "Pleasant site; lge pitches; pitches a little scruffy, but level; facs dated but clean." ♦ ltd 15 Mar-15 Oct. € 27.50 2014*

ROCHELLE, LA *7A1* (12km N Rural/Coastal) *46.25239, -1.11972* **Camp Municipal Les Misottes, 46 Rue de l'Océan, 17137 Esnandes [05 46 35 04 07 or 05 46 01 32 13 (Mairie); lesmisottes@yahoo.fr; www.campinglesmisottes.blogspot.com]** Fr N on D938 or N1327 turn W at Marans onto D105. In 7.5km turn S onto D9 then D202 to Esnandes. Enter vill, at x-rds strt, site on R in 200m. Fr La Rochelle D105 N to cent Esnandes, site sp. Med, mkd pitch, pt shd; wc (cont); shwrs inc; el pnts (10A) €2.85; Indtte; shops 500m; rest, bar 200m; snacks; playgrnd; pool; shgl beach 2km; canal fishing; 5% statics; dogs €1.60; poss cr; Eng spkn; adv bkg; quiet;CKE/CCI. "Site on the edge of marshlands; poor san facs (2009); liable to flood; vg." 1 Apr-15 Oct. € 8.70 2009*

ROCHELLE, LA *7A1* (5km S Rural/Coastal) *46.11659, -1.11939* **Camping Les Sables, Chemin du Pontreau, 17440 Aytré [05 46 45 40 30; fax 05 46 27 89 02; camping_les_sables@yahoo.fr; www.camping-les-sables.com]** Fr S (Rochefort) on D137, exit sp Aytré. At 2nd traff lts turn L & foll site sp. Lge, hdg pitch, pt shd; wc; chem disp; mv service pnt; baby facs; shwrs inc; el pnts (6A) €3; Indtte (inc dryer); shop; rest, snacks; bar; BBQ; playgrnd; 2 pools (1 htd, covrd); paddling pool; waterslide; cycle hire; games area; games rm; wifi; entmnt; 50% statics; dogs €1.50; phone; poss cr; Eng spkn; adv bkg; rlwy noise; ccard acc; CKE/CCI. "Vg." ♦ 1 May-31 Oct. € 26.00 2012*

ROCHELLE, LA *7A1* (8km S Coastal) *46.10409, -1.13093* **Camping Les Chirats-La Platère, Route de la Platère, 17690 Angoulins-sur-Mer [05 46 56 94 16; fax 05 46 56 65 95; contact@campingleschirats.fr; www.campingleschirats.fr]** Turn off N137 S of La Rochelle & go thro Angoulins-sur-Mer. Foll site sp fr vill N twd Aytré. After 300m turn L across rlwy at stn. Foll sp 'plage' & site. Lge, hdg/mkd pitch, hdstg, pt sl, pt shd; wc (some cont); chem disp; sauna; serviced pitches; shwrs inc; el pnts (6-10A) inc; gas; Indtte; shop & 2km; tradsmn; rest, snacks; bar; playgrnd; pools (1 htd, covrd); paddling pool; waterslide; jacuzzi; sand beach adj; fishing; fitness rm; games area; horseriding 1km; tennis 500m; TV rm; 10% statics; dogs €2.50; phone; poss cr; Eng spkn; adv bkg; quiet; ccard acc; CKE/CCI. "Gd facs; well-run site; aquarium worth a visit." ♦ Easter-30 Sep. € 27.00 2011*

See advertisement

⊞ **ROCHELLE, LA** *7A1* (2km W Urban/Coastal) *46.16041, -1.18578* **Camp Municipal de Port Neuf, Blvd Aristide Rondeau, Port Neuf, 17000 La Rochelle [05 46 43 81 20; fax 05 46 00 25 23; camping-portneuf@orange.fr]** On ring rd fr N on N11 turn R onto N237 sp Ile-de-Ré, then turn S onto N537 sp La Pallice. In 1.2km turn L dir Port Neuf (Ave Jean Guiton), & in 800m turn R to site, sp. If app fr airport side take care to avoid Ile-de-Ré toll booth. Lge, some hdstg, pt shd; htd wc (some cont); chem disp; baby facs; shwrs inc; el pnts (6A) €4 (poss rev pol); gas; Indttes nr; pool 2km; sand beach 1.5km; dogs €2.35; bus; poss cr; Eng spkn; some rd & aircraft noise; red low ssn;CKE/CCI. "Busy site in gd location; clean, well-maintained, gd facs but ltd low ssn; phone ahead to check space high ssn or open low ssn, espec mid-winter; when office clsd some parking along rd adj football pitch; min stay 2 nights high ssn; poss travellers; m'vans not allowed in old town; gd cycle path along seafront; most pitches under trees." € 20.00 2014*

"I like to fill in the reports as I travel from site to site"

You'll find report forms at the back of this guide, or you can fill them in online at www.caravaclub.co.uk/europereport.

"We must tell The Club about that great site we found"

Get your site reports in by mid-August and we'll do our best to get your updates into the next edition.

ROCHELLE, LA *7A1* (500m SW Urban/Coastal) *46.15050, -1.15859* **Camp Municipal Le Soleil, Ave Michel Crépeau, 17000 La Rochelle [05 46 44 42 53 or 05 46 51 51 25 (Mairie)]** App La Rochelle on N11, prepare to take L turn sp Port des Minimes when 2 lge concrete water towers come into view. Foll Port des Minimes to rlwy stn (clock tower). Turn R for site over mini-rndabt then L, then L again onto Quai Georges Simenon. Turn L onto Rue Sénac de Meilan, then turn onto Ave Michel Crépeau, site on L, sp. Or fr S on N137 take D937 sp Port des Minimes & rest as above. Lge, mkd pitch, unshd, some hdstg; wc; chem disp; mv service pnt adj; shwrs inc; el pnts (6A) €3.65; shops 1km; tradsmn; BBQ area; beach 1km; some Eng spkn; adv bkg; some noise fr rd & port;CKE/CCI. "Walking dist cent La Rochelle & marina; sm pitches, facs basic; ltd space for tourers; free m'van o'night area opp site ent; daily mkt in town; site poss full by 1400 - rec arr early; NH only." 15 May-29 Sep. € 13.00 2009*

ROCHELLE, LA *7A1* (3km NW Urban) *46.19190, -1.15853* **Camp Municipal Le Parc, Rue du Parc, 17140 Lagord [05 46 67 61 54 or 05 46 00 62 12 (Mairie); fax 05 46 00 62 01; contact@marie-lagord.fr; www.lagord.fr]** On N237 ring-rd N of La Rochelle, take D104 exit for Lagord. At rndabt in approx 800m turn L then 3rd L, site on L. Med, hdg/mkd pitch, pt shd; wc; chem disp; shwrs inc; el pnts (10A) €3.60 (poss rev pol); Indtte; supmkt 2km; BBQ (gas only); playgrnd; beach 4km; few statics; dogs €1.10; bus; Eng spkn; adv bkg; quiet;CKE/CCI. "Gd facs & pitches; helpful staff; red facs low ssn; twin axles extra; conv Ile de Ré; cycle paths to La Rochelle & Ile de Ré; gd value; excel." ♦ 15 Jun-15 Sep. € 9.20 2011*

ROCHELLE, LA *7A1* (5km NW Rural/Coastal) *46.19583, -1.1875* **Camping au Petit Port de l'Houmeau, Rue des Sartières, 17137 L'Houmeau [05 46 50 90 82; fax 05 46 50 01 33; info@aupetitport.com; www.aupetitport.com]** Exit N237 onto D104/D105 sp Lagord; at rndabt in 1km turn L onto D104; in 2.5km fork L onto D106 to L'Houmeau; at ent to town turn R into Rue des Sarthières sp Camping; site on R in 100m. Med, hdg/mkd pitch, hdstg, terr, shd; wc; chem disp; mv service pnt; baby facs; shwrs inc; el pnts (10A) €4.60 (poss rev pol); lndtte (inc dryer); tradsmn; shops & rest 400m; snacks; bar; BBQ (gas); playgrnd; shgl beach 1.5km; cycle hire; games rm; wifi; dogs €2; bus 400m; poss cr; Eng spkn; adv bkg rec; quiet; red low ssn; ccard acc;CKE/CCI. "Pleasant, friendly site; helpful owners; clean facs; no vehicle access 2230-0730; gd walking & cycling; under new management (2013); conv Ile de Ré bdge; excel." ♦ 1 Apr-30 Sep. € 30.00 2014*

RONCE LES BAINS see Tremblade, La *7B1*

RONDE, LA see Courçon *7A2*

"I need an on-site restaurant"

We do our best to make sure site information is correct, but it is always best to check any must-have facilities are still available or will be open during your visit.

ROYAN *7B1* (6km NE Rural) *45.64796, -0.95847* **FFCC Camping Le Bois Roland, 82 Route de Royan, 17600 Médis [tel/fax 05 46 05 47 58; contact@le-bois-roland.com; www.le-bois-roland.com]** On N150 Saintes-Royan rd, site sp on R 100m beyond Médis vill sp. Med, pt shd; wc (some cont); chem disp; shwrs inc; el pnts (5-10A) €4.20-5.20; gas; lndtte (inc dryer); shop & 600m; tradsmn; snacks; bar; playgrnd; pool; paddling pool; sand beach 4km; entmnt; TV; dogs €2.80; phone; poss cr; adv bkg; Eng spkn; quiet; ccard acc; red low ssn; CKE/CCI. "Attractive, wooded site; friendly, family-run; facs poss stretched high ssn; waiting area avail; vg." ♦ 1 May-30 Sep. € 19.00 2010*

ROYAN *7B1* (5km E Rural) *45.62991, -0.94626* **Camping Le Clos Fleuri, 8 Impasse du Clos Fleuri, 17600 Médis [05 46 05 62 17; fax 05 46 06 75 61; clos-fleuri@wanadoo.fr; www.le-clos-fleuri.com]** On N150 Saintes-Royan rd turn S in Médis dir Semussac. Well sp. Med, hdg/mkd pitch, shd; wc (some cont); baby facs; fam bathrm; sauna; shwrs inc; el pnts (5-10A) €5-6.50; lndtte; shop in ssn & 2km; tradsmn; rest, snacks & bar in ssn; playgrnd; pool; paddling pool; sand beach 7km; games area; ltd entmnt; TV; 10% statics; dogs €3.50; phone; Eng spkn; adv bkg; quiet; ccard acc; red low ssn; CKE/CCI. "Lovely, peaceful, family-run site; san facs clean but dated; rec for young families; access poss diff lge o'fits; some pitches dark due o'hanging trees; excel, under-used site." ♦ 1 Jun-15 Sep. € 29.00 2010*

⊞ **ROYAN** *7B1* (1.7km SE Coastal) *45.61817, -1.00425* **Camping La Triloterie, 44 ter, Ave Aliénor d'Aquitaine, 17200 Royan [05 46 05 26 91; fax 05 46 06 20 74; info@campingroyan.com; www.campingroyan.com]** Fr Royan PO, foll sp Bordeaux N730, on E of rd. Med, shd; htd wc; chem disp; mv service pnt; baby facs; shwrs inc; el pnts (4-12A) €4-6 (poss rev pol); shops 500m; BBQ; playgrnd; waterslide; sand beach 900m; wifi; entmnt; some statics; dogs €1.50; phone; poss cr/noisy high ssn; some rd noise; red low ssn. "Excel site; conv for Royan town cent & St. George de Didonne." € 23.00 2011*

ROYAN *7B1* (5km SE Coastal) *45.58345, -0.98720* **Camping Bois-Soleil, 2 Ave de Suzac, 17110 St Georges-de-Didonne [05 46 05 05 94; fax 05 46 06 27 43; camping.bois.soleil@wanadoo.fr; www.bois-soleil.com]** Fr A10 exit junc 35 dir Saintes & Royan; on app Royan foll St Georges-de-Didonne sp onto bypass D25/D730/D25/D25E; go over 2 rndabts (with underpass between); at 3rd rndabt turn L sp Meschers-sur-Gironde; site on R in 500m. Site well sp. Lge, hdg/mkd pitch, hdstg, terr, pt shd; htd wc (some cont); chem disp; mv service pnt; baby facs; shwrs inc; el pnts (6A) inc (poss rev pol); gas; lndtte (inc dryer); shop; tradsmn; rest, snacks; bar; BBQ (gas); playgrnd; htd pool; paddling pool; dir access to sand beach adj; tennis; cycle hire; games area; wifi; entmnt; TV rm; 30% statics; dogs €3 (not acc end Jun-Aug inc); phone; poss cr; Eng spkn; adv bkg rec (ess Jul/Aug); ccard acc; red low ssn; CKE/CCI. "Superb wooded site in vg location nr beach; popular & busy; generous pitches, some sandy; excel, clean san facs; vg shop & rest; many sandy beaches nrby." ♦ 2 Apr-9 Oct. € 42.00 (3 persons) (CChq acc) 2012*

See advertisement

ROYAN *7B1* (6km SE Coastal) *45.59253, -0.98713* **Camping Idéal, Ave de Suzac, 17110 St Georges-de-Didonne [05 46 05 29 04; fax 05 46 06 32 36; info@ideal-camping.com; www.ideal-camping.com]** Fr Royan foll coast rd sp St Georges-de-Didonne. Site sp on D25 2km S of St Georges, opp Cmp Bois-Soleil. Lge, mkd pitch, shd; wc (some cont); chem disp; shwrs inc; el pnts (6-10A) €4.50-5.50; gas; lndtte; shop; tradsmn; rest, snacks; bar; playgrnd; htd pool; paddling pool; waterslide; jacuzzi; sand beach 200m; tennis 500m; cycle hire; horseriding 300m; games area; games rm; entmnt; some statics; no dogs; phone; poss noisy (bar); ccard acc; red low ssn; CKE/CCI. "Helpful staff; site popular with families." ♦ 7 May-5 Sep. € 37.10 (3 persons) 2014*

See advertisement

ROYAN *7B1* (9km SE Rural) *45.59750, -0.90055* **Camping Bois De La Chasse, 17 Chemin de la Motte Ronde, 17120 Semussac [0546223771; boisdelachasse@orange.fr; www.boisdelachasse.com]** D730 fr Royan. Look for Tractor Monument at an island, turn next R sp Semussac into Rue de Didonne; after 500m turn L at sp D244 ARCES into Pl. de l'Eglise, then slight R into Rue du Lignou; turn L into Chemin de la Motte Ronde. Site is sp on L after 200m. Med, mkd pitch, pt shd; wc; chem disp; mv service pnt; shwrs inc; el pnts (6A) €5.10; gas; lndtte; sm shop; tradsmn; BBQ; playgrnd; 25% statics; dogs €1.80; phone; bus 500m; no twin-axles; Eng spkn; adv bkg; quiet; ccard acc; CKE/CCI. "Gd base for Royan/ Gironde; level pitches; local supmkt nrby; owner lives onsite; gd cycling; vg site." ♦ 01 Apr-31 Oct. € 19.78 2011*

ROYAN *7B1* (16km SE Coastal) *45.55713, -0.94655* **Camping Soleil Levant, Allée de la Langée, 17132 Meschers-sur-Gironde [05 46 02 76 62; fax 05 46 02 50 56; info@camping-soleillevant.com; www.camping-soleillevant.com]** Take D145 coast rd fr Royan to Talmont. At Meschers turn R foll camp sp twd port; sp. Med, pt shd; wc (some cont); chem disp; shwrs inc; el pnts (10A) €5.10; gas 1km; lndtte; snacks; bar; shop; playgrnd; sand beach 1.5km; free pool & paddling pool; entmnt (jul-aug);watersports & horseriding adj; 20% statics; dogs €3.50; adv bkg; quiet; ccard acc; red low ssn; CKE/CCI. "Gd, busy site; sm pitches, some diff to get into; v clean san facs; port & rest 300m; vill shop & daily mkt 500m; visits to Cognac & Bordeaux distilleries." 1 Apr-30 Sep. € 26.00 2014*

ROYAN *7B1* (2km NW Urban) *45.64470, -1.04160* **Camping Le Royan, 10 Rue des Bleuets, 17200 Royan [05 46 39 09 06; fax 05 46 38 12 05; camping.le.royan@wanadoo.fr; www.le-royan.com]** Take D25 by-pass fr Royan dir La Palmyre. Site sp. Lge, mkd pitch, hdstg, pt sl, pt shd; wc (some cont); chem disp; mv service pnt; baby facs; some serviced pitches; shwrs inc; el pnts (10A) inc; gas; lndtte (inc dryer); shop; rest, snacks; bar; BBQ; playgrnd; htd pool; paddling pool; waterslide; spa; sand beach 2.5km; lake sw 3km; solarium; games area; games rm; cycle hire; entmnt; TV; 55% statics; dogs €4; poss cr; adv bkg; rd noise; ccard acc; red low ssn/long stay/CKE/CCI. "Friendly, helpful owners; excel pool complex." ♦ 1 Apr-10 Oct. € 34.50 (3 persons) 2009*

ROYAN *7B1* (4km NW Urban/Coastal) *45.6309, -1.0498* **Campéole Camping Clairefontaine, 6 Rue du Colonel Lachaud, Pontaillac, 17200 Royan [05 46 39 08 11; fax 05 46 38 13 79; clairefontaine@campeole.com; www.camping-clairefontaine.com / www.campeole.com]** Foll Pontaillac sp fr Royan. Site sp in Clairefontaine (& Pontaillac). Lge, mkd pitch, pt shd; wc (some cont); chem disp; mv service pnt; fam bthrm; serviced pitches; shwrs inc; el pnts (10A) €4.10; gas; lndtte; tradsmn; shop; rest, snacks; bar; BBQ; playgrnd; 2 pools; sand beach 300m; tennis; casino 300m; wifi; TV rm; many statics; dogs €3; phone; Eng spkn; adv bkg (fee + dep req); quiet; ccard acc; red low ssn; CKE/CCI. "Lovely coastline; gd for family holiday; helpful owner; clean, unisex san facs; ltd touring pitches, some sm; gd security; site poss dusty; vg walking & cycling; coastal path Pontaillac to Royan; gd site; easy walk/bike/bus into town; nice sw; bar & shop onsite." ♦ 5 Apr-28 Sep. € 55.30 (3 persons) 2014*

⊞ **RUFFEC** *7A2* (5km NE Rural) *46.07505, 0.26055* **Camping Rural La Renardière, La Renardiere, 16700 Taizé-Aizie [05 45 30 15 81; larenardiere16700@orange.fr; www.la-renardiere.eu]** Fr N, leave Civray on D1/D8; in 8km pass x-rds (L turn sp Lizant, R turn sp Voulème); take next L turn (dir Le Gros Chêne) bef x-ing Rv Charente; foll sm rd up hill; site in 1km on R bef hamlet of Le Gros Chêne. Sm, some hdg/ mkd pitch, hdstg, pt shd; htd wc; chem disp; fam bthrm; shwrs inc; el pnts (10A) inc; lndtte; tradsmn; snacks & meals; BBQ; pool; lake sw & fishing 3km; cycle hire; games rm; wifi; dogs €1; adv bkg; quiet; ccard acc; red long stay; CKE/CCI. "CL-type site; friendly British owners; basic san facs low ssn; vg pool; excel; v spacious with great views; gd for walking; v relaxing." € 17.50 2013*

RUFFEC *7A2* (11km E Rural) *45.99658, 0.31950* **Camping Municipal Du Val De L'Argentor, 3 Rue Du Val L'Argentu, 16700 Nanteuil En Vallée [05 45 31 82 67; fax 05 45 30 08 52; nanteuil-en-vallée.mairie@wanadoo.fr]** Fr Nanteuil-En Vallee head SW on D172 twd D740. Turn L onto D740. Take 1st R onto D187. Site on R in 400m. Sm, pt shd; wc; chem disp; mv service pnt; shwrs inc; el pns (16A) inc; shops; rest; snacks; bar; BBQ; 0% statics; dogs; twin axles; quiet; CCI. "Walking dist to Nanteuil (500m); vr nice quiet site; excel." 1 Jun- 30 Sep. € 8.00 2014*

> “Satellite navigation makes touring much easier”
>
> Remember most sat navs don't know if you're towing or in a larger vehicle – always use yours alongside maps and site directions.

RUFFEC *7A2* (3km SE Rural) *46.01500, 0.21304* **Camping Le Réjallant, Les Grands Champs, 16700 Condac [05 45 31 29 06 or 05 45 31 07 14; fax 05 45 31 34 76; cdc-ruffec-charente@wanadoo.fr]** Site sp fr N10 & fr town. App 1km fr turn-off. Med, hdg/mkd pitch, pt sl, shd; wc; chem disp (wc); shwrs inc; el pnts (10A) inc; Indtte; tradsmn; snacks; rest & bar 100m; sm playgrnd; rv sw, fishing 100m; dogs; Eng spkn; quiet; ccard not acc; CKE/CCI. "Some pitches v lge; clean facs - water poss v hot; shwrs ltd; gates open 0700-2100 high ssn; no entry/exit 1100-1600 low ssn; great for families." 15 May-15 Sep. € 13.00 2009*

⊞ **RUFFEC** *7A2* (10km W Rural) *46.00722, 0.09664* **Camping à la Ferme de Chassangne (Peloquin), Chassagne, 16240 Villefagnan [05 45 31 61 47; fax 05 45 29 55 87; contact@campingdechassagne.fr; www.campingdechassagne.fr]** Exit N10 onto D740 W to Villefagnan. Site 1.8km SE of vill on D27. Sm, pt sl, pt shd; wc; chem disp (wc); shwrs; el pnts (10A) inc; Indtte; farm produce; shop, rest, snacks, bar 1.8km; playgrnd; pool; gites avail; dogs €1; poss cr; adv bkg; quiet. "Vg CL-type site; excel pool; gd cycle rtes." ♦ ltd € 12.50 2011*

ST ANDRE DE LIDON see Cozes *8B1*

ST ANGEAU see Mansle *7B2*

ST AUGUSTIN (CHARENTE MARITIME) see St Palais sur Mer *7B1*

ST CHRISTOPHE *7A3* (2.5km NE Rural) *46.01467, 0.87679* **Camping En Campagne, Essubras, 16420 St Christophe [05 45 31 67 57; info@encampagne.com; www.encampagne.com]** Fr D82 St Christophe foll site sp for 2.5km. Sm, hdg pitch, pt shd; htd wc; chem disp; mv service pnt; baby facs; shwrs inc; el pnts (6-10A); inc; Indtte; rest; bar; playgrnd; htd pool; games area; dogs; Eng spkn; adv bkg; quiet. "Vg." 1 Apr-1 Oct. € 18.35 2010*

ST CLEMENT DES BALEINES *7A1* (500m East Rural/Coastal) *46.24041, -1.56070* **Camping Les Baleines, Chemin Devaude, 17590 St. Clement-des-Baleines [05 46 29 40 76; fax 05 46 29 67 12; camping.lesbaleines@wanadoo.fr; www.camping-lesbaleines.com]** Fr bdge foll sp for Phare De Baleines. Sp 500m bef lighthouse. Do not foll SatNav. Narr vill rds. Lge, hdg/mkd pitch, pt shd, wc; chem disp; mv service pnt; baby facs; shwrs (10A) €5-6; gas 4km; Indtte (inc dryer); shop 500m; rest 500m; snacks 500m; bar 500m; BBQ; playgrnd; sand beach adj; games area; games rm; internet; wifi; tv rm; 10% statics; dogs €2.10-3.10; phone; bus 200m; twin axles; poss cr; Eng spkn; ccard acc; red low ssn; CKE/CCI. "Vg, quiet site in natural surroundings; helpful staff; clean modern shwrs; direct access to beach; 5mins walk to lighthouse." ♦ 22 Apr-20 Sep. € 48.00 2014*

ST CLEMENT DES BALEINES (ILE DE RE) *7A1* (850m S Coastal) *46.22567, -1.54424* **FFCC Camping La Côte Sauvage, 336 Rue de la Forêt, 17590 St Clément-Des-Baleines [05 46 29 46 63; fax 04 73 77 05 06; contact@lesbalconsverts.com; www.lesbalconsverts.com]** Fr cent of vill, foll sp to site at edge of forest. Lge, mkd pitch, pt sl, pt shd; wc; chem disp; mv service pnt; baby facs; shws inc; el pnts (10A) €4 (poss long lead req); shop 300m; tradsmn; snacks; shgl beach adj; cycle rtes adj; sw; wifi; dogs €3; phone; Eng spkn; quiet; red low ssn; CKE/CCI. "Gd location; some pitches uneven; gd modern san facs; poss unrel opening dates; gd." ♦ 6 Apr-29 Sep. € 29.00 (CChq acc) 2013*

ST CYR (VIENNE) see Jaunay Clan *4H1*

ST DENIS D'OLERON *7A1* (3.7km S Coastal) *46.00480, -1.38480* **Camping Les Seulières, 1371 Rue des Seulières, 17650 Saint-Denis-d'Oléron [33 546 479 051; campinglesseulieres@wanadoo.fr; www.campinglesseulieres.fr]** Fr D734 Cheray-Saint-Denis-d'Oleron. L twd La Jausiere, cont onto Grande Rue a Chaucre and foll sp to campsite. Med, mkd pitch, pt shd; wc; baby facs; shwrs inc; el pnts (10A); gas; Indtte (inc dryer); shop 3km; tradsmn; bar; pool; sandy beach 0.3km; entmnt; wifi; 45% statics; dogs €2; bus 8km; poss cr; Eng spkn; adv bkg; quiet; ccard acc; CCI. "Very nice beach; sep cycling rtes (plan provided)." ♦ ltd 1 Apr-31 Oct. € 30.45 2014*

SAINTES *7B2* (500m N Urban) *45.75511, -0.62871* **Camp Municipal au Fil de l'Eau, 6 Rue de Courbiac, 17100 Saintes [05 46 93 08 00 or 06 75 24 91 96 (mob); fax 05 46 93 61 88; campingaufildeleau@sfr.fr; www.camping-saintes-17.com]** Well sp as 'Camping Municipal' fr rndbts on by-pass N & S on D150 & D137 (thro indus area), adj rv. If app fr W on D128 (N side of Saintes), turn R at rndabt onto Rue de l'Abbatoir; in 800m turn L into Rue de Courbiac; site on R in 200m. NB 1st Mon in month street mkt & many rds clsd. Lge, pt shd; wc; chem disp; shwrs inc; el pnts (10A) €3.60; Indtte; shop; supmkt 1.5km; snacks; rest high ssn; bar; BBQ; playgrnd; sm pool; rv sw, fishing & boating adj; wifi; dogs €1.60; train 2km; Eng spkn; adv bkg; ccard acc; red low ssn/long stay; CKE/CCI. "Excel site; vg, clean san facs; excel rest; grnd poss boggy when wet; gd touring base; mkt Wed & Sat; easy walk to attractive Roman town; huge open site, efficent recep; site being upgraded (2014); friendly staff; gd NH just off A10; rest clsd on Sundays." ♦ 20 Apr-15 Oct. € 22.65 2014*

ST FORT SUR GIRONDE *7B2* (4km SW Rural) *45.43278, -0.75185* **Camping Port Maubert, 8 Rue de Chassillac, 17240 St Fort-sur-Gironde [05 46 04 78 86; fax 05 46 04 16 79; bourdieu.jean-luc@wanadoo.fr; www.campingportmaubert.com]** Exit A10 junc 37 onto D730 dir Royan. Foll sp Port Maubert & site. Sm, hdg/mkd pitch, shd; wc (some cont); chem disp; mv service pnt; shwrs inc; el pnts (10A) €3.50; gas; Indtte; shop 4km; tradsmn; bar; BBQ; playgrnd; pool; sand beach 25km; cycle hire; games rm; TV; some statics; dogs €2; Eng spkn; adv bkg; quiet; ccard acc; red long stay/ CKE/CCI. "Pleasant, well-run site; low ssn ltd facs, OK NH."
1 Apr-30 Oct. € 12.40 2014*

ST GEORGES DE DIDONNE see Royan *7B1*

ST GEORGES D'OLERON (ILE D'OLERON) *7A1* (5km E Coastal) *45.98738, -1.29347* **Camping La Gautrelle (CC de F), Plage des Saumonards, 17190 St Georges-d'Oléron [05 46 47 21 57; fax 05 46 75 10 74; lagautrelle.ccdf@wanadoo.fr; www.campingclub.asso.fr]** Fr viaduct, take D734 to St Pierre. At 3rd traff lts, turn R to Sauzelle, thro vill & L for St Georges & immed to R sp CCDF La Gautrelle. Site at end of lane in approx 1.5km & adj to beach. Lge, mkd pitch, shd; wc; shwrs inc; el pnts (6A) inc (long cable req); shops adj; sand beach; fishing; some statics; dogs €2.32; adv bkg; quiet; CKE/CCI. "Splendid beaches; forest walks, fishing; ltd el pnts."
♦ 1 Apr-30 Sep. € 19.85 2009*

ST GEORGES D'OLERON (ILE D'OLERON) *7A1* (6km E Coastal) *45.96820, -1.24483* **Camp Atlantique Signol, Ave des Albatros, Boyardville, 17190 St Georges-d'Oléron [02 51 20 41 94; contact@signol.com; www.signol.camp-atlantique.co.uk/en]** Cross bdge onto Ile d'Oléron & cont on main rd twd St Pierre-d'Oléron. Turn R at Dolus-d'Oléron for Boyardville & foll sp in vill. Lge, hdg/mkd pitch, pt sl, pt shd; wc; mv service pnt; chem disp; baby facs; shwrs inc; el pnts (6A) €4.60; gas; Indtte; shops adj; tradsmn; bar; playgrnd; htd pool; paddling pool; sand beach 800m; 60% statics;1 dog per pitch €4; Eng spkn; adv bkg; red low ssn. "Size of pitches variable; gd san facs; impressive pool complex; gd site & facs; vg facs and activities for kids; 50yrds to shops & rests." ♦
1 May-30 Sep. € 29.80 (CChq acc) 2014*

See advertisement

ST GEORGES D'OLERON (ILE D'OLERON) *7A1* (800m SE Rural) *45.97310, -1.32020* **Chadotel Camping Le Domaine d'Oléron, La Jousselinière, 17190 St Georges-d'Oléron [05 46 76 54 97 or 02 51 33 05 05 (LS); fax 02 51 33 94 04; info@chadotel.com; www.chadotel.com]** After x-ing Viaduct (bdge) onto island foll sp dir St Pierre d'Oléron & St Georges-d'Oléron on D734; turn R on rndabt immed see Leclerc supmkt on R; at next rndabt turn L sp 'Le Bois Fleury'; pass airfield 'Bois 'Fleury' on R; take next R & then immed L. Site on L in 500m. Lge, mkd pitch, terr, pt shd; wc; chem disp; mv service pnt; baby facs; shwrs inc; el pnts (6A) inc; gas; Indtte (inc dryers); shop; snacks; bar; BBQ (gas only) sep area; playgrnd; pool; waterslide; paddling pool; sand beach 3km; cycle hire; games area; wifi; entmnt; games/TV rm; 40% statics; dogs €3.20; no c'vans/m'vans over 8m high ssn; Eng spkn; adv bkg ess high ssn; poss noise fr nrby sites w/end high ssn; ccard acc; red long stay/low ssn; CKE/CCI. "Popular, well-organised, clean site; friendly, helpful staff; lovely pool; cycle paths; excel."
♦ 5 Apr-20 Sep. € 31.00 SBS - A41 2011*

"There aren't many sites open at this time of year"

If you're travelling outside peak season remember to call ahead to check site opening dates – even if the entry says 'open all year'.

ST GEORGES D'OLERON (ILE D'OLERON) *7A1* (4km SW Coastal) *45.95386, -1.37932* **Camping Les Gros Joncs, Les Sables Vigniers, 17190 St Georges-d'Oléron [05 46 76 52 29; camping.gros.joncs@wanadoo.fr; www.les-gros-joncs.fr]** Fr Ile d'Oléron toll bdge, by-passing Le Château-d'Oléron, NW on D734 to St Pierre-d'Oléron & St Georges-d'Oléron. At Chéray, foll sps to site. V lge, pt shd; wc; shwrs; el pnts (10A) €3; Indtte; shop; rest, snacks; bar; playgrnd; htd pool; paddling pool; jacuzzi; rocky beach 200m; sand beach 1km; games area; TV; some statics; dogs €3; adv bkg; quiet. "Excel pool; great location; clean facs; rec." ♦
23 Mar-23 Oct. € 43.00 (3 persons) 2011*

See advert on next page

ST GEORGES D'OLERON (ILE D'OLERON) *7A1* (3km W Coastal) *45.94756, -1.37386* **Camping Le Suroit, L'Ileau de la Grande Côte, 17190 St Georges-d'Oléron [05 46 47 07 25 or 06 80 10 93 18 (mob); fax 05 46 75 04 24; camping@lesuroit.fr; www.camping-lesuroit.com]** Fr Domino cent foll sp for beach, turn L for L'Ileau. Strt at x-rds. Fork L for La Cotinière, site on R in 150m. Lge, mkd pitch, shd; htd wc; baby facs; shwrs inc; el pnts (10A) €4; gas; lndtte; shop; rest, snacks; bar; BBQ; playgrnd; htd, covrd pool; sand beach adj; tennis; games area; cycle hire; entmnt; TV; some statics; dogs €4; adv bkg; quiet; red low ssn. "Excel, well-organised site." ♦ 4 Apr-3 Oct. € 25.00 2009*

ST GEORGES D'OLERON (ILE D'OLERON) *7A1* (3km W Coastal) *45.96119, -1.37032* **Camping Les Grosses Pierres, Les Sables Vigniers, 17190 St Georges-d'Oléron [02 51 27 37 80; fax 05 46 76 54 85; info@vagues-oceanes.com; www.camping-vagues-oceanes.com]** Site sp fr D734. Lge, mkd pitch, some hdstg, terr, pt shd; wc; chem disp; shwrs inc; el pnts (10A) inc; gas; lndtte (inc dryer); shop; rest, snacks; bar; BBQ; playgrnd; 2 pools (1 htd, covrd); paddling pool; waterslide; sand beach 900m; games rm; wifi; entmnt; 95% statics; dogs; phone; Eng spkn; adv bkg; ccard acc; CKE/CCI. 3 Apr-18 Sep. € 35.00 2010*

⊞ **ST GEORGES LES BAILLARGEAUX** *4H1* (1km S Rural) *46.66452, 0.39477* **Camping Le Futuriste, 86130 St Georges-les-Baillargeaux [05 49 52 47 52; fax 05 49 37 23 33; camping-le-futuriste.@wanadoo.fr; www.camping-le-futuriste.fr]** N of Poitiers on D910. Exit at Furutoscope/St Georges. Then foll sp. Sm, hdg pitch, mkd pitch, pt shd; wc; chem disp; mv service pnt; shwrs inc; lndtte (inc dryer); el pnts inc; shop; rest; playgrnd; htd covrd pool; games rm; wifi; dogs; twin axles; Eng spkn; quiet; CCI. "Lovely little site; nice pool with gd waterslide for kids & adults." € 33.00 2014*

ST HILAIRE LA PALUD *7A2* (5km NW Rural) *46.28386, -0.74344* **Flower Camping Le Lidon, Le Lidon, 79210 St Hilaire-la-Palud [05 49 35 33 64; fax 05 49 35 32 63; info@le-lidon.com; www.le-lidon.com]** Exit A10 junc 33 onto E601 then N248 & N11 S. At Epannes foll D1 N to Sansais, then D3 to St Hilaire-la-Palud. Foll sp Canal du Mignon & site. NB Access to site over narr angled bdge, extreme care needed - v diff lge o'fits. Med, hdg/mkd pitch, pt shd; wc; chem disp; mv service pnt; baby facs; fam bthrm; shwrs inc; el pnts (10A) inc; gas 4km; lndtte; ice; shop; tradsmn; rest, snacks; bar; BBQ; playgrnd; htd pool; paddling pool; rv fishing; canoe hire; cycle hire; wifi; entmnt; 5% statics; dogs €2.50; some Eng spkn; adv bkg; quiet; ccard acc; red low ssn; CKE/CCI. "Secluded site in Marais Poitevin Regional Park (marsh land); gd sized pitches; excel clean san facs; gd walking, cycling, birdwatching; vg." ♦ 9 Apr-29 Sep. € 26.00 (CChq acc) 2011*

ST JEAN D'ANGELY *7B2* (500m W Rural) *45.94868, -0.53645* **Camping Val de Boutonne, 56 Quai de Bernouet, 17400 St Jean-d'Angély [05 46 32 26 16; fax 05 46 32 29 54; info@valba.net; www.campingcharentemaritime17.com]** Exit A10 at junc 34; head SE on D939; turn R at 1st rndabt into town. Site sp. Med, mkd pitch, shd; wc (some cont); chem disp; mv service pnt; shwrs inc; el pnts (10A) €4; lndtte; sm shop; tradsmn; rest, snacks, bar 200m; playgrnd; aquatic cent 500m; wifi; TV rm; 10% statics; dogs €2; phone adj; Eng spkn; adv bkg; quiet; ccard acc; red long stay; CKE/CCI; "Pleasant, friendly, well-kept site by Rv Boutonne; helpful owners; new pool (2013); gd, clean san facs, outdated; poss open in Oct - phone ahead; vg; lake with sm boating facs; rec; gd nh just off the A10; 10min walk to historic town; lge Sat mkt." ♦ 1 Apr-30 Sep. € 22.35 2014*

ST JUST LUZAC see Marennes *7B1*

⊞ **ST LAURENT DE CERIS** *7B3* (4.6km NE Rural) *45.95902, 0.52880* **Camp Laurent, Le Fournet, 16450 St Laurent de Ceris Charente [06 02 22 37 15; lecamplaurent@gmail.com]** Fr St Claud on D174. Fr St Laurent de Ceris turn R at rest onto D15. Take 2nd L on D345, Le Fournet sp at junc. Site on R in about 1km. Sm, pt sl, pt shd; wc; chem disp (green only); mv service pnt; shwrs; el pnts (10A) €3; shops 1.5km; rest 1.5km; bar 1.5km; BBQ; pool; internet; wifi; dogs; twin axles; Eng spkn; adv bkg; quiet. "Adult only site; suitable for all units; Eng owners; beside sm rv; v clean facs; helpful, friendly welcome; lakes with beach nrby; new owners." ♦ € 17.00 2014*

⊞ **ST MAIXENT L'ECOLE** *7A2* (1.5km SW Urban) *46.40836, -0.21856* **Camp Municipal du Panier Fleuri, Rue Paul Drévin, 79400 St Maixent-l'Ecole [05 49 05 53 21; fax 05 49 76 50 90]** Take D611 twd Niort, at 2nd set of traff lts nr top of hill out of town turn L. Foll camping sps into ent. Med, mkd pitch, pt sl, pt shd; wc (some cont); mv service pnt; shwrs inc; el pnts (10A); tradsmn; rest, snacks, bar 1km; playgrnd; htd pool adj; tennis; dogs; quiet; ccard not acc. "Warden on site am & eve, if office locked go to house nr wc block; ltd/basic facs low ssn; interesting town; NH en rte Spain." 2010*

> "That's changed – Should I let The Club know?"
>
> If you find something on site that's different from the site entry, fill in a report and let us know. See www.caravanclub.co.uk/europereport.

STE MARIE DE RE (ILE DE RE) *7A1* (1km S Coastal) *46.14504, -1.31509* **Camp Municipal La Côte Sauvage, La Basse Benée 17740 Ste Marie-de-Ré [05 46 30 21 74 or 05 46 30 21 24 (LS); fax 05 46 30 15 64; camping.stemarie @ orange.fr; www.mairie-sainte-marie-de-re.fr]** Site sp fr main rd. V narr rds thro town. Med, mkd pitch, pt shd; wc; chem disp; mv service pnt; shwrs inc; el pnts (16A) €3.50; shop; supmkt 2km; snacks; bar; playgrnd; sand beach adj; fishing; quiet; ccard acc; red low ssn; CKE/CCI; "Excel location but poss windy; helpful owners; gd value snack bar; free parking for m'vans adj; highly rec." 1 Apr - 19 Oct. € 15.00 2013*

⊞ **STE MARIE DE RE (ILE DE RE)** *7A1* (4km NW Coastal) *46.16112, -1.35428* **Camping Les Grenettes, Route De L'Ermitage, 17740 Ste Marie De Re [05 46 30 22 47; fax 05 46 30 24 64; contact@hotel-les-grenettes.com; www.campinglesgrenettes.com]** Foll sp for D201 'Itinéraire Sud' after toll bdge in the dir of Le Bois-de-Plage; after approx 2km turn L. Med, mkd pitches, pt shd; wc; chem disp; mv service pnt; baby facs; shwrs inc; el pnts (6A) €4.50; gas; shop; rest; BBQ; playgrnd; pool; water slide; paddling pool; sea 200m; fishing; tennis; cycle hire; entmnt; wifi; TV; statics; dogs €4; Eng spkn; adv bkg; ccard acc. "V nice site close to sea; v gd rest." € 32.00 2011*

> "I like to fill in the reports as I travel from site to site"
>
> You'll find report forms at the back of this guide, or you can fill them in online at www.caravaclub.co.uk/europereport.

ST MARTIN DE RE (ILE DE RE) *7A1* (4km E Coastal/Urban) *46.18194, -1.33110* **Flower Camping de Bel Air, Route de la Noué, 17630 La Flotte-en-Ré [05 46 09 63 10; camping.bel-air@flowercampings.com; www.bel-air-camping.com]** Fr toll bdge take D735 to La Flotte. Turn R at rndabt to town into Route de la Noué, site sp. Lge, hdg/mkd pitch, pt shd; wc (some cont); chem disp; mv service pnt; shwrs inc; el pnts (6A) €3.84; lndtte; rest, snacks; bar; playgrnd; beach 800m; tennis; games rm; entmnt; wifi; phone; adv bkg; quiet. "Walk to shops, harbour, beach etc; gd; friendly staff." ♦ 30 Mar-3 Nov. € 29.00 2013*

ST MARTIN DE RE (ILE DE RE) *7A1* (2km SE Coastal) *46.18370, -1.30820* **FFCC Camping Les Peupliers, 17630 La Flotte-en-Ré [05 46 09 62 35; fax 05 46 09 59 76; contact@lespeupliers.com; www.les-peupliers.com]** Site sp fr D735, Route du Fort-la-Prée, main rd on Ile-de-Ré. Lge, hdg/mkd pitch, pt shd, wc; chem disp; mv service pnt; shwrs inc; el pnts (5A) inc; lndtte; shop; supmkt 900m; tradsmn; rest, snacks; bar; BBQ (gas only); playgrnd; htd pool; paddling pool; sand beach 800m; games area; wifi; entmnt; TV rm; 80% statics; dogs €5; phone; Eng spkn; adv bkg rec; quiet; ccard acc; CKE/CCI. "Sea views; some pitches sm; ltd touring ptiches; poss cr low ssn; gd sports facs." ♦ 30 Apr-24 Sep. € 35.00 (3 persons) 2010*

ST MARTIN DE RE (ILE DE RE) *7A1* (5km SE Rural) *46.18740, -1.34390* **Camping La Grainetière, Route St Martin, 17630 La Flotte-en-Ré [05 46 09 68 86; fax 05 46 09 53 13; la-grainetiere@orange.fr; www.la-grainetiere.com]** 10km W fr toll bdge, site sp on La Flotte ring rd. Med, pt shd; wc; chem disp; mv service pnt; baby facs; shwrs inc; el pnts (10A) €4.50; gas; lndtte; shop; tradsmn; playgrnd; htd pool; sand beach 3km; cycle hire; wifi; TV rm; 70% statics; dogs €4.50; poss cr; Eng spkn; adv bkg; rd noise; red low ssn; CKE/CCI; "Beautiful, clean, wooded site; haphazard pitching; helpful owners; gd san facs; gd pool; daily mkt; vg." ♦ 2 Apr- 30 Sep. € 23.00 2013*

See advert on next page

POITOU-CHARENTES

ST MARTIN DE RE (ILE DE RE) *7A1* (800m S Urban) *46.19913, -1.36682* **Camp Municipal Les Remparts, Rue Les Remparts, 17410 St Martin-de-Ré [05 46 09 21 96; fax 05 46 09 94 18; camping.stmartindere@wanadoo.fr; www.saint-martin-de-re.fr]** Foll D735 fr toll bdge to St Martin; sp in town fr both ends. Med, hdg/mkd pitch, pt sl, pt shd; wc; chem disp; mv service pnt; shwrs inc; el pnts (10A) €3.70; Indtte; shop; snacks; BBQ; playgrnd; pool 3km; sand beach 1.3km; dogs €2; Eng spkn; adv bkg; quiet; ccard acc; red low ssn; CKE/CCI. "Busy site in brilliant location; san facs dated but clean; gd basic rest; poss children's groups mid-ssn; some pitches boggy when wet; gd cycling; site poss unkempt end ssn; vg mkt; beautiful situation on o'skirts of a lovely town, gd size pitches." ♦ 12 Mar-18 Nov. € 23.00 (3 persons) 2013*

"We must tell The Club about that great site we found"

Get your site reports in by mid-August and we'll do our best to get your updates into the next edition.

ST PALAIS SUR MER *7B1* (1km N Rural/Coastal) *45.65163, -1.10898* **Camping Le Logis, 22 Rue des Palombes, 17420 St Palais-sur-Mer [05 46 23 20 23 or 05 46 22 38 22; fax 05 46 23 10 61 or 05 46 23 65 10; reservations@yukadivillages.com; www.yukadivillages.com]** On rd N out of Royan, after vill of St Palais-sur-Mer, site sp on R after petrol stn. V lge, pt sl, terr, shd; htd wc (some cont); chem disp; baby facs; shwrs inc; el pnts (6A) inc; Indtte (inc dryer); shop & 2km; tradsmn; snacks; bar; BBQ; playgrnd; pool; paddling pool; waterslide; aquapark; shgl beach 1km; tennis; games area; wifi; entmnt; TV; 35% statics; dogs; poss cr; Eng spkn; adv bkg; ccard acc; red low ssn. "La Palmyre zoo nr; excel water park." 17 May-7 Sep. € 38.50 2010*

ST PALAIS SUR MER *7B1* (7km N Rural) *45.67550, -1.09670* **Camping Le Logis du Breuil, 17570 St Augustin [05 46 23 23 45; fax 05 46 23 43 33; info@logis-du-breuil.com; www.logis-du-breuil.com]** N150 to Royan, then D25 dir St Palais-sur-Mer. Strt on at 1st rndabt & 2nd rndabt; at next rndabt take 2nd exit dir St Palais-sur-Mer. At next traff lts turn R dir St Augustin onto D145; site on L. NB Sat Nav can direct thro diff & narr alt rte. Lge, mkd pitch, pt shd, pt sl; wc (some cont); chem disp; mv service pnt; baby facs; shwrs inc; el pnts (6A) inc (50m cable poss req); gas; Indtte (inc dryer); shop; supmkt; rest, snacks; bar; BBQ (gas/elec); playgrnd; pool; paddling pool; sand beach 5km; fishing 1km; tennis; cycle hire; horseriding 400m; golf 3km; excursions; games area; games rm; wifi; entmnt; games/TV rm; 10% statics; dogs €3; no c'vans over 12m; phone; poss cr; Eng spkn; adv bkg; ccard acc; red low ssn; CKE/CCI. "Nice peaceful site; lge pitches in wooded area; gd alt to cr beach sites; friendly owner; san facs clean; gd for young families; excel." ♦ 10 May-29 Sep. € 27.50 SBS - A04 2011*

See advert on next page

ST PALAIS SUR MER *7B1* (8km N Rural) *45.68888, -1.11034* **Camping Les Vignes, 3 Rue des Ardilliers, 17570 St Augustin [tel/fax 05 46 23 23 51; campinglesvignes17@alicepro.fr; www.campinglesvignes17.com]** On app Royan on D733, after x-ing D14 turn R sp St Palais (by-pass Royan cent). At rndabt on D25 foll sp St Augustin. Site on R. Med, mkd pitch, pt shd; wc (some cont); shwrs; el pnts (5-10A) €3.90-4.70; gas; Indtte; shop; tradsmn; rest, snacks; bar; playgrnd; pool, paddling pool 200m; waterslides; cycle hire; wifi; entmnt; 70% statics; dogs €1.50; phone; adv bkg; red long stay/low ssn; CKE/CCI. "Remote, peaceful, welcoming site; basic facs, ltd low ssn; immac pools." ♦ Easter-1 Nov. € 16.00 2009*

ST PALAIS SUR MER *7B1* (500m NE Coastal) *45.64245, -1.07677* **Camping de Bernezac, 2 Ave de Bernezac, 17420 St Palais-sur-Mer [05 46 39 00 71; fax 05 46 38 14 46; acccf-ber@wanadoo.fr; www.acccf.com]** Foll sp off Royan-St Palais coast rd. Med, pt shd; wc; chem disp; mv service pnt; 50% serviced pitches; baby facs; shwrs inc; el pnts (6A) €3.70 (poss rev pol); Indtte; shop 800m; rest, snacks; BBQ; playgrnd; beach adj; lake fishing 1km; entmnt; TV; 30% statics; dogs €1; Eng spkn; adv bkg; quiet. "Helpful, friendly staff." 15 Mar-15 Oct. € 20.80 2009*

 You can now fill in site reports online

ST PALAIS SUR MER *7B1* (1.5km E Rural/Coastal) *45.64656, -1.07300* **Camping Les Ormeaux, 44 Ave de Bernezac, 17420 St Palais-sur-Mer [05 46 39 02 07; fax 05 46 38 56 66; campingormeaux@aliceadsl.fr; www.camping-ormeaux.com]** Foll sp fr D25 Royan-St Palais rd. Rec app ent fr R. Ent & camp rds narr. Lge, pt shd; wc; baby facs; shwrs inc; el pnts (6A) €7.50; gas; Indtte; shop; snacks; bar; playgrnd; htd pool; sand beach 800m; entmnt; TV; 98% statics; dogs €4; quiet; red low ssn. "Ltd touring area & access diff for lge o'fits or m'vans - tents or sm m'vans only." ♦ 1 Apr-31 Oct. € 27.00 (3 persons) 2009*

ST PALAIS SUR MER *7B1* (2km E Coastal) *45.64396, -1.06325* **Camping Le Val Vert, 108 Ave Frédéric Garnier, 17640 Vaux-sur-Mer [05 46 38 25 51; fax 05 46 38 06 15; camping-val-vert@wanadoo.fr; www.val-vert.com]** Fr Saintes on N150 dir Royan; join D25 dir St Palais-sur-Mer; turn L at rndabt sp Vaux-sur-Mer & Centre Hospitaliers; at traff lts ahead; at 2nd rndabt take 3rd exit & then turn immed R. Site on R in 500m. Med, hdg pitch; wc; chem disp; mv service pnt; baby facs; shwrs inc; el pnts (6A) €5.50 or (10A) €6.00; gas; Indtte; shop; rest, snacks; gas/elec BBQ; playgrnd; htd pool; paddling pool; sand beach 900m; watersports; fishing; cycle hire; tennis 400m; horseriding & golf 5km; games area; games rm; some wifi; entmnt; dogs €3.40; no c'vans/m'vans over 6.50m high ssn; adv bkg; ccard acc; red low ssn. "Well-kept, family-run site; gd sized pitches; unisex san facs; no twin-axles; a stream runs alongside site; sh walk to pleasant vill; daily mkt in Royan; excel." ♦ ltd 12 Apr-28 Sep. € 31.30 (3 persons) (CChq acc) SBS - A25 2013*

ST PALAIS SUR MER *7B1* (2km SE Coastal/Urban) *45.64272, -1.07183* **Camping Nauzan-Plage, 39 Ave de Nauzan-Plage, 17640 Vaux-sur-Mer [05 46 38 29 13; fax 05 46 38 18 43; info@campinglenauzanplage.com; www.campinglenauzanplage.com]** Take either coast rd or inland rd fr Royan to Vaux-sur-Mer; site not well sp. Lge, mkd pitch, pt shd; wc; chem disp; baby facs; shwrs inc; el pnts (10A) €5.50; gas; Indtte; shop; supmkt 1km; rest, snacks; bar; playgrnd; sm pool; sand beach 450m; tennis 200m; games/TV rm; 10% statics (sep area) dogs €5; adv bkg (rec Jul/Aug); quiet; red low ssn/long stay; CKE/CCI. "Gd site; helpful staff; gd cycling rtes." ♦ 1 Apr-30 Sep. € 32.00 (3 persons) 2010*

ST PALAIS SUR MER *7B1* (3km NW Coastal) *45.6500, -1.1193* **Camping La Côte de Beauté, 157 Ave de la Grande Côte, 17420 St Palais-sur-Mer [05 46 23 20 59; fax 05 46 23 37 32; campingcotedebeaute@wanadoo.fr; www.camping-cote-de-beaute.com]** Fr St Palais-sur-Mer foll sp to La Tremblade & Ronce-les-Bains. Site on D25, 50m fr beach, look for twin flagpoles of Camping Le Puits de l'Auture & lge neon sp on R; site in 50m. Med, hdg pitch, shd; htd wc; baby facs; shwrs inc; el pnts (6A) €4.20; Indtte; supmkt adj; tradsmn; rest, snacks; bar; playgrnd; sand beach 200m across rd; tennis, cycle hire adj; golf 2km; some statics; dogs €3; adv bkg; quiet; red low ssn. "Clean, tidy site; friendly staff; steep descent to beach opp - better beach 600m twd La Tremblade; cycle track to St Palais & Pontaillac." 1 May-30 Sep. € 25.80 (3 persons) 2010*

ST PALAIS SUR MER *7B1* (3km NW Coastal) *45.6482, -1.1108* **Camping La Grande Côte, 167 Ave de la Grande Côte, 17420 St Palais-sur-Mer [tel/fax 05 46 23 20 18; info@campinglagrandecote.com; www.campinglagrandecote.com]** Fr Royan, take D25 thro St Palais, site on R where rd runs close to sea. Look for flags. Med, mkd pitch, pt shd; htd wc; baby facs; shwrs inc; el pnts (6A) €4.20; gas; Indtte; rest adj; bar; BBQ; sand beach 200m; dogs €3; bus; quiet; CKE/CCI. "Helpful staff; excel site." ♦ 1 May-12 Sep. € 23.60 2009*

ST PIERRE D'OLERON (ILE D'OLERON) *7B1* (3km W Coastal) *45.90164, -1.30266* **Camping La Perroche Leitner, 18 Rue de Renclos de la Perroche, 17310 St Pierre-d'Oléron [05 46 75 37 33; fax 05 49 85 12 57; camping-la-perroche-leitner@wanadoo.fr]** Site about 10km fr bdge on W coast of Ile d'Oléron. Fr bdge foll sp to Grande Village/Vert-Bois/La Remigeasse & La Perroche. Well sp. Med, hdg/mkd pitch, hdstg, terr, pt shd; wc (some cont); chem disp; mv service pnt; shwrs inc; el pnts (10A) inc; gas; Indtte; shop; tradsmn; BBQ; playgrnd; direct access sand beach 200m; games area; dogs €2.80; Eng spkn; quiet; ccard acc; red low ssn. "Superb site; site staff connect/disconnect el pnts." ♦ 1 Apr-15 Sep. € 28.70 2010*

POITOU-CHARENTES

ST PIERRE D'OLERON (ILE D'OLERON) *7B1* (3.5km W Coastal) *45.92394, -1.34273* **FFCC Camp Municipal La Fauche Prère, Ave des Pins, La Cotinière, 17310 St Pierre d'Oléron [05 46 47 10 53; fax 05 46 75 23 44; camping@saint-pierre-oleron.com; www.saint-pierre-oleron.com]** Fr bdge foll D734 N to St Pierre-d'Oléron. Turn L onto D274 for La Cotinière, site bef vill on L, sp. Med, mkd pitch, pt sl, shd; wc; chem disp (wc); mv service pnt; baby facs; shwrs €0.80; el pnts (12A) €4; Indtte; shop; playgrnd; sand beach adj; dogs €2; poss cr; CKE/CCI. "Direct access to beach; most pitches sandy; gd." 1 Apr-30 Sep. € 18.00 (3 persons) 2010*

"I need an on-site restaurant"

We do our best to make sure site information is correct, but it is always best to check any must-have facilities are still available or will be open during your visit.

ST SAVIN *7A3* (1km N Rural) *46.56892, 0.86772* **Camp Municipal Moulin de la Gassotte, 10 Rue de la Gassotte, 86310 St Savin-sur-Gartempe [05 49 48 18 02; fax 05 49 48 28 56; saint.savin@ag86.fr; www.saintsavin.com]** E fr Chauvigny on D951 to St Savin; fr St Savin N on D11; well sp. Fr S on D5 cross rv; meet D951, turn R & site on R. Fr S on D11 use 'poids lourds' (heavy vehicles) rec rte to meet D951. Sm, pt shd; wc; chem disp; mv service pnt; shwrs inc; el pnts (12A) €2.70; Indry rm; shop, rests & bars 500m; tradsmn; playgrnd; rv fishing adj; TV; quiet; CKE/CCI. "Beautiful, peaceful site by rv; helpful warden; san facs old but clean; sh walk to vill; murals in Abbey restored by UNESCO." ♦ 14 May-15 Sep. € 6.80 2011*

ST SAVINIEN *7B2* (1km S Rural) *45.87789, -0.68441* **Camping L'Ile aux Loisirs (La Grenouillette), 17350 St Savinien [05 46 90 35 11; fax 05 46 91 65 06; contact@ileauxloisirs.com; www.ileauxloisirs.com]** Fr St Jean-d'Angély take D18 to St Savinien. Site on S side of town; cross rv bdge in vill; site on L after 300m. Med, pt shd; wc; shwrs inc; el pnts (6A) €4.50; (rev pol); Indtte; shop; bar; snacks; playgrnd; pool adj; tennis & mini-golf nrby; entmnt; dogs €1; adv bkg; quiet, some rd noise; red low ssn; ccard acc. "Pleasant, well-run site; attractive town." 1 Apr-22 Sep. € 16.00 2009*

ST SAVINIEN *7B2* (5km SW Rural) *45.85243, -0.70660* **Camping du Petit Bonheur, 14 Rue du Port, 17350 Crazannes [05 46 74 44 25 or 06 75 04 40 91 (mob); contact@dupetit-bonheur.com; www.dupetit-bonheur.com]** Fr St Savinien take D18 for 700m, turn L onto D119 sp Crazannes. Site on L on ent vill. Med, mkd pitch, pt sl, pt shd; wc (some cont); chem disp; baby facs; shwrs inc; el pnts (6A) €4.30; gas; Indtte; shops 300m; tradsmn; BBQ (gas/elec); playgrnd; htd pool; rv sw, fishing 100m; internet; 5% statics; dogs €1; adv bkg; quiet; red low ssn; CKE/CCI. "Peaceful, CL-type site nr Rv Charente; new san facs planned for 2011; gd cycling." 1 Mar-31 Oct. € 15.50 2010*

ST SORNIN see Marennes *7B1*

ST TROJAN LES BAINS (ILE D'OLERON) *7B1* (1.5km SW Rural) *45.82947, -1.21632* **Camping La Combinette, 36 Ave des Bris, 17370 St Trojan-les-Bains [05 46 76 00 47; fax 05 46 76 16 96; la-combinette@wanadoo.fr; www.combinette-oleron.com]** Fr toll bdge stay on D26 for 1km, L onto D275 & L onto D126 to St Trojan-les-Bains. Strt ahead at rndabt with figure sculpture, then R at next rndabt sp Campings. In 1km turn L at rd fork, site on R in 1km. Lge, shd; wc; baby facs; shwrs inc; el pnts (5-10A) €3-3.90; gas; Indtte; shop; rest, snacks; playgrnd; pool; beach; 2km; sauna; spa; gym; games area; cycle hire; wifi; entmnt; dogs €2.20; poss cr; quiet. "Gd touring base; some super pitches; friendly owners; facs poss stretched high ssn; poss flooding in heavy rain; vg." ♦ 1 Apr-31 Oct. € 24.70 2010*

ST VARENT *4H1* (2km S Rural) *46.89741, -0.24147* **Camp Municipal La Grande Versenne, 79330 St Varent [05 49 67 62 11 (Mairie); fax 05 49 67 67 87; villestvarent@wanadoo.fr]** Site sp on D938 at Bouillé-St Varent. Sm, hdg pitch, pt shd; wc; baby facs; shwrs inc; el pnts (10A) €2.50; supmkt nr; playgrnd; rv nrby; no statics; dogs €0.50; adv bkg; quiet. "Friendly staff; gd NH." ♦ 1 Apr-31 Oct. € 9.50 2012*

ST YRIEIX SUR CHARANTE see Angouleme *7B2*

SAUJON *7B1* (1.5km N Rural) *45.68646, -0.94000* **Aire Naturelle Le Logis de la Lande (Renouleau), Route de l'Ilatte, 17600 Saujon [05 46 02 84 31 or 06 77 38 62 98 (mob); christianerenouleau@wanadoo.fr; http://camping-lalande.monsite-orange.fr]** Fr N150 Saujon by-pass turn onto D1 dir Le Gua. At end slip rd turn L & at rndabt foll sp L'Ilatte. Site in 500m on R immed after R bend. Avoid Saujon cent. Sm, pt sl, pt shd; wc; chem disp; shwrs; el pnts (6A) €4; Indry rm; shop, rest, snacks & bar 2km; playgrnd; beach 12km; dogs €2 poss cr; v quiet. "Pleasant, well-kept, CL-type site; san facs clean but ltd in number; inland fr cr coast, not full peak ssn; excel." Apr-Oct. € 11.80 2010*

"Satellite navigation makes touring much easier"

Remember most sat navs don't know if you're towing or in a larger vehicle – always use yours alongside maps and site directions.

SECONDIGNY *4H1* (500m S Rural) *46.60486, -0.41599* **Camp Municipal du Moulin des Effres, 79130 Secondigny [05 49 95 61 97; fax 05 49 63 55 48; contact@campingmoulindeseffres.fr; www.campings-poitou-charentes.com]** D949 to Secondigny, S onto D748. Site sp on L in 800m on lakeside. Med, mkd pitch, pt sl, pt shd; wc; chem disp; shwrs inc; el pnts (6-10A) inc; Indtte (inc dryer); shops 500m; tradsmn; rest 400m; snacks; pool; paddling pool; lake fishing adj; tennis; wifi; entmnt; TV; 10% statics; dogs; phone; poss cr; quiet; ccard acc; red low ssn; CKE/CCI. "In pleasant surroundings nr attractive vill; poss travellers." 1 Apr-31 Oct. € 19.50 2011*

SIREUIL see Angouleme *7B2*

SURGERES *7A2* (500m S Urban) *46.10180, -0.75376* **Camping La Gères, 10 Rue de la Gères, 17700 Surgères [05 46 07 79 97 or 06 64 03 89 32 (mob); fax 05 46 27 16 78; contact@campingdelageres.com; www.campingdelageres.com]** Site sp in Surgères, on banks of Rv Gères, & fr Surgères by-pass. Sm, mkd pitch, pt shd; wc (cont); mv service pnt; shwrs; el pnts (6A) €3.50; Indtte (inc dryer); shop 300m; rest, snacks & bar 800m; pool & tennis 800m; dogs €1.50; phone; poss cr; ccard acc; CKE/CCI. "Adj to park; m'vans extra charge; poss travellers; NH only." 1 Apr-30 Sep. € 16.50 2009*

SURIS *7B3* (1km N Rural) *45.85925, 0.63739* **Camping La Blanchie, 16270 Suris [tel/fax 05 45 89 33 19 or 06 35 43 21 39 (mob); contact@lablanchie.co.uk; www.lablanchie.co.uk]** Fr N141 halfway bet Angoulême & Limoges take D52 S at La Péruse to Suris; in 3km turn E up a narr lane to site. Sm, some hdstg, pt sl, pt shd; wc; chem disp; shwrs inc; el pnts (10A) €4; bbq; lake/rv sw & sand beach 2.5km; tennis, golf, Futuroscope nrby; wifi; some statics; dogs; c'van storage; twin axles; Eng spkn; adv bkg; quiet; red long stay; CKE/CCI. "Welcoming, friendly British owners; clean site in lovely area; ltd facs; gd touring base; poor." ♦ ltd 1 Apr-30 Sep. € 20.40 2014*

TREMBLADE, LA *7B1* (3km W Rural) *45.75849, -1.17420* **Camping Le Pacha, Rue Bouffard, 17390 La Tremblade [05 46 36 14 44 or 06 16 38 45 46]** Sp fr D25 bypass around La Tremblade. Med, shd; wc; shwrs inc; el pnts (10A); tradsmn; snacks; bar; playgrnd; pool; beach 5km; entmnt; TV; some statics; dogs; quiet. "Peaceful site amongst pine trees; san facs old, could be cleaner (2009); Viaduct de la Seudre 3km." Easter-15 Oct. € 22.00 2009*

VAUX SUR MER see St Palais sur Mer *7B1*

VILLEFAGNAN see Ruffec *7A2*

VIVONNE *7A2* (500m E Rural) *46.42511, 0.26409* **Camp Municipal, Chemin de Prairie, 86370 Vivonne [05 49 43 25 95 or 05 49 43 41 05 (Mairie); fax 05 49 43 34 87; vivonne@cg86.fr]** Exit N10 where it by-passes Vivonne & ent town. Site in municipal park to E of town. Med, pt shd; wc; shwrs €2; el pnts (10A) €2.35; Indtte; playgrnd; noise fr rlwy, quieter w/end. "Welcoming, helpful resident warden; clean facs; sh walk to town cent; worth a visit; as gd as ever; ideal NH." ♦ May-Sep. € 17.00 2014*

VIVONNE *7A2* (5km E Rural) *46.42640, 0.33154* **Club Soleil de Poitiers, Domain Bois de la Pardière (Naturist), Route d'Aslonnes, 86370 Château-Larcher [05 49 43 56 02; la-pardiere@laposte.net; http://assoc.wanadoo.fr/club.soleil.poitiers]** Exit N10 at Vivonne onto D742 to Château-Larcher; turn L onto D88; site on R in 1.2km. Sm, mkd pitch, pt shd; wc; chem disp; shwrs; el pnts €3.40; Indry rm; shops 2km; BBQ; pool; games rm; dogs free; Eng spkn; adv bkg; quiet. "Simple site; friendly welcome; gd clean san facs; gd touring base or NH; excel." 26 Jun-30 Sep. € 13.70 2011*

VOUILLE *4H1* (450m NW Urban) *46.63968, 0.16488* **Camp Municipal, Chemin de la Piscine; 86190 Vouillé [05 49 51 90 10 (after 1800) or 05 49 54 20 30 (Mairie); fax 05 49 51 14 47; vouille@cg86.fr; www.tourisme-vienne.com]** Fr Parthenay take N149 twds Vouillé; go thro Vouillé & turn R onto D43 by Super U. At bottom of hill turn R twds town cent; site sp behind Cheval Blanc rest nr rvside. Sm, mkd pitch, shd; wc; chem disp (wc); shwrs inc; el pnts (3A); Indry rm; shop; supmkt 1km; rest 500m; bar; playgrnd adj; fishing; dogs; quiet. "Site yourself; useful NH; ideal Futuroscope." ♦ 1 May-30 Aug. € 10.00 2011*

Provence

Regional Introduction

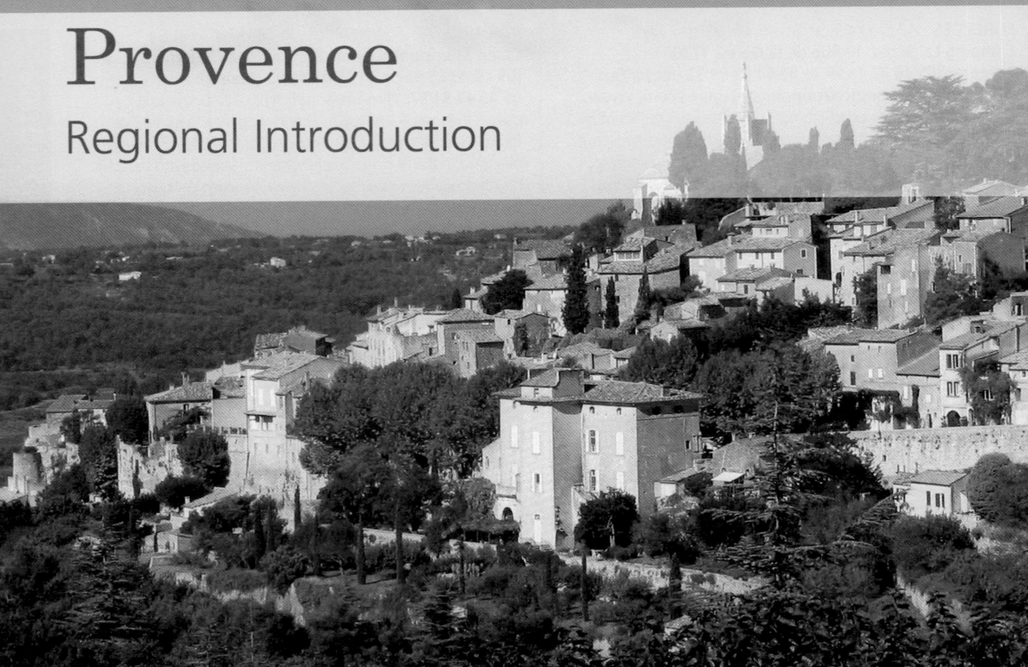

Bonnieux hillside village

Welcome to Provence

Rich in historic and cultural heritage, Provence is a mix of stunning landscapes, festivals, food markets and beautiful architecture.

As well as offering a relaxed atmosphere, this region is full of authentic and ancient customs that are still celebrated and shared with visitors today.

There are plenty of photo opportunities as you explore the sleepy hilltop villages, such as Bonnieux, and stroll through the quaint towns of Provence. You can't help but become immersed in the history and serene lifestyle of this region.

Local highlights

The use of olive oil, herbs and fresh catches from the sea dominate local cuisine and lamb from the area, most notably from Sisteron, is regarded as having a particular taste and quality.

Provence is the oldest winegrowing region in France, famous for its sunshine and its rosé. The best way to understand what makes the wine so distinctive is to meet some of the winemakers at their estates on the Provence Wine Route – they will happily show their produce.

Major towns and cities

- Aix en Provence – a town of authentic Provençal houses and historical sites.
- Toulon – picturesque old city of ancient fountains and daily markets.
- Marseilles – a cosmopolitan capital with a charming old port.
- Briançon – a city renowned for its health in the heart of the southern Alps.

Regional attractions

- Les-Baux-de-Provence – perched on a rocky outcrop, this village is carved into the stone.
- Gorges du Verdon – offers stunning views and lots of activities in which to get involved .
- Calanque du Sugiton – great for hiking with breathtaking views of the Mediterranean.
- St Paul de Mausolee – a historical asylum in Saint-Rémy-de-Provence where Van Gogh was treated and painted 200 pieces of artwork.

Find out more

www.visitprovence.com

Tel: (0)4 94 18 53 00 Toulon Tourist Office
Tel: (0)4 92 21 08 50 Briançon Tourist Office

AGAY See also site listed under St Raphaël.

AGAY *10F4* (4km E Coastal) *43.43740, 6.89165* **Camping Azur Rivage, Blvd Eugène Brieux, 83530 Anthéor [04 94 44 83 12; fax 04 94 44 84 39; info@camping-azur-rivage.com; www.camping-azur-rivage.com]** On D559 heading NE dir Cannes pass Agay. Opp sandy cove at Anthéor, turn L under viaduct. Med, shd; wc (mainly cont); chem disp; mv service pnt; shwrs; el pnts (6A) €5; gas; Indtte (inc dryer); shop; rest, snacks; bar; cooking facs; BBQ; playgrnd; pool; paddling pool; dir access to sand beach across rd; fishing; wifi; some statics; dogs €2; poss cr; adv bkg; some rlwy noise; red low ssn. "Virtually under rlwy viaduct but excel, v clean site; pitches sm." ♦ 1 Apr-30 Sep. € 40.00 (4 persons) 2009*

AGAY *10F4* (1.5km S Coastal) *43.41995, 6.85696* **Royal Camping, Plage de Camp-Long, 83530 Agay [tel/fax 04 94 82 00 20; contact@royalcamping.net; www.royalcamping.net]** On D559 twd St Raphaël. Turn at sp Tiki Plage & site. Stop in ent rd at recep bef ent site. Sm, mkd pitch, hdstg, pt shd; wc; chem disp; shwrs inc; el pnts (6A) €3.50; gas; Indtte; shops; tradsmn; rest, snacks, bar 300m; sand beach adj; wifi; some statics; dogs; phone; bus 200m; poss cr; Eng spkn; adv bkg; quiet but some rd/rlwy noise; CKE/CCI. "Gd walks; some pitches adj to beach in sep area; vg." ♦ ltd 7 Feb-10 Nov. € 29.00 2009*

AGAY *10F4* (2km W Coastal) *43.41787, 6.84828* **Campéole Camping Le Dramont, 986 Blvd de la 36ème Division du Texas, 83530 Agay [04 94 82 07 68; fax 04 94 82 75 30; dramont@campeole.com; www.camping-mer.com / www.campeole.com]** W fr Agay on D559 (D1098) dir St Raphaël; site on L in 1.8km. Or E fr St Raphaël on D559; site on R in 7km. Lge, mkd pitch, hdstg, pt sl, pt shd; wc; chem disp; mv service pnt; baby facs; shwrs inc; el pnts €4.10; gas adj; Indtte (inc dryer); shop; rest, snacks & bar adj; playgrnd; shgl beach adj; scuba diving adj; games area; games rm; wifi; entmnt; 50% statics; dogs €3.90; phone; bus adj; poss cr; Eng spkn; ccard acc; red low ssn. "Walking fr site; great discovery on cr coast; gd." ♦ 20 Mar-10 Oct. € 39.00 2009*

AGAY *10F4* (600m NW Coastal) *43.43376, 6.85245* **Camping des Rives de l'Agay, Ave de Gratadis, 83530 Agay [04 94 82 02 74; fax 04 94 82 74 14; reception@lesrivesdelagay.fr; www.lesrivesdelagay.fr]** Fr Agay take D100 dir Valescure, site in 400m on L. NB Dangerous bend & steep ent. Med, hdg/mkd pitch, shd; htd wc; chem disp; baby facs; shwrs inc; el pnts (6A) €3.60; gas; Indtte; shop; rest, snacks; bar; htd pool; paddling pool; sand beach 500m; entmnt; some statics; dogs €3; poss cr; Eng spkn; adv bkg; poss noisy; CKE/CCI. "San facs & pool v clean; gd pool with shd; excel site." ♦ 11 Mar-2 Nov. € 28.00 (3 persons) 2013*

AGAY *10F4* (5km NW Rural) *43.45408, 6.83254* **Esterel Caravaning, Ave des Golfs, 83530 Agay/St Raphaël [04 94 82 03 28; fax 04 94 82 87 37; contact@esterel-caravaning.fr; www.esterel-caravaning.fr]** Fr A8 foll sps for St Raphaël & immed foll sp 'Agay (par l'interieur)/Valescure' into D100/Ave des Golfs, approx 6km long. Pass golf courses & at end of rd turn L at rndabt twds Agay. Site ent immed after a L hand bend. Lge, hdg/mkd pitch, hdstg, terr, pt sl, pt shd; htd wc; chem disp; mv service pnt; shwrs inc; baby facs; individual san facs to some pitches (extra charge); el pnts (10A) inc (poss rev pol); gas; Indtte; shop; rest, snacks; bar; no BBQ; playgrnd; htd, covrd pools inc padding pool; waterslide; sand beach 3km; lake sw 20km; 8 local golf clubs; tennis; squash; cycle hire; archery; games rm; entmnt; undergrnd disco; wifi; TV rm; 50% statics; dogs €4; twin-axles acc (rec check in adv); poss cr; Eng spkn; adv bkg; ccard acc; red low ssn/long stay; CKE/CCI. "Superbly situated, busy site adj Esterel forest; friendly, helpful staff; gd san facs; gd for families - excel leisure activities; excel rest & shop; now classified as a 5 star site; conv Gorges du Verdon, Massif de l'Estérel, Monaco, Cannes & St Tropez; min stay 1 week high ssn (Sun to Sun); various pitch prices; ltd lge pitches avail; some pitches v sl & poss diff; ltd facs low ssn; mkt Wed; excel." ♦ 5 Apr-27 Sep. € 49.00 SBS - C21 2011*

See advert on next page

AIGUILLES *9D4* (1km NE Rural) *44.78783, 6.88849* **Camp Municipal Le Gouret, 05470 Aiguilles-en-Queyras [04 92 46 74 61 or 04 92 46 70 34; fax 04 92 46 79 05; www.aiguilles.com]** Fr Aiguilles on D947 dir Abriès, sp to site on R across rv bdge. Lge, shd; wc; chem disp; mv service pnt; baby facs; shwrs inc; el pnts (3-10A) €2.20-3.20; Indtte; shop, rest, snacks, bar 700m; BBQ; playgrnd; games area; some statics; dogs €1; phone; bus 100m; quiet. "Site on bank of Rv Guil; random pitching in lge area of larch forest; excel cent for Queyras National Park; vg." 1 Jun-15 Sep. € 11.80 2013*

AIX EN PROVENCE *10F3* (9km E Rural) *43.51771, 5.54128* **FFCC Camping Ste Victoire, Quartier La Paradou, 13100 Beaurecueil [04 42 66 91 31; fax 04 42 66 96 43; campingvictoire@orange.fr; www.campingsaintevictoire.com]** Exit A8/E80 junc 32 onto D7n dir Aix, then R onto D58 & foll sp for 3km. Sm, hdg/mkd pitch, hdstg, shd; htd wc (some cont); chem disp; mv service pnt; baby facs; shwrs inc; el pnts (6A) €3.40 (some rev pol & poss no neutral); Indtte; shop 3km; tradsmn; playgrnd; pool 9km; rv 1km; archery; cycle hire; wifi; TV; dogs €1.10; phone; bus; adv bkg; quiet, some rd noise; red low ssn/long stay; no ccard acc; CKE/CCI. "Well-run site in attractive hilly, wooded area; friendly, helpful owners; clean, basic, dated san facs, ltd low ssn; various pitch sizes; lge o'fits poss diff manoeuvring; some pitches too soft for lge o'fits when wet; no twin axles; no lighting at night; gd walking & climbing." ♦ 3 Feb-14 Nov. € 29.00 2014*

AIX EN PROVENCE *10F3* (2.5km SE Urban) *43.51250, 5.47196* **Camping L'Arc-en-Ciel, 45 Ave Henri Malacrida, Pont des 3 Sautets, 13100 Aix-en-Provence [04 42 26 14 28; camping-arcenciel@neuf.fr; www.campingarcenciel.com]** Fr E or W exit A8 at junc 31 for D7n dir SE; (turn N for 300m to 1st rndabt where turn R; in 200m at 2nd rndabt turn R again onto D7n dir SE); pass under m'way; site ent immed on R; sp. Take care at ent. NB Access easier if go past site for 1km to rndabt, turn round & app fr S. Sm, hdg/mkd pitch, terr, shd; htd wc; chem disp; shwrs inc; el pnts (6A) €3.60 (poss rev pol); gas; Indtte; shops nr; tradsmn; rest, snacks, bar 100m; BBQ; playgrnd; lge pool; fishing; canoeing; games area; golf 1km; TV; dogs; phone; bus adj; Eng library; poss cr; Eng spkn; adv bkg; m'way noise not too intrusive; ccard not acc; CKE/CCI. "Delightful, well-kept, well-run site; friendly, helpful owner; some pitches sm; some steep site rds, tow avail; gd clean facs; superb pool; if recep clsd use intercom in door; gd dog walk adj; bus to Marseille; conv NH nr a'route; highly rec." 1 Apr-30 Sep. € 24.00 2013*

"There aren't many sites open at this time of year"

If you're travelling outside peak season remember to call ahead to check site opening dates – even if the entry says 'open all year'.

⊞ **AIX EN PROVENCE** *10F3* (3km SE Urban) *43.51556, 5.47431* **Airotel Camping Chantecler, Val-St André, 13100 Aix-en-Provence [04 42 26 12 98; fax 04 42 27 33 53; info@campingchantecler.com; www.campingchantecler.com]** Fr town inner ring rd foll sps Nice-Toulon, after 1km look for sp Chantecler to L of dual c'way. Foll camp sp past blocks of flats. Well sp in Val-St André. If on A8 exit at junc 31 sp Val-St André; R at rndabt; R at Rndabt; L at 2nd traff lts onto Ave Andre Magnan; R ar rndabt; site sp. If app fr SE on D7n turn R immed after passing under A8. Lge, hdg pitch, hdstg, sl, pt terr, pt shd; htd wc; chem disp; mv service pnt; shwrs inc; el pnts (5A) €4.10 (long lead poss req); gas; Indtte; shop; tradsmn; rest in ssn; snacks; bar; BBQ (gas/elec); playgrnd; pool; entmnt; TV; dogs €3.60; bus; poss cr; adv bkg; some rd noise; ccard acc; site clsd 1 & 2 Jan; red long stay/low ssn; CKE/CCI. "Lovely, well-kept, wooded site; facs ltd low ssn; some site rds steep - gd power/weight ratio rec; access poss diff some pitches; rec request low level pitch & walk to pitch bef driving to it; ent narr; recep clsd 12.30-13.30; gd pool; conv city; vg touring base; access diff to some pitches, refurb san facs now htd & excel (2014)." ♦ € 36.00 2014*

ANNOT *10E4* (1km N Rural) *43.97195, 6.65777* **Camping La Ribière, Route de Fugeret, 04240 Annot [04 92 83 21 44; info@la-ribiere.com; www.la-ribiere.com]** On N202 exit at Les Scaffarels to Annot on D908. Site 1km beyond vill on L bank of rv. Med, mkd pitch, some hdstg, pt shd; htd wc (some cont); chem disp; shwrs €0.80; el pnts (10A) €3.40; Indtte; shops 1km; rest, snacks; bar; playgrnd; fishing; games rm; wifi; 30% statics; dogs €1; adv bkg; quiet. "Interesting medieval vills & gorges." 27 Feb-24 Oct. € 13.00 2010*

APT *10E3* (9km N Rural) *43.92050, 5.34120* **Domaine des Chenes Blancs, Route de Gargas, 84490 St Saturnin-lès-Apt [04 90 74 09 20 or 06 63 90 37 66; contact@leschenesblancs.com; www.vaucluse-camping.com]** Fr W on D900 twd Apt, at NW o'skts of Apt turn N on D101, cont approx 2km turn R on D83 into Gargas; thro Gargas & in 4km turn L at camp sp; site on R in 300m. Narr rd. Lge, hdg pitch, shd; wc; mv service pnt; shwrs inc; el pnts (6A) inc; Indtte; shop; tradsmn; rest, snacks; bar; BBQ; playgrnd; htd pool; paddling pool; lake fishing 5km; games area; entmnt; TV rm; dogs €4; poss cr; Eng spkn; adv bkg rec; quiet; red low ssn; ccard acc. "Well-run, popular site in gd location; pitches amongst oaks poss diff lge o'fits; steel pegs req due stony grnd; friendly staff; vg, modern san facs; nice pool; excel touring base; lots of facs." ♦ 1 Apr-31 Oct. € 43.55 (CChq acc) 2014*

APT *10E3* (500m NE Urban) *43.87753, 5.40302* **Camp Municipal Les Cèdres, 63 Impasse de la Fantaisie, 84400 Apt [tel/fax 04 90 74 14 61 / 04 90 74 14 61 (mob); lucie.bouillet@yahoo.fr; www.camping-les-cedres.fr]** In town turn N off D900 onto D22 twd Rustrel, site sp. Site on R in 200m immed after going under old rlwy bdge. Med, mkd pitch, pt shd; htd wc (some cont); chem disp; mv service pnt; shwrs inc; el pnts (6-10A) €3.50; gas; Indtte; shop & snacks (high ssn); cooking facs; playgrnd; entmnt; wifi; dogs €1; poss cr; adv bkg; ccard acc; CKE/CCI. "Excel site in lovely location; sm pitches; pitching poss haphazard low ssn; friendly staff; clean san facs; some pitches muddy when wet; cycle tracks; conv Luberon vills & ochre mines; phone ahead to check open low ssn; v lge mkt Sat; gd NH; site in 2 parts; popular; gd touring cent; Saturday mkt." ♦ 15 Feb-15 Nov. € 17.85 2014*

APT *10E3* (2km SE Rural) *43.86636, 5.41275* **Camping Le Luberon, Route de Saignon, 84400 Apt [04 90 04 85 40; fax 04 90 74 12 19; leluberon@wanadoo.fr; www.camping-le-luberon.com]** Exit Apt by D48 sp Saignon & site on R in 2km. Sharp turn into site. Med, mkd pitch, pt sl, pt shd; wc; chem disp; baby facs; shwrs inc; el pnts (6A) €4.50; gas; Indtte; shops 2km; tradsmn; rest, snacks; bar; BBQ; playgrnd; pool; fishing, sailing 3km; TV; 20% statics; dogs €3.50; phone; poss cr; Eng spkn; adv bkg; quiet; ccard acc; red low ssn; CKE/CCI. "Pitches well laid-out in woodland; well-run, clean site; helpful owners; poss not suitable teenagers; gd." ♦ ltd 3 Apr-25 Sep. € 20.00 2009*

ARGENTIERE LA BESSEE, L' *9C3* (2.5km S Rural) *44.77775, 6.55798* **Camp Municipal Les Ecrins, 05120 L'Argentière-la-Bessée [04 92 23 03 38; fax 04 92 23 09 89; contact@camping-les-ecrins.com; www.camping-les-ecrins.com]** Fr L'Argentière on N94, turn R onto D104, site sp. Med, some mkd pitch, pt shd, htd wc (some cont); shwrs inc; el pnts (10A) €2.40; Indtte; shop; snacks; playgrnd; pool, tennis 300m; games area; dogs €2.10; phone; adv bkg; rd/rlwy noise. "Mountain scenery." ♦ 20 Apr-15 Sep. € 14.20 2013*

⊞ **ARGENTIERE LA BESSEE, L'** *9C3* (5km S Rural) *44.75765, 6.57995* **FFCC Camping Le Verger, 05310 La Roche-de-Rame [tel/fax 04 92 20 92 23; info@campingleverger.com; www.campingleverger.com]** S fr Briançon on N94; site 500m L of rd bef vill; sp. Sm, hdg pitch, terr, shd; wc; chem disp; mv service pnt; shwrs inc; el pnts (3-10A) €2.10-3.60; Indtte; shop 5km; rest, snacks, bar 1km; lake sw 1km; TV; 25% statics; dogs free; phone; bus 5km; Eng spkn; adv bkg; quiet; red low ssn. "Grass pitches in orchard; excel, well-maintained facs; excel." € 15.50 2010*

ARGENTIERE LA BESSEE, L' *9C3* (4km NW Rural) *44.82455, 6.52575* **Campéole Camping Le Courounba, Le Village, 05120 Les Vigneaux [04 92 23 02 09; fax 04 92 23 04 69; courounba@campeole.com; www.camping-courounba.com / www.campeole.com]** Take N94 S fr Briançon to L'Argentiere-la-Bessée, turn R onto D994E dir Vallouise. Site on L over rv bdge. Lge, hdstg, pt shd; htd wc; chem disp; mv service pnt; baby facs; shwrs inc; el pnts (6A) €4.10 (poss long lead req); Indtte (inc dryer); shop 500m; tradsmn; rest, snacks; bar; BBQ; playgrnd; htd pool; paddling pool; waterslide; fishing; tennis; cycle hire; horseriding nr; wifi; entmnt; TV; 20% statics; dogs; phone; Eng spkn; adv bkg; quiet; ccard acc; red low ssn; CKE/CCI. "Gd site, beautifully situated in woods by rv in mountains; gd clean san facs; no site lighting." ♦ 16 May-23 Sep. € 39.60 2013*

ARGENTIERE LA BESSEE, L' *9C3* (8km NW Rural) *44.84354, 6.48989* **Camping Indigo Vallouise (formerly Les Chambonnettes), 05290 Vallouise [04 92 23 30 26 or 06 82 23 65 09 (mob); fax 04 92 22 34 03; vallouise@camping-indigo.com; www.camping-indigo.com]** Take N94 Briançon-Gap, on N o'skts of L'Argentière-la-Bessée take D994 W dir Vallouise. In cent of Vallouise turn L over bdge & immed L, site in 200m on rvside. Med, mkd pitch, pt sl, pt shd; htd wc; chem disp; mv service pnt; shwrs inc; el pnts (10A) €5.30; Indtte (inc dryer); shops 200m; tradsmn, rest 300m, snacks, bar 500m; BBQ; playgrnd; pool 3km; tennis; games rm; games area; internet; wifi; TV; 25% statics; dogs €1.80; phone; twin axles; poss cr; Eng spkn; adv bkg; quiet; red low ssn; ccard acc; CKE/CCI. "Mountain scenery; gd facs; gd cent for walking, skiing, canoeing; white-water rafting at nrby rv; interesting vill; gd." ♦ ltd 1 Jun-15 Sep. € 32.00 2014*

ARLES *10E2* (8km NE Rural) *43.72336, 4.71861* **Camp Municipal des Pins, Rue Michelet, 13990 Fontvieille [04 90 54 78 69; fax 04 90 54 81 25; campingmunicipal.lespins@wanadoo.fr; www.fontvieille-provence.com]** Take D570 fr Arles to Avignon; in 2km turn R on D17 to Fontvieille; at far end of vill turn R & foll sp. Med, pt sl, shd; wc; chem disp; shwrs inc; el pnts (6A) €3; gas fr Shell g'ge in vill; Indtte; shops 1km; playgrnd; pool 500m high ssn; tennis in vill; TV rm; dogs €1.50; bus; poss cr; Eng spkn; adv bkg; red long stay: CKE/CCI. "Delightful, quiet site in pines; friendly staff; vg facs; 15-20 mins walk to lively vill; quiet forest walks; tight access/exit long o'fits; site closes last Sunday in Sep; mosquitoes!" Easter-30 Sep. € 13.00 2014*

ARLES *10E2* (7km E Rural) *43.64799, 4.70625* **Camping La Bienheureuse, 13280 Raphèle-les-Arles [04 90 98 48 06; fax 04 90 98 37 62; contact@labienheureuse.com; www.labienheureuse.com]** Fr Arles E on D453, site on L 5km after Pont-de-Crau. W fr Salon-de-Provence on A54/N113; exit N113 junc 12 onto N1435 to St Martin-de-Crau; cont past St Martin-de-Crau on N1435; in 2km rd becomes D435 to Raphèle-les-Arles; site on R 900m after Raphèle-les-Arles. Med, hdg pitch, pt shd; wc; chem disp; shwrs inc; el pnts (10A); Indtte; snacks; bar; playgrnd; pool; paddling pool; horseriding nr; entmnt; wifi; 50% statics; dogs €2.50; phone; bus adj; twin-axles acc; Eng spkn; adv bkg; quiet; CKE/CCI. "Pleasant site; obliging British owners; 700m to shops/bar in vill; gd facs; gd dog walk along nrby lanes and canal." ♦ 1 Mar-31 Oct. € 20.00 2014*

ARLES *10E2* (2km SE Urban) *43.66981, 4.64422* **Camping Le City, 67 Route de la Crau, 13200 Arles [04 90 93 08 86 / 06 13 46 28 22 (mob); contact@camping-city.com; www.camping-city.com]** Fr town cent foll rd to Pont-de-Crau. Site well sp on L in 2km. Or exit N113 at junc 7 sp Arles & Pont de Crau; at rndabt go L alongside arches; site on R in 350m; well sp. Med, mkd pitch, pt shd; wc (some cont); chem disp; mv service pnt; baby facs; shwrs inc; el pnts (5A) €4; gas 1km; Indtte; shop; supmkt 1km; tradsmn; rest, snacks; bar; playgrnd; pool; paddling pool; sand beach 25km; tennis; cycle hire; entmnt; TV; many statics; dogs €2; bus; some Eng spkn; quiet; CKE/CCI. "Vg site; modern, clean san facs - low ssn ltd & poss upstairs; walk to town cent; Roman Amphitheatre well worth seeing." ♦ 1 Mar-30 Sep. € 24.00 2014*

ARLES *10E2* (4km SE Urban) *43.65942, 4.65416* **Camping Les Rosiers, 145 Draille Marseillaise, Pont-de-Crau, 13200 Arles [04 90 96 02 12; fax 04 90 93 36 72; lesrosiers.arles@wanadoo.fr; www.arles-camping-club.com]** Exit Arles E by D453 sp Pont-de-Crau or junc 7 fr N113 dir Raphèle-les-Arles; 200m after exit vill take 1st exit at rndabt then R at Flor Hotel sp on D83E. Site in 50m on R adj hotel. Med, pt shd; htd wc (some cont); mv service pnt; shwrs inc; chem disp; el pnts (6A) €4; Indtte; shop 500m; rest; bar; playgrnd; pool; games area; entmnt; TV; many statics; dogs €1.50; bus fr rndabt; no c'vans/m'vans over 5.50m allowed (but poss not enforced); poss cr; Eng spkn; some rd & rlwy noise; red low ssn. "Many mosquitoes; red facs low ssn; v muddy after rain; visit Les Baux citadel early morning bef coach parties arr; gd birdwatching; poss no site lighting low ssn; conv Arles." 3 Apr-31 Oct. € 17.00 2010*

ARLES *10E2* (14km W Rural) *43.66200, 4.47380* **Camping Caravaning Crin-Blanc, Hameau de Saliers, 13123 Albaron [04 66 87 48 78; fax 04 66 87 18 66; camping-crin.blanc@wanadoo.fr; www.camping-crin-blanc.com]** E fr St Gilles on D572 twd Arles; in 3km turn R onto D37 sp Saliers; site sp. Lge, pt shd; wc (some cont); chem disp; mv service pnt; baby facs; shwrs; el pnts (10A) inc; gas; Indtte (inc dryer); shop; tradsmn; rest, snacks; bar; BBQ; playgrnd; htd pool; paddling pool; tennis; horseriding; wifi; 70% statics; dogs €2.50; Eng spkn; adv bkg; quiet; red low ssn; ccard acc; CKE/CCI. "Poss muddy; mosquitoes; bird reserve." ♦ 1 Apr-30 Sep. € 24.00 2010*

ASPRES SUR BUECH *9D3* (1km S Rural) *44.51497, 5.74347* **Camping L'Adrech, Route de Sisteron, 05140 Aspres-sur-Buëch [04 92 58 60 45; fax 04 92 58 78 63; ladrech.camping@wanadoo.fr; www.campingladrech.com]** Site on L of D1075 fr Aspres. Med, hdg pitch, hdstg, pt sl, pt shd; wc; chem disp; shwrs; el pnts (6-10A) €4-6.50; gas; Indtte; shop & 1km; tradsmn; snacks; BBQ; playgrnd; fishing; rv/lake 5km; games area; entmnt; 50% statics; dogs €1; phone; poss cr; Eng spkn; adv bkg; quiet; ccard acc; CKE/CCI. "Wooded site; lovely views; lge pitches; helpful, friendly owner; remote location; ltd facs low ssn; useful NH." ♦ 1 Apr-1 Nov. € 10.00 2014*

ASPRES SUR BUECH *9D3* (8km NW Rural) *44.53048, 5.68371* **FFCC Aire Naturelle La Source (Pardoe), 05140 St Pierre-d'Argençon [tel/fax 04 92 58 67 81; info@lasource-hautesalpes.com; www.lasource-hautesalpes.com]** Fr D1075 at Aspres-sur-Buëch turn onto D993 dir Valence to St Pierre-d'Argençon; site sp. Or fr N on D93, cont onto D993 over Col de Cabre; site sp on L bef St Pierre-d'Argençon. Med, mkd pitch, pt sl, pt shd; wc; chem disp; mv service pnt; shwrs inc; el pnts (6/10A) €4; Indtte (inc dryer); tradsmn; rest, snacks; bar; BBQ; games area; wifi; dogs €1.50; twin axles; Eng spkn; adv bkg; quiet; ccard acc; red long stay; CKE/CCI. "Peaceful, well-kept CL-type site in woodland/open field; friendly, helpful British owners; clean san facs; chambre d'hôte on site; highly rec." ♦ ltd 15 Apr-15 Oct. € 13.50 2014*

AUBIGNAN see Carpentras *10E2*

⊞ **AUPS** *10E3* (300m SE Rural) *43.62525, 6.23103* **Camping Les Prés, 181 Route de Tourtour, 83630 Aups [04 94 70 00 93; fax 04 94 70 14 41; lespres.camping@wanadoo.fr; www.campinglespres.com]** Fr cent of Aups on rd to Tourtour, site on R. Rough rd. Med, hdg/mkd pitch, pt shd; htd wc; baby facs; fam bthrm; shwrs inc; el pnts (4-6A) €3.70; gas; Indtte; shop 300m; tradsmn; rest, snacks; bar; playgrnd; pool; entmnt; TV rm; some statics; adv bkg; quiet. "Peaceful, friendly site; recep clsd 1200 to 1500; ent not rec for lge o'fits." € 15.50 2012*

AUPS *10E3* (500m W Rural) *43.62455, 6.21760* **International Camping, Route de Fox-Amphoux, 83630 Aups [04 94 70 06 80; fax 04 94 70 10 51; info@internationalcamping-aups.com; www.internationalcamping-aups.com]** Site on L on D60 nr vill cent. Lge, hdg/mkd pitch, pt shd; wc; chem disp; shwrs inc; el pnts (16A) €5.30; Indtte; shop; tradsmn; snacks & rest high ssn; bar; pool; tennis; games rm; entmnt; many statics (sep area); dogs €1; Eng spkn; rec adv bkg high ssn; quiet; ccard acc; red low ssn. "Vg site in beautiful area; lge pitches; gd rest." 1 Apr-30 Sep. € 19.00 2009*

AUPS *10E3* (1km NW Rural) *43.63631, 6.20793* **Camping St Lazare, Route de Moissac, 83630 Aups [04 94 70 12 86; fax 04 94 70 01 55; camping.caravaning.st-lazare@orange.fr]** NW fr Aups twd Régusse on D9, site sp. Med, hdg/mkd pitch, pt sl, pt shd; wc (some cont); chem disp; baby facs; shwrs inc; el pnts (10A) €4; gas; Indtte; shop 1.5km; snacks; playgrnd; pool; paddling pool; games area; cycle hire; entmnt; 25% statics; dogs €1; phone; TV; 10% statics; adv bkg rec; CKE/CCI. "Excel touring base; poss unkempt low ssn; vg, quiet site." 1 Apr-30 Sep. € 16.00 2009*

AVIGNON *10E2* (4km NE Rural) *43.97651, 4.88475* **Camping du Grand Bois, 1340 Chemin du Grand Bois, Quartier La Tapy, 84130 Le Pontet [04 90 31 37 44; fax 04 90 31 46 53; campinglegrandbois@orange.fr; www.campinglegrandbois.webeasysite.fr]** Exit A7/E714 at junc 23 onto D53 S, Chemin du Pont Blanc. At rndabt turn onto Chemin du Grand Bois, site on R, sp. Med, hdg pitch, pt shd; wc; chem disp; shwrs inc; el pnts (5A) €3; Indtte; shop; hypmkt 3km; tradsmn; rest, snacks; playgrnd; cycle hire; wifi; TV; dogs €2; phone; Eng spkn; adv bkg; quiet; ccard acc; CKE/CCI. "Superb location; plenty of rm; family-run alt to main Avignon sites; ltd facs; helpful staff; insects poss a problem." ♦ 15 May-15 Sep. € 26.00 2009*

AVIGNON *10E2* (8km S Urban) *43.88361, 4.87010* **Camping de la Roquette, 746 Ave Jean Mermoz, 13160 Châteaurenard [04 90 94 46 81; fax 09 72 14 01 53; contact@camping-la-roquette.com; www.camping-la-roquette.com]** Exit A7/D907 Avignon S to Noves; take D28 to Châteaurenard 4km; foll sp to site & Piscine Olympic/Complex Sportiv. Med, hdg/mkd pitch, pt shd; wc; chem disp; some serviced pitches; mv service pnt; baby facs; shwrs inc; el pnts (10A) €4; Indtte; shops 1.5km; tradsmn; rest, snacks; bar; playgrnd; pool; paddling pool; tennis; wif; dogs €2; phone; TV; Eng spkn; adv bkg rec; quiet but rd noise; ccard acc; red low ssn; CKE/CCI. "Gd touring cent; sm pitches; owners friendly, helpful; clean facs; gd walks." ♦ ltd 1 Apr-31 Oct. € 37.00 2013*

"That's changed – Should I let The Club know?"

If you find something on site that's different from the site entry, fill in a report and let us know. See www.caravanclub.co.uk/europereport.

⊞ **AVIGNON** *10E2* (500m NW Urban) *43.95216, 4.79946* **FFCC Camping Bagatelle, 25 allée Antoine Pinay - Ile de la Barthelasse, 84000 Avignon [04 90 86 30 39; fax 04 90 27 16 23; camping.bagatelle@wanadoo.fr; www.campingbagatelle.com]** Exit D907 at Avignon Nord. After passing end of old bdge bear L, then onto new Daladier bdge & take immed R turn over bdge foll sp to Barthelasse & Villeneuve-lès-Avignon. Caution - do not foll Nîmes sp at more southerly bdge (Pont d'Europe). Lge, mkd pitch, pt shd; htd wc; mv service pnt; baby facs; shwrs inc; el pnts (6-10A) €3.50-4.50; gas; Indtte; shop; rest; pool 100m; playgrnd; boating; fishing; tennis 2km; games area; entmnt; dogs €2.40; some traffic noise at night; ccard acc; red low ssn/CKE/CCI. "Busy site on rv bank; sm pitches; helpful staff; facs dated but clean, ltd low ssn & poss stretched high ssn; narr site rds, suggest find pitch bef driving in; if recep unmanned, go to bar or supmkt to check in; free ferry to town; site low lying & poss damp; highly rec." ♦ € 37.05 2014*

PROVENCE

PROVENCE

AVIGNON *10E2* (1km NW Urban) *43.95670, 4.80222* **Camping du Pont d'Avignon, 10 Chemin de la Barthelasse, 84000 Avignon [04 90 80 63 50; fax 04 90 85 22 12; camping.lepontdavignon@orange.fr; www.camping-avignon.com]** Exit A7 junc 23 Avignon Nord dir Avignon Centre (D225) then Villeneuve-les-Avignon. Go round wall & under Pont d'Avignon; then cross rv dir Villeneuve, Ile de la Barthelasse. Turn R onto Ile de la Barthelasse. Lge, hdg/mkd pitch, mostly shd; wc; chem disp; mv service pnt; baby facs; shwrs inc; el pnts (6-10A); gas; Indtte; shop; rest, snacks; bar; BBQ; cooking facs; playgrnd; pool; paddling pool; tennis; games area; games rm; wifi; entmnt; TV; dogs €2.70; phone; car wash; poss cr; Eng spkn; adv bkg ess high ssn; quiet but some rd, rlwy & rv barge noise; ccard acc; red low ssn/long stay; CKE/CCI. "Superb, well-run, busy site; welcoming, helpful staff; lovely pool; gd sized pitches but most with high kerbs; poss flooded low ssn; extra for c'vans over 5.50m; Avignon festival Jul/Aug; best site for Avignon - 20 mins walk or free ferry; rec arr early even low ssn; san facs ltd but recently refurbished (2014)." ♦ 2 Mar - 23 Nov. € 40.20 2014*

BANDOL *10F3* (3km NW Rural) *43.15980, 5.72905* **Camping Le Clos Ste Thérèse, Route de Bandol, 83270 St Cyr-sur-Mer [04 94 32 12 21; fax 04 94 32 29 62; camping@clos-therese.com; www.clos-therese.com]** Fr Bandol take D559 twd St Cyr & Marseilles. Site on R after 3km. Caution - site ent sharp U turn fr rd. Site service rds steep & narr; not suitable lge vans. Med, terr, shd; htd wc; chem disp; shwrs; el pnts (6-10A) €4-5.20; gas; Indtte; supmkt 1km; rest, snacks; bar; playgrnd; 2 pools (1 htd); paddling pool; sand beach 4km; golf, tennis, horseriding nr; entmnt; TV rm; 30% statics; dogs €2.30; adv bkg rec; some daytime rd noise. "Many beaches & beauty spots in area; tractor will site c'vans." ♦ 5 Apr-30 Sep. € 22.50 2013*

BANDOL *10F3* (6km NW Coastal) *43.17236, 5.69641* **Camping Les Baumelles, 1 Roiute de la Madrague, 83270 St Cyr-sur-Mer [04 94 26 21 27; fax 04 94 88 76 13; baumellesloisirs@aol.com; www.campinglesbaumelles.net]** Fr Bandol take coast rd D559 NW to St Cyr. Turn L by statue on rd to La Madrague. Foll this coast rd 1.5km. Site on L at junc of coast rd. V lge, some mkd pitch; pt sl, shd; wc; baby facs; shwrs inc; el pnts (10A) €3.50; gas adj; Indtte; shop; rest, snacks; bar; playgrnd; sand beach adj; golf 2km; entmnt; TV; 60% statics; dogs €2; poss cr; Eng spkn; quiet; ccard not acc. "Great location, even if site below average." ♦ 1 Apr-30 Oct. € 27.00 2011*

BANON *10E3* (1.5km S Rural) *44.02607, 5.63088* **Camping L'Epi Bleu, Les Gravières, 04150 Banon [04 92 73 30 30 or 06 15 61 68 63 (mob); campingepibleu@aol.com; www.campingepibleu.com]** Fr D4100 8km S of Forcalquier turn R onto D5 N thro St Michel-L'Observatoire & Revest twd Banon (approx 25km). Turn L on D51 twds Simiane-la-Rotunde. Site on R in 500m immed bef town, sp at junc. Med, shd; wc; mv service pnt; baby facs; shwrs inc; el pnts (10A) €5; Indtte; shop; rest, snacks; bar; BBQ; playgrnd; htd pool; paddling pool; games area; entmnt; TV; some statics; dogs €3; adv bkg; quiet; red low ssn; CKE/CCI. "Vg, wooded site; pleasant owners; gd walking & cycling tours." ♦ 15 Apr-15 Oct. € 13.50 (CChq acc) 2010*

BARCELONNETTE *9D4* (2km SE Rural) *44.38166, 6.67603* **Camping La Chaup, Route du Sauze, 04400 Enchastrayes [04 92 81 02 82]** Fr D900 at W end of Barcelonnette turn R twds La Sauze & Enchastrayes; site sp. Sm, mkd pitch, sl, unshd; htd wc (some cont); shwrs €1.50; el pnts (6A) €3.90; Indtte; shop & snacks nrby; BBQ; playgrnd; rv & lake 2km; dogs €1; poss cr; adv bkg; quiet; CKE/CCI. "Relaxing site with mountain views; friendly owners." 1 Jun-15 Sep. € 9.70 2010*

⊞ **BARCELONNETTE** *9D4* (1km S Urban) *44.38294, 6.63470* **Camping Le Tampico, 70 Ave Emile Aubert, 04400 Barcelonnette [tel/fax 04 92 81 02 55; le-tampico@wanadoo.fr; www.letampico.fr]** Exit Barcelonnette onto D902 sp Col d'Allos & Col de la Cayolle; site on R in 1.3km. NB Do not app fr Col d'Allos or Col de la Cayolle. Med, mkd pitch, pt shd; htd wc; chem disp; baby facs; fam bthrm; shwrs inc; el pnts (6A) €3.50-6.00; gas; Indtte; ice; tradsmn; rest, snacks; bar; BBQ (gas, charcoal); playgrnd; white water canoeing/rafting; htd pool 2km; games area; TV; 10% statics; dogs €1.50; phone; wifi; bus; poss cr; Eng spkn; adv bkg; quiet; ccard acc; red long stay. "Lovely wooded site; mountain views; friendly owner; walk to town by rv; vg walking & outdoor activities; vg." ♦ ltd € 16.00 2011*

BARCELONNETTE *9D4* (500m W Rural) *44.38393, 6.64281* **Camping du Plan, 52 Ave Emile Aubert, 04400 Barcelonnette [tel/fax 04 92 81 08 11; legaudissart@orange.fr; www.campingduplan.fr]** Exit town on D902 sp Col d'Allos & Col de la Cayolle. Site on R. Sm, mkd pitch, pt shd; wc; shwrs inc; el pnts (3-10A) €2.95-4.25 gas; Indtte; shop; tradsmn; rest; dogs €1; adv bkg; quiet. "Garden site; helpful owners; unisex san facs; lovely views & walks; pleasant vill; excel." 25 May-30 Sep. € 13.00 2013*

BARCELONNETTE *9D4* (6km W Rural) *44.39229, 6.57340* **Camping Le Fontarache, 04580 Les Thuiles [tel/fax 04 92 81 90 42; reception@camping-fontarache.fr; www.camping-fontarache.fr]** Site sp fr D900 on ent Les Thuiles fr Barcelonnette. Lge, mkd pitch, some hdstg, pt shd; wc (some cont); chem disp; mv service pnt; shwrs inc; el pnts (6A) €3.20; Indtte; shop 100m; tradsmn; snacks; BBQ; playgrnd; htd pool; paddling pool; fishing; kayaking; tennis; games area; wifi; entmnt; TV; some statics; dogs €3; poss cr; Eng spkn; adv bkg; quiet. "Pleasant, scenic site." ♦ 1 Jun-5 Sep. € 19.00 2010*

BARCELONNETTE *9D4* (6km W Rural) *44.39686, 6.54605* **Domaine Loisirs de l'Ubaye, Vallée de l'Ubaye, 04340 Barcelonnette [04 92 81 01 96; fax 04 92 81 92 53; info@loisirsubaye.com; www.loisirsubaye.com]** Site on S side of D900. Lge, mkd pitch, terr, shd; wc; shwrs inc; el pnts (6A) €3.50; Indry rm; gas; shop; rest, snacks; bar; playgrnd; htd pool; rv adj; watersports; cycle hire; entmnt; TV rm; statics; dogs €3.50; phone; red low ssn/long stay; CKE/CCI. "Magnificent scenery." ♦ 1 Apr-30 Oct. € 24.00 2013*

BEAUMES DE VENISE see Carpentras *10E2*

BEAURECUEIL see Aix en Provence *10F3*

BEDOIN *10E2* (1.5km NE Rural) *44.13363, 5.18738* **Camping Domaine de Bélézy (Naturist), 84410 Bédoin [04 90 65 60 18; fax 04 90 65 94 45; info@belezy.com; www.belezy.com]** Fr Carpentras D974 to Bédoin. Go thro vill & turn R at rndabt sp Mont Ventoux. In 300m turn L & foll sp to site. Lge, pt sl, shd; htd wc (some cont); chem disp; mv service pnt; sauna; steam rm; baby facs; shwrs inc; el pnts (12A) €5.60; gas; Indtte; shop; rest, snacks; bar; cooking facs; playgrnd; 2 htd pools; paddling pool; tennis; games area; horseriding 2km; golf 20km; wifi; entmnt; TV rm; 20% statics; phone; sep car park high ssn; poss cr; Eng spkn; adv bkg; quiet; ccard acc; red long stay/low ssn; INF card. "Delightful, peaceful, well-kept site in lovely location; warm welcome, helpful staff; extensive facs; many acitivies; some sm & awkward pitches; gd base for Mt Ventoux, Côtes du Rhône; excel; no pets; pitches v close together." ♦ 2 Apr-2 Oct. € 41.00 (3 persons) 2013*

BEDOIN *10E2* (1km W Rural) *44.12468, 5.17249* **Camp Municipal de la Pinède, Chemin des Sablières, 84410 Bédoin [04 90 65 61 03; fax 04 90 65 95 22; la-pinede.camping.municipal@wanadoo.fr]** Take D938 S fr Malaucène for 3km, L onto D19 for 9km to Bédoin. Site adj to vill & sp. Med, sl, terr, shd; htd wc; mv service pnt; shwrs inc; el pnts (10A) inc; Indtte; shops in vill; snacks; playgrnd; pool (high ssn); dogs €1; quiet; ccard not acc; CKE/CCI. "Pool clsd Mon; 5 min walk to vill; mkt Mon." 15 Mar-31 Oct. € 14.70 2010*

BELGENTIER see Cuers *10F3*

BLAUVAC see Carpentras *10E2*

⊞ **BOLLENE** *9D2* (4.2km N Rural) *44.30918, 4.75426* **Camping Le Barry, Quartier St Pierre de Sénos, 84500 Bollène [04 90 30 13 20; fax 04 90 40 48 64; contactvalleedebarry@orange.fr; www.valleedebarry.com]** Exit A7 junc 19 at Bollène onto D26 twd Pierrelatte. Foll sp 'Site Troglodytique'. Sm, shd; own san; chem disp; mv service pnt; el pnts (10A) inc; gas; rest; bar; BBQ (gas/elec); playgrnd; pool; games area; games rm; internet; many statics; Eng spkn; quiet; ccard acc; CKE/CCI. "Mainly superior park homes; ltd facs low ssn; access to pool up steep slope; NH or sh stay only." € 17.00 2010*

⊞ **BOLLENE** *9D2* (5.5km E Rural) *44.29811, 4.78645* **FFCC Camping et Centre Equestre La Simioune, Quartier Guffiage, 84500 Bollène [04 90 30 44 62; fax 04 90 30 44 77; la-simioune@wanadoo.fr; www.la-simioune.fr]** Exit A7 junc 19 onto D994/D8 dir Carpentras (Ave Salvatore Allende D8). At 3rd x-rd turn L into Ave Alphonse Daudet dir Lambique & foll rd 3km to sp for camping on L, then site 1km. Sm, pt sl, shd; wc; chem disp; baby facs; shwrs €1; el pnts (6A) €3; Indtte; shops & supmkt 4km; tradsmn; rest; bar; BBQ; playgrnd; pool; paddling pool; horseriding; entmnt; 10% statics; dogs €2; adv bkg rec high ssn; quiet; redCKE/CCI. "In pine forest; facs ltd in winter; pony club for children & adults; NH only." € 14.00 2011*

BOLLENE *9D2* (6km SW Rural) *44.24335, 4.72931* **FFCC Camping La Pinède en Provence, Quartier des Massanes, 84430 Mondragon [04 90 40 82 98; fax 09 59 92 16 56; contact@camping-pinede-provence.com; www.camping-pinede-provence.com]** Exit A7 junc 19 dir Bollène & take D26 S, site 1.5km N of Mondragon. Steep access. Med, mkd pitch, pt sl, terr, pt shd; htd wc; chem disp; mv service pnt; baby facs; shwrs inc; el pnts (8-13A) €4.40-4.85; Indtte; shop; BBQ; playgrnd; pool; some statics; dogs €2; adv bkg; quiet; red low ssn; CKE/CCI. "Gd, clean site; gd touring base; conv Ardèche Gorge." 14 Feb-14 Nov. € 20.00 2013*

BONNIEUX *10E2* (1km W Rural) *43.81893, 5.31170* **Camp Municipal du Vallon, Route de Ménerbes, 84480 Bonnieux [tel/fax 04 90 75 86 14 / 06 48 08 46 79 (mob); campingvallon@wanadoo.fr]** Fr Bonnieux take D3 twd Ménerbes, site sp on L on leaving vill. Med, mkd pitch, terr, pt shd; wc (some cont); chem disp; shwrs inc; el pnts (10A) €3.80; Indtte; shop; tradsmn; snacks; bar; playgrnd; wifi; dogs €2; some Eng spkn; quiet; red low ssn; CKE/CCI. "Beautiful, quaint, 'olde worlde' site in wooded area; friendly warden; basic facs but clean; gd walking & mountain biking; attractive hilltop vill; gd touring base; gd rest in walking dist." 15 Mar-15 Oct. € 19.00 2013*

BORMES LES MIMOSAS see Lavandou, Le *10F3*

BRIANCON *9C4* (5km NE Rural) *44.93905, 6.68323* **Camp Municipal l'Iscle du Rosier, Le Rosier, 05100 Val-des-Prés [04 92 21 06 01; fax 04 92 21 46 46]** Fr Briançon on N94 E & take 3rd L after leaving Briançon (5km) sp Le Rosier. Foll rd thro until Le Rosier, site on L after bdge. Med, pt shd; wc (some cont); chem disp; shwrs inc; el pnts (5-10A) €3.50-5.20; gas; Indtte; shop; snacks; bar; BBQ; playgrnd; 5% statics; dogs €1.70; phone; bus adj; Eng spkn; quiet. "Nice, well-kept site by rv; friendy, helpful staff; superb walking, cycling & climbing nrby; conv Col de Montgenèvre rd; gd bus service." ♦ 15 Jun-15 Sep. € 10.00 2011*

⊞ **BRIANCON** *9C4* (6km NE Rural) *44.93034, 6.68169* **Camp Municipal du Bois des Alberts, 05100 Montgenèvre [04 92 21 16 11 or 04 92 21 52 52; fax 04 92 21 98 15; www.montgenevre.com]** Take N94 fr Briançon sp Italie. In 4km turn L onto D994, site 200m past Les Alberts vill on L. Lge, hdstg, shd; htd wc (some cont); chem disp; mv service pnt; baby facs; shwrs inc; el pnts (6-10A) €4.25 (rev pol); Indtte; shop; tradsmn; rest, snacks, bar high ssn; playgrnd; fishing; kayak tuition; tennis; games area; cycle & walking paths; fishing; x-country skiing; 30% statics; adv bkg; quiet; ccard acc; CKE/CCI. "Pleasant, friendly site in pine trees; random pitching; facs dated but clean, ltd low ssn; lge pine cones can fall fr trees - park away fr tall ones; gd touring base; nice site." ♦ € 13.00 2013*

BRIANCON *9C4* (3.8km SW Rural) *44.87737, 6.61634* **Camping Les Cinq Vallées, St Blaise, 05100 Briançon [04 92 21 06 27; fax 04 92 20 41 69; infos@camping5vallees.com; www.camping5vallees.com]** S of Briançon by N94 to vill St Blaise. Ent on L. Med, pt sl, pt shd; wc; chem disp; mv service pnt; baby facs, shwrs inc; el pnts (10A) inc; Indtte; rest; shop; snacks; bar; playgrnd; htd pool; games rm; TV rm; many statics; some noise fr by-pass. "Vg site, free bus pass fr office." ♦ 1 Jun-30 Sep. € 21.20 2014*

PROVENCE

BRIGNOLES *10F3* (1km E Rural) *43.40573, 6.07885* **Camp Municipal, 786 Route du Lac, 83170 Brignoles [tel/fax 04 94 69 20 10; campingbrignoles@aol.com]** Exit A8 junc 35 onto D554/D N7 E dir Le Luc/Nice/Fréjus; turn R at rndabt by Intermarché supmkt dir Centre Ville; site on R in 300m. Or fr E on D N7, at edge of town at Intermarché rndabt cont strt on dir Centre Ville; site on R in 300m. Med, hdg pitch, pt shd; wc; chem disp; shwrs inc; el pnts (10A) €3; gas; lndtte; Aldi supmkt opp; snacks; playgrnd; municipal pool 500m; 10% statics; phone; dogs €1.50; Eng spkn; some rd noise; adv bkg; ccard acc; red low ssn; CKE/CCI. "Well-run site by friendly family; some sm pitches; san facs clean but need update; site tired end ssn (2010); NH." 27 Mar-15 Oct. € 12.80 2010*

BRIGNOLES *10F3* (9km SE Rural) *43.33919, 6.12579* **Camping La Vidaresse, 83136 Ste Anastasie-sur-Issole [04 94 72 21 75; fax 04 98 05 01 21; contact@campinglavidaresse.com; www.campinglavidaresse.com]** On DN7 2km W of Brignoles at rndabt take D43 dir Toulon. In about 10km turn L at rndabt to D15. Do not ent vill, go strt & site is approx 250m on R. Med, hdg/mkd pitch, terr, pt shd; wc (some cont); chem disp; mv service pnt; shwrs inc; el pnts (10A) €5 (poss rev pol); gas; lndtte; shop in vill 1km & 5km; rest high ssn; snacks & bar (all ssn); BBQ (gas/elec only); playgrnd; htd, covrd pool; paddling pool; sand beach 40km; tennis; games area; fishing 200m; wifi; 40% statics; dogs €3; poss cr; adv bkg; ccard acc; red low ssn; CKE/CCI. "Well-managed, family site in lovely area; peaceful; friendly & helpful; facs adequate; excel pool; gd touring base Haute Provence, Gorges du Verdon & Riviera; vineyard adj; gd." ♦ 20 Mar-30 Sep. € 25.00 2014*

BRILLANE, LA *10E3* (3km W Rural) *43.93305, 5.86777* **Camping Le Moulin de Ventre, 04300 Niozelles [04 92 78 63 31 or 06 63 51 53 55 (mob); fax 04 92 79 86 92; moulindeventre@aol.com; www.moulin-de-ventre.com]** Exit A51 junc 19 at La Brillane; turn R onto D4096, then L onto D4100 sp Niozelles & Forcalquier. Site in 3km on L just after bdge, adj Rv Lauzon. Med, hdg/mkd pitch, pt sl, pt shd; htd wc; chem disp; mv service pnt; serviced pitches; baby facs; shwrs inc; el pnts (10A) inc; gas; lndtte (inc dryer); sm shop & 2km; tradsmn; rest, snacks; bar; BBQ (gas); playgrnd; pool; paddling pool; rv beach, fishing, boat hire adj; wifi; entmnt; games/TV rm; 10% statics; dogs €3; twin-axles acc (rec check in adv); phone; Eng spkn; adv bkg; quiet; ccard acc; red low ssn/long stay; CKE/CCI. "Pleasant, peaceful, wooded site by lake & rv; well-run; rvside pitches have drop to rv; excel touring base; lavendar fields in flower Jun/Jul." ♦ 12 Apr-29 Sep. € 34.00 2014*

CABRIERES D'AIGUES see Pertuis *10E3*

CADENET *10E3* (10km NE Rural) *43.76871, 5.44970* **Camping Lou Badareu, La Rasparine, 84160 Cucuron [04 90 77 21 46; fax 04 90 77 27 68; contact@loubadareu.com; www.loubadareu.com]** In Cadenet foll sp for church (église) onto D45 dir Cucuron; S of Cucuron turn onto D27 (do not go into town); site is E 1km. Well sp fr D27. Sm, mkd pitch, pt sl, pt shd; ltd wc (own san rec); chem disp; shwrs inc; el pnts (10A) €4.50 (long lead poss req); lndtte; shop & 1km; tradsmn; playgrnd; pool; few statics; dogs €1.80; phone; quiet; CKE/CCI. "Pretty farm site in cherry orchard; friendly, helpful owner; sep access for high vans." ♦ 1 Apr-15 Oct. € 11.00 2011*

CADENET *10E3* (10km NE Rural) *43.75667, 5.44448* **FFCC Camping Le Moulin à Vent, Chemin de Gastoule, 84160 Cucuron [04 90 77 25 77; fax 04 90 77 28 12; camping_bressier@yahoo.fr; www.le-moulin-a-vent.com]** Fr A51 exit junc 15 to Pertuis. N on D56 fr Pertuis to Cucuron. Site sp S fr Cucuron vill dir Villelaure. Med, hdg/mkd pitch, pt sl, terr, shd; wc (cont); chem disp; mv service point; baby facs; shwrs inc; spa; el pnts inc (6-10A) €3-4; lndry rm; shop; tradsmn; rest, snacks & bar 2km; playgrnd; htd pool 4km; wifi; 10% statics; dogs €2.70; poss cr; Eng spkn; adv bkg; quiet; CKE/CCI. "Spacious pitches, but access poss diff; friendly, helpful staff; no twin-axles; vg." ♦ ltd 1 Apr-15 Oct. € 14.50 2011*

CADENET *10E3* (2km SW Rural) *43.71968, 5.35479* **Camping Val de Durance, Les Routes, 84160 Cadenet [04 90 68 37 75 or 04 42 20 47 25 (LS); fax 04 90 68 16 34; info@homair.com; www.homair.com]** Exit A7 at Cavaillon onto D973 dir Cadenet. In Cadanet take D59, site sp. Lge, hdg pitch, pt shd; wc; chem disp; shwrs inc; el pnts (4-10A) inc (long lead req); gas; lndtte; shop & 2km; rest, snacks; bar; BBQ; playgrnd; pool; paddling pool; rv sw & beach; archery; canoeing; cycling; games area; wifi; entmnt; TV; 70% statics; dogs €5; adv bkg; red low ssn; ccard acc; CKE/CCI. "Dir access to lake; adj Luberon Park; noisy entmnt till late most evenings high ssn." ♦ 06 Apr - 29 Sep. € 32.00 2013*

CANNET DES MAURES, LE *10F3* (4km N Rural) *43.42140, 6.33655* **FFCC Camping Domaine de la Cigalière, Route du Thoronet, 83340 Le Cannet-des-Maures [tel/fax 04 94 73 81 06; campinglacigaliere@wanadoo.fr; www.campings-var.com]** Exit A8 at Le Cannet-des-Maures onto D17 N dir Le Thoronet; site in 4km on R, sp. Med, hdg/mkd pitch, pt sl, hdstg, pt shd; wc; baby facs; chem disp; mv service pnt; shwrs inc; el pnts (6A) €4; lndtte; snacks; bar; BBQ (gas/elec); playgrnd; htd pool; 20% statics; dogs €2; quiet; CKE/CCI. "Peaceful site; lge pitches; St Tropez 44km; vg site." ♦ ltd 1 Apr-30 Sep. € 20.00 2014*

CARCES *10F3* (500m SE Urban) *43.47350, 6.18826* **Camping Les Fouguières, Quartier Les Fouguières, 83570 Carcès [34 94 59 96 28 or 06 74 29 69 02 (mob); fax 34 94 59 96 28; info@camping-les-fouguieres.com; www.camping-les-fouguieres.com]** Exit A8 junc 35 at Brignoles onto D554 to Le Val; then take D562 to Carcès. Site sp off D13. Med, pt shd; wc; mv service pnt; shwrs inc; el pnts (14A) €3; gas; lndtte; snacks; playgrnd; htd pool; Rv Caramy runs thro site; rv sw, fishing & canoeing nrby; wifi; TV; many statics; dogs €2; phone; bus; Eng spkn; quiet; red low ssn. "Pleasant, clean, well-shd site; friendly, helpful owner; interesting, medieval town; Lake Carcès 2km; don't miss Entrecasteaux chateau; mkt Sat; excel." ♦ 6 Feb-26 Nov. € 28.00 2014*

CAROMB see Malaucène *10E2*

CARPENTRAS *10E2* (5km N Rural) *44.09723, 5.03682* **Camping Le Brégoux, Chemin du Vas, 84810 Aubignan [04 90 62 62 50 or 04 90 67 10 13 (LS); camping-lebregoux@wanadoo.fr; www.camping-lebregoux.fr]** Exit Carpentras on D7 sp Bollène. In Aubignan turn R immed after x-ing bdge, 1st R again in approx 250m at Club de Badminton & foll site sp at fork. Lge, hdg/mkd pitch, hdstg, pt shd; wc; chem disp; mv service pnt; baby facs; shwrs inc; el pnts (6-10A) inc (poss long lead req); lndtte; shops, rest, bars etc 1km; BBQ; sm playgrnd; pool 5km in ssn; tennis; go-karting, golf nrby; entmnt; games rm; wifi; TV; 2% statics; dogs €1.90; phone; poss v cr; Eng spkn; adv bkg; poss noisy high ssn; ccard acc; CKE/CCI. "Popular site in beautiful area; lge pitches & gd access; helpful, friendly staff; new unisex san facs, excel; gates clsd 2200-0700; poss flooding in heavy rain; excel walking & cycling nrby; gd value; gd." ♦ ltd 1 Mar-31 Oct. € 14.54 2014*

CARPENTRAS *10E2* (7km N Rural) *44.12246, 5.03437* **Camp Municipal de Roquefiguier, 84190 Beaumes-de-Venise [04 90 62 95 07 or 04 90 62 94 34 (Mairie); camping.roquefiguier@orange.fr; www.beaumes-de-venise.fr]** Leave A7 exit 22, take N7 S then L onto D950 sp Carpentras. At rndabt after Sarrians sp turn L onto D21 to Beaumes-de-Venise. Cross Beaumes & foll site sp. Turn L bef Crédit Agricole to site on R. Med, hdg/mkd pitch, pt sl, terr, pt shd; wc (some cont); chem disp; mv service pnt; baby facs; shwrs inc; el pnts (6A) €3.00; lndtte; BBQ; pool in vill; playgrnd,mini golf; wifi; dogs €1.45; phone; no adv bkg; quiet; ccard acc; CKE/CCI. "Gd site; gd views; facs clean; steel pegs req for pitches; poss diff access lge o'fits; steep access some pitches; gate clsd 1900-0830; 5 mins walk to Beaumes-de-Venise; wine caves adj; mkd walks & cycle ways; conv for Mt Ventoux, Orange & Avignon. MD Tues, excel hot shwrs." ♦ 1 Mar-31 Oct. € 13.65 2014*

CARPENTRAS *10E2* (7km E Rural) *44.08057, 5.11385* **Camping Le Ventoux, 1348 Chemin La Combe, 84380 Mazan [tel/fax 04 90 69 70 94; info@camping-le-ventoux.com; www.camping-le-ventoux.com]** Take D974 twd Bédoin; after 7km turn R at x-rds on D70 sp Mazan. Site on R in 300m. Sm, mkd pitch, pt shd; wc; chem disp; mv service pnt; baby facs; shwrs inc; el pnts (6A) €3.50 (poss rev pol); gas; lndtte (inc dryer); shop (high ssn) & 3km; tradsmn; rest, snacks; bar; BBQ; playgrnd; pool; lake fishing 4km; entmnt; 25% statics; dogs €2.50; phone; poss cr; Eng spkn; adv bkg (ess high ssn); quiet; ccard acc; red low ssn; CKE/CCI. "Busy site, even low ssn - bkg rec; friendly, helpful Dutch owners; excel rest; wine-tasting area; excel." ♦ ltd 1 Mar-1 Nov. € 19.00 2011*

CARPENTRAS *10E2* (12km E Rural) *44.02904, 5.19974* **Camp Municipal Aéria, Le Portail, 84570 Blauvac [tel/fax 04 90 61 81 41 (Mairie)]** E fr Carpentras on D942; E of Mazan fork onto D150. Site 100m N of Blauvac vill cent. Sm, mkd pitch, pt shd; wc (some cont); shwrs; el pnts (10A) €2; shop; rest, snacks; bar; playgrnd. "Superb, quiet site on hilltop with view; basic facs; warden calls am & pm; may be exposed in bad weather." 15 Mar-15 Oct. € 8.00 2009*

CARPENTRAS *10E2* (10km SE Rural) *44.01428, 5.17098* **Camping Font Neuve, Rte de Méthamis, 84570 Malemort-du-Comtat [04 90 69 90 00 or 04 90 69 74 86; fax 04 90 69 91 77; camping.font-neuve@libertysurf.fr; http://camping.font.neuve.free.fr]** Fr Malemort take Méthanis rd D5; as rd starts to rise look for sp on L to site. NB Take care narr app rds. Med, hdg pitch, terr, pt shd; wc (some cont); chem disp; serviced pitches; baby facs; shwrs inc; el pnts (10A) €4.50; lndtte; tradsmn; rest, snacks; bar; playgrnd; pool; tennis; entmnt; TV; some statics; dogs €1.70; adv bkg req high ssn; quiet. "Friendly, family-run site; gd rest; immac san facs." ♦ 1 May-30 Sep. € 16.50 2011*

CARPENTRAS *10E2* (500m S Urban) *44.04379, 5.05363* **FLOWER Camp Lou Comtadou, 881 Ave Pierre de Coubertin, Route de St Didier, 84200 Carpentras [04 90 67 03 16 or 06 09 36 67 56 (mob); fax 04 90 46 01 81; info@campingloucomtadou.com; www.campingloucomtadou.com / www.flowercampings.com]** Exit A7 junc 22 or 23 to Carpentras; foll sp dir St Didier thro one-way system onto D4; in 200m turn L into Ave Pierre de Coubertin. Site sp in 500m. Med, hdg/mkd pitch, hdstg, shd; htd wc; chem disp; baby facs; shwrs inc; el pnts (6A) €3; lndtte; ice; shop; tradsmn; rest, snacks; BBQ; playgrnd; pool; wifi; dogs €3; phone; bus adj; Eng spkn; quiet; ccard acc; red low ssn; CKE/CCI. "Well-kept, clean site; lge pitches; attractive walled town; excel." ♦ 1 Apr-30 Sep. € 19.60 2010*

CARPENTRAS *10E2* (6km S Urban) *43.99917, 5.06591* **Camp Municipal Coucourelle, Ave René Char, 84210 Pernes-les-Fontaines [04 90 66 45 55 or 04 90 61 31 67 (Mairie); fax 04 90 61 32 46; www.perneslesfontaines.fr]** Take D938 fr Carpentras to Pernes-les-Fontaines; then take D28 dir St Didier (Ave René Char pt of D28). Site sp (some sps easily missed). Foll sp sports complex, site at rear of sw pool. Sm, hdg/mkd pitch, shd; wc; chem disp; mv service pnt; shwrs inc; el pnts (10A) €3.50 gas 1km; lndtte; shops & rests 1km; BBQ; playgrnd; pool, sw & fishing 2.5km; tennis adj; dogs €0.50; poss cr; adv bkg; quiet; ccard acc; CKE/CCI. "Pleasant, well-run site; views of Mont Ventoux; most pitches lge but some sm & narr; gd, clean facs; m'vans can park adj to mv point free when site clsd; gates close 1930; no twin-axles; free use of adj pool; attractive old town, easy parking; adv bkg rec low ssn; vg." ♦ 1 Apr-30 Sep. € 12.00 2011*

CARPENTRAS *10E2* (6km S Rural) *44.00611, 5.03861* **Camping Les Fontaines, 125 Chemin de la Chapelette, Route de la Sudre, 84210 Pernes-les-Fontaines [04 90 46 82 55; fax 04 90 63 42 91; campinglesfontaine@gmail.com; www.campingfontaines.fr]** Take D938 S fr Carpentras to Pernes-les-Fontaines. On o'skts of Pernes turn L into Route de la Sudre, site sp in 1km on R, well sp. Med, hdg/mkd pitch, pt shd; wc; chem disp; mv service pnt; baby facs; shwrs inc; el pnts (6A) €4.50; lndtte; shop & 1km; tradsmn; supmkt nr; rest, snacks; bar; BBQ; playgrnd; pool complex; games area; wifi; entmnt; TV rm; 30% statics; dogs €3; Eng spkn; adv bkg; quiet; red low ssn; CKE/CCI. "Vg, newly developed site; clean, modern san facs; friendly, helpful owners; view of Mt Ventoux." ♦ 1 Apr-31 Oct. € 24.00 (CChq acc) 2010*

CARPENTRAS *10E2* (4km SW Rural) *44.0398, 5.0009* **Camp Municipal de Bellerive, 54 Chemin de la Ribière, 84170 Monteux [04 90 66 81 88 or 04 90 66 97 52 (TO); camping. bellerive@orange.fr; www.provenceguide.com]** Site on N edge of Monteux cent, sp off ring rd Monteux N, immed after rlwy x-ing. Sm, hdg/mkd pitch, some hdstg, pt shd; some serviced pitches; wc; chem disp; shwrs inc; el pnts (6-10A) €2.50; Indtte; shops 500m; rest, snacks, bar 500m; playgrnd; pool 4km; some statics; dogs €1; phone; bus; poss cr; quiet, but poss noise fr park adj (music); red long stay; CKE/CCI. "Gd, busy site; rec arr early high ssn; helpful, friendly warden lives adj; gd security; vg, clean, modern san facs; trees a problem for sat TV - choose pitch carefully; park adj gd for children; 5 min walk to vill; poss muddy when wet; poss some workers' statics low ssn; Mistral blows early & late ssn; gd touring base." ♦ 1 Apr-15 Oct. € 13.40 2013*

CARPENTRAS *10E2* (7km NW Urban) *44.07981, 4.97693* **Camp Muncipal de la Sainte Croix, Quartier Ste Croix, 84260 Sarrians [tel/fax 04 90 65 43 72; campingdestecroix@orange.fr; www.camping-sainte-croix.com]** Fr Carpentras on D950 dir Orange; in 7km turn L at rndabt on o'skts of Sarrians onto D221; site in 200m on R. Sm, hdg/mkd pitch, some hdstg, pt shd; wc; chem disp; shwrs inc; el pnts €3.50; Indtte; shop 500m; snacks; bar; BBQ; playgrnd; pool; rv sw 5km; tennis; 20% statics; dogs €2; phone; poss cr; adv bkg; red low ssn; CKE/CCI. "Pleasant site; helpful warden; clean facs; gd touring base." ♦ ltd 30 Mar-31 Oct. € 17.50 2009*

CARQUEIRANNE see Hyères *10F3*

⊞ **CARRY LE ROUET** *10F2* (750m W Coastal) *43.33024, 5.13747* **Camping Lou Souleï, 68-72 Avenue Draïo de la Mar, 13620 Carry-le-Rouet [04 42 44 75 75; fax 04 42 44 57 24; lousoulei@wanadoo.fr; www.lousoulei. com]** Fr Martigues take A55 & exit dir Carry-le-Rouet. Site on beach rd. V lge, hdg/mkd pitch, hdstg, pt shd; htd wc; chem disp; serviced pitch; shwrs inc; el pnts (6A) inc; Indtte; shop adj; rest, snacks; bar; playgrnd; htd pool; beach adj; games rm; games area; entmnt; TV rm; 60% statics; dogs; phone; poss cr; Eng spkn; adv bkg; red low ssn. "Gd base for Marseille, Camargue, Aix, etc; red facs low ssn." € 51.00 (4 persons) 2010*

CASSIS *10F3* (1.5km N Coastal) *43.22417, 5.54126* **Camping Les Cigales, Ave de la Marne, 13260 Cassis [04 42 01 07 34; fax 04 42 01 34 18; www.campingcassis. com]** App Cassis on D41E, then at 2nd rndabt exit D559 sp Cassis, then turn 1st R sp Les Calanques into Ave de la Marne, site immed on R. Avoid town cent as rds narr. Lge, hdg/ mkd pitch, hdstg, pt sl, pt shd; wc (some cont); chem disp; mv service pnt; shwrs inc; el pnts (3A) €2.60 (poss long lead req); gas; Indtte; shop; tradsmn; rest, snacks; bar; playgrnd; shgl beach 1.5km; 30% statics; dogs €1.10; phone; rd noise some pitches; Eng spkn; ccard acc; CKE/CCI. "Gd base for Calanques; v busy w/ends; attractive resort, but steep walk to camp site; poss tired san facs end ssn; poss diff lge o'fits due trees; v strong pegs req to penetrate hardcore." 15 Mar-15 Nov. € 16.50 2009*

CASTELLANE *10E3* (1.5km N Rural) *43.85598, 6.49563* **Camping Le Provençal, Route de Digne, 04120 Castellane [tel/fax 04 92 83 65 50; accueil@camping-provencal. com; www.camping-provencal.com]** Fr N on D4085 at foot of Col de Lècques site on R on LH bend. Fr Castellane site on D4085 in 1km on L. Med, mkd pitch, pt sl, pt shd; wc; chem disp; baby facs; shwrs inc; el pnts (6A) inc; Indtte; shop; supmkt 500m; tradsmn; snacks; bar; pool, tennis 1.5km; dogs €2; some rd noise; red low ssn. "Gd, clean site; fine scenery, friendly owners; conv Gorges du Verdon." 1 May-15 Sep. € 18.00 2009*

CASTELLANE *10E3* (2km SE Rural) *43.83833, 6.54194* **Camping La Ferme de Castellane, Quartier La Lagne, 04120 Castellane [04 92 83 67 66 or 06 82 82 02 91; accueil@camping-la-ferme.com; www.camping-la-ferme. com]** Fr Castellane take D6085 dir Grasse. In 1km turn R then site in 1km, sp. Narr app rd with passing places. Sm, mkd pitch, terr, pt shd; wc; chem disp; mv service pnt; baby facs; shwrs inc; el pnts €3.50; Indtte (inc dryer); tradsmn; shop, rest, snacks, bar 2km; sm playgrnd; pool 2km; games rm; wifi; TV rm; 25% statics; dogs €1; bus 2km; Eng spkn; adv bkg; quiet; ccard acc; red low ssn; CKE/CCI. "Vg, clean, friendly site; gd touring base." ♦ 27 Mar-20 Sep. € 17.00 2010*

CASTELLANE *10E3* (5km SE Rural) *43.81631, 6.57296* **RCN Camping Les Collines de Castellane, Route de Grasse, 04120 La Garde [04 92 83 68 96; fax 04 92 83 75 40; info@ rcn-lescollinesdecastellane.fr; www.rcn-campings.fr]** Fr Castellane, take D4085 for 5km to La Garde, go thro vill & foll sp. Site on R in 1km. Lge, terr, pt shd; wc; mv service pnt; baby facs; shwrs inc; el pnts (10A) inc; gas; Indtte; shop; rest, snacks; bar; playgrnd; pool; lake sw 5km; games area; organised activites inc watersports, rock climbing, paragliding, hiking; entmnt, TV; dogs €6; Eng spkn; adv bkg; red low ssn. "Friendly owners; peaceful site on steep hillside with views; main site rd v steep." ♦ 17 Apr-25 Sep. € 39.50 2009*

CASTELLANE *10E3* (300m SW Urban) *43.84623, 6.50995* **Camping Frédéric Mistral, 12 Ave Frédéric Mistral, 04120 Castellane [04 92 83 62 27; contact@camping-fredericmistral.com; www.camping-fredericmistral. com]** In town turn onto D952 sp Gorges-du-Verdon, site on L in 100m. Med, mkd pitch, pt shd; htd wc; chem disp; some serviced pitches; shwrs inc; el pnts (6A) €3 (poss rev pol); gas 200m; shops adj; supmkt nr; rest; bar; snacks; pool 200m; 2% statics; wifi; poss cr; adv bkg; quiet; red low ssn; CKE/CCI. "Friendly owners; gd san facs but poss stretched in ssn; gd base for gorges etc; gd." ♦ 1 Mar-11 Nov. € 14.00 2014*

CASTELLANE *10E3* (500m SW Rural) *43.84570, 6.50447* **Camping Notre Dame, Route des Gorges du Verdon, 04120 Castellane [tel/fax 04 92 83 63 02; camping-notredame@wanadoo.fr; www.camping-notredame.com]** N fr Grasse on D6085, turn L in Castellane at sq onto D952 to site on R in 500m. Sm, pt shd; wc; chem disp; mv service pnt; shwrs inc; el pnts (6A) €3.50; gas; Indtte; sm shop; rest 600m; playgrnd; 20% statics; dogs free; phone; poss cr; Eng spkn; adv bkg; some rd noise; red low ssn; CKE/CCI. "Ideal touring base; helpful owners; poss a bit unkempt early ssn; excel." ♦ ltd 1 Apr-15 Oct. € 16.00 2009*

CASTELLANE *10E3* (1.5km SW Rural) *43.83921, 6.49370* **Camping Domaine du Verdon, 04120 Castellane [04 92 83 61 29; fax 04 92 83 69 37; contact@camp-du-verdon.com; www.camp-du-verdon.com / www.les-castels.com]** Fr Castellane take D952 SW twd Grand Canyon du Verdon & Moustiers-Ste Marie. After 1.5km turn L into site. NB To avoid Col de Lèques with hairpins use N202 & D955 fr Barrême instead of D6085. V lge, hdg/mkd pitch; pt shd; wc (some cont); chem disp; mv service pnt; ltd baby facs; shwrs inc; el pnts (6A) inc; gas; Indtte (inc dryer); shop; rest, snacks; bar; BBQ (gas/elec); playgrnd; htd pool; waterslides; paddling pool; rv fishing adj; canoeing; horseriding nrby; archery; games area; wifi; entmnt; games/TV rm; dogs €3; no c'vans/m'vans over 8m; poss cr; Eng spkn; poss noisy; ccard acc; red low ssn; CKE/CCI. "Excel site by rv; gd sized pitches; gd, clean san facs, modern & dated blocks; quiet, rural walk to town; mkt Wed & Sat." ♦ 15 May-15 Sep. € 34.00 (3 persons) 2011*

CASTELLANE *10E3* (12km SW Rural) *43.79596, 6.43733* **Camp Municipal de Carajuan, 04120 Rougon [04 92 83 70 94; fax 04 92 83 66 49; campingverdon.carajuan@gmail.com; www.rougon.fr]** Fr N on D4085 turn R on D952 & foll sps for 16km to rv bank of Gorges du Verdon nr Carajuan bdge; site on L. Fr E on D952 ignore turning to Rougon; site sp in 5km. Med, mkd pitch, pt shd; wc; chem disp (wc); shwrs inc; el pnts (6A) €2.70; Indtte; shop 10km; tradsmn; snacks; playgrnd; 10% statics; dogs €1.20; phone; bus Jul/Aug; poss cr; quiet; Eng spkn; adv bkg; quiet; red long stay; CKE/CCI. "Natural, unspoilt site nr rvside with shingle beach (no sw); friendly staff; basic, dated facs, poss unclean low ssn; gd walking; fair; gd morning sun despite valley." 21 Mar-30 Sep. € 11.40 2014*

CASTELLANE *10E3* (9km W Rural) *43.82276, 6.43143* **Camping Indigo Gorges du Verdon, Clos d'Aremus, 04120 Castellane [04 92 83 63 64; fax 04 92 83 74 72; aremus@camping-gorgesduverdon.com; www.camping-gorgesduverdon.com]** On D6085 fr Grasse turn L on D952 in Castellane. Camp in 9km on L. Look for sp Chasteuil on R of rd; site in 500m. Lge, mkd pitch, shd; wc; chem disp; mv service pnt; shwrs inc; el pnts (6A) inc; gas; Indtte; sm shop; rest, snacks; bar; playgrnd; htd pool; fishing; boating; canoeing; games area; games rm; wifi; entmnt; TV; 10% statics; dogs free; poss cr; Eng spkn; adv bkg ess; red low ssn; CKE/CCI. "Some sm pitches; rd along Gorges du Verdon poss diff for lge o'fits." ♦ 26 Apr-15 Sep. € 28.50 (3 persons) 2013*

CASTELLANE *10E3* (2km NW Rural) *43.85861, 6.49795* **Kawan Village Camping International, Route Napoléon, La Palud, 04120 Castellane [04 92 83 66 67; fax 04 92 83 77 67; info@camping-international.fr; www.camping-international.fr]** Site sp fr D4085 & D602. Lge, hdg pitch, pt sl, pt shd; htd wc; chem disp; mv service pnt; serviced pitches; baby facs; shwrs inc; el pnts (6A) €4.50; gas; Indtte (inc dryer); sm supmkt; tradsmn; rest, snacks; bar; playgrnd; pool; lake sw & sand beach 5km; games area; golf; horseriding; wifi; entmnt; TV rm; 50% statics; dogs €2; adv bkg; Eng spkn; ccard acc; red low ssn; CKE/CCI. "Busy site; friendly, helpful owners; main san facs vg, some dated, but clean; most pitches on gentle slope; conv Gorges de Verdon; gd walking; gd." ♦ 31 Mar-1 Oct. € 22.45 (CChq acc) 2013*

CAVAILLON *10E2* (8km E Rural) *43.84220, 5.13284* **Camp Municipal Les Royères du Prieuré, La Combe-St Pierre, 84660 Maubec [04 90 76 50 34; fax 04 32 52 91 57; camping.maubec.provence@wanadoo.fr; www.campingmaubec-luberon.com]** Heading E fr Cavaillon on D2, thro vill of Robion, in 400m at end vill sp turn R to Maubec. Site on R in 1km bef old vill. (Avoid any other rte with c'van). Diff access at ent, steep slope. Sm, terr, pt shd; wc (mainly cont); shwrs inc; shops 1km; el pnts (6-10A) €3-4; Indtte; playgrnd; 30% statics; dogs €2; poss cr; quiet; CKE/CCI. "Awkward site for lge o'fits - otherwise vg; san facs stretched high ssn; conv A7." 1 Apr-15 Oct. € 10.00 2009*

CAVAILLON *10E2* (10km E Rural) *43.85568, 5.16803* **Camping Les Boudougnes (Guiraud), Les Chênes, Petit-Coustellet, 84580 Oppède [tel/fax 04 90 76 96 10]** Fr N180 in Coustellet, take D2 dir Cavaillon. After 1km turn L onto D3 sp Ménerbes. Turn L at x-rds, site on L in approx 2km just after hamlet of Petit-Coustellet. Take care, hump at ent to lane leading to site, danger of grounding. Sm, pt shd; wc; chem disp (wc); shwrs inc; el pnts (6A) €1; shop 700m; snacks; playgrnd; dogs free; adv bkg; CKE/CCI. "Pleasant, peaceful farm site on edge Luberon National Park; parking among oak trees; levelling blocks req; old facs but clean; nr lavender museum; Oppède-le-Vieux worth visit; rec." 10 Apr-1 Oct. € 9.60 2011*

CAVAILLON *10E2* (1km S Rural) *43.82107, 5.03723* **Camp Municipal de la Durance, 495 Ave Boscodomini, 84300 Cavaillon [04 90 71 11 78; fax 04 90 71 98 77; contact@camping-durance.com; www.camping-durance.com]** S of Cavaillon, nr Rv Durance. Fr A7 junc 25 foll sp to town cent. In 200m R immed after x-ing rv. Site sp (Municipal Camping) on L. Lge, pt shd; htd wc; chem disp; baby facs; shwrs; el pnts (4A-10A) €2.50- 6.50; shops 1.5km; snacks; pool adj; paddling pool; fishing; tennis; games area; TV; 30% statics; dogs €1.50; poss cr; adv bkg; some noise during early am. "Site OK; NH only." 1 Apr-30 Sep. € 13.70 2011*

CAVAILLON *10E2* (8km S Rural) *43.78182, 5.04040* **Camping de la Vallée Heureuse, Quartier Lavau, 13660 Orgon [04 90 44 17 13; fax 04 90 55 16 49; information@camping-lavalleheureuse.com; www.camping-lavalleeheureuse.com]** Sp in Organ town cent. Lge, mkd pitch, terr, shd; wc; chem disp; mv service pnt; baby facs; shwrs inc; el pnts €3.50; gas 1km; Indtte; tradsmn; rest & snacks 1km; bar; BBQ; supmkt 10k; playgrnd; pool; lake sw 500m; wifi; TV; dogs €1.70; poss cr; Eng spkn; adv bkg; v quiet; red low ssn; CKE/CCI. "Site in old quarry in beautiful position; friendly, helpful staff; superb san facs; gd pool; gd walking; interesting area; conv m'way; isolated site, vill 1.5km." 15 Mar-15 Oct. € 19.00 (CChq acc) 2012*

CAVAILLON *10E2* (12km SW Rural) *43.76058, 4.95154* **FFCC Camping Les Oliviers, Ave Jean Jaurès, 13810 Eygalières [04 90 95 91 86; fax 04 90 95 91 86; campinglesoliviers13@gmail.com; www.camping-les-oliviers.com]** Exit A7 junc 25; D99 dir St Rémy-de-Provence; in 8km camping sp on L; in vill well sp. Sm, hdg pitch, pt shd; htd wc; el pnts (6A) inc; shop, rest, snacks, bar 250m; BBQ; playgrnd; dogs €1; bus 3km; adv bkg; quiet. "Lovely, friendly site in olive grove nr scenic vill; quiet site; facs rustic but v clean; pitches cramped for lge o'fits; simple site." 30 Mar-5 Oct. € 18.00 2014*

⊞ **CAVAILLON** *10E2* (7km W Rural) *43.83331, 4.94650* **Camp Municipal St Andiol, 13670 St Andiol [tel/fax 04 90 95 01 13]** Exit Avignon on N7 & D7n to St Andiol, site on R of D7n past vill. Sm, hdg pitch, pt shd; wc; shwrs inc; el pnts (6-10A) €3-4; gas; Indtte; snacks; shop in vill; bar; BBQ; pool; tennis 1km; golf 15km; entmnt; dogs €1; some rd noise; CKE/CCI. "Facs adequate; NH only." € 16.50 2010*

CAVALAIRE SUR MER *10F4* (1.5km NE Rural) *43.18220, 6.51610* **Kawan Village Cros de Mouton, Chemin de Cros de Mouton, 83240 Cavalaire-sur-Mer [04 94 64 10 87 or 04 94 05 46 38; fax 04 94 64 63 12; campingcrosdemouton@wanadoo.fr; www.crosdemouton.com]** Exit A8 junc 36 dir Ste Maxime on D125/D25, foll sp on D559 to Cavalaire-sur-Mer. Site sp on coast app fr Grimaud/St Tropez & Le Lavandou; diff access. Lge, mkd pitch, terr, mainly shd; wc; chem disp; mv service pnt; serviced pitches; baby facs; shwrs inc; el pnts (10A) €4.50; gas; Indtte; shop; rest, snacks; bar; playgrnd; htd pool; paddling pool; sand beach 1.8km; cycle hire; wifi; TV rm; some statics; dogs €2; phone; Eng spkn; adv bkg (ess Jul/Aug book by Jan); quiet; ccard acc; red low ssn; CKE/CCI. "Attractive, well-run, popular site in hills behind town - rec adv bkg even low ssn; lge pitches avail; poss diff access to pitches due steep site rds - help avail; pleasant, welcoming staff; gd san facs; gd pool; vg rest & bar; excel." ♦ 15 Mar-3 Nov. € 29.60 2013*

See advertisement

CAVALAIRE SUR MER *10F4* (3km NE Coastal) *43.19450, 6.55495* **Sélection Camping, 12 Blvd de la Mer, 83420 La Croix-Valmer [04 94 55 10 30; fax 04 94 55 10 39; camping-selection@wanadoo.fr; www.selectioncamping.com]** Off N559 bet Cavalaire & La Croix-Valmer, 2km past La Croix at rndabt turn R sp Barbigoua, site in 200m. Lge, hdg/mkd pitch, terr, shd; htd wc; chem disp; mv service pnt; baby facs; private bthrms avail; shwrs inc; el pnts (10A) €5; gas; Indtte (inc dryer); shop; tradsmn; rest, snacks; bar; playgrnd; htd pool; paddling pool; sand beach 400m; games area; wifi; entmnt; TV rm; 20% statics; dogs (not acc Jul/Aug) €4; phone; bus; poss cr; Eng spkn; adv bkg ess high ssn; quiet. "Excel location; sm pitches; vg san facs; excel pool; excel site." ♦ 15 Mar-15 Oct. € 35.00 (3 persons) 2012*

CAVALAIRE SUR MER *10F4* (900m S Urban) *43.16956, 6.53005* **Camping de La Baie, Blvd Pasteur, 83240 Cavalaire-sur-Mer [04 94 64 08 15 or 04 94 64 08 10; contact@camping-baie.com; www.camping-baie.com]** Exit A8 sp Ste Maxime/St Tropez & foll D25 & D559 to Cavalaire. Site sp fr seafront. Lge, mkd pitch, pt sl, pt shd; htd wc; baby facs; shwrs inc; el pnts (10A) €5; Indtte; shop; rest, snacks; bar; BBQ; playgrnd; htd pool; paddling pool; jacuzzi; sand beach 400m; sailing; watersports; diving 500m; games area; games rm; internet; 10% statics; dogs €4; bus to St Tropez & Toulonl poss cr; Eng spkn; adv bkg; quiet; ccard acc; red low ssn. "Well-run, busy site; pleasant staff; excel pool & facs; nr shops, beach, marina & cafes; cycle paths; gd location; poss cr; sm pitches; narr rd." ♦ 15 Mar-15 Nov. € 66.50 (3 persons) 2014*

CAVALAIRE SUR MER *10F4* (500m SW Coastal) *43.17203, 6.52461* **Camping La Pinède, Chemin des Mannes, 83240 Cavalaire-sur-Mer [04 94 64 11 14; camping.lapinede83@orange.fr; www.la-pinede.com]** Sp on R (N) of N559 on S o'skts of Cavalaire. Lge, mkd pitch, pt sl, shd; wc; shwrs inc; el pnts (5A) €3; shop; gas; Indtte; tradsmn; snacks; playgrnd; sand beach 500m; poss cr; adv bkg ess; quiet but noisy nr rd; red low ssn. "Cavalaire pleasant, lively resort." ♦ 15 Mar-15 Oct. € 27.00 2014*

CAVALAIRE SUR MER *10F4* (1km W Coastal) *43.16681, 6.51910* **Camping Bonporteau, 83240 Cavalaire-sur-Mer [04 94 64 03 24; fax 04 94 64 18 62; contact@bonporteau.fr; www.camping-bonporteau.com]** Sp on S side of N559 Cavalaire-Toulon rd, approx 100m on R after rndabt. Lge, sl, terr, shd; htd wc; shwrs inc; el pnts (10A) €5; gas; Indtte; shop; supmkt 500m; rest, snacks; bar; playgrnd; htd pool; jacuzzi; sand beach 200m; cycle hire; TV; some statics; dogs €4.50; min 1 week's stay Jul/Aug; adv bkg; red low ssn; quiet. "Gd cycle rte to town, beach & port." 15 Mar-15 Oct. € 41.50 (3 persons) 2009*

CERESTE *10E3* (2.5km SW Rural) *43.84564, 5.56394* **Camping Bois de Sibourg (Vial-Ménard), 04280 Céreste [04 92 79 02 22 or (mobs) 06 30 88 63 29 or 06 70 64 62 01; campingsibourg@orange.fr; www.sibourg.com]** W fr Céreste on D900/D4100; turn L in 2km (site sp); site on L in 1km. Sm, pt shd; wc (cont); shwrs inc; el pnts (6A) €2.80; dogs free; phone; Eng spkn; CKE/CCI. "Delightful 'green' farm site; St Michel l'Observatoire 15km; gd NH or longer; excel." 15 Apr-15 Oct. € 9.60 2014*

CERESTE *10E3* (6km W Rural) *43.84361, 5.49666* **Camping à la Ferme (Bouscarle), Les Monguets, 84400 Castellet-en-Luberon [04 90 75 28 62]** Fr W on D900 (Apt) ignore Camping à la Ferme sp to R nr St Martin-de-Castillon (v narr rd). Cont 2km to La Bègude & turn R onto D233 dir Le Boisset. Site 3km on R, well sp. Sm, pt sl, shd; wc; chem disp (wc); shwrs inc; el pnts (4A) €3 (long lead req); shop 6km; no statics; dogs €1; poss cr; some Eng spkn; adv bkg; CKE/CCI. "Excel, scenic CL-type site on fruit farm; friendly owners; excel walking, cycling." Easter-1 Nov. € 13.00 2009*

CHARLEVAL see Cadenet *10E3*

CHATEAU ARNOUX *10E3* (3km NE Rural) *44.10611, 6.01556* **Camping Sunêlia L'Hippocampe, Route Napoléon, 04290 Volonne [04 92 33 50 00; fax 04 92 33 50 49; camping@l-hippocampe.com; www.l-hippocampe.com]** Exit A51 junc 21 onto D4085 12km S of Sisteron twd Volonne vill over rv. Turn R on D4 on ent vill & foll camp sp 1km. Lge, hdg/mkd pitch, some hdstg, pt shd; wc; chem disp; mv service pnt; baby facs; serviced pitches; shwrs inc; el pnts (10A) inc (poss rev pol); Indtte (inc dryer); shop; tradsmn; rest; bar; BBQ (elec/gas); playgrnd; 2 pools (1 htd); paddling pool; waterslide; rv sw & beach 150km; fishing; canoeing; rafting; tennis; cycle hire; games area; games rm; wifi; entmnt; TV rm; some statics; dogs €2; Eng spkn; adv bkg; quiet; ccard acc; red low ssn/long stay; CKE/CCI. "Pleasant, busy, well-run site; spacious, well-screened pitches; various pitch sizes/prices, some by lake; some pitches poss diff due trees; excel." ♦ Easter-30 Sep. € 40.00 (CChq acc) 2009*

See advertisement

CHÂTEAUNEUF DU PAPE see Sorgues

CHORGES *9D3* (9km NE Rural) *44.56169, 6.34642* **Campéole Camping Le Clos du Lac, Route des Lacs, 05160 St Apollinaire [04 92 44 27 43; fax 04 92 43 46 93; clos-du-lac@campeole.com; www.camping-closdulac.com / www.campeole.com]** N94 to Chorges, then take D9 to St Apollinaire. Take D509 to NW of vill, site in 2.2km, sp. Med, terr, pt shd; htd wc; chem disp; baby facs; shwrs inc; el pnts (7A) €4.10; Indtte; shop; tradsmn; playgrnd; lake sw & beach adj; fishing; watersports; games area; some statics; dogs €1.80; Eng spkn; adv bkg; quiet; ccard acc; red low ssn. "Pleasant, peaceful, well-kept site in lovely location; gd facs." ♦ 22 May-25 Sep. € 14.00 (CChq acc) 2009*

CHORGES *9D3* (2.5km E Rural) *44.53515, 6.30231* **Camping Le Rio Claret, Les Chabes, 05230 Chorges [tel/fax 04 92 50 62 16; rio-claret@wanadoo.fr; www.camping-lerioclaret.com]** Fr Gap foll N94 E dir Embrun; take main rd by-passing Chorges & 4km past traff lts look for sp to site. Turn L at junc (narr lane), turn R & R again to site. Sm, mkd pitch, pt shd; wc (some cont); chem disp; mv service pnt; shwrs inc; el pnts (4-10A) €2.80-4.20; Indry rm; tradsmn; shop 2.4km; rest, snacks; bar; playgrnd; pool; lake sw & beach 2km; TV; 10% statics; dogs €2.20; phone; adv bkg; some rd noise at lower level. "Conv touring base; spectacular views; helpful, pleasant owners; gd san facs; nice pool; conv Lac de Serre-Ponçon; boat excursions; day trip to Italy via Briançon." ♦ 1 Jun-30 Sep. € 16.00 2010*

CHORGES *9D3* (5km E Rural) *44.52289, 6.34125* **Camping Club Le Roustou, 05230 Prunières [04 92 50 62 63; fax 04 92 50 90 48; info@campingleroustou.com; www.campingleroustou.com]** E fr Gap on N94. Site on side of Lac de Serre-Ponçon. Do not attempt to go to Prunières vill, always stay on N94. Lge, mkd pitch, hdstg, terr, pt shd; wc; chem disp; mv service pnt; baby facs; shwrs inc; el pnts (4A) inc; Indtte; shops 10km; tradsmn; snacks; bar; playgrnd; pool (no shorts); beach & lake sw adj; canoe hire; tennis; cycle hire; games area; wifi; TV; dogs €2; poss cr; Eng spkn; quiet; red low ssn; ccard acc; CKE/CCI. "Beautiful views; excel scenery; relaxing area; always park on E side in case of poss problem with wind; excel." 1 May-30 Sep. € 20.00 2010*

CHORGES *9D3* (6km E Rural) *44.52701, 6.35876* **Camping Le Nautic, Lac de Serre-Ponçon, 05230 Prunières [04 92 50 62 49; fax 04 92 53 58 42; campinglenautic@wanadoo.fr; www.campinglenautic.com]** Fr Gap or Embrun take N94, site sp bet Savines & Chorges. Med, terr, shd; wc; chem disp; mv service pnt; shwrs; el pnts (6A) €3; gas; lndtte; shop; tradsmn; snacks; bar; playgrnd; pool; shgl beach & lake sw; boating; wifi; dogs €2; adv bkg; quiet. "Beautiful location; lake sw excel in sheltered bay; vg san facs." ♦ 15 May-15 Sep. € 20.35 2010*

CHORGES *9D3* (10km SW Rural) *44.47581, 6.26330* **Camping La Viste, Le Belvédère de Serre-Ponçon, 05190 Rousset [04 92 54 43 39; fax 04 92 54 42 45; camping@laviste.fr; www.laviste.fr]** N on A51 or D1085 twds Gap; take D942 sp Barcelonnette; after Espinasses turn L onto D3 to Barrage de Serre-Ponçon; then L onto D103. Site on L. NB D3 long, v steep climb, hairpin bends. Med, hdg/mkd pitch, pt sl, pt shd; wc; chem disp; mv service pnt; shwrs inc; el pnts (5A) €3.30; gas; lndtte; shop & 4km; tradsmn; rest, snacks; bar; BBQ; playgrnd; pool; lake sw 2km; some statics; dogs €2.40; phone; adv bkg; quiet; ccard acc; CKE/CCI. "Ltd facs low ssn; site o'looks Lac de Serre-Poncon (amenity area); site rds narr; access diff lge o'fits; gd walking." ♦ ltd 15 May-15 Sep. € 18.20 2009*

CIOTAT, LA *10F3* (4km NE Coastal) *43.18733, 5.65810* **Campsite La Baie des Anges (formerly Les Oliviers), Chemin des Plaines Baronnes, 13600 La Ciotat [04 42 83 15 04; fax 04 42 83 94 43; info@homair.com; www.camping-laciotat.fr / www.homair.com]** Fr La Ciotat, foll D559 coast rd sp Bandol & Toulon. Site in 4km, look for lge sp on L. Caution x-ing dual c'way. V lge, pt sl, terr, shd; wc; chem disp; shwrs inc; el pnts (6A) (poss rev pol); gas; lndtte; shops 300m; rest, snacks, bar 300m; playgrnd; pool; sand/shgle beach 800m; tennis; 80% statics; dogs; bus 300m; poss v cr; Eng spkn; adv bkg; quiet but some noise fr main rd & rlwy adj; ccard acc; CKE/CCI. "Sea views many pitches; friendly staff; gd touring base." ♦ 12 Apr-1 Oct. € 50.00 2014*

⊞ **CIOTAT, LA** *10F3* (3km E Coastal) *43.18938, 5.64605* **Camping Santa Gusta, Domaine de Fontsainte, 13600 La Ciotat [04 42 83 14 17; santagusta@wanadoo.fr; www.santagusta.com]** Foll D559 coast rd fr La Ciotat twd Les Lecques to Total filling stn on R. Site down by filling stn. Lge, pt sl, pt shd; wc (cont); chem disp (wc); shwrs inc; el pnts (5A) €2.90; lndtte; shop; rest, snacks, bar high ssn; playgrnd; rocky beach adj; boat-launching facs; wifi; entmnt; 95% statics; dogs; poss cr; quiet; CKE/CCI. "San facs open 0730-2000; adj beach not suitable for bathing; ltd facs low ssn; smart card access; NH only." € 19.50 2009*

COLMARS *9D4* (400m S Rural) *44.17731, 6.62151* **Aire Naturelle Les Pommiers, Chemin des Mélèzes, 04370 Colmars-les-Alpes [04 92 83 41 56; fax 04 92 83 40 86; contact@camping-pommier.com; www.camping-pommier.com]** Fr N on D908 on ent Colmars take 1st R over rd bdge & foll site sp. Col d'allos on D908 v narr, best to avoid. Sm, pt terr, pt shd; wc (some cont); chem disp; mv service pnt; shwrs inc; el pnts (10A) €2; lndtte; shop 400m; tradsmn; rest, snacks, bar 400m; BBQ; htd pool 800m; dogs €2; phone; adv bkg; CKE/CCI. "Beautifully-situated, well-maintained CL-type site nr medieval town; friendly owner; gd walking." ♦ ltd 1 May-1 Oct. € 15.50 2014*

COLMARS *9D4* (1km S Rural) *44.17472, 6.61629* **Camping Le Bois Joly, Chemin des Buissières, 04370 Colmars-les-Alpes [04 92 83 40 40; fax 04 92 83 50 60; camping-le-bois-joly@sfr.fr; www.colmars-les-alpes.fr]** Fr S on D955 & D908 twds Colmars, go thro Beauvezer & Villars-Colmars. Ignore two other sites en rte. Site sp. Sm, mkd, hdstg, shd; wc (some cont); chem disp (wc); mv service pnt; shwrs inc; el pnts (6A) €2.43; gas; lndtte; rest, snacks, bar & shop 1km; BBQ; tradsmn high ssn; rv fishing adj; no dogs; phone; adv bkg; quiet; CKE/CCI. "Well-kept, wooded site with gd atmosphere; gd facs; ideal base for walking in Haute Provence; friendly owners." 1 May-1 Oct. € 11.10 2014*

See advertisement

COMPS SUR ARTUBY *10E3* (1km NW Rural) *43.71543, 6.49862* **Camp Municipal du Pontet, 83840 Comps-sur-Artuby [04 94 76 91 40; mairie-comps-sur-artuby@wanadoo.fr]** Fr Comps-sur-Artuby take D71 sp Grand Canyon du Verdon. Site sp on R in 1km. Med, mkd pitch, terr, pt shd; wc (some cont); chem disp (wc); shwrs inc; el pnts (6A) €3; shop; rest; bar; dogs; phone; quiet; CKE/CCI. "Vg, well-laid out, wooded site; conv Gorges du Verdon; easy access." 16 May-31 Oct. € 7.50 2010*

CUCURON see Cadenet *10E3*

CUERS *10F3* (6km W Rural) *43.23243, 6.00645* **Camping Les Tomasses, 83210 Belgentier [04 94 48 92 70; fax 04 94 48 94 73; camping.tomasses@wanadoo.fr; www.camping-tomasses.fr]** 1st rte rec for sm o'fits only: Exit A8 junc 34 St Maximin onto N7; after Tourves take D205 then D5/D554 sp Solliès-Pont; after Belgentier in 1.5km turn R at yellow sp, site in 200m on L. Or exit A57 at junc 7 onto D554 dir Belgentier; approx 1.5km bef vill; sp on L. Med, hdg/mkd pitch, pt shd; wc (mainly cont); chem disp (wc); shwrs inc; el pnts (6A) €4; gas; lndtte; shop; rest, snacks; bar; BBQ; playgrnd; pool; tennis; entmnt; 10% statics; dogs €2.20; phone; bus 300m; adv bkg; quiet; red low ssn; CKE/CCI. "Pretty CL-type site; friendly management; twin-axles welcome; acces poss diff lge o'fits." ♦ ltd 1 Apr-15 Sep. € 20.00 2011*

DIGNE LES BAINS *10E3* (1km NE Rural) *44.10011, 6.24915* **Camping Notre Dame du Bourg, Route de Barcelonnette, 04000 Digne-les-Bains [04 92 31 04 87; contact@campingdubourg-alpes-provence.com; www.campingdubourg-alpes-provence.com]** Fr rndabt by rv bdge take main st (Boulevard Gassendi) thro cent town, sp D900 La Javie, Barcelonnette. Camp sp on R. Med, unshd; wc; shwrs inc; el pnts (4A) inc; lndtte; shops 1.5km; playgrnd; pool 1.5km; tennis; games area; entmnt; TV; 40% statics; dogs €1.50; quiet. "Views fr terr areas but poss diff access lge o'fits; recep manned ltd hrs; pleasant town; thermal baths; beautiful, fascinating area." ♦ 1 Apr-31 Oct. € 16.50 2009*

DIGNE LES BAINS *10E3* (1.5km SE Rural) *44.08646, 6.25028* **Camping Les Eaux Chaudes, 32 Ave des Thermes, 04000 Digne-les-Bains [04 92 32 31 04; fax 04 92 34 59 80; info@campingleseauxchaudes.com; www.campingleseauxchaudes.com]** Fr S foll N85 sp 'Centre Ville' over bdge keeping L to rndabt, turn 1st R sp Les Thermes (D20). Past Intermarché, site on R 1.6km after leaving town. Med, mkd pitch, pt shd; htd wc; chem disp; shwrs inc; el pnts (4-10A) €2-3.50 (poss rev pol); gas; lndtte; shops 1.5km; snacks; pool; lake sw 3km; games area; wifi; 50% statics; dogs €1.50; poss cr; adv bkg; quiet; red low ssn; CKE/CCI. "Pleasant site with plenty shd; vg san facs; gd pool; gd touring base; 500m fr thermal baths; National Geological Reserve in town cent; phone ahead low ssn to check open." ♦ ltd 1 Apr-31 Oct. € 31.50 2013*

DRAGUIGNAN *10F3* (2km S Rural) *43.51796, 6.47836* **Camping La Foux, Quartier La Foux, 83300 Draguignan [tel/fax 04 94 68 18 27; www.camping-lafoux.com]** Fr A8, take Le Muy intersection onto N555 N to Draguignan. Site ent on R at ent to town sp Sport Centre Foux. Fr Draguignan, take N555 S; just after 'End of Draguignan' sp, double back at rndabt & turn R. Lge, pt sl, unshd; wc; shwrs inc; el pnts (4-10A) €3.50-5; lndtte; shop; rest; bar; playgrnd; sand beach 20km; rv adj; fishing; entmnt; TV rm; dogs €3.90; poss cr; quiet. "Friendly staff; clean, dated san facs; care needed long vehicles on ent site; unshd, but many trees planted (2011); poss flooding when wet; easy access to Riviera coast." 20 Jun-30 Sep. € 16.00 2011*

EMBRUN *9D3* (6km N Rural) *44.60290, 6.52150* **FFCC Camping Les Cariamas, Fontmolines, 05380 Châteauroux-les-Alpes [04 92 43 22 63 or 06 30 11 30 57 (mob); p.tim@free.fr; http://les.cariamas.free.fr]** Fr Embrun on N94; in 6km slip rd R to Châteauroux & foll sp to site. Site in 1km down narr but easy lane. Med, mkd pitch, pt sl, terr, pt shd; wc; chem disp; mv service pnt; baby facs; shwrs inc; el pnts (6A) €3.15; lndtte; shop 1km; tradsmn; rest, snacks; bar; BBQ; playgrnd; htd pool; lake sw adj; fishing; watersports; tennis 500m; cycle hire; wifi; 20% statics; dogs €2.50; phone; Eng spkn; adv bkg; some rd noise; red low ssn; CKE/CCI. "Excel for watersports & walking; mountain views; National Park 3km." 1 Apr-30 Oct. € 21.50 2012*

"I need an on-site restaurant"

We do our best to make sure site information is correct, but it is always best to check any must-have facilities are still available or will be open during your visit.

EMBRUN *9D3* (1km SE Urban) *44.55440, 6.48610* **Camping La Vieille Ferme, La Clapière, 05200 Embrun [04 92 43 04 08; fax 04 92 43 05 18; info@campingembrun.com; www.campingembrun.com]** On N94 fr Gap, cross Rv Durance just bef Embrun town, take 1st R sp La Vieille Ferme. Med, mkd pitch, pt shd; wc; chem disp; mv service pnt; shwrs inc; el pnts (6-10A) €3-5; lndtte; supmkt nr; rest, snacks; bar; playgrnd; rv 200m, lake 400m; watersports; rafting; canyonning; entmnt; some statics; dogs €2; Eng spkn; adv bkg; red long stay; quiet. "Friendly, family-run site; gd facs; pretty town." ♦ 1 May-30 Sep. € 27.00 2010*

EMBRUN *9D3* (4km S Rural) *44.54808, 6.49638* **Camping Les Grillons, Route de la Madeleine, 05200 Embrun [tel/fax 04 92 43 32 75; info@lesgrillons.com; www.lesgrillons.com]** Fr Embrun take N94 twds Gap; over bdge; L at rndabt onto D40. Turn L at 1st sharp bend; site on L in 400m. Med, mkd/hdg pitch, pt sl, pt shd; wc; chem disp; shwrs inc; el pnts (3-10A) €3.20-4; lndtte; tradsmn; snacks high ssn; BBQ; playgrnd; htd pool; paddling pool; lake sw & fishing 2km; tennis; games area; 5% statics; dogs €2; phone; Eng spkn; adv bkg; red low ssn; CKE/CCI. "Helpful, pleasant owners." 15 May-10 Sep. € 15.00 2010*

ENTRECHAUX see Vaison la Romaine *9D2*

PROVENCE

ENTREVAUX *10E4* (1.5km NW Rural) *43.96163, 6.79830* **Camping Le Brec, 04320 Entrevaux [tel/fax 04 93 05 42 45; info@camping-dubrec.com; www.camping-dubrec.com]** Site sp on R just after bdge 2km W of Entrevaux on N202. Rd (2km) to site narr with poor surface, passing places & occasional lge lorries. Med, mkd pitch, pt sl, pt shd; htd wc; chem disp; mv service pnt; baby facs; shwrs inc; el pnts (10A) €3 (poss long lead req); Indtte; tradsmn; snacks; BBQ; watersports cent, rv sw, fishing, boating/canoeing adj; wifi; TV; 10% statics; dogs €1; phone; train 2km; poss cr; Eng spkn; adv bkg; quiet; ccard acc; red CKE/CCI. "In beautiful area lake on site; friendly family owners; popular with canoeists; easy rv walk to town; beautiful area; gd." ♦ ltd 15 Mar-15 Oct. € 17.00 2013*

FAYENCE *10E4* (3km E Rural) *43.60659, 6.74855* **Camping Les Prairies, Chemin des Maures, 83440 Callian [04 94 76 48 36; fax 04 94 85 72 21; info@campingdesprairies.com; http://campingdesprairies.com]** Site on D562 3km W fr junc with D37. Site next to Renault g'ge. Fr A8 exit junc 39 onto D37 to D562 (gd rd) & as above. Med, mkd pitch, pt sl, pt shd; wc; chem disp; shwrs inc; el pnts (10A) €4; Indtte; shops 400m; supmkt 800m; playgrnd; pool; fishing, sailing 5km; wifi; 70% statics; dogs €2; poss noisy; Eng spkn; adv bkg; CKE/CCI. "Modern san facs; nice." ♦ 1 Apr-31 Oct. € 21.00 2009*

FAYENCE *10E4* (10km S Rural) *43.58449, 6.69016* **Camping Le Parc, Quartier Trestaure, 83440 St Paul-en-Forêt [04 94 76 15 35; fax 04 94 84 71 84; campingleparc@wanadoo.fr; www.campingleparc.com]** Fr D562 midway bet Draguinan & Grasse turn S onto D4. Site sp on L. Exit A8 junc 39, N on D37 for 11km, at junc with D562 turn L for 10km; L onto D4 for 900m; sm sp, L into sm lane, site on bend. Med, mkd pitch, shd; htd wc; chem disp; mv service pnt; shwrs inc; el pnts (10A) €5; gas; Indtte; shop; tradsmn; rest; snacks, bar high ssn; playgrnd; pool; lake 6km; beach 25km; tennis; fishing; wifi; entmnt; 10% statics; dogs €4.10; poss cr; adv bkg; quiet; red low ssn; CKE/CCI; "Conv hill vills of Provence; gd rests in St Paul; vg." 6 Apr-30 Sep. € 36.00 (CChq acc) 2013*

FAYENCE *10E4* (6km W Rural) *43.3500, 6.39590* **Camping La Tuquette (Naturist), The High Suanes 83440 Fayence [04 94 76 19 40; fax 04 94 76 23 95; robert@tuquette.com; www.tuquette.com]** Fr Fayence take N562. At km 64.2 sp turn R, site ent 100m. Sm, mkd pitch, terr, pt shd; wc; chem disp; shwrs ind; el pnts (6A) €4.60; Indtte; shop 6km; tradsmn; snacks; bar; BBQ; playgrnd; 2 htd pools; wifi; some statics; dogs €2; poss cr; Eng spkn; adv bkg; quiet; INF card. "Vg, clean site; friendly owners." ♦ 10 Apr-26 Sep. € 36.40 2013*

FONTAINE DE VAUCLUSE see Isle sur la Sorgue, L' *10E2*

FONTVIEILLE see Arles *10E2*

FORCALQUIER *10E3* (500m E Urban) *43.96206, 5.78718* **Camping Indigo Forcalquier, Route de Sigonce, 04300 Forcalquier [04 92 75 27 94; fax 04 92 75 18 10; forcalquier@camping-indigo.com; www.camping-indigo.com]** Fr A51 exit junc 19 La Brillane onto D4100 to Forcalquier. Site sp. Med, mkd pitch, pt sl, pt shd; wc (some cont); chem disp; mv service pnt; baby facs; some serviced pitches; shwrs inc; el pnts (10A) €5.20 (long lead poss req); Indtte (inc dryer); shop 500m; tradsmn; rest, snacks; bar; playgrnd; htd pool; paddling pool; games area; wifi; TV rm; some statics; dogs €4; phone; Eng spkn; adv bkg; quiet; red low ssn; CKE/CCI. "Pleasant site in lovely location; excel m'van facs; access for lge o'fits & m'vans poss diff due v narr site rds & awkward corners; walking dist fr town cent." ♦ ltd 17 Apr-29 Sep. € 38.70 2014*

⊞ **FORCALQUIER** *10E3* (8km SE Rural) *43.89752, 5.80609* **FLOWER Camping La Rivière, Lieu-Dit 'Les Côtes', 04300 St Maime [04 92 79 54 66; fax 04 92 79 51 03; contact@camping-lariviere.com; http://camping-lariviere.com / www.flowercampings.com]** S fr Sisteron on D4085, then D4096. Turn R at Voix onto D13, site on R in about 5km. Med, hdg/mkd pitch, pt shd; wc; chem disp; shwrs; el pnts (10A) inc; Indry rm; sm shop & 8km; tradsmn; rest, snacks; bar; BBQ; playgrnd; pool; lake fishing adj; games area; games rm; internet; entmnt; TV rm; 50% statics; dogs €2.50; poss cr; adv bkg; some rd noise; ccard acc; CKE/CCI. "Vg, relaxing, friendly site; gd touring base for hilltop towns." ♦ 12 Apr-27 Sep. € 35.50 2014*

FORCALQUIER *10E3* (6km S Urban) *43.91096, 5.78210* **FFCC Camping l'Eau Vive, 04300 Dauphin [tel/fax 04 92 79 51 91; info@leauvive.fr; www.leauvive.fr]** S fr Forcalquier on D4100 dir Apt; in 2.5km turn L onto D13 (at Mane); site on R in 3km. Or fr D4096, turn onto D13 at Volx; site on L in 6km (800m past Dauphin). Med, mkd pitch, shd; htd wc; chem disp; shwrs inc; el pnts (3-6A) €3.50-4.50; Indtte; shop; supmkt 6km; snacks; BBQ (gas, sep area); playgrnd; 2 pools; paddling pool; tennis; cycle hire; games area; games rm; child entmnt; TV; dogs €3.50; bus 800m; Eng spkn; adv bkg; quiet; ccard not acc; red low ssn. "Well-run site; helpful owners; vg pools; vg for children; excel." 1 Apr-31 Oct. € 21.00 2009*

FORCALQUIER *10E3* (4km NW Rural) *43.97235, 5.73800* **Camping Le Domaine des Lauzons (Naturist), 04300 Limans [04 92 73 00 60; fax 04 92 73 04 31; leslauzons@wanadoo.fr; www.camping-lauzons.com]** Exit A51 junc 19 onto N100 dir Avignon; in Forcalquier at rndabt turn L onto D950/D313 sp Banon; site on R in approx 6km. Lge site sp. Diff app. Med, mkd pitch, pt sl, terr, pt shd; wc; chem disp; baby facs; sauna; shwrs inc; el pnts (6A) €4.50; gas; Indtte (inc dryer); ice; sm shop; supmkt 6km; tradsmn; rest, snacks; bar; BBQ (gas or charcoal sep area); playgrnd; 2 htd pools; waterslides; pony rides; archery; games area; games rm; many activities; wifi; entmnt; TV; 25% statics; dogs €4; phone; poss cr; some Eng spkn; adv bkg; quiet; ccard acc; INF req. "Pleasant site in wooded valley; wonderful scenery; excel family site; helpful, friendly staff; most san facs modern, ltd low ssn; excel pool area; walks fr site; Forcalquier lovely town; excel touring base; access diff lge o'fits, tractor help avail." ♦ ltd 1 Apr-30 Sep. € 30.00 2010*

"Satellite navigation makes touring much easier"

Remember most sat navs don't know if you're towing or in a larger vehicle – always use yours alongside maps and site directions.

FREJUS *10F4* (2.5km N Urban) *43.46290, 6.7257* **Camping Les Pins Parasols, 3360 Rue des Combattants d'Afrique du Nord, 83600 Fréjus [04 94 40 88 43; fax 04 94 40 81 99; lespinsparasols@wanadoo.fr; www.lespinsparasols.com]** Fr A8 exit junc 38 sp Fréjus cent. Fr E'bound dir foll Bagnols sp at 2 rndabts & Fréjus cent/Cais at 3rd. Fr W'bound dir foll Bagnols at 3 rndabts & Fréjus cent/Cais at 4th. Site on L in 500m. Lge, hdg/mkd pitch, terr, pt sl, pt shd, htd wc; chem disp; san facs on individual pitches; baby facs; shwrs inc; el pnts (6A) inc; gas; Indtte; shop; tradsmn; rest, snacks; bar; playgrnd; pool; paddling pool; waterslide; sand beach 6km; tennis; wifi; entmnt; TV rm; 30% statics; dogs €2.90; phone; adv bkg; Eng spkn; quiet; red low ssn; CKE/CCI. "Pleasant, family-run site; clean san facs; tractor to terr pitches; some lge pitches; excel." ♦ 2 Apr-24 Sep. € 29.00 2011*

See advert on previous page

*Last year of report

FREJUS *10F4* (5km SW Rural) *43.39890, 6.67531* **Camping Domaine de la Bergerie, Vallée-du-Fournel, Route du Col-du-Bougnon, 83520 Roquebrune-sur-Argens [04 98 11 45 45; fax 04 98 11 45 46; info@domainelabergerie.com; www.domainelabergerie.com]** On DN7 twd Fréjus, turn R onto D7 sp St Aygulf & Roquebrune-sur-Argens; after passing Roquebrune, site sp in approx 6km on R. V lge, hdg/mkd pitch, terr, pt shd; wc; chem disp; sauna; some serviced pitches; baby facs; shwrs inc; el pnts (6A) inc (extra for 10A); gas; lndtte (inc dryer); supmkt; rest, snacks; bar; playgrnd; 2 pools (1 htd, covrd); paddling pool; waterslide; jacuzzi; lake fishing; sand beach 7km; tennis; games area; mini-farm; archery; wifi; entmnt; 70% statics in sep area; dogs €3.10-5.10; Eng spkn; adv bkg; quiet; ccard acc; red low ssn/long stay. "Well-organised site; entmnt/activities for all ages; early bkg ess for summer; excel." ♦ 28 Apr-30 Sep. € 38.50 2011*

See advert on previous page

"There aren't many sites open at this time of year"

If you're travelling outside peak season remember to call ahead to check site opening dates – even if the entry says 'open all year'.

FREJUS *10F4* (8km W Rural) *43.44535, 6.65790* **Camping Le Moulin des Iscles, Chemin du Moulin des Iscles, 83520 Roquebrune-sur-Argens [04 94 45 70 74; fax 04 94 45 46 09; moulin.iscles@wanadoo.fr; www.campingdesiscles.com]** Twd Fréjus on DN7, turn R onto D7 to St Aygulf sp Roquebrune. Site on L after passing thro Roquebrune vill. Med, mkd pitch, shd; htd wc (some cont); chem disp; baby facs; shwrs inc; el pnts (6A) €2.70; lndtte (inc dryer); shop; tradsmn; rest, snacks; bar; BBQ; playgrnd; rv fishing; canoeing; water skiing nrby; sand beach 12km; games rm; wifi; entmnt; TV rm; 10% statics; dogs €1.30; adv bkg; quiet; red low ssn/long stay; ccard acc. "Excel well-kept, well-run site by rv; helpful owners; gd security." ♦ 1 Apr-30 Sep. € 24.50 (3 persons) (CChq acc) 2010*

FREJUS *10F4* (8km W Rural) *43.47866, 6.63991* **Camping Leï Suves, Quartier du Blavet, 83520 Roquebrune-sur-Argens [04 94 45 43 95; fax 04 94 81 63 13; camping.lei.suves@wanadoo.fr; www.lei-suves.com]** Exit A8 junc 36 at Le Muy, thro Le Muy twd Fréjus on DN7. After 5km turn L (under a'route, not into Roquebrune-sur-Argens) at sp. Foll sp to camp 4km N of Roquebrune. Lge, mkd pitch, terr, pt shd; wc; chem disp; baby facs; shwrs inc; el pnts (6A) €4.50; gas; lndtte (inc dryer); shop; tradsmn; rest, snacks; bar; BBQ (gas only); playgrnd; htd pool; paddling pool; sand beach 14km; lake sw & fishing 3km; tennis; games rm; entmnt; excursions; wifi; 45% statics; dogs €3.50; phone; Eng spkn; adv bkg; quiet; ccard acc; red low ssn; CKE/CCI. "V pleasant location in pine forest; well-maintained, family-run site; facs clean; excel pool; some sm pitches; conv Côte d'Azur." ♦ 2 Apr-15 Oct. € 42.00 2011*

See advertisement

FREJUS *10F4* (10km W Rural) *43.45070, 6.63320* **Village camping Les Pêcheurs, Quartier Verseil, 83520 Roquebrune-sur-Argens [04 94 45 71 25; fax 04 94 81 65 13; info@camping-les-pecheurs.com; www.camping-les-pecheurs.com]** Exit A8 junc 36 dir Le Muy, onto DN7 then D7 sp Roquebrune; camp 800m on L (bef bdge over Rv Argens) at ent to vill. Alt rte, leave A8 at junc 37, turn R at rndabt twrds Le Muy and cont as above. Lge, hdg/mkd pitch, hdstg, pt shd; htd wc; chem disp; mv service pnt; baby facs; sauna; spa; jacuzzi; shwrs inc; el pnts (10A) €5.50; gas; lndtte (inc dryer); shop; tradsmn; rest, snacks; bar; BBQ (gas/elec); playgrnd; htd pool; paddling pool; sand beach 11km; lake sw, fishing, canoeing adj; spa & jacuzzi; tennis 2km; horseriding; cycle hire 1km; wifi; entmnt; TV rm; 25% statics; dogs €3.20; phone; Eng spkn; adv bkg; quiet; ccard acc; red low ssn/CKE/CCI. "Lovely site; popular with families; helpful staff; some pitches v shady; some site rds/pitch access tight for lge o'fits, OK with mover; gd walking, cycling." ♦ 5 Apr-29 Sep. € 58.00 SBS - C08 2014*

See advert on next page

FREJUS *10F4* (3km NW Rural) *43.46335, 6.7247* **Camping Le Fréjus, 3401, rue des Combattants, d'Afrique du Nord, 83600 FREJUS [04 94 19 94 60; fax 04 94 19 94 69; contact@lefrejus.com; www.lefrejus.com]** Exit A8 junc 38, at 1st rndabt turn L, then L at 2nd rndabt & L again at 3rd rndabt, Site on R in 200m. Lge, mkd pitch, pt sl, pt terr, pt shd; htd wc (some cont); chem disp; mv service pnt; baby facs; shwrs inc; el pnts (10A) inc; gas high ssn; Indtte; shop high ssn & 500m; tradsmn, rest & snacks high ssn; bar; playgrnd; htd pool; waterslide; sand beach 6km; tennis; games rm; entmnt; internet; wifi; 80% statics; dogs(leashed) €4; Eng spkn; adv bkg; quiet; ccard acc; red low ssn; CKE/CCI. "Ideal position for coast bet Cannes & St Tropez; lge pitches; pleasant, friendly staff; gd san facs; muddy after rain; quiet low ssn; v gd site; basin cold water at each pitch." ♦ 15 Jan-15 Dec. € 37.00 2013*

"That's changed – Should I let The Club know?"

If you find something on site that's different from the site entry, fill in a report and let us know. See www.caravanclub.co.uk/europereport.

FREJUS *10F4* (4km NW Urban) *43.46616, 6.72203* **Camping La Baume - La Palmeraie, Route de Bagnoles, Rue des Combattants d'Afrique du Nord, 83600 Fréjus [04 94 19 88 88; fax 04 94 19 83 50; reception@labaume-lapalmeraie.com; www.labaume-lapalmeraie.com]** Fr A8 exit junc 38 sp Fréjus cent. Fr E'bound dir foll Bagnols sp at 2 rndabts & Fréjus cent/Cais at 3rd. Fr W'bound dir foll Bagnols at 3 rndabts & Fréjus cent/Cais at 4th. Site on L in 300m. V lge, pt sl, pt shd; htd wc; shwrs; el pnts (6A) inc; gas; Indtte; shop; rest, snacks; bar; playgrnd; 5 pools (1 htd, 2 covrd); sand beach 5km; waterslide; tennis; horseriding; entmnt; many tour ops statics; dogs €4; adv bkg ess Jul/Aug; quiet, except N pt of site adj to m'way; 15% red low ssn." ♦ 1 Apr-30 Sep. € 51.00 (3 persons) 2012*

See advert on next page

FREJUS *10F4* (4km NW Coastal) *43.44545, 6.72683* **Yelloh! Village Domaine du Colombier, 1052 Rue des Combattants d'Afrique du Nord, 83600 Fréjus [04 94 51 56 01 or 04 94 51 52 38 (LS); fax 04 94 51 55 57; info@clubcolombier.com; www.clubcolombier.com / www.yellohvillage.co.uk]** Fr E (Nice) on A8 exit junc 38 sp Fréjus. Go strt over 3 rndabts, turn R at 4th rndabt, then R again at next rndabt, site on R. Fr W (Aix-en-Provence) exit A8 junc 38 & turn R at 1st rndabt, then L at intersection. Site on L. Lge, hdg/mkd pitch, hdstg, terr, pt shd; htd wc (some cont); chem disp; mv service pnt; 30% serviced pitches; baby facs; shwrs inc; el pnts (16A) inc; gas; Indtte; supmkt; tradsmn; rest, snacks; bar; BBQ (elec); playgrnd; htd pool & waterslides; sand beach 4km; tennis; sports area; games rm; excursions; wifi; entmnt; TV rm; 85% statics/tour ops; dogs €4; poss cr; Eng spkn; adv bkg; quiet but poss noise fr disco; ccard acc; red low ssn; CKE/CCI. "Well-organised, clean site in pine forest with exotic trees; excel." ♦ 9 Apr-10 Oct. € 49.00 (3 persons) 2009*

"I like to fill in the reports as I travel from site to site"

You'll find report forms at the back of this guide, or you can fill them in online at www.caravaclub.co.uk/europereport.

FREJUS *10F4* (6km NW Rural) *43.46944, 6.67805* **Camping La Bastiane, 1056 Chemin des Suvières, 83480 Puget-sur-Argens [04 94 55 55 94; fax 04 94 55 55 93; info@labastiane.com; www.labastiane.com]** Exit A8 at junc 37 Puget/Fréjus. At DN7 turn R dir Le Muy & in 1km turn R immed after 2nd bdge. Foll sp to site. Fr DN7 turn L at traff lts in Puget, site is 2km N of Puget. Lge, hdg/mkd pitch, pt sl, shd; wc; chem disp; baby facs; fam bthrm; shwrs inc; el pnts (6A) inc; Indtte; shop; tradsmn; rest, snacks; bar; BBQ (elec); playgrnd; htd pool; paddling pool; sand beach 7km; watersports; tennis; cycle hire; games area; games rm; cinema; wifi; entmnt; TV; car wash area; 40% statics; dogs €4; phone; poss cr; Eng spkn; adv bkg; quiet; ccard acc; red long stay/low ssn/CKE/CCI. "Excel, family-run, friendly site; conv m'way (no m'way noise)." ♦ 3 Apr-22 Oct. € 40.00 2010*

GAP *9D3* (1.5km N Rural) *44.58030, 6.08270* **Camping Alpes-Dauphiné, Route Napoléon, 05000 Gap [04 92 51 29 95; fax 04 92 53 58 42; info@alpesdauphine.com; www.alpesdauphine.com]** On N85, sp. Med, mkd pitch, some hdstg, pt sl, terr, pt shd; htd wc; chem disp; mv service pnt; baby facs; shwrs inc; el pnts (6A) €3; gas; lndtte (inc dryer); shop; tradsmn; rest, snacks; bar; playgrnd; htd pool; paddling pool; games area; wifi; TV; 20% statics; dogs €2.10; phone; poss cr; Eng spkn; adv bkg rec high ssn; quiet; ccard acc; red low ssn; CKE/CCI. "Pleasant site with views; modern, well maintained san facs; m'vans need levellers; gd touring base; lack of maintenance early ssn (2011); conv NH; gd site; excel rest." ♦ 13 Apr-20 Oct. € 33.50 2014*

GAP *9D3* (10km S Rural) *44.45708, 6.04785* **Camp Municipal Le Chêne, Route de Marseille, 05130 Tallard [04 92 54 13 31 or 04 92 54 10 14 (Mairie); fax 04 92 54 00 81; mairie.tallard@wanadoo.fr]** Fr S take N85 twds Gap; turn R at traff lts onto D942; site on R after 3km. Fr Gap take N85 S; turn L at traff lts, D942; site on R 3km. Med, mkd pitch, hdstg, sl, terr, pt shd; wc (some cont); shwrs inc; el pnts (6A) inc; lndtte; shop 2km; rest; bar; playgrnd; htd pool; tennis; BBQ; entmnt; phone; dogs; adv bkg; CKE/CCI. "Poss unsuitable for lgs o'fits, sm pitches." 15 Jun-31 Aug. € 15.20 2011*

GAP *9D3* (8km SW Rural) *44.49914, 6.02901* **Camping Les Bonnets, Le Haut-du-Village, 05000 Neffes [04 92 57 93 89 or 06 88 73 13 59; camping.les.bonnets@wanadoo.fr; www.camping-les-bonnets.com]** N85 SW fr Gap, turn R onto D46, site sp 1km fr vill. Med, mkd pitch, pt shd; htd wc; baby facs; shwrs; el pnts (6-10A) €3.30-4.20; lndtte; shop; supmkt 5km; rest; bar 1km; playgrnd; pool; fishing 3km; games area; entmnt; wifi; TV rm; some statics; dogs €1.50; quiet; red low ssn. "Well-kept farm site in beautiful area; friendly owner; excel pool; v ltd facs & rather run-down early ssn (2011)." 1 Apr-30 Sep. € 13.50 2011*

GARDE FREINET, LA see Grimaud *10F4*

GASSIN see St Tropez *10F4*

GORDES *10E2* (2km N Rural) *43.92689, 5.20207* **Camping Les Sources, Route de Murs, 84220 Gordes [04 90 71 12 48; fax 04 90 72 09 43; campingdessources@wanadoo.fr; www.campingdessources.com]** Fr A7 junc 24, E on D973; then D22; then D900 twds Apt. After 18km at Coustellet turn N onto D2 then L on D15 twds Murs; site on L in 2km beyond Gordes. Med, mkd pitch, hdstg, terr, pt shd; wc (some cont); chem disp; mv service pnt; baby facs; shwrs inc; el pnts (6A) €4.40 (long lead poss req); lndtte; shop & 2km; rest, snacks; bar; playgrnd; pool; cycle hire; games area; games rm; entmnt; 25% statics; dogs €5; Eng spkn; adv bkg; quiet; red low ssn/long stay; ccard acc; CKE/CCI. "Lovely location & views; friendly staff; modern, clean san facs; gd pool; access rds narr; sm pitches v diff lge o'fits; ask for easy pitch & inspect on foot; some steep rds to pitches as site on hillside; 24 hr security barriers; gd walking; mkt Tues." 12 Apr-27 Sep. € 38.40 2014*

GORDES *10E2* (10km NE Rural) *43.94069, 5.22925* **Camp Municipal Les Chalottes, 84220 Murs [04 90 72 60 84 or 04 90 72 60 00 (Mairie); fax 04 90 72 61 73; contact@communedemurs-vaucluse.fr; www.communedemurs-vaucluse.fr]** W on D900 fr Avignon, L onto D2 at Coustellet. Do not turn L sp Gordes but cont 3.5km & turn L D102 sp Joucas/Mura. Or fr Apt twd Avignon on D900, R to D4 after 4km site sp to Murs. Do not app site thro Gordes. NB 2.5t weight restriction on S app. Sm, mkd pitch, pt sl, pt shd; wc (some cont); chem disp; shwrs inc; el pnts (6A) €2; tradsmn; playgrnd; dogs; phone; quiet; CKE/CCI. "Peaceful, pretty site among pines; gd walks; vill 1.8km." Easter-15 Sep. € 10.00 2009*

GRAVE, LA *9C3* (1km E Rural) *45.04508, 6.31052* **Camping de la Meije, 05320 La Grave [tel/fax 04 76 79 93 34 or 06 08 54 30 84 (mob); nathalie-romagne@wanadoo.fr; www.camping-delameije.com]** On D1091 travelling fr W site ent end of vill immed after last building. Site sp easily missed, by stream below vill. Fr E awkward app fr Briançon (sharp L-hand turn) cont & turn in parking area 150m. NB Rec app fr W. Sm, hdg/mkd pitch, pt sl, pt shd; wc (cont); chem disp (wc); baby facs; fam bthrm; shwrs inc; el pnts (4A) €3; lndtte; shop; tradsmn; rest, snacks; bar; BBQ; playgrnd; htd pool high ssn; tennis; games area; dogs €1; bus; poss cr; Eng spkn; adv bkg; quiet; red 5 days+; CKE/CCI. "Well-kept site in superb setting; mountain views; poss cr early & mid-July due La Marmotte cycle race & Tour de France." ♦ 15 May-20 Sep. € 13.40 2010*

GRAVESON *10E2* (1km SE Rural) *43.84408, 4.78080* **Camping Les Micocouliers, 445 Route de Cassoulen, 13690 Graveson [04 90 95 81 49; micocou@free.fr; www.camping-les-micocouliers-provence.fr]** Leave A7 junc 25 onto D99 St Rémy-de-Provence then D5 N past Maillane, site on R. Med, hdg/mkd pitch, unshd; wc; chem disp; mv service pnt; shwrs inc; el pnts (4-13A) €4.40-7.; lndtte; shop 1km; tradsmn; rest, bar 1km; BBQ; pool; tennis 1km; cycle hire; games area; wifi; 8% statics; dogs €2; phone; Eng spkn; adv bkg rec; red low ssn/CKE/CCI. "Peaceful but busy site; pretty & well-kept; friendly, helpful owners; excel, immac san facs; lovely sm pool; vg cycling; attractive, interesting area; excel." ♦ 15 Mar-15 Oct. € 39.00 2014*

GREOUX LES BAINS *10E3* (1.2km S Rural) *43.75158, 5.88185* **Camping Le Verseau, Route de St Pierre, 04800 Gréoux-les-Bains [04 92 77 67 10 or 06 22 72 93 25 (mob); info@camping-le-verseau.com; www.camping-le-verseau.com]** Fr W on D952 to Gréoux. Go under bdge then bear L just bef petrol stn. Cross rv (narr bdge), site on R in 500m. Med, hdg pitch, pt sl, pt shd; wc; chem disp; mv service pnt; baby facs; shwrs inc; el pnts (10A) €3.50; lndtte; shop 1km; tradsmn; rest, snacks; bar; BBQ (gas/elec); playgrnd; pool; tennis 1km; wifi; entmnt; dogs €2; phone; adv bkg; quiet; CKE/CCI. "Friendly owners; interesting spa town; great views." 1 Mar-31 Oct. € 17.50 2010*

GREOUX LES BAINS *10E3* (8km SW Rural) *43.72899, 5.81277* **Camp Municipal du Verdon, 83560 Vinon-sur-Verdon [04 92 78 81 51; camping@vinon-sur-verdon.fr; www.campingduverdon.com]** Exit A51 junc 17 onto D952 N to Vinon-sur-Verdon (dir Gréoux-Les-Bains); cross rv bdge in vill; site on R in 100m. Sm, shd; wc (some cont); mv service pnt; shwrs inc; el pnts (5A) €2.60; Indtte; shop 500m; playgrnd; rv fishing & sw adj; kayaking; games area; dogs €0.80; phone; quiet. ♦ 15 May-30 Sep. € 9.70 2010*

GRIGNAN see Valréas *9D2*

GRIMAUD *10F4* (2km E Rural) *43.27924, 6.56409* **Aire Naturelle (Lyons), Les Cagnignons, 83310 Grimaud [04 94 56 34 51; fax 04 94 56 51 26; lyons.cagnignons@wanadoo.fr]** Leave A8 at junc 36 onto D125/D25 at Le Muy sp Ste Maxime then onto D559 dir St Tropez. Take R onto D14 sp Grimaud & 3rd rd on R to site. Sm, terr, shd; wc; chem disp; shwrs inc; el pnts (3-6A) €3-3.50; Indtte; basic playgrnd; pool adj, tennis 500m; sand beach 2km; horseriding 2km; phone; 30% statics; dogs €1.60; adv bkg; quiet; no ccard acc; CKE/CCI. "Clean site; away fr bustle of St Tropez; not rec teenagers; some pitches ltd for long o'fits." ♦ Easter-30 Sep. € 18.00 2009*

GRIMAUD *10F4* (4.5km NW Rural) *43.29180, 6.49210* **Camping de Berard, 83680 La Garde-Freinet [tel/fax 04 94 43 21 23; camping.berard@wanadoo.fr; http://camping.berard.pagesperso-orange.fr]** Exit A8 junc 13 onto D558 to La Garde-Freinet; pass thro vill on D558; site on L in 5km. Sp fr N & S. Site midway bet La Garde-Freinet & Grimaud. Med, terr, pt shd; wc; chem disp; baby facs; shwrs; el pnts (6A) inc; Indtte; shop; tradsmn; rest; take-away; bar; BBQ; playgrnd; pool; paddling pool; sandy beach 8km; games area; games rm; entmnt; wifi; 60% statics; dogs; phone; Eng spkn; adv bkg; quiet, a little rd noise; CKE/CCI. "Friendly, family-run site in hills; well-spaced; san facs dated but clean & plentiful; some pitches v shady; La Garde-Freinet has all shops & excel rests; highly rec if want site close to coast without noise/crowds; vg." ♦ 1 Mar-31 Oct. € 20.00 2011*

GRIMAUD *10F4* (3km E Coastal) *43.28527, 6.57972* **Domaine des Naïades ACF, St Pons-les-Mûres, 83310 Grimaud [04 94 55 67 80; fax 04 94 55 67 81; info@lesnaiades.com; www.lesnaiades.com]** Exit A8 junc 36 (for Le Muy) onto D125/D25 dir St Maxime; join D559 W dir St Tropez & Grimaud. After 5km at rndabt opp Camping Prairies de la Mer turn R sp St Pons-les-Mûres; site sp & ent 500m on L. Lge, terr, shd, mkd pitch; wc (some cont); chem disp; mv service pnt; baby facs; shwrs inc; el pnts (10A) inc (poss rev pol); Indtte (inc dryer); shops; rest, snacks; bar; BBQ (elec); playgrnd; Olympic-sized htd pool; paddling pool; waterslides; sand beach 900m; watersports; cycle hire; games area; wifi; entmnt; games/TV rm; many statics; dogs €6; no c'vans/m'vans over 6m high ssn; min 7 nights Jul/Aug; poss cr; adv bkg ess; quiet except noisy disco & dog kennels adj; ccard acc; red low ssn/long stay; CKE/CCI. "Gd views; gd recep; mixed reports on san facs (2009); chem disp up many steps (2010); pitch access poss diff lge o'fits due steep hills & tight bends; gd for families; 24hr security." ♦ 31 Nov-21 Oct. € 55.00 (3 persons) 2011*

GRIMAUD *10F4* (3.5km E Coastal) *43.27630, 6.56000* **Camping La Pinède, 83310 Grimaud [04 94 56 04 36; fax 04 94 56 30 86; pinede-grimaud@sfr.fr; www.lapinede-camping.com]** Exit Grimaud E on D14; after junc with D61 cont on D14 for 1km; site on R. Lge, pt shd; wc; chem disp; mv service pnt; baby facs; shwrs; el pnts (10A) inc; Indtte (inc dryer); tradsmn; rest, snacks; bar; playgrnd; htd covrd pool; paddling pool; games rm; wifi; entmnt; some statics; dogs €4; red low ssn. 1 Apr-31 Oct. € 34.00 (CChq acc) 2010*

GRIMAUD *10F4* (4km E Coastal) *43.27080, 6.57320* **Camping Club Holiday Marina, Le Ginestel, 83310 Grimaud [04 94 56 08 43; fax 04 94 56 23 88; info@holiday-marina.com; www.holiday-marina.com]** Exit A8 junc 36 onto D125/D25 dir Ste Maxime; turn R onto D559 dir St Tropez (sea on your L); in approx 6km pass under sm flyover at Port Grimaud. Site on R in approx 500m past flyover just after Villa Verde garden cent. Lge, hdg/mkd pitch, pt shd; htd wc; chem disp; serviced pitches; pitches have private bthrms; shwrs inc; el pnts (16A) inc; Indtte; sm shop; tradsmn; rest, snacks; bar; BBQ (elec); playgrnd; htd pool; paddling pool; jacuzzi; sand beach 950m; fishing; boating; cycle hire; games rm; wifi; entmnt; sat TV; 70% statics; dogs €3; no c'vans/m'vans over 12m; deposit for barrier card & bathrm; sep car park; British owners; poss cr; adv bkg ess high ssn; rd noise; ccard acc; min 3 nights; red low ssn/long stay; lge pitches extra charge; CKE/CCI. "Lovely pool area; excel sports facs; helpful staff; some pitches poss tight - pitches avail for lge m'vans; recep clsd 1230-1400; conv all Côte d'Azur." ♦ 1 Mar-3 Jan. € 55.00 2011*

GRIMAUD *10F4* (4km E Coastal) *43.28375, 6.59165* **Camping Les Mûres, St Pons-les-Mûres, 83310 Grimaud [04 94 56 16 17; fax 04 94 56 37 91; info@camping-des-mures.com; www.camping-des-mures.com]** Exit Ste Maxime on D559 twd St Tropez, site in 5km visible on both sides of rd midway bet Ste Maxime & Grimaud. V lge, mkd pitch, pt sl, pt shd; wc (some cont); chem disp; shwrs inc; el pnts (6A) inc (poss rev pol); gas; Indtte; shop; rest, snacks; bar; playgrnd; sand beach adj; boat hire; water-skiing; games area; entmnt; some statics; dogs €2; poss cr; quiet but rd noise & disco (high ssn); adv bkg; red low ssn; CKE/CCI. "Well-run, clean site; site has own beach, beach pitches with views avail; v ltd facs low ssn." 4 Apr-3 Oct. € 35.00 2009*

GRIMAUD *10F4* (4km E Coastal) *43.28083, 6.58250* **Camping Les Prairies de la Mer, St Pons-les-Mûres, 83360 Grimaud [04 94 79 09 09; fax 04 94 79 09 10; prairies@riviera-villages.com; www.riviera-villages.com]** Leave A8/E80 at Ste Maxime/Draguignan exit. Take DD125/D25 twd Ste Maxime. Site on L of D559 heading SW, 400m bef St Pons-les-Mûres with rndabt at ent. Site opp Marina Village. V lge, mkd pitch, hdstg, pt shd; wc; chem disp; mv service pnt; shwrs inc; el pnts (6-10A) inc; gas; Indtte; shop; supmkt; rest, snacks; bar; playgrnd; sand beach adj; fishing; watersports; entmnt; 85% statics; dogs; phone; bus; poss cr; adv bkg ess high ssn; some rd noise; ccard acc; red low ssn; CKE/CCI. "Popular, well-run beach site; gd recep; pitches tight for med to lge o'fits & poss dusty high ssn; gd san facs; Port Grimaud sh walk; gd entmnt; gd." ♦ 23 Mar-13 Oct. € 55.00 2013*

GRIMAUD *10F4* (4.5km E Coastal) *43.28205, 6.58614* **Camping de la Plage, 98 Route National, St Pons-les-Mûres, 83310 Grimaud [04 94 56 31 15; fax 04 94 56 49 61; campingplagegrimaud@wanadoo.fr; www.camping-de-la-plage.fr]** Fr St Maxime turn onto D559 sp to St Tropez; site 3km on L on both sides of rd (subway links both parts). Lge, pt shd; wc; chem disp; mv service pnt; shwrs inc; el pnts (4-16A) €4.70-14.; gas; Indtte; shop; rest, snacks; bar; playgrnd; sand beach on site; tennis; wifi; entmnt; dogs €2.20; poss cr; some rd noise; adv bkg ess high ssn (rec bkg in Jan - non-rtnable bkg fee); ccard acc; red low ssn; CKE/CCI. "Pitches adj beach or in shd woodland - some sm; site tired but lovely situation & views compensate (2011); clean facs but need refurb; cycle tracks; site poss flooded after heavy rain; used every yr for 44 yrs by one CC member (2011); conv for ferry to St Tropez, rec as beautiful, helpful friendly efficient staff." ♦ 11 Apr-13 Oct. € 35.00 2014*

⊞ **GRIMAUD** *10F4* (2km SE Rural) *43.26414, 6.53365* **FFCC Camping Domaine du Golfe de St Tropez, Chemin des Vignaux, 83310 Grimaud [04 94 43 26 95; fax 04 94 43 21 06; info@golfe-st-tropez.com; www.golfe-st-tropez.com]** Sp down lane, Carraire de St Pierre, nr junc of D14 & D61 or off D558. Med, hdg/mkd pitch, pt shd; wc; chem disp; shwrs inc; el pnts (6-10A) €4-5; rest, snacks; playgrnd; pool; beach 3.5km; 40% statics; dogs €3; phone; ccard acc. "Conv for Port Grimaud & beaches." € 20.00 2009*

GUILLESTRE *9D4* (800m SW Rural) *44.65854, 6.63836* **Camping La Rochette (formerly Municipal), 05600 Guillestre [tel/fax 04 92 45 02 15; guillestre@aol.com; www.campingguillestre.com]** Exot N94 onto D902A to Guillestre. In 1km fork R on side rd at camp sps. Site on L in 1km. Lge, mkd pitch, pt shd; wc (some cont); shwrs inc; el pnts (6-10A) €2.80-3.40; gas; Indtte; shop; snacks; BBQ; playgrnd; pool, tennis adj; fishing; dir access to rv; sports area; entmnt; dogs free; phone; poss cr; adv bkg; quiet; red low ssn. "Spectacular views; lge pitches; Dutch-owned site; helpful staff; superb san facs; conv Queyras National Park." ♦ 15 May-30 Sep. € 15.20 2012*

HYERES *10F3* (4km E Coastal) *43.12050, 6.18464* **Camping Port Pothuau, 101 Chemin des Ourlèdes, 83400 Hyères [04 94 66 41 17; fax 04 94 66 33 09; pothuau@free.fr; www.campingportpothuau.com]** Fr Hyères E twds Nice on D98, turn R on D12 sp Salins d'Hyères. Site 2nd on R. Lge, mkd pitch, shd; wc; some serviced pitches; shwrs; el pnts (6-10A) inc (check rev pol/earth & poss long lead req); gas; Indtte; shop; rest, snacks; bar; playgrnd; pool; paddling pool; sand beach 1km; tennis; games area; cycle hire; TV; 90% statics; dogs €3; red low ssn. "Nr interesting town of Hyères; excursions to peninsula of Giens; basic facs; vg." 3 Apr-17 Oct. € 36.00 2010*

HYERES *10F3* (8km E Rural) *43.13017, 6.21650* **Camping De La Pascalinette, 1800 Ancien Chemin de Heyeres, BP 19, 83250 La Londe-les-Maures [04 94 66 82 72; www.var-camping.eu]** Site sp on D98 E of Hyères. Lge, mkd pitch, shd; wc; baby facs; shwrs inc; el pnts (10A) inc; gas; Indtte; shop; rest, snacks; BBQ; playgrnd; htd pool; paddling pool; sand/shgl beach 3km; games rm; entmnt; wifi; TV; statics; dogs €4 adv bkg; CKE/CCI. "V gd site in a great location; gd pool." ♦ 1 Apr-30 Sep. € 39.00 2011*

HYERES *10F3* (8km E Coastal) *43.1186, 6.24693* **Miramar Camping, 1026 Blvd Louis Bernard, 83250 La Londes-les-Maures [04 94 66 80 58 or 04 94 66 83 14; fax 04 94 66 80 98; camping.miramar.lalonde@wanadoo.fr; www.provence-campings.com/azur/miramar]** On D98 in cent of La Londes-les-Maures, turn S at traff lts; in 1km turn R over white bdge & foll rd for 1.5km dir Port Miramar; site on R 150m bef port. Lge, hdg/mkd pitch, shd; wc; chem disp; shwrs inc; el pnts (4-10A) €4.50-6.50; Indtte; v sm shop & 2km; rest, snacks; bar; sand beach 200m; games rm; 25% statics; no dogs; phone; bus 2km; poss cr; Eng spkn; quiet; ccard acc; CKE/CCI. "Vg shd; beach, port, rests & shops 200m, but food shops 2km; vg marina; excel site out of ssn; vg." ♦ ltd 1 May-30 Sep. € 22.00 2013*

HYERES *10F3* (4km SE Coastal) *43.05611, 6.14750* **Campéole Camping Eurosurf, Plage de la Capte, 83400 Hyères [04 94 58 00 20; fax 04 94 58 03 18; eurosurf@campeole.com; www.camping-hyeres.com / www.campeole.com]** Fr A8 take A57 as far as Hyères, foll sps to Giens & Les Iles, site is just outside La Capte vill on L on D97. V lge, mkd pitch, pt sl, pt shd; wc; chem disp; mv service pnt; baby facs; shwrs inc; el pnts (10A) inc; gas; Indtte; shop; tradsmn; rest, snacks; bar; no BBQ; playgrnd; sand beach adj; watersports; diving cent; 50% statics; dogs €3.90; phone; poss cr; no adv bkg; some rd noise; ccard acc; red low ssn. "Some areas of soft sand where pitches not mkd; excel for watersports; gd location." ♦ ltd 13 Mar-3 Nov. € 43.00 2010*

HYERES *10F3* (5km SE Coastal) *43.10103, 6.16955* **Camping Domaine du Ceinturon III, Rue du Ceinturon, L'Ayguade, 83400 Hyères [04 94 66 32 65; fax 04 94 66 48 43; contact@ceinturon3.fr; www.ceinturon3.fr]** Fr Hyères take L'Ayguade rd sp airport. At T-junc in L'Ayguade turn R. Site 400m twd Hyères harbour & adj airport on D42. Fr NE on D42 drive thro L'Ayguade, turn R at traff lts just after end of vill sp. Lge, hdg/mkd pitch, shd; htd wc (some cont); chem disp; serviced pitch; shwrs inc; el pnts (6-10A) €3-4; gas; Indtte (inc dryer); shop high ssn; tradsmn; rest, snacks; bar; playgrnd; htd pool; paddling pol; beach adj, tennis; wifi; TV rm; 15% statics; dogs €3.85; phone; bus; poss cr; Eng spkn; adv bkg ess Jul/Aug; quiet but some daytime noise fr adj airport; no ccard acc; CKE/CCI. "Excel, popular, busy site; sm pitches; helpful owners; excel cycle paths in area." ♦ 27 Mar-30 Sep. € 23.00 2010*

HYERES *10F3* (8km S Coastal) *43.04100, 6.14340* **Camping La Presqu'île de Giens, 153 Route de la Madrague, Giens, 83400 Hyères [04 94 58 22 86; fax 04 94 58 11 63; info@camping-giens.com; www.camping-giens.com]** Fr Toulon A570 dir Hyères. Thro palm-lined main street in Hyères dir Giens-les-Iles & foll sp to La Capte & Giens past airport on L, thro La Capte, turn R at rndabt to site on L, sp. Lge, pt sl, terr, pt shd; htd wc; mv service pnt; baby facs; shwrs inc; el pnts (15A) €5; gas; Indtte (inc dryer); shop; tradsmn; snacks; playgrnd; sand beach 600m; fishing & boat excursions; cycle hire; games area; games rm; wifi; entmnt; TV; 75% statics; dogs €3; poss cr; adv bkg; quiet; red low ssn. "Sm pitches, layout cramped; access to pitches awkward/steep lge o'fits; sister site La Tour Fondue has easier access; ltd water pnts; gd clean san facs; pleasant, helpful staff." ♦ 2 Apr-9 Oct. € 24.00 (CChq acc) 2011*

PROVENCE

HYERES *10F3* (9km S Coastal) *43.02980, 6.15490* **Camping La Tour Fondue, Ave des Arbanais, 83400 Giens [04 94 58 22 86; fax 04 94 58 11 63; info@camping-latourfondue.com; www.camping-latourfondue.com]** D97 fr Hyères, site sp. Med, hdg pitch, pt sl, pt terr, pt shd; wc; chem disp; mv service pnt; shwrs inc; el pnts (6A) €4.70; Indtte; rest, snacks; bar; beach adj; games area; entmnt; some statics; dogs €2.90 (not allowed on beach); no adv bkg; ccard acc. "Pleasant, sister site of Camping Presqu'île de Giens with easier access; sm pitches; only water point at 'Sanitaires' (by recep)." 5 Apr-2 Nov. € 44.45 2014*

HYERES *10F3* (13km S Coastal) *43.04156, 6.12799* **Camping International, 1737 Route de la Madrague, Presqu'ile de Giens, 83400 Hyères [04 94 58 90 16; fax 04 94 58 90 50; thierry.coulomb@wanadoo.fr; www.international-giens.com]** S fr Hyères on D97 dir Giens, once past La Capte foll sp La Bergerie & La Madrague, site sp. Lge, mkd pitch, hdstg, terr, pt shd; wc; chem disp; mv service pnt; baby facs; shwrs inc; el pnts (6A) €5; gas; Indtte (inc dryer); shop; tradsmn; rest, snacks; bar; no BBQ; playgrnd; htd pool; paddling pool; adj; sand beach 400m; tennis adj; watersports; windsurfing tuition; skin-diving; horseriding; solarium; wifi; entmnt; 60% statics; no dogs; Eng spkn; adv bkg; quiet; CKE/CCI. "Excel family site; many activities for all ages; gd beach; gd walking." 26 Mar-5 Nov. € 38.50 2010*

HYERES *10F3* (6km W Rural) *43.11442, 6.05609* **FLOWER Camping Le Beau Vezé, Route de la Moutonne, 83320 Carqueiranne [tel/fax 04 94 57 65 30; info@camping-beauveze.com; www.camping-beauveze.com / www.flowercampings.com]** Fr Toulon take D559 E dir Carqueiranne. Approx 2km after Le Pradet turn L onto D76 twd La Moutonne. Site on R in 1.5km. Med, mkd pitch, terr, pt shd; htd wc (some cont); chem disp; baby facs; shwrs inc; el pnts (4A) €4; gas; Indtte; shop; rest, snacks; bar; BBQ (gas only); playgrnd; 2 pools; paddling pool; waterslide; beach 4km; tennis; cycle hire; wifi; entmnt; few statics; dogs €2.50; poss cr; adv bkg; quiet but some rd noise; red low ssn; ccard not acc. "Poss diff access some pitches for lge o'fits; no twin-axle c'vans; mkt Thu." ♦ 1 May-15 Sep. € 29.00 (CChq acc) 2010*

ISLE SUR LA SORGUE L' *10E2* (2km E Rural) *43.91451, 5.07181* **Camping Airotel La Sorguette, 871 Route d'Apt, 84800 L'Isle-sur-la-Sorgue [04 90 38 05 71; fax 04 90 20 84 61; info@camping-sorguette.com; www.camping-sorguette.com]** Fr L'Isle-sur-la-Sorgue take D901 twd Apt, on L site in 1.5km, sp. Med, hdg/mkd pitch, pt shd; wc; chem disp; mv service pnt; shwrs inc; el pnts (10A) €4.70; gas; Indtte; shop; tradsmn; rest nr; BBQ; playgrnd; beach adj; trout-fishing adj; canoeing (not for faint-hearted!); tennis; games area; wifi; 10% statics; dogs €3.50; adv bkg; poss cr; Eng spkn; quiet; ccard acc; red low ssn; CKE/CCI. "Lovely, well-run site; useful & busy; friendly, helpful staff; beware low trees; dated but clean san facs; rvside walk to attractive town; Sun mkt (shuttle fr site); highly rec." ♦ ltd 15 Mar-15 Oct. € 23.00 2013*

ISLE SUR LA SORGUE L' *10E2* (5km NW Rural) *43.92980, 4.98320* **Camping Domaine du Jantou, 535 Chemin des Coudelières, 84250 Le Thor [04 90 33 90 07; fax 04 90 33 79 84; jantou@franceloc.fr; www.campings-franceloc.fr]** Exit A7 at Avignon Nord onto D942 sp Carpentras. Turn S onto D6; in 8km join D901 E sp Le Thor. Site sp bef vill. App fr E fork R at sharp bend, thro town gate take L turn after passing church & L. Med, hdg/mkd pitch, pt shd; wc; chem disp; mv service pnt; baby facs; shwrs inc; el pnts (16A) €4; Indtte (inc dryer); shop; snacks; playgrnd; 2 htd, covrd pools; paddling pools; waterslide; cycle hire; games area; games rm; wifi; wifi; entmnt; TV rm; 60% statics; dogs €5; phone; Eng spkn; adv bkg; quiet; ccard acc; CKE/CCI. "Vg, attractive site by Rv Sorgue; sm pitches, ltd access; conv Avignon, Camargue." ♦ ltd 3 Apr-26 Sep. € 26.50 2010*

ISLE SUR LA SORGUE, L' *10E2* (5km E Rural) *43.91087, 5.10665* **Camping La Coutelière, Route de Fontaine-de-Vaucluse, 84800 Lagnes [04 90 20 33 97; fax 04 90 20 27 22; info@camping-lacouteliere.com; www.camping-lacouteliere.com]** Leave L'Isle-sur-la-Sorgue by D900 dir Apt, fork L after 2km sp Fontaine-de-Vaucluse. Site on L on D24 bef ent Fontaine. Med, hdg pitch, shd; wc; shwrs inc; el pnts (10A) €4.40; Indtte; rest, snacks; bar; playgrnd; pool; canoeing nr; tennis, entmnt; 40% statics; dogs €4.50; phone; Eng spkn; adv bkg; quiet; red low ssn; CKE/CCI. "Attractive, busy site by rv; walking/cycling on canal towpath; 2km easy cycle ride to Fontaine; ltd san facs low ssn; poss unkept low ssn; lovely area; gd." ♦ 1 Apr-15 Oct. € 43.00 2014*

ISSAMBRES, LES see St Aygulf *10F4*

ISTRES *10F2* (6km S Coastal) *43.46958, 5.02420* **Camping Félix de la Bastide, Allée Plage d'Arthur, 13920 St Mitre-les-Remparts [04 42 80 99 35; fax 04 42 49 96 85; info@campingfelix.com; www.campingfelix.com]** S fr Istres on D5 to end of built up area. At 2nd rndabt turn L (foll sp); approx 2km on L. Med, hdg/mkd pitch, pt shd; wc; chem disp; shwrs inc; el pnts (6A) €3 (poss rev pol); gas 2km; Indry service; shop; tradsmn; rest; bar; BBQ; playgrnd; pool; paddling pool; shgl beach & lake adj; watersports; games area; wifi; dogs €1.50; phone; poss cr; Eng spkn; adv bkg; poss noise fr dogs barking & club nrby; red long stay. "Spacious pitches; poss strong winds; friendly Dutch owners; san facs poss stretched high ssn; beautiful scenery." 1 Apr-1 Nov. € 17.50 2009*

JAUSIERS see Barcelonnette *9D4*

JONQUIERES see Orange *10E2*

"I need an on-site restaurant"

We do our best to make sure site information is correct, but it is always best to check any must-have facilities are still available or will be open during your visit.

LAVANDOU, LE *10F3* (2km E Coastal) *43.14471, 6.38084* **Caravaning St Clair, Ave André Gide, 83980 Le Lavandou [04 94 01 30 20; fax 04 94 71 43 64; patrick.martini@ wanadoo.fr / lesmandariniers@orange.fr; www. caravaningsaintclair.com]** N559 thro Le Lavandou twd St Raphaël; after 2km at sp St Clair turn R immed after bend 50m after blue 'caravaning' sp (easy to overshoot). Med, mkd pitch, shd; htd wc (cont); mv service pnt; shwrs inc; el pnts (16A) €4.10 (rev pol); lndtte; shops 100m; rest, bar nrby; playgrnd; sand beach adj; fishing; boat hire; wifi; TV rm; dogs €2; no tents; poss cr; adv bkg ess Jul-Aug; some noise fr rd; no ccard acc; red low ssn. "Popular with British; pitch & ent screened by trees; conv beach & rests; quiet site." ♦ Apr-Oct. € 30.00 (3 persons) 2013*

LAVANDOU, LE *10F3* (2km S Coastal) *43.11800, 6.35210* **Camping du Domaine, La Favière, 2581 Route de Bénat, 83230 Bormes-les-Mimosas [04 94 71 03 12; fax 04 94 15 18 67; mail@campdudomaine.com; www. campdudomaine.com]** App Le Lavandou fr Hyères on D98 & turn R on o'skts of town clearly sp La Favière. Site on L in 2.3km about 200m after ent to Domaine La Favière (wine sales) - ignore 1st lge winery. If app fr E do not go thro Le Levandou, but stay on D559 until sp to La Favière. V lge, mkd pitch, terr, pt shd, 75% serviced pitch; wc; chem disp; mv service pnt; baby facs; shwrs inc; el pnts (10A) inc (long lead poss req); gas; lndtte (inc dryer); shop; supmkt; tradsmn; rest, snacks; bar; BBQ (gas); playgrnd; sand beach adj; tennis; games rm; wifi; entmnt; TV rm; 10% statics; dogs (not acc Jul/ Aug); phone; poss cr; Eng spkn; adv bkg ess high ssn; quiet; ccard acc; red low ssn; CKE/CCI. "Lge pitches, some with many trees & some adj beach (direct access); well-organised site with excel facs; gd walking & attractions in area." ♦ ltd 30 Mar-31 Oct. € 48.00 2013*

See advertisement

LAVANDOU, LE *10F3* (1.5km SW Coastal) *43.13386, 6.35224* **Camping Beau Séjour, Quartier St Pons, 83980 Le Lavandou [04 94 71 25 30; beausejourvar@orange.fr]** Take Cap Bénat rd on W o'skts of Le Lavandou. Site on L in approx 500m. Med, mkd pitch, pt shd; wc; shwrs inc; el pnts (3A) €4; supmkts 400m; rest, snacks & bar adj; beach 900m; poss cr; no adv bkg; rd noise on W side. "Well-kept, clean site; gd sized pitches." ♦ Mid Apr-30 Sep. € 17.60 2014*

LAVANDOU, LE *10F3* (2.7km W Urban) *43.13630, 6.35439* **Camping St Pons, Ave Maréchal Juin, 83960 Le Lavandou [04 94 71 03 93; info@campingsaintpons.com; www.campingstpons.com]** App fr W on D98 via La Londe. At Bormes keep R onto D559. At 1st rndabt turn R sp La Favière, at 2nd rndabt turn R, then 1st L. Site on L in 200m. Med, mkd pitch, shd; wc (some cont); chem disp; shwrs inc; el pnts (6A) inc; lndtte; shop adj; rest, snacks, bar high ssn; sand beach 800m; playgrnd; entmnt; 10% statics; dogs €3.90; phone; poss cr; Eng spkn; some rd noise; red low ssn; CKE/CCI. "Much improved site; helpful owner." 25 Apr-3 Oct. € 26.20 2009*

⊞ **LAVANDOU, LE** *10F3* (9km W Rural) *43.16262, 6.32152* **Camping Manjastre, 150 Chemin des Girolles, 83230 Bormes-les-Mimosas [04 94 71 03 28; fax 04 94 71 63 62; manjastre@infonie.fr; www.campingmanjastre.com]** App fr W on D98 about 3km NE of where N559 branches off SE to Le Lavandou. Fr E site is 2km beyond Bormes/Collobrières x-rds; sp. Lge, hdg/mkd pitch, v sl, terr, pt shd; htd wc; chem disp; mv service pnt; baby facs; shwrs inc; el pnts (10A) €4.70; lndtte (inc dryer); shop; rest, snacks; bar; BBQ; playgrnd; pool; paddling pool; sand beach 8km; wifi; TV; 10% statics; dogs €1.50 (not acc Jul/Aug); poss cr; Eng spkn; adv bkg; quiet; red low ssn; CKE/CCI. "Lovely site in vineyard on steep hillside (but one san facs block at bottom of hill); c'vans taken in & out by tractor; facs poss stretched in ssn; winter storage avail." ♦ € 27.00 (3 persons) (CChq acc) 2010*

LONDES LES MAURES, LA see Hyeres *10F3*

MALAUCENE *10E2* (4km N Rural) *44.20101, 5.12535* **FFCC Camping Aire Naturelle La Saousse (Letilleul), La Madelaine, 84340 Malaucène [04 90 65 14 02]** Fr Malaucène take D938 N dir Vaison-la-Romaine & after 3km turn R onto D13 dir Entrechaux where site sp. After 1km turn R, site 1st on R. Sm, hdg pitch, terr, shd; wc; chem disp; shwrs inc; el pnts (5A) €2.50; lndry rm; tradsmn high ssn; shop, rest, snacks, bar, pool 4km; no statics; dogs; adv bkg rec; quiet; ccard not acc; red low ssn; CKE/CCI. "CL-type site o'looking vineyards with views to Mt Ventoux; some pitches in woods with steep incline - rec pitch on lower level for easy access; friendly, helpful owners; basic, clean facs; v peaceful, excel." 1 Apr-30 Sep. € 14.00 2012*

MALAUCENE *10E2* (8km S Rural) *44.12383, 5.10968* **Camping Le Bouquier, Route de Malaucène, 84330 Caromb [tel/fax 04 90 62 30 13; lebouquier@wanadoo.fr; www.lebouquier.com]** Fr Malaucène S on D938 for 8km; turn L D13 sp Caromb; site 800m on L just bef vill. Or NE fr Carpentras on D974 then D13; site on R 1.5km after Caromb cent. NB App fr N (D939/D13) avoids lge speed humps in Caromb. Med, hdg/mkd pitch, hdstg, terr, pt shd, htd wc; chem disp; shwrs inc; el pnts (10A) €3; lndtte; shops 1.5km; tradsmn; snacks; bar; BBQ (gas/elec); playgrnd; htd pool; lake sw 1km; gd walking/cycling; wifi; 5% statics; dogs €1.60; phone; poss cr; Eng spkn; adv bkg; quiet but some rd noise; ccard not acc; red low ss; CKE/CCI. "Well-kept site; attractive scenery; helpful staff; excel san facs; steps to disabled facs; steel pegs req; gd touring base; no twin-axles; vg." ♦ ltd 3 Apr-1 Oct. € 15.00 2011*

MALAUCENE *10E2* (400m NW Rural) *44.17789, 5.12533* **Camping Le Bosquet, Route de Suzette, 84340 Malaucène [04 90 65 24 89 or 04 90 65 29 09; fax 04 90 65 12 52; camping.lebosquet@wanadoo.fr; www.provence.guideweb.com/camping/bosquet/]** Fr S on D938 dir Vaison-la-Romaine turn L onto D90 at Malaucène dir Suzette. Site on R in 300m. Do not tow thro Malaucène. Sm, hdg pitch, all hdstg, terr, pt shd; htd wc; chem disp; baby facs; shwrs inc; el pnts (10A) €3.20 (poss rev pol); gas; lndtte; shop 600m; tradsmn; snacks; bar; playgrnd; pool; 2% statics; dogs €1; phone; adv bkg; quiet; ccard not acc; red low ssn; CKE/CCI. "Clean san facs; friendly owner; gd touring base Mt Ventoux; mkt Wed; easy walk to the town." ♦ 5Apr-14 Oct. € 16.30 2014*

MALEMORT DU COMTAT see Carpentras *10E2*

MALLEMORT see Salon de Provence *10E2*

MANOSQUE *10E3* (4km E Rural) *43.82352, 5.85424* **Camping Oxygene, 04210 Valensole [tel/fax 04 92 72 41 77; info@camping-oxygene.com; www.camping-oxygene.com]** Exit A51 junc 18 onto D907 E dir Vinon-sur-Verdon; in 1km turn L at rndabt onto D4 N dir Oraison; site in 2.5km on L, at Les Chabrands, just bef Villedieu. Med, hdg/mkd pitch, pt shd; wc; chem disp; mv service pnt; baby facs; shwrs inc; el pnts (6-10A) €3.50-4.50; lndtte (inc dryer); tradsmn; snacks; bar; BBQ (gas/elec); pool; horseriding, angling, canyoning, rafting & paragliding nrby; games area; gym; dogs €2.50; no twin-axles; quiet; ccard not acc; red low ssn. "Peaceful, well-kept site with hill views; excel well-run site; vg pool; many places of interest nrby, inc Gorges du Verdon; vg farm shop nrby." ♦ 20 Apr-17 Sep. € 33.50 2014*

MANOSQUE *10E3* (1.5km W Rural) *43.82986, 5.76384* **FFCC Camping Les Ubacs, 1138 Ave de la Repasse, 04100 Manosque [04 92 72 28 08; fax 04 92 87 75 29; lesubacs.manosque@ffcc.fr]** Exit A51 junc 18 onto D907 dir Manosque; then D907 dir Apt; site sp at last rndabt on W side of Manosque. NB easy to overshoot. Med, hdg/mkd pitch,pt sl, pt shd; wc (cont); mv service pnt; shwrs inc; el pnts (3-9A) €3.34-4.20; lndtte; shop; rest, snacks (high ssn); bar; playgrnd; pool (high ssn); tennis; lake sw 5km; entmnt; dogs €1; ccard acc; red long stay/low ssn/CKE/CCI. "Conv Gorges du Verdon; helpful." 1 Apr-30 Sep. € 15.40 2013*

MAUBEC see Cavaillon *10E2*

MAUSSANE LES ALPILLES see Mouriès *10E2*

MAZAN see Carpentras *10E2*

MONDRAGON see Bollène *9D2*

MONTAGNAC MONTPEZAT see Riez *10E3*

MONTAUROUX see Fayence *10E4*

MONTEUX see Carpentras *10E2*

MONTGENEVRE see Briançon *9C4*

MONTMAUR *9D3* (500m E Rural) *44.56866, 5.88326* **Camping Mon Repos, Le Cadillon, 05400 Montmaur [04 92 58 03 14; campingmonrepos@gmail.com]** Fr D994 Veynes-Gap, foll D937 N, turning R at bdge to keep on D937. Site sp. Sm, pt sl, shd; wc; chem disp; mv service pnt 6km; shwrs inc; el pnts (2-5A) €2-3; gas; Indtte; shop; tradsmn; snacks; playgrnd; pool 6km; entmnt; TV rm; 30% statics; dogs €1; quiet; Eng spkn; CKE/CCI. "Friendly, family-run site; excel walking." ♦ ltd 1 May-30 Sep. € 10.00 2009*

⊞ **MONTMAUR** *9D3* (7km SE Rural) *44.55003, 5.95114* **Camping au Blanc Manteau, Route de Céüse, 05400 Manteyer [92 57 82 56 or 92 57 85 89; pierre.wampach@wanadoo.fr; www.campingaublancmanteau.fr]** Take D994 fr Veynes twd Gap, past Montmaur; site sp fr vill of La Roche-des-Arnauds on D18 in 1km. Sm, mkd pitch, pt shd; htd wc (some cont); chem disp; baby facs; shwrs inc; el pnts (10A) €5.35; Indtte; shops 750m; snacks; bar; playgrnd; htd pool; tennis; adv bkg. "Gd sized pitches; some daytime rd noise; pleasant owner; pretty, in wooded area with beautiful views of mountains." ♦ € 24.00 2014*

MONTMEYAN *10E3* (500m S Rural) *43.63830, 6.06080* **Camping Le Château de L'Eouvière, 83670 Montmeyan [tel/fax 04 94 80 75 54; contact@leouviere.com; www.leouviere.com]** Fr Montmeyan take D13 dir Fox-Amphoux; site 500m on R out of Montmeyan. Med, mkd pitch, terr, pt shd; wc; chem disp; baby facs; shwrs inc; el pnts (10A) €4 (poss rev pol); Indtte; tradsmn; rest, snacks; bar; BBQ (el only on pitch); playgrnd; pool; games rm; wifi; TV; no statics; dogs €1.50; Eng spkn; adv bkg; Eng spkn; quiet; red low ssn; no ccard acc. "Peaceful site in lovely area; friendly owners; diff access; steep slopes/uneven steps; poorly lit; adequate san facs." ♦ 1 May-31 Sep. € 27.00 2010*

MORMOIRON *10E2* (4km E Rural) *44.05713, 5.22798* **Camping Les Verguettes, Route de Carpentras, 84570 Villes-sur-Auzon [04 90 61 88 18; fax 04 90 61 97 87; info@provence-camping.com; www.provence-camping.com]** E on D942 fr Carpentras dir Sault. Site at ent to Villes-sur-Auzon beyond wine cave. Or at Veulle-les-Roses turn E onto D68. Cont thro Sottenville-sur-Mer. Site on L in 2km. Lge, hdg/mkd pitch, pt sl, pt shd; htd wc; chem disp; shwrs inc; el pnts (6A) inc; Indtte; shops 1km; rest; pool; paddling pool; tennis; games rm; fishing 300m; tennis; wifi; TV rm; dogs €2.60- 3.60; adv bkg rec all times; quiet; red low ssn. "Scenic location; gd walking & cycling; friendly, helpful owner; families with children sited nr pool, others at end of camp away fr noise; poss muddy when it rains; sm pitches not suitable lge o'fits; red facs low ssn; new toilet/shower block." ♦ 23 Mar - 30 Sep. € 24.50 2013*

MORNAS *10E2* (2km E Rural) *44.21540, 4.74530* **Camping Domaine Le Beauregard, Route d'Uchaux, 84550 Mornas [04 90 37 02 08; fax 04 90 37 07 23; beauregard@franceloc.fr; www.camping-beauregard.com / www.campings-franceloc.fr]** Exit A7 at Bollène, then N7 twd Orange. On N end of Mornas turn L on D74 to Uchaux, site after 1.7km, sp. Lge, pt sl, shd; htd wc (some cont); chem disp; mv service pnt; shwrs inc; el pnts (6-10A) €3.30-4.40; gas; Indtte; shop; rest, snacks; bar; BBQ; playgrnd; 2 pools (1 htd, covrd); paddling pool; games rm; tennis; golf; horseriding; cycle hire; wifi; entmnt; dogs €4.15; 80% statics; adv bkg rec high ssn; quiet; Eng spkn; ccard acc; red CKE/CCI. "Open until 2230; phone ahead to check open low ssn; gd san facs; many derelict vans; poorly maintained & ltd facs low ssn." ♦ 3 Apr-26 Sep. € 28.00 2010*

MOURIES *10E2* (2km E Rural) *43.68207, 4.91769* **Camping à la Ferme Les Amandaies (Crouau), Mas de Bou Malek, 13890 Mouriès [04 90 47 50 59; fax 04 90 47 61 79]** Fr Mouriès take D17 E sp Salon-de-Provence. Site sp on R 200m past D5 junc. Foll site sp to farm in 2km. Sm, pt shd; wc; shwrs inc; el pnts €2 (rec long lead) (poss rev pol); tradsmn; BBQ; dogs; quiet. "Simple CL-type site; a few lge pitches; friendly owners; dated, dimly-lit san facs; conv coast & Avignon; book in using intercom on LH wall at ent to shwr block." 15 Mar-10 Oct. € 13.00 2009*

MOURIES *10E2* (7km NW Urban) *43.72138, 4.80950* **Camp Municipal Les Romarins, Route de St Rémy-de-Provence, 13520 Maussane-les-Alpilles [04 90 54 33 60; fax 04 90 54 41 22; camping-municipal-maussane@wanadoo.fr; www.maussane.com]** Fr Mouriès N on D17, turn onto D5 on o'skts of vill dir St Rémy-de-Provence, turn immed L site on R adj municipal pool. Med, hdg pitch, pt shd; wc; chem disp; baby facs; shwrs inc; el pnts (4A) €3.50; gas 200m; Indtte; shops 200m; BBQ; playgrnd; pool adj inc; tennis free; cycle hire; internet; TV; dogs €2.50; buses in ssn; adv bkg rec; quiet, but some rd noise; red long stay; ccard acc; CKE/CCI. "Well-kept, well-run site in lovely area; on edge of vill; excel san facs; some pitches diff m'vans due low trees; gd security; excel." ♦ 15 Mar-15 Oct. € 19.50 2009*

MOUSTIERS STE MARIE *10E3* (300m S Rural) *43.83963, 6.22150* **Camping Le Vieux Colombier, Quartier St Michel, 04360 Moustiers-Ste Marie [tel/fax 04 92 74 61 89 or 04 92 74 61 82 (LS); Contact@lvcm.fr; http://camping.vieux.colombier.pagesperso-orange.fr/]** Fr Moustiers go E on D952 dir Castellane. Site on R in 300m opp g'ge. NB Steep, winding access rd. Med, mkd pitch, sl, terr, pt shd; htd wc; 80% serviced pitches; chem disp; mv service pnt; baby facs; shwrs inc; el pnts (3-6A) €2.70-3.40 (rev pol); gas; Indtte; shop 600m; snacks; bar; BBQ; playgrnd; lake sw 5km; wifi; canoeing; windsurfing; dogs €2; Eng spkn; adv bkg ess high ssn; quiet; ccard acc; CKE/CCI. "Helpful staff; steep terrs, park at top & walk down; gd, clean san facs; steep uphill walk to lovely vill; conv Gorges du Verdon; gd walking; vg." ♦ ltd 1 Apr-30 Sep. € 14.00 2009*

PROVENCE

MOUSTIERS STE MARIE *10E3* (1km SW Rural) *43.84371, 6.21475* **FFCC Camping St Jean, Route de Riez, 04360 Moustiers-Ste Marie [tel/fax 04 92 74 66 85; camping-saint-jean@wanadoo.fr; www.camping-saint-jean.com]** On D952 opp Renault g'ge & petrol stn. Med, some hdg pitch, pt sl, pt shd; htd wc (some cont); chem disp; mv service pnt; baby facs; shwrs inc; el pnts (6-10A) €3.60-4.70; gas; lndtte; sm shop & 700m; tradsmn; snacks; BBQ (elec/gas); playgrnd; fishing; sand beach, lake sw & boating 4km; climbing nr; cycle rtes; games area; games rm; wifi; TV; 10% statics; dogs €2.10; poss cr; Eng spkn; adv bkg; quiet; ccard acc; red low ssn; CKE/CCI. "Excel site in lovely location by rv; dated san facs (2010); some pitches diff lge o'fits; easy uphill walk to beautiful vill; conv Gorges du Verdon; gd value." ♦ ltd 1 Apr-16 Oct. € 16.50 2011*

MOUSTIERS STE MARIE *10E3* (500m W Rural) *43.84497, 6.21555* **Camping Manaysse, 04360 Moustiers-Ste Marie [04 92 74 66 71; fax 04 92 74 62 28; www.camping-manaysse.com]** Fr Riez take D952 E, pass g'ge on L & turn L at 1st rndabt for Moustiers; site on L off RH bend; strongly advised not to app Moustiers fr E (fr Castellane, D952 or fr Comps, D71) as these rds are diff for lge vehicles/c'vans - not for the faint-hearted. Med, mkd pitch, pt sl, pt shd; wc (some cont); chem disp; mv service pnt; shwrs inc; el pnts (6-10A) €2.50-3.50; shops 500m; tradsmn; supmkt 10m, playgrnd; dogs €0.50; adv bkg; quiet; CKE/CCI. "Welcoming, family-run site; super views; gd unisex san facs; cherry trees on site - avoid parking under during early Jun; steep walk into vill; lge o'fits do not attempt 1-way system thro vill, park & walk; gd." ♦ ltd 1 Apr-24 Oct. € 14.00 2012*

MUY, LE *10F4* (1km E Rural) *43.46832, 6.59202* **RCN Camping Domaine de la Noguière, 1617 Route de Fréjus, 83490 Le Muy [04 94 45 13 78; fax 04 94 45 92 95; info@rcn-domainedelanoguiere.fr; www.rcn-domainedelanoguiere.fr]** Exit A8 junc 37 dir Roquebrune-sur-Argens & Puget-sur-Argens & take DN7 for 8km. Site on R. V lge, mkd pitch, some hdstg, pt shd; htd wc; baby facs; shwrs inc; el pnts (6A) inc; gas; lndtte (inc dryer); shop; tradsmn; rest, snacks; bar; BBQ; playgrnd; pool complex; waterslides; sand beach 15km; lake fishing 2km; tennis; games area; games rm; wifi; entmnt; TV; statics; dogs €6; adv bkg; quiet. ♦ 19 Mar-30 Oct. € 44.00 (CChq acc) 2011*

NANS LES PINS *10F3* (1km N Rural) *43.37535, 5.78510* **Camping Village Club La Sainte Baume, Quartier Delvieux Sud, 83860 Nans-les-Pins [04 94 78 92 68; fax 04 94 78 67 37; ste-baume@wanadoo.fr; www.saintebaume.com]** Exit A8 junc 34 dir St Maximin onto D560. Cross N7 & at next lge junc turn R onto D560 then immed L onto D80. Site 600m after sp Nans-les-Pins, L at traff lts then up private rd to site. Lge, mkd pitch, pt sl, shd; wc; chem disp; mv service pnt; baby facs; shwrs inc; el pnts (6A) inc; gas; lndtte (inc dryer); shop; rest, snacks; bar; BBQ; playgrnd; 3 pools; waterslide; jacuzzi; sand beach 35km; cycle hire; games area; gym; horseriding; wifi; TV; 90% statics; dogs €5; adv bkg; ccard acc; red low ssn. "Friendly staff; modern san facs; some pitches diff access; ltd facs low ssn; path into pleasant vill; mkt Wed am; excel." ♦ 1 Apr-30 Sep. € 33.00 (CChq acc) 2010*

NEVACHE *9C3* (6km W Rural) *45.03399, 6.54543* **Camp Municipal de Foncouverte, 05100 Névache [04 92 21 38 21 or 04 92 21 49 95; michel.goiran@orange.fr]** Fr Briançon take N94 NE twd Italian border dir Turin, then L onto D994 sp Névache. Rd is narr with passing places. Site is 2nd in vill. Med, pt sl, pt shd; wc; shwrs €1.20; lndry rm; shop; tradsmn; Eng spkn; quiet. "Vg for walkers; diff lge o'fits; no c'vans or m'vans allowed on rds W of Névache 0900-1800 in summer." 1 Jun-20 Sep. € 9.50 2009*

NIOZELLES see Brillane, La *10E3*

OPPEDE see Cavaillon *10E2*

ORANGE *10E2* (10km NE Rural) *44.16222, 4.93531* **Camping des Favards (Formerly Aire Naturelle Domaine), 1335 Route d'Orange, 84150 Violès [04 90 70 90 93; fax 04 90 70 97 28; campingfavards@gmail.com; www.favards.com]** Fr N exit A7 junc 19 Bollène. Foll D8 dir Carpentras & Violès. In Violès foll dir Orange & look for camp sp. Fr S exit A7 junc 22 sp Carpentras, take dir Avignon, then dir Vaison-la-Romaine to Violès. Avoid cent of Orange when towing. Sm, hdg/mkd pitch, unshd; htd wc (some cont); baby facs; shwrs inc; el pnts (6-10A) €3 (poss rev pol); lndry rm; tradsmn; snacks; bar; playgrnd; pool; dogs €1; poss cr; Eng spkn; adv bkg; quiet; ccard acc; red low ssn; wifi; CKE/CCI. "Well-kept site; excel pitches - some v lge (extra charge); superb san facs, poss stretched; wine-tasting on site high ssn; gd touring base; poss dust clouds fr Mistral wind; pitches muddy when wet; gd." ♦ 15 Apr-4 Oct. € 16.60 2014*

ORANGE *10E2* (8km SE Urban) *44.11472, 4.90314* **Camp Municipal Les Peupliers, Ave Pierre-de-Coubertin, 84150 Jonquières [04 90 70 67 09; fax 04 90 70 59 01; mairie@jonquieres.fr; www.jonquieres.fr]** Exit junc 22 fr A7 onto N7 S. In 2km turn L (E) onto D950. In 5km at rndabt turn L onto D977. In 200m turn L sp Jonquières, site on L in 2km, sp in vill. Site behind sports complex. Sp not obvious. Med, mkd pitch, pt shd; wc; chem disp; shwrs inc; el pnts (4A) inc; gas 500m; lndtte; wifi, shop, rest, snacks, bar 500m; playgrnd; pool, tennis adj; dogs €2.50; phone; poss cr; adv bkg; noise fr airfield (week days); ccard acc; CKE/CCI. "Excel, well-run, busy site; friendly & welcoming owners; vg, clean san facs; need care with high o'fits due trees; gates close 2200; Roman ruins nrby; popular long stay; vg o'night stop." 23 Apr-2 Oct. € 27.00 2014*

ORPIERRE *9D3* (500m E Rural) *44.31110, 5.69650* **Camping Les Princes d'Orange, Flonsaine, 05700 Orpierre [04 92 66 22 53; fax 04 92 66 31 08; campingorpierre@wanadoo.fr; www.camping-orpierre.com]** N75 S fr Serres for 11km to Eyguians. Turn R in Eyguians onto D30, 8km to Orpierre, turn L in vill to site (sp). Med, mkd pitch, hdstg, pt sl, terr, pt shd; wc; chem disp; mv service pnt; baby facs; shwrs inc; el pnts (10A) €4.50; gas; lndtte; shop; snacks; bar; playgrnd; htd pool; waterslide; tennis; games area; entmnt; TV; fishing; some statics; dogs €1.60; adv bkg; red low ssn; CChq acc. "Rock-climbing area; gd walking; beautiful, interesting vill." ♦ 1 Apr-31 Oct. € 44.70 (CChq acc) 2014*

PERNES LES FONTAINES see Carpentras *10E2*

PERTUIS *10E3* (1.5km E Urban) *43.69014, 5.52489* **Camping Les Pinèdes du Luberon, Ave Pierre Augier, Quartier St Sépulcre, 84120 Pertuis [04 90 79 10 98; fax 04 90 09 03 99; pinedes-luberon@franceloc.fr; www.campinglespinedes.com]** Exit Pertuis on D973 twd Manosque. After 1km fr cent of Pertuis turn R foll sp Camping & Piscine. In 2km pass pool to site 100m on brow of hill. Lge, hdg/mkd pitch, hdstg, terr, pt sl, pt shd; htd wc; chem disp; mv service pnt; baby facs; shwrs inc; el pnts (6-10A) €4-8; gas; Indry rm; shop & 2km; playgrnd; aquatic cent with 2 pools & waterslide; trampolines; entmnt; 95% statics; dogs €5; phone; quiet; red long stay; ccard acc (high ssn); red low ssn; CKE/CCI. "Spacious, attractive, well-kept site; now privately owned & few touring pitches; san facs need update (2011); mkt high ssn; vg." ♦ 15 Mar-15 Oct. € 25.00 2011*

"There aren't many sites open at this time of year"

If you're travelling outside peak season remember to call ahead to check site opening dates – even if the entry says 'open all year'.

PERTUIS *10E3* (6km SW Rural) *43.64410, 5.45468* **Camping Messidor (Naturist), Route de St Canadet, 13610 Le Puy-Ste Réparade [04 42 61 90 28; fax 04 42 50 07 08; messidor@online.fr; www.messidor.fr]** S fr Pertuis on D956/D556 twds Aix-en-Provence; after 5km turn R onto D561 twds Le Puy-Ste Réparade & Silvacane. At ent to vill take sp Aix-en-Provence via St Canadet (D13). Cross canal & turn immed 2nd R. Med, terr, pt sl, pt shd; wc; shwrs inc; el pnts (4A) €3.20; Indtte; shop 3km; tradsmn; rest, snacks; bar; pool; paddling pool; rv fishing & watersports; tennis; 50% statics; dogs €2; Eng spkn; adv bkg; quiet; INF card req. "Gd facs & pool; lovely views fr some pitches; sh walk to bus stop for Aix." 1 Apr-30 Sep. € 23.00 (CChq acc) 2009*

PEYNIER see Trets *10F3*

PRUNIERES see Chorges *9D3*

PUGET SUR ARGENS see Fréjus *10F4*

PUIMOISSON *10E3* (8km NE Rural) *43.89836, 6.18011* **Camping à la Ferme Vauvenières (Sauvaire), 04410 St Jurs [tel/fax 04 92 74 44 18; contact@ferme-de-vauvenieres.fr; www.ferme-de-vauvenieres.fr]** Fr Riez take D953 N to 1km beyond Puimoisson then fork R onto D108 sp St Jurs & site sp. Sm, pt shd; wc; chem disp; shwrs inc; el pnts (6A) €2.90; Indtte; shops 2km; BBQ; lake sw 2.5km; games area; dogs €0.75; Eng spkn; adv bkg; quiet; CKE/CCI. "Peaceful, basic site off beaten track; wonderful views; lavendar fields; friendly Dutch owner; clean san facs, poss stretched if site full; gd for mountain walking; D17 to Majastres v narr; vg mkt on Wed & Sat in Riez." 1 Apr-1 Oct. € 17.50 2014*

RAMATUELLE see St Tropez *10F4*

REGUSSE *10E3* (2.5km NW Rural) *43.66031, 6.15103* **Village-Camping Les Lacs du Verdon, Domaine de Roquelande, 83630 Régusse [04 94 70 17 95; fax 04 94 70 51 79; info@homair.com; www.homair.com]** Fr W exit A8 junc 34 at St Maximin onto D560 Barjols, Tavernes, Montmeyan then D30 to Régusse. At rndabt in Régusse turn L twd St Jean & foll sp. Fr E exit A8 junc 36 Le Muy then Draguignan then D557 to Villecroze, Aups & Régusse. At rndabt turn R twd St Jean & foll sp. Lge, mkd pitch, pt shd; wc; chem disp; mv service pnt; shwrs inc; el pnts (6A) inc; gas; Indtte; shop; rest, snacks; bar; BBQ; playgrnd; pool; tennis; entmnt; internet; TV rm; 10% statics; dogs €5; poss cr; Eng spkn; adv bkg ess high ssn; quiet; ccard acc; CKE/CCI. "Beautiful area; mainly gravel pitches under pine trees; diff lge o'fits without mover due to trees." ♦ 1 Apr-30 Sep. € 31.00 2010*

RIEZ *10E3* (5km N Rural) *43.86953, 6.13160* **Camp Municipal Les Lavandes, Chemin de Touires, 04410 Puimoisson [04 92 74 71 49]** N fr Riez on D953 to Puimoisson in 5km; turn L onto D56; site in 1km on R. Med, mkd pitch, pt shd; wc (cont) (own san rec); shwrs inc; shop, rest & snacks 1km; dogs €1.50; quiet; ccard not acc;CKE/CCI. "Pleasant, clean site; mountain views; ramp to gd basic facs; conv Gorges du Verdon & Lac de Ste Croix - gd sw & beach; gd walking & cycling." ♦ 1 Jun-30 Sep. € 9.40 2009*

RIEZ *10E3* (500m SE Urban) *43.81306, 6.09931* **Camping Rose de Provence, Rue Edouard Dauphin, 04500 Riez [tel/fax 04 92 77 75 45; info@rose-de-provence.com; www.rose-de-provence.com]** Exit A51 junc 18 onto D82 to Gréoux-les-Bains then D952 to Riez. On reaching Riez strt across rndabt, at T-junc turn L & immed R, site sp. Med, mkd pitch, pt shd; wc; chem disp; shwrs inc; el pnts (6A) inc; Indtte; rest, snacks, bar 500m; playgrnd; jacuzzi; lake sw 10km; tennis adj; 5% statics; dogs €1.90; phone; adv bkg; no ccard; red low ssn; CKE/CCI; "Beautiful, well-kept site; helpful, friendly owners; gd san facs; nice vill; conv Verdon Gorge." ♦ ltd 3 Apr-3 Oct. € 17.70 2013*

ROQUE D'ANTHERON, LA see Cadenet *10E3*

ROQUEBRUNE SUR ARGENS see Fréjus *10F4*

ROSANS *9D3* (1.5km N Rural) *44.39547, 5.46094* **Camping Tamier Naturiste (Naturist), Route du Col de Pomerol, Tamier 05150 Rosans [04 92 66 61 55 or 06 80 23 64 81 (mob); fax 04 92 87 47 24; tamier@wanadoo.fr; www.naturisme-tamier.fr]** Off D94/D994 Serres to Nyons rd; turn N onto D25 at Rosans. Site sp in vill. Med, mkd pitch, terr, pt shd; htd wc; chem disp; shwrs inc; el pnts (6A) inc; Indtte; shop; tradsmn; rest, snacks; bar; playgrnd; pool; games area; some statics; TV; adv bkg; quiet; ccard acc; red low ssn. "Wonderful scenery; friendly owners; v steep access rd; suggest park in upper car park nr ent bef going to recep." 15 Apr-15 Oct. € 23.40 2009*

ROUSSET see Chorges *9D3*

ROUSSILLON *10E2* (2.5km SW Rural) *43.88973, 5.27596* **Camping L'Arc-en-Ciel, Route de Goult, 84220 Roussillon [04 90 05 73 96; contact@camping-arc-en-ciel.fr; www.camping-arc-en-ciel.fr]** Take D900 W out of Apt, then R on D201 sp Roussillon, then R on D4 for 1.5km, then L on D104 twd Roussillon. Take L fork twd Goult, site well sp 2.5km on L. No access for c'vans & m'vans in Roussillon vill. Med, mkd pitch, hdstg, pt sl, terr, pt shd; wc (some cont); chem disp; shwrs inc; el pnts (4A) €3.80; gas; lndry rm; sm shop & 2.5km (uphill); tradsmn; snacks; bar; playgrnd; pool; children's pool; games area; phone; adv bkg; quiet; CKE/CCI; dogs €3.50. "Tranquil woodland site; tight access some pitches; poss diff lge o'fits due trees; helpful staff; old san facs; beware rd humps & drainage channels on site access rds; some pitches poss diff lge o'fits; worth a detour; vg." ♦ 15 Mar-31 Oct. € 16.00 2014*

STE ANASTASIE SUR ISSOLE see Brignoles *10F3*

ST ANDIOL see Cavaillon *10E2*

ST APOLLINAIRE see Chorges *9D3*

ST AYGULF *10F4* (500m N Coastal) *43.39151, 6.72648* **Camping de St Aygulf Plage, 270 Ave Salvarelli, 83370 St Aygulf Plage [04 94 17 62 49 or 06 12 44 36 52 (mob); fax 04 09 81 03 16; info@campingdesaintaygulf.fr; www.campingdesaintaygulf.fr]** Fr Roquebrunne on D7 at rndabt 100m after vill sp St Aygulf take 3rd exit leading to Rue Roger Martin du Gard. Keep turning L. Fr Fréjus on D559, rd bends R after bdge over beach access, turn R bef rd climbs to L. V lge, hdg/mkd pitch, shd; wc; chem disp; shwrs inc; el pnts (5A) €3.50; gas; lndtte; shop; rest, snacks; bar; playgrnd; dir access to sand beach adj; watersports & sports facs nr; fishing; games area; entmnt; statics; dogs €3; extra for twin-axles & v lge m'vans; adv bkg; ccard acc; red low ssn/long stay; CKE/CCI; "Gd." 24 Apr-25 Sep. € 34.00 2013*

ST AYGULF *10F4* (4km S Coastal) *43.40963, 6.72491* **Camping Le Plage d'Argens, 541 route Départementale 559 (RN 98), 83370 St Aygulf [04 94 51 14 97; fax 04 94 51 29 44; camping.lepontdargens@yahoo.fr; www.camping-caravaning-lepontdargens.com]** Well sp fr D559 bet Fréjus & St Aygulf, by Rv Argens. If app fr W pass site on R & return via next rndbt. Lge, mkd pitch, pt shd; htd wc; chem disp; mv service pnt; baby facs; shwrs; el pnts (6A) €2; gas; lndtte (inc dryer); shop; tradsmn; hypmkt 1km; rest, snacks; bar; playgrnd; htd pool; paddling pool; sand beach adj; cycle hire; wifi; TV rm; 5% statics; dogs €2.50; poss cr; Eng spkn; adv bkg; some rd noise; ccard acc; CKE/CCI. "Excel, well-run site by rv; sh walk to uncrowded beach (pt naturist); excel facs & pool; cycle track to St Aygulf & pt way to Fréjus." 1 Apr-20 Oct. € 30.00 2013*

See advertisement

"That's changed – Should I let The Club know?"

If you find something on site that's different from the site entry, fill in a report and let us know. See www.caravanclub.co.uk/europereport.

ST AYGULF *10F4* (2km W Rural) *43.40691, 6.70923* **Camping Les Lauriers Roses, Route de Roquebrune, 83370 St Aygulf [04 94 81 24 46; fax 04 94 81 79 63; lauriersroses-camping@orange.fr; www.info-lauriersroses.com]** Exit A8 at junc 37 Puget-sur-Argens onto DN7 to Fréjus. At 1st rndabt after Fréjus town sp, turn R to St Aygulf at junc immed after rndabt. Pass under rlwy bdge & turn R onto D8. After bdge with traff lts foll rd up to junc & turn L onto D7, site in 1.5km on R. Med, mkd pitch, pt sl, terr, pt shd; wc; chem disp; baby facs; shwrs inc; el pnts (6-10A) €4-6; gas; lndtte; shop 500m; rest; bar; BBQ (gas only); playgrnd; htd pool & paddling pool; fitness area; sand beach 2km; games rm; entmnt; wifi; 10% statics; dogs €1.85; Eng spkn; adv bkg; quiet; ccard acc; CKE/CCI. "Excel, family-run, wooded site on hillside; diff acc some pitches for lge o'fits (max 8m) - owner assists with siting c'vans; no arr bet 1200-1500; mkt Tue & Fri." ♦ ltd 23 Apr-10 Oct. € 34.00 2011*

ST AYGULF *10F4* (2.5km W Coastal) *43.36566, 6.71264* **Camping Au Paradis des Campeurs, La Gaillarde-Plage, 83380 Les Issambres [04 94 96 93 55; fax 04 94 49 62 99; www.paradis-des-campeurs.com]** Exit A8/E80 junc 37 at Puget-sur-Argens onto DN7 to by-pass Fréjus, then onto D559 twd Ste Maxime. Site on R 2km after passing thro St Aygulf, on LH bend bef hill. Or exit junc 36 onto D125 to Ste Maxime, then D559 dir Fréjus. Site on L after ent Les Issambres. Med, mkd pitch, hdstg, pt sl, terr, pt shd; htd wc; chem disp; mv service pnt; baby facs; fam bthrm; 30% serviced pitches (extra charge); shwrs inc; el pnts (6A) €4 (poss rev pol); gas 2km; Indtte; shop; tradsmn; rest, snacks; bar; BBQ; playgrnd; sand beach adj; cycle hire; golf 4km; games rm; internet; TV rm; dogs €3; poss cr; Eng spkn; quiet; ccard acc; red low ssn; CKE/CCI. "V popular low ssn; direct access via underpass to beach; excel san facs; superb views fr top level pitches - worth extra; gates shut at night & guarded; helpful owners; old rd to St Aygulf suitable for cycling; excel; adj beach small." ♦ 1 Apr-5 Oct. € 43.30 (3 persons) 2014*

ST AYGULF *10F4* (5km NW Rural) *43.41626, 6.70598* **Camping L'Etoile d'Argens, Chemin des Etangs, 83370 St Aygulf [04 94 81 01 41; fax 04 94 81 21 45; info@etoiledargens.com; www.etoiledargens.com]** Exit A8 at junc 37 Puget-sur-Argens onto DN7 to Fréjus & D559 to St Aygulf, or fr DN7 take D7 to St Aygulf by-passing Fréjus & turn onto D8 to site. Lge, hdg/mkd pitch, shd; 25% serviced pitches; wc; chem disp; baby facs; shwrs inc; el pnts (10A) inc; gas; Indtte; shop; tradsmn; rest, snacks; bar; no BBQ; playgrnd; htd pool; sand beach 3km; rv fishing; tennis; archery; golf 1.5km; wifi; entmnt; 40% statics; dogs €5; poss cr; Eng spkn; adv bkg; quiet; ccard acc; red low ssn; CKE/CCI. "Friendly, helpful owners; gd facs, poss unclean low ssn; excel pool complex; ferry down rv to beach in ssn; vg." ♦ 1 Apr-30 Sep. € 59.00 2014*

ST CYR SUR MER (VAR) see Bandol *10F3*

ST JURS see Puimoisson *10E3*

ST LAURENT DU VERDON *10E3* (2km W Rural) *43.71066, 6.05789* **Domaine Naturiste d'Enriou (Naturist), 04500 St Laurent-du-Verdon [04 92 74 41 02; fax 04 92 74 01 20; domaine.enriou@voila.fr; www.domainedenriou.com]** Fr Riez foll D11 S, site on D311 to St Laurent-du-Verdon & sp fr D11/D311 junc immed N of Quinson. Med, shd; wc; chem disp; shwrs inc; el pnts (3-6A) €3.60-4; gas; shops; rest, snacks; playgrnd; 2 pools; sw lake 500m; canoes; archery; fishing; entmnt; TV; few statics; dogs €3.80; adv bkg; v quiet; INF card req. "Vg, friendly, peaceful site; lovely spot; conv Gorges du Verdon." 15 May-30 Sep. € 26.50 2009*

⊞ **ST LEGER LES MALEZES** *9D3* (300m E Rural) *44.64551, 6.20436* **Camping La Pause, Route du Barry, 05260 St Léger-les-Mélèzes [04 92 50 44 92; fax 04 92 50 77 59; info@camping-la-pause.fr; www.camping-la-pause.com]** Fr N85 Route Napoléon turn E onto D14 St Laurent-du Cros. At La Plaine take D113 to St Léger, site sp. Med, pt shd; htd wc; baby facs; chem disp; mv service pnt; shwrs inc; el pnts (2-10A) €2-10; gas; Indtte (inc dryer); shop 100m; rest, snacks; bar; BBQ; playgrnd; htd pool; tennis; horseriding; games area; games rm; wintersports; entmnt; 60% statics; dogs €1.50; adv bkg; quiet. € 13.00 2010*

STES MARIES DE LA MER *10F2* (700m E Coastal) *43.45633, 4.43576* **Camping La Brise, Rue Marcel Carrière, 13460 Les Stes Maries-de-la-Mer [04 90 97 84 67; fax 04 90 97 72 01; info@camping-labrise.fr; www.camping-labrise.fr]** Sp on o'skts on all rds. Take N570 fr Arles or D58 fr Aigues-Mortes. V lge, unshd; htd wc (mainly cont); mv service pnt; shwrs inc; el pnts (16A) €4.90; Indtte (inc dryer); sm shop & 500m; rest 500m; snacks; BBQ; 2 htd pools; paddling pool; beach adj; fishing; fitness area; wifi; entmnt; TV rm; some statics; dogs €5.20; site clsd mid-Nov to mid-Dec; red low ssn; CChq acc. "Gd facs; v cr Aug; poss mosquitoes; gd security; beach improved with breakwaters; m'vans can use free municipal car park with facs; recep open fr 0900-1700 but clsed 1200-1400; vg winter NH; pitches poorly mrkd, dirty & dusty." ♦ 1 Jan-12 Nov, 15 Dec-31 Dec. € 23.20 (CChq acc) 2014*

STE MAXIME *10F4* (5km NE Coastal) *43.33028, 6.66800* **Camping Les Cigalons, La Nartelle, 83120 Ste Maxime [04 94 96 05 51; fax 04 94 96 79 62; contact@campingcigalon.fr; www.campingcigalon.fr]** Site on D559 E of Ste Maxime, go thro La Nartelle & turn L into lane immed after seafood rest. Site on L after 25m. Med, mkd pitch, pt sl, shd; wc; chem disp; shwrs; el pnts (10A) €4; Indtte; sm shop; rest, snacks, bar adj; paddling pool; sand beach adj; wifi; some statics; dogs €2.50; poss cr; adv bkg; v quiet. "Site in gd position; friendly owners; dated san facs; sm v hard compacted earth pitches; car parking poss diff." ♦ 4 Apr-17 Oct. € 26.00 2010*

> “I like to fill in the reports as I travel from site to site”
>
> You'll find report forms at the back of this guide, or you can fill them in online at www.caravaclub.co.uk/europereport.

ST MAXIMIN LA STE BAUME *10F3* (3km S Rural) *43.42848, 5.86498* **Camping Caravaning Le Provençal, Route de Mazaugues, 83470 St Maximin-la-Ste Baume [04 94 78 16 97; fax 04 94 78 00 22; camping.provencal@wanadoo.fr; www.camping-le-provencal.com]** Exit St Maximin on N560 S twd Marseilles. After 1km turn L onto D64. Site on R after 2km. Lge, mkd pitch, pt sl, shd; wc; mv service pnt; shwrs inc; el pnts (6-10A) €3.40-4.40; gas; Indtte; shop & 3km; rest high ssn; snacks; bar; playgrnd; pool; TV; some statics; adv bkg; CKE/CCI. "Gd NH." 1 Apr-30 Sep. € 16.00 2012*

ST PAUL EN FORET see Fayence *10E4*

ST PIERRE D'ARGENCON see Aspres sur Buëch *9D3*

ST RAPHAEL See also sites listed under Agay.

ST RAPHAEL *10F4* (4.5km N Rural) *43.44611, 6.80610* **Douce Quiétude, 3435 Blvd Jacques Baudino, 83700 St Raphaël [04 94 44 30 00; fax 04 94 44 30 30; info@douce-quietude.com; www.douce-quietude.com / www.les-castels.com]** Exit A8 at junc 38 onto D37 then D100 sp Agay. Foll sp Valescure-Boulouris, site sp. NB c'vans not permitted on St Raphaël seafront. Lge, hdg/mkd pitch, hdstg, pt sl, pt shd; wc; chem disp; baby facs; serviced pitches; shwrs; el pnts (10A) inc; gas; Indtte (inc dryer); shop; tradsmn; rest; takeway; bar; BBQ (gas only); playgrnd; 2 pools (1 htd); waterslide; paddling pool; waterslide; sand beach 5km; cycle hire; gym; games area; games rm; wifi; entmnt; TV; many tour ops statics; dogs €5; phone; bus; poss v cr; Eng spkn; adv bkg; noise fr entmnt high ssn; ccard acc; red low ssn; CKE/CCI. "Lge pitches; excel facs; noisy disco nightly high ssn; sm touring pitches mostly amongst statics; vg." ♦ 30 Apr-8 Oct. € 54.00 (3 persons) (CChq acc) 2011*

> "We must tell The Club about that great site we found"
>
> Get your site reports in by mid-August and we'll do our best to get your updates into the next edition.

ST REMY DE PROVENCE *10E2* (500m E Urban) *43.78836, 4.84093* **Camping Pégomas, Ave Jean Moulin, 13210 St Rémy-de-Provence [tel/fax 04 90 92 01 21; contact@campingpegomas.com; www.campingpegomas.com]** On D99 fr W dir Cavaillon, ignore R fork to St Rémy 'Centre Ville' (& Sat Nav!). Pass twin stone sculptures on rndabt, at 2nd rndabt turn into Ave Jean Moulin , site on R in 400m - v sharp turn into site. Fr E Exit A7 junc 25 on D99 W dir St Rémy. Ignore sp 'Centre Ville', pass under aquaduct & across rndabt. At next rndabt turn L into Ave Jean Moulin, then as above. Do not attempt to tow thro town. Med, hdg/mkd pitch, shd; htd wc (mainly cont); chem disp; mv service pnt; baby facs; shwrs inc; el pnts (6A) €3.50 (poss rev pol & long lead req); gas; Indtte (inc dryer); shop 300m; tradsmn; snacks; bar; playgrnd; pool & paddling pool high ssn; games area; entmnt; wifi; TV rm; dogs €1.70; phone; poss cr; Eng spkn; adv bkg; quiet; ccard acc; red low ssn/long stay; CKE/CCI. "Well-run, busy site; clean san facs; lge o'fits poss diff some sm pitches; gd pool; gd touring base; recep clsd 2000 hrs, lge lay-by outside; mkt Wed am; excel for walking; lovely site." 17 Mar-1 Nov. € 46.00 2014*

ST REMY DE PROVENCE *10E2* (1km NW Rural) *43.7967, 4.82378* **Camping Monplaisir, Chemin Monplaisir, 13210 St Rémy-de-Provence [04 90 92 22 70; fax 04 90 92 18 57; reception@camping-monplaisir.fr; www.camping-monplaisir.fr]** Exit D99 at St Rémy onto D5 going NW dir Maillane, in 110m turn L & foll sp in 500m. Avoid going thro town. Med, hdg pitch, hdstg, shd; htd wc; chem disp; mv service pnt; baby facs; fam bthrm; shwrs inc; el pnts (10A) €4.20; gas; Indtte; shop; supmkt 500m; tradsmn; snacks, bar high ssn; BBQ (gas/elec); playgrnd; pool; paddling pool; cycle hire; wifi; entmnt; dogs €2; phone; bus 1km; Eng spkn; adv bkg; quiet; ccard acc; red long stay/low ssn; CKE/CCI. "Immac, well-run site; mostly gd sized pitches; clean, modern san facs; gd touring base; highly rec; site clsd last Sat in Oct; excel site." ♦ 11 Mar-19 Oct. € 30.00 2014*

ST TROPEZ *10F4* (6km SE Rural) *43.21804, 6.57830* **Camping Moulin de Verdagne, Route du Brost, 83580 Gassin [04 94 79 78 21; fax 04 94 54 22 65; info@moulindeverdagne.com; www.moulindeverdagne.com]** Foll N559 N fr Cavalaire for 6km. Take 1st R after town traff lts in La Croix-Valmer, site sp on R. Site in 2km, surrounded by vineyards. Rough app rd/track. Med, mkd pitch, terr, pt shd; wc (some cont); chem disp; shwrs inc; el pnts (6A) €4; Indtte; shop 4km; tradsmn; rest, snacks; bar; playgrnd; pool; sand beach 5km; dogs €3; 60% statics; phone; poss cr; Eng spkn; quiet; ccard acc; red low ssn/long stay. "Vg site; friendly recep; tight bends & narr pitches poss diff long o'fits; pool 2m deep." 1 Apr-31 Oct. € 24.00 2011*

ST TROPEZ *10F4* (7km S Rural) *43.21442, 6.63914* **Campéole Camping La Croix du Sud, Loumède, Route des Plages, 83350 Ramatuelle [04 94 79 89 21; fax 04 94 79 89 21; croix-du-sud@campeole.com; www.camping-saint-tropez.com / www.campeole.com]** App St Tropez fr W on D98A, turn R at traff lts at W o'skts onto D93 sp Ramatuelle. Site on R in 7km opp filling stn. Med, mkd pitch, pt sl, terr, pt shd; wc; baby facs; shwrs; el pnts (6A) €4.10; gas; Indtte; shop; tradsmn; rest, snacks; playgrnd; htd pool; sand beach 1.7km; games area; entmnt; TV; 50% statics; dogs €3.90; poss cr; Eng spkn; quiet; red low ssn; CKE/CCI. "Sm pitches, access poss diff." 2 Apr-2 Oct. € 39.00 2009*

> "I need an on-site restaurant"
>
> We do our best to make sure site information is correct, but it is always best to check any must-have facilities are still available or will be open during your visit.

ST TROPEZ *10F4* (7km S Rural) *43.24092, 6.57404* **Parc Saint James Gassin, Parc Montana, Route de Bourrian, 83580 Gassin [04 94 55 20 20; fax 04 94 56 34 77; gassin@camping-parcsaintjames.com; www.camping-parcsaintjames.com]** Exit A8 at junc 36 St Tropez; after Port-Grimaud foll sp Cavalaire-sur-Mer S on D559 where clearly sp. V lge, hdg/mkd pitch, hdstg, terr, pt shd; htd wc; shwrs inc; el pnts (6A) inc; Indtte; shop; rest, snacks; bar; BBQ; playgrnd; htd pool; paddling pool; spa/jacuzzi; beach 4km; tennis; games area; games rm; entmnt (child & adult); internet; golf 12km; 50% statics; dogs €5; phone; Eng spkn; adv bkg ess high ssn; quiet but some rd noise; ccard acc; red long stay/low ssn. "Conv St Tropez; scenic drives; vg site in a great location." ♦ 9 Jan-18 Nov. € 40.00 2011*

ST TROPEZ *10F4* (7km S Coastal) *43.23198, 6.65924* **Riviera Villages Kon-Tiki, Plage de Pampelonne, 83350 Ramatuelle [04 94 55 96 96; fax 04 94 55 96 95; kontiki@riviera-villages.com; www.riviera-villages.com]** Foll Ramatuelle on D93 sp fr St Tropez; site sp on L. V lge, mkd pitch, pt sl, pt shd; wc; chem disp; baby facs; shwrs inc; el pnts (6A) inc; gas; Indtte; shop; rest, snacks; bar; playgrnd; sand beach adj; watersports; tennis; archery; entmnt; TV; mainly statics; dogs; poss cr; adv bkg ess high ssn; quiet; red low ssn; ccard acc; CKE/CCI. "Touring area sm & poss a bit unkempt end of ssn; some sm pitches; coastal walks; conv St Tropez & hill vills." 1 Apr-31 Oct. € 40.00 2009*

"Satellite navigation makes touring much easier"

Remember most sat navs don't know if you're towing or in a larger vehicle – always use yours alongside maps and site directions.

ST TROPEZ *10F4* (8km S Rural) *43.20596, 6.65083* **Yelloh! Village Les Tournels, Route de Camarat, 83350 Ramatuelle [04 94 55 90 90; fax 04 94 55 90 99; info@tournels.com; www.tournels.com / www.yellohvillage.co.uk]** Exit A8 at Le Muy dir St Maxime, St Tropez. Take D61 dir Ramatuelle then foll sp 'Le Plages' & Camarat lighthouse. V lge, mkd pitch, terr, shd; htd wc (some cont); chem disp; mv service pnt; some serviced pitches; sauna; shwrs inc; el pnts (5A) inc; gas; lndtte; shops; rest, snacks; bar; playgrnd; htd pool; paddling pool; sand beach 1.5km; (shuttle bus high ssn); tennis; games area; fitness rm; cycle hire; wifi; entmnt; TV; 90% statics; dogs €4; Eng spkn; adv bkg; quiet; ccard acc; red low ssn; CKE/CCI. "Peaceful site on wooded hillside; well-kept & well-run; lower pitches full long term winter o'fits; lovely views upper terr levels but access via steep, narr rd - poss diff long o'fits, mechanical help avail." 1 Apr-6 Nov. € 59.00 2011*

See advertisement

ST VINCENT LES FORTS *9D3* (1km N Rural) *44.45682, 6.36529* **Campéole Camping Le Lac, Le Fein, 04340 St Vincent-les-Forts [04 92 85 51 57; fax 04 92 85 57 63; lac@campeole.com; www.camping-montagne.com / www.campeole.com]** W fr Barcelonnette on D900/D900b, past St Vincent-les-Forts dir Le Lautaret. Turn R onto D7 & foll narr steep winding rd to end, site sp o'looking lake. Lge, mkd pitch, terr, sl, pt shd; wc; chem disp; mv service pnt; baby facs; shwrs inc; el pnts (6A) €4.10; lndtte (inc dryer); shop; tradsmn; rest, snacks; bar; BBQ; playgrnd; pool; paddling pool; lake sw & beach 500m; fishing; watersports; tennis; horseriding; games area; games rm; wifi; child entmnt; 30% statics; dogs €3.50; phone; Eng spkn; adv bkg; quiet; ccard acc; red low ssn; CKE/CCI. "Simple site in superb scenic location; many leisure activities; vg walking in area; vg." ♦ 20 May-25 Sep. € 25.00 2012*

SALERNES *10F3* (4km E Rural) *43.55360, 6.29781* **Camping Club Le Ruou, Les Esparrus, 83690 Villecroze-les-Grottes [04 94 70 67 70; fax 04 94 70 64 65; info@leruou.com; www.leruou.com]** Fr Draguignan take D557 thro Flayosc, then D560 dir Salernes. Site sp on L. Med, mkd pitch, terr, shd; htd wc; chem disp; mv service pnt; baby facs; el pnts (6-10A) €4.20-6; gas; lndtte (inc dryer); shop; rest, snacks; bar; BBQ: playgrnd; htd pool; paddling pool; waterslide; fishing; games area; archery; wifi; entmnt; games/TV rm; adv bkg; 35% statics; dogs €3.20; adv bkg; quiet. ♦ 1 Apr-31 Oct. € 28.00 2011*

PROVENCE

SALERNES *10F3* (650m NW Rural) *43.56606, 6.22561* **Camp Municipal Les Arnauds, 83690 Salernes [04 94 67 51 95; fax 04 94 70 75 57; lesarnauds@ville-salernes.fr; www.village-vacances-lesarnauds.com]** W fr Draguignan on D557 thro Salernes; site sp on L on W o'skts of town; to avoid town cent turn R at rndabt on E o'skts sp Villecroze; take 1st L at next 2 rndabts & foll site sp. Med, hdg/mkd pitch, pt shd; wc; chem disp; baby facs; shwrs; el pnts (10A) inc; Indtte (inc dryer); bar; playgrnd; tennis; wifi; dogs €2; Eng spkn; adv bkg; quiet; ccard acc; red low ssn; CKE/CCI. "Excel, rvside site & san facs; warm welcome; gd night lighting; some sm pitches poss diff lge o'fits; no twin-axles; no entry 1200-1500; take torch into shwrs, lights on sh time switch." ♦ 2 May-30 Sep. € 26.50 2014*

SALLES SUR VERDON, LES *10E3* (1.9km N Rural) *43.78129, 6.21298* **Camp Municipal Les Ruisses, 83630 Les Salles-sur-Verdon [04 98 10 28 15; fax 04 98 10 28 16; lesruissescamping@orange.fr; www.sallessurverdon.com]** Fr Moustiers foll D957, site on L just bef Les Salles. Lge, mkd pitch, pt shd; wc (some cont); baby facs; shwrs inc; el pnts (6A) €3.20; Indtte; shop, snacks, bar high ssn; playgrnd; shgl beach & lake nr; fishing; dogs €1.70; no adv bkg; quiet; ccard acc; CKE/CCI. "Pleasant site; ltd facs low ssn but gd hot shwrs & clean facs." ♦ 15 Feb-15 Nov. € 19.00 2013*

"There aren't many sites open at this time of year"

If you're travelling outside peak season remember to call ahead to check site opening dates – even if the entry says 'open all year'.

SALLES SUR VERDON, LES *10E3* (2km E Rural) *43.77574, 6.24561* **FFCC Camping L'Aigle, Quartier St Pierre, 83630 Aiguines [tel/fax 04 94 84 23 75; contact@camping-aigle.fr; www.camping-aigle.fr]** Fr D957 fr Les Salles or Moustiers turn onto D19 & cont for approx 7km. Site sp 1km beyond vill. Rd steep, winding & with hairpins & vill narr for lge o'fits. Med, sl, terr, pt shd; wc; mv service pnt; baby facs; shwrs inc; el pnts (6A) inc; Indtte; rest, snacks; BBQ; playgrnd; ent barrier; dogs €3; phone; Eng spkn; quiet; ccard acc; red low ssn; CKE/CCI. "Lake views; clean, modern facs; steep, twisting access to terr pitches poss diff lge o'fits; highly rec." ♦ 24 Aug-19 Sep. € 29.00 2010*

SALLES SUR VERDON, LES *10E3* (500m W Rural) *43.77552, 6.20719* **Camping La Source, Lac de Sainte Croix, Quartier Margaridon, 83630 Les Salles-sur-Verdon [04 94 70 20 40; fax 04 94 70 20 74; contact@camping-la-source.eu; www.camping-la-source.eu]** Fr Moustiers on D957, foll sp Camping Les Pins (adj) via rd round vill. Med, hdg/mkd pitch, hdstg, pt terr, pt shd; wc (some cont); chem disp; child/baby facs; serviced pitches; shwrs inc; el pnts (10A) €3.80 (poss rev pol); gas; Indtte; shop, rest, snacks, bar 500m; BBQ; playgrnd; dir access to lake; lake sw & shgl beach adj; watersports; canoe hire; TV rm; dogs €2.20; phone; Eng spkn; adv bkg; quiet; ccard acc; red low ssn; CKE/CCI. "Excel facs; superb situation; well-run site conv Gorges du Verdon; friendly, helpful owners; gates clsd 2200-0700; some sm pitches - manhandling poss req; highly rec." ♦ 15 Apr-10 Oct. € 17.40 2010*

SALLES SUR VERDON, LES *10E3* (500m W Rural) *43.77628, 6.2090* **FFCC Camping Les Pins, Lac de Sainte Croix, 83630 Les Salles-sur-Verdon [04 98 10 23 80; fax 04 94 84 23 27; campinglespins83@orange.fr; www.campinglespins.com]** Fr Moustiers on D957 to Les Salles-sur-Verdon. Site clearly sp in vill on lakeside, via track round vill. Med, hdg/mkd pitch, hdstg, terr, pt shd; wc; chem disp; mv service pnt; serviced pitches; baby facs; shwrs inc; el pnts (6A) inc; gas; Indtte; shop 200m, tradsmn; bar; playgrnd; shgl beach & lake sw 200m; fishing; canoe hire; watersports; wifi; dogs €1.95; Eng spkn; adv bkg; quiet; ccard acc; red low ssn/long stay/CKE/CCI. "Lovely views; excel, friendly site; busy high ssn, facs poss stretched; gd touring base." ♦ 1 Apr-16 Oct. € 23.00 2011*

SALON DE PROVENCE *10E2* (12km NE Rural) *43.72125, 5.20495* **FFCC Camping Durance Luberon, Domaine du Vergon, 13370 Mallemort [04 90 59 13 36; fax 04 90 57 46 62; duranceluberon@orange.fr; www.campingduranceluberon.com]** Exit A7 junc 26 onto D7n dir Aix-en-Provence. In 11km turn L at rndabt onto D561 dir Charleval (passing Pont-Royal golf course). In 1km turn L dir Mallemort, site on R in 1km, sp. Med, hdg/mkd pitch, pt shd; htd wc; chem disp; mv service pnt; shwrs inc; el pnts inc (6-10A) €3.80-4.50; gas; Indtte; sm shop & 3km; tradsmn; rest adj; snacks; bar; BBQ; playgrnd; htd pool; paddling pool; rv fishing 1km; tennis; cycle hire; horseriding adj; wifi; 5% statics; dogs €2; phone; Eng spkn; adv bkg; quiet; red low ssn; ccard not acc; CKE/CCI. "Gd site with lge pitches; friendly owners; clean, modern san facs; gd touring base; excel." ♦ 1 Apr-30 Sept. € 22.00 2013*

SALON DE PROVENCE *10E2* (5km NW Rural) *43.67820, 5.06480* **Camping Nostradamus, Route d'Eyguières, 13300 Salon-de-Provence [04 90 56 08 36; fax 04 90 56 65 05; gilles.nostra@gmail.fr; www.camping-nostradamus.com]** Exit A54/E80 junc 13 onto D569 N sp Eyguières. After approx 1.5km turn R opp airfield onto D72d, site on R in approx 4km just bef T-junc. Or fr N exit A7 junc 26 dir Salon-de-Provence. Turn R onto D17 for 5km dir Eyguières, then L onto D72, site on L. Med, hdg/mkd pitch, pt shd; wc; chem disp; mv service pnt; baby facs; shwrs inc; el pnts (4-6A) €2.95-5.15; gas; Indtte (with dryer); shop 3km; tradsmn; rest, snacks; bar; BBQ; playgrnd; pool; paddling pool; games area; wifi; entmnt; TV; 15% statics; dogs €3; phone; Eng spkn; adv bkg (bkg fee); quiet; ccard acc; red low ssn; CKE/CCI. "Pleasant site; busy high ssn; welcoming owner with vg sense of humour!; poss diff access lge o'fits; dusty when dry; gd walking." ♦ 1 Mar-30 Nov. € 23.65 2014*

SANARY SUR MER *10F3* (4km NE Urban) *43.13147, 5.81483* **Campasun Mas de Pierredon, 652 Chemin Raoul Coletta, 83110 Sanary-sur-Mer [04 94 74 25 02; fax 04 94 74 61 42; pierredon@campasun.com; www.campasun-pierredon.fr]** Take D11 fr Sanary, cross m'way & 1st L. Site on R in approx 1km. Med, shd; htd wc; chem disp; mv service pnt; shwrs inc; el pnts (10A) inc; Indtte; shop; supmkt 800m; rest, snacks; bar; playgrnd; htd pool; paddling pool; waterslides; beach 3km; tennis; wifi; entmnt; TV; dogs €4; poss cr; adv bkg rec; rd noise; red low ssn; red CKE/CCI; "Gd family site." ♦ 19 Apr-30 Sep. € 47.00 2013*

⊞ **SANARY SUR MER** *10F3* (2km SE Urban) *43.11271, 5.82915* **Camping Les Playes, 419 Rue Grand, 83140 Six-Fours-les-Plages [04 94 25 57 57, 06 08 25 97 32 (mob) or 06 72 09 62 79 (mob); fax 04 94 07 19 90; camplayes@wanadoo.fr; www.camplayes.com]** Fr Six-Fours-les-Plages foll sp 'Camping Les Playes'. Site situated bet D11 & D63. Med, mkd pitch, hdstg, pt sl, terr, shd; htd wc; chem disp; shwrs inc; el pnts (10A) €4.50; Indtte; shops 300m; tradsmn; rest, snacks; bar; htd pool; beach 1.5km; wifi; dogs €4; bus 300m; poss cr; adv bkg; quiet; ccard acc; red low ssn; CKE/CCI. "Site on hillside on edge of wood; friendly recep; ltd space for tourers, rec phone ahead; poss diff lge o'fits; gd." € 30.00 2011*

SANARY SUR MER *10F3* (1.5km W Coastal) *43.12400, 5.78695* **Campasun Parc Mogador, 167 Chemin de Beaucours, 83110 Sanary-sur-Mer [04 94 74 53 16; fax 04 94 74 10 58; mogador@campasun.eu; www.campasun-mogador.eu]** Fr A50 exit junc 12 dir Bandol. Camping sp on R bef Sanary (for 2 sites). Lge, pt shd; htd wc; mv service pnt; baby facs; shwrs inc; el pnts (10A) inc; gas; Indtte (inc dryer); ltd shop; rest, snacks; bar; playgrnd; htd pool; paddling pool; shgl beach 800m; fishing, watersports 1km; games area; wifi; entmnt; TV; 40% statics; dogs €2.40 (not acc Jul/Aug); bus nrby; adv bkg rec; quiet; red low ssn. "Busy site; gd sized pitches; excel, modern san facs; narr site rds & overgrowing trees poss diff lge o'fits; poss muddy after heavy rain; attractive port." ♦ 14 Mar-6 Nov. € 40.30 2011*

"That's changed – Should I let The Club know?"

If you find something on site that's different from the site entry, fill in a report and let us know. See www.caravanclub.co.uk/europereport.

SAULT *10E3* (2km NE Rural) *44.10165, 5.42260* **Camp Municipal du Defends, Route de St Trinit, 84390 Sault [04 90 64 07 18 or 04 90 64 02 30 (Mairie); campingsault@wanadoo.fr]** NE fr Sault on D950 dir St Trinit; site on R in 2km. Med, some mkd pitch, shd; wc; chem disp; shwrs inc; el pnts (6A) €3.70 (poss long lead req); gas 1km; supmkt 1km; BBQ; playgrnd; 10% statics; dogs; phone adj; poss cr; Eng spkn; CKE/CCI. "Site in woodland; conv Mont Ventoux & Gorges de la Nesque; gd cycling; gd." 7 Apr-30 Sep. € 12.70 2011*

SAVINES LE LAC *9D3* (2km SW Rural) *44.51812, 6.38445* **Camp Municipal Les Eygoires, Route de Barcelonnette, 05160 Savines-le-Lac [04 92 44 20 48 or 04 92 44 20 03 (Mairie); fax 04 92 44 39 71; camping.municipal.savinelelac@orange.fr; www.savines-le-lac.fr]** Take N94 to Savines. Site on D954 on N side of rd. Lge, mkd pitch, terr, pt shd; wc (some cont); baby facs; shwrs; el pnts (5A) €3.40; Indtte; shop; snacks; bar; playgrnd; lake sw & shgl beach; sailing; some statics; dogs €1.70; adv bkg; quiet. 10 May-13 Sep. € 14.85 2010*

⊞ **SEPTEMES LES VALLONS** *10F3* (1km NE Urban) *43.40688, 5.36185* **Camping Le Verdière, 4 Chemin de la Haute Bédoule, 13240 Septèmes-les-Vallons [04 91 65 59 98 or 06 28 19 20 25 (mob); fax 04 91 65 59 98; camping.laverdiere@wanadoo.fr; www.camping-la-verdiere.com]** Exit A51 junc 1 onto D543 dir Septèmes-les-Vallons; at 5-pnt rndabt in 1km take 2nd exit; at next rndabt in 800m turn R under m'way; immed turn R again (on other side m'way) into Chemin de la Haute Bédoule; site on L in 800m. NB Take care using Sat Nav, can take to m'way running alongside site but no turning for 1km in either dir. Sm, pt shd; wc; el pnts (6A) €2.50; shops nrby; supmkt 1km; bar; pool; internet; 40% statics; dogs €3; 70% statics; bus & train 1km; Eng spkn; rd noise; red low ssn. "Touring pitches shady; gd san facs; OK." € 21.50 2011*

SEYNE *9D3* (800m S Rural) *44.34270, 6.35896* **Camping Les Prairies, Haute Gréyère, 04140 Seyne-les-Alpes [04 92 35 10 21; fax 04 92 35 26 96; info@campinglesprairies.com; www.campinglesprairies.com]** Fr Digne-les-Bains, take D900 N to Seyne. Turn L on ent Seyne onto D7, site sp beside Rv La Blanche. Med, mkd pitch, pt shd; htd wc; chem disp; mv service pnt; baby facs; shwrs inc; el pnts (10A) €3.50; gas; Indtte; shop 800m; tradsmn; rest 800m; snacks; bar; BBQ; playgrnd; htd pool; tennis 300m; horseriding 500m; dogs €2; phone; Eng spkn; adv bkg; quiet; ccard acc; red low ssn; CKE/CCI. "Immac, tidy, peaceful site; excel; beautifully sited and maintained; rest fr mid June; highly rec." 18 Apr-12 Sep. € 34.00 2014*

SISTERON *10E3* (2.5km N Rural) *44.21467, 5.93643* **Camp Municipal Les Prés Hauts, 44 Chemin des Prés Hauts, 04200 Sisteron [tel/fax 04 92 61 00 37 or 04 92 61 19 69; contact@camping-sisteron.com; www.camping-sisteron.com]** On W of D951. Lge, hdg pitch, pt sl, pt shd; wc; chem disp; serviced pitches; shwrs inc; el pnts (10A) €4 (poss rev pol); Indtte; shop & 1.5km; playgrnd; pool; tennis; fishing; entmnt; dogs €2; Eng spkn; quiet; ccard acc; red low ssn; CKE/CCI. "Lovely, well-kept, busy site; excel location, gd views; lge pitches & gd for m'vans; helpful, friendly warden; site yourself low ssn; vg facs, ltd low ssn; interesting old town, gd mkt; conv a'route; vg; ent Barrier clsd at 20.00; Stunning pool; huge pitches; gd facs; friendly helpful staff; handy for m'way." ♦ 1 Apr - 30 Sep. € 21.50 2014*

SIX FOURS LES PLAGES see Sanary Sur Mer *10F3*

SORGUES *10E2* (5km NW Rural) *44.04163, 4.82493* **Camping L'Art de Vivre, Islon St Luc , 84230 Châteauneuf-du-Pape [04 90 02 65 43; www.camping-artdevivre.com]** Exit A7 junc 22 onto D907 S dir Sorgues; in 11km (just bef Sorgues) turn R onto D17 dir Châteauneuf-du-Pape; in 4km, bef vill, turn L at site sp; site in 1km. Site well fr D17. Med, mkd pitch, shd; wc; chem disp; mv service pnt; shwrs inc; el pnts (10A) €4; Indtte (inc dryer); rest, snacks; bar; BBQ; pool; games area; games rm; internet; dogs €2.50; Eng spkn; m'van o'night area; ccard acc. "Site situated in woodland nr rv; new enthusiastic owners (2011); gd walks & cycling; wine-growing area; gd." 3 Apr-15 Oct. € 15.00 2011*

SUZE LA ROUSSE see Bollène *9D2*

TALLARD see Gap *9D3*

*Last year of report

⊞ **TARADEAU** *10F3* (3km S Rural) *43.44116, 6.42766* **Camping La Vallée de Taradeau, Chemin La Musardière, 83460 Taradeau [tel/fax 04 94 73 09 14; campingdetaradeau@hotmail.com; www.campingdetaradeau.com]** Exit A8 junc 13 & take DN7 to Vidauban. Opp Mairie take D48 dir Lorgues then D73 N twd Taradeau for 1.5km. Site sp - rough app rd - on rvside. Med, mkd pitch, shd; htd wc; mv service pnt; shwrs inc; el pnts (2-10A) €2.50-6.50; Indtte; rest, snacks; bar; playgrnd; pool; caneoing; games area; games rm; wifi; entmnt; some statics; dogs €3; adv bkg; quiet; CKE/CCI. "Pleasantly situated site; friendly, helpful staff; vg pool." € 22.00 2011*

⊞ **TARASCON** *10E2* (5km SE Urban) *43.78638, 4.71789* **Camp Municipal du Grès, 33 Ave du Docteur Barbarin, 13150 St Etienne-du-Grès [04 90 49 00 03 or 06 11 42 45 68; campingmunicipaldugres@wanadoo.fr; www.campingalpilles.com]** Fr Arles take N570 dir Avignon D99 E dir St Rémy. Site sp on o'skts of St Etienne. Sm, hdg pitch, pt shd; wc (some cont); chem disp; mv service pnt; san fans; el pnts (16A) €4 ; shop 1km; wifi; no statics; dogs €1; quiet; CKE/CCI. "Gd, peaceful site; lge pitches; friendly staff; gd san facs, recently updated." € 14.00 2014*

TARASCON *10E2* (5km SE Rural) *43.76744, 4.69331* **Camping St Gabriel, Route de Fontvieille, 13150 Tarascon [04 90 91 19 83; contact@campingsaintgabriel.com; www.campingsaintgabriel.com]** Take D970 fr Tarascon, at rndabt take D33 sp Fontvieille, site sp 100m on R. Med, hdg pitch, shd; htd wc; chem disp; mv service pnt; shwrs inc; el pnts (6A) €3.30; gas; Indtte; shop; rest adj; snacks; bar; playgrnd; htd pool; rv fishing; games rm; wifi; TV; 30% statics; dogs €2; bus 3km; site clsd mid-Feb & Xmas/New Year; adv bkg; quiet but some rd noise; CKE/CCI. "Well-kept, charming site; excel base for Camargue & Arles; modern san facs; sm pitches poss not suitable lge o'fits; gd." ♦ 1 Mar-30 Nov. € 17.00 (CChq acc) 2010*

THOR, LE see Isle sur la Sorgue, L' *10E2*

⊞ **TRETS** *10F3* (4km SW Rural) *43.44178, 5.62847* **Camping Le Devançon, Chemin de Pourachon, 13790 Peynier [04 42 53 10 06; fax 04 42 53 04 79; infos@ledevancon.com; www.ledevancon.com]** Leave A8 at Canet or Pas-de-Trets or leave D6 at Trets & take D908 to Peynier. In vill cont on D908 sp Marseille. Site on R at end vill after g'ge. Med, mkd pitch, all hdstg, pt sl, shd; htd wc; chem disp; mv service pnt; shwrs inc; el pnts (3-10A) €3-5; gas; Indtte; shop; tradsmn; snacks; rest & bar (high ssn) BBQ; playgrnd; pool; paddling pool; sand beach 30km; tennis; entmnt; TV rm; 50% statics; dogs €1; some Eng spkn; adv bkg; quiet; ccard acc; red long stay/CKE/CCI. "Excel facs & site; helpful owner; poss diff manoeuvring onto pitches for lge o'fits; few water points; ltd facs low ssn; gd touring area." ♦ € 19.00 2010*

VACQUEYRAS see Carpentras *10E2*

VAISON LA ROMAINE *9D2* (500m NE Urban) *44.24518, 5.07886* **Camping du Théâtre Romain, Chemin du Brusquet, 84110 Vaison-la-Romaine [04 90 28 78 66; fax 04 90 28 78 76; info@camping-theatre.com; www.camping-theatre.com]** Fr town cent foll sp for Théâtre Romain & site. Ent to Chemin du Busquet on rndabt at Théâtre Romain. Or site sp off Orange-Nyons rd thro town (do not ent town cent). Med, hdg/mkd pitch, pt shd; htd wc (some cont); chem disp; mv service pnt; serviced pitches; baby facs; shwrs inc; el pnts (5-10A) €3-4.50; gas 500m; Indtte (inc dryer); shop 500m; tradsmn; bar; BBQ; playgrnd; pool; games rm; wifi; some statics; dogs €2; Eng spkn; adv bkg ess high ssn (bkg fee); quiet; ccard acc; red low ssn; CKE/CCI. "Excel, well-kept site; busy low ssn due long stay residents, rec book in adv; mainly gd sized pitches but some sm; most pitches suitable m'vans; clean, unisex san facs; attractive town; mkt Tues; highly rec; excel as usual; old Roman town centre, 10 mins walk fr campsite." ♦ 15 Mar-5 Nov. € 37.50 2014*

VAISON LA ROMAINE *9D2* (4km NE Rural) *44.26240, 5.12950* **Camping L'Ayguette, 84110 Faucon [04 90 46 40 35 or 06 18 47 33 42 (mob); fax 04 90 46 46 17; info@ayguette.com; www.ayguette.com]** Exit Vaison NE on D938, R on D71, thro St Romain-en-Viennois. Then R onto D86 sp Faucon. Site on R, well sp. Med, mkd pitch, terr, shd; htd wc; chem disp; baby facs; shwrs inc; el pnts (10A) €2.50 (poss long lead req); Indtte; shop, supmkt 4km; tradsmn; snacks; bar; BBQ; playgrnd; htd pool; wifi; dogs €1.80; adv bkg; quiet; ccard acc; red low ssn/long stay; CKE/CCI. "Excel, well-run site; lge pitches in forest setting; friendly, helpful owners; excel mod facs inc hairdryers & children's shwrs; tractor tow avail." 19 Apr-27 Sep. € 38.00 2014*

VAISON LA ROMAINE *9D2* (4km NE Rural) *44.26806, 5.10651* **Camping Le Soleil de Provence, Route de Nyons, Quartier Trameiller, 84110 St Romain-en-Viennois [04 90 46 46 00; fax 04 90 46 40 37; info@camping-soleil-de-provence.fr; www.camping-soleil-de-provence.fr]** Leave A7 at junc 19 Bollène onto D94 dir Nyons. After Tullette turn R onto D20 & then D975 to Vaison-la-Romaine; fr Vaison take D938 sp Nyons; in 4km R & in 150m L to site; well sp. Lge, terr, hdg/mkd pitch, pt shd; htd wc; chem disp; some serviced pitches; shwrs inc; el pnts (10A) €4.50; gas; Indtte; shop; tradsmn; rest high ssn; snacks; bar; playgrnd; pool; paddling pool; wifi; entmnt; dogs: poss cr; adv bkg; quiet, but weekly disco eves; ccard not acc; red low ssn; CKE/CCI. "Popular, scenic, family-run site; gd pools; lovely town; poss strong Mistral winds Sep; mkt Tues; excel." ♦ 15 Mar-31 Oct. € 30.00 2014*

⊞ **VAISON LA ROMAINE** *9D2* (800m SE Rural) *44.23440, 5.08955* **FFCC Camping Club International Carpe Diem, Route de St Marcellin, 84110 Vaison-la-Romaine [04 90 36 02 02; fax 04 90 36 36 90; contact@camping-carpe-diem.com; www.camping-carpe-diem.com / www.campings-franceloc.fr]** S on A7 exit Orange; foll sp to Vaison; at Vaison on Nyons rd (D938) turn S at rndabt by supmkt dir Carpentras. In 1km turn L at junc to St Marcellin, site immed on L. Lge, hdg/mkd pitch, terr, pt shd; wc (some cont); chem disp; mv service pnt; shwrs inc; el pnts (6-10A) €4.70-5.70; gas; lndtte; shop on site & 800m; tradsmn; pizzeria, snacks, bar high ssn; playgrnd; 2 pools; paddling pool; waterslide; entmnt; internet; TV rm; 10% statics; dogs €5; site clsd 21 Dec-16 Jan; poss cr; Eng spkn; adv bkg; red low ssn; ccard acc; CKE/CCI. "Lively site; helpful staff; poss dust fr nrby quarry; poss muddy pitches; gd san facs; gd cent for Provence." ♦ € 31.00 2013*

VAISON LA ROMAINE *9D2* (6km SE Rural) *44.23728, 5.14959* **Camping Les Trois Rivières, Quarter des Jonches, 84340 Entrechaux [04 90 46 01 72; fax 04 90 46 00 75; doc@camping-3rivieres.com; www.camping-les3rivieres.com]** Take D938 fr Vaison twd Malaucène for 3.5km. Turn E onto D54 to Entrechaux; site well sp at rndabts at both ends of vill. Narr app rd. Med, pt sl, shd; wc (mostly cont); shwrs; el pnts (3-10A) €2.50-4.50; gas; lndtte; shop 2km; rest, snacks; bar; playgrnd; rv shgl beach, sw & fishing; horseriding; games rm; some statics; wifi; entmnt; TV; some statics; dogs €2; poss cr; quiet; adv bkg; red low ssn. "Tranquil site in Les Gorges du Toulourenc; access diff lge o'fits most pitches; 3km fr Entrechaux; nice walks." 1 Apr-30 Sep. € 14.50 2010*

VAISON LA ROMAINE *9D2* (5km NW Rural) *44.26446, 5.05242* **Camping Domaine de La Cambuse, Route de Villedieu, 84110 Vaison-la-Romaine [04 90 36 14 53 or 06 32 18 15 54 (mob); dom.lacambuse@wanadoo.fr; www.domainelacambuse.com]** Fr Vaison-la-Romaine N on D51 sp Villedieu. After 4km fork R onto D94 sp Villedieu. Site on R after 300m. Sm, terr, pt shd; wc (some cont); chem disp; shwrs inc; el pnts (6A) €3; gas 4km; tradsmn; snacks, bar in ssn; pool; paddling pool; 5% statics; dogs €1.52; phone; poss cr; quiet; CKE/CCI. "Site in vineyard on hillside; friendly, helpful owners." 1 May-15 Oct. € 12.00 2014*

VALENSOLE *10E3* (5.4km E Rural) *43.83862, 6.02029* **Domaine du Petit Arlane (Naturist), Route de Riez, 04210 Valensole [04 92 74 82 70; fax 04 92 74 99 35; contact@domainepetitarlane.fr; www.domainepetitarlane.fr]** Leave A51 junc 18 to Valensole 15km, fr Valensole take D6 signed Riez, site on L 5km (v bendy rds). Med, mkd pitch, some hdstg, pt sl, some terr; chem disp; mv service pnt; shwrs; el pnts (6- 15A) €3.90-8; gas 5km; lndtte (inc dryer); tradsmn; rest; snacks; bar; BBQ; playgrnd; pool; games area; internet; wifi; tv rm; dogs leashed €3.30; twin axles; Eng spkn; adv bkg; ccard acc; 10% statics; inf card advised. "Beautiful site, many pitches face lakes; gd local walks fr local villages; bkg ess." ♦Ltd 26 Apr-30 Sep. € 25.20 2013*

VALLOUISE see Argentière La Bessée, L' *9C3*

VALREAS *9D2* (1km N Rural) *44.39264, 4.99245* **Camping La Coronne, Route de Pègue, 84600 Valréas [04 90 35 03 78; fax 04 90 35 26 73; la.coronne@wanadoo.fr; www.campings-vaucluse.com]** Fr Nyons take D538 W to Valréas. Exit town on D10 rd to Taulignan, immed after x-ing bdge over Rv Coronne turn R into D196 sp Le Pègue. Site on R in 100m on rvside. Sp app fr E but easy to miss; app fr W; well sp in Valréas. Med, hdg/mkd pitch, pt shd; wc (some cont); chem disp; mv service pnt; shwrs inc; el pnts (6A) inc; gas; lndtte; shop; tradsmn; rest; snacks; bar; BBQ; playgrnd; pool; paddling pool; fishing; wifi; entmnt; TV; dogs €4; phone; poss cr; Eng spkn; adv bkg; quiet; ccard acc; red low ssn; CKE/CCI. "Sm pitches; excel pool; facs need refurb & poss unclean; site clsd 2200-0700." ♦ ltd 1 Apr-31 Oct. € 22.00 2011*

PROVENCE

VERNET, LE *9D3* (800m N Rural) *44.28170, 6.39080* **Camping Lou Passavous, Route de Roussimat, 04140 Le Vernet [04 92 35 14 67; fax 04 92 35 09 35; loupassavous@orange.fr; www.loupassavous.com]** Fr N on A51 exit junc 21 Volonne onto N85 sp Digne. Fr Digne N on D900 to Le Vernet; site on R. Fr S exit A51 junc 20 Les Mées onto D4, then N85 E to Digne, then as above. Sm, pt sl, pt shd; htd wc; chem disp; baby facs; shwrs inc; el pnts (10A) €3.75; lndtte; shop; tradsmn; rest, snacks; bar; playgrnd; pool; fishing; games area; wifi; entmnt; TV; some statics; dogs €1.50; poss cr; Eng spkn; adv bkg; quiet; ccard acc; CKE/CCI. "Scenic location; gd, clean facs; Dutch owners; gd walking." ♦ 15 Apr-1 Oct. € 18.50 2009*

VEYNES *9D3* (2km SW Rural) *44.51889, 5.79880* **FFCC Camping Les Rives du Lac, Les Iscles, 05400 Veynes [04 92 57 20 90; contact@camping-lac.com; www.camping-lac.com]** Off D994. Sp on lakeside. Med, mkd pitch, hdstg, pt sl, pt shd; wc; chem disp; mv service pnt; baby facs; shwrs; el pnts (10A) €3.50; lndtte; snacks; bar; BBQ; playgrnd; cvred pool; paddling pool; lake sw & beach adj with games in high ssn; watersports; mountain biking; climbing; open air cinema twice weekly; wifi; dogs €2.50; bus 500m; phone; adv bkg; quiet, occasional rlwy noise; ccard acc; red low ssn; CKE/CCI. "Attractive, well-run site on shore of sm lake; welcoming staff; san facs excel; something for all ages." 1 May-30 Sep. € 23.00 2013*

VIGNEAUX, LES see Argentiere la Bessee, L' *9C3*

VILLARS COLMARS see Colmars *9D4*

VILLECROZE LES GROTTES see Salernes *10F3*

VILLES SUR AUZON see Mormoiron *10E2*

VIOLES see Orange *10E2*

VISAN see Valréas *9D2*

VOLONNE see Château Arnoux *10E3*

Rhône-Alpes

Regional Introduction

Mont Blanc

Welcome to Rhône-Alpes

A very attractive region to visit, the Rhône-Alpes has a stunning landscape. The mountains house popular winter resorts that provide skiing and snowboarding opportunity as well as many other activities.

If it's a slower pace that you are after, the spas in the hilly towns and villages offer relaxation. The lakes of Lémain, Bourget and Annecy, as well as rivers and springs of the area have all encouraged the development of spa-tourism and many well being centres.

With so much to see and do in the area, Rhône-Alpes is well suited to providing visitors with whatever style of holiday they are looking for.

Local highlights

For a real taste of the Rhône-Alpes region sample raclette – a simple grilled cheese dish with potatoes and pickles.

La Grande Odyssée dog sled race is held in the heart of the Alps each year and you can watch the teams race through the ancient village of Bonneval-sur-Arc and the Mont Cenis mountain pass.

Major towns and cities

- Aix-les-Bains – an Alpine spa resort with Roman connections.
- Chambéry – an old city with fascinating historical and religious sites.
- Chamonix-Mont-Blanc – famous resort, best known for its winter sports.
- Grenoble – this city is a cultural, research and industrial centre with many art museums.
- Lyon – a diverse regional capital with a Roman influenced history.

Regional attractions

- Mont Blanc – ride up by cable car or tramway to see the amazing views.
- Archaeological Museum, Grenoble – found on a historical site and full of ancient burials.
- Ardéche Gorge – great for activities like hiking and kayaking.
- Parc de la Téte d'Or, Lyon – explore the rose garden, zoo and lake.

Find out more

www.rhonealpes-tourisme.com

Tel: (0)4 26 73 31 59 Rhône-Alpes Tourist Board

ABRETS, LES *9B3* (2km E Rural) *45.54065, 5.60834* **Kawan Village Le Coin Tranquille, 6 Chemin des Vignes, 38490 Les Abrets [04 76 32 13 48; fax 04 76 37 40 67; contact@coin-tranquille.com; www.coin-tranquille.com]** Fr N exit A43 at junc 10 Les Abrets & foll D592 to town cent. At rndbt at monument take D1006 twd Chambéry/Campings; cont for 500m then turn L sp Le Coin Tranquille; cross level x-ing & cont for 500m to site. Fr S on A48 exit junc 10 at Voiron onto D1075 to Les Abrets; turn R at rndabt onto D1006 twd Le Pont-de-Beauvoisin, then as above. Lge, hdg/mkd pitch, pt shd; wc (some cont); chem disp; mv service pnt; baby facs; shwrs inc; el pnts (6A) inc (poss rev pol & long lead poss req); gas; lndtte (inc dryer); shop; tradsmn; rest, snacks; bar; BBQ; playgrnd; pool; paddling pool; cycle hire; archery; horseriding & fishing 7km; golf 15km; games area; games rm; wifi; entmnt; TV rm; dogs €1.50; Eng spkn; no c'vans/m'vans over 8m unless bkd in adv; adv bkg ess high ssn; noisy high ssn; ccard acc; red low ssn; CKE/CCI. "Well-kept, well-run site in gd location; lge narr pitches; busy/noisy site, but some quiet pitches avail; helpful & friendly staff; well-kept, clean san facs, ltd low ssn; lovely pool; vg activities for children; poss flooding in wet weather; excel." ♦ 1 Apr-31 Oct. € 33.50 (CChq acc) SBS - M05 2012*

ABRETS, LES *9B3* (3km S Rural) *45.47079, 5.54688* **Camping Le Calatrin (formerly Municipal), 799 Rue de la Morgerie, 38850 Paladru [04 76 32 37 48; fax 04 76 32 42 02; le.calatrin@gmail.com; www.camping-paladru.fr]** S fr Les Abrets on D1075; turn R onto D50 to Paladru; site 1km beyond vill on L, on brow of hill. Or exit A48 junc 9 & foll sp 'Lac de Paladru'; 3km after rndabt junc of D50 & D17, site on R (by another rndabt). Med, hdg/mkd pitch, terr, shd; wc (some cont); chem disp; mv service pnt; baby facs; shwrs inc; el pnts (10A) €4 (long lead poss req); gas; lndtte; shop & 500m; tradsmn; snacks; bar; BBQ; playgrnd; lake sw & shgl beach adj; fishing; watersports; cycle hire; tennis 500m; games area; games rm; entmnt; wifi; TV; 30% statics; dogs €3.50; bus 200m; Eng spkn; adv bkg; quiet; no twin-axles; red low ssn/long stay; CKE/CCI. "Attractive site; direct access to lake; lge pitches; welcoming & helpful owners; gd recreational facs; nice walks; excel." ♦ 1 Apr-30 Sep. € 17.00 2013*

ABRETS, LES *9B3* (8km S Rural) *45.46736, 5.55857* **Camping International Le Lac, La Veronnière, 38620 Montferrat [04 76 32 31 67; fax 04 76 32 38 15; infos@camping-interdulac.com]** D1075 5km S of Les Abrets turn R onto D50 dir Paladru. Turn L sp La Veronnière, site on R on lakeside. Lge, mkd pitch, pt shd; wc; chem disp; shwrs inc; el pnts (6A) inc; lndtte; tradsmn; rest, snacks; bar; BBQ; playgrnd; lake sw & shgl beach; fishing; sailing; wifi; 25% statics; dogs €1.30; phone; Eng spkn; adv bkg; quiet; ccard acc; CKE/CCI. "Lovely lake; plenty of activities; gd touring base & conv NH; shwrs need refurb (2010)." ♦ 30 Apr-30 Sep. € 18.00 2010*

ABRETS, LES *9B3* (11km SW Rural) *45.44621, 5.53183* **Camp Municipal le Bord du Lac, 687 route du Bord du Lac, 38850 Bilieu [04 76 06 67 00 or 04 76 06 62 41 (Mairie); fax 04 76 06 67 15; camping.bilieu@live.fr; www.camping-bilieu.com]** S on D1075 fr Les Abrets. Turn R onto D50. Just bef Paladru, turn L to Charavines. site on R on ent Bilieu, by lakeside. Med, mkd pitch, pt sl, terr, pt shd; htd wc; chem disp; shwrs inc; el pnts (10A) €3; lndtte; tradsmn; playgrnd; wifi; 10% statics; poss cr; quiet; ccard acc; CKE/CCI. "Nice site by lake; san facs v gd; staff helpful; no sw in lake fr site, only boat launch; pitch access poss diff; gd." 1 Apr-30 Sep. € 23.30 2013*

AILLON LE JEUNE see Châtelard, Le *9B3*

AIX LES BAINS *9B3* (10km N Urban) *45.78484, 5.94262* **FFCC Camping Beauséjour, La Rippe, 73410 Albens [04 79 54 15 20 or 06 43 33 01 93 (mob); www.campingbeausejour-albens.com]** N fr Aix-les-Bains on D1201 dir Annecy to Albens; in Albens turn L at traff lts in town cent; site in 600m on L, over sm bdge. Site sp at traff lts. Med, pt sl, pt shd; htd wc (some cont); chem disp; mv service pnt; shwrs inc; el pnts (6-10A) €3-3.80; gas; lndtte; ice; shops & rest 500m; BBQ; playgrnd; games area; dogs €1; phone adj; bus 500m; adv bkg; quiet, some rd & rlwy noise; ccard acc; red low ssn; CKE/CCI. "Friendly, pleasant site; rarely full; no twin-axles; vg." 15 Jun-15 Sep. € 8.00 2010*

AIX LES BAINS *9B3* (7km SW Rural) *45.65511, 5.86142* **Camp Municipal L'Ile aux Cygnes, La Croix Verte, 501 Blvd Ernest Coudurier, 73370 Le Bourget-du-Lac [04 79 25 01 76; fax 04 79 25 32 94; camping@lebourgetdulac.fr; www.lebourgetdulac.fr]** Fr N foll Bourget-du-Lac & Lac sp soon after Tunnel Le Chat. Fr Chambéry take D1504 dir Aix-les-Bains; foll sp to Le Bourget-du-Lac & Le Lac, bear R at Camping/Plage sp to site at end of rd. Lge, shd; wc; mv service pnt; baby facs; shwrs inc; el pnts (6A) inc; gas; lndtte (inc dryer); shop; tradsmn; rest, snacks; bar; playgrnd; private lake beach & sw; waterslide; boating; watersports; entmnt; wifi; TV; some statics; dogs €1.50; phone; bus; adv bkg; quiet; red low ssn; CKE/CCI. "On beautiful lake; mountain scenery; grnd stoney." ♦ 28 Apr-30 Sep. € 23.00 2013*

AIX LES BAINS *9B3* (3km W Rural) *45.70005, 5.88666* **Camp Municipal International du Sierroz, Blvd Robert Barrier, Route du Lac, 73100 Aix-les-Bains [04 79 61 21 43; fax 04 79 63 35 08; info@camping-sierroz.com; www.camping-sierroz.com]** Fr Annecy S on D1201, thro Aix-les-Bains, turn R at site sp. Keep to lakeside rd, site on R. Nr Grand Port. Lge, hdg/mkd pitch, shd; htd wc; chem disp; mv service pnt; baby facs; shwrs inc; el pnts (6A) inc; gas; lndtte; shop; tradsmn; rest, snacks; bar; playgrnd; pool 1km; games area; golf 4km; TV; 5% statics; dogs €1.60; bus (ask at recep for free pass); poss cr; adv bkg; quiet; ccard acc; red low ssn; CKE/CCI. "Pleasant location; lake adj for watersports; lge pitches; poss travellers & v unclean facs low ssn (June 2010)." ♦ 15 Mar-15 Nov. € 28.00 2014*

⊞ **ALBERTVILLE** *9B3* (450m NNE Urban) *45.67922, 6.39636* **Camp Municipal Les Adoubes, Ave du Camping, 73200 Albertville [04 79 32 06 62 or 06 85 84 02 56; hello(at) camping-albertville.fr; www.camping-albertville.fr]** Site is 200m fr town cent; over bdge on banks of Rv Arly. Med, mkd pitch, pt sl, pt shd; htd wc; chem disp; mv service pnt; shwrs inc; el pnts (10A) €3.50; gas; Indtte (inc dryer); shop 200m; rest, bar 200m; BBQ; wifi; TV rm; 5% statics; dogs; twin axles; poss cr; Eng spkn; adv bkg; some rd noise; ccard acc; red CKE/CCI. "Excel site in excel location; plenty of rm, even high ssn; v helpful staff; site yourself if recep clsd; well kept; 10% red for CC memb; under new management; site being upgraded for 2015." € 10.25 2014*

⊞ **ALBERTVILLE** *9B3* (2km SE Urban) *45.66501, 6.42232* **Camping La Maladière, 2263 Route de Tours, 73200 Albertville [tel/fax 04 79 37 80 44; camping@camping-lamaldiere.com; www.camping-lamaladiere.com]** SE fr cent Albertville take N90 twds Moûtiers. After approx 4km turn off sp La Bâthie & Tours-en-Savoie. Turn L under D90 & L onto D990 thro Tours-en-Savoie. Site 300m after exit sp on R. Sm, pt shd; htd wc; shwrs inc; el pnts (5-10A) €3-4.50; playgrnd; wifi; mostly statics; dogs €1.20; poss cr; adv bkg; quiet. "Well-kept site; friendly; gd clean san facs; conv Fréjus tunnel; gd NH." ♦ € 11.00 2010*

ALEX see Annecy *9B3*

ALLEMONT/ALLEMOND see Bourg d'Oisans, Le *9C3*

ALLEVARD *9B3* (11km S Rural) *45.31869, 6.08430* **Camp Municipal Neige & Nature, Chemin de Montarmand, 38580 La Ferrière-d'Allevard [tel/fax 04 76 45 19 84; contact@neige-nature.fr; www.neige-nature.fr]** Fr Allevard take D525A S to La Ferrière; foll sp Collet & Le Pleynet. Sm, hdg/mkd pitch, pt sl, terr, pt shd; htd wc; chem disp; baby facs; shwrs; el pnts (10A) €3.90; gas 200m; Indtte; shop 200m; snacks; bar; playgrnd; rv & lake fishing; games area; entmnt; TV; dogs free; Eng spkn; adv bkg; quiet; ccard not acc; red long stay. "Excel, scenic site; helpful owners; many mkd walks." ♦ ltd 15 May-15 Sep. € 17.00 2010*

ANNECY *9B3* **For more sites nr Lake Annecy see also Doussard and Faverges.**

ANNECY *9B3* (8km SE Rural) *45.88990, 6.22367* **Camping La Ferme de Ferrières, 74290 Alex [04 50 02 87 09; fax 04 50 02 80 54; campingfermedesferrieres@voila.fr; www.camping-des-ferrieres.com]** Take D909 on E side of lake out of Annecy twds Thônes; look out for sp on L after turn off to Château de Menthon. Site off D909 approx 1km W of Alex. Med, pt sl, terr, pt shd; wc (cont); chem disp; baby facs; shwrs inc; el pnts (5A) €2.80; Indtte; shop & 2km; tradsmn; snacks; playgrnd; lake sw 6km; dogs €1; poss cr; quiet; phone; adv bkg; CKE/CCI. "Spectacular views; peaceful, clean site away fr crowds; friendly & accommodating owner; high standard san facs; pitches muddy when wet; gd NH." ♦ ltd 15 May-30 Sep. € 20.30 2014*

ANNECY *9B3* (8km SE Rural) *45.86305, 6.19690* **Camping Le Clos Don Jean, Route du Clos Don Jean, 74290 Menthon-St-Bernard [tel/fax 04 50 60 18 66; donjean74@wanadoo.fr; www.clos-don-jean.com]** Fr N site clearly sp fr vill of Menthon. L uphill for 400m. Med, mkd pitch, pt sl, pt shd; wc (some cont); chem disp; mv service pnt; shwrs inc; el pnts (3-6A) €2.60-3.00; gas; Indtte; shop; playgrnd; lake sw 900m; dogs €1; poss cr; Eng spkn; quiet; CKE/CCI; "Excel site in orchard; clean san facs, ltd low ssn; fine views chateau & lake; walk to lake." ♦ ltd 1 Jun-15 Sep. € 21.00 2012*

ANNECY *9B3* (9km SE Urban) *45.82672, 6.18861* **Camp Municipal Les Champs Fleuris, 631 Voie Romaine, Les Perris, 74410 Duingt [04 50 68 57 31, 06 78 99 20 74 (mob) or 04 50 68 67 07 (Mairie); fax 04 50 77 03 17; camping@duingt.fr; www.camping-duingt.com]** Fr Annecy take D1508 sp Albertville. Site on R bef Duingt vill (2km after St Jorioz). Foll sp Camping Le Familial, over cycle path & turn L. Med, mkd pitch, pt sl, terr, pt shd; htd wc; chem disp; mv service pnt; shwrs inc; el pnts (3-10A) €2.50-5.25; gas 1km; Indtte; shops 1km; tradsmn; rest, snacks; bar; BBQ; playgrnd; lake sw 750m; wifi; 3% statics; dogs €1.85; phone; bus 200m; poss cr; Eng spkn; adv bkg; quiet; CKE/CCI. "Pleasant site with mountain scenery; busy high ssn; gd sized pitches; friendly, helpful warden; facs basic but clean; vg lakeside beach; gd walking & cycling; cycle track fr site along old rlwy into Annecy; v cr if Tour de France in area; poss muddy after heavy rain; gd." ♦ 23 Apr-17 Sep. € 15.50 2011*

ANNECY *9B3* (10km SE Rural) *45.82423, 6.18523* **Camping Le Familial, 400 Route de Magnonnet, 74410 Duingt [tel/fax 04 50 68 69 91; contact@annecy-camping-familial.com; www.annecy-camping-familial.com]** Fr Annecy on D1508 twd Albertville. 5km after St Jorioz turn R at site sp Entrevernes onto D8, foll sp past Camping Champs Fleuris. Sm, mkd pitch, some hdstg, pt sl, pt shd; wc; shwrs inc; el pnts (6A) €3.40; Indtte; tradsmn; playgrnd; lake & shgl beach 500m; TV rm; dogs €1.70; some Eng spkn; adv bkg rec Jul/Aug; quiet but rd noise; CKE/CCI. "Gd site in scenic area; gd atmosphere; generous pitches; friendly owner; communal meals & fondu evenings; conv lakeside cycle track." ♦ ltd 1 Apr-30 Sep. € 26.00 2014*

ANNECY *9B3* (10km SE Rural) *45.84070, 6.16450* **Camping Le Solitaire du Lac, 615 Route de Sales, 74410 St Jorioz [04 50 68 59 30 or 06 88 58 94 24 (mob); fax 04 50 68 59 30; contact@campinglesolitaire.com/campinglesolitaire@wanadoo.fr; www.campinglesolitaire.com]** Exit Annecy on D1508 twd Albertville. Site sp on N o'skts of St Jorioz. Med, mkd pitch, pt shd; wc; chem disp; mv service pnt; shwrs inc; el pnts (5A) €3.50; water to MH's charge €0.20 per 60l; gas; Indtte; supmkt 2km; tradsmn; pizza; snacks; bar & 2km; BBQ; playgrnd; lake sw; boat-launching; cycle hire; games area; cycle track; wifi; TV rm; 10% statics; dogs €2.60; poss v cr high ssn; some Eng spkn; adv bkg; v quiet; ccard acc; red low ssn/long stay; CKE/CCI. "Nice, well-run site in excel location; popular but quiet; sm pitches; clean, modern san facs; direct access to Lake Annecy; sh walk to public beach & water bus; cycle path nr; gd touring base; no twin-axles; excel; perfect for boating & cycling." 5 Apr-20 Sep. € 34.00 2014*

ANNECY *9B3* (12km SE Rural) *45.80153, 6.15166* **Aire Naturelle Le Combarut (Cottard), Chef-Lieu Le Verger, 74410 St Eustache [04 50 32 00 20]** Take D1508 S fr Annecy to Sévrier, turn R onto D912, site on farm just bef St Eustache. Sm, shd; wc (cont); mv service pnt; shwrs €1.20; el pnts (4A) €2.20; shop 5km; pool 15km; dogs €1; quiet. "Basic facs but clean; gd mountain views; diff access on winding rds, but not diff with care." 15 Jun-15 Sep. € 12.00 2010*

ANNECY *9B3* (1.5km S Rural) *45.89100, 6.13236* **Camp Municipal Le Belvédère, 8 Route du Semnoz, 74000 Annecy [04 50 45 48 30; fax 04 50 51 81 62; camping@ville-annecy.fr; www.annecy.fr]** Exit A41 junc 16; initially foll sp 'Albertville' into town; then foll sp 'Le Lac' and 'Le Semnoz'; site is on R off Route du Semnoz (Route du Semnoz is A41). 'Le Semnoz is a mountain running S fr Annecy. Lge, mkd pitch, pt sl, terr, pt shd; htd wc; chem disp; shwrs inc; el pnts (16A) €3.20 (poss rev pol); gas; Indtte; shop; tradsmn; rest, snacks; playgrnd; cycle hire; sailing; fishing; forest walks; excursions; wifi; TV; sep statics area; dogs free; phone; poss cr; Eng spkn; adv bkg; poss noisy; ccard acc; CKE/CCI. "Lovely, tidy site in beautiful setting; well lit at night; sm pitches; staff helpful; san facs OK; steep footpath to old town; excel; v friendly helpful staff, rec adv bkg." ♦ 29 Mar-13 Oct. € 30.60 2013*

ANNECY *9B3* (5km S Urban) *45.85482, 6.14395* **Camping au Coeur du Lac, Les Choseaux, 74320 Sévrier [04 50 52 46 45; fax 04 50 19 01 45; info@aucoeurdulac.com; www.campingaucoeurdulac.com]** S fr Annecy on D1508 sp Albertville. Pass thro Sévrier cent. Site on L at lakeside 1km S of Sévrier. 300m after McDonald's. Med, mkd pitch, terr, pt sl, pt shd, some hdstg; wc (some cont); chem disp; mv service pnt; shwrs inc; el pnts (4A) €3.60, long cable rec; Indtte; shop; supmkt 2km; snacks; playgrnd; lake sw; grass & shgl beach; cycle/boat hire; entmnt; dogs free low ssn (not acc high ssn); bus nrby; poss cr; some Eng spkn; adv bkg ess high ssn; quiet; ccard acc; red low ssn; CKE/CCI. "Busy site in lovely location; gd views of lake fr upper terr; tight for lge o'fits - sm, sl pitches; gd san facs; gd access to lake beach & cycle path; excel, espec low ssn; v popular site." ♦ 1 Apr-30 Sep. € 36.60 2014*

ANNECY *9B3* (6km S Rural) *45.84333, 6.14175* **Camping Le Panoramic, 22 Chemin des Bernets, Route de Cessenaz, 74320 Sévrier [04 50 52 43 09; info@camping-le-panoramic.com; www.camping-le-panoramic.com]** Exit A41 junc 16 Annecy Sud onto D1508 sp Albertville. Thro Sévrier to rndabt at Cessenaz (ignore all prior sp to site) & take 1st R onto D10. In 200m turn R up hill to site in 2km. Lge, mkd pitch, pt sl, terr, pt shd; htd wc; chem disp; shwrs inc; el pnts (4-6A) €3.20-4.20 (some rev pol); Indtte; shop; supmkt 2km; tradsmn; rest, snacks; bar; playgrnd; pool; beach 2km; lake sw; games rm; wifi; TV; dogs €1.60; poss cr; Eng spkn; quiet; ccard acc; red low ssn; CKE/CCI. "Fantastic views fr many pitches; blocks/wedges ess for sl pitches; excel pool/bar area; rec for families; new san facs (2012); excel views of lake; v friendly staff; high rec." ♦ ltd 18 Apr-30 Sep. € 36.50 2014*

ANNECY *9B3* (6.5km S Urban) *45.84412, 6.15354* **Camping de l'Aloua, 492 Route de Piron, 74320 Sévrier [04 50 52 60 06; fax 04 50 52 64 54; camping.aloua@wanadoo.fr; www.camping-aloua-lac-annecy.com]** Foll sp for Albertville D1508 S fr Annecy. Site on E side, approx 1.4km S of Sevrier vill. Turn L at Champion supmkt rndabt & foll sp twd lake. Lge, pt hdg/mkd pitch, shd; wc (some cont); chem disp; mv service pnt; shwrs inc; el pnts (2-10A) €2.50-4.80; gas 400m; Indtte; shop; supmkt 400m; tradsmn; rest, snacks; bar; playgrnd; shgl beach 300m; lake sw, fishing, boating & watersports adj; archery; entmnt; TV; dog €2; phone; poss cr; quiet, but rd noise; Eng spkn; adv bkg; red low ssn; CKE/CCI. "Gd base for lake (no dir access fr site); cycle track around lake; night security; poss noisy at night with youths & some rd noise; basic san facs; pleasant owners; well run & maintained site; nr lac Annecy, Carrefour & g'ge; bike track or bus to Annecy; vg." ♦ 19 Apr-20 Sep. € 29.70 2014*

ANNECY *9B3* (6.5km S Rural) *45.84806, 6.15129* **FFCC Camping Les Rives du Lac, 331 Chemin du Communaux, 74320 Sévrier [04 50 52 40 14; lesrivesdulac-annecy@ffcc.fr; www.lesrivesdulac-annecy.com]** Take D1508 S fr Annecy sp Albertville, thro Sévrier sp FFCC. Turn L 100m past (S) Lidl supmkt, cross cycle path & turn R & foll sp FFCC keeping parallel with cycle path. Site on L in 400m. Med, mkd pitch, pt shd; wc (some cont); chem disp; mv service pnt; baby facs; shwrs inc; el pnts (10A) €4; Indtte; shops 500m; BBQ; playgrnd; private shgl beach; lake sw; sailing; fishing; walking; wifi; entmnt; dogs €1.20; bus nr; poss cr; Eng spkn; adv bkg; quiet; red CC members (not Jul/Aug)/long stay/low ssn/ CKE/CCI. "Beautiful situation; generous pitches; helpful staff; excel new toilet block; water bus to Annecy nr; gd touring base; gd walking, sailing & cycling; cycle rte adj." ♦ 01 Apr-30 Sep. € 23.00 (CChq acc) 2014*

ANNECY *9B3* (9km S Rural) *45.49484, 6.1055* **Camping International du Lac d'Annecy, 1184 Route d'Albertville, 74410 St Jorioz [tel/fax 04 50 68 67 93; contact@camping-lac-annecy.com; www.camping-lac-annecy.com]** Fr Annecy take D1508 sp Albertville. Site on R just after St Jorioz. Med, hdg/mkd pitch, some hdstg, pt shd; wc; chem disp; mv service pnt; baby facs; fam bthrm; shwrs inc; el pnts (6-10A) €4-5.60; gas; Indtte; shop & 2km; tradsmn; rest, snacks; bar; BBQ (gas/elec); playgrnd; htd pool; lake sw 2km, shgl beach; cycle hire; games area; TV rm; 30% statics; dogs €2.50; bus 500m; phone; poss cr; Eng spkn; adv bkg; quiet; ccard acc; red low ssn; CKE/CCI. "Lovely site; gd san facs; excel for touring lake area; site ent tight for med/lge o'fits (2009); vg cycling; gd rest nrby." 8 May-18 Sep. € 36.00 2012*

ANNECY *9B3* (9km S Rural) *45.82995, 6.18215* **Village Camping Europa, 1444 Route d'Albertville, 74410 St Jorioz [04 50 68 51 01; fax 04 50 68 55 20; info@camping-europa.com; www.camping-europa.com]** Fr Annecy take D1508 sp Albertville. Site on R 800m S of St Jorioz dir Albertville. Look for lge yellow sp on o'skirts of St Jorioz. Lge, hdg/mkd pitch, pt shd, wc; chem disp; mv service pnt; some serviced pitches; baby facs; shwrs inc; el pnts (6A) €3.80; Indtte; tradsmn; rest, snacks; bar; BBQ (gas); playgrnd; htd pool; waterslides; jacuzzi; beach (lake) 700m; windsurfing; boat hire; fishing; tennis 700m; cycle hire; cycle track adj; wifi; TV rm; dogs €3; Eng spkn; adv bkg; quiet but main rd adj; ccard acc; quiet; red long stay/low ssn; CKE/CCI. "Peaceful site; friendly staff; facs stretched high ssn; vg rest; excel for m'vans; conv Chamonix & Mont Blanc; variable pitch prices; some pitches tight lge o'fits; gd tourist base; excel; no water points around site, collect fr toilet block." ♦ 26 Apr-20 Sep. € 53.80 2014*

ANNECY *9B3* (7km SW Rural) *45.86131, 6.05214* **Aire Naturelle La Vidome (Lyonnaz), 74600 Montagny-les-Lanches [tel/fax 04 50 46 61 31; j.lyonnaz@wanadoo.fr; www.lavidome.fr]** Exit Annecy on D1201 sp Aix-les-Bains/Chambéry; after 6km at Le Treige turn R sp Montagny-les-Lanches. In 1km turn R in Avulliens; site on R in 100m. Sm, pt sl, pt shd; wc; chem disp; shwrs; el pnts (3-10A) €2.10-4; Indtte; hypermkt 3km; meals avail; playgrnd; pool 3km; beach & mini-golf 10km; fishing 1km; horseriding 1km; dogs €0.80; quiet but some rd noise; adv bkg; gd views; CKE/CCI. "Excel site; friendly owners; vg san facs; access poss tight for lge o'fits; gd touring base." 1 May-30 Sep. € 15.00 2014*

"I need an on-site restaurant"

We do our best to make sure site information is correct, but it is always best to check any must-have facilities are still available or will be open during your visit.

ANNECY *9B3* (9km SW Rural) *45.86183, 6.09029* **Aire Naturelle Le Pré Ombragé (Metral), Chef-Lieu, 74600 Montagny-les-Lanches [04 50 46 71 31; fax 04 50 57 20 04; lepreombrage@wanadoo.fr]** Exit Annecy on D1201 sp Aix-les-Bains/Chambéry, after 8km at Le Treige turn R sp Montagny-les-Lanches; site sp in vill. Sm, pt sl, pt shd; wc; shwrs inc; el pnts (6A) inc; shops 2.5km; BBQ; playgrnd; pool; dogs €0.50; adv bkg; quiet; CKE/CCI. "Friendly, family-run, basic site in orchard; excel views." 15 Jun-30 Sep. € 12.00 2010*

ANNECY *9B3* (8km NW Rural) *45.97811, 6.03564* **Camping La Caille, 18 Chemin de la Caille, 74330 La Balme-de-Sillingy [04 50 68 85 21; fax 04 50 68 74 56; contact@aubergedelacaille.com; www.aubergedelacaille.com]** Fr Annecy take D1508 dir Bellgarde-sur-Valserine. Strt on at rndabt at end of La Balme-de-Sillingy, foll sp. At mini-rndabt strt on, site on R in 1km. Sm, hdg/mkd pitch, pt sl, shd; wc; chem disp; el pnts (4-12A) €3-5; Indtte; shop 750m; tradsmn; rest, snacks; bar; playgrnd; pool; 25% statics; dogs €4; adv bkg; quiet; CKE/CCI. "Gd, well-kept site." ♦ 1 May-30 Sep. € 21.00 2010*

ANNONAY *9C2* (1km N Urban) *45.25799, 4.67426* **Camp Municipal de Vaure, Rue Mathieu Duret, 07100 Annonay [04 75 33 73 73 or 04 75 33 46 54; fax 04 75 34 62 36; www.mairie-annonay.fr]** Sp fr o'skts of town & foll sp St Etienne. Fr St Etienne & NW on D1082 & D820 twd Annonay. For R onto D206 S & foll camping/piscine sp to site. Sm, hdg/mkd pitch, pt shd; wc (some cont); shwrs inc; el pnts (6-10A) €2.50-3.50; Indtte; snacks; bar; supmkt adj; htd, covrd pool; paddling pool; tennis; games area; few statics; dogs €1.50; poss cr; quiet. "Helpful staff; gd; basic facs." 1 Apr-31 Oct. € 10.00 2014*

ANSE see Villefranche sur Saône *9B2*

ARECHES see Beaufort *9B3*

ARS SUR FORMANS see Villefranche sur Saône *9B2*

ARTEMARE see Virieu le Grand *9B3*

AUBENAS *9D2* (3km N Rural) *44.64268, 4.37925* **Camping Domaine de Gil, Route de Vals-les-Bains, 07200 Ucel [04 75 94 63 63; fax 04 75 94 01 95; info@domaine-de-gil.com; www.domaine-de-gil.com]** Fr Aubenas NE on D104 to St Privat. Cross bdge over Rv Ardèche 1km. At Pont d'Ucel, turn L along D578 twds Ucel; site 3km on L. Med, hdg/mkd pitch, pt shd; wc; chem disp; mv service pnt; serviced pitch; baby facs; shwrs inc; el pnts (10A) €5 (poss rev pol); Indtte; shop; tradsmn; rest, snacks; bar; BBQ (gas/elec); playgrnd; htd pool; tennis; canoeing; wifi; entmnt; TV; 75% statics; dogs €3; phone; adv bkg ess in Aug; quiet; ccard acc; red low ssn; CKE/CCI. "Neat, clean site in scenic area; lge pitches; excel, family site; efficient, helpful staff; gd, clean san facs; vg." ♦ 18 Apr-20 Sep. € 31.00 2009*

AUBENAS *9D2* (7km N Urban) *44.66920, 4.36343* **Camping au Fil de la Volane, Quartier du Stade, 07600 Vals-les-Bains [04 75 37 46 85; camping.aufildelavolane@wanadoo.fr; www.campingaufildelavolane.com]** Fr Aubenas NW on N102 dir Le Puy-en-Velay; in 3.5km take D578 to Vals-les-Bains. Clearly sp at N end of town by sports complex. Med, mkd pitch, terr, shd; wc (cont); chem disp (wc); mv service pnt; fam bthrm; shwrs inc; el pnts (10A) inc; Indtte (inc dryer); shops 500m; snacks; bar; BBQ; playgrnd; pool; entmnt; rv fishing & sw adj; few statics; dogs €1; phone; quiet; red low ssn. "Lovely, peaceful site; helpful owners; rv walk to spa town; vg." 1 Apr-30 Sep. € 18.00 2009*

AUBENAS *9D2* (2km E Rural) *44.61885, 4.43220* **Camping Le Plan d'Eau, Route de Lussas, 07200 St Privat [tel/fax 04 75 35 44 98; info@campingleplandeau.fr; www.campingleplandeau.fr]** Exit A7 at Montélimar dir Aubenas. Bef Aubenas turn R at rndabt onto D104 dir St Privat. In approx 1km turn R twd Lussas & foll site sp. Site on R on rvside. Med, mkd pitch, pt shd; wc; chem disp; baby facs; shwrs inc; el pnts (8A) €4.20; Indtte (inc dryer); shop adj; (rest, snacks; bar; clsd low ssn); BBQ (gas only); cooking facs; playgrnd; htd pool; games rm; wifi; entmnt; TV rm; 25% statics; dogs €2.70; phone; Eng spkn; adv bkg; quiet; red long stay/CKE/CCI. "Vg, peaceful site; gd san & sports facs." 26 Apr-13 Sep. € 43.00 2012*

AUBENAS *9D2* (7km E Rural) *44.60495, 4.47126* **Ludocamping, Route de Lavilledieu, 07170 Lussas [04 75 94 21 22; fax 04 75 88 60 60; info@ludocamping.com; www.ludocamping.com]** SE fr Aubenas on N102 twd Montélimar. Turn L after 10km in vill Lavilledieu onto D224 sp Lussas. Site sp on R in 4km. Med, mkd pitch, terr, pt shd; wc; chem disp; shwrs inc; el pnts (6A) €3 (poss rev pol); gas; Indtte; shop; rest in vill 600m; bar; playgrnd; htd pool; paddling pool; dogs €1.50; poss cr; Eng spkn; adv bkg; quiet. "Gd walking country; peaceful; facs poss stretched in high ssn; Dutch owned; excel." ♦ 1 Apr-15 Oct. € 27.00 2010*

AUBENAS *9D2* (7km SE Rural) *44.56401, 4.46119* **Camping Les Rives d'Auzon, Route de St Germain, 07170 Lavilledieu [tel/fax 04 75 94 70 64; contact@camping-rivesdauzon.fr; www.camping-rivesdauzon.fr]** Fr Aubenas on N102 turn R immed after Lavilledieu, sp St Germain (D103) site on L. Sm, pt shd; wc (some cont); mv service pnt; shwrs; el pnts (6A) €3.50; Indry rm; shop; rest, snacks; bar; playgrnd; pool; TV rm; entmnt; dogs €2; Eng spkn; adv bkg; some rd noise. "Friendly owner; beautiful location; poss diff for lge o'fits due trees." 6 Apr-30 Sep. € 17.00 2009*

AUBENAS *9D2* (8km SE Rural) *44.55315, 4.44855* **Camping à la Ferme Le Bardou (Boule), 07170 St Germain [tel/fax 04 75 37 71 91; info@lebardou.com; www.lebardou.com]** On N102 Aubenas-Montélimar turn S at Lavilledieu on D103, site on L in 2km. Site ent fairly narr bet stone houses in St Germain. Sm, pt shd; wc (some cont); chem disp; shwrs inc; el pnts (6A) €3.50; shops 150m; pool; fishing adj; some statics; dogs; adv bkg; red low ssn; quiet. "Lovely views; pleasant site low ssn; helpful owners; clean, basic facs but poss inadequate high ssn; gd." 1 Apr-31 Oct. € 16.00 2011*

AUBENAS *9D2* (3km S Urban) *44.59671, 4.37644* **Camping Les Acacias, 07200 St Etienne-de-Fontbellon [04 75 93 67 87; fax 04 75 93 71 77; camping-les-acacias@wanadoo.fr; www.camping-les-acacias.fr]** Fr Aubenas travel thro cent of St Etienne. Turn 2nd R at rndabt S of Leclerc hypmkt & foll sps. Fr S turn off D104 N of Lachapelle to St Etienne. At next rndabt turn L & foll sp. NB Do not tow thro vill. Sm, mkd pitch, pt shd; wc (cont); chem disp; mv service pnt; baby facs; shwrs inc; el pnts (6A) €2.70 (poss rev pol); Indtte; shops 1.5km; rest, snacks, bar high ssn; BBQ; playgrnd; pool; entmnt; dogs €0.70; Eng spkn; adv bkg; quiet; no ccard acc; red low ssn; CKE/CCI. "Pleasant site; mover needed most pitches; irreg office hrs, pitch & call in when open; gd touring cent." 3 Apr-3 Oct. € 11.00 2010*

AUBENAS *9D2* (8km S Rural) *44.54113, 4.41495* **Camping Les Roches, 07200 Vogüé [tel/fax 04 75 37 70 45; hm07@free.fr; www.campinglesroches.fr]** Fr Aubenas take D104 S. Then L onto D579 to Vogüé. Site on L 1.5km past Vogüé - do not turn twd Vogüé, but cont in dir Vogüé Gare. Med, pt sl, shd; wc (most cont); mv service pnt; baby facs; shwrs inc; el pnts (6-10A) inc; Indtte (inc dryer); shop; rest, snacks; bar; playgrnd; pool; tennis; games area; entmnt; TV; some statics; dogs free; adv bkg; quiet. "Pleasant site; pitch yourself, warden calls." ♦ 8 May-31 Aug. € 28.00 2010*

AUBENAS *9D2* (10km S Rural) *44.53693, 4.41039* **Camping Les Peupliers, 07200 Vogüé [04 75 37 71 47; fax 04 75 37 70 83; girard.jean-jacques@club-internet.fr; www.campingpeupliers.com]** Fr Aubenas take D104 S twd Alès. In 2km, turn L onto D579 dir Vogüé/Vallon Pont d'Arc. In 9km, pass L turn to Vog é. Immed after x-ing rv, turn R at rndabt. Site on R in 300m, (2nd site of 3 on rd). Lge, mkd pitch, pt shd; wc (some cont); chem disp; mv service pnt; baby facs; shwrs inc; el pnts (6A) €4.10; gas; Indtte; shop; rest, snacks; bar; BBQ; playgrnd; pool; rv & shgl beach adj; entmnt; some statics; dogs €2.30; phone; poss cr; adv bkg; quiet; ccard acc; CKE/CCI. "Gd touring base; access to rv for canoeing & fishing; basic site well worn facs but clean." 5 Apr-30 Sep. € 24.00 2011*

AUBENAS *9D2* (10km S Rural) *44.53416, 4.40690* **Domaine du Cros d'Auzon, 07200 St Maurice-d'Ardèche [04 75 37 75 86; fax 04 75 37 01 02; camping.auzon@wanadoo.fr; www.camping-cros-auzon.com]** Take D104 S fr Aubenas for 2km; at island turn L onto D579. After 9km, pass L turn to Vog é vill, cross rv & turn R immed. Site 600m on R, 1km fr Vog é stn. Lge, hdg/mkd pitch, pt shd; htd wc; chem disp; mv service pnt; serviced pitch; child/baby facs; shwrs inc; el pnts (6A) inc; gas; Indtte; shop 1km; tradsmn; rest, snacks; bar; playgrnd; pool; waterslide; fishing; cycle hire; tennis; entmnt; games/TV rm; cinema; 70% statics; dogs €3; Eng spkn; adv bkg; quiet; red low ssn/long stay; ccard acc; CKE/CCI. "Gd touring base; poss long walk to shwrs; excel." ♦ 3 Apr-18 Sep. € 29.50 2010*

AUBENAS *9D2* (7km NW Rural) *44.65157, 4.32384* **Camp Municipal le Pont des Issoux, Allée de Vals, 07380 Lalevade-d'Ardèche [04 75 94 14 09 (Mairie) or 04 75 94 01 92 (LS); fax 04 75 94 01 92; contact@campingdesissoux.com; www.campingdesissoux.com/livredor.php]** Fr Aubenas, N102 sp Mende & Le Puy-en-Velay; Lalevade in 10km; R in vill; well sp. Med, mkd pitch, pt shd; wc (mostly cont); chem disp (wc); shwrs inc; el pnts (10A) €3.10 (poss rev pol); gas; Indtte; supmkt adj; rest, snacks & bar 250m, playgrnd; lake sw & shgl beach adj; tennis & children's park nrby; wifi; dogs €1.20; bus 250m; poss cr; Eng spkn; adv bkg; quiet; CKE/CCI. "Pleasant, shady site beside Rv Ardèche; friendly, helpful warden; san facs dated but clean, poss scruffy low ssn; no twin-axles; close to vill; conv touring base; vg." ♦ 1 Apr-15 Oct. € 11.50 2013*

AUBERIVES SUR VAREZE *9B2* (8km E Rural) *45.42830, 4.92823* **Kawan Village Camping Le Bontemps, 5 Impasse du Bontemps, 38150 Vernioz [04 74 57 83 52; fax 04 74 57 83 70; info@campinglebontemps.com; www.camping-lebontemps.com]** Take N7 S fr Vienne. At Le Clos turn L onto D37 thro Cheyssieu & Vernioz, site approx 9km E of Vernioz. Fr S, on N7 N of vill of Auberives R onto D37, site on R in 8km. Tight ent - rec swing wide. NB Also sp Hotel de Plein Air. Lge, mkd pitch; terr, pt shd; wc; mv service pnt; baby facs; shwrs inc; el pnts (6A) inc (poss long lead req); Indtte (inc dryer); shop; rest, snacks; bar; BBQ; playgrnd; pool; paddling pool; fishing lake; wildlife sanctuary; tennis; games area; games rm; wifi; entmnt; TV; 30% statics; dogs €3; no c'vans/m'vans over 10m high ssn; adv bkg; ccard acc; red low ssn; CKE/CCI. "Attractive, well-kept site; popular NH high ssn; helpful staff; excel sports facs; vg NH." ♦ 5 Apr-26 Sep. € 41.00 (CChq acc) SBS - M10 2013*

AUBERIVES SUR VAREZE *9B2* (1km S Rural) *45.41284, 4.81358* **Camping des Nations, 38550 Clonas-sur-Varèze [04 74 84 95 13 or 04 74 84 97 17; fax 04 74 79 93 75; contact@campingdesnations.com]** Fr Vienne S on N7; site sp on R in 12km. Or fr S exit A7 junc 12 onto N7 dir Vienne; do not go into Clonas vill; site on L adj Hotel des Nations. Med, hdg/mkd pitch, shd; htd wc; chem disp; shwrs inc; el pnts (9A) inc; tradsmn; rest nr; snacks; pool; bbq; dogs €1; adv bkg (ess high ssn); quiet; ccard not acc; rd noise fr N71; CKE/CCI. "Pleasant, well-kept, well-laid out site; gd sized pitches; gd, clean san facs; site muddy when wet; poss under-used; ltd facs low ssn; poss irreg cleaning end of ssn; useful NH/touring base for Spain & the Med; vg site." ♦ 1 Mar-31 Oct. € 31.00 2014*

AUSSOIS see Modane *9C4*

AUTRANS *9C3* (450m E Rural) *45.17520, 5.54770* **Kawan Village au Joyeux Réveil, Le Château, 38880 Autrans [04 76 95 33 44; fax 04 76 95 72 98; camping-au-joyeux-reveil@wanadoo.fr; www.camping-au-joyeux-reveil.fr]** Fr Villard-de-Lans take D531 to Lans-en-Vercors & turn L onto D106 to Autrans. On E side of vill site sp at 1st rndabt. NB App on D531 fr W fr Pont-en-Royans not rec - v narr rd & low tunnels. Med, mkd pitch, pt sl, pt shd; htd wc; chem disp; mv service pnt; baby facs; shwrs inc; el pnts (2-10A) €2-8; gas; Indtte (inc dryer); shop 300m; tradsmn; rest 300m; snacks; bar; BBQ; playgrnd; htd pool; paddling pool; waterslide; rv fishing; tennis 300m; cycle hire; golf 20km; games area; wifi; TV rm; cab TV to pitches; 60% statics; dogs; bus 300m; phone; quiet; adv bkg; Eng spkn; red low ssn; ccard acc; CKE/CCI. "Site in Vercors National Park with excel views; winter sport facs, 1050m altitude; modern san facs; excel." ♦ ltd 1 Dec-31 Mar & 1 May-30 Sep. € 30.00 2009*

BAIX *9D2* (2km W Rural) *44.70527, 4.73794* **Camping Le Merle Roux, 07210 Baix [04 75 85 84 14; fax 04 75 85 83 07; www.lemerleroux.com]** Fr A7/E15 exit junc 16. Foll sp Le Pouzin, x-ing Rv Rhône. Turn L onto D86 (S), go thro Le Pouzin, in 2km immed bef rlwy x-ing, turn R twd Privas; in 500m turn L at sp & foll rd approx 2km. Single track rd to site, not rec low powered car + lge c'van. Med, pt sl, terr, pt shd; wc; chem disp; shwrs inc; el pnts (6A) inc; Indtte; shop; tradsmn; rest, snacks; bar; no BBQ; playgrnd; pool; 15% statics; dogs €2.50; adv bkg; quiet; red low ssn; CKE/CCI. "Scenic site; welcoming Dutch owners; excel facs & pitches; poss diff to reverse onto pitch; excel." 1 Apr-31 Oct. € 31.00 2010*

BALAZUC *9D2* (1km NE Rural) *44.51199, 4.38667* **FFCC Camping La Falaise, Hameau Les Salles, 07120 Balazuc [tel/fax 04 75 37 74 27; /www.camping-balazuc.com]** Sp on D579 on rvside. Sm, hdg pitch, pt sl, shd; wc; chem disp; baby facs; shwrs inc; el pnts (6A) €3.80; gas; Indtte; shop; tradsmn; snacks; bar; playgrnd; rv beach; canoe hire; dogs €1.50; phone; poss cr; Eng spkn; adv bkg; CKE/CCI. "Site beside Rv Ardèche; helpful and friendly owners; vg." ♦ 1 Apr-30 Sep. € 21.00 2013*

BALAZUC *9D2* (2km E Rural) *44.50778, 4.40333* **Camping Le Chamadou, Mas de Chaussy, 07120 Balazuc [04 75 37 00 56; fax 04 75 37 70 61; infos@camping-le-chamadou.com; www.camping-le-chamadou.com]** Fr Ruoms foll D579 dir Aubenas. After approx 9km turn R under viaduct, site sp. Keep R up narr rd to site. App recep on foot fr car pk. Med, hdg pitch, hdstg, pt sl, pt shd; htd wc; chem disp; baby facs; fam bthrm; shwrs inc; el pnts (10A) €4.20 (some rev pol); Indtte; shop & 3km; tradsmn; snacks; bar; BBQ (elec); playgrnd; pool; paddling pool; waterslide; rv & beach 1.5km; canoe & kayak hire; wifi; entmnt; TV rm; some statics; dogs €2.60; phone; poss cr; Eng spkn; adv bkg rec; v quiet; ccard acc; CKE/CCI. "Excel, well-run, family site; panoramic views; most pitches spacious." 1 Apr-31 Oct. € 24.00 2010*

BALBIGNY *9B1* (3km NW Rural) *45.82558, 4.16196* **Camping La Route Bleue, Route D56 du Lac de Villerest, Pralery, 42510 Balbigny [tel/fax 04 77 27 24 97 or 06 85 52 98 66 (mob); camping.balbigny@wanadoo.fr; www.camping-de-la-route-bleue.fr]** Fr N on D1082, take 1st R after a'route (A89/72) junc N of Balbigny onto D56. Fr S on D1082, turn L at RH bend on N o'skirts of Balbigny, D56, sp Lac de Villerest & St Georges-de-Baroille. Well sp. Med, hdg/mkd pitch, pt sl, pt shd; chem disp; mv service pnt; wc; shwrs inc; el pnts (6-10A) inc (poss long lead req); Indtte; shops 1.5km; tradsmn; rest, snacks; bar; playgrnd; pool & paddling pool; rv adj; fishing; games rm; sports complex adj; adv bkg; quiet; ccard acc; red low ssn/long stay; CKE/CCI. "Nice site on rv bank; views over rv some pitches; helpful & welcoming staff; san facs need update (2010); ltd el pnts (2010); extra for twin-axles; conv A72; excel; lovely area." ♦ ltd 15 Mar-31 Oct. € 16.00 2013*

BARBIERES *9C2* (1km NE Rural) *44.97942, 5.16357* **Camping Combe d'Oyans, 26300 Rochefort-Samson [04 75 47 33 23; fax 04 75 82 90 57; combe-doyans@orange.fr; www.combedoyans.fr]** Exit A49 junc 7 onto D149 to Chatuzange; cont on D149 for 5.5km to rndabt just bef Barbières; turn L onto D125 to Rochfort-Samson; cont thro vill; in 600m cont over x-rds; site on R in 500m. Sm, hdg/mkd pitch, terr, pt shd; wc; chem disp (wc); shwrs inc; el pnts €3; shops 3km; tradsmn; snacks; playgrnd; htd pool; 15% statics; dogs €1; phone adj; adv bkg; ccard not acc; red low ssn; CKE/CCI. "Conv Vercors Massif; gd walking, cycling, rockclimbing; children's activity camping adj; vg." ♦ 6 May-29 Sep. € 17.00 2009*

BARBIERES *9C2* (1km SE Rural) *44.94470, 5.15100* **Camping Le Gallo-Romain, 1090 Route de Col de Tourniol, 26300 Barbières [tel/fax 04 75 47 44 07; info@legalloromain.net; www.legalloromain.net]** Exit A49 junc 7 onto D149 dir Marches & Barbières. Go thro vill & ascend Rte du Col de Tourniol for 2km, site on R, well sp. Med, mkd pitch, pt sl, terr, pt shd; wc; chem disp; baby facs; shwrs inc; el pnts (6A) €3.75; Indtte; shop & 1km; rest, snacks; bar; BBQ; playgrnd; pool; entmnt; internet; TV; 15% statics; dogs €5.50; phone; poss cr; Eng spkn; adv bkg; quiet; no ccard acc; red low ssn; CKE/CCI. "Mountain setting; welcoming, friendly, helpful Dutch owners; ltd facs low ssn; gd; nice location." ♦ 22 Apr-30 Sep. € 46.00 2013*

BATHIE, LA see Albertville *9B3*

BEAUFORT *9B3* (300m NW Rural) *45.72160, 6.56418* **Camp Municipal Le Domelin, Domelin, 73270 Beaufort [tel/fax 04 79 38 33 88 or 04 79 38 33 15 (LS)]** Fr Albertville take D925 dir Beaufort & Bourg-St Maurice; site on L just bef ent Beaufort 100m up side rd (after passing D218B); clearly sp. NB App fr E (Bourg-St Maurice) rd v diff for towing. Med, mkd pitch, pt sl, pt shd; htd wc (some cont); chem disp; baby facs; shwrs inc; el pnts (10A) €2.65; Indtte; shops, rest, snacks & bar 1km; playgrnd; htd pool 1km; dogs; phone; bus 1km; poss cr; adv bkg; ccard acc; CKE/CCI. "Quiet, pleasant site; vg walking; attractive town; gd touring base." 1 Jun-30 Sep. € 11.84 2009*

BEAUREPAIRE *9C2* (850m E Urban) *45.33825, 5.06101* **Camp Intercommunal, Ave Charles de Gaulle, 38270 Beaurepaire [04 74 84 64 89 or 04 74 84 67 29; fax 04 74 79 24 14; camping.beaurepaire@orange.fr; www.territoire-de-beaurepaire.fr]** Sp in town on L of Beaurepaire-Romans rd, adj pool & stadium. Med, shd; wc (some cont); shwrs inc; el pnts (10A) €2.50; shops 250m; 2 supmkts nr; pool & tennis nrby; rv fishing; games rm; wifi; dogs €0.50; quiet; mkt Wed am. 15 Apr-15 Oct. € 8.00 2010*

BEAUREPAIRE *9C2* (10km S Rural) *45.25332, 5.02803* **Camping du Château, Route de Romans, 26390 Hauterives [04 75 68 80 19; fax 04 75 68 90 94; contact@camping-hauterives.com; www.camping-hauterives.com]** Take D538 S to Hauterives, site sp in vill adj Rv Galaure. Med, mkd pitch, pt shd; wc; mv service pnt; shwrs; el pnts (6-10A) €2.50-3; Indtte; snacks; sm supmkt adj; playgrnd; htd pool; paddling pool; rv & fishing adj; tennis; games area; some statics; dogs €2.20; adv bkg; quiet. "Gd NH; friendly; gd pool; Do not use SatNav, inaccurate." ♦ 1 Apr-30 Sep. € 26.50 2012*

BEAUVOIR EN ROYANS see St Marcellin *9C2*

BELLENTRE *9B4* (2km E Rural) *45.57576, 6.73553* **Camping L'Eden, 73210 Landry [04 79 07 61 81; fax 04 79 07 62 17; info@camping-eden.net; www.camping-eden.net]** Fr N90 Moûtiers to Bourg-St Maurice at 20km turn R sp Landry; site on L after 500m adj Rv Isère. Med, hdg/mkd pitch, hdstg, pt shd; htd wc; chem disp; shwrs inc; el pnts (10A) €4-6; gas; Indtte (inc dryer); shop; tradsmn; snacks; bar; playgrnd; htd pool; games rm; TV; dogs €1.50; phone; ski bus; poss cr; Eng spkn; adv bkg; quiet; ccard acc. "Gd cent mountain sports; helpful, friendly owner; red facs low ssn; ltd site lighting; poss unkempt end of ssn." 15 Dec-5 May & 25 May-15 Sep. € 21.00 2010*

⊞ **BELLENTRE** *9B4* (3km SE Rural) *45.56057, 6.73956* **Camping de Montchavin, 73210 Bellentre [04 79 07 83 23; fax 04 79 07 80 18; info@montchavin-lescoches.com; www.montchavin-lescoches.com]** On N90 fr Moûtiers to Bourg-St Maurice (ignore site sps on N90); at 20km turn R onto D87E sp Landry & Montchavin-les-Coches; in 1km turn R onto D220, in 500m turn L onto D225; site in 7km on L at Montchavin. Med, mkd pitch, terr, pt shd; htd wc; mv service pnt; shwrs inc; el pnts (4-10A) €3.80-€7.60; gas; Indtte; shops 500m; pool in vill; games area; chairlift 200m; 60% statics; site clsd Oct; adv bkg (ess Jul/Aug & winter); quiet; ccard acc. "Site at 1200m; steep hill to shops; walking in summer, skiing in winter; magnificent setting." € 13.00 2009*

BELLEY *9B3* (8km E Rural) *45.76860, 5.76985* **Camping Du Lac du Lit du Roi, La Tuilière, 01300 Massignieu-de-Rives [04 79 42 12 03; fax 04 79 42 19 94; info@camping-savoie.com; www.camping-savoie.com]** Fr D1504 turn E onto D992 to Massignieu-de-Rives, site sp. Site on NE of lake nr Les Mures. Med, hdg/mkd pitch, terr, pt shd; htd wc; chem disp; mv service pnt; shwrs inc; el pnts (10A) inc (long lead req); gas; Indtte (inc dryer); shop 8km; tradsmn; rest, snacks; bar; BBQ; playgrnd; pool; lake sw & beach; boating; tennis; cycle hire; wifi; TV rm; 20% statics; dogs €4; phone; Eng spkn; adv bkg (fee); ccard acc; red long stay/low ssn; CKE/CCI. "Superb location; many pitches on lake with lovely views; some lge pitches, others v sm; lack of site maintenance (2010); few water pnts (2009); v friendly site, idyllic location." ♦ 10 Apr-3 Oct. € 30.00 2013*

BILIEU see Abrets, Les *9B3*

BLACERET see Villefranche sur Saône *9B2*

BOEN SUR LIGNON *9B1* (1km S Urban) *45.73688, 4.00777* **Camping Municipal Domaine De Giraud, Rue de Camping, 42130 Boen Sur Lignon [04 77 24 08 91; camping.boen@orange.fr; www.boen.fr]** Fr Clermont Ferrand head E on D2089. Cont onto D1089. Site well sp immed on exiting Boen sur Lignon. Med, mkd pitch, pt sl, pt shd; wc; chem disp; baby facs; shwr; el pnts (10A); BBQ; playgrnd; games area; games rm; tv rm; 4% statics; dogs; twin axles; Eng spkn; no ccard acc; CCI. "Peaceful, well run site, 10 mins stroll fr town cent with rest, bars, shops, supermkts & Indtte; sports facs nrby; vg". ♦ ltd 20 Mar-20 Oct. € 15.60 2014*

BOLLENE *9D2* (7km E Rural) *44.29124, 4.83837* **FFCC Camping Le Pont du Lez, Ave es Côtes du Rhône, 26790 Suze-la-Rousse [tel/fax 04 75 98 82 83; camping-lepontdulez@wanadoo.fr; www.campinglepontdulez.fr]** E fr Bollène on D94 to Suze-la-Rousse; L in vill sq; R immed bef rv bdge. Sm, pt shd; wc; shwrs inc; el pnts (6-10A) €3.40 (long lead poss req); Indtte; shop 300m; supmkt 7km; snacks; bar; playgrnd; fishing; games area; TV; dogs €1.40; no twin-axles; red low ssn; CKE/CCI. "Lovely but decrepit (2009); basic, clean facs - hot water to shwrs only; lovely area." 1 Apr-30 Sep. € 12.80 2009*

BONNEVILLE *9A3* (500m NE Rural) *46.08206, 6.41288* **Camp Municipal Le Bois des Tours, 314 Rue des Bairiers, 74130 Bonneville [04 50 97 04 31 or 04 50 25 22 00 (Mairie)]** Fr A40 junc 16 take D1203, or fr Cluses take D1205 to Bonneville. Cross rv bdge into town cent; site sp. Med, pt shd; wc (some cont); chem disp; shwrs; el pnts (5A) €2.50; shops 500m; BBQ; playgrnd; poss cr peak ssn; adv bkg; quiet. "Well-maintained, immac site; gd san facs." 1 Jul-6 Sep. € 8.00 2012*

BOUGE CHAMBALUD see St Rambert d'Albon *9C2*

BOURDEAUX *9D2* (1km SE Rural) *44.57854, 5.12791* **Camping Les Bois du Châtelas, Route de Dieulefit, 26460 Bourdeaux [04 75 00 60 80; fax 04 75 00 60 81; contact@chatelas.com; www.chatelas.com]** Fr N exit A7 m'way junc 16 onto D104, head twd Crest. Shortly bef Crest turn R onto D538 S thro Bourdeaux & cont dir Dienlefit (still on D538), site in 1km on L, well sp. Med, mkd pitch, terr, pt shd; htd wc; chem disp; mv service pnt; baby facs; sauna; shwrs inc; el pnts (10A) inc; gas; Indtte; shop; tradsmn; rest, snacks; bar; BBQ (gas/elec); cooking facs; playgrnd; 2 pools (1 htd covrd); paddling pool; waterslide; rv & horseriding 5km; games area; fitness rm; games rm; cycle hire; wifi; entmnt; TV rm; 30% statics; dogs €5; no c'vans/m'vans over 8m high ssn; phone; Eng spkn; adv bkg ess high ssn; ccard acc; red low ssn; CKE/CCI. "In lovely, scenic area; site on steep slope; gd walking." ♦ 11 Apr-13 Sep. € 34.70 SBS - M11 2011*

BOURDEAUX *9D2* (300m S Rural) *44.58389, 5.13615* **FFCC Camp Municipal Le Gap des Tortelles, 26460 Bourdeaux [tel/fax 04 75 53 30 45; info@campingdebourdeaux.com; www.campingdebourdeaux.com]** Foll camping/piscine sp in vill. Gd app fr S via D94 & D70 fr Nyons. Sm, terr, pt shd; wc; mv service pnt; shwrs inc; el pnts (6A) €2.80; Indtte; shop, 600m; rest; bar; playgrnd; sw rv; tennis adj; few statics; dogs €2; adv bkg; quiet. "Attractive area away fr tourist scene; helpful warden; sh path into vill." ♦ 1 Apr-30 Sep. € 11.00 2009*

BOURDEAUX *9D2* (4km NW Rural) *44.59583, 5.11127* **Kawan Village Le Couspeau, Quartier Bellevue, 26460 Le Poët-Célard [04 75 53 30 14; fax 04 75 53 37 23; info@couspeau.com; www.couspeau.com]** Fr D538 Crest-Bourdeaux; pass thro Saou & after several kms turn R over bdge to Le Poët-Célard, site sp in vill. Med, terr, mkd pitch, sl, pt shd; wc; chem disp; serviced pitches; baby facs; shwrs inc; el pnts (6A) €3 (poss rev pol); gas; Indtte; sm shop; tradsmn; rest, snacks, bar high ssn; playgrnd; 2 htd pools (1 covrd); paddling pool; rv & fishing; canoeing; tennis; cycle hire; horseriding 4km; wifi; TV rm; 20% statics; dogs €2; Eng spkn; adv bkg; quiet; ccard acc; min 6 days high ssn; red low ssn; CKE/CCI. "On steep hillside; gd views; site rds steep; tractor assistance avail on arr/dep; excel." ♦ 15 Apr-14 Sep. € 32.00 2010*

⊞ **BOURG ARGENTAL** *9C2* (2km E Rural) *45.29910, 4.58183* **Camping Domaine de l'Astrée, L'Allier, 42220 Bourg-Argental [tel/fax 04 77 39 72 97 or 04 77 39 63 49 (OT); prl@bourgargental.fr]** S fr St Etienne on D1082 to Bourg-Argental, thro town, site well sp on R soon after rndabt & opp filling stn. Fr Annonay or Andance site on L of D1082 at start of Bourg-Argental, adj rv. Sm, mkd pitch, some hdstg, pt shd; wc; chem disp (wc); shwrs inc; el pnts (4-6A) inc (long cable poss req); gas; Indtte; shop 250m; snacks; BBQ; playgrnd; htd pool 600m; paddling pool; waterslide; fishing; tennis; games rm; cycle hire; 60% statics; dogs €1.60; phone; poss cr; some rd noise; red low ssn; ccard acc; red low ssn; CKE/CCI. "Pleasant site with modern facs; vg." ♦ € 20.00 2013*

BOURG D'OISANS, LE *9C3* (1.5km NE Rural) *45.06557, 6.03980* **Camping à la Rencontre du Soleil, Route de l'Alpe-d'Huez, La Sarenne, 38520 Le Bourg-d'Oisans [04 76 79 12 22; fax 04 76 80 26 37; rencontre.soleil@wanadoo.fr; www.alarencontredusoleil.com]** Fr D1091 approx 800m E of town turn N onto D211, sp 'Alpe d'Huez'. In approx 500m cross sm bdge over Rv Sarennes, then turn immed L to site. (Take care not to overshoot ent, as poss diff to turn back). Med, hdg/mkd pitch, pt shd; htd wc (some cont); chem disp; mv service pnt; baby facs; shwrs inc; el pnts (10A) inc; Indtte; supmkt 300m; tradsmn; rest, snacks; bar; BBQ; playgrnd; htd pool; fishing; tennis; games area; horseriding 1.5km; wifi; entmnt; TV/games rm; 45% statics; dogs €1; no c'vans/m'vans over 7m high ssn; adv bkg ess; rd noise; ccard acc; red low ssn; CKE/CCI. "Busy site with lovely views; various pitch sizes/shapes; excel, spotless san facs, some unisex; helpful owner; excel rest; La Marmotte cycle race (early Jul) & Tour de France usually pass thro area & access poss restricted; pitches poss flooded after heavy rain, but staff excel at responding; mkt Sat; highly rec." 1 May-30 Sep. € 38.00 2012*

BOURG D'OISANS, LE *9C3* (1.5km NE Rural) *45.06401, 6.03895* **Camping La Cascade, Route de l'Alpe d'Huez, 38520 Le Bourg-d'Oisans [04 76 80 02 42; fax 04 76 80 22 63; lacascade@wanadoo.fr; www.lacascadesarenne.com]** Fr W drive thro Le Bourg-d'Oisans & cross bdge over Rv Romanche. Approx 800m E of town turn onto D211, sp Alpe-d'Huez. Site on R in 600m. Med, mkd pitch, pt shd; htd wc; chem disp; baby facs; shwrs; el pnts (16A) €4.30; Indtte; supmkt 1km; snacks; bar high ssn; playgrnd; htd pool high ssn; some statics; dogs free; poss cr; Eng spkn; adv bkg; quiet; ccard acc; CKE/CCI. "Friendly site; discounts for ski passes fr recep." 1Jan-30 Sep / 12 Dec-31 Dec. € 45.80 2013*

> **"Satellite navigation makes touring much easier"**
>
> Remember most sat navs don't know if you're towing or in a larger vehicle – always use yours alongside maps and site directions.

⊞ **BOURG D'OISANS, LE** *9C3* (1.5km NE Rural) *45.06357, 6.03772* **Camping La Piscine, Route de l'Alpe d'Huez, 38520 Le Bourg-d'Oisans [04 76 80 02 41; fax 04 76 11 01 26; infos@camping-piscine.com; www.camping-piscine.com]** Fr D1091 approx 800m E of town, take D211 sp Alpe d'Huez. After 1km turn L into site. Fountains at ent. Med, mkd pitch, pt shd; htd wc (some cont); chem disp; shwrs inc; el pnts (16A) inc; Indtte; shops 1.5km; tradsmn; snacks; bar; BBQ; playgrnd; htd pool (summer); paddling pool; rv adj; tennis 2km; entmnt; wifi; TV; 10% statics; dogs €1; phone; poss cr; Eng spkn; adv bkg; quiet but with some rd noise; red long stay/low ssn; ccard acc; CKE/CCI. "Excel site; excel lge pool; facs stretched high ssn & when La Marmotte cycle race (early Jul) & Tour de France in area; ski slopes 10-18km." ♦ € 30.00 2011*

BOURG D'OISANS, LE *9C3* (500m SE Rural) *45.05258, 6.03561* **Camping Le Colporteur, Le Mas du Plan, 38520 Le Bourg-d'Oisans [04 76 79 11 44 or 06 85 73 29 19 (mob); fax 04 76 79 11 49; info@camping-colporteur.com; www.camping-colporteur.com]** W fr Briançon on D1019 to Le Bourg-d'Oisans. Ent town, pass Casino supmkt, site sp on L; 150m to sw pool - 2nd site sp, site 50m - sp on side of house. Fr Grenoble on A480 exit 8 onto N85, cont on D1019 to Le Bourg-d'Oisans. Foll sp R in cent of town. Med, hdg/mkd pitch, hdstg, pt shd; wc; chem disp; baby facs; shwrs inc; el pnts (6-15A) €4.50; Indtte; shops 500m; tradsmn; rest, snacks; bar; BBQ; playgrnd; htd pool opp; waterslide; lake sw 10km; fishing; tennis; squash; mountain bikes; rockclimbing; horseriding; cycle hire 200m; entmnt; games rm; wifi; TV; 10% statics; dogs €2; Eng spkn; adv bkg; quiet; ccard acc; red low ssn; CKE/CCI. "Well-organised, high standard site; lge pitches; gd security; mountain scenery; many activities; conv National Park des Ecrins." ♦ 14 May-18 Sep. € 26.00 2011*

BOURG D'OISANS, LE *9C3* (13km SE Rural) *44.98611, 6.12027* **Camping Le Champ du Moulin, Bourg d'Arud, 38520 Vénosc [04 76 80 07 38; fax 04 76 80 24 44; info@champ-du-moulin.com; www.champ-du-moulin.com]** On D1091 SE fr Le Bourg-d'Oisans sp Briançon for about 6km; turn R onto D530 twd La Bérarde & after 8km site sp. Turn R to site 350m after cable car stn beside Rv Vénéon. NB Site sp bef vill; do not cross rv on D530. Med, mkd pitch, pt shd; wc; chem disp; mv service pnt; baby facs; shwrs inc; sauna; el pnts (6-10A) €4.60-5.60 (extra charge in winter; poss rev pol); gas; Indtte (inc dryer): sm shop; tradsmn; rest, snacks; bar; BBQ; playgrnd; htd pool adj; fishing, tennis, rafting & horseriding nr; wifi; games/TV rm; 20% statics; dogs €1.70; no c'vans/m'vans over 10m; poss cr; Eng spkn; adv bkg ess; quiet; ccard acc; red long stay/low ssn; CKE/CCI. "Lovely, well-run site by alpine torrent (unguarded); friendly, helpful owners; ltd facs low ssn; access to pitches poss diff lge o'fits; ideal for walking, climbing & relaxing; lots of outdoor activities to enjoy; cable car to Les Deux Alpes adj (closes end Aug); mkt Tue Vénosc (high ssn); highly rec." ♦ 1 Jan-30 Apr, 1Jun-15 Sep, 15 Dec-31 Dec. € 35.00 SBS - M03 2014*

BOURG D'OISANS, LE *9C3* (4km NW Rural) *45.09000, 6.00750* **Camping Ferme Noémie, Chemin Pierre Polycarpe, Les Sables, 38520 Le Bourg-d'Oisans [tel/fax 04 76 11 06 14 or 06 87 45 08 75 (mob); ferme.noemie@orange.fr; www.fermenoemie.com]** On D1091 Grenoble to Briançon; Les Sables is 4km bef Le Bourg-d'Oisans; turn L next to church, site in 400m. Sm, mkd pitch, unshd; htd wc; chem disp; mv service pnt; shwrs inc; el pnts (16A) €3.50; Indtte; tradsmn; shop, rest, snacks & bar 3km; BBQ (gas); playgrnd; pool 3km; fishing; skiing; cycling; walking; games area;wifi internet; 25% statics; dogs free; phone; bus 500m; poss cr; adv bkg; quiet; red long stay; ccard acc; CKE/CCI. "Simple site in superb location with excel facs; helpful British owners; lots of sports; gd touring base lakes & Ecrins National Park; excel site." ♦ 22 Apr-30 Oct. € 28.50 2014*

BOURG D'OISANS, LE *9C3* (7km NW Rural) *45.11595, 6.00591* **Camping Le Château de Rochetaillée, Chemin de Bouthéon, 38520 Rochetaillée [04 76 11 04 40; fax 04 76 80 21 23; jcp@camping-le-chateau.com; www.camping-le-chateau.com / www.les-castels.com]** On D1091 fr Grenoble turn 7km bef Le Bourg-d'Oisans onto D526 sp Allemont. Site is 50m on L. Med, pt shd; wc; chem disp; baby facs; shwrs inc; el pnts (6A) €4.10; Indtte; shop; rest, snacks; bar; BBQ; playgrnd; pool; spa; games area; games rm; gym; entmnt; dogs €1; 5% statics; quiet; red low ssn; CKE/CCI. "Vg site with mountain views; helpful staff; san facs clean & modern." ♦ 13 May-14 Sep. € 31.00 2010*

BOURG D'OISANS, LE *9C3* (7km NW Rural) *45.11388, 6.00785* **RCN Camping Belledonne, Rochetaillée, 38520 Le Bourg-d'Oisans [04 76 80 07 18; fax 04 76 79 12 95; belledonne@rcn.fr; www.rcn-campings.fr]** Fr S of Grenoble take N85 to Vizille then D1091 twd Le Bourg-d'Oisans; in approx 25km in Rochetaillée turn L onto D526 sp Allemont. Site 100m on R. Med, hdg pitch, shd; wc (some cont); chem disp; mv service pnt; sauna; baby facs; sauna; shwrs inc; el pnts (6A) inc; Indtte (inc dryer); shop; rest, snacks; bar; BBQ; playgrnd; 2 htd pools & paddling pool; fishing 500m; windsurfing; tennis; horseriding; games area; wifi; entmnt; games/TV rm; dogs €7; no twin-axles; no c'vans/m'vans over 7.50m high ssn; Eng spkn; quiet; ccard acc; red low ssn; CKE/CCI. "Beautiful, well-run site in lovely location; friendly Dutch owners; access to many pitches tight; no twin-axles; gd for teenagers; excel pool with views; many walks; gd touring base; La Marmotte cycle race (early Jun) & Tour de France usually pass thro area & access poss restricted; mkt Sat; excel san facs, gd rest; v helpful staff." ♦ 19 Apr-19 Sep. € 52.00 SBS - M02 2014*

BOURG D'OISANS, LE *9C3* (8km NW Rural) *45.12914, 6.04130* **Camp Municipal Le Plan, 38114 Allemont/Allemond [04 76 80 76 88 or 04 76 80 70 30 (Mairie); fax 04 76 79 80 28; info@camping-leplan-allemont.com; www.camping-leplan-allemont.com]** At Rochetaillée on D1091 fr Grenoble turn N 7km bef Le Bourg-d'Oisans on D526 sp Allemont site on R at N end of vill below dam. Med, mkd pitch, hdstg; pt shd; htd wc; chem disp; shwrs inc; el pnts (16A) €2.50; Indtte; snacks; shops in vill; pool adj high ssn only; no statics; dogs €0.50; adv bkg; quiet, some rd noise; ccard acc high ssn; CKE/CCI. "In quiet vill with lovely mountain scenery; excel, clean facs; helpful staff." ♦ 1 May-30 Sep. € 9.70 2010*

BOURG EN BRESSE *9A2* (1km NE Urban) *46.20943, 5.24013* **FFCC Camp Municipal de Challes, 5 Alleée du Centre Nautique, 01000 Bourg-en-Bresse [04 74 45 37 21 or 04 74 22 92 20 (LS); fax 04 74 45 59 95; camping-municipal-bourgenbresse@wanadoo.fr; www.bourgenbresse.fr]** Fr N or S ON N83 foll sp Camping/Piscine/Stade. Site opp stadium. Med, hdstg, shd; wc (most cont); chem disp; shwrs inc; el pnts (6-16A) €2.50 (poss rev pol); Indry rm; hypermkt nr; snacks; rest; BBQ; htd, covrd pool & sports grnd adj; lake sw 2km; wifi; 10% statics; bus adj; poss cr; adv bkg; some rd noise; ccard acc; long stay/CKE/CCI. "Vg, well maintained site; site poss full by 1800; suitable lge o'fits; gd shwr block; gd touring base; daytime noise fr stadium; poss workers staying on site (no problem); mkt Wed." 1 Apr-15 Oct. € 20.00 2014*

BOURG EN BRESSE *9A2* (11km NE Rural) *46.29078, 5.29078* **Camp Municipal du Sevron, Chemin du Moulin, 01370 St Etienne-du-Bois [04 74 30 50 65 or 04 74 30 50 36 (Mairie); fax 04 74 25 85 72; mairie@st-etienne-du-bois.fr; www.st-etienne-du-bois.fr]** On D1083 at S end of vill of St Etienne-du-Bois on E side of rd. Sm, hdg pitch, shd; wc; chem disp; shwrs inc; el pnts (10A) €2.05; shops 300m; tennis; rv fishing; dogs €1.06; Eng spkn; ccard not acc. "Gd NH; dated but clean facs; friendly; sm pitches; late arr get v sm pitches; poss rd & rlwy noise; gd shwrs & plenty hot water." 1 Mar-25 Oct. € 12.00 2014*

BOURG EN BRESSE *9A2* (13km SE Rural) *46.14705, 5.33159* **Camp Municipal de Journans, Rue de Boisserolles/ Montée de Lachat, 01250 Journans [04 74 42 64 71 or 04 74 51 64 45; fax 04 74 42 64 83; mairiejournans@ wandadoo.fr]** Exit A40 junc 7, turn L onto D1075, then L onto D64 dir Tossiat & Journans. Or SE fr Bourg-en-Bresse on D1075 for 9.5km E onto D64 to Journans. Site sp on D52. Sm, mkd pitch, sl terr, pt shd; wc (some cont); shwrs inc; el pnts (5-10A) €2.60; shops 1km (Tossiat); dog €1; poss cr; quiet; CKE/CCI. "Pleasant setting, gd views; helpful warden calls pm; some pitches diff for c'vans; v quiet low ssn; poss mkt traders; excel value." 1 May-15 Sep. € 8.00 2010*

BOURG EN BRESSE *9A2* (20km SE Rural) *46.12775, 5.4282* **Camping de l'Ile Chambod, Route du Port, 01250 Hautecourt-Romanèche [04 74 37 25 41; fax 04 74 37 28 28; camping.chambod@free.fr; www. campingilechambod.com]** Fr S exit A42 junc 9 onto D1075 dir Geneva. In 1km turn L onto N84 dir Nantua. At Poncin turn L at traff lts dir Ile Chambod & site. Fr N turn S off D979 in Hautecourt at x-rds (site sp). Site sp in 4km off D59. At rvside cont for 500m. Med, mkd pitch; pt shd; wc; mv service pnt; baby facs; shwrs inc; el pnts (5-10A) €2.90-3.90 (poss rev pol); gas; lndtte; shop; rest, snacks; BBQ; playgrnd; pool; lake 100m; fishing/boat hire 400m; cycle hire; games area; games rm; internet; entmnt; 10% statics; dogs €1.20; poss cr; Eng spkn; adv bkg; quiet; ccard acc; red low ssn. "Lovely, picturesque, remote site opp lake & adj rv; superb san facs; helpful manager; rest ltd menu; gd for families; gd cycling; 2 nights min w/end; conv Geneva; highly rec." ♦ 22 Apr-25 Sep. € 16.00 2011*

BOURG ST ANDEOL *9D2* (1.5km N Rural) *44.38131, 4.64840* **Camping Le Lion, Chemin du Chenevrier, 07700 Bourg-St Andéol [tel/fax 04 75 54 53 20; contact@campingdulion; www.campingdulion.com]** Exit A7 at junc 18 or 19 onto N7. At Pierrelatte turn W on D59 to Bourg-St Andéol. Site sp fr cent town dir Viviers. Med, mkd pitch, shd; wc; shwrs inc; el pnts (6A) €3; lndtte; shop; snacks; bar; playgrnd; pool; games area; games rm; dir access to rv; wifi; some statics; dogs €1.70; poss cr; adv bkg; quiet; red low ssn. "Peaceful site in woodland setting; some modern san facs, some need update; muddy when wet; highly rec." 1 Apr-15 Sep. € 21.00 2011*

BOURG ST MAURICE *9B4* (1km E Rural) *45.62241, 6.78503* **Camping Le Versoyen, Route des Arcs, 73700 Bourg-St Maurice [04 79 07 03 45; fax 04 79 07 25 41; leversoyen@ wanadoo.fr; www.leversoyen.com]** Fr SW on N90 thro town turn R to Les Arcs. Site on R in 1km. Do not app fr any other dir. Lge, hdstg, pt shd; wc; chem disp; mv service pnt; sauna; shwrs inc; el pnts (4-10A) €4.60-5.20; lndtte; shops 200m; playgrnd; 2 pools adj; tennis adj; games area; entmnt; fishing, canoeing; dogs €1; Eng spkn; quiet; red low ssn; red CKE/CCI. "Excel for winter sports; mountain views; mkd walks fr site; rvside walk to town; well-organised site; dated but clean facs." ♦ 1 Jan-24 Apr, 25 May-3 Nov, 14 Dec-31 Dec. € 32.00 2013*

BOURG ST MAURICE *9B4* (8km S Rural) *45.53100, 6.77530* **Camping Les Lanchettes, Route de Boverêche-Nancroix, 73210 Peisey-Nancroix [04 79 07 93 07; fax 04 79 07 88 33; lanchettes@free.fr; www.camping-lanchettes.com]** Fr Moûtiers foll N90 NE twds Bourg-St Maurice. In 20km turn R sp Landry & Peisey-Nancroix. Up v steep rd with hairpin bends for 6km. Site 1km beyond Nancroix. Long steep ascent with many hairpin bends. Med, pt sl, terr, pt shd; htd wc; chem disp; mv service pnt; shwrs inc; el pnts (3-10A) €3.40-8.40; gas adj; lndtte (inc dryer); shop 200m (summer); tradsmn; rest, snacks; bar; playgrnd; rv fishing; tennis 100m; games area; ski cent in winter; wifi; TV rm; some statics; dogs €1.20; adv bkg; CKE/CCI. "Lovely setting in National Park; excel for outdoor pursuits, walking." ♦ 10 Dec-29 Apr & 4 Jun-25 Sep. € 14.00 2010*

BOURGET DU LAC, LE see Aix Les Bains *9B3*

BRAMANS LE VERNEY see Modane *9C4*

BUIS LES BARONNIES *9D2* (300m N Urban) *44.27558, 5.27830* **Camp Municipal, Quartier du Jalinier, 26170 Buis-les-Baronnies [04 75 28 04 96 or 06 60 80 40 53 (mob)]** Fr Vaison-la-Romaine S on D938; turn L onto D54/D13/D5 to Buis-les-Baronnies; cont N onto D546; at bend turn R over rv bdge; turn L along rv, then 1st R. Site split into 2 either side of sw pool; recep in upper site. Med, hdg/mkd pitch, pt sl, pt shd; wc; chem disp; shwrs inc; el pnts (6A) €3; lndry rm; pool nrby; 5% statics; dogs €1.20; phone; wifi; bus 300m; poss cr; quiet, but poss noise fr pool; CKE/CCI. "Lovely views; san facs dated but clean; not suitable lge o'fits but lger, more accessible pitches on lower level; attractive town; gd mkt Wed & Sat; fair." 1 Mar-11 Nov. € 11.20 2014*

BUIS LES BARONNIES *9D2* (7km E Rural) *44.26325, 5.37744* **Camping/Gîte du Lièvre (Taponnier), 26170 La Roche-sur-les-Buis [04 75 28 11 49; fax 04 75 28 19 26; gitedulievre@ wanadoo.fr; www.gitedulievre.com]** In Buis-les-Baronnies travel N on D546; at edge of town after x-ing rv turn R onto D159; foll for 10km to Poët-en-Percip; site sp on L; 3km down unmade rd. Sm, mkd pitch, hdstg, terr, pt shd; wc (some cont); chem disp (wc); shwrs inc; el pnts (3A) €2.50 (poss long lead req); tradsmn; rest, snacks; bar; playgrnd; pool; mountain bike trails; horseriding; some statics; adv bkg; quiet; no ccard acc; CKE/CCI. "Site on farm; scenic but v isolated at 3,000 feet; views of Mt Ventoux; walks; climbing." May-Oct. € 17.00 2010*

BUIS LES BARONNIES *9D2* (4km SW Rural) *44.25190, 5.24370* **Camping La Gautière, La Penne-sur-l'Ouvèze, 26170 Buis-les-Baronnies [04 75 28 02 68; fax 04 75 28 24 11; accueil@camping-lagautiere.com; www.camping-lagautiere.com]** On D5 Vaison-la-Romaine to Buis-les-Baronnies rd, on L. Sm, mkd pitch, pt shd; htd wc; shwrs inc; el pnts (3-10A) €3-4.60; gas; lndtte; shop & 4km; snacks; bar; BBQ; playgrnd; pool; climbing at Rocher St Julien & Gorges d'Ubrieux; horseriding & fishing nr; games area; games rm; 5% statics; dogs €2.50; phone; bus adj; Eng spkn; adv bkg; quiet; ccard acc; CKE/CCI. "Beautiful situation; haphazard pitch size; diff for o'fits over 6m; helpful owners." 1 Apr-16 Nov. € 17.50 2013*

CHABEUIL see Valence *9C2*

CHALLES LES EAUX see Chambéry *9B3*

CHAMBERY *9B3* (5km E Rural) *45.55151, 5.98416* **Camp Municipal Le Savoy, Parc des Loisirs, Chemin des Fleurs, 73190 Challes-les-Eaux [tel/fax 04 79 72 97 31; camping73challes-les-eaux&wanadoo.fr; www.ville-challesleseaux.com]** On o'skts of town app fr Chambéry on D1006. Pass airfield, lake & tennis courts on L, L at traff lts just bef cent of Challes-les Eaux sp Parc de Loisirs, at Hôtel Les Neiges de France foll camp sp to site in 100m. Fr A41 exit junc 20, foll sp Challes-les-Eaux, then 'Centre Ville', then D1006 N. Med, mkd pitch, hdstg, shd; wc; chem disp; serviced pitches; shwrs; el pnts (6-10A) €2.90; gas; lndtte; shop, rest adj; snacks in ssn; lake sw, fishing, tennis adj; dogs €1; bus; adv bkg; quiet but some rd noise; ccard acc; red long stay. "Well-designed, well-run, clean site in beautiful setting; diff sized pitches; level (suitable wheelchairs); friendly, helpful staff; excel modern san facs; excel walking; well run site, rec hotel school rest in term time." ♦ 1 May-30 Sep. € 16.00 2013*

CHAMBERY *9B3* (10km SW Rural) *45.53804, 5.79973* **Camping Les Peupliers, Lac d'Aiguebelette, 73610 Lépin-le-Lac [04 79 36 00 48 / 06 66 10 09 99 (mob); fax 04 79 44 12 48; info@camping-lespeupliers.net; www.camping-lespeupliers.net]** Exit A43 junc 12 & foll sp Lac d'Aiguebelette (D921). Turn L at rndabt & foll rd on L of lake. Site on R after sm vill. Lge, hdg/mkd pitch, pt shd; wc; chem disp; shwrs inc; el pnts (6A) €3.50; lndtte; shop 3km; tradsmn; rest 3km; snacks; bar; playgrnd; lake sw adj; fishing; wifi; dogs €1.20 (NO SW); poss cr; quiet; ccard acc; red low ssn; CKE/CCI. "Pleasant site in beautiful setting, espec lakeside pitches; friendly, helpful owner; busy w/ends." 1 Apr-30 Oct. € 24.00 2014*

CHAMBERY *9B3* (11km SW Rural) *45.53990, 5.77940* **Camping Le Curtelet, 73610 Lépin-le-Lac [tel/fax 04 79 44 11 22; lecurtelet@wanadoo.fr; www.camping-le-curtelet.com]** Fr A43 E to Chambéry exit junc 12 onto D921 bef Tunnel L'Epine sp Lac d'Aiguebelette. Foll rd round lake, turn L on D921D to Lépin-le-Lac. Site sp after stn on L over level x-ing. Med, mkd pitch, pt sl, pt shd; wc; chem disp; baby facs; shwrs inc; el pnts (2-6A) €2.30-3; lndtte; shop 1km; tradsmn; bar; BBQ; playgrnd; lake sw; sand beach adj; dogs €1.40; Eng spkn; adv bkg; some rlwy noise at top of site; red low ssn; CKE/CCI. "Beautiful scenery; well-maintained site; no twin-axles due terrain; public beach adj poss scruffy low ssn; highly rec." 15 May-30 Sep. € 15.00 2009*

CHAMBERY *9B3* (12km W Rural) *45.55582, 5.79095* **Camping Le Sougey, Lac Rive Ouest, 73610 St Alban-de-Montbel [04 79 36 01 44; fax 04 79 44 19 01; info@camping-sougey.com; www.camping-sougey.com]** Fr A43 E to Chambéry take D921 sp Lac d'Aiguebelette. On W side of lake 3km to site on L. Med, hdg/mkd pitch, some hdstg, pt sl, pt shd; wc; chem disp; 30% serviced pitches; baby facs; shwrs inc; el pnts (6A) inc; gas; lndtte (inc dryer); shop; rest, snacks; bar; playgrnd; lake sw & fishing adj; tennis; horseriding; cycle hire; archery; entmnt; TV; 20% statics; dogs €1.80; Eng spkn; adv bkg rec high ssn; quiet; red low ssn; ccard acc. "Attractive area; spacious site; helpful staff." ♦ 1 May-11 Sep. € 21.00 2010*

CHAMONIX MONT BLANC *9B4* (2km NE Rural) *45.9378, 6.8925* **Camping La Mer de Glace, 200 Chemin de la Bagna, Praz de Chamonix, 74400 Chamonix [04 50 53 44 03; fax 04 50 53 60 83; info@chamonix-camping.com; www.chamonix-camping.com]** Foll sp on D1506 thro Chamonix dir Argentière & Swiss Frontier; site well sp on R in 3km but ent under bdge 2.4m. Rec, to avoid low bdge cont to 1st rndabt in Praz-de-Chamonix & foll sp to site (R at rndabt). Med, hdg/mkd pitch, hdstg, pt sl, pt shd; htd wc (some cont); chem disp; mv service pnt; baby facs; shwrs inc; el pnts (10A) €3; gas 500m; lndtte (inc dryer); shop, rest & bar 500m; tradsmn; snacks; BBQ; playgrnd; htd pool 2km; sports cent nr; wifi; dogs free; phone adj; bus & train 500m; poss cr; Eng spkn; no adv bkg, arr early high ssn; quiet but helicopter noise; ccard not acc; red low ssn; CKE/CCI. "Well-run, wooded site with superb views; sm pitches; helpful staff; vg facs; v conv trains/buses; close to Flégère lift; path to town via woods & rv; excel." ♦ 29 Apr-2 Oct. € 26.80 2014*

CHAMONIX MONT BLANC *9B4* (7km NE Rural) *45.97552, 6.92224* **Camping Le Glacier d'Argentière, 161 Chemin des Chosalets, 74400 Argentière [04 50 54 17 36; fax 04 50 54 03 73; info@campingchamonix.com; www.campingchamonix.com]** On Chamonix-Argentière D1506 rd bef Argentière take R fork twd Argentière cable car stn. Site immed on R. Med, pt sl, pt shd; wc; chem disp; shwrs inc; el pnts (2-10A) €2.60+.03 per extra amp; lndtte; shops 1km; tradsmn; BBQ; dogs €0.50; phone adj; poss cr; adv bkg; Eng spkn; quiet; CKE/CCI; wifi; games area. "Alpine excursions; cable cars adj; mountain views; friendly, helpful owners; gd friendly site; Alpine views; quiet relaxed site; bus stop 1 min; 10 min walk to Argentiere Vill', train stn & cable car; mkd paths fr site." ♦ 15 May-30 Sep. € 18.00 2014*

CHAMONIX MONT BLANC *9B4* (1km SW Rural) *45.91466, 6.86138* **Camping Iles des Barrats, 185 Chemin de l'Ile des Barrats, 74400 Chamonix [tel/fax 04 50 53 51 44; campingiledesbarrats74@orange.fr; www.campingdesbarrats.com]** Fr Mont Blanc tunnel take 1st L on app Chamonix, foll sp to hospital, site opp hospital. Do not go into town. Sm, mkd pitch, pt sl, unshd; wc; chem disp; mv service pnt; shwrs inc; el pnts (5-10A) €3.30-4.30; gas; lndtte; shops 1km; tradsmn; sw 250m; dogs €1; poss cr; Eng spkn; adv bkg; quiet; CKE/CCI. "Great little site; superb mountain views; friendly family owners; immac facs; 10 mins level walk to town; 10 mins cable car Mont Blanc; excel; bus & train pass fr recep; site open fr 1st Monday in Jun until 3rd Sunday in Sep." 2 Jun-21 Sep. € 38.00 2014*

CHAMONIX MONT BLANC *9B4* (3km SW Rural) *45.90578, 6.83673* **Camping Les Ecureuils, Rue Chemin des Doux, Les Bossons, 74400 Chamonix [tel/fax 04 50 53 83 11; contact@campingdesecureuils.fr; www.campingdesecureuils.fr]** Fr St Gervais on D1205 twd Chamonix. L fork to vill. L at x-rd. Under rlwy, sharp R. Site at end of rd. NB Not suitable twin-axles due narr app thro v sm tunnel under rlwy. Sm, mkd pitch, hdstg, pt shd; wc; shwrs inc; el pnts (6A) €3.30; lndtte; shop 3km tradsmn; internet; some statics; poss v cr; adv bkg; quiet; ccard acc; CKE/CCI. "Warm welcome; helpful owners; v sm pitches - not suitable lge o'fits; vg." 15 Apr-30 Sep. € 13.00 2011*

"There aren't many sites open at this time of year"

If you're travelling outside peak season remember to call ahead to check site opening dates – even if the entry says 'open all year'.

⊞ **CHAMONIX MONT BLANC** *9B4* (3.5km SW Rural) *45.90203, 6.83716* **Camping Les Deux Glaciers, 80 Route des Tissières, Les Bossons, 74400 Chamonix [04 50 53 15 84; fax 04 50 55 90 81; info@les2glaciers.com; www.les2glaciers.com]** Exit Mont Blanc tunnel foll sps Geneva turn L on D1506 (Chamonix-Geneva rd), in 2km turn R for Les Bossons & L under bdge. Fr W foll sps Chamonix & Mont Blanc tunnel. On dual c/way turn R at sp 'Les Bossons' & site after Mercure Hotel; adj Les Cimes site; site clearly sp fr D1205. Med, sl, pt shd; htd wc; chem disp; shwrs inc; baby facs; el pnts (6-10A) €2.50-7; lndtte (inc dryer); shop; tradsmn; rest, snacks; bar; playgrnd; pool & skating rink 4km; games rm; table tennis; wifi; dogs free; bus; Eng spkn; CKE/CCI. "Pleasant, well-kept site in wonderful location just under Mont Blanc; roomy pitches; clean facs; poss diff site for lge o'fits over 6m; if recep clsd pitch & wait until 1730; ideal for walking; funicular adj to Glacier des Bossons; rec arr early high ssn; highly rec." ♦ 1 Jan- 15 Nov, 15 Dec- 31 Dec. € 28.00 2014*

CHANAS see St Rambert d'Albon *9C2*

CHANTEMERLE LES BLES see Tain l'Hermitage *9C2*

CHAPELLE EN VERCORS, LA *9C3* (6.5km N Rural) *45.02534, 5.44370* **Camping La Porte St Martin, 26420 St Martin-en-Vercors [04 75 45 51 10; infos@camping-laportestmartin.com; www.camping-laportestmartin.com]** Sp 200m N of vill on D103. (D531 fr Villard-de-Lans W not rec for c'vans). Med, mkd pitch, pt terr, pt shd; wc; shwrs inc; el pnts (10A) €2.80; lndtte; tradsmn; shops, rest, snacks & bar 500m; pool; paddling pool; wifi; some statics; dogs €2; phone; Eng spkn; quiet; red low ssn; CKE/CCI. "Superb mountain views fr most pitches; excel walking." ♦ 1 May-30 Sep. € 14.00 2010*

CHAPELLE EN VERCORS, LA *9C3* (2km E Rural) *44.96808, 5.43048* **Camping Les Myrtilles, Les Chaberts, 26420 La Chapelle-en-Vercors [tel/fax 04 75 48 20 89; camping.des.myrtilles@wanadoo.fr; http://camping.des.myrtilles.pagesperso-orange.fr]** Fr A49/E713 exit 8 to N532 St Nazaire-en-Royans, then D76 thro St Thomas-en Royans, then D216 to St Laurent-en-Royans. Take D2 around E flank of Combe Laval (2 sh 2-lane tunnels). Fr Col de la Machine foll D76 S 1km, then D199 E over Col de Carri to La Chapelle. Fr S fr Die, foll D518 over Col de Rousset. (D76 over Combe Laval, D531 fr Villard-de-Lans & D518 fr Pont-en-Royans over Grandes Goulet not suitable for c'vans). Med, pt sl, pt shd; wc; chem disp; shwrs inc; el pnts (4-6A) €2.45-3; lndtte; shop 1km; snacks; bar; playgrnd; htd pool; rv fishing 2km; 20% statics; dogs €1.50; adv bkg; v quiet; red low ssn; CKE/CCI. "Beautiful setting; excel walking, caves & gorges; gates locked 2200-0700." ♦ 1 May-15 Sep. € 14.50 2010*

CHARLIEU *9A1* (950m E Urban) *46.15851, 4.18088* **FFCC Camp Municipal de la Douze, Rue Riottier, 42190 Charlieu [04 77 69 01 70 or 06 65 34 77 39 (mob); fax 04 77 69 07 28; camp-charlieu@voila.fr]** N fr Roanne on D482 to Pouilly-sous-Charlieu, then E on D487 to Charlieu town cent, site sp in town, by sw pool. NB Do not confuse with Camp Municipal Pouilly-sous-Charlieu which is sp fr main rd. Med, hdg/mkd pitch, pt shd; wc; chem disp; mv service pnt; shwrs inc; el pnts (6A) inc; lndtte; shops 1km; snacks; bar; playgrnd; pool adj; sports area; fishing, boating adj; entmnt; 40% statics; poss cr; Eng spkn; adv bkg; CKE/CCI. "Gd clean san facs; facs poss stretched high ssn, excel low ssn; vg value." ♦ 1 Apr-30 Sep. € 11.00 2009*

CHARLIEU *9A1* (4km W Rural) *46.15003, 4.11204* **FFCC Camp Municipal Les Ilots, Rue de Marcigny, 42720 Pouilly-sous-Charlieu [04 77 60 80 67; fax 04 77 60 79 44; mairie.pouilly-sous-charlieu42@wanadoo.fr]** N fr Roanne on D482 sp Pouilly-sous-Charlieu. Site sp on ring rd 1km N of town, turn E into stadium. Med, mkd pitch, pt shd; htd wc (cont); mv service pnt; shwrs inc; el pnts (6A) €3; gas; lndtte; shops 1km; rest, bar 500m; playgrnd; pool; fishing; games area; poss cr; Eng spkn; quiet; ccard not acc; red CKE/CCI. "Lge pitches grouped in circles." 15 May-15 Sep. € 7.00 2009*

CHARMES SUR L'HERBASSE see St Donat sur l'Herbasse *9C2*

CHATEAUNEUF SUR ISERE see Valence *9C2*

CHATEAUNEUF SUR ISERE *9C2* (5km W Rural) *44.99710, 4.89333* **Le Soleil Fruité, Les Pèches, 26300 Châteauneuf-sur Isère [04 75 84 19 70; fax 04 75 78 05 85; contact@lesoleilfruite.com; www.lesoleilfruite.com]** Fr Valence, take A7 dir Lyon. Take exit 14 Valence Nord twd Bourg les Valence. At rndabt take 1st exit onto N7. Turn R onto D877 and foll sp. Med; hdg pitch; mkd pitch; pt shd; wc; baby facs; shwrs; el pnts (6A); lndtte (inc dryer); rest; snacks; bar; BBQ; playgrnd; htd covrd pool; htd paddling pool; waterslide; bike hire; games area; entmnt; tv; wifi; Eng spkn; adv bkg; CCI. "Immac site; lovely pool; gd rest; sh drive to vill." ♦ 26 Apr-15 Sep. € 44.00 2014*

CHATEL *9A4* (1.5km SW Rural) *46.25768, 6.83023* **Camping Caravaneige L'Oustalet, 1428 Route des Freinets, 74390 Châtel [04 50 73 21 97; fax 04 50 73 37 46; oustalet@valdabondance.com; www.oustalet.com]** Fr Thonon-les-Bains, take D902 & D22 to Châtel. Site sp fr church in cent. Med, hdg/mkd pitch, unshd; htd wc; mv service pnt; sauna; shwrs inc; el pnts (3-10A) €4-7.50; gas; Indtte; shop, rest, bar 100m; playgrnd; htd, covrd pool high ssn; tennis; games rm; wifi; entmnt; some statics; dogs €2.10; adv bkg rec winter; quiet; red low ssn. "Excel, well-kept site; excel clean facs; vg indoor pool; gd mountain walks; conv for ski lifts; ski bus stop adj." ♦ 19 Jun-5 Sep & 19 Dec-25 Apr. € 25.00 2010*

CHATELARD, LE *9B3* (500m NW Rural) *45.68783, 6.13078* **Camping Les Cyclamens, 73630 Le Châtelard [04 79 54 80 19 or 07 86 86 03 58 (mob); contact@camping-cyclamens.com; www.camping-cyclamens.com]** Exit A41 junc 14 at Grésy-sur-Aix onto D911 E to Le Châtelard; turn R at rndabt at ent to Le Châtelard onto Route du Champet; in 600m turn R to site. Or S fr Annecy on D508/D1508; in 3km fork R onto D912/D911 to Le Châtelard; then as bef. Site well sp. Sm, pt sl, pt shd; wc; chem disp; mv service pnt; baby facs; shwrs inc; el pnts (2-10A) €2.40-3.10; gas; Indtte; supmkt 400m; tradsmn; BBQ; rv sw 1km, lake sw 5km; fishing; kayaking; rock-climbing; paragliding; canyoning; horseriding; games rm; wifi; dogs; €0.80; bus 600m; Eng spkn; adv bkg; quiet; red low ssn/long stay; CKE/CCI. "Attractive site with stunning views; lge pitches; friendly staff; clean san facs; easy access to walks; excel." ♦ 22 Apr-30 Sep. € 12.00 2011*

CHATILLON EN DIOIS *9D3* (600m E Urban) *44.69450, 5.48817* **Camp Municipal Les Chaussières, 26410 Châtillon-en-Diois [04 75 21 10 30 or 04 75 21 14 44 (Mairie); fax 04 75 21 18 78; camping.chatillonendiois@wanadoo.fr; www.camping-chatillonendiois.com]** Fr Die take D93 S for 6km then L on D539 to Châtillon (8km) site sp on R on ent to town. Med, mkd pitch, pt shd; wc (some cont) chem disp; mv service pnt; shwrs inc; el pnts (10A) €3.60; ice; shop 200m; snacks & bar 200m; BBQ; playgrnd; pool adj; canoeing; fishing; tennis; horseriding; cycling; entmnt; 30% statics; dogs €2.10; phone; poss cr; Eng spkn; adv bkg; quiet; ccard acc; red low ssn; CKE/CCI. "Wardens off site 1130- 1630; pleasant sweet site, wardens friendly and helpful." 1 Apr-1 Nov. € 25.70 2014*

CHATILLON SUR CHALARONNE *9A2* (500m SE Urban) *46.11622, 4.96172* **FFCC Camp Municipal du Vieux Moulin, Ave Jean Jaurès, 01400 Châtillon-sur-Chalaronne [04 74 55 04 79; fax 04 74 55 13 11; campingvieuxmoulin@orange.fr; www.camping-vieuxmoulin.com]** Exit A6 junc 30 to Châtillon-sur-Chalaronne; pick up D7 on S site of vill; site on R in 400m. Ave Jean Jaurès is pt of D7. Site sp in town. Med, hdg pitch, hdstg, shd; wc (some cont); chem disp; baby facs; shwrs inc; el pnts (10A) €4 (long lead req on some pitches); Indtte (inc dryer); supmkt 200m; rest & bar adj; snacks; playgrnd; pool adj inc; fishing; leisure cent adj; 50% statics; dogs €2; phone; adv bkg; quiet, noisy eves high ssn; ccard acc; red CKE/CCI. "Lovely site in picturesque area; helpful warden; immac facs, ltd low ssn; check office opening hrs for early dep; if office clsd ring bell, warden will open barrier; lovely medieval town cent; excel model rlwy; mkt Sat; site remains excellent, new municipal pool under construction next door." ♦ 1 May-30 Sep. € 23.00 2014*

CHAVANNES SUR SURAN *9A2* (500m E Rural) *46.26601, 5.42819* **Camp Municipal, Le Village, 01250 Chavannes-sur-Suran [04 74 51 70 52; fax 04 74 51 71 83; mairiechavannessuran@wanadoo.fr]** Turn E off N83 at St Etienne-du-Bois onto D3, cross D52 bef Treffort (v narr rds). Then steep climb & bends & after 6km turn N onto D936 sp Chavannes. Turn E at town hall (Mairie), site sp. Fr Bourg-en-Bresse turn E onto D936 sp Jasseron about 1km after joining N83 in Bourg. Foll D936 for approx 18km to Chavannes. Sm, hdg/mkd pitch, pt shd; wc; chem disp (wc); shwrs inc; el pnts (5A) inc (poss rev pol & poss long lead req); shop 500m; BBQ; quiet. "Pretty rvside site in beautiful area; lge pitches; site self, warden calls; clean san facs; excel cycling, fishing, walking; attractive vill; Cize-Bolozon viaduct worth visit; highly rec." ♦ ltd 1 May-30 Sep. € 11.50 2010*

CHAZELLES SUR LYON *9B2* (3km E Rural) *45.63454, 4.42789* **Camping d'Hurongues, 69590 Pomeys [04 78 48 44 29; campinghurongues@orange.fr; www.camping-hurongues.com]** Fr N on D389/D1089 turn S onto D103, thro Chazelles-sur-Lyon, exit on D2, twd St Symphorien-sur-Coise. Site on L 3km fr Chazelles. Med, pt sl, terr, pt shd; htd wc (some cont); chem disp; mv service pnt; baby facs; shwrs; el pnts (13A) €3; Indtte (inc dryer); shop; tradsmn; rest 3km; snacks; BBQ; htd, covrd pool adj; tennis; cycle hire; games area; some statics; dogs €3; phone; sep car park high ssn; adv bkg; quiet. ♦ 16 Apr-16 Oct. € 17.00 (CChq acc) 2010*

CHENS SUR LEMAN **see Douvaine** *9A3*

CLELLES *9C3* (4km N Rural) *44.85118, 5.62478* **FFCC Camp Municipal de la Chabannerie, 38930 St Martin-de-Clelles [tel/fax 04 76 34 00 38; camping.chabannerie@yahoo.fr; www.camping-isere.fr]** D1075 fr Grenoble, after St Michel-les-Portes look for rest on R. Turn L after 300m to St Martin-de-Clelles, site sp. Site well sp fr N & S. Sm, mkd pitch, hdstg, terr, shd; wc; chem disp; baby facs; shwrs inc; el pnts (10A) €3.50; gas 5km; Indtte; shop 5km; rest, snacks; bar; no BBQs; playgrnd; pool; games area; TV rm; 4% statics; dogs €1; phone; Eng spkn; adv bkg; quiet, rd noise some pitches; ccard acc; red low ssn/long stay/CKE/CCI. "Pitches in pine trees; conv Vercours National Park & mountains; pleasant staff; some san facs dated; low ssn san facs poss unclean (2011); beautiful pool; sm pitches & steep site rds, access diff lge o'fits; gd walking; tranquil site with 38 species of orchids in ssn." ♦ 1 May-30 Sep. € 15.50 2011*

CLEON D'ANDRAN *9D2* (200m SE Urban) *44.60985, 4.93715* **Camp Municipal Les Cigales, Rue de Piscine, 26450 Cléon-d'Andran [06 87 90 40 80 (mob) or 04 75 90 12 73 (Mairie); mairie.cleon.andran@wanadoo.fr]** Fr A7 leave at junc 16 sp Privas/Crest. S fr Crest on D538. In 5km take D6. In 11km at Cléon-d'Andran turn L in vill, in 100m turn R. Sm, shd; wc (cont); shwrs inc; el pnts €2.50; Indtte; shop 500m; playgrnd; pool; dogs €1; quiet; CKE/CCI. 1 Jul-31 Aug. € 11.00 2010*

RHONE-ALPS

CLUSAZ, LA *9B3* (6km N Rural) *45.93972, 6.42777* **Camping L'Escale, Route de la Patinoire, 74450 Le Grand-Bornand [04 50 02 20 69; fax 04 50 02 36 04; contact@ campinglescale.com; www.campinglescale.com]** Exit A41 junc 17 onto D16/D909 E dir La Clusaz. At St Jean-de-Sixt turn L at rndabt sp Le Grand Bornand. After 1.5km foll camping sp on main rd & at junc turn R sp for site & 'Vallée du Bouchet'. Site is 1st exit R at rndabt at end of this rd. D4 S fr Cluses not rec while towing as v steep & winding. Med, mkd pitch, pt sl, terr, pt shd; htd wc; chem disp; mv service pnt; serviced pitch in summer; baby facs; shwrs inc; el pnts (10A) inc poss rev pol); gas; Indtte (inc dryer); shop 250m; tradsmn; rest, snacks; bar; BBQ; playgrnd; 2 pools (1 htd, covrd); paddling pool; fishing; wintersports; cycle hire 250m; tennis; archery; wifi; games/ TV rm; 20% statics; dogs €2.30; no c'vans over 8.50m or m'vans over 8m high ssn, Feb & wk of New Year; skibus; poss cr; adv bkg ess; ccard acc; red low ssn; CKE/CCI. "Family-run site in scenic area; gd san facs; vg rest; sh walk to attractive vill; free use htd ski/boot rm in winter; boggy in wet weather; vg mkt Wed" ♦ 27 May-28 Sep & 9 Dec-6 Apr. € 29.80 SBS - M07 2013*

CLUSAZ, LA *9B3* (2km E Rural) *45.90921, 6.45208* **Camping Le Plan du Fernuy, 1800 Route des Confins, 74220 La Clusaz [04 50 02 44 75; fax 04 50 32 67 02; fernuy@ franceloc.fr; www.plandufernuy.com / www.campings-franceloc.fr]** Fr Annecy take D909 to La Clusaz (32km). Turn L for Les Confins & site on R in 2km. Med, mkd pitch, pt sl, unshd; wc; chem disp; shwrs inc; baby rm; el pnts (4-13A) €4-8; gas; Indtte (inc dryer); shop; snacks; bar; playgrnd; htd, covrd pool; paddling pool; wifi; TV; some statics; dogs €5; free ski bus; poss cr; quiet. "Site at 1200m alt; excel site & facs; poss diff lge o'fits." ♦ 12 Jun-5 Sep & 2 Jan-24 Apr. € 25.00 2010*

CONDRIEU *9B2* (4km N Rural) *45.50949, 4.77330* **Camping Domaine du Grand Bois (Naturist), Tupin et Semons, 69420 Condrieu [04 74 87 89 00 or 04 74 87 04 29; fax 04 74 87 88 48; domainedugrandbois@free.fr; www. domainedugrandbois.fr]** Fr Vienne take D502 dir Rive-de-Gier; site well sp after x-ing Rv Rhône. NB Do not app fr Condrieu - v steep with hairpins. Lge, sl, pt shd; wc (most cont); chem disp (wc); shwrs inc; el pnts (6A) €4.50; shop 6km; snacks; bar; playgrnd; pool; TV; 75% statics; phone; poss cr; adv bkg; quiet; INF card. "Spectacular views; v basic san facs." ♦ ltd 15 Apr-15 Oct. € 17.56 2013*

CONDRIEU *9B2* (2km SE Rural) *45.42413, 4.78251* **Camping Le Daxia, Route du Péage, 38370 St Clair-du-Rhône [04 74 56 39 20; fax 04 74 56 45 57; info@campingledaxia. com; www.campingledaxia.com]** S fr Vienne on D386; turn L in Condieu sp D28 Les Roches-de-Condrieu & Le Péage-de-Roussillon; foll sp A7 Valance & 'Camping' onto D4. Site on L well sp fron Condrieu. Med, hdg/mkd pitch, pt shd; wc; chem disp; mv service pnt; baby facs; shwrs inc; el pnts (5-6A) €2.40-2.85; Indtte; shop 1km; sm rest, snacks; bar; BBQ; playgrnd; pool; paddling pool; games rm, wifi; dogs €1.85; adv bkg; quiet; CKE/CCI; "Vg site; on edge of sm rv with beach." ♦ ltd 1 Apr-30 Sep. € 19.00 2013*

CORDELLE see Roanne *9A1*

CORPS *9C3* (250m W Urban) *44.81909, 5.94323* **Camping Municipal Les Aires, Route du Sautet, 38970 Corps [04 76 30 03 85; fax 04 76 81 12 28; www.isere-tourisme. com]** Fr N85, Route de Napoleon, Grenoble to Gap. Vill of Corps turn R on D537, site on L in 400m. Sm, mkd pitch, pt shd; wc; chem disp; shwrs; el pnts (6A) inc; Indry rm; games rm; 30% statics; dog; "Quiet site; san facs old but clean; in pretty vill on the Route de Napoleon." 06 Apr-30 Sep. € 13.40 2013*

⊞ **CREMIEU** *9B2* (5km NW Rural) *45.74829, 5.22486* **Camping à la Ferme des Epinettes, 11 Rue de l'Eglise, 38460 St Romain-de-Jalionas [tel/fax 04 74 90 94 90 or 06 19 31 03 50 (mob); info@camping-cremieu.com; www. camping-cremieu.com]** N fr Crémieu on D517; in 3km site sp on R, immed bef rndabt on edge of St Romain-de-Jalionas. 200m after turning R off D517 (into Rue de l'Eglise), turn L into Rue des Epinettes & site ent. Site on R in 100m. Sm, mkd pitch, pt shd; htd wc; chem disp (wc); shwrs inc; el pnts (16A); Indry rm; shops etc 5km; jacuzzi; 20% statics; dogs €1; no twin-axles; quiet; red low ssn. "Gd NH for interesting & historic town of Lyon and Crémieu; helpful owners; ltd facs low ssn; gd touring base; Pérouges worth visit; trams/metro fr Meyzieu to Lyon; rec; lovely, peaceful site." ♦ ltd € 17.00 2014*

CREST *9D2* (5km E Rural) *44.71095, 5.08960* **Gervanne Camping, Quartier Bellevue, 26400 Mirabel-et-Blacons [04 75 40 00 20; fax 04 75 40 03 97; info@gervanne-camping.com; www.gervanne-camping.com]** Exit A7 junc 16 Loriol onto D104/D164, turn off onto D93. Site E of Mirabel-et-Blacons on both sides or rd. Recep by shop. Lge, hdg/mkd pitch, pt shd; htd wc; chem disp; mv service pnt; shwrs inc; baby facs; el pnts (6A) €4; gas; Indtte (inc dryer); shop; tradsmn; rest, snacks; bar; BBQ (gas/elec); playgrnd; htd pool; rv sw & beach adj; canoeing; kayaking; canyoning; cycle hire; games area; games rm; wifi; TV; 12% statics; dogs €3; poss cr; Eng spkn; adv bkg (ess high ssn); quiet; ccard acc; red low ssn; CKE/CCI. "Excel, family-run site in beautiful area by Rv Drôme; gd sized pitches; vg pool complex; vg rest; poss soft after rain - no hdstg." ♦ 2 Apr-30 Sep. € 23.00 2011*

CREST *9D2* (500m S Urban) *44.72410, 5.02755* **Camping Les Clorinthes, Quai Soubeyran, 26400 Crest [04 75 25 05 28; fax 04 75 76 75 09; clorinthes@wanadoo.fr; www. lesclorinthes.com]** S fr Crest twd Nyons on D538, cross bdge cont to rndabt,take last exit foll sp to site. Lge, hdg/mkd pitch, some hdstg, pt sl, pt shd; wc; chem disp; baby facs; shwrs; el pnts (6A) €3.90; gas; Indtte (inc dryer); shop & 500m; tradsmn; snacks; bar; pool; paddling pool; rv sw adj; sports complex 500m; wifi; entmnt; TV; 20% statics; dogs €2.80; phone; adv bkg; poss cr; quiet, some train noise; red low ssn; CKE/CCI. "Well-maintained site in beautiful situation; dir access rv; gd, modern san facs; easy walk or cycle to vill." ♦ ltd 10 Apr-19 Sep. € 27.50 2014*

CREST *9D2* (8km W Rural) *44.72717, 4.92664* **Camping Les Quatre Saisons, Route de Roche-sur-Grâne, 26400 Grane [04 75 62 64 17; fax 04 75 62 69 06; contact@camping-4-saisons.com; www.camping-4saisons.com]** Exit A7 at junc for Loriol or Crest, take D104 E for 18km. Turn R thro vill twd Roche-sur-Grane, site well sp. If a lge unit, access thro 4th junc to Grane. Site well sp fr Crest. Med, pt sl, terr, pt shd; wc; chem disp; mv service pnt; baby facs; shwrs inc; el pnts (6A) €4; Indtte; shop; tradsmn; rest 800m; snacks; bar; BBQ; htd pool; paddling pool; tennis; cycle hire; games area; wifi; TV; some statics; dogs; phone; poss cr; adv bkg; Eng spkn; quiet; ccard acc; red long stay/low ssn; CKE/CCI. "Beautiful views; well-run site; pleasant, helpful owner; sm & lge pitches; excel san facs; gd pool; Grane (supmkt, rest etc) in walking dist; some pitches far fr el pnts and san facs up steep hill; paths a bit uneven - need attention; pleasant stay." ♦ 1 May-15 Sep. € 27.00 (CChq acc) 2013*

CULOZ see Ruffieux *9B3*

DARBRES *9D2* (10km NE) *44.63370, 4.50740* **Camping Les Charmilles, Le Clapas, 07170 Darbres, Ardèche [tel/fax 04 75 88 56 27; info@campinglescharmilles.fr; www.campinglescharmilles.fr]** E fr Aubenas on D259; turn L on D224 at Lussas; fork R after Darbres & site in 2km on L sp. Steep app. Med, terr, pt shd; wc; chem disp; shwrs inc; el pnts (5-10A) inc; rest, snacks; shop; 2 pools; dog €2; adv bkg; few statics; Eng spkn; some noise to 2300; "free tow if in trouble on app." ♦ 27 Aprr-30 Sep. € 44.50 2013*

DARDILLY see Lyon *9B2*

DIE *9D2* (300m N Rural) *44.75444, 5.37778* **FFCC Camping La Riou-Merle, Route de Romeyer, 26150 Die [tel/fax 04 75 22 21 31; lerioumerle@gmail.com; www.camping-lerioumerle.com]** Fr Gap on D93 heading twd Valence. Cont on D93 twd town cent; R on D742 to Romeyer. Site on L in 200m. On D93 fr Crest foll sp round town cent onto D742. Med, pt sl, pt shd; wc (some cont); chem disp; mv service pnt; shwrs inc; el pnts (10A) €4.20; Indtte; shops in town; rest; playgrnd; pool; fishing; wifi; 30% statics; dogs €2; Eng spkn; quiet; red low ssn. "Clean site; friendly, helpful staff; gd san facs; attractive town." 1 Apr-15 Oct. € 17.00 2011*

DIE *9D2* (2km NW Rural) *44.76250, 5.34674* **Camping de Chamarges, Route de Crest, 26150 Die [tel/fax 04 75 22 14 13 or 04 75 22 06 77; campingchamarges@orange.fr]** Foll D93 twd Valence, site on L by Rv Drôme. Med, mkd pitch, pt shd; wc (some cont); chem disp; shwrs inc; el pnts (3-6A) €2.90-3.60; gas; shop 1km; rest, snacks; bar; BBQ (gas); playgrnd; pool; rv sw, fishing & canoeing adj; entmnt; TV; wifi; dogs €1.60; phone; Eng spkn; rec adv bkg high ssn; quiet; ccard acc; CKE/CCI. "Beautiful mountainous area; vg; friendly owners." ♦ 1 Apr-13 Sep. € 12.00 2012*

DIEULEFIT *9D2* (1km SW Urban) *44.52129, 5.06126* **Le Domaine des Grands Prés, Chemin de la Bicoque, 26220 Dieulefit [04 75 49 94 36 or 06 30 57 08 43 (mob); info@lesgrandspres-dromeprovencale.com; www.lesgrandspres-dromeprovencale.com]** Fr N of A7 take exit 17 twd Dieulefit/Montelimar. At rndabt, take 2nd exit onto N7. Turn L onto D74. Drive thro the vill of Souzet, La Batie-Rolland & la Begude de Mazenc. Campsite located bef town on S side of the rd on the R. Med, mkd pitch, hdstg, pt shd; wc; chem disp; baby facs; shwrs; el pnts (10A) €3.70; Indtte (inc dryer); BBQ; pool; paddling pool; playgrnd; wifi; tv rm; dogs €2; bus 0.2km; poss cr; Eng spkn; adv bkg; quiet; ccard acc; CCI. "Site on o'skirts of vill with all facs with unusual accomodations. ♦ 20 Mar-1 Nov. € 31.00 2014*

DIVONNE LES BAINS *9A3* (3km N Rural) *46.37487, 6.12143* **Camping Indigo Divonne, Quartier Villard, 01220 Divonne-les-Bains [04 50 20 01 95 or 04 42 20 47 25 (LS); fax 04 50 20 00 35; info@homair.com; www.homair.com]** Exit E62 dir Divonne-les-Bains approx 12km N of Geneva. Fr town on D984, foll sp to site. Lge, hdg/mkd pitch, sl, terr, shd; htd wc; shwrs inc; chem disp; el pnts (4A) €5; gas; Indtte; shop, snacks & rest in ssn; bar; supmkts 3km; lake sw 3km; htd pool; paddling pool; lake sw 3km; tennis; games area; entmnt in ssn; TV rm; 50% statics; dogs €5; Eng spkn; adv bkg; quiet; ccard acc; red low ssn; CKE/CCI. "Helpful owner; levellers req; Lake Geneva 8km." 4 Apr-18 Oct. € 26.00 2014*

DOUSSARD *9B3* (1.5km N Rural) *45.79120, 6.21599* **Camping International de Lac Bleu, Route de la Plage, 74210 Doussard [04 50 44 30 18 or 04 50 44 38 47; fax 04 50 44 84 35; contact@camping-lac-bleu.com; www.camping-lac-bleu.com]** S fr Annecy on D1508 twd Albertville. Site on L in 20km just past Bout-du-Lac & bef Camp La Nublière. Lge, hdg/mkd pitch, pt sl, pt shd; wc; chem disp; mv service pnt; some serviced pitches; shwrs inc; el pnts (8A) €3.90; gas adj; Indtte; shop 2km; hypmkt 4km; rest & snacks in high ssn; bar; playgrnd; pool; lake beach adj; watersports; wifi; dogs €4; phone; bus adj; poss cr; Eng spkn; adv bkg; rd noise some pitches; red low ssn/long stay; ccard acc; CKE/CCI. "Excel lakeside location; some lge pitches; gd watersports; cycle path to Annecy; ltd facs low ssn." ♦ 4 Apr-26 Sep. € 29.00 2009*

DOUSSARD *9B3* (2.5km N Rural) *45.79534, 6.20589* **Camping L'Idéal, 715 Route de Chaparon, 74210 Lathuile [04 50 44 32 97; fax 04 50 44 36 59; info@camping-ideal.com; www.camping-ideal.com]** Take Annecy Sud exit fr A41, foll Albertville sp on D1508 on W side of lake. In vill of Brédannaz R at traff lts, immed L on narr rd for 100m; site on R after 2km. Lge, mkd pitch, pt sl, pt shd; wc; chem disp; shwrs inc; el pnts (6A) €3.90; gas; Indtte; shop; rest, snacks; bar; BBQ: playgrnd; htd, covrd pool; waterslide; lake sw 800m; games area; entmnt; TV; 15% statics; dogs €3.20; phone; poss cr high ssn; adv bkg; quiet; red long stay; CKE/CCI. "Pleasant, family-run site; less cr than lakeside sites; views of mountains & lake." 1 May-23 Sep. € 23.00 2009*

"I like to fill in the reports as I travel from site to site"

You'll find report forms at the back of this guide, or you can fill them in online at www.caravaclub.co.uk/europereport.

DOUSSARD *9B3* (3km N Rural) *45.80256, 6.20960* **Camping La Ravoire, Route de la Ravoire, Bout-du-Lac, 74210 Doussard [04 50 44 37 80; fax 04 50 32 90 60; info@camping-la-ravoire.fr; www.camping-la-ravoire.fr]** Fr Annecy, turn R at traff lts in Bredanaz, then immed L & foll rd across cycle track & uphill for 1km, at vill take L fork, site immed on L. Fr Albertville on B1508, turn L opp Complex Sportif, Bout de Lac sp Lathule; cont, x-ing cycle track to rndabt; turn R & cont 2km past other sites; at junc turn sharp R, site immed on L. Med, hdg/mkd pitch, hdstg, pt sl, pt shd; htd wc; chem disp; mv service pnt (poss diff access); serviced pitches; baby facs; shwrs inc; el pnts (5A) inc (poss rev pol); gas; Indtte (inc dryer); sm shop; tradsmn; supmkt 5km; rest 800m; snacks; bar; playgrnd; htd pool; paddling pool; waterslide; lake sw 800m; fishing, golf, horseriding, sailing & windsurfing adj; cycle hire; games area; TV rm; some statics; dogs; phone; poss cr; Eng spkn; adv bkg rec Jul/Aug; quiet; ccard acc; red low ssn; CKE/CCI. "Excel, well-kept, busy site with mountain views; friendly staff & atmosphere; immac facs; lake ferry fr Doussard; cycle paths adj." ♦ 8 May-14 Sep. € 40.40 (CChq acc) 2014*

See advertisement

DOUSSARD *9B3* (3km N Rural) *45.80302, 6.20608* **Camping Le Taillefer, 1530 Route de Chaparon, 74210 Doussard [tel/fax 04 50 44 30 30; info@campingletaillefer.com; www.campingletaillefer.com]** Fr Annecy take D1508 twd Faverges & Albertville. At traff lts in Bredannaz turn R, then immed L for 1.5km; site immed on L by vill sp 'Chaparon'. Do NOT turn into ent by Bureau but stop on rd & ask for instructions as no access to pitches fr Bureau ent. Or, to avoid Annecy, fr Faverges, along D1508, turn L (sp Lathuile) after Complex Sportif at Bout-du-Lac. Turn R at rndabt (sp Chaparon), site is on R after 2.5km. Sm, mkd pitch, pt sl, terr, pt shd; wc; chem disp; mv service pnt; shwrs inc; el pnts (6A) €4.50 (check rev pol); Indtte (inc dryer); sm shop & 3km; tradsmn; snacks & bar (high ssn); BBQ (gas/charcoal only); playgrnd; lake sw 1km; shgl beach 3km; tennis 100m; watersports 2km; sailing; rafting; canyoning; climbing; cycle hire; games/TV rm; dogs €2.50; no c'vans/m'vans over 8m high ssn; Eng spkn; adv bkg; quiet, some rd noise; ccard not acc; red low ssn/long stay. "Peaceful, simple, family-run site nr Lake Annecy; fantastic mountain views; access some pitches poss diff due steep terraces; friendly, helpful owners; dated, clean san facs; vg rest in easy walking dist; mkt Mon; worth another visit." ♦ 1 May-29 Sep. € 21.00 SBS - M06 2014*

DOUSSARD *9B3* (500m NW Rural) *45.79115, 6.21298* **Camping Le Polé, 1430 Route du Bout du Lac, 74210 Lathuile [04 50 44 32 13 or 06 88 04 68 70 (mob); contact@camping-le-pole.fr; www.camping-le-pole.fr]** S fr Annecy on D1508 dir Albertville; in 14km at Bout-du-Lac turn R dir Lathuile; site on L in 70m, just after cylce track. Or N fr Faverges on D1508; in 8km turn sharp L after passing Camping International du Lac Bleu; site on L. Med, hdg/mkd pitch, pt shd; wc; chem disp; baby facs; shwrs inc; el pnts (2-6A) €3.50-7; Indry rm; ice; shops 3km; tradsmn rest 2km; snacks 500m; bar 200m; BBQ; playgrnd; pool; paddling pool; lake sw adj; games area; games rm; TV; 50% statics; dogs €2.50; phone; Eng spkn; adv bkg; quiet. "Quiet, scenic site in busy area high ssn; helpful manager; gd pool; cycle path adj; gd walks; vg." ♦ 1 Jun-30 Sep. € 15.50 2009*

DOUVAINE *9A3* (8km NE Rural) *46.36812, 6.32809* **Camping Mathieu Le Léman 1, 74140 Yvoire [04 50 72 84 31; fax 04 50 72 96 33; www.campingsmathieu.com]** Exit D1005 at Sciez (bet Geneve & Thonon) onto D25 sp Yvoire; site in 10km; at Yvoire foll camping sp. NB Narr ent to site. Med, mkd pitch, pt sl, pt shd; wc (mainly cont); chem disp; mv service pnt; shwrs inc; el pnts (6A) €2.50; Indtte; tradsmn; shop, snacks & bar 500m; BBQ; playgrnd; lake sw 500m; 75% statics; dogs €1; Eng spkn; adv bkg; quiet; red low ssn; ccard not acc; CKE/CCI. "Excel site above beautiful medieval vill; friendly owner; lge pitches, some sloping; clean san facs; gd lake sw; adj site Mathieu Le Léman 2 open Jul-Aug only - same ownership, sep recep & facs; conv Geneva & Thonon-les-Bains." 1 Apr-28 Oct. € 14.50 2010*

DOUVAINE *9A3* (4km NW Rural) *46.32441, 6.26101* **Camping Lémania II, Plage de Tougues, 74140 Chens-sur-Léman [04 50 94 22 43 or 06 16 42 90 25 (mob); contact@camping-nautique.com; www.camping-nautique.com]** Fr Geneva dir Thonon on D1005 turn L onto D20 dir Tougues at Douvaine. Site sp. Med, pt shd; wc (some cont); chem disp; shwrs inc; el pnts (5A); Indtte; shop 300m; rest, snacks 200m; shgl beach on lake 200m; some statics; dogs; red low ssn. "Gd lake sw nr; gd NH." 1 May-30 Sep. € 15.00 2010*

ECHELLES, LES *9B3* (6km NE Rural) *45.45679, 5.81327* **Camping La Bruyère, Hameau Côte Barrier, 73160 St Jean-de-Couz Chartreuse [04 79 65 79 11/ 04 79 65 74 27 (ls) / 06 29 47 27 43 (mob); camping-labruyere@orange.fr; www.campingsavoie.com]** Heading S on D1006 Chambéry-Lyon rd, after x-ing Col de Coux 15km S of Chambéry take D45 to St Jean-de-Couz; site sp. Med, hdg pitch, pt sl, pt shd; wc (most cont); chem disp; shwrs inc; el pnts (4-10A) €2.90-5.90; gas; shop; Indtte; tradsmn; rest, snacks high ssn; bar; BBQ; playgrnd; volleyball; football; video games; TV rm; 3% statics; dogs €1; adv bkg; quiet. "Peaceful site; magnificent scenery; friendly, helpful owner; vg, clean facs; gd walking area; Chartreuse caves open to public adj; vg base for touring Chartreuse mountains; waymarked walks fr site; site well looked after." 15 May-30 Sep. € 11.00 2013*

ECHELLES, LES *9B3* (200m SE Urban) *45.43462, 5.75615* **Camping L'Arc-en-Ciel, Chemin des Berges, 38380 Entre-Deux-Guiers [tel/fax 04 76 66 06 97; info@camping-arc-en-ciel.com; www.camping-arc-en-ciel.com]** Fr D520 turn W sp Entre-Deux-Guiers. On ent vill turn R into Ave de Montcelet dir Les Echelles & R again in 100m. Site sp fr D520. Med, some hdg/mkd pitch, pt sl, pt shd; wc (some cont); chem disp; shwrs inc; el pnts (2-4A) €2.50-4.30; gas; Indtte; shops, rest, snacks & bar nrby; 40% statics; dogs €1.10; poss cr; red low ssn; CKE/CCI. "Conv La Chartreuse area with spectacular limestone gorges; gd." ♦ ltd 1 Mar-15 Oct. € 31.70 2014*

ECLASSAN see St Vallier *9C2*

ENTRAIGUES *9C3* (500m W Rural) *44.90064, 5.94606* **Camp Municipal Les Vigneaux, 38740 Entraigues [04 76 30 17 05 or 06 43 76 22 66 (mob); camping.murielbillard@orange.fr]** S on D1085 (N85) fr La Mure, turn L on D114, fork R on D26 to Valbonnais. This rd becomes D526. Site on L on ent Entraigues, 4km beyond Lake Valbonnais. Ent on bend in rd, more diff if ent fr Bourg-d'Oisans. Sm, mkd pitch, pt shd; wc; mv service pnt; shwrs inc; el pnts (5A) €2 (poss rev pol); Indtte; shops 100m; rv 100m; lake 4km; fishing; 15% statics; dogs €1; adv bkg; quiet; red long stay; CKE/CCI. "Clean facs; National Park adj; warden visits am & pm." ♦ 1 May-30 Sep. € 12.00 2010*

EVIAN LES BAINS *9A3* (4km E Rural) *46.40033, 6.64546* **Camping de Vieille Eglise, Route des Prés Parrau, 74500 Lugrin [04 50 76 01 95; campingvieilleeglise@wanadoo.fr; www.camping-vieille-eglise.com]** D21 fr Evian via Maxilly, or turn S off D1005 at Tourronde, sp. Med, hdg/mkd pitch, pt terr, pt sl, pt shd; wc; chem disp; mv service pnt; baby facs; private san facs avail; shwrs inc; el pnts (4-10A) €3.25-4.50; gas; Indtte (inc dryer); shop; supmkt 300m; rest 2km; BBQ; playgrnd; htd pool; paddling pool; shgl beach & lake fishing 1km; games area; wifi; entmnt; 50% statics; dogs €2; adv bkg; quiet; ccard acc; red long stay; CKE/CCI. "View of Lac Léman." ♦ 10 Apr-14 Oct. € 20.00 (CChq acc) 2011*

EVIAN LES BAINS *9A3* (6km W Rural) *46.39388, 6.52805* **FFCC Camping Les Huttins, 350 Rue de la Plaine, Amphion-les-Bains, 74500 Publier [tel/fax 04 50 70 03 09; campingleshuttins@gmail.com; www.camping-leshuttins.com]** Fr Thonon on D1005 twds Evian, at start of Amphion turn L onto Rte du Plaine sp; ent 200m on R after rndabt. Fr Evian on D1005 twds Thonon, at end of Amphion turn R & foll sp. Med, mkd pitch, shd; wc (some cont); chem disp; mv service pnt; shwrs inc; el pnts €3; gas; Indtte; shop; hypermkt 300m; rest, bar 400m; BBQ; playgrnd; pool & sports complex 200m; lake sw 400m; tennis adj; TV; 5% statics; dogs €1; Eng spkn; adv bkg; quiet; red low ssn. "Spacious, simple, relaxed site in beautiful area; enthusiastic, helpful owners; basic, clean san facs; gd base for Lake Léman; poss unrel opening dates - phone ahead; excel; site run by siblings." 1 May-30 Sep. € 27.00 2014*

EXCENEVEX see Thonon les Bains *9A3*

FAVERGES *9B3* (2km N Rural) *45.79090, 6.21630* **Campéole Camping La Nublière, 30 Allée de la Nublière, 74210 Doussard [04 50 44 33 44; fax 04 50 44 31 78; nubliere@campeole.com; www.camping-nubliere.com / www.campeole.com]** Fr Annecy take D1508 twd Albertville, site on L in 20km, 300m after Camp du Lac Bleu. Fr Faverges NW on D1508. Lge, mkd pitch, pt shd, wc (some cont); chem disp; mv service pnt; shwrs inc; el pnts (6A) €4.10; gas; Indtte (inc dryer); shop; rest, snacks; bar; BBQ; playgrnd; lake sw adj; boating; golf; cycle hire; games area; wifi; entmnt; dogs €3.50; poss cr; adv bkg; poss noisy; ccard acc; red low ssn. "Helpful staff; gd san facs." ♦ 30 Apr-19 Sep. € 22.50 2010*

RHONE-ALPS

FAVERGES *9B3* (7.3km NW Urban) *45.77510, 6.22585* **Camping La Serraz, Rue de la Poste, 74210 Doussard [04 50 44 30 68; info@campinglaserraz.com; www.campinglaserraz.com]** Exit Annecy on D1508 twd Albertville. At foot of lake ignore sp on R for Doussard Vill & take next turn R. Site on L in 1km, bef PO, sp. Med, pt shd; wc; chem disp; mv servie pnt; baby facs; sauna; shwrs; el pnts (16A) inc; Indtte (inc dryre); rest; BBQ; playgrnd; htd pool; paddling pool; games area; lake sw 1km; games rm; bike hire; entmnt; wifi; 50% statics; dogs €2.50; twin axles; Eng spkn; adv bkg; quiet; CCI. "Excel site; diving course for 8-14 year olds in Jul & Aug. spa opening 2014". ♦ ltd 19 Apr-14 Sep. € 49.00 2014*

FERRIERE D'ALLEVARD, LA see Allevard *9B3*

FEURS *9B2* (1km N Urban) *45.75457, 4.22595* **Camp Municipal Le Palais, Route de Civens, 42110 Feurs [tel/fax 04 77 26 43 41; www.camping-rhonealpes.com]** Site sp fr D1082 on N o'skts of town. Lge, pt shd; htd wc; chem disp (wc); mv service pnt; shwrs inc; el pnts (6A) €3.05; gas; sm shop; tradsmn; snacks; playgrnd; pool adj; mostly statics; dogs €0.61; phone; quiet; CKE/CCI. "Pleasant, spacious, beautifully-kept site; busy, espec w/ends; clean san facs." ♦ 1 Apr-31 Oct. € 15.00 2013*

"We must tell The Club about that great site we found"

Get your site reports in by mid-August and we'll do our best to get your updates into the next edition.

FLEURIE *9A2* (500m SE Rural) *46.18758, 4.69895* **Camp Municipal La Grappe Fleurie, La Verne, 69820 Fleurie [04 74 69 80 07; fax 04 74 59 85 18; camping@fleurie.org; www.camping-beaujolais.fr]** S dir Lyon on D306 turn R (W) at S end of Romanèche onto D32; 4km to vill of Fleurie (beware sharp turn in vill & narr rds) & foll site sp. Med, hdg/mkd pitch, terr, pt shd; wc; chem disp; mv service pnt; serviced pitches; shwrs inc; baby facs; el pnts (10A) inc; gas; Indtte; tradsmn; shop, rest, snacks, bar 500m; playgrnd; pool; tennis; dog €3.10; wifi; entmnt; some statics; poss cr; Eng spkn; adv bkg rec Jul/Aug; ccard acc; red low ssn/CKE/CCI. "Clean, well-run, busy site; friendly staff; excel san facs; lovely pool; gates & wash rms clsd 2200-0700; clean,spacious san facs; path to town thro vineyards (uphill); wine tasting; sm mkt Sat; excel." ♦ 21 Mar-22 Oct. € 30.00 2014*

⊞ **FLUMET** *9B3* (1.5km NE Rural) *45.82216, 6.53512* **Camping Le Vieux Moulin, 73590 Flumet [tel/fax 04 79 31 70 06; amrey@hotmail.fr]** Fr Albertville go N on D1212 & cont past Flumet for 1km. Turn R, watch for sp. Med, mkd pitch, hdstg, pt shd; htd wc; chem disp; mv service pnt; shwrs inc; el pnts (3-10A) €5.05-10; Indtte; tradsmn; rest nr; playgrnd; ski lifts 200m; 20% statics; dogs €1.20; phone; poss cr; Eng spkn; some rd noise; CKE/CCI. "Gd touring base by sm rv; friendly staff; superb san block but ltd; ltd facs low ssn outside ski ssn; gd boot & drying rm; highly rec." ♦ € 13.50 2010*

FRANGY *9A3* (4km E Rural) *46.01060, 5.97610* **Camping Le Chamaloup, 74270 Contamine-Sarzin [04 50 77 88 28 or 06 72 80 09 84 (mob); fax 04 50 77 99 79; camping@chamaloup.com; www.chamaloup.com]** Exit A40 junc 11 onto D1508 dir Annecy, thro Frangy. Site sp on L in 10km. Med, hdg/mkd pitch, pt shd; htd wc; chem disp; serviced pitches; mv service pnt; baby facs; shwrs inc; el pnts (16A) €4; gas; Indtte; shop; tradsmn; snacks; bar; BBQ; htd pool; games rm; wifi; entmnt; 20% statics; dogs €2; poss cr; Eng spkn; rd noise; some noise fr bar music; adv bkg; ccard acc; CKE/CCI. "Friendly owners; rv & fish pond (fenced-off) on site." ♦ 1 May-15 Sep. € 22.00 2010*

GEX *9A3* (500m E Urban) *46.33430, 6.06744* **Camping Les Genêts, 400 Ave des Alpes, 01170 Gex [04 50 42 84 57 or 06 79 17 13 69 (mob); les.2b@hotmail.fr; http://campinglesgenets.unblog.fr]** Fr all dir head for 'Centre Ville'; at rndabt take D984 twd Divonne/Lausanne. Site sp to R (tight turn) after rlwy sheds (poor sp in town) & Musée Sapeurs Pompiers. Med, hdg pitch, hdstg, pt sl, pt shd; wc (some cont); chem disp; shwrs inc; el pnts (16A) €2.90; gas 500m; Indtte; shops 500m; tradsmn; snacks; bar; playgrnd; games area; TV rm; dogs €1; phone; gates clsd 2200-0800; Eng spkn; adv bkg; quiet; ccard acc; CKE/CCI. "Excel attractive site; excel games facs/playgrnd; friendly, helpful staff; clean san facs; quiet with lots of privacy; conv Geneva; wifi in recp; 20 mins fr Geneva airport." ♦ 25 May-30 Sep. € 13.25 2014*

GIVORS *9B2* (7km NW Urban) *45.61498, 4.67068* **Camp Municipal de la Trillonnière, Monts du Lyonnais, Rue de la Loire, 69440 Mornant [04 78 44 16 47 or 04 78 44 00 46 (Mairie); fax 04 78 44 91 70; mairiemornant@wanadoo.fr; www.ville-mornant.fr]** Exit A7 at Givors & foll sp for St Etienne via D488, thro Givors onto D2 till sp seen for Mornant via D34, cont on D34 up hill for 7km, cross D342 & cont 1km to o'skts of Mornant, L at junc island & site on L. Med, pt sl, pt shd; wc; chem disp; shwrs; el pnts (10A) inc; shops, rest, snacks bar 500m; pool 250m; dogs €1; adv bkg; some rd noise; access for vans 0815-1015 & 1700-2200. 1 May-30 Sep. € 14.00 2009*

GLUIRAS see Ollières sur Eyrieux, Les *9D2*

GRAND BORNAND, LE see Clusaz, La *9B3*

GRANE see Crest *9D2*

GRAVIERS see Vans, Les *9D1*

GRENOBLE *9C3* (10km S Rural) *45.08553, 5.69872* **Camping à la Ferme Le Moulin de Tulette (Gaudin), Route du Moulin de Tulette, 38760 Varces-Allières-et-Risset [04 76 72 55 98; tulette@wanadoo.fr; http://moulindetulette.pagesperso-orange.fr/]** Fr A51, exit junc 12 to join D1075 N, Varces in approx 2km. Turn R at traff lts & foll sp to site, (approx 2km fr D1075). If driving thro Grenoble look for sp Gap - D1075 diff to find; on ent Varce foll site sp. Sm, mkd pitch, pt sl, pt shd; wc; chem disp; baby facs; shwrs inc; el pnts (5-10A) €2.50; shop 1km; tradsmn; sm pool; dogs €1; poss cr; Eng spkn; adv bkg; quiet; CKE/CCI. "Peaceful, picturesque, well-kept site with views; friendly, helpful owners; facs ltd but clean - stretched high ssn; gd base for touring/x-ing Alps." ♦ 1 May-30 Sep. € 19.00 2014*

GRENOBLE *9C3* (7km SW Urban) *45.16687, 5.69897* **Camping Caravaning Les 3 Pucelles, 58 Rue des Allobroges, 38180 Seyssins [04 76 96 45 73; fax 04 38 12 87 51; amico.francoise @ gmail.com; www.camping-trois-pucelles.com]** On A480 in dir of rocade (by-pass) S exit 5B, on R after supmkt then foll sp to R then L. Clearly sp. Well sp fr m'way. Sm, hdg pitch, hdstg, pt shd; htd wc (some cont); chem disp; shwrs inc; el pnts (16A) meter; Indtte; ice shop; tradsmn; rest, snacks; bar; playgrnd; pool; 70% statics; phone; bus nr; poss cr; noise fr indus area; CKE/CCI. "Site pt of hotel campus run by friendly family; sm pitches; san facs need refurb; conv Grenoble by bus/tram; NH only; poorly maintained." € 21.00 2014*

HAUTECOURT ROMANECHE see Bourg en Bresse *9A2*

HAUTERIVES see Beaurepaire *9C2*

LABLACHERE *9D2* (4km NW Rural) *44.47955, 4.17096* **Camping Le Ch'ti Franoi, Route de Planzolles, 07230 Lablachère [04 75 36 64 09; info@campinglechti.com; www.campinglechti.com]** Exit D104 to Lablachère; cont thro vill onto D4 dir Planzolles; site on L in 4km, just bef Cédat. Sm, pt sl, pt shd; wc; chem disp (wc); shwrs inc; el pnts (3A) inc (10-16A extra); Indry rm; shop; tradsmn; rest, snacks; bar; BBQ; playgrnd; pool; entmnt; TV rm; 75% statics; dogs €4; adv bkg. "Welcoming, friendly, helpful British owners." 1 Apr-31 Oct. € 24.00 2009*

LAC D'ISSARLES, LE *9C1* (2km E Rural) *44.81805, 4.05352* **Camping La Plaine de la Loire, Pont-de-Laborie, 07470 Le Lac-d'Issarlès [04 66 46 25 77 or 06 24 49 22 79 (mob); fax 04 66 46 21 55; campinglaplainedelaloire@ifrance.com; http://campinglaplainedelaloire.ifrance.com]** Fr S on N102 take D16 sp Le Lac-d'Issarles. After Coucouron (5km) site on R after Pont-de-Laborie. Med, mkd pitch, pt shd; wc (cont); chem disp; shwrs inc; el pnts (6A) €4; gas; Indtte; shop; tradsmn; snacks; playgrnd; rv sw adj; games area; 5% statics; dogs €0.80; adv bkg; quiet; CKE/CCI. "Lovely, tranquil site; long uphill walk to lake; m'van 'aire' adj lake." ♦ 5 Jun-15 Oct. € 10.00 2010*

LAFFREY see Vizille *9C3*

LALLEY *9D3* (300m S Rural) *44.75490, 5.67940* **Camping Belle Roche, Chemin de Combe Morée, 38930 Lalley [04 76 34 75 33 or 06 86 36 71 48 (mob); fax 04 76 34 75 33; camping.belleroche@gmail.com / contact@camping-belleroche.com; www.campingbelleroche.com]** Off D1075 at D66 for Mens; down long hill into Lalley. Site on R thro vill. Med, some hdg pitch, hdstg, pt sl, pt shd; wc; chem disp; mv service pnt; baby facs; shwrs inc; el pnts (10A) €4 (poss rev pol, poss long lead req); gas; Indtte; shop 500m; tradsmn; rest, snacks; bar; BBQ; playgrnd; htd pool; tennis 500m; games area; entmnt; wifi; TV rm; some statics; dogs €1.50; poss cr; adv bkg; quiet; ccard acc over €20; red low ssn; CKE/CCI. "Well-kept, scenic site; spacious pitches but little shd; friendly, welcoming owners; clean, vg modern san facs, poss stretched high ssn; pleasant pool area; nr Vercors National Park; vg walking/cycling; don't miss The Little Train of La Mure; conv NH; v nice site; highly recommended superb in every way." ♦ 26 Mar-15 Oct. € 30.00 2014*

LAMASTRE *9C2* (5km NE Rural) *45.01053, 4.62366* **Camping Les Roches, 07270 Le Crestet [04 75 06 20 20; fax 04 75 06 26 23; camproches@nordnet.fr; www.campinglesroches.com]** Take D534 fr Tournon-sur-Rhône dir Lamastre. Turn R at Le Crestet & foll sp for site, 3km fr vill. Sm, mkd pitch, hdstg, terr, pt shd; wc (some cont); chem disp; mv service pnt; baby facs; shwrs inc; el pnts (6A) €5.; Indtte; shop; tradsmn; rest, snacks; bar; BBQ; playgrnd; htd pool; rv sw adj; fishing; tennis 3km; games area; TV rm; 30% statics; dogs €4.50; bus 1km; Eng spkn; adv bkg; quiet; ccard acc; 5% red CKE/CCI. "Friendly family-run site; clean facs; lovely views; gd base for touring medieval vills; gd walking; site rd steep." ♦ 1 May-30 Sep. € 32.20 2013*

LANSLEBOURG MONT CENIS *9C4* (300m SW Rural) *45.28417, 6.87380* **Camp Municipal Les Balmasses, Chemin du Pavon, 73480 Lanslebourg-Mont-Cenis [tel/fax 04 79 20 52 77 / 06 19 46 28 18 (mob); info@camping-les-balmasses.com; www.camping-les-balmasses.com]** Fr Modane, site on R on rv on ent to town. Med, mkd pitch, pt shd; wc (some cont); shwrs inc; el pnts (6-10A) €4.50-5.40; Indtte; shop 500m; BBQ; playgrnd; dogs; phone; Eng spkn; CKE/CCI. "Pleasant, quiet site by rv; mountain views; clean facs; conv NH bef/after Col du Mont-Cenis." ♦ ltd 1 Jun-20 Sep. € 14.00 2014*

LARGENTIERE *9D2* (4km SE Rural) *44.50347, 4.29430* **Camping Les Châtaigniers, Le Mas-de-Peyrot, 07110 Laurac-en-Vivarais [04 75 36 86 26; chataigniers@hotmail.com; www.chataigniers-laurac.com]** Fr Aubenas S on D104 dir Alès; site sp fr D104. Site on one of minor rds leading to Laurac-en-Vivarais. Med, mkd pitch, pt sl, pt shd; wc, chem disp; baby facs; shwrs; el pnts (10A) €3; Indtte; BBQ (gas); playgrnd; pool & sun area; 15% statics; dogs €2; poss cr; adv bkg; quiet, but rd noise on lower terr; red low ssn. "Attractive site; some pitches deep shd; gd pool; sh uphill walk to vill shops & auberge; vg." ♦ 1 Apr-30 Sep. € 17.00 2011*

LARGENTIERE *9D2* (1.6km NW Rural) *44.56120, 4.28615* **Domaine Les Ranchisses (formerly Kawan Village Les Ranchisses), Route de Rocher, Chassiers, 07110 Largentière [04 75 88 31 97; fax 04 75 88 32 73; reception@lesranchisses.fr; www.lesranchisses.fr]** Exit A7/E15 junct 17/18 (Montelimar N or S) on to N7 dir Montelimar to take N102. Fr Aubenas S on D104 sp Alès. 1km after vill of Uzer turn R onto D5 to Largentière. Go thro Largentière on D5 in dir Rocher/Valgorge; site on L in 1.5km. DO NOT use D103 bet Lachapelle-Aubenas & Largentière - too steep & narr for lge vehicles & c'vans. NB Not rec to use Sat Nav dirs to this site. Lge, mkd pitch, pt shd; wc; chem disp; mv service pnt; baby facs; shwrs inc; el pnts (10A) inc; gas; Indtte (inc dryer); shop; rest, snacks; bar; BBQ (gas/elec only) playgrnd; 3 htd pools (1 covrd); paddling pool; rv sw, fishing; canoeing; wellness centre; tennis; cycle hire; games area; games rm; wifi; entmnt; TV; 30% statics; dogs €3.60; c'vans/m'vans over 7m by request; poss cr; adv bkg ess; ccard acc; red low ssn. "Lovely, well-run, busy site adj vineyard; gd sized pitches; friendly, helpful staff; gd, immac san facs; excel rest & takeaway; lovely pools; gd choice of sporting activities; poss muddy when wet; noisy rd adj to S end of site; mkt Tues am; first class; 5 star site in lovely location." ♦ 12 Apr-21 Sep. € 68.00 (CChq acc) SBS - C32 2014*

RHONE-ALPS

LARNAS *9D2* (2.5km SW Rural) *44.43674, 4.57728* **Camping Le Domaine d'Imbours, 07220 Larnas [04 75 54 39 50; fax 04 75 54 39 20; info@domaine-imbours.com; www.domaine-imbours.com / www.campings-franceloc.fr]** Fr Bourg-St Andéol on D86 take D4 to St Remèze. Do not exit on D462 which has sp for tourists for Imbours site. In St Remèze turn R on D362 to Mas-du-Gras & D262 twd Larnas & site. Do not attempt app to site via D262 thro St Montant. Lge, mkd pitch, some hdstg, pt sl, pt shd; wc; shwrs inc; el pnts inc; Indtte; shop; rest, snacks; bar; playgrnd; htd, pool complex; waterslide; tennis; cycle hire; entmnt; some statics; dogs €4.30; poss cr; adv bkg (ess Jul/Aug); quiet. "Many sports activities; beautiful area." ♦ 1 Jul-26 Aug. € 30.00 (3 persons) 2010*

LATHUILE see Doussard *9B3*

LESCHERAINES *9B3* (2.5km SE Rural) *45.70279, 6.11158* **Camp Municipal de l'Ile, Base de Loisirs, Les Iles du Chéran, 73340 Lescheraines [tel/fax 04 79 63 80 00; contact@iles-du-cheran.com; www.iles-du-cheran.com]** Fr Lescheraines foll sp for Base de Loisirs. Lge, mkd pitch, pt shd; wc; chem disp; mv service pnt; baby facs; shwrs inc; el pnts (6-10A) €2.40-3.50; gas 1km; Indtte; shop; rest 500m; snacks; bar; wifi; BBQ; playgrnd; lake sw; canoe & boat hire; fishing; wifi; entmnt; 5% statics; dogs €1.50; phone; Eng spkn; quiet; red low ssn; CKE/CCI. "Beautiful, scenic, lakeside setting; v helpful staff; gd walks." ♦ 19 Apr-28 Sep. € 16.50 2014*

LUC EN DIOIS *9D3* (6km N Rural) *44.68144, 5.44720* **Kawan Village L'Hirondelle, Bois de St Ferréol, 26410 Menglon [tel/fax 04 75 21 82 08; contact@campinghirondelle.com; www.campinghirondelle.com]** Foll D93 S twd Luc-en-Diois, in 6km at Pont-de-Quart turn L on D539 sp Châtillon, in 5km turn R on D140 sp Menglon, Recoubeau, site on R in 150m over rv. Med, shd; wc (some cont); baby facs; shwrs inc; el pnts (3-6A) €3.35-4.40 (long lead poss req); Indtte (inc dryer); shop; rest, snacks; bar; BBQ; playgrnd; htd pool complex; waterslide; rv fishing; archery; games area; wifi; entmnt; TV rm; 10% statics; dogs €3.20; Eng spkn; adv bkg; quiet. "Well-run, clean site; most pitches in woodland - some diff access; lovely area." ♦ 23 Apr-10 Sep. € 28.00 2010*

LUGRIN see Evian les Bains *9A3*

LUS LA CROIS HAUTE see St Julien en Beauchêne *9D3*

LYON *9B2* (12km E Rural) *45.79082, 4.99223* **Camping Le Grand Large, 81 Rue Victor Hugo, 69330 Meyzieu [04 78 31 42 16; fax 04 72 45 91 78; camping.grand.large@wanadoo.fr]** Exit N346 junc 6, E onto D6 dir Jonage. In approx 2 km turn L twd Le Grand Large (lake), site in 1km. Lge, pt shd; htd wc (mainly cont); chem disp; mv service pnt; shwrs inc; el pnts (5A) inc; gas; Indtte; shop 2km; snacks; pool 2km; lake sw & beach adj; boating, fishing in lake; games area; entmnt; TV; 90% statics; dogs €1; bus 1km; train 2km; poss cr; quiet; adv bkg; ccard acc; CKE/CCI. "Pleasant location; san facs scruffy & unclean (2011); stn 2km for trains to Lyon; mainly statics and chalets; NH only high ssn." 1 Apr-31 Oct. € 28.00 (3 persons) 2013*

⊞ **LYON** *9B2* (7km SW Urban) *45.68702, 4.78636* **Camping des Barolles, 88 Ave Foch, 69230 St Genis-Laval [04 78 56 05 56; fax 04 72 67 95 01; contact@campingdesbarolles.fr; www.campingdesbarolles.fr]** Exit A7 at Pierre-Bénite cent onto A450 & exit at Basses-Barolles; foll sp. Or fr D342 to St Genis-Laval cent main sq (Place Joffre) then take Ave Foch SW to site. Sm, hdstg, terr, pt shd; wc; mv service pnt; shwrs; el pnts (6-16A) €4.20-9.50; gas; Indtte; shop, snacks, bar 200m; playgrnd; wifi; some statics; dogs €2.50; site clsd Nov; quiet; twin-axles extra. "Excel site conv Lyon; friendly recep; gd san facs; NH only." € 15.00 2011*

⊞ **LYON** *9B2* (8km NW Urban) *45.81948, 4.76168* **Camping Indigo Lyon, Ave de la Porte de Lyon, 69570 Dardilly [04 78 35 64 55; fax 04 72 17 04 26; lyon@camping-indigo.com; www.camping-indigo.com]** Fr D306 Paris rd, take Limonest-Dardilly-Porte de Lyon exit at Auchan supmkt. Fr A6 exit junc 33 Porte de Lyon. Site on W side of A6 adj m'way & close to junc, foll sp (poss obscured by trees) for 'Complexe Touristique'. Fr E take N ring rd dir Roanne, Paris, then as above. Lge, hdg/mkd pitch, hdstg, pt shd; htd wc; chem disp; mv service pnt; serviced pitches; mv service pnt; baby facs; shwrs inc; el pnts (6-10A) €4.70-7.50; gas 100m; Indtte (inc dryer); hypmkt 200m; rest & bar 100m; playgrnd; pool; games rm; internet; TV rm; some statics; dogs €4; phone; bus/train to city nr; extra for twin-axle c'vans; Eng spkn; adv bkg; rd noise; ccard acc; red low ssn; CKE/CCI. "Well-run, secure site; Lyon easy by bus & metro, tickets can be bought fr recep; gd touring base for interesting area; helpful recep; gd, clean san facs; cafes nrby." ♦ € 33.00 (CChq acc) 2014*

MACON *9A2* (8km S Rural) *46.25167, 4.82610* **Base de loisirs du lac de Cormoranche, Les Luizant, 01290 Cormoranche-sur-Saône [03 85 23 97 10; fax 03 85 23 97 11; contact@lac-cormoranche.com; www.lac-cormoranche.com]** Exit A26 junc 29 sp Mâcon Sud onto N6 S to Crêches-sur-Saône. Turn L in town at traff lts onto D31 sp Cormoranche, then D51A. Cross rv, site sp on L. Alt rte: exit N6 in Mâcon & turn E onto D1079 dir St Laurent-sur-Saône then take D933 S to Pont-de-Veyle. Cont on D933 & foll sp to Cormoranche. Med, hdg/mkd pitch, pt shd; htd wc; chem disp; mv service pnt; shwrs inc; el pnts inc; Indtte (inc dryer); shop; tradsmn; rest, snacks; bar; playgrnd; lake sw & sand beach adj; fishing; cycle hire; entmnt; TV rm; 25% statics; dogs €2.20; poss cr; Eng spkn; adv bkg; quiet; ccard acc; CKE/CCI. "Spacious pitches, some with narr access; vg." ♦ 1 May-30 Sep. € 26.00 2013*

MALARCE SUR LA THINES see Vans, Les *9D1*

MANTENAY MONTLIN *9A2* (750m W Rural) *46.42218, 5.09208* **Camp Municipal du Coq, 01560 Mantenay-Montlin [04 74 52 66 91 or 04 74 52 61 72 (Mairie); cdec.sainttrivierdecourtes@wanadoo.fr]** Exit A40 junc 5 Bourg-en-Bresse Nord onto D975 to Mantenay-Montlin; site sp in vill on D46. Or exit A39 junc 10 to St Trivier-de-Courtes, then S to Mantenay. Sm, hdg/mkd pitch, pt shd; wc (cont); chem disp; shwrs inc; el pnts (6A) €1.70; shop, rest & bar 400m; playgrnd; tennis; dogs €1.50; bus 400m; quiet; red long stay; ccard acc. "Vg rvside site in pretty area; lge pitches; san facs old but clean; warden calls pm; poss v soft after rain; conv NH just off D975." 1 Jun-15 Sep. € 11.50 2010*

MARS see St Agrève *9C2*

MARSANNE *9D2* (2.5km NE Rural) *44.64870, 4.87930* **Camping Les Bastets, Quartier Les Bastets, 26740 Marsanne [04 75 90 35 03; fax 04 75 90 35 05; contact@ campinglesbastets.com; www.campinglesbastets. com]** Exit A7 junc 17 onto N7; pass thro Les Tourettes & La Coucourde to Marsanne. In La Coucourde turn L onto D74 & in 6km L onto D105 thro Marsanne. Site sp fr D105. App fr N on D57 not rec. Med, hdg/mkd pitch, sl, terr, pt shd; htd wc; chem disp; mv service pnt; baby facs; fam bthrm; shwrs inc; el pnts (10A) €4; Indtte (inc dryer); shop; tradsmn; rest, snacks; bar; BBQ; playgrnd; pool; archery; cycle hire; games area; games rm; golf 10km; wifi; entmnt; TV rm; 10% statics; dogs €4; Eng spkn; adv bkg; quiet; red low ssn. "Tractor tow to pitches - not rec to attempt under own steam; pleasant site with gd views; beautiful area; vg." ♦ ltd 1 Apr-15 Oct. € 22.00 (CChq acc) 2009*

MAYRES *9D1* (500m S Rural) *44.66723, 4.08965* **Camping La Chataigneraie, Hameau de Cautet, 07330 Mayres [tel/ fax 04 75 87 20 40 or 04 75 87 20 97]** Fr Aubenas on N102; L after Mayres vill, over Ardèche bdge, up hill in 500m. Sm, mkd pitch, terr, pt shd; wc (cont); shwrs inc; el pnts (3-6A) €2.50-4; tradsmn; rv sw 2km; dogs €1; quiet; ccard acc. "Vg CL-type site; secluded by tributary of Rv Ardèche; helpful owners." ♦ ltd Easter-1 Nov. € 13.00 2009*

MEAUDRE see Villard de Lans *9C3*

MEGEVE *9B3* (2km SW Rural) *45.84120, 6.58887* **FFCC Camping Gai Séjour, 332 Route de Cassioz, 74120 Megève [tel/fax 04 50 21 22 58]** On D1212 Flumet-Megève rd, site on R 1km after Praz-sur-Arly, well sp. Med, mkd pitch, sl (blocks needed), pt shd; wc; chem disp; shwrs inc; el pnts (4A); Indry rm; shops, rest, bar 1km; dogs; Eng spkn; adv bkg; quiet; CKE/ CCI. "Pleasant site with gd views, lge pitches; gd walks; 40km fr Mont Blanc; helpful owners; no free parking in Megeve." 6 Jan-15 Sep. € 14.70 2014*

MERIBEL *9B3* (2km N Rural) *45.40779, 6.55883* **Camping Le Martagon, Le Raffort, Route de Méribel, 73550 Les Allues [04 79 00 56 29; fax 04 79 00 44 92; contact@ restaurant-martagon.com; www.restaurant-martagon. com]** Fr Moûtiers on D915 S to Brides-les-Bains then D90 S dir Méribel. Site on L at Le Raffort. Park in public car park & go to rest. Sm, hdstg, terr, unshd; htd wc; chem disp; mv service pnt; shwrs inc; el pnts (13A) €6; gas 200m; Indtte; shop 2km; tradsmn; rest; bar; no statics; dogs; adv bkg; rd noise; ccard acc. "Ski bus every 20 mins at site ent; ski lift 100m; htd boot rm; mountain-biking in summer." ♦ 1 Dec-30 Apr & 1 Jul-31 Aug. € 26.00 2011*

MEYRAS *9D2* (1km S Rural) *44.66846, 4.28329* **Camping Le Ventadour, Pont de Rolandy, 07380 Meyras [tel/ fax 04 75 94 18 15; info@leventadour.com; www. leventadour.com]** Sp fr N102, on rvside, W of Pont-de-Labeaume. Med, pt shd; htd wc; shwrs inc; el pnts (6-10A) €3.20-4.20 (poss rev pol); Indtte; shop; supmkt 5km; tradsmn; snacks; bar; gas BBQ; playgrnd; fishing; wifi; some statics; dogs €2; Eng spkn; adv bkg; quiet; ccard acc. "Helpful owners; easy access; gd, clean facs; attractive site." 17 Apr-3 Oct. € 20.00 2010*

MEYRIEU LES ETANGS *9B2* (800m SE Rural) *45.50790, 5.20850* **Camping Base de Loisirs du Moulin, Commune du Pays St Jeannais, 38440 Meyrieu-les-Etangs [04 74 59 30 34; fax 04 74 58 36 12; contact@camping-meyrieu.com; www.camping-meyrieu.com]** Exit A43 at junc 8. Enter Bourgoin & foll sp for La Gare to pick up D522 SW twd St Jean-de-Bournay. Site next to lake 1km fr D522, sp. Med, mkd pitch, hdstg, terr, pt shd; wc; shwrs; el pnts (6-10A) €2.90-4.50; Indry rm; shop; rest; lake sw; pedalos; fishing; canoeing; archery; games rm; entmnt in ssn; TV; dogs €1.80; phone; adv bkg; quiet. "Views across lake; sm pitches; hdstg on all pitches for car; clean san facs & site; vg, nice site." ♦ 6 Apr-30 Sep. € 15.00 2013*

MEYZIEU see Lyon *9B2*

MODANE *9C4* (10km NE Rural) *45.22870, 6.78116* **Camp Municipal Val d'Ambin, Plan de l'Eglise, 73500 Bramans-le-Verney [04 79 05 03 05 or 06 16 51 90 91 (mob); fax 04 79 05 23 16; campingbramans@gmail.com; www. camping-bramansvanoise.com]** 10km after Modane on D1006 twd Lanslebourg, take 2nd turning R twd vill of Bramans, & foll camping sp, site by church. App fr Lanslebourg, after 12km turn L at camping sp on D306 at end of vill. Med, unshd; htd wc; baby facs; shwrs; el pnts (12-16A) €3.70-5.20; Indtte (inc dryer); shops, rest, snacks, bar nr; BBQ: playgrnd; pool 10km; games area; entmnt; TV; some statics; dogs €1.60; no adv bkg; poss cr; quiet. "Away-from-it-all site worth the climb; beautiful area; gd dog walk adj; excel, brilliant site; great for walkers & outdoor enthusiasts; v well rec." 1 May-30 Oct. € 23.00 2014*

⊞ **MODANE** *9C4* (1km W Rural) *45.19437, 6.66413* **Camping Les Combes, Refuge de La Sapinière, Route de Bardonnèche, 73500 Modane [04 79 05 00 23 or 06 10 16 54 61 (mob); fax 04 79 05 00 23; camping-modane@wanadoo.fr; http://camping-modane.chez-alice. fr]** Exit A43 junc 30 onto D1006 thro Fourmeaux to o'skirts Modane; at Casino supmkt turn R onto D215; site in 500m on bend on hill (at junc with D216). Fr Fréjus tunnel site on L 1km bef Modane. Med, pt sl, pt shd; htd wc (some cont); chem disp; shwrs inc; el pts (6A) €3; Indtte; shop 1km; tradsmn; snacks; bar; playgrnd; pool 1km; tennis; winter sports; wifi; 10% statics; dogs €1.50; quiet. "Excel & conv NH for Fréjus tunnel; warm welcome; superb scenery; ltd san facs; low ssn recep opens 1700 - site yourself." € 13.00 2014*

MONESTIER DE CLERMONT *9C3* (700m SW Urban) *44.91515, 5.62809* **Camping Les Portes du Trièves, Chemin de Chambons, 38650 Monestier-de-Clermont [04 76 34 01 24/ 04 76 34 06 20 (ls); fax 04 76 34 19 75; camping.lesportesdutrieves@wanadoo.fr; www. campingisere.com]** Turn W off D1075. Sp in vill. 700m up steep hill adj sw pool & school. Fr Grenoble take A51 to S end of vill & foll sps to site. Sm, hdg/mkd pitch, hdstg, terr, pt shd; htd wc; chem disp; mv service pnt; shwrs inc; el pnts (6A) €2.70; Indtte (inc dryer); shop, rest, snacks & bar 800m; playgrnd; htd pool 200m; tennis adj; lake 10km; games rm; wifi; dogs free; bus 500m; quiet; Eng spkn; adv bkg; red long stay; CKE/CCI. "Attractive, immac, well-run site; friendly, helpful staff; clean san facs but sm; watersports at lake; spectacular countryside; train to Grenoble; gd NH." 1 May-30 Sep. € 21.00 2013*

MONTAGNY LES LANCHES see Annecy *9B3*

RHONE-ALPS

MONTALIEU VERCIEU *9B2* (1.5km NE Rural) *45.82756, 5.42052* **Camp Municipal La Vallée Blue, 38390 Montalieu-Vercieu [04 74 88 63 67; fax 04 74 88 62 11; camping.valleebleue@wanadoo.fr; www.camping-valleebleue.com]** S fr Ambérieu-en-Bugey on D1075; in 15km (nr Porcieu-Amblagnieu) site sp on L. Med, pt sl, pt shd; wc (some cont); chem disp; mv service pnt; shwrs; el pnts (6A) €3; gas; lndtte; sm shop; tradsmn; snacks; playgrnd; htd pool; aquapark; paddling pool; games area; dogs €1.90; phone; bus; ccard acc; red low ssn/long stay; CKE/CCI. "Immed access to Rv Rhône; conv NH fr D1075; vg." ♦ ltd 4 Apr-25 Oct. € 15.00 2009*

MONTBRISON *9B1* (1.5km S Urban) *45.59133, 4.07806* **Camp Municipal Le Surizet, 31 Rue du Surizet, Moingt, 42600 Montbrison [04 77 58 08 30; fax 04 77 58 00 16]** Fr St Etienne on D8, at rndabt junc with D204 turn L sp St Anthème & Ambert. Cross rlwy & turn R in 400m, site sp. Med, pt shd; wc; chem disp; mv service pnt; shwrs; el pnts (5-10A) inc; lndtte; shop 1km; BBQ sep area; playgrnd; pool; fishing; pool, tennis 2km; 60% statics; dogs €0.85; bus (every hr); quiet; adv bkg; CKE/CCI. "Pleasant, well-kept site; no twin-axles; vg value; highly rec NH or sh stay." 15 Apr-15 Oct. € 13.00 2009*

MONTBRUN LES BAINS *10E3* (500m E Rural) *44.17621, 5.44767* **Camp Municipal Le Pré des Arbres, 26570 Montbrun-les-Bains [04 75 28 85 41 or 04 66 46 22 43 (LS); fax 04 75 28 81 16; camping@montbrunlesbains.com; www.montbrunlesbainsofficedutourisme.fr]** Site well sp in Montbrun. Sm, mkd pitch, terr, pt shd; wc; shwrs; el pnts (15A) €3.40; pool, tennis adj; some statics; dogs; quiet. "Gd, clean site; warden visits; walking dist to pleasant town & spa; thermal baths; interesting area." 15 Mar-15 Nov. € 10.00 2011*

MONTFERRAT see Abrets, Les *9B3*

MONTMELIAN *9B3* (5km SE Rural) *45.47745, 6.04111* **FFCC Camping L'Escale, La Gare, 73800 Ste Hélène-du-Lac [04 79 84 04 11 or 06 20 40 32 22 (mob); campingescale@wanadoo.fr; www.camping-savoie-escale.com]** Exit A43 junc 22 onto D923 dir Pontcharra & Les Mollettes; after x-ing A43 site on R. Med, hdg pitch, pt shd; wc; baby facs; shwrs inc; el pnts (6A) inc; gas; lndtte; rest, snacks; bar; BBQ; playgrnd; pool; wifi; 30% statics; dogs €1.50; poss cr; adv bkg; some rd & rlwy noise; CKE/CCI. "Gd san facs." 15 Feb-15 Oct. € 16.00 2010*

MONTREVEL EN BRESSE *9A2* (500m E Rural) *46.33911, 5.13615* **Camping La Plaine Tonique, Base de Plein Air, 01340 Montrevel-en-Bresse [04 74 30 80 52; fax 04 74 30 80 77; plaine.tonique@wanadoo.fr; www.laplainetonique.com]** Exit A40 junc 5 Bourg-en-Bresse N onto D975; at Montrevel-en-Bresse turn E onto D28 dir Etrez & Marboz; site sp on L in 400m. Or exit A6 junc 27 Tournus S onto D975. V lge, hdg/mkd pitch, shd; wc; chem disp; mv service pnt; baby facs; shwrs inc; el pnts (10A) inc; lndtte; shop; rest, snacks; bar; BBQ; playgrnd; 3 htd, covrd pools; 2 paddling pools; 2 waterslides; lake beach & sw adj; watersports; fishing; tennis; cycle hire; games area; archery; mountain biking; entmnt; TV; dogs €2.10; Eng spkn; adv bkg; quiet; ccard acc; red low ssn. "Excel, busy, family site; superb leisure facs; vg clean san facs; some pitches boggy after rain." ♦ 11 Apr-25 Sep. € 30.00 2012*

MORESTEL *9B3* (8km S Urban) *45.63521, 5.57231* **Camping Les Avenières (Formerly Les Epinettes), 6 Rue du Stade, 38630 Les Avenières [tel/fax 04 74 33 92 92; infos@camping-les-avenieres.com]** S fr Morestel on D1075, turn onto D40 to Les Avenières, site well sp. Med, hdg/mkd pitch, hdstg, pt shd; htd wc; chem disp; mv service pnt; baby facs; shwrs inc; el pnts (10A); lndtte; shop; tradsmn; rest, snacks; bar; BBQ; playgrnd; pool adj; rv sw 2km; entmnt; TV rm; 35% statics; dogs; phone; adv bkg; noise fr adj stadium; red low ssn; ccard acc; CKE/CCI. "Phone ahead low ssn to check open." ♦ 1 May-30 Sep. € 27.00 2014*

MORESTEL *9B3* (800m SW Urban) *45.67694, 5.46587* **Camp Municipal La Rivoirette, Rue François Perrin, 38510 Morestel [04 74 80 14 97; info@morestel.com; www.morestel.com]** Foll camping sps in town. Site by sports complex on D517. (NB No Entry sps do not apply to campers). Med, pt shd; wc; shwrs inc; el pnts (8A) €2.70; supmkt 1km; pool & sports complex adj; dogs; quiet. "Sm, poss awkward pitches; twin-axles extra charge; ent barrier operated by adj sw pool staff; excel NH." 1 May-30 Sep. € 11.00 2010*

MORZINE *9A3* (7km SW Rural) *46.15070, 6.64307* **Camping La Grange au Frêne, Les Cornuts, 74260 Les Gets [04 50 75 80 60 ou 04 50 75 80 55; fax 04 50 75 84 39; www.alpensport-hotel.com]** Fr Morzine go S on D902 to Les Gets. Site sp at end of vill. Sm, hdg/mkd pitch, terr, pt sl, pt shd; htd wc; 50% serviced pitches; baby facs; shwrs inc; el pnts (2-4A) €3-5; lndtte; shop 3km; tradsmn; rest, snacks & bar 3km; playgrnd; climbing; golf, tennis & adventure park nr; games rm;TV rm; dogs; phone; Eng spkn; adv bkg; quiet. "Excel site." ♦ 24 Jun-15 Sep. € 17.00 2010*

MORZINE *9A3* (3km NW Rural) *46.19510, 6.67715* **Camping-Caravaneige Les Marmottes, 74110 Essert-Romand [tel/fax 04 50 75 74 44 or 06 12 95 00 48 (mob); contact@campinglesmarmottes.com; www.campinglesmarmottes.com]** Exit A40 junc 18 or 19 onto D902 twd Morzine, then turn L onto D328 to Essert-Romand. Fr A40 take junc 18 to Morzine. Sm, hdstg, unshd; wc; chem disp; serviced pitches; baby facs; shwrs inc; el pnts (3-10A) €4.50-8; lndtte; shop 2km; tradsmn; playgrnd; lake sw 3km; TV; some statics; dogs €1; ski-bus; Eng spkn; adv bkg; quiet; red long stay; CKE/CCI. "Specialises in winter c'vanning for skiers; tractor to tow to pitch in snow." ♦ 21 Jun-7 Sep & 22 Dec-13 Apr. € 16.50 2009*

MOUTIERS *9B3* (3km N Rural) *45.50700, 6.49097* **Camping Eliana, 188 Rue des Pommiers, 73260 Aigueblanche [04 79 24 23 87 or 06 73 57 17 76; campingeliana@hotmail.com; www.campingeliana.com]** Fr Albertville take N90 S & exit 38 for Aigueblanche. Foll sp in vill for 'Camping' on D97 dir La Léchère. Site on L 700m after supmkt; well sp. NB Final L turn fr D97 is thro a NO ENTRY sign. Sm, hdg/mkd pitch, terr, shd; htd wc; chem disp; mv service pnt; shwrs inc; el pnts (4-10A) €2-3.80; gas 1km; lndtte; shop 1km; tradsmn; rest, snacks; bar; BBQ; htd pool 500m; cycle hire; wifi; some statics; dogs €0.30; quiet; CKE/CCI. "Well-managed site in orchard; gd, clean facs; warden calls 1800; sm pitches poss diff lge o'fits; gd walking & cycling." ♦ ltd 1 Apr-31 Oct. € 9.00 2010*

MOUTIERS *9B3* (4km S Rural) *45.45294, 6.56232* **Camping La Piat, Ave Greyffié de Bellecombe, 73570 Brides-les-Bains [04 79 55 22 74; fax 04 79 55 28 55; campinglapiat@wanadoo.fr; www.camping-brideslesbains.com]** Fr Moûtiers on D915 to Brides-les-Bains into town cent. Turn R onto Ave Greyffié de Bellecombe & foll sp to site. Med, mkd pitch, some hdstg, pt sl, terr, pt shd; wc (some cont); chem disp; mv service pnt; baby facs; shwrs inc; el pnts (3-10A) €2.10-3.70; gas; Indtte; shops, rest, snacks & bar 500m; tradsmn; playgrnd; pool adj; 10% statics; dogs €0.90; phone adj; bus 500m; ski lift 500m; poss cr; Eng spkn; adv bkg; quiet but some rd noise; ccard acc; red low ssn; CKE/CCI. "Gd mountain base; Brides-les-Bains is thermal spa town specialising in obesity treatments; some pitches v muddy in wet weather." ♦ 10 Apr-16 Oct. € 10.80 2010*

> "I need an on-site restaurant"
>
> We do our best to make sure site information is correct, but it is always best to check any must-have facilities are still available or will be open during your visit.

NANTUA *9A3* (1km W Urban) *46.14999, 5.60017* **Camp Municipal Le Signal, 17 Ave du Camping, 01130 Nantua [04 74 75 02 09 or 06 71 76 36 17 (mob); contact@camping-nantua.fr; www.camping-nantua.fr]** E on D1084 fr Pont d'Ain, rd passes alongside Nantua lake on R. At end of lake bef ent town turn R & foll sps. Sm, hdg/mkd pitch, unshd; wc; mv service pnt; shwrs inc; el pnts (16A) €2.50; shops 200m; rest, snacks; playgrnd; lake sw 300m; sports cent nr; some statics; dogs free; poss cr; quiet. "Attractive, spacious, well-kept site in lovely setting; friendly staff; town & shops mins away; conv for m'way; Lidl store 3 mins away." 15 Apr-15 Oct. € 18.00 2014*

NEYDENS see St Julien en Genevois *9A3*

NOIRETABLE *9B1* (1km S Rural) *45.80817, 3.76844* **Camp Municipal de la Roche, Route de la Roche, 42440 Noirétable [04 77 24 72 68; fax 04 77 24 92 20]** Leave A72/E70 junc 4 sp Noirétable; thro toll & turn SW onto D53. Ignore narr tourist rte sp to W; cont downhill to T-junc & turn R onto D1089. Take next L & site on R in 750m. Sm, mkd pitch, hdstg, pt terr, pt sl, pt shd; htd wc (cont); shwrs €1.50; el pnts (10A) €2.80; supmkt 1km; snacks, bar nr; playgrnd, lake adj; ccard not acc. "Warden lives on site, but barrier poss locked low ssn; rec phone ahead." 1 Apr-1 Nov. € 7.00 2011*

NYONS *9D2* (1km NE Rural) *44.36523, 5.15365* **Camping Les Clos, Route de Gap, 26110 Nyons [04 75 26 29 90; fax 04 75 26 49 44; info@campinglesclos.com; www.campinglesclos.com]** Fr rndabt in town cent take D94 sp Gap & site on R in 1km. Med, hdg/mkd pitch, hdstg, pt shd; wc; chem disp; shwrs inc; baby facs; el pnts (10A) inc; gas; Indtte; shop; rest 1km; snacks; bar; BBQ (gas/elec only); playgrnd; pool; shgl rv beach & fishing; entmnt (ltd); 20% statics; dogs €2.20; phone; poss v cr; Eng spkn; adv bkg; ccard acc; red low ssn; CKE/CCI. "Quiet, well-kept site in lovely area; friendly, helpful staff; excel touring base." ♦ 1 Apr-30 Sep. € 22.00 2010*

NYONS *9D2* (12km NE Rural) *44.42569, 5.21904* **Camping de Trente Pas, 26110 St Ferréol-Trente-Pas [04 75 27 70 69; contact@campingtrentepas.com; www.campingtrentepas.com]** Exit A7 junc 19 Bollène onto D994 & D94. L on D70 to St Ferréol-Trente-Pas. Site 100m fr vill on banks of stream. Med, shd; wc; shwrs; el pnts (6A) €3.10; Indry rm; sm shop & snacks high ssn; shop 2km; rest 200m; bar; playgrnd; pool; games rm; tennis; cycle hire; horseriding 4km; entmnt; TV; 5% statics; dogs €2; quiet; red low ssn. "Peaceful site nr rv; scenic area, views fr site; gd, clean san facs; gd pool; on flood plain; excel value; rec." 1 May-31 Aug. € 15.00 2011*

NYONS *9D2* (12km NE Rural) *44.43507, 5.21248* **FFCC Camping Le Pilat, 26110 St Ferréol-Trente-Pas [04 75 27 72 09; fax 04 75 27 72 34; info@campinglepilat.com; www.campinglepilat.com]** Fr D94 N or Nyons turn N at La Bonté onto D70 to St Ferréol, site sp 1km N of vill. Med, hdg pitch, shd; wc; chem disp; shwrs inc; el pnts (6A) €4; Indtte; shop high ssn & 3km; tradsmn; snacks; playgrnd; pool (solar heated); paddling pool; games area; outdoor gym; entmnt; TV; 25% statics; dogs €1.50 high ssn; phone; poss cr; Eng spkn; quiet; red low ssn; CKE/CCI. "Site among lavender fields; pleasant, helpful owners; gd clean san facs; gd walking & off-rd cycling; Thurs mkt Nyons; excel." ♦ 1 Apr-30 Sep. € 23.60 2012*

NYONS *9D2* (12km E Rural) *44.34319, 5.28357* **Camp Municipal Les Cigales, Allée des Platanes, 26110 Ste Jalle [04 75 27 34 88 or 04 75 27 32 78 (mairie); mairie.saintejalle@orange.fr]** Fr Nyons take D94 dir Serres; in 10 km at Curnier turn R onto D64 to Ste-Jalle. In vill turn R onto D108 dir Buis-les-Baronnies. Site on R in 300m. NB Dist by rd fr Nyons is 20km. Sm, hdg pitch, pt shd; wc; chem disp; shwrs inc; el pnts (10A) €2.20; Indtte; shop, rest, snacks, bar 200m; playgrnd; 15% statics; dogs; adv bkg; quiet. "Vg site in attractive old vill." 1 May-30 Sep. € 7.40 2009*

⊞ **NYONS** *9D2* (6km SW Rural) *44.32830, 5.08380* **Camping Domaine Le Sagittaire, Le Pont de Mirabel, 26110 Vinsobres [04 75 27 00 00; fax 04 75 27 00 39; camping.sagittaire@wanadoo.fr; www.le-sagittaire.com / www.campings-franceloc.fr]** Fr Nyons on D94, sp Orange, site on L just after junc with D4, well sp. Lge, hdg pitch, pt shd; htd wc; chem disp; shwrs inc; el pnts (6-10A) €4.70-5.70; gas; Indtte; shop; tradsmn; rest, snacks, bar in ssn; playgrnd; htd, covrd pool; waterslide; tennis; cycle hire; entmnt; TV; 25% statics; dogs €5; poss cr; adv bkg; quiet but some rd noise on edge of site; ccard acc; red long stay/low ssn; CKE/CCI. "Part of holiday complex in attractive, uncommercialised area." € 31.00 2009*

NYONS *9D2* (7km SW Rural) *44.32942, 5.06605* **Camp Municipal Chez Antoinette, Champessier, 26110 Vinsobres [04 75 27 61 65 or 04 75 27 64 49 (Mairie); fax 04 75 27 59 20; camping-municipal@club-internet.fr]** Fr Nyons on D94 sp Orange. Turn R 500m after junc with D4 twd Vinsobres vill. Site 500m on L bef vill. Sm, mkd pitch, pt shd; htd wc; chem disp; shwrs inc; el pnts (6A) €2.70; Indry rm; BBQ; playgrnd; adv bkg; quiet; ccard acc; CKE/CCI. "Peaceful, v popular site; cramped san facs; steep unhill walk to vill; excel touring area." ♦ Easter-31 Oct. € 8.00 2009*

NYONS *9D2* (4km NW Rural) *44.40829, 5.07993* **Camping Les Terrasses Provençales, Les Barroux, Novézan, 26110 Venterol [tel/fax 04 75 27 92 36; lesterrassesprovencales@gmail.com; www.lesterrassesprovencales.com]** Exit A7/E15 at junc 18 sp Nyons. Join D541 E twd Nyons. Site in Venterol, sp bet Valréas & Nyons. Med, hdg/mkd pitch, hdstg, terr, pt shd; wc; chem disp; baby facs; fam bthrm; shwrs inc; el pnts (10A) €3.85 (poss rev pol); lndtte; shop; tradsmn; tradsmn; rest; bar; BBQ; playgrnd; htd pool; cycle hire; games area; wifi; TV; dogs €2; poss cr; some Eng spkn; quiet; ccard acc; CKE/CCI. "Owner will tow c'van onto terr pitch; excel." ♦ 1 Apr-30 Sep. € 17.00 2010*

OLLIERES SUR EYRIEUX, LES *9D2* (500m N Rural) *44.80730, 4.61500* **Kawan Village Le Mas de Champel, Route de La Voulte-sur-Rhône, 07360 Les Ollières-sur-Eyrieux [04 75 66 23 23; fax 04 75 66 23 16; info@masdechampel.com; www.masdechampel.com]** Fr D86 W on D120 at La Voulte-sur-Rhône or D21 at Beauchastel. Rds join at St Laurent-du-Pape. Cont on D120, turn R soon after D2 on ent Les Ollières bef descent into vill. Site sp. Med, terr, unshd; htd wc; chem disp; mv service pnt; shwrs inc; el pnts (10A) inc; lndtte (inc dryer); shops 1km; rest, snacks; bar; playgrnd; htd pool complex; paddling pool; fishing; canoeing; cycle hire; games area; guided walks; cycle hire; solarium; wifi; entmnt; TV; some statics; poss cr; adv bkg; quiet. "Pleasant site in lovely countryside." ♦ 16 Apr-30 Sep. € 24.00 2009*

OLLIERES SUR EYRIEUX, LES *9D2* (2.5km S Rural) *44.78155, 4.61790* **Camping Le Chambourlas, Chambon de Bavas, 07360 Les Ollières-sur-Eyrieux [04 75 66 24 31; fax 04 75 66 21 22; info@chambourlas.com; www.chambourlas.com]** Fr Privas take D2 dir Le Cheylard; site on R in 14km at Les Ollières. D2 a v slow, twisty rd. Steep site ent. Med, mkd pitch, shd; wc; chem disp; baby facs; shwrs inc; el pnts (10A) inc; gas; lndtte; shop; rest, snacks; bar; BBQ; playgrnd; pool; paddling pool; lake sw & fishing; canoe hire; games area; wifi; TV rm; 10% statics; dogs €2.50; adv bkg; ccard acc. "Lovely site; lge pitches; warm welcome; gd walks fr site." ♦ Easter-30 Sep. € 31.50 2009*

OLLIERES SUR EYRIEUX, LES *9D2* (10km NW Rural) *44.82895, 4.52295* **L'Ardechois Camping, Le Chambon, 07190 Gluiras [04 75 66 61 87; fax 04 75 66 63 67; ardechois.camping@wanadoo.fr; www.ardechois-camping.fr]** Exit A7 junc 15 or 16 & cross rv onto D86. Turn W at Beauchastel onto D21/D120 dir Le Cheylard to St Sauveur-de-Montagut. In St Sauveur foll D102 St Pierreville & Mézilhac. Site approx 8km on bank Rv Glueyre on both sides D102 - steep access to pitches. Med, hdg/mkd pitch, terr, shd; htd wc; chem disp; mv service pnt; baby facs; shwrs inc; el pnts (6-10A) inc; gas; lndtte (inc dryer); shop & 8km; tradsmn; rest high ssn; snacks; bar; BBQ; playgrnd; htd pool; paddling pool; rv & sand beach adj; cycle hire; games area; wifi; entmnt; TV rm; 70% statics; dogs €4; Eng spkn; adv bkg ess in ssn; ccard acc; red low ssn/snr citizens; CKE/CCI. "Wonderful, friendly, family site in glorious countryside; helpful Dutch owners; excel rest; organised walks, picnics." ♦ 30 Apr-30 Sep. € 27.50 (CChq acc) 2009*

OYONNAX *9A3* (8km E Rural) *46.25530, 5.55705* **Camping Les Gorges de l'Oignin, Rue du Lac, 01580 Matafelon-Granges [04 74 76 80 97; camping.lesgorgesdeloignin@wanadoo.fr; www.gorges-de-loignin.com]** Exit A404 junc 9 onto D979 dir Bourg-en-Bresse; in 700m turn R onto D18 to Matafelon-Granges; foll sp. NB Fr Oyonnax 22km by rd. Med, hdg/mkd pitch, hdstg, terr, pt shd; htd wc; chem disp; baby facs; excel hot shwrs inc; el pnts (10A) €3.40; lndtte; ltd shop or 3km; supmkt 15km; rest, snacks; bar; BBQ; playgrnd; 2 pools; paddling pool; lake sw adj; games area; wifi; TV rm; 10% statics; dogs €2.40; phone; Eng spkn; adv bkg; quiet; red low ssn; CKE/CCI. "Beautiful site on lake - boat launching; friendly, helpful staff; Jura National Park; Rv Ain gorges; excel." 15 Apr-25 Sep. € 20.80 2012*

PACAUDIERE, LA *9A1* (200m E Rural) *46.17512, 3.87639* **Camp Municipal Beausoleil, Route de Vivans, 42310 La Pacaudière [04 77 64 11 50 or 04 77 64 30 18 (Mairie); fax 04 77 64 14 40; lapacaudiere@wanadoo.fr; www.camping-rhonealpes.com]** NW on N7 Roanne to Lapalisse; turn R in La Pacaudière, D35; site well sp; fork R in 50m; site ent in 400m. Sm, hdg pitch, hdstg, sl, unshd; wc; chem disp; shwrs inc; el pnts (10A); gas; lndtte; shop; supmkt 500m; playgrnd; public pool high ssn; TV rm; quiet. "Pleasant NH in beautiful countryside; ltd facs low ssn; interesting area; Sat mkt." 1 May-30 Sep. € 13.50 2014*

PASSY see Sallanches *9A3*

PEISEY NANCROIX see Bourg St Maurice *9B4*

PELUSSIN *9B2* (1km SE Rural) *45.41375, 4.69143* **Camping Bel'Epoque du Pilat, La Vialle, Route de Malleval, 42410 Pélussin [04 74 87 66 60; contact@camping-belepoque.fr; www.camping-belepoque.fr]** Exit A7 junc 10 just S of Lyon foll N86 dir Serrières; in Chavanay turn R onto D7 to Pélussin, then at rndabt turn L and foll D79 S & foll site sp. Rec do not use SatNav! Sm, hdg pitch, pt sl, pt shd; htd wc; chem disp; mv service pnt; baby facs; fam bthrm; shwrs inc; el pnts (6A) €3.50; gas; lndtte; shop 1.5km; tradsmn; rest, snacks; bar; BBQ; playgrnd; htd pool; paddling pool; tennis; games area; wifi; child entmnt; dogs €2.50; phone; train 10km; Eng spkn; adv bkg; quiet; ccard acc; CKE/CCI; "In nature reserve; excel touring base; vg walking; vg, peaceful site; supmkt in Pélussin." 5 Apr-28 Sep. € 33.00 2014*

PENNE SUR L'OUVEZE, LA see Buis les Baronnies *9D2*

POET LAVAL, LE *9D2* (2km SE Rural) *44.52889, 5.02300* **Camp Municipal Lorette, 26160 Le Poët-Laval [04 75 91 00 62 or 04 75 46 44 12 (Mairie); fax 04 75 46 46 45; camping.lorette@wanadoo.fr; www.campinglorette.fr]** Site 4km W of Dieulefit on D540. Med, mkd pitch, pt shd; wc; chem disp (wc); mv service pnt; shwrs inc; el pnts (6A) €2; lndtte; shop; tradsmn; rest 500m; snacks; playgrnd; pool; tennis; no statics; dogs €1.10; bus; phone; quiet; CKE/CCI. "Well-kept site with views; lge pitches; clean, modern facs; nr lavender fields (Jun/Jul); mkt in Dieulefit Fri; excel." ♦ 1 May-30 Sep. € 12.20 2013*

POET LAVAL, LE *9D2* (8km W Rural) *44.56423, 4.90788* **Camping à la Ferme des Roures (Gontard), Route de St Gervais, Les Roures, 26160 La Bégude-de-Mazenc [04 75 46 21 80; gitesfrance@ferme-des-roures.com]** Fr Montélimar E on D540 for 15km. Turn L onto D74 dir St Gervais. Foll sp for site. Sm, pt sl, shd; wc; chem disp; shwrs inc; el pnts (10A) €2.30 (poss rev pol); Indtte; gas & shop 4km; dogs €0.75; quiet; CKE/CCI. "Site in wood in pleasant area; friendly, helpful owners; clean facs." ♦ 1 May-15 Sep. € 8.50 2010*

POMEYS see Chazelles sur Lyon *9B2*

POMMEROL see Rémuzat *9D2*

PONCIN see Pont d'Ain *9A2*

PONT D'AIN *9A2* (800m E Urban) *46.04680, 5.34446* **Camping de l'Oiselon, Rue E'mile Lebreüs, 01160 Pont-d'Ain [tel/fax 04 74 39 05 23; campingoiselon@free.fr]** Fr A42 exit Pont-d'Ain foll D90 to vill. In vill cent turn R on D1075. Turn L immed after x-ing Rv L'Ain. Foll rd passing tennis club on L. Site on L, clearly sp. Lge, pt shd; wc; chem disp; baby facs; shwrs inc; el pnts (6-10A) €2.40-3.10 (poss rev pol); shops; rest, snacks; BBQ; playgrnd; pool; rv sw & beach; fishing; canoeing; tennis adj; horseriding 5km; cycle hire; games area; entmnt; 30% statics; dogs free; poss cr; Eng spkn; adv bkg; quiet (poss some noise fr disco); CKE/CCI. "Gd, well-run site with easy access; helpful, friendly staff; gd clean san facs; site needs TLC (early ssn 2010); gd NH." ♦ 16 Mar-13 Oct. € 20.00 2012*

PONT DE VAUX *9A2* (3.5km NE Rural) *46.44394, 4.98313* **Camping Les Ripettes, St Bénigne, 01190 Chavannes-sur-Reyssouze [03 85 30 66 58; info@camping-les-ripettes.com; www.camping-les-ripettes.pagesperso-orange.fr]** Take D2 fr Pont-de-Vaux sp St Trivier-des-Courtes for 3km. Immed after water tower on R turn L onto D58 sp Romenay, then immed L. Site well sp on L in 100m. Med, hdg/mkd pitch, pt sl, pt shd; htd wc; chem disp; mv service pnt; shwrs inc; el pnts (10A) €3.50; Indtte; shop & 3.5km; tradsmn; snacks; playgrnd; 2 pools; games area; wifi; 1 static; dogs €1.50; phone; Eng spkn; adv bkg rec high ssn; quiet, but some rd noise; ccard acc; red low ssn; CKE/CCI. "Lovely, popular site in beautiful location; spacious pitches; friendly, helpful owner; immac facs; gd pool area; gd touring base; hard to beat!" ♦ ltd 1 Apr-30 Sep. € 25.00 2013*

PONT DE VAUX *9A2* (5km W Rural) *46.44710, 4.89890* **Camping aux Rives du Soleil, 01190 Pont-de-Vaux [tel/fax 03 85 30 33 65; info@rivesdusoleil.com; www.rivesdusoleil.com]** Leave D306 (N6) at Fleurville (bet Mâcon & Tournus) onto D933A dir Pont-de-Vaux. In 1km cross rv; site immed on R. Well sp. Lge, pt shd, wc; chem disp; mv service pnt; baby facs; shwrs inc; el pnts (6A) €3.50 (poss rev pol); gas; Indtte; shop; rest, snacks; bar; BBQ; playgrnd; pool; paddling pool; rv beach adj; fishing; boating; entmnt; TV; 15% statics; dogs €3.50; poss cr; Eng spkn; adv bkg; some rlwy noise; red long stay/low ssn. "Pleasant site adj rv & canal; Dutch owners; san facs need update; conv NH fr A6." 24 Apr-17 Oct. € 20.00 2010*

PONT EN ROYANS *9C2* (1.3km W Rural) *45.06193, 5.33398* **Camp Municipal Les Seraines, 38680 Pont-en-Royans [04 76 36 06 30 or 04 76 36 03 09 (Mairie); fax 04 76 38 92 37; mairie.pont.en.royans@wanadoo.fr]** App on D531 fr E or D518 fr St Marcellin fr N, site sp on ent town. Sm, hdg pitch, hdstg, pt terr, pt shd; wc (mainly cont); chem disp; mv service pnt; shwrs inc; el pnts (4A) €3; Indtte; shops 500m; playgrnd; lake 8km; rv adj; tennis; entmnt; poss cr; statics; dogs; quiet but some rd noise; CKE/CCI. "Site in 2 adj parts; helpful warden; rvside walk to town." 15 Apr-30 Sep. € 9.50 2010*

PONT ST ESPRIT *9D2* (6km NW Rural) *44.30388, 4.58443* **Camping Le Pontet, 07700 St Martin-d'Ardèche [04 75 04 63 07 or 04 75 98 76 24; fax 04 75 98 76 59; contact@campinglepontet.com; www.campinglepontet.com]** N86 N of Pont-St Esprit; turn L onto D290 at sp Gorges de l'Ardèche & St Martin-d'Ardèche, site on R after 3km, lge sp. Med, mkd, pt shd; wc; chem disp; mv service pnt; shwrs inc; el pnts (6A) €3.60 (rev pol); gas; Indry rm; tradsmn; shop, rest high ssn; snacks; bar; playgrnd; pool; rv sw 1km; wifi; 5% statics; dogs €3; phone; Eng spkn; adv bkg; quiet (poss noisy w/end); ccard not acc; red low ssn; CKE/CCI. "Vg; helpful owners; peaceful out of ssn." ♦ 8 Apr-25 Sep. € 19.00 2011*

PONT ST ESPRIT *9D2* (7.5km NW Urban) *44.30342, 4.56819* **Camp Municipal Le Village, Rue du Nord, 07700 St Martin-d'Ardèche [04 75 04 65 25; fax 04 75 98 71 38; denislaurent1@sfr.fr; www.ot-stmartin-ardeche.com]** N on D6086 fr Pont-St Esprit, turn L onto D290 at St Just. Foll D290 around St Martin-d'Ardèche, look out for site sp. Turn sharp R down under main rd & strt into site - take care if v high outfit. Med, mkd pitch, pt shd; wc; chem disp; shwrs inc; el pnts (4A) inc; Indtte; shop, rest, snacks, bar 200m; playgrnd; rv beach adj; fishing; tennis; adv bkg; quiet. "Nr lovely, quiet vill; popular site; san facs only adequate (2010); site poss unkempt low ssn." 28 Mar-28 Sep. € 13.00 2011*

PONT ST ESPRIT *9D2* (8km NW Rural) *44.30043, 4.57069* **Camping Indigo Le Moulin, 07700 St Martin-d'Ardèche [04 75 04 66 20; fax 04 75 04 60 12; moulin@camping-indigo.com; www.camping-indigo.com]** Exit A7 junc 19 to Bollène, then D994 to Pont-St Esprit & D6068/D86 to St Just. Turn L onto D290 to St Martin in 4km. Site on L on rvside. Med, pt sl, pt shd; htd wc; chem disp; mv service pnt; baby facs; shwrs inc; el pnts (10A) €4.90; Indtte (inc dryer); shop; rest 5km; snacks; bar; playgrnd; htd pool; paddling pool; rv sw & beach adj; fishing; canoe hire; tennis 500m; cycle hire; games area; internet; entmnt; TV rm; 5% statics; dogs €4; phone; Eng spkn; no adv bkg; ccard acc; quiet; red low ssn. "Friendly site; gd modern san facs; footpath to vill; rec." ♦ 22 Apr-1 Oct. € 245.00 2011*

⊞ **PONT ST ESPRIT** *9D2* (8km NW Rural) *44.34423, 4.60434* **FFCC Camping Les Truffières, 201 Route de St Ramèze, 07700 St Marcel-d'Ardèche [04 75 04 68 35 or 06 82 01 28 30 (mob); soulier.valerie@wanadoo.fr]** S fr Bourg-St Andéol, turn W on D201; in vill foll sp to site located approx 3km W of vill. Med, mkd pitch, terr, pt shd; htd wc; mv service pnt; shwrs inc; el pnts (6A) €6.60 (poss rev pol); gas; Indtte; shops 3km; rest, snacks; bar; playgrnd; pool; entmnt; 70% statics; dogs €1.60; adv bkg; quiet; red low ssn; CKE/CCI. "Friendly owners; glorious views; gd san facs; conv NH nr A7." ♦ € 17.00 2009*

PONTAIX *9D2* (2km E Rural) *44.76585, 5.27270* **Aire Naturelle La Condamine (Archinard), 26150 Pontaix [04 75 21 08 19; fax 04 74 04 46 12; aurelie.goderiaux@laposte.net]** W fr Die on D93; site on R just after D129. Fr E, 2km after Pontaix on L. Sm; wc; chem disp; shwrs inc; el pnts (10A) inc; lndry rm; shop 8km; BBQ; rv sw adj; dogs €1; adv bkg; quiet; CKE/CCI. "Excel CL-type site by Rv Drôme; helpful owner." ♦ 15 Apr-15 Oct. € 13.50 2011*

POULE LES ECHARMEAUX *9A2* (1.5km W Rural) *46.15028, 4.45419* **Camp Municipal Les Echarmeaux, 69870 Poule-les-Echarmeaux [06 89 90 33 64 (mob) or 06 79 30 46 62; fax 04 74 03 68 71; www.poulelesecharmeaux.eu]** Turn E off D385 to Poule-les-Echarmeaux, site sp. Sm, hdg pitch, terr, pt shd; wc; shwrs inc; el pnts inc; shop 500m; playgrnd; adv bkg. "Beautifully situated site adj lake; nr Beaujolais wine area; excel sh stay; mkd walks." 1 May-30 Sep. € 10.80 2013*

PRALOGNAN LA VANOISE *9B4* (500m S Rural) *45.37692, 6.72375* **Camp Municipal Le Chamois, Route de l'Isertan, 73710 Pralognan-la-Vanoise [04 79 08 71 54; fax 04 79 08 78 77; camping@pralognan.com; www.pralognan.com]** Fr Moûtiers take D915 to Pralognan. Pass under concrete bdge, turn SW & foll camping sp; keep L past recep of bigger Iseran site. Site on rvside. Lge, mkd pitch, terr, pt sl, unshd; htd wc (some cont); chem disp (wc); shwrs inc; el pnts (2-10A) €2.30-3.90; lndtte; shops 500m; htd pool 300m; rv fishing adj; dogs; poss cr; quiet. "Peaceful site in beautiful area; vg walks; friendly staff; cable car up mountain." 5 Jun-5 Sep. 2009*

PRALOGNAN LA VANOISE *9B4* (500m S Rural) *45.37667, 6.72236* **Camping Le Parc Isertan, Route de l'Isertan, 73710 Pralognan-la-Vanoise [04 79 08 75 24; fax 04 79 08 76 13; camping@camping-isertan.com; www.camping-isertan.com]** Fr Moûtiers, take D915 E to Pralognan. Pass under concrete bdge & foll camping sp. Site behind pool adj municipal site. Lge, hdstg, terr, pt shd; htd wc; chem disp; mv service pnt; baby facs; shwrs inc; el pnts (2-10A) €4-6.50; gas 500m; tradsmn; shop 500m; rest, snacks; bar; BBQ; playgrnd; drying rm & ski boot rm; htd, covrd pool & sports cent adj; horseriding 500m; some statics; dogs €1.50; phone; poss cr; Eng spkn; adv bkg; quiet; ccard acc; red low ssn/CKE/CCI. "Peaceful site with superb scenery; recep in hotel on site; vg walking; cable car in vill; cross country skiing at side of site; free naveltte to ski lift; new spa facs (2012); excel site." ♦ 18 Dec-18 Apr & 21 May-24 Sep. € 24.00 2012*

PRALOGNAN LA VANOISE *9B4* (13.7km NW Rural) *45.44274, 6.64874* **Camp Municipal Le Chevelu, Route de Chevelu, 73350 Bozel [06 49 23 10 34 or 04 79 55 03 06 (LS); camping.lechevelu.bozel@gmail.com; www.camping-bozel.com]** Foll D915 thro Bozel dir Pralognan. Site on R immed beyond vill. Med, mkd pitch, hdstg, pt sl, terr, shd; wc; chem disp; mv service pnt; shwrs inc; el pnts (6-10A) €3.50-4.50; lndtte (inc dryer); shops 1km; rest; café; playgrnd; lake fishing & sw 1 km; dogs €1.50; phone; Eng spkn; adv bkg; quiet; CKE/CCI. "In wood by rv; excel walking & climbing; vg; pleasant vill; lunchtime rest v popular with locals." ♦ ltd 1 Jun-30 Sep. € 16.40 2014*

PRESILLY see St Julien en Genevois *9A3*

PRIVAS *9D2* (8km NE Rural) *44.75721, 4.71298* **Camping L'Albanou, Quartier Pampelonne, 07000 St Julien-en-St Alban [04 75 66 00 97; camping.albanou@wanadoo.fr; www.camping-albanou.com]** Fr A7 exit junc 16 at Loriol dir Le Pouzin, go thro Le Pouzin on D104 dir Privas/Aubenas. Site in 6km on L just bef vill of St Julien-en-St Alban. Med, hdg/mkd pitch, pt sl, pt shd; wc; chem disp; mv service pnt; baby facs; shwrs inc; el pnts (6A) €3.50; lndtte; shops 1km; tradsmn; snacks; playgrnd; pool; rv fishing adj; wifi; some statics; dogs €2; Eng spkn; adv bkg (poss not by phone); quiet; red low ssn; CKE/CCI. "Superb, well-run, clean site by rv; gd sized pitches; friendly, helpful owners; super pool; sh walk to sm town; rec arr bef 1500 high ssn; a great site." 22 Apr-30 Sep. € 20.00 2011*

PRIVAS *9D2* (1.5km S Urban) *44.72668, 4.59730* **Kawan Village Ardèche Camping, Blvd de Paste, Quartier Ouvèze, 07000 Privas [04 75 64 05 80; fax 04 75 64 59 68; jcray@wanadoo.fr; www.ardechecamping.fr]** Exit A7 junc 16 dir Privas. App Privas cross rv bdge & at rndabt take 2nd exit. Site ent opp supmkt, sp. Lge, mkd pitch, pt sl, pt shd; wc (mainly cont); chem disp; mv service pnt; baby facs; fam bthrm; shwrs inc; el pnts (10A) inc; lndtte; shops adj; supmkt 100m; rest, snacks; bar; BBQ; playgrnd; htd pool; paddling pool; rv fishing; tennis adj; wifi; entmnt; TV rm; 80% statics; dogs €3.30; Eng spkn; adv bkg; quiet, but some rd noise fr D2; ccard acc; red low ssn/long stay; CKE/CCI. "Very gd friendly site with English speaking owners. gd rest and shady pitches. Interesting area to visit." ♦ 15 Apr-28 Sep. € 31.00 (CChq acc) 2013*

RECOUBEAU JANSAC see Luc en Diois *9D3*

REMUZAT *9D2* (9km NE Rural) *44.44598, 5.45913* **Aire Naturelle de Pommerol (Morin), Quartier Lemoulin, 26470 Pommerol [04 75 27 25 63 or 04 75 98 26 25 (LS); fax 04 75 27 25 63; camping.pommerol@wanadoo.fr]** Fr Rémuzat, take D61 N dir La Motte-Chalancon. In vill, turn R & cont on D61 for 6km dir La Charce, then turn R onto D138 sp Montmorin/Pommerol. In 1km bear R onto D338 to Pommerol. Site sp in 2km on R. Diff access for lge c'vans. Sm, terr, pt shd; htd wc; chem disp; shwrs inc; el pnts €2 (long lead req); lndtte; shop 9km; rest, snacks, bar, (high ssn only or 9km); BBQ; playgrnd; htd pool 10km; lake sw, beach 12km; dogs €2; Eng spkn; adv bkg; quiet; CKE/CCI. "Superb views; adv bkg ess high ssn." 1 Apr-30 Oct. € 11.00 2009*

REMUZAT *9D2* (350m S Rural) *44.41036, 5.35272* **Camp Municipal Les Aires, 26510 Rémuzat [04 75 27 81 43 or 04 75 25 85 78 (Mairie); camping.municipal@remuzat.fr; www.remuzat.com]** Fr Rosans take D94 W for approx 10km; then R onto D61 to Rémuzat; site on R at ent to vill, on rvside. Sm, hdg/mkd pitch, pt shd; wc; chem disp; baby facs; shwrs inc; el pnts (6-10A) €2.80-3.80; lndtte; shop nr; BBQ; dogs €2.30; poss v cr if rallies; quiet; CKE/CCI. "Beautiful site, vill & area; some sm pitches; helpful warden; san facs old but clean; site poss clsd if weather bad; excel." ♦ May-30 Sep. € 9.50 2010*

RIBES *9D2* (700m S Rural) *44.29545, 4.12436* **Camping Les Cruses, Ribes 07260 Joyeuse [33 04 75 39 54 69; les-cruses@wanadoo.fr; www.campinglescruses.com]** Head NW on rue du Mas de Laffont towards Le Chateâu after 120 mtrs turn L onto Le Chateâu. Turn R onto D550, sharp R twrds Laffont, L onto Laffont, sharp R twrd D450 after 41 mtrs turn L onto D450. Sm, mkd pitch, shd; htd wc; chem disp; mv service pnt; child/baby facs; shwrs; el pnts (10A) €4.30; Indtte; tradsmn; rest; snack bar; bar; BBQ; playgrnd; pool; beach 1km; games area; entmnt; internet; TV rm; wifi; dogs; Eng spkn; adv bkg; quiet; ccard acc; CCI. "Excellent on site pool and jacuzz; v helpful and friendly owners; near lively town and places to see." 01 Apr-30 Sep. € 29.00 2014*

ROANNE *9A1* (12km S Rural) *45.91576, 4.06108* **Camping De Mars, 56 route du Chateau de la Roche, 42123 Cordelle [04 77 64 94 42; campingdemars@yahoo.fr; www.camping-de-mars.com]** On D56 fr Roanne foll dir Lac Villarest; cross barrage & site 4.5km S of Cordelle well sp just off D56. Fr junc 70 on N7 to St Cyr-de-Favières. Foll sp to Château de la Roche on D17 & site on D56. Fr S take D56 immed after Balbigny; single track app, with restricted visibility. Or fr N82 exit for Neulise onto D26 to Jodard, then D56 twd Cordelle. Site on L in 11km. Med, pt sl, terr, pt shd, hdg pitch; wc; chem disp; serviced pitch; mv service pnt; shwrs; child/baby facs; el pnts (6A) inc; Indtte; shop; tradsmn; snacks; bar; playgrnd; pool; lake sw, fishing & watersports 500m; entmnt; 40% statics; Eng spkn; adv bkg rec high ssn; quiet; red long stay; CKE/CCI. "Peaceful; lovely views." ♦ ltd 01 Apr-15 Oct. € 22.00 (CChq acc) 2011*

See advertisement

ROANNE *9A1* (5km SW Rural) *45.98830, 4.04531* **Camping L'Orée du Lac, Le Barrage, 42300 Villerest [tel/fax 04 77 69 60 88; camping@loreedulac.net; www.loreedulac.net]** Take D53 SW fr Roanne to Villerest; site sp in vill. Sm, mkd pitch, pt sl, pt shd; wc; chem disp (wc); shwrs inc; el pnts (6A) €3.70; shop 400m; rest, snacks; bar; playgrnd; pool; rv 300m; lake 100m; fishing; watersports; entmnt; wifi; TV; dogs €2.50; phone; Eng spkn; adv bkg rec high ssn; quiet; red low ssn;CKE/CCI. "Attractive site nr medieval vill; much of site diff lge/med o'fits; lower pt of site diff when wet." 2 Apr-30 Sep. € 17.00 2012*

ROCHE DE GLUN, LA see Valence *9C2*

ROCHETTE, LA (SAVOIE) *9B3* (2km S Rural) *45.44983, 6.10299* **Camp Municipal Le Lac St Clair, Chemin de la Plaine, 73110 Détrier [04 79 25 73 55 or 04 79 25 50 32 (Mairie); campinglarochette@orange.fr; www.la-rochette.com]** Exit A41 at Pontcharra junc 22; foll D925 NE sp La Rochette & Albertville. Take 1st sp turn to La Rochette on R. Pass supmkt & boating pool. Site 300m on R. Med, pt sl, pt shd; wc; chem disp; baby facs; shwrs inc; baby facs; el pnts (16A) €3.50; Indry rm; shop 500m; tradsmn; bar; BBQ; playgrnd; some statics; dogs €1.20; phone; poss cr; quiet. "Gd base for W Alps; easy access fr m'way; clean, modern san facs; peaceful site." ♦ ltd 1 May-30 Sep. € 13.00 2009*

ROSANS *9D3* (4km W Rural) *44.38523, 5.42540* **Aire Naturelle Le Gessy (Cagossi), 26510 Verclause [tel/fax 04 75 27 80 39 or 06 84 14 69 01 (mob); legessy@hotmail.com; www.camping-legessy.com]** Site sp fr vill; 2km up steep, narr, winding rd. Sm, hdstg, sl, terr, pt shd; wc; chem disp (wc); shwrs inc; el pnts (6-10A) €3.50; supmkt & rest 2km; snacks; bar; playgrnd; pool; 10% statics; dogs €2; Eng spkn; adv bkg; quiet; CKE/CCI. "Spacious pitches; gd views; vg." 1 May-1 Oct. € 12.50 2010*

ROYBON *9C2* (1km S Rural) *45.24639, 5.24806* **Camping de Roybon, Route de St Antoine, 38940 Roybon [04 76 36 23 67; fax 04 76 36 33 02; info@campingroybon.com; www.campingroybon.com]** Fr Roybon go S on D71 & foll sp. Med, mkd pitch, pt sl, pt shd; wc; chem disp; shwrs inc; el pnts (6A) €3.50; shops 1km; playgrnd; sw & watersports in lake adj; dogs €2.65; adv bkg; quiet; red low ssn. "V peaceful; gd, modern facs new; vg." ♦ 15 Apr-15 Oct. € 16.80 2009*

RUFFIEUX *9B3* (500m W Rural) *45.84932, 5.83441* **Camping Le Saumont, 73310 Ruffieux [04 79 54 26 26; camping.saumont@wanadoo.fr; www.campingsaumont.com]** N fr Aix-les-Bains take D991 N to Ruffieux, sp just bef Ruffieux at junc with D904. Sm, hdg/mkd pitch, pt shd; wc; chem disp; serviced pitch; shwrs; el pnts (6A) inc; Indtte; shop 1.5km; snacks; bar; BBQ; playgrnd; 2 pools; lake & rv sw 2.5km; tennis; cycle hire; 10% statics; dogs €1.80; adv bkg; quiet; red low ssn. "Dusty rd thro site when hot & dry; muddy after rain." 1 May-26 Sep. € 20.00 2009*

RUFFIEUX *9B3* (4km W Rural) *45.85255, 5.79274* **Camping Le Colombier, Ile de Verbaou, 01350 Culoz [tel/fax 04 79 87 19 00; camping.colombier@free.fr; http://camping.colombier.free.fr]** W fr Ruffieux or N fr Belley on D904, site sp off rndabt 1km E of Culoz. Med, hdg/mkd pitch, hdstg, pt shd; wc (some cont); chem disp; mv service pnt; baby facs; shwrs inc; el pnts (10A) €3; Indtte; shop 1km; tradsmn; rest, snacks; bar; playgrnd; lake sw adj; tennis; cycle hire; wifi; TV; some statics; dogs €1; phone; Eng spkn; adv bkg; quiet; ccard acc; red low ssn/CKE/CCI. "Gd touring base; conv Annecy." ♦ 23 Apr-26 Sep. € 16.50 2010*

RUMILLY *9B3* (4km N Rural) *45.90229, 5.92738* **Camping Les Charmilles, Route de Seyssel, 74150 Vallières [04 50 62 10 60; fax 04 50 62 19 45; lescharmilles.camping@wanadoo.fr; www.campinglescharmilles.com]** Exit A41 junc 15 at Alby onto D3 to Rumilly; 4km N of Rumilly in Vallières exit D910 on D14 sp Seyssel. Site on L in 500m. Med, mkd pitch, pt shd; wc; baby facs; shwrs inc; el pnts (6A) €3.50; gas; Indtte; shops 500m; tradmsn; rest, snacks; bar; BBQ; playgrnd; pool; paddling pool; games area; wifi; entmnt; TV; 25% statics; dogs €2; phone; adv bkg; quiet; red low ssn. "Gd, modern san facs; pleasant situation." ♦ 1 Apr-31 Oct. € 15.50 2010*

RUMILLY *9B3* (3.5km S Rural) *45.84083, 5.96277* **Camping Le Madrid, Route de St Félix, 74150 Rumilly [04 50 01 12 57; contact@camping-le-madrid.com; www.camping-le-madrid.com]** S fr Rumilly on D910, take D3 L dir St Marcel for approx 600m & at 2nd rndabt turn R, site sp. Med, hdg/mkd pitch, some hdstg, pt shd; htd wc (some cont); chem disp; mv service pnt; baby facs; shwrs; el pnts (6-10A) €2.80-4.30; Indtte (inc dryer); shop 2km; tradsmn; rest, snacks; bar; BBQ; playgrnd; pool; paddling pool; fishing; cycle hire; games area; games rm; wifi; entmnt; 50% statics; dogs €2; adv bkg; quiet. "Pleasant owners; chosen for proximity to m'way; ideal for NH." ♦ 1 Apr-24 Oct. € 28.00 (CChq acc) 2014*

RUOMS *9D2* (2km N Rural) *44.47655, 4.35858* **Camping Les Coudoulets, Chemin de l'Ardèche, 07120 Pradons [04 75 93 94 95; fax 04 79 39 65 89; camping@coudoulets.com; www.coudoulets.com]** Site sp fr D579. Med, mkd pitch, shd; wc; chem disp; mv service pnt; baby facs; shwrs inc; el pnts (6A) €4; Indtte; shop 300m; rest, snacks; bar; playgrnd; htd pool; paddling pool; rv fishing nr; games area; 5% statics; dogs €2.50; Eng spkn; adv bkg; quiet. "Site o'looks Rv Ardèche; friendly, careful owners; excel pool." ♦ 18 Apr-19 Sep. € 25.00 2009*

RUOMS *9D2* (3km N Rural) *44.47375, 4.35325* **Camping du Pont des Champs des Souliers, Route de Chauzon, Chemin du Cirque de Gens, 07120 Pradons [04 75 93 93 98; campingdupont07@wanadoo.fr; www.campingdupontardeche.com]** S fr Aubenas on D104, on o'skts of town take D579 to Pradons. Thro vill, bef end vill sp turn R onto D308 opp Intermarché supmkt to Chauzon. Site 300m on L, site sp. Med, hdg/mkd pitch, pt shd; wc (some cont); chem disp; shwrs inc; el pnts (6-10A) €4.20 (poss rev pol); Indtte; shop 100m; rest 300m; snacks; bar; BBQ; playgrnd; htd pool; rv sw & sand beach adj; canoe hire; games area; wifi; TV; 15% statics; dogs €2.50; phone; bus; Eng spkn; adv bkg; quiet; red low ssn; CKE/CCI. "Friendly owners; lovely, rugged area; vg." ♦ 27 Mar-30 Sep. € 24.50 2010*

RUOMS *9D2* (3km S Rural) *44.42761, 4.33561* **Yelloh! Village La Plaine, 07120 Ruoms [04 75 39 65 83; fax 04 75 39 74 38; camping.la.plaine@wanadoo.fr; www.camping-la-plaine.com / www.yellohvillage.co.uk]** Exit Ruoms S on D579 dir Vallon-Pont-d'Arc; at junc in 2km turn S onto D111 dir St Ambroix. Site on L. Lge, hdg/mkd pitch, pt shd; wc; baby facs; shwrs inc; el pnts (6A) inc; Indtte; shop; tradsmn; rest, snacks; bar; BBQ; playgrnd; pool; paddling pool; rv sw, fishing & private beach; games area; games rm; fitness rm; entmnt; some statics; dogs €7; red low ssn; CKE/CCI. 16 Apr-17 Sep. € 41.00 2010*

RUOMS *9D2* (4km SW Urban) *44.43101, 4.32945* **Camping La Chapoulière, 07120 Ruoms [tel/fax 04 75 39 64 98 or 04 75 93 90 72; camping@lachapouliere.com; www.lachapouliere.com]** Exit Ruoms S on D579. At junc 2km S, foll D111 sp St Ambroix. Site 1.5km fr junc. Med, mkd pitch, pt sl, shd; wc; mv service pnt; baby facs; shwrs inc; el pnts (6A) €4; gas; Indtte; shop in ssn & 3km; rest, snacks; bar; pool; paddling pool; rv sw & fishing adj; canoeing; tennis 2km; games area; wifi; entmnt; TV; dogs €2.50; Eng spkn; adv bkg rec high ssn; quiet; red low ssn. "Beautiful pitches on rv bank; friendly; ltd facs low ssn; vg; excel modern san facs; lge pitches demarcated by trees." ♦ Easter-30 Sep. € 37.00 2014*

See advert on next page

SAHUNE see Rémuzat *9D2*

SAILLANS *9D2* (8km E Rural) *44.69579, 5.30393* **Camp Municipal La Colombe, 26340 Aurel [04 75 21 76 29 or 04 75 21 71 88; fax 04 75 21 71 89; bern.pera@wanadoo.fr]** E of Saillans on D93, in vill of Vercheny turn S onto D357. Bef vill of Aurel turn R by war memorial. Sm, mkd pitch, terr, shd; wc (cont); shwrs inc; el pnts; Indtte; shops 4km; rest, snacks; bar; playgrnd; pool; rv sw & fishing 5km; games area; some statics; v quiet. "Peaceful, mountain site; beautiful views." 1 May-30 Sep. 2009*

SAILLANS *9D2* (500m W Rural) *44.69511, 5.18124* **Camping Les Chapelains, 26340 Saillans [04 75 21 55 47; camping@chapelains.fr; www.chapelains.fr]** Fr W on D93 turn onto D493. Site well sp just bef Saillans vill boundary adj Rv Drôme. Sm, hdg/mkd pitch, pt shd; wc; shwrs inc; el pnts (4-10A); gas; Indtte; sm shop; rest; tradsmn; snacks; playgrnd; shgl beach; games area; dogs; Eng spkn; adv bkg; quiet; ccard not acc; CKE/CCI. "Attractive, well-run rvside site; some v sm pitches; new san facs; friendly, helpful warden; rv walk to vill; rest open low ssn." 15 Apr-15 Sep. € 21.00 2012*

ST AGREVE *9C2* (5km W Rural) *45.02423, 4.32760* **FFCC Camping La Prairie, Laillier, 07320 Mars [tel/fax 04 75 30 24 47; millardjf@camping-laprairie.com; www.camping-laprairie.com]** Fr St Agrève W on D120/D15, shortly bef Mars site sp to R. Sm, hdg/mkd pitch, pt shd; htd wc; chem disp; mv service pnt; baby facs; shwrs inc; el pnts (6A) €3; Indtte (inc dryer); shop, rest 5km; tradsmn; snacks; bar; BBQ; playgrnd; fishing 800m; games area; entmnt; 10% statics; dogs €0.50; phone; poss cr; adv bkg; quiet; CKE/CCI. "V attractive area; gd walking, cycling; golf course nrby; vg." ♦ 15 May-15 Sep. € 15.00 2010*

ST ALBAN AURIOLLES see Ruoms *9D2*

ST ALBAN DE MONTBEL see Chambéry *9B3*

ST COLOMBAN DES VILLARDS *9C3* (700m SW Rural) *45.29015, 6.22091* **Camping La Perrière, Route du Col du Glandon, 73130 St Colomban-des-Villards [04 79 59 16 07; fax 04 79 59 15 17; saint-colomban@franceloc.fr; www.campings-franceloc.fr]** Exit A43 junc 26 onto D927. Site at end of vill. Access rd narr & winding in places - not rec long o'fits. Sm, mkd pitch, hdstg, terr, pt shd; htd wc; mv service pnt; shwrs inc; el pnts €4; Indtte; shop 200m; BBQ; playgrnd; games area; phone; quiet. "Excel." ♦ 15 Jun-15 Sep. € 15.00 2009*

ST DONAT SUR L'HERBASSE *9C2* (6km N Rural) *45.14631, 5.02140* **FFCC Camping Les Falquets, Route de Margès, 26260 Charmes-sur-l'Herbasse [04 75 45 75 57 or 04 75 45 27 44 (LS); fax 04 75 45 66 17; info@lesfalquets.com; www.lesfalquets.com]** Exit A7 junc 13 onto D532 dir Romans-sur-Isère; at Chanos-Curson turn N onto D67 to Charmes (via St Donat-sur-l'Herbasse), then D121 dir Margès. Site sp in vill on rvside. Med, shd; wc (some cont); chem disp; shwrs inc; el pnts (6-10A) €2.80-3.50; Indtte; shop 3km; bar; playgrnd; lake sw, waterslide, windsurfing & tennis 3km; 25% statics; dogs free; phone; Eng spkn; adv bkg rec high ssn; quiet; red low ssn; CKE/CCI. "Pleasant, well-kept site; old facs but clean; helpful warden; sh walk to vill; gd." ♦ 1 May-31 Aug. € 13.00 2009*

ST DONAT SUR L'HERBASSE *9C2* (500m S Rural) *45.11916, 4.99290* **Camping Domaine Les Ulèzes, Route de Romans, 26260 St Donat-sur-l'Herbasse [tel/fax 04 75 47 83 20; contact@domaine-des-ulezes.com; www.domaine-des-ulezes.com]** Exit A7 junc 13 onto D532 dir Romans-sur-Isère. In 5km turn N onto D67 thro St Donat. Site on edge of vill off D53 dir Peyrins, well sp. Med, hdg/mkd pitch, pt shd; wc; chem disp; mv service pnt; shwrs inc; el pnts (6-10A) €3.50-4.50; gas 1km; Indtte; ice; shop; tradsmn; rest, snacks; bar; BBQ (gas/elec); playgrnd; htd pool; games area; games rm; wifi; entmnt; TV; 10% statics; dogs €2; no twin-axles; Eng spkn; adv bkg; quiet; ccard acc; red low ssn; CKE/CCI. "Lovely rvside site; gd size pitches; immac; excel facs; welcoming, friendly owners; canal-side walk to town; gd touring base; vg; rec; serviced pitches." ♦ 1 Apr-31 Oct. € 32.70 2014*

ST ETIENNE DE FONTBELLON see Aubenas *9D2*

ST EUSTACHE see Annecy *9B3*

ST FERREOL TRENTE PAS see Nyons *9D2*

STE FOY L'ARGENTIERE *9B2* (7km SE Rural) *45.65185, 4.56315* **Camp Municipal Les Verpillières, Les Plaines, 69850 St Martin-en-Haut [04 78 48 62 16; saintmartinenhaut@9business.fr; http://saintmartin.decideur.net]** Fr Craponne on W o'skts of Lyon SW on D311 to cent of St Martin-en-Haut; then take D122 S; site on L approx 200m fr x-rds. Site sp. Fr St Foy take D489 SE to Duerne, D34 to St Martin-en-Haut, then as above. This app not for lge o'fits, two 7-12% climbs out of St Foy & hairpins after Duerne. Med, mkd pitch, pt sl, shd; htd wc; shwrs; el pnts (10A) inc; Indtte; shops 500m; snacks; bar; playgrnd; tennis 300m; entmnt; 75% statics; poss cr; adv bkg; quiet. "Lovely wooded site with red squirrels; busy at w/end." 1 Apr-31 Oct. € 12.00 2011*

ST GALMIER *9B2* (2km E Rural) *45.59266, 4.33528* **Campéole Camping Val de Coise, Route de la Thiéry, 42330 St Galmier [04 77 54 14 82; fax 04 77 54 02 45; val-de-coise@campeole.com; www.camping-valdecoise.com / www.campeole.com]** Fr St Etienne take D1082 N. In 7km turn R onto D12 sp St Galmier; after x-ing rv bdge on o'skirts of vill turn R & foll Camping sp for 2km. Or fr N on D1082 look for sp to St Galmier about 1.5km S of Montrond-les-Bains & turn L onto D6 to St Galmier. On D12 in St Galmier at floral rndabt with fountain if app fr N go L & fr S go R, uphill & foll site sp. Site approx 1.5km fr rndabt. Med, mkd pitch, hdstg, pt sl, pt shd; wc; chem disp; baby facs; shwrs inc; el pnts (16A) €4.10; gas; Indtte; sm shop & 2km; tradsmn; rest & snacks 2km; BBQ; playgrnd; htd pool; paddling pool; fishing; tennis 2km; cycle hire; games area; games rm; wifi; entmnt; TV rm; 20% statics; dogs €2.60; phone; Eng spkn; adv bkg; v quiet; ccard acc; red low ssn; CKE/CCI. "Pleasant rvside site; helpful staff; facs poss stretched high ssn; highly rec." ♦ 11 Apr-12 Oct. € 30.00 2014*

ST GENIS LAVAL see Lyon *9B2*

ST GENIX SUR GUIERS *9B3* (300m SE Urban) *45.58878, 5.64252* **Les Bords du Guiers, Route de Pont Beauvoisin, 73240 Saint Genix sur Guiers [04 76 31 71 40; info@lesbordsduguiers.com; www.lesbordsduguiers.com/]** On reaching vill on D1516 foll sp Le-Pont-de-Beauvoisin, site 300 mtrs on R. Med, hdg/mkd pitch, pt shd; wc; chem disp; mv service pnt; shwrs; el pnts (8-10A); tradsmn; BBQ; pool; games area; games rm; wifi; dogs; twin axles; quiet; Eng spkn; red low ssn; supmkt 6km. "Excel, quiet site; cycle hire; v helpful owners; gd base for site seeing or star watching; town centre 5 mins walk; mkt day Wed." 30 Apr-25 Sept. € 21.00 2014*

ST GERMAIN see Aubenas *9D2*

ST GERVAIS LES BAINS *9B4* (10km SE Rural) *45.80275, 6.72207* **Camping Le Pontet, 2485 Route de Notre-Dame-de-la-Gorge, 74170 Les Contamines-Montjoie [04 50 47 04 04; fax 04 50 47 18 10; welcome@campinglepontet.fr; www.campinglepontet.fr]** Fr St Gervais take D902 to Les Contamines-Montjoie (sp); go thro vill & foll sp to Notre Dame-de-la-Gorge; site in 2km on L, clearly sp. Lge, mkd pitch, hdstg, pt shd; htd wc; chem disp; baby facs; shwrs inc; el pnts (2-10A) €3-9.90; Indtte; shops 2km; tradsmn; rest, snacks; playgrnd; fishing; lake adj; leisure/sports park adj; tennis; horseriding; ski lift 200m; dogs free; phone; Eng spkn; adv bkg; quiet; ccard acc. "Mkd alpine walks; excel new owners; owner is a ski instructor & mountain guide." ♦ 1 May-26 Sep & 1 Dec-30 Apr. € 25.00 2014*

ST GERVAIS LES BAINS *9B4* (2km S Rural) *45.87333, 6.72000* **Camping Les Dômes de Miage, 197 Route des Contamines, 74170 St Gervais-les-Bains [04 50 93 45 96; fax 04 50 78 10 75; info@camping-mont-blanc.com; www.camping-mont-blanc.com]** Exit A40 junc 21; fr N thro St Gervais, at sm rndabt in cent foll sp Les Contamines onto D902, site 2km on L. Med, mkd pitch, pt shd; htd wc (some cont); chem disp; mv service pnt; baby facs; shwrs inc; el pnts (6A) €3.50 (poss rev pol); gas; Indtte (inc dryer); shop; tradsmn; supmkt 7km; rest, bar adj; snacks; BBQ; playgrnd; htd pool, tennis 800m; fishing 1km; cycle hire 800m; games area; wifi; TV rm; lux chalet to rent; dogs €2 (free low ssn); bus adj; train 5.5km; Eng spkn; adv bkg (bkg fee); quiet; ccard acc; red low ssn; CKE/CCI; "Superb, well-kept, family-owned site in beautiful location; welcoming, helpful & friendly; immac san facs; conv Tramway du Mont Blanc excursions; mkt Thurs; excel." ♦ 12 May-13 Sep. € 37.50 2014*

See advertisement

ST JEAN DE COUZ see Echelles, Les *9B3*

ST JEAN DE MAURIENNE *9C3* (1.2km SE Urban) *45.27034, 6.35023* **Camp Municipal des Grands Cols, 422 Ave du Mont-Cenis, 73300 St Jean-de-Maurienne [tel/fax 04 79 64 28 02 or 06 64 09 77 48 (mob); info@campingdesgrandscols.com; www.campingdesgrandscols.com]** Site sp fr D1006 in St Jean-de-Maurienne; site behind shops 100m fr town cent behind trees/parking. Med, hdg/mkd pitch, hdstg, pt sl, pt shd; wc; chem disp; mv service pnt; 20% serviced pitches; shwrs inc; el pnts (16A) €3; Indtte; supmkt 1km; tradsmn; snacks; bar; playgrnd; pool 1.5km; lake 3km; games rm; TV; dogs €1; Eng spkn; quiet; ccard not acc; red low ssn; CKE/CCI. "Warm welcome; helpful staff; clean san facs; interesting town; excel for serious cycling; gd NH for Fréjus tunnel; excel." 17 May-30 Sep. € 31.00 2014*

ST JEAN DE MUZOLS see Tournon sur Rhône *9C2*

ST JEAN EN ROYANS *9C2* (6km NE Rural) *45.05917, 5.25353* **FFCC Camp Municipal, 26190 St Nazaire-en-Royans [04 75 48 41 18 or 04 75 48 40 63 (Mairie); contact@saint-nazaire-en-royans.com]** Exit A49 onto D1532 to St Nazaire-en-Royans, site is on E edge of vill on D76, 700m fr cent, well sp. Med, hdg pitch, pt sl, pt shd; wc (some cont); chem disp; shwrs inc; el pnts (6A) €3.80; Indtte; shops & rest 700m; playgrnd; dogs €1.22; no ccard acc; quiet; CKE/CCI. "Clean san facs; helpful warden; gate clsd 2200-0700; conv mountains of Vercors; aquaduct on Rv Isère worth seeing; excel." ♦ 1 May-30 Sep. € 9.00 2011*

ST JORIOZ see Annecy *9B3*

ST JULIEN EN BEAUCHENE *9D3* (7km N Rural) *44.66440, 5.70742* **Camping Le Champ La Chèvre, 26620 Lus-La-Croix-Haute [04 92 58 50 14; fax 04 92 58 55 92; info@campingchamplachevre.com; www.campingchamplachevre.com]** Turn E off D1075 thru Lus vill, site SE of vill nr sw pool on D505. Med, mkd pitch, pt sl, terr, pt shd; wc; chem disp; shwrs €1; el pnts (6A) €4.05; gas; Indtte; shops 300m; snacks; playgrnd; htd pool adj; fishing; some statics; dogs €2.65; poss cr; adv bkg; quiet; ccard acc; CKE/CCI. "Mountain views; helpful staff; excel pool; many waymarked walks; vg." ♦ ltd 27 Apr-30 Sep. € 16.40 (CChq acc) 2009*

ST JULIEN EN GENEVOIS *9A3* (5km SE Rural) *46.12015, 6.10565* **Camping La Colombière, 166 Chemin Neuf-Chef-Lieu, 74160 Neydens [04 50 35 13 14; fax 04 50 35 13 40; la.colombiere@wanadoo.fr; www.camping-la-colombiere.com]** Exit A40 junc 13 onto D1201 dir Cruseilles; in 1.75km turn L to Neydens; turn R at church; site on R in 200m. Site sp. NB: Do not go into St Julien-en-Genevois when towing. Med, hdg/mkd pitch, hdstg, pt sl, pt shd; htd wc; chem disp; mv service pnt; baby facs; shwrs inc; el pnts (6-10A) inc, extra for 15A; gas; Indtte (inc dryer); sm shop & 500m; farm produce; rest, snacks; bar; BBQ; playgrnd; 2 pools (1 sm htd, covrd); paddling pool; lake fishing 1km; cycle hire; wifi; entmnt; games/TV rm; 10% statics; dogs €2.50; no c'vans/m'vans over 10m high ssn; park & ride bus; poss cr; Eng spkn; adv bkg; quiet, but some rd & aircraft noise; ccard acc; red low ssn; CKE/CCI. "Family-owned site; friendly, helpful staff; boggy after heavy rain; conv Geneva - guided tours high ssn; open for m'vans all year; gd NH; excel." ♦ 4 Apr-10 Nov. € 29.00 SBS - M08 2013*

See advertisement

ST JULIEN EN ST ALBAN see Privas *9D2*

ST JUST EN CHEVALET *9B1* (1km NW Rural) *45.91459, 3.84026* **Camp Municipal Le Verdillé, 42430 St Just-en-Chevalet [tel/fax 04 77 65 17 82 or 04 77 65 00 62 (Mairie); campingleverdille@sfr.fr]** Exit A72 at junc 4, join D53 NE twd St Just-en-Chevalet. Foll sp in town to camping/piscine. Due to steep gradients avoid D1 when towing. Med, hdg pitch, pt sl, pt shd; wc (mainly cont); chem disp; mv service pnt; shwrs inc; el pnts (16A) €3; Indtte; shops & supmkt 500m; rest 500m; snacks, bar adj; htd pool & tennis adj; 10% statics; dogs €1.70; phone; Eng spkn; adv bkg; quiet; CKE/CCI. "Friendly owners." 1 May-30 Sep. € 19.00 2013*

ST LAGER BRESSAC see St Vincent de Barrès *9D2*

ST LAURENT DU PAPE see Voulte sur Rhône, La *9D2*

ST LAURENT EN BEAUMONT see Salle en Beaumont, La *9C3*

ST MARCELLIN *9C2* (7km E Rural) *45.12122, 5.33775* **Camping Château de Beauvoir, 38160 Beauvoir-en-Royans [04 76 64 01 79; fax 04 76 38 49 60; chateaudebeauvoir@wanadoo.fr]** On D1092 Romans to Grenoble, turn into narr uphill rd D518 to vill; L into site, sp. Care needed on app rd & ent gate narr. Sm, shd; htd wc; shwrs inc; el pnts (10A) €2; Indtte; shop 6km; bar; rest 2km; 10% statics; dogs; adv bkg rec; quiet; "Vg site on château lawn; gd walking." 1 Apr-31 Oct. € 11.60 2013*

ST MARTIN DE VALAMAS *9C2* (500m N Rural) *44.94249, 4.36779* **Camp Municipal La Teyre, 07310 St Martin-de-Valamas [04 75 30 47 16]** At N end of vill across single-track bdge. Well sp. Sm, mkd pitch, pt shd; wc (cont); chem disp (wc); shwrs inc; el pnts (6A) inc; Indry rm; playgrnd; games area; quiet. "Lge pitches; vg." ♦ ltd 1 May-30 Sep. € 12.00 2009*

ST MARTIN EN HAUT see Ste Foy l'Argentiere *9B2*

ST MARTIN EN VERCORS see Chapelle en Vercors, La *9C3*

"Satellite navigation makes touring much easier"

Remember most sat navs don't know if you're towing or in a larger vehicle – always use yours alongside maps and site directions.

ST MARTIN SUR LA CHAMBRE *9B3* (2km N Rural) *45.36883, 6.31458* **Camping Le Petit Nice, Notre Dame-de-Cruet, 73130 St Martin-sur-la-Chambre [tel/fax 04 79 56 37 72 or 06 76 29 19 39 (mob); campinglepetitnice@yahoo.fr; www.camping-petitnice.com]** Fr N on A43 exit junc 26 & foll sp to cent of La Chambre, thro town to rndabt & turn R into Rue Notre Dame-du-Cruet. Foll site sp & in 2km turn R thro housing, site on L in 200m. Sm, terr, pt shd; htd wc; chem disp; shwrs inc; el pnts (3-10A) €3; Indtte; shop & 2km; rest, snacks; bar; playgrnd; pool; wifi; 80% statics; dogs €1; poss cr; Eng spkn; adv bkg; quiet; CKE/CCI. "By stream with mountain views; clean, modern san facs." ♦ € 13.00 2009*

ST MAURICE D'ARDECHE see Aubenas *9D2*

RHONE-ALPS

ST MAURICE L'EXIL *9B2* (1.7km E Urban) *45.39760, 4.78836* **Camping La Colombière, 20 Rue Mata, La Colombier, 38550 Saint-Maurice l'Exile [(033) 474 862 567; contact@camping-lacolombiere.com; www.camping-lacolombiere.com]** Fr N7 turn off at exit St Maurice-l'Exile, foll sp to vill. Take exit rd sp Vienne (toll Free) via RN7 exit to vill and foll sp to site. Sm, hdg pitch, pt shd; wc (cont); mv service pnt; child baby facs; fam bthrm; shwes; lndry rm; el pnts 9A; dogs; playgrnd; htd indoor pool; games area; entmnt; wifi; waterslide; tennis; quiet; Eng spkn; ccard acc. "Lovely warm welcome." ♦ 1 Apr-31-Oct. € 18.50 2012*

"There aren't many sites open at this time of year"

If you're travelling outside peak season remember to call ahead to check site opening dates – even if the entry says 'open all year'.

⊞ **ST MICHEL DE MAURIENNE** *9C3* (500m SE Rural) *45.21276, 6.47858* **FFCC Camping Le Marintan, 1 Rue de la Provalière, 73140 St Michel-de-Maurienne [04 79 59 17 36; contact@gite-lemarintan.com; http://gite-lemarintan.com/camping]** Fr D1006 foll sp in town to 'Centre Touristique' & 'Maison Retraite'. Rue de la Provalière is a L turn fr D1006 immed bef rlwy bdge. Sm, hdg pitch, unshd; htd wc; chem disp; shwrs inc; el pnts inc; lndtte (inc dryer); shops in town; rest; bar; pool; some statics; dogs €1; quiet. "Gd touring base, but no character; conv for skiing at Val Thorens via gondola lift at Orelle." € 12.00 2013*

ST NAZAIRE EN ROYANS see St Jean en Royans *9C2*

ST NAZAIRE LE DESERT *9D2* (200m E Rural) *44.56952, 5.27750* **Camp Municipal, 26340 St Nazaire-le-Désert [04 75 26 42 99 or 04 75 27 52 31 (LS); info@camping-stnazaire.com; www.camping-stnazaire.com]** Well sp in St Nazaire-le-Désert. Med, mkd pitch, terr, shd; wc (own san rec); chem disp (wc); shwrs inc; el pnts €3; shops nrby; rest, snacks; bar; BBQ; playgrnd; htd pool; games rm; wifi; entmnt; dogs; phone; no twin-axles; poss cr; Eng spkn; adv bkg rec high ssn. "Busy, friendly site in beautiful location; v lge o'fits poss diff to pitch; gd." 1 May-30 Sep. € 10.00 2009*

ST PANTALEON LES VIGNES *9D2* (2km E Rural) *44.39752, 5.06099* **Camping Les Cyprès, Hameau Font de Barral, 26770 Saint Pantaleon les Vignes [06 81 53 78 03 / 06 82 27 19 14; contact@lescypres-camping.com; www.lescypres-camping.com]** D541 fir Nyons. Fr highway A7 exit Montèlimar-Sud Bollène or Orange Cent. Sm, pt sl, pt shd; wc; chem disp; shwrs inc; el pnts (4,6,10A) €2.50-3.60; shops 5km; tradsmn; rest 5km; snacks 5km; bar 5km; BBQ; playgrnd; games rm; wifi; dogs €1.80; twin axles; poss cr; quiet. "Beautiful surroundings; friendly owners." ♦ ltd 1 Apr-31 Oct. € 11.00 2014*

ST PAUL DE VARAX see Bourg en Bresse *9A2*

ST PAUL DE VEZELIN *9B1* (3.5km N Rural) *45.91159, 4.06615* **Camping d'Arpheuilles, Lac de Villerest, 42590 St-Paul-de-Vézelin [04 77 63 43 43; arpheuilles@wanadoo.fr; www.camping-arpheuilles.com]** Take D53 fr Roanne 10km. Turn L onto D8 twd St German-Laval. Turn L at Dancé onto D112 to St-Paul-de-Vézelin. Turn L on ent to vill. Or fr A72 exit junc 5 onto D8, then D26. V diff single track fr vill (3km) - v steep in places. Med, mkd pitch, pt sl, pt shd; wc (some cont); chem disp; mv service pnt; shwrs inc; el pnts (5-6A) €3; gas; lndtte; shop; tradsmn; rest, snacks; bar; BBQ; playgrnd; pool; paddling pool; lake sw & sand beach adj; TV; few statics; dogs free; phone; Eng spkn; adv bkg; 20% red 3+ days; quiet. "Beautiful location; helpful owner; well-managed with gd facs; various sports facs." 1 May-10 Sep. € 19.50 2010*

ST PIERRE D'ALBIGNY see Montmelian *9B3*

ST PIERRE DE CHARTREUSE *9C3* (2km S Rural) *45.32570, 5.79700* **Camping de Martinière, Route du Col de Porte, 38380 St Pierre-de-Chartreuse [04 76 88 60 36; fax 04 76 88 69 10; camping-de-martiniere@orange.fr; www.campingdemartiniere.com]** Site is situated on D520B thro Gorge-du-Guiers-Mort after St Pierre-de-Chartreuse. Med, mkd pitch, pt shd; htd wc; chem disp; mv service pnt; baby facs; shwrs inc; el pnts (2-10A) €2-7.20; gas; lndtte (inc dryer); shop; tradsmn; rest, snacks; bar; BBQ; playgrnd; pool; paddling pool; rv fishing 500m; 15% statics; dogs €1.50; phone; poss cr; Eng spkn; adv bkg, ess high ssn; quiet; red low ssn; ccard acc; red low ssn; CKE/CCI. "Excel site; lge pitches; friendly owner; excel mountain/hill walking, cycling; Grand Chartreuse Monastery 4km; vg; rte to site and area demanding, gd car/c'van ratio advised; beautiful site in lovely setting." 1 May-11 Sep. € 9.00 2013*

ST RAMBERT D'ALBON *9C2* (1.3km N Urban) *45.29992, 4.80722* **Camping des Claires, 26140 St Rambert-d'Albon [tel/fax 04 75 31 01 87; info@camping-des-claires.com; www.camping-des-claires.com]** Fr A7 exit junc 12 dir Chanas, turn S onto N7. In 1km turn R to St Rambert, turn R at rndabt by rlwy stn, under rlwy bdge & foll site sp. Med, pt sl, shd; wc; chem disp (wc); baby facs; shwrs inc; el pnts (6-10A) €4-8; gas; lndtte; tradsmn; rest, snacks; bar in vill; BBQ; playgrnd; pool; sports area; entmnt; 50% statics; dogs €1.40; phone adj; Eng spkn; some rlwy noise; CKE/CCI. "Pleasant site; friendly staff; old but clean san facs; excel NH." 1 Apr-15 Oct. € 15.50 2010*

ST REMEZE see Vallon Pont d'Arc *9D2*

ST ROMAIN DE JALIONAS see Cremieu *9B2*

ST THEOFFREY *9C3* (3.2km NE Rural) *44.99993, 5.77752* **FFCC Camping Ser-Sirant, Petichet, 38119 St Théoffrey [04 76 83 91 97; fax 04 76 30 83 69; campingsersirant@wanadoo.fr; www.euro-campsite.com]** N fr La Mure on N85 dir Grenoble. At traff lts in Petichet turn E, site on lakeside in 500m. Med, mkd pitch, pt terr, pt shd; wc; chem disp; mv service pnt; shwrs inc; el pnts (6-10A) €3-4.50; lndtte; shop 8km; tradsmn; rest 1km; snacks; sm playgrnd; lake sw & beach adj; watersports; dogs €1.50; phone; bus 1km; Eng spkn; adv bkg; quiet; CKE/CCI. "Gd site with views; most pitches req blocks; helpful owners; excel walking & cycling; highly rec." 1 May-Oct. € 17.00 2010*

ST VALLIER *9C2* (400m N Rural) *45.18767, 4.81225* **Camp Municipal Les Iles de Silon, 26240 St Vallier [04 75 23 22 17 or 04 73 23 07 66; camping.saintvallier@orange.fr; www.saintvallier.com/campings]** On N7 just N of town, clearly sp in both dirs on rvside. Med, hdg sm pitch size restriced, pt shd; wc; chem disp; shwrs inc; el pnts (10A) €2.30 (poss long cable req); Indtte; shop & 500m; snacks; BBQ; playgrnd; pool 1km; watersports; tennis adj; some statics; dogs €2.30; Eng spkn; adv bkg; quiet but some rlwy noise; ccard acc; CKE/CCI. "Attractive, gd quality site; views over rv; lge pitches; friendly warden; gd immac san facs; rec arr bef 1600 high ssn; cycle path along Rhône; gd value; cycle/walking track adj; excel well managed site; v gd facs and staff." ♦ ltd 15 Mar-15 Nov. € 7.00 2014*

ST VALLIER *9C2* (5km W Rural) *45.17917, 4.73960* **Camping L'Oasis, Le Petit Chaléat, 07370 Eclassan [04 75 34 56 23; fax 04 75 34 47 94; info@oasisardeche.com; www.oasisardeche.com]** Leave N7 at St Vallier, cross Rhône to Sarras. Then across D86 onto D6 sp St Jeure-d'Ay, in 7km turn R foll sp to site. App rd twisting & narr, many sharp bends & no passing places. Sm, hdg/mkd pitch, terr, pt shd, 80% serviced pitch; wc; chem disp; shwrs inc; el pnts (3-6A) €3.40-3.90; gas; Indtte; shop; tradsmn; rest, snacks; bar; playgrnd; pool; rv adj; archery; golf 10km; 20% statics; dogs €2.50; Eng spkn; adv bkg; quiet; ccard not acc; CKE/CCI. "Lovely setting by rv; tractor tow to pitch; not rec NH due diff app." 23 Apr-15 Sep. € 20.00 2010*

ST VINCENT DE BARRES *9D2* (1km SW Rural) *44.65659, 4.69330* **Camping Le Rieutord, 07210 St Vincent-de-Barrès [04 75 65 07 73; moncamping@wanadoo.fr; www.ardeche-sud-camping.com]** Fr N exit A7 junc 16 Loriol onto D104 & foll sp Le Pouzin then Chomérac (do not foll 1st sp St Vincent-de-Barrès - narr rd). At rndabt foll D2 dir Le Teil-Montélimar for 6km. When arr at St Vincent (vill on L), turn R & foll site sp for 1.5km. Fr S exit junc 18 Montélimar Sud, foll sps Montélimar then Privas. Cross Rv Rhône, go thro Rochemaure sp Privas. At Meysse turn L after bdge dir Privas. Foll D2 for 4.5km then turn L dir St Bauzile to site in 3km. Med, hdg pitch, pt sl, pt shd; htd wc; shwrs inc; el pnts (16A) €3; Indtte; shop; snacks; bar; cooking facs; playgrnd; pool; paddling pool; waterslide; tennis; games area; some statics; €2; no c'vans over 6m or twin-axles; Eng spkn; adv bkg; quiet CKE/CCI. "Tranquil site in beautiful setting nr old walled town; pleasant owners; gd touring base." 4 Apr-31 Oct. € 15.00 2010*

SALLANCHES *9A3* (2km SE Rural) *45.92470, 6.65528* **Camping Miroir du Mont Blanc, 1213 Chemin de Mont-Blanc-Plage, 74700 Sallanches [04 50 58 14 28 or 04 50 58 12 04 (LS); fax 04 50 93 95 23; beatrice.brosse2@wanadoo.fr]** Fr Geneva on D1205 into Sallanches. Take 1st L after 2nd set of traff lts (by PO) sp 'Hôpital'. Foll rd thro traff lits & over rndabt when rd turns sharp R & runs alongside m'way. In 2km site ent on R beside rndabt. Or exit A41 junc 21 or 22 dir Lac de Passy, site sp. Med, mkd pitch, shd; wc; shwrs inc; el pnts (6A) €2.50; gas 2km; Indry rm; shops 2km; tradsmn; rest, snacks; bar; playgrnd; pool & paddling pool 200m; waterslide; lake sw & sand/shgl beach adj; tennis; fishing; sailing; windsurfing 50m; entmnt; adv bkg rec; rd noise; red low ssn. "Situated bet m'way & rlwy." 15 May-15 Sep. € 13.00 2009*

SALLANCHES *9A3* (2km SE Rural) *45.92723, 6.64710* **Camping Mont Blanc Village L'Ecureuil, 490 Route des Follieux, 74700 Sallanches [04 50 58 43 67; fax 04 50 58 44 61; contact@camping-ecureuil.com; www.camping-ecureuil.com]** App fr Chamonix on D1205, turn R opp Ford g'ge ent Sallanches; strt on thro traff lts, over sleeping policemen, under rlwy bdge & fork R at Braconne rest; strt at next junc to site in 200m. Med, shd; wc; chem disp; mv service pnt; shwrs inc; el pnts (10A) €2.50; gas; Indtte (inc dryer); shops 1km; tradsmn; rest (not every day); bar; playgrnd; pool nr; lake sw & sand/shgl beach; games area; games rm; TV; some statics; dogs €1; poss cr; quiet; ccard acc; red low ssn; CKE/CCI. "Gd, clean, spacious site; mountain views; well drained after rain; excel." Easter-15 Oct. € 15.60 2009*

SALLANCHES *9A3* (4km SE Rural) *45.92388, 6.65042* **Camping Village Center Les Iles, Lac de Passy 245 Chemin de la Cavettaz, 74190 Passy [04 50 58 45 36 or 04 99 57 21 21; www.passy-mont-blanc.com / www.village-center.com]** E fr Geneva on A40, exit junc 21 onto D339 dir Passy; in 400m turn L onto D39 dir Sallanches; at rndabt in 1.5km turn L onto D199 dir Domancy; immed after rlwy x-ing in 500m turn R into Chemin de Mont Blanc Plage; site at end of rd in 1km. Or E fr Sallanches on D1205 dir Chamonix; in 3km turn L (1st into filter to turn L) onto D199; in 1km turn L immed bef level x-ing; site at end of rd. Lge, hdg/mkd pitch, pt shd; wc (some cont); baby facs; shwrs inc; el pnts (8A) inc; Indtte; shop & 3km; snacks; playgrnd; htd pool; shgl lake beach & sw adj; fishing; entmnt; statics; dogs €3; phone; Eng spkn; adv bkg; quiet; ccard acc high ssn; red low ssn; CKE/CCI; "Mountain views; conv Chamonix; vg site." ♦ 6 Apr-29 Sep. € 26.40 (CChq acc) 2013*

SALLE EN BEAUMONT, LA *9C3* (4km SE Rural) *44.87593, 5.83710* **Camping Belvédère de l'Obiou, Les Egats, 38350 St Laurent-en-Beaumont [tel/fax 04 76 30 40 80; info@camping-obiou.com; www.camping-obiou.com]** Clearly sp on D1085. Sm, pt sl, pt terr, pt shd; htd wc; chem disp; mv service pnt; baby facs; shwrs; el pnts (4-10A) €3-6 (poss rev pol); Indtte (inc dryer); shop 7km; tradsmn; rest, snacks; playgrnd; htd, covrd pool; games rm; wifi; TV; 5% statics; dogs €2; poss cr; Eng spkn; rd noise; red long stay/low ssn; CKE/CCI; "Superb, immac, family-run site; excel facs; helpful owners; excel rest & pool; picturesque & interesting area; gd local walks." ♦ 15 Apr-15 Oct. € 30.00 (CChq acc) 2013*

SALLE EN BEAUMONT, LA *9C3* (1.5km W Rural) *44.85573, 5.84503* **Camping Le Champ Long, Chemin de Bas-Beaumont, 38350 La Salle-en-Beaumont [04 76 30 41 81; fax 04 76 30 47 21; champlong38@orange.fr; www.camping-champlong.com]** S fr La Mure on N85 for approx 12km, turn R by primary school on ent La Salle-en-Beaumont. Well sp fr main rd. Med, hdg/mkd pitch, hdstg, terr, shd; wc; chem disp; mv service pnt; baby facs; shwrs inc; el pnts (10A) €3.50; Indtte (inc dryer); tradsmn; rest, snacks; bar; BBQ; playgrnd; pool; paddling pool; games area; games rm; wifi; entmnt; TV; 30% statics; dogs €2.30; Eng spkn; adv bkg; quiet; CKE/CCI. "Gd site for families; gd touring base - many sports/leisure activities nrby; friendly, helpful owners will assist with tractor if req; views fr some pitches; lge o'fits rec to pitch nr recep; excel." ♦ ltd 1 Apr-15 Oct. € 16.00 2010*

SAMOENS *9A3* (5km SE Rural) *46.07392, 6.83768* **Camp Municipal Le Pelly, 74740 Sixt-Fer-à-Cheval [04 50 34 12 17; fax 04 50 89 51 02; camping@sixtferacheval.net; www.sixtferacheval.com/camping/]** Take D907 NE fr Sixt. Site sp on R after 6km bef bdge over Rv Giffre. Med, pt sl, pt shd; wc; chem disp; baby facs; shwrs inc; el pnts (10A) inc; Indtte; tradsmn; snacks; bar; BBQ; playgrnd; horseriding 500m; dogs €1.55; phone; quiet. "Gd walking; alpine flowers & wildlife; helpful wardens." 1 Jun-13 Sep. € 12.00 2009*

⊞ **SAMOENS** *9A3* (750m S Rural) *46.07731, 6.71851* **Camping Caravaneige Le Giffre, La Glière, 74340 Samoëns [04 50 34 41 92; fax 04 50 34 98 84; camping.samoens@wanadoo.fr; www.camping-samoens.com]** Leave A40 at junc 15 sp Fillinges/St Jeoire. Foll D907 thro Taninges E for 11km, sp Samoëns. At W town boundary turn R immed after wooden arch over rd, foll sp to Parc des Loisirs. Site on R after sw pool & park. Lge, mkd pitch, pt shd; htd wc (few cont); chem disp; mv service pnt; baby facs; private san facs avail; shwrs inc; el pnts (6-10A) €3.20-4.75; Indtte (inc dryer); shops 750m; tradsmn; rest, snacks adj; BBQ; playgrnd; htd pool adj; fishing lake adj; tennis; cycle hire; htd ski storage/drying rm; Samoëns ski gondola 150m; wifi; TV rm; 5% statics; dogs €2; phone; poss cr; adv bkg ess high ssn; quiet; ccard acc; red CKE/CCI. "Friendly staff; some facs ltd low ssn; on arr, park on rdside bef checking in; excel winter site." ♦ € 30.70 2014*

⊞ **SAMOENS** *9A3* (5km W Rural) *46.08944, 6.67874* **Camp Municipal Lac et Montagne, 74440 Verchaix [tel/fax 04 50 90 10 12; www.verchaix.com]** Fr Taninges take D907 sp Samoëns for 6km, site to R of main rd in Verchaix. Med, shd; shwrs; el pnts (10A) €4.10; Indtte (inc dryer); shops nr; rest, bar adj; playgrnd; rv & lake adj; tennis; some statics; dogs €1.40; phone; adv bkg; quiet. "Gd touring base." ♦ € 8.50 2009*

SAMPZON see Vallon Pont d'Arc *9D2*

SERRIERES *9C2* (3km W Rural) *45.30872, 4.74622* **Camping Le Bas Larin, 88 Route de Larin Le Bas, 07340 Félines [tel/fax 04 75 34 87 93 or 06 80 05 13 89 (mob); camping.baslarin@wanadoo.fr; www.camping-bas-larin.com]** Exit A7 junc 12 Chanas or fr N7, exit at Serrières onto D1082; cross canal & rv; cont over rndabt up winding hill, camp on L nr hill top. Sp fr N7 & D1082, but easily missed - foll sp Safari de Peaugres. Med, terr, shd; wc; chem disp; baby facs; shwrs inc; el pnts (4-10A) €2.50-3.50; Indtte; shops 2km; rest adj; playgrnd; pool; paddling pool; games area; games rm; wifi; entmnt; some statics; dogs free; Eng spkn; some rd noise; CKE/CCI. "Friendly, family-run site; beautiful views; helpful staff; easy access pitches; popular with Dutch; excel." ♦ 1 Apr-30 Sep. € 17.00 2011*

SEVRIER see Annecy *9B3*

SEYSSEL *9B3* (400m N Urban) *45.96324, 5.83574* **Camping Le Nant Matraz, 15 Route de Genève, 74910 Seyssel [tel/fax 04 50 59 03 68]** On L of D992 sp Frangy. Lge supmkt opp. Med, mkd pitch, pt shd; wc (some cont); chem disp; mv service pnt; shwrs inc; el pnts (6A) inc; Indtte; shop adj; snacks; bar; BBQ; playgrnd; pool in town; boat hire; rv fishing; games rm; some statics; dogs; Eng spkn; adv bkg; rd/rlwy noise; ccard acc. "On banks of Rv Rhône." 1 Apr-30 Sep. € 15.00 2010*

⊞ **TAIN L'HERMITAGE** *9C2* (5km NE Rural) *45.10715, 4.89105* **Camping Chante-Merle, 26600 Chantemerle-les-Blés [04 75 07 49 73; fax 04 75 07 45 15; campingchantemerle@wanadoo.fr; www.campingchante-merle.fr/]** Exit A7 at Tain-l'Hermitage. After exit toll turn L twd town, next turn R (D109) to Chantemerle; site sp. Cont for 5km, site on L. Sm, hdg/mkd pitch, pt shd; htd wc; chem disp; serviced pitches; baby facs; shwrs inc; el pnts (10A) €4.50; Indtte; shops 300m; tradsmn; rest & snacks high ssn; bar; playgrnd; pool; tennis 500m; wifi; 10% statics; dogs €2; site clsd Jan; adv bkg ess; quiet but some rd noise; CKE/CCI. "Helpful manager; popular site; excel facs." ♦ € 23.00 2012*

TAIN L'HERMITAGE *9C2* (500m SE Urban) *45.06727, 4.84880* **Camp Municipal Les Lucs, 24 Ave du Président Roosevelt, 26600 Tain-l'Hermitage [tel/fax 04 75 08 32 82 or 04 75 08 30 32; camping.tainlhermitage@wanadoo.fr; www.campingleslucs.fr]** Fr N or S exit A7 junc 13 dir Tain-l'Hermitage onto N7. Cont N twd town cent; at fuel stn on R & Netto supmkt sp prepare to turn L in 80m; ent to site in 35m. Fr N on N7 prepare to turn R after fuel stn on R. Site alongside Rv Rhône via gates (locked o/night). Well sp adj sw pool/petrol stn. Med, hdg/mkd pitch, some hdstg, pt shd; wc (some cont); chem disp; mv service pnt; shwrs inc; el pnts (6A) inc (poss rev pol); Indtte; shops, snacks adj; playgrnd; dogs €1.40; phone; no twin-axles; Eng spkn; some rd/rlwy noise; red low ssn; ccard not acc; CKE/CCI. "Pretty, well-kept, well-run site by Rhône; lovely views; secure site; friendly staff; excel, clean, new (2014) san facs; no twin-axles, no c'vans over 5.50m & no m'vans over 6m (poss high ssn only); rvside walk to town; Valrhona chocolate factory shop nrby; mkt Sat; gd touring base; popular NH; highly rec; access gate with PIN." ♦ ltd 15 Mar-15 Oct. € 24.00 2014*

⊞ **TANINGES** *9A3* (1km S Rural) *46.09899, 6.58806* **Camp Municipal des Thézières, Les Vernays-sous-la-Ville, 74440 Taninges [04 50 34 25 59; fax 04 50 34 39 78; camping.taninges@wanadoo.fr; www.taninges.com]** Take D902 N fr Cluses; site 1km S of Taninges on L - just after 'Taninges' sp on ent town boundary; sp Camping-Caravaneige. Lge, pt shd; htd wc (some cont); chem disp; mv service pnt; shwrs inc; el pnts (6-10A) €2.50-4; Indtte (inc dryer); ltd shop; tradsmn; shops, rest, snacks, bar 1km; BBQ; playgrnd; pool at Samoens 11km; tennis; wifi; TV rm; dogs €1.30; phone; poss cr; Eng spkn; quiet; ccard acc; CKE/CCI. "Splendid site with magnificent views; peaceful & well-kept; lge pitches; friendly, helpful staff; excel facs; conv for N Haute Savoie & Switzerland to Lake Geneva; excel." ♦ € 22.60 2012*

THOISSEY *9A2* (1km SW Rural) *46.16512, 4.79257* **Camping Hortus - La Route des Vins, Ave du Port, 01140 Thoissey [04 74 04 02 97; info@camping-hortus.com; www.camping-hortus.com]** S on D306 turn L onto D9 thro Dracé. Turn sharp R immed after x-ing Rv Saône, site sp. Lge, mkd pitch, pt shd; htd wc; mv service pnt; shwrs inc; el pnts (10A) inc; lndtte; shop; rest, snacks; bar; BBQ; playgrnd; htd pool; paddling pool; rv beach & sw adj; fishing; watersports; tennis; games rm; games area; wifi; entmnt; TV; 2% statics; dogs €2; phone; poss cr; Eng spkn; adv bkg; quiet; ccard acc; CKE/CCI. "Vg touring base for vineyards; lge pitches; vg, modern san facs." ♦ 23 Apr-30 Sep. € 20.00 2011*

THONON LES BAINS *9A3* (3km NE Rural) *46.39944, 6.50416* **Camping Le Saint Disdille, 117 Ave de St Disdille, 74200 Thonon-Les-Bains [04 50 71 14 11; fax 04 50 71 93 67; camping@disdille.com; www.disdille.com]** Exit A41/A40 junc 14 Annemasse onto D1005 & foll sp Thonon twd Evian. At Vongy rndabt foll sp St Disdille & site. Site 200m fr Lake Geneva. V lge, mkd pitch, shd; wc; baby facs; shwrs; el pnts (6-10A) €4; gas; lndtte (inc dryer); shop; tradsmn; rest, snacks; bar; BBQ; playgrnd; lake sw & beach 200m; fishing; watersports; tennis; cycle hire; games area; games rm; wifi; entmnt; 30% statics; dogs €3; adv bkg ess; quiet; ccard acc; red low ssn; CKE/CCI. "Well-situated; well-equipped site; gd touring base for v nice area." ♦ 1 Apr-30 Sep. € 35.00 2013*

See advertisement

THONON LES BAINS *9A3* (10km W Rural) *46.35638, 6.35250* **Campéole Camping La Pinède, 74140 Excenevex [04 50 72 85 05 or 04 50 72 81 27 (Mairie); fax 04 50 72 93 00; pinede@campeole.com; www.camping-lac-leman.info / www.campeole.com]** On D1005 to Geneva, 10km fr Thonon, turn R at Camping sp. V lge, htd/mkd pitch, shd; htd wc; child facs; shwrs inc; chem disp; mv service pnt; child facs; el pnts (10A) €4.10; gas; lndtte; shop; rest, snacks; bar; BBQ; playgrnd; sports area; tennis; lake sw, fishing, watersports & sand beach adj; horseriding 1km; entmnt; internet; TV; 75% statics; dogs €3.50; poss cr; adv bkg; quiet; red low ssn. "Excel lakeside site; friendly & efficient staff." 2 Apr-10 Sep. € 24.00 (CChq acc) 2013*

⊞ **TOURNON SUR RHONE** *9C2* (500m N Rural) *45.07000, 4.83000* **FFCC Camping de Tournon HPA, Quai Farconnet, 1 Promenade Roche-de-France, 07300 Tournon-sur-Rhône [tel/fax 04 75 08 05 28; camping@camping-tournon.com; www.camping-tournon.fr]** Fr Tain l'Hermitage cross Rhône, turn R onto D86; in approx 1km R at end of car park; turn L after 50m, site on R on Rv Rhône. Or fr N on D86, sp on L by car park. Med, shd; htd wc (some cont); chem disp; mv service pnt; shwrs inc; el pnts (6-10A) €4-6.50; gas; lndtte; shop, rest, snacks & bar nr; playgrnd; pool 1km; canoeing; internet; some statics; dogs €2; phone; m'van o'night area; c'van storage avail; poss cr; Eng spkn; adv bkg rec; ccard not acc high ssn; red long stay/low ssn; CKE/CCI. "Pleasant, well-kept site in wooded location; rvside pitches; friendly owners; clean, dated san facs (unisex low ssn); some sm pitches & narr site rds poss diff lge o'fits; gd security; footbdge to Tain-l'Hermitage; fr mid-Jun rock concerts poss held nrby at w/end; gd; conv NH." ♦ € 25.00 2014*

TOURNON SUR RHONE *9C2* (6km N Rural) *45.12116, 4.80023* **FFCC Camping L'Iserand, Rue Royal, 07610 Vion [04 75 08 01 73; fax 04 75 08 55 82; iserand@tele2.fr; www.iserandcampingardeche.com]** Take D86 N fr Tournon, site 1km N of Vion on L. Med, hdg/mkd pitch, sl, terr, pt shd; htd wc (some cont); chem disp; mv service pnt; baby facs; shwrs inc; el pnts (10A) €3; gas; lndtte; shop on site & 1km; tradsmn; rest 1km; snacks; bar; BBQ; playgrnd; pool; beach; cycle hire; canoeing 1km; entmnt; TV rm; 20% statics; dogs €3; bus 1km; phone; poss cr; adv bkg; Eng spkn; rd & rlwy noise; red low ssn; CKE/CCI. "Excel site; friendly owner lives on site - will take low ssn visitors." 7 Apr-30 Sep. € 16.00 (CChq acc) 2009*

TOURNON SUR RHONE *9C2* (3km W Rural) *45.06650, 4.78830* **FFCC Camping Le Manoir, 222 Route de Lamastre, 07300 Tournon-sur-Rhône [04 75 08 02 50 or 06 70 00 06 13 (mob); fax 04 75 08 57 10; info@lemanoir-ardeche.com; www.lemanoir-ardeche.com]** Leave Tournon on D532 just bef x-ing rv, dir Lamastre. Site on R after 3km (4th site). Med, mkd pitch, pt shd; wc (50% cont); chem disp; mv service pnt; shwrs inc; el pnts (10A) €3.60; lndtte; shop 2.5km; tradsmn; snacks; bar; BBQ; playgrnd; pool; rv adj; TV rm; entmnt; 70% statics; dogs €2.50; phone; poss cr; adv bkg; quiet but some rd noise; ccard acc; red CKE/CCI. "Pleasant, family-run, rvside site; friendly, hard-working staff; gd facs; gd walking, vineyard tours; narr access to pitches poss diff lge o'fits; vg." ♦ 1 Apr-30 Sep. € 18.50 2010*

RHONE-ALPS

TOURNON SUR RHONE *9C2* (4km W Rural) *45.06786, 4.78516* **Camping Le Castelet, 113 Route du Grand Pont, 07300 St Jean-de-Muzols [04 75 08 09 48; fax 04 75 08 49 60; courrier@camping-lecastelet.com; www.camping-lecastelet.com]** Exit Tournon on D86 N; in 500m turn L on D532 twd Lamastre; in 4km turn R on D532 over bdge & turn immed R into site. Med, mkd pitch, some hdstg, terr, pt shd; wc (some cont); chem disp; baby facs; shwrs inc; el pnts (10A) €4.50; gas; Indtte; shop on site & supmkt 4km; tradsmn; bar; BBQ; playgrnd; pool; paddling pool; fishing; games rm; wifi; entmnt; TV; dogs €2; adv bkg; quiet, but some rd noise; red low ssn; ccard not acc. "Lovely, family-run site in beautiful setting; excel facs." 5 Apr-13 Sep. € 37.00 2014*

TREPT *9B2* (2.5km E Rural) *45.68701, 5.35190* **Camping les 3 Lacs du Soleil, La Plaine de Serrières, 38460 Trept [04 74 92 92 06; fax 04 74 92 93 35; info@les3lacsdusoleil.com; www.camping-les3lacsdusoleil.com]** Exit A432 at junc 3 or 3 & head twd Crémieu then Morestel. Trept bet these 2 towns on D517, site sp by lakes. Lge, pt shd; wc; chem disp; baby facs; shwrs inc; el pnts (6A) inc; Indtte (inc dryer); shop; tradsmn; rest, snacks; bar; BBQ (gas); playgrnd; pool complex; paddling pool; waterslides; lake sw & beach adj; fishing; tennis; archery; fitness rm; games area; horseriding 2km; wifi; entmnt; TV rm; 5% statics; dogs €2.50; phone; adv bkg; Eng spkn; quiet; ccard acc; red low ssn. "Gd family site; gd, modern san facs." ♦ 27 Apr-14 Sep. € 35.50 2011*

See advert on next page

TREVOUX see Villefranche sur Saône *9B2*

TULETTE *9D2* (2.2km S Rural) *44.26485, 4.93180* **Camping Les Rives de L'Aygues, 142 chemin des rives de l'Eygues, 26790 Tulette [tel/fax 04 75 98 37 50; camping.aygues@wanadoo.fr; www.lesrivesdelaygues.com]** Exit D94 at Tulette onto D193 S; site in 2.2km on L. Site sp. Med, hdg/mkd pitch, hdstg, shd; wc; chem disp; shwrs inc; el pnts (6A) €4.20; gas; tradsmn; snacks; bar; playgrnd; htd pool; direct access to rv; games area; internet; 5% statics; dogs €2.50; phone; Eng spkn; adv bkg; quiet; ccard acc; red low ssn; CKE/CCI. "Lovely, peaceful, family-run site in woodland by Rv Aygue; gd san facs; gd pool; vineyards & lavendar fields nr; excel." ♦ ltd 1 May-25 Sep. € 35.20 2013*

UGINE *9B3* (7km NW Rural) *45.76141, 6.33702* **Camping Champ Tillet, 28 Rue Chenevier, 74210 Marlens [04 50 44 33 74; fax 04 50 66 23 44; duchamptillet@wanadoo.fr; www.champtillet.com]** D1508 S fr Annecy after leaving Lake. Take by-pass past Faverges dir Ugine. After rndabt, site on R at junc bef Marlens, sp. Med, hdg pitch, pt shd; htd wc (some cont); chem disp (wc); baby facs; shwrs inc; el pnts (10A) €4. (poss rev pol); Indtte (inc dryer); shops adj; tradsmn; supmkts 3km; rest, snacks; playgrnd; pool; paddling pool; rv fishing 500m; cycle hire; wifi; some statics; dogs €1; some rd noise - adj extensive cycle track; red low ssn; ccard acc; CKE/CCI. "Gd walks; lovely views; barrier clsd 2300-0700; helpful staff; shops 4km." ♦ 1 Apr-30 Sep. € 39.00 2013*

VAL D'ISERE *9B4* (1km E Rural) *45.44622, 6.99218* **Camping Les Richardes, Le Laisinant, 73150 Val-d'Isère [tel/fax 04 79 06 26 60; campinglesrichardes@free.fr; http://campinglesrichardes.free.fr]** Leave Val d'Isère going E twds Col de l'Iseran on D902, site on R 1.5km bef Le Fornet vill. Med, pt sl, unshd; wc; shwrs €1; el pnts (3-6A) €1.90-3.80; pool 1.5km; dogs €0.50; quiet; CKE/CCI. "Peaceful site; delightful owner." 15 Jun-15 Sep. € 10.00 2009*

VALENCE *9C2* (7.5km N Rural) *44.99723, 4.89383* **Camping Le Soleil Fruité, Les Pêches, 26300 Chateauneuf-sur-Isère [04 75 84 19 70; fax 04 75 78 05 85; contact@lesoleilfruite.com; www.lesoleilfruite.com]** Exit A7 junc 14 Valence Nord onto D67 sp Chateauneuf-sur-Isère, site sp to W of village. Alt rte foll N7 turn onto D877 twrds Chateauneuf and foll sp to campsite. Med, hdg/mkd pitch, pt shd; wc; baby facs; chem disp; mv service pnt; shwrs inc; el pnts (6A) €4; Indtte (inc dryer); shop 8km; tradsmn; rest, snacks; bar; BBQ; playgrnd; pool; paddling pool; wifi; entmnt; TV; 15% statics; dogs €2 (not acc high ssn); no twin-axles; phone; poss cr; Eng spkn; adv bkg; quiet; ccard acc; red low ssn; CKE/CCI. "Vg, family-run site; lge pitches; friendly owner; excel, clean, modern san facs; rest/takeaway open early Jun (2011); ltd water pnts; cycle friendly; gd bar/rest." ♦ 26 Apr-15 Sep. € 44.00 2014*

VALENCE *9C2* (12km SE Rural) *44.91560, 5.06520* **Camping Sunêlia Le Grand Lierne, 26120 Chabeuil [04 75 59 83 14; fax 04 75 59 87 95; grand-lierne@franceloc.fr; www.grandlierne.com / www.campings-franceloc.fr]** Fr A7 S take Valence Sud exit dir Grenoble. After 8km take D68 on R twd Chabeuil. Turn L at rndabt on o'skts of vill & foll site sp on by-pass; do not go into vill. On arr, park in lay-by at end of app rd & walk to recep to book in. Or app off D125 NE of Chabeuil. Lge, some mkd pitch, hdstg, shd; wc; chem disp; baby facs; shwrs inc; el pnts (6-10A) €4-8; gas; Indtte; shop; rest, snacks; bar; BBQ (gas/elec); playgrnd; htd pool; whirlpool; waterslide; paddling pool; archery; golf 3km; games area; wifi; entmnt; games/TV rm; 80% statics; dogs €5 (no dogs Jul/Aug): no c'vans/m'vans over 7m high ssn; poss cr; Eng spkn; adv bkg rec; poss noisy high ssn; ccard acc; red low ssn; CKE/CCI. "Site in oak forest; friendly staff; clean san facs; gd facs & all-round entmnt; some sm pitches, poss diff lge o'fits; no twin-axles; gd for families; mkt Chabeuil Tue, mkt Valence Thur; gd but regimented!" ♦ 22 Apr-18 Sep. € 31.00 2010*

⊞ **VALENCE** *9C2* (3km S Urban) *44.91871, 4.87561* **Camp Municipal de l'Epervière, Chemin de l'Epervière, 26000 Valence [04 75 42 32 00; fax 04 75 56 20 67; eperviere26@orange.fr; www.valence-espaces-evenements.com]** Exit A7 at Valence Sud & turn N onto N7, site well sp fr N7. When app fr S on N7 turn L at traff lts 500m after Géant supmkt. Fr N on N7 look for R turn 2km S of Valence. Lge, hdstg, pt shd; htd wc; mv service pnt; shwrs inc; el pnts (10A) €4.90 (poss rev pol); Indtte; supmkt 500m; rest adj; rest, snacks; bar; playgrnd; htd pool; fishing in Rv Rhône; watersports cent adj; games area; TV; 30% statics; site clsd mid-Dec to mid-Jan; poss cr; Eng spkn; no adv bkg; rd noise; ccard acc; red low ssn; CKE/CCI. "Generous pitches in wooded area; clean, dated san facs; office opp side of rd behind other buildings & up steps; pool in hotel complex; poss unkempt low ssn; poss travellers; excel; v clean, bright, airy san facs; recep now at ent." ♦ ltd 17 Jan-16 Dec. € 17.50 2013*

VALENCE *9C2* (9km NW Rural) *45.00726, 4.84862* **Camp Municipal Les Vernes, 26600 La Roche-de-Glun [04 75 84 54 11 or 04 75 84 60 52 (Mairie); mairie.rdg@wanadoo.fr; www.ladrometourisme.com]** Turn W off N7 at Pont-d'Isère. On ent La Roche-de-Glun foll camping sp. Sm, hdg/mkd pitch, shd; wc (some cont); serviced pitches; chem disp; shwrs inc; el pnts (10A) €1.40; Indtte; shop 500m; BBQ; htd pool adj in ssn inc; sports cent adj; 50% statics; phone; poss cr; adv bkg; quiet; no ccard acc; red low ssn; CKE/CCI. "Pleasant site; friendly resident warden; gd, clean san facs; vg municipal pool adj; barrier clsd 2200-0700; vg value; vg NH." ♦ 1 May-30 Sep. € 14.00 2011*

VALLIERES see Rumilly *9B3*

VALLOIRE *9C3* (500m N Rural) *45.17000, 6.42960* **Camp Caravaneige Municipal Ste Thècle, Route des Villards, 73450 Valloire [04 79 83 30 11; fax 04 79 83 35 13; camping-caravaneige@valloire.net; www.valloire.net]** Exit A43 junc 29 onto D306 to St Michel-de-Maurienne, then onto D902 to Valloire. At vill mkt turn R over rv to site. Climb fr valley 15% gradient max. Med, mkd pitch, some hdstg, unshd; htd wc (cont); chem disp; mv service pnt; baby facs; fam bthrm; shwrs inc; el pnts (13A) €3.60; Indtte (inc dryer); shop 300m; rest 500m; bar 200m; playgrnd; pool; paddling pool; waterslide; fishing; tennis; fitness rm; wifi; TV rm; dogs free; phone 100m; bus; Eng spkn; adv bkg; quiet; red long stay; ccard acc. "Superb mountain scenery for walking & cycling; excel." ♦ ltd 12 Dec-23 Apr & 1 Jun-30 Sep. € 18.00 2010*

VALLON PONT D'ARC *9D2* (6km N Rural) *44.46611, 4.4125* **Domaine de Chadeyron, 07150 Lagorce Vallon-Pont-d'Arc [04 75 88 04 81 or 06 70 67 88 78 (mob); infos@campingchadeyron.com; www.campingdechadeyron.com]** Fr S Vallon Pont d'Arc take D390 sp St Remeze/Lagorce. R onto D1, foll sp to site. (NB Rd thro vill narr). Fr N (rec large o'fits) Vogue foll D579 sp Ruoms/Vallon Pont d'Arc, after 1.5km turn L D1 Rochecolmbe/Lagorce, 8km to site. Sm, mkd pitch, pt shd; wc; chem disp; mv service pnt; baby facs; shwr; el pnts (10A); Indtte; tradsmn; snack; bar; playgrnd; htd pool; paddling pool; rv 7km; entmnt; wifi; tv; 50% statics; dogs; twin axles; Eng spkn; adv bkg; CCI. "Gd walks; canoeing; vg site." ♦ ltd 5 Apr-12 Oct. € 41.00 2014*

VALLON PONT D'ARC *9D2* (9km E Rural) *44.39146, 4.51057* **Camping Carrefour de l'Ardèche, Route de Bourg-St Andéol, Quartier Gourdaud, 07700 St Remèze [04 75 04 15 75; fax 04 75 04 35 05; carrefourardeche@yahoo.fr; www.ardechecamping.net]** D4 E fr Vallon-Pont-d'Arc. Site on L on bend 500m after St Remèze vill. Med, mkd pitch, pt shd; wc; chem disp; baby facs; shwrs inc; el pnts (6A) €3.50; gas; Indtte; shop; snacks; bar; playgrnd; pool; cycle hire; canoeing; fishing 5km; entmnt; TV; dogs €2.50; adv bkg; quiet; ccard acc. "Surrounded by vineyards; vg." ♦ 15 Apr-30 Sep. € 20.00 2009*

VALLON PONT D'ARC *9D2* (1km SE Rural) *44.39783, 4.40005* **Camping Le Provençal, Route des Gorges, 07150 Vallon-Pont-d'Arc [04 75 88 00 48; fax 04 75 88 02 00; camping.le.provencal@wanadoo.fr; www.camping-le-provencal.fr]** Fr Aubenas take D579 thro Vallon-Pont-d'Arc to S. Turn L on D290 N of rv; site on R in 500m (middle of 3 sites). Fr Alès, N on D904/D104. At St Ambroix turn R onto D51 then D579 to Vallon-Pont-d'Arc. Lge, pt shd; htd wc; shwrs inc; el pnts (8A) €3.90; gas; Indtte; shop; rest, snacks; bar; playgrnd; htd pool; canoeing; fishing; sailing; tennis; internet; some statics; dogs €4; poss cr; Eng spkn; adv bkg; quiet; ccard acc. "Friendly, helpful staff; site at NW end of spectacular Gorges de l'Ardèche." ♦ 13 Apr-20 Sep. € 59.00 2014*

VALLON PONT D'ARC *9D2* (1km SE Rural) *44.39777, 4.39861* **Camping Nature Park L'Ardéchois, Route des Gorges de l'Ardèche, 07150 Vallon-Pont-d'Arc [04 75 88 06 63; fax 04 75 37 14 97; ardecamp@bigfoot.com; www.ardechois-camping.com / www.les-castels.com]** Fr Vallon take D290 Rte des Gorges & site on R bet rd & rv. Lge, hdg/mkd pitch, hdstg, pt sl, shd; htd wc; chem disp; mv service pnt; baby facs; fam bthrm; serviced pitch (extra charge); private bthrm avail (by reservation); shwrs inc; el pnts (6-10A) inc; gas; Indtte (inc dryer); shop; tradsmn; rest, snacks; bar; BBQ; playgrnd; htd pool; paddling pool; tennis; canoeing; games area; cycle hire; internet; entmnt; TV rm; dogs €7.70; Eng spkn; adv bkg; quiet; ccard acc; red low ssn; CKE/CCI. "Spectacular scenery; excel rvside site; helpful staff; price depends on size of pitch; gd san facs; 5 star site." ♦ 15 Apr-30 Sep. € 49.00 2011*

RHONE-ALPS

VALLON PONT D'ARC *9D2* (1.5km SE Rural) *44.39467, 4.39909* **Mondial Camping, Route des Gorges, 07150 Vallon-Pont-d'Arc [04 75 88 00 44; fax 04 75 37 13 73; reserv-info@mondial-camping.com; www.mondial-camping.com]** Fr N exit A7 Montélimar Nord junc 17 onto N7 then N102 dir Le Teil, Villeneuve-de-Berg. Turn S onto D103/ D579 dir Vog é, Ruoms then Vallon-Pont-d'Arc. Take D290, Rte des Gorges de l'Ardèche to site in 1.5km. Fr S exit A7 junc 19 at Bollène, dir Bourg-St Andéol, then D4 to St Remèze & Vallon-Pont-d'Arc. App to Vallon fr E thro Gorges de l'Ardeche not rec. Lge, hdg/mkd pitch, shd; htd wc; chem disp; mv service pnt; serviced pitches (extra charge); baby facs; shwrs inc; el pnts (6-10A) inc; gas; Indtte (inc dryer); shop; rest, snacks; bar; playgrnd; htd pool; paddling pool; waterslides & aqua park; canoeing; tennis adj; games rm; entmnt; internet; TV; some statics; dogs €4.50; phone; poss cr; Eng spkn; adv bkg; quiet; ccard acc; red low ssn/snr citizens; CKE/CCI. "Dir access to rv, Ardèche gorges & canoe facs; gd touring base; excel site." ♦ 1 Apr-30 Sep. € 42.00 2011*

VALLON PONT D'ARC *9D2* (3km SE Rural) *44.39333, 4.39465* **Camping Le Clapas, La Vernède, 07150 Salavas [04 75 37 14 76; contact@camping-le-clapas.com; www.camping-le-clapas.com]** D579 S fr Vallon-Pont-d'Arc to Salavas; 250m after Salavas turn L. Well sp. Med, mkd pitch, pt sl, shd; wc; chem disp; mv service pnt; shwrs inc; el pnts (10A) €3; Indtte; shop on site & 2km; rest 2km; snacks; bar; BBQ (gas/elec); playgrnd; direct access to private rv beach; rv sw; fishing; canoeing; rafting; canyoning; games area; games rm; wifi; entmnt; TV rm; dogs €2; poss cr; Eng spkn; adv bkg; quiet; ccard acc; red low ssn; CKE/CCI. "Beautiful, well-kept site by Rv Ardèche; friendly, helpful staff; poss diff lge o'fits; conv Ardèche Gorges; excel." ♦ ltd 23 Apr-20 Sep. € 20.00 2010*

VALLON PONT D'ARC *9D2* (800m W Rural) *44.40509, 4.37827* **Camping La Roubine, Route de Ruoms, 07150 Vallon-Pont-d'Arc [tel/fax 04 75 88 04 56; roubine.ardeche@wanadoo.fr; www.camping-roubine.com]** Site on W side of Vallon-Pont-d'Arc off D579, well sp by rvside. Med, hdg/mkd pitch, pt shd; htd wc; chem disp; mv service pnt; baby facs; shwrs inc; el pnts (10A) €4.50; gas; Indtte (inc dryer); shop; rest, snacks; bar; playgrnd; htd pool; sm waterslide; rv & sand beach adj; fishing; canoeing; tennis; cycle hire; games area; wifi; entmnt; TV rm; 20% statics; dogs €4; Eng spkn; adv bkg; quiet; ccard acc. "Excel, well-run site in lovely area; excel rest; guided walks high ssn." ♦ 23 Apr-9 Sep. € 47.00 2011*

VALLON PONT D'ARC *9D2* (2km W Rural) *44.41251, 4.35018* **Camping L'Arc en Ciel, Route de Ruoms, Les Mazes, 07150 Vallon-Pont-d'Arc [04 75 88 04 65; fax 04 75 37 16 99; info@arcenciel-camping.com; www.arcenciel-camping.com]** Fr Ruoms take D579 dir Vallon. After 4km bear R for Les Mazes. Pass thro vill & in about 1.7km bear L at camp sp. Lge, pt sl, pt shd; wc; baby facs; shwrs; el pnts (10A) €4; Indtte; shop; rest, snacks; bar; playgrnd; pool; paddling pool; shgl beach & rv; fishing; canoeing; tennis, horseriding nr; games rm; wifi; entmnt; some statics; dogs €3.50; poss cr; adv bkg; quiet; ccard acc; red low ssn. "Pleasant site on rv bank; excel." ♦ 3 Apr-1 Oct. € 31.00 2010*

VALLON PONT D'ARC *9D2* (2km W Rural) *44.40645, 4.36448* **Camping Le Beau Rivage, Les Mazes, 07150 Vallon-Pont-d'Arc [tel/fax 04 75 88 03 54; campingbeaurivage@wanadoo.fr; www.beaurivage-camping.com]** Take D579 W fr Vallon. After approx 1km bear L for Les Mazes at rndabt. After 800m turn L down side rd for site. Med, mkd pitch, terr, shd; wc (some cont); chem disp; baby facs; shwrs; el pnts (6A) €3.90; gas; Indry rm; shop on site & 2km; tradsmn; rest 2km; bar; BBQ; playgrnd; htd pool; fishing; sailing; canoe hire; entmnt; TV rm; 5% statics; dogs €2; phone; poss cr; Eng spkn; ccard acc; red low ssn; CKE/CCI. "Vg quality, clean, family site; dir access to rv; friendly owners; poss diff access some pitches for lge o'fits due trees; excel." 1 May-13 Sep. € 24.00 2009*

VALLON PONT D'ARC *9D2* (2.1km W Rural) *44.41517, 4.37796* **Domaine de L'Esquiras, chemin du Fez, 07150 Vallon-Pont-d'Arc [04 75 88 04 16; esquiras@orange.fr; www.camping-esquiras.com]** Fr Ruoms L at rndabt bef the Lidl nr the vill. Foll sp. Fr Vallon foll dir Ruoms. R after Lidl. Med, mkd pitch, pt sl, pt shd; wc; chem disp; mv service pnt; baby facs; fam bthrm; shwrs inc; gas; Indtte (inc dryer); shops; rest; snacks; bar; pool; rv 1km; games area; games rm; entmnt; internet; wifi; tv rm; wifi; dogs €3.50; phone; twin axles; poss cr; Eng spkn; adv bkg; quiet; ccard acc; red low ssn; CKE/CCI. "Lovely vill (10 min walk) with lots of bars & rest; caving, climbing or kayaking; excel." ♦ 12 Apr-21 Sep. € 45.00 2014*

VALLON PONT D'ARC *9D2* (5km NW Rural) *44.42900, 4.35515* **FLOWER Camping Le Riviera, 07120 Sampzon [04 75 39 67 57; fax 04 75 93 95 57; leriviera@wanadoo.fr; www.campingleriviera.com / www.flowercampings.com]** Fr Ruoms take D579 E twd Vallon-Pont-d'Arc. After 2km turn R over narr bdge twd Sampzon on D161. Site immed on L. Lge, mkd pitch, pt shd; wc; chem disp; mv service pnt; shwrs inc; el pnts (10A) inc; gas; Indtte; shop 100m; rest, snacks; bar; BBQ; playgrnd; pool; paddling pool; rv & shgl beach adj; tennis; games rm; cycle hire; horseriding; entmnt; TV rm; some statics; dogs €4; poss cr; some rd noise; red low ssn. "Attractive pools." 1 Apr-30 Sep. € 40.00 2009*

VALLORCINE *9A4* (1km SE Rural) *46.0242, 6.92370* **Camping des Montets, Le Buet, 74660 Vallorcine [04 50 54 60 45 or 04 50 54 24 13 (LS); fax 04 50 54 01 34; camping.des.montets@wanadoo.fr; http://camping-montets.com]** N fr Chamonix on D1506 via Col de Montets; Le Buet 2km S of Vallorcine; site sp nr Le Buet stn. Fr Martigny (Switzerland) cross border via Col de la Forclaz; then D1506 to Vallorcine; cont to Le Buet in 1km. Med, hdg/mkd pitch, pt shd; wc (some cont); chem disp (wc); shwrs inc; el pnts (3-6A) €2-3; Indtte; shops 1km; sm rest; tradsmn; snacks; tennis adj; no statics; dogs; train 500m; Eng spkn; quiet; red long stay; CKE/CCI. "Site with spectacular views; friendly owners; ltd flat pitches for c'vans/m'vans (others for tents in field), rec phone ahead; clean san facs; excel walking direct fr site; free train pass to Chamonix; vg." ♦ ltd 1 Jun-15 Sep. € 16.00 2011*

VALREAS *9D2* (8km W Rural) *44.41131, 4.89112* **Camping Les Truffières, 1100 Chemin de Bellevue-d'Air, Nachony, 26230 Grignan [tel/fax 04 75 46 93 62; info@lestruffieres.com; www.lestruffieres.com]** Fr A7 take D133 E twds Grignan. On W o'skts of vill turn S on D71. In 1km turn L at sp. Site is 200m on R. Fr Nyons take D538 W to Grignan. Sm, mkd pitch, shd; wc; chem disp; mv service pnt; shwrs inc; el pnts (10A) €4.20; gas; Indtte; shop 1km; tradsmn, rest, snacks high ssn; bar; communal BBQ only; playgrnd; pool; fishing; 5% statics; no dogs; Eng spkn; adv bkg; quiet; red low ssn; CKE/CCI. "Excel, well-wooded site by lavendar fields; pleasant owners; immac san facs; gd pool; some pitches diff access; site poss dusty; 20 min stroll to town." ♦ 20 Apr-30 Sep. € 31.50 2013*

VALREAS *9D2* (9.4km NW Rural) *44.41741, 4.90935* **Camp Municipal La Rochecourbière, Ave du Grillon, 26230 Grignan [04 75 46 50 06; mairie.grignan@wanadoo.fr; www.ville-grignan.fr]** Sp at E end of D541 bypass of Grignan; Ave du Grillon runs NE off D541; site in 100m. Do not go into town. Sm, hdg/mkd pitch, pt sl, pt shd; wc (some cont); chem disp (wc); shwrs inc; el pnts inc; dogs; quiet. "Unspoilt, simple site outside ramparts of historic town; clean, modern san facs; if office clsd site self or contact Mairie; gd." ♦ 1 Jul-31 Aug. € 13.00 2010*

VANS, LES *9D1* (3.5km NW Rural) *44.41613, 4.09229* **Camping Le Mas du Serre, 07140 Gravières [04 75 37 33 84; camping-le-mas-du-serre@wanadoo.fr; www.campinglemasduserre.com]** NW fr Les Vans on D901 dir Villefort; in 2km turn R onto D113 dir Gravières; in 1.5km turn R bef bdge. NB Awkward turn downhill. Foll site sp. Recep in cent of site. Med, pt sl, pt terr, hdstg, shd; wc (some cont); chem disp (wc); shwrs inc; el pnts (6A) €3 (long lead poss req); supmkt 4km; snacks; bar; pool; paddling pool; boating on rv nrby; canyoning & caves nrby; games area; entmnt; 10% statics; dogs €1.50; adv bkg; quiet; red low ssn. "Beautiful scenery; san facs clean but ltd; gd walking." 1 Apr-1 Oct. € 18.50 2009*

VANS, LES *9D1* (5km NW Rural) *44.43722, 4.08028* **Camping Les Gorges de Chassezac, Champ d'Eynes, 07140 Malarce-sur-la-Thines [04 75 39 45 12; campinggorgeschassezac@wanadoo.fr; www.campinggorgeschassezac.com]** Fr Les Vans cent, dir Gravière, approx 5km thro Gravière cont, site on L. Med, mkd pitch, pt sl, terr, shd; wc (many cont); chem disp; shwrs; el pnts (6A) €3; gas; Indtte; shop; tradsmn; snacks; bar; playgrnd; rv adj; TV; dogs €1; entmnt; poss cr; Eng spkn; adv bkg; quiet; CKE/CCI. "Peaceful site." ♦ ltd 1 May-31 Aug. € 14.00 2010*

VARCES ALLIERES ET RISSET see Grenoble *9C3*

VENOSC see Bourg d'Oisans, Le *9C3*

VERCHAIX see Samoëns *9A3*

VERNIOZ see Auberives sur Varèze *9B2*

⊞ **VILLARD DE LANS** *9C3* (800m N Rural) *45.07750, 5.55620* **Camping Caravaneige L'Oursière, 38250 Villard-de-Lans [04 76 95 14 77; fax 04 76 95 58 11; oursiere@franceloc.fr; www.camping-oursiere.fr]** Site clearly visible on app to town fr D531 Gorges d'Engins rd (13km SW Grenoble). App fr W on D531 not rec for c'vans & m'vans due o'hangs. Lge, terr, unshd; htd wc (some cont); chem disp; mv service pnt; baby facs; shwrs inc; el pnts (10A) €4-6; gas; Indtte; shops; snacks; rest; BBQ; playgrnd; pool & waterspark 800m; drying rm; wifi; 20% statics; dogs €5; poss cr; Eng spkn; adv bkg; quiet; ccard acc; red low ssn; CKE/CCI. "Excel all winter sports; under new ownership (2011); friendly owners; san facs need upgrade (2010)." ♦ € 28.00 2014*

⊞ **VILLARD DE LANS** *9C3* (10km N Rural) *45.12951, 5.53215* **Camping Caravaneige Les Buissonnets, 38112 Méaudre [04 76 95 21 04; fax 04 76 95 26 14; camping-les-buissonnets@wanadoo.fr; www.camping-les-buissonnets.com]** Fr Grenoble take D1532 to Sassenage then D531 to Lans-en-Vercors. Turn R at rndabt onto D106, site sp at ent to vill of Méaudre off D106. Approx 30km SW of Grenoble by rd & 18km as crow flies. Med, sl, unshd; htd wc; chem disp; mv service pnt; shwrs inc; el pnts (6-10A) €4-6; Indtte; shops 500m; snacks; rest 500m; pool 300m; playgrnd; games area; bus to ski slopes; clsd 1 Dec-10 Nov; Eng spkn; quiet; higher price in winter. "Gd skiing cent; conv touring Vercours; levellers ess; highly rec." ♦ € 14.50 2010*

> **"That's changed – Should I let The Club know?"**
>
> If you find something on site that's different from the site entry, fill in a report and let us know. See www.caravanclub.co.uk/europereport.

VILLARS LES DOMBES *9A2* (200m S Urban) *45.99763, 5.03163* **Camping Indigo Parc des Oiseaux, 164 Ave des Nations, 01330 Villars-les-Dombes [04 74 98 00 21 or 04 92 75 27 94; fax 04 74 98 05 82; camping@parcdesoiseaux.com; www.camping-indigo.com]** N fr Lyon on N83, site in town cent on R by sw pool. Lge, some hdstg, pt shd; wc; mv service pnt; shwrs inc; el pnts (10A) €4.50; Indtte (inc dryer); shop1km; tradsmn; rest, snacks; bar; BBQ gas; playgrnd; htd pool adj inc; paddling pool; rv fishing adj; tennis; cycle hire; games area; entmnt; 60% statics; dogs €3. "Excel site; lge pitches; modern,gd san facs; gd security; bird park 10 mins walk; popular NH." ♦ 29 Mar - 3 Nov. € 33.00 (CChq acc) 2014*

VILLEFRANCHE SUR SAONE *9B2* (10km E Rural) *45.99104, 4.81802* **FFCC Camp Municipal le Bois de la Dame, 521 Chemin du Bois de la Dame, 01480 Ars-sur-Formans [04 74 00 77 23 or 04 74 00 71 84 (Mairie); fax 04 74 08 10 62; mairie.ars-sur-formans@wanadoo.fr]** Exit A6 junc 31.1 or 31.2 onto D131/D44 E dir Villars-les-Dombes. Site 500m W of Ars-sur-Formans on lake, sp. Med, mkd pitch, pt sl, terr, pt shd; wc (cont); chem disp; shwrs inc; el pnts (6A) €3.10; Indtte; playgrnd; fishing lake; 60% statics; dogs €1.50; poss cr; adv bkg rec high ssn; CKE/CCI. "Average site, but pretty & interesting vill; ltd facs low ssn; no twin-axles; higher pitches have unguarded precipices." ♦ 1 Apr-30 Sep. € 12.00 2011*

VILLEFRANCHE SUR SAONE *9B2* (3km SE Rural) *45.97243, 4.75237* **Camp Municipal La Plage Plan d'Eau, 2788 Route de Riottier, 69400 Villefranche-sur-Saône [04 74 65 33 48; fax 04 74 60 68 18; campingvillefranche@voila.fr; www.villefranche.net]** Exit A6 junc 31.2 Villefranche. Fr N turn R at rndabt, cross over a'route & str over next rndabt; cont to site on R bef Rv Saône. Or fr S turn R at rndabt & cont to site as above. Look for sp on rndabt. Med, shd; wc (some cont); chem disp; mv service pnt; shwrs inc; el pnts (6A) €4; gas; lndry rm; shop 1km; tradsmn; snacks in ssn; bar; lake sw adj; fishing; wifi; 10% statics; adv bkg; quiet; ccard acc; CKE/CCI. "Busy site in gd position; easy access & nr m'way but quiet; a bit run down & san facs not v clean; gd walking; NH only." ♦ 1 May-30 Sep. € 15.60 2011*

VILLEFRANCHE SUR SAONE *9B2* (6km SE Rural) *45.93978, 4.76811* **Camp Municipal La Petite Saône, Rue Robert Baltié, 01600 Trévoux [tel/fax 04 74 00 14 16 or 04 74 08 73 73 (Mairie); mairie.trevoux@wanadoo.fr; http://ladombes.free.fr/Camping/Trevoux.htm]** Fr Villefranche take D306 S to Anse. Turn L onto D39/D6 for Trévoux, site sp in town, on bank of Rv Saône. Lge, pt shd; wc (mainly cont); shwrs; el pnts (6A) inc; shops 1km; playgrnd; rv fishing & sw adj; entmnt; 75% statics; dogs; adv bkg high ssn; quiet; m'van o'night area at ent; red/CKE/CCI. "Spacious rvside site nr vill; helpful staff; clean facs; well maintained; access poss diff lge o'fits due statics; gd cycling rtes nrby; Trévoux interesting history." ♦ 1 Apr-30 Sep. € 10.00 2012*

VILLEFRANCHE SUR SAONE *9B2* (5km S Rural) *45.94050, 4.72680* **Camping Les Portes du Beaujolais, 495 Ave Jean Vacher, 69480 Anse [04 74 67 12 87; fax 04 74 09 90 97; campingbeaujolais@wanadoo.fr; www.camping-beaujolais.com]** Exit A6 junc 31.2 at Villefranche & foll D306 S to Anse (foll sp Champion supmkt). Site well sp off D39, on banks of Rvs Saône & L'Azergues. Lge, hdg/mkd pitch, hdstg, pt shd; htd wc (some cont); chem disp; mv service pnt; shwrs inc; el pnts (10A) €5.50; lndtte; shop; supmkt 700m; snacks; bar; playgrnd; pool; paddling pool; lake sw; cycle hire; wifi; TV rm; 20% statics; dogs €2; phone; Eng spkn; adv bkg; rd noise fr A6 nrby & some rwly noise; red low ssn; CKE/CCI. "Pleasant, friendly site; pitches poss tired end of ssn; some pitches sm, uneven & diff lge o'fits; ltd facs low ssn & poss stretched high ssn; shwrs sometimes cold (2011); pool poss overcrowded; poss muddy when wet; lge field avail at rear but no shd; rvside walk; Anse 10 min walk - bus to Lyons; narr gauge rlwy adj; lge o'night area; conv NH." ♦ 1 Mar-31 Oct. € 37.50 2013*

VILLEFRANCHE SUR SAONE *9B2* (8km NW Rural) *46.04751, 4.66041* **Camping Domaine de la Maison Germain, Route de Salles, Impasse de Charpenay, 69460 Blaceret [04 74 67 56 36; patrick.bossan@wanadoo.fr; www.bossan.tk]** Exit A6 junc 31.1 onto D43 dir Arnas; cont to Blaceret then turn L onto D20; in 500m turn R into lane; recep on R, but site strt on. Sp 'Camping à la Ferme'. Sm, hdg pitch, pt shd; wc; shwrs inc; el pnts (10A) inc; rest; Eng spkn; adv bkg; quiet. "Charming, CL-type site on sm vineyard in heart of Beaujolais region; only 6 pitches, rec phone in adv; san facs clsd in cold weather but site open; site poss open 15 Mar-15 Nov, depending on weather (2011); conv NH." 1 Apr-31 Oct. € 16.00 2011*

VILLENEUVE DE BERG *9D2* (2km N Rural) *44.57251, 4.51041* **Camping Domaine Le Pommier, 07170 Villeneuve-de-Berg [04 75 94 82 81; fax 04 75 94 83 90; info@campinglepommier.com; www.campinglepommier.com]** Site off rndabt at E end of by-pass to Villeneuve-de-Berg on N102. If app fr Aubenas do not go thro town. Steep incline, poss req tractor. Lge, mkd pitch, hdstg, terr, pt sl, pt shd; htd wc; chem disp; mv service pnt; baby facs; fam bthrm; shwrs inc; el pnts (6A) €4; lndtte; supmkt; rest, snacks; bar; BBQ (gas); playgrnd; htd pools; waterslides; paddling pool; tennis; games area; games rm; cycle hire; wifi; entmnt; sound-proofed disco high ssn; TV rm; 30% statics; dogs €4; Eng spkn; adv bkg; quiet; ccard acc; red low ssn/long stay; CKE/CCI. "Vg Dutch-owned site; superb pool complex; excel san facs." ♦ 30 Apr-17 Sep. € 30.50 2010*

VILLENEUVE DE BERG *9D2* (5km E Rural) *44.58722, 4.52565* **FFCC Camping Les Arches, Le Cluzel, Route de Mirabel, 07580 St Jean-le-Centenier [04 75 36 75 45; info@camping-les-arches.com; www.camping-les-arches.com]** Situated midway bet Aubenas & Montélimar. Fr W leave N102 just bef St Jean-le-Centenier onto D458 dir Mirabel, site in 500m nr rlwy arches. Med, hdg/mkd pitch, terr, pt shd; htd wc; chem disp; mv service pnt; baby facs; shwrs inc; el pnts (10A) €3.90; lndtte; shop 5km; tradsmn; rest, snacks; bar; BBQ; playgrnd; rv sw & fishing; canoeing; entmnt; some statics; dogs €1.80; bus adj; poss cr; Eng spkn; quiet; ccard acc. "V pleasant site in 2 sections divided by sm rv; simple & immac; peaceful location; helpful owner." ♦ 24 Apr-20 Sep. € 20.00 2010*

VINSOBRES see Nyons *9D2*

VION see Tournon sur Rhône *9C2*

VIRIEU LE GRAND *9B3* (5km NE Rural) *45.87483, 5.68428* **Camping Le Vaugrais, Chemin de Vaugrais, 01510 Artemare [04 79 87 37 34; fax 04 79 87 37 46; contact@camping-le-vaugrais.fr; www.camping-le-vaugrais.fr]** N fr Belley on D1504 then D904 to Artemare; sp in vill. Well sp fr D904 on rvside. Sm, pt shd, hdg pitch; wc (some cont); chem disp (wc); baby facs; shwrs inc; el pnts (5A) €3.50; lndtte; shop 500m; tradsmn; snacks; bar; BBQ; playgrnd; pool; fishing; wifi; 1% statics; dogs €1; Eng spkn; adv bkg; quiet; red low ssn; CKE/CCI. "Charming site in gd location; some lge pitches with views; friendly owners; clean san facs, poss inadequate high ssn; nice pool; Artemare within walking dist; gd food at hotel in town; excel." ♦ ltd 1 Mar-9 Dec. € 18.00 SBS - M12 2011*

VIZILLE *9C3* (500m N Urban) *45.08660, 5.76814* **FFCC Camping Le Bois de Cornage, Chemin du Camping, 38220 Vizille [tel/fax 04 76 68 12 39; campingvizille@wanadoo.fr; www.campingvizille.com]** Site sp at x-rds of Rte Napoléon, N85 & Rte de Briançon D1091. Site on N o'skirts of town. Well sp. Med, hdg/mkd pitch, pt sl, terr, shd; wc; chem disp; mv service pnt; baby facs; shwrs inc; el pnts (10-16A) €4.50-5.50 (long lead poss req); gas 500m; lndtte; shops 200m; supmkt 500m; tradsmn; rest, snacks; bar; playgrnd; htd pool; gd cycling & climbing nrby; 10% statics; dogs €0.80; no vans over 5m acc; bus; poss v cr; Eng spkn; adv bkg rec high ssn; quiet; red long stay/low ssn; CKE/CCI. "Helpful owner; excel clean facs; mkd walks nrby; poss mosquitoes; frequent buses to Grenoble & Bourg-d'Oisans; vg." 24 Apr-10 Oct. € 16.00 2013*

VIZILLE *9C3* (7km S Rural) *45.02055, 5.77522* **Camp Municipal Napoléon, 38220 Laffrey [04 76 13 36 74; contact@mairie-laffrey.com; www.mairie-laffrey.com]** Exit Grenoble on D1085. S thro Vizille to Laffrey. Steep climb on narr rd. Site 200m S of vill at top of steep hill on Rte Napoléon. Site sp fr town. Med, mkd pitch, pt sl, pt shd; wc; shwrs inc; el pnts (6A) €3.50; Indtte; shop in ssn; snacks; lake sw & watersports; dogs €1.50; some rd noise. "Gd sized pitches." 15 Jun-15 Sep. € 11.50 2009*

VOGUE see Aubenas *9D2*

VONNAS *9A2* (300m NW Rural) *46.22152, 4.98805* **Camp Municipal Le Renom, 240 Ave des Sports, 01540 Vonnas [tel/fax 04 74 50 02 75; campingvonnas@wanadoo.fr; www.vonnas.com]** Fr Bourg-en-Bresse take D1079 W sp Mâcon. In 15km take D26 or D47 S to Vonnas; turn R in town cent (ignore sp on o'skts of town) & site on R in 300m by leisure cent. Med, hdg/mkd pitch, pt shd; wc; chem disp; baby facs; shwrs inc; el pnts (10A) €4.15; Indtte; shop 300m; BBQ; htd pool, tennis adj; rv fishing; 30% statics; dogs €1; quiet. "Warm welcome; interesting town; mkt Thurs; gd site, but expensive." ♦ ltd 30 Mar-29 Sep. € 19.00 (CChq acc) 2013*

VOULTE SUR RHONE, LA *9D2* (4km N Rural) *44.82663, 4.76171* **Camping La Garenne, Quartier La Garenne, 07800 St Laurent-du-Pape [tel/fax 04 75 62 24 62; info@lagarenne.org; www.lagarenne.org]** Well sp fr La Voulte. Fr Valence S on D86 La Voulte, approx 15km turn W onto D120; 300m after St Laurent-du-Pape cent, turn R bef PO. Med, pt terr, pt shd; wc; chem disp; shwrs inc; el pnts (6A) inc (poss rev pol); gas; Indtte; shop; rest, snacks; bar; playgrnd; pool; cycle hire; wifi; entmnt; dogs €2.50; poss v cr; Eng spkn; adv bkg; quiet; red low ssn/long stay; CKE/CCI. "Popular site; friendly, helpful Dutch owners; views fr terr pitches; gd clean san facs; sh walk to vill; vg." ♦ 1 Mar-1 Nov. € 33.50 2013*

VOULTE SUR RHONE, LA *9D2* (4km NE Rural) *44.82004, 4.81960* **Camp Municipal Les Voiliers, 07800 Beauchastel [04 75 62 24 04; fax 04 75 62 42 32; camping.lesvoiliers@orange.fr; www.camping-les-voiliers.fr]** S fr Valence on D86; in 15km at junc with D86E (nr Beauchastel), cont on D86 for 800m; turn L across Rhône in front of hydro stn; site in 400m. Site sp fr N & S on D86 & in Beauchastel. Med, terr, shd; htd wc (most cont); snacks; shwrs inc; el pnts (5A) €3; Indtte; shops 500m; snacks; bar; BBQ; playgrnd; pool; paddling pool; horseriding; canoeing; rv sw; tennis; games area; entmnt; 15% statics; dogs €2.50; poss cr; quiet; red low ssn. "Friendly; gd san facs; NH only." 1 Apr-31 Oct. € 18.00 2011*

YVOIRE see Douvaine *9A3*

Andorra

Regional Introduction

Pyrénées Mountains

Welcome to Andorra

Located in the heart of the Pyrénées, Andorra is known internationally for its ski resorts. The breathtaking mountains are also a paradise for nature lovers, with a large amount of the landscape thickly forested. Take a hike through the woodlands and discover wild rivers, picturesque lakes and stunning rock formations.

The official language of the country is Catalan, although French is also widely spoken. You'll also find many Catalan influences, such as folk music.

Local highlights

Cuisine is also heavily influenced by neighbouring Catalonia. The best way to try authentic Andorran gastronomy is to go to one of the stone-built, often family-run bordas (restaurants).

A speciality drink of the area is the refreshing granizado. It can be made from orange juice, coffee or liqueurs which are blended with crushed ice into a thick purée.

The variety and quality of winter sports sees Andorra host many annual events, such as the Pirena Dog Sled Race in January and ski and snowboarding championships.

Major towns and cities

- Andorra la Vella – the capital city of Andorra.
- Encamp – a town that combines historical buildings with modern architecture.
- Canillo – an old town with a historical 11th-century church.
- La Massana – catch a gondola directly to the Pal ski area.

Regional attractions

- Santa Coloma Church – a historic church with pre-Romanesque architecture.
- Compapedrosa Valley National Park – a stunning national park to explore, perfect for a day of hiking.
- Sant Joan de Caselles – the church dates from the 11th-century and has Italian and German influences in its architecture.
- Casa de la Vall – Andorra's old parliament building, full of historical artefacts and artwork of the region.

Find out more

www.visitandorra.com

Tel: (0)3 76 82 02 14 Andorra Tourist Office

SITES IN ANDORRA

⊞ **ANDORRA LA VELLA** *8G3* (600m S Urban) *42.50166, 1.51527* **Camping Valira, Ave de Salou, AD500 Andorra-la-Vella [tel/fax 722 384; campvalira@andorra.ad; www.campvalira.com]** Site on E site of main rd S fr Andorra-la-Vella; behind sports stadium; clearly sp. Lge, mkd pitch, hdstg, terr, pt shd; htd wc; chem disp; mv service pnt; shwrs inc; el pnts (3-10A) €3.50-6 (no earth); gas; Indtte; shop; rest, snacks; bar; playgrnd; htd covrd pool; paddling pool; wifi; dogs €2.10; Eng spkn; adv bkg; quiet, but some rd noise; red low ssn; CKE/CCI. "Conv NH for shopping; 25mins walk to main shops; excel immac facs; vg rest; beware of sudden storms blowing up." ♦ € 25.00 2012*

⊞ **CANILLO** *8G3* (300m ENE Urban) *42.56740, 1.60235* **Camping Pla, Ctra General s/n, AD100 Canillo [tel 851 333; fax 851 280; campingpla@cyberandorra.com; www.campingpla.cyberandorra.com]** App Canillo fr S, pass Tarrado petrol stn on R; take 1st exit at 1st rndabt opp lge hotel, over bdge & turn L to site. Med, mkd pitch, pt shd; htd wc; chem disp; baby facs; shwrs inc; el pnts (5-10A) €3; gas; Indtte; rest, snacks in town; bar; playgrnd; htd, covrd pool & sports facs in town; ski lift 100m; 75% statics; dogs; bus adj; Eng spkn; adv bkg; ccard not acc. "Excel location for skiing but poss unkempt/untidy low ssn." € 14.00 2011*

MASSANA, LA *8G3* (2km N Rural) *42.56601, 1.52448* **Camping Borda d'Ansalonga, Ctra General del Serrat, AD400 Ordino [tel 850 374; fax 735 400; campingansalonga@andorra.ad; www.campingansalonga.com]** Fr Andorra-la-Vella foll sp La Massana & Ordino. Turn L twd El Serrat, site on R, well sp. Lge, pt shd; htd wc; chem disp; baby facs; shwrs inc; el pnts (10A) €5.60; gas; Indtte; shop; tradsmn; rest; bar; BBQ; playgrnd; pool; games rm; winter statics for skiers; dogs; phone; Eng spkn; quiet; CKE/CCI. "Statics moved to storage area in summer; quieter than sites on main thro rte." 17 Oct-25 Apr & 15 Jun-15 Sep. € 24.00 2011*

⊞ **MASSANA, LA** *8G3* (2km NW Rural) *42.55361, 1.48916* **Camping Xixerella, Ctra de Pal, AD400 Erts [tel 836 613; fax 839 113; c-xixerella@campingxixerella.com; www.campingxixerella.com]** Fr Andorra la Vella take rd for La Massana; fr there foll sps for Xixerella & vill of Pal. Site on L. Med, terr, pt shd; htd wc; chem disp; shwrs; el pnts (5A) €5.90 (poss no earth); Indtte (inc dryer); shop; rest; bar; playgrnd; pool; crazy golf; wifi; entmnt; some statics; dogs €4.20; phone; site clsd Oct; Eng spkn; adv bkg; quiet; ccard acc; red long stay; CKE/CCI. "Lovely site, lovely setting; clean, modern facs; helpful staff; not all pitches level; no drying rm for ski gear; gd mountain walks; long walk to dispose of rubbish; site poss untidy/unkempt low ssn)." ♦ € 25.00 2010*

Far and away the best value
for touring Europe

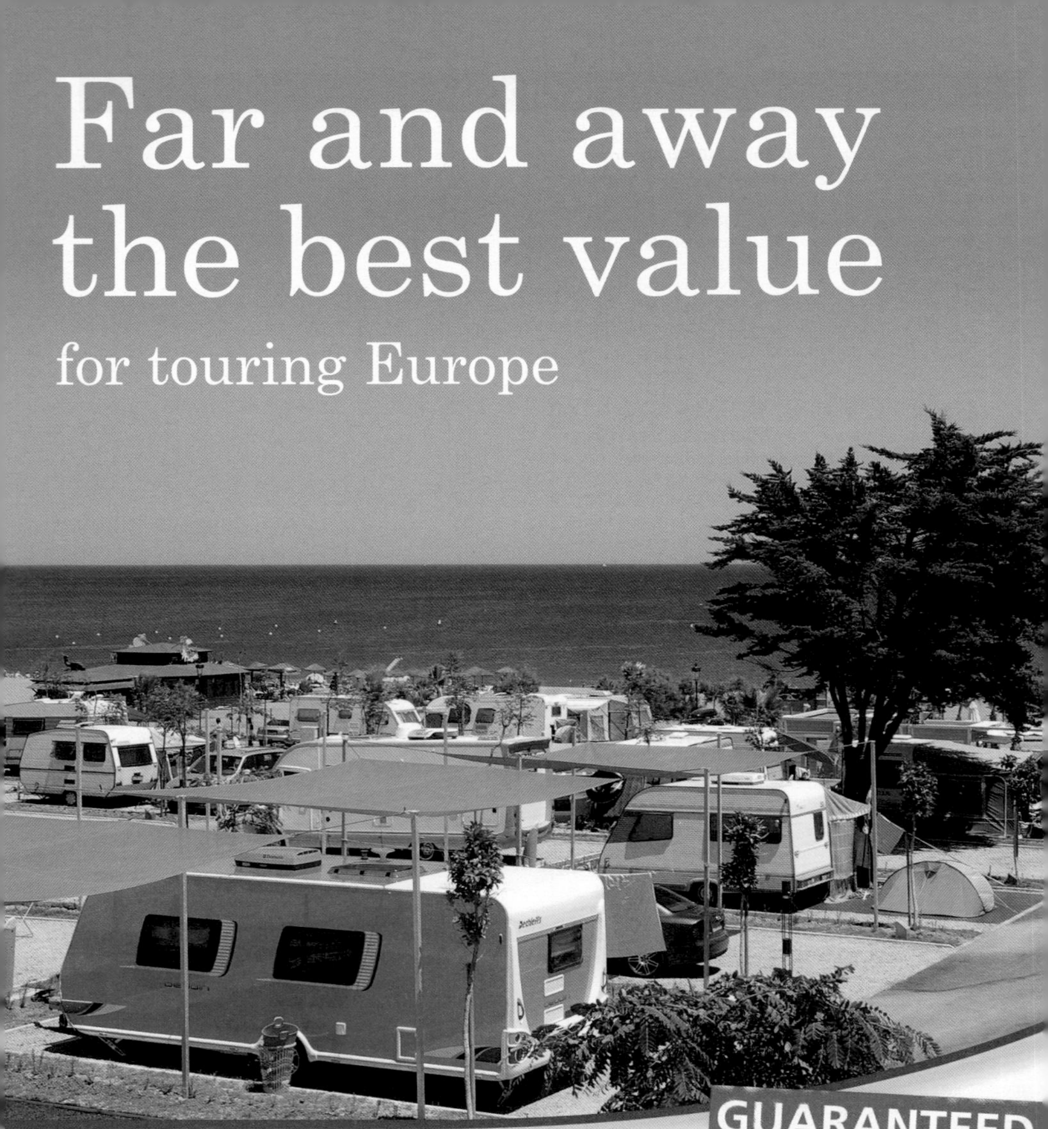

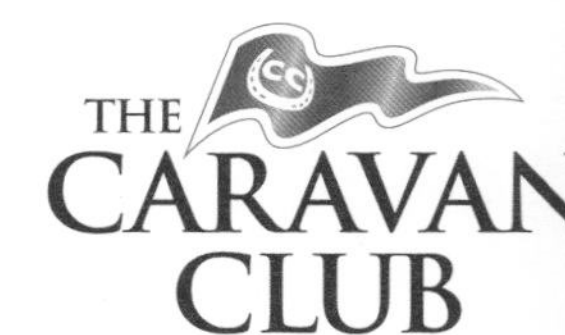

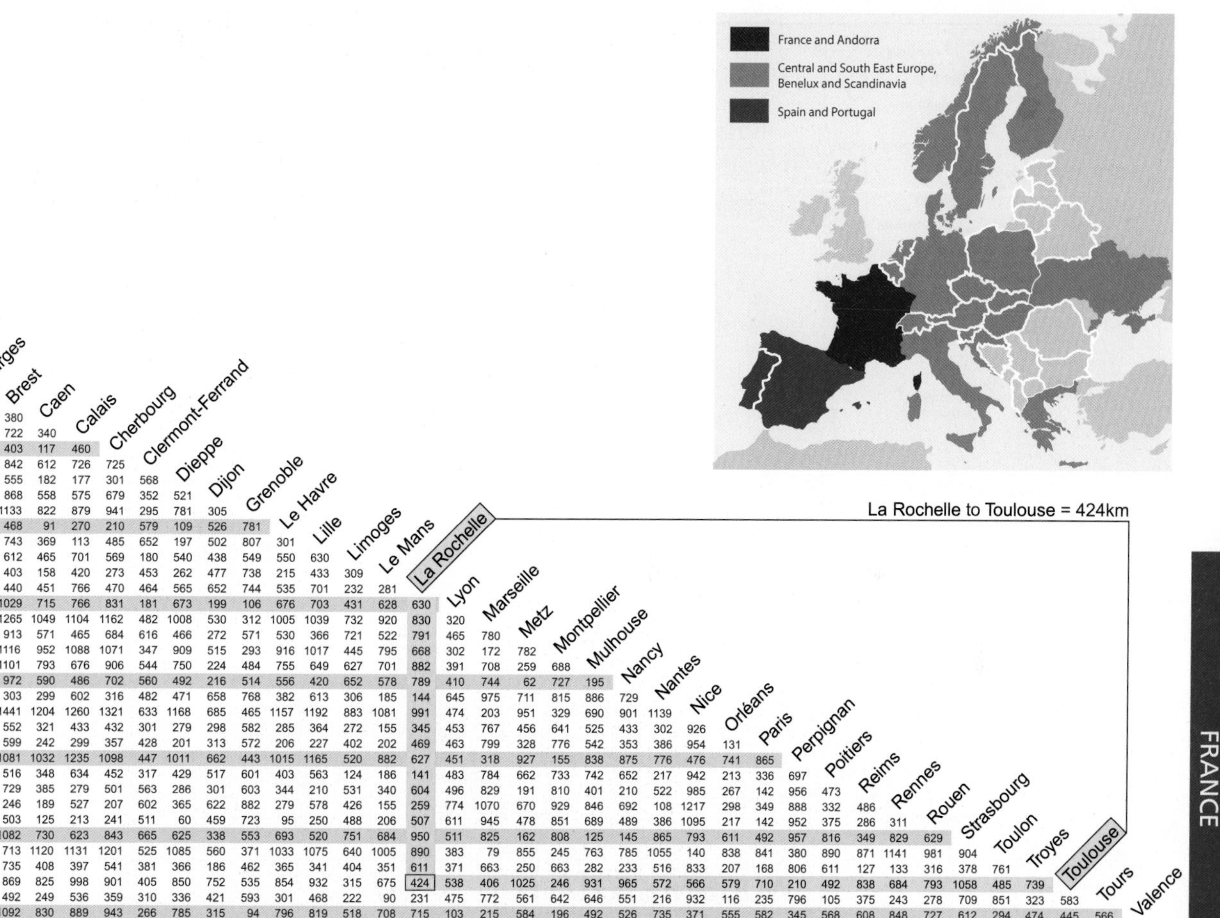

La Rochelle to Toulouse = 424km

	Andorra-la-Vella	Annecy	Bayonne	Besançon	Bordeaux	Bourges	Brest	Caen	Calais	Cherbourg	Clermont-Ferrand	Dieppe	Dijon	Grenoble	Le Havre	Lille	Limoges	Le Mans	La Rochelle	Lyon	Marseille	Metz	Montpellier	Mulhouse	Nancy	Nantes	Nice	Orléans	Paris	Perpignan	Poitiers	Reims	Rennes	Rouen	Strasbourg	Toulon	Troyes	Toulouse	Tours
Annecy	701																																						
Bayonne	415	912																																					
Besançon	861	230	1042																																				
Bordeaux	432	691	190	855																																			
Bourges	678	505	630	544	446																																		
Brest	1051	1092	822	965	632	672																																	
Caen	1026	790	775	659	581	425	380																																
Calais	1141	832	1067	653	884	553	722	340																															
Cherbourg	1085	910	843	773	657	549	403	117	460																														
Clermont-Ferrand	591	332	545	416	356	189	842	612	726	725																													
Dieppe	1052	751	863	613	679	388	555	182	177	301	568																												
Dijon	783	263	955	95	764	246	868	558	575	679	352	521																											
Grenoble	601	106	821	352	776	476	1133	822	879	941	295	781	305																										
Le Havre	1051	754	823	621	632	393	468	91	270	210	579	109	526	781																									
Lille	1105	756	1003	585	812	477	743	369	113	485	652	197	502	807	301																								
Limoges	516	580	409	501	225	189	612	465	701	569	180	540	438	549	550	630																							
Le Mans	873	709	624	569	434	275	403	158	420	273	453	262	477	738	215	433	309																						
La Rochelle	627	782	375	749	183	330	440	451	766	470	464	565	652	744	535	701	232	281																					
Lyon	615	143	828	258	538	353	1029	715	766	831	181	673	199	106	676	703	431	628	630																				
Marseille	477	401	695	572	650	663	1265	1049	1104	1162	482	1008	530	312	1005	1039	732	920	830	320																			
Metz	1084	528	1099	268	902	506	913	571	465	684	616	466	272	571	530	366	721	522	791	465	780																		
Montpellier	320	383	533	559	490	529	1116	952	1088	1071	347	909	515	293	916	1017	445	795	668	302	172	782																	
Mulhouse	989	358	1183	139	990	473	1101	793	676	906	544	750	224	484	755	649	627	701	882	391	708	259	688																
Nancy	1013	472	1081	206	898	480	972	590	486	702	560	492	216	514	556	420	652	578	789	410	744	62	727	195															
Nantes	762	886	522	750	329	369	303	299	602	316	482	471	658	768	382	613	306	185	144	645	975	711	815	886	729														
Nice	641	529	850	732	810	816	1441	1204	1260	1321	633	1168	685	465	1157	1192	883	1081	991	474	203	951	329	690	901	1139													
Orléans	748	532	651	399	462	125	552	321	433	432	301	279	298	582	285	364	272	155	345	453	767	456	641	525	433	302	926												
Paris	875	542	769	405	580	251	599	242	299	357	428	201	313	572	206	227	402	202	469	463	799	328	776	542	353	386	954	131											
Perpignan	158	533	491	702	451	631	1081	1032	1235	1098	447	1011	662	443	1015	1165	520	882	627	451	318	927	155	838	875	776	476	741	865										
Poitiers	663	629	436	613	248	192	516	348	634	452	317	429	517	601	403	563	124	186	141	483	784	662	733	742	652	217	942	213	336	697									
Reims	989	557	911	382	717	386	729	385	279	501	563	286	301	603	344	210	531	340	604	496	829	191	810	401	210	522	985	267	142	956	473								
Rennes	871	846	634	716	445	422	246	189	527	207	602	365	622	882	279	578	426	155	259	774	1070	670	929	846	692	108	1217	298	349	888	332	486							
Rouen	995	690	812	559	622	326	503	125	213	241	511	60	459	723	95	250	488	206	507	611	945	478	851	689	489	386	1095	217	142	952	375	286	311						
Strasbourg	1093	452	1256	261	1066	580	1082	730	623	843	665	625	338	553	693	520	751	684	950	511	825	162	808	125	145	865	793	611	492	957	816	349	829	629					
Toulon	551	480	760	623	718	725	713	1120	1131	1201	525	1085	560	371	1033	1075	640	1005	890	383	79	855	245	763	785	1055	140	838	841	380	890	871	1141	981	904				
Troyes	967	411	911	245	745	235	735	408	397	541	381	366	186	462	365	341	404	351	611	371	663	250	663	282	233	516	833	207	168	806	611	127	133	316	378	761			
Toulouse	203	626	295	802	240	504	869	825	998	901	405	850	752	535	854	932	315	675	424	538	406	1025	246	931	965	572	566	579	710	210	492	838	684	793	1058	485	739		
Tours	771	623	538	510	345	159	492	249	536	359	310	336	421	593	301	468	222	90	231	475	772	561	642	646	551	216	932	116	235	796	105	375	243	278	709	851	323	583	
Valence	519	178	729	360	683	443	1092	830	889	943	266	785	315	94	796	819	518	708	715	103	215	584	196	492	526	735	371	555	582	345	568	608	848	727	612	294	474	445	566

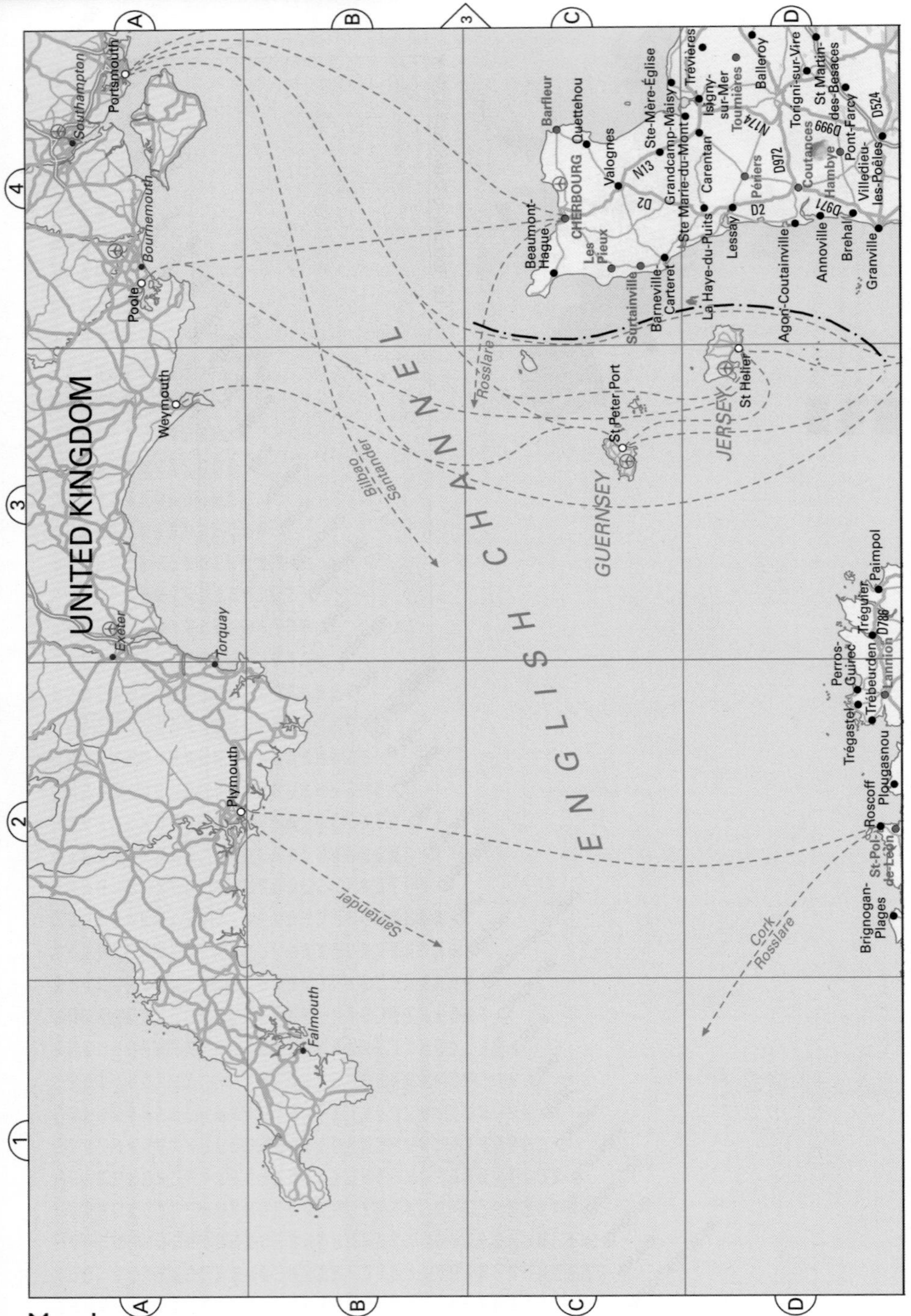

A B 3 C D

4

UNITED KINGDOM
Southampton
Portsmouth
Bournemouth
Poole
Weymouth
Exeter
Torquay
Plymouth
Falmouth

ENGLISH CHANNEL

Bilbao
Santander
Santander
Rosslare
Cork
Rosslare

GUERNSEY
St Peter Port
JERSEY
St Helier

Barfleur
Quettehou
CHERBOURG
Beaumont-Hague
Les Pieux
Valognes
Ste-Mère-Église
N13
D2
Grandcamp-Maisy
Ste Marie-du-Mont
Surtainville
Barneville-Carteret
La Haye-du-Puits
Carentan
Isigny-sur-Mer
Trévières
Tournières
Balleroy
N174
Lessay
Périers
D2
D972
Agon-Coutainville
Coutances
Torigni-sur-Vire
St Martin-des-Besaces
D999
Pont-Farcy
D524
Annoville
D971
Hambye
Villedieu-les-Poêles
Brehal
Granville

Paimpol
Tréguier
D786
Perros-Guirec
Trébeurden
Lannion
Trégastel
Plougasnou
Roscoff
St-Pol-de-Léon
Brignogan-Plages

3

2

1

A B C D

Map 1

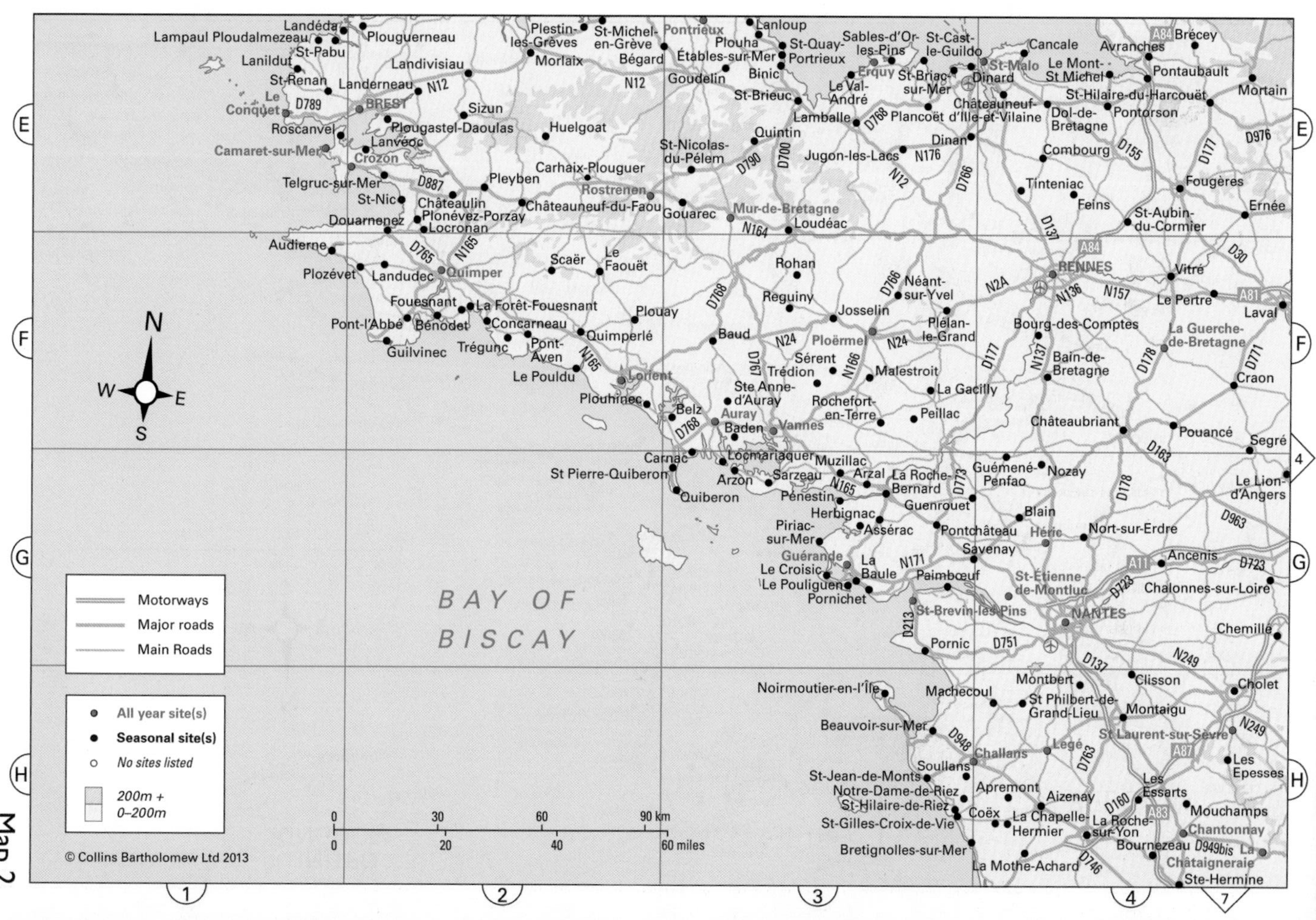
BAY OF BISCAY
Motorways
Major roads
Main Roads
All year site(s)
Seasonal site(s)
No sites listed
200m +
0–200m
© Collins Bartholomew Ltd 2013
0 30 60 90 km
0 20 40 60 miles
N
S
E
W
Lampaul Ploudalmezeau
Landéda
St-Pabu
Plouguerneau
Lanildut
St-Renan
Le Conquet
Landerneau
Landivisiau
Brest
Roscanvel
Plougastel-Daoulas
Sizun
Huelgoat
Camaret-sur-Mer
Lanvéoc
Crozon
Telgruc-sur-Mer
St-Nic
Châteaulin
Plonévez-Porzay
Locronan
Douarnenez
Pleyben
Carhaix-Plouguer
Rostrenen
Châteauneuf-du-Faou
Plestin-les-Grèves
Morlaix
St-Michel-en-Grève
Bégard
Pontrieux
Plouha
Lanloup
Étables-sur-Mer
St-Quay-Portrieux
Binic
Goudelin
St-Brieuc
Sables-d'Or-les-Pins
Erquy
Le Val-André
St-Cast-le-Guildo
St-Briac-sur-Mer
Dinard
St-Malo
Cancale
Lamballe
Plancoët
Châteauneuf-d'Ille-et-Vilaine
Dinan
Le Mont-St Michel
Avranches
Brécey
Pontaubault
Mortain
St-Hilaire-du-Harcouët
Dol-de-Bretagne
Pontorson
Combourg
Tinteniac
Feins
Fougères
St-Aubin-du-Cormier
Ernée
Quintin
St-Nicolas-du-Pélem
Jugon-les-Lacs
Gouarec
Mur-de-Bretagne
Loudéac
Audierne
Plozévet
Landudec
Quimper
Scaër
Le Faouët
Fouesnant
La Forêt-Fouesnant
Pont-l'Abbé
Bénodet
Concarneau
Guilvinec
Trégunc
Pont-Aven
Quimperlé
Plouay
Le Pouldu
Lorient
Plouhinec
Belz
Auray
Ste Anne-d'Auray
Baden
Vannes
Baud
Rohan
Reguiny
Josselin
Néant-sur-Yvel
Ploërmel
Plélan-le-Grand
Sérent
Trédion
Malestroit
Rochefort-en-Terre
La Gacilly
Peillac
Rennes
Vitré
Le Pertre
Laval
Bourg-des-Comptes
La Guerche-de-Bretagne
Bain-de-Bretagne
Craon
Châteaubriant
Pouancé
Segré
Le Lion-d'Angers
Carnac
St Pierre-Quiberon
Quiberon
Locmariaquer
Arzon
Sarzeau
Muzillac
Arzal
La Roche-Bernard
Pénestin
Guémené-Penfao
Nozay
Guenrouet
Herbignac
Piriac-sur-Mer
Assérac
Pontchâteau
Blain
Héric
Nort-sur-Erdre
Savenay
Guérande
La Baule
Le Croisic
Le Pouliguen
Pornichet
Paimbœuf
St-Étienne-de-Montluc
St-Brevin-les-Pins
Nantes
Ancenis
Chalonnes-sur-Loire
Chemillé
Pornic
Noirmoutier-en-l'Île
Machecoul
Montbert
St Philbert-de-Grand-Lieu
Clisson
Montaigu
Cholet
Beauvoir-sur-Mer
Challans
Legé
St Laurent-sur-Sèvre
Les Epesses
Soullans
St-Jean-de-Monts
Notre-Dame-de-Riez
St-Hilaire-de-Riez
St-Gilles-Croix-de-Vie
Apremont
Coëx
Aizenay
La Chapelle-Hermier
La Roche-sur-Yon
Les Essarts
Mouchamps
Chantonnay
Bournezeau
La Châtaigneraie
Ste-Hermine
Bretignolles-sur-Mer
La Mothe-Achard
N12
N164
N165
N24
N2A
N136
N157
N137
N166
N171
N176
N249
D789
D887
D765
D768
D767
D700
D790
D766
D137
D155
D177
D976
D30
D771
D178
D163
D963
D773
D213
D751
D723
D948
D763
D160
D746
D949bis
A84
A81
A11
A83
A87
E
F
G
H
1
2
3
4
7

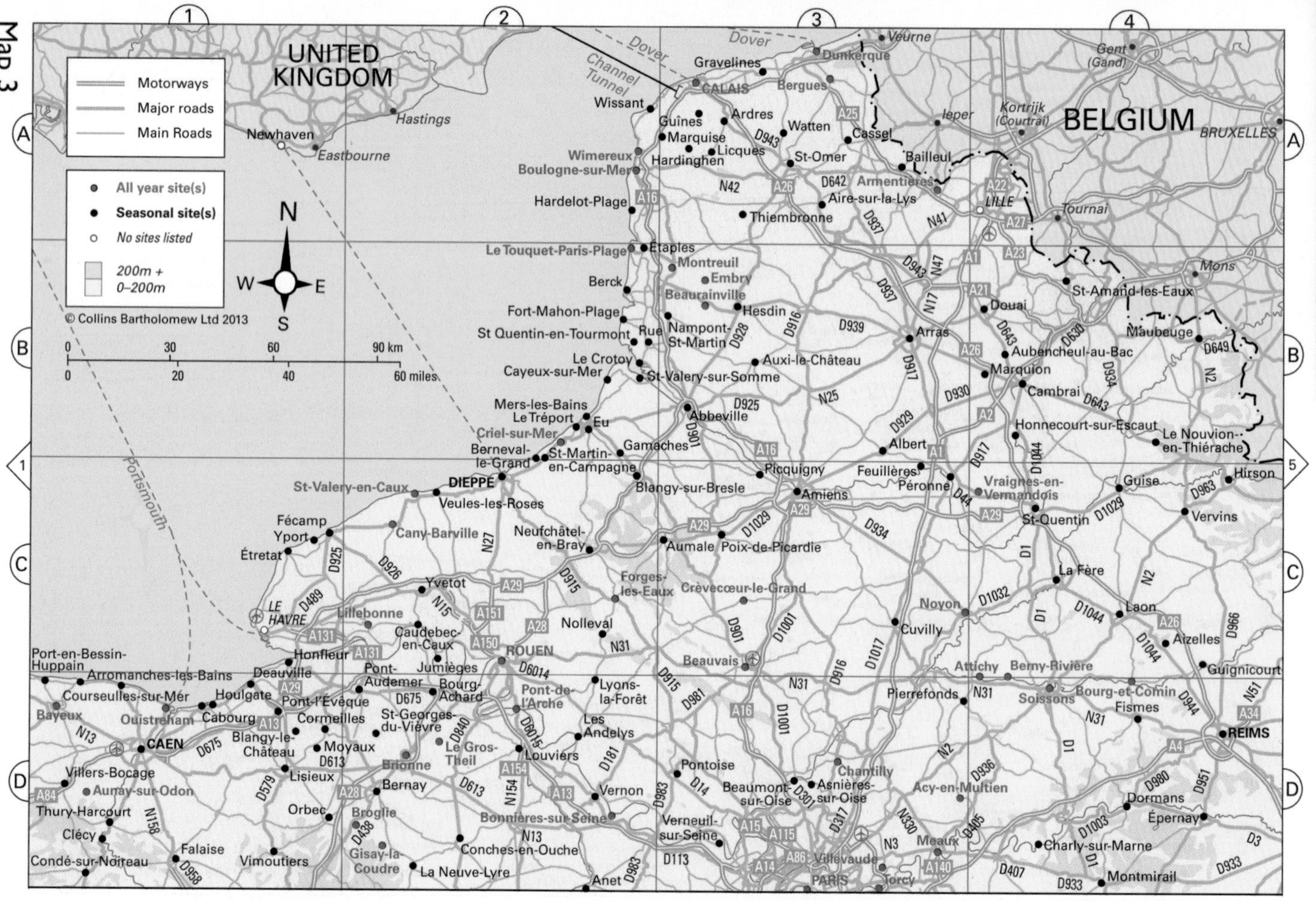

Motorways
Major roads
Main Roads
All year site(s)
Seasonal site(s)
No sites listed
200m +
0–200m
© Collins Bartholomew Ltd 2013
N
E
S
W
0
30
60
90 km
0
20
40
60 miles
UNITED KINGDOM
BELGIUM
BRUXELLES
Gent (Gand)
Kortrijk (Courtrai)
Ieper
Veurne
Tournai
Mons
Newhaven
Eastbourne
Hastings
Dover
Portsmouth
Channel Tunnel
CALAIS
Dunkerque
Gravelines
Bergues
Watten
Cassel
Bailleul
Armentières
LILLE
Wissant
Guînes
Marquise
Ardres
Licques
Hardinghen
St-Omer
Aire-sur-la-Lys
Thiembronne
Wimereux
Boulogne-sur-Mer
Hardelot-Plage
Étaples
Le Touquet-Paris-Plage
Montreuil
Embry
Beaurainville
Berck
Fort-Mahon-Plage
Nampont-St-Martin
Rue
St Quentin-en-Tourmont
Le Crotoy
St-Valery-sur-Somme
Cayeux-sur-Mer
Hesdin
Auxi-le-Château
Arras
Douai
Aubencheul-au-Bac
Marquion
Cambrai
St-Amand-les-Eaux
Maubeuge
Honnecourt-sur-Escaut
Le Nouvion-en-Thiérache
Hirson
Vervins
Guise
Vraignes-en-Vermandois
St-Quentin
Albert
Feuillères
Péronne
Abbeville
Gamaches
Blangy-sur-Bresle
Mers-les-Bains
Le Tréport
Eu
Criel-sur-Mer
St-Martin-en-Campagne
Berneval-le-Grand
DIEPPE
Picquigny
Amiens
Poix-de-Picardie
Aumale
Crèvecœur-le-Grand
Forges-les-Eaux
Neufchâtel-en-Bray
Nolleval
Veules-les-Roses
St-Valery-en-Caux
Cany-Barville
Fécamp
Yport
Étretat
LE HAVRE
Lillebonne
Yvetot
Caudebec-en-Caux
Jumièges
ROUEN
Pont-de-l'Arche
Lyons-la-Forêt
Les Andelys
Louviers
Vernon
Beauvais
Noyon
Cuvilly
La Fère
Laon
Aizelles
Guignicourt
REIMS
Berny-Rivière
Attichy
Soissons
Bourg-et-Comin
Fismes
Pierrefonds
Acy-en-Multien
Chantilly
Asnières-sur-Oise
Beaumont-sur-Oise
Pontoise
Verneuil-sur-Seine
Meaux
Torcy
Villevaudé
PARIS
Dormans
Épernay
Charly-sur-Marne
Montmirail
Honfleur
Pont-Audemer
Bourg-Achard
Le Gros-Theil
St-Georges-du-Vièvre
Brionne
Bernay
Broglie
Gisay-la-Coudre
La Neuve-Lyre
Conches-en-Ouche
Bonnières-sur-Seine
Anet
Deauville
Pont-l'Évêque
Cormeilles
Moyaux
Blangy-le-Château
Lisieux
Orbec
Vimoutiers
Houlgate
Cabourg
Ouistreham
CAEN
Arromanches-les-Bains
Courseulles-sur-Mer
Port-en-Bessin-Huppain
Bayeux
Villers-Bocage
Aunay-sur-Odon
Thury-Harcourt
Clécy
Condé-sur-Noireau
Falaise
A
B
C
D
1
2
3
4
5

Map 3

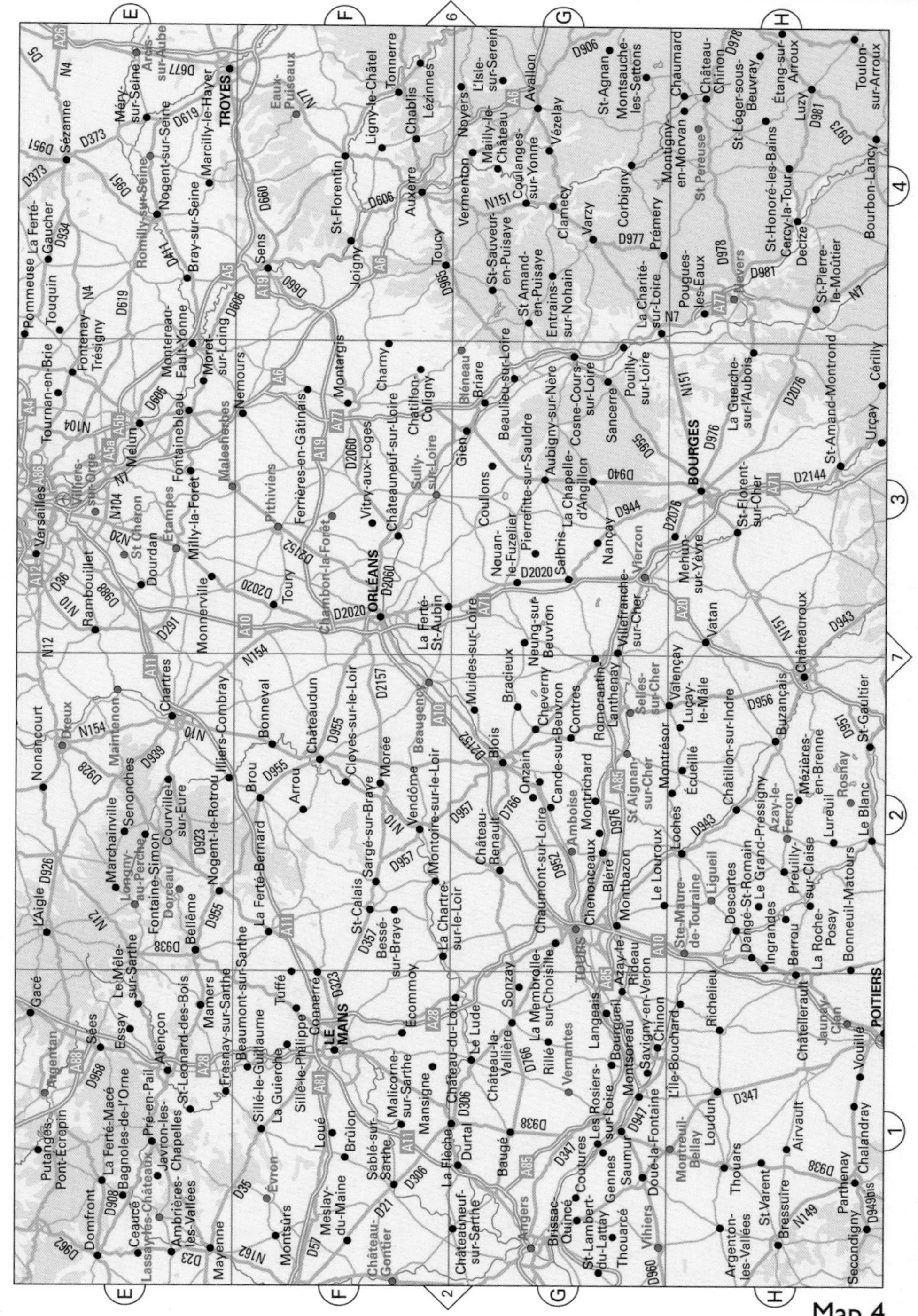

Map 4

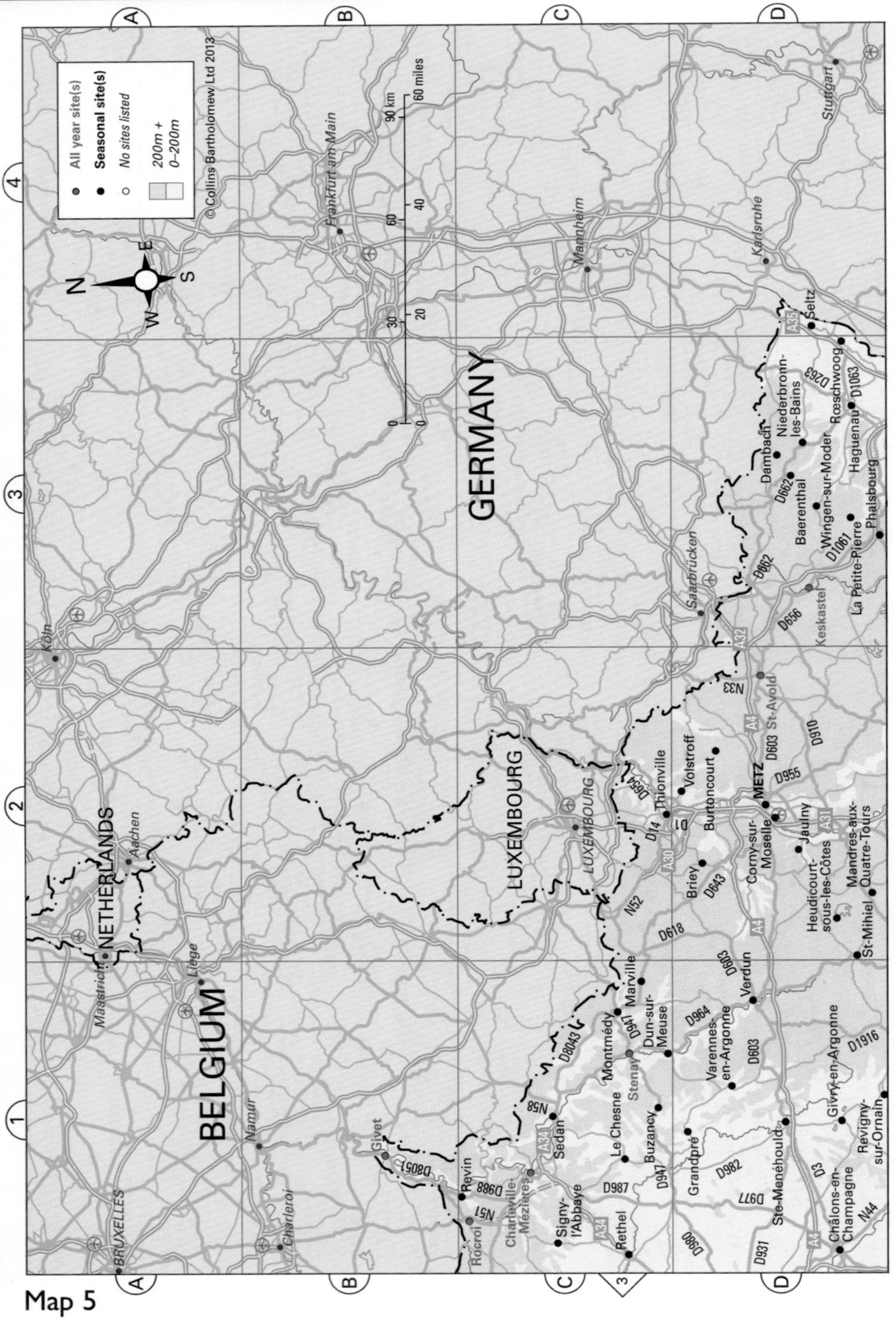

All year site(s)
Seasonal site(s)
No sites listed
200m +
0–200m

0 30 60 90 km
0 20 40 60 miles
N E S W
NETHERLANDS
BELGIUM
GERMANY
LUXEMBOURG
Maastricht
Aachen
Köln
Liège
Namur
BRUXELLES
Charleroi
Frankfurt am Main
Mannheim
Karlsruhe
Stuttgart
Saarbrücken
LUXEMBOURG
Givet
Rocroi
Revin
Charleville-Mézières
Signy-l'Abbaye
Rethel
Sedan
Le Chesne
Buzancy
Grandpré
Montmédy
Stenay
Dun-sur-Meuse
Marville
Varennes-en-Argonne
Verdun
Ste-Menehould
Châlons-en-Champagne
Givry-en-Argonne
Revigny-sur-Ornain
St-Mihiel
Heudicourt-sous-les-Côtes
Mandres-aux-Quatre-Tours
Jaulny
Corny-sur-Moselle
METZ
Briey
Thionville
Volstroff
Buttoncourt
St-Avold
Keskastel
La Petite-Pierre
Phalsbourg
Wingen-sur-Moder
Baerenthal
Haguenau
Dambach
Niederbronn-les-Bains
Rœschwoog
Seltz
D8051
D988
N51
A34
D987
D947
D982
D977
D980
D931
D3
N44
A4
N58
D8043
D947
D964
D603
D1916
D618
N52
D643
A30
D14
D1
D654
D603
D955
D910
N33
A32
D656
D662
D1061
D263
D1063
A35

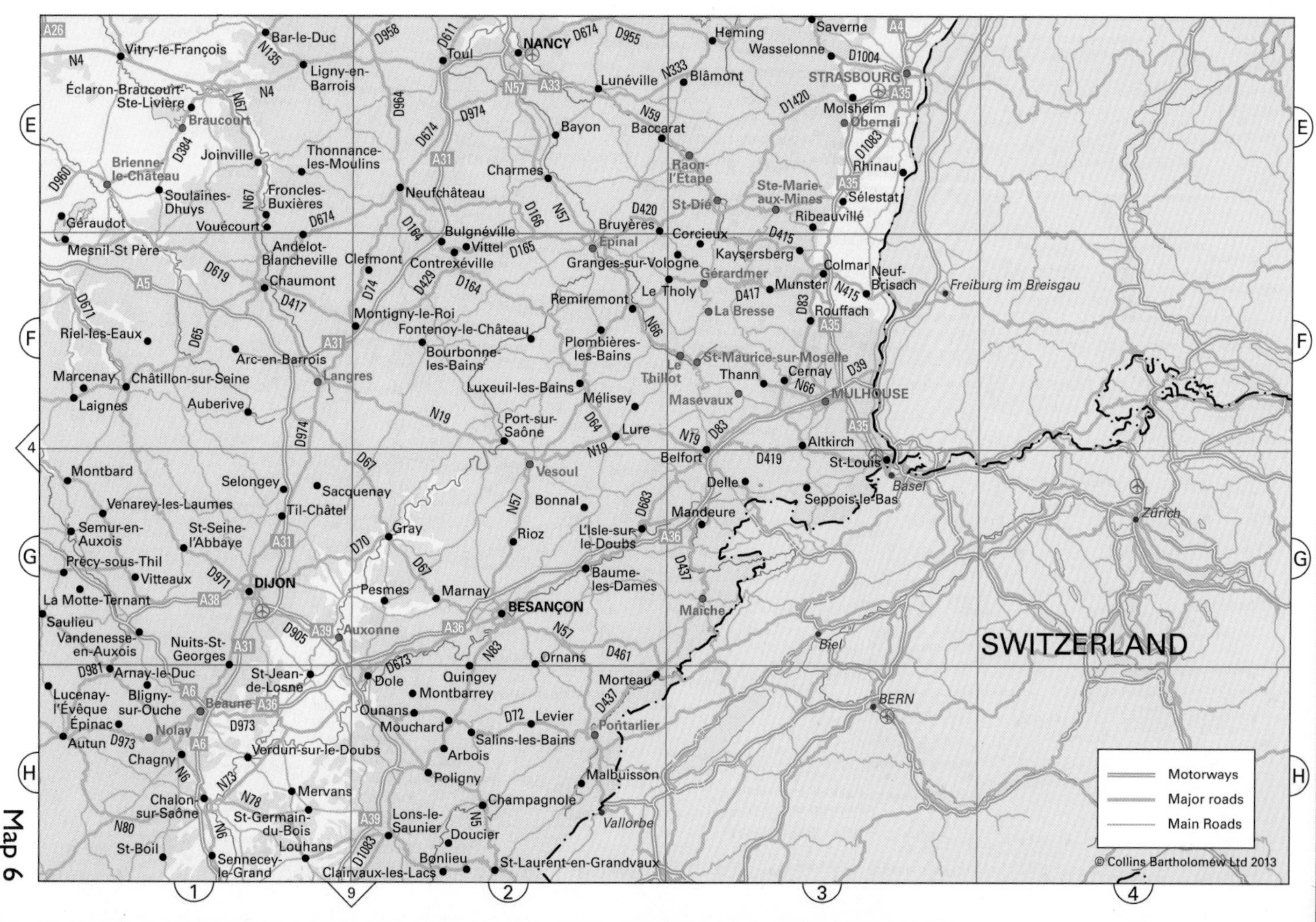
SWITZERLAND
Motorways
Major roads
Main Roads
© Collins Bartholomew Ltd 2013
NANCY
STRASBOURG
MULHOUSE
BESANÇON
DIJON
Basel
Zürich
BERN
Biel
Freiburg im Breisgau
Saverne
Wasselonne
Molsheim
Obernai
Sélestat
Rhinau
Ribeauvillé
Colmar
Neuf-Brisach
Rouffach
Munster
Kaysersberg
Ste-Marie-aux-Mines
Cernay
Thann
Altkirch
St-Louis
Seppois-le-Bas
Delle
Belfort
Mandeure
Maîche
Morteau
Pontarlier
Vallorbe
Malbuisson
Champagnole
St-Laurent-en-Grandvaux
Lure
Mélisey
Luxeuil-les-Bains
Plombières-les-Bains
Remiremont
Le Thillot
Masevaux
St-Maurice-sur-Moselle
La Bresse
Gérardmer
Le Tholy
Granges-sur-Vologne
Corcieux
St-Dié
Raon-l'Étape
Baccarat
Blâmont
Heming
Lunéville
Bayon
Charmes
Épinal
Bruyères
Toul
Vittel
Contrexéville
Bulgnéville
Neufchâteau
Vesoul
Port-sur-Saône
Rioz
Bonnal
L'Isle-sur-le-Doubs
Baume-les-Dames
Ornans
Levier
Salins-les-Bains
Arbois
Poligny
Lons-le-Saunier
Doucier
Bonlieu
Clairvaux-les-Lacs
Quingey
Montbarrey
Mouchard
Ounans
Dole
Marnay
Pesmes
Gray
Auxonne
Langres
Montigny-le-Roi
Fontenoy-le-Château
Bourbonne-les-Bains
Clefmont
Chaumont
Andelot-Blancheville
Thonnance-les-Moulins
Froncles-Buxières
Vouécourt
Joinville
Ligny-en-Barrois
Bar-le-Duc
Vitry-le-François
Éclaron-Braucourt-Ste-Livière
Braucourt
Brienne-le-Château
Soulaines-Dhuys
Géraudot
Mesnil-St Père
Riel-les-Eaux
Arc-en-Barrois
Châtillon-sur-Seine
Marcenay
Laignes
Auberive
Montbard
Selongey
Sacquenay
Til-Châtel
Venarey-les-Laumes
Semur-en-Auxois
St-Seine-l'Abbaye
Précy-sous-Thil
Vitteaux
La Motte-Ternant
Saulieu
Vandenesse-en-Auxois
Nuits-St-Georges
Arnay-le-Duc
St-Jean-de-Losne
Lucenay-l'Évêque
Bligny-sur-Ouche
Beaune
Épinac
Nolay
Autun
Chagny
Verdun-sur-le-Doubs
Mervans
Chalon-sur-Saône
St-Germain-du-Bois
Louhans
St-Boil
Sennecey-le-Grand
E
F
G
H
1
2
3
4
9

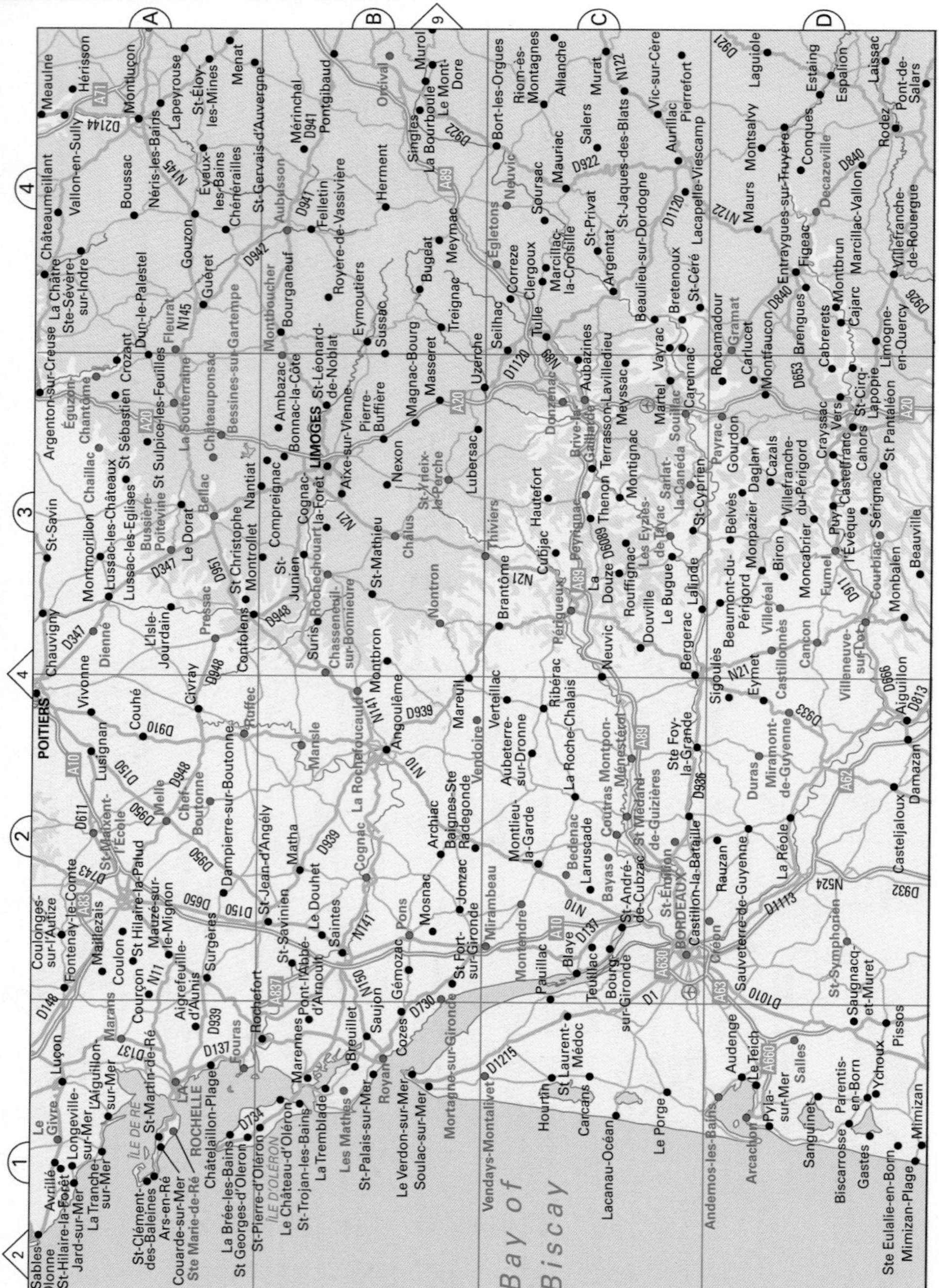

Map 7

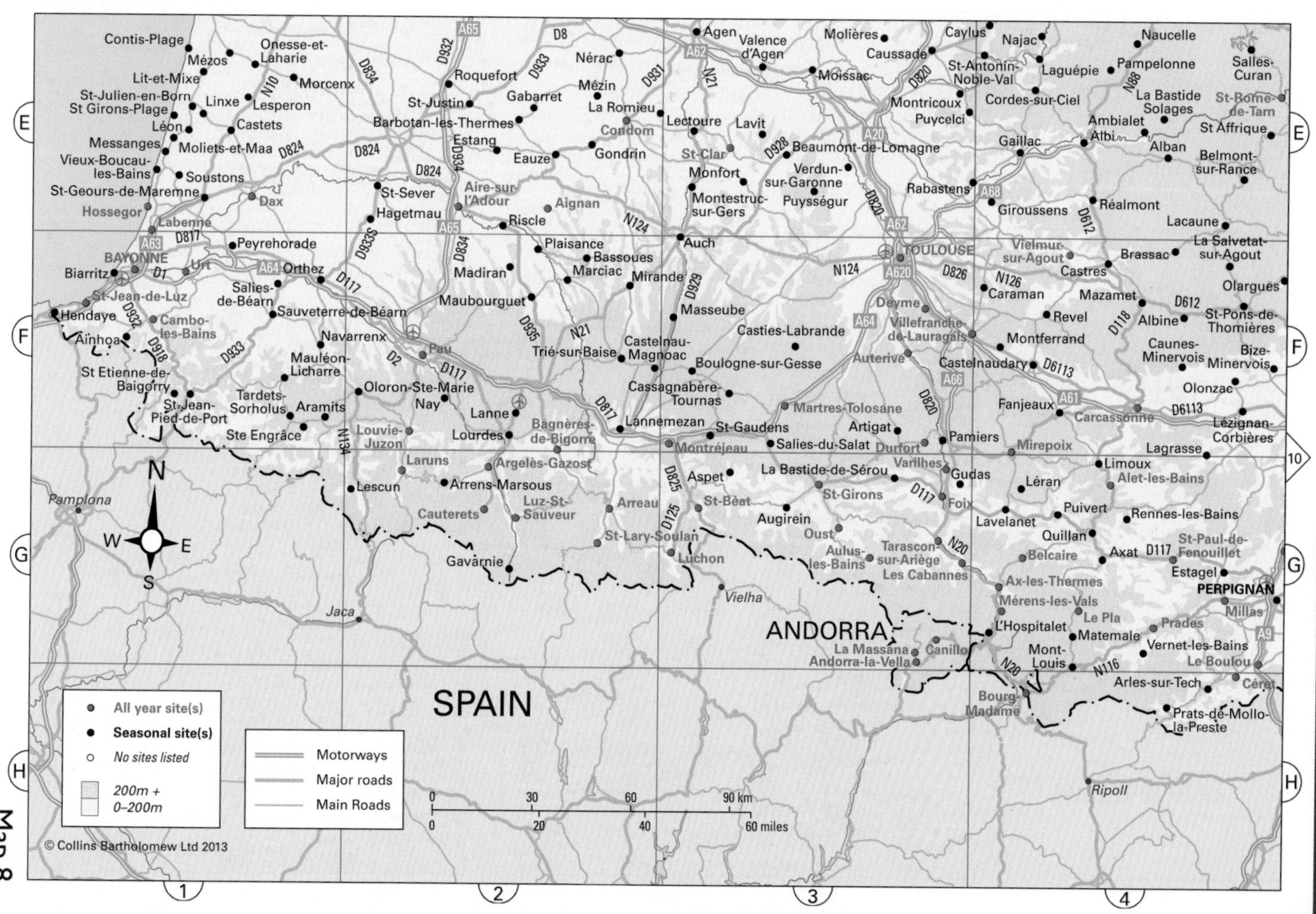

E
F
G
H
10
1
2
3
4
All year site(s)
Seasonal site(s)
No sites listed
200m +
0–200m
Motorways
Major roads
Main Roads
0 30 60 90 km
0 20 40 60 miles
N
S
E
W
SPAIN
ANDORRA
© Collins Bartholomew Ltd 2013
Contis-Plage
Mézos
Lit-et-Mixe
St-Julien-en-Born
St Girons-Plage
Léon
Linxe
Messanges
Vieux-Boucau-les-Bains
Moliets-et-Maa
Soustons
St-Geours-de-Maremne
Hossegor
Labenne
BAYONNE
Biarritz
Hendaye
St-Jean-de-Luz
Aïnhoa
Cambo-les-Bains
St Etienne-de-Baïgorry
St-Jean-Pied-de-Port
Onesse-et-Laharie
Morcenx
Lesperon
Castets
Dax
Peyrehorade
Urt
Salies-de-Béarn
Sauveterre-de-Béarn
Orthez
Tardets-Sorholus
Ste Engrâce
Mauléon-Licharre
Aramits
Navarrenx
Oloron-Ste-Marie
Louvie-Juzon
Lescun
Laruns
Roquefort
St-Justin
Barbotan-les-Thermes
Gabarret
Estang
Aire-sur-l'Adour
St-Sever
Hagetmau
Riscle
Madiran
Maubourguet
Pau
Nay
Lanne
Lourdes
Arrens-Marsous
Argelès-Gazost
Cauterets
Gavarnie
Luz-St-Sauveur
Bagnères-de-Bigorre
Nérac
Mézin
La Romieu
Condom
Gondrin
Eauze
Aignan
Plaisance
Bassoues
Marciac
Mirande
Trie-sur-Baïse
Castelnau-Magnoac
Lannemezan
Arreau
St-Lary-Soulan
Luchon
Vielha
Agen
Valence d'Agen
Lectoure
St-Clar
Lavit
Auch
Monfort
Montestruc-sur-Gers
Masseube
Cassagnabère-Tournas
St-Gaudens
Montréjeau
Aspet
St-Béat
Moissac
Molières
Caussade
Beaumont-de-Lomagne
Verdun-sur-Garonne
Puysségur
Castiès-Labrande
Boulogne-sur-Gesse
Martres-Tolosane
Salies-du-Salat
La Bastide-de-Sérou
Augirein
Oust
St-Girons
Aulus-les-Bains
Caylus
Najac
St-Antonin-Noble-Val
Montricoux
Puycelci
Rabastens
TOULOUSE
Deyme
Villefranche-de-Lauragais
Auterive
Castelnaudary
Artigat
Durfort
Varilhes
Pamiers
Gudas
Foix
Tarascon-sur-Ariège
Les Cabannes
La Massana
Canillo
Andorra-la-Vella
Naucelle
Pampelonne
Laguépie
Cordes-sur-Ciel
Gaillac
Giroussens
Vielmur-sur-Agout
Caraman
Revel
Montferrand
Fanjeaux
Mirepoix
Léran
Lavelanet
Belcaire
Ax-les-Thermes
Mérens-les-Vals
L'Hospitalet
Bourg-Madame
Salles-Curan
La Bastide Solages
Ambialet
Albi
Alban
St-Rome-de-Tarn
St Affrique
Belmont-sur-Rance
Réalmont
Lacaune
La Salvetat-sur-Agout
Brassac
Castres
Mazamet
Albine
Olargues
St-Pons-de-Thomières
Caunes-Minervois
Bize-Minervois
Olonzac
Lézignan-Corbières
Carcassonne
Lagrasse
Limoux
Alet-les-Bains
Puivert
Quillan
Rennes-les-Bains
Axat
St-Paul-de-Fenouillet
Estagel
PERPIGNAN
Millas
Prades
Le Pla
Matemale
Mont-Louis
Vernet-les-Bains
Le Boulou
Céret
Arles-sur-Tech
Prats-de-Mollo-la-Preste
Ripoll
Jaca
Pamplona
A63
A64
A65
A62
A20
A68
A620
A61
A66
A9
N10
N21
N124
N126
N134
N20
N116
N88
D8
D117
D6113
D612
D820
D817
D825
D929

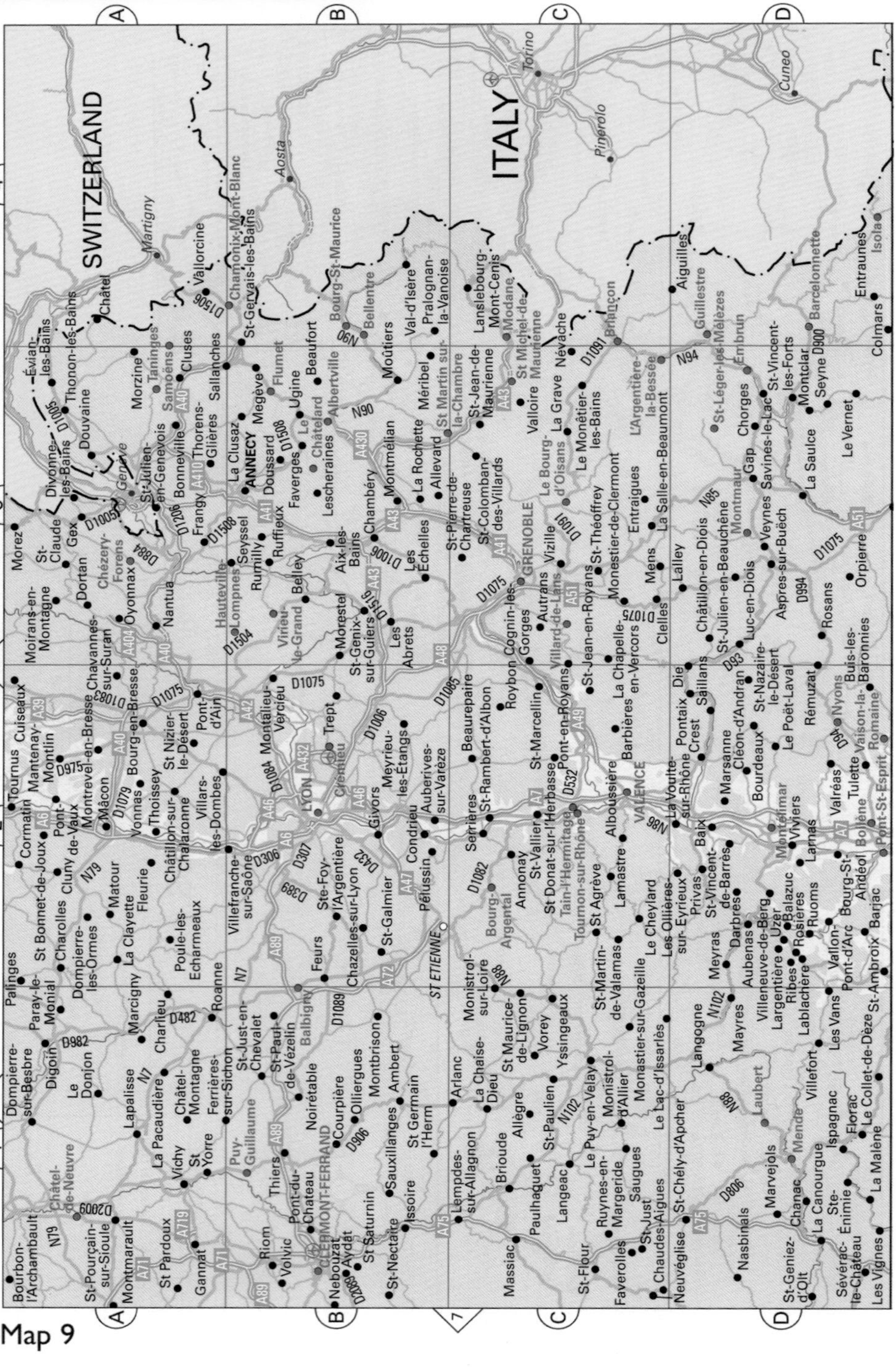

Map 9

SWITZERLAND

ITALY

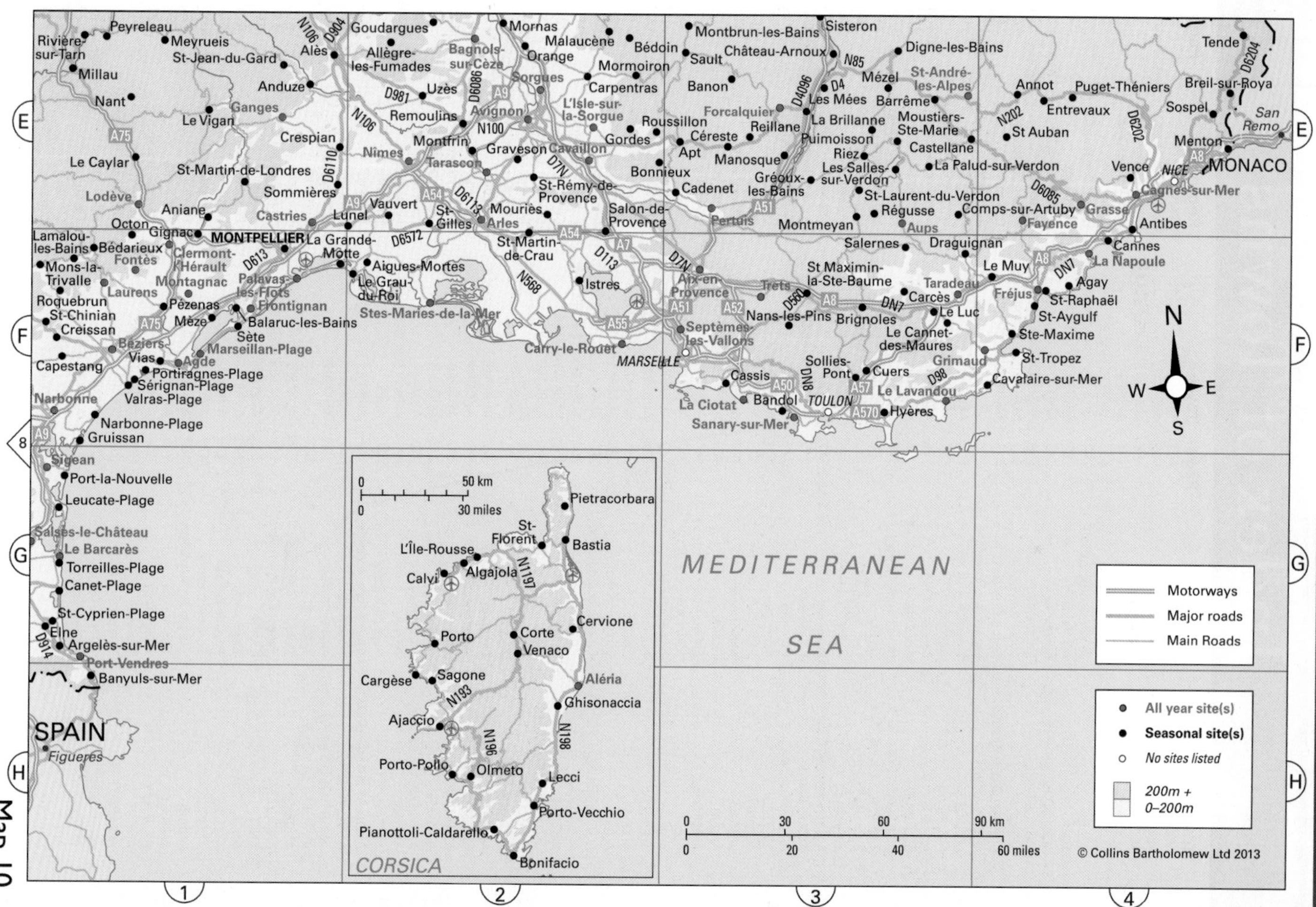
MONACO
MONTPELLIER
MARSEILLE
TOULON
NICE
SPAIN
CORSICA
MEDITERRANEAN
SEA
N
E
S
W
Motorways
Major roads
Main Roads
All year site(s)
Seasonal site(s)
No sites listed
200m +
0–200m
0 30 60 90 km
0 20 40 60 miles
0 50 km
0 30 miles
Rivière-sur-Tarn
Peyreleau
Meyrueis
St-Jean-du-Gard
Millau
Nant
Le Vigan
Ganges
Anduze
Alès
Goudargues
Allègre-les-Fumades
Bagnols-sur-Cèze
Uzès
Remoulins
Crespian
Le Caylar
St-Martin-de-Londres
Sommières
Lodève
Aniane
Castries
Lunel
Vauvert
Nîmes
Montfrin
Tarascon
Avignon
Sorgues
Mornas
Orange
Malaucène
Bédoin
Mormoiron
Carpentras
L'Isle-sur-la-Sorgue
Cavaillon
Graveson
St-Rémy-de-Provence
Mouriès
Arles
St-Gilles
Gordes
Roussillon
Bonnieux
Montbrun-les-Bains
Sault
Banon
Sisteron
Château-Arnoux
Digne-les-Bains
St-André-les-Alpes
Mézel
Les Mées
Barrême
Forcalquier
Céreste
Reillane
Apt
Manosque
La Brillanne
Puimoisson
Moustiers-Ste-Marie
Riez
Castellane
Les Salles-sur-Verdon
La Palud-sur-Verdon
Gréoux-les-Bains
Cadenet
Pertuis
St-Laurent-du-Verdon
Régusse
Montmeyan
Aups
Comps-sur-Artuby
Fayence
Annot
Puget-Théniers
Entrevaux
St Auban
Tende
Breil-sur-Roya
Sospel
San Remo
Menton
Vence
Cagnes-sur-Mer
Grasse
Antibes
Salon-de-Provence
Octon
Gignac
Lamalou-les-Bains
Bédarieux
Fontès
Clermont-l'Hérault
La Grande-Motte
Aigues-Mortes
Le Grau-du-Roi
St-Martin-de-Crau
Istres
Mons-la-Trivalle
Montagnac
Palavas-les-Flots
Laurens
Roquebrun
St-Chinian
Creissan
Pézenas
Frontignan
Mèze
Balaruc-les-Bains
Sète
Stes-Maries-de-la-Mer
Béziers
Marseillan-Plage
Capestang
Vias
Agde
Portiragnes-Plage
Sérignan-Plage
Valras-Plage
Narbonne
Narbonne-Plage
Gruissan
Carry-le-Rouet
Aix-en-Provence
Trets
Septèmes-les-Vallons
Nans-les-Pins
St Maximin-la-Ste-Baume
Brignoles
Salernes
Draguignan
Taradeau
Carcès
Le Luc
Le Cannet-des-Maures
Le Muy
Fréjus
Cannes
La Napoule
Agay
St-Raphaël
St-Aygulf
Ste-Maxime
St-Tropez
Grimaud
Cavalaire-sur-Mer
Cassis
La Ciotat
Bandol
Sanary-sur-Mer
Solliès-Pont
Cuers
Le Lavandou
Hyères
Sigean
Port-la-Nouvelle
Leucate-Plage
Salses-le-Château
Le Barcarès
Torreilles-Plage
Canet-Plage
St-Cyprien-Plage
Elne
Argelès-sur-Mer
Port-Vendres
Banyuls-sur-Mer
Figueres
Pietracorbara
St-Florent
Bastia
L'Île-Rousse
Algajola
Calvi
Cervione
Porto
Corte
Venaco
Cargèse
Sagone
Aléria
Ghisonaccia
Ajaccio
Porto-Pollo
Olmeto
Lecci
Porto-Vecchio
Pianottoli-Caldarello
Bonifacio
© Collins Bartholomew Ltd 2013

Index of Towns

Index of Towns

Index of Towns

Index of Towns

Index of Towns

Index of Towns

Index of Towns

Index of Towns

Index of Towns

Index of Towns

Index of Towns

Index of Towns

Index of Towns

Site Report Form

If campsite is already listed, complete only those sections of the form where changes apply or alternatively use the Abbreviated Site Report form on the following pages.

Sites not reported on for 5 years may be deleted from the guide

Year of guide used	20..........	Is site listed?	Listed on page no.	Unlisted	Date of visit	......../........./.........

A – CAMPSITE NAME AND LOCATION

Country		Name of town/village site listed under *(see Sites Location Maps)*			
Distance & direction from centre of town site is listed under *(in a straight line)*	....................km	eg N, NE, S, SW	Urban	Rural	Coastal
Site open all year?	Y / N	Period site is open *(if not all year)*	................./................. to ..../.................		
Site name			Naturist site	Y / N	
Site address					
Telephone		Fax			
E-mail		Website			

B – CAMPSITE CHARGES

Charge for outfit + 2 adults in local currency	PRICE		EL PNTS inc in this price?	Y / N	Amps ....

C – DIRECTIONS

Brief, specific directions to site (in km) *To convert miles to kilometres multiply by 8 and divide by 5 or use Conversion Table in guide*	
GPS	Latitude..*(eg 12.34567)* Longitude..*(eg 1.23456 or -1.23456)*

D – CAMPSITE DESCRIPTION

SITE size ie number of pitches	Small Max 50	SM	Medium 51-150	MED	Large 151-500	LGE	Very large 500+	V LGE	Unchanged

PITCH size	*eg small, medium, large, very large, various*	Unchanged

Pitch features if **NOT** open-plan/grassy	Hedged	HDG PITCH	Marked or numbered	MKD PITCH	Hardstanding or gravel	HDSTG	Unchanged
If site is **NOT** level, is it	Part sloping	PT SL	Sloping	SL	Terraced	TERR	Unchanged
Is site shaded?	Shaded	SHD	Part shaded	PT SHD	Unshaded	UNSHD	Unchanged

E – CAMPSITE FACILITIES

WC	Heated	HTD WC	Continental	CONT	Own San recommended	OWN SAN REC

Chemical disposal point	CHEM DISP	Dedicated point		WC only	
Motorhome waste discharge and water refill point		MV SERVICE PNT			
Child / baby facilities (bathroom)	CHILD / BABY FACS	Family bathroom		FAM BTHRM	
Hot shower(s)	SHWR(S)	Inc in site fee?	Y / N	Price....................*(if not inc)*	
ELECTRIC HOOK UP *if not included in price above*	EL PNTS	Price.....................................		Amps..	
Supplies of bottled gas	GAS	On site	Y / N	Or in .... Kms	
Launderette / Washing Machine	LNDTTE	Inc dryer Y / N		LNDRY RM *(if no washing machine)*	

You can also complete forms online: www.caravanclub.co.uk/europereport

CUT ALONG DOTTED LINE

F – FOOD & DRINK

Shop(s) / supermarket	SHOP(S) / SUPMKT	On site		or	.... kms
Bread / milk delivered	TRADSMN				
Restaurant / cafeteria	REST	On site		or	.... kms
Snack bar / take-away	SNACKS	On site		or	.... kms
Bar	BAR	On site		or	.... kms
Barbecue allowed	BBQ	Charcoal	Gas	Elec	Sep area
Cooking facilities	COOKING FACS				

G – LEISURE FACILITIES

Playground	PLAYGRND					
Swimming pool	POOL	On site		or ....km	Heated	Covered
Beach	BEACH	Adj		or ....km	Sand	Shingle
Alternative swimming *(lake)*	SW	Adj		or ....km	Sand	Shingle
Games /sports area / Games room	GAMES AREA	GAMES ROOM				
Entertainment in high season	ENTMNT					
Internet use by visitors	INTERNET	Wifi Internet		WIFI		
Television room	TV RM	Satellite / Cable to pitches		TV CAB / SAT		

H – OTHER INFORMATION

% Static caravans / mobile homes / chalets / cottages / fixed tents on site					................% STATICS
Dogs allowed	DOGS	Y / N	Price per night .... *(if allowed)*		
Phone	PHONE	On site	Adj		
Bus / tram / train	BUS / TRAM / TRAIN	Adj	or .... km		
Twin axles caravans allowed?	TWIN AXLES Y / N	Possibly crowded in high season			POSS CR
English spoken	ENG SPKN				
Advance bookings accepted	ADV BKG	Y / N			
Noise levels on site in season	NOISY	QUIET	If noisy, why?		
Credit card accepted	CCARD ACC	Reduction low season		RED LOW SSN	
Camping Key Europe or Camping Card International accepted in lieu of passport	CKE/CCI	INF card required *(If naturist site)*		Y / N	
Facilities for disabled	Full wheelchair facilities	♦	Limited disabled facilities	♦ ltd	

I – ADDITIONAL REMARKS AND/OR ITEMS OF INTEREST

Tourist attractions, unusual features or other facilities, eg waterslide, tennis, cycle hire, watersports, horseriding, separate car park, walking distance to shops etc	YOUR OPINION OF THE SITE:	
	EXCEL	
	VERY GOOD	
	GOOD	
	FAIR	POOR
	NIGHT HALT ONLY	
Your comments & opinions may be used in future editions of the guide, if you do not wish them to be used please tick		

J – MEMBER DETAILS

ARE YOU A:	Caravanner		Motorhomer		Trailer-tenter?	
NAME:			MEMBERSHIP NO:			
			POST CODE:			
DO YOU NEED MORE BLANK SITE REPORT FORMS?			YES		NO	

Please use a separate form for each campsite and do not send receipts. Owing to the large number of site reports received, it is not possible to enter into correspondence. Please return completed form to:

The Editor, Overseas Touring Guides, The Caravan Club
FREEPOST, PO Box 386, (RRZG-SXKK-UCUJ)
East Grinstead RH19 1FH

(Please use this address only when mailing from within the UK)

Site Report Form

If campsite is already listed, complete only those sections of the form where changes apply or alternatively use the Abbreviated Site Report form on the following pages.

Sites not reported on for 5 years may be deleted from the guide

Year of guide used	20.........	Is site listed?	Listed on page no.	Unlisted	Date of visit	......./......../........

A – CAMPSITE NAME AND LOCATION

Country		Name of town/village site listed under *(see Sites Location Maps)*			
Distance & direction from centre of town site is listed under *(in a straight line)*	..................km	eg N, NE, S, SW	Urban	Rural	Coastal
Site open all year?	Y / N	Period site is open *(if not all year)*	................/................ to ..../................		
Site name			Naturist site	Y / N	
Site address					
Telephone		Fax			
E-mail		Website			

B – CAMPSITE CHARGES

Charge for outfit + 2 adults in local currency	PRICE		EL PNTS inc in this price?	Y / N	Amps ....

C – DIRECTIONS

Brief, specific directions to site (in km) *To convert miles to kilometres multiply by 8 and divide by 5 or use Conversion Table in guide*	
GPS	Latitude...*(eg 12.34567)* Longitude...*(eg 1.23456 or -1.23456)*

D – CAMPSITE DESCRIPTION

SITE size ie number of pitches	Small Max 50	SM	Medium 51-150	MED	Large 151-500	LGE	Very large 500+	V LGE	Unchanged
PITCH size	*eg small, medium, large, very large, various*								Unchanged
Pitch features if **NOT** open-plan/grassy	Hedged	HDG PITCH	Marked or numbered	MKD PITCH	Hardstanding or gravel	HDSTG			Unchanged
If site is **NOT** level, is it	Part sloping	PT SL	Sloping	SL	Terraced	TERR			Unchanged
Is site shaded?	Shaded	SHD	Part shaded	PT SHD	Unshaded	UNSHD			Unchanged

E – CAMPSITE FACILITIES

WC	Heated	HTD WC	Continental	CONT	Own San recommended	OWN SAN REC
Chemical disposal point	CHEM DISP		Dedicated point		WC only	
Motorhome waste discharge and water refill point			MV SERVICE PNT			
Child / baby facilities (bathroom)	CHILD / BABY FACS		Family bathroom		FAM BTHRM	
Hot shower(s)	SHWR(S)		Inc in site fee?	Y / N	Price...................*(if not inc)*	
ELECTRIC HOOK UP *if not included in price above*	EL PNTS		Price....................................		Amps...	
Supplies of bottled gas	GAS		On site	Y / N	Or in .... Kms	
Launderette / Washing Machine	LNDTTE	Inc dryer Y / N		LNDRY RM *(if no washing machine)*		

You can also complete forms online: www.caravanclub.co.uk/europereport

CUT ALONG DOTTED LINE

F – FOOD & DRINK

Shop(s) / supermarket	SHOP(S) / SUPMKT	On site		or	.... kms
Bread / milk delivered	TRADSMN				
Restaurant / cafeteria	REST	On site		or	.... kms
Snack bar / take-away	SNACKS	On site		or	.... kms
Bar	BAR	On site		or	.... kms
Barbecue allowed	BBQ	Charcoal	Gas	Elec	Sep area
Cooking facilities	COOKING FACS				

G – LEISURE FACILITIES

Playground	PLAYGRND					
Swimming pool	POOL	On site		or ....km	Heated	Covered
Beach	BEACH	Adj		or ....km	Sand	Shingle
Alternative swimming *(lake)*	SW	Adj		or ....km	Sand	Shingle
Games /sports area / Games room	GAMES AREA	GAMES ROOM				
Entertainment in high season	ENTMNT					
Internet use by visitors	INTERNET	Wifi Internet		WIFI		
Television room	TV RM	Satellite / Cable to pitches		TV CAB / SAT		

H – OTHER INFORMATION

% Static caravans / mobile homes / chalets / cottages / fixed tents on site					................% STATICS
Dogs allowed	DOGS		Y / N	Price per night .... *(if allowed)*	
Phone	PHONE		On site	Adj	
Bus / tram / train	BUS / TRAM / TRAIN		Adj	or .... km	
Twin axles caravans allowed?	TWIN AXLES Y / N		Possibly crowded in high season		POSS CR
English spoken	ENG SPKN				
Advance bookings accepted	ADV BKG		Y / N		
Noise levels on site in season	NOISY	QUIET	If noisy, why?		
Credit card accepted	CCARD ACC		Reduction low season		RED LOW SSN
Camping Key Europe or Camping Card International accepted in lieu of passport	CKE/CCI		INF card required *(If naturist site)*		Y / N
Facilities for disabled	Full wheelchair facilities		♦	Limited disabled facilities	♦ ltd

I – ADDITIONAL REMARKS AND/OR ITEMS OF INTEREST

Tourist attractions, unusual features or other facilities, eg waterslide, tennis, cycle hire, watersports, horseriding, separate car park, walking distance to shops etc	YOUR OPINION OF THE SITE:	
	EXCEL	
	VERY GOOD	
	GOOD	
	FAIR	POOR
	NIGHT HALT ONLY	
Your comments & opinions may be used in future editions of the guide, if you do not wish them to be used please tick		

J – MEMBER DETAILS

ARE YOU A:	Caravanner		Motorhomer		Trailer-tenter?	
NAME:			MEMBERSHIP NO:			
			POST CODE:			
DO YOU NEED MORE BLANK SITE REPORT FORMS?			YES		NO	

Please use a separate form for each campsite and do not send receipts. Owing to the large number of site reports received, it is not possible to enter into correspondence. Please return completed form to:

The Editor, Overseas Touring Guides, The Caravan Club
FREEPOST, PO Box 386, (RRZG-SXKK-UCUJ)
East Grinstead RH19 1FH

(Please use this address only when mailing from within the UK)

Site Report Form

If campsite is already listed, complete only those sections of the form where changes apply or alternatively use the Abbreviated Site Report form on the following pages.

Sites not reported on for 5 years may be deleted from the guide

Year of guide used	20..........	Is site listed?	Listed on page no.	Unlisted	Date of visit	......../........./.........

A – CAMPSITE NAME AND LOCATION

Country		Name of town/village site listed under *(see Sites Location Maps)*			
Distance & direction from centre of town site is listed under *(in a straight line)*	...................km	eg N, NE, S, SW	Urban	Rural	Coastal
Site open all year?	Y / N	Period site is open *(if not all year)*	................./................. to ..../..................		
Site name		Naturist site	Y / N		
Site address					
Telephone		Fax			
E-mail		Website			

B – CAMPSITE CHARGES

Charge for outfit + 2 adults in local currency	PRICE		EL PNTS inc in this price?	Y / N	Amps ....

C – DIRECTIONS

Brief, specific directions to site (in km) *To convert miles to kilometres multiply by 8 and divide by 5 or use Conversion Table in guide*	
GPS	Latitude..*(eg 12.34567)* Longitude..*(eg 1.23456 or -1.23456)*

D – CAMPSITE DESCRIPTION

SITE size ie number of pitches	Small Max 50	SM	Medium 51-150	MED	Large 151-500	LGE	Very large 500+	V LGE	Unchanged

PITCH size	*eg small, medium, large, very large, various*	Unchanged

Pitch features if **NOT** open-plan/grassy	Hedged	HDG PITCH	Marked or numbered	MKD PITCH	Hardstanding or gravel	HDSTG	Unchanged
If site is **NOT** level, is it	Part sloping	PT SL	Sloping	SL	Terraced	TERR	Unchanged
Is site shaded?	Shaded	SHD	Part shaded	PT SHD	Unshaded	UNSHD	Unchanged

E – CAMPSITE FACILITIES

WC	Heated	HTD WC	Continental	CONT	Own San recommended	OWN SAN REC	
Chemical disposal point		CHEM DISP		Dedicated point		WC only	
Motorhome waste discharge and water refill point				MV SERVICE PNT			
Child / baby facilities (bathroom)		CHILD / BABY FACS		Family bathroom		FAM BTHRM	
Hot shower(s)		SHWR(S)		Inc in site fee?	Y / N	Price....................*(if not inc)*	
ELECTRIC HOOK UP *if not included in price above*		EL PNTS		Price...		Amps...	
Supplies of bottled gas		GAS		On site	Y / N	Or in ………………. Kms	
Launderette / Washing Machine		LNDTTE	Inc dryer Y / N			LNDRY RM *(if no washing machine)*	

You can also complete forms online: www.caravanclub.co.uk/europereport

CUT ALONG DOTTED LINE

F – FOOD & DRINK

Shop(s) / supermarket	SHOP(S) / SUPMKT	On site		or	.... kms
Bread / milk delivered	TRADSMN				
Restaurant / cafeteria	REST	On site		or	.... kms
Snack bar / take-away	SNACKS	On site		or	.... kms
Bar	BAR	On site		or	.... kms
Barbecue allowed	BBQ	Charcoal	Gas	Elec	Sep area
Cooking facilities	COOKING FACS				

G – LEISURE FACILITIES

Playground	PLAYGRND					
Swimming pool	POOL	On site		or ....km	Heated	Covered
Beach	BEACH	Adj		or ....km	Sand	Shingle
Alternative swimming *(lake)*	SW	Adj		or ....km	Sand	Shingle
Games /sports area / Games room	GAMES AREA	GAMES ROOM				
Entertainment in high season	ENTMNT					
Internet use by visitors	INTERNET	Wifi Internet		WIFI		
Television room	TV RM	Satellite / Cable to pitches		TV CAB / SAT		

H – OTHER INFORMATION

% Static caravans / mobile homes / chalets / cottages / fixed tents on site					................% STATICS
Dogs allowed	DOGS		Y / N	Price per night .... *(if allowed)*	
Phone	PHONE		On site	Adj	
Bus / tram / train	BUS / TRAM / TRAIN		Adj	or .... km	
Twin axles caravans allowed?	TWIN AXLES Y / N		Possibly crowded in high season		POSS CR
English spoken	ENG SPKN				
Advance bookings accepted	ADV BKG		Y / N		
Noise levels on site in season	NOISY	QUIET	If noisy, why?		
Credit card accepted	CCARD ACC		Reduction low season		RED LOW SSN
Camping Key Europe or Camping Card International accepted in lieu of passport	CKE/CCI		INF card required *(If naturist site)*		Y / N
Facilities for disabled	Full wheelchair facilities		♦	Limited disabled facilities	♦ ltd

I – ADDITIONAL REMARKS AND/OR ITEMS OF INTEREST

Tourist attractions, unusual features or other facilities, eg waterslide, tennis, cycle hire, watersports, horseriding, separate car park, walking distance to shops etc	YOUR OPINION OF THE SITE:	
	EXCEL	
	VERY GOOD	
	GOOD	
	FAIR	POOR
	NIGHT HALT ONLY	
Your comments & opinions may be used in future editions of the guide, if you do not wish them to be used please tick		

J – MEMBER DETAILS

ARE YOU A:	Caravanner		Motorhomer		Trailer-tenter?	
NAME:		MEMBERSHIP NO:				
		POST CODE:				
DO YOU NEED MORE BLANK SITE REPORT FORMS?		YES			NO	

Please use a separate form for each campsite and do not send receipts. Owing to the large number of site reports received, it is not possible to enter into correspondence. Please return completed form to:

The Editor, Overseas Touring Guides, The Caravan Club
FREEPOST, PO Box 386, (RRZG-SXKK-UCUJ)
East Grinstead RH19 1FH

(Please use this address only when mailing from within the UK)

Site Report Form

If campsite is already listed, complete only those sections of the form where changes apply or alternatively use the Abbreviated Site Report form on the following pages.

Sites not reported on for 5 years may be deleted from the guide

Year of guide used	20..........	Is site listed?	Listed on page no.	Unlisted	Date of visit	......../........./.........

A – CAMPSITE NAME AND LOCATION

Country		Name of town/village site listed under *(see Sites Location Maps)*				
Distance & direction from centre of town site is listed under *(in a straight line)*	...................km	eg N, NE, S, SW	Urban	Rural	Coastal	
Site open all year?	Y / N	Period site is open *(if not all year)*	................./................. to ..../..................			
Site name		Naturist site	Y / N			
Site address						
Telephone		Fax				
E-mail		Website				

B – CAMPSITE CHARGES

Charge for outfit + 2 adults in local currency	PRICE		EL PNTS inc in this price?	Y / N	Amps ....

C – DIRECTIONS

Brief, specific directions to site (in km) *To convert miles to kilometres multiply by 8 and divide by 5 or use Conversion Table in guide*	
GPS	Latitude...*(eg 12.34567)* Longitude..*(eg 1.23456 or -1.23456)*

D – CAMPSITE DESCRIPTION

SITE size ie number of pitches	Small Max 50	SM	Medium 51-150	MED	Large 151-500	LGE	Very large 500+	V LGE	Unchanged

PITCH size	*eg small, medium, large, very large, various*	Unchanged

Pitch features if **NOT** open-plan/grassy	Hedged	HDG PITCH	Marked or numbered	MKD PITCH	Hardstanding or gravel	HDSTG	Unchanged
If site is **NOT** level, is it	Part sloping	PT SL	Sloping	SL	Terraced	TERR	Unchanged
Is site shaded?	Shaded	SHD	Part shaded	PT SHD	Unshaded	UNSHD	Unchanged

E – CAMPSITE FACILITIES

WC	Heated	HTD WC	Continental	CONT	Own San recommended	OWN SAN REC
Chemical disposal point	CHEM DISP		Dedicated point		WC only	
Motorhome waste discharge and water refill point			MV SERVICE PNT			
Child / baby facilities (bathroom)	CHILD / BABY FACS		Family bathroom		FAM BTHRM	
Hot shower(s)	SHWR(S)		Inc in site fee?	Y / N	Price.....................*(if not inc)*	
ELECTRIC HOOK UP *if not included in price above*	EL PNTS		Price..		Amps..	
Supplies of bottled gas	GAS		On site	Y / N	Or in .... Kms	
Launderette / Washing Machine	LNDTTE	Inc dryer Y / N	LNDRY RM *(if no washing machine)*			

You can also complete forms online: www.caravanclub.co.uk/europereport

CUT ALONG DOTTED LINE

F – FOOD & DRINK

Shop(s) / supermarket	SHOP(S) / SUPMKT	On site		or	.... kms
Bread / milk delivered	TRADSMN				
Restaurant / cafeteria	REST	On site		or	.... kms
Snack bar / take-away	SNACKS	On site		or	.... kms
Bar	BAR	On site		or	.... kms
Barbecue allowed	BBQ	Charcoal	Gas	Elec	Sep area
Cooking facilities	COOKING FACS				

G – LEISURE FACILITIES

Playground	PLAYGRND					
Swimming pool	POOL	On site		or ....km	Heated	Covered
Beach	BEACH	Adj		or ....km	Sand	Shingle
Alternative swimming *(lake)*	SW	Adj		or ....km	Sand	Shingle
Games /sports area / Games room	GAMES AREA	GAMES ROOM				
Entertainment in high season	ENTMNT					
Internet use by visitors	INTERNET	Wifi Internet		WIFI		
Television room	TV RM	Satellite / Cable to pitches		TV CAB / SAT		

H – OTHER INFORMATION

% Static caravans / mobile homes / chalets / cottages / fixed tents on site					................% STATICS
Dogs allowed	DOGS	Y / N	Price per night .... *(if allowed)*		
Phone	PHONE	On site	Adj		
Bus / tram / train	BUS / TRAM / TRAIN	Adj	or .... km		
Twin axles caravans allowed?	TWIN AXLES Y / N	Possibly crowded in high season			POSS CR
English spoken	ENG SPKN				
Advance bookings accepted	ADV BKG	Y / N			
Noise levels on site in season	NOISY	QUIET	If noisy, why?		
Credit card accepted	CCARD ACC	Reduction low season		RED LOW SSN	
Camping Key Europe or Camping Card International accepted in lieu of passport	CKE/CCI	INF card required *(If naturist site)*		Y / N	
Facilities for disabled	Full wheelchair facilities	♦	Limited disabled facilities	♦ ltd	

I – ADDITIONAL REMARKS AND/OR ITEMS OF INTEREST

Tourist attractions, unusual features or other facilities, eg waterslide, tennis, cycle hire, watersports, horseriding, separate car park, walking distance to shops etc	YOUR OPINION OF THE SITE:	
	EXCEL	
	VERY GOOD	
	GOOD	
	FAIR	POOR
	NIGHT HALT ONLY	
Your comments & opinions may be used in future editions of the guide, if you do not wish them to be used please tick		

J – MEMBER DETAILS

ARE YOU A:	Caravanner		Motorhomer		Trailer-tenter?	
NAME:		MEMBERSHIP NO:				
		POST CODE:				
DO YOU NEED MORE BLANK SITE REPORT FORMS?		YES		NO		

Please use a separate form for each campsite and do not send receipts. Owing to the large number of site reports received, it is not possible to enter into correspondence. Please return completed form to:

The Editor, Overseas Touring Guides, The Caravan Club
FREEPOST, PO Box 386, (RRZG-SXKK-UCUJ)
East Grinstead RH19 1FH

(Please use this address only when mailing from within the UK)

Site Report Form

If campsite is already listed, complete only those sections of the form where changes apply or alternatively use the Abbreviated Site Report form on the following pages.

Sites not reported on for 5 years may be deleted from the guide

Year of guide used	20..........	Is site listed?	Listed on page no.	Unlisted	Date of visit	......../........./.........

A – CAMPSITE NAME AND LOCATION

Country		Name of town/village site listed under *(see Sites Location Maps)*			
Distance & direction from centre of town site is listed under *(in a straight line)*	...................km	eg N, NE, S, SW	Urban	Rural	Coastal
Site open all year?	Y / N	Period site is open *(if not all year)*	................./................. to ..../..................		
Site name				Naturist site	Y / N
Site address					
Telephone		Fax			
E-mail		Website			

B – CAMPSITE CHARGES

Charge for outfit + 2 adults in local currency	PRICE		EL PNTS inc in this price?	Y / N	Amps ....

C – DIRECTIONS

Brief, specific directions to site (in km) *To convert miles to kilometres multiply by 8 and divide by 5 or use Conversion Table in guide*	
GPS	Latitude...*(eg 12.34567)* Longitude...*(eg 1.23456 or -1.23456)*

D – CAMPSITE DESCRIPTION

SITE size ie number of pitches	Small Max 50	SM	Medium 51-150	MED	Large 151-500	LGE	Very large 500+	V LGE	Unchanged

PITCH size	*eg small, medium, large, very large, various*	Unchanged

Pitch features if **NOT** open-plan/grassy	Hedged	HDG PITCH	Marked or numbered	MKD PITCH	Hardstanding or gravel	HDSTG	Unchanged
If site is **NOT** level, is it	Part sloping	PT SL	Sloping	SL	Terraced	TERR	Unchanged
Is site shaded?	Shaded	SHD	Part shaded	PT SHD	Unshaded	UNSHD	Unchanged

E – CAMPSITE FACILITIES

WC	Heated	HTD WC	Continental	CONT	Own San recommended	OWN SAN REC
Chemical disposal point	CHEM DISP	Dedicated point		WC only		
Motorhome waste discharge and water refill point	MV SERVICE PNT					
Child / baby facilities (bathroom)	CHILD / BABY FACS	Family bathroom		FAM BTHRM		
Hot shower(s)	SHWR(S)	Inc in site fee?	Y / N	Price....................*(if not inc)*		
ELECTRIC HOOK UP *if not included in price above*	EL PNTS	Price..		Amps..		
Supplies of bottled gas	GAS	On site	Y / N	Or in .... Kms		
Launderette / Washing Machine	LNDTTE	Inc dryer Y / N	LNDRY RM *(if no washing machine)*			

You can also complete forms online: www.caravanclub.co.uk/europereport

CUT ALONG DOTTED LINE

F – FOOD & DRINK

Shop(s) / supermarket	SHOP(S) / SUPMKT	On site		or	.... kms
Bread / milk delivered	TRADSMN				
Restaurant / cafeteria	REST	On site		or	.... kms
Snack bar / take-away	SNACKS	On site		or	.... kms
Bar	BAR	On site		or	.... kms
Barbecue allowed	BBQ	Charcoal	Gas	Elec	Sep area
Cooking facilities	COOKING FACS				

G – LEISURE FACILITIES

Playground	PLAYGRND					
Swimming pool	POOL	On site		or ....km	Heated	Covered
Beach	BEACH	Adj		or ....km	Sand	Shingle
Alternative swimming *(lake)*	SW	Adj		or ....km	Sand	Shingle
Games /sports area / Games room	GAMES AREA	GAMES ROOM				
Entertainment in high season	ENTMNT					
Internet use by visitors	INTERNET	Wifi Internet		WIFI		
Television room	TV RM	Satellite / Cable to pitches		TV CAB / SAT		

H – OTHER INFORMATION

% Static caravans / mobile homes / chalets / cottages / fixed tents on site				...............% STATICS
Dogs allowed	DOGS	Y / N	Price per night .... *(if allowed)*	
Phone	PHONE	On site	Adj	
Bus / tram / train	BUS / TRAM / TRAIN	Adj	or .... km	
Twin axles caravans allowed?	TWIN AXLES Y / N	Possibly crowded in high season		POSS CR
English spoken	ENG SPKN			
Advance bookings accepted	ADV BKG	Y / N		
Noise levels on site in season	NOISY / QUIET	If noisy, why?		
Credit card accepted	CCARD ACC	Reduction low season		RED LOW SSN
Camping Key Europe or Camping Card International accepted in lieu of passport	CKE/CCI	INF card required *(If naturist site)*		Y / N
Facilities for disabled	Full wheelchair facilities	♦	Limited disabled facilities	♦ ltd

I – ADDITIONAL REMARKS AND/OR ITEMS OF INTEREST

Tourist attractions, unusual features or other facilities, eg waterslide, tennis, cycle hire, watersports, horseriding, separate car park, walking distance to shops etc	YOUR OPINION OF THE SITE:
	EXCEL
	VERY GOOD
	GOOD
	FAIR / POOR
	NIGHT HALT ONLY
Your comments & opinions may be used in future editions of the guide, if you do not wish them to be used please tick	

J – MEMBER DETAILS

ARE YOU A:	Caravanner		Motorhomer		Trailer-tenter?
NAME:		MEMBERSHIP NO:			
		POST CODE:			
DO YOU NEED MORE BLANK SITE REPORT FORMS?		YES		NO	

Please use a separate form for each campsite and do not send receipts. Owing to the large number of site reports received, it is not possible to enter into correspondence. Please return completed form to:

The Editor, Overseas Touring Guides, The Caravan Club
FREEPOST, PO Box 386, (RRZG-SXKK-UCUJ)
East Grinstead RH19 1FH

(Please use this address only when mailing from within the UK)

Site Report Form

If campsite is already listed, complete only those sections of the form where changes apply or alternatively use the Abbreviated Site Report form on the following pages.

Sites not reported on for 5 years may be deleted from the guide

Year of guide used	20..........	Is site listed?	Listed on page no.	Unlisted	Date of visit	......../........./.........

A – CAMPSITE NAME AND LOCATION

Country		Name of town/village site listed under *(see Sites Location Maps)*				
Distance & direction from centre of town site is listed under *(in a straight line)*	...................km	eg N, NE, S, SW	Urban	Rural	Coastal	
Site open all year?	Y / N	Period site is open *(if not all year)*	................../.................. to ..../..................			
Site name			Naturist site	Y / N		
Site address						
Telephone		Fax				
E-mail		Website				

B – CAMPSITE CHARGES

Charge for outfit + 2 adults in local currency	PRICE		EL PNTS inc in this price?	Y / N	Amps ....

C – DIRECTIONS

Brief, specific directions to site (in km) *To convert miles to kilometres multiply by 8 and divide by 5 or use Conversion Table in guide*	
GPS	Latitude...*(eg 12.34567)* Longitude...*(eg 1.23456 or -1.23456)*

D – CAMPSITE DESCRIPTION

SITE size ie number of pitches	Small Max 50	SM	Medium 51-150	MED	Large 151-500	LGE	Very large 500+	V LGE	Unchanged

PITCH size	*eg small, medium, large, very large, various*	Unchanged

Pitch features if **NOT** open-plan/grassy	Hedged	HDG PITCH	Marked or numbered	MKD PITCH	Hardstanding or gravel	HDSTG	Unchanged

If site is **NOT** level, is it	Part sloping	PT SL	Sloping	SL	Terraced	TERR	Unchanged

Is site shaded?	Shaded	SHD	Part shaded	PT SHD	Unshaded	UNSHD	Unchanged

E – CAMPSITE FACILITIES

WC	Heated	HTD WC	Continental	CONT	Own San recommended	OWN SAN REC
Chemical disposal point	CHEM DISP	Dedicated point		WC only	
Motorhome waste discharge and water refill point	MV SERVICE PNT				
Child / baby facilities (bathroom)	CHILD / BABY FACS	Family bathroom	FAM BTHRM		
Hot shower(s)	SHWR(S)	Inc in site fee?	Y / N	Price...................*(if not inc)*	
ELECTRIC HOOK UP *if not included in price above*	EL PNTS	Price...	Amps..		
Supplies of bottled gas	GAS	On site	Y / N	Or in .... Kms	
Launderette / Washing Machine	LNDTTE	Inc dryer Y / N	LNDRY RM *(if no washing machine)*		

CUT ALONG DOTTED LINE

You can also complete forms online: www.caravanclub.co.uk/europereport

F – FOOD & DRINK

Shop(s) / supermarket	SHOP(S) / SUPMKT	On site		or	.... kms
Bread / milk delivered	TRADSMN				
Restaurant / cafeteria	REST	On site		or	.... kms
Snack bar / take-away	SNACKS	On site		or	.... kms
Bar	BAR	On site		or	.... kms
Barbecue allowed	BBQ	Charcoal	Gas	Elec	Sep area
Cooking facilities	COOKING FACS				

G – LEISURE FACILITIES

Playground	PLAYGRND					
Swimming pool	POOL	On site		or ....km	Heated	Covered
Beach	BEACH	Adj		or ....km	Sand	Shingle
Alternative swimming *(lake)*	SW	Adj		or ....km	Sand	Shingle
Games /sports area / Games room	GAMES AREA	GAMES ROOM				
Entertainment in high season	ENTMNT					
Internet use by visitors	INTERNET	Wifi Internet		WIFI		
Television room	TV RM	Satellite / Cable to pitches		TV CAB / SAT		

H – OTHER INFORMATION

% Static caravans / mobile homes / chalets / cottages / fixed tents on site					................% STATICS
Dogs allowed	DOGS		Y / N	Price per night .... *(if allowed)*	
Phone	PHONE		On site	Adj	
Bus / tram / train	BUS / TRAM / TRAIN		Adj	or .... km	
Twin axles caravans allowed?	TWIN AXLES	Y / N	Possibly crowded in high season		POSS CR
English spoken	ENG SPKN				
Advance bookings accepted	ADV BKG		Y / N		
Noise levels on site in season	NOISY	QUIET	If noisy, why?		
Credit card accepted	CCARD ACC		Reduction low season		RED LOW SSN
Camping Key Europe or Camping Card International accepted in lieu of passport	CKE/CCI		INF card required *(If naturist site)*		Y / N
Facilities for disabled	Full wheelchair facilities		♦	Limited disabled facilities	♦ ltd

I – ADDITIONAL REMARKS AND/OR ITEMS OF INTEREST

Tourist attractions, unusual features or other facilities, eg waterslide, tennis, cycle hire, watersports, horseriding, separate car park, walking distance to shops etc	YOUR OPINION OF THE SITE:	
	EXCEL	
	VERY GOOD	
	GOOD	
	FAIR	POOR
	NIGHT HALT ONLY	
Your comments & opinions may be used in future editions of the guide, if you do not wish them to be used please tick		

J – MEMBER DETAILS

ARE YOU A:	Caravanner		Motorhomer		Trailer-tenter?	
NAME:			MEMBERSHIP NO:			
			POST CODE:			
DO YOU NEED MORE BLANK SITE REPORT FORMS?			YES		NO	

Please use a separate form for each campsite and do not send receipts. Owing to the large number of site reports received, it is not possible to enter into correspondence. Please return completed form to:

The Editor, Overseas Touring Guides, The Caravan Club
FREEPOST, PO Box 386, (RRZG-SXKK-UCUJ)
East Grinstead RH19 1FH

(Please use this address only when mailing from within the UK)

Abbreviated Site Report Form

Use this abbreviated Site Report Form if you have visited a number of sites and there are no changes (or only small changes) to their entries in the guide. If reporting on a new site, or reporting several changes, please use the full version of the report form. **If advising prices,** these should be for an outfit, and 2 adults for one night's stay. **Please indicate high or low season prices and whether electricity is included.**

Remember, if you don't tell us about sites you have visited, they may eventually be deleted from the guide.

Year of guide used	20..........	Page No.	....	Name of town/village site listed under	
Site Name				Date of visit	.... /....... /........
GPS	Latitude.......................(eg 12.34567) Longitude.......................(eg 1.23456 or -1.23456)				
Site is in: Andorra / Austria / Belgium / Croatia / Czech Republic / Denmark / Finland / France / Germany / Greece / Hungary / Italy / Luxembourg / Netherlands / Norway / Poland / Portugal / Slovakia / Slovenia / Spain / Sweden / Switzerland					
Comments:					
Charge for outfit + 2 adults in local currency	High Season	Low Season	Elec inc in price?	Y / N	.............amps
			Price of elec (if not inc)		.............amps

Year of guide used	20..........	Page No.	....	Name of town/village site listed under	
Site Name				Date of visit	.... /....... /........
GPS	Latitude.......................(eg 12.34567) Longitude.......................(eg 1.23456 or -1.23456)				
Site is in: Andorra / Austria / Belgium / Croatia / Czech Republic / Denmark / Finland / France / Germany / Greece / Hungary / Italy / Luxembourg / Netherlands / Norway / Poland / Portugal / Slovakia / Slovenia / Spain / Sweden / Switzerland					
Comments:					
Charge for outfit + 2 adults in local currency	High Season	Low Season	Elec inc in price?	Y / N	.............amps
			Price of elec (if not inc)		.............amps

Year of guide used	20..........	Page No.	....	Name of town/village site listed under	
Site Name				Date of visit	.... /....... /........
GPS	Latitude.......................(eg 12.34567) Longitude.......................(eg 1.23456 or -1.23456)				
Site is in: Andorra / Austria / Belgium / Croatia / Czech Republic / Denmark / Finland / France / Germany / Greece / Hungary / Italy / Luxembourg / Netherlands / Norway / Poland / Portugal / Slovakia / Slovenia / Spain / Sweden / Switzerland					
Comments:					
Charge for car, caravan & 2 adults in local currency	High Season	Low Season	Elec inc in price?	Y / N	.............amps
			Price of elec (if not inc)		.............amps

Please fill in your details and send to the address on the reverse of this form.
You can also complete forms online: www.caravanclub.co.uk/europereport

CUT ALONG DOTTED LINE

Year of guide used	20..........	Page No.	....	Name of town/village site listed under	
Site Name				Date of visit	.... /....... /........
GPS	Latitude...(eg 12.34567) Longitude...(eg 1.23456 or -1.23456)				
Site is in: Andorra / Austria / Belgium / Croatia / Czech Republic / Denmark / Finland / France / Germany / Greece / Hungary / Italy / Luxembourg / Netherlands / Norway / Poland / Portugal / Slovakia / Slovenia / Spain / Sweden / Switzerland					
Comments:					
Charge for outfit + 2 adults in local currency	High Season	Low Season	Elec inc in price?	Y / N	.............amps
			Price of elec (if not inc)		.............amps

Year of guide used	20..........	Page No.	....	Name of town/village site listed under	
Site Name				Date of visit	.... /....... /........
GPS	Latitude...(eg 12.34567) Longitude...(eg 1.23456 or -1.23456)				
Site is in: Andorra / Austria / Belgium / Croatia / Czech Republic / Denmark / Finland / France / Germany / Greece / Hungary / Italy / Luxembourg / Netherlands / Norway / Poland / Portugal / Slovakia / Slovenia / Spain / Sweden / Switzerland					
Comments:					
Charge for outfit + 2 adults in local currency	High Season	Low Season	Elec inc in price?	Y / N	.............amps
			Price of elec (if not inc)		.............amps

Year of guide used	20..........	Page No.	....	Name of town/village site listed under	
Site Name				Date of visit	.... /....... /........
GPS	Latitude...(eg 12.34567) Longitude...(eg 1.23456 or -1.23456)				
Site is in: Andorra / Austria / Belgium / Croatia / Czech Republic / Denmark / Finland / France / Germany / Greece / Hungary / Italy / Luxembourg / Netherlands / Norway / Poland / Portugal / Slovakia / Slovenia / Spain / Sweden / Switzerland					
Comments:					
Charge for outfit + 2 adults in local currency	High Season	Low Season	Elec inc in price?	Y / N	.............amps
			Price of elec (if not inc)		.............amps

Your comments & opinions may be used in future editions of the guide, if you do not wish them to be used please tick ....

Name ....

Membership No. ....

Post Code ....

Are you a Caravanner / Motorhomer / Trailer-Tenter?

Do you need more blank Site Report forms? YES / NO

Please return completed forms to:
The Editor, Overseas Touring Guides
The Caravan Club
FREEPOST
PO Box 386 (RRZG-SXKK-UCUJ)
East Grinstead
RH19 1FH
(Please use this address only when mailing from within the UK)

You can also complete forms online: www.caravanclub.co.uk/europereport

Abbreviated Site Report Form

Use this abbreviated Site Report Form if you have visited a number of sites and there are no changes (or only small changes) to their entries in the guide. If reporting on a new site, or reporting several changes, please use the full version of the report form. **If advising prices,** these should be for an outfit, and 2 adults for one night's stay. **Please indicate high or low season prices and whether electricity is included.**

Remember, if you don't tell us about sites you have visited, they may eventually be deleted from the guide.

Year of guide used	20..........	Page No.	....	Name of town/village site listed under	
Site Name				Date of visit	.... /....... /........
GPS	Latitude..(eg 12.34567) Longitude..(eg 1.23456 or -1.23456)				
Site is in: Andorra / Austria / Belgium / Croatia / Czech Republic / Denmark / Finland / France / Germany / Greece / Hungary / Italy / Luxembourg / Netherlands / Norway / Poland / Portugal / Slovakia / Slovenia / Spain / Sweden / Switzerland					
Comments:					
Charge for outfit + 2 adults in local currency	High Season	Low Season	Elec inc in price?	Y / N	.............amps
			Price of elec (if not inc)		.............amps

Year of guide used	20..........	Page No.	....	Name of town/village site listed under	
Site Name				Date of visit	.... /....... /........
GPS	Latitude..(eg 12.34567) Longitude..(eg 1.23456 or -1.23456)				
Site is in: Andorra / Austria / Belgium / Croatia / Czech Republic / Denmark / Finland / France / Germany / Greece / Hungary / Italy / Luxembourg / Netherlands / Norway / Poland / Portugal / Slovakia / Slovenia / Spain / Sweden / Switzerland					
Comments:					
Charge for outfit + 2 adults in local currency	High Season	Low Season	Elec inc in price?	Y / N	.............amps
			Price of elec (if not inc)		.............amps

Year of guide used	20..........	Page No.	....	Name of town/village site listed under	
Site Name				Date of visit	.... /....... /........
GPS	Latitude..(eg 12.34567) Longitude..(eg 1.23456 or -1.23456)				
Site is in: Andorra / Austria / Belgium / Croatia / Czech Republic / Denmark / Finland / France / Germany / Greece / Hungary / Italy / Luxembourg / Netherlands / Norway / Poland / Portugal / Slovakia / Slovenia / Spain / Sweden / Switzerland					
Comments:					
Charge for car, caravan & 2 adults in local currency	High Season	Low Season	Elec inc in price?	Y / N	.............amps
			Price of elec (if not inc)		.............amps

Please fill in your details and send to the address on the reverse of this form.

You can also complete forms online: www.caravanclub.co.uk/europereport

CUT ALONG DOTTED LINE

Year of guide used	20..........	Page No.	....	Name of town/village site listed under	
Site Name				Date of visit	.... /....... /........
GPS	Latitude...(eg 12.34567) Longitude...(eg 1.23456 or -1.23456)				

Site is in: Andorra / Austria / Belgium / Croatia / Czech Republic / Denmark / Finland / France / Germany / Greece / Hungary / Italy / Luxembourg / Netherlands / Norway / Poland / Portugal / Slovakia / Slovenia / Spain / Sweden / Switzerland

Comments:

Charge for outfit + 2 adults in local currency	High Season	Low Season	Elec inc in price?	Y / N	.............amps
			Price of elec (if not inc)		.............amps

Year of guide used	20..........	Page No.	....	Name of town/village site listed under	
Site Name				Date of visit	.... /....... /........
GPS	Latitude...(eg 12.34567) Longitude...(eg 1.23456 or -1.23456)				

Site is in: Andorra / Austria / Belgium / Croatia / Czech Republic / Denmark / Finland / France / Germany / Greece / Hungary / Italy / Luxembourg / Netherlands / Norway / Poland / Portugal / Slovakia / Slovenia / Spain / Sweden / Switzerland

Comments:

Charge for outfit + 2 adults in local currency	High Season	Low Season	Elec inc in price?	Y / N	.............amps
			Price of elec (if not inc)		.............amps

Year of guide used	20..........	Page No.	....	Name of town/village site listed under	
Site Name				Date of visit	.... /....... /........
GPS	Latitude...(eg 12.34567) Longitude...(eg 1.23456 or -1.23456)				

Site is in: Andorra / Austria / Belgium / Croatia / Czech Republic / Denmark / Finland / France / Germany / Greece / Hungary / Italy / Luxembourg / Netherlands / Norway / Poland / Portugal / Slovakia / Slovenia / Spain / Sweden / Switzerland

Comments:

Charge for outfit + 2 adults in local currency	High Season	Low Season	Elec inc in price?	Y / N	.............amps
			Price of elec (if not inc)		.............amps

Your comments & opinions may be used in future editions of the guide, if you do not wish them to be used please tick ....

Name ....

Membership No. ....

Post Code ....

Are you a Caravanner / Motorhomer / Trailer-Tenter?

Do you need more blank Site Report forms? YES / NO

Please return completed forms to:
The Editor, Overseas Touring Guides
The Caravan Club
FREEPOST
PO Box 386 (RRZG-SXKK-UCUJ)
East Grinstead
RH19 1FH
(Please use this address only when mailing from within the UK)

You can also complete forms online: www.caravanclub.co.uk/europereport

Abbreviated Site Report Form

Use this abbreviated Site Report Form if you have visited a number of sites and there are no changes (or only small changes) to their entries in the guide. If reporting on a new site, or reporting several changes, please use the full version of the report form. **If advising prices,** these should be for an outfit, and 2 adults for one night's stay. **Please indicate high or low season prices and whether electricity is included.**

Remember, if you don't tell us about sites you have visited, they may eventually be deleted from the guide.

Year of guide used	20..........	Page No.	....	Name of town/village site listed under	
Site Name				Date of visit	.... /....... /........
GPS	Latitude..(*eg 12.34567*) Longitude..(*eg 1.23456 or -1.23456*)				

Site is in: Andorra / Austria / Belgium / Croatia / Czech Republic / Denmark / Finland / France / Germany / Greece / Hungary / Italy / Luxembourg / Netherlands / Norway / Poland / Portugal / Slovakia / Slovenia / Spain / Sweden / Switzerland

Comments:

Charge for outfit + 2 adults in local currency	High Season	Low Season	Elec inc in price?	Y / N	.............amps
			Price of elec (if not inc)		.............amps

Year of guide used	20..........	Page No.	....	Name of town/village site listed under	
Site Name				Date of visit	.... /....... /........
GPS	Latitude..(*eg 12.34567*) Longitude..(*eg 1.23456 or -1.23456*)				

Site is in: Andorra / Austria / Belgium / Croatia / Czech Republic / Denmark / Finland / France / Germany / Greece / Hungary / Italy / Luxembourg / Netherlands / Norway / Poland / Portugal / Slovakia / Slovenia / Spain / Sweden / Switzerland

Comments:

Charge for outfit + 2 adults in local currency	High Season	Low Season	Elec inc in price?	Y / N	.............amps
			Price of elec (if not inc)		.............amps

Year of guide used	20..........	Page No.	....	Name of town/village site listed under	
Site Name				Date of visit	.... /....... /........
GPS	Latitude..(*eg 12.34567*) Longitude..(*eg 1.23456 or -1.23456*)				

Site is in: Andorra / Austria / Belgium / Croatia / Czech Republic / Denmark / Finland / France / Germany / Greece / Hungary / Italy / Luxembourg / Netherlands / Norway / Poland / Portugal / Slovakia / Slovenia / Spain / Sweden / Switzerland

Comments:

Charge for car, caravan & 2 adults in local currency	High Season	Low Season	Elec inc in price?	Y / N	.............amps
			Price of elec (if not inc)		.............amps

Please fill in your details and send to the address on the reverse of this form.

You can also complete forms online: www.caravanclub.co.uk/europereport

CUT ALONG DOTTED LINE

Year of guide used	20..........	Page No.	....	Name of town/village site listed under		
Site Name					Date of visit	.... /....... /........
GPS	Latitude..(eg 12.34567) Longitude..(eg 1.23456 or -1.23456)					
Site is in: Andorra / Austria / Belgium / Croatia / Czech Republic / Denmark / Finland / France / Germany / Greece / Hungary / Italy / Luxembourg / Netherlands / Norway / Poland / Portugal / Slovakia / Slovenia / Spain / Sweden / Switzerland						
Comments:						
Charge for outfit + 2 adults in local currency	High Season	Low Season	Elec inc in price?	Y / N	.............amps	
			Price of elec (if not inc)		.............amps	

Year of guide used	20..........	Page No.	....	Name of town/village site listed under		
Site Name					Date of visit	.... /....... /........
GPS	Latitude..(eg 12.34567) Longitude..(eg 1.23456 or -1.23456)					
Site is in: Andorra / Austria / Belgium / Croatia / Czech Republic / Denmark / Finland / France / Germany / Greece / Hungary / Italy / Luxembourg / Netherlands / Norway / Poland / Portugal / Slovakia / Slovenia / Spain / Sweden / Switzerland						
Comments:						
Charge for outfit + 2 adults in local currency	High Season	Low Season	Elec inc in price?	Y / N	.............amps	
			Price of elec (if not inc)		.............amps	

Year of guide used	20..........	Page No.	....	Name of town/village site listed under		
Site Name					Date of visit	.... /....... /........
GPS	Latitude..(eg 12.34567) Longitude..(eg 1.23456 or -1.23456)					
Site is in: Andorra / Austria / Belgium / Croatia / Czech Republic / Denmark / Finland / France / Germany / Greece / Hungary / Italy / Luxembourg / Netherlands / Norway / Poland / Portugal / Slovakia / Slovenia / Spain / Sweden / Switzerland						
Comments:						
Charge for outfit + 2 adults in local currency	High Season	Low Season	Elec inc in price?	Y / N	.............amps	
			Price of elec (if not inc)		.............amps	

Your comments & opinions may be used in future editions of the guide, if you do not wish them to be used please tick ....

Name ....

Membership No. ....

Post Code ....

Are you a Caravanner / Motorhomer / Trailer-Tenter?

Do you need more blank Site Report forms? YES / NO

Please return completed forms to:
The Editor, Overseas Touring Guides
The Caravan Club
FREEPOST
PO Box 386 (RRZG-SXKK-UCUJ)
East Grinstead
RH19 1FH
(Please use this address only when mailing from within the UK)

You can also complete forms online: www.caravanclub.co.uk/europereport

Abbreviated Site Report Form

Use this abbreviated Site Report Form if you have visited a number of sites and there are no changes (or only small changes) to their entries in the guide. If reporting on a new site, or reporting several changes, please use the full version of the report form. **If advising prices,** these should be for an outfit, and 2 adults for one night's stay. **Please indicate high or low season prices and whether electricity is included.**

Remember, if you don't tell us about sites you have visited, they may eventually be deleted from the guide.

Year of guide used	20..........	Page No.	....	Name of town/village site listed under	
Site Name				Date of visit	.... /....... /........
GPS	Latitude...(eg 12.34567) Longitude...(eg 1.23456 or -1.23456)				
Site is in: Andorra / Austria / Belgium / Croatia / Czech Republic / Denmark / Finland / France / Germany / Greece / Hungary / Italy / Luxembourg / Netherlands / Norway / Poland / Portugal / Slovakia / Slovenia / Spain / Sweden / Switzerland					
Comments:					
Charge for outfit + 2 adults in local currency	High Season	Low Season	Elec inc in price?	Y / N	.............amps
			Price of elec (if not inc)		.............amps

Year of guide used	20..........	Page No.	....	Name of town/village site listed under	
Site Name				Date of visit	.... /....... /........
GPS	Latitude...(eg 12.34567) Longitude...(eg 1.23456 or -1.23456)				
Site is in: Andorra / Austria / Belgium / Croatia / Czech Republic / Denmark / Finland / France / Germany / Greece / Hungary / Italy / Luxembourg / Netherlands / Norway / Poland / Portugal / Slovakia / Slovenia / Spain / Sweden / Switzerland					
Comments:					
Charge for outfit + 2 adults in local currency	High Season	Low Season	Elec inc in price?	Y / N	.............amps
			Price of elec (if not inc)		.............amps

Year of guide used	20..........	Page No.	....	Name of town/village site listed under	
Site Name				Date of visit	.... /....... /........
GPS	Latitude...(eg 12.34567) Longitude...(eg 1.23456 or -1.23456)				
Site is in: Andorra / Austria / Belgium / Croatia / Czech Republic / Denmark / Finland / France / Germany / Greece / Hungary / Italy / Luxembourg / Netherlands / Norway / Poland / Portugal / Slovakia / Slovenia / Spain / Sweden / Switzerland					
Comments:					
Charge for car, caravan & 2 adults in local currency	High Season	Low Season	Elec inc in price?	Y / N	.............amps
			Price of elec (if not inc)		.............amps

Please fill in your details and send to the address on the reverse of this form.

You can also complete forms online: www.caravanclub.co.uk/europereport

CUT ALONG DOTTED LINE

Year of guide used	20..........	Page No.	....	Name of town/village site listed under		
Site Name					Date of visit	.... /....... /........
GPS	Latitude...(*eg 12.34567*) Longitude...(*eg 1.23456 or -1.23456*)					
Site is in: Andorra / Austria / Belgium / Croatia / Czech Republic / Denmark / Finland / France / Germany / Greece / Hungary / Italy / Luxembourg / Netherlands / Norway / Poland / Portugal / Slovakia / Slovenia / Spain / Sweden / Switzerland						
Comments:						
Charge for outfit + 2 adults in local currency	High Season	Low Season	Elec inc in price?	Y / N	.............amps	
			Price of elec (if not inc)		.............amps	

Year of guide used	20..........	Page No.	....	Name of town/village site listed under		
Site Name					Date of visit	.... /....... /........
GPS	Latitude...(*eg 12.34567*) Longitude...(*eg 1.23456 or -1.23456*)					
Site is in: Andorra / Austria / Belgium / Croatia / Czech Republic / Denmark / Finland / France / Germany / Greece / Hungary / Italy / Luxembourg / Netherlands / Norway / Poland / Portugal / Slovakia / Slovenia / Spain / Sweden / Switzerland						
Comments:						
Charge for outfit + 2 adults in local currency	High Season	Low Season	Elec inc in price?	Y / N	.............amps	
			Price of elec (if not inc)		.............amps	

Year of guide used	20..........	Page No.	....	Name of town/village site listed under		
Site Name					Date of visit	.... /....... /........
GPS	Latitude...(*eg 12.34567*) Longitude...(*eg 1.23456 or -1.23456*)					
Site is in: Andorra / Austria / Belgium / Croatia / Czech Republic / Denmark / Finland / France / Germany / Greece / Hungary / Italy / Luxembourg / Netherlands / Norway / Poland / Portugal / Slovakia / Slovenia / Spain / Sweden / Switzerland						
Comments:						
Charge for outfit + 2 adults in local currency	High Season	Low Season	Elec inc in price?	Y / N	.............amps	
			Price of elec (if not inc)		.............amps	

Your comments & opinions may be used in future editions of the guide, if you do not wish them to be used please tick ....

Name ....

Membership No. ....

Post Code ....

Are you a Caravanner / Motorhomer / Trailer-Tenter?

Do you need more blank Site Report forms? YES / NO

Please return completed forms to:
The Editor, Overseas Touring Guides
The Caravan Club
FREEPOST
PO Box 386 (RRZG-SXKK-UCUJ)
East Grinstead
RH19 1FH
(Please use this address only when mailing from within the UK)

You can also complete forms online: www.caravanclub.co.uk/europereport

Abbreviated Site Report Form

Use this abbreviated Site Report Form if you have visited a number of sites and there are no changes (or only small changes) to their entries in the guide. If reporting on a new site, or reporting several changes, please use the full version of the report form. **If advising prices,** these should be for an outfit, and 2 adults for one night's stay. **Please indicate high or low season prices and whether electricity is included.**

Remember, if you don't tell us about sites you have visited, they may eventually be deleted from the guide.

Year of guide used	20..........	Page No.	....	Name of town/village site listed under	
Site Name				Date of visit	.... /....... /........
GPS	Latitude..(eg 12.34567) Longitude..(eg 1.23456 or -1.23456)				
Site is in: Andorra / Austria / Belgium / Croatia / Czech Republic / Denmark / Finland / France / Germany / Greece / Hungary / Italy / Luxembourg / Netherlands / Norway / Poland / Portugal / Slovakia / Slovenia / Spain / Sweden / Switzerland					
Comments:					
Charge for outfit + 2 adults in local currency	High Season	Low Season	Elec inc in price?	Y / N	.............amps
			Price of elec (if not inc)		.............amps

Year of guide used	20..........	Page No.	....	Name of town/village site listed under	
Site Name				Date of visit	.... /....... /........
GPS	Latitude..(eg 12.34567) Longitude..(eg 1.23456 or -1.23456)				
Site is in: Andorra / Austria / Belgium / Croatia / Czech Republic / Denmark / Finland / France / Germany / Greece / Hungary / Italy / Luxembourg / Netherlands / Norway / Poland / Portugal / Slovakia / Slovenia / Spain / Sweden / Switzerland					
Comments:					
Charge for outfit + 2 adults in local currency	High Season	Low Season	Elec inc in price?	Y / N	.............amps
			Price of elec (if not inc)		.............amps

Year of guide used	20..........	Page No.	....	Name of town/village site listed under	
Site Name				Date of visit	.... /....... /........
GPS	Latitude..(eg 12.34567) Longitude..(eg 1.23456 or -1.23456)				
Site is in: Andorra / Austria / Belgium / Croatia / Czech Republic / Denmark / Finland / France / Germany / Greece / Hungary / Italy / Luxembourg / Netherlands / Norway / Poland / Portugal / Slovakia / Slovenia / Spain / Sweden / Switzerland					
Comments:					
Charge for car, caravan & 2 adults in local currency	High Season	Low Season	Elec inc in price?	Y / N	.............amps
			Price of elec (if not inc)		.............amps

Please fill in your details and send to the address on the reverse of this form.
You can also complete forms online: www.caravanclub.co.uk/europereport

CUT ALONG DOTTED LINE

Year of guide used	20..........	Page No.	....	Name of town/village site listed under		
Site Name					Date of visit	.... /....... /........
GPS	Latitude...(eg 12.34567) Longitude...(eg 1.23456 or -1.23456)					

Site is in: Andorra / Austria / Belgium / Croatia / Czech Republic / Denmark / Finland / France / Germany / Greece / Hungary / Italy / Luxembourg / Netherlands / Norway / Poland / Portugal / Slovakia / Slovenia / Spain / Sweden / Switzerland

Comments:

Charge for outfit + 2 adults in local currency	High Season	Low Season	Elec inc in price?	Y / N	.............amps
			Price of elec (if not inc)		.............amps

Year of guide used	20..........	Page No.	....	Name of town/village site listed under		
Site Name					Date of visit	.... /....... /........
GPS	Latitude...(eg 12.34567) Longitude...(eg 1.23456 or -1.23456)					

Site is in: Andorra / Austria / Belgium / Croatia / Czech Republic / Denmark / Finland / France / Germany / Greece / Hungary / Italy / Luxembourg / Netherlands / Norway / Poland / Portugal / Slovakia / Slovenia / Spain / Sweden / Switzerland

Comments:

Charge for outfit + 2 adults in local currency	High Season	Low Season	Elec inc in price?	Y / N	.............amps
			Price of elec (if not inc)		.............amps

Year of guide used	20..........	Page No.	....	Name of town/village site listed under		
Site Name					Date of visit	.... /....... /........
GPS	Latitude...(eg 12.34567) Longitude...(eg 1.23456 or -1.23456)					

Site is in: Andorra / Austria / Belgium / Croatia / Czech Republic / Denmark / Finland / France / Germany / Greece / Hungary / Italy / Luxembourg / Netherlands / Norway / Poland / Portugal / Slovakia / Slovenia / Spain / Sweden / Switzerland

Comments:

Charge for outfit + 2 adults in local currency	High Season	Low Season	Elec inc in price?	Y / N	.............amps
			Price of elec (if not inc)		.............amps

Your comments & opinions may be used in future editions of the guide, if you do not wish them to be used please tick ....

Name ....

Membership No. ....

Post Code ....

Are you a Caravanner / Motorhomer / Trailer-Tenter?

Do you need more blank Site Report forms? YES / NO

Please return completed forms to:
The Editor, Overseas Touring Guides
The Caravan Club
FREEPOST
PO Box 386 (RRZG-SXKK-UCUJ)
East Grinstead
RH19 1FH
(Please use this address only when mailing from within the UK)

You can also complete forms online: www.caravanclub.co.uk/europereport

Index

Index

PEFC Certified
This product is from sustainably managed forests and controlled sources
PEFC
PEFC/16-33-254
www.pefc.org